30 Romantic Weekends for Two

We have 30 Romantic Weekends for Two

WIN a Romantic weekend for 2

to be won in the AA Lifestyle Guide Free Prize Draw with the Virgin Hotel Collection

The Virgin Hotel Collection offers you an unbeatable experience of the highest standards of service, the friendliest welcome, adventurous, award-winning cuisine complemented by the finest wines and immaculate attention to detail to make your stay that little bit special. Splendid architecture reflecting past centuries houses luxurious interiors that enhance the ambience and individual style of each property. Beautiful scenery in secluded surroundings will ensure that your stay is peaceful, relaxing and one to remember.

A bouquet of flowers for every winner courtesy of Interflora

A total of 6 Prize Draws throughout the year, with 5 winners per draw.

Draws will be made on the last day of December 96 and then February, April, June, August and October 97.

For more information on the Virgin Hotel Collection, please call 0800 716 919

HOW TO ENTER

Just complete (in capitals, please) and send off this card or, alternatively, send your name and address on a **stamped** postcard to the address overleaf (no purchase required). Entries limited to one per household and to residents of the UK and Republic of Ireland. This card will require a stamp if posted in the Republic of Ireland.

MR/MRS/MISS/MS/OTHER, PLEASE STATE: ____________________

NAME: ____________________

ADDRESS: ____________________

POSTCODE: ____________________

TEL.NOS: ____________________

Are you an AA Member ? Yes/No

Have you bought this or any other AA Lifestyle Guide before? Yes/No
If yes, please indicate the year of the last edition you bought:

The AA Hotel Guide	19____
AA Best Restaurants	19____
AA Bed and Breakfast Guide	19____
AA Camping and Caravanning (Britain & Ireland)	19____
AA Camping and Caravanning (W. Country & S. England)	19____
AA Camping and Caravanning (Europe)	19____

If you do not wish to receive further information or special offers on
AA Publishing ☐ Virgin Hotel Collection ☐ please tick the box

HG97

Terms and Conditions

1. Five winners will be drawn for each of six prize draws to take place on 31 December, 1996, 28 February, 30 April, 30 June, 29 August, 31 October, 1997.

2. Closing date for receipt of entries is 1 day prior to the relevant draw date. Final close date for receipt of entries is 30 October 1997.

3. Entries received after any draw date except the final one will go forward into the next available draw. Entries will be placed in one draw only. Only one entry per household accepted.

4. Winners will be notified by post within 14 days of the relevant draw date. Prizes will be valid for 3 months from the relevant draw date. Prizes are not transferable and there will be no cash alternative.

5. Each prize is comprised of two nights with dinner, bed and a champagne breakfast on one morning, offered by Virgin Hotels. The package will be for two people sharing a double/twin room at any of the UK hotels in the Virgin Hotel Collection. Dates subject to availability. The prize does not include other meals and drinks (except as stated), special activities such as golf etc. (these will be charged as taken), or travelling expenses.

6. All hotel accommodation, services and facilities are provided by Virgin Hotels and AA Publishing is not party to your agreement with Virgin Hotels in this regard.

7. The prize draw is open to anyone resident in the UK or the Republic of Ireland over the age of 18 other than employees of the Automobile Association or Virgin Hotels, their subsidiary companies, their families or agents

8. For a list of winners, please send a stamped, self-addressed envelope to AA Lifestyle Guide winners, Publishing Admin, Fanum House, Basing View, Basingstoke, Hants RG21 4EA.

9. If this card is posted in the Republic of Ireland it must have a stamp.

BUSINESS REPLY SERVICE
Licence No BZ 343

PLEASE NOTE: Requires a stamp if posted in Eire

AA Lifestyle Guide Prize Draw

AA PUBLISHING
FANUM HOUSE
BASING VIEW
BASINGSTOKE
HANTS RG21 4EA

AA

The Hotel Guide 1997

In association with Royal Mail

This edition published October 1996

Mapping is produced by the Cartographic Department of the Automobile Association. Maps

Directory compiled by the AA's Hotels and Touring Services Department and generated from the AA's establishment database

The contents of this publication are believed correct at the time of printing. Nevertheless, the publishers cannot be held responsible for any errors or omissions or for changes in the details given in this guide or for the consequences of any reliance on the information provided by the same. Assessments of AA inspected establishments are based on the experience of the Hotel and Restaurant Inspectors on the occasion of their visit(s) and therefore descriptions given in this guide necessarily contain an element of subjective opinion which may not reflect or dictate a reader's own opinion on another occasion. We have tried to ensure accuracy in this guide but things do change and we would be grateful if readers would advise us of any inaccuracies they may encounter.

Typeset and colour repro by Microset Graphics Ltd, Basingstoke
Printed by bpc magazines (Milton Keynes) Ltd, England

Advertisement Sales
Head of Advertisement Sales: Christopher Heard, telephone 01256 20123 ext. 21544
Advertisement Production: Karen Weeks, telephone 01256 20123, ext. 21545

Cover design and introductory pages by Design Fx, Chelsea, London
The cover photograph shows Eastwell Manor Hotel at Ashburton, Kent. Eastwell Manor is one of the Virgin Collection of Hotels
A CIP catalogue record for this book is available from the British Library
ISBN 0-7495-1381 0 AA Ref. 56494

Published by AA Publishing, a trading name of Automobile Association Developments Limited, whose registered office is Norfolk House, Priestley Road, Basingstoke, Hampshire RG24 9NY. Registered number 1878835

Published in the USA by Hunter Publishing, Inc, 300 Raritan Centre, Edison NJ 08818
USA ISBN 1-55650-759-3

CONTENTS

New AA Hotel Booking Service, One Call is all it takes

telephone 0990 050505

Members can now let the AA take the strain out of finding somewhere to stay in the UK and Ireland - and save time and money into the bargain. All you need to do is make one telephone call to the AA Hotel Booking Service to tell us your requirements (whereabouts you want to stay, what your budget is, what facilities you need) and we do all the hard work, at no extra charge to you, of finding you the right place at the right price from among the thousands of AA star-rated hotels and recommended Bed & Breakfast establishments.

In most circumstances, the AA Hotel Booking Service can negotiate an advantageous room rate as well, so you could be saving money as well as the time it would take you on your own to find and contact a number of hotels or B & Bs before finding the accommodation to match your requirements.

You may need a hotel in the Lake District that will take pets; a city-centre hotel in Glasgow with parking on the premises; a B & B within 10 miles of the Eurotunnel terminus at Ashford, or a country hotel suitable for your firm's conference for 70 delegates.

The AA Hotel Booking Service can research all of that, and much more - for example, hotels with golf courses, sports centres, swimming pools, facilities for children, award-winning restaurants, executive accommodation, four-poster beds, etc. You may be travelling around Britain and Ireland and need a number of convenient overnight stops, so you can make just one telephone call to give AA Hotel Booking Service your list and we can work out a complete itinerary for you.

All you need to do to take advantage of this new AA service is to give your credit card details when you make your telephone call to place your accommodation request. AA Hotel Booking Service will call you back within the hour to confirm the booking and the documentation will be sent to you through the post, or by fax.

Full listings of more than 4000 AA star-rated hotels can be found in the AA Members' Handbook or the AA Hotel Guide and of more than 3500 AA recommended Bed & Breakfast establishments (including small private hotels, guest houses, farmhouses and inns) in the AA Bed & Breakfast Guide. These two guides are published every year, the Handbook every two years.

All AA listed accommodation can also be found at the AA's Inernet site, whose address is: http://www.theaa.co.uk/hotels

IT'S SO SIMPLE

Decide on your preferred location, budget and the facilities you require
Call AA Hotel Booking Service on 0990 050505

Quote your AA Membership Number
An experienced hotel reservations consultant will give you all the help you need, at no extra charge to you, tell you your room rate, what the discount is, and make the booking for you

Use Access/Mastercard, Barclaycard/Visa or American Express and your reservation is guaranteed - even for late arrivals and last-minute bookings

If you don't want to pay by credit card you can still use the service, but you will have to send a deposit direct to the hotel

Written confirmation of the reservation will give you peace of mind

Enjoy your stay and simply settle your bill with the hotel in the usual way

Remember, though, that if you cancel a reservation once it has been made you may be liable for at least part of the cost

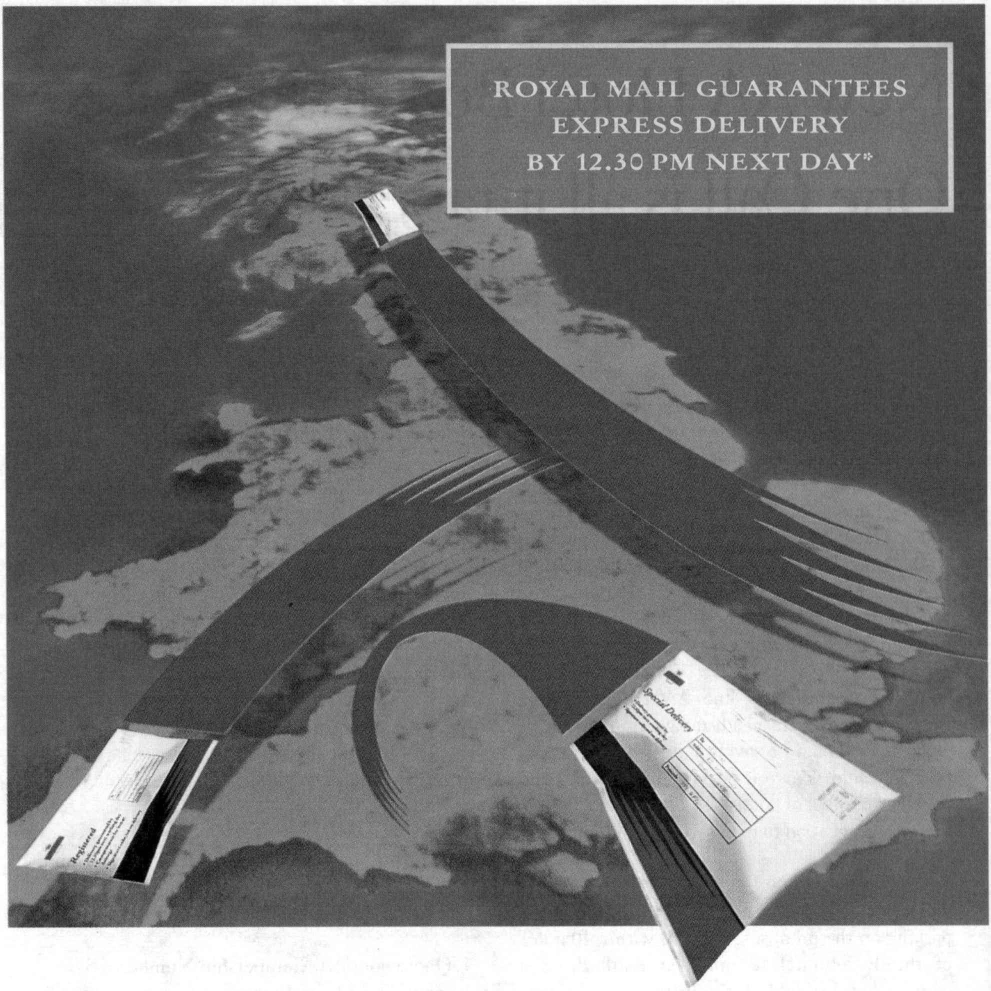
ROYAL MAIL GUARANTEES
EXPRESS DELIVERY
BY 12.30 PM NEXT DAY*

AA Star-Rating, Classification & Award Schemes

How the AA classifies hotels and what the percentage score means

Hotels applying to join the AA scheme are visited anonymously by the AA's professional hotel inspectorate. Only after testing the accommodation and services and having paid their bill do inspectors introduce themselves in order to make a thorough inspection of the entire premises.

Once given a star-rating, the hotel is visited annually. If there is a change of ownership, the new owners must re-apply for assessment and star rating. Star ratings rise from one to five. They denote an internationally accepted standard, ranging from the simplest to the most luxurious hotel. The following explanations tell you what you might expect at each star rating:

★ Usually privately owned and run, one-star hotels tend to be small, with a more personal atmosphere than larger ones. Furnishings and services will be good but simple; not all bedrooms may have en suite facilities. Some hotels may not offer all the expected hotel services - e.g. lunch service may be limited.

★★ May include group-owned as well as proprietor-owned hotels. At this star rating they are usually small to medium sized. At least half the bedrooms will have en suite bath/shower rooms. and may also have phones and TVs.

★★★ Three-star hotels offer a greater range of facilities and services, including full reception service as well as more formal restaurant and bar arrangements. Bedrooms should all have en suite facilities, mostly with baths.

★★★★ Usually large hotels with spacious accommodation,offering high standards of comfort and food. All bedrooms will have en suite bathrooms with bath and shower and private suites will usually also be available. The range of services should include porterage, room service, formal reception and probably a choice of styles of restaurant.

★★★★★ Five stars denote large. luxury hotels offering the highest international standards of accommodation, facilities, services and cuisine.

PERCENTAGE SCORES

The percentage score for each hotel, printed in the guide entry in red after the star rating, reflects an inspector's subjective assessment of the quality of facilities, services and hospitality, based on his or her personal experience during the visit. Every aspect of service, from reception to check out, the degree of comfort in bedrooms and day rooms, the quality of the food, the standard of housekeeping, the efficiency of management and the attitude of the staff, is assessed and marked according to a carefully devised scale, in order to arrive at the final percentage. Guests can use that percentage to choose between any number of hotels with the same star rating, or to decide whether one with fewer stars but a high quality score may offer better value for money.

Between 50 and 59 per cent indicates that the hotel satisfies AA requirements for sound levels of comfort, facilities and services.

Between 60 and 69 per cent indicates that the hotel offers a generally high standard of comfort, facilities and services, and in several respects exceeds expectations at its star rating.

Between 70 and 85 per cent indicates an all round level of excellence in most departments and a hotel whose main concern is to offer the highest standards..

Red Star Hotels are not given percentage scores because the award of red stars in itself signifies that these hotels are the very best in their star rating and have been assessed as offering outstanding quality in every aspect of their operation.

TOWN HOUSE HOTELS

This classification denotes small, personally run town-centre hotels which concentrate on privacy, high-quality room service and luxuriously furnished bedrooms and suites. They often do not have the public rooms or formal dining arrangements traditionally associated with hotels, but are usually in areas well served by restaurants.

COUNTRY HOUSE HOTELS

Country House Hotels offer a relaxed, informal atmosphere with an emphasis on personal welcome. They are usually, but not always, in a secluded or rural setting and should offer peace and quiet, regardless of location.

COMPANY-OWNED HOTELS WITH STAR RATING

Some company-owned hotels and hotels that belong to marketing consortia have developed a strong corporate identity with a nationally or internationally recognised quality image which they promote by displaying their company logo against their entry.

BRAND-NAME HOTELS

Some well known hotel companies offer such a consistent style of service and level of facilities at each of their hotels that the AA recognises the brand name as a quality standard. All are regularly inspected by the AA to ensure that they live up to the aims of brand, and information about what each of these brand names offers is given on page 21.

LODGES

Useful budget accommodation, for an overnight stay, Lodges are outside the star-rating scheme, because they offer consistent standards of accommodation and service. They are usually to be found conveniently near to main roads and motorways

★ RED STAR AWARDS

These awards are made annually to a select number of hotels as a recognition of excellence within their star rating. This is the AA's supreme award for hotels and to earn it, they must consistently provide outstanding levels of hospitality, service, food and comfort. Because of this a percentage score is considered to be unnecessary. Red star hotel entries are highlighted by a colour panel and a photograph. There is a quick reference list on page 8.

ROSETTE AWARDS

The AA makes annual rosette awards on a rising scale of one to five for the quality of food served in hotel restaurants. Only hotels offering the highest international standards of cuisine and service will merit the AA's top awards of four or five rosettes.

One rosette denotes simple, carefully prepared food, based on good quality, fresh ingredients, cooked in such a way as to emphasise honest flavours. Sauces and desserts will be home-made and the cooking will equate to first-class home cooking.

Two rosettes denote cooking that displays a high degree of competence on the part of the chef. The menus should include some imaginative dishes, making use of very good raw ingredients, as well as some tried and tested favourites. Flavours should be well balanced and complement or contrast with one another, not over-dominate.

❀❀❀ Only cooking of the highest national standard receives three or more rosettes. Menus will be imaginative; dishes should be accurately cooked, demonstrate well developed technical skills and a high degree of flair in their composition. Ingredients will be first-class, usually from a range of specialist suppliers, including local produce only if its quality is excellent. Most items - breads, pastries, pasta, petits fours - will be made in the kitchens, but if any are bought in, for example, breads, the quality will be excellent.

❀❀❀❀ At this level, cuisine should be innovative, daring, highly accomplished and achieve a noteworthy standard of consistency, accuracy and flair throughout all the elements of the meal. Excitement, vibrancy and superb technical skill will be the keynotes.

❀❀❀❀❀ Five rosettes is the supreme accolade, made to chefs at the very top of their profession. This award recognises superlative standards of cuisine at an international level, evident at every visit in every element of the meal. Creativity, skill and attention to detail will produce dishes cooked to perfection, with intense, exciting flavours in harmonious combinations and faultless presentation. Menus may be innovative or classical, and may use luxury ingredients like lobster, truffles, foie gras, etc., often in unexpected combinations and with secret ingredients that add an extra dimension of taste and interest.

Using the Guide

ANYTOWN Anyshire Map 04 SU49	1. TOWN NAME
★★★64% **Typical Hotel**	2. HOTEL NAME
Marcham Rd AB00 XY1 ☎ 01235 55456 FAX 01235 55417 RS Xmas	3. RESTRICTED SERVICE
A modern purpose-built hotel, the Typical is located within easy reach of the A34 Oxford to Newbury road. The bedrooms are spacious and well equipped.	4. ACCOMMODATION DETAILS
63 en suite (bth/shr) No smoking in 14 bedrooms CTV in all bedrooms STV No dogs (ex guide dogs) Night porter 85P Xmas English & French Cuisine V meals Coffee am Tea pm	5. HOTEL FACILITIES
ROOMS: (incl. cont. bkfst) d £50-£69 **LB** MEALS: Lunch £7.25-£9.95 Dinner £7.95-£10.95 *	7. MEALS
CONF: Thtr 140 Class 80 Board 48 Del from £90 CARDS: ▬ ▬ ▬ (£)	8. PAYMENT DETAILS

1.TOWN NAME

Listed in the directory in alphabetical order by country: England, Channel Islands, Isle of Man, Scotland, Wales and Ireland.

After the town name comes the administrative county or region. Towns on islands are listed under the island (e.g. Wight, Isle of). The map ref gives the map page number, then the National Grid Ref. To find the location, read the first figure across and the second figure vertically within the lettered square.

2. HOTEL NAME

The star rating, percentage score for quality and any other special awards or classifications (see the Bookmark for symbols and abbreviations) precede the hotel name. If the hotel name is in italic type, it indicates that the information that follows has not been confirmed by the hotel management.

The postal address follows and then, if the hotel belongs to a company or consortium, the company name (for the index of companies and consortia with central reservation numbers, please refer to the Contents page). In some cases, the company or consortium may display its own logo beside that of the hotel name.

Where a telephone number is shown as 'due to change to' the fax number will also change. Please note that some hotel groups use a central telex or fax service, so you should specify the name and location of the hotel when booking

3. RESTRICTED SERVICE

Some hotels operate a restricted service during less busy months. This may be a reduction of the restaurant service, or some leisure facilities may be unavailable. Please check when booking.

4. ACCOMMODATION DETAILS

The first figure shows the number of letting bedrooms, followed by the numbers of rooms that have en suite bath or shower and WC.

Bedrooms in an annexe/extension are noted only if they are equivalent to (or better than) those in the main building. Facilities and prices may differ from those in the main building. In some hotels, all the bedrooms are in an annexe/extension.

5. HOTEL FACILITIES

(For the key to symbols and abbreviations, see the bookmark inside the back cover.)

fmly family bedrooms

CTV/TV colour/black & white television in lounge or in bedrooms. Check when booking

STV satellite TV channels at no extra cost, but check details when booking.

No dogs no dogs allowed in bedrooms. Guide dogs for the blind may be an exception, but, even where hotels allow dogs, they may forbid some breeds, and may exclude dogs from certain areas of the hotel, especially the dining room. It is essential to check the conditions before booking.

Prices are provided by hoteliers in good faith and are indications not firm quotations. 'LB' means leisure or special break package; 'Off Peak' any lower price or concessions available at certain times. Check when booking. In some hotels children can sleep in the parents' room at no extra cost. Check when booking. Prices for the Republic of Ireland are shown Irish Punts (IR£).

Night porter At some hotels, the night porter may be there only between certain hours or on certain nights. However, four and five star hotels must have a night porter always on duty.

No coaches. This information is supplied by the hotels in good faith. Inns, however, have well defined legal obligations towards travellers, and in the event of a query, the customer must approach the proprietor or the local licensing authority.

Wkly live entertainment entertainment should be available at least once a week all year. Some hotels provide entertainment only in summer or on special occasions, so even if the entry indicates nothing, it is worth checking.

No children indicates that children cannot be accommodated. A minimum age may be specified (e.g. No children 4yrs - no children under four years). If nothing appears, it means that the hotel will take children, but may have no special facilities(e.g. no cots or high chairs). It is essential to check when booking. See also below.

Ch fac indicates establishments with special facilities for children, which will include baby intercom or possibly babysitting, playroom or playground, laundry facilities, drying and ironing facilities, cots, high chairs and special meals.

CONF. denotes conference facilities available & numbers that can be accommodated theatre style (Thtr); classroom (Class); boardroom (Board) and minimum overnight delegate rate (del).

6. FACILITIES FOR TRAVELLERS WITH DISABILITIES

Full details of hotels suitable for travellers with disabilities will be found in the AA *Guide for the Disabled Traveller* on sale in book shops or in AA shops, where it is free to members.
Guests with any disability should notify hotels in advance in case of an emergency.

7. MEALS

Details of the style of food, last dinner orders, and price range are given. If there is a fixed-price menu(s), this is the price range quoted. If the words '& alc' follow, it means an à la carte menu is available. and its prices may be much higher.. See also paragraph on page 16.

V meals a choice of vegetarian dishes is normally available,but check first.

Coffee am/Tea pm morning coffee and/or afternoon tea are served to chance callers. All four and five star hotels serve morning coffee and, normally, afternoon tea to resident guests.

8. CREDIT & CHARGE CARDS & DISCOUNT OFFERS FOR AA MEMBERS

Access/Eurocard/Mastercard

American Express   Barclaycard/Visa

Diners   Connect

Delta   Switch

Check the position on credit/charge cards when booking. They may be subject to a surcharge.

(£) Discount off the room rate for AA members showing a current AA membership card plus the Discount Card included at the back of this guide, which details terms and conditions.

GET IT RIGHT

Have you ever waited for a postcard from your family and friends? Rushing to the letter box every morning, throwing envelopes in all directions to find that it has not arrived? You are not alone. This scene of frantic anticipation happens to many, many people on a daily basis.

Aside from Aunty Flossie forgetting to pop the postcard in the post, a common reason for delivery delays is that the mail is not properly addressed and does not have a postcode. Royal Mail is able to sort correctly addressed mail automatically by machine, which means that your mail can be processed approximately 20 times faster than if it had been sorted by hand.

A correct postal address is needed to ensure that your mail reaches its destination first time and is not literally sent round the houses. Are you aware that there is a right and wrong way to address your mail? Many a heated discussion has taken place between generations as to how an address should be set out. Royal Mail, the experts in written communication, recommend a standard format.

Although many people would have us believe otherwise, the address should not be indented nor should it include any punctuation marks at all. Importantly, the Post Town should be written in capital letters and there should always be a postcode written as the last line of the address.

It all seems a lot to take in and remember but it's worth it in the long run. Once your mail is correctly addressed it will be with the postman and delivered to its destination before you can say "I didn't know you should write it like that".

For further information about correct addressing visit your local Post Office or call your local Royal Mail Business Centre on 0345 950 950.

USEFUL INFORMATION - BRITAIN

Information specifically relating to Northern Ireland and the Republic of Ireland will be found on pages 16-17.

BOOKING

Book as early as possible, particularly during the peak holiday periods from the beginning of June to the end of September, at public holiday weekends and, in some parts of Scotland, during the skiing season. Some hotels ask for a deposit, or even full payment in advance, specially for one-night bookings from chance callers. Not all hotels, however, will take advance bookings for bed and breakfast for overnight or short stays. Some will not make reservations from mid week.

CANCELLATION

Once the booking has been confirmed, notify the hotel immediately if you are in any doubt as to whether you can keep to your reservation. If the hotel cannot relet your accommodation you may be liable to pay about two-thirds of the price you would have paid if you had stayed there. A deposit will count towards this payment.

In Britain it is accepted that a legally binding contract has been made as soon as an intending guest accepts an offer of accommodation, either in writing or on the telephone. Illness is not accepted as a release from this contract. You are advised to effect insurance cover, for example, AA Travelsure, against possible cancellation.

COMPLAINTS

If you have a complaint about the food, services or facilities at the hotel, we strongly advise you to take the matter up with the management there and then, in order to give the hotelier a chance to put things right straight away. If this personal approach fails, AA members may inform AA Hotel Services, Fanum House, Basing View Basingstoke, Hampshire RG21 4EA. The AA does not, however, undertake to obtain compensation for complaints.

FIRE PRECAUTIONS

As far as we can discover, every hotel in Great Britain listed in this book has applied for and not been refused a fire certificate. The Fire Precautions Act does not apply to the Channel Islands, the Republic of Ireland, or the Isle of Man, which exercise their own rules.

LICENCE TO SELL ALCOHOL

Unless otherwise stated, all establishments listed are licensed. Hotel residents can obtain alcoholic drinks at all times, if the owner is prepared to serve them. Non-residents eating at the hotel restaurant can have drinks with their meals.
Licensing laws differ in England, Wales, Scotland, the Republic of Ireland, the Isle of Man, the Isles of Scilly and each of the islands forming the Channel Islands.
Public houses are generally open from mid morning to early afternoon, and from about 6 or 7pm until 11pm, but closing time can be slightly earlier or later. Some licensees stay open all afternoon.

Children under 14 (or 18 in Scotland) may be excluded from bars where no food is served. Those under 18 are not allowed to purchase or consume alcoholic drinks.

Club Licence. This means that drinks can be served only to club members. An interval of 48 hours must elapse between joining and ordering.

MEALS

In some parts of Britain, particularly in Scotland, high tea (i.e., a savoury dish, followed by bread and butter, scones, cake, etc.), is served in the early evening instead of dinner. However, the alternative of dinner may be available on request. The last time at which high tea or dinner maybe ordered is shown, but there may be some variation at weekends. On Sunday some hotels serve the main meal at lunch time, and only a cold supper in the evening.

PAYMENT

Most hotels will only accept cheques in payment of accounts if notice is given and identification (e.g., a cheque card) produced. Not all hotels take travellers' cheques, even from leading banks and agencies. If a hotel accepts credit/ charge cards, the information is shown at the end of the entry (see p.14 for details).

PRICES

The AA encourages the use of the Hotel Industry Voluntary Code of Booking Practice, which aims to ensure that guests know precisely how much they will have to pay, and what services and facilities that includes, before committing themselves to a financially binding agreement. If the price has not previously been confirmed in writing, guests should be given a card stipulating the total obligatory charge when they register at reception.

The Tourism (Sleeping Accommodation Price Display) Order of 1977 compels hotels, motels, guest houses, farmhouses, inns and self-catering accommodation with four or more letting bedrooms, to display in entrance halls the minimum and maximum prices charged for each category of room. This Order complements the Voluntary Code of Booking Practice.

Tariffs shown are the minimum and maximum for one or two persons but they may vary without warning. Please see the note on Prices in 'Using the Guide'.
Please note that some hotels charge half-board (bed, breakfast and dinner) whether you eat the dinner or not, and some hotels, particularly in holiday areas, may only accept full-board bookings.

MEAL PRICES

Please see the appropriate paragraph in 'Using the Guide'. Remember that à la carte menus may be considerably dearer than set menus.
With the exception of the Channel Islands, where VAT does not apply, all prices quoted are inclusive of VAT and of service where applicable.

IRELAND
(NORTHERN IRELAND & REPUBLIC OF IRELAND)

Please also see the sections on pages 7, 11 & 19 on AA Star Rating, Classification & Awards Schemes, Using the Guide,and Brand-name Hotels

PRICES

In the Republic, prices are quoted in Punts, indicated by the symbol IR£. Please consult your bank or the daily paper for the current exchange rate. Hotels must display tariffs, either in the bedrooms or at reception. Application of VAT and service charges varies, but all prices quoted must be inclusive of VAT.

TELEPHONE NUMBERS

Area codes for numbers in the Republic of Ireland apply only within the Republic. If dialling from outside, you should check the telephone directory. Area codes for numbers in Britain and N. Ireland cannot be used directly from the Republic.

FIRE PRECAUTIONS

The Fire Services (NI) Order 1984 covers establishments accommodating more than 6 people, which must have a certificate from the Northern Ireland Fire Authority. Places accommodating fewer than 6 persons need adequate exits.

Republic of Ireland: safety regulations are a matter for local authority regulations, but AA officials inspect emergency notices, fire-fighting equipment and fire exits. For your own and others' safety, you must read the emergency notices displayed and be sure you understand them.

LICENSING REGULATIONS

Northern Ireland: public houses open from 11.30-23.00, and on Sun 12.30-14.30 and 19.00-22.00. Hotels can serve residents without restriction. Non-residents can be served from 12.30-22.00 on Christmas Day. Children under 18 are not allowed in the bar area and may neither buy nor consume liquor in hotels.

Republic of Ireland: General licensing hours at present are 10.30-23.00 (23.30 in summer), Mon - Sat. On Sun and St Patrick's Day (17th March), 12.30-14.00 and 16.00-23.00. Hotels, however, can serve residents without restriction. There is no service on Christmas Day or Good Friday.

Central Reservation Telephone Numbers

Best Western	0181 541 0033
Brend	01271 44496
Campanile	0181 569 6969
Consort	01904 643151
Copthorne	0800 414741
Country Club	0800 221222
De Vere	01925 639499
Forestdale	0800 378640
Forte	0800 404040
Friendly	0800 444444
Granadalodge	0800 555300
Hilton	0171 734 6000
Holiday Inn	0800 897121
Ibis	0181 7463233
Independents	0800 885544
Inter-Continental	0345 581444
Leading Hotels	0800 181123
Logis of Great Britain	01865 875888
Marriott & Courtyard	0800 221222
Menzies	01773 829133
Minotels	01253 292000
Novotel	0181 748 3433
Pavilion	0800 555300
Principal	0800 454454
Queens Moat Houses	01708 766677
Radisson Edwardian	0800 374411
Regal	0345 697699
Roadchef	0800 834719
Savoy Group	0171 872 8080
Scottish Highland	0131 557 2368
Sheraton	0800 353535
Shire	01282 416987
Small Luxury Hotels	01372 361873
Swallow	0191 419 4666
Thistle/Mt Charlotte	0800 181716
Toby	0345 665544
Travel Inn	01582 414341
Travelodge	0800 850950
Virgin	0800 716919

Hotel Groups

In recent years many hotel companies have developed clearly identifiable 'brand' umbrellas to distinguish groups of their hotels that share the same important characteristics and services. In the directory, we show these hotels without a star rating and with the brand symbol because it is more accurate to recognise them by brand name, than by star rating, although they are still annually inspected against a defined set of standards. Each brand and its aims is described below.

CAMPANILE

There are 360 Campanile hotels in seven European countries. All are run by a husband and wife team. Reception is open every day from 7am (8am at weekends) to 11pm. There is free parking; a relaxed and friendly Bistro restaurant - which offers breakfast, lunch and dinner; a licensed bar and a conference room. Bedrooms have en suite bathroom, remote-control TV plus Sky, direct-dial phone, desk area and tea/coffee-making facilities. There are specially equipped rooms for travellers with disabilities.

All room offer the same tariff throughout the country and can be made available to sleep up to three people.
£35.75 per room (Mon-Thu)
£29.95 per room (Fri-Sun)
£16.00 day delegate rate includes TV

FORTE POSTHOUSE

There are over 80 Forte Posthouses throughout the country. All are ideally situated for the business and leisure traveller, and have free car parking.

All the comfortable bedrooms offer en-suite bathrooms, tea/coffee-making facilities, colour interactive TV with pay movies, direct-dial telephone, hair-dryer, trouser-press and mini-bar. Pricing by room means that the value for money improves with the number of occupants - particularly popular with families. Fifty per cent of the bedrooms are for non-smokers. Many locations offer leisure centres with indoor swimming pools. An informal theme is carried through the restaurants to the bar and lounge, which offer an 'Anytime' menu for light meals. Room service is also available.

All major credit cards are accepted.
For central reservations, call free on 0800 404040

TRAVELODGE

There are over 160 Travelodges conveniently situated on major roads, throughout the UK. Each Travelodge room has an en suite bathroom, large, soft towels, tea/coffee-making facilties, TV including Sky channels (except Welcome Break). and radio alarm. Travelodge rooms can accommodate three adults and a child under 12, or two adults and two children up to the age of 16. Please check family type when you book. Travelodge charge for a room and not the number of occupants in the room.

Travelodges offer fax facilities (except Welcome Break) and lodges on Granada Service Areas offer a direct dial telephone in each room (except Grantham, and Sutton Scotney north and south)

Rooms for guests with limited mobility are available and include accessible bathrooms and an alarm call system.

Ample free parking is provided at each Travelodge and there is a family restaurant adjacent (except at Dudley and Nuneaton, Bedworth).

For information on individual Travelodge room rates and to make your booking, call Roomline free of charge on 0800 850 950, 7am - 10pm, 7 days a week.

HILTON NATIONAL

Hilton National is a domestic chain of more than 20 first-class, modern hotels located in key business areas on or near major motorway networks throughout Britain.

All bedrooms have private bathroom with shower and wc, remote-control TV, radio, direct-dial telephone, work space, hair-dryer, trouser-press and tea/coffee-making facilities. Bedrooms include executive, family, no-smoking, and most hotels will have at least one room specially equipped for disabled guests. Hotels feature extensive conference and banqueting facilities, including boardrooms and training rooms, business centres, car parking, and most have an indoor leisure centre. Restaurants offer the choice between a carvery and an à la carte menu. Room service is available for light meals.

All major credit cards are accepted.

For central reservations, call 0171 734 6000.

RADISSON EDWARDIAN

Radisson Edwardian Hotels' policy is to provide elegant hotel accommodation with high levels of service in the very heart of London's West End and near Heathrow. This includes concierge service, on-site parking at Heathrow, 24-hour room service, separate cocktail bar or wine bar, lounge service, and restaurants with international cuisine.

Bedroom decoration ranges from smart to luxurious, and all rooms have en suite facilities, CTV (with in-house movies at selected hotels) hair-dryer, trouser-press and direct-dial telephone. Suites are available.

The hotels offer luxurious furnishings and restful surroundings reminiscent of a country-house atmosphere, yet are ideally situated for London's shopping districts, theatres, museums and night life. They can also offer guests corporate hospitality at the top sporting occasions as well as a theatre and arts programme. Radisson Edwardian is the 'Preferred Partner' for Hertz, the 'London Hotel Partner' for British Airways and has a marketing partnership with Radisson International Hotels and SAS Hotels Worldwide.

The Savoy Court and Pastoria are smaller hotels offering a more informal range of services.

All major credit cards are accepted.

ROADCHEF LODGES

RoadChef Lodges offer high specification rooms at affordable prices in popular locations suited to both the business and private traveller. All rooms have private bathroom, CTV (including satellite channels), radio, self-dial telephone, tea and coffee-making facilities, hair-dryer and trouser press. Fax and photocopying facilities are available at Reception.

TRAVEL INN

Travel Inn is a rapidly expanding national network of high-quality, low-cost accommodation. There are nearly 150 properties, located on major 'A' roads and near motorways. They have ample parking, and are typically affiliated to an adjacent family restaurant and pub, such as Beefeater or Brewers' Fayre, serving breakfast, lunch and dinner. They are modern buildings, landscaped sympathetically with their surroundings, and include ground-floor rooms and at least one with special facilities for disabled travellers, as well as no-smoking rooms.

All bedrooms are a good size, with en suite bathroom, shower and w.c. Every room has remote-control CTV, radio/alarm clock, tea/coffee-making facilities and individually controlled central heating. The price is charged per room per night, accommodating up to two adults and two children aged up to 16 years old (family rooms are available at most Travel Inns). Reception is manned 24 hours a day.

All major credit cards are accepted.

For central reservations, call 01582 414341.

AA Award Winners for 1996/97

AA INSPECTORS' CHOICE HOTEL OF THE YEAR AWARDS

Photographs of these hotels have been used as the section operners for the appropriate country sections of the Hotels Directory.

ENGLAND

Carlyon Bay Hotel (Brend Group),
St Austell, Cornwall

SCOTLAND

Kirroughtree Hotel,
Newton Stewart, Dumfries & Galloway

WALES

Penhelig Arms Hotel (Welsh Rarebits),
Aberdovey, Gwynedd

IRELAND

Park Hotel (Relais & Chateau),
Kenmare, Co Kerry

COURTESY AND CARE AWARDS

ENGLAND

LONDON

Cannizaro House Hotel (Thistle),
SW19 *General Manager, Mr R Slade*

SOUTH-EAST

Bishop's Table Hotel (Consort),
Farnham, Surrey *Proprietor, Mr KK Verjee*

Donnington Valley Hotel,
Newbury, Berkshire
Managing Director, Mr I Leslie

SOUTH-WEST

Croyde Bay Hotel, Croyde, Devon
Proprietors, Mr and Mrs A Penny

Royal Crescent Hote (Queen's Moat House), Bath, Somerset
General Manager, Mr R Stevenson

MIDLANDS

Cottage in the Wood (Consort),
Malvern, Hereford & Worcester
Owners, Mrs M Pattin and family

Elms Hotel, Abberley,
Hereford & Worcester
Owners, Marcel and Corinna Frichot

NORTH

Wind in the Willows, Glossop, Derbyshire
Proprietor, Mr P Marsh

Vermont Hotel (TAZ Leisure),
Newcastle upon Tyne, Tyneside
General Manager, Nicky Hislop

IRELAND

NORTHERN IRELAND

Culloden House (Hastings), Belfast
Manager, Mr P Weston,
Deputy, Ms J McLornan

REPUBLIC OF IRELAND

Cahernane Hotel, Killarney, Co. Kerry
General Manager, Mr C O'Connell

SCOTLAND

Manor House Hotel, Oban, Argyllshire
General Manager, Miss M Wijker

Rufflets Country House Hotel,
St Andrews, Fife
Owner, Mrs A Russell, Manager, Mr J Angus

WALES

Bear Hotel, Crickhowell, Powys
Proprietors, Mr and Mrs Hindmarsh

Dolserau Hall, Dolgellau, Gwynedd
Proprietors, Mr and Mrs P Kaye

THISTLE HOTELS

Britain's Best Hotels

RED STAR AWARDS

A select number of hotels have gained this year's highest AA award that of Red Stars. Only about 3.2 per cent - around 144 - of the total number of star-rated hotels in Britain and Ireland gain this accolade, and there are only 10 new award winners this year. The new awards are highlighted and the hotels are presented in country and county order. For the full entry for each of these hotels, please refer to the appropriate country directories.

ENGLAND

BUCKINGHAMSHIRE

Aylesbury: ★★★★ **Hartwell House**
Taplow: ★★★★★ **Cliveden**

CHESHIRE

Chester: ★★★★ **Chester Grosvenor**
Nantwich ★★★ **Rooker y Hall**
Sandiway: ★★★ **Nunsmere Hall Country House**

CORNWALL & ISLES OF SCILLY

Liskeard: ★★ **Well House**
St Martin's ★★★ **St Martin's on the Isle**
Tresco: ★★★ **Island**

CUMBRIA

Alston: ★★ **Lovelady Shield**
Brampton: ★★★ **Farlam Hall**
Grasmere: ★★★ **Michael's Nook Country House**
Grasmere: ★ **White Moss House**
Howtown: ★★★ **Sharrow Bay Country House**
Keswick: ★ **Swinside Lodge**
Watermillock: ★★★ **Leeming House**
Watermillock: ★ **Old Church**
Windermere: ★★ **Holbeck Ghyll Country House**
Windermere: ★★ **Miller Howe**
Witherslack: ★ **Old Vicarage Country House**

DERBYSHIRE

Baslow: ★★★ **Cavendish Hotel**
★★ **Fischer's Baslow Hall**

DEVON

Barnstaple: ★ **Halmpstone Manor**
Chagford: ★★★ **Gidleigh Park**
Lewdown: ★★ **Lewtrenchard Manor**
Lynton ★ **Highcliffe Hotel**
South Molton: ★★ **Whitechapel Manor**
Whimple : ★★ **Woodhayes**

DORSET

Evershot: ★★★ **Summer Lodge**
Gillingham: ★★★ **Stock Hill Country House**
Wareham : ★★★ **Priory**
Wimborne Minster :
★★ **Beechleas**

ESSEX

Dedham: ★★★ **Maison Talbooth**

GLOUCESTERSHRE

Buckland: ★★★ **Buckland Manor**
Charingworth: ★★★ **Charingworth Manor**
Cheltenham: ★★★ **Greenway**
Cheltenham: ★★★ **Hotel on the Park**
Chipping Camden:
★★★ **Cotswold House**
Lower Slaughter:
★★★ **Lower Slaughter Manor**
Tetbury: ★★★ **Calcot Manor**
Tetbury: ★★★ **Close Hotel**
Thornbury: ★★★ **Thornbury Castle**

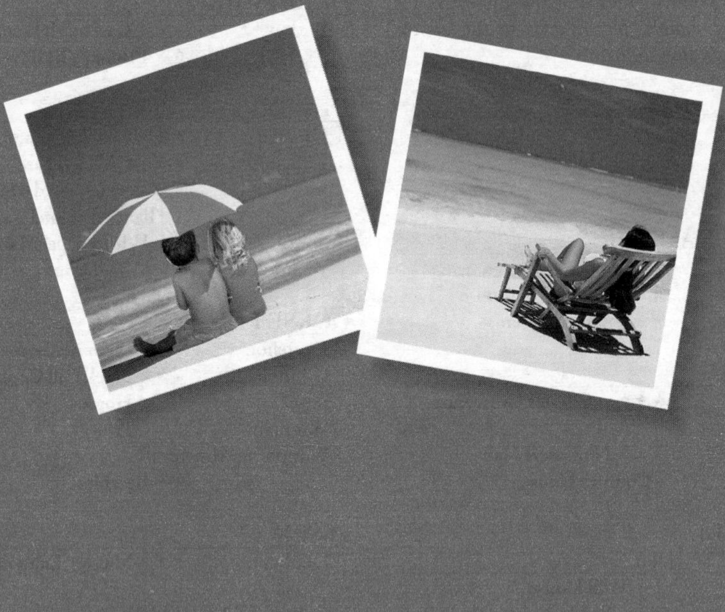

HAMPSHIRE

Highclere: ★★★ **Hollington Country House**
Lymington: ★★ **Gordleton Mill**
New Milton: ★★★★★ **Chewton Glen**
Rotherwick: ★★★★ **Tylney Hall**

HEREFORD & WORCESTER

Broadway: ★★★★ **Lygon Arms**
Leominster: ★ **Marsh Country Hotel**

KENT

Cranbrook ★★ **Kennel Holt Hotel**

LEICESTERSHIRE

Melton Mowbray: ★★★★ **Stapleford Park**

LONDON NW1

★★★★★ **Landmark**

LONDON SW1

★★★★★ **The Berkeley**
★★★★★ **Hyde Park**
★★★★★ **Lanesborough**
★★★★ **Goring**
★★★★ **Halkin**

LONDON SW3

★★★★ **Capital**

LONDON W1

★★★★★ **Claridges**
★★★★★ **Connaught**
★★★★★ **Dorchester**
★★★★★ **Four Seasons**
★★★★ **Athenaeum**
★★★★ **Brown's**

LONDON WC2

★★★★★ **Savoy**

NORFOLK

Blakeney: ★★ **Morston Hall**
Grimston: ★★★ **Congham Hall Country House**

NORTHUMBERLAND

Powburn: ★★ **Breamish House**

OXFORDSHIRE

Great Milton: ★★★★ **Le Manoir aux Quat' Saisons**

RUTLAND

Oakham ★★★ **Hambleton Hall**

SOMERSET

Bath ★★★ **Priory**
★★★ **Queensberry**
Dulverton: ★★ **Ashwick House**
Hinton Charterhouse: ★★★ **Homewood Park**
Hunstrete: ★★★ **Hunstrete House**
Porlock: ★★ **The Oaks**
Ston Easton ★★★★ **Ston Easton Park**
Taunton: ★★★ **Castle**
Wiveliscombe: ★★ **Langley House**
Yeovil: ★ **Little Barwick House**

SUFFOLK

Hintlesham: ★★★★ **Hintlesham Hall**

SURREY

Bagshot: ★★★★ **Pennyhill Park**
Gatwick ★★ **Langshott Manor**

SUSSEX - EAST

Battle: ★★★ **Netherfield Place**
Forest Row: ★★★★ **Ashdown Park**
Uckfield: ★★★ **Horsted Place Sporting Estate & Hotel**

SUSSEX - WEST

Amberley: ★★★ **Amberley Castle**
East Grinstead: ★★★ **Gravetye Manor**
Turners Hill: ★★★ **Alexander House**

WARWICKSHIRE

Leamington Spa: ★★★ **Mallory Court**
Leamington Spa: ★ **Lansdowne**

WEST MIDLANDS

Hockley Heath: ★★★ **Nuthurst Grange Country House**
Sutton Coldfield : ★★★★ **New Hall**

WILTSHIRE

Castle Combe: ★★★★ **Manor House**
Colerne: ★★★★ **Lucknam Park**

YORKSHIRE-NORTH

Bolton Abbey: ★★★ **Devonshire Arms Country House**
York: ★★★ **Grange**
York: ★★★ **Middlethorpe Hall**

CHANNEL ISLES-JERSEY

Rozel Bay: ★★★ **Chateau la Chaire**
St Saviour: ★★★★ **Longueville Manor**

SCOTLAND

ABERDEENSHIRE

Ballater: ★★ **Balgonie House**
Banchory: ★★★ **Banchory Lodge**
Bridge of Marnoch: ★★ **Old Manse of Marnoch**
Kildrummy: ★★★ **Kildrummy Castle**

ARGYLL & BUTE

Port Appin ★★★ **Airdes Hotel**

CITY OF GLASGOW

Glasgow: ★★★ **One Devonshire Gardens**

DUMFRIES & GALLOWAY

Auchencairn: ★★ **Collin House**
Moffat ★ **Well View**
Portpatrick: ★★ **Knockinaaam Lodge**

EAST LOTHIAN

Gullane: ★★★ **Greywalls**

FIFE

Markinch: ★★★★ **Balbirnie House**
Peat Inn: ★★ **Peat Inn**

HIGHLAND

Arisaig: ★★★ **Arisaig House**
Fort William: ★★★★ **Inverlochy Castle**
Inverness: ★★ **Dunain Park**
Kingussie ★★ **The Cross**
Whitebridge: ★★ **Knockie Lodge**

NORTH AYRSHIRE

Brodick ★★ **Kilmichael Country House**

PERTHSHIRE & KINROSS

Auchterarder: ★★★★★ **Gleneagles**
Blairgowrie ★★★ **Kinloch House**
Dunkeld: ★★★ **Kinnaird**

SOUTH AYRSHIRE

Maybole: ★★ **Ladyburn**
Turnberry: ★★★★★ **Turnberry Hotel**

STIRLING

Dunblane ★★★ Cromlix House

WALES

ABERCONWY & COLWYN

Betws-y-Coed ★★ **Tan-y-Foel Hotel**
Conwy ★★ **Old Rectory**
Llandudno ★★★ **Bodysgallen Hall**
Llandudno: ★★ **St Tudno**

ANGLESEY - ISLE OF

Llangefni: ★★★ **Tre-Ysgawen Hall**

CARDIGANSHIRE

Eglwysfach: ★★ **Ynyshir Hall**

DENBIGHSHIRE

Llandrillo: ★★ **Tyddyn Llan Country House**

GWYNEDD

Talsarnau: ★★ **Maes y Neuadd**

POWYS

Llangamarch Wells: ★★★ **Lake Country House**
Llyswen: ★★★★ **Llangoed Hall**

IRELAND

CO CLARE
Ballyvaughan: ★★★ **Gregans Castle**

CO CORK
Mallow: ★★★ **Longueville House**

CO DOWN
Annalong: ★★ **Glassdrumman Lodge**

CO GALWAY
Cashel: ★★★ **Cashel House**
Galway ★★★★ **Glenlo Abbey**

CO KERRY
Kenmare: ★★★★ **Park**
Kenmare: ★★★★ **Sheen Falls Lodge**

CO KILDARE
Straffan: ★★★★★ **Kildare Hotel & Country Club**

CO KILKENNY
Thomastown: ★★★★ **Mount Juliet Hotel**

CO LIMERICK
Adare: ★★★★ **Adare Manor**

CO WEXFORD
Gorey: ★★★ **Marlfield House**

CO WICKLOW
Rathnew: ★★★ **Tinakilly Country House & Restaurant**

Britain's Best Hotel Restaurants

with three or more AA Rosette Awards

Listed below are hotel restaurants where the cooking presentation of dishes and service are of such an exceptionally high standard as to merit the AA's three highest awards for quality of cuisine:

✿✿✿✿✿ Five rosettes is the supreme accolade, made to chefs at the very top of their profession. This award recognises superlative standards of cuisine at an international level, evident at every visit in every element of the meal. Creativity, skill and attention to detail will produce dishes cooked to perfection, with intense, exciting flavours in harmonious combinations and faultless presentation. Menus may be innovative or classical, and may use luxury ingredients like lobster, truffles, foie gras, etc. often in unexpected combinations and with secret ingredients that add an extra dimension of taste and interest.

✿✿✿✿ At this level, cuisine should be innovative, daring, highly accomplishedand achieve a noteworthy standard of consistency, accuracy and flair throughout all the elements of the meal. Excitement, vibrancy and superb technical skill will be the keynotes.

✿✿✿ Only cooking of the highest national standard receives three or more rosettes. Menus will be imaginative; dishes should be accurately cooked, demonstrate well developed technical skills and a high degree of flair in their composition. Ingredients will be first-class, usually from a range of specialist suppliers, including local produce only if its quality is excellent. Most items - breads, pastries, pasta, petits fours - will be made in the kitchens, but if any are bought in, for example, breads, the quality will be excellent.

✿✿✿✿✿ FIVE ROSETTES

LONDON

SW1: ✿✿✿✿✿ **The Restaurant, Hyde Park Hotel**

W1: ✿✿✿✿✿ **Nico at Ninety, Grosvenor House Hotel**

OXFORDSHIRE

Great Milton: ✿✿✿✿✿ **Le Manoir aux Quat' Saisons**

✿✿✿✿ FOUR ROSETTES

CUMBRIA

Grasmere: ✿✿✿✿ **Michael's Nook**

DEVON

Chagford: ✿✿✿✿ **Gidleigh Park**

LONDON

SW3: ✿✿✿✿ **Capital**

RUTLAND

Oakham: ✿✿✿✿ **Hambleton Hall**

SOMERSET

Taunton: ✿✿✿✿ **Castle**

✿✿✿ THREE ROSETTES - ENGLAND

BEDFORDSHIRE

Flitwick: ✿✿✿ **Flitwick Manor**

BERKSHIRE

Maidenhead: ✿✿✿ **Fredrick's**

Yattendon: ✿✿✿ **Royal Oak**

BUCKINGHAMSHIRE

Taplow: ✿✿✿ **Cliveden**

CHESHIRE

Chester: ✿✿✿ **The Chester Grosvenor**
✿✿✿ **Crabwall Manor**
Nantwich: ✿✿✿ **Rookery Hall**
Sandiway: ✿✿✿ **Nunsmere Hall**

CORNWALL

Liskeard: ✿✿✿ **Well House**
Padstow: ✿✿✿ **Seafood Restaurant**
St Martin's ✿✿✿ **St Martin's on the Isle**

CUMBRIA

Howtown: ✿✿✿ **Sharrow Bay**
Watermillock:
✿✿✿ **Rampsbeck**

DERBYSHIRE

Baslow: ✿✿✿ **Fischer's**

DEVON

Gulworthy: ✿✿✿ **Horn of Plenty**
Lifton: ✿✿✿ **Arundell Arms**
South Molton:
✿✿✿ **Whitechapel Manor**

DORSET

Evershot: ✿✿✿ **Summer Lodge**
Gillingham: ✿✿✿ **Stock Hill Country House**

GLOUCESTERSHIRE

Buckland (nr Broadway):
✿✿✿ **Buckland Manor**
Cheltenham:
✿✿✿ **Greenway**
Lower Slaughter:
✿✿✿ **Lower Slaughter Manor**
✿✿✿ **Washbourne Court**
Stow-on-the-Wold:
✿✿✿ **Wyck Hill House**
Upper Slaughter:
✿✿✿ **Lords of the Manor**

GREATER MANCHESTER

Bury: ✿✿✿ **Normandie**

HAMPSHIRE

Lymington: ✿✿✿ **Gordleton Mill**
New Milton: ✿✿✿ **Chewton Glen**
Highclere: ✿✿✿ **Hollington Country House**

HERTFORDSHIRE

Ware: ✿✿✿ **Marriott Hanbury Manor**

KENT

Ashford: ✿✿✿ **Eastwell Manor**
Dover: ✿✿✿ **Wallet's Court**
Folkestone ✿✿✿ **Sandgate**

LONDON

SW1: ✿✿✿ **Halkin**
SW1: ✿✿✿ **Lanesborough**
SW1: ✿✿✿ **Sheraton Park Tower**
W1: ✿✿✿ **Connaught**
W1: ✿✿✿ **Dorchester**
W1: ✿✿✿ **Inter-Continental**
W1: ✿✿✿ **Le Meridien Picadilly**
W1: ✿✿✿ **London Hilton on Park Lane**
W1: ✿✿✿ **Ritz**
W1: ✿✿✿ **St George's**
W11: ✿✿✿ **Halcyon**
WC2: ✿✿✿ **The Savoy**

OXFORDSHIRE

Moulsford: ✿✿✿ **Beetle & Wedge**

RUTLAND

Oakham: ✿✿✿ **Hambleton Hall**

SHROPSHIRE

Worfield: ✿✿✿ **Old Vicarage**

SOMERSET

Bath: ✿✿✿ **Royal Crescent Hotel**
Hinton Charterhouse:
✿✿✿ **Homewood Park**
Hunstrete: ✿✿✿ **Hunstrete House**
Ston Easton:
✿✿✿ **Ston Easton Park**
Williton: ✿✿✿ **White House**

SUFFOLK

Hintlesham:
✿✿✿ **Hintlesham Hall**

SURREY

Bagshot: ✿✿✿ **Pennyhill Park**

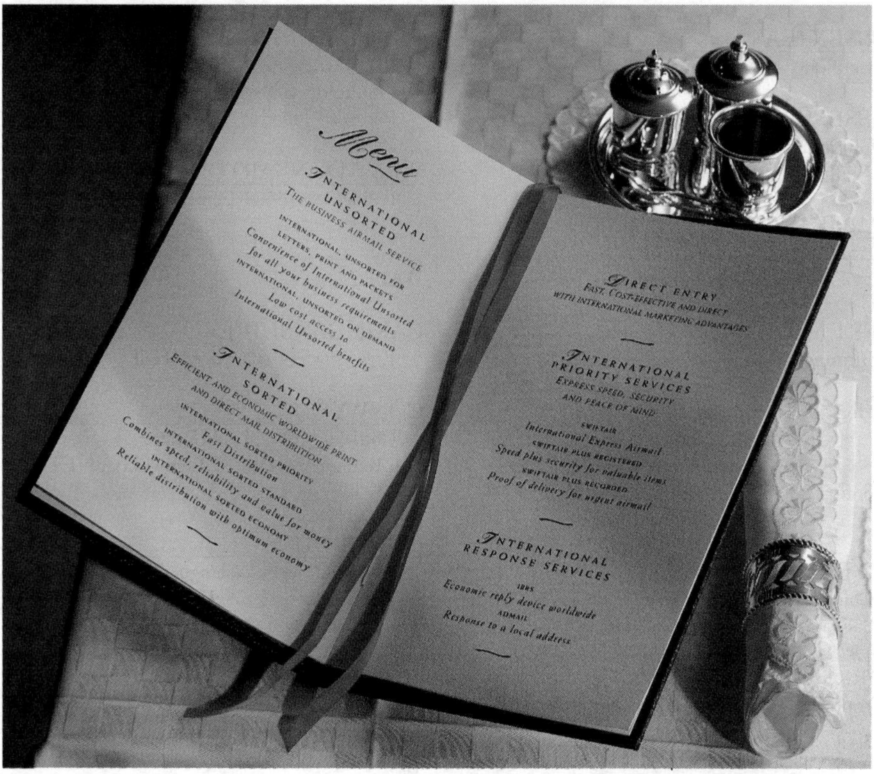
Menu
INTERNATIONAL UNSORTED
The business airmail service
INTERNATIONAL UNSORTED FOR LETTERS, PRINT AND PACKETS
Convenience of International Unsorted for all your business requirements
INTERNATIONAL UNSORTED ON DEMAND
Low cost access to International Unsorted benefits
INTERNATIONAL SORTED
EFFICIENT AND ECONOMIC WORLDWIDE PRINT AND DIRECT MAIL DISTRIBUTION
INTERNATIONAL SORTED PRIORITY
Fast Distribution
INTERNATIONAL SORTED STANDARD
Combines speed, reliability and value for money
INTERNATIONAL SORTED ECONOMY
Reliable distribution with optimum economy
DIRECT ENTRY
FAST, COST-EFFECTIVE AND DIRECT WITH INTERNATIONAL MARKETING ADVANTAGES
INTERNATIONAL PRIORITY SERVICES
EXPRESS SPEED, SECURITY AND PEACE OF MIND
SWIFTAIR
International Express Airmail
SWIFTAIR PLUS REGISTERED
Speed plus security for valuable items
SWIFTAIR PLUS RECORDED
Proof of delivery for urgent airmail
INTERNATIONAL RESPONSE SERVICES
IBRS
Economic reply device worldwide
ADMAIL
Response to a local address

SUSSEX (EAST)

Uckfield: ❀❀❀ **Horsted Place**

SUSSEX (WEST)

Climping: ❀❀❀ **Bailiffscourt**
Midhurst: ❀❀❀ **Angel**

WARWICKSHIRE

Leamington Spa:
❀❀❀ **Mallory Court**

WEST MIDLANDS

Birmingham:
❀❀❀ **Swallow Hotel**
Hockley Heath:
❀❀❀ **Nuthurst Grange Country House**
Sutton Coldfield:
❀❀❀ **New Hall**

WILTSHIRE

Colerne: ❀❀❀ **Lucknam Park**
Salisbury: ❀❀❀ **Howard's House**

YORKSHIRE - NORTH

York: ❀❀❀ **Middlethorpe Hall**

CHANNEL ISLANDS

JERSEY

St Saviour: ❀❀❀ **Longueville Manor**

SCOTLAND

ARGYLL & BUTE

Port Appin: ❀❀❀ **Airds**

CITY OF GLASGOW

Glasgow: ❀❀❀ **One Devonshire Gardens**

DUMFRIES & GALLOWAY

Auchencairn:
❀❀❀ **Collin House**
Portpatrick: ❀❀❀ **Knockinaam Lodge**

FIFE

Peat Inn: ❀❀❀ **Peat Inn**

HIGHLAND

Fort William:
❀❀❀ **Inverlochy Castle**
Kingussie: ❀❀❀ **The Cross**

PERTHSHIRE & KINROSS

Blairgowrie: ❀❀❀ **Kinloch House**
Dunkeld: ❀❀❀ **Kinnaird Hotel**
Perth: ❀❀❀ **Newmiln Country Estate**

WEST DUNBARTONSHIRE

Balloch: ❀❀❀ **Cameron House**

WALES

CARDIGANSHIRE

Eglwysfach: ❀❀❀ **Ynishir Hall**

CONWY

Conwy: ❀❀❀ **Old Rectory**
Llandudno: ❀❀❀ **St Tudno** GWYNEDD

GWYNEDD

Llyswen: ❀❀❀ **Llangoed Hall**
Reynoldston: ❀❀❀ **Fairy Hill**
Talsarnau: ❀❀❀ **Maes y Neuadd**

MONMOUTHSHIRE

Whitebrook: ❀❀❀ **Crown at Whitebrook**

IRELAND

CO CORK

Mallow: ❀❀❀ **Longueville House**

CO DONEGAL

Donegal: ❀❀❀ **Harvey's Point Country Hotel**

CO DUBLIN

Dublin: ❀❀❀ **Hibernian Hotel**

CO KERRY

Kenmare: ❀❀❀ **Park Hotel Kenmore**
Killarney: ❀❀❀ **Aghadoe Heights**

CO KILDARE

Straffan: ❀❀❀ **Kildare Hotel & Country Club**

CO LIMERICK

Adare: ❀❀❀ **Dunraven Arms**

Romantic Hotels

ENGLAND

ABBERLEY, The Elms
ABBOT'S SALFORD, Salford Hall
ALDERMINSTER, Ettington Park
ALFRISTON, The Star Inn
ALSTON, Lovelady Shield
ALTARNUN, Penhallow Manor
AMBERLEY, Amberley Castle
AMBLESIDE, Nanny Brow
AMBLESIDE, Wateredge
AMERSHAM, The Crown
APPLEBY-IN-WESTMORLAND, Tufton Arms
APPLETON-LE-MOORS, Appleton Hall
ARNCLIFFE, Amerdale House
ASHBOURNE, Callow Hall
ASHFORD, Eastwell Manor
AUSTWICK, The Traddock
AXMINSTER, Lea Hill
AYLESBURY, Hartwell House

BAGSHOT, Pennyhill Park
BALSALL COMMON, Nailcote Hall
BAMBURGH, Waren House
BANBURY, Whately Hall
BANBURY, Wroxton House
BASINGSTOKE, Audleys Wood
BASLOW, Fischer's Baslow Hall
BASSENTHWAITE, Castle Inn
BASSENTHWAITE, Overwater Hall
BATH, Bath Spa
BATH, Old Mill
BATH, Priory
BATH, Queensberry
BATH, Royal Crescent
BATTLE, Burnt Wood House
BEAULIEU, Montagu Arms
BELPER, Makeney Hall
BIBURY, Swan
BICESTER, Bignell Park Hotel & Restaurant
BINGLEY, Oakwood Hall
BIRMINGHAM, Jonathans'
BIRMINGHAM, J Lombard Room Restaurant & Mill House
BIRMINGHAM, J Swallow
BLACKBURN, Millstone
BLAKENEY, Morston Hall
BOLTON ABBEY, Devonshire Arms
BOLTON, Last Drop
BOSHAM, Millstream
BOURNEMOUTH, Langtry Manor
BRAITHWAITE, Ivy House
BRAMPTON, Farlam Hall
BREADSALL, Marriott Breadsall Priory
BRIGHTON, The Grand
BRISTOL, Swallow Royal
BROADWAY, The Lygon Arms
BROCKENHURST, New Park Manor
BROCKENHURST, Rhinefield House
BROCKENHURST, Whitley Ridge
BROME, Cornwallis Arms
BUCKLAND, Buckland Manor
BURFORD, Golden Pheasant
BURFORD, The Bay Tree
BURLEY, Burley Manor
BURTON UPON TRENT, Riverside
BUXTON, Lee Wood
CAMBERLEY, Frimley Hall
CASTLE ASHBY, Falcon
CASTLE COMBE, Castle Inn
CASTLE COMBE, Manor House
CHAGFORD, Easton Court
CHAGFORD, Gidleigh Park
CHAGFORD, Mill End
CHARINGWORTH, Charingworth Manor
CHELMSFORD, Pontlands Park
CHELTENHAM, Greenway
CHELTENHAM, Hotel on the Park
CHENIES, Bedford Arms Thistle
CHESTER, Blossoms
CHESTER, Chester Grosvenor
CHILLINGTON, White House
CHIPPING CAMPDEN, Cotswold House
CHOLLERFORD, George
CIRENCESTER, Stratton House
CLANFIELD, Plough at Clanfield
CLIMPING, Bailiffscourt
COGGESHALL, White Hart
COLERNE, Lucknam Park
CRANBROOK, Kennel Holt

CRATHORNE, Crathorne Hall
CROSBY-ON-EDEN, Crosby Lodge
CROYDE, Croyde Bay House
CUCKFIELD, Ockenden Manor
DARTFORD, Rowhill Grange
DEDHAM, Maison Talbooth
DORKING, Burford Bridge
DOVER, Wallett's Court
DUNSTER, Luttrell Arms
EASINGTON, Grinkle Park
EAST GRINSTEAD, Gravetye Manor
EVESHAM, Riverside
EVESHAM, Mill At Harvington
FOLKESTONE, Sandgate
GITTISHAM, Combe House
GLOSSOP, Wind in the Willows
GLOUCESTER, Hatton Court
GRASMERE, Gold Rill
GRASMERE, Michael's Nook
GRASMERE, Prince of Wales Thistle
GRASMERE, Swan
GRASMERE, White Moss House
GREAT MILTON, Le Manoir Aux Quat' Saisons
GRIMSTON, Congham Hall
GUILDFORD, Angel Posting House and Livery
HACKNESS, Hackness Grange Country
HALIFAX, Holdsworth House
HARROGATE, Old Swan
HARROGATE, White House
HASTINGS & ST LEONARDS, Beauport Park
HAYES, Radisson Edwardian
HELMSLEY, Black Swan
HELSTON, Nansloe Manor
HINCKLEY, Sketchley Grange
HINTLESHAM, Hintlesham Hall
HOCKLEY HEATH, Nuthurst Grange
HOLFORD, Combe House
HORLEY, Stanhill Court
HORTON-CUM-STUDLEY, Studley Priory
HOWTOWN, Sharrow Bay
HUNSTRETE, Hunstrete House
HURSTBOURNE TARRANT, Esseborne Manor
HYTHE, Hythe Imperial
KESWICK, Keswick
KESWICK, Swinside Lodge
KINGSBRIDGE, Buckland-Tout-Saints
KNARESBOROUGH, Dower House
LASTINGHAM, Lastingham Grange
LAVENHAM, Swan
LEAMINGTON SPA, Adams
LEEDS, 42 The Calls
LEEDS, Haley's Hotel & Restaurant
LEEDS, Oulton Hall
LEICESTER, Belmont House
LEWDOWN, Lewtrenchard Manor
LEWES, Shelleys
LIFTON, Arundell Arms
LISKEARD, Well House
LONDON NW1, Landmark
LONDON SW19, Cannizaro House
LONDON SW1,
LONDON SW1, Berkeley
LONDON SW1, Halkin
LONDON SW1, Hyatt Carlton Tower
LONDON SW1, Lowndes
LONDON SW1, Stafford
LONDON SW3
LONDON SW3, Capital
LONDON W1, Athenaeum
LONDON W1, Berkshire
LONDON W1, Brown's
LONDON W1, Claridge's
LONDON W1, Connaught
LONDON W1, Dorchester
LONDON W1, Inter-Continental
LONDON W1, Langham Hilton
LONDON W1, Leonard
LONDON W1, London Hilton on Park Lane
LONDON W1, May Fair Inter-Continental
LONDON W1, Le Meridien Piccadilly
LONDON W1, Ritz
LONDON W1, Westbury
LONDON W2
LONDON W2, Whites
LONDON WC1, Blooms
LONDON WC2, Hampshire
LONDON WC2, Savoy
LONDON WC2, Waldorf Meridien
LONG MELFORD, Bull
LOWER BEEDING, South Lodge
LOWER SLAUGHTER, Lower Slaughter Manor
LOWER SLAUGHTER, Washbourne Court

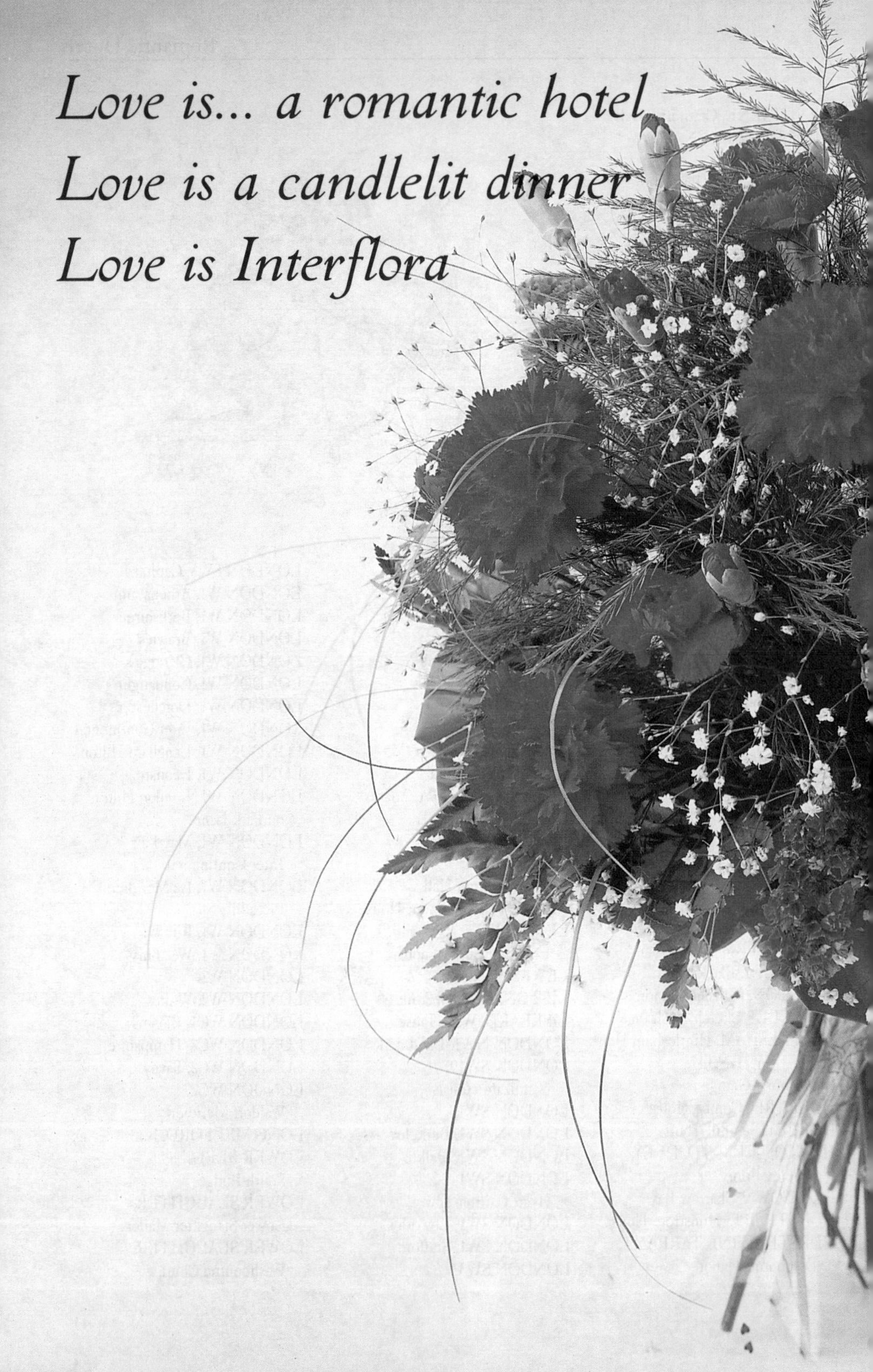
Love is... a romantic hotel
Love is a candlelit dinner
Love is Interflora

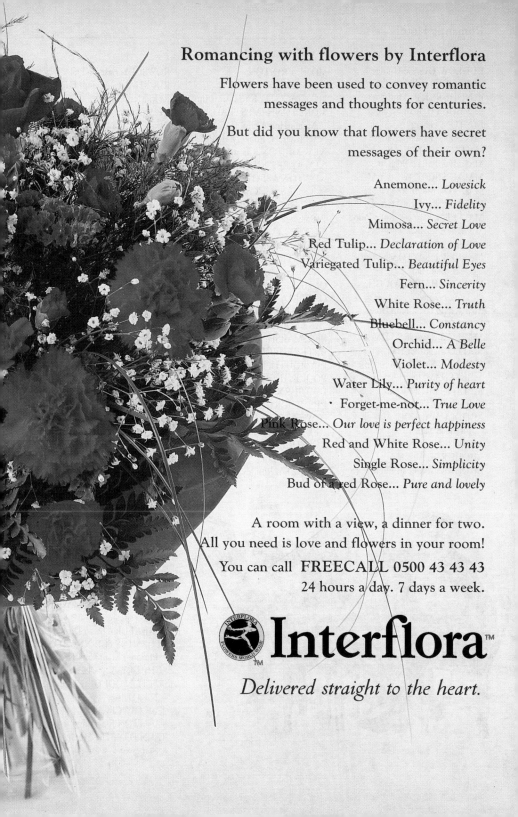

LUDLOW, Overton Grange
LUDLOW, Feathers at Ludlow
LYNDHURST, Parkhill
LYNMOUTH, Rising Sun
LYNTON, Hewitts
LYNTON, Highcliffe House
MAIDENHEAD, Fredrick's
MALMESBURY, Old Bell
MALMESBURY, Whatley Manor
MALTON, Burythorpe House
MALTON, Newstead Grange
MALVERN, Cottage in the Wood
MANCHESTER, Victoria & Albert
MARKET DRAYTON, Goldstone Hall
MARKET HARBOROUGH, Three Swans
MARKINGTON, Hob Green
MARLOW, Compleat Angler
MARLOW, Danesfield House
MATLOCK, Riber Hall
MAWNAN SMITH, Meudon
MELKSHAM, Beechfield House
MELTON MOWBRAY, Stapleford Park
MIDDLE WALLOP, Fifehead Manor
MIDDLEHAM, Millers House
MIDHURST, Angel
MIDHURST, Spread Eagle
MONK FRYSTON, Monk Fryston Hall
MONTACUTE, Kings Arms Inn
MORETONHAMPSTEAD, Manor House
NANTWICH, Rookery Hall
NEW MILTON, Chewton Glen
NEWBY BRIDGE, Lakeside
NEWTON ABBOT, The Ilsington Country
NORTHALLERTON, Solberge Hall
NUTFIELD, Nutfield Priory
OAKHAM, Hambleton Hall
OSWESTRY, Pen-y-Dyffryn Country
OUNDLE, Talbot
OXFORD, The Randolph
PAINSWICK, Painswick
PANGBOURNE, Copper Inn
PEASMARSH, Flackley Ash
PETERBOROUGH, Orton Hall
PLYMOUTH, Kitley
POOLE, Haven
POWBURN, Breamish House
PRESTBURY, White House Manor
REDRUTH, Aviary Court
ROSEDALE ABBEY, Milburn Arms
ROTHLEY, Rothley Court
ROWSLEY, East Lodge
RUCKHALL, Ancient Camp Inn
RYE, Mermaid Inn
ST ALBANS, Noke Thistle
ST AUSTELL, Boscundle Manor
ST KEYNE, Old Rectory House
ST MARTIN'S, St Martin's on the Isle
ST MARY'S, Star Castle
ST MAWES, Idle Rocks
SALCOMBE, Tides Reach
SALISBURY, Howard's House
SCARBOROUGH, Wrea Head Country
SCILLY, ISLES OF, TRESCO, New Inn
SCILLY, ISLES OF, TRESCO, Island
SEAHOUSES, Olde Ship
SENNEN, Old Success Inn
SETTLE, Falcon Manor
SHEFFIELD, Whitley Hall
SHREWSBURY, Albright Hussey
SILCHESTER, Romans
SIMONSBATH, Simonsbath House
SIX MILE BOTTOM, Swynford Paddocks
SOUTH MOLTON, Marsh Hall
STANSTEAD ABBOTS, Briggens House
STOKE GABRIEL, Gabriel Court
STON EASTON, Ston Easton Park
STOW-ON-THE-WOLD, Grapevine
STOW-ON-THE-WOLD, Wyck Hill House
STRATFORD-UPON-AVON, Billesley Manor
STRATFORD-UPON-AVON, Shakespeare
STREATLEY, Swan Diplomat
STURMINSTER NEWTON, Plumber Manor
SUDBURY, Boar's Head
SUTTON COLDFIELD, New Hall
TAPLOW, Cliveden
TAUNTON, Farthings
TAUNTON, The Mount Somerset

TELFORD, Madeley Court
TETBURY, Calcot Manor
TETBURY, The Close
THORNTON HOUGH, Thornton Hall
TINTAGEL, Trebrea Lodge
TORQUAY, Imperial
TORQUAY, Osborne
TURNERS HILL, Alexander House
TWO BRIDGES, Prince Hall
UPHOLLAND, Holland Hall
UPPER SLAUGHTER, Lords of the Manor
WAKEFIELD, Waterton Park
WALSALL, Fairlawns at Aldridge
WARE, Marriott Hanbury Manor
WARMINSTER, Bishopstrow House
WATERMILLOCK, Leeming House
WATERMILLOCK, Old Church
WATERMILLOCK, Rampsbeck
WELLS, Swan
WENTBRIDGE, Wentbridge House
WEST WITTON, Wensleydale Heifer Inn
WEYBRIDGE, Ship Thistle
WHEDDON CROSS, Raleigh Manor
WILMSLOW, Mottram Hall
WINCHESTER, Lainston House
WINDERMERE, Burn How Garden House
WINDERMERE, Fayrer Garden House
WINDERMERE, Gilpin Lodge
WINDERMERE, Hillthwaite House
WINDERMERE, Holbeck Ghyll
WINDERMERE, Langdale Chase
WINDERMERE, Linthwaite House
WINDERMERE, Miller Howe
WINDERMERE, Wild Boar
WINDSOR, Castle
WINDSOR, Oakley Court
WINSFORD, Royal Oak Inn
WOODBRIDGE, Seckford Hall
WOODSTOCK, Bear
WOOKEY HOLE, Glencot House
WORFIELD, Old Vicarage
YARMOUTH, George
YATTENDON, Royal Oak
YORK, Dean Court
YORK, Fairfield Manor
YORK, Grange
YORK, Middlethorpe Hall
YORK, Mount Royale

CHANNEL ISLANDS

ROZEL BAY, Chateau La Chaire
SARK, Stocks Island
ST SAVIOUR, Longueville Manor

SCOTLAND

ABERFELDY, Guinach House
ABOYNE, Birse Lodge
ALLOA, Gean House
ARCHIESTOWN, Archiestown
ARDELVE, Conchra House
ARDENTINNY, Ardentinny
ARDUAINE, Loch Melfort
ARDVASAR, Ardvasar
ARISAIG, Arisaig House
AUCHENCAIRN, Balcary Bay
AUCHENCAIRN, Collin House
AUCHTERARDER, Auchterarder House
AUCHTERARDER, Cairn Lodge
AUCHTERHOUSE, Old Mansion House
BALLATER, Balgonie
BALLATER, Darroch Learg
BALLOCH, Cameron House
BALQUHIDDER, Monachyle Mhor
BANCHORY, Banchory Lodge
BANCHORY, Raemoir House
BANCHORY, Tor-na-Coille
BLAIRGOWRIE, Kinloch House
BRAEMAR, Invercauld Arms
BRIDGE OF MARNOCH, Old Manse of Marnoch
BRODICK, Auchrannie
CANNICH, Mullardoch House
CHIRNSIDE, Chirnside Hall
CONTIN, Coul House
DINGWALL, Kinkell House
DULNAIN BRIDGE, Muckrach Lodge
DUNBLANE, Cromlix House

EDINBURGH, Balmoral
EDINBURGH, Caledonian
EDINBURGH, Marriott Dalmahoy
EDINBURGH, Norton House Hotel & Restaurant
EDINBURGH, Sheraton Grand
ELGIN, Mansion House
ERISKA, Isle of Eriska
FORRES, Ramnee
FORT WILLIAM, Inverlochy Castle
FORT WILLIAM, Moorings
GIFFORD, Tweeddale Arms
GLAMIS, Castleton House
GLASGOW, Malmaison
GLASGOW, One Devonshire Gardens
GLASGOW, Devonshire Hotel of Glasgow
GLENFINNAN, Princes House
GLENROTHES, Rescobie
GRANTOWN-ON-SPEY, Garth
GULLANE, Greywalls
HUMBIE, Johnstounburn House
INVERGARRY, Glengarry Castle
INVERMORISTON, Glenmoriston Arms
INVERNESS, Bunchrew House
INVERNESS, Culloden House
INVERNESS, Dunain Park
INVERNESS, Loch Ness House
ISLE ORNSAY, Hotel Eilean Iarmain
ISLE ORNSAY, Kinloch Lodge
KELSO, Sunlaws House Hotel & Golf Course
KILCHRENAN, Ardanaiseig

KILCHRENAN, Taychreggan
KILDRUMMY, Kildrummy Castle
KILFINAN, Kilfinan
KINGUSSIE, The Cross
LETHAM, Fernie Castle
MARKINCH, Balbirnie House
MAYBOLE, Ladyburn
MUIR OF ORD, Ord House
MUIR OF ORD, Dower House
NEWBURGH, Udny Arms
NEWTON STEWART, Kirroughtree
OBAN, Manor House
ONICH, Allt-Nan-Ros
PEAT INN, The Peat Inn
PEEBLES, Cringletie House
PERTH, Huntingtower
PERTH, Newmiln Country Estate
PITLOCHRY, Pine Trees
PLOCKTON, Haven
PORT APPIN, Airds
PORT OF MENTEITH, Lake
PORTPATRICK, Knockinaam Lodge
PORTREE, Rosedale
ROTHES, Rothes Glen
ST ANDREWS, Rufflets
ST ANDREWS, St Andrews Golf Hotel
ST BOSWELLS, Dryburgh Abbey
SCALASAIG, Colonsay
SKEABOST BRIDGE, Skeabost House
SPITTAL OF GLENSHEE, Dalmunzie House
STEWARTON, Chapeltoun House
STRACHUR, Creggans Inn
STRONTIAN, Kilcamb Lodge
TORRIDON, Loch Torridon
TURNBERRY, Turnberry Hotel
WHITEBRIDGE, Knockie Lodge

WALES

ABERDYFI, Penhelig Arms
ABERDYFI, Plas Penhelig
ABERSOCH, Porth Tocyn
BALA, Pale Hall
BARMOUTH, Ty'r Graig Castle
BEAUMARIS, Ye Olde Bulls Head Inn
BEDDGELERT, Sygun Fawr
BETWS-Y-COED, Craig-y-Dderwen
BETWS-Y-COED, Tan-y-Foel
BONTDDU, Bontddu Hall
BRIDGEND, Coed-y-Mwstwr
CAERNARFON, Seiont Manor
CHEPSTOW, Marriott St Pierre
CONWY, Old Rectory
CRICCIETH, Bron Eifion
CRICCIETH, Parciau Mawr
DOLGELLAU, Dolmelynllyn Hall
DOLGELLAU, Penmaenuchaf Hall
FISHGUARD, Tregynon Country Farmhouse
LLANBEDR, Cae Nest Hall
LLANDDEINIOLEN, Ty'n Rhos
LLANDEGLA, Bod Idris Hall
LLANDRILLO, Tyddyn Llan
LLANDUDNO, Bodysgallen Hall
LLANDUDNO, St Tudno
LLANGAMMARCH WELLS, Lake
LLANGOLLEN, Bryn Howel
LLANRWST, The Priory
LLYSWEN, Llangoed Hall
NANNERCH, Old Mill
NORTHOP, Soughton Hall
PEMBROKE, Court
PENRHYNDEUDRAETH, Hotel Portmeirion
REYNOLDSTON, Fairyhill
RUTHIN, Ruthin Castle
TAL-Y-LLYN, Minffordd
TAL-Y-LLYN, Tyn-y-Cornel
TALSARNAU, Hotel Maes y Neuadd
TREFRIW, Hafod House

NORTHERN IRELAND

ANNALONG, Glassdrumman Lodge
BALLYMENA, Galgorm Manor
MAGHERA, Ardtara

REPUBLIC OF IRELAND

CLIFDEN, Rock Glen
GALWAY, Glenlo Abbey
KENMARE, Sheen Falls Lodge
KILLARNEY, Muckross Park Hotel Ltd
RECESS, Lough Inagh Lodge
THOMASTOWN, Mount Juliet Hotel

Romance is in the Air

As you take a quick glance through this guide you will notice a number of rose motifs beside hotel entries. This is because we have designated 1997 as the Year for Romance for no better reason than that any time is a fine time for romance. And what better way to spend a romantic evening or weekend with your loved one than in one of the 400 or more hotels which have been specially selected by our inspectorate as being particularly romantic in this year's guide, See the quick reference list starting on page 40. Remember also to enter our readers' Prize Draw, and you may ebe the lucky winner of a free romantic weekend break at a hotel in the Virgin Collection, with dinner and a champagne breakfast, plus a bouquet of flowers from Interflora. See the card inside the front cover for details.

Romantic Review

We sent out a survey to the hotels our inspectors had nominated to discover how romantic they really are; whether they provide champagne-and-roses weekend breaks, have wedding ceremonies performed in their grounds and whether they organise something special for Valentine's Day. As well as the answers to these questions we were given a lot more information which only strengthens the view that as a nation we really are a bunch of misty-eyed romantics!

In this Hotel, I thee Wed...

Since the revision of the wedding laws last year in England and Wales, many hotels are now licensed to hold the actual wedding ceremony on their premises rather than just the reception. And very popular venues they have proved to be too! Since the change in the laws Farthings Hotel in Somerset has organised 20 wedding ceremonies in its grounds and has 40 more planned for this year. The Greenway in Gloucestershire was one of the first hotels in England to obtain a licence and weddings are held in the oak-panelled Marriage Ceremony room. At Chewton Glen in Hampshire the ceremony is conducted in the sunlit Morning Room while 70 acres of gardens and parkland provide plenty of room for the guests to wander around in afterwards. The Savoy in London has two rooms licensed for weddings: the Lancaster Ballroom and the Abraham Lincoln Room.

ROMANCE IS IN THE AIR

The Savoy's popularity is based on its fame and its location overlooking the River Thames, yet other hotels make equally attractive venues because of their romantic appearance and gardens, or, as in the case of Knockinaam Lodge in Scotland, its proximity to the Irish Sea. The hotel is surrounded on three sides by cliffs which plunge dramatically into the foaming waters, but the hotelier didn't reveal whether all brides-to-be are automatically kitted out with sou'westers to put on over their wedding dresses!

Scotland, of course, has been performing wedding ceremonies in hotels for centuries. The Isle of Eriska Hotel has not only been used as a wedding venue for many years, but the owner, Robin Buchanan-Smith, is a minister of the Church of Scotland and so performs the wedding ceremonies at the hotel himself, making the whole event a truly family-run affair.

MYTH AND LEGEND

Two hotels are specially memorable for their romantic associations. Lainston House, outside Winchester, was the secret venue in 1742 for the wedding of the feisty Lady Elizabeth Chudleigh and Viscount Hervey. There were no witnesses at this clandestine wedding and soon after the event Viscount Hervey went away to sea. On his return 25 years later he found that his wife had bigamously married the Duke of Kingston. The result of the lawsuit that followed was the introduction of the wedding banns, which still have to be read in public on three occasions before a wedding can take place, unless a special licence is obtained.

Nick Wainford, the proprietor of the Well House Hotel in Liskeard, Cornwall, tells of the legend of St Keyne's Well, which lies next to his hotel and has attracted romantic couples since the 15th century. St Keyne, who lived in the area in the early Middle Ages, desired 'Peace on Earth' above all things and was concerned that wives were merely the property of their husbands. She therefore put a spell on the well, which dictated that whoever drank its water - whether man or wife - would be master for life. This legend has attracted many couples to Well House, but rather than racing to the well Nick Wainford suggests that the couple share a glass together and enjoy life in peaceful harmony!

'I hastn'd as soon as the wedding was done,
And left my wife in the porch:
But, i'faith she had been wiser than me,
For she took a bottle to Church!

LOVE IS ALL AROUND

Hotels play an important role in the process of a blossoming romance - they are the places where lovers go for an intimate candlelit meal on Valentine's Day, and where sometimes under the influence of champagne, soft music and good food some couples give in to temptation. At 42 The Calls in Leeds the night porter witnessed a rather unconventional use of the lift, while at the Swallow Royal Hotel in Bristol an amorous couple were discovered in the early hours of the morning making love on top of a grand piano in the front lobby!

ROMANCE IS IN THE AIR

THE COMEDY OF ERRORS

Since the time of those star-crossed lovers Romeo and Juliet the course of true love has never run smoothly - but at least they didn't have a wedding reception to organise. A lot of hotels have horror stories of staff tripping up into the wedding cake and of wedding cakes melting in heat waves. Then there are bees in the bride's bouquet, and the owners of Nutfield Priory in Redhill recall one very embarrassing wedding reception where the bride's buttons burst open, followed by the general manager having to ask the mother-in-law to return the silver cruets she had smuggled into her handbag... .

The knight-to-the-rescue award must go, however, to the Oulton Hall Hotel in West Yorkshire. The bride and groom were travelling from the church by horse-drawn carriage so they were expected to arrive after their guests, yet as the minutes ticked by and there was still no sign of the happy couple. A few minutes later the phone rang and an out-of-breath groom gasped 'the nag's gone lame!' The hotel organised its minibus to gallop up to save the day

A FISHY TALE

Many are the practical jokes played on departing newly weds. Many seem to involve fish. Ockendon Manor Hotel in West Sussex remembers a couple's car which was completely covered in clingfilm with a kipper left on the radiator, while the Royal Crescent Hotel in Bath recalls a similar incident of a kipper being concealed in the column of the car's steering wheel. The Hotel on the Park in Cheltenham tells of a couple departing on a touring holiday eventually discovering a mackerel decomposing under the driver's car seat! It's hard to say whether that was preferable to the three geese and one duck which waddled out of a couple's BMW in Devon... Chewton Glen's recollection of 25 hidden alarm clocks going off at all times throughout the night in the Bridal Suite seems quite mild in comparison.

ROMANCE IS IN THE AIR

A WHIRLPOOL ROMANCE

Hoteliers will bend over backwards to make an evening memorable for the romantic couple; it seems that nothing is too difficult to arrange. Nearly all our nominated hotels provide a four poster bed, champagne and flowers in the bedroom if they know their guests are celebrating a honeymoon or anniversary there. The Castle Inn at Castle Combe provides the lovers with a room with a jacuzzi in which many a proposal has taken place, while the Ancient Camp Inn near Eaton Bishop offers the River Room, which looks straight onto the River Wye. In the bathroom the bath has been raised by two feet, allowing bathers a similar view! At the Compleat Angler in Marlow the management will arrange a boat trip along the Thames with a guitarist to serenade the couple, while on one occasion 42, The Calls at Leeds filled a room - on request - with 90 bunches of daffodils!

POPPING THE QUESTION

When asked about the most romantic thing which has taken place at a hotel, we were flooded with replies. We never realised there were so many ways to ask the question, 'Will you marry me?' One innovative chap had a word with the barman at the Millstone Hotel in Lancashire, and placed an engagement ring in an ice cube which was served in a pre-dinner drink to his girlfriend. It must have come as quite a surprise to her - and he was very lucky she didn't swallow the diamond. The Waterton Park Hotel in Wakefield recalls a similar incident where a man carrying 10 balloons proposed to his girlfriend. The engagement ring had been placed in one of them and the girlfriend had to pop all the balloons to find it!

For sheer romance it's hard to beat the tale from Le Manoir Aux Quat'Saisons at Great Milton. When the couple arrived the lady was whisked upstairs to the round Dovecot bedroom, where a bottle of champagne and note telling her to look out the window were waiting for her. Outside was her boyfriend, clutching a red rose with a violinist beside him. He read some poetry and then proposed, and everyone was delighted - and relieved! - when the lady said yes.

Yet it isn't always the man who asks the all-important question. The Greenway at Cheltenham remembers one couple who had just finished dinner at the hotel. The lady then signalled to the head waiter, who brought out a surprise cake with the words 'Will You Marry Me?' piped across the top. Coffee was served when he accepted!

England

Inspectors' Choice Hotel of the Year: Carlyon Bay, St Austell

A

ABBERLEY Hereford & Worcester Map 07 SO76

★★★78% **Elms**

WR6 6AT (on A443 between Worcester and Tenbury Wells 2m beyond Great Witley)
☎ 01299 896666 FAX 01299 896804

The Elms is a very special hotel not least for the warmth of welcome offered by Marcel and Corinna Frichot and their highly professional staff who strike exactly the right balance of warmth and correctness. The grounds alone are worth a visit with manicured lawns to the front and a formal garden to the rear which affords excellent views over the lovely countryside. Rooms are all very spacious and are full of the nice extra touches which mark out a hotel of this class. The foyer features some remarkable time-pieces and the lounge and bar are full of comfy sofas where it is easy to relax and be tempted to sample some of the large range of malt whiskies. The cuisine is very French in feel. Owners and staff here have won the AA Courtesy and Care Award for 1996/7.

16 en suite (bth/shr) CTV in all bedrooms Night porter 61P Tennis (hard) Croquet lawn Putting green Xmas English & French Cuisine V meals Coffee am Tea pm No smoking in restaurant Last d 9pm

ROOMS: (incl. bkfst) s £75-£90; d £110-£135 * **LB**
MEALS: Lunch £12.50-£15.95 Dinner fr £22.50&alc
CONF: Thtr 60 Class 30 Board 24 Del from £130
CARDS:

ABBOT'S SALFORD Warwickshire Map 04 SP05

★★★❀❀77% **Salford Hall**

WR11 5UT (8m W of Stratford-upon Avon on B439)
☎ 01386 871300 FAX 01386 871301
Closed 24-30 Dec

Salford Hall is a beautifully restored 15th-century manor house which still retains many of it's charming period features including exposed beams. Staff are a great asset here and are ably directed by General Manager Sally Pearce. Bedrooms are superbly equipped most featuring mini bars and a wealth of extras. The fabrics and furnishings used throughout are bold and stylish but are still in keeping with the character of the house. The clubby bar with its leather seating is popular for relaxing. There are also a wealth of leisure activities for the sporty and some for hedonists who want to escape activity. The cuisine served in the smart restaurant continues to impress and is based round a modern interpretation of regional cuisine. Our inspector particularly enjoyed his starter of seared scallops with saffron noodles and sun dried tomatoes.

14 en suite (bth/shr) 19 annexe en suite (bth/shr) CTV in all bedrooms No dogs (ex guide dogs) 51P No coaches Tennis (hard) Snooker Sauna Solarium V meals Coffee am Tea pm No smoking in restaurant Last d 9.30pm

ROOMS: (incl. bkfst) s £75-£105; d £105-£140 * **LB**
MEALS: Lunch fr £15.25 Dinner £22.50-£35
CONF: Thtr 50 Class 35 Board 25 Del from £110
CARDS: Connect

£

See advertisement under STRATFORD-UPON-AVON

ABINGDON Oxfordshire Map 04 SU49

★★★64% **Abingdon Lodge**

Marcham Rd OX14 1TZ ☎ 01235 553456 FAX 01235 554117

A modern purpose-built hotel, Abingdon Lodge is located within easy reach of the A34 Oxford to Newbury road. The bedrooms are spacious and well equipped and a friendly young team of staff provides competent service. There is a choice of three menus at dinner and a popular carvery at lunch time.

63 en suite (bth/shr) No smoking in 14 bedrooms CTV in all bedrooms STV No dogs (ex guide dogs) Night porter 85P Wkly live entertainment Xmas English & French Cuisine V meals Coffee am Tea pm Last d 10pm

ROOMS: s £61-£72; d £69-£84 **LB**
OFF-PEAK: s £49-£72; d £49-£84
MEALS: Lunch £7.25-£9.95 Dinner £7.95-£10.95*
CONF: Thtr 140 Class 80 Board 48 Del from £99
CARDS:

£

★★★64% **Upper Reaches**

FORTE Heritage

Thames St OX14 3JA (on A415 in Abingdon follow signs for Dorchester and turn left just before the Broad Face public house) ☎ 01235 522311
FAX 01235 555182

There is an interesting history to parts of this 17th-century building linking it to the nearby abbey. The enclosed working water mill in the restaurant is an attractive feature. Most of the bedrooms are located in the main building, which is surrounded by the river Thames, while some are in a modern extension. The kitchen, under chef Phillip Edwards, produces tasty and well crafted dishes - some of the delicious bread is freshly baked.

19 en suite (bth/shr) 6 annexe en suite (bth/shr) (2 fmly) No smoking in 10 bedrooms CTV in all bedrooms 80P Xmas V meals Coffee am Tea pm No smoking in restaurant Last d 9.30pm

ROOMS: s £90-£96; d £98-£105 **LB**
MEALS: Sunday Lunch £12.95-£14.95 High tea £4.50-£6.50 Dinner £18.95-£20
CONF: Thtr 70 Class 45 Board 35 Del from £110
CARDS: Connect

ACCRINGTON Lancashire Map 07 SD72

★★★ 66% ***Dunkenhalgh***

Macdonald Hotels

Blackburn Rd, Clayton le Moors BB5 5JP (adj to M65,junct 7) ☎ 01254 398021 FAX 01254 872230

Dunkenhalgh is a handsome period house at the end of a tree-lined drive. It has been considerably extended in recent years with an excellent leisure club and additional bedrooms housed in cottage-style annexes. Decanters of sherry, fresh fruit and mineral water feature in all rooms, which are currently being upgraded with attractive fabrics and colour schemes.

37 en suite (bth/shr) 42 annexe en suite (bth/shr) (13 fmly) No smoking in 10 bedrooms CTV in all bedrooms STV Night porter 400P Indoor swimming pool (heated) Snooker Sauna Solarium Gym Steam room Wkly live entertainment International Cuisine V meals Coffee am Tea pm

CARDS:

ACLE Norfolk Map 05 TG41

Travelodge

Travelodge

NR13 3BE (junc A47 & Acle Bypass)

☎ 01493 751970 FAX 01493 751970

This modern building offers accommodation in smart, spacious and well equipped bedrooms, suitable for family use, and all with en suite bathrooms. Meals may be taken at the nearby family restaurant. For information on room rates and to make a booking, call Roomline free of charge on 0800 850950. For more details about Travelodge, consult the Contents page under Hotel Groups.

40 en suite (bth/shr)

ADDERBURY Oxfordshire Map 04 SP43

★★ 68% **Red Lion**

The Green, Oxford Rd OX17 3LU (3m S of Banbury Cross, on A423)

☎ 01295 810269 FAX 01295 811906

Pre-dating the Civil War, this lovely stone-built coaching inn has character, comfort and style. It serves good bar snacks, and a more extensive dinner menu which can be served in one of the bar-lounges or the restaurant. There is a definite French influence to the home-cooked food, with dishes such as lamb provençale and boeuf bourguignon. Much of the fish is from the proprietor's own Cornish fishing boat. Bedrooms are very smart and decorative.

14 rms (13 bth/shr) (3 fmly) CTV in all bedrooms 24P Xmas English & French Cuisine V meals Coffee am Tea pm No smoking area in restaurant Last d 10pm

ROOMS: (incl. bkfst) s £47.50; d £65 * **LB**

MEALS: Lunch £11.95&alc Dinner £15-£25alc*

CONF: Board 12 Del from £95

CARDS:

indicates a Town House Hotel. Please consult the section on AA Star Rating at the front of the book.

ADLINGTON Lancashire Map 07 SD61

★★ 66% **Gladmar**

Railway Rd PR6 9RG (off A6 near railway station)

☎ 01257 480398 FAX 01257 482681

Closed 25 Dec

This immaculately maintained and privately owned hotel, where Bill Beaumont grew up, is conveniently situated just off the A6, close to the railway station. The first thing you will notice are the well maintained gardens which guests are free to use. The public areas include a comfortable lounge with an open fire, a characterful bar, which features a number of celebrity photographs, and a spacious dining room where a good range of popular dishes is available. Bedrooms, some of which are on the ground floor but all of which are en suite, are comfortably furnished and well equipped. Mr Duffy and his enthusiastic staff make every effort to ensure guests are comfortable and are being well looked after.

20 en suite (bth/shr) (1 fmly) CTV in all bedrooms STV No dogs (ex guide dogs) 30P V meals Coffee am Tea pm No smoking area in restaurant Last d 9pm

ROOMS: (incl. bkfst) s fr £37; d £49-£58 * **LB**

OFF-PEAK: (incl. bkfst) s fr £28; d £39-£48

MEALS: Lunch £5.50-£7.50 High tea fr £3.50 Dinner £11.50-£15.50*

CONF: Thtr 40 Board 14 Del from £76

CARDS:

ALCESTER Warwickshire Map 04 SP05

★★★ 65% **Kings Court**

Kings Coughton B49 5QQ (1m N on A435)

☎ 01789 763111 FAX 01789 400242

Closed 24-30 Dec

This hotel is set in four acres of grounds and gardens around the original Tudor farmhouse. Recent construction of a new complex of bedrooms has provided comfortable, spacious rooms well suited to both the business guest and tourist; there are also four beamed bedrooms within the original farmhouse. Public rooms include an open-plan dining room, attractive reception lobby and beamed public bar.

4 en suite (bth/shr) 38 annexe en suite (bth/shr) (3 fmly) CTV in all bedrooms 120P V meals Coffee am Tea pm No smoking area in restaurant

ROOMS: (incl. bkfst) s fr £52; d fr £74 **LB**

OFF-PEAK: (incl. bkfst) s £31; d £52

MEALS: Sunday Lunch fr £10.50alc

CARDS:

ALDEBURGH Suffolk Map 05 TM45

★★★ 70% **Wentworth**

Wentworth Rd IP15 5BD (turn off A12 on to A1094, leave church on left and turn left at bottom of hill)

☎ 01728 452312 FAX 01728 454343

contd.

Closed 28 Dec-8 Jan
This well established family run hotel offers a comfortable relaxing environment and a helpful service throughout the smart and inviting public rooms, which include several delightful lounge areas with open fires, a small bar and a large decorative restaurant. The accommodation is split between the individually styled main house bedrooms, most of which have sea views, and the newly created bedrooms in the adjacent Darfield House; these new rooms are stylish, spacious and very well appointed.
31 rms (24 bth 4 shr) 7 annexe en suite (bth/shr) No smoking in 7 bedrooms CTV in all bedrooms 30P No coaches Xmas English & French Cuisine V meals Coffee am Tea pm No smoking area in restaurant Last d 9pm
ROOMS: (incl. bkfst) s £56-£61; d £90-£110 * **LB**
MEALS: Lunch £13.50-£14.50 Dinner £12.50-£15.50
CARDS:

See advertisement on opposite page

★★★69% **White Lion**

Market Cross Place IP15 5BJ (from A12 at Saxmundham take A1094 approx 5m on seafront)
☎ 01728 452720 FAX 01728 452986
This long established and very popular well known hotel enjoys a prime position overlooking the sea a short distance from the famous Moot Hall museum. Personally run by the Mackrill family the atmosphere is very friendly and relaxed with many guests having become regulars and returning year after year. Bedrooms continue to be upgraded and all come particularly well equipped. The '1563' beamed restaurant continues to feature sea fresh shellfish and seafood whilst the buttery bar adds a further good dimension at lunchtime. There is a comfortable and well furnished lounge, smart bar and good reception foyer and the service is helpful and attentive.
38 en suite (bth/shr) (1 fmly) CTV in all bedrooms 15P Xmas English & French Cuisine V meals Coffee am Tea pm Last d 9pm
ROOMS: (incl. bkfst) s £59.50-£69.50; d £84-£104 * **LB**
MEALS: Sunday Lunch £11.95 High tea £6.50 Dinner £17.95&alc
CONF: Thtr 120 Class 50 Board 50 Del from £88
CARDS:

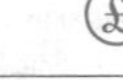

★★★63% **The Brudenell**

The Parade IP15 5BU (on seafront, adjoining Fort Green car park) ☎ 01728 452071
FAX 01728 454082
This quietly located hotel faces the sea and almost, unique for Aldeburgh, has its own outdoor seaward patio. Most of the bedrooms are decorated to a contemporary and well maintained standard.
47 en suite (bth/shr) (1 fmly) No smoking in 11 bedrooms CTV in all bedrooms Lift Night porter 22P Xmas V meals Coffee am Tea pm No smoking in restaurant Last d 8.45pm
ROOMS: s £65-£72.50; d £80-£95 * **LB**
OFF-PEAK: s £50-£65; d £65-£80
MEALS: Lunch £8.45-£11.95 Dinner £15.95-£18.95*
CONF: Thtr 50 Del from £75
CARDS:

★★66% **Uplands**
Victoria Rd IP15 5DX (on A1094, opposite church)
☎ 01728 452420 FAX 01728 454872
Closed 23 Dec-3 Jan
The Uplands is a small family-run hotel which offers quiet surroundings. The public rooms are comfortable, providing a small bar, pleasant restaurant and comfortable lounge; the adjacent conservatory looks out onto the walled gardens. Accommodation styles and sizes vary, with period furnishings in the main house, whilst the garden cottage annexes are generally larger but more modestly furnished. All rooms are well maintained.
12 rms (9 bth/shr) 8 annexe en suite (bth/shr) (2 fmly) CTV in all bedrooms No dogs (ex guide dogs) 22P No coaches No children 12yrs V meals Coffee am No smoking in restaurant Last d 8.30pm
ROOMS: (incl. bkfst) s £35-£45; d fr £63 * **LB**
MEALS: Dinner fr £14.50&alc*
CARDS:

ALDERLEY EDGE Cheshire Map 07 SJ87

★★★70% **Alderley Edge**
Macclesfield Rd SK9 7BJ ☎ 01625 583033 FAX 01625 586343
This sandstone house which dates from 1850, and was formerly the home of one of Manchester's cotton kings, occupies a wonderful position half way up 'The Edge' and commands magnificent views of the Cheshire Plain. Well equipped bedrooms include individually named 'deluxe' rooms, some with four poster beds. Day rooms include a comfortable lounge and lounge bar, both smartly furnished with deep cushioned sofas, and an interesting conservatory restaurant. An ambitious variety of eloquently described dishes is available from three menus. Typical of the style are dishes like seared collop of foie gras with rasin brioche and onion marmalade, or more simply, a main course of cod with a flaked potato and cheese crust served with torn cabbage and roast peppers, an excellent comination of flavours and textures.
32 en suite (bth/shr) CTV in all bedrooms No dogs (ex guide dogs) Night porter 90P Wkly live entertainment Xmas English & Continental Cuisine V meals Coffee am Last d 10pm
ROOMS: s £87-£125; d £99.50-£125 * **LB**
OFF-PEAK: (incl. bkfst) s £36; d £67
MEALS: Lunch £13.50-£15.50&alc Dinner £22.95&alc*
CONF: Thtr 120 Class 80 Board 40 Del from £95
CARDS:

ALDERMINSTER Warwickshire Map 04 SP24

★★★★77% **Ettington Park**

CV37 8BU (5m S of Stratford) ☎ 01789 450123
FAX 01789 450472
Ettington Park is a magnificent Grade 1 listed Victorian Gothic mansion set in 40 acres of beautiful gardens and parkland on the banks of the River Stour. Its location makes it ideal for visiting the many attractions nearby, such as Warwick, Stratford-upon-Avon and the Cotswolds. Within the house there are some superb architectural features such as the rococo ceiling and crested panelling in the Oak Room restaurant, original Minton-tiled flooring and stained glass windows. Bedrooms have recently benefited from considerable investment, all now have the elegant fabrics and stylish bathrooms which they deserve and many have views of the gardens and the 12th-century chapel which stands in the grounds.
48 en suite (bth/shr) (5 fmly) CTV in all bedrooms STV No dogs (ex guide dogs) Lift Night porter 90P Indoor swimming pool (heated) Tennis (hard) Fishing Riding Sauna Solarium Croquet lawn Clay pigeon shooting Archery English & French Cuisine V meals Coffee am Tea pm No smoking in restaurant Last d 9.30pm
ROOMS: (incl. bkfst) s £120-£225; d £165-£315 * **LB**
MEALS: Lunch fr £17 High tea fr £9.25 Dinner fr £30
CONF: Thtr 65 Class 40 Board 48 Del from £170
CARDS:

See advertisement under STRATFORD-UPON-AVON

ALDERSHOT Hampshire Map 04 SU85

★★★69% ***Potters International***
1 Fleet Rd GU11 2ET (access via A325 and A321 towards Fleet)
☎ 01252 344000 FAX 01252 311611
This one-year-old hotel and leisure complex is located on the edge of town, on the site of an old officers' mess. The bedrooms are spacious and well equipped with attractive decor. Extensive public areas include a coffee shop serving light meals and a more formal restaurant; there

are also several conference rooms and a business centre. The leisure club offers a fitness room with extensive modern equipment and a good sized pool with sauna, jacuzzi and steam bath.
101 en suite (bth/shr) No smoking in 10 bedrooms CTV in all bedrooms STV No dogs (ex guide dogs) Lift Night porter 120P Indoor swimming pool (heated) Sauna Solarium Gym Pool table Jacuzzi/spa English & French Cuisine V meals Coffee am Tea pm Last d 10.30pm
CARDS:

Travel Inn

Wellington Av GU11 1SQ (M3 junct 4 take A325 signed Aldershot & Farnham, at rdbt A325/A323 turn lt toward town centre on A323)
☎ 01252 344063 FAX 01252 344073
Purpose-built accommodation, offering spacious, well equipped bedrooms, all with en suite bathrooms. Meals may be taken at the nearby family restaurant. For more information about Travel Inns, consult the Contents page under Hotel Groups.
40 en suite (bth/shr)
ROOMS: d £35.50 *

ALDWARK North Yorkshire Map 08 SE46

★★★ 70% ***Aldwark Manor***
YO6 2NF ☎ 01347 838146 FAX 01347 838867
This impressive 19th-century manor house has been carefully changed into a comfortable and well furnished hotel, which includes two lounges and an elegant restaurant. It is surrounded on all sides by a well laid out golf course. The bedrooms are generally very spacious and all are well furnished and thoughtfully equipped. Service is attentive, provided by a keen and friendly staff.
17 en suite (bth/shr) 3 annexe en suite (bth/shr) (2 fmly) CTV in 18 bedrooms STV Night porter 52P Golf 18 Fishing Coarse fishing European Cuisine V meals Coffee am Tea pm Last d 9.30pm
CARDS:

ALFRETON Derbyshire Map 08 SK45

Travelodge

Old Swanwick Colliery Rd DE55 1HJ
(junc A38/A61) ☎ 01773 520040 FAX 01773 520040
This modern building offers accommodation in smart, spacious and well equipped bedrooms, suitable for family use, and all with en suite bathrooms. Meals may be taken at the nearby family restaurant. For information on room rates and to make a booking, call Roomline free of charge on 0800 850950. For more details about Travelodge, consult the Contents page under Hotel Groups.
61 en suite (bth/shr)

ALFRISTON East Sussex Map 05 TQ50

★★★ 66% **The Star Inn**

BN26 5TA (7m off A27 at Drusillas roundabout)
☎ 01323 870495 FAX 01323 870922
Several bedrooms are available on the ground floor of this extended hotel. There is a sympathetically added extension of more modern bedrooms while the original lot are housed in the main building proper, which has a great deal of character. Its history dates back to the 13th century, and although it has since been renovated, some parts retain the period charm such as the flagstoned bar.
34 en suite (bth/shr) No smoking in 10 bedrooms CTV in all bedrooms 29P Xmas V meals Coffee am Tea pm No smoking in restaurant Last d 9pm

ROOMS: s £67.50; d £87.50 * **LB**
MEALS: Lunch £16.95&alc Dinner £18.95&alc*
CONF: Thtr 40 Class 20 Board 30 Del from £95
CARDS:

★★★ 63% ***Deans Place***
BN26 5TW ☎ 01323 870248 FAX 01323 870918
This creeper-clad hotel stands in its own grounds on the southern fringes of the village. Bedrooms vary in size and standards, and there is a range of public areas suited to both leisure and conference guests. The restaurant might have a particular theme for its wine or food and afternoon cream teas are readily available.
36 en suite (bth/shr) (3 fmly) No smoking in 4 bedrooms CTV in all bedrooms STV No dogs (ex guide dogs) Night porter 150P Outdoor swimming pool (heated) Croquet lawn French Cuisine V meals Coffee am Tea pm Last d 9.30pm
CARDS:

ALNWICK Northumberland Map 12 NU11

★★★ 61% **White Swan**
Bondgate Within NE66 1TD ☎ 01665 602109 FAX 01665 510400
An impressive feature of this 300 year old hotel, situated in the centre of the town, is the elegant banqueting suite with its ceilings floors and walls made with the oak panelling from the smoking room of the SS Olympic. Another interesting area is the lounge bar which features fishing tackle memorabilia. Bedrooms vary in shape and size, but all have modern facilities and several of the original rooms have characteristic high ceilings. The hotel has its own private car park.
58 en suite (bth/shr) (4 fmly) No smoking in 15 bedrooms CTV in all bedrooms Night porter 30P Wkly live entertainment Xmas English & French Cuisine V meals Coffee am Tea pm No smoking in restaurant Last d 9.30pm

contd.

ROOMS: (incl. bkfst) s fr £62; d fr £74 **LB**
MEALS: Lunch £10.95-£16.95 High tea fr £7.75 Dinner fr £17.95*
CONF: Thtr 200 Class 80 Board 15 Del £79
CARDS:

ALRESFORD Hampshire Map 04 SU53

★★61% **Swan**
11 West St SO24 9AD (off A31) ☎ 01962 732302 & 734427 FAX 01962 735274
RS 25-26 Dec
This former coaching inn, where Cromwell is believed to have stayed, has been skilfully extended to provide de luxe rooms in a modern annexe, and standard rooms in the main house. Stan's Bar is a popular rendezvous and the recently unearthed crypt bar has great character. The bedrooms in the house are gradually being upgraded with bright attractive colour schemes.
23 rms (10 bth) (4 fmly) CTV in all bedrooms 75P International Cuisine V meals Coffee am Tea pm No smoking area in restaurant Last d 9.30pm
ROOMS: (incl. bkfst) s £35-£40; d fr £45 * **LB**
MEALS: Lunch £4.85-£10.95 High tea £2.50 Dinner £11.25&alc*
CONF: Thtr 90 Class 60 Board 40 Del from £50
CARDS:

See advertisement on opposite page

ALSAGER Cheshire Map 07 SJ75

★★★66% **Manor House**
Audley Rd ST7 2QQ (signposted from railway station)
☎ 01270 884000 FAX 01270 882483
RS 25-30 Dec
Oak-beamed bars and the similarly beamed Ostlers Restaurant are reminiscent of the style of the old farmhouse site on which the hotel has been built, and although the buildings are modern it does have the ambience of a country hotel. Bedrooms are comfortably furnished and have all modern facilities; one has a four-poster bed and two have been designed for disabled guests. There are very good meeting and conference facilities and also an indoor swimming pool. The attractive patio gardens make it an ideal venue for weddings.
57 en suite (bth/shr) (4 fmly) No smoking in 12 bedrooms CTV in all bedrooms STV Night porter 178P Indoor swimming pool (heated) Jacuzzi/spa English & French Cuisine V meals Coffee am Tea pm Last d 9.30pm
ROOMS: (incl. bkfst & dinner) s £69; d £79 * **LB**
MEALS: Lunch fr £10.95&alc Dinner £18.50&alc*
CONF: Thtr 180 Class 108 Board 82 Del £95
CARDS:

ALSTON Cumbria Map 12 NY74

★★★65% ***Nent Hall Country House***
CA9 3LQ ☎ 01434 381584 FAX 01434 382668
MINOTEL Great Britain
Despite its roadside position on the A689 three miles east of Alston, this attractive hotel enjoys a moorland setting and has ample gardens on two sides. Bedrooms are smart and modern, but public areas retain the ambience of a comfortable country house, and Dorothy and Eric Peacock provide personal service which is enhanced by the friendly and relaxed atmosphere. During the winter months services to non-residents can be restricted, particularly at lunch time.
19 rms (18 bth/shr) (2 fmly) CTV in 18 bedrooms 48P V meals Coffee am Tea pm Last d 8.45pm
CARDS:

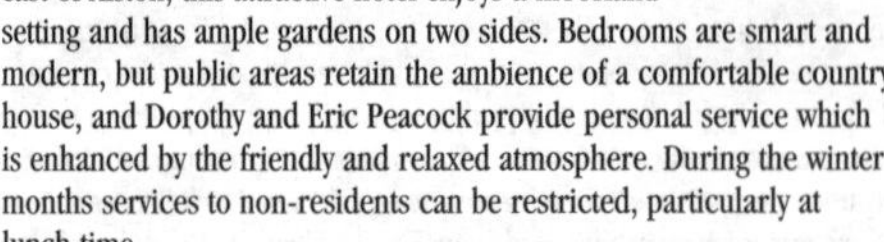

RED STAR HOTEL

★★ **Lovelady Shield Country House**
CA9 3LF (2m E, signposted off A689 where it joins the B6294) ☎ 01434 381203 & 381305 FAX 01434 381515
Closed 3 Jan-5 Feb
Situated just outside Alston, a picturesque hilltop market town with cobbled streets, this lovely country house lies in its own carefully tended grounds shielded by the wooded hillside and bordered by the River Nent. Mr and Mrs Lyons and their dedicated team provide personal service, a quiet and relaxing atmosphere and a really warm welcome. The reception rooms comprise an elegant drawing room, a small bar and dining room. Bedrooms are generously proportioned and carefully furnished to maximise their comfort. The dinner menu is short, well balanced and appealing, with capable cooking producing robust flavours. Breakfasts run to kedgeree, kippers and croissant.
12 en suite (bth/shr) (1 fmly) CTV in all bedrooms 20P No coaches Tennis (hard) Croquet lawn Xmas English & French Cuisine Coffee am Tea pm No smoking in restaurant Last d 8.30pm
ROOMS: (incl. bkfst) s £49.50-£59.50; d £95-£115 **LB**
OFF-PEAK: (incl. bkfst) s £35-£45; d £60-£80
MEALS: Lunch £15.95 High tea £4.95-£7.95alc Dinner £25.45
CONF: Class 12 Board 12 Del from £69
CARDS:

★★68% **Lowbyer Manor Country House**
CA9 3JX (on the edge of town) ☎ 01434 381230 FAX 01434 382937
Lying on the edge of the village, this interesting 17th-century manor house is set on several levels and offers a friendly country house atmosphere. The inviting lounge has lots of reading material, whilst downstairs there is the attractive restaurant and cosy bar complete with an inglenook fireplace, exposed stone walls and oak beams.
8 en suite (bth/shr) 4 annexe en suite (bth) CTV in all bedrooms 14P Xmas V meals Coffee am Tea pm Last d 9pm
ROOMS: (incl. bkfst) s £34; d £68 **LB**
MEALS: Lunch £8.50 High tea £8.50 Dinner £16.50-£25.50alc
CONF: Board 10 Del £60
CARDS:

ALTARNUN Cornwall & Isles of Scilly Map 02 SX28

★★76% **Penhallow Manor Country House**
PL15 7SJ (in village next to the church)
☎ 01566 86206 FAX 01566 86179
Closed 3 Jan-14 Feb

An elegant former rectory built in Georgian style in 1842, now a comfortable small hotel, personally owned and run by John and Julia Cubbage. Each of the seven bedrooms is individually furnished and decorated, with co-ordinating wallpapers and soft furnishings; every modern facility is provided. The public areas are spacious and comfortable, with the lounge or bar being the ideal venue for a pre-dinner aperitif. Each evening a short table d'hÙte menu is offered, using the very best of local fish, meat and vegetables, Julia Cubbage being an imaginative and skilful cook. Breakfast is served in the conservatory overlooking the church.

7 en suite (bth/shr) No smoking in all bedrooms CTV in all bedrooms 10P No coaches Fishing Croquet lawn Art courses No children 12yrs Xmas English & French Cuisine V meals Coffee am Tea pm No smoking in restaurant Last d 8.45pm

ROOMS: (incl. bkfst) s £34.50-£49.50; d £69-£99 * **LB**

OFF-PEAK: (incl. bkfst) s fr £28.50; d £39.50-£49.50

MEALS: Bar Lunch fr £1.75 Dinner fr £19.50

CONF: Thtr 30 Class 16 Board 16 Del from £54

CARDS:

See advertisement under LAUNCESTON

ALTHORPE Lincolnshire Map 08 SE80
See also Scunthorpe

★★65% **Lansdowne House**

Main St DN17 3HJ (leave M181 at junc 3 onto A18 towards Doncaster continue over iron bridge, keep left at road fork, hotel on right) ☎ 01724 783369 FAX 01724 783369

This attractive Victorian house stands in two acres of grounds on the edge of the village. Its comfortable bedrooms are all well equipped and most are very spacious; three are set in a rear, separate, extention. A good range of home-cooked food is available and service is friendly and polite.

7 en suite (bth/shr) 3 annexe en suite (bth/shr) (5 fmly) CTV in all bedrooms No dogs (ex guide dogs) 40P English & French Cuisine V meals Coffee am Tea pm Last d 10pm

ROOMS: (incl. bkfst) s £39.50-£49.50; d £49.50-£75 *

CARDS:

ALTON Hampshire Map 04 SU73

★★★66% **Alton House**

Normandy St GU34 1DW (turn off A31, close to railway station) ☎ 01420 80033 FAX 01420 89222

Closed 25-26 Dec RS 27-29 Dec

This busy hotel is located on the edge of the town and is popular with the business and leisure guest. The bedrooms are being steadily upgraded, and they are all spacious and well equipped. The restaurant offers a daily set menu and a carte served by the friendly staff. There is an attractive rear garden and outdoor pool, also an adjoining health and fitness club. The hotel has several function and conference rooms.

39 en suite (bth/shr) (3 fmly) No smoking in 2 bedrooms CTV in all bedrooms STV No dogs (ex guide dogs) Night porter 54P Outdoor swimming pool (heated) Tennis (hard) Snooker Solarium Gym

Croquet lawn Jacuzzi/spa Xmas English & Continental Cuisine V meals Coffee am Tea pm Last d 9.15pm

ROOMS: s £45-£57.50; d £57.50-£85 * **LB**

OFF-PEAK: s £35-£40; d £40-£50

MEALS: Lunch £10.95-£12.95&alc High tea £3-£7 Dinner £12.95&alc*

CONF: Thtr 150 Class 80 Board 50 Del from £90

CARDS:

★★★66% **Grange**

London Rd GU34 4EG (on E outskirts) ☎ 01420 86565 FAX 01420 541346

Closed 23-31 Dec

This family-run hotel is quietly situated on the edge of the town. It has been sympathetically extended to provide modern well equipped accommodation. The bedrooms are spacious and individually decorated with attractive co-ordinating fabrics, and some of the rooms are on the ground floor. A piano bar overlooks the 2-acre garden and the Terrace Room is available for private parties and conferences. Guests may dine in Truffles Restaurant or there is a lighter menu available in the bar.

26 en suite (bth/shr) 4 annexe en suite (bth/shr) (2 fmly) No smoking in 2 bedrooms CTV in all bedrooms STV 48P Croquet lawn Putting green No children 3yrs English & French Cuisine V meals Coffee am Tea pm No smoking in restaurant Last d 9.30pm

ROOMS: (incl. bkfst) s £52.50-£57.50; d £67.50-£77.50 **LB**

MEALS: Lunch £10.95-£25alc Dinner £15-£25alc*

CONF: Thtr 80 Class 30 Board 40 Del from £83.50

CARDS:

indicates a Country House Hotel. Please consult the section on AA Star Rating at the front of the book.

★★★62% ***Swan***

High St GU34 1AT ☎ 01420 83777 FAX 01420 87975

This well established town centre hotel is a popular venue and both residents and non-residents enjoy the hotel's character, comfortable lounges, bar and large restaurant. Bedrooms are tastefully furnished and comprehensively equipped with modern facilities. We are pleased to report the long-awaited upgrading programme to the public areas appears to be taking shape. Ample car parking is available at the rear.

36 en suite (bth/shr) (2 fmly) No smoking in 15 bedrooms CTV in all bedrooms Night porter 70P English, French & Italian Cuisine V meals Coffee am Tea pm Last d 9.30pm

CARDS:

ALTON Staffordshire Map 07 SK04

★★62% **Bull's Head Inn**

High St ST10 4AQ ☎ 01538 702307 FAX 01538 702065

This popular old inn, full of character, stands in the centre of the village and is ideally situated for Alton Towers. Bedrooms are bright and comfortably furnished. Public areas include a busy lounge bar with exposed beams and an open fire as well as a spacious restaurant offering a short selection of popular dishes.

6 rms (5 shr) CTV in all bedrooms No dogs 15P No coaches V meals Coffee am No smoking in restaurant Last d 9.30pm

ROOMS: (incl. bkfst) s £35-£40; d £40-£50 *

OFF-PEAK: (incl. bkfst) s £25-£30; d £35-£40

MEALS: Bar Lunch £6.75-£16.75alc Dinner £6.75-£16.75alc*

CARDS:

ALTRINCHAM Greater Manchester Map 07 SJ78

★★★❀71% **Woodland Park**

Wellington Rd, Timperley WA15 7RG (off the A560) ☎ 0161 928 8631 FAX 0161 941 2821

This busy, privately-owned hotel which offers attractively decorated and well equipped accommodation is conveniently situated within easy reach of Manchester city centre, the airport and both the M6 and M56 motorways. The impressive and tastefully decorated public areas, which include a conservatory, various lounges, meeting rooms and a nightclub, are both luxuriously and comfortably furnished. In the restaurant guests can choose from a good range of carefully prepared dishes.

45 en suite (bth/shr) (3 fmly) No smoking in 2 bedrooms CTV in all bedrooms STV No dogs (ex guide dogs) Night porter 151P International Cuisine V meals Coffee am Tea pm Last d 10pm

ROOMS: (incl. bkfst) s £69.50; d £86 *

MEALS: Lunch fr £5 Dinner fr £13.95*

CONF: Thtr 200 Class 120 Board 50 Del from £86.50

CARDS:

★★★66% **Cresta Court**

Church St WA14 4DP (on A56) ☎ 0161 927 7272 FAX 0161 926 9194

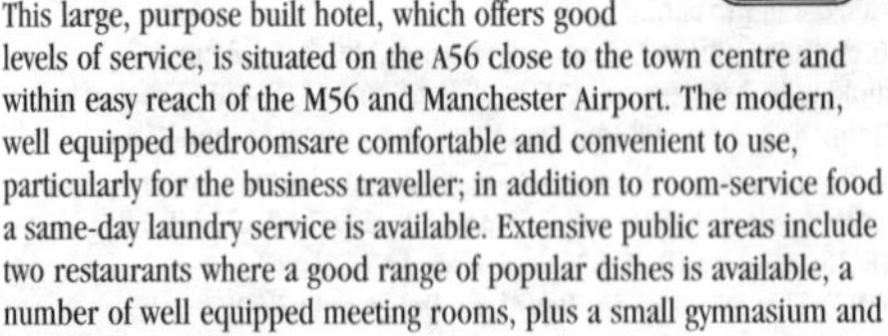

This large, purpose built hotel, which offers good levels of service, is situated on the A56 close to the town centre and within easy reach of the M56 and Manchester Airport. The modern, well equipped bedroomsare comfortable and convenient to use, particularly for the business traveller; in addition to room-service food a same-day laundry service is available. Extensive public areas include two restaurants where a good range of popular dishes is available, a number of well equipped meeting rooms, plus a small gymnasium and solarium.

138 en suite (bth/shr) (5 fmly) No smoking in 12 bedrooms CTV in all bedrooms STV Lift Night porter 200P Solarium Gym English & French Cuisine V meals Coffee am Tea pm No smoking in restaurant Last d 9.45pm

ROOMS: (incl. bkfst) s £65-£70; d £85-£95 **LB**

OFF-PEAK: (incl. bkfst) s £36-£40; d £70-£78

MEALS: Lunch £10&alc Dinner £12&alc*

CONF: Thtr 400 Class 100 Board 40 Del from £94

CARDS:

★★★63% **Bowdon**

Langham Rd, Bowdon WA14 2HT (M6 leave junct 19 to airport continue until 2nd roundabout head for Bowdon/Altrincham hotel is in Langham Road)

☎ 0161 928 7121 FAX 0161 927 7560

A converted and extended Victorian house situated in a pleasant residential area, but within easy reach of major motorways and Manchester International Airport. Extensive refurbishment has been undertaken to both bedrooms and public areas, in recent months, including the attractive restaurant which has attained a good reputation locally. There are also good facilities for business meetings and conferences.

82 en suite (bth/shr) No smoking in 6 bedrooms CTV in all bedrooms Night porter 164P Pool table Xmas English & French Cuisine V meals Coffee am Tea pm No smoking area in restaurant Last d 10pm

ROOMS: s £63-£68; d £82-£115 * **LB**

MEALS: Lunch fr £4.50&alc High tea fr £6&alc Dinner fr £15.95&alc*

CONF: Thtr 130 Class 60 Board 48 Del from £90

CARDS:

★66% **The Unicorn**

329 Hale Rd, Halebarns WA15 8SS (on A538, near M56)

☎ 0161 980 4347 FAX 0161 903 9187

Hospitality is a strength at this informal and friendly hotel, which offers modern freshly decorated, en suite bedrooms. A good range of popular dishes is available from the menu or from the daily-changing 'specials' on the blackboard, and the open-plan public areas include a comfortable lounge bar and a small restaurant. The hotel is ideally located in the centre of the village, close to the airport and the M56.

5 en suite (bth/shr) CTV in all bedrooms No dogs (ex guide dogs) 27P No coaches V meals Coffee am

ROOMS: (incl. bkfst) s £25-£35; d £35-£50 *

CONF: Thtr 50 Class 50 Board 30

CARDS:

ALVELEY Shropshire Map 07 SO78

★★★★65% **Mill Hotel & Restaurant**

WV15 6HL (between Kidderminster/Bridgnorth, turn off A442 signposted Enville/Turley Green) ☎ 01746 780437 FAX 01746 780850

This modern hotel is set in several acres of pretty grounds and is located just off the A442 at Alveley. The hotel has been built around a 16th-century flour mill and the original water wheel is still a feature in the public bar. Well appointed bedrooms include three with four-poster beds and these, together with the attractive grounds, attract many local weddings. Public areas include extensive function suites and these are also popular for business meetings. The restaurant offers a wide choice of food and staff are friendly and caring.

21 en suite (bth/shr) (3 fmly) CTV in all bedrooms No dogs Lift Night porter 200P Pool table English & Continental Cuisine V meals Coffee am Tea pm No smoking in restaurant Last d 10.15pm

ROOMS: (incl. cont bkfst) s £45-£61.50; d £55-£85 * **LB**

MEALS: Lunch £8.70-£12.95&alc Dinner fr £17.50&alc*

CONF: Thtr 200 Class 200 Board 100 Del from £85

CARDS:

See advertisement under BRIDGNORTH

ALVESTON Gloucestershire Map 03 ST68

★★★ 75% **Alveston House**

BS12 2LJ (near A38, between juncts 14 & 16 of M5)
☎ 01454 415050 FAX 01454 415425
Alveston House is a comfortable hotel offering a good range of facilities and services to suit commercial guests and tourists alike. Bedrooms have been tastefully decorated and the public areas, including a range of meeting rooms, are smartly maintained. A good choice of imaginative, freshly prepared dishes is offered in Quincey's, the attractive restaurant.
30 en suite (bth/shr) (1 fmly) CTV in all bedrooms STV 75P English & French Cuisine V meals Coffee am Tea pm Last d 9.30pm
ROOMS: (incl. bkfst) s £67.50-£71.50; d £77.50-£85 * **LB**
MEALS: Lunch £16.50 Dinner £16.50*
CONF: Thtr 85 Class 48 Board 50 Del from £91.50
CARDS: 

See advertisement under BRISTOL

Forte Posthouse Alveston
Thornbury Rd BS12 2LL (close to M4/M5 interchange, on A38) ☎ 01454 412521
FAX 01454 413920
Suitable for both the business and leisure traveller, this bright hotel provides modern accommodation in well equipped bedrooms with en suite bathrooms. For more details about Forte Posthouse hotels, consult the Contents page for the section on Hotel Groups.
74 en suite (bth/shr)
ROOMS: d £49-£69 *
CONF: Thtr 100 Class 40 Board 40 Del £99

ALWALTON Cambridgeshire Map 04 TL19

★★★★ 65% **Swallow**

Peterborough Business Park, Lynchwood PE2 6GB (opposite East of England Showground)
☎ 01733 371111 FAX 01733 236725
Standing opposite the East of England Showground in eleven acres of attractively landscaped grounds west of Peterborough near the A1, this modern two-storey hotel offers extensive conference and leisure facilities. The well equipped bedrooms are spacious and the introduction of colourful fabrics has helped soften the functionality of the original design. Spacious public areas are bright and include a choice of restaurants and a coffee lounge serving light refreshments throughout the day. Extensive car parking is available.
163 en suite (bth/shr) (10 fmly) No smoking in 89 bedrooms CTV in all bedrooms STV Night porter 200P Indoor swimming pool (heated) Sauna Solarium Gym Putting green Jacuzzi/spa Beauty therapist Hairdressing Wkly live entertainment Xmas English & French Cuisine V meals Coffee am Tea pm Last d 10.30pm
ROOMS: (incl. bkfst) s fr £95; d fr £110 * **LB**
OFF-PEAK: (incl. bkfst) s fr £55; d fr £85
MEALS: Lunch fr £14 Dinner fr £17.50&alc*
CONF: Thtr 300 Class 160 Board 160 Del from £125
CARDS:

Travelodge

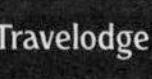

Great North Rd PE7 3UR (on A1, southbound)
☎ 01733 231109 FAX 01733 231109
This modern building offers accommodation in smart, spacious and well equipped bedrooms, suitable for family use, and all with en suite bathrooms. Meals may be taken at the nearby family restaurant. For information on room rates and to make a booking, call Roomline free of charge on 0800 850950. For more details about Travelodge, consult the Contents page under Hotel Groups.
32 en suite (bth/shr)

AMBERLEY Gloucestershire Map 03 SO80

★★ 65% ***Amberley Inn***
GL5 5AF (on A46) ☎ 01453 872565
FAX 01453 872738
This small traditional inn is in a prominent position with expansive views over the open grasslands of Minchinhampton Common onto Woodchester Valley. It boasts a welcoming atmosphere with friendly service from its mostly local staff, congenial bars serving a good range of meals and draught ales, and cosy public rooms.
10 rms (9 bth) 4 annexe en suite (bth) (1 fmly) CTV in all bedrooms 30P No coaches English & French Cuisine V meals Coffee am Tea pm Last d 9.30pm
CARDS:

AMBERLEY West Sussex Map 04 TQ01

RED STAR HOTEL

★★★ **Amberley Castle**
BN18 9ND (SW of village, off B2139)
☎ 01798 831992 FAX 01798 831998
White peacocks and suits of armour are found within the massive 14th-century walls of Amberley Castle. The small number of bedrooms allows for a certain level of cosiness and a good service is provided by a newly established team of staff. The bedrooms are immaculately decorated in personalised individual styles; each has a spa bath and there are plenty of extras including video recorders. In the Queen's Room restaurant, new menus are evolving under the guidance of chef Simon Thyer whose menus include the unusual Castle Cuisine with its medieval inspiration. Breakfast in particular is a sumptuous affair of well cooked dishes, all served in a cheerful and caring manner.
15 en suite (bth/shr) CTV in all bedrooms STV No dogs (ex guide dogs) 50P No coaches Croquet lawn Jacuzzi/spa English & French Cuisine V meals Coffee am Tea pm Last d 9.30pm
CONF: Thtr 60 Class 24 Board 32
CARDS:

AMBLESIDE Cumbria Map 07 NY30
See also Elterwater

★★★ 74% **Rothay Manor**
Rothay Bridge LA22 0EH (0.25m SW on Coniston road)
☎ 015394 33605 FAX 015394 33607
Closed 2 Jan-9 Feb
An elegant Regency-style house, Rothay Manor is set in beautifully

contd.

landscaped gardens only a short distance from the town centre. It has many modern facilities but retains traditional values and an atmosphere of warmth and relaxation. The individually-styled bedrooms include some ground-floor rooms and two in an adjacent bungalow with their own sitting rooms. Light lunches are available during the week with a full lunch on Sunday, and afternoon tea is served (on the lawn in summer); but dinner is the main meal with a fixed-price menu of three, four, or five courses.

15 en suite (bth/shr) 3 annexe en suite (bth/shr) (7 fmly) CTV in all bedrooms No dogs (ex guide dogs) 45P Nearby leisure centre free to guests Xmas English & French Cuisine V meals Coffee am Tea pm No smoking in restaurant Last d 9pm
ROOMS: (incl. bkfst) s fr £78; d £118-£132 * **LB**
MEALS: Lunch £13-£16&alc Dinner £23-£29*
CONF: Thtr 25 Board 20 Del from £92
CARDS:

See advertisement on opposite page

★★★ 69% Regent
Waterhead Bay LA22 0ES (1m S A591) ☎ 015394 32254
FAX 015394 31474
Recognised in the summer by the splash of colour from its flowers and hanging baskets, this family-run hotel lies just across the road from Waterhead Bay on the south side of the town. Attractive public areas feature inviting and comfortable lounges, whilst smartly turned out staff contribute to the friendly and relaxing atmosphere. Bedrooms are nicely decorated and enhanced by tasteful fabrics, whilst those contained in a courtyard building to the rear offer a particularly good level of comfort.
24 en suite (bth/shr) (7 fmly) No smoking in 4 bedrooms CTV in all bedrooms 30P Indoor swimming pool (heated) Jacuzzi/spa Wkly live entertainment Xmas English & French Cuisine V meals Coffee am Tea pm No smoking in restaurant Last d 8.30pm
ROOMS: (incl. bkfst) s £45-£59; d £89-£130 * **LB**
OFF-PEAK: (incl. bkfst) s £39-£59; d £69-£99
MEALS: Bar Lunch £5-£15alc Dinner fr £18.50&alc
CONF: Board 20
CARDS:

★★★ 63% The Salutation
CONSORT HOTELS
Lake Rd LA22 9BX (take A591 to Ambleside and follow one way system down Wansfell Road into Compston Road. At traffic lights take right hand lane back into village) ☎ 015394 32244 FAX 015394 34157
Conveniently situated in the town centre with its own car park behind it, this hotel has grown from a mid 17th-century hostelry on the old coach route between Kendal and Whitehaven. Today it meets the demands of modern travellers more than adequately by providing recently modernised, well equipped bedrooms, an attractively decorated restaurant, a comfortable lounge bar, a public bar and a games room.
29 en suite (bth/shr) (4 fmly) CTV in all bedrooms STV 41P Pool table Free membership of nearby leisure club Xmas English & French Cuisine V meals Coffee am Tea pm No smoking in restaurant Last d 9pm

ROOMS: (incl. bkfst) s £37.50-£50.50; d £75-£91
OFF-PEAK: (incl. bkfst) s £32.50-£42.50; d £65-£75
MEALS: Bar Lunch £5-£13 Dinner fr £18.50&alc
CONF: Thtr 40 Board 16 Del from £65.50
CARDS:

See advertisement on opposite page

★★ 77% Wateredge
Borrans Rd, Waterhead LA22 0EP (on A591, at Waterhead Bay, adj Steamer Pier) ☎ 015394 32332
FAX 015394 31878
Closed mid Dec-early Feb
This delightful family-run hotel lies in attractive and secluded gardens leading down to the shores of Lake Windermere. Two 17th-century fishermen's cottages have been sympathetically extended to combine period charm with modern comfort. Set within the oldest part are the oak-beamed, split-level dining rooms, the cosy bar and elegant lounges overlooking the gardens. Bedrooms are tastefully decorated and individual; many are well proportioned and the five studio suites offer a high level of comfort with a private patio or balcony. There is a commitment to the use of fresh produce whether it be for the six course dinners or hearty breakfasts. The home-baked afternoon teas are also to be recommended and can be taken either in the lounges or in the gardens. Friendly staff provide cheery and enthusiastic service throughout.
18 en suite (bth/shr) 5 annexe en suite (bth/shr) (1 fmly) CTV in all bedrooms 25P No coaches Rowing boat Free use of Leisure Club No children 7yrs Coffee am Tea pm No smoking in restaurant Last d 8.30pm
ROOMS: (incl. bkfst & dinner) s £76; d £138-£178 **LB**
OFF-PEAK: (incl. bkfst & dinner) s £62-£68; d £106-£162
MEALS: Bar Lunch £7.45-£8.95alc Dinner fr £26.90*
CARDS:

See advertisement on opposite page

★★ 72% Borrans Park
Borrans Rd LA22 0EN (from A591 turn left at Waterhead traffic lights, hotel 0.5m on right, entrance opposite rugby club) ☎ 015394 33454
FAX 015394 33003

contd.

A former farmhouse, this peacefully situated small hotel is convenient for Ambleside centre. It has comfortable lounges, one with a log fire and lots of books, and the bedrooms are prettily decorated and thoughtfully equipped bedrooms. The set dinner is well produced and includes only the best of local produce. It may feature lamb, pork or trout and there is always a good home-made soup. The sweet trolley often makes two journeys around the tables and the English cheese board is well chosen.
12 en suite (bth/shr) (2 fmly) No smoking in all bedrooms CTV in all bedrooms No dogs 20P No coaches Free use of local leisure club V meals No smoking in restaurant Last d 6pm
ROOMS: (incl. bkfst) s £29-£39; d £58-£78 **LB**
MEALS: Dinner £16
CARDS:

See advertisement on opposite page

★★72% **Laurel Villa**
Lake Rd LA22 0DB (on A591 approx. 0.5m from centre of village)
☎ 015394 33240
Closed Xmas
This elegant Victorian house lies on the Windermere road, and is run under the personal supervision of the proprietor Mr Seedhouse, who ensures the best of care for his guests. The pretty bedrooms are furnished in pine and have many extra touches such as fresh fruit and flowers and detailed embroidery samplers. Public areas include a choice of comfortable lounges and a bright dining room, where home-cooked 4-course dinners are offered, usually at 7pm. The wine list is exclusively English.
8 en suite (bth/shr) No smoking in 2 bedrooms CTV in all bedrooms No dogs 10P No coaches No children 16yrs Coffee am No smoking in restaurant Last d 7.30
ROOMS: (incl. bkfst) s £50; d £60-£80 **LB**
MEALS: Dinner £20-£25
CARDS:

★★72% **Skelwith Bridge**
Skelwith Bridge LA22 9NJ (2.5m W A593) ☎ 015394 32115
FAX 015394 34254
Situated at the junction of the Coniston and Elterwater roads, this hotel offers relaxing public areas which include both foyer and main lounge, a residents' library bar and a spacious lounge bar using stone from an original barn. Meals can be taken here as well as in the restaurant. Bedrooms are all individual and well equipped, and some are in a traditional slate stone house.
23 en suite (bth/shr) 6 annexe en suite (bth/shr) (3 fmly) No smoking in 6 bedrooms CTV in all bedrooms 60P No coaches Fishing Pool table Jacuzzi/spa English & French Cuisine V meals Coffee am Tea pm No smoking in restaurant Last d 9pm
ROOMS: (incl. bkfst) s £40.50-£46; d £75-£110 * **LB**
OFF-PEAK: (incl. bkfst) s £25.50-£30; d £50-£60
MEALS: Sunday Lunch £9.95 Dinner £17.95-£18.50*
CONF: Thtr 45 Class 25 Board 25 Del from £55
CARDS:

See advertisement on opposite page

★★ 71% **Nanny Brow Country House**
Clappersgate LA22 9NF (on A593, 1.5m from Ambleside) ☎ 015394 32036 FAX 015394 32450
Set in several acres of mature grounds and gardens, this charming country house affords beautiful views over the River Brathey towards the Langdale Valley. Bedrooms include some suitable for families and several have four-poster beds for that special occasion; garden suites are also available and some of these have private sitting rooms and patio areas. An elegant drawing room with a cheerful log fire is provided for residents and the bar is situated in a conservatory extension and is furnished with comfortable settees and armchairs.
18 rms (17 bth/shr) (3 fmly) No smoking in 6 bedrooms CTV in all bedrooms STV 20P Fishing Solarium Croquet lawn Putting green Jacuzzi/spa Free use of private leisure club Xmas V meals Coffee am Tea pm No smoking in restaurant Last d 8.45pm
ROOMS: (incl. bkfst & dinner) s £60-£65; d £125-£135 **LB**
OFF-PEAK: (incl. bkfst & dinner) s £55-£60; d £110-£120
MEALS: Lunch £12.50-£16.50 High tea £4.75-£12.75 Dinner £22.50-£27.50
CONF: Thtr 30 Class 30 Board 20 Del from £75
CARDS:

See advertisement on opposite page

★★70% **Fisherbeck**
Lake Rd LA22 0DH (S of Ambleside on A591) ☎ 015394 33215
FAX 015394 33600
Closed 25 Dec-10 Jan
Conveniently situated on the A591 from Windermere, this delightful hotel combines very comfortable accommodation with high standards of service and hospitality. Tastefully furnished and decorated bedrooms have many modern features, those at the front also enjoying magnificent views of Loughrigg and the surrounding fells; some are on the ground floor and look out onto neat gardens. As well as a choice of lounges there is the Tannery Bar, serving residents and non residents alike with both lunches and dinners, an alternative to the attractive split-level dining room's varied menu of British and international dishes. On-site parking facilities are available.
20 rms (18 bth/shr) (3 fmly) CTV in all bedrooms No dogs 24P No coaches Free use of nearby Leisure Complex International Cuisine V meals Coffee am Tea pm No smoking area in restaurant Last d 8.30pm
MEALS: Bar Lunch fr £8.65 Dinner fr £16.95*
CARDS:

★★70% **Waterhead**
Best Western
Lake Rd LA22 0ER ☎ 015394 32566
FAX 015394 31255
With just the main road between it and the bay, this hotel offers pleasant views to the lakeside, where one can sit in the gardens and watch the boats, resident ducks and swans. There are two bars as well as a restaurant, whilst bedrooms, which vary in size and style, are all well equipped. The hotel offers a good range of services and hospitality by the enthusiastic young staff is first class.
26 en suite (bth/shr) (3 fmly) No smoking in 5 bedrooms CTV in all bedrooms 50P Use of sister hotel's leisure facilities Wkly live entertainment Xmas English & French Cuisine V meals Coffee am Tea pm No smoking in restaurant Last d 9pm
ROOMS: (incl. bkfst) s £39.50; d £79-£110 * **LB**
OFF-PEAK: (incl. bkfst) d £79-£95
MEALS: Lunch £6.95-£10.95 High tea fr £5.75 Dinner fr £18.95
CONF: Thtr 40 Class 15 Board 30 Del from £65
CARDS:

See advertisement under WINDERMERE

A

★★69% **Elder Grove**
Lake Rd LA22 0DB (on A591, half a mile S of village centre)
☎ 015394 32504 FAX 015394 32504
Closed mid Nov-mid Feb
A double-fronted Lakeland-stone house offers good accommodation and friendly service. Bedrooms are well equipped and public areas comprise two very comfortable first-floor lounges and an attractive dining room with exposed stone walls where delicious four-course evening meals are served.
12 en suite (bth/shr) (1 fmly) CTV in all bedrooms 12P No coaches English & Continental Cuisine V meals Coffee am Tea pm Last d 8.15pm
ROOMS: (incl. bkfst) s £22-£27.50; d £44-£55 **LB**
MEALS: Bar Lunch £2.50-£6alc Dinner £16-£16.50&alc
CARDS:

See advertisement on page 65

★★68% **Kirkstone Foot Country House**
Kirkstone Pass Rd LA22 9EH ☎ 015394 32232 FAX 015394 32232
Closed 3 Jan-10 Feb
Once a 17th-century manor house, this friendly hotel lies in its own gardens with grounds sloping down to a small stream, on the Kirkstone Pass road, north of the town centre. There is an inviting lounge with reading material and a cosy beamed restaurant, whilst the well equipped bedrooms have been upgraded to a bright modern standard.
12 en suite (bth/shr) 14 annexe rms (1 bth 1 shr) (1 fmly) CTV in 12 bedrooms No dogs 36P Xmas V meals Coffee am Tea pm No smoking in restaurant Last d 8.30pm
ROOMS: (incl. bkfst & dinner) s £56-£62; d £112-£124 * **LB**
OFF-PEAK: (incl. bkfst & dinner) s £48-£54; d £96-£108
MEALS: High tea fr £6 Dinner £19.95-£20.95*
CONF: Thtr 40 Class 35 Board 26 Del from £58
CARDS:

★★66% Crow How
Rydal Rd LA22 9PN (0.75m N, on A591) ☎ 015394 32193
FAX 015394 32193
Closed Dec-Jan (ex New Year) RS Feb & Nov
This comfortable Victorian country house enjoys a secluded location in two acres of grounds off the A591 between Ambleside and Rydal Water. It offers traditionally furnished en suite bedrooms with television sets and tea/coffee making facilities. Guests can relax in the very comfortable lounge or a cosy bar, and the candlelit dining room serves a four-course evening meal.
9 rms (7 bth 1 shr) (2 fmly) CTV in all bedrooms 9P No coaches European Cuisine V meals No smoking in restaurant Last d 5.30pm
ROOMS: (incl. bkfst) s £24-£32.50; d £48-£65 * LB
OFF-PEAK: (incl. bkfst) s £18; d £36-£58
MEALS: Dinner £14
CARDS:

★★65% Glen Rothay
Rydal LA22 9LR (1.25m N of Ambleside on A591)
☎ 015394 32524 & 33099 FAX 015394 31079
RS 1-22 Dec & 5-31 Jan
This 17th-century house lies in its own grounds by the roadside almost midway between Ambleside and Grasmere, by Rydal Water. Now a family-run hotel, it has a friendly and informal atmosphere. Both the cosy bar and the historic oak lounge have open fires in season, whilst good home-cooked meals are served in the attractive dining room.
11 en suite (bth/shr) (2 fmly) No smoking in all bedrooms CTV in all bedrooms STV 35P No coaches Fishing Xmas V meals Coffee am No smoking in restaurant Last d 8.30pm
ROOMS: (incl. bkfst) s £27.50-£32.50; d £55-£90 * LB
MEALS: Bar Lunch £9.95-£12.25 Dinner £13.95-£16.95
CARDS:

★★62% *Horseshoe*
Rothay Rd LA22 0EE (On A591) ☎ 015394 32000 FAX 015394 31007
Closed 7 Jan-9 Feb
Situated close to the town centre and with good views of the surrounding fells from upper floors, this hotel offers bright modern bedrooms and public rooms which include an attractive lounge and a cosy bar.
19 en suite (bth/shr) (2 fmly) No smoking in 10 bedrooms CTV in all bedrooms 19P European Cuisine V meals Coffee am Tea pm Last d 8.30pm
CARDS:

See advertisement on opposite page

★65% *Gables*
Compston Rd LA22 9DJ (follow one-way system, hotel is on left on cul-de-sac to parish church, in front of bowling green) ☎ 015394 33272
Closed Nov-mid Dec & Jan-mid Feb RS Xmas, New Year & mid Feb-Easter
This well established hotel has been run by the friendly Robinson family for over forty years and is situated opposite St Mary's Church and the local tennis courts. Bedrooms are neat and modern and many are attractively decorated with coordinating wallpapers and fabrics. There is a comfortable lounge for residents, and a fixed menu offering enjoyable food is served in the dining room.
13 en suite (bth/shr) (4 fmly) CTV in all bedrooms 7P No coaches
CARDS:

AMERSHAM Buckinghamshire Map 04 SU99

★★★62% The Crown
High St HP7 0DH ☎ 01494 721541
FAX 01494 431283
FORTE Heritage
The Georgian façade of the Crown hides an Elizabethan interior, with inglenooks, beams and wall paintings testifying to its historic past. Although bedrooms vary in shape and size, they are attractively furnished and film goers will be interested to know that some of the more romantic scenes from "Four Weddings and a Funeral" were shot here. An abundance of flowers and hanging baskedts makes the courtyard an attractive feature.
19 en suite (bth/shr) 4 annexe en suite (bth/shr)
No smoking in 7 bedrooms CTV in all bedrooms
32P Xmas V meals Coffee am Tea pm No smoking in restaurant Last d 9.30pm
ROOMS: s £90; d £105-£120 * LB
OFF-PEAK: s £65-£90; d £75-£120
MEALS: Lunch £11.95-£21.95 High tea £1.40-£6.95
Dinner £19.95-£29.95*
CONF: Thtr 30 Class 18 Board 24 Del £135
CARDS:

AMESBURY Wiltshire Map 04 SU14

★★62% Antrobus Arms
15 Church St SP4 7EU (from rdbt on A303 proceed through town on one way system to T junct, turn left hotel on left) ☎ 01980 623163
FAX 01980 622112
This traditionally styled hotel offers a warm welcome, and the popular public rooms include a comfortably furnished lounge and a cosy bar where a log fire burns in the winter months. Good home-cooked meals are served in the wood panelled restaurant, and the bedrooms vary in size but are neatly presented.
20 rms (14 bth/shr) (2 fmly) CTV in all bedrooms STV 15P Xmas English & French Cuisine V meals Coffee am Tea pm No smoking in restaurant Last d 9.30pm
ROOMS: (incl. bkfst) s £35-£46; d £61-£75 LB
MEALS: Lunch £12.95-£15.95 Dinner £13.95-£16.95
CONF: Thtr 40 Board 20
CARDS:

See advertisement on opposite page

Travelodge
Travelodge
Countess Services SP4 7AS (junc A345 & A303 eastbound) ☎ 01980 624966 FAX 01980 624966
This modern building offers accommodation in smart, spacious and well equipped bedrooms, suitable for family use, and all with en suite bathrooms. Meals may be taken at the nearby family restaurant. For information on room rates and to make a booking, call Roomline free of charge on 0800 850950. For more details about Travelodge, consult the Contents page under Hotel Groups.
32 en suite (bth/shr)

AMPFIELD Hampshire Map 04 SU32

★★★70% Potters Heron
Winchester Rd SO51 9ZF (off A31)
☎ 01703 266611 FAX 01703 251359
COUNTRY CLUB Hotel Group
RS 1-6 Jan
Situated close to the New Forest, this thatched roof hotel retains many original features and offers cosy, comfortable public areas and a

choice of dining options. The galleried pub at Potters keeps a selection of real ales and provides an excellent alternative to the more formal Garden Restaurant. Spacious bedrooms, many with balconies, are particularly well equipped and there is a good range of room service. Friendly staff provide prompt service.
54 en suite (bth/shr) (4 fmly) No smoking in 32 bedrooms CTV in all bedrooms STV Lift Night porter 150P Sauna ch fac Xmas Mediterranean Cuisine V meals Coffee am Tea pm No smoking in restaurant Last d 10pm
ROOMS: s £75-£85; d £75-£85 * **LB**
OFF-PEAK: (incl. bkfst) s fr £40; d fr £50
MEALS: Lunch £11.95-£13.95&alc Dinner £17.50-£18.50&alc
CONF: Thtr 150 Class 70 Board 45 Del from £95
CARDS: 

ANDOVER Hampshire Map 04 SU34

★★61% **Danebury**
High St SP10 1NX]from A303 take B3057 to Stockbridge. After 0.5m turn left after traffic lights and left again after 200yds) ☎ 01264 323332
FAX 01264 334021
The two bars at the Danebury are the focal point of the hotel which is popular with locals, but equally its relaxed atmosphere attracts business people throughout the week. Bedrooms are mostly of a good size, soundly furnished and very well equipped to include satellite TV and complimentary mineral water. It is wise to ask for directions to the rear car park which can be difficult to find.
23 en suite (bth/shr) No smoking in 6 bedrooms CTV in all bedrooms STV No dogs (ex guide dogs) 40P V meals Coffee am Tea pm No smoking area in restaurant

contd.

ROOMS: (incl. bkfst) s £49.50; d £59.50 * LB
OFF-PEAK: (incl. bkfst) s £39.50; d £49.50
MEALS: Sunday Lunch £5.95-£8.95*
CARDS:

ANSTY Warwickshire Map 04 SP38

★★★64% ***Ansty Hall***
CV7 9HZ (close to M69 & junct 2 of M6) ☎ 01203 612222 FAX 01203 602155
A house of charm and character, this 17th-century red-brick manor house stands in eight acres of mature gardens on the edge of Ansty village, just a few minutes from the M6. Bedrooms are housed in the original building, an extension and the converted stables; all are furnished to a good standard and most are spacious. The hotel is popular as a conference/wedding venue. Staff are cheerful and helpful.
25 en suite (bth/shr) 6 annexe en suite (bth/shr) (1 fmly) No smoking in 4 bedrooms CTV in all bedrooms Night porter 50P English & French Cuisine V meals Coffee am Tea pm Last d 9.30pm
CARDS:

APPLEBY-IN-WESTMORLAND Cumbria Map 12 NY62

★★★❀ 74% **Appleby Manor Country House**
Best Western
Roman Rd CA16 6JB ☎ 017683 51571
FAX 017683 52888
Closed 24-26 Dec
This period mansion sits in attractive grounds high above the town, with fine views of the valley and Appleby Castle. It has been sympathetically extended to blend modern amenities with its traditional features. Family-run, it was a 1995 winner of the AA's Courtesy and Care award. There are three styles of bedrooms - the modern garden rooms, traditional main house rooms and smart coach house rooms just across the courtyard. At dinner, a full carte offers imaginative dishes and generous portions. Afterwards, guests may enjoy a malt from the impressive range of whiskies.
23 en suite (bth/shr) 7 annexe en suite (bth/shr) (8 fmly) CTV in all bedrooms STV 53P Indoor swimming pool (heated) Sauna Solarium Pool table Croquet lawn Jacuzzi/spa Steam room Table tennis International Cuisine V meals Coffee am Tea pm No smoking in restaurant Last d 9pm
ROOMS: (incl. bkfst) s £74-£99; d £108-£118 LB
OFF-PEAK: (incl. bkfst) s £69-£89; d £88-£108
MEALS: Lunch £16-£30alc Dinner £16-£30alc
CONF: Thtr 38 Class 25 Board 26 Del from £67.81
CARDS:

See advertisement on opposite page

★★★❀69% **Tufton Arms**
CONSORT CROWN
Market Square CA16 6XA (on B6260)
☎ 017683 51593 FAX 017683 52761
Set in a popular market town, this family-run hotel is stylishly furbished to reflect its Victorian character. The elegant bedrooms include lavish suites and studio rooms, along with two characterful mews rooms; there are also some simpler economy rooms. The conservatory restaurant features a set-price dinner menu as well as a carte offering less formal dishes.
21 en suite (bth/shr) (4 fmly) No smoking in 2 bedrooms CTV in all bedrooms STV 17P Fishing Shooting Xmas English & French Cuisine V meals Coffee am Last d 9.30pm
ROOMS: (incl. bkfst) s £45-£95; d £65-£140 * LB
MEALS: Lunch £9.75-£20alc Dinner £19.50-£29.50&alc
CONF: Thtr 100 Class 60 Board 50 Del from £90
CARDS:

★★68% ***Royal Oak Inn***
Bongate CA16 6UN ☎ 017683 51463
FAX 017683 52300
Closed 25 Dec
This charming extended coaching inn beside the old main road on the south side of town retains original oak beams, wood panelling and log fires. The attractively decorated bedrooms vary in size and include some large stylish rooms. Other facilities include two bars serving real ales, two lounge areas, a restaurant and a small flagstoned dining room. Hearty home-cooked country cuisine is served in the restaurant, dining room and downstairs lounge.
9 rms (7 bth/shr) (1 fmly) CTV in all bedrooms 10P International Cuisine V meals Coffee am Last d 9pm
CARDS:

See advertisement on opposite page

★62% **White Hart**
34 Boroughgate CA16 6XG ☎ 017683 51598 & 51598
FAX 017683 51598
This family-run hotel lies in the town centre and offers a wide range of bar meals which can also be served in the dining room to complement the à la carte dinner menu.
9 rms (5 bth/shr) (1 fmly) CTV in all bedrooms ch fac Xmas V meals Coffee am Tea pm Last d 9pm
ROOMS: (incl. bkfst) s £27-£37.50; d £39-£60 *
OFF-PEAK: (incl. bkfst) s £24-£27; d £33-£55
MEALS: Sunday Lunch £7.50-£15.95alc Dinner £9.95-£18.95alc*
CARDS:

★61% ***Courtfield***
Bongate CA16 6UP (on Brough road) ☎ 017683 51394
This former Victorian vicarage sits in its own large gardens well back from the main road. It's a family-run hotel with a friendly atmosphere, comfortable public rooms and home-cooked meals. Bedrooms are pleasant, the best being in the main house; those in the annexe are more modest, but this is reflected in the price.
5 rms (1 bth 1 shr) 3 annexe rms (1 bth 1 shr) (1 fmly) CTV in 6 bedrooms 22P No coaches V meals Coffee am Tea pm Last d 8pm

APPLETON-LE-MOORS North Yorkshire Map 08 SE78

★★ 71% **Appelton Hall Country House**

YO6 6TF ☎ 01751 417227 & 417452
FAX 01751 417540

Norma and Graham Davies are quite delightful hosts and welcome guests to their elegantly furnished Victorian country house, which stands on the edge of the village amidst award-winning gardens. A most inviting and comfortable lounge is provided and a roaring log fire burns in the hearth on colder days. Bedrooms are attractively decorated and thoughtfully equipped, and Norma's cooking is of some considerable note. Appleton Hall is a perfect place at which to relax and unwind.

10 en suite (bth/shr) CTV in all bedrooms Lift 30P No coaches Croquet lawn No children 12yrs Xmas English & Continental Cuisine Coffee am Last d 8.30pm

ROOMS: (incl. bkfst & dinner) s £50-£60; d £100-£120 * **LB**

MEALS: Dinner £19.95

CARDS:

See advertisement on this page

ARNCLIFFE North Yorkshire Map 07 SD97

★★ 74% Amerdale House

BD23 5QE ☎ 01756 770250 FAX 01756 770250
Closed mid Nov-mid Mar

This former manor house stands in its own lovely gardens on the edge of the village, surrounded by beautiful Dales scenery. Nigel and Paula Crapper are very friendly hosts who provide a warming family style of service, attaching great importance to the comfort of their guests. Relaxing public rooms have been further improved by the addition of a cosy library lounge, whilst the very well furnished bedrooms are a sheer delight to occupy. Nigel is a fine chef, and the excellent dinners featured on his daily-changing short-choice menu are complemented by a well chosen wine list.

10 en suite (bth/shr) 1 annexe en suite (bth) (3 fmly) CTV in all bedrooms No dogs (ex guide dogs) 30P No coaches No smoking in restaurant Last d 8.30pm
ROOMS: (incl. bkfst & dinner) s £66.50; d £119 * **LB**
MEALS: Dinner £25*
CARDS:

ARUNDEL West Sussex Map 04 TQ00

★★★ 66% Norfolk Arms

Forestdale Hotels

High St BN18 9AD (in centre of High Street)
☎ 01903 882101 FAX 01903 884275

An 18th-century town-centre coaching inn built by the 10th Duke of Norfolk, the Norfolk Arms retains a congenial traditional feel in its cosy lounge and two bars; one bar is popular with locals and both are warmed by welcoming log fires in winter. At the time of our last visit a redecoration programme was in hand for the public areas. The premier bedrooms are the most spacious, while those in a separate wing are modern and uniform in style. A friendly atmosphere is created by a willing team of staff.

21 en suite (bth) 13 annexe en suite (bth) (4 fmly) No smoking in 3 bedrooms CTV in all bedrooms Night porter 34P Xmas International Cuisine V meals Coffee am Tea pm No smoking area in restaurant Last d 10pm
ROOMS: (incl. bkfst) s fr £65; d £80-£90 * **LB**
OFF-PEAK: (incl. bkfst) s fr £78.50; d £106-£116
MEALS: Lunch £7.95-£10.95 High tea fr £5 Dinner fr £16.95*
CONF: Thtr 100 Class 40 Board 40 Del from £85
CARDS:

★★★ 60% The Swan

27-29 High St BN18 9AG ☎ 01903 882314 FAX 01903 883759

Combining a very popular and lively tap room pub atmosphere this popular Victorian hotel set in the heart of the town features a range of good quality non-smoking bedrooms together with a tastefully appointed restaurant and a small combined reception and residents lounge. The bedrooms which vary in shape and size have been attractively furnished and equipped with modern amenities and beds are particularly comfortable and good quality. Room service is available and light refreshments throughout the day and Chef Michael Collis offers an extensive range of freshly prepared interesting dishes cooked to order in the candle lit Restaurant. Other features include a good range of bar meals, real ales and informal and friendly service.

15 en suite (bth/shr) (5 fmly) No smoking in all bedrooms CTV in all bedrooms No dogs (ex guide dogs) Night porter 15P Xmas English & Continental Cuisine V meals Coffee am Tea pm
ROOMS: (incl. bkfst) s £45-£50; d £50-£70 * **LB**
CARDS:

★★ 75% Burpham Country

Old Down, Burpham BN18 9RJ (3m NE off A27) ☎ 01903 882160
FAX 01903 884627

Reputed to have been a hunting lodge for the Duke of Norfolk, parts of this house date from c1710. It has also been a rectory but is now a small country house hotel set in peaceful village surroundings at the base of the South Downs. The accommodation has been completely upgraded and improved and the well proportioned bedrooms come well equipped with every modern facility. Sparkling chandeliers grace the entrance hall and elegant décor is complemented by co-ordinated fabrics and quality soft furnishings. Bar-lounge comfort is enhanced by a feature gas flame fire, and the restaurant is adorned with fresh flowers and soft candlelight. Swiss born Marianne Walker does the cooking and offers a daily menu of freshly prepared dishes, fresh seafood and memorable desserts coming in for lots of praise.

10 en suite (bth/shr) CTV in all bedrooms No dogs 12P No coaches Croquet lawn No children 10yrs Xmas English, French & Swiss Cuisine V meals No smoking in restaurant Last d 8.45pm
ROOMS: (incl. bkfst) s fr £35; d £72-£79 **LB**
MEALS: Dinner £18.50
CARDS:

See advertisement on opposite page

Travel Inn

Crossbush BN18 9PQ v 01903 882655
FAX 01903 884381

Purpose-built accommodation, offering spacious, well equipped bedrooms, all with en suite bathrooms. Meals may be taken at the nearby family restaurant. For more information about Travel Inns, consult the Contents page under Hotel Groups.
40 en suite (bth/shr)

ASCOT Berkshire Map 04 SU96

★★★★ 69% The Royal Berkshire

London Rd, Sunninghill SL5 0PP (on A329) (Hilton) ☎ 01344 23322
FAX 01344 27100

A much extended, refurbished 18th-century mansion, the Royal Berkshire is an interesting and largely successful mixture of old and new. A new wing provides bedrooms of a uniformly good standard, while those in the main house come in every shape and size, but are also comfortable. There is an elegant lounge and a smart restaurant serving enjoyable food, of a style in keeping with the surroundings.

63 en suite (bth/shr) CTV in all bedrooms Night porter 150P Indoor swimming pool (heated) Tennis (hard) Squash Sauna Gym Croquet lawn Putting green Jacuzzi/spa Xmas European Cuisine V meals Coffee am Tea pm Last d 9.30pm
ROOMS: s £70-£200; d £215-£305 * **LB**
MEALS: Lunch £24.75&alc Dinner £35.50&alc
CARDS:

See advertisement under WINDSOR

★★★★ 68% The Berystede

FORTE Heritage

Bagshot Rd, Sunninghill SL5 9JH ☎ 01344 23311
FAX 01344 872301

Standing in nine acres of wooded grounds this turreted and timber-framed former Victorian residence has been considerably extended in a contrastingly modern style. The best bedrooms, which are generously-sized, are in the main house together

with the comfortable and attractively appointed day rooms which include various lounges, a small bar and a tastefully furnished restaurant. Here, new chef Iain McCormack is pleasing diners with his seasonal modern menus which often feature Scottish fish and dishes such as roquefort and walnut mousse with parma ham or a broth of rhubarb and orange. The hotel is well managed and staff are friendly and willing.

91 en suite (bth/shr) (6 fmly) No smoking in 36 bedrooms CTV in all bedrooms STV Lift Night porter 241P Outdoor swimming pool (heated) Croquet lawn Putting green Wkly live entertainment Xmas European Cuisine V meals Coffee am Tea pm No smoking in restaurant Last d 10pm

ROOMS: s £115-£170; d £125-£180 **LB**

OFF-PEAK: (incl. bkfst & dinner) s fr £80; d fr £100

MEALS: Lunch £15.95-£18.95 Dinner £24.50-£26.50&alc*

CONF: Thtr 120 Class 55 Board 50 Del from £145

CARDS:

★★71% ***Highclere***

19 Kings Rd, Sunninghill SL5 9AD (opposite Sunninghill Post Office)

☎ 01344 25220 FAX 01344 872528

Every aspect of the service and fabric of this hotel is a little bit more special than the average two star establishment. Care and attention is lavished on the property and the guests by Mr and Mrs Rees, and a new conservatory at the back has provided more space for the bar and lounge.

11 en suite (bth/shr) (1 fmly) No smoking in 3 bedrooms CTV in all bedrooms STV No dogs (ex guide dogs) 14P No coaches European Cuisine V meals Coffee am Last d 9.30pm

CARDS:

★★66% **Brockenhurst**

Brockenhurst Rd SL5 9HA (on A330) ☎ 01344 21912

FAX 01344 873252

This large Edwardian house is located on the A330 to the south of Ascot, with a large rear lawn and plenty of parking space. Catering for both business and leisure guests, the resident owners provide a friendly and informal atmosphere. There are two types of bedroom but they are all generally spacious and well maintained.

11 en suite (bth/shr) (2 fmly) CTV in all bedrooms No dogs 32P No coaches Xmas French Cuisine Coffee am Tea pm Last d 9.30pm

ROOMS: (incl. cont bkfst) s £69-£89; d £79-£100 * **LB**

MEALS: Lunch £5-£13&alc Dinner £15&alc*

CONF: Thtr 50 Class 25 Board 30 Del from £94

CARDS:

ASHBOURNE Derbyshire Map 07 SK14

★★★ 75% **Callow Hall**

Mappleton Rd DE6 2AA (take A515 through Ashbourne toward Buxton, turn left at Bowling Green pub on left, then first right)

☎ 01335 343403 & 342412 FAX 01335 343624

Closed 25-26 Dec

A tree-lined drive overlooking the valleys of Bentley Brook and the River Dove leads to the home of the Spencer family. This mellow early Victorian house is swathed in Virginia creeper and rich in architectural features. Inside, it is furnished with a harmonious but eclectic range of polished period antiques and contemporary pieces. Malaysian prints sit comfortably next to gilt-framed portraits and deep, comfortably worn Chesterfields next to rattan backed armchairs. The atmosphere is welcoming and the service unobtrusive but attentive and professional. Bedrooms, some of generous proportions, are similarly furnished, all having large bathrooms. The food is a very strong feature - breads, preserves and the breakfast sausages and bacon are made or cured by David and Anthony Spencer. Dishes are predominantly modern English and rely the best produce available. Sauces are really good.

contd.

16 en suite (bth/shr) (2 fmly) CTV in all bedrooms No dogs (ex guide dogs) 21P No coaches Fishing ch fac English & French Cuisine V meals No smoking in restaurant Last d 8.45pm
ROOMS: (incl. bkfst) s £65-£85; d £95-£120 * **LB**
MEALS: Lunch £15.50 Dinner £30&alc*
CONF: Thtr 30 Board 16
CARDS:

See advertisement on page 69

★★★68% **Ashbourne Lodge**
Derby Rd DE6 1XH (on A52, on SE outskirts) ☎ 01335 346666
FAX 01335 346549
This modern purpose-built hotel lies just outside the town and comprises a well equipped bedroom wing, Alberts (an all-day brasserie), Milldale (a more formal restaurant), and a leisure club.
50 en suite (bth/shr) (5 fmly) No smoking in 11 bedrooms CTV in all bedrooms STV No dogs (ex guide dogs) Lift Night porter 200P Indoor swimming pool (heated) Sauna Gym Pool table ch fac V meals Coffee am Tea pm No smoking area in restaurant Last d 10pm
ROOMS: (incl. bkfst) s fr £65; d fr £82 * **LB**
MEALS: Bar Lunch fr £10 Dinner £15.95-£25*
CONF: Thtr 200 Class 100 Board 80 Del from £85
CARDS:

★★62% ***Greenman Royal***
St John's St DE6 1GH (in town centre) ☎ 01335 345783
FAX 01335 346613
Instantly recognisable by the huge sign that stretches from one side of the street to the other, this characterful hotel offers attractively decorated and neatly furnished accommodation. The bedrooms do vary in size and refurbishment work on the larger rooms, situated in the older part of the building, was about to commence. A bright, coffee shop/restaurant and a cosy lounge bar form the main part of the public areas and the hotel does have a newly decorated conference and banqueting suite. Ample parking is available at the rear of the hotel.
9 en suite (bth/shr) CTV in all bedrooms 30P No coaches V meals Coffee am Tea pm
CARDS:

See advertisement on opposite page

ASHBURTON Devon Map 03 SX77

★★★64% **Holne Chase**
Two Bridges Rd TQ13 7NS (3m N on Two Bridges/Tavistock road (unclass)) ☎ 01364 631471 FAX 01364 631453
In a lovely woodland setting Holne Chase Hotel has a comfortable, friendly atmosphere. Bedrooms are individually decorated, with attractive coordinated soft furnishings. The restaurant serves local produce cooked with care to produce honest dishes with natural flavours.
12 en suite (bth/shr) 6 annexe en suite (bth/shr) (6 fmly) CTV in all bedrooms 40P No coaches Fishing Croquet lawn Putting green Xmas V meals Coffee am Tea pm No smoking in restaurant Last d 9pm
ROOMS: (incl. bkfst) s fr £50; d £100-£140 * **LB**
MEALS: Lunch fr £16&alc High tea fr £10 Dinner fr £25&alc*
CONF: Thtr 20 Class 20 Board 20 Del from £95
CARDS:

See advertisement on opposite page

★★69% **Dartmoor Lodge**
MINOTEL Great Britain
Peartree Cross TQ13 7JW (turn off A38 at Peartree Junction and follow 'Hotel & Services' signs)
☎ 01364 652232 FAX 01364 653990
RS Nov-Feb
This popular hotel, situated just off the main A38 halfway between Plymouth and Exeter, offers well equipped bedrooms, a character bar and various function rooms. A wide range of dishes is served from a choice of menus in the attractive beamed restaurant, where the atmosphere is relaxed and friendly.
30 en suite (bth/shr) (8 fmly) No smoking in 5 bedrooms CTV in all bedrooms STV Lift Night porter 100P Xmas V meals Coffee am Tea pm No smoking area in restaurant Last d 9pm
ROOMS: s fr £34; d fr £45 **LB**
MEALS: Lunch £7.95 Dinner £5-£16&alc*
CONF: Thtr 84 Class 48 Board 32 Del from £80
CARDS:

ASHBY-DE-LA-ZOUCH Leicestershire Map 08 SK31

★★★64% **The Fallen Knight**
Kilwardby St LE65 2FQ ☎ 01530 412230 FAX 01530 417596
The hotel, at the edge of the town's shopping centre is a superbly renovated and refurbished old building. Very much in the contemporary mode the public rooms extend beyond a comfortably furnished lounge style bar to an elegant dining room and conference rooms as well. The choice of food available is good ranging from light bar meals to more formal eating. The bedrooms are furnished to a similar style and quality though the rooms in the older part have more character and are more individual.
24 en suite (bth/shr) (3 fmly) CTV in all bedrooms Lift 50P No coaches Xmas English & Mediterranean Cuisine V meals Coffee am Last d 10.30pm
ROOMS: (incl. bkfst) s £62-£68; d £79-£90
OFF-PEAK: (incl. bkfst) s £40-£50; d £60-£70
MEALS: Lunch £9.95-£13.95 Dinner £13.95-£17.50
CONF: Thtr 70 Class 50 Board 40 Del from £85
CARDS:

ASHFORD Kent Map 05 TR04

★★★★ 75% **Eastwell Manor**
THE Virgin HOTEL COLLECTION
Eastwell Park, Boughton Lees TN25 4HR (on A251, 200 yds on left when entering Boughton Aluph)
☎ 01233 219955 FAX 01233 635530
This fine hotel, featured on the front cover of this guide, is set in 62 acres of the magnificent gardens and grounds of Eastwell Park on the outskirts of Ashford. Its rich history is reflected in stunning architecture and comfortable public rooms with stonework, open fires, antiques, and wood panelling. Bedrooms are spacious and decorated with sumptuous fabrics, catering for guests' comforts with many thoughtful extras. Friendly staff provide excellent levels of service, and in the kitchens chef Ian Mansfield continues to cook to a high standard. His seasonally changing menus offer a balanced range of dishes making creative use of good local ingredients.

23 en suite (bth/shr) No smoking in 4 bedrooms CTV in all bedrooms STV Lift Night porter 60P No coaches Tennis (hard) Snooker Croquet lawn Putting green Boule Xmas English & French Cuisine V meals Coffee am Tea pm No smoking in restaurant Last d 9.30pm
ROOMS: s £113-£235; d £145-£255 * **LB**
MEALS: Lunch £19.50-£25&alc Dinner fr £25&alc*
CONF: Thtr 100 Class 40 Board 36 Del £155
CARDS:

★★★★66% **Ashford International**
Simone Weil Av TN24 8UX (off junct 9, M20) ☎ 01233 219988
FAX 01233 627708
This is a modern purpose-built hotel which has as a public area feature a naturally lit boulevard with boutiques and eating outlets. The Alhambra is the more formal restaurant and there is a brasserie as well as the Florentine cafe which serves light snacks. The bedrooms are spacious and decorated in two distinct styles. The hotel is suitable for social and business meetings as well as groups of holidaymakers.
200 en suite (bth/shr) (4 fmly) No smoking in 57 bedrooms CTV in

all bedrooms Lift Night porter 400P Indoor swimming pool (heated) Snooker Sauna Solarium Gym Jacuzzi/spa European Cuisine V meals Coffee am Tea pm No smoking area in restaurant Last d 10pm
ROOMS: s £84; d £98 * **LB**
MEALS: Lunch £12.50-£12.90 Dinner £16.90&alc*
CONF: Thtr 400 Class 160 Board 100
CARDS:

★★★ 64% **Master Spearpoint**
Canterbury Rd, Kennington TN24 9QR (on A28 1m N of town centre, 0.5m from junct 9 of M20)
☎ 01233 636863 FAX 01233 610119

Best Western

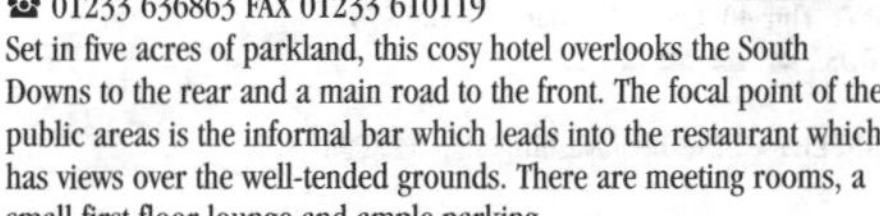

Set in five acres of parkland, this cosy hotel overlooks the South Downs to the rear and a main road to the front. The focal point of the public areas is the informal bar which leads into the restaurant which has views over the well-tended grounds. There are meeting rooms, a small first floor lounge and ample parking.
34 en suite (bth/shr) (1 fmly) CTV in all bedrooms STV Night porter 60P International Cuisine V meals Coffee am Tea pm No smoking area in restaurant Last d 9.45pm
ROOMS: (incl. bkfst) s £65; d £75 * **LB**
OFF-PEAK: (incl. bkfst) s £57.50; d £65
MEALS: Lunch £4.95-£5.95 Dinner fr £5.95*
CONF: Thtr 75 Class 40 Board 40 Del £85
CARDS:

Forte Posthouse Ashford
Canterbury Rd TN24 8QQ (off A28)
☎ 01233 625790 FAX 01233 643176

FORTE Posthouse

Suitable for both the business and leisure traveller, this bright hotel provides modern accommodation in well equipped bedrooms with en suite bathrooms. For more details about Forte Posthouse hotels, consult the Contents page for the section on Hotel Groups.
60 en suite (bth/shr)
CONF: Thtr 120 Class 65 Board 40 Del £99

Travel Inn
Maidstone Rd, Hothfield Common TN26 1AP (on A20, between Ashford & Charing)
☎ 01233 712571 FAX 01233 713945

travel inn

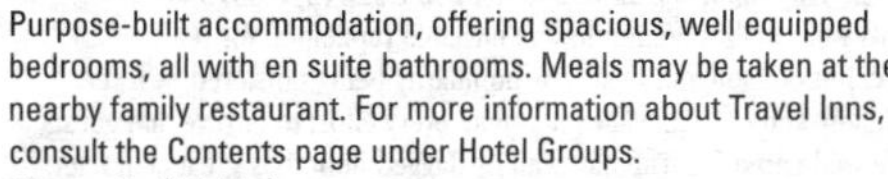

Purpose-built accommodation, offering spacious, well equipped bedrooms, all with en suite bathrooms. Meals may be taken at the nearby family restaurant. For more information about Travel Inns, consult the Contents page under Hotel Groups.
40 en suite (bth/shr)
ROOMS: d £35.50 *

ASHFORD-IN-THE-WATER Derbyshire Map 07 SK17

★★★ ❀❀ 70% **Riverside Country House**
Fennel St DE45 1QF (on main village street beside the Sheep Wash Bridge) ☎ 01629 814275 FAX 01629 812873
The individually styled bedrooms at this delightful riverside hotel encompass a good range of comfort and quality, though all share the same modern facilities. The candlelit restaurant is intimate and elegant, with crystal glistening on the polished oak tables, provideing the perfect setting for some excellent cooking. Quality ingredients are prepared with flair and independence in a straightforward modern style. In the summer, home-cured beef was chunkily sliced, tender and moist, served with a tangy dressed salad, fresh olives and a lid of parmesan. Loin of tuna, toasted crisply to seal in its freshness, came with fresh anchovy and tiny sautéed potatoes. A variety of puddings included lemon crème brûlée and pear fritters.
15 en suite (bth/shr) No smoking in all bedrooms CTV in all bedrooms 30P No coaches Croquet lawn Putting green Xmas

contd.

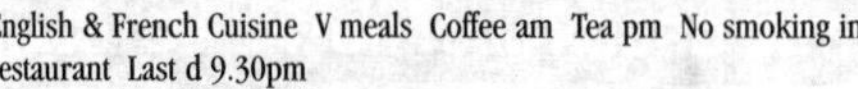

English & French Cuisine V meals Coffee am Tea pm No smoking in restaurant Last d 9.30pm
ROOMS: (incl. cont bkfst) s £75-£85; d £85-£150 * **LB**
MEALS: Lunch £14.50-£18.95 Dinner £19.50-£29.95&alc*
CONF: Thtr 25 Class 20 Board 12 Del from £125
CARDS:

★★71% **Ashford**
Church St DE45 1QB (next to the Post Office) ☎ 01629 812725
FAX 01629 814749
Cheerful young staff and owners help to create a friendly, relaxed atmosphere at this small inn. The bar and food operations are popular with guests and locals, and include an all-day lounge and bar menu and a good restaurant choice, plus daily dishes from the blackboard. Accommodation is attractive in its rustic style, most rooms have oak-beamed ceilings, and all are nicely colour co-ordinated and well equipped, with en suite bathrooms.
7 en suite (bth/shr) (1 fmly) CTV in all bedrooms 50P Xmas International Cuisine V meals Coffee am No smoking in restaurant Last d 9pm
ROOMS: (incl. bkfst) s £50-£55; d £75-£95 * **LB**
MEALS: Lunch £10.50-£16.25alc Dinner £14-£20alc*
CARDS:

ASHTON-UNDER-LYNE Greater Manchester Map 07 SJ99

★★69% **York House**

York Place, Richmond St OL6 7TT (close to junct A635/A6017) ☎ 0161 330 5899 FAX 0161 343 1613
Closed 26 Dec & 1 Jan RS Sun
Developed from a number of Victorian houses, this long-established privately-owned and personally-run hotel is quietly situated amongst beautiful gardens, a short distance from the city. Whilst the bedrooms vary in size, they are all thoughtfully equipped and have a good range of facilities; twelve rooms are situated just opposite the main hotel. Attractively furnished public areas are full of character and include a welcoming reception hall, part-panelled bar and anelegant restaurant where a good range of carefully prepared dishes is available.
24 en suite (bth/shr) 10 annexe en suite (bth/shr) (2 fmly) CTV in all bedrooms STV Night porter 34P Reduced cost at local gym/pool English & French Cuisine V meals Coffee am Tea pm Last d 9.30pm
ROOMS: (incl. bkfst) s £49-£58; d £72-£75 **LB**
OFF-PEAK: (incl. bkfst) s £35; d £66
MEALS: Lunch £5-£9.95&alc Dinner £8-£26alc*
CONF: Thtr 50 Class 20 Board 22 Del from £79
CARDS:

★63% **Welbeck House**
324 Katherine St OL6 7BD ☎ 0161 344 0751 FAX 0161 343 4278
This friendly, privately-owned hotel offers neat, no frills accommodation, all of which is en suite. The public areas include a spacious lounge bar furnished with leather chesterfield sofas, opposite which is a small dining room where a short choice of popular dishes served at dinner.
8 en suite (shr) (2 fmly) CTV in all bedrooms STV Night porter 15P No coaches Sauna Pool table Games room V meals Last d 8.45pm
ROOMS: (incl. bkfst) s fr £35; d fr £45 * **LB**
OFF-PEAK: (incl. bkfst) s fr £29.50; d fr £42
MEALS: Dinner £8-£15&alc*
CARDS:

ASKRIGG North Yorkshire Map 07 SD99

★★✿✿68% **King's Arms Hotel & Clubroom Restaurant**
Market Place DL8 3HQ (half a mille off A684 in centre of village)
☎ 01969 650258 FAX 01969 650635
Standing in the centre of the village which is famous as the location for the TV series based on James Herriot's 'All Creatures Great and Small', this lovely old inn dates back to 1760. Much of its original character and charm is retained, especially in the bars where locals mix with tourists. The bedrooms are furnished in the style of the house. Food is now under the control of John Barber, who offers a very interesting menu using local fresh produce which is attractively presented. Service is very friendly and courteous.
11 en suite (bth/shr) (1 fmly) CTV in all bedrooms 17P Xmas English & French Cuisine V meals Coffee am Tea pm No smoking in restaurant Last d 9pm
ROOMS: (incl. bkfst) s £50-£70; d £75-£108 * **LB**
MEALS: Lunch fr £9.25 Dinner fr £25*
CONF: Thtr 40 Class 20 Board 30 Del £75
CARDS:

ASPLEY GUISE Bedfordshire Map 04 SP93

★★★69% **Moore Place**
The Square MK17 8DW (from junct 13 of M1 follow signs for Husborne Crawley) ☎ 01908 282000 FAX 01908 281888
Closed 26-30 Dec
This red brick Georgian mansion is set in the cetre of a quiet village, yet is convenient for junction 13 of the M1. Accommodation is divided between the main house and a courtyard extension which provides attractive bedrooms with a good range of equipment. Room sizes vary between spacious executive rooms and smaller standard rooms; a delightful suite is also available. Public areas include a reception with foyer seating, a cocktail bar and an airy Victorian-style conservatory restaurant serving a good choice of food on imaginative menus.
39 en suite (bth/shr) 15 annexe en suite (bth/shr) CTV in all bedrooms STV Night porter 50P ch fac English & French Cuisine V meals Coffee am Tea pm Last d 9.30pm
ROOMS: (incl. bkfst) s £68-£95; d £90-£175 * **LB**
OFF-PEAK: (incl. bkfst) s £52.50; d £85-£175
MEALS: Lunch £5.95-£19.09alc Dinner £15.95-£19.95alc*
CONF: Thtr 50 Class 32 Board 24 Del from £105
CARDS:

ASTON CLINTON Buckinghamshire Map 04 SP81

★★★✿✿75% **Bell Inn**
HP22 5HP (on A41) ☎ 01296 630252 FAX 01296 631250
This well established inn has an enviable reputation for both accommodation and meals, its popularity being bolstered by a very friendly and efficient staff who make every effort to ensure that guests are well cared for. The bar, with its flagged floor, has great character, and the restaurant features a splendid hand-painted mural based on a garden theme. New chef Giles Stonehouse has added modern touches to some of the well trusted favourites that are very much part of the Bell Inn tradition, and menus offer very good value for money. Bedrooms are priced according to size and type; all are spacious and well equipped, but each is different in style and some have patios with direct access to the gardens.
6 en suite (bth/shr) 15 annexe en suite (bth/shr) (6 fmly) CTV in all bedrooms Night porter 200P Croquet lawn ch fac Xmas English & French Cuisine V meals Coffee am Tea pm No smoking area in restaurant Last d 9.45pm
ROOMS: d £55-£90 * **LB**
MEALS: Lunch £10-£19.75 Dinner £17.95-£25&alc*
CONF: Class 20 Board 20 Del from £125
CARDS:

ATCHAM Shropshire Map 07 SJ50

★★62% ***Mytton & Mermaid Hotel***
SY5 6QG ☎ 01743 761220
This former coaching inn dates back to the early 18th century and has a very interesting history. It stands alongside the River Severn some 3

miles east of Shrewsbury. The bedrooms vary in both size and style and all have modern equipment. Some rooms are located on the ground floor of a former stable block and guests can park directly outside. In addition to an attractive garden, public areas include a large restaurant, a traditionally furnished lounge bar and an attractively appointed, comfortable lounge. There is also a self contained suite for conferences and other functions. An entertainment room is used for disco's three nights a week and country and western music on a fourth.
16 rms

ATHERSTONE Warwickshire Map 04 SP39

★★ 73% **Chapel House**
Friar's Gate CV9 1EY ☎ 01827 718949 FAX 01827 717702
Closed 24-26 Dec
Set beside the church, partly enclosed by a high brick wall, this hotel is an oasis of friendly hospitality and good cooking. The kitchen team offer a monthly changing menu and great care is taken in all their preparations, from the canapés to the petits fours. A sample winter meal from a three or four-course menu comprised veal and smoked bacon terrine, baked cod in parsley butter sauce, and a chocolate and Amaretto mousse. The flavours are exact and the cooking near faultless. Bedrooms vary considerably in style but they are all comfortable.
13 en suite (bth/shr) CTV in all bedrooms No dogs (ex guide dogs) No coaches English & French Cuisine V meals Last d 9.30pm
ROOMS: (incl. bkfst) s £45-£60; d £60-£75 * **LB**
MEALS: Lunch £14-£31alc Dinner £14-£31alc*
CONF: Board 20
CARDS:

See advertisement on this page

ATTLEBOROUGH Norfolk Map 05 TM09

★★ 65% **Sherbourne Country House**
Norwich Rd NR17 2JX (at Parish Church follow signs for A11 to Norwich. Hotel 200yds on right.) ☎ 01953 454363
FAX 01953 453509
This small friendly hotel sits on the edge of the town in its own grounds with ample private car parking. Bedrooms are light and inviting, each individually styled and thoughtfully equipped, and most have modern en suite bathrooms. The smart public areas are divided between a lounge bar and two small dining rooms, where a good choice of interesting meals are served.
8 rms (5 bth/shr) No smoking in 2 bedrooms CTV in all bedrooms 40P No coaches Jacuzzi/spa Wkly live entertainment French Cuisine V meals Coffee am Tea pm No smoking area in restaurant Last d 9pm
ROOMS: (incl. bkfst) s £29-£55; d £50-£75 * **LB**
MEALS: Lunch £2.95-£15alc Dinner £6.95-£17alc
CONF: Thtr 24 Class 24 Board 17 Del from £75
CARDS:

AUSTWICK North Yorkshire Map 07 SD76

★★ 67% **The Traddock**

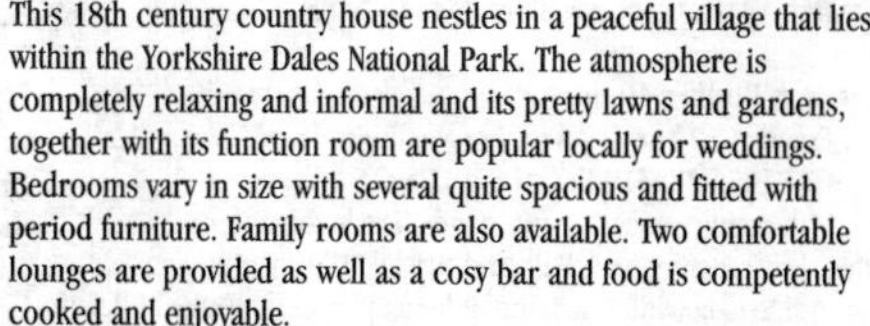

LA2 8BY (4m N of Settle, off A65)
☎ 015242 51224 FAX 015242 51224
This 18th century country house nestles in a peaceful village that lies within the Yorkshire Dales National Park. The atmosphere is completely relaxing and informal and its pretty lawns and gardens, together with its function room are popular locally for weddings. Bedrooms vary in size with several quite spacious and fitted with period furniture. Family rooms are also available. Two comfortable lounges are provided as well as a cosy bar and food is competently cooked and enjoyable.
11 en suite (bth/shr) (3 fmly) No smoking in all bedrooms CTV in all bedrooms No dogs (ex guide dogs) 15P Croquet lawn Putting green Xmas International Cuisine V meals Coffee am No smoking in restaurant Last d 9pm

ROOMS: (incl. bkfst) s £35-£40; d £65-£75 * **LB**
OFF-PEAK: (incl. bkfst) s £30-£35; d £60-£70
MEALS: Sunday Lunch £8.95-£17.85alc Dinner fr £17.50&alc*
CONF: Thtr 70 Class 30 Board 20 Del from £60
CARDS:

AXBRIDGE Somerset Map 03 ST45

★★ 65% **Oak House**
The Square BS26 2AP (2m E of Cheddar, 0.25m off A371)
☎ 01934 732444 FAX 01934 733112
Situated in the Square of this ancient town of Axbridge, the Oak House was originally three cottage properties. Attracting both business and leisure users, the hotel has a cosy, relaxed atmosphere. Piggy's Bistro provides an intimate style of dining with dishes being advertised on blackboards. Meals are prepared using fresh, local produce, the cooking being simple retaining the natural flavours. Bedrooms are well equipped and are currently under going upgrading.
10 en suite (bth/shr) (2 fmly) CTV in all bedrooms English & French Cuisine V meals Coffee am Tea pm No smoking area in restaurant Last d 9.15pm
ROOMS: (incl. bkfst) s £40; d £54-£59.50 * **LB**
MEALS: Lunch £10.85-£20.85alc Dinner £10.85-£20.85alc*
CONF: Thtr 40 Class 40 Board 22
CARDS:

AXMINSTER Devon Map 03 SY29See Chardstock

★★★ 73% **Fairwater Head**
Hawkchurch EX13 5TX (turn off B3165 (Crewkerne to Lyme Regis Road) hotel signposted to Hawkchurch) ☎ 01297 678349
FAX 01297 678459
Closed 4 Dec-2 Mar

contd.

This charming Edwardian house, set in well kept gardens amidst rolling countryside yet close to the coast of East Devon and Dorset, provides warm personal service and a peaceful atmosphere. Comfortable bedrooms, some of which are situated in a separate house in the garden, are attractive, with co-ordinating soft furnishings and fresh flowers. There is a choice of relaxing lounges, an elegant drawing room and a spacious dining room where 4-course dinners are based on fresh local produce.
14 en suite (bth/shr) 7 annexe en suite (bth/shr) CTV in all bedrooms 30P No coaches Croquet lawn Bowls Xmas English & French Cuisine V meals Coffee am Tea pm Last d 8.15pm
ROOMS: (incl. bkfst & dinner) s £67.50-£84; d £126-£149 * **LB**
MEALS: Lunch fr £6.50 Dinner fr £20&alc*
CARDS:

See advertisement under LYME REGIS

★★ 78% **Lea Hill**
Membury EX13 7AQ ☎ 01404 881881 881388
This beautiful thatched Devon long house nestles in the heart of the countryside near Axminster, and parts of it dates as far back as the 1300s. Sympathetically restored, the house now offers nine luxurious bedrooms with modern en suite facilities. The rooms are individually decorated and comfortably furnished with nice personal touches. Resident proprietors Hilary and Jim Reaney offer a warm welcome and ensure a relaxed atmosphere; there is a cosy bar and the restaurant offers good home-cooked food using local produce. In the summer months guests may take advantage of the lovely gardens with views across the countryside.
9 annexe en suite (bth/shr) (2 fmly) No smoking in all bedrooms CTV in all bedrooms 25P Croquet lawn ch fac Xmas English & French Cuisine Coffee am Tea pm No smoking in restaurant Last d 8.30pm
ROOMS: (incl. bkfst) s £47-£53; d £74-£86 **LB**
OFF-PEAK: (incl. bkfst) s £45-£51; d £70-£82
MEALS: Lunch £18-£26.25 High tea £5.95 Dinner £18-£26.25
CARDS:

See advertisement under AXMINSTER

See advertisement on opposite page

AYLESBURY Buckinghamshire Map 04 SP81

RED STAR HOTEL

★★★★ **Hartwell House**
Oxford Rd HP17 8NL (signposted 2m SW on A418) ☎ 01296 747444 FAX 01296 747450
RELAIS & CHATEAUX. Relais Gourmands
There is much to please the eye in this 90-acre estate which is dominated by the supremely elegant hotel building. It dates from 1600 but was altered by Georgian architects, and delightful features such as delicate ceiling plasterwork and a Jacobean great staircase have been carefully preserved. The bedrooms ooze character and comfort including some more recently built rooms in a converted stable block. They have the advantage of being closer to the health centre complex, complete with Buttery coffee shop and separately contained function rooms. The kitchen, under Roger Barstow, maintains a classical style of cooking as reflected in a recent meal of chicken sausage with puréed potatoes, grilled seabass with clams and a parsley cream sauce, and a trio of English desserts (treacle tart, rice pudding and steamed sponge).
31 en suite (bth/shr) 16 annexe en suite (bth/shr) No smoking in 12 bedrooms CTV in all bedrooms Lift Night porter 91P No coaches Indoor swimming pool (heated) Tennis (hard) Fishing Sauna Solarium Gym Croquet lawn Jacuzzi/spa Treatment room Wkly live entertainment No children 8yrs Xmas V meals Coffee am Tea pm No smoking in restaurant Last d 9.45pm
ROOMS: s £105-£130; d £160-£260 * **LB**
MEALS: Lunch £18.45-£24.90&alc Dinner £39.90&alc
CONF: Thtr 100 Class 40 Board 40 Del from £185
CARDS:

★★★ 62% **Holiday Inn Garden Court**
Buckingham Rd, Watermead HP19 3FY (A41 into Aylesbury follow ring road, pick up A413 towards Buckingham, hotel on the right hand side)
☎ 01296 398839 FAX 01296 394108
Holiday Inn Garden Court
This modern hotel is quietly located on the outskirts of town on the A413 Buckingham road. It has large, comfortable bedrooms which are well equipped. Public areas are restricted in size and style of operation and include an informally run bar and restaurant.
40 en suite (bth/shr) No smoking in 20 bedrooms CTV in all bedrooms STV Night porter 37P V meals Coffee am No smoking area in restaurant
ROOMS: s ~~£44-£54~~; d £44-£54 *
CONF: Thtr 30 Class 20 Board 25 Del from £90
CARDS:

Forte Posthouse Aylesbury
Aston Clinton Rd HP22 5AA (on A41)
☎ 01296 393388 FAX 01296 392211
FORTE Posthouse
Suitable for both the business and leisure traveller, this bright hotel provides modern accommodation in well equipped bedrooms with en suite bathrooms. For more details about Forte Posthouse hotels, consult the Contents page for the section on Hotel Groups.
94 en suite (bth/shr)
ROOMS: d fr £79 *
CONF: Thtr 110 Class 80 Board 40 Del £109

BABBACOMBE See Torquay

BADMINTON Gloucestershire Map 03 ST88

★★ 66% **Bodkin House**
Petty France GL9 1AF (on A46, 6m N of junct 18 on M4) ☎ 01454 238310 FAX 01454 238422
This 17th-century coaching inn stands beside the A46, within easy reach of both Bath and Bristol. The surrounding countryside is beautiful, much of it being part of the Duke of Beaufort's estate. Run in a friendly and relaxed style by Brian and Tricia Neve, with spacious bedrooms, well equipped and with modern facilities, the hotel also features comfortable public rooms. The split-level dining room is most attractive, and the bar has a stone flagged floor.

B

8 en suite (bth/shr) (2 fmly) CTV in all bedrooms 35P Hot air ballooning ch fac Xmas English & French Cuisine V meals Coffee am Tea pm No smoking in restaurant Last d 9.30pm
ROOMS: (incl. bkfst) s £45-£49; d £70-£80 **LB**
OFF-PEAK: (incl. bkfst) s £42-£45; d £55-£65
MEALS: Lunch £7.45-£14.95&alc High tea fr £5.75 Dinner £9.95-£14.95&alc*
CONF: Thtr 20 Class 12 Board 12
CARDS:

See advertisement on this page

BAGSHOT Surrey Map 04 SU96

Red Star Hotel

★★★★ **Pennyhill Park**
London Rd GU19 5ET (on A30)
☎ 01276 471774 FAX 01276 473217

This fine manor house, set in an estate of 120 acres, is covered in creepers and surrounded by flagged terraces and formal gardens. The architecture of the house has been carefully restored and, despite the more recent inclusion of modern facilities, preserves all the elegance and dignity of the Victorian era. The public rooms are lavishly furnished with beautiful tapestries and a host of paintings, all of which enhance the magnificent surroundings. The intimate restaurant has a timbered ceiling, and here the interesting menus and the cooking skills of Karl Edmunds continue to impress. Excellent leisure facilities are provided, and since they are at a distance from the main building, do not intrude. Plans are afoot to develop the kitchens and to add a second restaurant and bar, and also to refurbish the reception area.
22 en suite (bth/shr) 54 annexe en suite (bth/shr) No smoking in 31 bedrooms CTV in all bedrooms No dogs (ex guide dogs) Night porter 250P Outdoor swimming pool (heated) Golf 9 Tennis (hard) Fishing Riding Sauna

contd.

Solarium Croquet lawn Archery Clay pigeon shooting Xmas English & French Cuisine V meals Coffee am Tea pm No smoking in restaurant Last d 10.30pm
ROOMS: s fr £135; d fr £155 * **LB**
CONF: Thtr 60 Class 35 Board 35
CARDS:

See advertisement on opposite page

BAINBRIDGE North Yorkshire Map 07 SD99

★★65% **Rose & Crown**
Village Green DL8 3EE (on A684 in centre of village)
☎ 01969 650225 FAX 01969 650735
This 15th-century inn stands at the head of the village overlooking the delightful green. It is well cared for in all areas, and provides comfortable bedrooms together with adequate and inviting bars. There is also a cosy residents' lounge, and a good range of food is served either in the bar or the oak-floored restaurant. Service is friendly and very honest.
12 en suite (bth/shr) (1 fmly) CTV in all bedrooms 65P Fishing Pool table V meals Coffee am No smoking area in restaurant Last d 9.30pm
ROOMS: (incl. bkfst) s £30-£34.50; d £48-£57 **LB**
MEALS: Lunch £9.20-£11.95alc High tea £5.50-£7.50alc Dinner £14.95-£23.45alc
CARDS:

BAKEWELL Derbyshire Map 08 SK26

★★★70% **Hassop Hall**
Hassop DE45 1NS (take B6001 for approx. 2m into Hassop, hotel opposite church) ☎ 01629 640488 FAX 01629 640577
RS 24-26 Dec
Hassop Hall is a magnificent example of the English heritage. Its architecture and history dates back originally to the Domesday Book, with examples from the reign of Richard the Second, the Reformation and Civil War periods. Improvements to modernise, in the neo-classical mould were made in the early nineteenth century and more latterly by the present owners, the Chapman family who have exercised a determination to conserve this outstanding heritage and maintain the hall as a home and a successful hotel. Today hospitality is a speciality of the house and the bedrooms and reception rooms, overlooking magnificent gardens are comfortably furnished and warmed by open fires.
13 en suite (bth/shr) (2 fmly) CTV in all bedrooms Lift 80P Tennis (hard) Croquet lawn Wkly live entertainment V meals Last d 9pm
ROOMS: s £65-£109; d £79-£119 * **LB**
MEALS: Lunch £9.95-£17.95 Dinner £18.75-£27.95*
CARDS:

★★★63% ***Rutland Arms***
The Square DE45 1BT ☎ 01629 812812 FAX 01629 812309
This historic hotel offers a variety of accommodation, including some spacious rooms in the main building and more compact but equally well furnished and equipped ones in the courtyard. Public areas include cosy and comfortable lounges, a lounge bar, and the adjacent Rutland Tavern which serves real ales and a good range of bar meals. Head chef Peter Saunders produces mouth-watering dishes in the Four Seasons Restaurant.
20 en suite (bth) 16 annexe en suite (bth) (2 fmly) No smoking in 10 bedrooms CTV in all bedrooms Night porter 38P English & French Cuisine V meals Coffee am Tea pm Last d 9.30pm
CARDS:

★★ 74% **Croft Country House**
Great Longstone DE45 1TF (from Bakewell follow A6 towards Buxton turn right on to A6020, turn left at sign to Great Longstone, entrance on right 0.25m into village) ☎ 01629 640278
Closed 2 Jan-1 Feb

This hotel is set in a picturesque village in the heart of the Peak National Park and although its décor and furnishings reflect the Victorian period from which the house dates the amenities are thoroughly modern. The galleried lounge with its polished floors is at the centre with each of the comfortably furnished reception rooms leading off. Above, each of the individually styled bedrooms leads off the landing overlooking the lounge. The food is fresh and wholesome.
9 en suite (bth/shr) CTV in all bedrooms No dogs (ex guide dogs) Lift 40P No coaches Xmas British & Continental Cuisine V meals Coffee am Tea pm No smoking in restaurant Last d 7pm
ROOMS: (incl. bkfst) s £60; d £97.50 **LB**
MEALS: Dinner £21.75-£21.75
CARDS:

See advertisement on opposite page

★★67% **Milford House**
Mill St DE45 1DA (off A6 near town centre) ☎ 01629 812130
Closed Nov-Mar
The Hunt family take great pride in their Georgian residence, which is set in its own attractive grounds only three hundred yards from the bustle of the town. Old-fashioned hospitality is one of the memorable aspects of a stay at Milford House, the traditional English home cooking served at dinner another. Bar meals are also available to residents by prior arrangement. Individually designed bedrooms vary from the attractive to the more functional, but all are comfortable and immaculately maintained.
12 en suite (bth/shr) CTV in all bedrooms STV No dogs 17P No coaches Croquet lawn No children 10yrs V meals Last d 7.30pm
ROOMS: (incl. bkfst) s £35-£45; d £67-£80
MEALS: Sunday Lunch £5-£14 Dinner £13-£20
CARDS:

BALDOCK Hertfordshire Map 04 TL23

Travelodge
Great North Rd, Hinxworth SG7 5EX (on A1, southbound) v 01462 835329 FAX 01462 835329
This modern building offers accommodation in smart, spacious and well equipped bedrooms, suitable for family use, and all with en suite bathrooms. Meals may be taken at the nearby family restaurant. For information on room rates and to make a booking, call Roomline free of charge on 0800 850950. For more details about Travelodge, consult the Contents page under Hotel Groups.
40 en suite (bth/shr)

BALSALL COMMON West Midlands Map 04 SP27

★★★74% **Nailcote Hall**
Nailcote Ln, Berkswell CV7 7DE (on B4101)
☎ 01203 466174 FAX 01203 470720
Nailcote Hall is a charming Elizabethan manor house steeped in the history of Cromwell and the Civil War. The house remains largely unspoilt and is well refurbished with contemporary wall coverings and

contd.

fabrics accentuating the heavy timbers, oak floors and panelling and open fires. The leisure facilities are of excellent quality, housed mainly in the Mediterranean-style annexe centred around the eponymous Rick's Place bistro. In the intimate candlelit Tudor surroundings of the Oak Room, the cuisine continues to impress. The style is modern and the quality of produce very good. Cured ham from Serrano was served with a light butter and chive sauce rounded off with tender asparagus spears, followed by a cassoulet of fish drizzled with a vinaigrette of chilli, coriander and basil. Desserts also live up to expectations. Service is friendly, attentive and skilled.

21 en suite (bth/shr) 17 annexe en suite (bth/shr) (2 fmly) CTV in all bedrooms Lift Night porter 200P Indoor swimming pool (heated) Golf 9 Tennis (hard) Snooker Solarium Gym Croquet lawn Putting green Jacuzzi/spa Wkly live entertainment Xmas English & French Cuisine V meals Coffee am Tea pm No smoking in restaurant Last d 11pm

ROOMS: (incl. bkfst) s £120; d £130 **LB**

MEALS: Lunch £18.50 Dinner £25.50-£37*

CONF: Thtr 150 Class 80 Board 45 Del from £152.75

CARDS:

★★ 72% Haigs

Kenilworth Rd CV7 7EL (on A452 4m N of Kenilworth and 6m S of junct 4 of M6. 5m S of M42 junct 6) ☎ 01676 533004

FAX 01676 535132

Closed 26 Dec-3 Jan & Etr

Haigs is a small owner-managed hotel which is well placed for the area's business users. It is a perfect specimen within its classification with an unusually high degree of professionalism and attention to food. The varied menu might include sweet roasted peppers topped with ewes' cheese, olives and tomatoes, followed by red snapper on a pungent lime and ginger sauce, and to finish a delicious almond tart. The bread, served warm, would rival that of any top English restaurant.

14 rms (13 bth/shr) CTV in all bedrooms 22P No coaches English & French Cuisine V meals Coffee am No smoking in restaurant Last d 9.30pm

ROOMS: (incl. bkfst) s £35-£52.50; d £62.50-£67.50

OFF-PEAK: (incl. bkfst) s £35-£42.50; d fr £55

MEALS: Sunday Lunch £11.95 Dinner £16.95&alc

CONF: Thtr 35 Class 25 Board 20 Del from £80

CARDS:

See advertisement under BIRMINGHAM (NATIONAL EXHIBITION CENTRE)

BAMBURGH Northumberland Map 12 NU13

★★ 75% Waren House

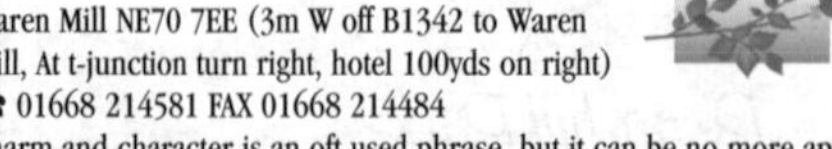

Waren Mill NE70 7EE (3m W off B1342 to Waren Mill, At t-junction turn right, hotel 100yds on right)

☎ 01668 214581 FAX 01668 214484

Charm and character is an oft used phrase, but it can be no more aptly used than to describe this delightful country house, which is set in six acres of woodland and gardens just five minutes east of the A1 along the B1342. Though Georgian in origin it reflects a rich tapestry of periods and is appealingly personalised by portraits, photographs and mementoes of the Laverack family. Objects d'art adorn every wall, seat and corridor, with cats and dolls being predominant themes. Bedrooms are magnificent and each has a particular style, such as Victorian, Edwardian, nursery or oriental, and there are two suites. Public rooms are more classical in style, there being an elegant dining room plus a drawing room and adjoining library in which to relax.

7 en suite (bth/shr) No smoking in all bedrooms CTV in all bedrooms STV 20P No coaches Tennis (hard) Croquet lawn No children 14yrs Xmas European Cuisine No smoking in restaurant Last d 8.30pm

ROOMS: (incl. bkfst) s £80-£100; d £110-£165 * **LB**

OFF-PEAK: (incl. bkfst) s fr £55

MEALS: Dinner £22.50*

CONF: Board 20 Del from £85

CARDS:

★★ 69% *Lord Crewe Arms*

Front St NE69 7BL (just below the castle) ☎ 01668 214243

FAX 01668 214273

Closed Nov-1 Apr

This former coaching inn lies in the centre of the village, where the impressive Bamburgh Castle dominates the skyline. It is now a family-run hotel offering a choice of lounges, bars and restaurants (one closed on Mondays), along with attentive service.

25 rms (20 bth/shr) (1 fmly) CTV in all bedrooms 34P No coaches No children 5yrs English & French Cuisine V meals Coffee am Last d 9pm

CARDS:

★★ 61% The Mizen Head

Lucker Rd NE69 7BS (turn off the A1 onto the B1341 for Bamburgh the hotel is the first building on the left as you enter the village)

☎ 01668 214254

Situated on the edge of the village, this welcoming holiday hotel is run by the resident owners, who provide friendly service. Bedrooms are neat, with some good-sized family rooms. A wide range of reasonably priced meals is served in both the bar and dining room.

15 rms (11 bth/shr) (4 fmly) CTV in all bedrooms 30P V meals Coffee am No smoking in restaurant Last d 8pm

ROOMS: (incl. bkfst) s £30.50-£42; d £44-£74.50 **LB**

OFF-PEAK: (incl. bkfst) s £23-£35; d £38-£58

MEALS: Lunch £6.70 Dinner £12.50&alc

CARDS:

★ 62% Sunningdale

21-23 Lucker Rd NE69 7BS (turn off A1 onto B1341 at Warenford. Hotel on right on entering village) ☎ 01668 214334

Closed Nov-Feb

This friendly family-run hotel lies just a few minutes walk from the centre of the village. It offers two comfortable lounges and a residents' bar and games room. Bedrooms come in a variety of styles, with unusually, the better ones being without en-suite bathrooms. Those with this facility are compact and more modestly furnished, being contained mainly in a rear extension.

21 rms (6 bth) (4 fmly) CTV in 10 bedrooms 16P Snooker Pool table Games room V meals Coffee am Tea pm No smoking area in restaurant Last d 6pm

ROOMS: (incl. bkfst) s £16-£30; d £32-£50 **LB**

MEALS: Dinner £8

CARDS:

BAMFORD Derbyshire Map 08 SK28

★★ 69% Yorkshire Bridge Inn

Ashopton Rd, Yorkshire Bridge S30 2AB (on A6013)

☎ 01433 651361 FAX 01433 651812

This deservedly busy and convivial roadside inn has been completely

refurbished in a contemporary country style. The atmosphere and character is harmonious, easy and welcoming. The bar meals are the most popular side of the business. The open-plan lounge bar extends into a pretty conservatory which is a dedicated no smoking area. The Garden Room to one side is reserved for residents and leads on to a purpose-built accommodation wing. Each of the well designed bedrooms is thoughtfully furnished with warm pine free-standing units and has coordinated printed wall coverings to accentuate the country feel. Bathrooms are very good.

10 en suite (bth/shr) (1 fmly) CTV in all bedrooms STV No dogs (ex guide dogs) 12P No coaches Xmas English & Continental Cuisine V meals Coffee am Tea pm No smoking area in restaurant Last d 9pm

ROOMS: (incl. bkfst) s £38-£45; d £49.50-£59.50 *

MEALS: Bar Lunch £2.75-£5.95alc Dinner £4.95-£10.50alc*

CONF: Thtr 30 Board 16 Del from £60

CARDS:

★★60% ***Marquis of Granby***

Hathersage Rd S30 2BH (beside A625) ☎ 01433 651206

This characterful inn is situated beside the A625 between Hathersage and Castleton, only two miles from Ladybower reservoir, and is in ideal location for walkers or those guests wishing to explore the Peak District National Park. Bedrooms, all of which are en-suite, are , comfortable and adequately equipped. One room and some other areas of the hotel, have the most magnificent panelling originally from the S.S. Olympic A good range of traditional tasty dishes are available in the small restaurant, which overlooks the gardens and where the service is friendly and informal. In addition bar meals are also available in the comfortable bar. The hotel also benefits from a large function suite and a smaller room which can be used for private dining or smaller meetings.

7 en suite (bth/shr) (2 fmly) CTV in all bedrooms 100P Fishing V meals Coffee am Tea pm

CARDS:

BAMPTON Devon Map 03 SS92

★★72% **Bark House**

Oakford Bridge EX16 9HZ (7m N of Tiverton on the A396)

☎ 01398 351236

Closed Dec-Feb

This delightful little hotel, built of old stone in the last century, was once a tannery. It is set in the beautiful Exe valley, one the edge of Exmoor, within easy reach of the north coast of Devon and Somerset, and the south coasts of Devon and Dorset. The house is surrounded by its own pretty garden, on a sloping hillside; it is comfortable and cosy, with log fires, low beamed ceilings, and paintings, prints and books. The bedrooms are equipped with modern facilities and thoughtful extras like tissues and reading material. Douglas and Pauline West have been running the Bark House in a relaxed and informal manner since 1983. The welcome is warm, the housekeeping immaculate, and the atmosphere friendly. Pauline provides a set menu every evening, offering a range of traditional dishes based on fresh produce.

6 rms (2 bth 2 shr) (1 fmly) CTV in 5 bedrooms 14P No coaches No children 5yrs English, French & American Cuisine Coffee am Tea pm No smoking in restaurant Last d 8.30pm

ROOMS: (incl. cont bkfst) s £19-£34; d £38-£56 *

MEALS: Lunch £7.50-£10 Dinner £14.50

CARDS:

BANBURY Oxfordshire Map 04 SP44

★★★72% **Wroxton House**

Wroxton OX15 6QB (follow A422 from Banbury, 2.5m to Wroxton, hotel on right on entering village)

☎ 01295 730777 FAX 01295 730800

contd.

This charming hotel converted from three old cottages is at the centre of the lovely village of Wroxton and is clearly signposted from Banbury. Staff under the capable management of Roger Swatkins are well trained, professional and make a real effort to make their guests feel welcome. The bedrooms vary in style from the more traditionally furnished older wing to modern rooms well suited to the business guest. New chef Franc Peigne is gaining a reputation for his well presented flavoursome food which marries local produce with sound technical skills.
29 en suite (bth/shr) 3 annexe en suite (bth/shr) (1 fmly) No smoking in 6 bedrooms CTV in all bedrooms STV Night porter 100P English & French Cuisine V meals Coffee am Tea pm No smoking in restaurant Last d 9.15pm
MEALS: Lunch £15.50-£17 Dinner £22.50-£24
CONF: Thtr 50 Class 20 Board 25 Del from £110
CARDS:

See advertisement on page 79

★★★ 67% **Whately Hall**
Banbury Cross OX16 0AN ☎ 01295 263451
FAX 01295 271736

FORTE Heritage

This former coaching inn occupies a central location overlooking overlooking Banbury Cross. The well equipped bedrooms, most of which have been refurbished to a high standard, vary in size and style. For summer months there is also a garden and terrace. Public areas include spacious, comfortably furnished lounges and in the restaurant a good choice of well prepared dishes is available. The service here is especially friendly.
73 en suite (bth/shr) No smoking in 24 bedrooms CTV in all bedrooms Lift Night porter 80P Croquet lawn Xmas V meals Coffee am Tea pm No smoking in restaurant Last d 9.30pm
ROOMS: s £70-£85; d £78-£95 * **LB**
OFF-PEAK: d £53-£60
MEALS: Lunch £13.95-£15&alc Dinner £21.50-£23&alc*
CONF: Thtr 90 Class 80 Board 40 Del from £120
CARDS:

★★★ 65% **Banbury House**
Oxford Rd OX16 9AH (approx 200yds from Banbury Cross on the A423) ☎ 01295 259361
FAX 01295 270954
Closed 24-30 Dec

CONSORT HOTELS

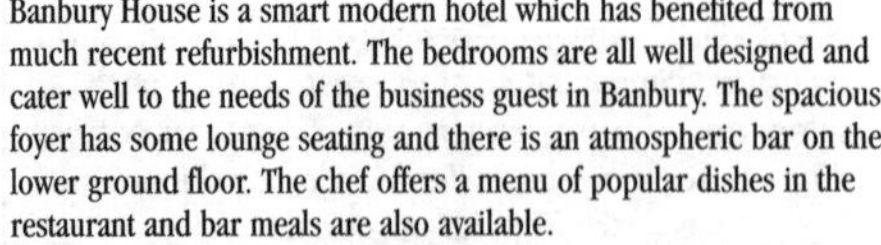

Banbury House is a smart modern hotel which has benefited from much recent refurbishment. The bedrooms are all well designed and cater well to the needs of the business guest in Banbury. The spacious foyer has some lounge seating and there is an atmospheric bar on the lower ground floor. The chef offers a menu of popular dishes in the restaurant and bar meals are also available.
49 en suite (bth/shr) (4 fmly) No smoking in 10 bedrooms CTV in all bedrooms STV Night porter 50P Continental Cuisine V meals Coffee am Tea pm Last d 9.30pm
ROOMS: s £71-£81; d £81-£110 * **LB**
OFF-PEAK: (incl. dinner) s £33-£43; d £66-£86
MEALS: Sunday Lunch £5.50-£6.50 High tea £5 Dinner £17&alc

CONF: Thtr 60 Class 35 Board 30
CARDS:

BARFORD Warwickshire Map 04 SP26

★★★ 66% **The Glebe at Barford**
Church St CV35 8BS (leave M40 at junct 15 take exit A429 Barford/Wellesboune at mini island turn left, hotel 100 mtrs on right)
☎ 01926 624218 FAX 01926 624625
A former rectory has been considerably modernised and extended to create this friendly hotel. Bedrooms are contemporary in decor and have excellent beds, while public facilities include an indoor swimming pool and several function rooms that make the hotel popular with commercial visitors. Andrew Wheeler offers well prepared seasonal menus with a strong emphasis on simple flavours.
41 en suite (bth/shr) (3 fmly) CTV in all bedrooms STV Lift Night porter 70P Indoor swimming pool (heated) Sauna Solarium Gym Croquet lawn Jacuzzi/spa Steam room Xmas English & Continental Cuisine V meals Coffee am Tea pm Last d 10pm
ROOMS: (incl. bkfst) s £90; d £110 * **LB**
MEALS: Lunch fr £3.75 Dinner fr £16.25*
CONF: Thtr 130 Class 50 Board 60 Del from £135
CARDS:

BAR HILL Cambridgeshire Map 05 TL36

★★★ 64% **Cambridgeshire Moat House**
CB3 8EU (turn off A14 Huntingdon to Cambridge road at Bar Hill junction, follow road all way over flyover to roundabout, hotel opposite)

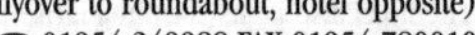

☎ 01954 249988 FAX 01954 780010
This is a purpose built hotel with extensive grounds, which include a championship golf course. Bedrooms are practically furnished and have recently benefited from smart new bathrooms with power showers and a co-ordinated colour scheme. Aubrey's restaurant has an informal sporting theme and the bar features satellite TV. Although the leisure club is compact, the swimming pool is a good size.
99 en suite (bth/shr) (8 fmly) CTV in all bedrooms Night porter 200P Indoor swimming pool (heated) Golf 18 Tennis (hard) Gym Pool table Putting green Jacuzzi/spa beauty treatments Wkly live entertainment Mediterranean Cuisine V meals Coffee am Tea pm No smoking area in restaurant Last d 10pm
ROOMS: s £79-£90; d £79-£95 **LB**
MEALS: Lunch £11.25-£15.50&alc Dinner £13.50-£15.50&alc*
CONF: Thtr 200 Class 80 Board 40
CARDS:

BARNHAM BROOM Norfolk Map 05 TG00

★★★ 72% **Barnham Broom**
NR9 4DD (signposted from A11 and A47)
☎ 01603 759393 FAX 01603 758224

Best Western

This successful golfing hotel also proves popular for its extensive range of leisure and conference facilities. Bedrooms have recently been redecorated to look warmer and more welcoming, and provide all the usual amenities. Diners have a good choice of eating options, with either a la carte menus within the newly refurbished restaurant, or informal dining within the Sports bar buttery, where all day snacks and refreshments are served. Two 18 hole golf courses, a good swimming pool, supervised gymnasium and squash courts are only a few of the leisure pursuits available.
52 en suite (bth/shr) (8 fmly) CTV in all bedrooms No dogs (ex guide dogs) Night porter 200P Indoor swimming pool (heated) Golf 36 Tennis (hard) Squash Snooker Sauna Solarium Gym Putting green Jacuzzi/spa Hairdressing salon Beautician Xmas English & Continental Cuisine V meals Coffee am Tea pm No smoking in restaurant Last d 9.30pm
ROOMS: (incl. bkfst) s £62-£67.50; d £85-£90 **LB**

MEALS: Lunch £9.95-£16&alc Dinner £15.50-£16&alc
CONF: Thtr 150 Class 70 Board 40 Del from £92
CARDS:

See advertisement under NORWICH

BARNSDALE BAR SERVICE AREA North Yorkshire Map 08 SE51

Travelodge
Wentbridge WF8 3JB (on A1, southbound)
☎ 01977 620711 FAX 01977 620711
This modern building offers accommodation in smart, spacious and well equipped bedrooms, suitable for family use, and all with en suite bathrooms. Meals may be taken at the nearby family restaurant. For information on room rates and to make a booking, call Roomline free of charge on 0800 850950. For more details about Travelodge, consult the Contents page under Hotel Groups.
56 en suite (bth/shr)

BARNSLEY South Yorkshire Map 08 SE30
See also Tankersley

★★★66% **Ardsley House**
Doncaster Rd, Ardsley S71 5EH (on A635)
☎ 01226 309955 FAX 01226 205374

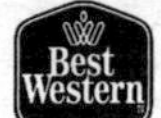

A Georgian house with modern extensions on the A635 Doncaster road about two miles from the town. It provides well equipped bedrooms which have been thoughtfully designed for the business traveller, although there is also a delightful bridal suite. Spacious public rooms include a comfortable lounge foyer which leads to a delightful restaurant where good value and well produced meals are available. Other facilities include a friendly bar, extensive conference rooms and also closed circuit TV in the car park.
73 en suite (bth/shr) (3 fmly) No smoking in 35 bedrooms CTV in all bedrooms Night porter 300P Wkly live entertainment Xmas English & French Cuisine V meals Coffee am Tea pm No smoking in restaurant Last d 10.30pm
ROOMS: s £46-£65; d £55-£70 **LB**
OFF-PEAK: (incl. bkfst) s £34; d £65
MEALS: Lunch fr £5.95 Dinner fr £16.95*
CONF: Thtr 350 Class 250 Board 40
CARDS:

See advertisement on this page

★★★58% **Queens Hotel**
Regent St S70 2HQ ☎ 01226 731010 FAX 01226 248719
Located in the centre of town this charming hotel offers a popular bar, a small restaurant and a range of meeting rooms. Bedrooms are well equipped but vary in size and are simply appointed. Service is friendly and enthusiastic.
51 en suite (bth/shr) (13 fmly) No smoking in 16 bedrooms CTV in all bedrooms STV Night porter 150P Xmas European Cuisine V meals Coffee am Tea pm No smoking in restaurant Last d 9.30pm
ROOMS: (incl. bkfst) s £35-£40; d £45-£50
OFF-PEAK: (incl. bkfst) s £30-£35; d £40-£45

MEALS: Sunday Lunch £4.95-£7.50 High tea 50p-£6.25 Dinner £13.95
CONF: Thtr 120 Class 40 Board 60
CARDS:

Travelodge
520 Doncaster Rd S70 3PE (at Stairfoot roundabout A633/A635) ☎ 01226 298799
FAX 01226 298799

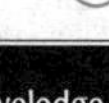

This modern building offers accommodation in smart, spacious and well equipped bedrooms, suitable for family use, and all with en suite bathrooms. Meals may be taken at the nearby family restaurant. For information on room rates and to make a booking, call Roomline free of charge on 0800 850950. For more details about Travelodge, consult the Contents page under Hotel Groups.
32 en suite (bth/shr)

BARNSTAPLE Devon Map 02 SS53

★★★67% **Barnstaple Hotel**
Braunton Rd EX31 1LE (on the outskirts of Barnstaple on A361) (Brend) ☎ 01271 76221 FAX 01271 24101
This purpose built hotel, located on the west side of Barnstaple, affords easy access to the town centre and the North Devon coastline. The bedrooms, equipped with modern facilities and recently refurbished, are on long corridors around the main building. The smart public areas include a bar-lounge, extensive leisure facilities, a selection of meeting rooms and an attractive restaurant offering a choice of menus.
57 en suite (bth) (6 fmly) CTV in all bedrooms STV Night porter Air conditioning 250P Indoor swimming pool (heated) Outdoor swimming pool (heated) Snooker Sauna Solarium Gym Jacuzzi/spa Wkly live entertainment ch fac Xmas English & French Cuisine V meals Coffee am Tea pm Last d 9pm

contd.

3

ROOMS: s £47-£52; d £57-£67 * LB
OFF-PEAK: s £35-£40; d £45-£55
MEALS: Lunch £16-£26alc Dinner £15&alc*
CONF: Thtr 250 Class 250 Board 250
CARDS:

★★★65% **Royal & Fortescue**
Boutport St EX31 1HG (follow A361 along Barbican Rd signposted town centre, turn right into Queen St & left (oneway) Boutport St hotel on left) (Brend) ☎ 01271 42289 FAX 01271 42289
Benefiting from its central location in the town, and its two car parks, this hotel has seen many improvements over the years. The public areas, including a large bar-lounge, coffee shop lounge and restaurant, are very attractive. Most of the bedrooms have been modernised and, though they vary in shape and size, all are well equipped.
47 en suite (bth/shr) (5 fmly) CTV in all bedrooms STV Lift Night porter 40P Wkly live entertainment Xmas English & French Cuisine V meals Coffee am Tea pm Last d 9pm
ROOMS: s £45-£50; d £55-£65 * LB
OFF-PEAK: s £33-£38; d £43-£53
MEALS: Lunch £8.50&alc Dinner £15&alc*
CONF: Thtr 50 Class 50 Board 50
CARDS:

★★★62% **Park**
Taw Vale EX32 9AE (opposite Rock Park, 0.5m from town centre) (Brend) ☎ 01271 72166 FAX 01271 23157
Overlooking the Park, within easy walking distance of Barnstaple Bridge and the town centre, this modern hotel offers bedrooms in a variety of sizes, some in a separate period building across the courtyard. Public areas include a spacious first-floor function suite and a smart lounge bar opening into a dining room.
25 en suite (bth/shr) 17 annexe en suite (bth/shr) (7 fmly) CTV in all bedrooms STV Night porter 80P Wkly live entertainment Xmas English & French Cuisine V meals Coffee am Tea pm Last d 9pm
ROOMS: s £42-£47; d £52-£62 * LB
OFF-PEAK: s £30-£35; d £40-£50
MEALS: Lunch £8&alc Dinner £15&alc*
CONF: Thtr 150 Class 150 Board 150
CARDS:

RED STAR HOTEL

★ **Halmpstone Manor**
Bishop's Tawton EX32 0EA (5m S off A377, leave A377 at Bishop's Tawton opposite petrol station and follow unclassified road for 2m then turn right at Halmpstone Manor sign)
☎ 01271 830321 FAX 01271 830826
Closed Jan & Nov
A manor house surrounded by farmland has been owned by the Stanburys since 1947 and is now run by second generation Charles and Jane who continue to provide an informal atmosphere and excellent customer care. Bedrooms are individually furnished and well equipped. Guests dine in a candlelit panelled dining room with a choice of two fixed-price menus; dishes feature herbs from the garden, fish from Bideford Quay and other local produce. Our inspector was impressed by a piping hot crab soufflé and a fillet of Devon beef served with caramelised shallots. Vegetables are beautifully cooked and home-made desserts are served from a trolley.
5 en suite (bth/shr) CTV in all bedrooms 12P No coaches No children 12yrs Xmas English & French Cuisine V meals Coffee am Tea pm Last d 9pm
ROOMS: (incl. bkfst) s £65-£70; d £100-£130 * LB
MEALS: Dinner £30
CARDS:

Cedars Lodge Inn
Bickington Rd EX31 2HP (turn off A39 at Roundswell, pass Sainsburys on right and continue for 200yds) ☎ 01271 71784 FAX 01271 25733
A recently renovated Victorian house has a comfortable bar and attractive conservatory, both serving a wide range of food. Spacious bedrooms of a good standard are in lodges set round a courtyard in the grounds.
30 annexe rms (13 bth 15 shr) (5 fmly) No smoking in 6 bedrooms CTV in all bedrooms STV No dogs Night porter 120P Squash V meals Coffee am Tea pm No smoking area in restaurant Last d 10pm
ROOMS: s £38; d £50 *
MEALS: Lunch £6-£15alc Dinner £6-£15alc*
CONF: Thtr 200 Class 100 Board 30 Del from £56.50
CARDS:

BARROW-IN-FURNESS Cumbria Map 07 SD16

★★64% **Lisdoonie**
307/309 Abbey Rd LA14 5LF (on A590) ☎ 01229 827312
FAX 01229 820944
Closed Xmas & New Year
A friendly, family-run hotel, situated on what was the original approach road to the town from the east before the by-pass was built, offers bedrooms in a variety of sizes and shapes; each is comfortably furnished, however, and a good all-round standard of accommodation is provided. The pleasant dining room serves a range of dishes, and there is also a large function room with its own separate entrance and bar.
12 en suite (bth/shr) (2 fmly) CTV in all bedrooms 30P English & French Cuisine V meals Coffee am Tea pm Last d 7.30pm
ROOMS: (incl. bkfst) s £25-£41; d £36-£51 * LB
CONF: Class 255
CARDS:

BARTON Lancashire Map 07 SD53

★★★67% **Barton Grange**
Garstang Rd PR3 5AA (from M6 junct 32 follow A6, signed Garstang ,for two and half miles, hotel on the right) ☎ 01772 862551 FAX 01722 861267

This friendly and popular hotel is situated alongside the International Garden Centre on the A6, about six miles north of Preston. It is particularly noted for its hospitality and the staff are all sensitive to guests' needs and spontaneous in their approach. Many of the bedrooms have recently been upgraded and new rooms have also been opened in the Garden House, just over the car park. The public rooms are comfortably furnished.
43 en suite (bth/shr) 8 annexe en suite (bth/shr) (4 fmly) CTV in all bedrooms STV No dogs (ex guide dogs) Lift Night porter 250P Indoor swimming pool (heated) Snooker Sauna Gym Jacuzzi/spa Games room Xmas English & French Cuisine V meals Coffee am

Tea pm No smoking in restaurant Last d 9.45pm
ROOMS: (incl. bkfst) s £59-£73; d £69-£85 * **LB**
MEALS: Lunch £9.95-£10.50 High tea £4-£7alc
Dinner £18-£20&alc*
CONF: Thtr 350 Class 200 Board 60 Del from £86.50
CARDS:

BARTON MILLS Suffolk Map 05 TL77

Travelodge
IP28 6AE (on A11) ☎ 01638 717675
FAX 01638 717675
This modern building offers accommodation in smart, spacious and well equipped bedrooms, suitable for family use, and all with en suite bathrooms. Meals may be taken at the nearby family restaurant. For information on room rates and to make a booking, call Roomline free of charge on 0800 850950. For more details about Travelodge, consult the Contents page under Hotel Groups.
32 en suite (bth/shr)

BARTON-ON-SEA Hampshire Map 04 SZ29

★★ 74% **The Cliff House**
Marine Dr West BH25 7QL (turn off A337 on to Sea Road at Barton-on-Sea. Hotel at end of road on cliff top) ☎ 01425 619333
FAX 01425 612462
This popular personally-run hotel is superbly located on the cliff top, with uninterrupted views over Christchurch Bay. The public rooms, which include a cosy bar and a comfortable coffee lounge are attractively furnished with antiques and pretty chintzes. The bedrooms which have been given similar thought to detail offer many extra touches and modern facilities. Owner James Simpson oversees the kitchen and produces good imaginative home cooking.
9 en suite (bth/shr) No smoking in all bedrooms CTV in all bedrooms STV No dogs (ex guide dogs) 50P No coaches No children 10yrs Xmas International Cuisine V meals Coffee am No smoking in restaurant Last d 9pm
ROOMS: (incl. bkfst) s £35-£45; d £60-£80 * **LB**
OFF-PEAK: (incl. bkfst) s fr £30; d fr £50
MEALS: Lunch fr £11.95&alc Dinner fr £16.95&alc*
CARDS:

BARTON STACEY Hampshire Map 04 SU44

Travelodge
SO21 3NP (on A303) ☎ 01264 720260
FAX 01264 720260
This modern building offers accommodation in smart, spacious and well equipped bedrooms, suitable for family use, and all with en suite bathrooms. Meals may be taken at the nearby family restaurant. For information on room rates and to make a booking, call Roomline free of charge on 0800 850950. For more details about Travelodge, consult the Contents page under Hotel Groups.
20 en suite (bth/shr)

BARTON UNDER NEEDWOOD Staffordshire Map 07 SK11

Travelodge (Northbound)
DE13 8EG (on A38,northbound) ☎ 01283 716343
FAX 01283 716343
This modern building offers accommodation in smart, spacious and well equipped bedrooms, suitable for family use, and all with en suite bathrooms. Meals may be taken at the nearby family restaurant. For information on room rates and to make a booking, call Roomline free of charge on 0800 850950. For more details about Travelodge, consult the Contents page under Hotel Groups.
20 en suite (bth/shr)

Travelodge (Southbound)
Rykneld St DE13 8EH (on A38, southbound)
☎ 01283 716784 FAX 01283 716784
This modern building offers accommodation in smart, spacious and well equipped bedrooms, suitable for family use, and all with en suite bathrooms. Meals may be taken at the nearby family restaurant. For information on room rates and to make a booking, call Roomline free of charge on 0800 850950. For more details about Travelodge, consult the Contents page under Hotel Groups.
40 en suite (bth/shr)

BASILDON Essex Map 05 TQ78

★★★ 66% **Chichester**
Old London Rd, Wickford SS11 8UE (off A129)
☎ 01268 560555 FAX 01268 560580
A friendly and relaxed atmosphere prevails at this modern, family-run, commercial hotel, which stands in landscaped grounds surrounded by open farmland. Diners can take an informal bar meal in the character Stable Bar or choose from a set-priced menu in the Gallery Restaurant. Most of the immaculately maintained bedrooms are set around an attractive garden courtyard, and each room is comfortably appointed and well equipped.
2 en suite (bth/shr) 32 annexe en suite (bth/shr) CTV in all bedrooms No dogs (ex guide dogs) Night porter 150P No children 5yrs English & French Cuisine V meals Last d 9.15pm
ROOMS: s £45.50-£53.50; d £55.50 *
MEALS: Lunch £9.50-£11.50 Dinner £11.25-£14.25alc*
CARDS:

Campanile
Pipps Hill, Southend Arterial Rd SS14 3AE (exit A127 at Basildon/Billericay turn off and turn left at next 2 roundabouts) ☎ 01268 530810
FAX 01268 286710

The bar and Bistro restaurant provide meals and refreshments. Bedrooms are well equipped and have en suite bathrooms. For more details about Campanile, consult the Contents page under Hotel Groups.
100 annexe en suite (bth/shr)
ROOMS: d £29.95-£36.50 *
CONF: Thtr 40 Class 24 Board 24

Forte Posthouse Basildon
Cranes Farm Rd SS14 3DG (off A1235, via A127)
☎ 01268 533955 FAX 01268 530119
Suitable for both the business and leisure traveller, this bright hotel provides modern accommodation in well

contd.

equipped bedrooms with en suite bathrooms. For more details about Forte Posthouse hotels, consult the Contents page for the section on Hotel Groups.
110 en suite (bth/shr)
ROOMS: d £69 *
CONF: Thtr 300 Class 80 Board 80 Del from £77

Travel Inn
Felmores, East Mayne SS13 1BW (take A127 towards Basildon) v 01268 522227
FAX 01268 530092
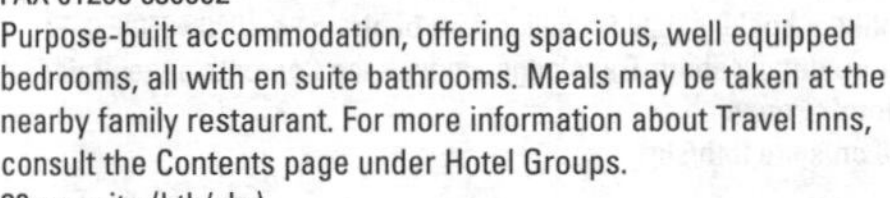
Purpose-built accommodation, offering spacious, well equipped bedrooms, all with en suite bathrooms. Meals may be taken at the nearby family restaurant. For more information about Travel Inns, consult the Contents page under Hotel Groups.
32 en suite (bth/shr)

Travel Inn

High Rd, Fobbing, Stanford le Hope SS17 9NR v 01268 554500 FAX 01268 581752
Purpose-built accommodation, offering spacious, well equipped bedrooms, all with en suite bathrooms. Meals may be taken at the nearby family restaurant. For more information about Travel Inns, consult the Contents page under Hotel Groups.
40 en suite (bth/shr)
ROOMS: (incl. bkfst) d £35.50 *

BASINGSTOKE Hampshire Map 04 SU65
See also Odiham, Sherfield on Loddon & Stratfield Turgis

★★★★ **Tylney Hall**

RG27 9AZ BASINGSTOKE ☎ 01256 764881
FAX 01256 768141
(For full entry see Rotherwick)

★★★★ 72% **Audleys Wood**

Alton Rd RG25 2JT (1.5m S of Basingstoke on A339)
☎ 01256 817555 FAX 01256 817500
Set in seven acres of well kept grounds, which include a croquet lawn, this extended Victorian residence offers comfortable and attractively appointed accommodation. Spacious bedrooms are mostly contained in a modern wing and feature marble bathrooms, while the few in the main house have a touch of Victorian grandeur. Public areas retain much of their original character with fine dark wood panelling and handsome fireplaces. The striking restaurant with its unusual vaulted ceiling and small minstrels' gallery, makes an agreeable setting for the enjoyable, attractively presented food of chef Christopher Cleveland. Typical of his style might be succulent guinea fowl with girolles, asparagus and a caramel flavoured Madeira sauce.
71 en suite (bth/shr) (6 fmly) No smoking in 25 bedrooms CTV in all bedrooms STV Night porter 100P Croquet lawn Putting green Bicycles Archery ch fac Xmas British & French Cuisine V meals Coffee am Tea pm Last d 9.45pm
ROOMS: s £48-£95; d £96-£115 * **LB**
OFF-PEAK: (incl. bkfst) s £48; d £96
MEALS: Lunch £14.95-£17.95&alc Dinner £19-£28.50&alc*
CONF: Thtr 50 Class 20 Board 26 Del from £130
CARDS:

★★★ 73% **Romans**
Little London Rd RG7 2PN ☎ 0118 970 0421
FAX 0118 970 0691
(For full entry see Silchester)

★★★ 68% ***Basingstoke Country***
Nately Scures, Hook RG27 9JS (leave M3 exit 5 take turning on roundabout to Newnham/Basingstoke, proceed 0.5m until reaching T junct, turn left onto A30, hotel is 200yd on right)
☎ 01256 764161 FAX 01256 768341
This popular business hotel is conveniently located between Basingstoke and Hook, with easy motorway access. The bedrooms are spacious and well equipped: they include executive rooms, junior suites and disabled rooms. The leisure facilities are extensive including a sizeable pool and well equipped fitness suite. The restaurant offers and an interesting set menu and carte, as well as a 24-hour room service menu.
70 en suite (bth/shr) (8 fmly) No smoking in 14 bedrooms CTV in all bedrooms STV Lift Night porter 164P Indoor swimming pool (heated) Sauna Solarium Gym V meals Coffee am Tea pm Last d 9.45pm
CARDS:

★★★ 68% **Centrecourt Hotel, Tennis & Health Club**
Centre Dr, Chineham RG24 8FY (off A33 Reading Road behind the Chineham Shopping Centre via Great Binfields Road)
☎ 01256 816664 FAX 01256 816727
This modern purpose-built complex is ideally located in the Chineham area of Basingstoke, with easy access to the M3, M4 and business areas. The hotel has extensive leisure facilities centred around a large number of indoor and outdoor tennis courts. There is a new fitness suite with full-time trainers, a dance and work out studio and an indoor pool. The bedrooms are spacious and well equipped, some have balconies overlooking the courts. The open-plan public areas have a relaxed and friendly atmosphere.
50 en suite (bth/shr) (6 fmly) No smoking in 25 bedrooms CTV in all bedrooms STV No dogs (ex guide dogs) Lift Night porter 120P Indoor swimming pool (heated) Tennis (hard) Sauna Solarium Gym Jacuzzi/spa Steam room English & Continental Cuisine V meals Coffee am Tea pm Last d 9.30pm
ROOMS: (incl. bkfst) s £85-£100; d £100-£115 * **LB**
OFF-PEAK: (incl. bkfst) s £50; d £50
MEALS: Lunch £14.95&alc Dinner £17.95&alc*
CONF: Thtr 100 Class 40 Board 40 Del from £95
CARDS:

★★★ 61% **Ringway**
Popley Way, Aldermaston Roundabout, Ringway North (A339) RG24 9NV (Hilton) ☎ 01256 20212 FAX 01256 842835
Conveniently positioned just off the ring road, this busy commercial hotel provides practical but well equipped bedrooms. Public areas are relaxed and informal and the staff are cheerful and friendly.
134 en suite (bth/shr) (26 fmly) No smoking in 34 bedrooms CTV in all bedrooms STV Lift Night porter 250P Indoor swimming pool (heated) Sauna Gym Pool table American Cuisine V meals Coffee am Tea pm Last d 9.45pm
CARDS:

★★★ 56% **Wheatsheaf**
RG25 2BB ☎ 01256 398282 FAX 01256 398253
(For full entry see North Waltham)

★★56% **Red Lion**
24 London St RG21 7NY ☎ 01256 28525 FAX 01256 844056
Centrally situated for the town and business areas, this hotel provides well equipped bedrooms of varying standards, and popular bars. Between the à la carte, bar snack and coffee house menus a good range of eating options is offered. Meeting rooms and car parking are also available.
58 en suite (bth/shr) (2 fmly) No smoking in 2 bedrooms
CTV in all bedrooms STV Lift Night porter 62P Pool table
Xmas V meals Coffee am Tea pm No smoking area in restaurant
Last d 9pm
ROOMS: (incl. bkfst) s £70-£90; d £90-£110 *
OFF-PEAK: (incl. bkfst) s fr £25; d fr £45
MEALS: Lunch £10-£15alc Dinner £15-£22.50alc
CONF: Thtr 40 Class 40 Board 20 Del from £89.50
CARDS:

Forte Posthouse Basingstoke
FORTE Posthouse
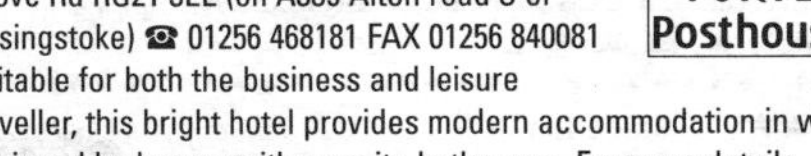
Grove Rd RG21 3EE (on A339 Alton road S of Basingstoke) ☎ 01256 468181 FAX 01256 840081
Suitable for both the business and leisure traveller, this bright hotel provides modern accommodation in well equipped bedrooms with en suite bathrooms. For more details about Forte Posthouse hotels, consult the Contents page for the section on Hotel Groups.
84 en suite (bth/shr)
ROOMS: d £79 *
CONF: Thtr 150 Class 80 Board 80

Hilton National Basingstoke

Old Common Rd, Black Dam RG21 3PR (via M3 junct 6 or M4 junct 11 onto A33 into Basingstoke)
☎ 01256 460460 FAX 01256 840441
This is a bright, modern hotel, with an informal restaurant, aimed at both the business and leisure guest. All bedrooms have en suite bathrooms and a range of modern facilities. For more information about Hilton National hotels, consult the Contents page under Hotel Groups.
141 en suite (bth/shr)
ROOMS: s £89.50-£109.50; d £89.50-£109.50 *
CONF: Thtr 150 Class 80 Board 50 Del from £120

Travel Inn
travel inn
Basingstoke Leisure Park, Worting Rd RG22 6PG
☎ 01256 811477 FAX 01256 819329
Purpose-built accommodation, offering spacious, well equipped bedrooms, all with en suite bathrooms. Meals may be taken at the nearby family restaurant. For more information about Travel Inns, consult the Contents page under Hotel Groups.
40 en suite (bth/shr)
ROOMS: d £35.50 *

Travelodge
Travelodge
Stag and Hounds, Winchester Rd RG22 5HN (off A30) ☎ 01256 843566 FAX 01256 843566
This modern building offers accommodation in smart, spacious and well equipped bedrooms, suitable for family use, and all with en suite bathrooms. Meals may be taken at the nearby family restaurant. For information on room rates and to make a booking, call Roomline free of charge on 0800 850950. For more details about Travelodge, consult the Contents page under Hotel Groups.
32 en suite (bth/shr)

❀ Rosette symbols denote the quality of food in hotel restaurants on a rising scale of 1-5.

BASLOW Derbyshire Map 08 SK27

RED STAR HOTEL

★★★❀❀ **Cavendish**
DE45 1SP (on A619) ☎ 01246 582311 FAX 01246 582312
This traditionally run hotel, where old fashioned courtesies still apply, enjoys the most enviable position on the edge of the Chatsworth estate. The public rooms and bedrooms are beautifully furnished and the main feature of the hotel apart from the comfortable sofas, open fires and the huge vases of fresh flowers is the unique collection of pictures, from Victorian fine art to twentieth century graffiti. Simply but very effectively decorated bedrooms are all of a good size and are furnished with sumptuous beds and deep cushioned chairs. The informal

contd.

Garden Room conservatory, with magnificent views of the garden offers a good range of lighter dishes whilst in the restaurant a range of more formal and involved dishes featuring home-made and local produce are available. Interesting combinations such as monkfish pan-fried in sage butter served with a sweet tomato and pepper relish or English calf's liver roasted in Parma ham with an orange and caper berry dressing are typical starters; main courses are no less interesting and may include wind dried tuna served with a spiced pear salad and olive oil or roast saddle of rabbit with a mustard and white wine sauce.
24 en suite (bth/shr) CTV in all bedrooms STV No dogs (ex guide dogs) Night porter 50P No coaches Fishing Putting green Xmas European Cuisine V meals Coffee am Tea pm No smoking in restaurant Last d 10pm
ROOMS: s fr £79; d fr £99 * **LB**
MEALS: Lunch fr £32.25&alc Dinner fr £32.25&alc*
CONF: Thtr 25 Board 18 Del from £140
CARDS:

RED STAR HOTEL

★★ **Fischer's Baslow Hall**

Calver Rd DE45 1RR (on the A623 between Baslow & Calver) ☎ 01246 583259
FAX 01246 583818
Closed 25-26 Dec
On the edge of the town, Max and Susan Fischer's cosy country home is both a haven for discerning business types and a discreet retreat for lovers of good food. Set in attractive grounds, this typical Derbyshire manor house has sumptuous bedrooms, a few with original bath tubs. Public rooms centre around the restaurant and the slightly more casual 'Café-Max', but there's a very attractive lounge with a log fire and drinks trolley. Max Fischer's highly acclaimed cuisine is worth travelling for and there's certainly no better or committed chef for many miles around. The efficient team of smart staff exude friendly hospitality.
6 en suite (bth/shr) CTV in all bedrooms No dogs (ex guide dogs) 40P No coaches Xmas European Cuisine V meals Coffee am Tea pm No smoking in restaurant
ROOMS: (incl. cont bkfst) s £75-£90; d £95-£120 * **LB**
MEALS: Lunch £18-£24.75 Dinner £42
CONF: Thtr 40 Board 18 Del from £125
CARDS:

Make the weekend extra special with flowers from INTERFLORA. Freecall 0500 43 43 43.

BASSENTHWAITE Cumbria Map 11 NY23

★★★★ 64% **Armathwaite Hall**
CA12 4RE ☎ 017687 76551 FAX 017687 76220
This magnificent 17th-century mansion lies in four hundred acres of park and woodland at the northern end of Bassenthwaite Lake. The impressive public rooms have superb crafted woodwork and imposing fireplaces, while bedrooms are in the country house style with a choice of standards and sizes. The Hall has its own well equipped leisure complex which includes health and sports facilities, a children's club, a farm park and a bar.
43 en suite (bth/shr) (4 fmly) CTV in all bedrooms STV Lift Night porter 100P Indoor swimming pool (heated) Tennis (hard) Fishing Riding Snooker Sauna Solarium Gym Croquet lawn Putting green Jacuzzi/spa Beauty salon Xmas English & French Cuisine V meals Coffee am Tea pm No smoking in restaurant Last d 9.30pm
ROOMS: (incl. bkfst) s £50-£120; d £110-£190 * **LB**
MEALS: Lunch £14.95 High tea fr £5 Dinner £29.95&alc*
CONF: Thtr 120 Class 50 Board 60 Del from £99
CARDS:

★★★ 67% **Castle Inn**
CA12 4RG (on A591, 6m N of Keswick) ☎ 017687 76401 FAX 017687 76604

Best Western

With indoor and outdoor leisure facilities designed to attract both the conference and tourist market, this ever-expanding hotel also has a choice of restaurants, a comfortable lounge bar, spacious foyer lounge and a conservatory.
Bedrooms offer a variety of styles and sizes, with some beautiful large superior rooms.
49 en suite (bth/shr) (8 fmly) No smoking in 14 bedrooms CTV in all bedrooms Night porter 100P Indoor swimming pool (heated) Tennis (grass) Riding Snooker Sauna Solarium Gym Pool table Jacuzzi/spa Badminton Table tennis Golf practice net Xmas English & Continental Cuisine V meals Coffee am Tea pm Last d 9.15pm
ROOMS: (incl. bkfst) s £59-£75; d £98-£130 **LB**
OFF-PEAK: (incl. bkfst & dinner) s £69-£85; d £118-£150
MEALS: Lunch fr £10 Dinner fr £19.95&alc*
CONF: Thtr 200 Class 100 Board 40 Del from £75
CARDS:

See advertisement under KESWICK

★★ 72% **Overwater Hall**
Ireby CA5 1HH (from Keswick on A591, turn right at Castle Inn crossroads, 2m along this road, turn right at sign in wall) ☎ 017687 76566
FAX 017687 76566
This imposing 19th-century mansion lies in 18 acres of gardens and woodland close to Overwater Tarn. An authentic country house hotel in every sense, it offers lovely public rooms, including a cosy bar where the counter is a baby grand piano. The comfortable bedrooms are individually furnished and several are particularly well proportioned. Stephen Bore and Angela Hyde provide hospitable attention, whilst Adrian Hyde presents an imaginative five course, daily changing dinner menu. A watercress and orange soup was a highlight of one meal, preceded by a terrine of chicken filled with a mousse of apricots and pistachio nuts on a sweet yellow pepper cream. Main course was roast Barbary duck, compote of wild mushrooms and a sage and grain mustard sauce. A chocolate, rum and pineapple crème brûlee proved an unusual dessert, but do leave room for the well presented cheese board.
13 en suite (bth/shr) (4 fmly) CTV in all bedrooms 25P Fishing Putting green ch fac Xmas English & French Cuisine V meals Coffee am Tea pm No smoking in restaurant Last d 9pm

Percentage scores give you a comparison of quality within each star rating. See 'How to Use the Guide".

ROOMS: (incl. bkfst & dinner) s £48.50-£51; d £97-£102 * LB
OFF-PEAK: (incl. bkfst & dinner) s £40-£45.50; d £80-£90
MEALS: Sunday Lunch £12.50 High tea fr £2.95 Dinner £16.50-£25*
CARDS:

★★ 65% **Ravenstone**
CA12 4QG (4.5m N of Keswick on Carlisle road A591)
☎ 01768 776240 FAX 01768 776240
Closed Nov-Feb
This fine 19th-century dower house sits in an elevated position tucked into a hillside commanding panoramic view across the valley towards Bassenthwaite Lake. Family run, the house retains much of its original character, with splendid oak panelling, staircase and fireplaces, as well as antiques and period pictures. There is a comfortable lounge, well proportioned dining room, a cosy bar and a games room. How appropriate that the owner should be a wood craftsman by profession. He has matched much of the woodwork with that of his own, as well as hand-crafting the furniture in most of the bedrooms, two of which have superb four-poster beds.
20 en suite (bth/shr) (2 fmly) CTV in all bedrooms 25P No coaches Snooker Pool table Table tennis Xmas V meals Coffee am No smoking in restaurant Last d 7.30pm
ROOMS: (incl. bkfst) s fr £30; d fr £60
MEALS: Dinner £12.50
See advertisement under KESWICK

BATH Somerset Map 03 ST76
See also Colerne & Hinton Charterhouse

★★★★★ 67% **Bath Spa**
FORTE Heritage
Sydney Rd BA2 6JF ☎ 01225 444424
FAX 01225 444006
Enjoying an enviable elevated position overlooking the city this imposing Georgian property has been sympathetically modernised. A luxury hotel has retained its elegance and grandeur of days gone by and now promotes commendable modern surroundings. Public rooms are inviting and offer a cosy, intimate ambience. The two restaurants are in contrasting styles; the Alfresco serves lighter meals in an airy colonnade and the Vellore is a more formal dining option in the former ballroom.
98 en suite (bth/shr) (3 fmly) No smoking in 31 bedrooms CTV in all bedrooms STV Lift Night porter 162P Indoor swimming pool (heated) Tennis (hard) Sauna Solarium Gym Croquet lawn Putting green Jacuzzi/spa Beauty treatment Hair salon Wkly live entertainment ch fac Xmas International Cuisine V meals Coffee am Tea pm No smoking in restaurant Last d 9.30pm
ROOMS: s £119-£139; d £149-£189 * LB
MEALS: Lunch £16.50&alc High tea £4.75-£10.25alc Dinner £35&alc*
CONF: Thtr 140 Class 72 Board 55 Del from £159
CARDS:

Courtesy & Care Award

★★★★ 77% **The Royal Crescent**
16 Royal Crescent BA1 2LS
☎ 01225 739955 FAX 01225 339401

Forming the centre of John Wood's world-famous architectural masterpiece, this fine Georgian property offers all the grace and elegance one might expect from a Bath townhouse. Individually designed bedrooms are furnished with antiques and equipped with modern conveniences such as two telephones and power showers. Some are contained in the Dower House, which also houses the bar and restaurant, and stands in a walled garden to the rear of the hotel. This makes a fine setting for the imaginative and enjoyable cooking of chef Steven Blake, who continues to offer some of the best food in Bath. A recent meal featured quail with braised cabbage and a truffled jus, lightly smoked turbot with spinach and a delicate tomato sauce and ended with an excellent apple tart with cinnamon ice cream.
Management and staff have won the AA Courtesy and Care Award for 1996/7.
25 en suite (bth/shr) 21 annexe en suite (bth/shr) (8 fmly) CTV in all bedrooms No dogs (ex guide dogs) Lift Night porter 32P Croquet lawn Plunge pool Wkly live entertainment Xmas English & French Cuisine V meals Coffee am Tea pm No smoking area in restaurant Last d 9.30pm
ROOMS: s £105; d £175 * LB
OFF-PEAK: s £95; d £155
MEALS: Lunch £12.50-£18.50 Dinner £33.50-£55&alc
CONF: Thtr 70 Class 30 Board 26 Del from £140
CARDS:

See advertisement on page 89

★★★★ 68% **Combe Grove Manor Hotel & Country Club**
Brassknocker Hill, Monkton Combe BA2 7HS (2m SE of Bath)
☎ 01225 834644 FAX 01225 834961
Based around an elegant Georgian manor house, this hotel enjoys stunning views over beautiful countryside. The house itself is stylishly furnished, and there are two restaurants, the Georgian and the less formal Manor Vaults. Most of the bedrooms are in the Garden Lodge, and these have balconies with garden furniture. There are a superb leisure centre with both wet and dry sections and a popular beauty treatment room. Sports facilities in the grounds include tennis, jogging trails, a golf driving range and an outdoor pool.
9 en suite (bth/shr) 31 annexe en suite (bth/shr) (11 fmly) CTV in all bedrooms STV No dogs Night porter 150P Indoor swimming pool (heated) Outdoor swimming pool (heated) Golf 5 Tennis (hard) Sauna Solarium Gym Croquet lawn Putting green
contd.

Jacuzzi/spa Aerobics Xmas V meals Coffee am Tea pm No smoking in restaurant Last d 9.30pm
ROOMS: (incl. cont bkfst) s fr £98; d fr £98 * LB
MEALS: Lunch £13.50-£16.50 Dinner £19.50*
CONF: Thtr 100 Class 40 Board 36 Del £145
CARDS:

RED STAR HOTEL

★★★ **The Priory**

Weston Rd BA1 2XT ☎ 01225 331922
FAX 01225 448276

Although only a mile from the centre of Bath, two acres of attractive and well-tended gardens give this extended Georgian property very much the air of a country house. A relaxed and civilised atmosphere pervades the comfortable public areas which abound in fresh flowers and objets d'art. Extensive refurbishment has improved standards and increased the number of bedrooms, which are now tastefully decorated and thoughtfully equipped and feature marbled bathrooms, and rich fabrics. Attractively presented menus offer an interesting choice of largely classically-inspired dishes, the highlight of a recent meal being some excellent monkfish on a bed of spinach with a creamy whole grain mustard sauce. Cheerful service includes comprehensive evening room service and early morning tea.
18 en suite (bth/shr) (3 fmly) No smoking in 2 bedrooms CTV in all bedrooms No dogs (ex guide dogs) Night porter 21P No coaches Indoor swimming pool (heated) Outdoor swimming pool (heated) Sauna Solarium Gym Croquet lawn Jacuzzi/spa Xmas French Cuisine V meals Coffee am Tea pm No smoking in restaurant Last d 9.30pm
ROOMS: (incl. bkfst) s £115; d £155-£225 * LB
OFF-PEAK: (incl. bkfst & dinner) s £140; d £195-£260
MEALS: Lunch £12.50-£20.50 Dinner £28&alc*
CONF: Thtr 60 Class 30 Board 24 Del from £120
CARDS:

RED STAR HOTEL

★★★ **Queensberry**

Russel St BA1 2QF (100mtrs from the Assembly Rooms) ☎ 01225 447928
FAX 01225 446065
Closed 24-30 Dec RS Sun

This delightful Bath-stone town house hotel, built in 1772 by John Wood, is situated in a quiet side street, only minutes from the centre of the city. The whole property has been lovingly decorated and furnished with great flair by Stephen and Penny Ross. Tastefully appointed bedrooms are generously proportioned and boast comfortable sofas, modern bathrooms and thoughtful extras. There are two small lounges on the ground floor, one with an honesty bar, but the heart of the operation is decidedly the Olive Tree restaurant. Offering a contemporary, informal atmosphere and modern bistro cookery with more than a hint of the Mediterranean, the restaurant, with its starched linen and candlelit tables is justifiably very popular, so guests should ensure they book in advance. Throughout, service is relaxed but efficient and staff are friendly and willing.

22 en suite (bth/shr) CTV in all bedrooms No dogs (ex guide dogs) Lift Night porter 5P English, French & Italian Cuisine V meals Coffee am Tea pm No smoking area in restaurant Last d 10pm
ROOMS: (incl. cont bkfst) s £89-£125; d £115-£180 LB
MEALS: Lunch £10.50-£12.50&alc Dinner £19&alc*
CONF: Thtr 16 Board 16
CARDS:

★★★ 74% **Cliffe**

Crowe Hill BA3 6HY (A36 from Bath and after approx 3m at traffic lights take B3108 to Lower Limpley Stoke. At sharp left hand bend take minor road to village) ☎ 01225 723226 FAX 01225 723871

From its elevated position overlooking the picturesque Avon Valley, this converted 19th-century country house enjoys glorious views. Bedrooms are tastefully decorated and well equipped; some have direct access from the car park. Public areas include an attractive lounge, an adjacent bar lounge and a delightful restaurant serving an interesting range of dishes featuring fresh local produce and a good vegetarian choice. Resident proprietors Barbara and Richard Okill extend a warm welcome to their guests and, along with a team of friendly staff, assure them of attentive service. The hotel is surrounded by three acres of terraced gardens which feature an outdoor heated pool and sun patio.
11 en suite (bth/shr) (3 fmly) CTV in all bedrooms 40P No coaches

B

Outdoor swimming pool (heated) Xmas English & French Cuisine V meals Coffee am Tea pm No smoking area in restaurant Last d 9.30pm
ROOMS: (incl. bkfst) s £66.50-£77; d £77-£105 **LB**
MEALS: Lunch £15 High tea fr £4 Dinner £19-£24alc
CARDS:

See advertisement on this page

★★★65% **Francis**

FORTE Heritage

Queen Square BA1 2HH (on the trunk road A4 in the centre of the city) ☎ 01225 424257
FAX 01225 319715
An established hotel, the Francis has dominated the lower side of Queens Square for over 100 years, and it continues to offer a traditional atmosphere and welcome. Public rooms include a smart restaurant and cosy lounges where afternoon tea is a real treat. Most of the bedrooms have benefited from upgrading and are comfortably furnished and well equipped; hopefully the remaining rooms will soon be completed.
94 en suite (bth/shr) (1 fmly) No smoking in 38 bedrooms CTV in all bedrooms Lift Night porter 30P Xmas V meals Coffee am Tea pm No smoking area in restaurant Last d 9.30pm
ROOMS: s fr £80; d fr £100 * **LB**
MEALS: Lunch fr £13.95 Dinner fr £18.95*
CONF: Thtr 80 Class 40 Board 30 Del from £115
CARDS:

★★★64% **The Abbey Hotel**

Best Western

North Pde BA1 1LG ☎ 01225 461603
FAX 01225 447758
This hotel forms part of a handsome Georgian terrace close to the river and the Abbey in the centre of the city. Restricted parking is available outside and there is a public car park a short walk

contd.

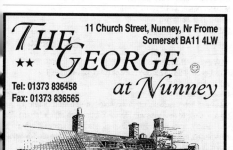

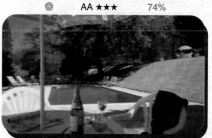

away. Bedrooms are equipped with modern comforts and the public areas include a smart bar lounge and a formal restaurant where a choice of menus is available.
56 en suite (bth/shr) (4 fmly) CTV in all bedrooms STV Lift Night porter Xmas British & French Cuisine V meals Coffee am Tea pm No smoking in restaurant Last d 9.15pm
ROOMS: (incl. bkfst) s £55-£65; d £89-£99 * **LB**
MEALS: Lunch £4.50-£8.75alc Dinner fr £15.50&alc
CONF: Thtr 35 Class 15 Board 24 Del from £69
CARDS:

★★★ 63% **Pratts**
South Pde BA2 4AB ☎ 01225 460441
FAX 01225 448807

Forestdale Hotels

Centrally positioned and part of an attractive Georgian terrace, this long-established hotel has been run for many years by loyal manager Dennis Meakin. Public rooms retain their traditional atmosphere, with a cosy writing room, in addition to two comfortably furnished lounges. Due to architectural restraints bedrooms tend to vary with some being more spacious than others; the third floor rooms have lower ceilings and smaller windows.
46 en suite (bth/shr) (2 fmly) No smoking in 2 bedrooms CTV in all bedrooms Lift Night porter Xmas English & French Cuisine V meals Coffee am Tea pm No smoking in restaurant Last d 9.30pm
ROOMS: (incl. bkfst) s £55.95-£65; d £85.90-£95 * **LB**
OFF-PEAK: (incl. bkfst & dinner) s £68.50-£78.50; d £112-£122
MEALS: Sunday Lunch fr £10.50 High tea fr £5 Dinner fr £14.75*
CONF: Thtr 50 Class 12 Board 30 Del from £85
CARDS:

★★ 70% **The Old Mill**
Tollbridge Rd, Batheaston BA1 7DE
☎ 01225 858476 FAX 01225 852600

This delightful hotel, converted from an old flour mill, in its own gardens nestling beside the River Avon, is full of character. Many of the bedrooms in the main house are spacious and enjoy river views, while those in the adjacent lodge enjoy the same facilities although more compact. The restaurant featuring a revolving floor, powered by the waterwheel, gently turns, transporting diners through all the river views. With an excellent range of function rooms and car park , The Old Mill adds up to a unique experience.
16 en suite (bth/shr) 10 annexe en suite (shr) (5 fmly) CTV in all bedrooms No dogs (ex guide dogs) 50P Fishing English & French Cuisine V meals Coffee am Tea pm No smoking area in restaurant Last d 9.30pm
ROOMS: (incl. bkfst) s £32-£50; d £44-£70 **LB**
MEALS: Lunch fr £6.95 Dinner £10-£15alc
CONF: Thtr 100 Del from £55.76
CARDS:

See advertisement on opposite page

★★ 69% **Duke's**
Great Pulteney St BA2 4DN ☎ 01225 463512
FAX 01225 483733
Tim and Rosalind Forester and their team of staff offer a warm welcome at their stylish small hotel, where modern comforts have been combined with the elegance and charm of the fine Georgian building. Bedrooms are attractively decorated and well equipped, and the public rooms include a choice of lounges, one with a bar. There is a small restaurant on the lower ground floor, where the menu offers a short choice of freshly prepared and interesting dishes. Unrestricted overnight parking is available outside the hotel, which is only a few minutes walk from some of the city's most popular attractions, and there is a multi-storey car park close by.
22 en suite (bth/shr) (4 fmly) CTV in all bedrooms 1P No coaches V meals Coffee am Tea pm No smoking in restaurant Last d 8.30pm

ROOMS: (incl. bkfst) s £55-£65; d £65-£95 **LB**
MEALS: Dinner £12.50-£18.50*
CONF: Thtr 20 Class 20 Board 20 Del from £85
CARDS:

See advertisement on opposite page

★★ 69% **Siena**
25 Pulteney Rd BA2 4EZ ☎ 01225 425495 FAX 01225 469029
This fine Victorian property within walking distance of the city centre benefits from its own car park and a relaxed and friendly atmosphere. Whilst in the past few years the house has been carefully restored, many of the original features, such as marble fire surrounds and ornate cornices, have been retained. Bedrooms have been comfortably equipped with modern facilities, and those at the rear have views of the county cricket ground and Bath's medieval abbey. Public areas include an attractive bar and a smart dining room where a short carte offers a selection of interesting dishes.
15 en suite (bth/shr) (3 fmly) No smoking in 6 bedrooms CTV in all bedrooms STV Night porter 15P V meals No smoking area in restaurant Last d 8.30pm
ROOMS: (incl. bkfst) s £42.50-£57.50; d £67.50-£85 * **LB**
OFF-PEAK: (incl. bkfst) s £37.50-£52.50; d £62.50-£80
MEALS: Dinner £13.75-£16.95&alc*
CONF: Thtr 22 Board 20
CARDS:

See advertisement on opposite page

★★ 64% **Haringtons**
8/10 Queen St BA1 1HE (in centre of Bath) ☎ 01225 461728
FAX 01225 444804
Closed 24-26 Dec
This small hotel, tucked away in a cobbled street behind Queens Square, close to the shops and theatre, continues to offer a relaxed and friendly atmosphere. The bedrooms, which are gradually being refurbished, vary in size, and the restaurant and bar have already been tastefully decorated and furnished. The interesting menu includes a popular selection of fish, meat and vegetarian dishes, prepared from quality ingredients.
12 rms (8 bth/shr) (4 fmly) CTV in all bedrooms STV No dogs (ex guide dogs) No coaches English & French Cuisine V meals Coffee am
ROOMS: (incl. bkfst) s £40-£55; d £49-£75 * **LB**
OFF-PEAK: (incl. bkfst) s £35-£50; d £49-£65
CARDS:

★★ 64% **Wentworth House**
106 Bloomfield Rd BA2 2AP (off A367) ☎ 01225 339193
FAX 01225 310460
Closed 14 Dec-7 Jan
This attractive Victorian property stands with its own parking in a quiet residential area just a fifteen minute walk or a bus ride from the city centre. Bedrooms have been tastefully furnished and equipped with modern comforts. Public areas include a cosy lounge bar and a bright and airy dining room serving a short choice of dishes on the fixed

contd.

THE SHAW COUNTRY HOTEL

Bath Road, Shaw, Nr Melksham, Wiltshire
Tel: (01225) 702836/790321

This 400 year old farmhouse is a supremely comfortable Country Hotel set in its own grounds with a glowing reputation for good food, extensive wine list and personal service. All thirteen bedrooms are en-suite with colour TV, telephone, beverage facilities and fresh fruit. Several four poster bedrooms one jacuzzi bath. Only 9 miles from Bath it makes an excellent touring centre for the City and its surrounding attractions with no parking problems.

Double room £59 to £78. Single room £40
Weekend B&B and evening meal
Double room £70 up to £90. Single room £45

The Old Mill

Under New Ownership

TOLLBRIDGE ROAD
BATHEASTON
BATH BA1 7DE
Tel: 01225 858476
Fax: 01225 852600

In a picturesque position on the banks of the river Avon just 1.4 miles from the centre of Bath.

All bedrooms are en suite with the majority having river views, there are some with 4-poster beds.

Dine in the Water Wheel Restaurant while the floor gently revolves giving changing views of the historic toll bridge, revolving water wheel, pretty gardens and the river and its wild life.

Free private parking.

Special short breaks available all year.

Siena Hotel

24/25 Pulteney Road
Bath, Avon BA2 4EZ
Tel: 01225 425495 Fax: 01225 469029

AA
★★

An elegant Victorian villa within a few minutes level walk of the City Centre. Set in landscaped gardens and overlooking Bath's medieval Abbey, the Siena Hotel offers today's discerning business and leisure traveller quality accommodation, excellent home cuisine, licensed bar, use of gardens, unlimited free golf (Mon-Fri) at the nearby Entry Hill Golf Club, a high standard of personal service and the advantage of a private car park. Friendly staff, warm and comfortable ambience create an ideal location for a memorable stay.

★★ 69%

DUKES HOTEL

Great Pulteney Street
Bath, Avon
BA2 4DN

Telephone: (01225) 463512 Fax: (01225) 483733

Family run Grade I Townhouse situated on Europe's most elegant Georgian boulevard – a short stroll from the Roman Baths/Abbey.

We offer a peaceful and relaxed atmosphere emphasising personal service and excellent food. Our traditional English breakfast includes Dukes' own marmalade and freshly squeezed orange juice. Dinner is prepared from the finest local produce complemented by our reasonably priced selection of wines carefully chosen by a Master of Wines.

Our gracious conference room is an ideal location for meetings/seminars.

priced dinner menu. The hotel has its own garden and outdoor swimming pool.
18 rms (16 bth/shr) CTV in all bedrooms No dogs (ex guide dogs) 18P Outdoor swimming pool No children 5yrs No smoking in restaurant
ROOMS: (incl. bkfst) s £38-£45; d £48-£70 * **LB**
MEALS: Dinner fr £17.50*
CARDS:

★★61% **Georges**
2-3 South Pde BA2 4AA (in town centre midway between Abbey and Raileay station) ☎ 01225 464923 & 425336 FAX 01225 425471
Right in the heart of the city, this friendly hotel has a good range of well equipped bedrooms. There is a popular bar and a Greek bistro restaurant.
19 en suite (bth/shr) (5 fmly) CTV in all bedrooms No dogs (ex guide dogs) Night porter Wkly live entertainment English & Continental Cuisine V meals Coffee am Tea pm No smoking area in restaurant Last d 11pm
ROOMS: (incl. bkfst) s £40-£45; d £55-£65 * **LB**
OFF-PEAK: (incl. bkfst) s fr £40; d fr £50
MEALS: Sunday Lunch £6-£12alc Dinner £9.50-£16alc*
CARDS:

TOWN HOUSE HOTEL

Fountain House Hotel Suites
9-11 Fountain Buildings, Lansdown Rd BA1 5DV ☎ 01225 338622 FAX 01225 445855
This rather unusual establishment is set in the heart of Bath and only offers suites. These are comfortable, attractively decorated and well furnished, boasting fully fitted kitchens and smartly presented bathrooms with two bathrooms in larger suites. There are no public areas, other than the office where friendly staff are able to help with any queries. Room service is limited to the delivery of a breakfast basket, hot cross buns at Easter, scones and freshly baked rolls. A lift is available to all floors.
13 en suite (bth/shr) 1 annexe en suite (bth) CTV in 13 bedrooms STV Lift Night porter 3P No coaches
ROOMS: (incl. cont bkfst) s £100-£138; d £130-£219 * **LB**
CARDS:

Hilton National Bath
Walcot St BA1 5BJ v 01225 463411
FAX 01225 463411

This is a bright, modern hotel, with an informal restaurant, aimed at both the business and leisure guest. All bedrooms have en suite bathrooms and a range of modern facilities. For more information about Hilton National hotels, consult the Contents page under Hotel Groups.
150 en suite (bth/shr)

BATLEY West Yorkshire Map 08 SE22

★★66% **Alder House**
Towngate Rd, off Healey Ln WF17 7HR ☎ 01924 444777
FAX 01924 442644
This attractive Georgian house is tucked away is a quiet corner and has been carefully furnished and thoughtfully equipped throughout. There is a cosy dining room, with a good range of dishes available and the modern bedrooms are a delight to occupy. Solidly warm and friendly service is provided by a dedicated staff.
20 en suite (bth/shr) (1 fmly) CTV in all bedrooms 52P English & Continental Cuisine V meals Coffee am Tea pm No smoking in restaurant Last d 9pm

ROOMS: (incl. bkfst) s £48-£57; d £62-£74 **LB**
OFF-PEAK: (incl. bkfst) s £35-£37; d £50-£53
MEALS: Lunch £8.95-£11 Dinner £15.25-£19.75&alc*
CONF: Thtr 80 Class 40 Board 35 Del from £75
CARDS:

See advertisement on opposite page

BATTLE East Sussex Map 05 TQ71

RED STAR HOTEL

★★★ **Netherfield Place**
Netherfield TN33 9PP (turn off A21 onto A2100 to Battle. After level crossing take second turning right, hotel approx 1.5m on left)

☎ 01424 774455 FAX 01424 774024
Closed 2 wks Xmas, New Year & 2wks Jan
This charming country house is tucked away in the countryside near historic Battle. Proprietors Michael and Helen Collier and their young team of professional highly-skilled staff ensure guests quickly feel at home. The bedrooms are all individually styled by Mrs Collier and feel like rooms in a grand house rather than being typical hotel bedrooms. There is a wealth of quality extras and beds are properly turned down. The lounge and bar are elegantly proportioned and the latter has a fine selection of malt whiskies and cognacs. The restaurant showcases the cuisine of young chef Sue Kessick who , under the guidance of Mr Collier, presents a well conceived range of dishes. Some of the over-elaborate flavour combinations have been done away with and the food is now more gutsy and honest.
14 en suite (bth/shr) (1 fmly) CTV in all bedrooms No dogs (ex guide dogs) 32P No coaches Tennis (hard) Croquet lawn Putting green Clay pigeon & archery by arrangement ch fac V meals Coffee am Tea pm Last high tea 5pm
ROOMS: (incl. bkfst) s £60-£90; d fr £110 * **LB**
OFF-PEAK: (incl. bkfst & dinner) d £155
MEALS: Lunch fr £11.50&alc High tea £2.50-£10.50 Dinner fr £11.50&alc
CONF: Thtr 60 Class 40 Board 30 Del from £130
CARDS:

★★★71% **Powdermills**
Powdermill Ln TN33 0SP ☎ 01424 775511 FAX 01424 774540
This 18th-century former manor house set in 150 acres of park and woodland has been skilfully converted and considerably extended into an elegant privately-owned hotel. Accommodation has much to recommend it, and offers guests a choice between rooms in the original house or those in a new wing or recently constructed balcony suites; two rooms have four-poster beds. The Orangery Restaurant

features the able talents of chef Paul Webbe whose cooking continues to grow in stature with his exciting and well constructed pâtisserie coming in for lots of praise. Service is very attentive and friendly and personally supervised by proprietors Julie and Douglas Cowpland. The new Pavilion Function Suite will accommodate up to 250 persons. Other facilities include a seven-acre fishing lake and three smaller lakes stocked with trout.

25 en suite (bth/shr) 10 annexe en suite (bth/shr) CTV in all bedrooms 101P Outdoor swimming pool Fishing Xmas V meals Coffee am Tea pm No smoking area in restaurant Last d 9pm

ROOMS: (incl. bkfst) s £55; d £80-£115 **LB**

MEALS: Lunch £14.50-£15.50 Dinner £18.50&alc

CONF: Thtr 250 Class 50 Board 16 Del from £95

CARDS:

See advertisement on page 95

★★★ 67% ***Burnt Wood House***

Powdermill Ln TN33 0SU ☎ 01424 775151

FAX 01424 775151

With lovely country views from the rear of the house this friendly family-run hotel stands in its own woodland with an attractive garden full of interesting wildlife. Whilst bedrooms vary in shape and size, they are all well furnished in a modern and co-ordinated style. There is a very comfortable lounge, and a smaller bar lounge and dining room overlooking the rear gardens. Personally run by Mike and Heather Hoggarth the atmosphere is very relaxed and informal.

10 en suite (bth/shr) (2 fmly) CTV in all bedrooms STV 30P No coaches Outdoor swimming pool (heated) Tennis (hard) Riding Croquet lawn V meals Coffee am Tea pm Last d 9.30pm

CARDS:

B

★★61% **The George**

23 High St TN33 0EA (turn off A21 onto B2100, hotel is half a mile from rdbt in middle of High St on the right) ☎ 01424 774466 FAX 01424 774853

This traditional high street coaching inn has been refurbished in a modern style yet retains some of its original charm with an attractive spiral staircase. Bedrooms tend to vary in size and location but all offer an extensive range of modern facilities and are suitable for both tourist and business guests. The informal restaurant offers a range of competitively priced dishes and the small bar attracts a good local trade.

15 en suite (bth/shr) (4 fmly) No smoking in 5 bedrooms CTV in all bedrooms 36P Xmas European Cuisine V meals Coffee am Tea pm No smoking area in restaurant Last d 9.30pm

ROOMS: (incl. bkfst) s £35-£50; d £50-£65 * **LB**

MEALS: Lunch £11.50 Dinner £11.50*

CONF: Thtr 60 Class 30 Board 30 Del £60

CARDS: 

£

BAWTRY South Yorkshire Map 08 SK69

★★★65% **The Crown**

High St DN10 6JW ☎ 01302 710341 FAX 01302 711798

A former 17th-century posting house situated in the town centre has been tastefully modernised in keeping with the character of the building. Some of the bedrooms have been furnished and decorated to a very high standard, and although others are more modest, they are modern and well equipped; one room features a beautiful four-poster bed. A menu of British and regional dishes is available in the restaurant, and bar meals are served in the oak-panelled Crown Bar.

57 en suite (bth/shr) No smoking in 18 bedrooms CTV in all bedrooms Night porter 50P Xmas V meals Coffee am Tea pm No smoking in restaurant Last d 9.30pm

ROOMS: s £46-£56; d £56-£66 * **LB**

MEALS: Sunday Lunch £10.30 Dinner £14.95&alc*

CONF: Thtr 150 Class 80 Board 60 Del from £65

CARDS:

BEACONSFIELD Buckinghamshire Map 04 SU99

★★★★62% **Bellhouse**

Oxford Rd HP9 2XE (2m E A40) ☎ 01753 887211 FAX 01753 888231

The Mediterranean-style facade and hall area of this hotel set the tone for a comfortable stay. This same smart yet informal style does not fully extend to the bedrooms which are being refurbished on a gradual basis. The staff have made strides in providing levels of service in keeping with this classification of hotel and another highlight is the attractively configured leisure centre. The banqueting and meeting facilities are well used at weekends.

136 en suite (bth/shr) (11 fmly) No smoking in 86 bedrooms CTV in all bedrooms STV Lift Night porter 405P Indoor swimming pool (heated) Squash Snooker Sauna Solarium Gym Jacuzzi/spa Beauty therapy room Xmas English & Continental Cuisine V meals Coffee am Tea pm No smoking in restaurant Last d 9.45pm

ROOMS: (incl. bkfst) s £115-£135; d £135-£155 * **LB**

MEALS: Lunch £13.50 Dinner £19.50&alc*

CONF: Thtr 450 Class 220 Board 40 Del from £140

CARDS:

★★62% **White Hart Toby**

Aylesbury End HP9 1LW (on A40) ☎ 01494 671211 FAX 01494 670704

RS 24 Dec-2 Jan

A branded restaurant and spacious public bar occupy most of the public areas of this inn, which dates back to the 16th century. Apart from a few bedrooms in the main building, accommodation is housed in a purpose built annexe.

5 en suite (bth/shr) 28 annexe en suite (bth/shr) No smoking in 14 bedrooms CTV in all bedrooms STV No dogs (ex guide dogs) Night porter 100P Xmas V meals Coffee am Tea pm No smoking in restaurant Last d 10.30pm

ROOMS: (incl. bkfst) s £69.50-£79.50; d £79.50-£110 * **LB**

OFF-PEAK: (incl. bkfst) s £36-£38; d fr £58

MEALS: Lunch £5-£15alc Dinner £10-£20alc*

CONF: Thtr 80 Class 30 Board 30 Del from £88

CARDS:

BEAMINSTER Dorset Map 03 ST40

★★★68% **Bridge House**

3 Prout Bridge DT8 3AY (off A3066, 100yds from Town Square) ☎ 01308 862200 FAX 01308 863700

Dating from the 13th century, The Bridge House nestles in the heart of Beaminster. The bedrooms are divided between the main house and the coach house. All rooms are very well equipped and attractively decorated, those in the main house bing very spacious. The public rooms are comfortably furnished, the log fires, beamed ceilings and array of Thomas Hardy books all add to the relaxing atmosphere. The elegant Georgian dining room offers a perfect setting in which to enjoy the imaginative menu, where the best possible use is made of local produce.

9 en suite (bth/shr) 4 annexe en suite (bth/shr) CTV in all bedrooms 22P No coaches Xmas International Cuisine Coffee am Tea pm No smoking in restaurant Last d 9pm

ROOMS: (incl. bkfst) s £53-£70; d £60-£99 * **LB**

OFF-PEAK: (incl. bkfst) s £48-£63; d £54-£90

MEALS: Lunch £11.95-£13.95 Dinner £18.95*

CONF: Class 16 Del from £95

CARDS:

BEAMISH Co Durham Map 12 NZ25

★★★66% **Beamish Park**

Beamish Burn Rd NE16 5EG (off A6076, close to Causey Arch Inn) ☎ 01207 230666 FAX 01207 281260

This modern, comfortable hotel in open countryside just off the A6076 is close to the Beamish open air museum and other heritage sites. The bedrooms are well furnished and comfortable, whilst the inviting public rooms include two dining styles and a delightful lounge which is attached to the elegant restaurant. Chef Clive Imber continues to produce fine dishes from his carefully chosen menu which uses the best local produce that is available. A recent addition is an excellent golf driving range, and there are plans to add a nine hole golf course. Value for money is exceptionally good.

47 en suite (bth/shr) (7 fmly) CTV in all bedrooms STV Night porter 100P Golf 9 Floodlit golf driving range English & French Cuisine V meals Coffee am Tea pm No smoking area in restaurant

ROOMS: s £33-£46; d £58-£67 * **LB**
OFF-PEAK: (incl. bkfst) s £25.50; d £51
MEALS: Lunch £9.70-£19.75 Dinner £20.50*
CONF: Thtr 30 Class 10 Board 25 Del from £59
CARDS:

BEAULIEU Hampshire Map 04 SU30

★★★ 75% **Montagu Arms**
Palace Ln SO42 7ZL ☎ 01590 612324
FAX 01590 612188

This charming creeper clad hotel is the picturesque location of Beaulieu where the donkeys and cows gather in the car-park. The bedrooms are individually decorated and retain many of their original features. The public rooms include a cosy lounge and a bright conservatory overlooking the pretty walled garden. Chef Simon Fennell offers an imaginative menu which offers a good range of dishes using good locally sourced ingredients, the homemade bread is particularly memorable.

24 en suite (bth/shr) (3 fmly) CTV in all bedrooms Night porter 86P Pool table Xmas French Cuisine V meals Coffee am Tea pm No smoking in restaurant Last d 9.30pm
ROOMS: (incl. bkfst) s fr £69.90; d £98.90-£185.90 * **LB**
OFF-PEAK: (incl. bkfst & dinner) s fr £69.90; d £109-£199
MEALS: Lunch £12.90-£16.50 Dinner fr £23.90&alc*
CONF: Thtr 30 Class 16 Board 24 Del from £109
CARDS:

See advertisement on page 97

★★★ 61% **Beaulieu**
Beaulieu Rd SO42 7YQ (off B3056) ☎ 01703 293344
FAX 01703 292729
This small popular hotel is located in the heart of the Forest between Lyndhurst and Beaulieu. With its own adjoining pub it has a good buzz in the summer months. The bedrooms are well equipped and comfortably furnished. Facilities include an indoor swimming pool and steam room, and an outdoor children's play area. A daily changing menu is offered in the restaurant which has lovely Forest views.

15 en suite (bth/shr) 3 annexe en suite (bth/shr) (2 fmly) CTV in all bedrooms 60P Indoor swimming pool (heated) Steam room ch fac Xmas V meals Coffee am Tea pm Last d 8.45pm
ROOMS: (incl. bkfst) s £50; d £79-£89 **LB**
MEALS: Bar Lunch £2.75 High tea fr £4.50 Dinner £17.50&alc*
CONF: Thtr 60 Class 40 Board 30 Del from £75
CARDS:

BEBINGTON Merseyside Map 07 SJ38

Travelodge
New Chester Rd L62 9AQ (on A41, northbound off, jucnt 5 on M63) ☎ 0151 327 2489
FAX 0151 327 2489

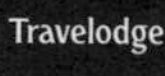

contd.

B

B

This modern building offers accommodation in smart, spacious and well equipped bedrooms, suitable for family use, and all with en suite bathrooms. Meals may be taken at the nearby family restaurant. For information on room rates and to make a booking, call Roomline free of charge on 0800 850950. For more details about Travelodge, consult the Contents page under Hotel Groups.
31 en suite (bth/shr)

BECKINGTON Somerset Map 03 ST85

★★ 76% **Woolpack Inn**
BA3 6SP (on A36) ☎ 01373 831244 FAX 01373 831223
Occupying a central position in the village, this former coaching inn dates back to the 16th century. Attracting both business and the leisure guests, for the well appointed bedrooms, the enjoyable, imaginative food and the friendly relaxed atmosphere. Whilst retaining the character of the building, each bedroom is individually furnished and equipped with every modern comfort. David Woolfall's innovative, fresh dishes are served at both midday and during the evening and guests have the option of eating in the attractive flagstone floored bar, the Garden room overlooking the terraced walled garden or in the no smoking restaurant area.
12 en suite (bth/shr) No smoking in 4 bedrooms CTV in all bedrooms STV 16P No coaches No children 5yrs Xmas English & French Cuisine V meals Coffee am Tea pm No smoking area in restaurant Last d 10pm
ROOMS: (incl. bkfst) s £59; d £69-£89 **LB**
MEALS: Lunch £15-£28alc Dinner £15-£28alc*
CONF: Thtr 30 Class 20 Board 20 Del from £95
CARDS:

£

Travelodge
BA3 6SF (A36) ☎ 01373 830251 FAX 01373 830251
This modern building offers accommodation in smart, spacious and well equipped bedrooms, suitable for family use, and all with en suite bathrooms. Meals may be taken at the nearby family restaurant. For information on room rates and to make a booking, call Roomline free of charge on 0800 850950. For more details about Travelodge, consult the Contents page under Hotel Groups.
40 en suite (bth/shr)

BEDALE North Yorkshire Map 08 SE28

★★ 62% **Motel Leeming**
The Great North Rd DL8 1DT (at A1/A684 junct, 12m S of Scotch Corner) ☎ 01677 422122
FAX 01677 424507
Situated next to the A1 but insulated from it, this family-owned motel offers good value for money and friendly service. Bedrooms are modern and well equipped and are mainly compact, whilst the public areas include a restaurant and a 24-hour café.
40 en suite (bth/shr) (8 fmly) No smoking in 12 bedrooms CTV in all bedrooms STV Night porter 210P Xmas V meals Coffee am Tea pm No smoking in restaurant Last d 10pm
ROOMS: s £39.50; d £39.50 **LB**
OFF-PEAK: s £29.95; d £29.95
MEALS: Lunch £6-£10alc Dinner £12.95&alc
CONF: Thtr 90 Class 40 Board 30
CARDS:

£

★★ 60% **White Rose**
Bedale Rd DL7 9AY (on A684, E of A1 junc)
☎ 01677 422707 & 424941 FAX 01677 425123
Situated in a convenient location for the A1, this mainly business-style hotel provides modern bedrooms which are also well equipped. A very good range of reasonably-priced food is available either in the bar or the friendly restaurant.
18 en suite (bth/shr) (2 fmly) CTV in all bedrooms 50P Pool table V meals Coffee am Tea pm No smoking area in restaurant Last d 9.30pm
ROOMS: (incl. bkfst) s £31; d £45 *
OFF-PEAK: (incl. bkfst) s fr £22; d fr £35
MEALS: Lunch £7.95 High tea £7.75 Dinner £11.95&alc
CARDS:

£

BEDFORD Bedfordshire Map 04 TL04

★★★ 72% **Woodlands Manor**
Green Ln, Clapham MK41 6EP (2m N A6)
☎ 01234 363281 FAX 01234 272390
Closed between Xmas & New Year RS Aug
Woodlands Manor is situated within wooded gardens and grounds on the outskirts of the small village of Clapham, two miles north of Bedford. The character of this manor house has been retained by good use of sympathetic furnishings and decor, which has resulted in comfortable and elegantly appointed public rooms; the restaurant is a particularly good example, with its high ceilings, large windows and polished tables. The accommodation is all pleasantly furnished, most with cherry wood furniture and coordinated colour schemes; room sizes vary from comfortable through to spacious and a well proportioned suite is also available. Attentive professional service is one of the strengths of this pleasing country house.
22 en suite (bth/shr) 3 annexe en suite (bth/shr) No smoking in 11 bedrooms CTV in all bedrooms STV No dogs (ex guide dogs) Night porter 100P Croquet lawn No children 7yrs Xmas English & French Cuisine V meals Coffee am Tea pm No smoking in restaurant Last d 9.45pm
ROOMS: (incl. bkfst) s £59.50-£75; d £75-£85 * **LB**
OFF-PEAK: (incl. bkfst) s £50-£55; d £65-£75
MEALS: Lunch £15.75-£15.95&alc Dinner fr £19.75&alc*
CONF: Thtr 30 Class 20 Board 20 Del from £110
CARDS:

★★★ 68% **The Barns**
Cardington Rd MK44 3SA (on A603 1.5m E of Bedford) ☎ 01234 270044 FAX 01234 273102
This popular riverside hotel has been sympathetically developed around a 17th-century manor house and medieval tithe barn. Modern, well equipped bedrooms form part of the more recent extensions and are all of good size and smartly decorated. The public areas retain much of the character of the original buildings and include cosy bars and a smart restaurant overlooking the River Ouse, where a set menu and carte choices are offered; snacks are also available in the Riverside Bar. Prompt services are carried out by a friendly team.
48 en suite (bth/shr) No smoking in 16 bedrooms CTV in all bedrooms STV Night porter 90P Fishing Sauna Solarium Xmas International Cuisine V meals Coffee am Tea pm No smoking area in restaurant Last d 9.45pm

ROOMS: s £72-£74; d £72-£74 * **LB**
MEALS: Lunch £12.50-£14.50&alc Dinner £16.95-£18.95&alc
CONF: Thtr 120 Class 40 Board 40 Del from £105
CARDS:

★★★66% **Bedford Moat House**

2 Saint Mary's St MK42 0AR (from junct 13 on M1 follow signs for town centre hotel is on right just before bridge crossing river Great Ouse)
☎ 01234 799955 FAX 01234 340447
RS Bank hols
This large contemporary hotel in the town centre occupies a commanding position on the south bank of the River Great Ouse, its airy restaurant overlooking the water. Extensive conference facilities and comfortable, well maintained bedrooms make this a convenient base for business use.
100 en suite (bth/shr) (20 fmly) No smoking in 22 bedrooms CTV in all bedrooms Lift Night porter 72P Solarium Gym Xmas English & Continental Cuisine V meals Coffee am Tea pm No smoking area in restaurant Last d 10pm
ROOMS: d £57-£65 * **LB**
MEALS: Lunch £10.95-£15 High tea £5-£12.50 Dinner £13.50-£22&alc*
CONF: Thtr 400 Class 150 Board 50 Del £99
CARDS:

BEER Devon Map 03 SY28

★★64% **Anchor Inn**
EX12 3ET (turn off A3052 following signs for Beer, continue through the village to slip road for beach Anchor Inn on the right)
☎ 01297 20386 FAX 01297 24474
Closed 25-29 Dec
This popular inn is situated right on the seafront and offers smart bedrooms, most of which have sea views and en suite facilities. The cosy bars have open fires in the winter months and are known for their range of real ales. The restaurant offers a wide choice of dishes and specialises in fish and seafood.
8 rms (5 bth/shr) (2 fmly) CTV in all bedrooms No dogs No coaches International Cuisine V meals Coffee am Last d 9.30pm
ROOMS: (incl. bkfst) d £49-£59 * **LB**
OFF-PEAK: (incl. bkfst) d £36.76-£44.26
MEALS: Lunch £8&alc Dinner £6-£20alc
CARDS:

BEETHAM Cumbria Map 07 SD47

★62% **Wheatsheaf**
LA7 7AL (1m S of Milnthorpe, next to the church off A6)
☎ 015395 62123
Closed 25 Dec
Located in the centre of the historic village, this friendly family-run hotel offers a good standard of accommodation and serves reasonably priced meals in the bars and the upstairs dining room.
6 en suite (bth/shr) CTV in all bedrooms 50P V meals Coffee am No smoking in restaurant Last d 8.30pm
ROOMS: (incl. bkfst) s £30; d £40 * **LB**
MEALS: Lunch £6.30-£11.30alc Dinner £9.25&alc*
CARDS:

BELFORD Northumberland Map 12 NU13

★★★64% **Blue Bell**
Market Place NE70 7NE (centre of village on left of St Mary's church)
☎ 01668 213543 FAX 01668 213787
Lying in the centre of the village, this creeper-clad former coaching inn has been modernised but still retains much of its Georgian character. It has a friendly atmosphere, pleasant public rooms including two

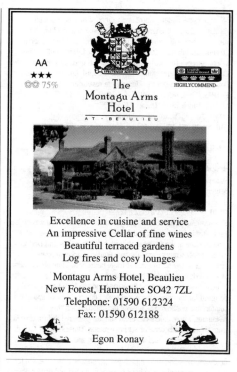

restaurants, and well equipped bedrooms.
17 en suite (bth/shr) (1 fmly) No smoking in 4 bedrooms CTV in all bedrooms 17P Pool table Xmas English & French Cuisine V meals Coffee am Tea pm No smoking in restaurant Last d 9pm
ROOMS: (incl. bkfst) s £38-£40; d £78-£92 * **LB**
OFF-PEAK: (incl. bkfst) s £34-£42
MEALS: Lunch £8.95-£9.50 High tea £5.25 Dinner £21*
CONF: Thtr 140 Class 120 Board 30 Del from £55
CARDS:

⌂ **Purdy Lodge**
Adderstone Services NE70 7JU ☎ 01668 213000
FAX 01668 213111
This conveniently situated lodge forms part of a roadside complex and provides practical accommodation with several family rooms. All the bedrooms look out over fields to the rear of the lodge and are insulated from the noise of the road. Public areas include a 24-hour café lounge bar and cottage-style restaurant.
20 en suite (bth/shr) (4 fmly) CTV in all bedrooms Night porter 60P Xmas V meals Coffee am Tea pm Last d 10pm
ROOMS: s £37.50; d £37.50
MEALS: Lunch £7.50-£20&alc High tea £9-£20&alc Dinner £9-£27.50&alc
CARDS:

BELLINGHAM Northumberland Map 12 NY88

★★68% **Riverdale Hall**

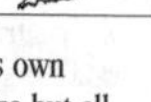

NE48 2JT (turn off B6320, after bridge, hotel on left)
☎ 01434 220254 FAX 01434 220457
A popular family hotel standing in its own grounds to the west of the village off the B6320, the hotel overlooks its own cricket pitch and the North Tyne river. Bedrooms vary in size but all

contd.

B

offer the same modern amenities. A range of menus, including vegetarian dishes, is offered in both the restaurant and bar, and a young team of staff provide particularly friendly and helpful service.
20 en suite (bth/shr) (6 fmly) CTV in all bedrooms 60P Indoor swimming pool (heated) Fishing Sauna Croquet lawn Putting green Cricket field Petanque Xmas English & Danish Cuisine V meals Coffee am Tea pm No smoking area in restaurant Last d 9.30pm
ROOMS: (incl. bkfst) s £40-£45; d £69-£78 * **LB**
MEALS: Lunch £8.45 Dinner £18&alc*
CONF: Thtr 40 Board 20 Del from £65
CARDS:

BELPER Derbyshire Map 08 SK34

★★★ 75% **Makeney Hall Country House**
Makeney, Milford DE56 0RS (turn off A6 between Belper and Duffield at Milford, signposted Makeney. Hotel is 0.25m further along on left)
☎ 01332 842999 FAX 01332 842777
This beautifully restored and preserved Victorian mansion was built in 1896. It stands in 6 acres of delightful grounds and gardens and is situated close to the A6, near Milford, between Belper and Derby, which is only 4 miles away. The well equipped accommodation includes a variety of sizes and styles of bedrooms. Some are contained in a cleverly converted outbuilding and surround a small courtyard. Nine of these are on ground floor level and two have been specially designed for the convenience of disabled guests. The well appointed, comfortable public rooms include the oak panelled "Lavinia's" restaurant, where diners can enjoy soundly prepared dishes, chosen from either the a la carte or set price menus. Other facilities include private dining rooms and a range of meeting and conference rooms for up to 150 delegates. The hotel is also a popular venue for other functions, including wedding receptions and it is in fact licensed for marriage ceremonies. The hotel is privately owned and personally run, with a dedicated and professional team of staff, who go to great lengths to ensure that guests are comfortable and contented.
27 en suite (bth/shr) 18 annexe en suite (bth/shr) No smoking in 6 bedrooms CTV in all bedrooms STV Lift Night porter 150P Pool table Croquet lawn Putting green V meals Coffee am Tea pm No smoking area in restaurant Last d 9.45pm
ROOMS: s £75-£135; d £75-£135 * **LB**
MEALS: Lunch £10.50-£14.50 Dinner £22.50-£25&alc*
CONF: Thtr 180 Class 80 Board 50 Del £120
CARDS:
See advertisement under DERBY

See advertisement on opposite page

★★61% **Lion**
Bridge St DE56 1AY (on A6) ☎ 01773 824033
FAX 01773 828393
MENZIES HOTELS
In the centre of the town - but amply provided with parking space - this hostelry serves as a meeting place for local residents. Extended and modernised a few years ago, it now has a good range of thoughtfully designed and fully co-ordinated rooms. A livelier lounge bar which serves bar meals supplements both the cocktail bar and restaurant.
19 rms (13 bth/shr) (1 fmly) No smoking in 6 bedrooms CTV in all bedrooms Night porter 25P Xmas English & Continental Cuisine V meals Coffee am Tea pm Last d 9.30pm
ROOMS: d £47.50-£54.50 * **LB**
OFF-PEAK: d £35-£40
MEALS: Lunch fr £8.95&alc Dinner £12.50-£20alc*
CONF: Thtr 130 Class 60 Board 40 Del from £65
CARDS:

BELTON Lincolnshire Map 08 SK93

★★★★75% **Belton Woods**
NG32 2LN (2m N of Grantham on A607)
☎ 01476 593200 FAX 01476 574547
DE VERE HOTELS
Set in 470 acres of Lincolnshire countryside to the north east of Grantham, this large modern hotel offers an impressive range of leisure activities, as well as extensive conference and function facilities. Spacious and comfortable public areas include a choice of restaurants and bars. Bedrooms, some in a separate wing, offer all the expected comforts for an hotel of this style. Smartly uniformed staff provide friendly and attentive service.
136 en suite (bth/shr) No smoking in 48 bedrooms CTV in all bedrooms STV No dogs (ex guide dogs) Lift Night porter 500P Indoor swimming pool (heated) Golf 45 Tennis (hard) Squash Snooker Sauna Solarium Gym Croquet lawn Putting green Jacuzzi/spa Hair & beauty salon Steamroom Xmas English & French Cuisine V meals Coffee am Tea pm No smoking area in restaurant Last d 9.30pm
ROOMS: (incl. bkfst) s £115; d £125 * **LB**
MEALS: Lunch £12.50-£16.50 High tea £8.75-£16.50 Dinner £12.50-£21&alc*
CONF: Thtr 275 Class 130 Board 80 Del from £115
CARDS:

BERKELEY Gloucestershire Map 03 ST69

★★63% **The Old Schoolhouse**
Canonbury St GL13 9BG (1.5m off A38 next to Berkley Castle)
☎ 01453 811711 FAX 01453 511761
As its name suggests, this was the town's primary school, and it still retains much of the charm of former times. There is an impressive lounge with a large log fire, and this leads into an attractive restaurant, where an appealing menu offers a good range of home-cooked dishes using fresh natural ingredients. The bedrooms are spacious, pretty and comfortable, and some of them enjoy views to the castle.
7 en suite (bth/shr) (1 fmly) CTV in all bedrooms No dogs (ex guide dogs) 15P International Cuisine V meals Coffee am Tea pm No smoking in restaurant Last d 9.30pm
ROOMS: (incl. bkfst) s £38.50; d £48.50 * **LB**
MEALS: Lunch £8.50&alc Dinner £13.95&alc*
CARDS:

BERKELEY ROAD Gloucestershire Map 03 ST79

★★65% **Prince of Wales**
GL13 9HD (on A38, 6m S of M5 junc 13 and 6m N of junc 14)
☎ 01453 810474 FAX 01453 511370
Conveniently situated within 20 minutes drive of both Gloucester and Bristol and close to junctions 13 and 14 of the M5, this much modernised hotel offers comfortable and very well equipped bedrooms in tune with 20th-century requirements, in contrast to its popular and traditional bar which harks back to its origins as a Victorian coaching inn. An informal restaurant overlooking the garden offers a good choice of enjoyable dishes.

41 en suite (bth/shr) (1 fmly) No smoking in 6 bedrooms CTV in all bedrooms STV Night porter 150P pool table English & French Cuisine V meals Coffee am Tea pm No smoking area in restaurant Last d 9.30pm
ROOMS: s £39-£45; d £45-£50 *
OFF-PEAK: s £30-£35; d £39-£45
MEALS: Lunch £5.95-£12alc Dinner £8-£19.50alc*
CONF: Thtr 200 Class 60 Board 60 Del from £50
CARDS:

BERWICK-UPON-TWEED Northumberland Map 12 NT95

★★★ 70% ***Marshall Meadows Country House***
TD15 1UT ☎ 01289 331133 FAX 01289 331438
This Georgian mansion sits in wooded grounds, flanked by farmland, and is a popular venue for weddings and conferences, as well as attracting a business and tourist clientele. The stylish bedrooms are comfortable and well equipped, whilst public room include a cosy bar, inviting lounge and two-tier restaurant with two varied menus, one featuring speciality dishes such as char-grilled wild boar or fillet of English ostrich.
18 en suite (bth/shr) (2 fmly) CTV in all bedrooms 87P Tennis (hard) Croquet lawn International Cuisine V meals Coffee am Tea pm Last d 9.50pm
CARDS:

See advertisement on this page

★62% **Queens Head**
Sandgate TD15 1EP (in town centre opposite swimming pool and adjacent to town walls) ☎ 01289 307852 FAX 01289 307852
Decent sized, well equipped bedrooms feature in this unpretentious commercial and tourist hotel, which is situated close to the town centre and its historic garrison walls. The emphasis is on bar meals, and breakfast is a set affair except for a choice of cereals.
6 en suite (bth/shr) (5 fmly) CTV in all bedrooms V meals Coffee am No smoking area in restaurant Last d 9pm
ROOMS: (incl. bkfst) s £25-£30; d £45-£50 * **LB**
MEALS: Lunch £7.50-£10.50 High tea fr £6.50 Dinner fr £12.95
CARDS:

BEVERLEY East Riding of Yorkshire Map 08 TA03

★★★65% **Beverley Arms**

North Bar Within HU17 8DD (opposite St Marys Church, just before North Bar) ☎ 01482 869241 FAX 01482 870907
An attractive hotel with a distinctive Georgian façade situated opposite St Mary's Church and close to the town centre. In summer colourful floral displays are a feature, especially in the courtyard in the centre of the building, which is visible from the popular flagstoned lounge where snacks and light meals are served during the day. Bedrooms are well equipped, but those in the older part of the hotel have the most character. There are an attractively appointed restaurant and a comfortable lounge bar as well as a number of meeting rooms and good parking facilities.
57 en suite (bth/shr) (4 fmly) No smoking in 27 bedrooms CTV in all bedrooms Lift Night porter 70P V meals Coffee am Tea pm No smoking in restaurant Last d 9.30pm
MEALS: Lunch £7-£8.25&alc High tea £3-£10alc Dinner £16.95&alc*
CONF: Thtr 60 Class 40 Board 30 Del from £65
CARDS:

★★★63% **Tickton Grange**

Tickton HU17 9SH (3m NE on A1035)
☎ 01964 543666 FAX 01964 542556
RS 25-29 Dec

contd.

This elegant Georgian house stands in four acres of well tended grounds on the A1035 to the north of Beverley and retains much of its original charm. The well equipped bedrooms are individually decorated and designed; one room has an Georgian four-poster bed. The lounge bar is comfortable and the well furnished restaurant serves enjoyable dinners and offers views overlooking the garden. Service is relaxed and caring.
18 en suite (bth/shr) (2 fmly) CTV in all bedrooms STV 65P Croquet lawn Putting green V meals Coffee am Tea pm
ROOMS: s £49.50-£55; d £59.50-£65 * **LB**
OFF-PEAK: s fr £39.50; d fr £49.50
MEALS: Lunch £12.95&alc*
CONF: Thtr 80 Class 60 Board 35 Del from £86.50
CARDS:

★★ 70% **The Manor House**
Northlands, Walkington HU17 8RT (4m SW off B1230)
☎ 01482 881645 FAX 01482 866501
This charming hotel is set in the heart of the countryside and is furnished in the country house genre. Bedrooms are spacious and elegantly furnished in period style. The restaurant consists of an elegant dining room and a comfortable conservatory overlooking some of the hotel's grounds. It serves a choice of excellent set-price menus based on fresh local ingredients in dishes such as pan-fried calves' liver with buttered fried onions, green back bacon and a marvellously glossy jus.
6 en suite (bth/shr) 1 annexe en suite (bth/shr) (1 fmly) CTV in all bedrooms 40P No coaches V meals Last d 9.15pm
ROOMS: s £65-£75; d £75-£100 **LB**
MEALS: Dinner £16.50&alc*
CONF: Thtr 20 Del from £85
CARDS:

★★ 67% ***Lairgate***
30-34 Lairgate HU17 8EP ☎ 01482 882141 FAX 01482 861067
This privately-owned, town-centre hotel offers a relaxed atmosphere and friendly informal service from the small team of staff. Bedrooms have modern facilities; some have four-poster beds and family rooms are available. Light, attractively decorated public areas include a comfortable lounge and bar, and the restaurant offers a good selection of dishes. Located in a one-way road system, access to the hotel's rear car park is found by taking the turning just before the hotel.
22 rms (9 bth 10 shr) (2 fmly) CTV in all bedrooms No dogs (ex guide dogs) Night porter 20P English & French Cuisine V meals Coffee am Tea pm Last d 9.45pm
CARDS:

BEWDLEY Hereford & Worcester Map 07 SO77

★★ 64% **The George**
Load St DY12 2AW (in town centre opposite town hall)
☎ 01299 402117 FAX 01299 401269
This former coaching inn is conveniently situated in the town centre. It dates back to 1506 and has a wealth of character, which is enhanced by such things as exposed beams, panelled walls and the magnificent Jacobean fireplace in the restaurant, as well as real fires in the two bars, one of which doubles as a coffee shop during the day. The modern furnished and equipped bedrooms vary in size and have benefited from recent refurbishment. Family accommodation and a room with a four-poster bed are both available. Other facilities include a function room for up to 120 guests.
13 rms (2 bth 8 shr) (1 fmly) CTV in all bedrooms No dogs (ex guide dogs) 50P English & French Cuisine V meals Coffee am Tea pm Last d 9.30pm
ROOMS: (incl. bkfst) s £40-£45; d £55-£65 * **LB**
MEALS: Lunch £9.50-£12.50 Dinner £10-£25alc*
CONF: Thtr 50 Class 50 Board 40 Del from £52
CARDS:

BEXHILL-ON-SEA East Sussex Map 05 TQ70

★★★ 58% **Grand**
Sea Rd TN40 1EE (turn off A259 coast road, hotel 50yds from main railway station) ☎ 01424 215437 FAX 01424 225028
Centrally situated close to the sea front and town centre this popular hotel is currently undergoing a complete program of refurbishment and upgrading. Completed bedrooms are furnished and decorated in the modern style and come equipped with all modern amenities. Public rooms comprise the Deerstalker bar which features live entertainment most evenings, two comfortable lounges and the attractive and well lit Chandelier Restaurant.
50 en suite (bth/shr) CTV in all bedrooms Lift Night porter Xmas English & French Cuisine V meals Coffee am Tea pm No smoking area in restaurant Last d 9pm
ROOMS: (incl. bkfst) s fr £49.50; d fr £65 * **LB**
MEALS: Lunch fr £10.50 Dinner fr £15*
CONF: Thtr 150 Class 80 Board 40 Del from £69.50
CARDS:

BEXLEY Greater London Map 05 TQ47

★★★★ 71% **Swallow**
1 Broadway DA6 7JZ (near junct 2 of M25)
☎ 0181 298 1000 FAX 0181 298 1234
SWALLOW HOTELS
This very modern, purpose-built hotel is located on the fringes of the town centre. It is linked to a covered municipal car park. The bedrooms are swish and well laid out and include smart marble bathrooms. There is a choice of two restaurants as well as full room service. The young team of staff make great efforts at creating a warm and welcoming atmosphere.
142 en suite (bth/shr) (16 fmly) No smoking in 53 bedrooms CTV in all bedrooms STV Lift Night porter Air conditioning 100P Indoor swimming pool (heated) Solarium Gym Jacuzzi/spa Steam room Xmas British & European Cuisine V meals Coffee am Tea pm No smoking area in restaurant Last d 11pm
ROOMS: (incl. bkfst) s £65-£105; d £80-£130 * **LB**
OFF-PEAK: (incl. bkfst) s £65-£75; d £80-£105
MEALS: Lunch £14-£19.25&alc Dinner £19.50-£26&alc*
CONF: Thtr 200 Class 120 Board 65 Del from £110
CARDS:

Forte Posthouse Bexley
FORTE Posthouse
Black Prince Interchange, Southwold Rd
DA5 1ND (follow A2 to exit signposted A220/A223 Black Prince interchange Bexley, Bexleyheath & Crayford) ☎ 01322 526900 FAX 01322 526113
Suitable for both the business and leisure traveller, this bright hotel provides modern accommodation in well equipped bedrooms with en suite bathrooms. For more details about Forte Posthouse hotels, consult the Contents page for the section on Hotel Groups.
103 en suite (bth/shr)
ROOMS: s £49-£79; d £49-£79 *
CONF: Thtr 70 Class 30 Board 30 Del from £109

BIBURY Gloucestershire Map 04 SP10

★★★ 74% **Swan**
GL7 5NW (off B4425, by bridge over the River Coln)
☎ 01285 740695 FAX 01285 740473
Set in gardens on the River Colne, this delightful creeper clad and honey-coloured 17th-century Cotswold inn is decorated with sumptuous fabrics and furnishings, including some fine period furniture. The bedrooms have all been individually furnished, many with antiques, to provide the highest standards of comfort with superb quality bathrooms, and lots of little extra touches. For light meals there is an all-day brasserie, and in the handsome, spacious main dining

room, chef Guy Bossom offers a fixed-price, 6-course dinner menu featuring some very interesting, if at times over-complicated, dishes. However, this year's inspection meal shows the promise of some good meals to come: an appetiser of local trout was served with a very rich, dark glace de viande, followed by a tartlette of pigeon and (slightly overcooked) foie gras with a celery and mushroom duxelle, then an excellent creamy celeriac and port soup. The main course partnered confit of salmon with potato cakes, squid, and very firm-textured confit of duck. A duo of white and dark chocolate mousseline with griollines cherries wasn't accurately described as it came with only white chocolate and strawberries but nonetheless enjoyable. Service is very attentive and friendly and professionally managed by the managing director/general manager Mr Heinz Sedlacek.
18 en suite (bth/shr) (1 fmly) CTV in all bedrooms No dogs (ex guide dogs) Lift 16P No coaches Fishing Xmas V meals Coffee am Tea pm No smoking in restaurant Last d 9.30pm
ROOMS: (incl. bkfst) s £86-£117; d £115-£210 **LB**
OFF-PEAK: (incl. bkfst) s £86-£97; d £115-£190
MEALS: Sunday Lunch fr £15.95 High tea £6-£9alc Dinner £21.50-£35&alc
CONF: Thtr 85 Class 60 Board 10 Del from £135
CARDS:

★★ 66% Bibury Court
GL7 5NT (beside the River Coln, behind St Marys Church)
☎ 01285 740337 & 740324 FAX 01285 740660
Closed 21-30 Dec
Situated on the edge of a charming Cotswold village, within walled landscaped gardens, this fine period building features flagstone floors, wood-panelled rooms and enormous minster log fires in the drawing room. Bedrooms are well proportioned, with a mixture of Art Deco and antique furnishings which blend surprisingly well, and there are huge Victorian-style baths.
20 en suite (bth) (2 fmly) CTV in all bedrooms 100P No coaches Fishing Squash Riding Pool table Croquet lawn Putting green English, French & Spanish Cuisine V meals Coffee am Tea pm No smoking area in restaurant
ROOMS: (incl. cont bkfst) s £44-£56; d £74-£82 * **LB**
MEALS: Lunch £15.50-£21.50alc*
CARDS:

See advertisement on this page

BICESTER Oxfordshire Map 04 SP52

★★ 74% Bignell Park Hotel & Restaurant
Chesterton OX6 8UE (on A4095 Witney road)
☎ 01869 241444 & 241192 FAX 01869 241444

This friendly hotel just outside Bicester has many features of real quality including the dramatic restaurant with its artwork, fireplace and exposed beams. The lounge is crammed with books, and there is a lovely grand piano and comfortable seating. the spacious bedrooms are stylishly furnished with some unusual pieces of furniture. Danish proprietor Erling Sorensen acts as host and his friendly dog is always on hand to extend a warm welcome.

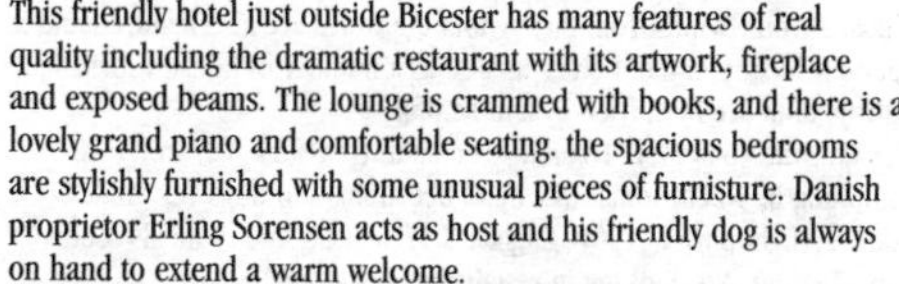

5 en suite (bth/shr) CTV in all bedrooms 40P No coaches No children 3yrs English & French Cuisine V meals Coffee am Last d 9.30pm
ROOMS: (incl. bkfst) s £65-£75; d £69-£85 *
MEALS: Lunch £12.50-£15&alc Dinner £18-£26alc*
CONF: Board 16
CARDS:

Travelodge
Cherwell Valley (M40 junct 10)
☎ Central Res 0800 850950 FAX 01869 345030
This modern building offers accommodation in smart, spacious and well equipped bedrooms, suitable for family use, and all with en suite bathrooms. Meals may be taken at the nearby family restaurant. For information on room rates and to make a booking, call Roomline free of charge on 0800 850950. For more details about Travelodge, consult the Contents page under Hotel Groups.
64 en suite (bth/shr)

BICKLEIGH Devon Map 03 SS90

★★ 65% *Fisherman's Cot*
EX16 8RW ☎ 01884 855237 & 855289 FAX 01884 855241
This small thatched hotel enjoys a setting beside the river Exe, and the popular bars and restaurants have been positioned to make the most of the delightful outlook. Bedrooms have been equipped with modern facilities, some are situated in a house and a bungalow across the car park. An extensive selection of dishes is available from a range of menus, as well as a carvery which offers various roast meats, vegetables and puddings.
23 en suite (bth/shr) (5 fmly) No smoking in 6 bedrooms CTV in all bedrooms 147P Fishing ch fac English & French Cuisine V meals Coffee am Tea pm Last high tea 5pm
CARDS:

BIDEFORD Devon Map 02 SS42
See also Landcross & Westward Ho!

★★★ 67% Royal
Barnstaple St EX39 4AE (at eastern end of Bideford Bridge) (Brend)
☎ 01237 472005 FAX 01237 478957
From its prominent position overlooking historic Bideford, this comfortable hotel offers a warm and friendly atmosphere. The bedrooms, some of which are very spacious, have been decorated with attractive floral fabrics and equipped with modern facilities. The public areas include a bar-lounge and the panelled Kingsley Room, which can

contd.

be used for private functions. A la carte and set-price menus are available in the restaurant.
31 en suite (bth/shr) (3 fmly) CTV in all bedrooms STV Night porter 70P Wkly live entertainment Xmas English & French Cuisine V meals Coffee am Tea pm Last d 9pm
ROOMS: s £42-£47; d £52-£62 * **LB**
OFF-PEAK: s £30-£35; d £40-£50
MEALS: Lunch £7.50 Dinner £15&alc*
CONF: Thtr 100 Class 100 Board 100
CARDS: 

★★68% **Yeoldon Country House**
Durrant Ln, Northam EX39 2RL (from Barnstaple follow A39 over River Torridge Bridge, at rdbt turn right onto A386 towards Northam then 3rd rightinto Durrant Ln) ☎ 01237 474400 FAX 01237 476618
Peacefully situated in its own grounds at the end of a long private drive, this delightful ivy-clad hotel overlooks the River Torridge. Individually styled bedrooms are brightly decorated and equipped with modern facilities, and the public areas include a comfortable bar lounge and a most attractive dining room. Sue and Kevin Jelley and their spaniel dog Duff, extend a warm welcome and invite guests to enjoy the "home from home" atmosphere of Yeoldon House.
10 en suite (bth/shr) (2 fmly) CTV in all bedrooms 22P No coaches Xmas English, French & Italian Cuisine V meals Coffee am Tea pm No smoking in restaurant Last d 9.30pm
ROOMS: (incl. bkfst) s £44-£53.50; d £75-£85 **LB**
OFF-PEAK: (incl. bkfst) s £39; d £65
MEALS: Lunch £9.50-£11.50 High tea fr £3.50 Dinner £15&alc
CARDS: 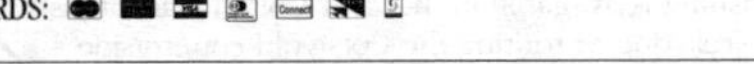

★★62% **Orchard Hill Hotel & Restaurant**
Orchard Hill, Northam EX39 2QY (A39 into town, over Newbridge to roundabout and turn left, then 2nd left into Orchard Hill. Hotel 800yds on left) ☎ 01237 472872 FAX 01237 423803
Set in an elevated position close to the centre of the ancient port of Bideford, this family-run hotel affords easy access to the North Devon link road. Bedrooms all have en suite facilities, TV and tea-making facilities, there is a comfortable lounge, and a choice of freshly prepared dishes is available in the candlelit restaurant.
9 en suite (bth/shr) (3 fmly) CTV in all bedrooms No dogs 12P No coaches No children 5yrs V meals No smoking in restaurant Last d 8pm
ROOMS: (incl. bkfst) s £30-£35; d £45-£50 * **LB**
MEALS: Dinner £10-£12&alc*
CARDS:

★★57% **Riversford**
Limers Ln EX39 2RG ☎ 01237 474239 & 470381 FAX 01237 421661
Owned and personally managed by the Jarrad family for over twenty years, this hotel offers a peaceful location along a quiet lane and overlooking the Torridge estuary, yet only a few minutes' walk from the ancient port of Bideford. Bedrooms are generally spacious and comfortably furnished. The open fire in the lounge provides a warm welcome in cooler months, whilst an extensive menu is offered in the dining room which is much patronised by locals as well as hotel guests.
13 en suite (bth/shr) (1 fmly) CTV in all bedrooms Night porter 17P Solarium ch fac Xmas English & French Cuisine V meals Coffee am Tea pm No smoking area in restaurant Last d 9.30pm
ROOMS: (incl. bkfst) s fr £40; d £55-£65 * **LB**
MEALS: Lunch £5-£25alc High tea fr £6alc Dinner £9.50-£17.50&alc*
CONF: Thtr 50 Class 25 Board 20
CARDS:

BIGBURY-ON-SEA Devon Map 03 SX64

★69% **Henley**
TQ7 4AR ☎ 01548 810240 FAX 01548 810020
Closed Nov-Mar
This cosy hotel is in an elevated position with dramatic views over Bigbury Bay and a footpath (127 steps) down to a private beach. Refurbishment continues and bedrooms are exceptionally well equipped and pleasant. A well balanced set-price menu is provided using fresh local produce. This is a no-smoking establishment.
8 en suite (bth/shr) (2 fmly) No smoking in all bedrooms CTV in all bedrooms STV 9P No coaches English & French Cuisine Coffee am Tea pm No smoking in restaurant Last d 8pm
ROOMS: (incl. bkfst & dinner) s £44-£54; d £88-£94 **LB**
OFF-PEAK: (incl. bkfst & dinner) s fr £40; d fr £80
MEALS: Dinner £16
CARDS:

BILBROUGH North Yorkshire Map 08 SE54

Travelodge
Tadcaster LS24 8EG (A64 eastbound)
☎ 01937 531823 FAX 01937 531823
This modern building offers accommodation in smart, spacious and well equipped bedrooms, suitable for family use, and all with en suite bathrooms. Meals may be taken at the nearby family restaurant. For information on room rates and to make a booking, call Roomline free of charge on **0800 850950**. For more details about Travelodge, consult the Contents page under Hotel Groups.
36 en suite (bth/shr)

BILLINGHAM See Stockton-on-Tees

BILLINGTON Lancashire Map 07 SD73

★★★★67% **Foxfields Country Hotel & Restaurant**
Whalley Rd BB7 9HY ☎ 01254 822556
FAX 01254 824613
This hotel is situated in attractive countryside just off the A59 between Preston and Clitheroe, only a short drive from the M6 motorway. It started life as a high class restaurant, but in recent years luxurious bedrooms have been added, many with their own lounges, and recently a leisure centre has been opened, considerably enhancing the hotel's facilities. Much emphasis is still placed on the restaurant operation and the new Expressions menu offers a wide choice of dishes with a local flavour. Wines from throughout the world are also featured and a good selection of half bottles as well as a number of house wines. Staff throughout are both friendly and helpful.
28 en suite (bth/shr) 16 annexe en suite (bth/shr) (27 fmly) No smoking in 5 bedrooms CTV in all bedrooms No dogs (ex guide dogs) Night porter 150P English & French Cuisine V meals Coffee am Tea pm No smoking in restaurant Last d 9.30pm
MEALS: Lunch £6.95-£10.45&alc Dinner £16.95-£19.45*
CARDS:

BINGLEY West Yorkshire Map 07 SE13

★★★66% **Oakwood Hall**

Lady Ln BD16 4AW ☎ 01274 564123 & 563569
FAX 01274 561477
Closed 25-31 Dec
Situated in a peaceful residential area, Oakwood Hall is a handsome Victorian house with many fine architectural features and a well tended garden. All the bedrooms are individually furnished and attention has been given to providing good writing desks and seating, as well as thoughtful extras such as mineral water and fresh fruit. Room service

menus have now been introduced.
20 en suite (bth/shr) CTV in all bedrooms Night porter 100P English & French Cuisine V meals Coffee am Tea pm Last d 9.30pm
ROOMS: (incl. bkfst) s £55-£65; d £75-£85
OFF-PEAK: (incl. bkfst) s fr £50; d fr £70
MEALS: Lunch £8.50-£12.50&alc Dinner fr £12.50&alc
CONF: Thtr 80 Class 50 Board 40 Del from £95
CARDS:

See advertisement on this page

BIRCH MOTORWAY SERVICE AREA (M62) Greater Manchester Map 07 SD80

Travelodge
M62 Service Area OL10 2HQ
☎ Central Res 0800 850950 FAX 01525 878450
This modern building offers accommodation in smart, spacious and well equipped bedrooms, suitable for family use, and all with en suite bathrooms. Meals may be taken at the nearby family restaurant. For information on room rates and to make a booking, call Roomline free of charge on 0800 850950. For more details about Travelodge, consult the Contents page under Hotel Groups.
55 en suite (bth/shr)

BIRDLIP Gloucestershire Map 03 SO91

★★★ 65% **Royal George**
GL4 8JH (on the B4070, off the A417)
☎ 01452 862506 FAX 01452 862277

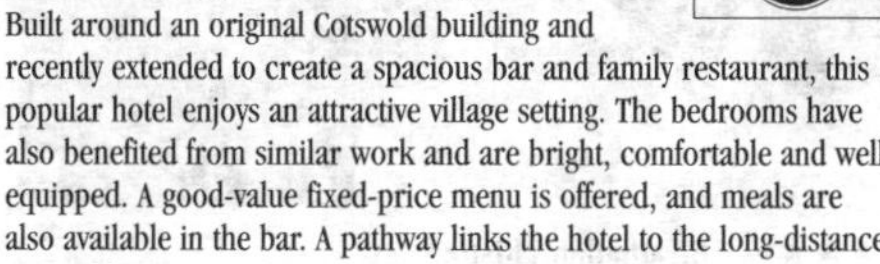

Built around an original Cotswold building and recently extended to create a spacious bar and family restaurant, this popular hotel enjoys an attractive village setting. The bedrooms have also benefited from similar work and are bright, comfortable and well equipped. A good-value fixed-price menu is offered, and meals are also available in the bar. A pathway links the hotel to the long-distance Cotswold Way.
34 en suite (bth/shr) (4 fmly) No smoking in 6 bedrooms CTV in all bedrooms STV No dogs (ex guide dogs) Night porter 120P Putting green Xmas English & Continental Cuisine V meals Coffee am Tea pm No smoking area in restaurant Last d 9.45pm
ROOMS: (incl. bkfst) s £59.50; d £75 * **LB**
OFF-PEAK: (incl. bkfst) s fr £30; d fr £50
MEALS: Sunday Lunch £5.50-£10.50 Dinner £12-£14.50&alc*
CONF: Thtr 100 Class 50 Board 40 Del £89
CARDS:

BIRKENHEAD Merseyside Map 07 SJ38

★★★ 68% **Bowler Hat**
2 Talbot Rd, Oxton L43 2HH (1m from junct 3 of M53)
☎ 0151 652 4931 FAX 0151 653 8127
This late Victorian house is situated in the pleasant residential area of Oxton, only a few minutes from junction 3 of the M53. Bedrooms have recently been refurbished to a good standard, and whilst those in the new wing are compact, those in the older part of the hotel are spacious and very comfortable. The restaurant - this year selected for a rosette award - offers a high standard of international cuisine in congenial surroundings; its four-course fixed-price menu is particularly good value. There are also facilities for weddings, conferences and all types of functions.
32 en suite (bth/shr) CTV in all bedrooms STV No dogs (ex guide dogs) Night porter 85P No coaches Wkly live entertainment Xmas International Cuisine V meals Coffee am Tea pm Last d 10pm
ROOMS: (incl. cont bkfst) s £67.50-£80.50; d £92.50-£127.50 **LB**
MEALS: Lunch £9.95-£12.95&alc High tea £10.95&alc
Dinner £17.95&alc*

contd.

CONF: Thtr 150 Class 80 Board 40 Del from £95
CARDS:

★★64% Riverhill
Talbot Rd, Oxton L43 2HJ (1m from M53 junct 3, along the A552 turn left onto B5151 at traffic lights hotel 0.5m on right)
☎ 0151 653 3773 FAX 0151 653 7162
The Riverhill Hotel is a Victorian house set in its own grounds at Oxton. The bedrooms, including two with four-posters, vary in shape and size but are well equipped with the business guest in mind. The popular restaurant offers a wide choice of interesting international dishes, and service is helpful and friendly.
16 en suite (bth/shr) (1 fmly) CTV in all bedrooms No dogs 30P No coaches English, French & Italian Cuisine V meals Last d 9.30pm
ROOMS: (incl. bkfst) s £39.95-£44; d £49-£65 *
OFF-PEAK: (incl. bkfst) s fr £29.95; d fr £39
MEALS: Lunch £9.95-£14.95&alc Dinner fr £14.95&alc*
CARDS:

BIRMINGHAM West Midlands Map 07 SP08
See also Great Barr, Bromsgrove, Lea Marston & Oldbury

★★★★★71% *Swallow*
12 Hagley Rd, Five Ways B16 8SJ ☎ 0121 452 1144
FAX 0121 456 3442

Still the best hotel in the city, the Swallow is ably run by general manager Brendan Carr. His dedicated team combine a genuine hospitality with stylish professionalism. An elegant marble lobby leads to a series of small but comfortable day rooms, and there is a choice of two dining options as well as 24-hour room service. Langtry's is the more informal eatery where chef de cuisine Jonathan Harrison specialises in modern British cuisine whilst the Sir Edward Elgar restaurant offers a fine dining experience, with a choice of imaginative menus, highly trained staff and a live pianist. Bedrooms are furnished and equipped to a high standard with restful colour schemes, quality extras and marble bathrooms.

98 en suite (bth/shr) No smoking in 54 bedrooms CTV in all bedrooms STV Lift Night porter Air conditioning 70P No coaches Indoor swimming pool (heated) Sauna Solarium Gym Hair & beauty salon Wkly live entertainment English & French Cuisine V meals Coffee am Tea pm Last d 10.30pm
CARDS:

★★★★66% Holiday Inn Crowne Plaza
Central Square B1 1HH ☎ 0121 631 2000
FAX 0121 643 9018

This hotel has been transformed by considerable refurbishment with bedrooms, delightful Conservatory Restaurant and Bar, and the facade all upgraded to a very high standard. Bedrooms are sizeable and comfortable and triple-glazed windows eliminate traffic noise from the busy city centre. There is a comprehensive leisure club as well as numerous conference and meeting rooms and the hotel offers special benefits to lady guests including an escort to the hotel car park.
284 en suite (bth/shr) (188 fmly) No smoking in 127 bedrooms CTV in all bedrooms STV Lift Night porter Air conditioning 50P Indoor swimming pool (heated) Sauna Solarium Gym Jacuzzi/spa Children's pool Beautician Xmas International Cuisine V meals Coffee am Tea pm No smoking area in restaurant Last d 10pm
ROOMS: s £108; d £118 * **LB**
OFF-PEAK: d fr £94
MEALS: Lunch £13.50-£14.95 Dinner fr £18.50
CONF: Thtr 150 Class 75 Board 40 Del from £145
CARDS:

★★★★64% The Copthorne Birmingham
Paradise Circus B3 3HJ ☎ 0121 200 2727
FAX 0121 200 1197
A stylish modern hotel at the heart of the city centre offers facilities which include a good conference and business centre, an attractive swimming pool and a supervised gym. Highly trained staff are very efficient, though not effusive, and Goldsmiths Restaurant has a menu to suit all tastes, featuring popular options like fish and chips, prawn Szechuan, lamb cobbler, baked salmon with crab mousse and 'the All American Dream Beefburger'. All dishes are competently prepared from fresh ingredients.
212 en suite (bth/shr) No smoking in 108 bedrooms CTV in all bedrooms STV No dogs (ex guide dogs) Lift Night porter 88P Indoor swimming pool (heated) Sauna Gym Jacuzzi/spa Xmas International Cuisine V meals Coffee am Tea pm No smoking area in restaurant Last d 11pm
ROOMS: s £110-£130; d £120-£140 **LB**
MEALS: Sunday Lunch £10.95-£25&alc Dinner £14.25-£25&alc*
CONF: Thtr 180 Class 120 Board 30 Del from £135
CARDS:

★★★★58% Strathallan Thistle
225 Hagley Rd, Edgbaston B16 9RY (on A456)
☎ 0121 455 9777 FAX 0121 454 9432
Prominently positioned on the A456 just outside the city centre, this modern commercially-biased hotel has an attractive and comfortable lobby area, and a popular bar and restaurant. Although the bedrooms are slowly being upgraded they are the weak area at present; arranged in circles, they are consequently wedged-shaped and compact. Bathrooms are equally limited in size and can be functional; the Club rooms are better. However in all other areas, particularly housekeeping, there are sound standards.
167 en suite (bth/shr) (1 fmly) No smoking in 55 bedrooms CTV in all bedrooms STV Lift Night porter 200P Pool table V meals Coffee am Tea pm No smoking in restaurant Last d 10pm
ROOMS: s £83-£95; d £93-£105 * **LB**
OFF-PEAK: (incl. bkfst) s fr £37.50; d fr £64
MEALS: Lunch £11.75-£25.50alc High tea fr £7.25alc Dinner £11.75-£25.50alc*
CONF: Thtr 170 Class 100 Board 50 Del from £72
CARDS:

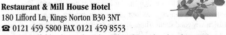

★★★77% Lombard Room Restaurant & Mill House Hotel
180 Lifford Ln, Kings Norton B30 3NT
☎ 0121 459 5800 FAX 0121 459 8553

Set in peaceful landscaped gardens, this elegant hotel and restaurant was once a paper mill and now provides excellent accommodation together with delightful food. Chef Anthony Morgan offers an interesting menu with both English and continental dishes being served with great care and flair. Pre dinner drinks are served in the spacious conservatory whilst the restaurant provides an elegant setting for Anthony's excellent cooking which is also backed by a well chosen wine list. The bedrooms, all of which are found in a separate building,

have been carefully designed and have been thoughtfully equipped and include fresh fruit, flowers and every conceivable extra. Guests can expect very attentive service which is both very friendly and delightfully professional.
10 annexe en suite (bth/shr) No smoking in 5 bedrooms CTV in all bedrooms No dogs (ex guide dogs) 40P No coaches Indoor swimming pool (heated) Jacuzzi/spa English & French Cuisine V meals Coffee am Tea pm No smoking in restaurant Last d 9.30pm
ROOMS: (incl. bkfst) s £85; d £95 * **LB**
MEALS: Lunch £15 Dinner £19.50*
CONF: Thtr 120 Class 50 Board 50 Del from £138
CARDS:

★★★69% **Westley**
80-90 Westley Rd, Acocks Green B27 7UJ (4m N of junct 4 on M42) ☎ 0121 706 4312
FAX 0121 706 2824

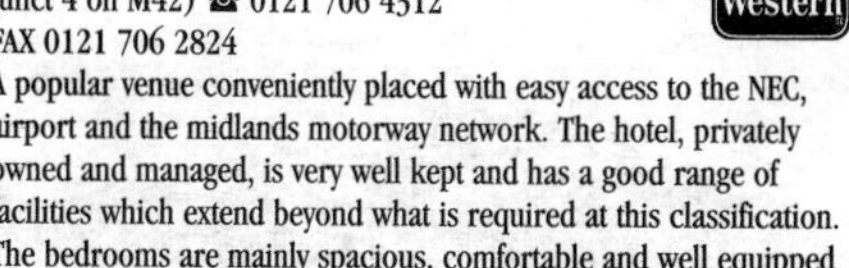

A popular venue conveniently placed with easy access to the NEC, airport and the midlands motorway network. The hotel, privately owned and managed, is very well kept and has a good range of facilities which extend beyond what is required at this classification. The bedrooms are mainly spacious, comfortable and well equipped with bold colour co-ordinated schemes. The public areas include a popular and convivial bar and brasserie as well the Seasons Carvery where both the carvery and the carte menus have a broad popular appeal. It is a most friendly hotel.
27 en suite (bth/shr) 9 annexe en suite (bth/shr) (1 fmly) CTV in 37 bedrooms STV Night porter 150P Wkly live entertainment English & French Cuisine V meals Coffee am Tea pm No smoking area in restaurant Last d 10pm
ROOMS: (incl. bkfst) s £74.50; d £84.50
OFF-PEAK: s fr £37.50; d fr £37.50
MEALS: Lunch £10.95-£16.95 Dinner £12.95&alc*
CONF: Thtr 250 Class 100 Board 100 Del from £85
CARDS:

★★★67% ***Birmingham Grand Moat House***
Colmore Row B3 2DA (opposite cathedral)
☎ 0121 236 7951 FAX 0121 233 1465
Closed 18-30 Dec
An elegant Victorian building with a colonnaded entrance, stands in the centre of the city opposite the Cathedral. Most of the bedrooms have now been upgraded to a very good modern standard to match the fine public rooms. There are two restaurants, "Chamberlain's" and the popular "Carvery at the Grand", and a further eating option downstairs in the club like atmosphere of "Colmores Bar". The banqueting and conference facilities feature an impressive ballroom with stone arched pillars, a musicians' gallery and a splendidly ornate ceiling.
173 en suite (bth/shr) (4 fmly) No smoking in 70 bedrooms CTV in all bedrooms Lift Night porter P English & French Cuisine V meals Coffee am Tea pm Last d 10.15pm
CARDS:

★★★67% **Westmead**
Redditch Rd, Hopwood B48 7AL (on A441, 1.5m from junct 2 of M42) ☎ 0121 445 1202
FAX 0121 445 6163
Situated to the south of Birmingham, the Westmead is conveniently placed for driving to the NEC. Bedrooms are modern and comfortably furnished and eating options include light meals in the bar or dining in the Colonial Restaurant.
58 en suite (bth/shr) (2 fmly) No smoking in 28 bedrooms CTV in all bedrooms STV No dogs (ex guide dogs) Night porter 155P Sauna Solarium International Cuisine V meals Coffee am No smoking area in restaurant Last d 10pm

ROOMS: s £75; d £75 * **LB**
OFF-PEAK: s £39; d £39
MEALS: Lunch £10.65-£19.15alc Dinner £10.65-£19.15alc*
CONF: Thtr 240 Class 120 Board 80 Del £95
CARDS:

★★★66% **Plough & Harrow**
135 Hagley Rd, Edgbaston B16 8LS
☎ 0121 454 4111 FAX 0121 454 1868
An inn has stood on the site of this hotel since 1612, and the older parts of the building (which date from the reign of Queen Anne) still portray the grand style of a more elegant era. Public rooms include a stylish lounge bar and restaurant. In complete contrast is the new wing where most of the modern bedrooms are housed. There are a small garden and a car park, and the hotel is only a few minutes' walk from the city centre.
44 en suite (bth/shr) No smoking in 9 bedrooms CTV in all bedrooms Lift Night porter 80P Xmas V meals Coffee am Tea pm No smoking in restaurant Last d 10pm
ROOMS: s £75; d £75 **LB**
OFF-PEAK: s £51; d £51
MEALS: Lunch £12.25&alc High tea fr £7.95 Dinner £16.95&alc
CONF: Thtr 70 Class 35 Board 30 Del from £110
CARDS:

★★★64% **Royal Angus Thistle**
St Chads, Queensway B4 6HY ☎ 0121 236 4211
FAX 0121 233 2195
Conveniently located beside the Inner Ring Road, this hotel has direct access into a large NCP car park at the second floor level. It is at this floor that spacious public areas can be found. We are pleased to report that the bedroom refurbishment is well in hand and those completed boast commendable standards in comfort in addition to a good range of equipment. Conferences can be catered for with a useful range of meeting rooms.
133 en suite (bth/shr) (4 fmly) No smoking in 30 bedrooms CTV in all bedrooms STV Lift Night porter Xmas English & French Cuisine V meals Coffee am Tea pm No smoking area in restaurant
Last d 10pmpm

contd.

ROOMS: s £83-£93; d £93-£103 * **LB**
OFF-PEAK: (incl. bkfst) s fr £50; d fr £60
MEALS: Lunch fr £11.95 Dinner fr £17.95*
CONF: Thtr 150 Class 80 Board 30
CARDS:

★★★63% **Novotel**

70 Broad St B1 2HT ☎ 0121 643 2000
FAX 0121 643 9796
A modern hotel is situated close to the city centre and offers value for money accommodation. Each functional bedroom has a double bed and sofa bed and the WC is conveniently separate from the bathroom. Other features include remotely controlled television with satellite, tea and coffee making facilities and an extended day and night room service menu.
148 en suite (bth/shr) (148 fmly) No smoking in 25 bedrooms CTV in all bedrooms STV Lift Air conditioning 57P Sauna Gym Jacuzzi/spa International Cuisine V meals Coffee am Tea pm Last d mdnt
ROOMS: s fr £73; d fr £83 * **LB**
OFF-PEAK: d fr £57
CONF: Thtr 250 Class 100 Board 100
CARDS:

★★★61% **Great Barr Hotel & Conference Centre**
Pear Tree Dr, Newton Rd B43 6HS BIRMINGHAM ☎ 0121 357 1141
FAX 0121 357 7557
(For full entry see Barr, Great)

★★★59% **Portland**
313 Hagley Rd, Edgbaston B16 9LQ (2m from city centre on A456)
☎ 0121 455 0535 FAX 0121 456 1841
This purpose-built red brick hotel stands on the A456 west of the city centre. Well equipped accommodation, ample car parking and a homely atmosphere make it popular, especially with business users.
63 en suite (bth/shr) No smoking in 7 bedrooms CTV in all bedrooms STV No dogs (ex guide dogs) Lift Night porter 80P English & French Cuisine V meals Tea pm No smoking area in restaurant Last d 9.45pm
ROOMS: (incl. bkfst) s £34.95-£49.95; d £52.50-£65 * **LB**
OFF-PEAK: (incl. bkfst) s £27.50-£36.95; d £42-£45
MEALS: Lunch £9.95-£13.95 Dinner £11.95-£13.95&alc
CONF: Thtr 100 Class 50 Board 50 Del from £61.95
CARDS:

★★71% **Oxford Hotel**

21 Oxford Rd B13 9EH (junct 3 M42, 3m S of Birmingham A435) ☎ 0121 449 3298
FAX 0121 442 4212
This character Victorian house, neatly set back within a quiet residential area, has been sympathetically restored and provides high standards of modern accommodation with relaxed and congenial public areas. Bedrooms tend to vary in size but all are well equipped and boast little extra personal touches to add to the guests' comfort. One of the strengths is the high level of hospitality and natural friendliness from Ann Molloy and her equally keen small team of staff.
15 en suite (bth/shr) 9 annexe en suite (bth/shr) (5 fmly) No smoking in 7 bedrooms CTV in all bedrooms STV Air conditioning 60P Snooker Pool table Xmas V meals Coffee am Tea pm No smoking in restaurant Last d 9.30pm
ROOMS: (incl. bkfst) s fr £79; d fr £89 **LB**
OFF-PEAK: (incl. bkfst) s fr £59; d fr £69
MEALS: Lunch £3.50-£10.50 High tea £2.95-£5.95
Dinner £3.95-£18.95
CONF: Thtr 70 Class 70 Board 40 Del from £99
CARDS:

★★70% **Copperfield House**

60 Upland Rd, Selly Park B29 7JS (off A441 at junct of Selly Park Rd and Upland Road)
☎ 0121 472 8344 FAX 0121 415 5655
This popular and immaculately maintained red brick mid-Victorian house stands in a pleasant residential area of Selly Oak just off the Pershore road. The en suite bedrooms, some of which have been refurbished to a very high standard, vary in size but are all comfortable and attractively furnished. Public areas include a traditionally furnished lounge and an attractive restaurant offering a small choice of interesting, carefully prepared dishes.
17 en suite (bth/shr) (2 fmly) CTV in all bedrooms 11P No coaches Xmas European Cuisine V meals Coffee am Tea pm Last d 8.30pm
ROOMS: (incl. bkfst) s £51-£61; d £61-£71 **LB**
OFF-PEAK: (incl. bkfst) s £41-£51; d £51-£61
CARDS:

★★68% **Robin Hood**

Stratford Rd, Hall Green B28 9ES (from junct 4 of M42 take A34 towards B'Ham city centre at island with traffic lights 4th exit Shirley Road 1st left into car park) ☎ 0121 745 9900 FAX 0121 733 1075
Situated beside the A34 at Hall Green, five miles from the centre of the city, this hotel provides a comfortable standard of accommodation. Well equipped bedrooms are contained in a modern purpose-built block while the various bars and attractive restaurant are housed in a former Victorian residence. The hotel also offers a smart new conference suite and extensive car parking.
30 en suite (bth/shr) No smoking in 16 bedrooms CTV in all bedrooms STV Night porter 200P Wkly live entertainment International Cuisine V meals Coffee am No smoking area in restaurant Last d 10pm
ROOMS: (incl. bkfst) s fr £59.95; d fr £69.95 * **LB**
OFF-PEAK: (incl. bkfst) s fr £31; d fr £53
CONF: Thtr 35 Class 35 Board 35 Del from £74
CARDS:

★★67% **Norwood**
87-89 Bunbury Rd, Northfield B31 2ET (turn left on A38 at Grosvenor shopping centre, 5m S of city centre) ☎ 0121 411 2202
FAX 0121 411 2202
This family owned and run hotel in found in a leafy suburb of Birmingham to the south of the city. Service is very friendly and natural with the Wall family being very much involved in the day to day running of the hotel. There is a lounge bar, and the bedrooms, which vary in size and shape, are all well equipped. The house is delightfully furnished and there is a collection of Beryl Cook prints around the walls. A good range of food is provided in the attractive restaurant which overlooks the garden.
18 en suite (bth/shr) CTV in all bedrooms STV 11P English & French Cuisine V meals Last d 8.30pm
ROOMS: (incl. bkfst) s £57.50-£65.75; d £65-£75 * **LB**
OFF-PEAK: (incl. bkfst) s £30-£40; d £45-£50
MEALS: Dinner £16.50

CONF: Thtr 40 Class 24 Board 20
CARDS:

★★65% **The Chamberlain**
Alcester St B12 0PJ ☎ 0121 606 9000 FAX 0121 606 9001
Situated in the Highgate area, a short distance from the actual city centre, this newly opened hotel originated in the 19th century as a charitable hostel. Now a Grade II listed building, it offers purpose-built bedrooms and comfortable public areas which include an attractive lobby, above-average conference and banqueting facilities and a self-service cafeteria. Service is simple, but the range of amenities available is that normally associated with a higher star rating.
250 en suite (bth/shr) No smoking in all bedrooms CTV in all bedrooms STV No dogs (ex guide dogs) Lift Night porter 200P English Cuisine V meals Coffee am Tea pm No smoking area in restaurant
ROOMS: (incl. bkfst) s £35; d £40
CONF: Thtr 400 Class 200 Board 112 Del from £49
CARDS:

★★65% **Westbourne Lodge**
27/29 Fountain Rd, Edgbaston B17 8NJ (off A456)
☎ 0121 429 1003 FAX 0121 429 7436
An attractive black and white gabled exterior distinguishes this well kept and very hospitable family-run hotel. Furnishings and facilities are regularly updated in line with its business guests' preferences. The restaurant includes a small bar where tasty home-cooked meals are served from either the set menu or the bar meal selection. Patio doors open onto a colourful terrace for summer use.
18 en suite (bth/shr) (4 fmly) No smoking in all bedrooms CTV in all bedrooms 12P English, French & Italian Cuisine V meals Coffee am Tea pm No smoking area in restaurant Last d 8.30pm
ROOMS: (incl. bkfst) s £45; d £55 * **LB**
OFF-PEAK: (incl. bkfst) s fr £35; d fr £45
MEALS: Lunch £10-£14.95 High tea fr £4 Dinner fr £14.95*
CARDS:

★★64% **Bearwood Court**
360-366 Bearwood Rd, Bearwood B66 4ET (on A4030)
☎ 0121 429 9731 FAX 0121 429 6175
RS Xmas Day
Located directly adjacent to the main road, with good access to the city, this family run hotel has been recently upgraded. Bedrooms tend to vary in size; some are quite compact but all are spotlessly clean and well equipped. Homely public rooms and an informal style of service promotes a welcoming atmosphere.
24 rms (17 bth/shr) (3 fmly) CTV in all bedrooms 22P No coaches ch fac V meals Coffee am Tea pm No smoking in restaurant
ROOMS: (incl. bkfst) s £25-£28; d £42-£48 *
CONF: Thtr 60 Class 40 Board 20
CARDS:

★★64% ***Hagley Court***
229 Hagley Rd, Edgbaston B16 9RP (on A456)
☎ 0121 454 6514 FAX 0121 456 2722
Closed Xmas-1 Jan
This impressive building, with its Regency facade, is conveniently situated just outside the city centre. Under the personal supervision of the resident proprietor, warm hospitality is the essence of this small, friendly hotel. Bedrooms, though some are compact, are clean, comfortable and well equipped.
27 en suite (bth/shr) (1 fmly) CTV in all bedrooms STV No dogs (ex guide dogs) Night porter 28P No coaches English & Continental Cuisine Coffee am Tea pm Last d 9.30pm
CARDS:

★★62% **Hotel Ibis**
Ladywell Walk B5 4ST ☎ 0121 622 6010
FAX 0121 622 6020
This modern hotel is situated within the Chinese quarter and forms part of the Acardian centre. The budget bedrooms are bright, all have en-suite showers, while the inviting public areas include a piano bar, lobby lounge and open plan restaurant set around a central fountain and atrium. There is also a good range of modern meeting rooms. The hotel does not have its own parking, but there is a multi story car park nearby and New Street Station in only five minutes' walk way.
159 en suite (bth/shr) No smoking in 40 bedrooms CTV in all bedrooms STV Lift Wkly live entertainment V meals Coffee am Tea pm No smoking area in restaurant
ROOMS: s £44-£46; d £44-£46 *
CONF: Thtr 140 Class 65 Board 60 Del from £70
CARDS:

★★61% ***Edgbaston Palace***
198 Hagley Rd B16 9PQ ☎ 0121 452 1577 FAX 0121 452 1577
Closed 24-26 Dec
A fine Georgian house and the former residence of the proprietor Mr Taylor, this hotel has grown steadily over the years, and the new wing of courtyard bedrooms is now open. The restaurant is a particularly good venue for functions, especially in summer as it opens onto an attractive stone courtyard. The bar reflects the owner's interest in motor racing, old racing-car wheels forming the base of the coffee tables.
30 rms (29 bth/shr) (4 fmly) CTV in all bedrooms STV Night porter 53P ch fac Continental Cuisine V meals Coffee am Tea pm Last d 9.30pm
CARDS:

★★60% **Fountain Court**
339-343 Fountain Court Hotel B17 8NH (on A456)
☎ 0121 429 1754 FAX 0121 429 1209
This family-run hotel is convenient for the city centre and the International Convention Centre, as well as being only ten minutes from the M5. Bedrooms are all en suite, and are attractively furnished. Public areas include a comfortable reception lounge, a bar, and a bright and spacious restaurant which serves a short set-price menu.
25 en suite (bth/shr) (4 fmly) CTV in all bedrooms 20P V meals Last d 8.30pm
CARDS:

★★54% **Sheriden House**
82 Handsworth Wood Rd, Handsworth Wood B20 2PL (on B4124)
☎ 0121 554 2185 & 0121 523 5960 FAX 0121 551 4761
Situated in a quiet suburb of the city, Sheriden House runs under the personal supervision of the resident proprietors. There is a well tended courtyard garden to the rear, whilst, inside, bedrooms are clean and brightly decorated. A choice of dishes is offered for dinner in the dining room.
11 rms (10 bth/shr) CTV in all bedrooms Night porter 30P English & French Cuisine V meals Coffee am Tea pm Last d 8.45pm
ROOMS: (incl. bkfst) s £26-£39; d £38-£54 * **LB**
OFF-PEAK: (incl. bkfst) s £22-£30; d £32-£42
MEALS: Lunch £10.95-£13&alc Dinner £13&alc*
CONF: Thtr 40 Class 25 Board 20 Del from £40.75
CARDS:

See advertisement on opposite page

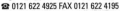

Campanile
55 Irving St B1 1DH (150yds from Dome Night Club, just off Bristol Street)
☎ 0121 622 4925 FAX 0121 622 4195
The bar and Bistro restaurant provide meals and refreshments. Bedrooms are well equipped and have en suite bathrooms. For more details about Campanile, consult the Contents page under Hotel Groups.
50 annexe en suite (bth/shr)
ROOMS: d fr £36.50 *
CONF: Thtr 35 Class 20 Board 20

Forte Posthouse Birmingham City

Smallbrook Queensway B5 4EW ☎ 0121 643 8171
FAX 0121 631 2528
Suitable for both the business and leisure traveller, this bright hotel provides modern accommodation in well equipped bedrooms with en suite bathrooms. For more details about Forte Posthouse hotels, consult the Contents page for the section on Hotel Groups.
251 en suite (bth/shr)
ROOMS: d £89-£99 *
CONF: Thtr 630 Class 380 Board 50 Del £119

Forte Posthouse Birmingham Great Barr
Chapel Ln B43 7BG ☎ 0121 357 7444
FAX 0121 357 7503
(For full entry see Barr, Great)

Travel Inn (Central)
20 Bridge St, Ladywood B1 2JH (follow signs for ICC, Bridge St is opposite ICC and Symphony Hall)
☎ 0121 633 4820 FAX 0121 633 4779
Purpose-built accommodation, offering spacious, well equipped bedrooms, all with en suite bathrooms. Meals may be taken at the nearby family restaurant. For more information about Travel Inns, consult the Contents page under Hotel Groups.
54 en suite (bth/shr)
ROOMS: d £35.50 *

Travel Inn (Central East)
Richard St, Waterlinks B7 4AA ☎ 0121 333 6484
FAX 0121 3336490
Purpose-built accommodation, offering spacious, well equipped bedrooms, all with en suite bathrooms. Meals may be taken at the nearby family restaurant. For more information about Travel Inns, consult the Contents page under Hotel Groups.
60 en suite (bth/shr)
ROOMS: (incl. bkfst) d £35.50 *

○ ***Burlington***
New St B2 4JH ☎ 0121 643 9191
112 rms

BIRMINGHAM AIRPORT West Midlands Map 07 SP18

★★★63% **Novotel**
B26 3QL (opp main passenger terminal)
☎ 0121 782 7000 FAX 0121 782 0445
Closed 25 Dec
This modern purpose-built hotel is directly opposite the main passenger terminal, linked with the monorail to the railway station and NEC. Accommodation is in the typical Novotel style; all the bedrooms are triple glazed, which mutes airport noise effectively. Public areas are modern and include a small bar and a grill-style restaurant which is open until midnight; light snacks and meals are available throughout the day. Whilst there is no hotel parking, guests can use the long-term NCP car park which provides a courtesy bus to and from the terminals.
195 en suite (bth/shr) No smoking in 130 bedrooms CTV in all bedrooms STV Lift Night porter Air conditioning Continental Cuisine V meals Coffee am Tea pm No smoking area in restaurant Last d mdnt
ROOMS: d £80-£119 *
MEALS: Lunch £16-£19 Dinner £16-£19*
CONF: Thtr 35 Class 20 Board 22 Del from £85
CARDS:

Forte Posthouse Birmingham Airport
Coventry Rd B26 3QW (from junct 6 of M42 take A45 towards Birmingham for 1.5m)
☎ 0121 782 8141 FAX 0121 782 2476
Suitable for both the business and leisure traveller, this bright hotel provides modern accommodation in well equipped bedrooms with en suite bathrooms. For more details about Forte Posthouse hotels, consult the Contents page for the section on Hotel Groups.
136 en suite (bth/shr)
ROOMS: d £69 *
CONF: Thtr 130 Class 100 Board 70 Del from £99

B

BIRMINGHAM (NATIONAL EXHIBITION CENTRE)
West Midlands Map 07 SP18

★★★ 74% **Nailcote Hall**
Nailcote Ln, Berkswell CV7 7DE ☎ 01203 466174 FAX 01203 470720
(For full entry see Balsall Common)

★★★ 60% **Arden Hotel & Leisure Club**
Coventry Rd, Bickenhill B92 0EH (from junc 6 of M42 take A45 towards Birmingham, hotel 0.25m on right hand side, just off B'ham Airport Island) ☎ 01675 443221 FAX 01675 443221
A successful family-run hotel, the Arden is constantly being updated to meet the demands of today's market, particularly business from the adjacent NEC. It offers a coffee shop, terraced water gardens, some eleven conference rooms and a leisure centre with a good sized pool.
146 en suite (bth/shr) (6 fmly) CTV in all bedrooms STV Lift Night porter 300P Indoor swimming pool (heated) Snooker Sauna Solarium Gym Jacuzzi/spa Wkly live entertainment French & Italian Cuisine V meals Coffee am Tea pm No smoking area in restaurant Last d 10pm
ROOMS: s £55-£69; d £66-£79 * **LB**
OFF-PEAK: (incl. bkfst) s £55; d £66
MEALS: Lunch £14&alc High tea £2.50 Dinner £14&alc*
CONF: Thtr 220 Class 60 Board 40 Del from £123
CARDS:
See advertisement under SOLIHULL

★★ 72% **Haigs**
Kenilworth Rd CV7 7EL BIRMINGHAM (NATIONAL EXHIBITION CENTRE) ☎ 01676 533004 FAX 01676 535132
(For full entry see Balsall Common)

BISHOP AUCKLAND Co Durham Map 08 NZ22

★★★64% ***Park Head***
New Coundon DL14 8QT (1m N on A688) ☎ 01388 661727
FAX 01388 661727
Park Head Hotel is a pleasant Victorian building with an extension of spacious bedrooms around a courtyard to the rear. All bedrooms are well equipped and the public rooms offer two dining styles together with a traditional bar. A good range of food is available at value for money prices and service is friendly and attentive. Excellent security car parking is provided.
8 en suite (bth/shr) 7 annexe en suite (bth) (3 fmly) CTV in all bedrooms Night porter 96P ch fac English, French & Italian Cuisine V meals Coffee am Tea pm Last d 9.45pm
CARDS:

★★61% **The Postchaise**
36 Market Pl DL14 7NX (follow signs for Bishop Auckland then for town centre/market place, hotel opposite town hall)
☎ 01388 661296 & 606312 FAX 01388 606312
An ancient town centre hostelry offering value for money with a lively atmosphere and a good range of bar meals.
12 en suite (bth/shr) CTV in all bedrooms No dogs (ex guide dogs) Night porter V meals Coffee am No smoking area in restaurant Last d 9pm
ROOMS: (incl. bkfst) s £29-£33; d £40-£45 *
MEALS: Sunday Lunch £5.95-£6.95 Dinner £3.10-£6.95&alc*
CONF: Board 30
CARDS:

BISHOP'S STORTFORD Hertfordshire Map 05 TL42

★★★★69% **Down Hall Country House**
Hatfield Heath CM22 7AS (leave B183 at Hatfield Heath, 5 miles turn right) ☎ 01279 731441 FAX 01279 730416
Set in 100 acres of parkland and landscaped gardens, this fine Victorian mansion provides elegantly furnished public rooms that are in keeping with the Italiante architecture; the spacious main lounge is a splendid example, combining modern day comforts with magnificent chandeliers and an ornate stone fireplace. Bedrooms come in two distinct styles, the new wing of bedrooms being comfortably proportioned and furnished with antique-style inlaid mahogany furniture, whereas the main house bedrooms are more individually appointed, with good use of bold colour schemes and comfortable seating. The hotel is particularly well geared to conferences and functions.
103 en suite (bth/shr) CTV in all bedrooms STV Lift Night porter 150P Indoor swimming pool (heated) Tennis (hard) Snooker Sauna Gym Croquet lawn Putting green Jacuzzi/spa Petanque Giant chess Whirlpool Xmas International Cuisine V meals Coffee am Tea pm Last d 9.45pm
ROOMS: s £90-£107; d fr £120 * **LB**
MEALS: Lunch £16.50&alc High tea £3-£20.10 Dinner £19.95&alc*
CONF: Thtr 290 Class 154 Board 84 Del from £130
CARDS:

BLACKBURN Lancashire Map 07 SD62
See also Langho

★★★59% **Blackburn Moat House**
Preston New Rd BB2 7BE (on A667/A6119 junct W of town) ☎ 01254 899988 FAX 01254 682435

Recent upgrading of public areas and many of the well equipped bedrooms has considerably enhanced this hotel, which is situated just west of the town at the junction of the A667 and A6119 roads. A unique feature of the hotel is its highly gabled banqueting suite situated on the first floor, adjoining other conference and meeting rooms. The business market is its main consideration during the week, but leisure guests will also find the hotel conveniently placed for visiting nearby tourist areas.
98 en suite (bth/shr) (2 fmly) No smoking in 50 bedrooms CTV in all bedrooms Lift Night porter 150P Pool table Xmas International Cuisine V meals Coffee am Tea pm No smoking area in restaurant Last d 10pm
ROOMS: d £69 * **LB**
OFF-PEAK: (incl. bkfst) s £45; d £33
CONF: Thtr 350 Class 150 Board 100 Del £99
CARDS:

★★74% **Millstone**
Church Ln, Mellor BB2 7JR (3m NW off A59)
☎ 01254 813333 FAX 01254 812628
This attractive, stone-built coaching inn is located at the crossroads in the quiet village of Mellor. The bar is the focal point of the building, where good food and cheer are served in equal measure. The cooking in the elegant restaurant shows an uncomplicated and caring approach to food, with tasty meals being produced. The bedrooms are furnished to a very high standard using good quality materials; the majority are in the main building but there are now some in a newly converted neighbouring building.
18 en suite (bth/shr) 6 annexe en suite (bth/shr) (1 fmly) No smoking in 4 bedrooms CTV in all bedrooms STV 40P No coaches Xmas V meals Coffee am Tea pm Last d 9.45pm
ROOMS: (incl. bkfst) s £73-£83; d £92-£102 * **LB**
OFF-PEAK: (incl. bkfst & dinner) d fr £84
MEALS: Lunch fr £12.95 Dinner fr £20alc*
CONF: Thtr 25 Class 15 Board 16 Del from £90
CARDS:

BLACKPOOL Lancashire Map 07 SD33

★★★★59% **De Vere**
East Park Dr FY3 8LL ☎ 01253 838866
FAX 01253 798800
Situated close to the zoo, this purpose built hotel offers the best leisure facilities in town. A championship golf course, driving range, state-of-the-art gym, 21-metre swimming pool and both tennis and squash courts will impress sporting enthusiasts. Refreshments are served in a choice of four bars, and meals are available in the restaurant or the comfort of your room.
166 en suite (bth/shr) (11 fmly) No smoking in 95 bedrooms CTV in all bedrooms STV Lift Night porter 500P Indoor swimming pool (heated) Golf 18 Tennis (hard) Squash Snooker Sauna Solarium Gym Pool table Jacuzzi/spa Aerobic studio Beauty room Xmas V meals Coffee am Tea pm No smoking in restaurant Last d 10pm
ROOMS: (incl. bkfst) s fr £95; d fr £105 * **LB**
MEALS: Lunch fr £11.95 Dinner fr £17.95
CONF: Thtr 600 Class 310 Board 30 Del from £135
CARDS:

★★★63% **Savoy**
Queens Promenade, North Shore FY2 9SJ ☎ 01253 352561
FAX 01253 500735
This large, popular hotel overlooks the North Promenade and offers generally smart, well equipped accommodation, including suites and family rooms which are constantly being upgraded and many have the most marvellous sea views. The characterful public areas include a busy restaurant, plentiful lounge areas and extensive conference and banqueting facilities.
131 en suite (bth/shr) (14 fmly) CTV in all bedrooms Lift Night porter 40P Xmas International Cuisine V meals Coffee am Tea pm No smoking area in restaurant Last d 9.30pm

ROOMS: (incl. bkfst) s £40-£75; d £80-£110 * **LB**
OFF-PEAK: (incl. bkfst) s £35-£45; d £70-£90
CARDS:

See advertisement on this page

★★★58% **Clifton**
Talbot Square FY1 1ND (from Blackpool town centre head towards the North Pier, hotel opposite) ☎ 01253 21481 FAX 01253 27345
This large Grade 1 listed Victorian hotel is well positioned near the north pier and tower, close to the town centre. It offers comfortable bedrooms including two newly refurbished suites which vary in size but are attractively decorated and well equipped. Extensive public areas include a choice of bars, a residents lounge with magnificent views and an ornately decorated restaurant which offers a good range of popular dishes.
77 en suite (bth/shr) (2 fmly) CTV in all bedrooms Lift Night porter Xmas English, French, Italian, Indian & Mexican Cuisine V meals Coffee am Tea pm No smoking area in restaurant Last d 9pm
ROOMS: (incl. bkfst) s £65; d £95 * **LB**
OFF-PEAK: (incl. bkfst) s £25-£65; d £50-£95
MEALS: Lunch £1.65-£8.95 High tea £5.95 Dinner £11.95
CONF: Thtr 200 Class 50 Board 40 Del from £55
CARDS:

★★70% **Brabyns**
Shaftesbury Av, North Shore FY2 9QQ
☎ 01253 354263 FAX 01253 352915

MINOTEL Great Britain

The hospitality of the Tibble family and their staff is a great strength at this small, traditionally run hotel. Quietly situated adjacent to The Promenade on the North Shore, the hotel offers a comfortably furnished lounge, with a bar and a panelled restaurant, where a good range of home-cooked dishes are served. Bedrooms, which vary in size, are all attractively decorated and thoughtfully equipped and include a number of rooms on the ground floor.
22 en suite (bth/shr) 3 annexe en suite (bth/shr) (10 fmly) CTV in all bedrooms STV 12P Xmas V meals Coffee am Tea pm No smoking area in restaurant Last d 7.30pm
ROOMS: (incl. bkfst) s £30-£35; d £50-£60 * **LB**
OFF-PEAK: (incl. bkfst) s £20-£25; d £40-£50
MEALS: Lunch £6.50-£7.50 Dinner £11-£12*
CARDS:

★★67% **Headlands**
611-613 South Prom FY4 1NJ (hotel at junc of promenade & Harrowside) ☎ 01253 341179 FAX 01253 342047
Closed 2-13 Jan
This popular family-run hotel stands on the promenade, just south of the Pleasure Beach. Bedrooms vary considerably in both size and shape, ranging from large family units to small doubles which are usually let for single occupancy; all of them have dark wooden furniture, modern facilities and an en suite bath or shower room. An attractively wood-panelled restaurant is the setting for out-of-season theme weekends featuring all the countries of Europe. Lounge and bar facilities are good, there is regular live entertainment, and the games room offers both table tennis and snooker. As well as a private car park, the hotel provides a number of lock-up garages.
43 en suite (bth/shr) (11 fmly) CTV in all bedrooms Lift 48P Snooker Solarium Pool table Wkly live entertainment Xmas V meals Coffee am Tea pm No smoking in restaurant Last d 8.30pm
ROOMS: (incl. bkfst) s £28.65-£37.45; d £57.30-£66.30 **LB**
OFF-PEAK: (incl. bkfst) s fr £25.30; d fr £50.60
MEALS: Lunch £6.50-£9.50 Dinner £12.50-£13.50*
CONF: Thtr 70 Class 70
CARDS:

B

★★66% Warwick
603-609 New South Promenade FY4 1NG (from M55 junct 4 take A5230 for South Shore then rt on A584, Promenade South)
☎ 01253 342192 FAX 01253 405776
The hotel is conveniently situated on the south shore, at the quieter end of the promenade overlooking the sea. The redecorated en suite bedrooms are comfortable and reasonably well equipped. Extensive public areas include a comfortable lounge, a large restaurant serving a good range of popular dishes and a public bar providing live entertainment in the evening. The hotel also has a newly refurbished swimming pool and solarium.
50 en suite (bth/shr) (11 fmly) CTV in all bedrooms Lift Night porter 30P Indoor swimming pool (heated) Solarium Pool table Table tennis Wkly live entertainment Xmas International Cuisine V meals Coffee am Tea pm No smoking area in restaurant Last d 8.30pm
ROOMS: (incl. bkfst) s £40-£46; d £68-£78 * **LB**
OFF-PEAK: (incl. bkfst) s £37-£39.50; d £74-£79
MEALS: Bar Lunch £3-£7alc Dinner £12.75-£15.25alc
CONF: Thtr 50 Class 24 Board 30 Del from £48
CARDS:

★★65% *Ruskin*
55-61 Albert Rd FY1 4PW (leaving the M55 at end, proceed N along Golden Mile, turn inland at Chapel St, bear left at the traffic lights, follow the road onto Albert Road) ☎ 01253 24063 FAX 01253 23571
Ideally situated in the centre of town, close to the Promenade and the Tower this very popular hotel, with its cheerful staff, offers bright, neatly furnished accommodation. The modern and very striking open-plan public areas, include a number of comfortable lounge areas, a bar and restaurant, where a daily changing fixed price menu is offered. Entertainment is regularly provided, guests also have the use of a games room and the hotel has a number of well equipped conference and banqueting suites.
72 en suite (bth/shr) (14 fmly) CTV in all bedrooms Lift Night porter 16P Pool table English, Chinese, French & Italian Cuisine V meals Coffee am Tea pm Last d 8.30pm
CARDS:

★★65% *Hotel Sheraton*
54-62 Queens Promenade FY2 9RP (1m N from Blackpool Tower on promenade towards Fleetwood) ☎ 01253 352723 FAX 01253 595499
Families enjoy the facilities of this large seafront hotel; these include a swimming pool and games room, evening entertainment, and for those who would prefer a little peace, a comfortable 'quiet' lounge. Bedrooms, all of which are en suite, vary in size, are comfortably furnished, have smart modern bathrooms, and some have been redecorated with attractive colour co-ordinated decor. A daily changing table d'hÙte menu offers a choice of dishes, some of them home-made, which are served in the spacious dining room.
119 en suite (bth/shr) (37 fmly) CTV in all bedrooms No dogs Lift Night porter 20P Indoor swimming pool (heated) Sauna Solarium Pool table Table tennis Darts V meals Coffee am Tea pm Last d 7.30pm
CARDS:

★★63% *Cliffs*
Queens Promenade FY2 9SG (on promenade, 1.5m N of Tower)
☎ 01253 595559 FAX 01253 500394
This large, privately owned and extremely popular hotel is ideally situated on Queens Promenade, north of the tower and within easy reach of the centre of town. The en suite bedrooms, including a number of spacious family rooms, vary in size and some have been redecorated more recently than others. Public areas offer an all day coffee shop, a smart newly redecorated restaurant, a well equipped leisure centre and a family room where children are entertained. The hotel also benefits from a number of conference and banqueting suites.
162 en suite (bth/shr) (28 fmly) CTV in all bedrooms No dogs (ex guide dogs) Lift Night porter 50P Indoor swimming pool (heated) Squash Snooker Sauna Solarium Gym Jacuzzi/spa English & French Cuisine V meals Coffee am Tea pm Last d 8.30pm
CARDS:

★★61% *Belgrave*
272 Queens Promenade FY2 9HD ☎ 01253 351570
Closed Jan RS Feb-Mar & Nov-Dec
Margaret and Barry Pike, the enthusiastic owners of this quietly situated hotel and their friendly team of staff, continue to make guests feel very welcome. Bedrooms include a family room and one or two rooms with four poster beds, and are all attractively decorated and well equipped. Public areas include a large lounge bar next to which is a dance floor, a smaller lounge and spacious restaurant where the four course daily changing menu proves excellent value.
33 en suite (shr) (7 fmly) CTV in all bedrooms STV No dogs Lift 16P Pool table V meals Coffee am Last d 7.15pm
CARDS:

★★61% *Revill's*
190-4 North Promenade FY1 1RJ ☎ 01253 25768
FAX 01253 24736
This much improved family-run hotel is well positioned on the North Promenade seafront, close to the North Pier and the town centre. The bedrooms vary in size and style, but most are en suite, and all are soundly decorated and comfortable. Spacious, attractive public areas include a choice of bars and the a newly redecorated non-smoking restaurant offering a small choice of well prepared dishes.
47 en suite (bth/shr) (10 fmly) CTV in all bedrooms No dogs Lift Night porter 23P Snooker V meals Coffee am Tea pm Last d 7.30pm
CARDS:

★★60% Claremont
270 North Prom FY1 1SA (0.5m N of Blackpool Tower)
☎ 01253 293122 FAX 01253 752409
This large hotel, which boasts a swimming pool and jacuzzi, is conveniently situated on the North Shore, within easy reach of The Tower and the town centre. The en suite bedrooms are bright and attractively decorated; some are in a wing, close to the main building. Extensive public areas include a spacious air-conditioned restaurant offering a choice of dishes, and a bar serving snacks. A good range of entertainment is also available and the hotel has an ample car park at the rear of the building.
143 en suite (bth/shr) 24 annexe en suite (bth) (51 fmly) CTV in all bedrooms STV No dogs (ex guide dogs) Lift Night porter 60P Indoor swimming pool (heated) Sauna Solarium Gym V meals Coffee am Tea pm No smoking area in restaurant
CONF: Thtr 280 Class 150 Board 150
CARDS:

★★56% Windsor & Westmorland
256-258 Queens Promenade, Bispham FY2 9HB ☎ 01253 354974
Free 0500 657807
This friendly family-run hotel situated by the promenade on the North Shore will be a popular venue for families. Accommodation standards are mixed, though the expected facilities are provided and improvements are on-going. At the time of our inspection early dinners were offered with a limited selection providing good value for money.
30 en suite (shr) (9 fmly) No smoking in 1 bedroom CTV in all bedrooms Lift 12P Xmas V meals Coffee am No smoking in restaurant
ROOMS: (incl. bkfst) s fr £25; d fr £50 * **LB**
CARDS:

★60% **Kimberley**
New South Promenade FY4 1NQ (off the Promenade)
☎ 01253 341184 FAX 01253 408737
Closed 3-15 Jan
Quietly situated in a crescent set back from the promenade, but within easy walking distance of the pleasure beach, this long established, privately owned hotel offers neat, soundly furnished accommodation. Guests can relax in the large sun lounge and enjoy a range of tasty dishes which is served by friendly staff in the restaurant.
54 rms (36 bth/shr) (8 fmly) CTV in all bedrooms Lift Night porter 26P No coaches Table tennis Darts Xmas English & Continental Cuisine Coffee am Tea pm Last d 0
ROOMS: (incl. bkfst) s £26.95-£31.25; d £49.50-£55.90 * **LB**
MEALS: Lunch fr £5.95 Dinner fr £11.50
CONF: Thtr 100 Class 70 Board 40
CARDS:

See advertisement on this page

Travel Inn

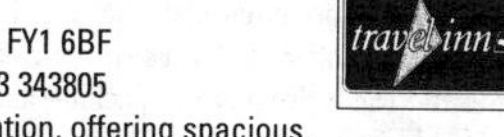

Yeadon Way, South Shore FY1 6BF
☎ 01253 341415 FAX 01253 343805
Purpose-built accommodation, offering spacious, well equipped bedrooms, all with en suite bathrooms. Meals may be taken at the nearby family restaurant. For more information about Travel Inns, consult the Contents page under Hotel Groups.
40 en suite (bth/shr)
ROOMS: (incl. bkfst) d £35.50 *

BLAKENEY Norfolk Map 09 TG04

★★★69% **The Blakeney**

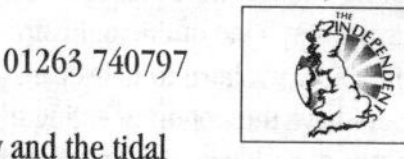

The Quay NR25 7NE (off A149) ☎ 01263 740797
FAX 01263 740795
Overlooking the National Trust quay and the tidal estuary, this privately owned hotel proves to be a popular yet peaceful retreat. Traditional services are professionally provided in spacious public areas; the restaurant provides well executed meals and the recently refurbished sun lounge offers really comfortable seating with delightful views over the salt marshes. New conference suites are likely to be popular with business guests during the quieter off-season months. The thoughtfully laid out bedrooms vary in size and styles and are graded and priced accordingly.
50 en suite (bth/shr) 10 annexe en suite (bth/shr) (4 fmly) CTV in all bedrooms Lift Night porter 60P No coaches Indoor swimming pool (heated) Snooker Sauna Gym Pool table Jacuzzi/spa Table tennis Xmas V meals Coffee am Tea pm No smoking in restaurant Last d 9.30pm
ROOMS: (incl. bkfst) s £48-£84; d £96-£168 * **LB**
MEALS: Lunch £5-£15alc High tea fr £4 Dinner fr £15*
CONF: Thtr 200 Class 70 Board 50 Del from £76
CARDS:

See advertisement on this page

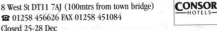

B

RED STAR HOTEL

★★❀❀ **Morston Hall**

Morston NR25 7AA (1m W of Blakeney on A149 Kings Lynn/Cromer Rd)
☎ 01263 741041 FAX 01263 740419
14 Feb-1 Jan
Morston Hall dates back to the 17th century and stands in a small coastal village and has delightful and well tended gardens. Hospitality and service is quite special here with the owners, Galton and Tracy Blackiston, being fully involved in the day to day running of the hotel. Lounges are a sheer delight to relax in and also includes a sunny conservatory whilst the elegant ding room is a perfect setting for Galton's excellent dinners. He provides a set price menu using only the best produce available and with presentation being a delight to the eye. An extensive wine list provides a wide choice. Morston Hall is located close to a small tidal quay and is an ideal base for exploring the wild and beautiful North Norfolk coast.
6 en suite (bth/shr) CTV in all bedrooms 40P No coaches Xmas V meals Coffee am Tea pm No smoking in restaurant Last d 8pm
ROOMS: (incl. bkfst & dinner) s £80-£120; d £140-£160 **LB**
MEALS: Sunday Lunch £15 Dinner £26
CARDS:

★★62% **Manor**
NR25 7ND (turn off A149 at St Mary's church)
☎ 01263 740376 FAX 01263 741116
Closed 4-23 Jan
The Manor is a well established hotel on the edge of the delightful village of Blakeney overlooking the saltings. Bedrooms are simply furnished, bathrooms are gradually being improved, and a good standard of housekeeping is maintained throughout. There are plenty of ground-floor rooms, spacious public rooms and a bowling green, making this an attractive venue for older guests.
8 en suite (bth/shr) 29 annexe en suite (bth/shr) (2 fmly) CTV in all bedrooms 60P Bowling green No children 14yrs Xmas English & Continental Cuisine V meals Coffee am Tea pm No smoking in restaurant Last d 9pm
ROOMS: (incl. bkfst) s £25-£33; d £56-£80 * **LB**
MEALS: Sunday Lunch fr £9.75alc Dinner fr £15.50&alc*

BLANCHLAND Northumberland Map 12 NY95

★★❀69% **Lord Crewe Arms**
DH8 9SP (10m S of Hexham via B6306) ☎ 01434 675251
FAX 01434 675337
This historic hotel dates from medieval times and is the focal point of an attractive conservation village. Bedrooms are split between the main house and a former estate building across the road; each is individual in style, but all combine modern comfort and a period feel. Public areas feature flagstone floors, original stonework and vaulted ceilings. The dining room overlooking the gardens is particularly impressive and serves a good variety of meat and vegetarian dishes.
10 en suite (bth/shr) 10 annexe en suite (bth/shr) (1 fmly) CTV in all bedrooms P Xmas V meals Coffee am Tea pm Last d 9.15pm
ROOMS: (incl. bkfst) s £75; d £110 * **LB**
MEALS: Sunday Lunch fr £14alc Dinner £26.50-£28alc
CONF: Thtr 30 Class 30 Board 24 Del from £75
CARDS:

BLANDFORD FORUM Dorset Map 03 ST80

★★★68% **Crown**

CONSORT HOTELS

8 West St DT11 7AJ (100mtrs from town bridge)
☎ 01258 456626 FAX 01258 451084
Closed 25-28 Dec
This attractive former coaching house is located in the centre of Blandford and offers an ideal setting for both business and leisure travellers. The bedrooms are spacious, attractively decorated and equipped to a good standard. There is a popular wood-panelled bar and restaurant, and a small comfortable lounge area. The smart self-contained function room is particularly well appointed for wedding receptions as well as conferences.
32 en suite (bth) (2 fmly) No smoking in 4 bedrooms CTV in all bedrooms STV 144P Fishing Shooting English & French Cuisine V meals Coffee am Tea pm Last d 9.15pm
ROOMS: (incl. bkfst) s fr £58; d fr £75 * **LB**
OFF-PEAK: (incl. bkfst) s fr £50; d fr £60
MEALS: Lunch £7.95-£13.75&alc Dinner £7.95-£13.75&alc*
CONF: Thtr 250 Class 200 Board 60 Del from £75
CARDS:

See advertisement on opposite page

BLOCKLEY Gloucestershire Map 04 SP13

★★★❀65% **Crown Inn**
High St GL56 9EX ☎ 01386 700245 FAX 01386 700247
This 16th-century former coaching inn has been sympathetically restored and extended by the Champion family, who have created a charming hotel in this pretty Cotswold village. Bedrooms feature quality pine furniture and fluffy bathrobes, setting the scene for a relaxing stay. One of the main strengths at the Crown is the friendly staff who work hard to deliver unaffected and considerate service. Diners have the option of eating in either the restaurant or the brasserie, both are presided over by chef Richard Smith whose imaginative modern cuisine is gaining recognition locally.
13 en suite (bth/shr) 8 annexe en suite (bth/shr) (2 fmly) CTV in all bedrooms 50P Wkly live entertainment Xmas English & Continental Cuisine V meals Coffee am Tea pm Last d 10pm
ROOMS: (incl. bkfst) s fr £60; d fr £84 * **LB**
MEALS: Lunch £7.95-£25alc Dinner £20-£30alc
CONF: Board 18 Del from £87.50
CARDS:

BLUNDELLSANDS Merseyside Map 07 SJ39

★★★64% **Blundellsands**
The Serpentine L23 6YB (from A565 to Liverpool turn left at College Rd (Merchant Taylors school) to roundabout. Turn left & take first right over bridge on to A6, Agnes Rd) ☎ 0151 924 6515
FAX 0151 931 5364
This friendly hotel, situated close to Crosby railway station, is a mixture of both modern and traditional styles and prides itself on its friendly service and a warm, comfortable atmosphere. The bedrooms, which vary in shape and size, are well appointed. The elegant Mauretania Restaurant, which resembles the famous liner's dining room, is the

most interesting of the public rooms which also include two bars, one serving light lunches and suppers. Extensive banqueting and conference suites and smaller meeting rooms are also a prominent feature of the hotel.
41 en suite (bth/shr) (3 fmly) No smoking in 5 bedrooms CTV in all bedrooms STV Lift Night porter 200P Wkly live entertainment English & French Cuisine V meals Coffee am Last d 9.30pm
ROOMS: (incl. bkfst) s fr £60.50; d fr £75 * **LB**
OFF-PEAK: (incl. bkfst) s fr £35; d fr £65
MEALS: Lunch £7.90-£9.90&alc Dinner £13.95-£14.25&alc*
CONF: Thtr 300 Class 200 Del from £79
CARDS:

BLYTH Nottinghamshire Map 08 SK68

★★★63% **Charnwood**
Sheffield Rd S81 8HF (A614 into Blyth village, turn right past church onto A634 Sheffield road. Hotel 0.5m on right past humpback bridge)
☎ 01909 591610 FAX 01909 591429
The Charnwood is an independently owned and managed hotel set in lovely landscaped gardens against a rural backdrop. The comfortably furnished coffee lounge leads into a large lounge-style bar and an attractively appointed restaurant both of which serve a comprehensive range of dishes and enjoy views of the garden. There are two distinct standards of accommodation and the superior one just that in every sense. 1996 should see the completion of a new wing of bedrooms.
34 en suite (bth/shr) (1 fmly) No smoking in 6 bedrooms CTV in all bedrooms STV No dogs (ex guide dogs) 70P Xmas English & French Cuisine V meals Coffee am Tea pm
ROOMS: (incl. bkfst) s £45-£55; d £70-£85 **LB**
OFF-PEAK: (incl. bkfst) s £35-£45; d £45-£50
CONF: Thtr 135 Class 60 Board 45 Del £72.50
CARDS:

Travelodge
Hilltop Roundabout S81 8HG (junct. A1M/A614)
☎ Central Res 0800 850950
This modern building offers accommodation in smart, spacious and well equipped bedrooms, suitable for family use, and all with en suite bathrooms. Meals may be taken at the nearby family restaurant. For information on room rates and to make a booking, call Roomline free of charge on 0800 850950. For more details about Travelodge, consult the Contents page under Hotel Groups.
39 en suite (bth/shr)

Travelodge

Travelodge
S81 8EL (on A1, southbound) ☎ 01909 591775
FAX 01909 591775
This modern building offers accommodation in smart, spacious and well equipped bedrooms, suitable for family use, and all with en suite bathrooms. Meals may be taken at the nearby family restaurant. For information on room rates and to make a booking, call Roomline free of charge on 0800 850950. For more details about Travelodge, consult the Contents page under Hotel Groups.
32 en suite (bth/shr)

Travelodge

BODMIN Cornwall & Isles of Scilly Map 02 SX06

★★63% **Westberry**
Rhind St PL31 2EL ☎ 01208 72772 FAX 01208 72212
Closed 5 days Xmas/New Year
A small family-run hotel, the Westberry is located near the town centre and offers soundly furnished accommodation. Spacious public areas include a sun lounge, bar and large dining room where a good selection of dishes is presented from the carte menu. An extensive range of bar meals is available at lunch time.

14 rms (6 bth 3 shr) 8 annexe en suite (bth/shr) (2 fmly) CTV in all bedrooms STV 30P Snooker Gym English Cuisine V meals Coffee am Tea pm
ROOMS: (incl. bkfst) s fr £25; d fr £50 * **LB**
CARDS:

BOGNOR REGIS West Sussex Map 04 SZ99

★★★64% **The Robin Hood**
Main Rd, Shripney PO22 9PA (on A29) ☎ 01243 822323
FAX 01243 841430
A very popular and well run free house c1780 with new and purpose-built good quality hotel accommodation. Bedrooms are spacious and all furnished to the same modern and co-ordinated standard. Other facilities include a new conservatory restaurant extension, a well appointed lively bar featuring a good range of real ales, a comfortable reception lobby lounge and separate breakfast room. The atmosphere is very convivial and friendly with attentive and competent service provided in the beamed restaurant, and well turned-out staff personally supervised by the proprietor Jim Lindsay.
24 en suite (bth/shr) (6 fmly) CTV in all bedrooms STV 80P V meals Coffee am Tea pm Last d 9pm
ROOMS: (incl. bkfst) s £37.50-£42.50; d £55-£65 * **LB**
CARDS:

★★★61% ***The Inglenook***
255 Pagham Rd, Nyetimber PO21 3QB ☎ 01243 262495 & 265411
FAX 01243 262668
A 16th century fully licensed free house cottage hotel wthe Inglenook has been skilfully extended to provide a range of bedrooms which vary in shape and size, some with four-poster beds and whirlpool baths. Whilst public rooms are compact they too have lots of old fashioned charm, and are furnished in the traditional style to retain the historic

contd.

atmosphere of the building. There is a cosy bar, a lounge and a double-sided restaurant, featuring real ale, log-burning fires and oak beams. Food includes local lobster and crab, an extensive range of bar meals, à la carte and fixed price menus. Other facilities are the function room which will accommodate up to 120 persons, an attractive garden and ample car parking.
18 en suite (bth/shr) (1 fmly) CTV in all bedrooms 35P V meals Coffee am Tea pm Last d 9.30pm
CARDS:

★★67% ***Black Mill House***

Princess Av, Aldwick PO21 2QU (at rbt junct with A259/A29 take Victoria Drive, signed Aldwick. At traffic lights turn rt into Aldwick Road)
☎ 01243 821945 & 865596 FAX 01243 821316
Quietly situated close to the sea, this 1930s hotel has been run by the Soothill family for many years and offers excellent value for money. Bedrooms are well equipped and furnished in modern style, while public areas include two lounges, a cosy bar and an attractive dining room offering a choice of menus together with bar meals and snacks. Room service is also available, and the Garden Room is a popular venue for local meetings and functions.
22 rms (18 bth/shr) 4 annexe rms (6 fmly) CTV in all bedrooms Lift 13P No coaches Putting green Table tennis ch fac English & French Cuisine V meals Coffee am Tea pm Last d 8.15pm
CARDS:

BOLDON Tyne & Wear Map 12 NZ36

★★★67% **Quality Friendly Hotel**

Witney Way NE35 9PE (junct A19/A184)
☎ 0191 519 1999 FAX 0191 519 0655
This modern hotel is conveniently situated in a business park, just off the A184, between Sunderland and Newcastle. The bedrooms are all very well equipped, and several have been designed for female guests who also have reserved parking spaces just outside the main entrance. There are also facilities for disabled persons. Conferences and business meetings are a feature of the hotel and there is also a small leisure centre which includes a swimming pool, sauna and solarium as well as a gymnasium.
82 en suite (bth/shr) (10 fmly) No smoking in 42 bedrooms CTV in all bedrooms STV Night porter 150P Indoor swimming pool (heated) Sauna Solarium Gym Xmas English & Continental Cuisine V meals Coffee am Tea pm No smoking area in restaurant Last d 9.30pm
ROOMS: s £67.50; d £87.50 **LB**
MEALS: Lunch £7.50-£9.95&alc Dinner £13.50&alc
CONF: Thtr 200 Class 100 Board 28 Del from £90
CARDS:

BOLTON Greater Manchester Map 07 SD70

★★★★64% **Georgian House**
Manchester Rd, Blackrod BL6 5RU (on A6, 1m from junct 6 of M61. Follow signs for Blackrod) ☎ 01942 814598 FAX 01942 813427
RS Xmas
The main restaurant is in the original Georgian house together with a very comfortable lounge and bar whilst most of the compact, but very well equipped bedrooms, are in more recent additions to the building at the side and rear. A popular hotel for all occasions the hotel has numerous banqueting and conference suites and also a very well equipped Sebastian Coe health club, complete with swimming pool and gymnasium.
100 en suite (bth/shr) (6 fmly) No smoking in 10 bedrooms CTV in all bedrooms STV Lift Night porter 250P No coaches Indoor swimming pool (heated) Snooker Sauna Solarium Gym Jacuzzi/spa Beauty therapy Steam room Hairdressers Wkly live entertainment English & French Cuisine V meals Coffee am Tea pm Last d 9.45pm
MEALS: Lunch £10-£12.90 High tea £1.50-£7 Dinner £14.50-£17.50&alc*
CONF: Thtr 300 Class 100 Board 40
CARDS:

★★★★63% **Bolton Moat House**

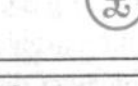

1 Higher Bridge St BL1 2EW (take A666, following signs for town centre north at 2nd set of traffic lights turn right, hotel on left) ☎ 01204 879988
FAX 01204 380777
An interesting feature of this large modern hotel, situated in the town centre, is its Cloisters Restaurant which was created from a church and still retains its stained glass windows and high arches. There is also the Bandstand Bar which provides a selection of hot and cold snacks. Bedrooms are all similarly furnished, in modern style and are particularly well equipped; several have been specially adapted for disabled persons.
128 en suite (bth/shr) (4 fmly) No smoking in 32 bedrooms CTV in all bedrooms STV No dogs (ex guide dogs) Lift Night porter 83P Indoor swimming pool (heated) Sauna Solarium Gym Jacuzzi/spa Wkly live entertainment English & Baltic Cuisine V meals Coffee am Tea pm No smoking area in restaurant Last d 10pm
ROOMS: s fr £89; d fr £105 * **LB**
MEALS: Lunch £10-£12.50&alc Dinner fr £15.50
CONF: Thtr 350 Class 120 Board 80 Del £105
CARDS:

★★★69% ***Last Drop***

The Last Drop Village, Hospital Rd, Bromley Cross BL7 9PZ (3m N off B6472) ☎ 01204 591131
FAX 01204 304122
The Last Drop Hotel is part of a village complex created from derelict 18th-century farm buildings located on a hillside three miles north of Bolton. The public areas are full of character, with a cobbled street, a carriage containing a public telephone, old farm implements and many other curiosities. Amenities include a pub, tea shop and baker,

together with comprehensive conference and banqueting facilities and an excellent leisure club. Some of the modern, well equipped bedrooms are located in various buildings around the village, and others are in the main hotel.

76 en suite (bth/shr) 7 annexe en suite (bth/shr) (27 fmly) No smoking in 32 bedrooms CTV in all bedrooms STV Night porter 400P Indoor swimming pool (heated) Squash Snooker Sauna Solarium Gym Pool table Jacuzzi/spa Craft shops & galleries Wkly live entertainment English & French Cuisine V meals Coffee am Tea pm Last d 9.45pm

CARDS:

★★★ 65% ***Egerton House***

Macdonald Hotels

Blackburn Rd, Egerton BL7 9PL (3m N A666)

☎ 01204 307171 FAX 01204 593030

This comfortable country house hotel is situated in 4 acres of mature grounds and gardens 3 miles north of Bolton and provides a relaxed and warm atmosphere in congenial surrounds. The bedrooms vary in shape and size, but all are very well equipped and comfortably furnished in keeping with the character of the house which is over 200 years old. A rosette has been awarded for the high standard of cuisine provided in the light and airy restaurant, which overlooks the gardens. Conferences and banquets can be catered for in the large Baronial hall, adjoining.

32 en suite (bth/shr) (8 fmly) No smoking in 14 bedrooms CTV in all bedrooms STV No dogs (ex guide dogs) Night porter 100P English & French Cuisine V meals Coffee am Tea pm

CARDS:

Forte Posthouse Bolton

Beaumont Rd BL3 4TA (on A58 W of town)

☎ 01204 651511 FAX 01204 61064

Suitable for both the business and leisure traveller, this bright hotel provides modern accommodation in well equipped bedrooms with en suite bathrooms. For more details about Forte Posthouse hotels, consult the Contents page for the section on Hotel Groups.

101 en suite (bth/shr)

ROOMS: s £69; d £45-£69 *

CONF: Thtr 130 Class 100 Board 50 Del from £60

BOLTON ABBEY North Yorkshire Map 07 SE05

RED STAR HOTEL

★★★ **Devonshire Arms Country House** BD23 6AJ (on B6160, 250yds N of junct with A59) ☎ 01756 710441 FAX 01756 710564

This fine hotel stands in beautiful grounds surrounded by Dales countryside, and is owned by the Duke of Devonshire. It provides every possible comfort for the discerning guest, meeting the needs of business people and tourists alike. Comfort and quality abound in the public rooms and a leisure centre is now provided for the more energetic. Every possible extra is supplied in the superbly furnished bedrooms including trouser presses, hairdryers, bathrobes and plenty of reading matter. Service and hospitality are quite special here and all staff are dedicated to ensuring that guests are well cared for throughout their stay. Quality cooking is provided in the elegant dining room, featuring local produce delightfully presented to the table.

41 en suite (bth/shr) No smoking in 12 bedrooms CTV in all bedrooms Night porter 150P Indoor swimming pool (heated) Tennis (hard) Fishing Sauna Solarium Gym Croquet lawn Putting green Jacuzzi/spa Clay pigeon shooting, Falconry Wkly live entertainment Xmas English & French Cuisine V meals Coffee am Tea pm No smoking area in restaurant Last d 10pm

ROOMS: (incl. bkfst) s £100-£110; d £140-£165 * **LB**

MEALS: Lunch £18.95-£21 Dinner £32.50-£35.50

CONF: Thtr 150 Class 80 Board 40 Del from £140

CARDS:

BONCHURCH See Wight, Isle of

BOREHAMWOOD Greater London Map 04 TQ19

★★★★ 65% **Elstree Moat House**

MOAT HOUSE

Barnet Bypass WD6 5PU (2m from junct 23 of M25)

☎ 0181 214 9988 FAX 0181 207 3194

The character and style of the public areas set the tone for this classification of hotel. Additionally there are two bars and several meeting rooms. Bedrooms are divided between two styles of décor but both types provide the same level of modern amenities which now include extra security measures.

130 en suite (bth/shr) (5 fmly) No smoking in 40 bedrooms CTV in all bedrooms STV No dogs (ex guide dogs) Lift Night porter 250P Indoor swimming pool (heated) Sauna Solarium Gym Pool table Jacuzzi/spa Steam room Beautician International Cuisine V meals Coffee am Tea pm No smoking area in restaurant Last d 9.45pm

ROOMS: s £98-£105; d £130-£140 *

MEALS: Lunch £12.95-£15&alc Dinner £16.90-£18.50&alc

CONF: Thtr 400 Class 100 Board 60 Del from £130

CARDS:

★★67% **Oaklands**
Studio Way WD6 5JY ☎ 0181 905 1455
FAX 0181 905 1370
This popular, good-value hotel is conveniently located approximately ten miles north of central London and only 25 minutes by train from Kings Cross. The well furnished bedrooms are equipped with every modern amenity; two bars are also available for guests' use. The Toby Grill features local Elstree cinematic and photographic memorabilia and offers a corporate grill menu and informal waitress service. Other facilities include function/meeting rooms and good car parking.
38 en suite (bth/shr) (1 fmly) No smoking in 13 bedrooms CTV in all bedrooms No dogs (ex guide dogs) Night porter 200P V meals Coffee am Last d 10.15pm
ROOMS: (incl. bkfst) s fr £72.50; d fr £82.50 **LB**
OFF-PEAK: (incl. bkfst) s fr £37.50; d fr £55
MEALS: Lunch £7.50-£19.15alc Dinner £10.25-£19.15alc
CONF: Thtr 35 Class 18 Board 20 Del from £77.50
CARDS:

BOROUGHBRIDGE North Yorkshire Map 08 SE36

★★★66% **Crown**
Horsefair YO5 9LB (0.5m from A1, at T junction in town centre) ☎ 01423 322328 FAX 01423 324512
Standing in the heart of the town, this historic hotel has been pleasantly furnished throughout with the public rooms being recently modernised. Several bedrooms retain the original character of the hotel whilst others are more modern, and all are well equipped. A good range of well produced food is available in the attractive restaurant and the hospitality is notable from a very attentive staff.
42 en suite (bth/shr) (2 fmly) CTV in all bedrooms Lift Night porter 60P Xmas International Cuisine V meals Coffee am Tea pm No smoking in restaurant Last d 9.30pm
ROOMS: (incl. bkfst) s £45-£47.25; d £69.95-£79.95 * **LB**
MEALS: Lunch £11.65-£13.85 High tea £1.25-£6.25 Dinner £17.95&alc
CONF: Thtr 200 Class 120 Board 120 Del from £65
CARDS:

See advertisement on opposite page

★★★65% **Rose Manor**
Horsefair YO5 9LL (on B6265) ☎ 01423 322245 FAX 01423 324920
This attractive country house-style hotel stands close to the town centre and provides generally spacious bedrooms all of which are well furnished and pleasantly decorated. There is a delightfully comfortable lounge, whilst the split-level restaurant offers a good range of well cooked dishes. There are extensive function facilities provided and service is friendly and professional.
17 en suite (bth/shr) (1 fmly) CTV in all bedrooms No dogs 100P V meals Coffee am Tea pm Last d 9pm
ROOMS: s fr £63; d £77-£82 * **LB**
MEALS: Lunch £9.50-£10.75 Dinner fr £17.50*
CONF: Thtr 250 Class 250 Board 25 Del from £95
CARDS:

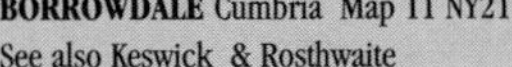

BORROWDALE Cumbria Map 11 NY21
See also Keswick & Rosthwaite

★★★ 74% **Borrowdale Gates Country House**
CA12 5UQ (from Keswick follow Borrowdale signs on B5289, after approx 4m turn right at sign for Grange, hotel is on right approx 0.25m through village) ☎ 017687 77204 FAX 017687 77254
Closed 3-26 Jan & 7-17 Dec
This family-run hotel sits in gardens surrounded by rugged fells in the beautiful Borrowdale valley. Inviting public rooms which include lounges complete with magazines and an open fire in cooler weather, a cosy bar and attractive restaurant, contribute to the comfortable and relaxing atmosphere, with all enjoying the splendid views. Staff are friendly and obliging, and this care also extends to the kitchen where the quality of the cooking is evident not only in the imaginative daily-changing dinner menu, but also in the home-baked afternoon teas and hearty breakfasts. Many of the bedrooms have been stylishly upgraded and a new wing will be in operation for 1997.
22 en suite (bth/shr) (2 fmly) CTV in all bedrooms No dogs (ex guide dogs) 35P No coaches ch fac Xmas English & French Cuisine V meals Coffee am Tea pm No smoking in restaurant Last d 8.45pm
ROOMS: (incl. bkfst & dinner) s £60-£75; d £110-£142.50 **LB**
OFF-PEAK: (incl. bkfst & dinner) s £52.50-£59.50; d £105-£120
MEALS: Lunch fr £7.50alc Dinner £24.50
CARDS:

★★★67% **Borrowdale**
CA12 5UY (on B5289 at south end of Lake Derwentwater)
☎ 017687 77224 FAX 017687 77338
This traditional tourist hotel lies in the spectacular Borrowdale valley some 15 minutes' drive south of Keswick. It features relaxing lounges and a spacious loung-bar leading to the gardens which provides an ideal setting for the comprehensive bar lunch menu. Dinner offers five-courses providing a mix of British and international dishes. Bedrooms vary in size but are all well equipped.
34 en suite (bth/shr) (8 fmly) CTV in all bedrooms 100P No coaches ch fac Xmas English & Continental Cuisine V meals Coffee am Tea pm No smoking area in restaurant Last d 9.15pm
ROOMS: (incl. bkfst & dinner) s £47-£53; d £84-£126 * **LB**
MEALS: Lunch £10.95&alc Dinner £13.50-£18.50
CONF: Class 30 Del from £79
CARDS:

BOSCASTLE Cornwall & Isles of Scilly Map 02 SX09

★★64% **The Wellington Hotel**
The Harbour PL35 0AQ ☎ 01840 250202
FAX 01840 250621
The 'Welly', as it is affectionately known, is steeped in history, parts dating back over 400 years. There is a choice of well equipped bedrooms, some of which are in the tower. French cuisine is accompanied by a wine list which includes several wines from the owner's vineyard (Madiran, in southwest France). Bar meals are also available. Ten acres of natural cliff and wooded hillside provide for enjoyable walks.

20 rms (10 bth 6 shr) CTV in all bedrooms 20P Pool table Games room Wkly live entertainment No children 7yrs Xmas English & French Cuisine V meals Coffee am No smoking area in restaurant Last d 9.30pm
ROOMS: (incl. bkfst) s £35; d £54-£60 * **LB**
OFF-PEAK: (incl. bkfst) s £14-£31; d £44-£56
MEALS: Bar Lunch £8.05-£13.25alc Dinner £16.95-£18.50*
CONF: Board 24 Del £65
CARDS:

BOSHAM West Sussex Map 04 SU80

★★★ 73% **The Millstream**
Bosham Ln PO18 8HL (4m W of Chichester on A259, turn left at Bosham roundabout, 1m turn right at T junction follow signs to church & quay hotel 0.5m on right) ☎ 01243 573234 FAX 01243 573459

This pretty, privately owned hotel and restaurant is situated in the peaceful village of Bosham, just a few miles from Chichester. The bedrooms are very comfortable and attractively decorated, each with an individual theme, and several now have impressive marbled bathrooms. Public rooms comprise a cocktail bar, elegantly furnished, spacious lounge overlooking the garden which has a stream running along the edge and the well appointed restaurant. Chef Bev Boakes offers a fixed price seasonal menu and interesting dishes which make good use of abundant local produce such as fresh fish, shellfish, game and poultry. An impressive list of wines contains an excellent range from around the world. Good service is provided from a competent and conscientious team of staff.

29 en suite (bth/shr) (2 fmly) CTV in all bedrooms Night porter 40P No coaches Sailing breaks, Bridge breaks Wkly live entertainment Xmas English & French Cuisine V meals Coffee am

contd.

Tea pm No smoking in restaurant Last d 9.30pm
ROOMS: (incl. bkfst) s fr £65; d fr £105 * **LB**
MEALS: Lunch £12.95-£15.95 Dinner fr £18.95*
CONF: Thtr 45 Class 20 Board 24 Del from £95
CARDS:

See advertisement under CHICHESTER

BOSTON Lincolnshire Map 08 TF34

★★★59% **New England**

49 Wide Bargate PE21 6SH (E side of town off John Adams Way) ☎ 01205 365255 FAX 01205 310597
A change of ownership and consequent upgrading has brought a new lease of life to this established market town hotel. The reception areas include an open-plan lounge popular with locals and visitors. Bedrooms are attractively co-ordinated and have been fitted with new bathroom suites.
25 en suite (bth/shr) (2 fmly) No smoking in 5 bedrooms CTV in all bedrooms Night porter Xmas V meals Coffee am Tea pm Last d 9.30pm
ROOMS: d £45-£49.50 * **LB**
OFF-PEAK: d £30-£35
MEALS: Lunch £8.95-£9.95 High tea £3.95 Dinner £12.50-£20alc
CONF: Thtr 40 Class 18 Board 25 Del from £60
CARDS:

★★66% **Comfort Friendly Inn**

Bicker Bar PE20 3AN (at junct of A17/A52)
☎ 01205 820118 FAX 01205 820228
A newly built hotel stands at the junction of the A52 and A17 at Bicker Bar, south of Boston. Well equipped modern bedrooms feature coordinated fabrics and attractive furnishings. Facilities include a small restaurant and bar and a mini-gym, and reasonably-priced meals are available all day. This is an ideal location for an overnight stay or as a base for those exploring the fen country and other parts of East Anglia.
55 en suite (bth/shr) (4 fmly) No smoking in 27 bedrooms CTV in all bedrooms STV Night porter Air conditioning 50P Gym Xmas English & Continental Cuisine V meals Coffee am Tea pm No smoking area in restaurant Last d 9.30pm
ROOMS: d £38.50-£49.50 **LB**
MEALS: Lunch £7.50-£9.75&alc Dinner £9.75&alc
CONF: Thtr 60 Class 20 Board 16 Del from £65
CARDS:

BOTLEY Hampshire Map 04 SU51

★★★★68% **Botley Park Hotel Golf & Country Club**

Macdonald Hotels

Winchester Rd, Boorley Green SO32 2UA (Boorley Green on B3354, approx 2m from village)
☎ 01489 780888 FAX 01489 789242
In 176 acres of landscaped parkland, yet near the M27, this modern hotel has, good-sized bedrooms (some suitable for disabled guests), comfortable lounges and choice of restaurants and bars. Services are promptly carried out by friendly staff. The hotel boasts an extensive range of sports and leisure facilities.
100 en suite (bth/shr) No smoking in 36 bedrooms CTV in all bedrooms STV Night porter 250P Indoor swimming pool (heated) Golf 18 Tennis (hard) Squash Snooker Sauna Solarium Gym Croquet lawn Jacuzzi/spa Aerobics studio Wkly live entertainment Xmas International Cuisine V meals Coffee am Tea pm No smoking in restaurant Last d 10pm
ROOMS: s £90; d £105 * **LB**
OFF-PEAK: (incl. bkfst & dinner) s £81; d £132
MEALS: Lunch £13.25 Dinner £21.95-£23.95&alc*
CONF: Thtr 240 Class 100 Board 60 Del from £130
CARDS:

BOURNE Lincolnshire Map 08 TF02

★★60% ***Angel***
Market Place PE10 9AE (in town centre) ☎ 01778 422346
FAX 01778 393990
Situated in the town centre, this traditional coaching inn provides a range of well equipped accommodation from spacious four-poster rooms to compact singles. The public bar is popular with the locals, and residents and diners have their own lounge bar, serving an attractive choice of bar food in addition to the carte and fixed-price menu in the dining room. Street parking to the front of the hotel is not advised; residents should follow signs to the free car park at the rear of the hotel.
14 en suite (bth/shr) (1 fmly) CTV in all bedrooms No dogs (ex guide dogs) English & French Cuisine V meals Coffee am Tea pm Last d 9.30pm
CARDS:

BOURNEMOUTH Dorset Map 04 SZ09
See also Christchurch & Poole

★★★★★62% **Royal Bath**

Bath Rd BH1 2EW ☎ 01202 555555
FAX 01202 554158
Surrounded by well tended gardens this large Victorian establishment enjoys fine views out to sea. Continued

refurbishment is improving the amenities at the hotel, which is a popular choice for conferences. Leisure guests are also well catered for with a health club housed in a pavilion in the grounds, spacious lounges and a choice of either the Garden Restaurant or the award winning Oscars. The latter provides an intimate setting and some imaginative menus which combine both classic and modern influences. Staff, particularly the porters, are friendly and courteous.
131 en suite (bth/shr) CTV in all bedrooms STV No dogs (ex guide dogs) Lift Night porter 70P Indoor swimming pool (heated) Sauna Solarium Gym Jacuzzi/spa Beauty salon Hairdressing Wkly live entertainment Xmas English & French Cuisine V meals Coffee am Tea pm No smoking area in restaurant Last d 10.15pm
ROOMS: (incl. bkfst) s £115-£290; d £140-£290 * **LB**
OFF-PEAK: (incl. bkfst & dinner) s £78-£150; d £156-£300
MEALS: Lunch fr £17&alc Dinner fr £23&alc
CONF: Thtr 450 Class 220 Board 100 Del from £100
CARDS:

★★★★69% **Norfolk Royale**
Richmond Hill BH2 6EN (from A338 follow signs 'Richmond Hill' and 'Town Square') (Leading CH) ☎ 01202 551521 FAX 01202 299729
This attractive Edwardian Hotel offers a good central location, just a few minutes walk from the town centre and gardens. The bedrooms are comfortable and smartly furnished, all with added comforts such as bathrobes, mini-bars and satellite TV. The public areas are extensive with a large open-plan lounge, a cosy cocktail bar and a conservatory restaurant. There is a small leisure area and a number of conference rooms. This year a new ballroom will reach completion.
95 en suite (bth/shr) (9 fmly) No smoking in 14 bedrooms CTV in all bedrooms STV No dogs (ex guide dogs) Lift Night porter 85P Indoor swimming pool (heated) Sauna Jacuzzi/spa Steamroom Whirlpool Xmas English & French Cuisine V meals Coffee am Tea pm No smoking area in restaurant Last d 10pm
ROOMS: (incl. bkfst) s £95-£110; d £130-£150 * **LB**
OFF-PEAK: (incl. bkfst) s £87.50-£97.50; d £135-£155
MEALS: Lunch £6.95-£10.95&alc Dinner £16.50-£19.50&alc*
CONF: Thtr 90 Class 45 Board 35 Del from £95
CARDS:

★★★★65% **Swallow Highcliff**
St Michaels Rd, West Cliff BH2 5DU
☎ 01202 557702 FAX 01202 292734

Boasting a commanding position on West Cliff, this hotel enjoys panoramic sea views. Since Swallow took over the management much of the hotel has been refurbished and a new leisure complex is now on line. Other facilities include extensive function and meeting rooms as well as a choice of restaurants. Bedrooms are comfortably appointed and thoughtfully equipped. A recent change of manager has seen improvements in service and staff attitudes.
107 en suite (bth/shr) 50 annexe en suite (bth/shr) (37 fmly) No smoking in 19 bedrooms CTV in all bedrooms STV Lift Night porter 130P Indoor swimming pool (heated) Outdoor swimming pool (heated) Tennis (hard) Snooker Sauna Solarium Gym Croquet lawn Putting green Jacuzzi/spa Badminton Golf driving net Xmas English & French Cuisine V meals Coffee am Tea pm No smoking in restaurant Last d 10pm
ROOMS: (incl. bkfst) s £82-£102; d £125-£145 * **LB**
MEALS: Lunch £9.75-£14.95 High tea £1.50-£10 Dinner £20-£25
CONF: Thtr 450 Class 180 Board 90 Del from £99.50
CARDS:

★★★71% **Chine**
Boscombe Spa Rd BH5 1AX ☎ 01202 396234 FAX 01202 391737
Tucked away in a peaceful corner of Boscombe this well run hotel is set in lovely gardens which stretch down to the chine below, and has enviable sea views. The bedrooms are spacious and comfortable, many

contd.

have balconies and all are well equipped and attractively decorated. The public areas are relaxed and have a friendly atmosphere. There is an elegant indoor pool and health suite, as well as the outdoor pool and a children's play area. This hotel is popular with both leisure and business guests and has extensive conference facilities. The restaurant has one of the best locations in the town and chef Paul Bingham provides an interesting range of skilfully prepared dishes.

86 en suite (bth/shr) (20 fmly) CTV in all bedrooms STV No dogs (ex guide dogs) Lift Night porter 54P Indoor swimming pool (heated) Outdoor swimming pool (heated) Sauna Solarium Putting green Games room Outdoor childrens play area ch fac Xmas English & French Cuisine V meals Coffee am Tea pm No smoking in restaurant Last d 8.30pm
ROOMS: (incl. bkfst) s £50-£61; d £90-£112 * **LB**
MEALS: Lunch £12.50 High tea £2.50-£17.50 Dinner £17.50*
CONF: Thtr 150 Class 50 Board 50 Del from £60
CARDS:

See advertisement on page 121

★★★ 70% **The Connaught**
West Hill Rd, West Cliff BH2 5PH (follow signs 'Town Centre West & BIC') ☎ 01202 298020
FAX 01202 298028
CONSORT HOTELS
This attractive modern hotel situated on the West Cliff is ideally located for the town centre and the beach. The extensive public areas include a bright conservatory bar and terrace, a ballroom with regular live entertainment, and a cosy lounge. The bedrooms are smartly decorated and well equipped, and many of them have balconies. Facilities include a leisure centre with a large pool, a sauna, steam-room and fitness suite, and there is also an outdoor pool.
60 en suite (bth/shr) (15 fmly) No smoking in 4 bedrooms CTV in all bedrooms STV Lift Night porter 45P Indoor swimming pool (heated) Outdoor swimming pool (heated) Snooker Sauna Solarium Gym Pool table Jacuzzi/spa Cardio-vascular suite Table tennis Wkly live entertainment Xmas English, French, Italian & Oriental Cuisine V meals Coffee am Tea pm No smoking area in restaurant Last d 9pm
ROOMS: (incl. bkfst) s £65-£95; d £110-£130 **LB**
OFF-PEAK: (incl. bkfst) s £49-£65; d £90-£110
MEALS: Lunch £9.25&alc High tea £2.20-£4.60 Dinner £15-£19.50&alc
CONF: Thtr 200 Class 70 Board 70 Del from £69
CARDS:

★★★ 70% **Elstead**
Knyveton Rd BH1 3QP ☎ 01202 293071 FAX 01202 293827
The Elstead is located in a quiet residential area on the East Cliff, and is being continually upgraded. Bedrooms have bright attractive decor and are well equipped; the public areas include a comfortable lounge and a smart bar. There is a smart new leisure suite comprising a large pool, fitness room with full range of cardio-vascular equipment, sauna and steam room. There are also several modern conference rooms
50 en suite (bth/shr) (4 fmly) No smoking in 5 bedrooms CTV in all bedrooms STV Lift Night porter 40P Indoor swimming pool (heated) Snooker Sauna Solarium Gym Pool table Jacuzzi/spa V meals Coffee am Tea pm No smoking in restaurant Last d 8.30pm
ROOMS: (incl. bkfst) s £34.50-£44.50; d £69-£75 * **LB**
MEALS: Lunch £7.95-£10.95 Dinner fr £12.50&alc
CONF: Thtr 80 Class 60 Board 40 Del from £69.50
CARDS:

See advertisement on opposite page

★★★ 69% **Hotel Courtlands**
16 Boscombe Spa Rd, East Cliff BH5 1BB
☎ 01202 302442 FAX 01202 309880
Best Western
This popular hotel is located close to Boscombe pier and the beach, and offers a friendly relaxed atmosphere. The bedrooms are attractively decorated and well equipped; and family rooms are available. Public rooms include two comfortable lounges overlooking the south-facing garden and swimming pool. The restaurant serves traditional meals and there is live music and dancing during the season. A leisure suite is provided with sauna, solarium and jacuzzi; and the outdoor pool has a paddling area.
60 en suite (bth/shr) (15 fmly) CTV in all bedrooms STV Lift Night porter 50P Outdoor swimming pool (heated) Sauna Solarium Pool table Jacuzzi/spa Free use of nearby Health Club Xmas English & French Cuisine V meals Coffee am Tea pm No smoking in restaurant Last d 8.30pm
ROOMS: (incl. bkfst) s £45-£47; d £80-£82 * **LB**
OFF-PEAK: (incl. bkfst) s £43; d £78
MEALS: Sunday Lunch fr £7.50 Dinner £17&alc*
CONF: Thtr 120 Class 85 Board 20 Del from £58
CARDS:

★★★ 69% **Piccadilly**
Bath Rd BH1 2NN (follow signs for 'Lansdowne')
☎ 01202 552559 FAX 01202 298235
This personally run hotel is situated a few minutes' walk from the seafront and town centre. It is especially popular for its ballroom dancing breaks for which many guests return regularly. The bedrooms have bright attractive decor and are well equipped. The smart public areas include a large open plan bar, a modern restaurant and a function room.
45 en suite (bth/shr) (2 fmly) CTV in all bedrooms STV No dogs (ex guide dogs) Lift Night porter 30P Ballroom dancing Xmas English & French Cuisine V meals Coffee am No smoking in restaurant Last d 8.30pm
ROOMS: (incl. bkfst) s £42-£52; d £64-£104 * **LB**
MEALS: Sunday Lunch fr £8.95alc Dinner fr £14.95alc*
CONF: Thtr 100 Class 50 Board 40 Del from £90
CARDS:

See advertisement on opposite page

★★★ 69% **Queens**
Meyrick Rd, East Cliff BH1 3DL ☎ 01202 554415 FAX 01202 294810
The Queens Hotel enjoys a good location on the East Cliff and attracts many conferences and groups. Bedrooms have bright attractive décor and modern bathrooms. The public areas are spacious and

comfortable. They include extensive conference facilities and The Queensbury Leisure Club, a smart leisure suite with an indoor pool and resident beauticians. Chef Will Summerell offers interesting menus.
114 en suite (bth/shr) (15 fmly) CTV in all bedrooms Lift Night porter 80P Indoor swimming pool (heated) Snooker Sauna Solarium Gym Pool table Jacuzzi/spa Beauty salon Games room Xmas English & French Cuisine V meals Coffee am Tea pm No smoking in restaurant Last d 8.30pm
ROOMS: (incl. bkfst) s £35-£52.50; d £70-£100 **LB**
OFF-PEAK: (incl. bkfst) s fr £30; d fr £60
MEALS: Lunch £8.25-£10.95 Dinner £16.95-£18.95
CONF: Thtr 220 Class 120 Board 50 Del from £55
CARDS:

See advertisement on page 125

★★★68% **Cadogan**
8 Poole Rd BH2 5QU (0.5m from spur road and by-pass. Follow signs B.I.C. from by-pass them right at rbt into Poole Road) ☎ 01202 763006 FAX 01202 766168
This popular family-owned hotel is located on the West Cliff, and provides a good base for visiting the town's attractions and the beach. The bedrooms are spacious and attractively decorated with modern en suite facilities. Public areas, although not extensive, are bright and comfortable with a relaxed friendly atmosphere. There is a daily set dinner menu and the value-for-money lunches attract a loyal local following.
54 en suite (bth/shr) (3 fmly) CTV in all bedrooms STV Lift Night porter 55P Wkly live entertainment Xmas English & French Cuisine V meals Coffee am Tea pm Last d 8.45pm
ROOMS: (incl. bkfst) s fr £46; d fr £85 **LB**
OFF-PEAK: (incl. bkfst) s fr £44; d fr £80
MEALS: Lunch fr £5.75 Dinner fr £13.50*
CONF: Thtr 70 Class 50 Board 35 Del from £50
CARDS:

★★★68% **East Anglia**
6 Poole Rd BH2 5QX (leave A338 at Bournemouth West rdbt, follow signs for B.I.C. and West Cliff, at next rdbt turn right into Poole Rd)
☎ 01202 765163 FAX 01202 752949
Closed 2-5 Jan
A well managed and privately owned hotel appealing to both the tourist and business person, the East Anglia lies on the west side of town with easy access to the town andmajor road links. It offers comfortable public areas and attractive bedrooms, the latter split between the main hotel and three adjacent buildings. The young, friendly staff provide attentive service.
47 en suite (bth/shr) 24 annexe en suite (bth/shr) (12 fmly) CTV in all bedrooms STV No dogs (ex guide dogs) Lift Night porter 70P Outdoor swimming pool (heated) Sauna Solarium Gym Pool table Jacuzzi/spa Xmas English & French Cuisine V meals Coffee am Tea pm No smoking in restaurant Last d 8.30pm
ROOMS: (incl. bkfst) s £42-£45; d £84-£90 * **LB**
MEALS: Sunday Lunch fr £9 Dinner fr £16
CONF: Thtr 150 Class 75 Board 60 Del from £65
CARDS:

★★★68% **Langtry Manor**
26 Derby Rd, East Cliff BH1 3QB ☎ 01202 553887 FAX 01202 290115

Langtry Manor brims over with history and is the perfect setting for a romantic break. Built in 1877 by Edward VII as a rendezvouz for his mistress Lillie Langtry, the house retains many of its original characteristics. The Edwardian theme is continued throughout the hotel with the staff dressing in costume and splendid weekend banquets. The bedrooms are individually furnished and several have four-poster beds; the Edward VII suite even has its own fireplace. The

contd.

B

high ceilinged dining hall has a minstrels' gallery, and the chef provides an interesting menu of fresh home prepared dishes.
14 en suite (bth/shr) 13 annexe en suite (bth/shr) (6 fmly) No smoking in 2 bedrooms CTV in all bedrooms 30P Xmas International Cuisine V meals Coffee am Tea pm No smoking in restaurant Last d 9pm
ROOMS: (incl. bkfst & dinner) s £59.75-£94.75; d £99.50-£179.50 * **LB**
MEALS: Bar Lunch £4-£9 High tea £5 Dinner £19.75&alc*
CONF: Thtr 100 Class 100 Board 50 Del from £75
CARDS:

★★★68% **Wessex**

Forestdale Hotels

West Cliff Rd BH2 5EU ☎ 01202 551911
FAX 01202 297354
Although the Wessex does not benefit from sea views, it has a convenient West Cliff location, good car parking and a superb leisure club. It is a popular choice for families in the summer, and it also makes a fine conference venue. Bedrooms are constantly being improved with attractive new decor, fabrics and additional modern facilities. The hotel has a relaxing atmosphere with a good range of services carried out by a friendly young team. The cooking of chef Wayne Fisher also continues to please with his more imaginative dishes which make good use of quality fresh produce.
85 en suite (bth/shr) (22 fmly) No smoking in 3 bedrooms CTV in all bedrooms STV Lift Night porter 250P Indoor swimming pool (heated) Outdoor swimming pool (heated) Snooker Sauna Solarium Gym Table tennis Xmas International Cuisine V meals Coffee am Tea pm No smoking area in restaurant Last d 9.15pm
ROOMS: (incl. bkfst) s £50-£65; d £85-£110 * **LB**
OFF-PEAK: (incl. bkfst & dinner) s £63.50-£78.50; d £112-£122
MEALS: Bar Lunch £3-£6 Dinner fr £14.95*
CONF: Thtr 400 Class 160 Board 160 Del from £85
CARDS:

★★★67% **Bay View Court**

35 East Overcliff Dr BH1 3AH ☎ 01202 294449 FAX 01202 292883
Located high on the East Cliff this family-run hotel enjoys beautiful views across the bay. The bedrooms vary in size but are attractive and well equipped. The lounges are comfortably furnished and south-facing, enjoying the benefits of the sun. There is also a heated indoor pool for guests' enjoyment.
64 en suite (bth/shr) (11 fmly) CTV in all bedrooms STV Lift Night porter 58P Indoor swimming pool (heated) Snooker Pool table Jacuzzi/spa Wkly live entertainment Xmas International Cuisine V meals Coffee am Tea pm No smoking in restaurant Last d 8.30pm
ROOMS: (incl. bkfst & dinner) s £39-£43; d £78-£86 * **LB**
MEALS: Lunch £6.50 High tea £1.50-£4.50alc Dinner £16*
CONF: Thtr 170 Class 85 Board 50 Del from £55
CARDS:

★★★67% **Cumberland**

East Overcliff Dr BH1 3AF ☎ 01202 290722 FAX 01202 311394
This popular hotel in a prime location on the East Cliff offers friendly, professional service. The well equipped bedrooms are attractively decorated and many have sea views and balconies. The public areas are spacious and comfortable, with a large lounge overlooking the outdoor pool and regular live entertainment. Guests also have use of the leisure club at the sister hotel, The Queens. The restaurant offers a daily-changing set menu, using fresh ingredients.
102 en suite (bth/shr) (12 fmly) CTV in all bedrooms Lift Night porter 65P Outdoor swimming pool (heated) Free use of pool etc at nearby hotel Wkly live entertainment Xmas British & Continental Cuisine V meals Coffee am Tea pm No smoking in restaurant Last d 8.30pm
ROOMS: (incl. bkfst) s £29.50-£47.50; d £59-£95 **LB**
MEALS: Lunch £6.95-£16.95 Dinner £13.95-£18.95
CONF: Thtr 120 Class 70 Board 45 Del from £49.50
CARDS:

See advertisement on opposite page

★★★67% **Hinton Firs**

Manor Rd, East Cliff BH1 3HB (from A338 turn west at St Paul's Rdbt across next 2 rdbts then immediately fork left to side of church, hotel on next corner)
☎ 01202 555409 FAX 01202 299607
This privately owned hotel offers a warm welcome and has a loyal returning clientele. It is located in a quiet residential area on the East Cliff and the hotel offers on-site parking, indoor and outdoor swimming pools and a health suite. The bedrooms vary in size but are well presented and attractively decorated. The public rooms are extensive with several comfortable lounges and a cosy bar.
46 en suite (bth/shr) 6 annexe en suite (bth) (12 fmly) CTV in all bedrooms No dogs Lift Night porter 40P No coaches Indoor swimming pool (heated) Outdoor swimming pool (heated) Sauna Pool table Jacuzzi/spa Games room Xmas English & French Cuisine V meals Coffee am Tea pm No smoking in restaurant Last d 8.30pm
ROOMS: (incl. bkfst & dinner) s £43-£51; d £68-£102 * **LB**
OFF-PEAK: (incl. bkfst & dinner) s £29.50-£39.50; d £59-£79
MEALS: Bar Lunch £2.50-£7.50 Dinner £13.25&alc*
CARDS:

See advertisement on opposite page

★★★66% **Hotel Collingwood**

11 Priory Rd, West Cliff BH2 5DF ☎ 01202 557575
This well run, privately owned hotel is ideally located for the BIC and the seafront. The bedrooms are being steadily upgraded and the public rooms are spacious, attractively presented and have a relaxing atmosphere. The hotel also has a good size swimming pool.
54 en suite (bth/shr) (16 fmly) CTV in all bedrooms STV Lift Night porter 55P Indoor swimming pool (heated) Snooker Sauna Solarium Gym Steam room Games room Xmas English & French Cuisine V meals Coffee am Tea pm No smoking in restaurant Last d 8.30pm
ROOMS: (incl. bkfst & dinner) s £47-£49; d £94-£98 **LB**
OFF-PEAK: (incl. bkfst) s £42-£44; d £84-£88
MEALS: Sunday Lunch fr £7.95 Dinner £16.95-£19.95
CARDS:

See advertisement on opposite page

★★★66% **Trouville**

Priory Rd BH2 5DH (close to International Centre) ☎ 01202 552262
FAX 01202 293324
The Deauville Restaurant is the formal dining room of the Trouville Hotel, a popular Bournemouth venue for conferences. Decorated in dark burgundy the room can appear dull and not at all cheery, despite the warm and friendly service provided by its bevy of knowledgeable and willing waiters. Diners eat early in Bournemouth so I was the only inhabitant by 8.30 pm one evening. The daily changing set menu

contd.

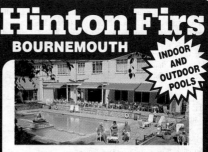

B

prepared by chef Alain Guyot is four courses for £15.95, and most visiting guests eat everything on offer. Menu choices try to please all tastes, with grills offered at an additional supplement. Desserts are offered buffet style and usually include at fresh fruit salad, a tart and several gateaux. The short wine list is predictable, with familiar wines not intended to intimidate infrequent imbibers. China is serviceable hotel ware. Unfortunately, despite advance notice of my arrival (their sister hotel had informed them of my intended visit), and presentation far exceeding the quality of ingredients on my plate, I feel the food here is not up to the standard required for entry into the Restaurant Guide. A visit to the kitchen revealed enormous containers of Knorr soup mix.
80 en suite (bth/shr) (21 fmly) CTV in all bedrooms Lift Night porter 60P Indoor swimming pool (heated) Sauna Solarium Gym Jacuzzi/spa Xmas English & French Cuisine V meals Coffee am Tea pm No smoking in restaurant Last d 8.30pm
ROOMS: (incl. bkfst & dinner) s £52-£57.50; d £104-£115 **LB**
MEALS: Lunch £8.25 High tea £5.75 Dinner £15.95&alc*
CONF: Thtr 100 Class 45 Board 50 Del from £55
CARDS:

See advertisement on page 125

★★★65% **Belvedere**
Bath Rd BH1 2EU ☎ 01202 297556 FAX 01202 294699
This family-run hotel which is located close to the centre of the town and the seafront offers bright spacious public areas and comfortable accommodation. There is a lively bar and the restaurant is very popular with locals for its good value meals. The bedrooms are steadily being upgraded and offer comfortable attractive accommodation, with modern facilities. There are some particularly spacious family rooms and some suitable for disabled guests.
62 en suite (bth/shr) (10 fmly) CTV in all bedrooms STV No dogs (ex guide dogs) Lift Night porter 55P Wkly live entertainment Xmas English & Continental Cuisine V meals Coffee am Tea pm Last d 9pm
ROOMS: (incl. bkfst) s £32-£46; d £72-£84 * **LB**
OFF-PEAK: (incl. bkfst) s £27-£32; d £50-£72
MEALS: Sunday Lunch fr £9.50 Dinner fr £12.50
CONF: Thtr 80 Class 30 Board 30 Del from £56
CARDS:

★★★65% **Marsham Court**
Russell Cotes Rd BH1 3AB ☎ 01202 552111 FAX 01202 294744
This well established privately owned hotel is located in an elevated position on the East Cliff and commands splendid views across the bay. The bedrooms, many with sea views, are spacious and the décor varies as they are being steadily upgraded with pretty bright colours. There is a comfortable lounge bar and the restaurant offers a daily changing menu.
86 en suite (bth/shr) (9 fmly) CTV in all bedrooms STV No dogs (ex guide dogs) Lift Night porter 100P Outdoor swimming pool (heated) Snooker Free swimming at BIC Xmas International Cuisine V meals Coffee am Tea pm Last d 9pm
ROOMS: (incl. bkfst & dinner) s £42-£52; d £64-£84 * **LB**
MEALS: Bar Lunch £6.50 High tea £5 Dinner fr £17
CONF: Thtr 200 Class 120 Board 80 Del from £65
CARDS:

See advertisement on opposite page

★★★65% **Pavilion**
22 Bath Rd BH1 2NS ☎ 01202 291266 FAX 01202 559264
This personally managed hotel is located in the town with easy access for the major routes, avoiding the centre. The bedrooms vary in size but are well equipped and attractively presented. The public areas are comfortable and have a relaxed atmosphere. The hotel has extensive function and conference facilities in a purpose built centre.
44 en suite (bth/shr) (6 fmly) CTV in all bedrooms Lift Night porter 40P Special rates for International Centre Wkly live entertainment Xmas English, French & Italian Cuisine V meals Coffee am Tea pm No smoking in restaurant Last d 8.30pm
ROOMS: (incl. bkfst & dinner) s £30-£40; d £60-£80 **LB**
OFF-PEAK: (incl. bkfst & dinner) s £25-£35; d £50-£70
MEALS: Lunch £7.50-£15 High tea £4.50-£6.50 Dinner £10-£14&alc*
CONF: Thtr 100 Class 50 Board 50 Del from £45
CARDS:

★★★65% **Suncliff**
29 East Overcliff Dr BH1 3AG ☎ 01202 291711 FAX 01202 293788
Located on the East Cliff, this large privately owned hotel offers glorious views. The bedrooms are bright and neatly furnished with modern facilities, and most have sea views. The public rooms are spacious and comfortably furnished, they include a conservatory and a TV room as well as a smart restaurant offering a set priced menu.
95 en suite (bth/shr) (29 fmly) CTV in all bedrooms Lift Night porter 60P Indoor swimming pool (heated) Squash Sauna Solarium Gym Pool table Jacuzzi/spa Table tennis Wkly live entertainment Xmas V meals Coffee am Tea pm No smoking area in restaurant Last d 8.45pm
ROOMS: (incl. bkfst & dinner) s £45-£57.50; d £90-£115 **LB**
OFF-PEAK: (incl. bkfst & dinner) s fr £39; d fr £78
MEALS: Sunday Lunch £6.25-£9.50alc Dinner £15-£20
CONF: Thtr 100 Class 70 Board 60 Del from £65
CARDS:

★★★64% **Anglo-Swiss**
16 Gervis Rd, East Cliff BH1 3EQ ☎ 01202 554794
FAX 01202 299615
Set amidst pine trees on the peaceful East Cliff, the Anglo Swiss hotel is just a short walk from the cliff top. The spacious bedrooms, some with balconies, are being continually upgraded and are bright and attractively decorated. Public areas are airy and relaxed, with a choice of lounges and 2 bars. There is a sauna and jacuzzi as well as exercise equipment for the energetic. The full size indoor pool opens onto the garden in the summer months.
57 en suite (bth/shr) 8 annexe en suite (bth/shr) (16 fmly) CTV in all bedrooms STV Lift Night porter 70P Indoor swimming pool (heated) Outdoor swimming pool (heated) Sauna Solarium Gym Pool table Jacuzzi/spa Wkly live entertainment ch fac Xmas French Cuisine V meals Coffee am Tea pm Last d 8.30pm
ROOMS: (incl. bkfst & dinner) s £55; d £110 **LB**
OFF-PEAK: (incl. bkfst & dinner) s £31-£55; d £62-£110
MEALS: Lunch £7 High tea £5 Dinner £15
CONF: Thtr 75 Class 30 Board 30 Del from £55
CARDS:

See advertisement on opposite page

★★★63% **Burley Court**
Bath Rd BH1 2NP ☎ 01202 552824 & 556704 FAX 01202 298514
Closed 2-10 Jan
This personally run hotel is very popular and many guests return regularly. The public areas are bright and airy and have a friendly atmosphere. Bedroom upgrading continues and most rooms are now

freshly decorated with quality furnishings. The remaining rooms are comfortable but more traditional in style. A daily changing menu is offered in the dining room, and in fine weather guests can enjoy the outdoor pool.
38 en suite (bth/shr) (8 fmly) No smoking in 8 bedrooms CTV in all bedrooms Lift Night porter 35P Outdoor swimming pool (heated) Solarium Pool table Free use of local indoor leisure pool Xmas English & French Cuisine Coffee am Tea pm No smoking in restaurant Last d 8.30pm
ROOMS: (incl. bkfst) s £29-£45; d £58-£78 **LB**
OFF-PEAK: (incl. bkfst) s fr £23; d £50-£78
MEALS: Lunch £7-£8.50 Dinner £13-£14.50
CARDS:

★★★63% Durley Hall
Durley Chine Rd, West Cliff BH2 5JS ☎ 01202 751000
FAX 01202 757585
Situated on the West Cliff this busy hotel continues to improve: the bedrooms vary in size but are well equipped. There is a smart leisure centre with a fitness room and solarium. The conservatory coffee shop serves snacks throughout the day, and there is a formal dining room for dinner.
70 en suite (bth/shr) 11 annexe en suite (bth/shr) (27 fmly) CTV in all bedrooms STV No dogs (ex guide dogs) Lift Night porter 150P Indoor swimming pool (heated) Outdoor swimming pool (heated) Sauna Solarium Gym Pool table Jacuzzi/spa Beauty therapist, Hairdresser Wkly live entertainment Xmas English & Continental Cuisine V meals Coffee am Tea pm No smoking area in restaurant Last d 8.45pm
ROOMS: (incl. bkfst & dinner) s £50-£68; d £100-£136 * **LB**
MEALS: Sunday Lunch £7.95 High tea £5 Dinner £16.50&alc
CONF: Thtr 200 Class 80 Board 35 Del from £60
CARDS: 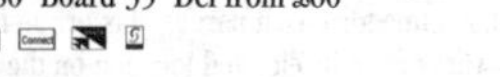

★★★63% Moat House
Knyveton Rd BH1 3QQ ☎ 01202 369988
FAX 01202 292221

MOAT HOUSE

Situated in a quiet tree-lined avenue, the Moat House attracts leisure business during the summer months and conference business at other times. Children are well catered for, with their own menu, a small leisure club and various activities during the season. Bedrooms vary from spacious, modern rooms to the very dated which are planned for refurbishment.
145 en suite (bth/shr) (20 fmly) No smoking in 20 bedrooms CTV in all bedrooms Lift Night porter 100P Indoor swimming pool (heated) Snooker Gym Pool table Putting green Table tennis, Indoor tennis, Playroom Xmas English & French Cuisine V meals Coffee am Tea pm No smoking area in restaurant
ROOMS: (incl. bkfst) s £37-£50; d £74-£100 * **LB**
OFF-PEAK: (incl. bkfst) s £35-£40; d £70-£90
MEALS: High tea fr £6 Dinner fr £16.95*
CONF: Thtr 1670 Class 811 Board 370
CARDS:

★★★62% Bournemouth Heathlands
12 Grove Rd, East Cliff BH1 3AY ☎ 01202 553336 FAX 01202 555937
This large popular hotel is located on the East Cliff a short walk from the sea, although it has an outdoor pool. The redecoration of the bedrooms continues, and the newly completed executive rooms are very smart. The public areas are spacious and attractive, and there is regular live entertainment. Also provided, is a full 'nanny' service for the children. The restaurant staff are young and friendly and a varied and interesting menu is offered. There is a fitness room with solarium and sauna.
114 en suite (bth/shr) (13 fmly) No smoking in 15 bedrooms CTV in all bedrooms STV Lift Night porter 80P Outdoor swimming pool (heated) Sauna Solarium Gym Jacuzzi/spa Health club Wkly live entertainment ch fac Xmas V meals Coffee am Tea pm

contd.

Last d 8.30pm
ROOMS: (incl. bkfst & dinner) s fr £44; d fr £88 * **LB**
OFF-PEAK: (incl. bkfst & dinner) s fr £35; d fr £70
MEALS: Lunch £6.50 Dinner £16.50*
CONF: Thtr 270 Class 102 Board 54 Del from £60
CARDS:

★★★62% Cliffeside
East Overcliff Dr BH1 3AQ ☎ 01202 555724 FAX 01202 555724
Positioned on the East Cliff this popular hotel owned by the Young family continues to improve. The bedrooms have all been upgraded and are bright and attractively decorated, many have marvellous sea views. The public areas are spacious and comfortable; the restaurant offers a set-price menu and overlooks the outdoor swimming pool.
62 en suite (bth/shr) (10 fmly) CTV in all bedrooms Lift Night porter 45P Outdoor swimming pool (heated) Pool table Table tennis Xmas English & French Cuisine V meals Coffee am Tea pm No smoking in restaurant Last d 8.30pm
ROOMS: (incl. bkfst) s £38.50-£48; d £77-£96 * **LB**
OFF-PEAK: (incl. bkfst & dinner) s £32.50-£39.50; d £65-£79
MEALS: Lunch £5.50-£10 High tea £3.50-£5 Dinner £17.95-£20*
CONF: Thtr 180 Class 140 Board 60 Del from £45
CARDS:
See advertisement on page 125

★★★62% Grosvenor
Bath Rd, East Cliff BH1 2EX ☎ 01202 558858 FAX 01202 298332
Ideally located close to the shops and only a short walk to the sea front this friendly and welcoming hotel offers a range of comfortable attractive bedrooms furnished in the modern style, most of which have recently been upgraded. There is a well furnished comfortable bar lounge, and a dinner dance is held in the pleasant restaurant every Saturday. Other facilities include a smart indoor leisure suite and a small games room.
40 en suite (bth/shr) (9 fmly) CTV in all bedrooms Lift Night porter 35P Indoor swimming pool (heated) Sauna Solarium Gym Wkly live entertainment Xmas French Cuisine V meals Coffee am Tea pm Last d 8.45pm
ROOMS: (incl. bkfst) s £32.50-£43.50; d £63-£87.50 * **LB**
MEALS: Lunch £5-£12 High tea £5.25-£7.50 Dinner £16
CONF: Class 40 Board 30
CARDS:

★★★61% Durlston Court
Gervis Rd, East Cliff BH1 3DD ☎ 01202 291488 FAX 01202 290335
Located on the East Cliff, The Durlston Court offers easy access to the town's attractions and beaches. The bedrooms are being steadily upgraded but are generally comfortable and spacious. The smartly refurbished public areas are bright and airy, the bar overlooks the pool and terrace, and there is a small health suite.
54 en suite (bth/shr) (16 fmly) CTV in all bedrooms STV Lift Night porter 50P Outdoor swimming pool (heated) Pool table Jacuzzi/spa Jacuzzi Wkly live entertainment Xmas English & French Cuisine V meals Coffee am Tea pm No smoking area in restaurant Last d 8.30pm
ROOMS: (incl. bkfst) s £45-£50; d £70-£80 * **LB**
MEALS: Bar Lunch £2.50-£6 Dinner £16.50
CONF: Thtr 100 Class 75 Board 50
CARDS:

★★★61% East Cliff Court
East Overcliff Dr BH1 3AN ☎ 01202 554545 FAX 01202 557456
The East Cliff Court is located on the cliff promenade and commands spectacular sea views. The public rooms are attractively decorated and comfortably furnished with French windows to the pool. The bedrooms are all smart and well equipped, most have now been upgraded and many have balconies. The restaurant provides an extensive buffet lunch and an evening set menu.
70 en suite (bth/shr) (10 fmly) CTV in all bedrooms STV Lift Night porter 100P Outdoor swimming pool (heated) Sauna Solarium Beauty salon Xmas English & French Cuisine V meals Coffee am Tea pm No smoking in restaurant Last d 8.45pm
ROOMS: (incl. bkfst & dinner) s £48-£57; d £96-£114 * **LB**
OFF-PEAK: (incl. bkfst & dinner) s £40-£50; d £80-£100
MEALS: Lunch £6.75-£7.95 High tea fr £5.25 Dinner fr £14.25*
CONF: Thtr 200 Class 80 Board 40 Del from £55
CARDS:

★★★59% New Durley Dean
Westcliff Rd BH2 5HE (off A338) ☎ 01202 557711
FAX 01202 292815
This popular and relaxing hotel offers a range of facilities and entertainments to suit all kinds of guest. The Green Room restaurant provides a short set-price menu with one or two supplementary dishes, while breakfast is a self-serve hot/cold buffet. Bedrooms vary in size but have modern furnishings and a good range of equipment.
112 en suite (bth/shr) (27 fmly) CTV in all bedrooms STV Lift Night porter 45P Indoor swimming pool (heated) Snooker Sauna Solarium Gym Jacuzzi/spa Table tennis Steam room Wkly live entertainment Xmas English & Continental Cuisine V meals Coffee am Tea pm No smoking in restaurant Last d 8.30pm
ROOMS: (incl. bkfst) s £49.50-£59; d £99-£118 * **LB**
OFF-PEAK: (incl. bkfst) s £24.75; d £49.50
MEALS: Sunday Lunch £4.95-£8.95 High tea fr £5.75 Dinner fr £14.90
CONF: Thtr 150 Class 70 Board 40 Del from £55
CARDS:

★★★58% Chesterwood
East Overcliff Dr BH1 3AR ☎ 01202 558057 FAX 01202 556285
A popular venue for coach parties, this privately-owned hotel enjoys fine sea views from its elevated location on the East Cliff. Bedrooms are slowly being upgraded and improved and some are particularly well proportioned, with the upper front-facing bedrooms having the best aspect overlooking the bay. Public rooms have been attractively furnished and decorated, with a comfortable bar lounge complemented by the Poole Drawing Room, spacious Hampshire Restaurant and entertainment function room. The furnished terrace overlooks an outdoor swimming pool and garden and there is ample car parking space.
47 en suite (bth/shr) 4 annexe en suite (bth) (13 fmly) CTV in all bedrooms No dogs (ex guide dogs) Lift Night porter 47P Outdoor swimming pool (heated) Wkly live entertainment ch fac Xmas V meals Coffee am Tea pm No smoking in restaurant
ROOMS: (incl. bkfst & dinner) s £37-£40; d £64-£80 * **LB**
CONF: Thtr 150 Class 100 Board 30
CARDS:

★★★58% Roundhouse
Lansdowne BH1 2PR (off A338) ☎ 01202 553262
FAX 01202 557698

REGAL
A Collection of Individual Hotels

This unusual building is circular in design with the first two floors forming useful car parking space. Bedrooms are comfortable and reasonably well equipped, but unfortunately the decor and furnishings are now rather tired and the public areas retain much of their original 1970s character.
98 en suite (bth/shr) (5 fmly) No smoking in 49 bedrooms CTV in all bedrooms Lift Night porter 86P Table tennis darts skittles Xmas V meals Coffee am Tea pm No smoking area in restaurant Last d 10pm
ROOMS: s £45-£55; d £53.50-£55 * **LB**
MEALS: Lunch £6.95-£8.95 High tea £2.50-£7.95alc Dinner £14.95-£15.95&alc*
CONF: Thtr 120 Class 50 Board 40 Del from £75
CARDS:

★★★55% **Embassy**
Meyrick Rd, East Cliff BH1 3DW ☎ 01202 290751 FAX 01202 557459
Situated on the east side of the town a short walk from the promenade, the Embassy is a popular venue for tours and conferences. The bedrooms are located in three buildings and vary in standard. There is a comfortable lounge bar and a small restaurant, also a large ballroom and an outdoor pool.
39 en suite (bth/shr) 33 annexe en suite (bth/shr) (12 fmly) CTV in all bedrooms STV Lift Night porter 75P Outdoor swimming pool (heated) Pool table Games room Xmas British & French Cuisine V meals Coffee am Tea pm No smoking in restaurant Last d 8.30pm
ROOMS: (incl. bkfst) s £22-£36; d £44-£72 **LB**
MEALS: Sunday Lunch £6.50-£7.50 High tea £4.75
Dinner £12.50-£14
CONF: Thtr 100 Class 60 Board 50 Del from £45
CARDS:

★★70% **Arlington**
Exeter Park Rd BH2 5BD ☎ 01202 552879 & 553012
FAX 01202 298317
RS Jan-Mar
This popular hotel has the advantage of a central location and is within walking distance of the BIC and the Pavilion Theatre. The loyal clientele return time and time again because of the friendly atmosphere and warm welcome. The bedrooms vary in size but are attractively decorated and well maintained; some of them enjoy lovely views of the Winter Gardens. The public areas are bright and comfortable.
28 en suite (bth/shr) 1 annexe en suite (shr) (6 fmly) CTV in 28 bedrooms STV No dogs Lift 21P No children 2yrs Xmas English & French Cuisine V meals Coffee am Tea pm No smoking area in restaurant Last d 8pm
ROOMS: (incl. bkfst & dinner) s £32.50-£39; d £65-£78 * **LB**
OFF-PEAK: (incl. bkfst & dinner) s £33; d £66
MEALS: Bar Lunch £4 Dinner £11*
CARDS:

★★68% **Durley Grange**
6 Durley Rd, West Cliff BH2 5JL ☎ 01202 554473 & 290743
FAX 01202 293774
Located in a quiet corner of the West Cliff, this popular hotel has been run by the Kirby family for over 16 years. The spotless bedrooms are bright, comfortable and well maintained. Public rooms include a spacious dining room serving home-cooked meals, and there is a smart residents' swimming pool with sauna and solarium.
50 en suite (bth/shr) (4 fmly) CTV in all bedrooms Lift Night porter 35P Indoor swimming pool (heated) Sauna Solarium Jacuzzi/spa Wkly live entertainment No children 5yrs Xmas English & Mediterranean Cuisine Coffee am No smoking in restaurant Last d 8pm
ROOMS: (incl. bkfst & dinner) s fr £20; d £40-£80 * **LB**
MEALS: Sunday Lunch £6-£8 Dinner £13*
CONF: Thtr 70 Class 40 Board 30 Del from £40
CARDS:

★★68% **West Cliff Towers**
12 Priory Rd BH2 5DG ☎ 01202 553319 FAX 01202 553319
This privately owned hotel is located on the West Cliff, within convenient walking distance of the beach, BIC and the town centre. The bedrooms are bright, spacious and attractively decorated with pretty co-ordinating fabrics. Public areas include a comfortable lounge and a separate games area. The lower ground floor restaurant offers a daily-changing menu of carefully prepared traditional dishes served by friendly staff.
27 en suite (bth/shr) (7 fmly) CTV in all bedrooms STV No dogs (ex guide dogs) Lift 27P table tennis Wkly live entertainment Xmas V meals Coffee am Tea pm No smoking in restaurant Last d 7.30pm

ROOMS: (incl. bkfst & dinner) s £30-£40; d £60-£80 **LB**
MEALS: Bar Lunch £2.50-£4.50 Dinner £9.95*
CARDS:

See advertisement on this page

★★68% **Whitehall**
Exeter Park Rd BH2 5AX (follow signs B.I.C. then turn into Exeter Park Road off Exeter Road) ☎ 01202 554682 FAX 01202 554682
Closed Nov-Feb
This well presented hotel is centrally located in a quiet cul-de-sac overlooking the park, close to the shops, seafront and BIC. Personally run by the Price family, the Whitehall offers a warm welcome and comfortable accommodation. The bedrooms are bright and attractively decorated with modern en suite facilities. There is a small well stocked bar and two lounges, one of which overlooks the garden.
49 rms (44 bth/shr) (5 fmly) CTV in all bedrooms Lift Night porter 25P Coffee am Tea pm No smoking in restaurant Last d 8pm
ROOMS: (incl. bkfst) s £25-£27; d £50-£54 * **LB**
OFF-PEAK: (incl. bkfst) d £25-£27
MEALS: Bar Lunch £1.50-£3.50 Dinner £12
CARDS:

★★67% **Chinehurst**
18-20 Studland Rd, Westbourne BH4 8JA ☎ 01202 764583
FAX 01202 762854
This friendly personally-run hotel is situated in the peaceful residential area of Alum Chine on the West Cliff. The public rooms are well appointed and overlook attractive woodland. There is a path down to the beach running through the garden and aviaries housing a collection of tropical birds and British birds of prey. The bedrooms are bright and well equipped and all have modern en suite facilities.
29 en suite (bth/shr) (4 fmly) No smoking in 4 bedrooms CTV in all bedrooms 14P Games room Bird gardens Xmas Continental Cuisine

contd.

V meals Coffee am Tea pm No smoking in restaurant Last d 8.30pm
ROOMS: (incl. bkfst) s £21-£28; d £42-£56 * LB
MEALS: Lunch £7.50&alc Dinner £15-£20&alc*
CONF: Thtr 60 Class 40 Board 40
CARDS:

★★67% **Durley Chine**
29 Chine Crescent, West Cliff BH2 5LB (follow signs for 'Bournemouth International Centre', 'West Cliff' and 'Town Centre')
☎ 01202 551926 FAX 01202 310671
This friendly family-run hotel has the best of both worlds, set in its own grounds with a beautiful tranquil garden, yet only minutes from the beach and town centre. The public rooms are comfortably furnished and both the lounge and the restaurant have balconies overlooking the gardens. The bedrooms are bright and spacious with attractive décor and furnishings.
23 en suite (bth/shr) 14 annexe en suite (bth/shr) (7 fmly) CTV in all bedrooms STV 40P Outdoor swimming pool (heated) Wkly live entertainment No children 5yrs Xmas English, French & Italian Cuisine Coffee am No smoking in restaurant Last d 7.30pm
ROOMS: (incl. bkfst & dinner) s £29-£40; d £58-£80 LB
OFF-PEAK: (incl. bkfst & dinner) s £26-£35; d £52-£70
MEALS: Sunday Lunch £11.50-£15 Dinner £11.50-£15
CARDS:

★★67% **Mansfield**
West Cliff Gardens BH2 5HL (from A338 follow signs for West Cliff, straight on at two rdbts via Cambridge & Durley Chine Rd)
☎ 01202 552659
Closed 2-15 Jan
Located in a quiet crescent on the West Cliff this hotel offers value for money comfortable accommodation in bedrooms. There is a cosy bar, and spacious lounges with entertainment on selected evenings. The daily changing menu offers generous portions of good home cooking, and a children's menu is also available.
30 en suite (bth/shr) (7 fmly) CTV in all bedrooms No dogs 12P No coaches Xmas V meals Coffee am Tea pm No smoking in restaurant Last d 8.30pm
ROOMS: (incl. bkfst & dinner) s £30-£34; d £60-£68 LB
OFF-PEAK: (incl. bkfst & dinner) s fr £27.50; d fr £55
MEALS: Sunday Lunch £7-£8 Dinner £9-£10
CARDS:

★★67% **Sun Court**
West Hill Rd, West Cliff BH2 5PH ☎ 01202 551343
FAX 01202 316747
This friendly family managed hotel, situated on the West Cliff close to the town centre, the sea-front and theatres, offers a welcoming atmosphere. Bedrooms vary in size but have been well equipped with modern comforts and the public rooms are spacious. There is an outdoor heated pool and sun terrace, and plenty of parking.
36 en suite (bth/shr) (4 fmly) CTV in all bedrooms Lift Night porter 50P Outdoor swimming pool (heated) Solarium Gym Facilities at sister hotel English, French, Italian & Spanish Cuisine V meals Coffee am Tea pm No smoking in restaurant Last d 8.30pm
MEALS: Sunday Lunch fr £6.25 Dinner £8.50*
CARDS:

★★67% **Ullswater**
West Cliff Gardens BH2 5HW (on entering Bournemouth follow signs to Westcliff, hotel just off Westcliff Road) ☎ 01202 555181
FAX 01202 317896
This popular, friendly hotel is situated on the West Cliff close to the beach and shops. The public areas are spacious and comfortable, and include a relaxing lounge and bar, and a very elegantly decorated dining room serving generous freshly-cooked evening meals. The bedrooms all have modern en suite facilities and are bright and attractively furnished.
42 en suite (bth/shr) (7 fmly) CTV in all bedrooms No dogs (ex guide dogs) Lift 10P Snooker Table tennis Wkly live entertainment Xmas English & French Cuisine Coffee am Tea pm No smoking in restaurant Last d 8pm
ROOMS: (incl. bkfst) s £25-£30; d £50-£60 LB
OFF-PEAK: (incl. bkfst) s £23-£25; d £46-£50
MEALS: Sunday Lunch fr £6.95 Dinner fr £10.50
CONF: Thtr 40 Class 30 Board 24 Del £47.50
CARDS:

★★66% **Hotel Riviera**
West Cliff Gardens BH2 5HL ☎ 01202 552845 FAX 01202 317717
Closed Dec-Mar RS 23 Dec-2 Jan
This long established family-run hotel enjoys a fine location, with direct access to the beach and lovely views from the terrace and bedrooms. The public rooms include a cosy bar which opens onto the pretty garden, and two comfortable lounges. The bedrooms are bright and cheerful with attractive decor.
34 en suite (bth/shr) (5 fmly) CTV in all bedrooms Lift Night porter 24P No coaches Xmas V meals Coffee am Tea pm No smoking in restaurant Last d 7.30pm
ROOMS: (incl. bkfst) s £23-£29; d £46-£58 LB
MEALS: Bar Lunch £1.70-£7 Dinner £9.50
CARDS:

★★65% **Croham Hurst**
9 Durley Rd South, West Cliff BH2 5JH (off A35 at Cambridge Rd roundabout, follow signs to BIC, hotel on the right just before Durley roundabout) ☎ 01202 552353 FAX 01202 311484
Closed 2 Jan-10 Feb
A popular family-run hotel is conveniently situated for easy access to the beach and town centre. There is a good range of well equipped en suite bedrooms in traditional and modern styles. A well furnished lounge area combines a bar and an attractive restaurant; the standard of cooking is high and service is friendly and attentive. Other attractions inlude ample car parking and a furnished garden terrace.
40 en suite (bth/shr) (10 fmly) CTV in all bedrooms STV No dogs (ex guide dogs) Lift 30P Wkly live entertainment Xmas V meals Coffee am No smoking in restaurant Last d 7.30pm
ROOMS: (incl. bkfst & dinner) s £25-£35; d £50-£70 * LB
OFF-PEAK: (incl. bkfst & dinner) s £22.50-£27; d £45-£54
MEALS: Sunday Lunch £6.50 Dinner £6.50-£10.50*
CARDS:
See advertisement on opposite page

★★64% ***Gresham Court***
4 Grove Rd, East Cliff BH1 3AX (take station exit off A338 towards East Cliff continue through 2 traffic islands into Gervis Rd)
☎ 01202 551732
Closed 2 Jan-12 Feb
This friendly East Cliff hotel is personally run by John and Pauline Moore and has a loyal return trade. Particularly popular with groups and sequence dancing is a speciality, however individuals are well looked after. The bedrooms are bright and well equipped, with traditional furnishings. Mrs Moore's cooking is generous and enjoyable.
34 en suite (bth/shr) (11 fmly) CTV in all bedrooms Lift 34P V meals Last d 7.30pm
CARDS:

★★64% ***Hartford Court***
48 Christchurch Rd BH1 3PE (on A35) ☎ 01202 551712 & 293682
This popular hotel is located on the eastern edge of the town and caters well for both the leisure and business guest. The bedrooms are well presented and there are several on the ground floor as well as some in the Coach House behind the main building. The smart public areas include a bar and a comfortable lounge; the dining room offers a simple set-price menu.

34 rms (27 bth/shr) 6 annexe en suite (bth/shr) (1 fmly) CTV in all bedrooms Lift 40P Coffee am Tea pm Last d 7.30pm
CARDS:

★★63% Lynden Court
8 Durley Rd, West Cliff BH2 5JL ☎ 01202 553894 FAX 01202 317711
Closed Jan
This small family run hotel is set on the West Cliff just a few minutes form the town and sea front . It offers spacious attractive rooms with modern ensuite facilities. The public rooms include a lounge bar with a separate pool table area, and a well presented dining room offering a daily set menu.
32 en suite (bth/shr) (3 fmly) CTV in all bedrooms STV Lift 20P Pool table Wkly live entertainment V meals Coffee am Tea pm No smoking in restaurant Last d 7.30pm
MEALS: Sunday Lunch £6-£7.50 Dinner £6-£7.50*
CARDS:

★★63% Montague
Durley Rd South BH2 5JH ☎ 01202 551074 FAX 01202 553948
Closed Dec-Feb
Ideally situated close to Durley Chine and only a short walk to the town centre this friendly and welcoming hotel is personally run by the resident proprietors Geoffrey and Barbara Ramsden. Bedrooms vary in shape and size but are all furnished and equipped in the modern style. There is a comfortable open-plan bar/lounge and reception, and an attractive, panelled dining room.
26 rms (22 bth/shr) (6 fmly) CTV in all bedrooms No dogs (ex guide dogs) 30P Outdoor swimming pool (heated) Pool table Xmas V meals Coffee am No smoking in restaurant Last d 7.30pm
ROOMS: (incl. bkfst & dinner) d £32-£35 * **LB**
OFF-PEAK: (incl. bkfst & dinner) d £25-£28
MEALS: Dinner £10-£15*
CARDS:

★★63% Winterbourne
Priory Rd BH2 5DJ (from A338 follow signs B.I.C. Hotel behind Centre) ☎ 01202 296366
FAX 01202 780073
Located high on the hill, this friendly hotel has views over the town and out to sea. The bedrooms are practically furnished and are being gradually upgraded. Public rooms include a lounge overlooking the garden and pool.
41 en suite (bth/shr) (12 fmly) CTV in all bedrooms STV Lift 33P Outdoor swimming pool (heated) Pool table Table tennis Climbing frame ch fac Xmas V meals Coffee am Tea pm No smoking in restaurant Last d 8pm
ROOMS: (incl. bkfst) s £25-£42; d £40-£74 * **LB**
OFF-PEAK: (incl. bkfst) s fr £25; d fr £40
MEALS: Bar Lunch £1.60-£4.65 High tea £3.75 Dinner £10-£14.50&alc
CONF: Thtr 90 Class 50 Board 36 Del from £47
CARDS:

★★61% Fircroft
4 Owls Rd, Boscombe BH5 1AE (off A338 signposted Boscombe Pier, hotel is 400yds from pier close to Christchurch Road) ☎ 01202 309771 FAX 01202 395644
An established hotel is conveniently located for the pier and the shops. The bright bedrooms vary in size but all are smartly furnished and well equipped. Spacious public areas include a choice of comfortable lounges and a restaurant serving traditional evening meals; an extensive bar snack menu is available at lunch.
51 en suite (bth/shr) (20 fmly) CTV in all bedrooms Lift Night porter 50P Indoor swimming pool (heated) Squash Snooker Sauna Solarium Gym Pool table Jacuzzi/spa sports at health club owned by hotel Xmas English & French Cuisine V meals Coffee am Tea pm No smoking in restaurant

ROOMS: (incl. bkfst) s £26-£35; d £52-£70 **LB**
MEALS: Bar Lunch £2-£4.50 Dinner £12.50
CONF: Thtr 200 Class 100 Board 40 Del £40
CARDS:

★★60% Cliff Court
15 Westcliff Rd BH2 5EX (on entering Bournemouth via Wessex Way, follow signs to International Centre (B3066) at 2nd rdbt turn right into West Cliff Road) ☎ 01202 555994 FAX 01202 780954
Centrally located on the West Cliff with easy access to the town centre and all the local attractions, this popular well managed hotel has a range of adequately furnished modern bedrooms all with en suite facilities. Public rooms comprise a comfortable bar lounge and attractive dining room. There is an automatic lift to all levels, reception and ample forecourt car parking.
38 en suite (bth/shr) CTV in all bedrooms Lift 38P Leisure facilities at nearby Club Wkly live entertainment Xmas V meals Coffee am Tea pm No smoking in restaurant
ROOMS: (incl. bkfst) s £18-£32; d £36-£64 * **LB**
CARDS:

★★60% Dean Park
41 Wimborne Rd BH2 6NB (turn off the Bournemouth By-Pass at the Richmond Hill rdbt, take the Wimborne road and hotel approx 0.5m on the right) ☎ 01202 552941 FAX 01202 556400
17 rms (16 bth/shr) (2 fmly) CTV in all bedrooms STV Night porter 45P No coaches Pool table International Cuisine V meals Coffee am Tea pm Last d 8.30pm
ROOMS: (incl. bkfst) s £22.50-£30; d £44-£52 * **LB**
OFF-PEAK: (incl. bkfst) s fr £20; d fr £40
MEALS: Lunch £4.75-£10.50 Dinner fr £10.50*
CARDS:

B

★★59% **Russell Court**
Bath Rd BH1 2EP ☎ 01202 295819 FAX 01202 293457
This popular coaching hotel offers bright well maintained rooms, some with sea views. The public rooms are spacious and comfortably furnished - there is a lounge bar and live entertainment is provided in the evenings. The young friendly staff provide cheerful attentive service.
62 rms (54 bth 4 shr) (6 fmly) CTV in all bedrooms No dogs (ex guide dogs) Lift Night porter 60P Wkly live entertainment Xmas V meals Coffee am Tea pm No smoking in restaurant Last d 8pm
ROOMS: (incl. bkfst & dinner) s £28-£36; d £56-£86 * **LB**
MEALS: Lunch £6.95 High tea £5-£7.50 Dinner £8.90-£19.90
CONF: Thtr 20
CARDS:

★★57% **County**
Westover Rd BH1 2BT ☎ 01202 552385 & 0500 141401
FAX 01202 297255
This centrally located hotel offers easy access to the seafront, shops and local amenities. The bedrooms vary in size and are being steadily upgraded; public areas include a quiet lounge bar and the popular 'Poets' bar which offers a lively music until midnight and commands a good crowd.
52 rms (37 bth 9 shr) (11 fmly) CTV in all bedrooms STV Lift Night porter 6P Use of Bournemouth International Pool Xmas Coffee am No smoking area in restaurant Last d 8pm
ROOMS: (incl. bkfst) s £19-£35; d £35-£68 * **LB**
MEALS: Sunday Lunch £5.25-£6.75 Dinner £10.50-£12.50
CARDS:

★★55% ***St George***
West Cliff Gardens BH2 5HL ☎ 01202 556075 FAX 01202 557330
Closed mid Nov - mid Dec & 3 Jan-Mar
This West Cliff hotel has a pretty garden and lovely sea views from many rooms including the large traditional lounge. Many guests return year after year to enjoy the amiable atmosphere. The bedrooms which are being gradually refurbished are bright and simply furnished with modern amenities.
22 rms (20 bth/shr) (5 fmly) CTV in all bedrooms STV Lift 4P Pool table ch fac V meals Coffee am Tea pm Last d 7.30pm

★66% ***Taurus Park***
16 Knyveton Rd BH1 3QN ☎ 01202 557374 FAX 01202 557374
The Taurus Park is situated on the East Cliff convenient for the town, station and major road links, and here the Ribas family offer a warm welcome. The bedrooms have bright, fresh décor and most have modern en suite facilities. Extensive public areas including a games room, an attractive dining room and popular bar. There is also plenty of private car parking.
43 rms (38 bth/shr) (7 fmly) CTV in all bedrooms No dogs Lift 20P No children 5yrs Last d 7.30pm

BOURTON-ON-THE-WATER Gloucestershire Map 04 SP12

★★❀70% **Dial House**
The Chestnuts, High St GL54 2AN (off A429) ☎ 01451 822244
FAX 01451 810126
This proudly maintained hotel is located in the centre of this busy village but conveniently set back from the road. Comfortable day rooms include two dining rooms. Bedrooms are well kept and mostly spacious. Service is assured by smartly uniformed and cheerful locals. The kitchen makes that extra effort using local produce to prepare good food.
10 en suite (bth/shr) No smoking in 2 bedrooms CTV in all bedrooms STV No dogs (ex guide dogs) 20P No coaches Croquet lawn Putting green No children 10yrs Xmas English & French Cuisine V meals Coffee am Tea pm No smoking in restaurant Last d 9.15pm
ROOMS: (incl. bkfst) s £25-£43; d £50-£100 **LB**
OFF-PEAK: (incl. bkfst) s fr £25; d fr £50
MEALS: Lunch £9.25-£15.45alc Dinner £15.95-£24.70alc
CONF: Class 16 Board 14 Del £75
CARDS:

See advertisement on opposite page

★★67% **Old Manse**
Victoria St GL54 2BX (centre of village, beside the River Windrush, near the War Memorial and the Motor Museum) ☎ 01451 820082
FAX 01451 810381
Situated at the heart of this much visited Cotswold village, the Old Manse is just a few feet from the stream which gives Bourton its suffix. The attractive bedrooms range from an impressive four-poster room with whirlpool bath and trompe l'oeil mural, to more cosy cottage-style accommodation. The busy bar is used by both locals and tourists and is open all day. A restaurant with an integral lounge offers food based round market fresh produce.
12 en suite (bth/shr) No smoking in 2 bedrooms CTV in all bedrooms 12P No coaches Wkly live entertainment Xmas V meals Coffee am No smoking in restaurant Last d 9.30pm
ROOMS: (incl. bkfst) s £39.50-£62.50; d £59-£119 * **LB**
OFF-PEAK: (incl. bkfst) s £33.50-£53; d £47-£95
MEALS: Lunch £6.25-£18.20 Dinner £15.95&alc*
CONF: Thtr 30 Class 20 Board 16 Del from £56.45
CARDS:

See advertisement on opposite page

★★65% **Chester House Hotel & Motel**
Victoria St GL54 2BU ☎ 01451 820286
FAX 01451 820471
Closed mid Dec-Jan
MINOTEL Great Britain
Close to the centre of one of the Cotswold's most delightful small towns, Chester House is personally run by proprietors Mr and Mrs Davies. All staff are particularly helpful and work hard to make their guests feel welcome. Rooms are generally spacious and there thoughtfully equipped, with some family rooms available; the hotel is well suited to both business and leisure guests. There is an attractive restaurant and separate breakfast room.
13 en suite (bth/shr) 10 annexe en suite (bth/shr) (6 fmly) CTV in all bedrooms 20P English & French Cuisine V meals Coffee am Last d 9.30pm
ROOMS: (incl. bkfst) s fr £49; d £59-£99 * **LB**
MEALS: Lunch £5.95-£7.50alc Dinner £13-£14*
CARDS:

★★65% **Old New Inn**
High St GL54 2AF (off A429) ☎ 01451 820467 FAX 01451 810236
Closed 25 Dec
Since the early 18th-century this inn has been providing shelter and food to all comers. What it may lack in modern comforts it makes up for with character, friendliness and setting. The owners maintain a traditional style, which includes the delivery of early morning tea to the bedroom door. There are four bars, and the well known model village stands next to the building.

16 rms (6 bth 2 shr) 4 annexe rms CTV in 19 bedrooms 31P No coaches English & French Cuisine V meals Coffee am Last d 8.30pm
ROOMS: (incl. bkfst) s £30-£36; d £60-£72 **LB**
MEALS: Lunch £10-£15 Dinner fr £18
CARDS:

BOVEY TRACEY Devon Map 03 SX87

★★★68% **Edgemoor**
Haytor Rd TQ13 9LE (from A382 follow signs for Haytor and Widecombe) ☎ 01626 832466 FAX 01626 834760
This charming, ivy-clad country house, built in the 1870s and peacefully set in two-acre gardens on the edge of Dartmoor, has been sympathetically modernised. Individually decorated bedrooms are thoughtfully equipped, while public areas include a bar lounge and quiet lounge - originally the school hall - as well as an attractive dining room.
12 en suite (bth/shr) 5 annexe en suite (bth/shr) (2 fmly) CTV in all bedrooms 45P No coaches ch fac English & French Cuisine V meals Coffee am Tea pm No smoking in restaurant Last d 9pm
ROOMS: (incl. bkfst) s £42.50-£49.50; d £75.50-£89 **LB**
MEALS: Lunch £10.95-£17.25 Dinner £19.50-£22
CONF: Thtr 90 Class 60 Board 30 Del from £60
CARDS:
See advertisement on this page

★★63% **Coombe Cross**

Coombe Cross TQ13 9EY (from A38 follow signs for Bovey Tracey and town centre, along High St & up the hill 400yds beyond the Parish Church, hotel on the left) ☎ 01626 832476 FAX 01626 835298
Closed 20 Nov-26 Dec
contd.

The Coombe Cross Hotel is set in half an acre of landscaped gardens in a residential area on the edge of Bovey Tracey, with distant moorland views. It offers a choice of comfortable lounges and a cosy dining room, which is soon to be refurbished. A well presented leisure facility was opened in 1993, available exclusively to residents at certain times during the day.
23 en suite (bth/shr) (2 fmly) CTV in 26 bedrooms Night porter 26P Indoor swimming pool (heated) Sauna Solarium Gym Jacuzzi/spa V meals Coffee am Tea pm No smoking in restaurant Last d 8.30pm
ROOMS: (incl. bkfst) s £39; d £56-£66 **LB**
MEALS: High tea £5-£7 Dinner £18.95*
CONF: Thtr 40 Class 60 Board 30 Del from £60
CARDS:

★★63% **Riverside Inn**
Fore St TQ13 9AF (hotel by bridge in town centre) ☎ 01626 832293 FAX 01626 833880
There is an informal atmosphere at this town centre inn with large, popular bars. Food options include bar snacks, a fixed-price menu and a carte. Guests are requested not to smoke in the bedrooms, which are comfortable and offer a good range of modern equipment.
10 en suite (bth/shr) CTV in all bedrooms STV Night porter 100P Fishing English & French Cuisine V meals Coffee am Tea pm No smoking area in restaurant Last d 9.30pm
ROOMS: (incl. bkfst) s £29.50; d £39.50 * **LB**
MEALS: Lunch £7-£16 Dinner £10-£28.50
CARDS:

BOWNESS ON WINDERMERE See Windermere

BOX Wiltshire Map 03 ST86

★★68% ***Box House***
London Rd SN13 8NR (on A4) ☎ 01225 744447 FAX 01225 743971
This handsome Georgian mansion, set in a beautiful walled garden, lies on the outskirts of the city The spacious bedrooms have been individually decorated and furnished with antique pieces, sympathetically combined with modern facilities. There is a choice of dining rooms, where an interesting selection of dishes is available from an à la carte menu, complemented by a range of fine wines from a well balanced list.
9 en suite (bth/shr) (1 fmly) CTV in all bedrooms Night porter 40P Outdoor swimming pool (heated) V meals Coffee am Tea pm Last d 9.30pm
CARDS:

BRACKLEY Northamptonshire Map 04 SP53

★★66% **Crown**
20-22 Market Square NN13 7DP (from M40 junc 10 take A43 into town, though Market Place for hotel on left) ☎ 01280 702210 FAX 01280 701840

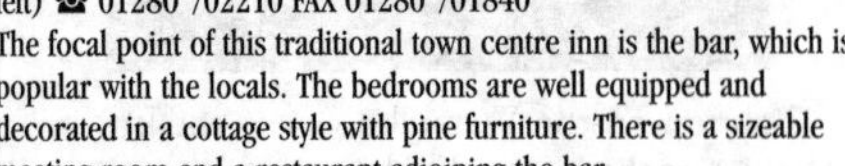

The focal point of this traditional town centre inn is the bar, which is popular with the locals. The bedrooms are well equipped and decorated in a cottage style with pine furniture. There is a sizeable meeting room and a restaurant adjoining the bar.
18 en suite (bth/shr) (2 fmly) CTV in all bedrooms 25P Xmas International Cuisine V meals Coffee am Tea pm Last d 9.30pm
ROOMS: (incl. bkfst) s £50; d £65 * **LB**
MEALS: Lunch £1.50-£4.50alc Dinner £9.50&alc*
CARDS:

Prices shown in the directory are meant as a guide only and are subject to change without warning. Please check before you book.

BRACKNELL Berkshire Map 04 SU86
See also Wokingham

★★★★76% **Coppid Beech**
John Nike Way RG12 8TF (from junct 10 on M4 take Wokingham/Bracknell option on to A329, in 2 miles at roundabout take B3408 to Binfield, hotel 200yds on the right hand side)
☎ 01344 303333 FAX 01344 301200
This impressive modern building is built in an Alpine style with peaks, wooden shutters and balconies. If offers an extensive range of amenities, which include indoor leisure, a night-club, and Bierkeller. Adjacent are also a ski-slope and ice-rink. Bedrooms are spacious and well equipped. There are a choice of eating options, and Rowans is the fine dining restaurant, where very capable and enjoyable cooking from a mixture of classic and modern styles can be enjoyed.
205 en suite (bth/shr) (6 fmly) No smoking in 138 bedrooms CTV in all bedrooms STV Lift Night porter Air conditioning 350P Indoor swimming pool (heated) Sauna Solarium Gym Jacuzzi/spa Wkly live entertainment Xmas V meals Coffee am Tea pm No smoking area in restaurant Last d 10.30pm
ROOMS: (incl. bkfst) s £120; d £145 **LB**
OFF-PEAK: (incl. bkfst) s £60; d £70
MEALS: Lunch £15.95-£19.95&alc Dinner £19.95&alc*
CONF: Thtr 400 Class 240 Board 24 Del from £150
CARDS:

See advertisement on opposite page

★★★72% **Stirrups Country House**
Maidens Green RG42 6LD (access via B3022)
☎ 01344 882284 FAX 01344 882300
Best Western
The subtle horse racing theme which the name implies is seen to best effect in the foyer where jockey's silks are displayed prominently. No long faces from the staff however, they are a welcoming bunch and are all very keen to make guests feel quickly at home with a professional and discreet approach to service. Bedrooms are smart and feature some quality dark wood furnishings, bright fabrics and wall coverings. Guests can expect an excellent range of extras in bedrooms and are well catered for whether visiting for pleasure or on business.
24 en suite (bth) (1 fmly) CTV in all bedrooms STV Lift Night porter 100P English & Continental Cuisine V meals Coffee am Last d 10pm
ROOMS: s £85.50-£95.50; d £89.50-£99.50 * **LB**
OFF-PEAK: s £30-£60; d £65-£75
MEALS: Lunch £10.50-£12.50 Dinner £16.25&alc*
CONF: Thtr 100 Class 50 Board 40 Del £112.50
CARDS:

Hilton National Bracknell
HILTON
Bagshot Rd RG12 0QJ ☎ 01344 424801
FAX 01344 487454
This is a bright, modern hotel, with an informal restaurant, aimed at both the business and leisure guest. All bedrooms have en suite bathrooms and a range of modern facilities. For more information about Hilton National hotels, consult the Contents page under Hotel Groups.
167 en suite (bth/shr)
ROOMS: s £115; d £115 *
CONF: Thtr 400 Class 90 Board 35 Del from £140

BRADFORD West Yorkshire Map 07 SE13
See also Shipley

★★★★63% **Cedar Court**
Mayo Av, Off Pooley Ln BD5 8HZ ☎ 01274 406606 & 406601
FAX 01274 406600
This impressive purpose built hotel is well positioned for access from both the M62 and M1 and is only eight miles from Bradford Airport.

Bedrooms, including no-smoking rooms, rooms designed for disabled guests, and those specifically for women guests, offer high levels of comfort, are well equipped and convenient to use. A good number of individually designed conference and banqueting suites are available and, at the time of our inspection, work had just begun on an impressive leisure facility which is to include a pool, gym and spa area.

127 en suite (bth/shr) (7 fmly) No smoking in 75 bedrooms CTV in all bedrooms Lift Night porter 350P Indoor swimming pool (heated) Sauna Solarium Gym Pool table Jacuzzi/spa Aerobic studio Beauty therapy Xmas International Cuisine V meals Coffee am Tea pm No smoking area in restaurant Last d 10pm
ROOMS: s £89; d £89 **LB**
OFF-PEAK: s £50; d £60
MEALS: Lunch fr £12.50 Dinner fr £18.50&alc*
CONF: Thtr 800 Class 500 Board 100 Del from £100
CARDS:

See advertisement on this page

★★★74% **Victoria**
Bridge St BD1 1JX ☎ 01274 728706 FAX 01274 736358
A designer-led, trendy hotel in the heart of the city. Owned by the successful Jonathan Wix, a name synonymous with quality within the hotel industry the Victoria is a rejuvenated period station hotel. The interior though contemporary compliments the architectural context of the original building. Mainly furnished in reds and blacks with ivory tones of decor, there are interesting modern oils and prints to all the walls. Bedrooms fan out from the broad avenues of corridors, each room is individually fashioned though similarly equipped with both video and CD players and good comfy armchairs. The public rooms include the lively public bar and Vic and Berts, a stylish brasserie serving good modern British and all-continents cuisine.
60 en suite (bth/shr) (3 fmly) No smoking in 21 bedrooms CTV in all bedrooms Lift Night porter 69P Sauna Gym Xmas V meals Coffee am Tea pm Last d 10.30pm
ROOMS: s £69-£89; d £69-£89 * **LB**
OFF-PEAK: s £35-£55; d £35-£55
MEALS: Lunch £7.95-£9.95&alc Dinner £7.95-£14.95&alc*
CONF: Thtr 180 Class 90 Board 50 Del £90.85
CARDS:

★★★68% **Pennington Midland**
Forster Square BD1 4HU ☎ 01274 735735 FAX 01274 720003
The old Midland Station Hotel has been completely restored to its former glory and is now very much part of the Bradford scene. The bedrooms are mainly spacious and have been thoughtfully equipped and pleasingly furnished whilst the public rooms include marble columns, ornate gilt-edged balustrades and sweeping staircases. The owners and their dedicated staff run the hotel in an efficient and friendly manner and a good range of food is available.
93 en suite (bth/shr) (10 fmly) No smoking in 30 bedrooms CTV in all bedrooms STV Lift Night porter 50P Pool table Y Wkly live entertainment English & Continental Cuisine V meals Coffee am Tea pm No smoking area in restaurant Last d 11pm
ROOMS: (incl. cont bkfst) s £59-£65; d £69-£75 * **LB**
OFF-PEAK: (incl. cont bkfst) s £35-£40; d £49-£54
MEALS: Lunch £10-£15&alc High tea £3.50-£6.50
Dinner £12-£17.50&alc
CONF: Thtr 500 Class 150 Board 100 Del from £80
CARDS:

See advertisement on opposite page

★★★67% **Courtyard by Marriott Leeds/Bradford**
The Pastures, Tong Ln BD4 0RP (off A450)
☎ 0113 285 4646 FAX 0113 285 3661
Situated in rural surroundings between Bradford and Leeds, this well managed hotel has been extended since its days as a vicarage. Half of the bedrooms are modern and well furnished, with the remainder scheduled for upgrading. There are two bars, one being a traditional pub serving bar meals and the other adjoins the spacious restaurant. Cheerful staff create a convivial atmosphere.
50 en suite (bth/shr) (5 fmly) No smoking in 28 bedrooms CTV in all bedrooms STV Lift Night porter 300P Sauna Solarium Gym Pool table Wkly live entertainment English, Italian & Indian Cuisine V meals Coffee am Tea pm No smoking area in restaurant
MEALS: Lunch £10-£15alc*
CONF: Thtr 300 Class 150 Board 100
CARDS:

★★★65% **Apperley Manor**
Apperley Ln, Apperley Bridge BD10 0PQ (on A658 Bradford to Harrogate road) ☎ 0113 250 5626 FAX 0113 250 0075
Situated in a convenient position for Leeds/Bradford airport, this modern, personally run hotel offers well furnished and thoughtfully equipped bedrooms together with adequate public areas. Well produced dishes are provided in the delightful restaurant, and there is a spacious and popular bar. Good conference facilities are also available. Resident owner Mrs Hodgson is always on hand to ensure that guests are well cared for and is she backed by a friendly and eager staff.
13 en suite (bth/shr) (2 fmly) CTV in all bedrooms No dogs (ex guide dogs) Lift Night porter 100P Jacuzzi in 2 bedrooms International Cuisine V meals Coffee am Tea pm No smoking area in restaurant
ROOMS: (incl. bkfst) s £59.50-£65; d £69.50-£79.50 *
OFF-PEAK: (incl. cont bkfst) s £25-£35; d £50-£70
MEALS: Lunch fr £9.50*
CONF: Thtr 80 Class 40 Del from £85
CARDS:

★★★64% **Novotel**

Merrydale Rd BD4 6SA (3m S adjacent to M606)
☎ 01274 683683 FAX 01274 651342
This is one of the first Novotels to be built in this country, but recent upgrading of public rooms, including the restaurant, has considerably enhanced the hotel and the foyer lounges are particularly comfortable. Bedrooms are serviceably furnished and ideal for families as well as business clientele. There are several meeting and function rooms, a sizeable car park and even a small outdoor swimming pool.

127 en suite (bth/shr) (127 fmly) No smoking in 42 bedrooms CTV in all bedrooms STV Lift Night porter Air conditioning 180P Outdoor swimming pool (heated) English & French Cuisine V meals Coffee am Tea pm No smoking area in restaurant
ROOMS: s fr £42.50; d fr £42.50 *
CONF: Thtr 300 Class 150 Board 100 Del £80
CARDS:

★★67% Park Grove

28 Park Grove, Frizinghall BD9 4JY (off A650 Keighley road) ☎ 01274 543444 FAX 01274 495619

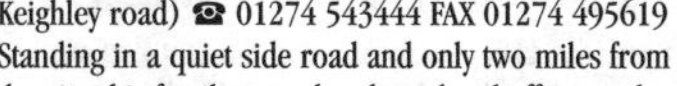

Standing in a quiet side road and only two miles from the city, this family-owned and run hotel offers modern and well equipped bedrooms. The Singh family are very much involved with the running of the hotel which provides predominantly Asian cuisine cooked to a very good standard; English food is also available from the extensive menu. Public areas consist of a cosy lounge bar which is attached to the very attractive restaurant; there is a small car park to the rear.
11 en suite (bth/shr) (2 fmly) CTV in all bedrooms STV No dogs Night porter 8P No coaches Croquet lawn English & Indian Cuisine V meals Last d 11pm
ROOMS: (incl. bkfst) s £42-£46; d £56-£58 * **LB**
OFF-PEAK: (incl. bkfst) s £40; d £50-£52
MEALS: Dinner £11-£15alc*
CARDS:

★★66% Dubrovnik
3 Oak Av, Manningham BD8 7AQ (1.5m from city centre. Take Keighley Road, Queens Road, first left after police station, then second left and hotel on right) ☎ 01274 543511 FAX 01274 480407
A spacious Victorian house with modern extensions standing in a quiet side road and about a mile from the city. It is family-owned and -run and the staff are very friendly and helpful. The bedrooms are of two styles, those in the newer extension being more spacious and generally more modern whilst they are all well equipped. A good range of food is available in the traditionally styled dining room.
46 en suite (bth/shr) (10 fmly) CTV in all bedrooms Night porter 70P ch fac Xmas English & Yugoslavian Cuisine V meals Coffee am Tea pm Last d 10pm
ROOMS: (incl. bkfst) s £56; d £73 * **LB**
OFF-PEAK: (incl. bkfst) s £38.50; d £62.75
MEALS: Lunch £3-£10&alc Dinner £15-£20&alc*
CONF: Thtr 250 Class 100 Board 60 Del from £60
CARDS:

★★66% Park Drive

12 Park Dr BD9 4DR (turn off A650 Keighley road into Emm Lane, at Lister Park turn 2nd right)
☎ 01274 480194 FAX 01274 484869
This pleasantly furnished hotel stands in a quiet residential area and has well tended gardens to the rear. It provides mainly spacious bedrooms which are well equipped, bright and fresh and a lounge bar

contd.

B

is also available for guests. Well prepared home cooking is available and service is both friendly and attentive from the resident owners.
11 en suite (bth/shr) (1 fmly) CTV in all bedrooms 10P No coaches V meals No smoking in restaurant Last d 8.30pm
ROOMS: (incl. bkfst) s £46; d £56 **LB**
OFF-PEAK: (incl. bkfst) s £30; d £48
MEALS: Dinner £12&alc
CONF: Thtr 20 Class 8 Board 12 Del £65
CARDS:

See advertisement on opposite page

BRADFORD ON AVON Wiltshire Map 03 ST86

★★★ 74% **Woolley Grange**
Woolley Green BA15 1TX (on B3105, 0.5m NE at Woolley Green)
☎ 01225 864705 FAX 01225 864059
Located in beautiful Wiltshire countryside this lovely hotel provides a perfect escape from the hustle and bustle of life, as well as someone to look after your children. The bedrooms are beautifully furnished with attractive antique pieces and thoughtful extras; many can accommodate families. The public areas offer several separate lounge and quiet seating areas while the staff provide unobtrusive but friendly service. The bright restaurant serves a good range of skilfully prepared dishes making full use of local produce, with delicious home-made breads and pastries being the highlight.
14 en suite (bth/shr) 8 annexe en suite (bth/shr) (7 fmly) CTV in all bedrooms Night porter 40P No coaches Outdoor swimming pool (heated) Tennis (grass) Pool table Croquet lawn Putting green Badminton Games room ch fac Xmas V meals Coffee am Tea pm No smoking in restaurant Last d 9.45pm
ROOMS: (incl. bkfst) s £90-£180; d £99-£200 **LB**
MEALS: Lunch £5-£20alc High tea fr £5 Dinner £29
CONF: Thtr 40 Class 40 Board 22 Del from £125
CARDS:

★★64% **The Swan**
1 Church St BA15 1LN (at N end of the bridge over the River Avon)
☎ 01225 868686 FAX 01255 868681
This 15th-century building stands in the centre of town, overlooking the River Avon to the rear. Extensive refurbishment followed a change of ownership three years ago, and all the bedrooms are now comfortable and well equipped; bars serve a selection of real ales and interesting bar meals, while the restaurant provides a fixed-price menu featuring fresh Brixham fish and local game from Tuesday to Saturday and at Sunday lunch time. The Coach House Room can be hired for weddings, functions and conferences.
12 en suite (bth/shr) (1 fmly) CTV in all bedrooms STV 15P Pool table International Cuisine V meals Coffee am Tea pm Last d 9.30pm
ROOMS: (incl. bkfst) s fr £40; d £52.50-£70 * **LB**
MEALS: Lunch fr £9.95alc Dinner £7.50-£15alc*
CONF: Thtr 60 Class 60 Board 40
CARDS:

BRAINTREE Essex Map 05 TL72

★★★61% **White Hart**
Bocking End CM7 9AB (in town centre)
☎ 01376 321401 FAX 01376 552628
Located in the centre of the town this hotel suits both business and leisure guests as well as being a popular venue for locals. Informal public areas include congenial bar, conservatory lounge and family restaurant. Bedrooms are modern, with the exception of a small number of character rooms in the main house, and all offer a good range of facilities.
31 en suite (bth/shr) (8 fmly) No smoking in 9 bedrooms CTV in all bedrooms STV No dogs (ex guide dogs) Night porter 52P Sauna Solarium Gym English & Continental Cuisine V meals Coffee am Tea pm No smoking area in restaurant Last d 10pm
ROOMS: (incl. bkfst) s £36-£59.50; d £52-£71 * **LB**
MEALS: Lunch £5-£15alc Dinner £5-£20alc*
CONF: Thtr 40 Class 16 Board 24 Del from £75
CARDS:

BRAITHWAITE Cumbria Map 11 NY22

★★71% **Ivy House**
CA12 5SY ☎ 017687 78338 FAX 017687 78113
Closed Jan
The Ivy House is a gracious 17th-century house in the centre of a peaceful and picturesque village nestling in the foothills of the Coledale round and Skiddaw. Nick and Wendy Shill are conscientious owners who are intimately involved, with Wendy in the kitchen and Nick providing the warm welcome. Extra touches of homeliness such as flowers, books and magazines add to the comfort of the cosy lounge, filled with deep armchairs and sofas, and featuring ancient timbers and open fires. The galleried restaurant, candlelit by night, serves a daily-changing 4-course dinner; the quality of the cooking is good.
12 en suite (bth/shr) CTV in all bedrooms 17P No coaches No children Xmas No smoking in restaurant Last d 7.30pm
ROOMS: (incl. bkfst & dinner) s £27-£30; d £54-£60 *
MEALS: Dinner £18.95*
CARDS:

★★67% **Middle Ruddings Country Inn & Restaurant**
CA12 5RY (off A66 N of Keswick. Turn off at Thornthwaite, not at 'Braithwaite/Whinlatter' sign) ☎ 017687 78436
FAX 017687 78438
This family-run hotel lies just off the A66 on the edge of the village and can be recognised by the large oak tree that dominates the front garden and under which one can sit, eat and drink in appropriate weather. The hotel is popular for its bar meals, but there is also a cosy lounge for those dining in the restaurant and the spacious and comfortable public areas are indeed a feature. Bedrooms are well equipped and one has its own balcony overlooking the rear garden.
11 en suite (bth/shr) (1 fmly) CTV in all bedrooms 14P No coaches Bowls English & French Cuisine V meals Coffee am Tea pm No smoking in restaurant Last d 8.45pm
ROOMS: (incl. bkfst) s £40; d £72 * **LB**
OFF-PEAK: (incl. bkfst) s fr £36; d fr £56
MEALS: Lunch £9.95 Dinner £13.95&alc*
CARDS:

★★65% **Cottage in the Wood**
Whinlatter Pass CA12 5TW (on B5292, 2m up the pass hotel on right)
☎ 017687 78409
Closed 17 Nov-11 Mar
This cosy little roadside hotel is surrounded by wooded hillsides, with striking views of distant peaks. Run in a friendly and informal manner by the owners, it has neat bedrooms which although lacking TVs (there is one in the tiny bar) do offer clock radios, hair dryers and electric blankets. The two larger rooms have four-posters. There is a relaxing lounge and a comfortable dining room which enjoys the views. The four course dinner is served around 7pm and although no choice is offered, dishes are home made and freshly cooked.
7 en suite (bth/shr) (2 fmly) No smoking in all bedrooms 20P No coaches Coffee am Tea pm No smoking in restaurant Last d 7pm
ROOMS: (incl. bkfst) d £62-£64 **LB**
OFF-PEAK: (incl. bkfst) s £31-£33; d £58-£62
MEALS: Dinner £14.50-£18.50
CARDS:

B

BRAMHALL Greater Manchester Map 07 SJ88

★★★67% **Bramhall Moat House**
Bramhall Ln South SK7 2EB (off A5102)
☎ 0161 439 8116 & 455 9988 FAX 0161 440 8071

Smart bedrooms and pleasant public areas are offered at this hotel which is situated in a peaceful residential area. A business centre has recently been added and further improvements to the services and facilities are planned, including the re-styling of the restaurant.
65 en suite (bth/shr) (3 fmly) No smoking in 13 bedrooms CTV in all bedrooms Night porter 132P Solarium Gym Xmas English & French Cuisine V meals Coffee am Tea pm No smoking in restaurant
ROOMS: s £85; d £100 * **LB**
OFF-PEAK: (incl. bkfst) s fr £25; d fr £50
CONF: Thtr 180 Class 50 Board 40 Del £118
CARDS:

BRAMHOPE West Yorkshire Map 08 SE24

Forte Posthouse Leeds/Bradford
Leeds Rd LS16 9JJ (on A660 N of village)
☎ 0113 284 2911 FAX 0113 284 3451

Suitable for both the business and leisure traveller, this bright hotel provides modern accommodation in well equipped bedrooms with en suite bathrooms. For more details about Forte Posthouse hotels, consult the Contents page for the section on Hotel Groups.
124 en suite (bth/shr)
ROOMS: d £59-£79 *
CONF: Thtr 160 Class 90 Board 50 Del from £78

BRAMPTON Cumbria Map 12 NY56

RED STAR HOTEL

★★★ **Farlam Hall**
Hallbankgate CA8 2NG (from A69 take A689 to Alston, the hotel is approx 2m on the left, not in village)
☎ 016977 46234 FAX 016977 46683
Closed 25-30 Dec
(Rosettes awarded for dinner only)

Dating in part from the 16th century, this delightful and historic country house stands in beautiful landscaped gardens complete with a stream and ornamental lake, two and a half miles east of Brampton on the A689. Lounges boast fine furnishings, open fires, reading material and games, and have a relaxed atmosphere. Bedrooms are individual in design and furnished in the style of the house; some have bathrooms designed by Joan Quinion featuring separate shower cubicles and TVs. The dining room is elegant, with fine china and silver on crisp linen over large well spaced tables. Barry Quinion's short but well structured daily-changing four-course dinner offers British cooking in the modern style. A roulade of salmon and halibut accompanied by a watercress coulis might be followed by best-end of local lamb served on a bed of home-made spinach with a rosemary and red wine sauce. Cheese will precede dessert which could be rhubarb and ginger parfait with rhubarb coulis. Levels of hospitality and service are excellent.
11 en suite (bth/shr) 1 annexe en suite (bth/shr) CTV in all bedrooms 35P No coaches Croquet lawn No children 5yrs V meals Coffee am Tea pm Last d 8.30pm
ROOMS: (incl. bkfst & dinner) s £105-£120; d £190-£220 * **LB**
MEALS: Dinner £28.50-£29.50
CONF: Thtr 12 Class 12 Board 12
CARDS:

★★66% ***Kirby Moor Country House***
Longtown Rd CA8 2AB (NW off A6071)
☎ 016977 3893 FAX 016977 41847

This Victorian country house lies on the edge of the town and has a pleasant outlook across grazing land. Stylishly renovated to retain its character, the hotel offers well equipped bedrooms in a variety of sizes. There is a cosy lounge with dispense bar and an attractive conservatory restaurant providing freshly prepared food.
6 rms (5 shr) (1 fmly) CTV in all bedrooms 16P International Cuisine V meals Coffee am Tea pm Last d 9pm
CARDS:

★★65% **Tarn End House**
Talkin Tarn CA8 1LS (from A69 take B6413 for 2m and turn off towards Talkin Village) ☎ 016977 2340 FAX 016977 2089
There is a friendly and relaxed atmosphere at this former estate farm house which enjoys an idyllic situation with gardens running down to the shores of Talkin Tarn, in attractive countryside south of Brampton. The hotel provides an ideal retreat and is also popular with golfers, the local course being on its doorstep. Bedrooms have been enhanced by Mrs Ball's choice of fabrics and interior design, a flare which is also reflected in the attractive lounge and dining room.
7 en suite (bth/shr) (1 fmly) CTV in all bedrooms 40P No coaches Xmas International Cuisine V meals Coffee am Tea pm No smoking in restaurant Last d 9pm
ROOMS: (incl. bkfst) s £32.50-£42.50; d £55-£67 **LB**
OFF-PEAK: (incl. bkfst) s £29.50-£39.50; d £55-£65
MEALS: Lunch £8.95-£12 Dinner £13.50-£17.50&alc
CARDS:

BRANDESBURTON East Riding of Yorkshire Map 08 TA14

★★68% **Burton Lodge**

YO25 8RU (on A165, adjoining Hainsworth Park Golf Club) ☎ 01964 542847 FAX 01964 542847
Situated on the edge of the town surrounded by landscaped gardens and a golf course, this modern-style house is very well furnished and maintained. A comfortable lounge overlooks the greens and a tennis court has recently been added for guests. The en suite bedrooms are bright and have recently had Sky television added to existing facilities such as hair dryers. A small choice dinner menu is provided and is very English in style; service is friendly and attentive.
8 rms (7 bth/shr) 2 annexe en suite (bth/shr) (2 fmly) CTV in all bedrooms STV 12P No coaches Golf 18 Tennis (grass) Putting green Pitch and putt V meals Coffee am Tea pm No smoking in restaurant Last d 9.15pm
ROOMS: (incl. bkfst) s £32-£35; d £42-£46 **LB**
OFF-PEAK: (incl. bkfst) s fr £30; d fr £40
MEALS: Dinner £12-£14
CARDS:

BRANDON Suffolk Map 05 TL78

★★★67% **Brandon House**

High St IP27 0AX ☎ 01842 810171
FAX 01842 814859
Closed 25-31 Dec
This red brick 18th-century manor house sits close to the town centre and has ample car parking. The public areas offer a large lounge bar and two eating options, with informal Cajun-style dining offered in the Garden Room or more formal dining from à la carte menus in the pleasantly appointed restaurant. Bedrooms are generally of comfortable proportions and all are very well equipped.
15 en suite (bth/shr) CTV in all bedrooms STV 40P No coaches English & French Cuisine V meals Coffee am Tea pm Last d 9pm
ROOMS: (incl. bkfst) s £49.50-£55; d £65-£70 * **LB**
MEALS: Lunch £15.95&alc Dinner £15.95&alc*
CONF: Thtr 70 Class 25 Board 20 Del £85
CARDS:

BRANDON Warwickshire Map 04 SP47

★★★64% **Brandon Hall**

FORTE Heritage

Main St CV8 3FW (off A428 to Rugby)
☎ 01203 542571 FAX 01203 544909
Peacefully situated in 17 acres of well tended lawns and woodland, this former shooting lodge is found by following signs for the village centre. Many of the bedrooms have now been upgraded, and future plans include revitalising the public areas which include a comfortably furnished lounge bar in the original house and a more recently built restaurant.
60 en suite (bth/shr) No smoking in 29 bedrooms CTV in all bedrooms Night porter 250P Squash Croquet lawn Putting green Xmas International Cuisine V meals Coffee am Tea pm No smoking in restaurant Last d 9.30pm
ROOMS: d £80 * **LB**
MEALS: Lunch £10.95-£14.95&alc Dinner £19.95&alc*
CONF: Thtr 90 Class 40 Board 40 Del from £110
CARDS:

BRANDS HATCH Kent Map 05 TQ56

★★★★59% **Brands Hatch Thistle**

THISTLE HOTELS

DA3 8PE (on A20 N of junct with M20)
☎ 01474 854900 FAX 01474 853220
This conference and leisure hotel is located at the main entrance of the world famous Grand Prix racing circuit. There are good facilities in the well-kept and individually styled bedrooms and in addition to a refurbished restaurant there is a brasserie in the lounge area.
137 en suite (bth/shr) (7 fmly) No smoking in 40 bedrooms CTV in all bedrooms STV Night porter 180P Xmas English & French Cuisine V meals Coffee am Tea pm No smoking area in restaurant Last d 10pm
ROOMS: s £79-£92; d £89-£102 * **LB**
OFF-PEAK: s £59-£69; d £72-£82
MEALS: Lunch fr £15.95&alc Dinner £21-£22&alc*
CONF: Thtr 270 Class 120 Board 50 Del from £95
CARDS:

★★★❀❀67% **Brandshatch Place**

Fawkham DA3 8NQ (From A20 follow signs Fawkham, Brands Hatch Paddock after 1 mile take third turn left under motorway bridge. Hotel second turn right)
☎ 01474 872239 FAX 01474 879652
There are views of the racing track's paddocks from this Georgian country house which is set in 12 acres of parkland. A major programme of upgrading is due to have been finished by the autumn of 1996. The bedrooms too have been smartly furnished. Serious intentions are evident in the kitchen under capable head chef, Mark Cheeseman. The cooking demonstrates sure-handed technique and an understanding of flavours. Wonderful home-made bread rolls and desserts.
29 en suite (bth/shr) 12 annexe en suite (bth/shr) (2 fmly) No smoking in 12 bedrooms CTV in all bedrooms STV Night porter 100P Indoor swimming pool (heated) Tennis (hard) Squash Snooker Sauna Solarium Gym Jacuzzi/spa Badminton Beauty therapy Steam room ch fac International Cuisine V meals Coffee am Tea pm No smoking in restaurant Last d 9.30pm
ROOMS: s £75; d £95-£125 * **LB**
MEALS: Lunch £14.25&alc Dinner £19.95-£25alc*
CONF: Thtr 150 Class 50 Board 35 Del from £125
CARDS:

BRANKSOME See Poole

BRANSCOMBE Devon Map 03 SY18

★★❀72% **The Masons Arms**
EX12 3DJ (turn off A3052 towards Branscombe, head down hill, hotel in the valley at the bottom of the hill) ☎ 01297 680300
FAX 01297 680500
A 14th-century inn, the Masons Arms is situated half a mile from the sea on the quiet road which runs through this lovely village surrounded by National Trust land. Individually decorated bedrooms (some of them contained in cottages immediately adjacent to the inn) are equipped with modern comforts and extras such as fresh flowers and sewing kits. The bar is built around a central fireplace, and what was once a rendezvous for smugglers is now the haunt of locals and residents alike. The restaurant features oak beams made of ships' timbers and a well balanced carte offering an interesting selection of local fish, meat and game.
8 en suite (bth/shr) 13 annexe en suite (bth/shr) CTV in all bedrooms 43P No coaches Xmas Caribbean & French Cuisine V meals Coffee am Tea pm No smoking area in restaurant
ROOMS: (incl. bkfst) s £22-£50; d £44-£80 * **LB**
CONF: Thtr 60 Class 20 Board 20 Del from £75
CARDS:

BRANSTON Lincolnshire Map 08 TF06

★★★68% ***Branston Hall***
Branston Park LN4 1PD ☎ 01522 793305 FAX 01522 790549
Branston Hall is a fine manor house set amid 88 acres of woodland and lakes in the heart of rural Lincolnshire. Most of the house's period architecture remains though it was a nursing home before its conversion to a hotel. The reception rooms lead off from a generously proportioned light oak-panelled lounge bar. The bedrooms are mostly spacious and comfortably furnished.
22 en suite (bth/shr) (2 fmly) CTV in all bedrooms Lift Night porter 150P Fishing English & French Cuisine V meals Coffee am Tea pm Last d 9.45pm
CARDS:

★★★62% **Moor Lodge**

Sleaford Rd LN4 1HU (3m S of Lincoln on B1188)
☎ 01522 791366 FAX 01522 794389
This fine old manor house lies in an area where paratroopers for the wartime raid on Arnheim trained and assembled. The majority of bedrooms have now been upgraded and several colour schemes have been used to good effect. Very extensive function facilities are provided and business and other meetings are also well catered for. There is a peaceful and relaxing atmosphere throughout the bar and lounge areas and staff are friendly and welcoming.
24 en suite (bth/shr) (2 fmly) No smoking in 1 bedroom CTV in all bedrooms Night porter 150P English & French Cuisine V meals Coffee am Tea pm Last d 9.45pm
ROOMS: (incl. bkfst) s £55-£65; d £75-£85 * **LB**
MEALS: Lunch £9.50-£20.25alc Dinner £9.50-£20.25alc*
CONF: Thtr 200 Class 80 Board 60 Del from £60
CARDS:

BRAY Berkshire Map 04 SU97

★★★★❀62% **Monkey Island**
SL6 2EE (exit M4 at junct 8/9 and take A308 signposted Windsor, take first left into Bray then first right into Old Mill Lane)
☎ 01628 23400 FAX 01628 784732
Closed 26 Dec-15 Jan RS Sat (no lunch in restaurant)
Monkey Island lies a mile downstream from Maidenhead on the Thames, near the village of Bray; access is by footbridge or boat. The grounds are well maintained and inhabited by fowl and rabbits. Bedrooms and public areas are in two separate buildings; the former are bright, modern and compact, the latter stylish, spacious and comfortable. Ian Butcher's ambitious cuisine is appropriate to the surroundings, and smartly presented staff are brisk and competent.
25 en suite (bth/shr) (3 fmly) CTV in all bedrooms No dogs Night porter 100P Fishing Croquet lawn Clay pigeon shooting/boating by request Wkly live entertainment English & French Cuisine V meals Coffee am Tea pm No smoking area in restaurant
ROOMS: s fr £90; d fr £110 * **LB**
MEALS: Lunch fr £20&alc Dinner fr £27&alc*
CONF: Thtr 150 Class 60 Board 50 Del from £160
CARDS:
See advertisement under MAIDENHEAD

★★★❀❀69% **Chauntry House**
SL6 2AB ☎ 01628 73991 FAX 01628 773089
This delightful house is situated in the peaceful village of Bray, just a few minutes walk from the river. The public rooms have an elegant charm and are comfortably furnished. The spacious bedrooms are individually decorated with attractive fabrics and antiques. There is a pretty garden where guests may sit and enjoy the tranquillity. Chef Chris Hope offers a fresh imaginative menu with some skilful prepared dishes. A recent meal started with a superb Crottin de Chavignol soufflé served with a spied rhubarb compote, the medley of sea bream and monkfish was also enjoyable.
13 en suite (bth/shr) 4 annexe en suite (bth/shr) CTV in all bedrooms STV 35P No coaches European Cuisine V meals Coffee am Tea pm No smoking in restaurant Last d 9.30pm
ROOMS: (incl. bkfst) s £80-£95; d £105-£135 *
MEALS: Lunch £10-£30&alc High tea £7.50 Dinner £21.50-£30&alc*
CONF: Board 22 Del from £120
CARDS:

BREADSALL Derbyshire Map 08 SK33

★★★★64% **Marriott Breadsall Priory**
Moor Rd DE7 6DL (0.5m N. Signposted off A61)
☎ 01332 832235 FAX 01332 833509
This extended period mansion is set in 400 acres of parkland. Guests have full membership of the Country Club which offers a host of facilities including golf, tennis, swimming, gym and its own stylish restaurant and lounge bar. Bedrooms are mostly contained within various modern wings which are a short walk from the original building and guests are advised to register before unloading.
14 en suite (bth/shr) 77 annexe en suite (bth/shr) (1 fmly) No smoking in 45 bedrooms CTV in all bedrooms STV No dogs (ex guide dogs) Lift Night porter 300P Indoor swimming pool (heated) Golf 18 Tennis (hard) Sauna Solarium Gym Croquet lawn Putting green Jacuzzi/spa Health/beauty salon Dance studio Xmas English & French Cuisine V meals Coffee am Tea pm
ROOMS: s fr £75; d fr £75 * **LB**
MEALS: Lunch £12.50&alc Dinner £17-£23&alc*
CONF: Thtr 120 Class 50 Board 36
CARDS:

B

BRENTWOOD Essex Map 05 TQ59

★★★★ 68% **Marygreen Manor**
London Rd CM14 4NR (on A1023) ☎ 01277 225252
FAX 01277 262809
A good level of services is provided by a professional team at this well established hotel, which is conveniently located for both the town and the M25. The Tudor main building retains of much its character throughout the public rooms and the three period bedrooms; the majority of bedrooms are contemporary in style and are arranged around the well tended garden to the rear of the property. The restaurant, with its exposed beams and tapestries, offers a range of menus that includes some imaginative and traditional dishes.
An all-day snack menu is also available in the lounge.
3 en suite (bth/shr) 30 annexe en suite (bth/shr) CTV in all bedrooms STV No dogs (ex guide dogs) Night porter 100P International Cuisine V meals Coffee am Tea pm No smoking area in restaurant Last d 10.15pm
ROOMS: s fr £97.50; d fr £110 * **LB**
OFF-PEAK: d fr £104.25
MEALS: Lunch £12-£16.50&alc Dinner £19.50-£25&alc*
CONF: Thtr 60 Class 20 Board 25 Del from £132.50
CARDS:

★★★ 59% **The New World**
Great Warley St, Warley CM13 3JP ☎ 01277 226418
FAX 01277 229795
The New World is a family owned and managed hotel, which sits on the B186 south of Brentwood and is easily accessible from junction 29 of the M25. The accommodation is divided between the main hotel and an adjacent building, and room styles and sizes vary. Public rooms include a bar and restaurant; a major development is scheduled for 1996 to create spacious, modern and comfortable public areas and an additional wing of modern bedrooms.
28 en suite (bth/shr) 10 annexe en suite (bth/shr) (6 fmly) CTV in all bedrooms Night porter 250P Outdoor swimming pool (heated) Tennis (hard) V meals Coffee am Tea pm Last d 10.30pm
ROOMS: (incl. bkfst) s £55; d £65 * **LB**
MEALS: Bar Lunch £3.50-£10alc Dinner £9-£19alc*
CARDS:

See advertisement on opposite page

Forte Posthouse Brentwood

Brook St CM14 5NF (close to M25/A12 interchange) v 01277 260260 FAX 01277 264264
Suitable for both the business and leisure traveller, this bright hotel provides modern accommodation in well equipped bedrooms with en suite bathrooms. For more details about Forte Posthouse hotels, consult the Contents page for the section on Hotel Groups.
145 en suite (bth/shr)
ROOMS: d £69-£89 *
CONF: Thtr 120 Class 60 Board 50 Del £119.50

BRIDGNORTH Shropshire Map 07 SO79
See also Alverley

★★ 65% **Croft**
Saint Mary's St WV16 4DW ☎ 01746 762416
This is a small, friendly, family-run hotel which dates back to the early 18th century. It lies within the narrow streets of the old town and is surrounded by similar buildings. Many exposed beams and wall timbers still feature and public rooms are cosy and full of character. Bedrooms vary in size and shape and modern facilities are provided.
12 rms (4 bth 6 shr) (3 fmly) CTV in all bedrooms No coaches ch fac V meals Coffee am Tea pm No smoking in restaurant Last d 8pm
ROOMS: (incl. bkfst) s £23.50-£40; d £44-£50 **LB**
MEALS: Lunch £8.50 Dinner £10.50
CARDS:

★★ 65% **Parlors Hall**
Mill St WV15 5AL ☎ 01746 761931 FAX 01746 767058
Located in the Low Town area of Bridgnorth, this 12th-century house was originally a private residence. It now provides comfortable bedrooms, all well equipped with modern amenities including en suite bath or shower rooms. Public rooms retain many original features with impressive oak-panelling in the bar and a superb carved fireplace in the restaurant. As well as a carte menu, which is available on most evenings, there is a popular carvery where even the largest appetites are satisfied. The hotel has its own car park.
15 en suite (bth/shr) (2 fmly) CTV in all bedrooms No dogs (ex guide dogs) 24P European Cuisine V meals Coffee am Tea pm Last d 9.45pm
CARDS:

See advertisement on opposite page

★★ 62% **Falcon**
Saint John St, Lowtown WV15 6AG ☎ 01746 763134
FAX 01746 765401
This 17th-century coaching inn is situated near the bridge at Lowtown. Many original oak beams remain but the interior has been extensively modernised over the years. The bars and restaurant are now in the open-plan mode and the bistro style meals on offer, prove very popular locally and offer good value for money. Bedrooms are equipped with modern facilities, family rooms are available and several rooms have individual videos. Staff are young and friendly and there is a warm atmosphere.
15 rms (5 bth 7 shr) (3 fmly) CTV in all bedrooms 200P English & French Cuisine V meals Coffee am Tea pm Last d 9.30pm
ROOMS: (incl. bkfst) s £35-£39; d £46-£49 * **LB**
OFF-PEAK: (incl. bkfst) s fr £30; d fr £40
MEALS: Lunch £7.50-£14.95alc Dinner £7.50-£15.90alc
CONF: Thtr 50 Class 30 Board 35 Del from £60
CARDS:

BRIDGWATER Somerset Map 03 ST33

★★★ 72% **Walnut Tree Hotel**

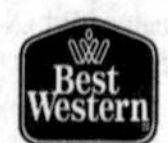

North Petherton TA6 6QA (on A38, 1m S of exit 24 on M5) ☎ 01278 662255 FAX 01278 663946
Proprietors Richard and Hilary Goulden have carefully modernised this 18th-century former coaching inn over the last decade. The majority of the bedrooms are now executive rooms, elegantly furnished and decorated; the facilities exceeding expectations for three stars. Two eating options are offered; the formal Sedgemoor restaurant with an interesting à la carte and the popular Cottage Room serving value for money meals.
32 en suite (bth) (5 fmly) CTV in all bedrooms STV No dogs (ex guide dogs) Night porter 70P Solarium Xmas European Cuisine V meals Coffee am Tea pm No smoking area in restaurant Last d 10pm
ROOMS: (incl. bkfst) s £56-£61; d £72-£80 **LB**
OFF-PEAK: (incl. bkfst) s £34-£42; d £42-£58
MEALS: Lunch £7.50-£12alc Dinner fr £15&alc*
CONF: Thtr 90 Class 46 Board 52 Del from £75
CARDS:

★★ 67% **Friarn Court**
37 St Mary St TA6 3LX (at junct of A38 & A39 turn into St Mary St)
☎ 01278 452859 FAX 01278 452988
Service is friendly and relaxed at this popular town centre hotel. Bedrooms fall into two categories, the executive rooms being more spacious than the standard ones. All are comfortable and tastefully furnished and constant improvements are always being made. Public areas include a cosy bar and more spacious restaurant, where during

the week a full à la carte menu is served, while on Sundays, bar snacks are provided.
16 en suite (bth/shr) (3 fmly) No smoking in 4 bedrooms CTV in all bedrooms No dogs (ex guide dogs) Night porter 14P International Cuisine V meals Coffee am Tea pm Last d 9pm
ROOMS: (incl. bkfst) s £39.90-£59.90; d fr £59.90 **LB**
OFF-PEAK: (incl. bkfst) s fr £35; d fr £45
MEALS: Bar Lunch £5.90-£12.90 High tea £3-£9 Dinner £5.90-£12.90&alc
CONF: Thtr 60 Class 40 Board 30
CARDS:

BRIDLINGTON East Riding of Yorkshire Map 08 TA16

★★★65% Expanse

North Marine Dr YO15 2LS (follow signs North Beach P, pass under railway arch for North Marine Drive. Hotel at bottom of hill)
☎ 01262 675347 FAX 01262 604928
Standing proudly overlooking the sea, this large traditional hotel enjoys panoramic views over the bay and is found on the north shore of the town. Comfortable public areas include a large bar and an inviting lounge, and service is relaxed and friendly. The modern bedrooms vary in size and all are well equipped.
48 en suite (bth/shr) (4 fmly) CTV in all bedrooms No dogs (ex guide dogs) Lift Night porter 30P No coaches Wkly live entertainment Xmas English & French Cuisine V meals Coffee am Tea pm Last d 9pm
ROOMS: (incl. bkfst) s £29.50-£42; d £59-£75 * **LB**
OFF-PEAK: (incl. bkfst) s £29.50-£39.50; d £55-£70
MEALS: Lunch £8.25-£9.25 Dinner fr £13.75*
CONF: Thtr 50 Class 30 Board 24
CARDS:

B

★★68% Revelstoke
1-3 Flamborough Rd YO15 2HU (take B1255 Flamborough Head road and in half mile turn right at mini-roundabout to intersection of the Promenade and Flamborough Rd) ☎ 01262 672362
FAX 01262 672362
This family-owned hotel offers a relaxing stay to both business and tourist guests. Spacious public areas include a delightful restaurant serving a daily carte. The en suite rooms vary in style and size but all provide well equipped modern accommodation. The hotel is conveniently located for the town and the seafront.
25 en suite (bth/shr) (5 fmly) CTV in all bedrooms STV No dogs 14P Wkly live entertainment English & French Cuisine V meals Coffee am Tea pm No smoking in restaurant Last d 9.30pm
ROOMS: (incl. bkfst) s £34-£40; d £50-£64 * **LB**
OFF-PEAK: (incl. bkfst) s £25-£34
MEALS: Lunch £5.50-£10.50 Dinner £12.50-£15&alc*
CONF: Thtr 250 Class 200 Board 100
CARDS:

BRIDPORT Dorset Map 03 SY49

★★★63% Haddon House
West Bay DT6 4EL (from A35, half mile along B3157, signposted to West Bay) ☎ 01308 423626 & 425323 FAX 01308 427348
This attractive family-run hotel is located in West Bay, a few minutes from the quay and seafront. The bedrooms are comfortably furnished and have modern en suite facilities. There is a spacious residents' lounge and a popular bar serving a wide range of food. The restaurant also offers an interesting menu of carefully prepared dishes.
13 en suite (bth/shr) (2 fmly) CTV in all bedrooms STV No dogs (ex guide dogs) 74P ch fac Xmas English & French Cuisine V meals Coffee am Last d 9pm
ROOMS: (incl. bkfst) d £50-£65 **LB**
CARDS:

★★66% Roundham House

Roundham Gardens, West Bay Rd DT6 4BD
☎ 01308 422753 & 425779 FAX 01308 421145
Closed Jan-Feb
This small, personally run hotel is located on the edge of West Bay and offers a friendly welcome. The bedrooms are spacious and well equipped, and there is a comfortable guest lounge. Good home cooked-meals are served in the bright restaurant where guests may enjoy sea views.
8 rms (4 bth 3 shr) (2 fmly) CTV in all bedrooms 13P European Cuisine V meals Coffee am Tea pm No smoking in restaurant Last d 8.30pm
ROOMS: (incl. bkfst) s £30-£35; d £50-£64 * **LB**
MEALS: Sunday Lunch £7.95-£9.95 Dinner fr £16.50&alc
CARDS:

★64% Bridge House
115 East St DT6 3LB (next to River Asker bridge) ☎ 01308 423371
FAX 01308 423371
This attractive 18th-century house is located on the eastern edge of the town and offers relaxing and friendly accommodation. The bedrooms are neat and simply furnished, with modern facilities. There is a small bar and the cellar restaurant offers good home-cooked evening meals using top quality local produce: the home-made bread is especially recommended. There is a small private car park.
10 en suite (bth/shr) (3 fmly) CTV in all bedrooms STV 12P Xmas V meals Coffee am No smoking in restaurant Last d 9pm
ROOMS: (incl. bkfst) s £26-£33; d £35-£47 **LB**
MEALS: Dinner £15&alc*
CONF: Thtr 20 Board 12 Del £50
CARDS:

★59% Bridport Arms
West Bay DT6 4EN (2m S off B3157 Weymouth road)
☎ 01308 422994 FAX 01308 425141
This popular thatched inn is situated on the beach at West Bay, overlooking the quay. The rooms are simply furnished, and some have en suite facilities. There are two residents' lounges, and a lively bar with good range of snacks. The restaurant offers an interesting menu of good home cooking.
8 rms (1 bth 5 shr) 5 annexe rms (3 fmly) CTV in 8 bedrooms V meals Coffee am No smoking area in restaurant Last d 9pm
ROOMS: (incl. bkfst) s £20-£28; d £40-£55 **LB**
MEALS: Lunch £7.75-£8.25 Dinner £9.50-£18alc
CARDS:

BRIGG Lincolnshire Map 08 TA00

★★65% Exchange Coach House Inn
Bigby St DN20 8EJ ☎ 01652 657633 FAX 01652 657636
A Grade 11 listed building standing in the centre of the town and providing modern, well furnished and pretty bedrooms which are situated in a collection of outbuildings to the rear. The main building provides an Oriental-style dining room together with a spacious bar and also a full-sized snooker table which is found on the first floor. The service is friendly and helpful and the hotel has the benefit of its own car park.
21 en suite (bth/shr) (1 fmly) CTV in all bedrooms STV 24P Snooker Pool table Wkly live entertainment American/Mexican Cuisine V meals Coffee am Tea pm No smoking area in restaurant Last d 11pm
ROOMS: (incl. bkfst) s £50-£60; d £60-£70 *
MEALS: Lunch £3.95-£8.95&alc High tea £1.50-£2.50 Dinner £5.95-£12.95&alc
CONF: Thtr 100 Class 50 Board 40 Del from £65
CARDS:

BRIGHOUSE West Yorkshire Map 07 SE12

Forte Posthouse Brighouse

Clifton Village HD6 4HW (on A644 just off junct 25 of M62) ☎ 01484 400400 FAX 01484 400068
Suitable for both the business and leisure traveller, this bright hotel provides modern accommodation in well equipped bedrooms with en suite bathrooms. For more details about Forte Posthouse hotels, consult the Contents page for the section on Hotel Groups.
94 en suite (bth/shr)
CONF: Thtr 200 Class 120 Board 60

BRIGHTON & HOVE East Sussex Map 04 TQ30

★★★★★61% Grand

DE VERE HOTELS

Kings Rd BN1 2FW (adjacent to Conference Centre)
☎ 01273 321188 FAX 01273 202694
This famous hotel has graced the Brighton seafront since 1864. The busy public rooms include the popular King's Restaurant, a Victorian marbled lounge bar and the seafront conservatory; other facilities include Hobden's Health Spa, a night club and a superb conference centre. Bedrooms vary in size, outlook and quality; the smart deluxe rooms have balconies. Further refurbishments are planned over the next two years.
200 en suite (bth/shr) (70 fmly) CTV in all bedrooms STV Lift Night porter 65P Indoor swimming pool (heated) Sauna Solarium Gym Jacuzzi/spa Hairdresser Masseur Steam room Wkly live entertainment Xmas English & French Cuisine V meals Coffee am Tea pm No smoking area in restaurant Last d 10pm
ROOMS: (incl. bkfst) s £75-£135; d £150-£250 * **LB**
OFF-PEAK: (incl. bkfst) s £64-£75; d £128-£165

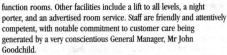

MEALS: Lunch fr £18 Dinner £25.50-£29*
CONF: Thtr 800 Class 420 Del from £160
CARDS:

★★★★ 72% **Brighton Thistle**

Kings Rd BN1 2GS (from Palace Pier rbt take Kings Rd for hotel in 0.5m on right)
☎ 01273 206700 FAX 01273 820692

Right on the seafront, this is a modern and well appointed hotel with light and airy public areas including a comfortable lounge and a well stocked bar. There is a spacious carvery restaurant and a more formal restaurant serving enjoyable dishes with balanced flavours. Bedrooms are spacious and well appointed.

204 en suite (bth/shr) No smoking in 40 bedrooms CTV in all bedrooms STV Lift Night porter Air conditioning 70P Indoor swimming pool (heated) Sauna Solarium Gym Wkly live entertainment Xmas English & French Cuisine V meals Coffee am Tea pm No smoking area in restaurant Last d 10pm
ROOMS: s £125-£150; d £145-£170 * **LB**
OFF-PEAK: (incl. bkfst) s £69-£94; d £102-£127
MEALS: Lunch £14.50-£16.50 Dinner £15.50&alc*
CONF: Thtr 300 Class 180 Board 120 Del from £120
CARDS:

★★★68% **Old Ship**
King's Rd BN1 1NR (on seafront between the piers)
☎ 01273 329001 FAX 01273 820718

Improvements continue at this long-established seafront hotel. The majority of the bedrooms are bright and modern with good facilities and smart fabrics. The public areas are spacious and smart and there are extensive conference and banqueting facilities. Staff are helpful and friendly and the dedicated guest relations manager is delighted to assist with itineraries and in planning activities.
The wine cellars are very special and a visit should be a part of everyone's stay.

152 en suite (bth/shr) (19 fmly) CTV in all bedrooms Lift Night porter 70P Xmas English & French Cuisine V meals Coffee am Tea pm No smoking in restaurant Last d 9.30pm
ROOMS: (incl. bkfst) s £65-£105; d £70-£110 * **LB**
MEALS: Lunch £14-£16&alc High tea £5.50-£12.50 Dinner £18-£19.95&alc
CONF: Thtr 300 Class 120 Board 60 Del from £65
CARDS:

★★★67% **Imperial**
First Av BN3 2GU ☎ 01273 777320
FAX 01273 777310

Completely refurbished and upgraded a few years ago, this professionally managed good quality hotel is conveniently located close to the sea. Bedrooms are particularly well designed and comfortable and range from superior doubles to spacious family rooms. Attractive public rooms comprise an elegant and tastefully furnished lounge, the popular Tates Bar and Hamiltons Brasserie, a furnished front terrace, and modern, well equipped conference and function rooms. Other facilities include a lift to all levels, a night porter, and an advertised room service. Staff are friendly and attentively competent, with notable commitment to customer care being generated by a very conscientious General Manager, Mr John Goodchild.

76 en suite (bth/shr) (2 fmly) No smoking in 10 bedrooms CTV in all bedrooms STV Lift Night porter Air conditioning 8P Xmas French/International Cuisine V meals Coffee am Tea pm Last d 9.30pm
ROOMS: (incl. bkfst) s £40-£70; d £55-£90 * **LB**
OFF-PEAK: (incl. bkfst) s £35-£55; d £45-£70
MEALS: Lunch £14.25&alc Dinner £14.25&alc*
CONF: Thtr 110 Class 50 Board 32
CARDS:

★★★64% **Courtlands**
21-27 The Drive BN3 3JE ☎ 01273 731055 FAX 01273 328295

The upgrading of this well run hotel continues with the refurbishment of the bedrooms bringing them up to a more modern standard. The sizes vary, some are quite spacious and all are well equipped with many modern facilities. The well appointed restaurant offers a choice of set price and a la carte menu and a well chosen wine list. Bar meals are also available in the comfortable cosy bar. The friendly staff give a helpful and attentive service to ensure guests stay is very enjoyable.

43 en suite (bth/shr) 12 annexe en suite (bth/shr) (2 fmly) CTV in all bedrooms No dogs (ex guide dogs) Lift Night porter 24P Indoor swimming pool (heated) Solarium Beach hut on promenade Xmas European Cuisine V meals Coffee am Tea pm No smoking area in restaurant Last d 9.30pm
ROOMS: (incl. bkfst) s £37.50-£52.50; d £55-£70 * **LB**
OFF-PEAK: (incl. bkfst) s £42.50; d £60
MEALS: Lunch £8.95-£9.95&alc High tea fr £6.25 Dinner £12.75&alc
CONF: Thtr 100 Class 50 Board 46 Del from £69.50
CARDS:

★★★60% ***Brighton Oak***
West St BN1 2RQ (hotel just behind Brighton Conference Centre)
☎ 01273 220033 FAX 01273 778000

This modern purpose-built hotel is conveniently located for both the seafront and the city centre. All bedrooms are practically furnished, if a little compact, but executive rooms have more space. The stylish foyer has an ocean liner theme with a feature staircase, open-plan bar and lounge, and spinnakers restaurant which serves popular modern food. Extensive conference facilities are available.

138 en suite (bth/shr) No smoking in 29 bedrooms CTV in all bedrooms STV Lift Night porter Air conditioning English & French Cuisine V meals Coffee am Tea pm Last d 10pm
CONF: Thtr 200 Class 80 Board 60 Del from £90
CARDS:

★★★59% ***The New Madeira Hotel***
19-23 Marine Pde BN2 1TL ☎ 01273 698331 FAX 01273 606193

Recently refurbished and upgraded this popular hotel is conveniently located facing the sea and the Palace Pier within walking distance of the town centre. Accommodation has been furnished in the modern style, and well designed open plan public areas provide reception, lounge, bar and restaurant facilities. Service is relaxed and informal and other facilities includes two well appointed smart conference rooms and the Catfish disco night club which opens on Friday and Saturday nights.

35 en suite (bth/shr) (4 fmly) CTV in all bedrooms STV No dogs (ex guide dogs) Lift Night porter 10P Wkly live entertainment No children 3yrs Last d 7.30pm
CARDS:

★★★59% *Sackville*
189 Kingsway BN3 4GU ☎ 01273 736292 FAX 01273 205759
Situated in an enviable position overlooking Hove Lawns, the bowling green and the sea, this distinctive Edwardian building with its famous green-coloured exterior has a range of individually furnished bedrooms which vary considerably in style and size, but are all well equipped, some with a balcony. There is a comfortable wood-panelled bar-lounge with Chesterfield seating, an adjoining sun lounge, and a well appointed restaurant. The conference and banqueting suites provide versatile facilities for up to 80 persons, and car parking can also be provided.
45 en suite (bth/shr) (2 fmly) CTV in all bedrooms Lift Night porter P Free swimming in sports centre opposite English & Chinese Cuisine V meals Coffee am Tea pm Last d 9.30pm
CARDS:

★★ 76% Topps
17 Regency Square BN1 2FG (opposite West Pier) ☎ 01273 729334 FAX 01273 203679
Closed 24-26 Dec RS Sun Mon & Jan (no restaurant)
(Rosettes awarded for dinner only)
A beautifully restored Regency building situated in the famous Regency Square close to the seafront. It is personally run by owners Paul and Pauline Collins in a friendly relaxed atmosphere, and provides a high level of service. The bedrooms are spacious and comfortably furnished, and equipped with many modern amenities, with several thoughtful extras. Pauline Collins' cooking is unpretentious but good, using quality fresh produce; a fixed-price menu is offered together with a well balanced and reasonably priced wine list. A generous freshly cooked English breakfast is served, continental is also available.
15 en suite (bth/shr) (3 fmly) CTV in all bedrooms No dogs (ex guide dogs) Lift No coaches English & French Cuisine V meals Last d 9.30pm
ROOMS: (incl. bkfst) s £45-£89; d £79-£109 **LB**
CARDS:

★★65% St Catherines Lodge
Seafront, Kingsway BN3 2RZ (opposite King Alfred Leisure Centre) ☎ 01273 778181 FAX 01273 774949
Privately owned by the Houlton family for over 25 years, this Regency-style hotel is located on the seafront in Hove. There is a good range of bedrooms including standard, those with full en suite facilities and the best which have recently been upgraded. Many of the original architectural features have been retained: a cosy wood-panelled bar, Victorian lounge and Regency restaurant (which can be used for private functions), and the Dutch room with its fine display of antique Delft ceramic tiles. Service is courteous, complemented by efficient reception facilities, 24-hour room service, early morning tea, and the personal supervisory management skills of the proprietor Mr John Houlton.
50 rms (40 bth/shr) (4 fmly) CTV in all bedrooms Lift Night porter 9P Games room Xmas European Cuisine V meals Coffee am Tea pm Last d 9pm
ROOMS: (incl. bkfst) s £36-£45; d £54-£65 **LB**
OFF-PEAK: (incl. bkfst) s £30-£36; d £50-£60
MEALS: Lunch £6-£8.25&alc Dinner £13.50&alc
CONF: Thtr 40 Class 24 Board 24 Del from £50
CARDS:

See advertisement on opposite page

BRISTOL Bristol Map 03 ST57

★★★★ 74% Swallow Royal

College Green BS1 5TA (in the city centre next to the cathedral) ☎ 0117 925 5100 FAX 0117 925 1515
Centrally positioned adjacent to the cathedral, this impressively restored hotel boasts an attractive Bath stone façade and has been fitted to the highest standards throughout. Bedrooms are modern but traditionally styled and richly furnished with comfortable armchairs, luxurious marbled bathrooms and air conditioning. The elegant marbled lobby opens onto stylish drawing rooms and a cocktail bar with a terrace. The new congenial residents' bar is situated on the lower floor. However, the star attraction is probably the grand Palm Court restaurant, where a harpist plays three nights a week. Here Michael Kitts and his brigade provide commendable cooking, with dishes such as scallops and langoustine with soya sauce; braised duck with parsnip mash and sugar prunes; and a light but intensely flavoured orange parfait with crystallised almonds.
242 en suite (bth/shr) (14 fmly) No smoking in 100 bedrooms CTV in all bedrooms STV Lift Night porter Air conditioning 200P Indoor swimming pool (heated) Sauna Solarium Gym Jacuzzi/spa Xmas International Cuisine V meals Coffee am Tea pm No smoking area in restaurant Last d 10.30pm
ROOMS: (incl. bkfst) s £99-£120; d £130-£135 * **LB**
OFF-PEAK: (incl. bkfst) s fr £65; d fr £95
MEALS: Lunch £12-£15 High tea fr £8.75 Dinner fr £19*
CONF: Thtr 300 Class 140 Board 30 Del from £150
CARDS:

★★★★ 71% Bristol Marriott

Lower Castle St BS1 3AD (from M32 follow signs 'City Centre' and 'Temple Meads' - do not take underpass)
☎ 0117 929 4281 FAX 0117 927 6377
Though the 70s façade gives no clue, this hotel has benefited from extensive refurbishment, including the terrace floor with its stylish lounge and two restaurants. The Brasserie serves breakfast and informal meals in a lively setting while Le Chateau, a more intimate venue, opens for dinner only and serves cooking of merit. The bedrooms offer a good level of comfort with air conditioning and power showers; additional luxuries are found on the executive floor, where guest have their own lounge. First-class conference facilities are self-contained and there is a smart leisure club. Parking is in the adjacent multi-storey, and valet parking is available.
289 en suite (bth/shr) (138 fmly) No smoking in 200 bedrooms CTV in all bedrooms STV Lift Night porter Air conditioning Indoor swimming pool (heated) Sauna Solarium Gym Jacuzzi/spa Steam

room Whirlpool International Cuisine V meals Coffee am Tea pm No smoking area in restaurant Last d 10.30pm
MEALS: Lunch £15 High tea £3-£8 Dinner £16*
CONF: Thtr 700 Class 400 Board 50 Del from £95
CARDS:

★★★★69% Aztec

Aztec West Business Park, Almondsbury BS12 4TS
(access via M5 (junct 16) & M4) ☎ 01454 201090
FAX 01454 201593

This original, modern hotel is well situated for both the M4 and M5 and successfully caters for its business clientele during the week. The well maintained leisure facilities allow for relaxed weekend entertainment. The building has been attractively designed to include a cosy bar lounge and a split-level restaurant; the hotel also has a nearby pub. Bedrooms are very well furnished and cleverly laid out.
109 en suite (bth/shr) (13 fmly) No smoking in 55 bedrooms CTV in all bedrooms STV Lift Night porter 240P Indoor swimming pool (heated) Squash Snooker Sauna Solarium Gym Jacuzzi/spa Steam room Xmas International Cuisine V meals Coffee am Tea pm No smoking area in restaurant Last d 9.45pm
ROOMS: (incl. bkfst) s £94-£134; d £114-£144 * LB
OFF-PEAK: (incl. bkfst & dinner) d fr £114
MEALS: Bar Lunch fr £10 Dinner fr £22alc*
CONF: Thtr 250 Class 120 Board 48 Del from £140
CARDS:

★★★★64% The Grand Thistle

Broad St BS1 2EL ☎ 0117 929 1645
FAX 0117 922 7619

This stylishly refurbished hotel is situated right in the centre of the city and boasts attractively appointed bedrooms which offer all the modern facilities expected by the business and leisure guest. Ladies are particularly well catered for with a dedicated floor of rooms offering special security arrangements. Public areas are extremely limited but include a choice of bars and eating options. Staff are cheerful and willing.

182 en suite (bth/shr) (8 fmly) No smoking in 23 bedrooms CTV in all bedrooms Lift Night porter 180P Xmas English & French Cuisine V meals Coffee am Tea pm No smoking area in restaurant Last d 10.30pm
ROOMS: s £89-£99; d £99-£109 * LB
MEALS: Lunch £14&alc Dinner £17.50&alc*
CONF: Thtr 600 Class 250 Board 70 Del from £80
CARDS:

★★★★64% Holiday Inn Crowne Plaza

Victoria St BS1 6HY ☎ 0117 976 9988
FAX 0117 925 5040

Convenient for Temple Meads railway station and the city centre this popular and strikingly modern hotel offers contemporary bedrooms which are well geared to the demands of the business guest. The busy open-plan public areas feature a marble

contd.

B

foyer, comfortable seating and an informal all-day restaurant.
128 en suite (bth/shr) (6 fmly) No smoking in 58 bedrooms CTV in all bedrooms STV Lift Night porter 150P Solarium Gym International Cuisine V meals Coffee am Tea pm Last d 9.45pm
CONF: Thtr 250 Class 80 Board 50
CARDS:

★★★70% **Berkeley Square**
15 Berkeley Square, Clifton BS8 1HB (from M32 follow signs for Clifton, take first turn left at traffic lights by Willis memorial Tower (University) into Berkeley Sq) ☎ 0117 925 4000 FAX 0117 925 2970
RS Sun evening
Set in an elegant and peaceful square close to the university, art gallery and Clifton village, this smart Georgian hotel has thoughtfully furnished and tastefully decorated rooms. There is a busy bar in the basement and the restaurant features Creole style dishes, or you may choose to have a light supper in the room. The hotel has its own garage across the square offering secure parking.
43 en suite (bth/shr) No smoking in 12 bedrooms CTV in all bedrooms STV Lift Night porter 20P Wkly live entertainment European & Creole Cuisine V meals Coffee am Tea pm Last d 10pm
ROOMS: (incl. bkfst) s £76-£86; d £102-£122 **LB**
OFF-PEAK: (incl. bkfst) s £49-£69; d £69-£90
MEALS: Bar Lunch £3-£9alc Dinner £15-£25alc*
CONF: Thtr 60 Class 40 Board 30
CARDS:

★★★69% **Jurys Bristol Hotel**
Prince St BS1 4QF ☎ 0117 923 0333
FAX 0117 923 0300
Best Western
Continued good work at this popular city centre hotel with now the majority of bedrooms refurbished to a good standard, and an attractive waterside bistro and terrace bar. Public rooms are bright with attractive marbled finished reception, choice of restaurant and congenial bars. Prompt services by a friendly and smartly turned out brigade with commendable range of room service normally associated with higher classified hotels. Conveniently positioned overlooking Bristol's watershed area guests have free overnight parking at the adjacent multi story car park.
186 en suite (bth/shr) No smoking in 35 bedrooms CTV in all bedrooms STV No dogs (ex guide dogs) Lift Night porter P Boules Discount at local Leisure Club Wkly live entertainment Xmas International Cuisine V meals Coffee am Tea pm No smoking area in restaurant
ROOMS: s fr £90; d fr £90 * **LB**
MEALS: Lunch £12.50*
CONF: Thtr 320 Class 130 Board 80
CARDS:

★★★66% **Redwood Lodge Hotel**

Beggar Bush Ln, Failand BS8 3TG (2m W of Clifton Bridge on B3129) ☎ 01275 393901
FAX 01275 392104
This rambling modern hotel is a popular venue for the conference and leisure guest and is conveniently placed for the city centre and the M5. Tucked back within a green field area, it offers tiered theatre-style meeting rooms and extensive sports and leisure facilities. An informal poolside grill room forms part of the leisure club, but residents can dine more formally in the split-level restaurant. The well equipped bedrooms are in separate wings; some have been more recently redecorated than others.
108 en suite (bth/shr) (4 fmly) No smoking in 81 bedrooms CTV in all bedrooms STV No dogs (ex guide dogs) Night porter 1000P Indoor swimming pool (heated) Outdoor swimming pool Tennis (hard) Squash Snooker Sauna Solarium Gym Pool table Xmas V meals Coffee am Tea pm No smoking area in restaurant
ROOMS: s £80; d £80 * **LB**
OFF-PEAK: (incl. bkfst) s £60-£70; d £70-£90
MEALS: Bar Lunch £4.95 Dinner £8.95-£25alc*
CONF: Thtr 175 Class 100 Board 50 Del £120
CARDS:

★★★65% **Henbury Lodge**
Station Rd, Henbury BS10 7QQ (4.5m NW of City centre off A4018)
☎ 0117 950 2615 FAX 0117 950 9532
This privately owned and family-run hotel is full of character and dates from 1760. It is situated in a quiet suburb of the city just off the A4018, half a mile from Junction 17 of the M5. The bedrooms, some in the adjoining stables conversion, are attractively decorated, and well equipped. The public areas are small, but brightly decorated, and there are magazines, newspapers and games for the guests. In the dining room, which opens out onto well tended gardens, a short, fixed-price menu offers a range of simple, freshly cooked dishes. A meal may begin with a small salad of fresh tuna with roast peppers, tomato and a balsamic vinegar dressing or fresh pasta with Mediterranean vegetables. Main courses range from a plainly grilled lamb cutlets with home-made red currant jelly to whole trout served en papillotte.
11 en suite (bth/shr) 8 annexe en suite (bth/shr) (4 fmly) No smoking in 6 bedrooms CTV in all bedrooms STV 24P No coaches Sauna Solarium Gym Xmas English & Continental Cuisine V meals Coffee am Tea pm No smoking in restaurant Last d 9.30pm
ROOMS: (incl. bkfst) s £68.50-£71.50; d £78.50-£81.50 **LB**
OFF-PEAK: (incl. bkfst) s fr £36; d fr £52
MEALS: Lunch fr £16.80 Dinner fr £16.80
CONF: Thtr 32 Board 20 Del from £95
CARDS:

★★★64% **Avon Gorge**
Sion Hill, Clifton BS8 4LD ☎ 0117 973 8955
FAX 0117 923 8125
Mount Charlotte Hotels MH
This popular city hotel benefits from its picturesque setting in Clifton, overlooking the Avon Gorge and the famous suspension bridge. Bedrooms are equipped to meet the needs of business guests and those at the rear enjoy the view. Public areas are gradually being refurbished; they include various function rooms, two bars - one with a popular terrace - and a bright restaurant. Prompt

contd.

services are carried out by a friendly young team.
76 en suite (bth/shr) (6 fmly) No smoking in 21 bedrooms CTV in all bedrooms Lift Night porter 23P Childrens activity play area Wkly live entertainment Xmas English & French Cuisine V meals Coffee am Tea pm Last d 10pm
ROOMS: (incl. bkfst) s £80-£90; d £90-£105 * **LB**
OFF-PEAK: (incl. bkfst) s fr £80; d fr £90
MEALS: Lunch £11.25&alc Dinner £15&alc*
CONF: Thtr 100 Class 50 Board 26 Del from £55
CARDS:

★★70% **Seeley's**
17-27 St Paul's Rd, Clifton BS8 1LX ☎ 0117 973 8544
FAX 0117 973 2406
Closed 24 Dec-2 Jan
A family-run hotel, close to Clifton village, the university and the city centre, Seeley's continues to improve. All the bedrooms are being upgraded, along with the restaurant and the attractive reception and bar areas. Some of the rooms are in adjacent buildings, but all are now equipped and furnished to the same high standard. Residents and locals enjoy an extensive selection of dishes in Le Chasseur restaurant. Conference facilities are also available.
37 en suite (bth/shr) 18 annexe en suite (bth/shr) (10 fmly) CTV in all bedrooms STV No dogs (ex guide dogs) Night porter 39P Sauna Solarium Gym Jacuzzi/spa ch fac International Cuisine V meals Coffee am Tea pm No smoking area in restaurant Last d 10.30pm
ROOMS: (incl. bkfst) s £50-£55; d £59-£69 * **LB**
OFF-PEAK: (incl. bkfst) s £35-£40; d £44-£50
MEALS: Bar Lunch £4-£5.50 Dinner £13&alc*
CARDS:

★★❀❀69% **Rodney Hotel**
Rodney Place, Clifton BS8 4HY ☎ 0117 973 5422 FAX 0117 946 7092
Closed 22 Dec-4 Jan
An attractive listed terrace property has limited parking to the front. The bedrooms are tastefully decorated and well equipped with the business traveller in mind. The Marguerite Restaurant continues to offer imaginative food cooked with care by head chef Wayne Hatenboer. A carte offers a varied choice of dishes which include an interesting selection of vegetarian food. A recent test meal started with a Mille Feuille of Mushrooms and asparagus in a shallot and basil broth, which was followed by some noisettes of lamb cooked pink exactly as requested, on a minted jus with some freshly cooked vegetables. The meal was completed with a chocolate mousse, flavoured with rum and served with a creme Anglaise.
31 en suite (bth/shr) No smoking in 9 bedrooms CTV in all bedrooms STV Night porter English & French Cuisine V meals Coffee am Tea pm
ROOMS: (incl. bkfst) s fr £54.50; d fr £74 *
OFF-PEAK: (incl. bkfst) s fr £38; d fr £58
MEALS: Lunch £7.95-£9.99 Dinner £12.95-£14.95*
CONF: Thtr 30 Class 20 Board 15
CARDS:

★★67% **Clifton**
St Pauls Rd, Clifton BS8 1LX ☎ 0117 973 6882 FAX 0117 974 1082
Closed 23-29 Dec
This popular hotel, situated just off Whiteladies Road, has benefited from extensive upgrading to some of the well equipped bedrooms. There is a smart lounge at reception and during summer months, drinks can be taken outside on the terrace. Racks Bar and Restaurant in the basement offers a lively informal atmosphere and an interesting selection of dishes on an imaginative menu. Street parking is unrestricted and garages are available by arrangement.
60 rms (48 bth/shr) (2 fmly) No smoking in 15 bedrooms CTV in all bedrooms STV Lift Night porter 20P English & French Cuisine V meals Coffee am Tea pm
ROOMS: (incl. bkfst) s £42-£58; d £56-£72 *
MEALS: Bar Lunch fr £3.50 Dinner fr £15*
CARDS:

★★62% **Glenroy**

CONSORT HOTELS

Victoria Square, Clifton BS8 4EW (junct 19 of M5, follow signs for Clifton come over suspension bridge and turn left after the bakery, hotel around corner on right) ☎ 0117 973 9058 FAX 0117 973 9058
Closed 24-31 Dec
Set in the attractive residential area of Clifton, this small hotel, with its own car park at the rear, offers accommodation geared to the business guest. The bedrooms, whilst equipped with modern comforts, do vary in size and several are situated in an adjacent building. Public areas include a congenial bar, open-plan with the popular carvery restaurant, and the Victoria and Albert conference rooms.
25 en suite (bth/shr) 19 annexe en suite (bth/shr) (9 fmly) CTV in all bedrooms STV Night porter 16P V meals Coffee am No smoking area in restaurant Last d 9.30pm
ROOMS: (incl. bkfst) s £47-£65; d £67-£75 *
OFF-PEAK: (incl. bkfst) s £39-£53; d £48-£57
MEALS: Sunday Lunch £8-£10 Dinner £8-£11*
CONF: Thtr 45 Class 16 Board 25 Del from £75
CARDS:

Forte Posthouse Bristol

FORTE Posthouse

Filton Rd, Hambrook BS16 1QX (100yds from junct 1 of M32 via A4174) ☎ 0117 956 4242
FAX 0117 956 9735
Suitable for both the business and leisure traveller, this bright hotel provides modern accommodation in well equipped bedrooms with en suite bathrooms. For more details about Forte Posthouse hotels, consult the Contents page for the section on Hotel Groups.
197 en suite (bth/shr)
ROOMS: d fr £79 *
CONF: Thtr 300 Class 130 Del from £109

Hilton National Bristol

Redcliffe Way BS1 6NJ (adjacent to St Mary Redcliffe church and 400yds from Temple Meads BR station) v 0117 926 0041 FAX 0117 923 0089
This is a bright, modern hotel, with an informal restaurant, aimed at both the business and leisure guest. All bedrooms have en suite bathrooms and a range of modern facilities. For more information about Hilton National hotels, consult the Contents page under Hotel Groups.
201 en suite (bth/shr)
ROOMS: s £70-£120; d £70-£120 *
CONF: Thtr 350 Class 200 Board 40 Del £140

Travelodge

Travelodge

Cribbs Causeway BS10 7TL v 0117 950 1530
FAX 0117 950 1530
This modern building offers accommodation in smart, spacious and well equipped bedrooms, suitable for family use, and all with en suite bathrooms. Meals may be taken at the nearby family restaurant. For information on room rates and to make a booking, call Roomline free of charge on 0800 850950. For more details about Travelodge, consult the Contents page under Hotel Groups.
40 en suite (bth/shr)

BRIXHAM Devon Map 03 SX95

★★★64% **Quayside**
King St TQ5 9TJ (overlooking the harbour) ☎ 01803 855751
FAX 01803 882733
An attractive hotel created from six period cottages enjoys panoramic

views across the bay to Torbay from its elevated position overlooking the inner harbour. Public areas include a cosy lounge, a snug residents' bar and the larger, busier Ernie Lister's Bar as well as an intimate restaurant specialising in fresh local fish; bedrooms have been modernised and provide all the expected comforts. A car park is available a short walk away.

30 en suite (bth/shr) (4 fmly) CTV in all bedrooms Xmas English & French Cuisine V meals Coffee am Tea pm No smoking in restaurant Last d 9.30pm
ROOMS: (incl. bkfst) s £45-£65; d £55-£75 * **LB**
MEALS: Dinner £20-£25alc*
CARDS:

See advertisement on this page

★★★60% **Berryhead**
Berryhead Rd TQ5 9AJ ☎ 01803 853225 FAX 01803 882084
This imposing property dates back to 1809 and enjoys glorious views from its stunning cliff-top position. The location became the inspiration for the many famous hymns of Rev. Henry Francis Lyte including 'Abide with me' written in the grounds. More recently as an informal hotel, the Berry Head offers comfortable accommodation and a range of facilities including popular bars and all day eating operations.
16 en suite (bth/shr) (2 fmly) CTV in all bedrooms 200P No coaches Croquet lawn Petanque Wkly live entertainment Xmas English & French Cuisine V meals Coffee am Tea pm No smoking area in restaurant Last d 9.30pm
ROOMS: (incl. bkfst) s £40-£55; d £80-£116 * **LB**
OFF-PEAK: (incl. bkfst) s £33-£45; d £66-£90
MEALS: Lunch fr £8.50&alc High tea fr £5 Dinner fr £16&alc
CONF: Thtr 350 Class 250 Board 40 Del from £55
CARDS: £

See advertisement on this page

★60% **Smugglers Haunt**
Church Hill East TQ5 8HH ☎ 01803 853050 & 859416
FAX 01803 858738
This 300 year old hotel is centrally located just a short walk from the harbour. The wide selection of bar meals and the extensive carte make it a popular dining venue. The bedrooms vary in size and are comfortably appointed; some have en suite facilities.
14 rms (4 bth) 2 annexe rms (2 fmly) CTV in all bedrooms Night porter Xmas English & French Cuisine V meals Coffee am Last d 10pm
ROOMS: (incl. bkfst) s fr £22; d fr £38 * **LB**
MEALS: Lunch £4.95-£7.25 Dinner fr £4.95&alc*
CARDS:

BROADSTAIRS Kent Map 05 TR36

★★★❀60% **Royal Albion**
Albion St CT10 1LU (on entering the town follow signs for seafront)
☎ 01843 868071 FAX 01843 861509
RS Sun

contd.

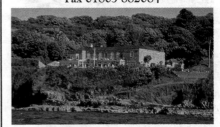

Located on the seafront with delightful views from some of the better bedrooms, this long-established hotel has been run by the Roger family for four generations. The bedrooms are slowly being upgraded and a new ground floor lounge sitting area has been created. Bedrooms are furnished in the modern style and all are well equipped. The main hotel provides the reception, public bar lounge and breakfast room, whilst the restaurant is located two doors away down the street in Marchesi's. Chef Steven Watson continues to produce capable standards of cooking with the seafood dishes coming in for the best praise, along with a great wine list. Staff are friendly and personally supervised by Peter, David and Nicola Roger, and the atmosphere is very relaxed and informal.
19 en suite (bth/shr) (3 fmly) No smoking in 3 bedrooms CTV in all bedrooms STV No dogs (ex guide dogs) Night porter 22P Xmas French Cuisine V meals Coffee am Tea pm No smoking area in restaurant Last d 9.30pm
ROOMS: s £45-£55; d £50-£60 * **LB**
MEALS: Lunch £12-£16 Dinner £16-£18*
CONF: Thtr 80 Class 60 Board 20
CARDS:

BROADWAY Hereford & Worcester Map 04 SP03
See also Buckland

RED STAR HOTEL

★★★★ **The Lygon Arms**

WR12 7DU (on A44 in centre of village)
(Leading Hotels)
☎ 01386 852255 FAX 01386 858611
It is encouraging to see continued investment and upgrading at this well established and famous hostelry. With sympathetic consideration to the original 16th-century coaching inn, a new state of the art conference suite has been added and now sits nicely with the splendid indoor pool and fitness centre. Public rooms have received similar good work which only adds to the cosiness and charm of the flagstone floors and wood panelling; the Great Hall dining room boasts heraldic panels and a minstrel's gallery. Initial exterior impressions of the rather austere bedroom block belie comfortable rooms with character. Although some are more opulent than others they offer quality surroundings with a host of antiques, objets d'art and welcoming little personal touches. A range of British dishes is offered from both the fixed-price menu and carte with pleasing results. Good use is made of quality ingredients with well executed and enjoyable dishes.
63 en suite (bth/shr) CTV in all bedrooms STV Night porter 104P No coaches Indoor swimming pool (heated) Tennis (hard) Snooker Sauna Solarium Gym Croquet lawn Jacuzzi/spa Beauty treatment Xmas International Cuisine V meals Coffee am Tea pm Last d 9.15pm
ROOMS: (incl. cont bkfst) s £117-£143; d £173-£229 * **LB**
CONF: Thtr 80 Class 48 Board 30
CARDS:

★★★ 68% **Dormy House**
Willersey Hill WR12 7LF (2m E off A44) ☎ 01386 852711
FAX 01386 858636
Closed 25 & 26 Dec RS Sat (restaurant closed for lunch)
This uniquely converted farmhouse dates back to the 17th century and stands in its own grounds in an elevated position high above the village of Broadway. The public areas are cosy, and the range of facilities have been recently extended by the addition of a gym, games room and sauna room. Bedrooms are individual in style, all equipped with modern comforts. Several are situated in the converted barns and stables. Chef Alan Cutler has been classically trained, and believes in using only the best quality ingredients, as is evident from the dishes he produces.
26 en suite (bth/shr) 23 annexe en suite (bth) (3 fmly) CTV in all bedrooms Night porter 80P No coaches Sauna Gym Pool table Croquet lawn Putting green Games room Nature/jogging trail English & French Cuisine V meals Coffee am Tea pm No smoking area in restaurant Last d 9.30pm
ROOMS: (incl. bkfst) s £63-£84; d £126-£152 * **LB**
MEALS: Lunch £18.50 Dinner £27.50&alc
CONF: Thtr 200 Class 100 Board 25 Del from £145
CARDS:

See advertisement on opposite page

★★★ 62% **Broadway**
The Green, High St WR12 7AA (set back from the High Street (A44), behind the village green) ☎ 01386 852401 FAX 01386 853879
Parts of this delightful old property date back to 1575 and the public areas have a wealth of charm and character. Set in the village centre, well back from the main road, it has a lovely garden and private car park behind it. Bedrooms, including one with a four-poster bed, one in a separate building and some on the ground floor, have predominantly modern appointments. Public areas include a spacious, attractively furnished restaurant with a beamed ceiling, a quaint and cosy bar, a comfortable lounge with an inglenook fireplace and a sun lounge. There are also a private dining room, a courtyard patio area and a cottage suitable for small conferences and meetings.
17 en suite (bth/shr) 1 annexe en suite (bth/shr) (1 fmly) No smoking in 4 bedrooms CTV in all bedrooms No dogs (ex guide dogs) 22P Xmas V meals Coffee am Tea pm No smoking in restaurant Last d 9pm
ROOMS: (incl. bkfst) s £45-£65; d £70-£85 * **LB**
MEALS: Sunday Lunch £8.95-£13.75&alc Dinner £16.95*
CONF: Thtr 20 Class 16 Board 14 Del £89
CARDS:

★★ 69% **Collin House**
Collin Ln WR12 7PB (1m NW off A44, signposted 'Willersey')
☎ 01386 858354
Closed 24-28 Dec
This charming 16th-century Cotswold stone house stands in its own grounds and gardens, just off the A44 on the road sign-posted to Willersley. Bedrooms are traditional in style, two rooms having four-poster beds, while public areas retain a wealth of charm and character, their exposed beams, stoneflagged floors and inglenook fireplaces enhanced by antique and period furnishings. Chefs Mark Brooks and Anthony Ike provide a wide choice of well prepared dishes on a carte supplemented by daily blackboard specials; a good range of bar meals are also available and the hotel is a popular dining venue for locals.
7 rms (5 bth 1 shr) No dogs 35P Outdoor swimming pool Croquet lawn V meals No smoking in restaurant Last d 9pm

ROOMS: (incl. bkfst) s fr £45; d fr £87 * LB
MEALS: Lunch fr £16 Dinner £16-£24*
CARDS:

BROCKENHURST Hampshire Map 04 SU30

★★★ 78% **New Park Manor**

Lyndhurst Rd SO42 7QH (on A337 1.5m from Lyndhurst) ☎ 01590 623467 FAX 01590 622268

Surrounded by parkland and with its own equestrian centre New Park Manor is not the classical English country house it appears to be. The owner and his capable general manager Arvid Oechies are both Dutch, as are many of the charming staff. Bedrooms are divided into two wings with the older wing having more character and charm but all are extremely comfortable with thoughtful extras such as fresh fruit and a guard cat to ensure visitors are not disturbed. The public areas are exceptional with an elegant bar and lounge and superbly appointed restaurant where chef Matthew Tilt serves an imaginative range of cuisine created where possible from local ingredients. Dishes such as mille feuille of potato and turnip with foie gras and wild mushrooms strike the correct forest note.

24 en suite (bth/shr) (4 fmly) No smoking in 4 bedrooms CTV in all bedrooms STV No dogs 60P Outdoor swimming pool (heated) Tennis (hard) Riding Solarium Croquet lawn Wkly live entertainment No children 7yrs Xmas English & French Cuisine V meals Coffee am Tea pm No smoking in restaurant Last d 9pm
ROOMS: (incl. bkfst) s £75; d £110 * LB
OFF-PEAK: (incl. bkfst) s £65; d £95
MEALS: Lunch fr £15 Dinner fr £27.50*
CONF: Thtr 80 Class 26 Board 30 Del from £105
CARDS:

See advertisement on page 155

★★★ 73% **Careys Manor**

SO42 7RH (on A337) ☎ 01590 623551
FAX 01590 622799

Originally a hunting lodge, Careys Manor stands in its own grounds on the edge of the village. The bedrooms are comfortably and attractively furnished and some have balconies overlooking the pretty garden. The public areas include a large but cosy lounge with a log fire, a cocktail

contd.

bar and a smart restaurant. The Health Club is very popular and offers a large pool, sauna and fitness room with qualified instructors. Le Blaireau Cafe provides an informal eating option in a typically French style, serving drinks and snacks all day. Chef Kevin Dorrington offers a more classical menu in the restaurant, making good use of local game and other produce.
15 en suite (bth/shr) 64 annexe en suite (bth/shr) No smoking in 28 bedrooms CTV in all bedrooms STV Night porter 180P Indoor swimming pool (heated) Sauna Solarium Gym Jacuzzi/spa Steam room Beauty therapists Xmas English & French Cuisine V meals Coffee am Tea pm No smoking in restaurant Last d 9.45pm
ROOMS: (incl. bkfst) s £69-£79; d £109-£129 * LB
OFF-PEAK: (incl. bkfst & dinner) s £69-£79; d £129-£149
MEALS: Lunch fr £13.95 Dinner fr £19.95&alc*
CONF: Thtr 100 Class 70 Board 40 Del from £125
CARDS:

See advertisement on opposite page

★★★ 73% ***Rhinefield House***

THE Virgin HOTEL COLLECTION

Rhinefield Rd SO42 7QB (take A35 towards Bournemouth. Turning to Rhinefield is 3m from Lyndhurst on the left) ☎ 01590 622922
FAX 01590 622800
This splendid mock-Elizabethan mansion was built in the late 19th century and lies in the heart of the New Forest. The impressive public rooms are popular with weddings at weekends; make sure you have a look at the fascinating Alhambra Room. The bedrooms are a good size and have undergone a very smart refurbishment during 1996. The gardens are formally laid out and are most interesting, and there are both indoor and outdoor leisure activities.

An extended range of services include 24-hour room service and an evening turndown.
34 en suite (bth/shr) No smoking in 12 bedrooms CTV in all bedrooms STV No dogs (ex guide dogs) Night porter 80P Indoor swimming pool (heated) Outdoor swimming pool (heated) Tennis (hard) Sauna Solarium Gym English & French Cuisine V meals Coffee am Tea pm Last d 10pm
CARDS:

★★★ 66% **Balmer Lawn**

Lyndhurst Rd SO42 7ZB (take A337 towards Lymington, house on left hand side behind village cricket green) (Hilton) ☎ 01590 623116
FAX 01590 623864
One of the best locations for access to all the Forest's attractions, this well established hotel has been extensively refurbished in recent years to provide comfortable public rooms and a good range of well equipped bedrooms. A cosy reception lounge extends into a cocktail bar and popular meeting room. Other attractions are the Hunting Lodge restaurant and a wide range of sporting and leisure facilities.
55 en suite (bth/shr) (11 fmly) No smoking in 35 bedrooms CTV in all bedrooms Lift Night porter 90P Indoor swimming pool (heated) Outdoor swimming pool (heated) Tennis (hard) Squash Sauna Gym Pool table Jacuzzi/spa Table tennis Xmas V meals Coffee am Tea pm No smoking in restaurant Last d 9.30pm
ROOMS: (incl. bkfst) s £48.75-£57.50; d £78.40-£110 * LB
OFF-PEAK: (incl. bkfst & dinner) s £40-£70; d £90-£110
MEALS: Lunch fr £8.50 High tea fr £4.95 Dinner fr £12.95*
CONF: Thtr 100 Class 40 Board 40 Del £110
CARDS:

★★★ 65% **Forest Park**

Forestdale Hotels

Rhinefield Rd SO42 7ZG (from A337 to Brockenhurst turn into Meerut Rd, follow winding road through Waters Green, 0.5m to a T junct, turn right into Rhinefield Road) ☎ 01590 622844 FAX 01590 623948
A popular destination for short breaks, this informally run hotel in the heart of the New Forest has benefited from a recent change of management. There are great walks to be enjoyed and the hotel also has its own riding stables and cosy gardens. Bedrooms vary; some are better than others, but all are well equipped.
38 en suite (bth/shr) (2 fmly) No smoking in 2 bedrooms CTV in all bedrooms 80P Outdoor swimming pool (heated) Tennis (hard) Riding Sauna ch fac Xmas English & French Cuisine V meals Coffee am Tea pm No smoking area in restaurant Last d 10pm
ROOMS: (incl. bkfst) s fr £65; d £85-£90 * LB
OFF-PEAK: (incl. bkfst & dinner) s fr £78.50; d £112-£122
MEALS: Lunch fr £6.95 High tea fr £5 Dinner fr £16.95*
CONF: Thtr 50 Class 20 Board 24 Del from £85
CARDS:

★★ 77% **Whitley Ridge Country House**

Beaulieu Rd SO4 7QL (access via B3055 towards Beaulieu) ☎ 01590 622354 FAX 01590 622856
Rennie and Sue Law have lovingly restored this former hunting lodge to create an intimate and friendly hotel which, although tucked away in the depths of the New Forest, is only 20 minutes' drive from the M27. All bedrooms are well equipped and have been furnished under the direction of Sue Law who has a keen eye for detail and wonderful taste in fabrics. The restaurant and two lounges are also most comfortable, with fresh flowers and books creating a country-house feeling. It is worth making a point of dining in for the excellent home cooking.
13 en suite (bth/shr) CTV in all bedrooms 30P Tennis (hard) Xmas English & French Cuisine V meals Coffee am Tea pm No smoking in restaurant Last d 9pm
ROOMS: (incl. bkfst) s £48-£56; d £78-£96 * LB
OFF-PEAK: (incl. bkfst) s £48-£54; d £78-£88
MEALS: Lunch £12-£12.50 Dinner £19.50-£20&alc*
CONF: Thtr 40 Class 40 Board 20 Del from £90
CARDS:

★★ 70% **Cloud**

Meerut Rd SO42 7TD (first turning right off A337 approaching Brockenhurst from Lyndhurst) ☎ 01590 622165 FAX 01590 622165
This delightful hotel is personally run by Avril Owton who continues to upgrade in all areas. The bedrooms are bright and comfortably furnished, with spotless modern en suite facilities; most rooms have lovely views over the New Forest. The public rooms include a smartly presented restaurant and several cosy little lounges with log fires in the winter months.
16 en suite (bth/shr) (3 fmly) CTV in all bedrooms 20P No coaches Xmas V meals Coffee am Tea pm No smoking in restaurant Last d 8.30pm
ROOMS: (incl. bkfst) s fr £48; d fr £80 * LB
MEALS: Lunch fr £5.95 High tea fr £5 Dinner fr £16*
CARDS:

★★ 67% ***Watersplash***

The Rise SO42 7ZP ☎ 01590 622344 FAX 01590 624047
This popular Victorian hotel has been in the Foster family for 37 years and is now run by the second generation. Robin and Judy continue to make improvements to all areas and are at present upgrading the

bedrooms, with co-ordinated décor and added facilities. The restaurant overlooks the pretty garden, and there is a comfortable residents' lounge and separate bar. The outdoor pool is particularly popular in the summer months.
23 en suite (bth/shr) (6 fmly) CTV in all bedrooms 29P Outdoor swimming pool (heated) Motor cruiser ch fac English & Continental Cuisine V meals Coffee am Tea pm Last d 8.30pm
CARDS:

BROMBOROUGH Merseyside Map 07 SJ38

Travel Inn

High St L62 7HZ (on A41) ☎ 0151 334 2917
FAX 0151 334 0443
Purpose-built accommodation, offering spacious, well equipped bedrooms, all with en suite bathrooms. Meals may be taken at the nearby family restaurant. For more information about Travel Inns, consult the Contents page under Hotel Groups.
31 en suite (bth/shr)
ROOMS: d £35.50 *

BROME Suffolk Map 05 TM17

★★★64% **Cornwallis Arms**

IP23 8AJ (off B1077, 50yds from junct with A140 in direction of Eye) ☎ 01379 870326
FAX 01379 870051
There are many attractive features to this 16th-century hotel, not least the long tree-lined avenue of limes, the topiary garden, a cricket pitch and an illuminated well in the character rustic bar. An elegant restaurant offers serious dining from a short interesting menu, or alternatively informal dining is available in the bar from an interesting

contd.

selection of daily blackboard specials. Bedrooms are individually furnished, well equipped and decorative, with period furniture and cheerful bold colour schemes; all have good modern bathrooms. At the time of our last visit considerable redecoration and alterations were scheduled, including the development of more comfortable areas within the public rooms.

11 en suite (bth/shr) (3 fmly) CTV in all bedrooms STV 100P No coaches Croquet lawn Xmas English & French Cuisine V meals Coffee am Tea pm No smoking area in restaurant Last d 9.30pm
ROOMS: (incl. bkfst) s £59.50-£69.50; d £74.50-£89.50 **LB**
MEALS: Lunch £12-£17 High tea £5.95-£8.95 Dinner £16.95-£22.95
CONF: Thtr 40 Class 20 Board 20 Del from £85
CARDS:

BROMLEY Greater London See LONDON SECTION plan 1 G1

★★★69% **Bromley Court**

Bromley Hill BR1 4JD (N, signposted off A21. Opposite Mercedes Benz garage on Bromley Hill)
☎ 0181 464 5011 FAX 0181 460 0899
A grand mansion with modern extensions standing just off the A21, amid three acres of well kept grounds in a residential area north-west of the town centre. Accommodation is spread over several areas, but though the rooms vary in shape and size all are well equipped. The attractive restaurant has a conservatory overlooking the garden and Chef Bob Hunt offers interesting and well cooked dishes. The restaurant also features dinner dancing and live entertainment on Friday and Saturday nights. Other facilities include the new leisure club, well furnished comfortable lounge bars, smart marble reception lobby and excellent facilities for all kinds of meetings.
116 en suite (bth/shr) (4 fmly) No smoking in 14 bedrooms CTV in all bedrooms STV Lift Night porter 100P Sauna Croquet lawn Putting green Jacuzzi/spa Xmas English & French Cuisine V meals Coffee am Tea pm No smoking area in restaurant Last d 10pm
ROOMS: (incl. bkfst) s £82-£85; d £91-£95
MEALS: Lunch £14.95&alc Dinner £17.95&alc
CONF: Thtr 150 Class 80 Board 45 Del from £100
CARDS:

BROMSGROVE Hereford & Worcester Map 07 SO97

★★★73% **Pine Lodge**
Kidderminster Rd B61 9AB (on A38) ☎ 01527 576600
FAX 01527 878981
Within easy reach of the Midlands motorway network, this Mediterranean-looking hotel is set in beautiful countryside. There are spacious open-plan public areas, two restaurants and all-day snacks in the terrace lounge. Bedrooms are a good size with comfortable chairs and there is a range of room services. Staff are smartly dressed and friendly.
114 en suite (bth/shr) (18 fmly) No smoking in 18 bedrooms CTV in all bedrooms STV Lift Night porter 250P Indoor swimming pool (heated) Snooker Sauna Solarium Gym Jacuzzi/spa Childrens play area ch fac English & Continental Cuisine V meals Coffee am Tea pm No smoking area in restaurant Last d 10pm
ROOMS: (incl. bkfst) s fr £89.50; d fr £99.50 * **LB**
OFF-PEAK: (incl. bkfst) s fr £29.95; d fr £59
CONF: Thtr 200 Class 140 Board 30
CARDS:

See advertisement on opposite page

BROOK (NEAR CADNAM) Hampshire Map 04 SU21

★★★67% **Bell Inn**
SO43 7HE (leave M27 junct 1 onto B3079, hotel a mile and a half on right) ☎ 01703 812214 FAX 01703 813958
This popular, well established hotel revolves around the golf course, although it is also an ideal base from which to visit the New Forest and surrounding sights. The bedrooms are comfortable and attractively furnished, and the public areas offer a cosy, friendly atmosphere. A wide range of fresh local produce is offered in both the oak-beamed bar and the restaurant. Non-golfers may prefer to relax in the comfort of the guest lounge.
22 en suite (bth) (3 fmly) No smoking in 11 bedrooms CTV in all bedrooms 150P Golf 18 Xmas English & French Cuisine V meals Coffee am Tea pm No smoking in restaurant Last d 9.30pm
ROOMS: (incl. bkfst) s £45-£59 * **LB**
MEALS: Lunch £8.50-£12.50&alc Dinner £23.50-£25.50*
CONF: Thtr 40 Class 60 Board 40 Del from £79
CARDS:

BROXTED Essex Map 05 TL52

★★★78% **Whitehall**
Church End CM6 2BZ ☎ 01279 850603 FAX 01279 850385
Closed 26-30 Dec
This friendly and well managed hotel dates back to the Tudor period and boasts good-sized, well equipped bedrooms. The Elizabethan character of the original building is reflected in log-burning fires and a timber-vaulted restaurant which serves soundly prepared meals in modern country style. A typical meal may start with lobster tortellini with Parma ham, sun-dried tomatoes and parmesan followed by monkfish tail with leeks and roasted shallots in a squid-ink sauce and finally ginger mousse with caramelised orange sauce. More adventurous diners might like to try the six-course surprise menu which depends on last-minute availability of ingredients. The hotel can also cater for conferences.
25 en suite (bth) (3 fmly) CTV in all bedrooms No dogs (ex guide dogs) Night porter 37P No coaches Outdoor swimming pool Tennis (hard) V meals Coffee am Tea pm Last d 9.30pm
ROOMS: (incl. bkfst) s £80; d £110-£140 * **LB**
MEALS: Lunch £13.50-£19.50 Dinner £13.50-£37.50*
CONF: Thtr 120 Class 80 Board 48 Del from £135
CARDS:

BROXTON Cheshire Map 07 SJ45

★★★66% **Broxton Hall Country House**
Whitchurch Rd CH3 9JS ☎ 01829 782321 FAX 01829 782330
Closed 25 Dec
This privately owned and personally run hotel is situated in five acres of lovely gardens very close to the roundabout where the A41 meets the A534 just south of Chester. The house itself is Tudor and has been decorated with real character. On cooler days the fire is lit in the front hall, the drawing room is comfortably furnished with deep cushioned sofas and in addition to the spacious bar the restaurant enjoys views across the terrace and gardens. It was here that a recent dinner was thoroughly enjoyed from the short fixed price menu. A first course of deliciously fresh mussels with a white wine, garlic and shallot sauce was followed by a very tender and well cooked rack of lamb. An enormous portion of bread and butter pudding finished a carefully prepared and well presented meal. The hotels' bedrooms are comfortably furnished and are in keeping with the style of the house.

Mr and Mrs Hedley and their small team of staff make every effort to ensure their guests are comfortable and well looked after.
12 en suite (bth/shr) (1 fmly) CTV in 11 bedrooms STV 30P No coaches Croquet lawn Wkly live entertainment No children 12yrs English & French Cuisine V meals Coffee am Tea pm Last d 9.30pm
ROOMS: (incl. bkfst) s £55-£60; d £70-£105 * LB
MEALS: Lunch £12-£22alc Dinner £23.90-£26.90*
CARDS:

○ ***Carden Park Hotel Golf & Health Resort***
CH3 9DQ (on A534) ☎ 01829 731000
83 en suite (bth/shr)

BRYHER See Scilly, Isles of

BUCKDEN North Yorkshire Map 07 SD97

★★65% **Buck Inn**
BD23 5JA (on B6160) ☎ 01756 760228 & 760342
FAX 01756 760227
(Rosette awarded for dinner only)
This delightfully attractive village inn and hotel stands in beautiful Dales countryside and retains much of the Georgian coaching house atmosphere, with open fires, stone floors and exposed beams. The pretty bedrooms are comfortable and well equipped, and the staff are caring and attentive. There is a very good range of dishes available, including extensive bar meals whilst the restaurant continues to gain a reputation for excellent cooking.
14 en suite (bth/shr) (2 fmly) CTV in all bedrooms 30P Xmas English & French Cuisine V meals Coffee am Tea pm No smoking in restaurant Last d 9.30pm
ROOMS: (incl. bkfst) s £31-£34; d £62-£68 * LB
MEALS: Lunch £10-£18 Dinner £14-£20*
CONF: Class 30 Del from £60
CARDS:

BUCKHURST HILL Essex Map 05 TQ49
See LONDON SECTION plan 5 F5

★★62% **The Roebuck**
North End IG9 5QY ☎ 0181 505 4636
FAX 0181 504 7826
REGAL
A Collection of Individual Hotels
This ivy-clad hotel was once an inn, and its bars have kept their appeal for local townsfolk. There is, however, a peaceful rural atmosphere about the hotel and the bedrooms offer sound standards of comfort in the traditional style.
29 en suite (bth/shr) No smoking in 10 bedrooms CTV in all bedrooms 40P Xmas V meals Coffee am Tea pm No smoking in restaurant Last d 10pm
ROOMS: s £70; d £80 * LB
OFF-PEAK: d £59.50
MEALS: Lunch £9.25-£12.95 Dinner £16.95&alc*
CONF: Thtr 200 Class 60 Board 14 Del £95
CARDS:

BUCKINGHAM Buckinghamshire Map 04 SP63

★★★71% **Villiers**
3 Castle St MK18 1BS ☎ 01280 822444 FAX 01280 822113
This town centre hotel has much to commend; primarily business-orientated, the conference facilities available are excellent with state of the art audio-visual equipment. Bedrooms have been carefully planned to maximise usable space and to ensure guests' comfort. There are two dining rooms, Henry's restaurant and a separate Italian trattoria. The stone-floored pub is popular with both guests and locals alike. Staff work hard to make guests feel welcome and are backed up by a professional management team.

contd.

38 en suite (bth/shr) (25 fmly) CTV in all bedrooms STV No dogs (ex guide dogs) Lift Night porter 53P Free membership of leisure club Wkly live entertainment ch fac Xmas English & Italian Cuisine V meals Coffee am Tea pm Last d 10pm
ROOMS: (incl. bkfst) s fr £70; d fr £89 *
OFF-PEAK: (incl. bkfst) s fr £55; d fr £79
MEALS: Sunday Lunch fr £14.95&alc High tea fr £8 Dinner £17.95-£21.25&alc*
CONF: Thtr 250 Class 100 Board 60 Del from £95
CARDS:

See advertisement on page 157

★★★66% **Buckingham Lodge**
Buckingham Ring Rd South MK18 1RY (on A421) ☎ 01280 822622 FAX 01280 823074
A modern purpose-built hotel designed with the needs of the business traveller in mind, there are extensive conference facilities, together with plenty of desk space provided in the well appointed bedrooms. An attractive well equipped leisure suite helps with relaxation, as does the open-plan restaurant and bar.
70 en suite (bth/shr) (6 fmly) No smoking in 24 bedrooms CTV in all bedrooms STV Night porter 120P Indoor swimming pool (heated) Snooker Sauna Solarium Gym Jacuzzi/spa Steam room Xmas English & French Cuisine V meals Coffee am Tea pm No smoking area in restaurant Last d 9.45pm
ROOMS: s £59-£74; d £59-£84 * **LB**
OFF-PEAK: s £49-£69; d £79
MEALS: Lunch £7.25-£10.50 Dinner £10.25-£11.95*
CONF: Thtr 160 Class 90 Board 50 Del from £105
CARDS:

BUCKLAND (NEAR BROADWAY) Gloucestershire Map 04 SP03

RED STAR HOTEL

★★★ **Buckland Manor**
WR12 7LY (off B4632) ☎ 01386 852626
FAX 01386 853557

Meticulous attention to detail remains the hallmark of this peacefully located Cotswold stone manor house, dating from the 13th-century. The gardens and grounds are immaculately kept, and guests can enjoy the private putting green, croquet lawns, tennis courts and a heated swimming pool. Inside, the house offers all the charm of the original architecture, carefully combined with modern comforts. Log fires burn in each of the sumptuously furnished sitting rooms, antique pieces reflect the tastes of several centuries, and beautiful flower arrangements complete the picture. Individually decorated bedrooms offer similar levels of comfort, some have four-poster beds and fireplaces and all the bathrooms use water drawn from the Manor's own spring. The cooking skills of chef Martyn Pearn and his team continue to impress. The monthly-changing carte offers dishes of interest, aptly supported by a selection of fine wines from around the world. A recent inspection meal started with feuillete of creamy scrambled free range eggs, served with an assortment of wild mushrooms in a richly flavoured Madeira sauce, and was followed by a succulent breast of chicken accompanied by fresh noodles and a creamy sauce delicately flavoured with Gewurztraminer wine. A lightly textured hot citrus soufflé, served with a raspberry sorbet and coulis, was chosen from the dessert list, which included a delicious range of hot and cold puddings.
13 en suite (bth/shr) (2 fmly) CTV in all bedrooms No dogs

30P No coaches Outdoor swimming pool (heated) Tennis (hard) Croquet lawn Putting green No children 12yrs Xmas International Cuisine V meals Coffee am Tea pm No smoking in restaurant
ROOMS: (incl. bkfst) s £165-£315; d £175-£325 *
MEALS: Lunch £27.50*
CARDS:

BUCKLERS HARD Hampshire Map 04 SU40

★★★58% **Master Builders House**
SO42 7XB ☎ 01590 616253 FAX 01590 616297
This 18th century house is beautifully located in its own pretty gardens running down to the river. Some bedrooms are located in the main house and retain much of their original character, two have four poster beds; the remainder of the bedrooms are in a modern annexe, all rooms are well equipped. The bright attractive restaurant takes full advantage of the lovely views and offers a daily menu and an interesting carte. There is also the popular Yachtsman's Bar which offers traditional pub fare.
6 rms (4 bth/shr) 17 annexe en suite (bth/shr) No smoking in 8 bedrooms CTV in all bedrooms 80P No coaches Fishing Clay pigeon shooting Boating English & French Cuisine V meals Coffee am Tea pm No smoking area in restaurant Last d 9.30pm
MEALS: Lunch £12.50-£15.45&alc High tea £6.95&alc Dinner £15.45&alc*
CONF: Thtr 50 Class 25 Board 30
CARDS:

BUDE Cornwall & Isles of Scilly Map 02 SS20

★★★67% **Hartland**
Hartland Ter EX23 8JY ☎ 01288 355661 FAX 01288 355664
Closed mid Nov-Etr (ex Xmas)
The Hartland overlooks the estuary and is only a minute's walk to the beach. This 1930s hotel is managed by a family who care about their guests: they still bring early morning tea to the well equipped modern rooms.

29 en suite (bth/shr) (2 fmly) CTV in all bedrooms Lift 30P Outdoor swimming pool (heated) Wkly live entertainment Xmas International Cuisine V meals Coffee am Tea pm Last d 8.30pm
ROOMS: (incl. bkfst) s £35-£45; d £58-£72 * **LB**
OFF-PEAK: (incl. bkfst) s £33-£41; d £54-£64
MEALS: Lunch £13.25-£14.25 Dinner £18-£19

★★★66% **Falcon**
Breakwater Rd EX23 8SD (turn off A39 into Bude and follow road to Widemouth bay. Hotel is on right as you cross over canal bridge).
☎ 01288 352005 FAX 01288 356359
The warm West Country hospitality and the family atmosphere make this hotel a most enjoyable place to stay. Bedrooms have been recently refurbished to a high standard and all are decorated using pretty pastel colours. Bathrooms are especially attractive and one room features a large whirlpool bath. Guests have the option of eating in the bar or choosing to dine in the more formal candlelit restaurant.
23 en suite (bth/shr) (5 fmly) CTV in all bedrooms STV 20P No coaches Sauna Solarium Gym Pool table Jacuzzi/spa French cuisine V meals Coffee am No smoking area in restaurant Last d 9.30pm
ROOMS: (incl. bkfst) s £33-£35; d £66-£70 **LB**
MEALS: Sunday Lunch £8.50 Dinner £16&alc
CONF: Thtr 60 Class 30 Board 30
CARDS:

See advertisement on this page

★★66% **Camelot**
Downs View EX23 8RE (turn off A39 into Bude, drive through Bude across Golf Course, hotel is on left overlooking golf course)
☎ 01288 352361 FAX 01288 355470
With its close proximity to the Bude and North Cornwall Golf Club, this much-extended Edwardian house is a popular venue for golfers. Privately owned and personally run, it provides well maintained, modern accommodation which includes bedrooms on the ground floor and a family room, all tastefully and attractively decorated. Public rooms include a comfortable lounge and cosy bar with a golfing theme; there is also a games room.
21 en suite (bth/shr) (3 fmly) CTV in all bedrooms STV No dogs (ex guide dogs) 21P No coaches Pool table Darts Table tennis V meals No smoking in restaurant Last d 8.30pm
ROOMS: (incl. bkfst) s £22-£26; d £44-£52 * **LB**
MEALS: Dinner £14&alc*
CARDS:

★★65% **Bude Haven**
Flexbury Av EX23 8NS ☎ 01288 352305
Situated in a quiet residential area away from the hurly burly of the town, this Edwardian house retains many original features. A friendly relaxed atmosphere is created by Margaret and Alan Bird, who are assisted by their daughter Sarah. Bedrooms are neatly furnished and decorated. In the dining room an interesting selection of dishes is available.

contd.

12 en suite (bth/shr) (2 fmly) CTV in all bedrooms No dogs (ex guide dogs) 8P No coaches Xmas V meals No smoking in restaurant Last d 7.30pm
ROOMS: (incl. bkfst) s £23-£28; d £40-£52 **LB**
OFF-PEAK: (incl. bkfst) s £20-£22; d £37-£39
MEALS: Bar Lunch £5.50-£7 Dinner £10
CARDS:

See advertisement on page 159

★★65% **Maer Lodge**

Crooklets Beach EX23 8NG (leave A39 at Stratton to Bude 1m. Turn right into The Strand and up Belle Vue past shops. Bear left at Somerfield to Crooklets Beach & turn right) ☎ 01288 353306 FAX 01288 353306
This former coaching inn in its own gardens is within easy reach of the beach and golf course. The Stanley family have been here for over thirty years and provide a warm welcome. Public areas include two comfortable lounges and a light, airy dining room where a pianist often plays. The bedrooms are comfortable and clean.
16 en suite (bth/shr) (4 fmly) No smoking in all bedrooms CTV in all bedrooms 15P Pool table Mini-golf Wkly live entertainment Xmas English & Continental Cuisine V meals Coffee am No smoking in restaurant
ROOMS: (incl. bkfst) s £32-£34.50; d £58-£63 * **LB**
OFF-PEAK: (incl. bkfst) s fr £29.50; d fr £53
MEALS: Dinner fr £8.50*
CONF: Class 60 Board 15
CARDS:

★★65% **St Margaret's**
Killerton Rd EX23 8EN ☎ 01288 352252 & 352401
FAX 01288 355995
This friendly, privately-owned and personally-run hotel is situated in a quiet residential area within easy reach of the town centre. Bedrooms have modern furnishings and are very well equipped; they include a ground floor room and family rooms. Downstairs there are a lounge bar, a separate lounge for non-smokers and a pleasant cottage-style restaurant which has a conservatory lounge overlooking the large, attractive garden.
10 en suite (bth/shr) (2 fmly) CTV in all bedrooms STV 4P No coaches Xmas English & Continental Cuisine V meals Coffee am Tea pm No smoking in restaurant Last d 8.30pm
ROOMS: (incl. bkfst) s £30; d £46-£52 * **LB**
OFF-PEAK: (incl. bkfst) d £40-£50
MEALS: Lunch fr £7.50 Dinner fr £12&alc*
CONF: Class 25 Board 25
CARDS:

★★64% **Penarvor**
Crooklets Beach EX23 8NE (on headland 50yds from Crooklets beach)
☎ 01288 352036 FAX 01288 355027
Closed Nov-Feb
This family-run hotel is very popular with golfers and offers many golfing breaks. The accommodation is comfortable and there is an open-plan bar and lounge which have recently been refurbished. The cuisine is predominantly English and served in the attractive dining room.
16 en suite (bth/shr) (3 fmly) CTV in all bedrooms STV 20P No coaches Pool table English & French Cuisine V meals Coffee am Tea pm No smoking in restaurant Last d 8pm
ROOMS: (incl. bkfst) s £22-£26; d £44-£52 * **LB**
MEALS: Bar Lunch £1-£4alc Dinner £14.50&alc*
CARDS:

★★62% **Atlantic House**
17-18 Summerleaze Crescent EX23 8HJ ☎ 01288 352451
Closed 11 Nov-2 Mar
This friendly, family-run hotel continues to improve. Accomodation is comfortable in well decorated bedrooms, a number of which have been upgraded with modern furnishings. Lounge facilities are limited but comfortable and there is an attractive dining room serving a set-price menu of simple English cuisine well prepared using good, fresh produce.
19 rms (12 bth/shr) (4 fmly) CTV in all bedrooms No dogs (ex guide dogs) 10P Pool table Games room Multi-activity sports V meals Coffee am Tea pm No smoking in restaurant Last d 8pm
ROOMS: (incl. bkfst & dinner) s £22.50; d £45 * **LB**
OFF-PEAK: (incl. bkfst & dinner) s £21; d £43
MEALS: Bar Lunch £2.50-£5 Dinner £13*
CARDS:

★★61% **Burn Court**
Burn View EX23 8DB (leave M5 at Exeter. Follow signs for Okehampton on A30. Take turn off for Bude)
☎ 01288 352872 352694 FAX 352872
Closed Jan
A popular resort hotel situated opposite the golf course offers well equipped bedrooms. Public areas are quite spacious and include an attractive dining room. A set-price menu is offered at dinner with limited choice, and the cooking is sound.
34 rms (5 bth 17 shr) (6 fmly) CTV in 22 bedrooms TV in 12 bedrooms 10P Xmas English Cuisine V meals Coffee am Tea pm Last d 9pm
ROOMS: (incl. bkfst) s £20-£33; d £40-£66 *
MEALS: Lunch £5.75 Dinner £5&alc*

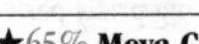

★65% **Meva Gwin**
Upton EX23 0LY (take Widemouth Bay road and continue for 1m)
☎ 01288 352347 FAX 01288 352347
Closed 5 Oct-Mar
Popular with walkers on the coastal footpath, the hotel stands to the southwest of the town with sweeping views of the coastline down to Trevose Head and Padstow. The bedrooms, some with balconies and deckchairs enabling guests to take advantage of the views, are spotlessly clean and well equipped. Public areas are cosy and the walls of the Surfers Bar are decorated with bright murals.
12 rms (4 bth 7 shr) (4 fmly) CTV in all bedrooms No dogs 44P c fac Coffee am Tea pm No smoking in restaurant Last d 7.30pm
ROOMS: (incl. bkfst) s £18-£22; d £40-£44 *
MEALS: Dinner £8.95
CARDS:

BUDOCK WATER Cornwall & Isles of Scilly Map 02 SW73

★★70% **Crill Manor**
Roscarrack Rd TR11 5BL (2.5m W on unclass rd) ☎ 01326 211880
FAX 01326 211229
The accommodation at this Victorian manor house has been completely upgraded to provide sumptuous non-smoking bedrooms with every modern amenity. Public areas include a spacious open-plan bar and lower lounge overlooking the garden and pool. The Four Seasons Restaurant features a limited choice, four-course, fixed-price menu of freshly prepared dishes.
11 en suite (bth/shr) 1 annexe en suite (bth) (1 fmly) No smoking in all bedrooms CTV in all bedrooms No dogs 12P No coaches Outdoor swimming pool (heated) No children 10yrs Xmas V meals Coffee am Tea pm No smoking in restaurant Last d 8.30pm
ROOMS: (incl. bkfst) s £32-£37.50; d £64-£75 * **LB**
MEALS: Sunday Lunch £10.50 Dinner £16.50&alc
CARDS:

★★65% **Penmorvah Manor**

Penjerrick TR11 5ED (at Hillhead roundabout take Maenporth road, at Falmouth Football Club turn right, through Budock village, hotel opposite Penjerrick Gardens) ☎ 01326 250277 FAX 01326 250509

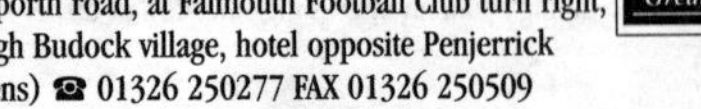

Hidden away in six acres of mature gardens and woodlands, this Victorian manor house is located within two miles of the centre of Falmouth. The majority of the no smoking bedrooms are located in a purpose built new wing, half the rooms being on the ground floor. In the candlelit restaurant a fixed-price menu is offered, with extra dishes which carry a supplementary charge. Activity holidays and leisure breaks are available and include a painters' workshop supervised by Ben Maile, and golfing holidays.
27 en suite (bth/shr) (1 fmly) No smoking in all bedrooms CTV in all bedrooms No dogs (ex guide dogs) 150P Pool table Croquet lawn Xmas English & French Cuisine V meals Coffee am Tea pm No smoking in restaurant Last d 8.30pm
ROOMS: (incl. bkfst) s £35-£40; d £70-£80 * **LB**
MEALS: Lunch £8.50 Dinner £15.50
CONF: Thtr 250 Class 100 Board 56 Del from £52.50
CARDS:
See advertisement under FALMOUTH

BUNWELL Norfolk Map 05 TM19

★★ 64% Bunwell Manor
Bunwell St NR16 1QU (off B1113) ☎ 01953 788304
A modestly furnished, attractive 18th-century house with extensive lawns, this hotel is a popular venue for weekend social gatherings. The public areas are welcoming and the friendly, ever-present owners oversee guests' welfare. Well cared for bedrooms come in a variety of shapes, as one would expect with a building of this age.
10 en suite (bth/shr) (2 fmly) CTV in all bedrooms 35P Croquet lawn Xmas V meals Coffee am No smoking area in restaurant Last d 9.30pm
ROOMS: (incl. bkfst) s fr £40; d fr £65 **LB**
MEALS: Lunch £9.50-£12.95&alc Dinner £12.95&alc
CONF: Thtr 30 Board 20
CARDS:

BURFORD Oxfordshire Map 04 SP21

★★★ 70% The Bay Tree

12-14 Sheep St OX18 4LW (off A40, down hill towards Burford, Sheep St 1st left)
☎ 01993 822791 FAX 01993 823008
This attractive old inn in the heart of Burford, the gateway to the Cotswolds, is built in the traditional manner from local stone. There are many delightful period features and particularly striking is the main stairwell with its heraldic decor. Bedrooms are furnished in a mixture of traditional and modern styles with some characterful pieces of furniture. There are some feature rooms with four poster and half tester rooms and the cottage rooms overlook a manicured two acre walled garden. Staff work hard to make their guests feel welcome.
23 en suite (bth/shr) CTV in all bedrooms 20P Croquet lawn Xmas V meals Coffee am Tea pm No smoking in restaurant Last d 9.30pm
ROOMS: (incl. bkfst) s fr £60; d £110-£195 * **LB**
MEALS: Lunch £12.95-£15.95 Dinner £19.95-£25*
CONF: Thtr 30 Class 20 Board 12 Del from £125
CARDS:

★★★ 62% Inn For All Seasons
The Barringtons OX18 4TN (3m W on A40) ☎ 01451 844324
FAX 01451 844375
Closed 25 & 26 Dec
This attractive 16th-century coaching inn offers guests a warm welcome and a pleasant, informal atmosphere. Service is efficient and friendly and meals in the original bar with its oak beams and exposed stone walls are rightly popular. Rooms are all individually styled and reflect the history of the building in their unusual shapes.
9 en suite (bth) 1 annexe en suite (bth/shr) (2 fmly) CTV in all bedrooms STV No dogs (ex guide dogs) 60P Clay pigeon shooting No children 10yrs English & Continental Cuisine V meals Coffee am Tea pm No smoking in restaurant Last d 10pm
MEALS: Lunch £2.95-£11.50 Dinner £16.50&alc
CONF: Thtr 25 Class 30 Board 30 Del £95
CARDS:

★★★ 61% Cotswold Gateway
Cheltenham Rd OX18 4HX (situated at the roundabout on the A40 Oxford/Cheltenham at junct with A361) ☎ 01993 822695
FAX 01993 823600
A conveniently located hotel situated on the A40 route to Cheltenham. The Cotswold Gateway attracts a loyal following in large part due to the friendly naturalness of the staff: service however can be more haphazard. Bedrooms are prettily decorated with pleasant fabrics and attractive furnishings, and two four-poster rooms are particularly good. There is a separate coffee shop and an olde worlde restaurant where traditional and modern dishes are served.
13 en suite (bth/shr) 8 annexe en suite (bth/shr) (4 fmly) No smoking in 1 bedroom CTV in all bedrooms No dogs (ex guide dogs) 60P Xmas English & French Cuisine V meals Coffee am Tea pm Last d 9.45pm
ROOMS: (incl. bkfst) s fr £49.50; d £65-£80 * **LB**
CONF: Thtr 40 Class 20 Board 24
CARDS:

★★ 67% Golden Pheasant

91 High St OX18 4QA (leave M40 at junct 8 and follow signs A40 Cheltenham into Burford)
☎ 01993 823223 & 823417 FAX 01993 822621
This characterful old inn on Burford's main street has many charming features which date back in part to the 1500's. Staff are welcoming and friendly and help to create an inviting yet informal atmosphere. Bedrooms can be a little compact but all are furnished with style featuring some attractive fabrics and period pieces of furniture, together with a wealth of useful extras. Meals can either be taken in the inviting bar or in the restaurant with its solid fuel stove.
12 rms (11 bth/shr) (1 fmly) CTV in all bedrooms 12P Xmas English & French Cuisine V meals Coffee am Tea pm No smoking area in restaurant Last d 9pm
ROOMS: (incl. bkfst) s £45-£60; d £65-£85 * **LB**
MEALS: Lunch £2.95-£13.50alc Dinner £8.75-£15.95alc*
CARDS:

Travelodge
Berry Barn OX7 5TB (A40) ☎ 01993 822699
FAX 01993 822699
Travelodge
This modern building offers accommodation in smart, spacious and well equipped bedrooms, suitable for family use, and all with en suite bathrooms. Meals may be taken at the nearby family restaurant. For information on room rates and to make a booking, call Roomline free of charge on 0800 850950. For more details about Travelodge, consult the Contents page under Hotel Groups.
40 en suite (bth/shr)

BURGH HEATH Surrey Map 04 TQ25

★★ 63% Heathside
Brighton Rd KT20 6BW (on S carriageway of A217)
☎ 01737 353355 FAX 01737 370857
Conveniently located on the southern carriageway of the A217 three miles from junction 8 of the M25, this popular hotel offers a range of facilities including some good quality bedrooms in modern style. There is an attractive restaurant with a conservatory extension and a small lobby bar lounge.
73 en suite (bth/shr) No smoking in 11 bedrooms CTV in all bedrooms STV Night porter 150P Indoor swimming pool (heated)
contd.

Golf 9 Sauna Gym English & French Cuisine V meals Coffee am Last d 9.45pm
ROOMS: (incl. bkfst) s £66-£76; d £76-£86 *
MEALS: Dinner £12.50&alc
CONF: Thtr 200 Class 50 Board 50 Del from £89
CARDS:

BURLEY Hampshire Map 04 SU20

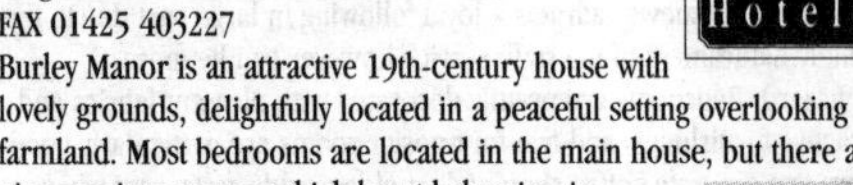

★★★63% Burley Manor

Ringwood Rd BH24 4BS ☎ 01425 403522
FAX 01425 403227

Forestdale Hotels

Burley Manor is an attractive 19th-century house with lovely grounds, delightfully located in a peaceful setting overlooking farmland. Most bedrooms are located in the main house, but there are nine spacious rooms, which boast balconies, in the converted stable block. Cosy, public rooms are warmed by log fires and the hotel offers a relaxed ambience.

21 en suite (bth/shr) 9 annexe en suite (bth/shr) (3 fmly) No smoking in 4 bedrooms CTV in all bedrooms 60P Outdoor swimming pool (heated) Fishing Riding Croquet lawn Xmas V meals Coffee am Tea pm No smoking area in restaurant Last d 9.45pm
ROOMS: (incl. bkfst) s fr £65; d £85-£110 * LB
OFF-PEAK: (incl. bkfst) s fr £78.50; d £112-£137
MEALS: Lunch fr £7.95 High tea fr £5 Dinner fr £17.20*
CONF: Thtr 60 Class 40 Board 40 Del from £85
CARDS:

★★★60% Moorhill House

BH24 4AG ☎ 01425 403285 FAX 01425 403715

Situated in the heart of the New Forest on the edge of Burley, this quiet hotel is being steadily upgraded. The bedrooms have been newly decorated with attractive co-ordinated fabrics and modern facilities. The public areas include two lounges overlooking the garden; a small swimming pool and whirlpool bath.

24 en suite (bth/shr) (7 fmly) CTV in all bedrooms 40P No coaches Indoor swimming pool (heated) Sauna Putting green Jacuzzi/spa ch fac Xmas V meals Coffee am Tea pm No smoking area in restaurant Last d 8.45pm
ROOMS: (incl. bkfst) s £50; d £79-£89 * LB
MEALS: Dinner £17.50&alc*
CONF: Thtr 54 Class 48 Board 28 Del from £75
CARDS:

BURNHAM Buckinghamshire Map 04 SU98

★★★68% Burnham Beeches

Grove Rd SL1 8DP (off A355 via 'Farnham Royal' roundabout) ☎ 01628 429955 FAX 01628 603994

MOAT HOUSE

This extended, squat Georgian manor house stands on the fringes of old woodland. The majority of the bedrooms are comfortable and sizeable and all are well equipped. The well presented team of staff make special efforts to ensure guests' welfare. The kitchen, under Laurence Bryant, produces exact, simple meals which deliver honest and full flavours.

75 en suite (bth/shr) (19 fmly) No smoking in 19 bedrooms CTV in all bedrooms STV No dogs (ex guide dogs) Lift Night porter 150P Indoor swimming pool (heated) Tennis (hard) Snooker Solarium Gym Croquet lawn Putting green Jacuzzi/spa Table tennis Xmas French Cuisine V meals Coffee am Tea pm No smoking area in restaurant Last d 10pm
ROOMS: s £98.50-£200; d £120-£200 * LB
MEALS: Lunch fr £22.50&alc Dinner fr £22.50&alc*
CARDS:

★★★61% Jarvis Grovefield

Taplow Common Rd SL1 8LP ☎ 01628 603131 FAX 01628 668078

This popular conference hotel is part Edwardian and part contemporary with a more recent extension providing spacious bedrooms. An attractive feature is the large garden which borders on open fields. The staff are upbeat and the kitchen is making great efforts at producing meals that show extra care and attention.

40 en suite (bth/shr) (5 fmly) No smoking in 8 bedrooms CTV in all bedrooms Lift Night porter 155P Golf 9 Fishing Croquet lawn Putting green Xmas English & French Cuisine V meals Coffee am Tea pm No smoking in restaurant Last d 10pm
ROOMS: (incl. bkfst) s £90-£110; d £100-£120 * LB
OFF-PEAK: (incl. bkfst) s £65-£75; d £75-£85
MEALS: Lunch £10.95-£15&alc High tea £7.50-£9.50 Dinner £20&alc*
CONF: Thtr 250 Class 80 Board 80 Del from £135
CARDS:

BURNHAM MARKET Norfolk Map 09 TF84

★★68% Hoste Arms

The Green PE31 8HD (signposted on B1155) ☎ 01328 738777
FAX 01328 730103

The Hoste Arms is an up market fashionable pub/restaurant/hotel in the centre of a delightful Georgian village. It is home from home for Paul Whittome who runs his inn with keen devotion, and his other passions for music and art are reflected in the regular jazz nights in the piano room and local artists work displayed in the galleried lounge on the first floor. Leading off from the flagstoned bar where real ale and scrumpy is served chilled straight from the barrel, is the award winning restaurant. This recently refurbished room looks smart with its raspberry painted walls, waxed panelling and polished floorboards, tables with starched white linen and candle lit at night. It here that Chef Leigh Diggins presents serious cooking through an interesting set priced menu of 2 or 3 courses; very good value for money for exciting quality dishes that are cooked with great flair and imagination.

12 en suite (bth/shr) 9 annexe en suite (bth/shr) (1 fmly) CTV in all bedrooms Night porter 60P No coaches Wkly live entertainment English, French & Mediterranean Cuisine V meals Coffee am Tea pm No smoking area in restaurant
ROOMS: (incl. bkfst) s £50-£60; d £68-£96 * LB
OFF-PEAK: (incl. bkfst) d fr £48
MEALS: Sunday Lunch £13-£20alc*
CONF: Thtr 30 Class 22 Board 24
CARDS:

BURNHAM-ON-SEA Somerset Map 03 ST34

★★63% Royal Clarence

31 The Esplanade TA8 1BQ ☎ 01278 783138
FAX 01278 792965

This family-run, seafront hotel is popular with both the business and the leisure markets. The well equipped bedrooms vary in size and decor, and some are due to be upgraded. The hotel owns its own brewery, and own brand names are sold alongside national favourites. In the Victorian-style dining room on the first floor both set price and à la carte menus are available.

19 rms (18 bth/shr) (2 fmly) CTV in all bedrooms 20P No coaches Pool table English & French Cuisine V meals Coffee am No smoking area in restaurant Last d 8.30pm
ROOMS: (incl. bkfst) s fr £37; d fr £54 * LB
MEALS: Sunday Lunch fr £7 High tea fr £3.50 Dinner fr £13.50&alc*
CONF: Thtr 200 Class 120 Board 24 Del from £57
CARDS:

For the key to symbols and abbreviations, please see the bookmark inside the back cover

BURNLEY Lancashire Map 07 SD83

★★★72% **Oaks**

Colne Rd, Reedley BB10 2LF (on A56 between Burnley and Nelson) ☎ 01282 414141
FAX 01282 433401

This Victorian manor house has been lovingly restored and extended to provide well laid out and comfortable bedrooms. The characterful public rooms are housed in the main building which include Quills restaurant, the Authors bar and there is also a cellar brasserie. There are some notable features to the building such as the grand staircase and some fine stained glass. The staff are well meaning and create a welcoming atmosphere.

52 en suite (bth/shr) (10 fmly) No smoking in 20 bedrooms CTV in all bedrooms STV Night porter 110P Indoor swimming pool (heated) Sauna Solarium Gym Jacuzzi/spa Xmas English & French Cuisine V meals Coffee am Tea pm No smoking area in restaurant Last d 9.45pm

ROOMS: (incl. bkfst) s £82-£102; d £102-£122 * **LB**
OFF-PEAK: (incl. bkfst & dinner) d fr £102
MEALS: Bar Lunch fr £10 Dinner fr £20alc*
CONF: Thtr 120 Class 48 Board 60 Del from £99
CARDS:

★★67% **Rosehill House**

Rosehill Av B11 2PW (0.5m S of Burnley town centre, off the A682)
☎ 01282 453931 FAX 01282 455628

This elegant stone-built house stands in its own grounds and is found in a quiet residential area of Burnley. The comfortable public rooms are a pleasure to occupy and feature beautiful ornate ceilings which add to the hotel's unique charm. Modern bedrooms meet all the needs of today's travellers whilst well prepared cooking is served in the intimate dining room. Service is provided by all the family who are supported by a very attentive and polite staff.

19 en suite (bth/shr) (1 fmly) No smoking in 1 bedroom CTV in all bedrooms STV 50P ch fac English & Continental Cuisine V meals Coffee am Tea pm No smoking in restaurant Last d 9.30pm

ROOMS: (incl. bkfst) s £35-£40; d £56-£65 * **LB**
OFF-PEAK: (incl. bkfst) s £27.50-£29.50; d £39.50-£62
MEALS: Lunch £5-£12 Dinner £12.50-£14.50&alc
CONF: Thtr 30 Class 20 Board 20 Del from £42
CARDS:

★★66% **Sparrow Hawk**

Church St BB11 2DN (on Inner Ring Road (A682), opposite St Peters Church) ☎ 01282 421551
FAX 01282 456506

Situated in the heart of the town, this Victorian hotel retains much of its period charm and has been extensively upgraded of late to provide modern, well furnished bedrooms and comfortable public areas. A good range of dishes is available in either the first-floor restaurant or mock-Tudor bar. Friendly, helpful service is provided by dedicated staff.

36 en suite (bth/shr) (2 fmly) No smoking in 18 bedrooms CTV in all bedrooms STV No dogs (ex guide dogs) Night porter 24P Pool table Wkly live entertainment Xmas European Cuisine V meals Coffee am No smoking area in restaurant Last d 9.30pm

ROOMS: (incl. bkfst) s £40-£49; d £45-£60
OFF-PEAK: (incl. bkfst) s fr £34; d fr £40
MEALS: Bar Lunch £6.95-£11.95 Dinner £11.95-£16.95
CONF: Thtr 80 Class 40 Board 30 Del from £39.50
CARDS: £

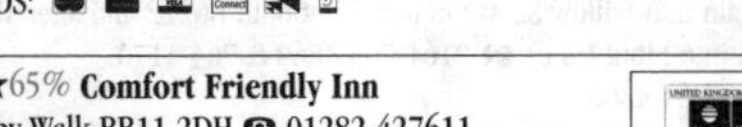

★★65% **Comfort Friendly Inn**

Keirby Walk BB11 2DH ☎ 01282 427611
FAX 01282 436370

This mainly commercial hotel situated in the centre of the town has ample parking, both outside and beneath the building. Bedrooms are compact but well equipped and include Premier Plus rooms which provide a higher standard of facilities. The smartly dressed staff are friendly and helpful, and traditional English food can be enjoyed in Malkins Restaurant. Cottons Café Bar, which also serves food, has recently been opened for both residents and non-residents and is a welcome addition to the hotel's amenities.

48 en suite (bth/shr) No smoking in 18 bedrooms CTV in all bedrooms STV Lift Night porter 75P Mini-gym Xmas English & Continental Cuisine V meals Coffee am Tea pm No smoking area in restaurant Last d 9.30pm

ROOMS: d £38.50-£49.50 **LB**
MEALS: Lunch £7.50-£9.95&alc Dinner £9.75&alc
CONF: Thtr 300 Class 80 Board 280 Del from £65
CARDS:  £

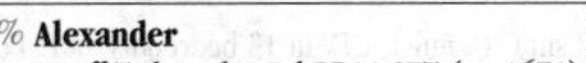

★★63% **Alexander**

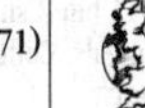

2 Tarleton Av, off Todmorden Rd BB11 3ET (on A671)
☎ 01282 422684 FAX 01282 424094

This small, privately owned and neatly maintained hotel is quietly situated just off the A671, almost next door to Towneley Hall. Bedrooms, some of which are situated in a wing immediately adjacent to the main building, are mostly en suite, freshly decorated, neatly furnished and well equipped with facilities, including cable TV. A good range of popular dishes from the fixed-price and carte menus is available in the bright, attractively decorated dining room and there is a small lounge bar.

13 rms (6 bth 4 shr) 3 annexe en suite (bth/shr) (1 fmly) CTV in all bedrooms STV No dogs (ex guide dogs) 18P ch fac English & Continental Cuisine V meals Coffee am Tea pm Last d 9pm

ROOMS: (incl. bkfst) s £25-£38; d £38-£49 *
MEALS: Sunday Lunch £7.75-£8.95&alc Dinner £12.50-£16.50*
CONF: Thtr 60 Class 25 Board 30 Del from £36
CARDS: £

Travel Inn

Queen Victoria Rd BB10 3EF ☎ 01282 450250
FAX 01282 452811

Purpose-built accommodation, offering spacious, well equipped bedrooms, all with en suite bathrooms. Meals may be taken at the nearby family restaurant. For more information about Travel Inns, consult the Contents page under Hotel Groups.

40 en suite (bth/shr)
ROOMS: (incl. bkfst) d £35.50 *

Travelodge

Travelodge

Cavalry Barracks, Barracks Rd BB11 4AS (junc A671/A679) ☎ 01282 416039 FAX 01282 416039

This modern building offers accommodation in smart, spacious and well equipped bedrooms, suitable for family use, and all with en suite bathrooms. Meals may be taken at the nearby family restaurant. For information on room rates and to make a booking, call Roomline free of charge on 0800 850950. For more details about Travelodge, consult the Contents page under Hotel Groups.

32 en suite (bth/shr)

BURNSALL North Yorkshire Map 07 SE06

★★❀66% **Red Lion**

By the Bridge BD23 6BU (on B6160 between Grassington and Bolton Abbey) ☎ 01756 720204 FAX 01756 720292

The Red Lion was once a ferryman's inn and dates back to the 16th century. It is set amongst the most beautiful Dales scenery and stands by the bridge and next to the river on which it has fishing rights. The hotel is full of its original charm with beamed ceilings and log fires whilst the bedrooms are well equipped and pleasantly furnished. Dinner is a special occasion here, when chef James Rowley proudly displays his cooking skills using only the best of local produce.

7 en suite (bth/shr) 4 annexe en suite (bth/shr) (2 fmly) CTV in all bedrooms No dogs 80P No coaches Fishing Xmas V meals Coffee am No smoking in restaurant Last d 9.30pm

ROOMS: (incl. bkfst) s £49-£55; d £79-£84 * **LB**

MEALS: Lunch £11.95-£15.95 Dinner fr £18.95*

CONF: Thtr 30 Class 10 Board 20 Del from £78.95

CARDS:

★★61% **Fell**

BD23 6BT (on B6160) ☎ 01756 720209 FAX 01756 720605

Standing in an elevated position and overlooking the village and the River Wharfe, this family-owned and run hotel is in the process of being extensively refurbished. There are good public rooms, whilst the modern bedrooms are adequately furnished and equipped. A good range of food is available either in the bar or the spacious dining room.

14 rms (11 bth 2 shr) (4 fmly) CTV in 13 bedrooms 60P Pool table Xmas V meals Coffee am Tea pm No smoking area in restaurant Last d 9pm

ROOMS: (incl. bkfst) s fr £33.50; d fr £55 * **LB**

MEALS: Lunch £7-£12 Dinner fr £14.95*

CONF: Thtr 70 Del from £65

CARDS:

BURRINGTON (NEAR PORTSMOUTH ARMS STATION)
Devon Map 03 SS61

★★★❀ 70% **Northcote Manor**

EX37 9LZ (leave A377 Exeter to Barnstaple road onto private forest drive opposite Portsmouth Arms Railway Station. Do not enter Burrington) ☎ 01769 560501 FAX 01769 560770

Closed 15 Nov-15 Mar

This stone-built, gabled manor house stands in twelve acres of pretty grounds with an all-weather tennis court and plans for a golf range. The bedrooms are all well presented with quality dark wood furnishings and pretty fabrics. The new Austrian chef gains our rosette award for his careful interpretation of well conceived dishes. An attractive baronial lounge and a more cosy bar complete the picture.

12 en suite (bth/shr) CTV in all bedrooms STV Night porter 20P No coaches Tennis (hard) Fishing Putting green Jacuzzi/spa No children 12yrs International Cuisine V meals No smoking in restaurant

ROOMS: (incl. bkfst) s £79-£139; d £109-£169 * **LB**

CONF: Thtr 50 Class 25 Board 12

CARDS:

BURTON UPON TRENT Staffordshire Map 08 SK22

★★★★67% **Hoar Cross Hall Health Spa**

Hoar Cross DE13 8QS (follow B5017 out of Burton for 4.5m then take unclass. road to Hoar Cross) ☎ 01283 575671 FAX 01283 575652

This impressive spa resort, which has a friendly and relaxed atmosphere, is set in beautiful grounds and is privately owned and personally run by the Joynes family. The magnificently appointed house provides 84 bedrooms and suites, all attractively decorated and well equipped and some their own roof terrace, whirlpool baths, saunas and four-poster beds. The modern and superbly equipped spa provides a huge range of facilities and treatments, there is also a boutique and hairdressing salon. Quite a good range of well prepared dishes is available in the restaurant or the spa, all helpfully colour coded to encourage healthier eating.

86 en suite (bth/shr) No smoking in 40 bedrooms CTV in all bedrooms STV No dogs (ex guide dogs) Lift Night porter 200P No coaches Indoor swimming pool (heated) Golf 9 Tennis (hard) Sauna Solarium Gym Croquet lawn Putting green Jacuzzi/spa Aerobic studio Treatment rooms No children 16yrs Xmas English & French Cuisine V meals No smoking in restaurant

ROOMS: (incl. bkfst & dinner) s fr £112; d fr £224 *

CONF: Thtr 150 Class 70 Board 50 Del from £125

CARDS:

See advertisement under BIRMINGHAM (NATIONAL EXHIBITION CENTRE)

★★★68% **Riverside**

Riverside Dr, Branston DE14 3EP (follow signs for Branston on A5121 until small humped bridge, over bridge and right turn into Warren Lane. Second left into Riverside Drive) ☎ 01283 511234 FAX 01283 511441

RS Xmas/New Year

This delightful riverside inn has grown over the years into a substantial hotel. It caters for all occasions from conferences to wedding ceremonies. The restaurant has fine views over the river and a comfortable lounge in which to enjoy a drink before dinner. The service is professional and friendly and the cooking caters for all popular tastes and includes an impressive hors d'oeuvre table and a noteworthy selection of wines. The modern bedrooms have excellent facilities and contemporary design.

22 en suite (bth/shr) CTV in all bedrooms STV Night porter 110P Fishing Wkly live entertainment English & French Cuisine V meals Coffee am Tea pm Last d 10pm

ROOMS: (incl. bkfst) s £28-£58; d £56-£68 *

MEALS: Lunch £8.95-£11.95&alc Dinner £16.95&alc*

CONF: Thtr 150 Class 30 Board 30

CARDS:

See advertisement on opposite page

BURTONWOOD MOTORWAY SERVICE AREA (M62)
Cheshire Map 07 SJ59

Travelodge

WA5 3AX (between junc 7 & 9 M62 westbound) ☎ 01925 710376

This modern building offers accommodation in smart, spacious and well equipped bedrooms, suitable for family use, and all with en suite bathrooms. Meals may be taken at the nearby family restaurant. For information on room rates and to make a booking, call Roomline free of charge on 0800 850950. For more details about Travelodge, consult the Contents page under Hotel Groups.

40 en suite (bth/shr)

BURY Greater Manchester Map 07 SD81

★★★❀❀❀70% **Normandie**

Elbut Ln, Birtle BL9 6UT (leave M66 at junct 2, first right and then first right again into Willow St. At top turn right onto B6222 and after 1m turn left into Elbut Lane) ☎ 0161 764 3869 & 764 1170 FAX 0161 764 4866

Closed 26 Dec-6 Jan & 1 wk at Etr RS weekends (restricted meal service)

Gillian Moussa has now been joined by daughter Jo in addition to her son Max in helping to run this long established hotel which has an enviable reputation for excellent food and providing old fashioned services, such as evening turndown and proper shoe cleaning. The hotel is located at the foot of the Pennines, just outside Bury, and enjoys the most wonderful panoramic views of Manchester. Two types of room are available, freshly decorated and spacious standard rooms and better appointed luxury rooms; all however, are comfortable and well equipped. Whist the hotel has a welcoming and relaxed atmosphere the real pleasure for guests is deciding which of Pascal Pommier's well executed dishes to choose, from the short set-price and carte menus.

20 en suite (bth/shr) 3 annexe en suite (bth/shr) CTV in all bedrooms No dogs (ex guide dogs) Lift Night porter 60P No coaches English & French Cuisine V meals Last d 9.30pm
ROOMS: (incl. cont bkfst) s £49-£69; d £59-£79 *
MEALS: Lunch £12.50&alc Dinner £15&alc
CONF: Thtr 14 Class 14 Board 14 Del from £105
CARDS:

★★★63% **Bolholt Country Park**

Walshaw Rd BL8 1PU (from M66 take turn-off for Bury Town Centre and after 50yds fork right and at 4-lane filter system take right hand lanes and signpost for Walshaw) ☎ 0161 764 5239 FAX 0161 763 1789

This much extended property is set in fifty acres of grounds on the outskirts of the town. Bedrooms vary in size and are located in two modern wings and a separate annexe a short walk across the garden; there are also several rooms on the ground floor. One of the hotel's greatest assets is the friendly informal service provided by the owner and his team of young staff.

38 en suite (bth/shr) 9 annexe en suite (bth/shr) (3 fmly) CTV in all bedrooms STV 300P Indoor swimming pool (heated) Fishing Sauna Solarium Gym Pool table Jacuzzi/spa Fitness & leisure centre Wkly live entertainment Xmas V meals Coffee am Tea pm No smoking in restaurant Last d 9.30pm
ROOMS: (incl. bkfst) s £44-£50; d £55-£61 * **LB**
MEALS: Lunch £8.95 Dinner £13.50&alc*
CONF: Thtr 300 Class 120 Board 40 Del from £75
CARDS:

BURY ST EDMUNDS Suffolk Map 05 TL86

★★★ 70% **Ravenwood Hall**

Rougham IP30 9JA (3m E off A14) ☎ 01359 270345 FAX 01359 270788

A warm welcome and cheerful service are just two of the strengths of Ravenwood Hall, which sits in pleasant countryside just outside Bury St Edmunds. The food is also worth a mention; diners can choose between a wide choice of bar meals or formal dining in the restaurant, a splendid room with carved timbers and a huge Tudor inglenook fireplace. The menus offer carefully prepared dishes, combining both classical and adventurous country cooking and the well chosen wine list should provide something to satisfy most tastes and pockets. Bedrooms are divided between the main house and the mews, each room being individually furnished with antique or period-style furniture.

7 en suite (bth) 7 annexe en suite (bth) No smoking in all bedrooms CTV in all bedrooms 153P Outdoor swimming pool (heated) Tennis (hard) Riding Croquet lawn Shooting & fishing parties Xmas V meals Coffee am Tea pm No smoking in restaurant Last d 9.30pm
ROOMS: (incl. bkfst) s £59-£79; d £79-£109 **LB**
MEALS: Lunch £18.95&alc High tea £8.95 Dinner £18.95&alc
CONF: Thtr 150 Class 80 Board 40 Del from £99
CARDS:

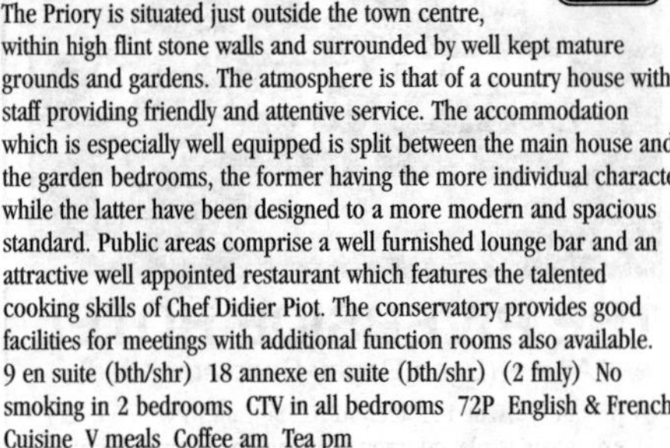

★★★69% **The Priory**
Tollgate IP32 6EH (off A1101) ☎ 01284 766181
FAX 01284 767604
The Priory is situated just outside the town centre, within high flint stone walls and surrounded by well kept mature grounds and gardens. The atmosphere is that of a country house with staff providing friendly and attentive service. The accommodation which is especially well equipped is split between the main house and the garden bedrooms, the former having the more individual character while the latter have been designed to a more modern and spacious standard. Public areas comprise a well furnished lounge bar and an attractive well appointed restaurant which features the talented cooking skills of Chef Didier Piot. The conservatory provides good facilities for meetings with additional function rooms also available.
9 en suite (bth/shr) 18 annexe en suite (bth/shr) (2 fmly) No smoking in 2 bedrooms CTV in all bedrooms 72P English & French Cuisine V meals Coffee am Tea pm
CONF: Thtr 40 Class 20 Board 24
CARDS:

★★★68% **Angel**
Angel Hill IP33 1LT ☎ 01284 753926 FAX 01284 750092
This characterful hotel near the cathedral offers warm hospitality, helpful service and comfortable accommodation in bedrooms which are spacious, attractively furnished and well equipped. Carpets may be a little shabby in the comfortably furnished public rooms, but some fine portraits hang on the walls of an attractive restaurant featuring well balanced carte and fixed-price menus of quality dishes skilfully prepared by chef Graham Mallia. On a recent visit our inspector enjoyed warm mousse of scallops garnished with mussels and cucumber, tournedos of beef (a good quality fillet, lightly pan-fried and served with delicious wild mushrooms and artichoke bottoms) and a light chocolate mousse set in a dark chocolate case and accompanied by a flavoursome coffee sauce. The reasonably priced wine list, though not very exciting, provides a suitable accompaniment for everything on the menu.
42 en suite (bth/shr) (4 fmly) CTV in all bedrooms Night porter 62P Xmas English & French Cuisine V meals Coffee am Tea pm No smoking in restaurant Last d 10pm
ROOMS: s fr £59; d £69-£105 * **LB**
OFF-PEAK: (incl. bkfst) s fr £35
MEALS: Lunch fr £13.95 Dinner fr £19.95&alc*
CONF: Thtr 160 Class 30 Board 40 Del from £92.50
CARDS:

★★★64% **Butterfly**
A14 (Bury East exit), Moreton Hall IP32 7BW (from A14 take Bury East exit and at roundabout take exit for Moreton Hall. Left at next roundabout) ☎ 01284 760884 FAX 01284 755476
The Butterfly sits on the outskirts of the town, easily accessible from the A14 at the junction with the A134. Friendly service is provided within the relaxed, informal public areas that are dominated by Walt's Bar and Restaurant. Bedrooms are modern in style and well laid out for business guests, and a range of ground floor, studio and ladies' rooms are available; new this year are the remote controlled TVs with satellite and pay movie channels. The business community find that the good car parking and flexible range of conference rooms are most convenient.
66 en suite (bth/shr) (2 fmly) No smoking in 10 bedrooms CTV in all bedrooms No dogs (ex guide dogs) Night porter 85P European & Oriental Cuisine V meals Coffee am Tea pm No smoking area in restaurant Last d 10pm
ROOMS: s fr £55; d fr £55 * **LB**
OFF-PEAK: s fr £45; d fr £45
MEALS: Lunch fr £9.75&alc Dinner fr £12.25&alc*
CONF: Thtr 40 Class 21 Board 22 Del from £85
CARDS:

See advertisement on opposite page

★★65% **The Suffolk**
38 The Buttermarket IP33 1DL ☎ 01284 753995
FAX 01284 750973
Situated close to the town square, this long established hotel has a bar and a coffee shop which are well patronised by the locals. Residents can also enjoy meals in the restaurant or their room. The standard of bedrooms varies but all are practical to use and equipped with modern conveniences.
33 en suite (bth/shr) (3 fmly) No smoking in 13 bedrooms CTV in all bedrooms Night porter 30P Xmas V meals Coffee am Tea pm No smoking in restaurant Last d 9.30pm
ROOMS: s £55; d £65 * **LB**
MEALS: Lunch £7.50-£10.95 Dinner £9-£21*
CONF: Thtr 30 Class 12 Board 20 Del from £85
CARDS:

BUTTERMERE Cumbria Map 11 NY11

★★69% **Bridge**
CA13 9UZ ☎ 017687 70252 FAX 017687 70252
This long-established family-run hotel sits by a stream in the centre of the village, surrounded by mountains in the beautiful Buttermere Valley. Public rooms have a welcoming atmosphere and include a cosy hall, relaxing lounge and smart dining room, whilst bar meals and real ales can be found in the beamed bar. The owners continue the long-standing tradition of serving home-baked afternoon teas to house guests. Bedrooms are also comfortable and most enjoy the superb views.
22 en suite (bth/shr) 60P No coaches Xmas English & French Cuisine V meals Coffee am Tea pm No smoking in restaurant Last d 8.30pm
ROOMS: (incl. bkfst & dinner) s £48.50-£56; d £97-£112 * **LB**
MEALS: Bar Lunch £3.50-£7.90alc Dinner £19.50*
CARDS:

BUXTON Derbyshire Map 07 SK07

★★★73% **Lee Wood**
13 Manchester Rd SK17 6TQ (NE on A5004, 300mtrs beyond the Devonshire Royal Hospital)
☎ 01298 23002 FAX 01298 23228
Closed 24-29 Dec
This is a friendly privately-owned hotel which has been in the same family for two generations. It has a loyal staff with long serving and very professional key members. A high standard of hospitality and comfort is offered throughout the hotel which is run along traditional lines. Bedrooms are each individually furnished and decorated with good modern facilities in generally spacious accommodation. The conservatory-style restaurant continues to offer good cooking skills and a predominantly British cuisine.
36 en suite (bth/shr) 2 annexe en suite (bth/shr) (2 fmly) No smoking in 7 bedrooms CTV in all bedrooms Lift Night porter 50P English & French Cuisine V meals Coffee am Tea pm No smoking area in restaurant Last d 9.30pm
ROOMS: (incl. bkfst) s £64-£68; d £82-£92 * **LB**
OFF-PEAK: (incl. bkfst) s £58-£64; d £74-£86
MEALS: Lunch £11.95-£12.95&alc High tea £5-£8 Dinner £17.50-£23
CONF: Thtr 120 Class 65 Board 40 Del from £85
CARDS:

★★★66% **Palace**
Palace Rd SK17 6AG (in town centre adjacent to railway station) ☎ 01298 22001 FAX 01298 72131
This impressive Victorian building overlooking the spa town provides recently upgraded bedrooms and elegant public areas.
122 en suite (bth/shr) (12 fmly) No smoking in 33 bedrooms CTV

in all bedrooms STV Lift Night porter 200P Indoor swimming pool (heated) Snooker Sauna Solarium Gym Croquet lawn Putting green Xmas English & Continental Cuisine V meals Coffee am Tea pm No smoking in restaurant Last d 10pm
ROOMS: (incl. bkfst) s fr £95; d fr £105 * **LB**
MEALS: Lunch fr £10.50 Dinner fr £16.50*
CONF: Thtr 375 Class 125 Board 60 Del £115
CARDS: 

★★★62% **Buckingham Hotel**
1 Burlington Rd SK17 9AS (on A53 overlooking the Pavilion Gardens) ☎ 01298 70481 & 72186
CONSORT HOTELS
This owner-managed, friendly and relaxing hotel was once the home of a local artist, George Ramsey, and the popular bar, in which a full range of bar meals is served, is named after him. There is also an equally popular carvery restaurant serving traditional roasts together with à la carte dishes. Many of the bedrooms which are spacious and comfortable overlook the Pavilion Gardens. All are well equipped and have every modern facility. The hotel is ideal for both business and leisure purposes and also has facilities for meetings and conferences.
30 en suite (bth/shr) (4 fmly) No smoking in 10 bedrooms CTV in all bedrooms STV Lift 20P Xmas International Cuisine V meals Coffee am Tea pm
ROOMS: (incl. bkfst) s fr £62; d fr £75 * **LB**
OFF-PEAK: (incl. bkfst) s fr £42; d fr £75
CONF: Thtr 40 Class 20 Board 16 Del from £75
CARDS: 

★★66% **Portland**
32 St John's Rd SK17 6XQ (on A53 opposite the Pavilion and Gardens) ☎ 01298 71493
FAX 01298 27464

This well established traditional hotel is located opposite the Pavillion and its gardens. A continuing refurbishment programme ensures that the hotel keep up to date. The Park Restaurant (a shaded conservatory) offers a good range of freshly cooked dishes. The flavours are distinctive and a main course of supreme of chicken stuffed with ham and cheese, wrapped in a buttery pastry case and served with a thick creamy sauce was most enjoyable.
25 en suite (bth/shr) (3 fmly) No smoking in 1 bedroom CTV in all bedrooms STV 18P Xmas English & French Cuisine V meals Coffee am Tea pm No smoking in restaurant Last d 9.30pm
ROOMS: (incl. bkfst) s fr £52; d fr £62 * **LB**
OFF-PEAK: (incl. bkfst) s fr £45; d fr £58
MEALS: Lunch £6.50-£11.95 High tea £3.65-£5 Dinner £18.50&alc*
CONF: Thtr 50 Class 30 Board 25 Del from £50
CARDS: 

★66% ***Hartington***
18 Broad Walk SK17 6JR ☎ 01298 22638 FAX 01298 22638
Closed 17 Dec-4 Jan RS Nov-Mar
This traditional, well maintained and personally run hotel which is quietly situated overlooking the Pavilion Gardens has been in the same hands for many years. The light, comfortable and attractively furnished bedrooms, including two on the ground floor, are also well equipped. The public areas include a comfortable dining room where a short choice of home-made dishes are available each evening and a first floor lounge which has a marvellous view. Access for cars is via Hartington Road, behind the hotel.
17 rms (3 bth 4 shr) (3 fmly) No smoking in 2 bedrooms CTV in all bedrooms No dogs (ex guide dogs) 15P Last d 8pm
CARDS:

CADNAM Hampshire Map 04 SU21

★★★60% **Bartley Lodge**
Lyndhurst Rd SO40 2NR (near junct of M27/A337) ☎ 01703 812248
FAX 01703 812075
Quietly situated in its own grounds, this former hunting lodge is just minutes from the M27/A35. Rooms vary in size but are well equipped, and there is a new addition of family rooms. The public areas include a new indoor pool with sauna and fitness suite and a cosy bar with TV room. There are also several conference rooms overlooking the attractive grounds.
31 en suite (bth/shr) (14 fmly) CTV in all bedrooms 60P Indoor swimming pool (heated) Tennis (hard) Sauna Gym Croquet lawn ch fac Xmas V meals Coffee am Tea pm No smoking in restaurant Last d 8.45pm
ROOMS: (incl. bkfst) s £50; d £79-£104 **LB**
MEALS: Lunch £17.50 Dinner £17.50&alc
CONF: Thtr 60 Class 40 Board 40 Del from £75
CARDS:

CALNE Wiltshire Map 03 ST97

★★69% **Hayle Farm**
Quemerford SN11 8UJ (3m E of Calne on the A4) ☎ 01249 813275
FAX 01249 813275
Situated at the foot of the Marlborough Downs, this old farmhouse overlooks the famous White Horse at Cherhill. The main house retains much of its original character with beamed ceilings and a large fireplace in the restaurant. The bedrooms are located in converted outbuildings and provide comfortable modern accommodation. All seven rooms have en suite bathrooms, direct dial telephones and TVs. Proprietors Stephen and Veronica Harding offer a warm welcome and

contd.

provide friendly attentive service. The menus change monthly and there are daily specials, carefully produced from quality local ingredients.
7 annexe en suite (bth/shr) CTV in all bedrooms 100P No coaches European Cuisine V meals Coffee am No smoking area in restaurant
ROOMS: (incl. bkfst) s £39-£45; d £49-£55 *
CARDS:

★★62% **Lansdowne Strand Hotel & Restaurant**

The Strand SN11 0EH (on A4) ☎ 01249 812488
FAX 01249 815323
This former coaching inn dating from the 16th century is situated in the centre of the market town of Calne on the edge of the Marlborough Downs. Since taking over the hotel in 1994, the Calleya family continue with an extensive programme of refurbishment. Bedrooms have been well equipped with modern comforts, some being situated in a building looking onto the courtyard. Guests have the option of dining in the bars or in a more formal restaurant.
21 en suite (bth/shr) 5 annexe en suite (bth/shr) (3 fmly) No smoking in 4 bedrooms CTV in all bedrooms 21P Xmas English & French Cuisine V meals Coffee am Tea pm Last d 9.30pm
ROOMS: (incl. bkfst) s £52.50; d £68.25 * **LB**
MEALS: Lunch £11.50&alc High tea £3.30-£6.75alc
Dinner £11.50&alc
CONF: Thtr 90 Class 28 Board 30 Del £70
CARDS:

CAMBERLEY Surrey Map 04 SU86

★★★68% **Frimley Hall**

Portsmouth Rd GU15 2BG ☎ 01276 28321
FAX 01276 691253
Peacefully situated at the end of a residential road, Frimley Hall is a handsome Victorian manor house in 4 acres of grounds. Once inside, the grand staircase, wood panelling and stained glass windows create a sense of the past and there are some original bedrooms which retain fine features. Day rooms include an elegant lounge where guests can enjoy pre-dinner drinks and the a smaller, beamed Sandhurst bar.

66 en suite (bth/shr) (2 fmly) No smoking in 16 bedrooms CTV in all bedrooms Night porter 100P Wkly live entertainment Xmas V meals Coffee am Tea pm No smoking in restaurant Last d 9.30pm
ROOMS: s £110-£130; d £120-£170 **LB**
OFF-PEAK: d fr £75
MEALS: Lunch £14-£18.25&alc Dinner £17.50-£20.75&alc*
CONF: Thtr 60 Class 30 Board 40 Del from £140
CARDS:

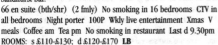

★★★65% **Lakeside International**
Wharf Rd, Frimley Green GU16 6JR (off A321) ☎ 01252 838000
FAX 01252 837857
An attractively situated modern hotel, the Lakeside International is chiefly geared to conferences and the corporate market, and the overall complex includes the renowned night club and a health and fitness club. Bedrooms are all furnished and equipped to the same standard the most attractive having a balcony and lakeside views. A spacious well appointed restaurant now offers a choice of menus and 24 hour room service is also provided. Live entertainment four nights a week makes the bar lounge a popular venue.
98 en suite (bth/shr) No smoking in 18 bedrooms CTV in all bedrooms No dogs (ex guide dogs) Lift Night porter 250P Indoor swimming pool (heated) Squash Snooker Sauna Solarium Gym Pool table Jacuzzi/spa Xmas English & French Cuisine V meals Coffee am Tea pm
ROOMS: (incl. bkfst) s fr £85; d fr £98 *
OFF-PEAK: (incl. bkfst) s fr £45; d fr £65
MEALS: Lunch £15.50 Dinner £15.50*
CONF: Thtr 100 Class 100 Board 36
CARDS:

★★69% **One Oak Toby**
114 Portsmouth Rd, Frimley GU15 1HS (leave M3 jct 4, follow A325 towards Frimley, hotel on left, past hospital) ☎ 01276 691939 FAX 01276 676088

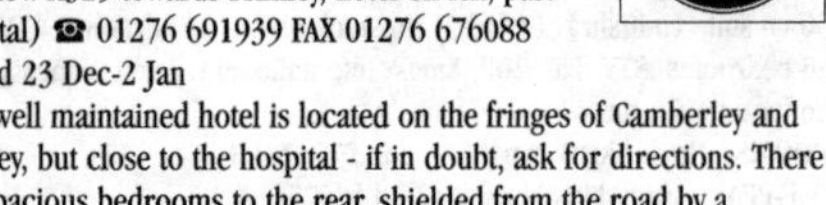

Closed 23 Dec-2 Jan
This well maintained hotel is located on the fringes of Camberley and Frimley, but close to the hospital - if in doubt, ask for directions. There are spacious bedrooms to the rear, shielded from the road by a company themed restaurant and an informal bar which was the building's previous sole purpose. It is now efficiently run by a welcoming team of staff.
40 en suite (bth/shr) No smoking in 10 bedrooms CTV in all bedrooms STV No dogs (ex guide dogs) Night porter 80P No coaches V meals Coffee am No smoking in restaurant Last d 10.30pm
ROOMS: (incl. bkfst) s £69.95; d £82 *
OFF-PEAK: (incl. bkfst) s £31; d £56-£59
MEALS: Lunch £9-£19.40alc Dinner £9-£19.40alc*
CONF: Thtr 30 Class 14 Board 18 Del £82
CARDS:

Travel Inn

221 Yorktown Rd, College Town GH15 4RT
☎ 01252 878181 FAX 01252 890648
Purpose-built accommodation, offering spacious, well equipped bedrooms, all with en suite bathrooms. Meals may be taken at the nearby family restaurant. For more information about Travel Inns, consult the Contents page under Hotel Groups.
40 en suite (bth/shr)
ROOMS: d £35.50 *

CAMBORNE Cornwall & Isles of Scilly Map 02 SW64

★★★69% **Tyacks**
27 Commercial St TR14 8LD (town centre opposite town clock) (St Austell Brewery) ☎ 01209 612424 FAX 01209 612435
This 18th century former coaching inn located in the centre of the town benefits from a large car park. The smart bedrooms are all very well equipped and have impressive bathrooms. Public areas which are spacious and equally well furnished include a smart residents' lounge and bar, a popular public bar and a well appointed restaurant; a choice of fixed price and carte choices are available, and an extensive range of food is also served in the bar.
15 en suite (bth/shr) (2 fmly) No smoking in 3 bedrooms CTV in all bedrooms STV No dogs (ex guide dogs) 43P Pool table Wkly live entertainment English & Continental Cuisine V meals Coffee am Last d 9.30pm
ROOMS: (incl. bkfst) s £42; d £70 * **LB**
MEALS: Lunch fr £15&alc Dinner fr £15&alc*
CARDS:

CAMBRIDGE Cambridgeshire Map 05 TL45

★★★★ 73% Cambridge Garden House

Granta Place, Mill Ln CB2 1RT ☎ 01223 259988
FAX 01223 316605
Sitting in 3 acres of grounds by the River Cam near the city centre, this hotel has very obliging staff, smart public rooms, including a lounge and a cocktail bar, and comfortable, well equipped bedrooms ranging from standard to executive and also some suites. Le Jardin Restaurant offers a good selection of modern and classical dishes, prepared by chef Alan Fuller from the freshest ingredients.
117 en suite (bth/shr) (4 fmly) No smoking in 42 bedrooms CTV in all bedrooms STV No dogs (ex guide dogs) Lift Night porter 150P Indoor swimming pool (heated) Fishing Sauna Solarium Gym Jacuzzi/spa Punting, beauty salon, steam room, Xmas International Cuisine V meals Coffee am Tea pm No smoking in restaurant Last d 9.45pm
ROOMS: s £105-£170; d £145-£195 * **LB**
MEALS: Lunch fr £17.50&alc High tea £6-£12alc Dinner fr £23&alc
CONF: Thtr 250 Class 100 Board 30 Del from £150
CARDS:

★★★★ 63% Holiday Inn

Downing St CB2 3DT ☎ 01223 464466
FAX 01223 464440
The easiest way to overcome the complex city centre road maze is to follow the signs to the Lions Yard car park. An efficient welcome and a valet car parking service awaits guests who arrive by car. The hotel is designed around a compact atrium, most of which is covered, which does sometimes create bottlenecks at peak periods of service. The bedrooms are well proportioned and the staff are well meaning.
199 en suite (bth/shr) No smoking in 100 bedrooms CTV in all bedrooms Lift Night porter Air conditioning 68P International Cuisine V meals Coffee am Tea pm Last d 10pm
ROOMS: s fr £99; d fr £125 * **LB**
MEALS: Sunday Lunch fr £11.95 Dinner fr £19.50*
CONF: Thtr 180 Class 40 Board 60 Del from £135
CARDS:

See advertisement on this page

★★★★ 61% University Arms

Regent St CB2 1AD ☎ 01223 351241
FAX 01223 461319
This fine Victorian building with a modern extension overlooks the famous Parkers Piece green. The public areas have some period style, especially the Octagon Lounge with its impressive domed ceiling. Most of the bedrooms have been upgraded now, though their size and outlook can vary considerably.
115 en suite (bth/shr) (16 fmly) No smoking in 38 bedrooms CTV in all bedrooms STV Lift Night porter 100P English & French Cuisine V meals Coffee am Tea pm Last d 9.45pm
CONF: Thtr 300 Class 100 Board 60 Del from £95
CARDS:

★★★ 71% Gonville

Gonville Place CB1 1LY (leave M11 jct 11 on A1309 follow signs to city centre, at 2nd mini rdbt turn right into Lensfield road, straight over jct with traffic lights)
☎ 01223 366611 FAX 01223 315470
A well established hotel which sits overlooking Parkers Piece, close to the city centre, that benefits from the provision of ample private car parking. Services are provided in a friendly and professional manner throughout the inviting public areas which are now air conditioned. The bedroom refurbishment is now complete, each of the new modern style bedrooms is well appointed and appealing with the richly coloured soft furnishings complimenting good dark wood furniture.

64 en suite (bth/shr) (1 fmly) No smoking in 12 bedrooms CTV in all bedrooms Lift Night porter 100P Xmas English & French Cuisine V meals Coffee am Tea pm Last d 8.45pm
ROOMS: (incl. bkfst) s fr £77; d fr £96 * **LB**
MEALS: Lunch fr £12.50&alc Dinner fr £15.95&alc
CONF: Thtr 200 Class 100 Board 50 Del from £92
CARDS:

★★★ 64% Cambridgeshire Moat House

CB3 8EU ☎ 01954 249988 FAX 01954 780010
(For full entry see Bar Hill)

★★★ 63% Royal Cambridge

Trumpington St CB2 1PY (leave M11 junct 11, follow signs for city centre. At 1st mini rdbt turn left into Fen Causeway, then first right for hotel) ☎ 01223 351631 FAX 01223 352972
An attractive Georgian hotel with convenient car parking, which sits just south of the city centre. Polite young staff provide a range of useful extra services, such as all-day service of snacks in the small lounge area, or the availability of room service for food and refreshments. Bedrooms are well maintained and quite comfortably appointed with rattan-style furniture.
46 en suite (bth/shr) (6 fmly) No smoking in 6 bedrooms CTV in all bedrooms STV Lift Night porter 80P V meals Coffee am Tea pm Last d 9.30pm
ROOMS: (incl. bkfst) s £75; d £87.50 * **LB**
MEALS: Lunch £4.95-£13.75&alc Dinner fr £13.75&alc*
CARDS:

★★ 70% *Cambridge Lodge*

139 Huntingdon Rd CB3 0DQ ☎ 01223 352833
FAX 01223 355166
RS Sat

contd.

C

Proprietors Sheila Hipwell and Darren Chamberlain ensure that guests receive a personal and caring service at this comfortable small hotel. Chef Peter Reynolds offers some imaginative dishes from both à la carte and set priced menus, which generally reflect a classical style of cooking with a French bias. Lighter snacks are also available in the lounge bar or through room service. Bedrooms are well appointed and most are of comfortable proportions.
11 rms (8 bth/shr) CTV in all bedrooms 20P No coaches English & Continental Cuisine V meals Last d 9.30pm
CARDS:

★★ 71% **Arundel House**
Chesterton Rd CB4 3AN (on A1303, overlooking the River Cam)
☎ 01223 367701 FAX 01223 367721
Closed 25-26 Dec
The Arundel House is only a short walk from the city centre, yet looks out over the River Cam and open parkland, known as Jesus Green. Public rooms are very smart following a recent expansion and refurbishment, the Victorian Conservatory is a delightful setting in which to enjoy food and refreshments from an all day lounge menu. The adjacent bar has a bright cheerful atmosphere, with beautiful chintz curtains, comfortable sofas and armchairs. A good choice of menus are offered within the attractively appointed restaurant, most tastes are catered for and the meals are reasonably priced. Bedrooms include the quiet coach house rooms; the more recent rooms are attractive with good use of bold soft furnishings and co-ordinated decor.
83 rms (77 bth/shr) 22 annexe en suite (bth/shr) (6 fmly) No smoking in 52 bedrooms CTV in all bedrooms No dogs Night porter 70P English, French & Italian Cuisine V meals Coffee am Tea pm No smoking area in restaurant Last d 9.30pm
ROOMS: (incl. cont bkfst) s £30-£59; d £57-£89 **LB**
MEALS: Lunch £9.75-£11.95&alc High tea £1.95-£6.55&alc Dinner £13.50-£15.95&alc
CONF: Thtr 50 Class 34 Board 32 Del from £72.50
CARDS:

★★68% **Centennial**
63-71 Hills Rd CB2 1PG ☎ 01223 314652 FAX 01223 315443
Closed 23 Dec-2 Jan
The Centennial is a friendly family-run hotel which offers quiet public areas and well furnished accommodation. A pleasant lounge area is provided on the ground floor, comfortably appointed with leather Chesterfields, and a bar and restaurant are available on the lower ground floor. Whilst bedroom sizes vary, they are all nicely appointed and well equipped, each with a modern en suite bathroom; room service to bedrooms is available.
39 en suite (bth/shr) (1 fmly) No smoking in 12 bedrooms CTV in all bedrooms No dogs Night porter 32P English & French Cuisine V meals Coffee am Tea pm Last d 9.30pm
ROOMS: (incl. bkfst) s £55-£65; d £69-£77 * **LB**
OFF-PEAK: (incl. bkfst) s £50-£58; d £65-£73
MEALS: Lunch £13.50-£16.50&alc Dinner £14-£17&alc*
CONF: Thtr 35 Class 25 Board 25
CARDS:

See advertisement on opposite page

Forte Posthouse Cambridge

FORTE Posthouse

Lakeview, Bridge Rd, Impington CB4 4PH (2.5m N,on N side of rdbt jct A45/B1049)
☎ 01223 237000 FAX 01223 233426
Suitable for both the business and leisure traveller, this bright hotel provides modern accommodation in well equipped bedrooms with en suite bathrooms. For more details about Forte Posthouse hotels, consult the Contents page for the section on Hotel Groups.
118 en suite (bth/shr)
ROOMS: d £59-£89 *
CONF: Thtr 60 Class 40 Board 30 Del from £119

CANNOCK Staffordshire Map 07 SJ91

★★★66% **Roman Way**

REGAL A Collection of Individual Hotels

Watling St, Hatherton WS11 1SH (on A5)
☎ 01543 572121 FAX 01543 502749
This purpose built hotel, named after the Roman road on which it lies, is conveniently close to junctions 11 and 12 of the M6. Attractive public areas include a marbled reception foyer, cocktail bar, restaurant and a lounge bar. There are also a number of meeting rooms which include a smart, newly refurbished boardroom. Guests have the choice of eating from the carvery in the lounge bar or in the restaurant. Otherwise, a short range of dishes, including hot food, is available from room service. Bedrooms are well appointed and all are equipped to the same standard.
56 en suite (bth/shr) (7 fmly) No smoking in 7 bedrooms CTV in all bedrooms Night porter 200P V meals Coffee am Tea pm Last d 9.30pm
ROOMS: s fr £59; d fr £64 * **LB**
OFF-PEAK: (incl. bkfst) s fr £45; d fr £45
MEALS: Sunday Lunch fr £8.50 Dinner fr £15*
CARDS:

Travel Inn

travel inn

Watling St, Longford WS11 1SJ (at junct of A5/A460) ☎ 01543 572721 FAX 01543 466130
Purpose-built accommodation, offering spacious, well equipped bedrooms, all with en suite bathrooms. Meals may be taken at the nearby family restaurant. For more information about Travel Inns, consult the Contents page under Hotel Groups.
38 en suite (bth/shr)
ROOMS: d £35.50 *

CANTERBURY Kent Map 05 TR15

★★★66% **Falstaff**

CCH COUNTRY CLUB Hotel Group

St Dunstans St, Westgate CT2 8AF (turn into St Peters Place off the A2 pass Westgate Towers into St Dunstans St hotel on right) ☎ 01227 462138
FAX 01227 463525
Many original features have benn retained within the walls of this beamed coaching inn which dates from the 16th century. The hotel stands next to the Westgate Tower, benefits from its own car park and offers easy access to the city centre, the M2 and M20. Bedrooms vary in size and have recently been improved to include smart bathrooms. Cosy public rooms comprise a comfortable lounge, an attractive restaurant and residents' bar. The Falstaff Tap, an ale and cider house, is situated in the grounds.
24 en suite (bth/shr) (2 fmly) No smoking in 15 bedrooms CTV in all bedrooms STV Night porter 50P Xmas English & French Cuisine V meals Coffee am Tea pm No smoking in restaurant Last d 9.30pm
ROOMS: s fr £68; d fr £75 * **LB**
MEALS: Lunch fr £12alc High tea fr £4 Dinner £20-£25alc*
CARDS:

★★★64% **The Chaucer**

FORTE Heritage

Ivy Ln CT1 1TU ☎ 01227 464427 FAX 01227 450397

This former Georgian residence located within easy walking distance of the city centre has a well-cared-for atmosphere. Bedrooms are comfortable and well looked after. There is an old-fashioned bar and an elegantly furnished restaurant.

42 en suite (bth/shr) No smoking in 19 bedrooms CTV in all bedrooms Night porter Xmas V meals Coffee am Tea pm No smoking in restaurant Last d 9.30pm

ROOMS: s fr £70; d fr £85 * **LB**

MEALS: Lunch £10.95-£12.50 Dinner £17.95-£18.95&alc

CONF: Thtr 100 Class 45 Board 45 Del from £98

CARDS:

★★75% **Ebury**

65/67 New Dover Rd CT1 3DX ☎ 01227 768433 FAX 01227 459187

Closed 16 Dec-14 Jan

Quietly situated set back from the New Dover Road in 2 acres of well kept mature garden this delightful family-run hotel has a very agreeable relaxing atmosphere. The accommodation has been attractively furnished and all bedrooms come particularly well equipped. A spacious and comfortable lounge forms the main part of the ground floor, along with a reception facility and well appointed restaurant which offers an interesting à la carte menu including char grills, home-made recipes and the promise of some good meals to come. Room service is available including continental breakfast and the attentive staff are personally supervised by owner Mr A P Mason.

15 en suite (bth/shr) (2 fmly) CTV in all bedrooms 31P No coaches Indoor swimming pool (heated) Jacuzzi/spa Exercise equipment V meals Coffee am Tea pm No smoking in restaurant Last d 8.30pm

ROOMS: (incl. bkfst) s £41-£48; d £60-£65 **LB**

MEALS: Bar Lunch £2-£7alc Dinner £8.50-£15alc*

CARDS:

★★66% **Canterbury**

MINOTEL Great Britain

71 New Dover Rd CT1 3DZ (on A2, Dover road)

☎ 01227 450551 FAX 01227 780145

The Canterbury is a popular family-run hotel ideally located not far from the city centre. It comprises a range of comfortable bedrooms, all furnished and equipped to the same standard, an attractive restaurant and breakfast room, a separate TV lounge, (which can be reserved for private meetings etc.), and a combined bar and reception. The French à la carte cuisine is worthy of note and holds out the promise of some good meals to come. Service is friendly and helpful, and forecourt car parking is available.

27 en suite (bth/shr) (3 fmly) CTV in all bedrooms Lift Air conditioning 50P French Cuisine V meals Coffee am Tea pm Last d 10pm

ROOMS: (incl. bkfst) s fr £40; d fr £55 * **LB**

MEALS: Lunch fr £8.50 Dinner fr £12.50*

CONF: Thtr 60 Class 30 Board 25 Del from £55

CARDS: £

Travelodge

Travelodge

A2 Gate Services, Dunkirk ME13 9LN (5m W on A2 northbound) ☎ 01227 752781 FAX 01227 752781

This modern building offers accommodation in smart, spacious and well equipped bedrooms, suitable for family use, and all with en suite bathrooms. Meals may be taken at the nearby family restaurant. For information on room rates and to make a booking, call Roomline free of charge on 0800 850950. For more details about Travelodge, consult the Contents page under Hotel Groups.

CARBIS BAY Map 02 SW53

See St Ives

CARCROFT South Yorkshire Map 08 SE50

Travelodge
Great North Rd DN6 9LF (on A1 northbound)
☎ 01302 330841 FAX 01302 330841
This modern building offers accommodation in smart, spacious and well equipped bedrooms, suitable for family use, and all with en suite bathrooms. Meals may be taken at the nearby family restaurant. For information on room rates and to make a booking, call Roomline free of charge on 0800 850950. For more details about Travelodge, consult the Contents page under Hotel Groups.
40 en suite (bth/shr)

CARLISLE Cumbria Map 11 NY45
See also Crosby-on-Eden

★★★73% **Crown**
Wetheral CA4 8ES ☎ 01228 561888
FAX 01228 561637
Considerate and well meaning levels of service and hospitality are to be found in this peacefully located hotel. Originally built as a farmhouse in the early 18th century it has evolved into a clever combination of old and new. It is well suited for conferences as well as leisure guests. The conservatory restaurant overlooks well tended gardens and in addition to a cocktail bar there is a more traditional bar, Waltons.
49 en suite (bth/shr) 2 annexe en suite (bth/shr) (3 fmly) No smoking in 10 bedrooms CTV in all bedrooms STV Night porter 80P Indoor swimming pool (heated) Squash Snooker Sauna Solarium Gym Jacuzzi/spa Children's splash pool Xmas International Cuisine V meals Coffee am Tea pm No smoking area in restaurant Last d 9.45pm
ROOMS: (incl. bkfst) s £92-£112; d £110-£130 * **LB**
OFF-PEAK: (incl. bkfst & dinner) d fr £130
MEALS: Bar Lunch fr £10 Dinner fr £20alc*
CONF: Thtr 175 Class 90 Board 50 Del from £115
CARDS:

★★★67% **Cumbria Park**
32 Scotland Rd, Stanwix CA3 9DG (1.5m N on A47)
☎ 01228 22887 FAX 01228 514796
Closed 25-26 Dec
Distinguished by its impressive brick façade, this long established family-run hotel is attractively furnished and offers relaxing lounge areas complete with daily papers and photographs of celebrity guests. Bedrooms come in a variety of sizes, but whilst all are individual, it's worth asking for one of the executive rooms, some of which have antique 4-poster beds.
48 en suite (bth/shr) (2 fmly) No smoking in 6 bedrooms CTV in all bedrooms STV No dogs (ex guide dogs) Lift Night porter 40P English & Italian Cuisine V meals Coffee am Tea pm Last d 9.45pm
ROOMS: (incl. bkfst) s £65-£82.50; d £82.50-£120 * **LB**
OFF-PEAK: (incl. bkfst) s £45-£70; d £55-£85
MEALS: Lunch fr £9.95 Dinner £15.95&alc*
CARDS:

★★★64% **Swallow Hilltop**
London Rd CA1 2PQ (S on A6) ☎ 01228 29255
FAX 01228 25238
Although this hotel is conveniently situated on the A6, it is set back from the road in an elevated position. The majority of bedrooms have now been upgraded to a smart modern standard; there are, however, still some less glamorous budget rooms. Both leisure and meeting facilities are available.
92 en suite (bth/shr) (6 fmly) No smoking in 24 bedrooms CTV in all bedrooms STV Lift Night porter 350P Indoor swimming pool (heated) Sauna Solarium Gym Massage Wkly live entertainment Xmas English & French Cuisine V meals Coffee am Tea pm Last d 9.45pm
ROOMS: (incl. bkfst) s £85; d £99 **LB**
MEALS: Lunch £9.50 Dinner £17.95
CONF: Thtr 500 Class 250 Board 90 Del £99
CARDS:

★★★60% **Central Plaza**
Victoria Viaduct CA3 8AL (in city centre, just N of main BR station on A6) ☎ 01228 20256 FAX 01228 514657
Offering accommodation in a variety of styles and standards, this Victorian property lies in the city centre close to the station.
84 en suite (bth/shr) (3 fmly) No smoking in 4 bedrooms CTV in all bedrooms STV Lift Night porter 12P Pool table Xmas English & French Cuisine V meals Coffee am Tea pm Last d 9.15pm
ROOMS: (incl. bkfst) s £60.50-£65.50; d £80-£89 * **LB**
MEALS: Dinner fr £18.50*
CARDS:

★★64% **County**
9 Botchergate CA1 1QS (opposite railway station) ☎ 01228 31316
FAX 01228 515456
Located in the city centre close to the railway station, this large commercial and tour hotel offers well equipped bedrooms, a comfortable lounge and a small restaurant featuring good-value meals on both carte and the carvery menu. There is a secure car park to the rear of the hotel.
84 en suite (bth/shr) (14 fmly) No smoking in 6 bedrooms CTV in all bedrooms STV Lift Night porter 100P Games room Xmas International Cuisine V meals Coffee am Tea pm No smoking in restaurant Last d 10pm
ROOMS: s £39.95-£64.95; d £49.95-£64.95 * **LB**
MEALS: Lunch £4.50-£6.90 Dinner fr £13.95*
CONF: Thtr 150 Class 75 Board 50 Del from £42
CARDS:

See advertisement on opposite page

★★60% **Pinegrove**
262 London Rd CA1 2QS (on A6) ☎ 01228 24828
FAX 01228 810941
Closed 25 & 31 Dec
This extended late-Victorian mansion lies on the main road south of the city centre. Public areas include a spacious restaurant and an attractive lounge bar, whilst bedrooms are of a reliable standard and well equipped. More practical accommodation may be offered in the adjacent Woodlands Hotel which is now part of the Pinegrove and operates mainly as an annexe.
28 rms (8 bth 19 shr) 4 annexe en suite (bth/shr) (8 fmly) CTV in all bedrooms STV 50P Pool table Darts English & French Cuisine V meals Coffee am Last d 9pm
ROOMS: (incl. bkfst) s £42; d £54 * **LB**
OFF-PEAK: (incl. bkfst) s fr £28; d fr £40
MEALS: Lunch fr £5.95 Dinner fr £14&alc*
CONF: Thtr 120 Class 100 Board 100 Del from £60
CARDS:

★62% **Vallum House Garden**
Burgh Rd CA2 7NB ☎ 01228 21860
Closed 25-26 Dec & 1 Jan
Situated in a west end residential area this small personally-run hotel has a friendly informal atmosphere and offers good value to both business guests and families. Bedrooms though variable in size and somewhat practical in style, are gradually being cosmetically improved. With no lounge, the bar is a popular rendezvous and the menus offer both light and substantial dishes at competitive prices.
9 rms (5 bth/shr) (1 fmly) CTV in all bedrooms 30P English, French & Italian Cuisine V meals Coffee am Tea pm No smoking in restaurant Last d 8.45pm

ROOMS: (incl. bkfst) s £25; d £40-£45 * **LB**
OFF-PEAK: (incl. bkfst) s £22; d £40
MEALS: Lunch £8.50-£15 High tea fr £5 Dinner £8.50-£15*
CARDS:

Forte Posthouse Carlisle
Parkhouse Rd CA3 0HR (junc 44/M6 take A7 into Carlisle hotel on right at first set of traffic lights) ☎ 01228 31201 FAX 01228 43178
FORTE Posthouse
Suitable for both the business and leisure traveller, this bright hotel provides modern accommodation in well equipped bedrooms with en suite bathrooms. For more details about Forte Posthouse hotels, consult the Contents page for the section on Hotel Groups.
93 en suite (bth/shr)
ROOMS: d £59-£79 *
CONF: Thtr 60 Class 32 Board 28

CARNFORTH Lancashire Map 07 SD47

★★60% **Royal Station**
Market St LA5 9BT (leave M6 junct 35 join A6 signed Carnforth & Morecambe, in 1m at x-rds in centre of Carnforth turn rt into Market Sq hotel opposite rly sta) ☎ 01524 732033 & 733636
FAX 01524 720267
As its name suggests, this long established hotel is ideally situated opposite the railway station and has quite a traditional feel. Bedrooms, all of which have modern en suite facilities, are generally spacious and quite well equipped but some, however, are beginning to show signs of wear. There are two bars where meals are served and one which benefits from a couple of pool tables and which is very popular with the locals. The hotel also has a large function room, in addition to a smaller meeting room and a small car park at the rear.
12 en suite (bth/shr) (1 fmly) CTV in all bedrooms 18P Pool table English & French Cuisine V meals Coffee am Tea pm Last d 9.30pm
ROOMS: (incl. bkfst) s £28; d £43 * **LB**
MEALS: Sunday Lunch £7.95-£13.20alc Dinner £7.95-£13.65alc*

CARDS:

CARPERBY North Yorkshire Map 07 SE08

★★65% **Wheatsheaf**
DL8 4DF (from A1 take west route on A684 to Wensley, turn right signposted Castle Bolton next village is Carperby) ☎ 01969 663216
FAX 01969 663019
Famous as the venue where James Herriot of 'All Creatures Great and Small' spent his honeymoon, the Wheatsheaf is a typical Dales inn and a comfortable hotel. It stands in beautiful countryside in the heart of the pretty village of Carperby. The bedrooms are pleasantly furnished (two with four-poster beds), whilst the public rooms are cosy and comfortable. The lounge features a 17th-century stone fireplace, and wood-panelling abounds and the service is naturally warm and friendly.
8 en suite (bth/shr) (1 fmly) CTV in all bedrooms 52P No coaches Trout fishing can be arranged No children 12yrs V meals Coffee am Tea pm Last d 9pm
ROOMS: (incl. bkfst) s £26-£28; d £50-£60 * **LB**
MEALS: Sunday Lunch fr £9.50 Dinner £12.50-£15*
CARDS:

CARTMEL Cumbria Map 07 SD37

★★74% **Aynsome Manor**
LA11 6HH (from junc 36 M6, follow A590 signed Barrow in Furness. Continue towards Cartmel turn left at end of dual carriageway. Hotel just before village) ☎ 015395 36653 FAX 015395 36016
Closed 2-26 Jan

Dating from the 16th century this historic manor house sits in its own gardens amidst farmland on the outskirts of the village, giving good views of the priory. Family-run, it offers a high level of personal service and hospitality. Public areas are a delight, whether one relaxes in the entrance lounge, cosy bar or magnificent upper lounge, all of which are enhanced by open fires in season. Good British cooking is exemplified by the five-course dinners and tasty breakfasts which grace the elegant dining room.
10 en suite (bth/shr) 2 annexe en suite (bth) (2 fmly) CTV in all bedrooms 20P No coaches Xmas V meals Coffee am No smoking in restaurant Last d 8.30pm
ROOMS: (incl. bkfst & dinner) s £52-£62; d £88-£104 **LB**
MEALS: Sunday Lunch £12 Dinner £15-£19.50
CARDS:

CASTLE ASHBY Northamptonshire Map 04 SP85

★★★73% **Falcon**
NN7 1LF ☎ 01604 696200 FAX 01604 696673
Best Western
Ongoing improvements at the Falcon have upgraded the bedrooms and public areas, and added a herb garden to the existing grounds. The chef maintains a straightforward approach to cooking which produces enjoyable dishes which are occasionally supplemented by seasonal menus, for example an asparagus menu in the late spring. The indefatigable owners, Mr and Mrs Watson, continue to oversee guests' welfare in a graceful fashion.
6 rms (5 bth/shr) 11 annexe en suite (bth/shr) CTV in all bedrooms STV 75P English & French Cuisine V meals Coffee am Tea pm Last d 9.30pm
ROOMS: (incl. bkfst) s £62.50; d £75 * **LB**
OFF-PEAK: (incl. bkfst) s £50; d £60
MEALS: Lunch £15.50-£19.50&alc Dinner £19.50&alc*
CONF: Thtr 30 Class 30 Board 20 Del from £90
CARDS:

CASTLE BROMWICH West Midlands Map 07 SP18

★★69% ***Bradford Arms***
Chester Rd B36 0AG ☎ 0121 748 7675
FAX 0121 776 7961
Situated beside the A47, this 18th century coaching inn offers comfortable accommodation in a modern purpose-built bedroom block. Rooms are attractively furnished, pleasantly appointed and well equipped. The main building contains a choice of popular bars and a spacious restaurant serving a good range of dishes both at lunch time and in the evening. Smartly uniformed staff provide friendly and cheerful service.
30 en suite (bth/shr) No smoking in 16 bedrooms CTV in all bedrooms STV Night porter 100P No coaches V meals Coffee am Last d 10.30pm
CARDS:

CASTLE COMBE Wiltshire Map 03 ST87

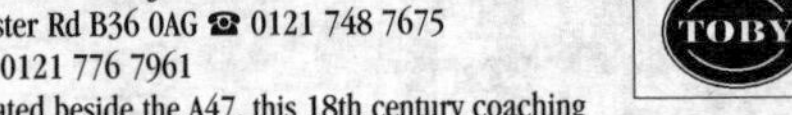

★★★★ **Manor House**
SN14 7HR (follow Chippenham signs from M4 junc17, onto A420 signed Bristol, then right onto B4039. Go through village, turn rt after crossing river bridge) ☎ 01249 782206 FAX 01249 782159
Set back within a picturesque location surrounded by parkland and Italianate gardens, the Manor House appears to go from strength to strength. Continued investment at this charming hotel has seen the addition of more superb bedrooms, in which the bathrooms in particular are unique. Bedrooms in the main house are lavishly furnished while those in the cottage are simpler, though this is reflected in the tariff. Manager Martin Clubbe and his equally dedicated team provide high service levels which are tempered with an abundance of enthusiasm and natural friendliness. Chef Mark Taylor's cooking continues to please with carefully prepared dishes and good use of first class ingredients. A recent inspection meal began with delicious scallops with a complementary curry sabayon, followed by a full-flavoured roast local partridge with roasted shallots. A rich Belgian chocolate soufflé was well presented and full of flavour.
17 en suite (bth/shr) 24 annexe en suite (bth/shr) CTV in all bedrooms No dogs (ex guide dogs) Night porter 100P No coaches Outdoor swimming pool (heated) Golf 18 Tennis (hard) Fishing Croquet lawn Jogging track Xmas English & French Cuisine V meals Coffee am Tea pm No smoking in restaurant Last d 10pm
ROOMS: s £100-£350; d £100-£350 * LB
MEALS: Lunch £16.95-£18.95 Dinner £35&alc
CARDS:

★★★67% **Castle Inn**
SN14 7HN (Take A420 to Chippenham follow signs for Castle Combe. Hotel is situated in the heart of the village) ☎ 01249 783030 FAX 01249 782315
Set in the market place of historic Castle Coombe, this famous hostelry can trace its origins back to the 12th-century and many features of the original construction remain today. The inn has recently undergone considerate restoration with care being taken to preserve the charm and character of the delightful building. Seven bedrooms have been individually decorated and there are many thoughtful extras such as fruit, mineral water and tasty home-made biscuits. A teddy bear is also provided to welcome you to the inn. An interesting selection of dishes is available in Oliver's Restaurant and more informal dining is on offer in the bar.
7 en suite (bth/shr) CTV in all bedrooms No dogs (ex guide dogs) N Xmas English Cuisine V meals Coffee am Tea pm No smoking in restaurant Last d 9pm
ROOMS: (incl. bkfst) s £60-£75; d £75-£90 * LB
MEALS: Lunch £1.95-£10 Dinner £1.95-£12*
CONF: Board 30
CARDS:

CASTLE DONINGTON Leicestershire Map 08 SK42
See also East Midlands Airport & Shardlow

★★★66% **The Priest House on the River**
Kings Mills DE74 2RR ☎ 01332 810649
FAX 01332 811141

This hotel dates from the 11th century when coins of the realm were struck here and was later the home of the priest of the local Abbey. It is situated at the end of a wooded, winding lane in a pictuesque spot on a bend of the River Trent, complete with watermills. It has a Gothic tower as its centrepiece, and the striking interior design continues this theme with arched windows and doorways. To the rear, a courtyard leads from the library, which is furnished with deep cushioned sofas and winged armchairs, dominated by a huge Adam fireplace. The restaurant faces the river and the bar is a convivial place to enjoy the local ales. The bedrooms, many of them with four poster beds, are furnished to a higher level of quality than is normally found at this classification.
25 en suite (bth/shr) 20 annexe en suite (bth/shr) (2 fmly) CTV in all bedrooms STV Night porter 150P Fishing Croquet lawn Archery Clay pigeon shooting Wkly live entertainment Xmas English Cuisine V meals Coffee am Tea pm No smoking area in restaurant Last d 9.30pm
ROOMS: s fr £75; d fr £85 * LB
MEALS: Lunch £15&alc Dinner £19.75&alc*
CONF: Thtr 150 Class 45 Board 36 Del from £125
CARDS:

★★★65% **Donington Manor**
High St DE74 2PP (1m into village on B5430 situated on left at traffic lights) ☎ 01332 810253
FAX 01332 850330
Closed 27-30 Dec
Owner Mr Grist's personal stewardship is reflected in the hospitality extended to his guests via a dedicated and well trained staff at this hotel, a graceful Georgian building just off the village centre. Bedrooms - which are constantly being upgraded - feature individual décor and furnishings together with some really striking bathrooms, the one formerly belonging to Elvis Presley being perhaps the most eye catching. Over half the bedrooms are superior in every sense and far above the expectations in this class of hotel. Locally it has a good reputation for functions, the attractive oak-panelled room beyond the bar being particularly popular for wedding receptions. The main Adam dining room has remarkable plasterwork.

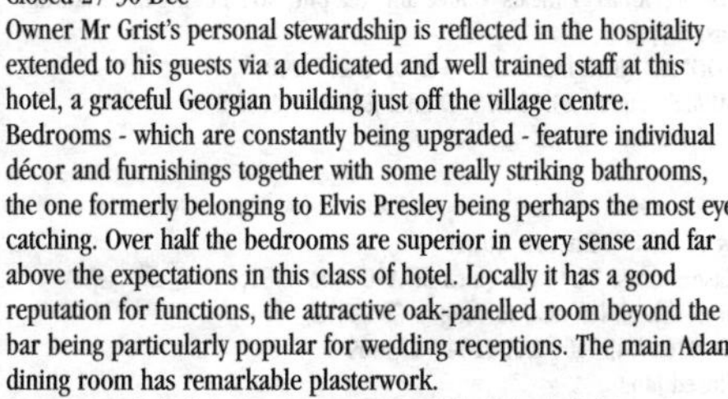

25 en suite (bth/shr) 1 annexe en suite (bth/shr) (1 fmly) CTV in all bedrooms STV No dogs (ex guide dogs) Night porter 60P English & French Cuisine V meals Coffee am Tea pm Last d 9.30pm
ROOMS: (incl. bkfst) s £57-£62.75; d £70.50-£75.50 * **LB**
OFF-PEAK: (incl. bkfst) s fr £35; d fr £60
MEALS: Lunch fr £8.90&alc Dinner fr £10.75&alc*
CONF: Thtr 80 Class 80 Board 20 Del from £60
CARDS:

★★60% **The Lady In Grey**
Wilne Ln DE72 2HA ☎ 01332 792331 FAX 01332 792331
(For full entry see Shardlow)

CATON Lancashire Map 07 SD56

★★60% ***Scarthwaite Country House***
Crook o Lune LA2 9HR (leave M6 at junct 34 onto A683 towards Caton hotel one and a half miles on right) ☎ 01524 770267
FAX 01524 770711
Convenient for the M6 motorway and nearby Lake District, this hotel was built in 1842 as a country retreat and stands in its own grounds. Bedrooms are individually furnished and have modern facilities. The attractive gardens are a pleasant setting for a drink or meal on a summer's evening, and make it a popular venue for weddings.
10 en suite (bth/shr) (1 fmly) No smoking in 2 bedrooms CTV in all bedrooms No dogs (ex guide dogs) Night porter 75P V meals Coffee am Tea pm Last d 9.30pm
CARDS:

CATTERICK BRIDGE North Yorkshire Map 08 SE29

★★59% **Bridge House**
DL10 7PE (3 miles S of Scotch Corner, on bridge opp Catterick Racecourse) ☎ 01748 818331 FAX 01748 818331
This family-owned and run hotel is found directly opposite the Catterick Bridge racecourse and was a former coaching house. It provides modestly furnished bedrooms together with friendly and attentive service whilst a good range of food is available in the spacious and traditional-style restaurant.
16 rms (4 bth 9 shr) (3 fmly) CTV in all bedrooms STV 70P Fishing Pool table English & French Cuisine V meals Coffee am Last d 9.15pm
ROOMS: (incl. bkfst) s £26-£36; d £42-£52 * **LB**
MEALS: Lunch £12.75-£20.50alc Dinner £12.75-£20.50alc*
CONF: Thtr 120 Class 80 Board 60 Del from £136
CARDS:

CAWSTON Norfolk Map 09 TG12

★64% **Grey Gables**
Norwich Rd NR10 4EY (1m S of Cawston village at Eastgate, 1m W B1149) ☎ 01603 871259
Closed 24-26 Dec
Mr and Mrs Snaith provide discreet hospitality and sound home-cooked food at their peaceful home. Bedrooms are well equipped and reflect the natural and easy-going surroundings. Drinks are served in the cosy lounge.
8 rms (5 bth 1 shr) (1 fmly) CTV in all bedrooms 20P No coaches Tennis (grass) English & French Cuisine V meals No smoking in restaurant Last d 9pm
ROOMS: (incl. bkfst) s £21-£40; d £42-£60 * **LB**
MEALS: Dinner £10-£20
CONF: Board 12 Del from £60
CARDS:

CHADDERTON Greater Manchester Map 07 SD90

Travel Inn
The Broadway OL9 8DW ☎ 0161 681 1373
FAX 0161 682 7974
Purpose-built accommodation, offering spacious, well equipped bedrooms, all with en suite bathrooms. Meals may be taken at the nearby family restaurant. For more information about Travel Inns, consult the Contents page under Hotel Groups.
40 en suite (bth/shr)
ROOMS: d £35.50 *

CHADDESLEY CORBETT Hereford & Worcester Map 07 SO87

★★★80% **Brockencote Hall Country House**
DY10 4PY (0.50 m W, off A448, opposite St Cassians Church) ☎ 01562 777876
FAX 01562 777872
This magnificent country house is set in 70 acres of landscaped grounds on the outskirts of the village. Proprietors Joseph and Allison Petitjean have extended the original house to provide accommodation which is tastefully furnished and appointed to a high standard. The spacious and comfortable bedrooms include rooms on ground-floor level, a room for disabled guests, and rooms with four-poster beds. The well proportioned public rooms include a choice of comfortable lounges, an elegant dining room, a room for private dining and facilities for small conferences. Didier Philipot has returned to the hotel as Head Chef and introduced a menu that features traditional French cuisine as well as lighter food with a simpler format.
17 en suite (bth/shr) (2 fmly) CTV in all bedrooms STV No dogs Lift 45P No coaches Croquet lawn Jacuzzi/spa Xmas French Cuisine V meals Coffee am Tea pm No smoking in restaurant Last d 9.30pm
ROOMS: (incl. bkfst) s £85-£95; d £115-£140 **LB**
MEALS: Lunch £18.50-£39.50 Dinner £23.50-£39.50
CONF: Thtr 30 Class 20 Board 20 Del £140
CARDS:

CHAGFORD Devon Map 03 SX78

RED STAR HOTEL

★★★ **Gidleigh Park**
TQ13 8HH ☎ 01647 432367 & 432225
FAX 01647 432574
Gidleigh has long been a mecca for those seeking all that is best in British hotel-keeping and few guests are likely to be disappointed by Paul and Kay Henderson's idyllic hideaway set in 45 acres of secluded grounds within

contd.

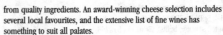

Dartmoor. The fabulous gardens are being restored and can provide hours of entertainment as they include an all-weather tennis court, bowling greens, several croquet lawns and a putting green. The mock-Tudor house built in the 1920s is delightfully furnished with fine English fabrics, antique furniture and stunning fresh flower arrangements. Individually styled bedrooms vary in size and outlook (reflected in the tariff) but not in quality and all have thoughtful extras. Under the direction of manager Catherine Endacott, the young staff provide charming, attentive and informed service. Crowning all of this is the cooking of chef Michael Caines, surely one of the most innovative young chefs in the country. Quality produce is consistently handled with great flair and creativity to produce finely balanced dishes which exhibit tremendous depth of flavour. The food, coupled with a stunning wine list, is likely to satisfy even the most demanding of gourmets.

12 en suite (bth/shr) 3 annexe en suite (bth/shr) CTV in all bedrooms STV 25P No coaches Tennis (hard) Fishing Croquet lawn Putting green Bowls French Cuisine V meals Coffee am Tea pm No smoking in restaurant Last d 9pm
ROOMS: (incl. bkfst & dinner) s £210-£350; d £325-£400 * LB
MEALS: Lunch £25-£55alc Dinner £55-£60alc*
CONF: Board 22 Del from £250
CARDS:

★★★ 75% Mill End
Sandy Park TQ13 8JN (2m N on A382)
☎ 01647 432282 FAX 01647 433106
Closed 7-15 Dec & 9-17 Jan
This former flour mill, peacefully set in its own well tended garden with six miles of salmon and trout fishing on the Teign, is ideally situated for exploring Dartmoor. Inside the hotel the atmosphere is that of a comfortable private house, well managed by the resident proprietors and their team of professional staff. Some of the bedrooms are modern and some old and chintzy, but they are all well equipped with modern facilities and thoughtful extra touches like fresh flowers. The daily-changing menu offers interesting dishes, freshly prepared from quality ingredients. An award-winning cheese selection includes several local favourites, and the extensive list of fine wines has something to suit all palates.
17 rms (15 bth/shr) (2 fmly) CTV in all bedrooms 21P No coaches Fishing Xmas V meals Coffee am Tea pm No smoking in restaurant Last d 9pm
ROOMS: (incl. bkfst) s £35-£50; d £79-£90 *
MEALS: Lunch £9.95-£15 Dinner £14.50-£28alc*
CARDS:

See advertisement on opposite page

★★ 72% Easton Court
Easton Cross TQ13 8JL (turn off A30 onto A382, hotel 4m on left near turning to Chagford)
☎ 01647 433469 FAX 01647 433469
Closed Jan
This delightful family-run hotel, situated on the outskirts of the picturesque moorland town of Chagford, retains all the character and charm of a building which dates back to the 15th century. Brightly decorated bedrooms have been equipped with modern facilities and thoughtful extras. Three cosy lounges, one with a bar, and another with a magnificent inglenook fireplace, boast low ceilings and exposed beams. A choice of dishes make up the daily-changing table d'hÙte menu, which emphasises fresh ingredients, honest flavours and competent cooking skills.
8 en suite (bth/shr) CTV in all bedrooms 20P No coaches No children 12yrs Xmas English & Continental Cuisine V meals Tea pm No smoking in restaurant Last d 8.30pm
ROOMS: (incl. bkfst & dinner) s fr £64; d fr £116 **LB**
OFF-PEAK: (incl. bkfst & dinner) s fr £50; d fr £90
MEALS: Dinner £22
CARDS:

CHALE See Wight, Isle of

CHARDSTOCK Devon Map 03 ST30

★★★ 73% Tytherleigh Cot
EX13 7BN (take Chardstock turn off A358 and continue for 0.75m. Hotel on right)
☎ 01460 221170 FAX 01460 221291
(Rosette awarded for dinner only)
A former cider house, this 14th-century grade II listed building has been extended to create an attractive village hotel. The bedrooms are housed in several converted buildings and they have a pleasant cottagey character, whilst providing good levels of comfort and facilities. The restaurant is in a conservatory overlooking the pond and outdoor swimming pool; there is a interesting daily menu as well as daily specials such as a tasty smoked salmon and seaweed roulade, or fresh local scallops. The wine list offers a good variety from Europe and the New World, with several half bottles.
3 en suite (bth) 16 annexe en suite (bth) CTV in all bedrooms STV 25P Outdoor swimming pool (heated) Sauna Solarium Gym No children 12yrs V meals Coffee am Tea pm Last d 9.30pm
CARDS:

CHARINGWORTH Gloucestershire Map 04 SP13

RED STAR HOTEL

★★★ Charingworth Manor
GL55 6NS (on B4035 3m E of Chipping Campden) ☎ 01386 593555
FAX 01386 593353

This 14th-century manor house enjoys delightful views of gently rolling Cotswold countryside from its elevated position in 50 acres of grounds and gardens just three miles from Chipping Campden. Inside, Charingworth retains many original features including exposed beams, flagstone floors and open fireplaces. An elegant leisure spa offers an indoor heated swimming pool, sauna, steam room and solarium, and there is also a tennis court in the grounds. The 24 individually designed bedrooms have been furnished with antiques and fine fabrics, carefully combined with modern comforts. The John Greville restaurant provides intimate surroundings in which to enjoy the interesting dishes prepared with care by chef Matthew Laughton and his brigade. A recent inspection meal started with a salad of succulent Cornish Scallops, served with crispy bacon and fresh tomatoes, and was followed by a shank of lamb, braised in beer and orange until tender and served with a purée of turnips. The dessert selection included light, richly flavoured tirimisu, attractively presented in a cup and saucer, and steamed apple and pear flapjack pudding.

26 en suite (bth/shr) CTV in all bedrooms Night porter 50P No coaches Indoor swimming pool (heated) Tennis (hard) Snooker Sauna Solarium Croquet lawn Xmas English & French Cuisine V meals Coffee am Tea pm No smoking in restaurant Last d 9.30pm

ROOMS: (incl. bkfst) s fr £95; d fr £132 * **LB**

MEALS: Lunch fr £15.95 Dinner fr £32.25&alc*

CARDS:

See advertisement under CHIPPING CAMPDEN

CHARLBURY Oxfordshire Map 04 SP31

★★66% The Bell

Church St OX7 3PP (3m W of A34) ☎ 01608 810278
FAX 01608 811447

Best Western

A historic inn in the ancient town of Charlbury, The Bell attracts a loyal local clientele who enjoy the relaxed atmosphere. The flagstone floored bar is very popular and Spanish tapas are served, reflecting the origins of proprietor Juan Claramonte. Rooms are cosy and attractively furnished. The restaurant serves reliable food in the traditional style. Its warm atmosphere is another of the hotel's attractions.

10 en suite (bth/shr) 4 annexe en suite (bth/shr) (1 fmly) CTV in all bedrooms 30P Clay pigeon shooting Xmas International Cuisine V meals Coffee am Tea pm Last d 9.15pm

ROOMS: (incl. bkfst) s fr £50; d £75 * **LB**

MEALS: Lunch £15&alc Dinner £15&alc

CONF: Thtr 55 Class 25 Board 20 Del £85

CARDS:

CHARLECOTE Warwickshire Map 04 SP25

★★★63% Charlecote Pheasant Country

CV35 9EW (leave M40 junc15, take A429 towards Cirencester through Barford village after 2m turn right into Charlecote, hotel opp Charlecote Manor Park)
☎ 01789 470333 FAX 01789 470222

RS Xmas/New Year

Conveniently positioned just outside Stratford, this large and unusual complex set in extensive grounds comprises a collection of buildings of various ages, ranging from purpose-built to converted farm buildings and house. There is a distinctly rustic feel to the public rooms, restaurant and bars. Bedrooms are well equipped and include ground floor and non-smoking; rooms range from the functional to the quite luxurious.

67 annexe en suite (bth/shr) (1 fmly) No smoking in 14 bedrooms CTV in all bedrooms STV No dogs (ex guide dogs) Night porter 120P Outdoor swimming pool (heated) Tennis (hard) ch fac International Cuisine V meals Coffee am Tea pm No smoking in restaurant Last d 9.45pm

MEALS: Lunch £11.50&alc High tea £6.75 Dinner £14.25&alc*

CARDS:

CHARMOUTH Dorset Map 03 SY39

★★66% Hensleigh

Lower Sea Ln DT6 6LW (at traffic lights incentre of village turn into Lower Sea Ln hotel on left approx 250 yds from junc)
☎ 01297 560830

Closed Nov-Feb

This friendly, family-run hotel is situated off the main street, just a few minutes walk from the sea. The bright en suite bedrooms are attractively presented with pretty fabrics and furnishings. There is a

contd.

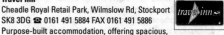

cosy bar, and the comfortable dining room extends into a spacious conservatory where good English home cooking is served.
11 en suite (bth/shr) (2 fmly) CTV in all bedrooms 15P No coaches No children 3yrs Coffee am Tea pm No smoking in restaurant Last d 7.45pm
ROOMS: (incl. bkfst) s £24-£26; d £48-£52 **LB**
MEALS: Dinner £13
CARDS: 

★★61% **Queen's Armes**
The Street DT6 6QF (in the centre of Charmouth village 0.5m off A35)
☎ 01297 560339 FAX 01297 560339
Closed end of Nov-3rd wk Feb
A traditional town-centre coaching inn, the Queen's Armes has played host to such historic notables as Catherine of Aragon and Charles II. Nowadays it is the haunt of walkers and holiday-makers coming to enjoy the beautiful coast and countryside. Modest bedrooms are attractively decorated and all have en suite facilities. A comfortable residents' lounge is provided and the restaurant offers a set menu of home-cooked food, including a good selection of vegetarian dishes by arrangement.
11 rms (5 bth 5 shr) (1 fmly) No smoking in all bedrooms CTV in all bedrooms 20P No coaches British, American & French Cuisine V meals Coffee am No smoking in restaurant Last d 8pm
ROOMS: (incl. bkfst) s £30; d £60 **LB**
OFF-PEAK: (incl. bkfst) s £25; d £50
MEALS: Dinner £7.25-£15alc*
CARDS:

CHARNOCK RICHARD Lancashire Map 07 SD51

★★★67% **Park Hall Hotel, Leisure & Conference Centre**
PR7 5LP (off A49 W of village. Follow brown tourist signs from M6/M61) (Granada) ☎ 01257 452090 FAX 01257 451838
Situated within the grounds of Camelot Theme Park, this unique hotel contains a number of bedrooms, a lounge bar and restaurant in the main building. A further range of chalet-style rooms are found in the 'Village' and are ideal for families seeking privacy. Other facilities include a recently extended leisure club with two pools and a conference centre.
54 en suite (bth/shr) 86 annexe en suite (bth/shr) (33 fmly) No smoking in 11 bedrooms CTV in all bedrooms STV No dogs (ex guide dogs) Lift Night porter 2600P Indoor swimming pool (heated) Squash Snooker Sauna Solarium Gym Pool table Jacuzzi/spa Steam room Weights room ch fac English, American, French & Mexican Cuisine V meals Coffee am Tea pm No smoking area in restaurant Last d 9.45pm
ROOMS: s £69.95-£90; d £69.95-£90 * **LB**
OFF-PEAK: (incl. bkfst & dinner) s £69.95-£90; d £99.90
MEALS: Lunch £9.50 High tea £2.50 Dinner £11.10-£18.75*
CONF: Thtr 750 Class 300 Del from £85
CARDS: 
See advertisement under PRESTON

CHARNOCK RICHARD MOTORWAY SERVICE AREA (M6)
Lancashire Map 07 SD51

Travelodge
Mill Ln PR7 5LR ☎ 01257 791746 FAX 01257 793596
This modern building offers accommodation in smart, spacious and well equipped bedrooms, suitable for family use, and all with en suite bathrooms. Meals may be taken at the nearby family restaurant. For information on room rates and to make a booking, call Roomline free of charge on 0800 850950. For more details about Travelodge, consult the Contents page under Hotel Groups.
100 en suite (bth/shr)

CHATTERIS Cambridgeshire Map 05 TL38

★67% **Cross Keys**
16 Market Hill PE16 6BA (at junct A141/142, opposite parish church)
☎ 01354 693036 & 692644 FAX 01354 693036
This small 16th-century inn sits in the town centre opposite the church of St Peter and St Paul. A cheerful and friendly staff help create a welcoming and informal environment in the cosy public rooms, which consist of an open plan lounge bar with a log fire, and a small restaurant. Guests have the option of bar meals in the lounge bar or a selection of à la carte dishes in the restaurant. Whilst bedroom sizes vary they are all nicely appointed and well equipped; each is individually decorated and most have en suite shower rooms. A narrow car park is available to the rear of the property.
7 rms (5 shr) (1 fmly) No smoking in 5 bedrooms CTV in all bedrooms 8P English & French Cuisine V meals Coffee am Tea pm Last d 10pm
ROOMS: (incl. bkfst) s £21-£32.50; d £32.50-£55 * **LB**
MEALS: Sunday Lunch £9 Dinner £9&alc
CARDS: 

CHEADLE Greater Manchester Map 07 SJ88

Travel Inn
Cheadle Royal Retail Park, Wilmslow Rd, Stockport SK8 3DG ☎ 0161 491 5884 FAX 0161 491 5886

Purpose-built accommodation, offering spacious, well equipped bedrooms, all with en suite bathrooms. Meals may be taken at the nearby family restaurant. For more information about Travel Inns, consult the Contents page under Hotel Groups.
40 en suite (bth/shr)
ROOMS: (incl. bkfst) d £35.50 *

CHEDDAR See Axbridge

CHELMSFORD Essex Map 05 TL70

★★★★70% **Pontlands Park Country**

West Hanningfield Rd, Great Baddow CM2 8HR
☎ 01245 476444 FAX 01245 478393
Closed 24 Dec-2 Jan (ex 31 Dec) RS Sat/Mon lunch & Sun dinner
Pontlands Park, located on the outskirts of Chelmsford in the village of Great Baddow, is a country house-style hotel which offers a professional service in pleasant surroundings. Public rooms are tastefully appointed, offering a cosy bar with an adjacent small conservatory, a comfortable quiet lounge and an attractive restaurant. Here chef Stephen Wright offers a balanced à la carte menu of interesting dishes in formal surroundings; alternatively light meals are available in the coffee shop adjoining Trimmers Leisure Centre. Bedroom sizes vary from the comfortable through to the spacious suites with four-posters and half-testers, which are particularly attractive with their cheerful soft furnishings.
17 en suite (bth/shr) (1 fmly) CTV in all bedrooms No dogs (ex guide dogs) Night porter 100P No coaches Indoor swimming pool (heated) Outdoor swimming pool (heated) Sauna Solarium Pool table Jacuzzi/spa Beauty salon Dance studio English, French & Italian Cuisine V meals Coffee am Tea pm Last d 9.45pm
MEALS: Lunch £15-£18&alc Dinner £15-£18&alc*
CARDS:

★★★64% **County**
Rainsford Rd CM1 2QA (from town centre continue past railway and bus station to hotel 300yds on left beyond traffic lights)
☎ 01245 491911, FAX 01245 492762
Closed 27-30 Dec
Professional service and a friendly atmosphere are the strengths of this town centre hotel, which also has the added bonus of a large private car park. The public rooms are decorative and comfortable; the

lounge bar is particularly appealing with its pastel shades and comfortable sofas. Diners have a good choice from carte and fixed-price menus of classical French and British cooking served within the restaurant; informal snacks can also be provided. The accommodation is cheerfully decorated and well equipped, although some bedrooms are more compact in nature.

28 en suite (bth/shr) 7 annexe en suite (bth/shr) CTV in all bedrooms Night porter 80P English & French Cuisine V meals Coffee am Tea pm No smoking area in restaurant Last d 9.30pm

ROOMS: (incl. bkfst) s £64; d £74-£92 * **LB**

OFF-PEAK: (incl. bkfst) s £28; d £56

MEALS: Lunch £15-£25alc Dinner £15-£25alc

CARDS:

★★★58% **South Lodge**

196 New London Rd CM2 0AR (leave A1016 onto B1007 towards town centre, at traffic lights turn left then immediately right)

☎ 01245 264564 FAX 01245 492827

A family-run hotel close to the A12 and the town centre offers comfortable accommodation in bedrooms divided between the main building and a separate one nearby. Public rooms include an attractive restaurant and bar.

25 en suite (bth/shr) 16 annexe en suite (bth/shr) (3 fmly) No smoking in 8 bedrooms CTV in all bedrooms Night porter 50P No coaches Games room International Cuisine V meals Coffee am Tea pm Last d 9.30pm

ROOMS: (incl. cont bkfst) s £49-£65; d £60-£80 *

MEALS: Lunch £13.50-£15.50&alc Dinner £13.50-£15.50&alc

CARDS:

Travel Inn

Chelmsford Service Area, Colchester Rd, Springfield CM2 5PY (at intersection of A12 Chelmsford by-pass & A130) ☎ 01245 464008 FAX 01245 464010

Purpose-built accommodation, offering spacious, well equipped bedrooms, all with en suite bathrooms. Meals may be taken at the nearby family restaurant. For more information about Travel Inns, consult the Contents page under Hotel Groups.

60 en suite (bth/shr)

ROOMS: d £35.50 *

CHELTENHAM Gloucestershire Map 03 SO92

See also Cleeve Hill

★★★★66% **Cheltenham/Gloucester Moathouse**

Shurdington Rd, Brockworth GL3 4PB

☎ 01452 519988 FAX 01452 519977

Situated close to junction 11A of the M5, this newly built hotel has been attractively designed in a contemporary style. On the ground floor there is the elegantly furnished lounge bar where guests can enjoy a cappuccino or a light meal whilst Coopers restaurant offers an upbeat atmosphere with a menu that includes combo s tarters made for sharing, chargrills, local specialities and carvery dinners and breakfasts. The bedrooms, all spacious have been fitted to a high specification, with king sized beds, easy chairs and smart modern bathrooms. Meetings and conferences are well catered for, with state-of-the-art rooms, a business centre and an excellent leisure club.

100 en suite (bth/shr) No smoking in 50 bedrooms CTV in all bedrooms Lift Night porter 212P Indoor swimming pool (heated) Sauna Solarium Gym Jacuzzi/spa dance studio Xmas V meals Coffee am Tea pm No smoking area in restaurant Last d 10pm

ROOMS: s fr £85; d fr £85

OFF-PEAK: (incl. bkfst) s fr £41; d fr £82

MEALS: Lunch fr £16.75 Dinner fr £16.75

CONF: Thtr 344 Class 120 Board 50 Del £118

CARDS:

★★★★ 66% **Golden Valley Thistle**

THISTLE HOTELS

Gloucester Rd GL51 0TS (1m from junct 11 of M5)

☎ 01242 232691 FAX 01242 221846

Conveniently close to junction 11 of the M5, this popular business hotel has good conference and function facilities. Public areas include a conservatory lounge and library restaurant offering a choice of menus. There are also a well equipped modern leisure centre with all-weather tennis courts, a lounge bar and a beauty salon. Bedrooms have recently benefited from upgrading, the executive rooms offering the best standards. Chef Ronnie Pharaoh provides seasonal carte and set-price menus where the emphasis is on flavour and texture, and extensive room service is also available.

124 en suite (bth/shr) (8 fmly) No smoking in 44 bedrooms CTV in all bedrooms STV Lift Night porter 250P Indoor swimming pool (heated) Tennis (hard) Sauna Solarium Gym Croquet lawn Putting green Jacuzzi/spa Beauty salon Xmas International Cuisine V meals Coffee am Tea pm No smoking area in restaurant Last d 9.45pm

ROOMS: s £89-£95; d £99-£150 * **LB**

OFF-PEAK: (incl. bkfst) s £41-£81; d £82-£117

MEALS: Lunch £15.50-£17.50&alc Dinner fr £21&alc*

CONF: Thtr 220 Class 120 Board 60 Del from £99

CARDS:

★★★★64% **Cheltenham Park**

Cirencester Rd, Charlton Kings GL53 8EA (on the A435, 2m SE of Cheltenham) ☎ 01242 222021 FAX 01242 226935

Cheltenham Park Hotel is located on the edge of the town with splendid views over the adjoining golf course. Now owned by the Paramount Hotel Group, the hotel is being extensively upgraded, and new leisure and restaurant facilities are due to have been completed in 1996. Bedrooms provide good, modern standards of comfort.

144 en suite (bth/shr) No smoking in 11 bedrooms CTV in all bedrooms STV Night porter 170P Indoor swimming pool (heated) Sauna Solarium Gym Jacuzzi/spa Steam room Xmas International Cuisine V meals Coffee am Tea pm No smoking in restaurant Last d 9.30pm

contd.

ROOMS: (incl. bkfst) s £85-£100; d £105-£130 * **LB**
MEALS: Lunch £12.50 Dinner £19.50&alc*
CONF: Thtr 350 Class 180 Board 45 Del from £135
CARDS:

See advertisement on opposite page

★★★★61% **The Queen's**
The Promenade GL50 1NN ☎ 01242 514724
FAX 01242 224145

FORTE Heritage

This elegant, traditional hotel, with its fine Regency pillared facade, is prominently situated in the centre of the town overlooking the Regency Gardens. Although not over large, there is a spacious feel to the lofty foyer area, cocktail bar and smart restaurant where enjoyable and more imaginative food standards are served. The hotel is in the process of upgrading and bedrooms tend to vary with the best rooms pleasantly appointed with chintz fabrics, solid furniture and marbled bathrooms.
74 en suite (bth/shr) (8 fmly) No smoking in 20 bedrooms CTV in all bedrooms STV Lift Night porter 85P Xmas International Cuisine V meals Coffee am Tea pm No smoking in restaurant Last d 9.45pm
ROOMS: s £75; d £90 * **LB**
MEALS: Lunch £14-£22.50 High tea £4.95-£7.50 Dinner £25-£30
CONF: Thtr 325 Class 200 Board 75 Del from £90
CARDS:

RED STAR HOTEL

★★★ **The Greenway**
Shurdington GL51 5UG (3m S on A46)
☎ 01242 862352 FAX 01242 862780

PRIDE OF BRITAIN MEMBER

Quietly situated amidst formal gardens and 7.5 acres of well manicured grounds with the rolling Cotswold hills beyond, this former Elizabethan manor house (c1587) offers an ideal location. Whilst retaining many of its original features little has changed since its total refurbishment and upgrading. Individually decorated quality bedrooms are located in the main house and eight further spacious rooms are in an adjacent Georgian coach house. Public areas combine the sumptuous comfort of the drawing room and foyer with the well appointed candlelit Conservatory Dining Room, which overlooks an illuminated sunken garden. Recently appointed chef de cuisine Peter Fairclough continues to maintain a very high standard with his exciting and daring innovative recipes which feature the good use of fresh local produce, herbs and spices. The wine list has been carefully compiled to represent a well balanced approach to complement the food.

Service is conscientious and competent and personally supervised by the proprietor Mr David A White.
11 en suite (bth/shr) 8 annexe en suite (bth/shr) No smoking in 8 bedrooms CTV in all bedrooms STV No dogs Night porter 50P No coaches Croquet lawn No children 7yrs Xmas V meals Coffee am Tea pm Last d 9.30pm
ROOMS: (incl. bkfst) s £87.50-£105; d £130-£190 * **LB**
OFF-PEAK: (incl. bkfst & dinner) s fr £95; d £150-£180
MEALS: Lunch £18-£19.50 Dinner £29.50-£32*
CONF: Thtr 30 Class 25 Board 22 Del from £129.50
CARDS:

RED STAR HOTEL

★★★ **Hotel On the Park**
38 Evesham Rd GL52 2AH (opposite Pittville Park) ☎ 01242 518898 FAX 01242 511526

This delightful small town house hotel, located on the Evesham Road overlooking Pittville Park and close to the race course, continues to offer accommodation of the highest standard. The bedrooms combine elegance, comfort and rich decorative detail with modern facilities; each with its own individual style. There are two charming lounges, with deep arm chairs, open fires and fresh flowers; one has a small bar. Chef Graham Mairs and his partner Donna Fox run the Restaurant on the Park as their own operation. A short selection of imaginative dishes is provided from both carte and table d'hÙte menus, which feature excellent quality ingredients. A recent inspection meal started with a quadrini of seafood, delicately flavoured prawns, scallops and salmon surrounding layers of fresh pasta which had been filled with a fish-flavoured mousseline, served with a light jus flavoured with aniseed. Lamb, taken as a main course, was succulent and tender, even though its flavour had been slightly lost in the strongly flavoured garlic accompaniments. A crispy thin apple, prune and Armagnac tart was stunning, the fruit textures and flavours enhanced by a caramelised sugar-based sauce, complemented by a tart passion fruit ice cream.
12 en suite (bth/shr) No smoking in 4 bedrooms CTV in all bedrooms STV 9P No coaches No children 8yrs Xmas V meals Coffee am Tea pm Last d 9.30pm
ROOMS: s fr £74.50; d £89.50-£109.50 * **LB**
MEALS: Lunch £16-£21 Dinner £21.50&alc*
CARDS:

★★★65% **Carlton**
Parabola Rd GL50 3AQ ☎ 01242 514453 FAX 01242 226487
A large white Regency building is located in the middle of a wide tree-lined road close to the town centre. High ceilings, lavish fabrics and smart bathrooms make the bedrooms quite distinctive, and some superior, spacious accommodation is contained in an adjacent building. The hotel has the added advantage of off-street parking.
62 en suite (bth/shr) 13 annexe en suite (bth/shr) (2 fmly) No

smoking in 20 bedrooms CTV in all bedrooms Lift Night porter 85P Xmas V meals Coffee am Last d 9.30pm
ROOMS: (incl. bkfst) s £59.50-£62.50; d £79.50-£83.50 * **LB**
OFF-PEAK: (incl. bkfst & dinner) s £39.50-£41.50; d £79-£83
MEALS: Lunch £12&alc Dinner £17&alc*
CONF: Thtr 225 Class 150 Board 100 Del from £65
CARDS:

★★★65% **Wyastone**
Parabola Rd GL50 3BG (from junct 11 M5,travel 3m to end of Lansdown Rd,at Montpellier (rdbt with ornate lampstand) 2nd left around Bank of Scotland into Parababola Rd) ☎ 01242 245549 FAX 01242 522659
Closed 24 Dec-3 Jan
A small, personally run hotel is located in a tree-lined road in the elegant Montpellier district, convenient for both the Promenade and shopping centre. Owners Eliane and John Osborne provide well equipped bedrooms, those in the main building generally being more spacious than the newer ones built to the rear. In the evenings, an à la carte menu is offered in the dining room.
13 en suite (bth/shr) (2 fmly) CTV in all bedrooms STV No dogs 13P No coaches Secluded patio garden No children 8yrs V meals No smoking in restaurant
ROOMS: (incl. bkfst) s £48-£56; d £68 * **LB**
OFF-PEAK: (incl. bkfst) s £38-£56; d £58
MEALS:*
CARDS:
See advertisement on this page

★★★64% **White House**
Gloucester Rd, Staverton GL51 0ST (leave M5 junc 11 onto A40 to Cheltenham, then left at roundabout hotel half a mile on left)
☎ 01452 713226 FAX 01452 857590
The White House is located off the M5 motorway approximately three miles to the west of Cheltenham. It has modern functional bedrooms which adequately cater for guests on residential courses and coach parties. The public areas are elegantly decorated and the staff show extra signs of friendliness.
48 en suite (bth/shr) (3 fmly) CTV in all bedrooms STV Night porter 70P Pool table English & French Cuisine V meals Coffee am Tea pm Last d 9.30pm
ROOMS: (incl. bkfst) s £75-£65; d fr £95
OFF-PEAK: (incl. bkfst) s fr £40; d fr £50
MEALS: Lunch fr £12 Dinner fr £15.50
CONF: Thtr 180 Class 70 Board 40 Del from £100
CARDS:

★★★63% **The Prestbury House Hotel & Restaurant**
The Burgage, Prestbury GL52 3DN (2m NE A46 from Cheltenham racecourse follow signs for Prestbury hotel is 2nd on the left half a mile from racecouse) ☎ 01242 529533 FAX 01242 227076
Friendly spirits allegedly inhabit this proud Regency building set in a small village to the north of Cheltenham. Staff are open and friendly,
contd.

kept busy by the frequent training courses and seminars held here. Modern bedrooms are housed in a converted coach house, and some of the bedrooms in the main building are gradually being upgraded.
8 en suite (bth/shr) 9 annexe en suite (bth/shr) (5 fmly) CTV in all bedrooms STV No dogs (ex guide dogs) 50P Riding Croquet lawn Clay pigeon shooting Xmas English, French & Italian Cuisine V meals Coffee am Tea pm No smoking area in restaurant Last d 9pm
ROOMS: (incl. bkfst) s £60-£75; d £70-£85 **LB**
OFF-PEAK: (incl. bkfst) s fr £58; d fr £65
MEALS: Lunch £15-£25&alc High tea £5-£7.50 Dinner £25&alc
CONF: Thtr 70 Class 30 Board 25 Del from £90
CARDS:

★★★61% **The Frog Mill**
Shipton Oliffe, Andoversford GL54 4HT (at junct of A40/A436, 0.5m from Andoversford traffic lights) ☎ 01242 820547 FAX 01242 820237
Easily accessible from Cheltenham but situated in the heart of the Cotswold countryside. The Frog Mill is an ancient building which has been welcoming travellers for many centuries. Now a modern hotel with impressive meeting facilities, all the bedrooms are attractive and well equipped. Guests have the choice of dining in either the formal restaurant or more casually in the stylish bar with its wine-inspired décor.
16 en suite (bth/shr) (4 fmly) CTV in all bedrooms STV 252P Golf 9 archery practice shooting ballooning English & Conitinental Cuisine V meals Coffee am Tea pm No smoking area in restaurant Last d 9.45pm
ROOMS: (incl. bkfst) s £38-£50; d £58-£80 * **LB**
OFF-PEAK: (incl. bkfst) s fr £38; d fr £58
MEALS: Bar Lunch £11.50-£17 Dinner £11.50-£17*
CARDS:
See advertisement on opposite page

★★★57% **Hotel De La Bere**
REGAL A Collection of Individual Hotels
Southam GL52 3NH (3m NE on B4632)
☎ 01242 237771 FAX 01242 236016
An imposing 15th-century building overlooking the racecourse, this hotel retains such original features as oak panelling, ornate plasterwork, beams and fireplaces. The long-awaited bedroom refurbishment is now in hand and a number of rooms had been improved at the time of our visit. Some accommodation is located in a converted coach house and the rest in the main building; the latter vary in size and shape and are in some cases accessed by winding corridors or old staircases.
32 en suite (bth/shr) 25 annexe en suite (bth) (2 fmly) No smoking in 14 bedrooms CTV in all bedrooms Night porter 150P Outdoor swimming pool (heated) Tennis (hard) Squash Sauna Solarium Gym Croquet lawn Badminton Xmas English & French Cuisine V meals Coffee am Tea pm No smoking in restaurant Last d 9.30pm
ROOMS: s £70; d £80 * **LB**
MEALS: Sunday Lunch £9.95-£11.95 Dinner £17.95&alc*
CONF: Thtr 100 Class 35 Board 40 Del from £85
CARDS:

★★68% **Charlton Kings**

London Rd, Charlton Kings GL52 6UU (2.5m SE on A40) ☎ 01242 231061 FAX 01242 241900
Surrounded by fields, yet only a short distance from the centre, this modern purpose-built hotel is privately owned and personally run. The bedrooms are well thought out and include modern extras as well as smart en suite facilities. The ground floor comprises a small lounge and bar area which leads into a modern bistro-style restaurant where simple meals are served. There is a caring, attentive attitude from the owner and his team.
14 en suite (bth/shr) (2 fmly) No smoking in 5 bedrooms CTV in all bedrooms 20P V meals Coffee am Tea pm Last d 8.45pm
ROOMS: (incl. bkfst) s £39-£69; d £62-£92 * **LB**
OFF-PEAK: (incl. bkfst) s £39-£69; d £62-£92

MEALS: Sunday Lunch £5.95-£11.85 Dinner £12.50-£15.95&alc*
CARDS:

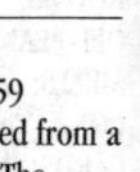

★★66% **George Hotel**
St Georges Rd GL50 3DZ ☎ 01242 235751 FAX 01242 224359
The George Hotel, located close to the town centre, was created from a row of terraced Regency houses and it continues to improve. The bedrooms are mostly spacious, modern in appearance and well equipped; a large bar and an elegant restaurant occupy the ground floor.
39 en suite (bth/shr) (1 fmly) No smoking in 2 bedrooms CTV in all bedrooms STV Night porter 30P English & French Cuisine V meals Coffee am Tea pm No smoking area in restaurant Last d 9pm
ROOMS: (incl. bkfst) s fr £56; d fr £66 **LB**
OFF-PEAK: (incl. bkfst) s fr £42; d fr £54
MEALS: Lunch fr £9.95 Dinner fr £13.50
CONF: Thtr 40 Class 24 Board 20 Del from £75
CARDS:

★★63% **Cotswold Grange**
Pittville Circus Rd GL52 2QH (from town centre follow signs 'Prestbury'. Turn right at first roundabout, hotel 200yds on left)
☎ 01242 515119 FAX 01242 241537
Closed 24 Dec-1 Jan RS Sun evening
This friendly informal hotel is located in a quiet tree-lined avenue close to the town centre. The Weaver family have run the hotel for twenty years and the warm atmosphere has led many guests to make return visits. Bedrooms are well equipped and smart. The bar is cosy and the attractive dining room serves tasty home cooked food.
25 en suite (bth/shr) (4 fmly) CTV in all bedrooms STV 20P V meals Coffee am Tea pm No smoking in restaurant Last d 7.30pm
ROOMS: (incl. bkfst) s £42-£45; d £55-£65 * **LB**
MEALS: Lunch £6-£14alc Dinner £10-£20alc
CARDS:

★★62% **Allards**
MINOTEL Great Britain
Shurdington GL51 5XA (1m S on A46, near junct 11A of M5) ☎ 01242 862498 FAX 01242 863017
This well looked after hotel is a combination of old and new, although the bedroom standards are similar throughout. It is run by a dedicated couple who maintain a minimum standard for the comfort of their guests. The dining room can sometimes be used for social or business functions.
12 en suite (bth/shr) (2 fmly) CTV in all bedrooms No dogs 31P Putting green Xmas English & French Cuisine V meals Coffee am No smoking in restaurant Last d 8.30pm
ROOMS: (incl. bkfst) s £42-£47; d £62-£67 *
OFF-PEAK: s fr £37; d fr £45
MEALS: Sunday Lunch fr £7.25 Dinner fr £11.95&alc
CONF: Thtr 20 Class 20 Board 20 Del from £55
CARDS:

★74% **Regency House**
50 Clarence Square GL50 4JR (N of town centre close to Pittville Park)
☎ 01242 582718 FAX 01242 262697
Closed 24 Dec-2 Jan
This charming Regency property has been carefully restored and is now a professionally maintained hotel. Bedrooms vary in size but are attractively decorated and well equipped. Public areas include a combined lounge and honesty bar where guests meet before dinner to choose from a short but well balanced set-price menu.
8 en suite (bth/shr) (3 fmly) No smoking in 4 bedrooms CTV in all bedrooms No dogs (ex guide dogs) No coaches French Cuisine Coffee am Tea pm No smoking in restaurant Last d 8pm
ROOMS: (incl. bkfst) s £34-£38; d £44-£52 * **LB**
MEALS: Lunch fr £10 High tea fr £7.50
Dinner £11.95-£16.95&alc*
CARDS:

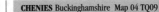

Travel Inn
Tewkesbury Rd, Uckington GL51 9SL (on A4019)
☎ 01242 233847 FAX 01242 244887
Purpose-built accommodation, offering spacious, well equipped bedrooms, all with en suite bathrooms. Meals may be taken at the nearby family restaurant. For more information about Travel Inns, consult the Contents page under Hotel Groups.
40 en suite (bth/shr)
ROOMS: d £35.50 *

CHELWOOD Somerset Map 03 ST66

★★73% **Chelwood House**
BS18 4NH (on A37 200yds S of junct with A368) ☎ 01761 490730
FAX 01761 490730
RS first two weeks Jan
Rudi and Jill Birk's little hotel provides a quality, country house atmosphere, and from its situation beside the A37 is easily accessible to the cities of Bath and Bristol. The charming Dower House is 300 years old and has been lovingly furnished to enhance the elegance of the architecture. Bedrooms are spacious, individually designed and equipped with modern comforts and personal touches. There is a cosy sitting room and an attractive conservatory restaurant which enjoys views of the courtyard and garden. Rudi's cooking skills continue to impress, and the interesting menu includes some speciality dishes from his Bavarian homeland.
11 en suite (bth/shr) (1 fmly) CTV in all bedrooms No dogs (ex guide dogs) 15P No coaches Croquet lawn No children 8yrs English, French & German Cuisine V meals Coffee am No smoking in restaurant Last d 9pm
ROOMS: (incl. bkfst) s £49-£55; d £69-£95 * **LB**
MEALS: Sunday Lunch £11.50-£13.90 Dinner £10.50-£20alc
CARDS:

CHENIES Buckinghamshire Map 04 TQ09

★★★72% **The Bedford Arms Thistle**
WD3 6EQ (off A404) ☎ 01923 283301
FAX 01923 284825
THISTLE HOTELS
This 19th-century building retains an inn-like character. The accommodation has been completely renovated to provide richly appointed bedrooms.
There is a traditional bar and panelled dining room serving a good range of dishes.
10 en suite (bth/shr) (1 fmly) No smoking in 3 bedrooms CTV in all bedrooms STV Night porter 120P No coaches English & French Cuisine V meals Coffee am Tea pm Last d 10pm
ROOMS: s fr £100; d fr £110 * **LB**
OFF-PEAK: (incl. bkfst) s fr £47; d fr £94
MEALS: Lunch fr £21alc Dinner £21*
CONF: Thtr 25 Class 10 Board 15 Del from £140
CARDS:

CHERTSEY Surrey Map 04 TQ06

★★★66% **The Crown**
7 London St KT16 8AP (adjacent to Old Town Hall) ☎ 01932 564657
FAX 01932 570839
A successful combination of the old and the new, The Crown has been completely refurbished, upgraded and extended. It now provides a range of well proportioned good quality bedrooms along with a well appointed public bar, garden bar and conservatory, and an attractive restaurant. Traditional home-cooked food features some interesting home-made recipes, bar meals, and · la carte dishes. Other facilities include a popular function suite and good town centre parking.
30 annexe en suite (bth/shr) (4 fmly) No smoking in 13 bedrooms CTV in all bedrooms STV Night porter 50P V meals Coffee am Tea pm No smoking area in restaurant Last d 10pm
MEALS: Lunch £7-£10&alc Dinner £13-£22alc*
CARDS:

See advertisement on opposite page

CHESHUNT Hertfordshire Map 05 TL30

★★★★62% **Cheshunt Marriott**
Halfhide Ln, Turnford EN10 6NG (off A1170) (Marriott)
☎ 01992 451245 FAX 01992 440120
Check for directions to locate this modern hotel off the A10. Air-conditioned bedrooms are a good size, de luxe ones overlook a pretty central garden. The busy Washington Bar and Restaurant offer a choice of informal eating options.
142 en suite (bth/shr) (37 fmly) No smoking in 92 bedrooms CTV in all bedrooms STV Lift Night porter Air conditioning 200P Indoor swimming pool (heated) Gym Jacuzzi/spa Wkly live entertainment Xmas English & French Cuisine V meals Coffee am Tea pm No smoking in restaurant Last d 9.30pm
ROOMS: d £75-£135 * **LB**
MEALS: Bar Lunch £5-£15alc Dinner £18.95-£27.95&alc*
CONF: Thtr 220 Class 100 Board 90 Del from £137
CARDS:

CHESSINGTON Greater London Map 04 TQ16

Travel Inn
Leatherhead Rd KT9 2NE (on A423)
☎ 01372 744060 FAX 01372 720889
Purpose-built accommodation, offering spacious, well equipped bedrooms, all with en suite bathrooms. Meals may be taken at the nearby family restaurant. For more information about Travel Inns, consult the Contents page under Hotel Groups.
42 en suite (bth/shr)
ROOMS: d £35.50 *

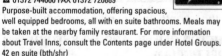

***STOP PRESS!** AA Members can book accommodation at many hotels in this guide through the AA Booking Service, usually at attractive discounts. See page 5 for details or telephone 0990 050505*

CHESTER Cheshire Map 07 SJ46
See also Puddington

RED STAR HOTEL

★★★★❀❀❀ **The Chester Grosvenor**
Eastgate CH1 1LT ☎ 01244 324024
FAX 01244 313246
Closed 25-26 Dec

Owned by the Duke of Westminster and run for many years by the charismatic Jonathan Slater, the Chester Grosvenor continues to provide guests with the exacting standards of service for which it is renowned; but this is not to suggest that it is stuffy, for staff manage to combine stylish professionalism with a warm and natural welcome. Understated quality and refined good taste are exemplified throughout the hotel, from the welcoming marbled foyer and grand old sweeping staircase, above which hangs the magnificent Grosvenor chandelier, to the small panelled library which serves as a cocktail bar and venue for afternoon tea. Bedrooms and suites are immaculate, of course. There are two restaurants, the authentic Brasserie serving anything from a cappuccino to beef and Guinness sausages with mashed potato, or the elegant Arkle restaurant where chef Paul Reed offers grand hotel cooking which earns our coveted three-rosette award. There is no stinting on luxuries with dishes such as a ballotine of foie gras and brawn with a crackling salad, veal with a truffle and Gruyère risotto and a successful combination of roasted seabass and scallops topped with caviar and served with creamed celeriac, girolles, braised celery and a red wine fumet.
86 en suite (bth/shr) CTV in all bedrooms STV No dogs (ex guide dogs) Lift Night porter Air conditioning Sauna Solarium Gym Wkly live entertainment British & French Cuisine V meals Coffee am Tea pm Last d 9.30pm
ROOMS: s £141-£158.62; d £211.50-£235 * **LB**
OFF-PEAK: s fr £100; d fr £140
MEALS: Lunch £18-£22.50 Dinner £37&alc*
CONF: Thtr 220 Class 120 Board 48 Del from £176.25
CARDS:

★★★★65% **Chester Moat House**
Trinity St CH1 2BD (from City Inner Ring Road follow signs 'Gateway Theatre') ☎ 01244 899988
FAX 01244 316118

Built in the late eighties, this city-centre hotel offers comfortable and well designed accommodation; the best rooms feature king-sized beds and spa baths. Public rooms are found on the first floor; there are a small leisure suite, spacious café bar and the Paddocks Restaurant,

which is planned for a re-fit to create a more informal brasserie atmosphere but retaining an intimate area for à la carte dining.
152 en suite (bth/shr) (4 fmly) No smoking in 91 bedrooms CTV in all bedrooms Lift Night porter 76P Sauna Solarium Gym Pool table Jacuzzi/spa Steam bath Xmas Continental Cuisine V meals Coffee am Tea pm No smoking area in restaurant Last d 10.30pm
ROOMS: s fr £100; d fr £140 **LB**
MEALS: Lunch fr £9.95 Dinner fr £19.95alc*
CONF: Thtr 600 Class 250 Board 120 Del from £139
CARDS:

★★★★ 65% **Mollington Banastre**

Parkgate Rd CH1 6NN (M56 to junct 16 at next rdbt turn left for Chester A540. Hotel is 2 miles down the A540 on right) ☎ 01244 851471 FAX 01244 851165
This comfortable hotel is situated in eight acres of attractive gardens and grounds on the A540, two miles north of Chester. Its many facilities include an extensive sports and leisure club. Recent upgrading of many bedrooms has considerably enhanced the accommodation, and family rooms with separate quarters for children have been introduced. The public areas have also been refurbished and the spacious lounge overlooking the gardens is particularly comfortable. A rosette has been awarded for the high standard of cuisine provided in The Garden Room Restaurant, and an alternative is provided by the informal Grill Room, overlooking the swimming pool.
63 en suite (bth) (12 fmly) No smoking in 5 bedrooms CTV in all bedrooms Lift Night porter 300P Indoor swimming pool (heated) Squash Riding Sauna Solarium Gym Pool table Croquet lawn Jacuzzi/spa Hairdressing Health & beauty salon Wkly live entertainment ch fac Xmas V meals Coffee am Tea pm No smoking in restaurant Last d 10pm
ROOMS: s £80; d £100 * **LB**
OFF-PEAK: (incl. bkfst) s £64; d £80
MEALS: Lunch £12.50-£18&alc Dinner £16-£23&alc
CONF: Thtr 300 Class 60 Board 50 Del from £90
CARDS:

★★★★ 62% **Queen**

City Rd CH1 3AH (follow signs for railway station, hotel is opposite) ☎ 01244 350100 FAX 01244 318483
This Victorian hotel is situated opposite the station with a private car park and an enclosed garden. It has been elegantly restored and its sumptuously refurbished public rooms are particularly impressive. Spacious bedrooms are well equipped and contain many extra items; there is also a suite with a separate sitting room. Service levels are good and include traditional afternoon tea and room service of all main meals.
126 en suite (bth/shr) (6 fmly) No smoking in 24 bedrooms CTV in all bedrooms STV Lift Night porter 100P Croquet lawn Xmas English & French Cuisine V meals Coffee am Tea pm No smoking in restaurant Last d 9.30pm
ROOMS: (incl. bkfst) s £75-£95; d £95-£108 * **LB**
OFF-PEAK: (incl. bkfst) s £54-£95; d £75-£108
MEALS: Lunch fr £13.95 Dinner fr £15.95*
CONF: Thtr 280 Class 100 Board 50 Del from £87.50
CARDS:

See advertisement on page 187

★★★ 79% **Crabwall Manor**

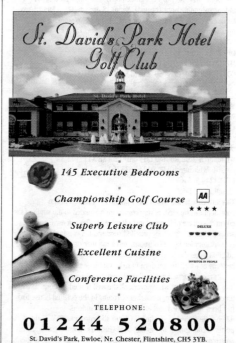

Parkgate Rd, Mollington CH1 6NE (NW off A540) ☎ 01244 851666 FAX 01244 851400
Crabwell Manor is conveniently positioned just outside the city in 17 acres of mature parkland; the building itself dates from the 1600's and is instantly recognisable by its fine red-brick frontage, distinctive turrets and clock tower. The elegant public rooms include the main hall with its high ceiling and splendid fireplace, a

contd.

C

cosy bar, snooker room and restaurant to which has been added a conservatory where Michael Truelove's fine cooking can be sampled; the service is highly polished and professional. All the bedrooms and suites are spacious and comfortably furnished and include many useful and thoughtful extras such as trouser presses and satellite TV. Bathrooms are also spacious and well equipped, most have separate showers, bidets and twin basins, in addition to hugely deep baths.
48 en suite (bth/shr) No smoking in 2 bedrooms CTV in all bedrooms STV No dogs (ex guide dogs) Night porter 120P Snooker Croquet lawn Heli pad Xmas English & French Cuisine V meals No smoking area in restaurant Last d 9.30pm
ROOMS: s fr £98.50; d fr £130 * **LB**
OFF-PEAK: (incl. bkfst) s fr £81.50; d fr £95
MEALS: Lunch £25-£40alc Dinner £25-£40alc*
CONF: Thtr 100 Class 60 Board 36 Del £140
CARDS:

★★★72% The Gateway To Wales
Welsh Rd, Sealand, Deeside CH5 2HX (4m NW via A548 towards Sealand and Queensferry) ☎ 01244 830332 FAX 01244 836190
A lot of thought and time has been spent in decorating and furnishing this modern, privately-owned, purpose-built hotel, which is conveniently situated four and a half miles from the city, literally at 'The Gateway To Wales', at the junction of the A550 and A548. All the well equipped bedrooms, including suites and a disabled room, have been very attractively decorated with co-ordinating furnishings and include several thoughtful touches. The period style public areas include the Louis XVI lounge bar and the Regency restaurant where a good choice of imaginative dishes, prepared by head chef Nicholas Walton,is available from the table d'hÙte or the fixed-price Five Step menus. Other facilities include a sixteen station gymnasium, attractive swimming pool, jacuzzi and saunas, as well as a good-sized conference and banqueting suite.
39 en suite (bth/shr) (4 fmly) No smoking in 8 bedrooms CTV in all bedrooms STV No dogs (ex guide dogs) Lift Night porter 51P Indoor swimming pool (heated) Sauna Solarium Gym Jacuzzi/spa European Cuisine V meals Coffee am Tea pm No smoking in restaurant Last d 9.30pm
ROOMS: (incl. bkfst) s £65; d £90 * **LB**
OFF-PEAK: (incl. bkfst) s £45; d £80
MEALS: Lunch £8.95-£16.95&alc Dinner £16.95&alc*
CONF: Thtr 110 Class 50 Board 50 Del £75
CARDS:

★★★66% Broxton Hall Country House
Whitchurch Rd CH3 9JS ☎ 01829 782321 FAX 01829 782330
(For full entry see Broxton)

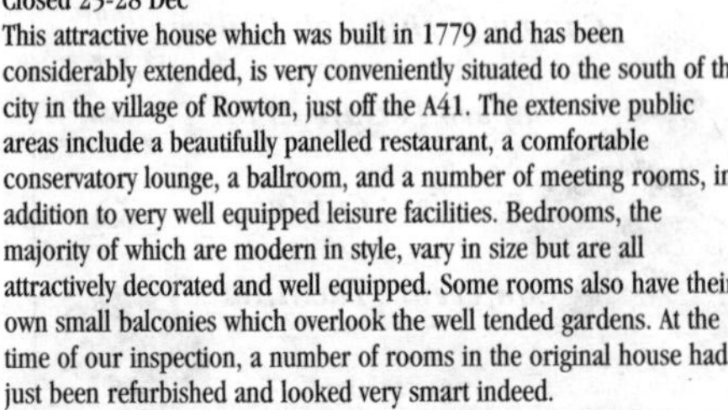

★★★66% Rowton Hall
Whitchurch Road,Rowton CH3 6AD (2m SE A41 towards Whitchurch) ☎ 01244 335262
FAX 01244 335464
Closed 25-28 Dec
This attractive house which was built in 1779 and has been considerably extended, is very conveniently situated to the south of the city in the village of Rowton, just off the A41. The extensive public areas include a beautifully panelled restaurant, a comfortable conservatory lounge, a ballroom, and a number of meeting rooms, in addition to very well equipped leisure facilities. Bedrooms, the majority of which are modern in style, vary in size but are all attractively decorated and well equipped. Some rooms also have their own small balconies which overlook the well tended gardens. At the time of our inspection, a number of rooms in the original house had just been refurbished and looked very smart indeed.
42 en suite (bth/shr) (4 fmly) CTV in all bedrooms STV Night porter 120P Indoor swimming pool (heated) Tennis (hard) Sauna Solarium Gym Jacuzzi/spa ch fac English & French Cuisine V meals Coffee am Tea pm Last d 9.30pm
ROOMS: (incl. bkfst) s £72-£78; d £88-£98 * **LB**
MEALS: Lunch £10.50-£13&alc Dinner fr £18.50&alc*
CONF: Thtr 200 Class 48 Board 50 Del from £95
CARDS:

★★★65% Blossoms
St John St CH1 1HL ☎ 01244 323186
FAX 01244 346433

FORTE Heritage

This long standing establishment is ideally situated right in the city centre and offers varying styles and sizes of accommodation, the majority of which has been refurbished to a high standard. Guests can choose to eat in the restaurant or in their rooms and can enjoy a drink in the cosy bar. Afternoon tea is also served in the lounge. The hotel has no car park and guests are directed to the nearby Newgate Street car park, where the hotel has a special arrangement with regard to charges.

64 en suite (bth/shr) (2 fmly) No smoking in 43 bedrooms CTV in all bedrooms Lift Night porter Wkly live entertainment Xmas V meals Coffee am Tea pm No smoking in restaurant Last d 9.45pm
ROOMS: s £75-£125; d £90-£125 * **LB**
MEALS: Lunch £12.50-£22 Dinner fr £18.95&alc
CONF: Thtr 100 Class 60 Board 60 Del from £95
CARDS:

★★★65% Hoole Hall
Warrington Rd, Hoole Village CH2 3PD (from junct 12 on M53 continue 0.5m on A56 towards city centre)
☎ 01244 350011 FAX 01244 320251

REGAL A Collection of Individual Hotels

An 18th-century hall standing in spacious grounds, this hotel has been modernised and extended to provide well equipped accommodation and very good facilities for business meetings, banquets and conferences. It is also much favoured by tour groups visiting the city of Chester and the surrounding area. The bedrooms include six executive rooms, which have spa baths, and a room on the ground floor for disabled guests. The hotel is only about 2 miles from the city centre and close to both the M53 and M56.
97 en suite (bth) (4 fmly) No smoking in 32 bedrooms CTV in all bedrooms Lift Night porter 200P ch fac International Cuisine V meals Coffee am Tea pm No smoking in restaurant Last d 10pm
ROOMS: (incl. bkfst) s fr £63; d fr £68 * **LB**
MEALS: Lunch fr £8.95&alc Dinner fr £17.25&alc*
CONF: Thtr 150 Class 65 Board 50 Del from £95
CARDS:

★★★63% Grosvenor Pulford
Wrexham Rd, Pulford CH4 9DG ☎ 01244 570560 FAX 01244 570809
This interesting Edwardian property offers very attractive, well equipped accommodation. The bedrooms, where effective use has been made of rich colourful fabrics and which give a 'quality' feel, include a number of suites with spiral staircases. Guests can enjoy a good range of well prepared dishes in the characterful restaurant, which at the time of our visit had just been smartly refurbished. The hotel also has an impressive enclosed courtyard and banqueting facilities.
42 en suite (bth/shr) (4 fmly) No smoking in 3 bedrooms CTV in all bedrooms STV No dogs (ex guide dogs) Night porter 150P Xmas V meals Coffee am Tea pm No smoking area in restaurant Last d 10pm
ROOMS: (incl. bkfst) s £50-£60; d £60-£70 *
MEALS: Sunday Lunch £10-£15 Dinner £10-£20*
CONF: Thtr 80 Class 40 Board 40
CARDS:
See advertisement on opposite page

★★★61% The Plantation Inn
Liverpool Rd CH2 1AG (on A5116 opposite James Edwards Garage)
☎ 01244 374100 FAX 01244 379240
Standing in its own grounds just outside the city walls, the Plantation is

a modern hotel with functional bedrooms and good executive rooms but a limited number of public rooms. These include a 'ritzy' bar and split-level restaurant with dance floor. Staff are smart and attentive.
75 en suite (bth/shr) (4 fmly) No smoking in 15 bedrooms CTV in all bedrooms STV Lift Night porter 90P Xmas English & Continental Cuisine V meals Coffee am Tea pm No smoking area in restaurant Last d 9.30pm
ROOMS: (incl. bkfst) s £50-£80; d £90-£100 * **LB**
MEALS: Lunch £9.95-£17&alc High tea £6-£9.95 Dinner £17.50&alc*
CARDS:

See advertisement on page 189

★★72% **Green Bough**
60 Hoole Rd CH2 3NL (leave M53/A55 at junction 12 and follow A56 into Chester) ☎ 01244 326241 FAX 01244 326265
Y
Green Bough is a large and impeccably maintained Victorian house, tastefully decorated and furnished in a style befitting its character. Facilities include an attractive restaurant, a bar, and a lounge with an ornately carved fireplace and panelled walls. Bedroom furnishings vary from modern to antique, and there are family, four-poster and ground-floor rooms available. The hotel is owned and run by Doreen and David Castle, who, with their loyal staff, provide friendly and attentive service.
12 en suite (bth/shr) 8 annexe en suite (bth/shr) (3 fmly) CTV in all bedrooms 21P Xmas V meals Coffee am Tea pm No smoking in restaurant Last d 8.30pm
ROOMS: (incl. bkfst) s £36-£44; d £52-£60 * **LB**
MEALS: Lunch fr £8.75 Dinner fr £12.50*
CARDS:

C

★★67% Cavendish
42-44 Hough Green CH4 8JQ (S on A549) ☎ 01244 675100
FAX 01244 681309
This privately owned, well maintained Georgian house is very enthusiastically managed, and ideally situated close to the city centre. On the ground floor the public areas include a gracious, richly furnished drawing room, and downstairs there is an open-plan lounge-bar and restaurant, with windows which open out on to the very well tended gardens and a small terrace. The spacious, well equipped bedrooms, all of which are en suite, also include rooms that are on the ground floor and two rooms with four-poster beds.
18 en suite (bth/shr) (4 fmly) CTV in all bedrooms STV No dogs Night porter 36P Xmas English & French Cuisine V meals Coffee am Tea pm No smoking in restaurant Last d 9pm
ROOMS: (incl. bkfst) s fr £45; d fr £55 * **LB**
MEALS: Lunch £15-£20 Dinner £15-£20
CARDS:

★★66% Dene

Hoole Rd CH2 3ND (0.75m E of city centre, from junct 12 of M53 take A56 towards Chester, hotel just after Alexander Park) ☎ 01244 321165
FAX 01244 350277
This friendly, privately owned hotel, which offers freshly decorated and well equipped accommodation, is situated in its own attractive grounds on the A56 between the city centre and the M53. The bedrooms, including ground floor and family rooms, vary in size, but all are comfortably furnished. Guests can relax in the comfortable lounge bar and enjoy a good range of dishes at dinner.
40 en suite (bth/shr) 8 annexe en suite (bth/shr) (5 fmly) No smoking in 6 bedrooms CTV in all bedrooms STV 55P Pool table V meals Coffee am Tea pm No smoking in restaurant Last d 9pm
ROOMS: (incl. bkfst) s £37-£38; d £47-£48 **LB**
MEALS: Sunday Lunch £7.25 Dinner £10-£18.50alc*
CONF: Thtr 30 Class 12 Board 15 Del £55
CARDS:

See advertisement on opposite page

★★65% Royal Oak

Warrington Rd, Mickle Trafford CH2 4EX
(3m NE A56) ☎ 01244 301391 FAX 01244 301948
Closed 24-26 Dec
This roadside inn provides practical accommodation for business and leisure guests, with modern bedrooms which are due to be re-decorated in late 1995. Good value traditional roasts are available in the popular restaurant; a comfortable bar adjoins, and meeting and conference facilities are also provided. There is a children's play area at the rear of the hotel and ample car parking at the front.
36 en suite (bth/shr) No smoking in 10 bedrooms CTV in all bedrooms Night porter 100P Pool table V meals Coffee am Tea pm No smoking in restaurant Last d 10pm
ROOMS: (incl. bkfst) s £32-£59; d £55-£66 * **LB**
MEALS: Lunch £8.95-£11.25&alc High tea £1.80 Dinner £8.95-£13.90&alc
CONF: Thtr 30 Class 16 Board 20 Del from £67.40
CARDS:

★★64% Brookside
Brook Ln CH2 2AN (0.5m from city, second turning at roundabout on A5116, Liverpool road) ☎ 01244 381943 FAX 01244 379701
This privately owned hotel, situated beside the A5116 just north of the city centre, offers bedrooms which all have modern furnishings and equipment though they vary in size. Public areas include a split-level restaurant with adjacent bar area and an attractive lounge; guests have the use of fitness equipment and other leisure facilities. There is a small conference room, and a private car park is located at the rear of the building.
26 en suite (bth/shr) (6 fmly) CTV in all bedrooms STV 13P Sauna Solarium Gym Pool table Xmas French Cuisine V meals No smoking area in restaurant Last d 9.30pm
ROOMS: (incl. bkfst) s £30-£34; d £42-£48 **LB**
OFF-PEAK: (incl. bkfst) s £30; d £40
MEALS: Dinner £9.95&alc
CONF: Class 25
CARDS:

★★63% Curzon
52/54 Hough Green CH4 8JQ (on A5104) ☎ 01244 678581
FAX 01244 680866
Closed 24 Dec-30 Dec
Continual improvements are being made to this already well maintained hotel which is conveniently situated on the A5104, a mile from the city centre. The style of service is informal and the atmosphere is friendly and relaxed. The bedrooms, all of which are en suite and include good sized family rooms and a room with a four-poster bed, all have high ceilings and are freshly decorated and well equipped. The public areas include a spacious dining room where a good range of popular dishes is served, and a comfortable lounge bar. Guests can also enjoy the very well tended gardens, and have use of the carport at the rear of the hotel.
16 en suite (bth/shr) (3 fmly) CTV in all bedrooms STV 16P No coaches Pool table Continental & Swiss Cuisine V meals No smoking in restaurant Last d 9pm
ROOMS: (incl. bkfst) s £35-£40; d £45-£65 * **LB**
MEALS: Bar Lunch £2.50-£8.50alc Dinner £15-£20&alc
CARDS:

★★58% Eaton

29/31 City Rd CH1 3AE ☎ 01244 320840
FAX 01244 320850
This small, privately owned, no-frills hotel is conveniently located within easy walking distance of the city centre and the railway station; it also benefits from its own secure car park. Bedrooms, most of which are en suite and include a number of family rooms, are well equipped, soundly furnished and some have recently been redecorated. A short choice of simple but well prepared dishes is available in the dining room, opposite which is a small, cheerfully decorated lounge bar.
18 rms (13 bth/shr) (4 fmly) CTV in all bedrooms 10P English & French Cuisine V meals Coffee am Tea pm No smoking in restaurant Last d 8pm
ROOMS: (incl. bkfst) s £29.50-£39.50; d £39.50-£49.50 * **LB**
OFF-PEAK: (incl. bkfst & dinner) s £37.50-£47.50; d £55-£65
MEALS: Bar Lunch £2.50-£8.95 Dinner £8.95-£11.95
CARDS:

★★58% Riverside
22 City Walls CH1 1SB ☎ 01244 326580 FAX 01244 311567
This friendly hotel is full of character, and enjoys an enviable position overlooking the River Dee, with its weir and salmon leap. Bedrooms, all of which are attractively furnished, are divided between the main hotel building and an annexe which was once home to the Recorder of

Chester. Guests can relax in the cosy bar and a good choice of popular dishes are available in the dining room.

12 en suite (bth/shr) 10 annexe en suite (bth/shr) (3 fmly) No smoking in 10 bedrooms CTV in all bedrooms No dogs (ex guide dogs) 22P No coaches English & French Cuisine V meals Coffee am No smoking in restaurant Last d 9pm
CONF: Thtr 20
CARDS:

See advertisement on this page

★63% **Leahurst Court**
74 Hoole Rd, Hoole CH2 3NL (1m from town centre on A56 situated on the right hand side, sitting back from main road) ☎ 01244 327542 FAX 01244 344889
Closed 24-31 Dec
This comfortable, family-run large Victorian house with spacious and attractive gardens standson the A56 between the city centre and the M53. Bedrooms vary in size and furniture, but all have modern equipment. Some rooms are located in a separate converted coach

contd.

house, with two on ground floor level. There is a pleasant dining room with cottage-style furniture, and a small lounge; there is no bar, but drinks are available in both these rooms.
8 rms (5 bth/shr) 6 annexe rms (4 shr) (3 fmly) CTV in all bedrooms No dogs (ex guide dogs) 17P No coaches No smoking in restaurant Last d 7pm
ROOMS: (incl. bkfst) s £21-£32; d £39-£46 * **LB**
MEALS: Dinner fr £10.45&alc*
CARDS:

Forte Posthouse Chester

Wrexham Rd CH4 9DL (near Wrexham junct on A483, off A55) ☎ 01244 680111 FAX 01244 674100
Suitable for both the business and leisure traveller, this bright hotel provides modern accommodation in well equipped bedrooms with en suite bathrooms. For more details about Forte Posthouse hotels, consult the Contents page for the section on Hotel Groups.
105 en suite (bth/shr)
ROOMS: d £79-£89 *
CONF: Thtr 100 Class 50 Board 40

CHESTERFIELD Derbyshire Map 08 SK37

★★★61% **Chesterfield**
Malkin St S41 7UA (from Chesterfield town centre follow signs to railway station hotel is diagonally across from station)
☎ 01246 271141 FAX 01246 220719
Follow signs to the station to reach this popular hotel where staff provide exceptionally helpful and cheerful service. Bedrooms are well equipped and the hotel also has an excellent leisure centre as well as banqueting and conference suites. The public areas, including Bejerano's Restaurant and Cocktail Bar are decorated in a 1920s theme.
73 en suite (bth/shr) (10 fmly) No smoking in 18 bedrooms CTV in all bedrooms STV Lift Night porter 100P Indoor swimming pool (heated) Snooker Sauna Solarium Gym Jacuzzi/spa Xmas International Cuisine V meals Coffee am Last d 9.45pm
ROOMS: (incl. bkfst) s £69-£75; d £79-£90 * **LB**
OFF-PEAK: (incl. bkfst) s £40-£45; d £67-£77
MEALS: Lunch £8-£15&alc Dinner £15&alc*
CONF: Thtr 200 Class 100 Board 80 Del from £80
CARDS:

★★68% ***Sandpiper***

Sheffield Rd, Sheepbridge S41 9EH ☎ 01246 450550
FAX 01246 452805
This modern complex consists of an extremely well furnished and equipped brick-built block of bedrooms, and a separate stone-faced hospitality block within the same grounds. The latter has a comfortably furnished reception and lounge combination which leads on to the bar-cum-restaurant area. There is a good range of popular dishes on offer, complemented by a carvery on the busier nights.
28 annexe en suite (bth/shr) (4 fmly) No smoking in 4 bedrooms CTV in all bedrooms STV No dogs (ex guide dogs) 220P English & French Cuisine V meals Coffee am Tea pm Last d 10pm
CARDS: 

★★65% **Abbeydale**

MINOTEL Great Britain

Cross St S40 4TD (from M1 or A61 follow A619 to island at end of Queens Park, turn right into Foljambe Rd, Compton St to T junct, turn right for 200yds,hotel on left) ☎ 01246 277849 FAX 01246 558223
Closed Xmas wk
Proprietors Peter and Marjorie Bramhill provide friendly personal service at their small hotel situated in a quiet residential area of the town. Cosy but appealing public rooms include a comfortable TV lounge, bar and dining room, while bedrooms (two of them on the ground floor) vary in size but are all immaculately kept and well equipped.
11 rms (9 bth/shr) (1 fmly) CTV in all bedrooms No dogs 15P No coaches V meals No smoking in restaurant Last d 8pm
ROOMS: (incl. bkfst) s fr £39; d fr £58 * **LB**
MEALS: Dinner fr £15&alc*
CARDS:

★★63% **Portland**
West Bars S40 1AY (in town centre overlooking Market Place)
☎ 01246 234502 & 234211 FAX 01246 550915
A busy Tudor-style Victorian hotel on the edge of the market place, the Portland attracts not only shoppers to its contemporary, open-plan lounge bar, but business guests as well, especially to the thoughtfully furnished and well designed bedrooms.
24 en suite (bth/shr) (7 fmly) CTV in all bedrooms No dogs (ex guide dogs) Night porter 30P Mainly grills V meals Coffee am Last d 9.45pm
ROOMS: (incl. bkfst) s £40-£50; d £50-£63 * **LB**
CARDS:

Travelodge

Travelodge

A61 Brimmington Rd, Inner Ring Rd, Wittington Moor S41 9BE (A61, N of town centre)
☎ 01246 455411 FAX 01246 455411
This modern building offers accommodation in smart, spacious and well equipped bedrooms, suitable for family use, and all with en suite bathrooms. Meals may be taken at the nearby family restaurant. For information on room rates and to make a booking, call Roomline free of charge on 0800 850950. For more details about Travelodge, consult the Contents page under Hotel Groups.
20 en suite (bth/shr)

CHICHESTER West Sussex Map 04 SU80

★★★★70% **Marriott Goodwood Park**

PO18 0QB ☎ 01243 775537 FAX 01243 520120
(For full entry see Goodwood)

★★★63% **The Dolphin & Anchor**

West St PO19 1QE (opposite Cathedral)
☎ 01243 785121 FAX 01243 533408
Once two hotels, but now combined, this historic building has an enviable position opposite from formidable cathedral. It has a vast ballroom and in addition to the smartly decorated restaurant there is an informally-run coffee shop. There are some cheerful members of staff.
49 en suite (bth/shr) (5 fmly) No smoking in 25 bedrooms CTV in all bedrooms Night porter 11P Xmas V meals Coffee am Tea pm No smoking in restaurant Last d 9pm
ROOMS: s fr £70; d fr £95 * **LB**
MEALS: Lunch £11-£14.50&alc High tea £5-£9 Dinner £15.95-£17.95&alc*
CONF: Thtr 180 Class 50 Board 40 Del from £75
CARDS:

★★★61% **Ship**
North St PO19 1NH ☎ 01243 778000 FAX 01243 788000
Close to the shopping area, this fine Georgian-style hotel was home to Admiral Sir George Murray during the Napoleonic period. The restaurant is named after him, and the hotel's nautical heritage is reflected in the two styles of bedroom. Admiral's Class are the more luxurious, but the Captain's Class are also very attractive. Lunchtime snacks are served in the Hornblower Bar and Lounge, but Murray's Restaurant offers more formal dining. Chef Robin Castle produces meals of a consistently high standard, a strong point being his use of fresh fish and well made sauces. There is a good hotel car park.

32 en suite (bth/shr) (4 fmly) CTV in all bedrooms Lift Night porter 38P Xmas English & French Cuisine V meals Coffee am Tea pm No smoking in restaurant Last d 9.30pm
ROOMS: (incl. bkfst) s £52-£69; d £80-£120 **LB**
OFF-PEAK: (incl. bkfst) s £46-£64; d £70-£90
MEALS: Lunch £12.50-£13&alc Dinner £19.50&alc
CONF: Thtr 70 Class 35 Board 30 Del £85
CARDS:

★★69% **Suffolk House**
3 East Row PO19 1PD (turn right off East St into Little London, follow into East Row, hotel on left. ☎ 01243 778899 FAX 01243 787282
A former town house in this Georgian city has been suitably modernised, yet has retained most original features. Bedrooms have every modern facility and lots of little extras: some rooms are on the ground floor and some have pleasant views over the rear, walled garden. A new lounge has been added, and the bar and restaurant offers a choice of menus, including the fixed-price at £12.50.
11 en suite (bth/shr) (2 fmly) No smoking in 2 bedrooms CTV in all bedrooms STV No dogs (ex guide dogs) No coaches English & French Cuisine No smoking in restaurant Last d 9pm
ROOMS: (incl. bkfst) s £52-£75; d £78.50-£110 * **LB**
MEALS: Sunday Lunch fr £9.50 Dinner fr £12.50&alc
CARDS:

See advertisement on this page

★★68% **Bedford**
Southgate PO19 1DP (from A27 (Chichester Bypass) continue N past level crossing at Chichester Station. Hotel 400yds on right)
☎ 01243 785766 FAX 01243 533175
RS Xmas week
The Bedford, which dates from about 1700, is ideally located within walking distance of the town centre. The accommodation is tastefully furnished and comprises a comfortable, open-plan bar and lounge, the attractive Terrace Garden Restaurant and a range of modern bedrooms to suit everyone. Room service is also available.
19 rms (16 bth/shr) (2 fmly) No smoking in 6 bedrooms CTV in all bedrooms No dogs 8P V meals No smoking area in restaurant Last d 8.30pm

contd.

ROOMS: (incl. bkfst) s £32-£45; d £68 * **LB**
MEALS: Bar Lunch £2.75-£6.50 Dinner £14&alc*
CARDS:

CHILDER THORNTON Cheshire Map 07 SJ37

Travel Inn
New Chester Rd L66 1QW (on A41)
☎ 0151 339 8101 FAX 0151 347 1401

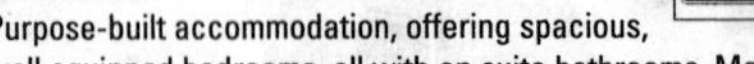

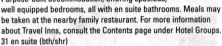

Purpose-built accommodation, offering spacious, well equipped bedrooms, all with en suite bathrooms. Meals may be taken at the nearby family restaurant. For more information about Travel Inns, consult the Contents page under Hotel Groups.
31 en suite (bth/shr)
ROOMS: d £35.50 *

CHIPPENHAM Wiltshire Map 03 ST97

★★★ 72% **Stanton Manor**
Stanton St Quintin SN14 6DQ (leave M4 junc17 onto A429 within 150yds turn 1st left signed Stanton St Quintin entrance to hotel on left just after church) ☎ 01666 837552 FAX 01666 837022
26 Dec-6 Jan
This delightful former manor house, set in five acres of gardens and woodland which feature an original dovecote for over 1,000 birds, is just a mile from junction 17 of the M4. Resident proprietors Elizabeth and Philip Bullock are experienced hoteliers and friendly hosts, and Stanton Manor offers a relaxed atmosphere. Spacious bedrooms have been attractively co-ordinated and equipped with every modern facility, and the public areas include a comfortable lounge and a separate bar. In the hotel's restaurant, the à la carte menu provides an interesting selection of fish, meat and game dishes, carefully prepared from fresh, and where possible, local produce.
10 en suite (bth/shr) CTV in all bedrooms No dogs (ex guide dogs) Night porter 40P No coaches Croquet lawn V meals Coffee am Tea pm No smoking in restaurant Last d 9.30pm
ROOMS: (incl. bkfst) s £68-£75; d £82-£95 **LB**
MEALS: Lunch £20 Dinner £20-£28alc*
CONF: Thtr 30 Class 15 Board 20 Del from £85
CARDS:

CHIPPERFIELD Hertfordshire Map 04 TL00

★★★ 62% **The Two Brewers Inn**

The Common WD4 9BS (turn left in centre of village, hotel overlooks common) ☎ 01923 265266
FAX 01923 261884
The Two Brewers is a 16th century inn overlooking the common and cricket ground. There is a lounge and bar, the latter serving a range of ales, popular with locals. Bedrooms, in an adjoining wing are smart and comfortable.
20 en suite (bth/shr) No smoking in 8 bedrooms CTV in all bedrooms 25P Xmas V meals Coffee am Tea pm No smoking in restaurant Last d 9.30pm
ROOMS: s £85; d £100 **LB**
OFF-PEAK: d £70
MEALS: Lunch £10.95-£14.95&alc Dinner £16.95-£18.95&alc*
CONF: Thtr 25 Class 15 Board 20 Del from £115
CARDS:

CHIPPING Lancashire Map 07 SD64

★★★ 70% **The Gibbon Bridge**
PR3 2TQ (jn.32 on M6, follow A6 Garstang,turn right for Goosnarg/Longridge follow signs for Chipping, into village turn right at T junct. Hotel in 0.75m) ☎ 01995 61456 FAX 01995 61277
With views across the open countryside of the Trough of Bowland this magnificent hotel, which is situated in its own award-winning gardens, has been owned and enthusiastically run by Janet Simpson for the last 14 years. The comfortable and attractively decorated bedrooms include a number of large suites, some with split-level sitting rooms and others with real fires and four-poster beds. Guests also have the use of the well equipped leisure facilities which include a gymnasium, steam rooms and a beauty treatment room, as well as a tennis court. Head chef Grace Holland produces carefully prepared dishes using as many vegetables and herbs from the hotel's garden. The service from the young staff, whilst informal, is attentive and friendly.
15 en suite (bth/shr) 15 annexe en suite (bth/shr) CTV in all bedrooms STV No dogs (ex guide dogs) Lift Night porter 252P Tennis (hard) Fishing Sauna Solarium Gym Fishing Xmas V meals Coffee am Tea pm No smoking in restaurant Last d 9pm
ROOMS: (incl. bkfst) s £60-£100; d £80-£160 * **LB**
MEALS: Lunch £12&alc Dinner £18*
CARDS:

CHIPPING CAMPDEN Gloucestershire Map 04 SP13

RED STAR HOTEL

★★★ **Cotswold House**
The Square GL55 6AN (on B4081 signposted to Chipping Campden into village. Turn right into High St at T junct Cotswold House is located at the square in the High Street) ☎ 01386 840330 FAX 01386 840310
Closed 23-26 Dec
Dating back to the 17th-century and situated in Chipping Campden's historic high street, this hotel is an ideal base for exploring the Cotswolds and Shakespeare's country. The rooms are elegantly furnished, with antiques and works of art complementing the many period features, such as a splendid spiral staircase. Log fires blaze invitingly in winter, and there are always beautiful arrangements of fresh flowers. Each bedroom has its own theme, and thoughtful extras such as bottled water and fresh fruit are provided. For informal dining Forbes Brasserie is open all day, while the Garden Room Restaurant offers a more polished style. A recent inspection meal started with duck pancakes, served with a piquant sauce, and was followed by fillet of turbot accompanied by a smooth Vermouth butter sauce. The selection of mouth watering puddings included a zesty steamed marmalade pudding with a butterscotch sauce, and passion fruit mousse surrounded by fresh fruit.
15 en suite (bth/shr) CTV in all bedrooms STV No dogs 15P No coaches Croquet lawn Wkly live entertainment No children 7yrs V meals Coffee am Tea pm No smoking in restaurant Last d 9.30pm
ROOMS: (incl. bkfst) s £70-£80; d £100-£140 **LB**
OFF-PEAK: (incl. bkfst & dinner) s £75-£85; d £120-£150

MEALS: Sunday Lunch fr £15.75alc Dinner £17-£19.50&alc*
CONF: Thtr 30 Board 20 Del from £106.50
CARDS:

See advertisement on this page

★★★ 68% Seymour House
High St GL55 6AH ☎ 01386 840429 FAX 01386 804369
Parts of this mainly Georgian building date from the early 1700s and its Cotswold stone façade is full of character. Bedrooms vary in size and comfort but are all well equipped, including the self-contained rooms in the cottage annexe. In addition to the split restaurant (half conservatory and half formal Balloon Room) there is a new bar serving John Heckles' enjoyable cuisine; Italian food and innovative fish dishes such as seabass with three mushrooms and truffle oil are a speciality.
11 en suite (bth/shr) 5 annexe en suite (bth/shr) CTV in all bedrooms STV No dogs (ex guide dogs) 28P Xmas English, French & Italian Cuisine V meals Coffee am Tea pm No smoking in restaurant Last d 10pm
ROOMS: (incl. bkfst) s £53-£95; d £66-£140 * **LB**
MEALS: Lunch £2.50-£12alc High tea £5-£15 Dinner £20.95-£30*
CONF: Thtr 40 Board 26 Del from £85
CARDS:

★★★65% Three Ways
Mickleton GL55 6SB (situated on B4632 Stratford upon Avon to Broadway Road, Hotel in centre of Mickleton Village) ☎ 01386 438429
FAX 01386 438118
Close to many of the attractions of the North Cotswolds, the sleepy village of Mickleton is like a corner of England from years gone by. Three Ways House has been acquired by experienced hoteliers Peter

contd.

Henderson and Simon Coombe; the enthusiasm of the new owners has rubbed off on their staff, who take delight in offering a warm welcome and a high standard of service. Bedrooms do look a little dated at present, but all are well equipped and have many personal touches. A programme of ongoing refurbishment has begun and is beginning to bear fruit already. This home of 'The Pudding Club' has a reputation for serving traditional English nursery puddings such as spotted dick or syrup sponge, all served, of course, with lashings of custard.

40 en suite (bth/shr) (5 fmly) CTV in all bedrooms Night porter 37P Wkly live entertainment Xmas English & Continental Cuisine V meals Coffee am Tea pm No smoking in restaurant Last d 9.30pm
ROOMS: (incl. bkfst) s £52-£55; d £80-£90 **LB**
MEALS: Lunch £12-£16 High tea £1.50-£4.25alc Dinner £18-£19&alc*
CONF: Thtr 130 Class 40 Board 35 Del from £90
CARDS: 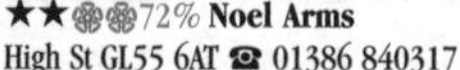

See advertisement on opposite page

★★72% **Noel Arms**
High St GL55 6AT ☎ 01386 840317
FAX 01386 841136
The Noel Arms dates from the 14th century and was built to serve visiting wool merchants to the historic town of Chipping Campden one of the Cotswolds most attractive towns. Much improved in recent times the hotel bedrooms are in two styles more traditional in the older part of the hotel and modern in the new courtyard wing. A stylish new wine bar with brasserie style food complements the more formal panelled restaurant where the food takes a modern English tack.
26 en suite (bth/shr) (1 fmly) CTV in all bedrooms 40P Membership of leisure club V meals Coffee am Tea pm No smoking in restaurant Last d 9.30pm
MEALS: Sunday Lunch £9.25-£10.75 Dinner £15.75-£17.75
CONF: Thtr 60 Class 40 Board 35 Del from £85
CARDS:

CHIPPING NORTON Oxfordshire Map 04 SP32

★★65% **The Crown & Cushion**
23 High St OX7 5AD (the Hotel is located on the High Street of Chipping Norton) ☎ 01608 642533 FAX 01608 642926
Located at the centre of town on Chipping Norton's historic market place this former coaching inn dates back to 1497. The frontage which is rather unprepossessing belies the extent of the building and the range of facilities offered within. The hotel is built of Cotswold stone and encloses a courtyard to the rear. All the bedrooms are well furnished with decor based round either dark wood or mellow pine. All offer the expected modern comforts and several make features of four poster beds. There is a modern leisure centre where guests can swim, play squash and exercise in the gym. There are also extensive conference and banqueting facilities which have all amenities self contained.

30 en suite (bth/shr) 10 annexe rms (3 shr) (10 fmly) No smoking in 3 bedrooms CTV in all bedrooms 34P Indoor swimming pool (heated) Squash Snooker Solarium Gym Jacuzzi/spa Xmas European Cuisine V meals Coffee am Tea pm No smoking in restaurant Last d 9pm
ROOMS: (incl. bkfst) s £43-£58; d £69-£95 * **LB**
MEALS: Sunday Lunch £5.90-£6.90 Dinner £18&alc
CONF: Thtr 200 Class 70 Board 60 Del from £70
CARDS:

See advertisement under STRATFORD-UPON-AVON

★★63% **White Hart**
16 High St OX7 5AD (opposite Market Sq on High St (A44)) ☎ 01608 642572 FAX 01608 644143
There is an 18th-century façade to this building, parts of which date back to the 13th century. A few of the bedrooms are spacious and have some wonderful older world character, and the majority are more contemporary. The restaurant has introduced a modern style of menu.
14 en suite (bth/shr) 5 annexe en suite (bth) CTV in all bedrooms STV 26P Xmas British & French Cuisine V meals Coffee am Tea pm No smoking in restaurant Last d 9pm
ROOMS: (incl. bkfst) s £35-£60; d £45-£90 **LB**
MEALS: Lunch £5.95-£9.95 Dinner £9.95-£13.95
CONF: Thtr 60 Class 20 Board 24 Del from £55
CARDS:

CHITTLEHAMHOLT Devon Map 03 SS62

★★★70% **Highbullen**
EX37 9HD ☎ 01769 540561 FAX 01769 540492
The excellent leisure facilities provided by this hotel - a fine Victorian Gothic mansion set in 60 acres of parkland - include an 8-hole golf course (now being increased to 18 holes), outdoor and indoor swimming pools and facilities for tennis, squash and snooker. The majority of its comfortable, well equipped bedrooms are contained in additional buildings, and main house public areas include a library, an elegant sitting room furnished in keeping with the character of the house and a small sun lounge; there is also a spacious relaxed restaurant where set-price menus offer a very good choice of dishes. Provençale fish soup, for example, might be followed by tender loin of pork cooked in apple juice and brandy and served with home-made apple sauce, the meal ending with a traditional favourite like sticky toffee pudding. A fine wine list of 200 bins includes some first growth and fine burgundies.
12 en suite (bth) 25 annexe en suite (bth/shr) CTV in all bedrooms No dogs (ex guide dogs) 60P No coaches Indoor swimming pool (heated) Outdoor swimming pool (heated) Golf 18 Tennis (hard) Fishing Squash Snooker Sauna Solarium Gym Croquet lawn Putting green Hairdressing Beauty treatment Massage No children 8yrs International Cuisine V meals Coffee am Tea pm No smoking in restaurant Last d 9pm
ROOMS: (incl. cont bkfst & dinner) s £62.50-£75; d £105-£160 * **LB**
OFF-PEAK: (incl. cont bkfst & dinner) d £85-£140

MEALS: Bar Lunch £2.50-£7.50&alc Dinner £18.50
CONF: Board 20
CARDS:

CHOLLERFORD Northumberland Map 12 NY97

★★★ 70% **George**

NE46 4EW ☎ 01434 681611 FAX 01434 681727
This comfortable and characterful hotel, which is peacefully set in well tended gardens on the edge of the village, close to where the old Roman road crosses the River Tyne, offers comfortable well equipped accommodation. The bedrooms are divided between the main house and a more recently added wing. The public areas enjoy views over the gardens to the river beyond. An interesting range of very well prepared dishes is available from the good value four-course, or the five-course Gourmet menus.

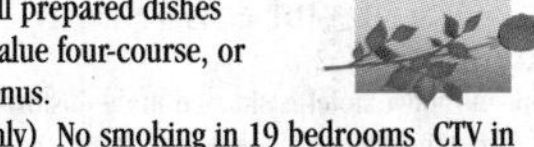

46 en suite (bth/shr) (5 fmly) No smoking in 19 bedrooms CTV in 50 bedrooms STV Night porter 70P Indoor swimming pool (heated) Fishing Sauna Solarium Putting green Jacuzzi/spa Jogging track Exercise equipment International Cuisine V meals Coffee am Tea pm Last d 9.30pm
CONF: Thtr 60 Class 30 Board 32
CARDS:

CHORLEY Lancashire Map 07 SD51
See also Clayton-le-Woods

★★★68% **Shaw Hill Hotel Golf & Country Club**
Preston Rd, Whittle-le-Woods PR6 7PP (2m N A6)
☎ 01257 269221 FAX 01257 261223
The testing championship golf course is a major attraction at this handsome and sympathetically extended Georgian mansion which is situated beside the A6 two miles north of Chorley. Recent improvements include completion of a new conference centre and the creation of an elegant new a la carte restaurant which overlooks the golf course. There is also a choice of contrasting bars and comfortable lounges. Bedrooms range from spacious and tastefully appointed suites, executive and superior rooms, to the more modest standard rooms on the ground floor.
26 en suite (bth/shr) 4 annexe en suite (bth/shr) (1 fmly) CTV in all bedrooms STV Night porter 200P Golf 18 Fishing Snooker Xmas International Cuisine V meals Coffee am Tea pm Last d 9.45pm
ROOMS: (incl. bkfst) s £60-£85; d £80-£105 * LB
OFF-PEAK: (incl. bkfst) s £50-£75; d £65-£95
MEALS: Lunch £12.95&alc Dinner £18.95&alc
CARDS:

See advertisement on this page

★★★67% **Park Hall Hotel, Leisure & Conference Centre**
PR7 5LP PRESTON (Granada) ☎ 01257 452090 FAX 01257 451838
(For full entry see Charnock Richard)

CHRISTCHURCH Dorset Map 04 SZ19

★★★ 75% **Waterford Lodge**

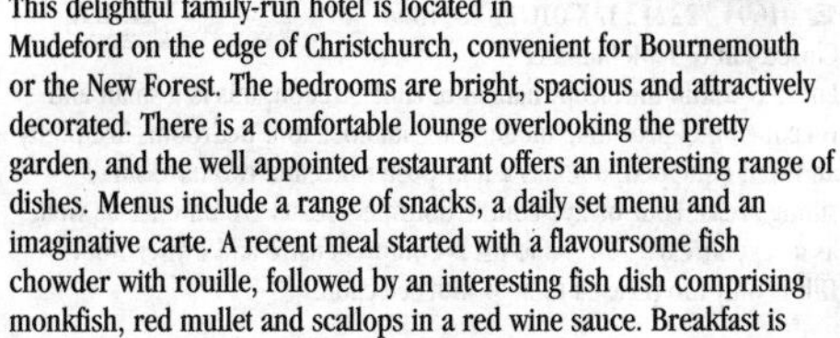

87 Bure Ln, Friars Cliff, Mudeford BH23 4DN (2m E off B3059) ☎ 01425 272948 FAX 01425 279130
This delightful family-run hotel is located in Mudeford on the edge of Christchurch, convenient for Bournemouth or the New Forest. The bedrooms are bright, spacious and attractively decorated. There is a comfortable lounge overlooking the pretty garden, and the well appointed restaurant offers an interesting range of dishes. Menus include a range of snacks, a daily set menu and an imaginative carte. A recent meal started with a flavoursome fish chowder with rouille, followed by an interesting fish dish comprising monkfish, red mullet and scallops in a red wine sauce. Breakfast is

contd.

notable for the excellent local sausages and good toasted home-made bread.

17 en suite (bth) (1 fmly) CTV in all bedrooms 38P No coaches Xmas English & French Cuisine V meals Coffee am Tea pm Last d 9pm
ROOMS: (incl. bkfst) s £80-£85; d £100-£110 * **LB**
OFF-PEAK: (incl. bkfst) s £74-£79; d £98-£108
MEALS: Lunch £10.95-£14.95&alc Dinner £23-£25&alc*
CONF: Thtr 100 Class 48 Board 36 Del from £79
CARDS:

See advertisement on opposite page

★★★ 68% **The Avonmouth**

FORTE Heritage

95 Mudeford BH23 3NT (approaching Christchurch on A35 fron Lyndhurst, turn left at roundabout and right at next roundabout and continue for 1m)
☎ 01202 483434 FAX 01202 479004
Superbly located alongside Mudeford quay, the Avonmouth appeals to leisure and business guests alike, and is attractive to families with children in the summer months. Public rooms are traditional in style, but the bedrooms are modern with pretty decor and good standards of comfort. The garden rooms offer that little extra in independence with their own garden patios. Chef Mark Walters produces worthy cooking with good use of local fish.
27 en suite (bth/shr) 14 annexe en suite (bth/shr) (3 fmly) No smoking in 14 bedrooms CTV in all bedrooms Night porter 100P No coaches Outdoor swimming pool (heated) Croquet lawn Putting green Golf practice net Xmas V meals Coffee am Tea pm Last d 8.45pm
ROOMS: s £65-£72.50; d £90-£105 * **LB**
MEALS: Sunday Lunch £11.95 Dinner £18.95&alc*
CONF: Thtr 60 Class 25 Board 24 Del from £85
CARDS:

★★ 65% **Fisherman's Haunt**
Salisbury Rd, Winkton BH23 7AS (2.5m N on B3347)
☎ 01202 477283 & 484071 FAX 01202 478883
Closed 25 Dec
This popular hotel is located on the edge of the town with lovely views over the River Avon and water meadows. Bedrooms are well equipped with fridges, satellite TV, hairdryers and modern ensuite bathrooms, some are in the main house and others are situates in tow cottages. The public areas include a lively bar with good local trade; and guests may dine in the restaurant or choose from a wide range of bar snacks.
4 rms (3 bth/shr) 15 annexe rms (13 bth/shr) (3 fmly) CTV in all bedrooms STV 75P V meals Coffee am Tea pm No smoking area in restaurant
ROOMS: (incl. bkfst) s £37.50; d £52.50 * **LB**
MEALS: Sunday Lunch £8.75*
CARDS:

★★ 64% ***Kings Arms***

TOBY

18 Castle St BH23 1DT ☎ 01202 474117
FAX 01202 471562
This attractive hotel is situated in the historic town of Christchurch, overlooking the church and castle. The smart restaurant and bars are attractively appointed and offer an extensive range of well cooked food. Bedrooms are comfortable and retain much of their original character; some are in a separate cottage behind the main house. Ample private car-parking is available.
32 en suite (bth/shr) (2 fmly) CTV in all bedrooms Lift Night porter 52P British & Continental Cuisine V meals Coffee am Tea pm Last d 10.30pm
CARDS:

Travel Inn

Somerford Rd BH23 3QG (on B3059 roundabout towards Somerford) ☎ 01202 485376
FAX 01202 474939
Purpose-built accommodation, offering spacious, well equipped bedrooms, all with en suite bathrooms. Meals may be taken at the nearby family restaurant. For more information about Travel Inns, consult the Contents page under Hotel Groups.
38 en suite (bth/shr)
ROOMS: d £35.50 *

CHURCH STRETTON Shropshire Map 07 SO49

★★★ 60% ***Stretton Hall***
All Stretton SY6 6HG (turn off A49 at traffic lights, drive over railway bridge continuing to junct at top of town. Turn right and hotel is 1.5m on right hand side) ☎ 01694 723224 FAX 01694 724364
Set in extensive gardens in the small village of All Stretton, just north of Church Stretton, this impressive former country house is steadily upgrading accommodation which includes some ground floor bedrooms and a room with a four-poster bed. The pleasant restaurant is furnished with period items, while an attractive lounge bar features panelled walls and a striking fireplace. Rooms are also available for private dinner parties and small conferences.
14 en suite (bth/shr) (1 fmly) CTV in all bedrooms 70P V meals Coffee am Tea pm Last d 10pm
CARDS:

See advertisement on opposite page

★★ 71% **Mynd House**
Little Stretton SY6 6RB (2m S B4370)
☎ 01694 722212 FAX 01694 724180
Closed Jan & 1 wk Summer
Located within the sleepy hamlet of Little Stretton, this is a small and relaxing hotel providing modern accommodation. Bedrooms are pretty and well equipped; one has a four-poster bed and two have small sitting areas. Four or five-course Gourmet menus are on offer as well as a regular carte. The wine list is comprehensive and owner Robert Hill is only too pleased to help with selection.

7 en suite (bth/shr) No smoking in all bedrooms CTV in all bedrooms 16P No coaches Jacuzzi/spa English, French & Italian Cuisine V meals Coffee am Tea pm No smoking in restaurant Last d 8.45pm
ROOMS: (incl. bkfst) s £38-£45; d £60-£100 * **LB**
OFF-PEAK: (incl. bkfst) s £35-£40; d £60-£90
MEALS: Bar Lunch £4-£7alc Dinner £24-£26alc
CONF: Thtr 15 Class 20 Board 12
CARDS:

CIRCENCESTER Gloucestershire Map 04 SP00

★★★69% **Stratton House**
Gloucester Rd GL7 2LE (just outside town on A417)
☎ 01285 651761 FAX 01285 640024

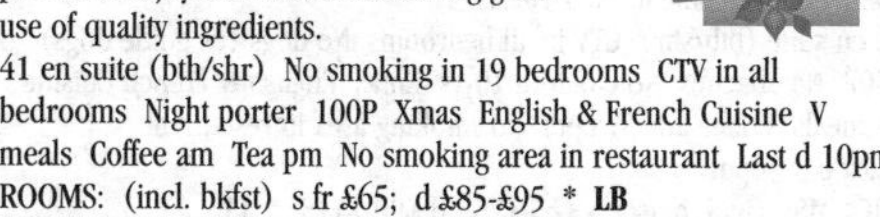

Sympathetically extended, this attractive 17th-century manor house offers a new wing of spacious premier rooms and a function suite. Original rooms in the main house are more compact but are equipped to the same standard. Cosy day rooms include a split-level drawing room and a restaurant overlooking the garden. There is also a congenial bar. Chef Simon Walsh produces enjoyable fresh food making good use of quality ingredients.
41 en suite (bth/shr) No smoking in 19 bedrooms CTV in all bedrooms Night porter 100P Xmas English & French Cuisine V meals Coffee am Tea pm No smoking area in restaurant Last d 10pm
ROOMS: (incl. bkfst) s fr £65; d £85-£95 * **LB**
OFF-PEAK: (incl. bkfst & dinner) s fr £78.50; d £112-£122
MEALS: Lunch fr £11.25 High tea fr £2.50 Dinner fr £17.75*
CONF: Thtr 150 Class 50 Board 40 Del £85
CARDS:

★★★ 66% **The Crown of Crucis**
Ampney Crucis GL7 5RS (take A417 to Fairford, hotel is approx 2.5m on left hand side of road) ☎ 01285 851806 FAX 01285 851735
Closed 24-30 Dec
This attractive hotel consists of two buildings, an original Cotswold stone inn, which now houses the bar and dining rooms, and a more modern bedroom block built round a courtyard. It stands on the edge of the village and Ampney Brook runs by its car park. Modern, well maintained bedrooms offer all the expected comforts. Cuisine is modern British in style and the hearty portions served offer good value for money.
25 en suite (bth/shr) CTV in all bedrooms 82P V meals Coffee am Tea pm Last d 10pm
ROOMS: (incl. bkfst) s £52; d £74 * **LB**
OFF-PEAK: (incl. bkfst) s £36; d £52
CONF: Thtr 80 Class 40 Board 25 Del from £76
CARDS:

★★★ 62% **King's Head**

Market Place GL7 2NR (town centre, opposite prominent church tower) ☎ 01285 653322
FAX 01285 655103
Closed 27-30 Dec
A landmark hotel in the centre of town, the King's Head is benefiting from improvements to its public areas, and the bedrooms are earmarked for similar treatment. The building is a sprawling complex of creaking floorboards and variously shaped rooms. It has two bars, a choice of lounges, a restaurant and a small car park to the rear.
66 en suite (bth/shr) (3 fmly) CTV in all bedrooms Lift Night porter 25P Pool table Skittle alley Xmas V meals Coffee am Tea pm Last d 9pm
ROOMS: (incl. bkfst) s £68; d £86 **LB**
MEALS: Bar Lunch fr £4.95 Dinner £14.95-£19.95*
CONF: Thtr 250 Class 75 Board 50 Del from £75
CARDS:

See advertisement on opposite page

★★ 76% **The New Inn**
GL7 5AN ☎ 01285 750651 FAX 01285 750657
(For full entry see Coln St Aldwyns)

★★ 59% **Corinium Court**
12 Gloucester St GL7 2DG ☎ 01285 659711 FAX 01285 885807
A property with a 400-year-old history, this former wool merchant's house makes a cosy hotel, just a quarter of a mile from the centre of town. Bedroom standards vary and more attention is paid to public areas which focus around the restaurant, converted from an old barn. A large car park is provided at the rear.
16 en suite (bth/shr) (1 fmly) CTV in all bedrooms 25P English & Italian Cuisine V meals Coffee am Tea pm No smoking in restaurant Last d 9.30pm
ROOMS: (incl. bkfst) s £40-£45; d £50-£65 * **LB**
MEALS: Bar Lunch £2.10-£12.50 Dinner £6.50-£12.50&alc*
CARDS:

CLACTON-ON-SEA Essex Map 05 TM11

★ 69% **Chudleigh**
13 Agate Rd, Marine Pde West CO15 1RA ☎ 01255 425407
FAX 01255 425407
RS Oct-Etr (evening meals optional)
This small friendly family-run hotel, which sits between the town centre and the sea, offers comfortably appointed bedrooms that are immaculately maintained and individually decorated in a light and cheerful style; most bedrooms have comfortable seating and a good range of facilities. The public rooms consist of a small lounge and a restaurant with a dispense bar.
10 en suite (bth/shr) (2 fmly) CTV in all bedrooms 7P No coaches No smoking in restaurant Last d 7pm
ROOMS: (incl. bkfst) s £29.95-£31; d £45-£47
OFF-PEAK: (incl. bkfst) s £25-£29.95; d £42.50-£45
MEALS: Dinner £9.50-£11
CARDS:

CLANFIELD Oxfordshire Map 04 SP20

★★★ 66% **Plough at Clanfield**

Bourton Rd OX18 2RB (on A4095/B4020)
☎ 01367 810222 FAX 01367 810596
Closed 28-30 Dec

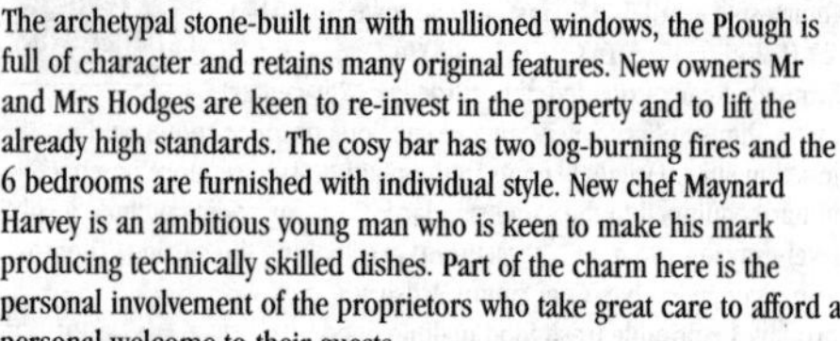

The archetypal stone-built inn with mullioned windows, the Plough is full of character and retains many original features. New owners Mr and Mrs Hodges are keen to re-invest in the property and to lift the already high standards. The cosy bar has two log-burning fires and the 6 bedrooms are furnished with individual style. New chef Maynard Harvey is an ambitious young man who is keen to make his mark producing technically skilled dishes. Part of the charm here is the personal involvement of the proprietors who take great care to afford a personal welcome to their guests.
6 en suite (bth/shr) CTV in all bedrooms No dogs (ex guide dogs) 30P No coaches No children 10yrs Xmas English & French Cuisine V meals Coffee am Tea pm No smoking area in restaurant Last d 9.30pm
ROOMS: (incl. bkfst) s £65-£75; d £90-£115 * **LB**
MEALS: Sunday Lunch £16-£17alc Dinner £26.50-£30.50alc*
CONF: Thtr 10 Class 10 Board 10 Del £99.50
CARDS:

CLAVERDON Warwickshire Map 04 SP16

★★★ 76% **Ardencote Hotel & Country Club**
Lye Green Rd CV35 8LS ☎ 01926 843111 FAX 01926 842646
Although it is quite a small hotel with only 18 rooms, the facilities available at Ardencote are of the type one would associate with a far larger hotel and are unsurpassed in this classification. The staff are a friendly team who, under the direction of affable manager Paul Williams, look after their guests with courtesy and care. Bedrooms are also well equipped with pretty fabrics and smart furnishings. There is a choice of four eating venues, the principal two being The Palms conservatory-style restaurant and the more formal Oak Room. Chef Didier Benemet cooks in a simple classical way using fresh ingredients.
18 en suite (bth/shr) (1 fmly) CTV in all bedrooms STV No dogs (ex guide dogs) Night porter 100P No coaches Indoor swimming pool (heated) Tennis (hard) Fishing Squash Sauna Solarium Gym Putting green Jacuzzi/spa Xmas V meals Coffee am Tea pm No smoking in restaurant Last d 9.30pm
ROOMS: (incl. bkfst) s £50-£87.50; d £70-£130 * **LB**
MEALS: Lunch fr £14.95 Dinner fr £21.95*
CONF: Thtr 130 Class 80 Board 40 Del from £70
CARDS:

CLAYTON-LE-WOODS Lancashire Map 07 SD52

★★★ 65% ***Pines***
PR6 7ED (on A6, 1m S of M6 junc 29) ☎ 01772 38551
FAX 01772 629002
Closed 25 & 26 Dec
This characterful, privately owned and enthusiastically run hotel, which is within very easy reach of the M6 offers attractive, thoughtfully equipped bedrooms, quite a number of which have their own sitting areas. The public areas include an elegant lounge, magnificent 'Crystal' dining room for private parties, as well as a spacious restaurant and a number of well equipped meeting rooms. Future plans include adding a conservatory which will offer a less formal eating option, although at

the time of our inspection these plans were still being finalised.
39 en suite (bth/shr) No smoking in 8 bedrooms CTV in all bedrooms STV No dogs Night porter 100P No coaches V meals Coffee am Tea pm Last d 9.30pm
CARDS:

CLEARWELL Gloucestershire Map 03 SO50

★★★65% **Wyndham Arms**
GL16 8JT (in centre of village on the B4231) ☎ 01594 833666
FAX 01594 836450
A charming 14th-century inn located in the Forest of Dean, the Wyndham Arms has been modernised and extended to create a comfortable hotel, where the Stanford family have been welcoming guests for the last 20 years. All the bedrooms are well equipped, but those in the new wing are larger. Some have been fitted with grab rails and wider doors for disabled guests. The restaurant offers an extensive carte, and bar meals are served in the historic bar, which is popular with locals and tourists alike.
5 en suite (bth/shr) 12 annexe en suite (bth/shr) (3 fmly) CTV in all bedrooms 54P International Cuisine V meals Coffee am Tea pm No smoking in restaurant Last d 9.30pm
ROOMS: (incl. bkfst) s £49.50; d £61-£65 **LB**
OFF-PEAK: (incl. bkfst) s £49.50; d £61-£65
MEALS: Lunch £12.95-£13.75&alc Dinner £18.25&alc
CONF: Thtr 56 Class 30 Board 22 Del from £90
CARDS:

CLEATOR Cumbria Map 11 NY01

★★★66% **Ennerdale Country House**
CA23 3DT ☎ 01946 813907 FAX 01946 815260
This fine period mansion lies in its own gardens on the A5086 north of Egremont and southeast of Whitehaven. Attracting a business, corporate and wedding market, it offers stylish well equipped bedrooms (including two with four-posters), an elegant restaurant and adjoining bar, and a less formal American-style bar/diner adorned with bric-a-brac depicting the States. Staff are friendly, attentive and contribute to a relaxed atmosphere.
22 en suite (bth/shr) CTV in all bedrooms STV 65P ch fac Xmas International Cuisine V meals Coffee am Tea pm No smoking in restaurant Last d 9.30pm
ROOMS: (incl. bkfst) s £75-£85; d £85-£105 **LB**
MEALS: Lunch £7.95-£10.95 High tea £3.95-£7.95 Dinner £15.95-£18.50&alc
CONF: Thtr 150 Class 100 Board 40 Del from £95
CARDS:

CLECKHEATON West Yorkshire Map 07 SE12

Travel Inn
Whitehall Rd BD19 6HG ☎ 01582 414341
FAX 01582 400024
Purpose-built accommodation, offering spacious, well equipped bedrooms, all with en suite bathrooms. Meals may be taken at the nearby family restaurant. For more information about Travel Inns, consult the Contents page under Hotel Groups.
40 en suite (bth/shr)

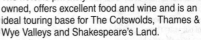

CLEETHORPES Lincolnshire Map 08 TA30

★★★69% **Kingsway**
Kingsway DN35 0AE (junct of A1098 and seafront)
☎ 01472 601122 FAX 01472 601381
Closed 25-26 Dec
This seafront hotel has been in the same family now for four generations and continues to be professionally run. The lounges are

contd.

very inviting and include one for non-smokers. The restaurant is traditional in style, offering classical French and English cooking backed by a well-balanced wine list. Bright, fresh and well-equipped bedrooms are provided , along with attentive service from a well turned out staff. There is ample car parking, some of which is under cover.
50 en suite (bth/shr) CTV in all bedrooms STV No dogs (ex guide dogs) Lift Night porter 50P No coaches No children 5yrs English & French Cuisine V meals Coffee am Last d 9pm
ROOMS: (incl. bkfst) s £56-£63; d £79 * **LB**
MEALS: Lunch £10-£13.50&alc Dinner £16.50*
CARDS:

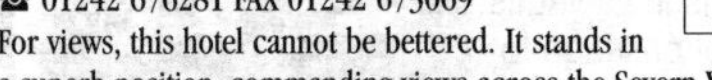

CLEEVE HILL Gloucestershire Map 03 SO92

★★★65% **Rising Sun**
GL52 3PX (on the B4632, 4m N of Cheltenham)
☎ 01242 676281 FAX 01242 673069
For views, this hotel cannot be bettered. It stands in a superb position, commanding views across the Severn Valley to the Malvern Hills and beyond. Spacious public areas include a large restaurant with striking decor, a bar and a reception lounge. Bedrooms are not large, but they offer a good range of facilities and the more dated among them were scheduled for refurbishment at the time of our visit. There is an enthusiastic new management team, and staff are friendly and obliging.
24 en suite (bth/shr) (2 fmly) No smoking in 6 bedrooms CTV in all bedrooms STV Night porter 75P Sauna Xmas English & French Cuisine V meals Coffee am Tea pm No smoking area in restaurant Last d 10pm
ROOMS: (incl. bkfst) s £59.50; d £75 * **LB**
OFF-PEAK: (incl. bkfst) s £40; d £60
MEALS: Lunch £6.95-£10.95 Dinner £12-£14.50&alc*
CONF: Thtr 40 Class 20 Board 30 Del £85
CARDS:

CLEOBURY MORTIMER Shropshire Map 07 SO67

★★73% **Redfern**
DY14 8AA (on A4117) ☎ 01299 270395
FAX 01299 271011
Good food and friendly, informal service are provided at this family-run hotel. The bedrooms, some of which are located in an adjacent building, have every modern facility, including satellite TV, trouser presses and welcoming decanters of sherry. There are a restaurant with a wide range of dishes, an all-day coffee shop and a pizza parlour. The food is well cooked, and everything - including the bread - is produced in the hotel's kitchen.
5 en suite (bth/shr) 6 annexe en suite (bth/shr) (4 fmly) CTV in all bedrooms STV 20P No coaches Clay pigeon shooting Pheasant shooting English & French Cuisine V meals Coffee am Tea pm No smoking in restaurant Last d 9.30pm
MEALS: Lunch £4.95-£9&alc Dinner £9.50-£17.25&alc*
CONF: Thtr 30 Class 30 Board 20 Del from £60
CARDS:

CLEVEDON Somerset Map 03 ST47

★★★60% **Walton Park**
Wellington Ter BS21 7BL ☎ 01275 874253
FAX 01275 343577
From its position overlooking the Bristol Channel, on the northern outskirts of the town, this Victorian hotel enjoys glorious views across to Wales. Bedrooms have been equipped with modern comforts, and the public areas include a popular bar and meeting rooms.
40 en suite (bth/shr) (4 fmly) CTV in all bedrooms STV Lift Night porter 50P English & French Cuisine V meals Coffee am Tea pm No smoking area in restaurant Last d 9.30pm
ROOMS: (incl. bkfst) s £40-£69.95; d £70-£90.90 **LB**
MEALS: Sunday Lunch £11.95 Dinner £14.50-£15.85&alc
CONF: Thtr 150 Class 80 Board 80 Del from £70
CARDS:

CLIMPING West Sussex Map 04 SU90

★★★78% **Bailiffscourt**
BN17 5RW ☎ 01903 723511 FAX 01903 723107
Bailiffscourt is a wonderful deception, a perfectly preserved medieval house that was built only 50 years ago! Architecturally and aesthetically correct in every detail, this delightful hotel has been tastefully furnished throughout, and is full of character and charm. Accommodation is available in the main house bedrooms and in superb garden rooms. Many have four poster beds, open log fires and beautiful views. Chef Chris Colmer offers an exciting collection of dishes in the elegant dining room. Superb flavours, colours and textures are interestingly combined, and fish features prominently. Two good examples might be a roasted Whitby cod with a spiced crust and a sweet pimento fondue or Scottish salmon with a pasta rösti, nage of blue cheese and spinach. Among the desserts, a hot walnut tart with orange and aniseed sorbet can be recommended.
10 en suite (bth/shr) 17 annexe en suite (bth/shr) CTV in all bedrooms Night porter 60P Outdoor swimming pool (heated) Tennis (hard) Croquet lawn Golf practice area Clay pigeon Xmas English & French Cuisine V meals Coffee am Tea pm No smoking in restaurant Last d 9.45pm
ROOMS: (incl. bkfst) s £85-£110; d £100-£275 **LB**
MEALS: Lunch £18.50 Dinner £30
CONF: Thtr 50 Board 22 Del £135
CARDS:

CLOVELLY Devon Map 02 SS32

★★62% ***Red Lion***
The Quay EX39 5TF (Turn off A39 at Clovelly Cross on to B3237. Proceed to bottom of hill and take first turning on left to harbour)
☎ 01237 431237 FAX 01237 431044
A quaint 18th-century inn, full of character and charm, overlooks the quay in this delightful village. Its bedrooms provide modern facilities without detracting from the character of the building, and most have glorious views. The bars have beamed ceilings and open fireplaces, and a selection of simple dishes is offered on the small dining room's set-price menu. Limited car parking is available, together with a Land Rover 'ferry service' for those reluctant to climb Clovelly's famous steep, cobbled street.
12 en suite (bth/shr) (1 fmly) CTV in all bedrooms No dogs 12P V meals Coffee am Tea pm Last d 8.30pm
CARDS:

COALVILLE Leicestershire Map 08 SK41

Bardon Hall
Beveridge Ln, Bardon Hill LE67 2TB (1m W of junct 22 of M1, on A50) ☎ 01530 813644
FAX 01530 815425
This is an attractive complex, set in extensive grounds, which include the Stardust Cabaret Club, an exhibition centre and very well furnished and equipped accommodation in mews-style annexes. The pub-style restaurant is informal and popular.
35 en suite (bth/shr) No smoking in 4 bedrooms CTV in all bedrooms No dogs (ex guide dogs) 150P English & Continental Cuisine V meals Coffee am Tea pm No smoking in restaurant
ROOMS: s fr £39.50; d fr £39.50 *
OFF-PEAK: s fr £28.50; d fr £28.50
MEALS: Lunch fr £4.95*

CONF: Thtr 200 Class 100 Board 60 Del from £75
CARDS: 

See advertisement on this page

COBHAM Surrey Map 04 TQ16

Hilton National Cobham
Seven Hills Rd South KT11 1EW ☎ 01932 864471
FAX 01932 868017

HILTON

This is a bright, modern hotel, with an informal restaurant, aimed at both the business and leisure guest. All bedrooms have en suite bathrooms and a range of modern facilities. For more information about Hilton National hotels, consult the Contents page under Hotel Groups.
149 en suite (bth/shr)
ROOMS: d £135-£150 *
CONF: Thtr 300 Class 150 Board 30 Del from £130

COCKERMOUTH Cumbria Map 11 NY13

★★★65% **The Trout**
Crown St CA13 0EJ (next to Wordsworth House and Mineral Museum)
☎ 01900 823591 FAX 01900 827514
This long-established hotel lies by the banks of the River Derwent, right next to the birthplace of William Wordsworth. Public areas, which include an attractive restaurant, are cosy and inviting, whilst bedrooms in the original building come in a variety of sizes. A new extension of 12 bedrooms will be up and running by the end of 1996.
30 en suite (bth/shr) (4 fmly) No smoking in 12 bedrooms CTV in all bedrooms STV Night porter 60P Fishing Xmas English, French & Italian Cuisine V meals Coffee am No smoking in restaurant Last d 9.30pm
ROOMS: (incl. bkfst) s £59.95-£95; d £76.95-£120 **LB**
MEALS: Lunch £9.95-£12.95&alc Dinner £16.95-£18.95&alc*
CONF: Thtr 50 Class 30 Board 25
CARDS: 

★★★62% ***Broughton Craggs***
Great Broughton CA13 0XW (leave A66 2m W of town, signposted Great Broughton. Over River Derwent and up Little Brow to T-junction. Turn right.) ☎ 01900 824400 FAX 01900 825350
Set in its own grounds on the edge of the village of Great Broughton just off the A66 two miles west of Cockermouth, this hotel enjoys splendid views across the valley of the River Derwent to distant fells. It has a relaxed and informal atmosphere and its versatile public areas make it a popular venue for weddings and small conferences.
14 en suite (bth/shr) (1 fmly) CTV in all bedrooms No dogs (ex guide dogs) 60P English & French Cuisine V meals Coffee am Tea pm Last d 9pm
CARDS:

★★67% **Derwent Lodge**
Bassenthwaite Lake, Embleton CA13 9YA ☎ 017687 76606
FAX 017687 76766
The Derwent Lodge started off as a farmhouse in the small hamlet adjacent to the main road. More recently it has been upgraded, under new management, into a friendly hotel which has the convivial character of an inn. The facilities are thoroughly modern and the furnishings are of a contemporary style.
15 en suite (bth/shr) (5 fmly) CTV in all bedrooms STV No dogs (ex guide dogs) 30P Jacuzzi/spa Xmas V meals Coffee am Tea pm No smoking in restaurant Last d 9.30pm
ROOMS: (incl. bkfst) s £35-£42; d £45-£55 * **LB**
OFF-PEAK: (incl. bkfst) s £30-£35; d £40-£45
MEALS: Sunday Lunch £6.95-£10.95&alc High tea £1.50-£3.50 Dinner £8.95-£13.95&alc*
CARDS:

See advertisement on this page

COGGESHALL Essex Map 05 TL82

★★★❀❀67% **White Hart**
Market End CO6 1NH ☎ 01376 561654
FAX 01376 561789

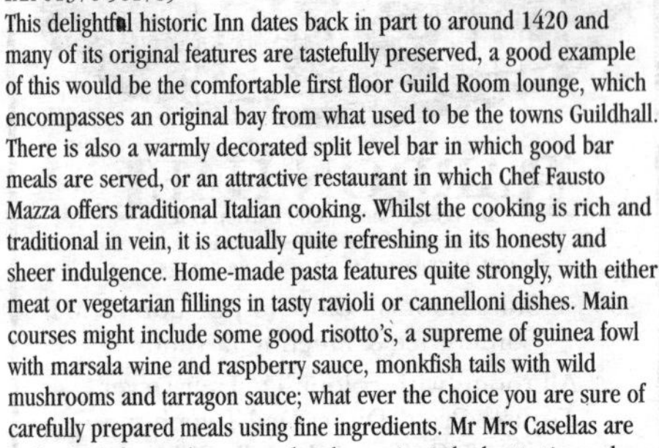

This delightful historic Inn dates back in part to around 1420 and many of its original features are tastefully preserved, a good example of this would be the comfortable first floor Guild Room lounge, which encompasses an original bay from what used to be the towns Guildhall. There is also a warmly decorated split level bar in which good bar meals are served, or an attractive restaurant in which Chef Fausto Mazza offers traditional Italian cooking. Whilst the cooking is rich and traditional in vein, it is actually quite refreshing in its honesty and sheer indulgence. Home-made pasta features quite strongly, with either meat or vegetarian fillings in tasty ravioli or cannelloni dishes. Main courses might include some good risotto's, a supreme of guinea fowl with marsala wine and raspberry sauce, monkfish tails with wild mushrooms and tarragon sauce; what ever the choice you are sure of carefully prepared meals using fine ingredients. Mr Mrs Casellas are enthusiastic hosts who ensure that the service is both attentive and professional throughout the hotel.
18 en suite (bth/shr) (1 fmly) CTV in all bedrooms STV No dogs 47P No coaches French & Italian Cuisine V meals Coffee am Last d 10pm
ROOMS: (incl. bkfst) s £55.35-£61.50; d £87.30-£97 * **LB**
OFF-PEAK: (incl. bkfst) s £49.20-£59.85; d fr £77.60
MEALS: Lunch £14-£29.50alc Dinner £14-£29.50alc*
CONF: Thtr 30 Class 10 Board 22 Del from £85
CARDS:

See advertisement on opposite page

COLCHESTER Essex Map 05 TL92

★★★69% **George**
116 High St CO1 2XE (200yds beyond Town Hall)
☎ 01206 578494 FAX 01206 761732
RS Xmas
This 15th-century coaching inn has now been fully refurbished, the public rooms are inviting and tastefully decorated with bold, cheerful colour schemes. The open-plan lounge and bar area is comfortably appointed and welcoming, and a lounge menu of light snacks or full meals is available all day. The restaurant also offers some imaginative choices from a brasserie style menu, supplemented by a blackboard of daily specials. Bedrooms have been refurbished to a very good modern standard and some retain the character of the building with exposed oak beams, brick-work and original fireplaces; all have a good range of facilities and there are two suites available.
45 en suite (bth/shr) (2 fmly) No smoking in 29 bedrooms CTV in 47 bedrooms STV Night porter 46P International Cuisine V meals Coffee am Tea pm No smoking area in restaurant Last d 10pm
ROOMS: s £34-£57.50; d £42.50-£63 * **LB**
MEALS: Lunch £5.95-£16.95alc Dinner £10.95-£15.95*
CONF: Thtr 80 Class 35 Board 40 Del from £78
CARDS:

★★★68% **Marks Tey**
London Rd, Marks Tey CO6 1DU (off A12/A120 junction) ☎ 01206 210001 FAX 01206 212167
Attractive accommodation and a range of conference suites are offered at this hotel, which is situated on the A12 at the junction with the A120. Bedrooms are thoughtfully equipped and laid-out, each room has co-ordinated soft furnishings and decor, and ornate dark wood furniture. Plans for a leisure complex and a coffee lounge had been somewhat delayed, but should be in place during 1997, these new facilities will further enhance the appeal and comfort of the public areas.
110 en suite (bth/shr) (12 fmly) No smoking in 16 bedrooms CTV in all bedrooms STV No dogs (ex guide dogs) Night porter 200P Tennis (hard) Gym Pool table English & French Cuisine V meals Coffee am Tea pm
ROOMS: s £62.50; d £69 **LB**
OFF-PEAK: s £45; d £45
MEALS: Lunch £13.50&alc Dinner £13.50&alc*
CONF: Thtr 200 Class 100 Board 60 Del £90
CARDS:

★★★68% **Rose & Crown**
East St CO1 2TZ ☎ 01206 866677 FAX 01206 866616
The Rose and Crown is a character hotel which retains much of its historic charm. The Tudor bar with its heavy timbers and exposed brickwork is a particular attraction to visitors. The accommodation is divided between modern new wing rooms, three cottage bedrooms and the original building where rooms are traditional in character and also include four-poster bedrooms. The hotel is professionally managed and offers above average levels of service in the bar and restaurant.
30 en suite (bth/shr) (4 fmly) No smoking in 5 bedrooms CTV in all bedrooms STV No dogs (ex guide dogs) Night porter 50P English, French & Italian Cuisine V meals Coffee am Tea pm No smoking area in restaurant Last d 10pm
ROOMS: (incl. bkfst) s £58; d £58 * **LB**
MEALS: Lunch £12.95&alc Dinner £12.95&alc*
CONF: Thtr 100 Class 40 Board 60 Del from £75
CARDS:

★★★65% **Butterfly**
Old Ipswich Rd CO7 7QY (A12/A120 Ardleigh Junction)
☎ 01206 230900 FAX 01206 231095
Overlooking a lake and close to the road network, this two-storey hotel was opened in 1992. Twin and double rooms are charged by the room and studio singles are particularly comfortable for the business traveller. The restaurant appeals to all tastes; breakfast is a buffet operation.
50 en suite (bth/shr) (2 fmly) No smoking in 11 bedrooms CTV in all bedrooms STV No dogs (ex guide dogs) Night porter 85P European & Oriental Cuisine V meals Coffee am Tea pm No smoking area in restaurant Last d 10pm
ROOMS: s fr £55; d fr £55 * **LB**
OFF-PEAK: s fr £45; d fr £45
MEALS: Lunch fr £9.75&alc Dinner fr £12.25&alc*
CONF: Thtr 80 Class 40 Board 40 Del from £62.50
CARDS:
See advertisement under BURY ST EDMUNDS

★★★62% ***Red Lion***
High St CO1 1DJ ☎ 01206 577986 FAX 01206 578207
The entrance to this hotel dating from Elizabethan times is down an alley off the High Street. The restaurant, with its fireplace and beams, was originally the Great Hall. Bedrooms in the old part are furnished in keeping with the building while those in the newer wing have modern furniture. There is a snug lounge for guests.
24 en suite (bth/shr) CTV in all bedrooms No dogs (ex guide dogs) Night porter English & French Cuisine V meals Coffee am Tea pm Last d 9.30pm
CARDS:

See advertisement on opposite page

★★★62% **Wivenhoe House**
Wivenhoe Park CO4 3SQ (follow signs to Colchester & University of Essex, enter University Campus & follow green signs to Wivenhoe Park Hotel) ☎ 01206 863666 FAX 01206 868532
Closed 25 Dec-1 Jan
An elegant 18th-century red brick building with a modern wing, this hotel is located within the campus of the university. The accommodation styles differ between the main house and new wing rooms, the former being more individual in style and varying in size, whereas the new rooms, designed primarily for the conference

delegate, tend to be more spacious ans modern. The restaurant offers a carte supplemented by a daily set menu which incorporates some carvery dishes. An extensive range of well equipped meeting rooms - some of them air conditioned - are available for seminars and conferences.
47 en suite (bth/shr) CTV in all bedrooms Night porter 80P Pool table Croquet lawn Putting green Tennis Squash & Gym at university English & Continental Cuisine V meals Coffee am No smoking in restaurant Last d 8.45pm
ROOMS: s £46-£57.50; d £46-£57.50 *
MEALS: Lunch £11.50-£13.10 Dinner £7.50-£20alc*
CONF: Thtr 80 Class 48 Board 40 Del from £80
CARDS:

★★70% Kingsford Park
Layer Rd CO2 0HS (form jun A12/A604 follow signs for Mersea at staggered junc with B1026, Layer Rd turn right) ☎ 01206 734301 FAX 01206 734512
An elegant 18th-century house standing in 18 acres of grounds on the B1026 Maldon road, this hotel is a popular venue for both social and business functions; it offers a flexible range of suites together with a small lounge and bar area adjacent to the modern conservatory restaurant, which provides a good choice of meals from an Italian carte. Service is both professional and attentive. Accommodation varies in size and styles, with the generally spacious bedrooms all being individually furnished and decorated, as well as provided with a good range of facilities.
10 en suite (bth/shr) (2 fmly) CTV in all bedrooms Night porter 103P Croquet lawn ch fac Xmas Italian & Mediterranean Cuisine V meals Coffee am Tea pm No smoking area in restaurant
ROOMS: (incl. bkfst) s £55-£75; d £65-£95 **LB**
CONF: Thtr 100 Class 44 Board 38 Del from £95
CARDS:

Forte Posthouse Colchester
FORTE Posthouse
Abbotts Ln, Eight Ash Green CO6 3QL (off A604) ☎ 01206 767740 FAX 01206 766577
Suitable for both the business and leisure traveller, this bright hotel provides modern accommodation in well equipped bedrooms with en suite bathrooms. For more details about Forte Posthouse hotels, consult the Contents page for the section on Hotel Groups.
110 en suite (bth/shr)
ROOMS: d £69-£79 *
CONF: Thtr 150 Class 70 Board 60 Del £99

COLEFORD Gloucestershire Map 03 SO51

★★★ 65% The Speech House

Forest of Dean GL16 7EL (on B4226 between Cinderford and Coleford) ☎ 01594 822607 FAX 01594 823658
This 17th-century hunting lodge is set in the heart of the Forest of Dean. Comfortably appointed bedrooms, several with 4-poster beds, have been tastefully refurbished and offer all the modern facilities whilst retaining their original charm. In comparison the public areas are less sumptuous, the beamed restaurant clearly reflecting its former use as a courthouse for the Foresters of Dean. The cooking of Mark Barnet continues to please with his more imaginative menus in which he makes good use of quality produce and ingredients. Service from a small staff is willing and friendly.
14 en suite (bth/shr) No smoking in 5 bedrooms CTV in all bedrooms 41P Xmas V meals Coffee am Tea pm No smoking in restaurant Last d 9pm
ROOMS: s £65; d £95 * **LB**
OFF-PEAK: s £50; d £80
MEALS: Sunday Lunch fr £13.95alc Dinner £21.95&alc

contd.

CONF: Thtr 40 Class 20 Board 15 Del from £95
CARDS:

COLERNE Wiltshire Map 03 ST87

RED STAR HOTEL

★★★★ ❀❀❀ ***Lucknam Park***
SN14 8AZ (leave M4 at junct 17, take A350 to Chippenham, then A420 towards Bristol for 3 miles. At village of Ford, turn south towards Colerne)
☎ 01225 742777 FAX 01225 743536
This magnificent Palladian mansion dates from 1720 and is set in 500 acres of its own parkland, yet only six miles from the Georgian city of Bath. Managing director Robert Carter's background in interior design shows in the elegant public rooms and the individually decorated and furnished bedrooms which include many suites. Similar high standards are evident in the leisure facilities which include a health and beauty suite, pool, gymnasium (soon to be extended) and the equestrian centre. Head chef Alexander Venables continues to provide imaginative menus, with robust flavours and great artistry in the style of presentation. Organic local produce is much used and is gaining acclaim. A recent inspection meal started with a delicious ceviche of monkfish, followed by a roasted Hereford duck breast on a shallot tart served with a crème de mûres sauce, accompanied by perfectly cooked baby vegetables. A well risen Grand Marnier soufflé completed the meal, served with lemon grass ice cream, orange segments and discs of caramel, an interesting combination of textures and flavours. Staff are professional, smartly uniformed and provide efficient, discreet service.
24 en suite (bth) 18 annexe en suite (bth) CTV in all bedrooms No dogs (ex guide dogs) Night porter 90P No coaches Indoor swimming pool (heated) Tennis (hard) Riding Snooker Sauna Solarium Gym Croquet lawn Jacuzzi/spa Whirlpool Beauty salon Steam room English & French Cuisine V meals Coffee am Tea pm Last d 9.30pm
CARDS:

COLESHILL Warwickshire Map 04 SP28

★★★62% **Grimstock Country House**
Gilson Rd, Gilson B46 1AJ (off A446 W of Coleshill) ☎ 01675 462121 & 462161 FAX 01675 467646
This large, privately owned hotel stands in its own spacious grounds convenient for the M42 and the NEC. Bedrooms are modern and offer a good range of amenities such as in-house movies. The attractive restaurant overlooks the grounds and the cosy bar is comfortably furnished. An extensive range of conference facilities contained in a purpose-built suite is popular with the local business community.
44 en suite (bth/shr) (1 fmly) CTV in all bedrooms STV Night porter 80P Xmas English & French Cuisine V meals Coffee am Tea pm Last d 9.30pm
ROOMS: (incl. bkfst) s £65-£70; d £76-£80 * **LB**
OFF-PEAK: (incl. bkfst) s fr £45; d fr £55
MEALS: Lunch £5-£12alc High tea £4.50-£6.50alc Dinner £14-£15&alc*
CONF: Thtr 100 Class 60 Board 50 Del from £93.50
CARDS:

★★66% **Coleshill**
152 High St B46 3BG ☎ 01675 465527
FAX 01675 464013

This popular coaching inn is situated in the town centre, only a short drive from the M6 and M42, and is convenient for the NEC and airport. Bedrooms are modern and well equipped though they tend to vary in size; some, including those at ground level, are in a separate house on the opposite side of the road. The lounge bar is full of character and the attractive restaurant congenial.
15 en suite (bth/shr) 8 annexe en suite (bth/shr) No smoking in 8 bedrooms CTV in all bedrooms STV No dogs (ex guide dogs) Night porter 48P English & French Cuisine V meals Coffee am Tea pm No smoking area in restaurant Last d 10pm
ROOMS: (incl. bkfst) s £65; d £75 * **LB**
OFF-PEAK: (incl. bkfst) s £35; d £60
MEALS: Sunday Lunch £4.95-£8.95&alc Dinner £10-£14.50&alc*
CONF: Thtr 150 Class 40 Board 40 Del £85
CARDS:

COLN ST-ALDWYNS Gloucestershire Map 04 SP10

★★❀❀76% **New Inn**
GL7 5AN (8m E of Cirencester, between Bibury and Fairford)
☎ 01285 750651 FAX 01285 750657
Time appears to languish in this most charming and traditional of Cotswold villages, where the 'New' of New Inn dates from Elizabethan times. This is a genuine country inn, with attractive accommodation and a small restaurant that has gained a high local reputation for its imaginative interpretation of traditional dishes. Service is professional.
8 en suite (bth/shr) 4 annexe en suite (bth/shr) (2 fmly) CTV in all bedrooms No dogs (ex guide dogs) 22P No coaches Xmas English & Mediterranean Cuisine V meals Coffee am Tea pm No smoking in restaurant Last d 9.30pm
ROOMS: (incl. bkfst) s £55-£70; d £79-£95 **LB**
OFF-PEAK: (incl. bkfst) s fr £45; d fr £65
MEALS: Lunch fr £14.50 Dinner fr £22.50
CONF: Thtr 20 Board 12 Del from £99.50
CARDS:

COLSTERWORTH Lincolnshire Map 08 SK92

Travelodge
NG33 5JR (on A1 southbound at junct with B151/B676) ☎ Central Res 0800 850950
FAX 01476 861078

This modern building offers accommodation in smart, spacious and well equipped bedrooms, suitable for family use, and all with en suite bathrooms. Meals may be taken at the nearby family restaurant. For information on room rates and to make a booking, call Roomline free of charge on 0800 850950. For more details about Travelodge, consult the Contents page under Hotel Groups.
31 en suite (bth/shr)

Travelodge
NG33 5JJ (at roundabout of junc A1/A151)
☎ 01476 861181 FAX 01476 861181
This modern building offers accommodation in

Travelodge

smart, spacious and well equipped bedrooms, suitable for family use, and all with en suite bathrooms. Meals may be taken at the nearby family restaurant. For information on room rates and to make a booking, call Roomline free of charge on 0800 850950. For more details about Travelodge, consult the Contents page under Hotel Groups.
32 en suite (bth/shr)

COLYFORD Devon Map 03 SY29

★★ 75% **Swallow Eaves**
Swan Hill Rd EX13 6QJ (on A3052, in centre of village, opposite village store) ☎ 01297 553184
Closed Jan
This delightful little hotel is personally run by Jane and John Beck who have deservedly built up a good local reputation for good service, food and hospitality. The bedrooms which are continually being upgraded, are very comfortable and attractively decorated with lots of extra, thoughtful touches. Jane serves a daily menu of carefully prepared dishes using quality local ingredients, and husband John ensures the smooth running of the restaurant and creates a relaxed atmosphere. Guests have the added bonus of being able to use a local heated swimming pool.
8 en suite (bth/shr) No smoking in 5 bedrooms CTV in all bedrooms No dogs (ex guide dogs) 10P No coaches Free use of nearby Swimming Club No children 14yrs Coffee am Tea pm No smoking in restaurant Last d 8.30pm
ROOMS: (incl. bkfst) s £37-£47; d £54-£74 **LB**
OFF-PEAK: (incl. bkfst) s £30-£40; d £40-£58
MEALS: Bar Lunch fr £4.50 Dinner fr £18.50
CARDS:

COLYTON Devon Map 03 SY29

★★ 68% **White Cottage**
Dolphin St EX13 6NA (on B3161) ☎ 01297 552401
FAX 01297 553897
Centrally situated in the village and ideally placed for touring the Dorset and East Devon coastline, this small, character hotel with thatched roof and attractive garden is run by resident proprietors who provide both a warm welcome and caring service. Home-cooked dinners are offered on both the carte and extensive bar snack menus, while the bedrooms - though they vary in size - are all well equipped with modern facilities.
6 en suite (bth/shr) (1 fmly) CTV in all bedrooms No dogs (ex guide dogs) 16P N No children 14yrs V meals Coffee am Tea pm No smoking in restaurant Last d 8.30pm
ROOMS: (incl. bkfst) s fr £36.50; d £63-£67 * **LB**
MEALS: Lunch £8.75 Dinner £19.50*

COMBE MARTIN Devon Map 02 SS54

★★ 61% ***Rone House***
King St EX34 0AD ☎ 01271 883428
Closed Nov-Feb (ex 23-27 Dec) RS Feb-Mar
Modestly furnished but comfortable and suitably equipped accommodation is provided by this small family-run hotel in the centre of the town. A compact lounge with colour TV also offers a number of video tapes for guests' use, while the dining room serves a range of uncomplicated English dishes - a short selection of vegetarian choices supplementing its set-price menus and carte.
11 rms (4 bth 4 shr) (4 fmly) CTV in all bedrooms 15P No coaches Outdoor swimming pool (heated) International Cuisine V meals Last d 9.30pm
CARDS:

CONGLETON Cheshire Map 07 SJ86

★★★ 65% **Lion & Swan**
Swan Bank CW12 1JR ☎ 01260 273115 FAX 01260 299270
Dating from Tudor times, this former coaching inn stands in the town centre. It has a lot of character, with exposed beams, an ornately carved fireplace in the restaurant and period-style furniture throughout. Bedrooms of different sizes are comfortable, with modern facilities, and there is one with an antique four-poster bed.
21 en suite (bth/shr) (2 fmly) No smoking in 3 bedrooms CTV in all bedrooms 49P Xmas English, French & Portuguese Cuisine V meals Coffee am Tea pm Last d 9.45pm
ROOMS: (incl. bkfst) s £31-£59; d £52-£72 * **LB**
MEALS: Lunch fr £7.95 Dinner fr £14.95&alc*
CONF: Thtr 110 Class 70 Board 40 Del from £92
CARDS:

See advertisement on this page

CONISTON Cumbria Map 07 SD39

★★ 65% **Black Bull**
Yewdale Rd LA21 8DU (in centre of village)
☎ 015394 41335 & 41668 FAX 015394 41168
This 16th-century coaching inn stands in the centre of the village right by the side of a stream, and some of its bedrooms, which are contained in an adjacent slate stone cottage and house, share a patio which overlooks the stream. The focal point of the inn is a spacious lounge bar with a coal fire and photographs of Donald Campbell and Bluebird. A good range of meals is served here and in the dining room. The inn brews its own ale and guests can have a tour of the brew house to see how beer is made.
10 en suite (bth/shr) 5 annexe en suite (bth/shr) (3 fmly) No smoking in 1 bedroom CTV in all bedrooms 15P Pony trekking

contd.

Sailing Wind Surfing Xmas English & French Cuisine V meals Coffee am Tea pm
ROOMS: (incl. bkfst) s fr £35; d fr £50 * **LB**
CARDS:

★★65% Sun
LA21 8HQ (signposted from village centre, off A593)
☎ 01539 441248
This 16th-century inn, now a family-run hotel, occupies a picturesque position above the village and many of its bedrooms enjoy fine views. Its association with Donald Campbell of Bluebird fame is recorded by the many photographs and archive items. The typical Lakeland bar boasts good real ale and an extensive menu, and there is a comfortable and relaxing residents' lounge next to the dining room.
11 rms (7 bth 3 shr) CTV in all bedrooms 20P Xmas English & Continental Cuisine V meals Coffee am Tea pm No smoking in restaurant Last d 9pm
ROOMS: (incl. bkfst) s £50; d £50-£70 * **LB**
OFF-PEAK: (incl. bkfst) s £25-£37; d £45-£60
MEALS: Lunch £8.95-£15.50alc Dinner £15.50
CONF: Class 20
CARDS:

★★63% Yewdale
Yewdale Rd LA21 8LU (opposite St Andrews Church & Barclays Bank)
☎ 015394 41280 FAX 015394 41662
This friendly family-run hotel which lies right in the centre of the village offers decent sized bedrooms, a lounge bar and a versatile dining room serving teas and snacks as well as dinners.
12 rms (2 bth 8 shr) (4 fmly) CTV in all bedrooms 6P Xmas English, Continental & Oriental Cuisine V meals Coffee am Tea pm No smoking in restaurant
ROOMS: (incl. bkfst) s £23.95-£33.50; d £47.90-£67 * **LB**
OFF-PEAK: (incl. bkfst) s £17-£25; d £34-£50
MEALS: Bar Lunch £2.95-£5.95alc
CARDS:

★ 73% Old Rectory
Torver LA21 8AX (2.5m S of Coniston) ☎ 015394 41353
FAX 015394 41156
This friendly, family-run Victorian house lies in three acres of gardens and grounds amidst farmland, two miles south of Coniston. The atmosphere is peaceful and relaxing, with magazines and board games in the lounge. There is no bar, but a limited selection of drinks is available and the well equipped bedrooms include mini bars. Dinner is the main occasion, served at 7.30pm. The set four course menu of country house cooking places emphasis on fresh ingredients and a choice is offered for dessert. Breakfasts are equally impressive, but expect to wait until 9am if you wish to enjoy a cooked meal. Most of the bedrooms are well proportioned, although three standard rooms are more compact; all are cheerfully decorated and have good en suite bathrooms.
8 en suite (bth/shr) (2 fmly) No smoking in all bedrooms CTV in all bedrooms 10P No coaches Xmas English & Continental Cuisine No smoking in restaurant Last d 7.30pm
ROOMS: (incl. bkfst & dinner) s £27.50-£30; d £50-£74 **LB**
OFF-PEAK: (incl. bkfst & dinner) s £17.50-£24.50; d £35-£49
MEALS: Dinner £13*
CARDS:

CONSTANTINE BAY Cornwall & Isles of Scilly Map 02 SW87

★★★ 77% Treglos
PL28 8JH (turn right at Constantine Bay stores, hotel 50 yards on left) ☎ 01841 520727
FAX 01841 521163
Closed 6 Nov-11 Mar
Just a short walk from the beach and set in attractive gardens and grounds, this hotel has spectacular views over the north Cornish coastline and has been in the same family ownership for over 30 years. Roaring log fires and fresh flowers are a feature of the tastefully furnished lounges, one of which is specifically for bridge players. Bedrooms are spacious and comfortable, many enjoying the splendid views, and all are well equipped. In the restaurant, Paul Becker's 5-course menus offer something for every taste, and at dinner the hors d'oeuvres buffet is always a popular choice, along with the array of Cornish cheeses.

CONSORT CROWN

44 en suite (bth/shr) (12 fmly) CTV in all bedrooms Lift Night porter 58P No coaches Indoor swimming pool (heated) Snooker Pool table Croquet lawn Jacuzzi/spa Converted 'boat house' for table tennis English & French Cuisine V meals Coffee am Tea pm No smoking in restaurant Last d 9.15pm
ROOMS: (incl. bkfst & dinner) s £46-£69; d £92-£138 * **LB**
MEALS: Lunch £11.50&alc High tea £7 Dinner £21&alc*
CONF: Board 20 Del from £60
CARDS:
See advertisement under PADSTOW

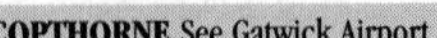

COPTHORNE See Gatwick Airport

CORBY Northamptonshire Map 04 SP88

★★★61% Rockingham Forest
Rockingham Rd NN17 1AE (just off A427)
☎ 01536 401348 FAX 01536 266383

REGAL A Collection of Individual Hotels

A low, modern, red-brick building stands near the Rockingham Triangle to the north of the town. Business people constitute the majority of guests here as its spacious lounges are ideal for informal eating and small gatherings.
70 en suite (bth/shr) No smoking in 33 bedrooms CTV in all bedrooms Night porter 150P Pool table Xmas International Cuisine V meals Coffee am Tea pm No smoking in restaurant Last d 10pm
ROOMS: (incl. bkfst) s fr £60; d fr £70 * **LB**
MEALS: Lunch £7.50-£12.50&alc Dinner £14.95&alc*
CONF: Thtr 400 Class 250 Board 40 Del from £79.50
CARDS:

CORFE CASTLE Dorset Map 03 SY98

★★★ 67% Mortons House
East St BH20 5EE (on A351 between Wareham/Swanage)
☎ 01929 480988 FAX 01929 480820
This attractive manor house is ideally placed for enjoying the beautiful countryside or visiting the beaches. The public areas are traditionally furnished and have a relaxed atmosphere. There is a comfortable lounge where a log fire burns in the winter months, and a pretty walled garden where guests may enjoy afternoon tea in the summer months. Bedrooms are attractively decorated and well equipped, some have views of the castle. The stylish restaurant offers an interesting selection of freshly cooked dishes and imaginative home made desserts.
14 en suite (bth/shr) 3 annexe en suite (bth/shr) (1 fmly) No smoking in 3 bedrooms CTV in all bedrooms 40P No coaches Jacuzzi/spa Xmas English & French Cuisine V meals Coffee am Tea pm No smoking in restaurant Last d 8.30pm
ROOMS: (incl. bkfst) s £60-£75; d £80-£96 * **LB**
OFF-PEAK: (incl. bkfst) s £60; d £60-£70
MEALS: Lunch £15.50 Dinner £20&alc
CONF: Thtr 45 Board 20 Del £100
CARDS:

CORNHILL-ON-TWEED Northumberland Map 12 NT83

★★★ 69% Tillmouth Park
TD12 4UU (on A698) ☎ 01890 882255 FAX 01890 882540
A late-Victorian country house is set in colourful mature grounds near

the border, a superb base from which to explore the historic Scottish borders and Northumberland. Comfortable public areas are dominated by the galleried lounge, while the recently refurbished bedrooms combine period style with modern amenities. A choice of eating places includes an informal bistro and a gracious dining room where the chef creates honest flavours using local produce. Fishing, golfing and shooting can all be arranged locally.

12 en suite (bth/shr) 2 annexe en suite (bth/shr) (1 fmly) CTV in all bedrooms 50P Croquet lawn Clay pigeon shooting Xmas English & French Cuisine V meals Coffee am Tea pm Last d 9.30pm

ROOMS: (incl. bkfst) s £80-£170; d £110-£145 * **LB**

MEALS: Lunch £11.50-£25&alc Dinner £25&alc

CONF: Thtr 50 Class 20 Board 20 Del £100

CARDS:

CORSE LAWN Hereford & Worcester Map 03 SO83

★★★ 68% ***Corse Lawn House***

GL19 4LZ (on B4211 5m SW of Tewkesbury)

☎ 01452 780479 & 780771 FAX 01452 780840

An elegant Queen Anne Grade II listed building set back from the village green provides character surroundings and a relaxed ambience. Most of its bedrooms are well proportioned and all successfully blend modern facilities with a range of antiques; thoughtful extras include fresh fruit and personalised items. Baba Hine's cooking is worthy of note - our inspector particularly enjoyed smooth hot crab sausage set off by fresh tomato sauce with chickpeas, bright fillet of hake and best end of lamb with lentil crust during a recent visit - and a bistro, Just Corse Lawn, offers an imaginative range of dishes in an atmosphere less formal than that of the restaurant; a comprehensive classical wine list is available in both.

19 en suite (bth/shr) CTV in all bedrooms STV 52P No coaches Outdoor swimming pool (heated) Tennis (hard) Croquet lawn English & French Cuisine V meals Coffee am Tea pm Last d 10pm

CARDS:

COVENTRY West Midlands Map 04 SP37

See also Brandon, Meriden & Nuneaton

★★★★ 59% **De Vere**

Cathedral Square CV1 5RP (follow signs for cathedral, turn right at first lights & bear left at next lights, hotel on the left) ☎ 01203 633733 FAX 01203 225299

This large modern hotel in the city centre lies next to the famous cathedral. Bedrooms are all a good size, and the views vary. Public areas are limited to the popular Daimlers Bar and Bentleys Restaurant, where guests can choose from a carvery or an imaginative a la carte menu. A useful facility is the reserved parking in and direct access from the adjacent car park.

190 en suite (bth/shr) (9 fmly) No smoking in 20 bedrooms CTV in all bedrooms Lift Night porter 130P Xmas English & French Cuisine V meals Coffee am Tea pm No smoking area in restaurant Last d 10pm

ROOMS: (incl. bkfst) s £50-£95; d £50-£105 * **LB**

OFF-PEAK: (incl. bkfst) s fr £40; d fr £50

MEALS: Sunday Lunch fr £8.95 Dinner fr £18*

CONF: Thtr 400 Class 250 Board 32 Del from £75

CARDS:

★★★ 72% **Brooklands Grange Hotel & Restaurant**

Holyhead Rd CV5 8HX (on A4114, off A45 at Allesley roundabout)

☎ 01203 601601 FAX 01203 601277

Closed 26-28 Dec & 1-2 Jan

Behind the Jacobean façade of Brooklands Grange there lies a thoroughly modern and comfortable business hotel, noted for the warmth and concern of its staff. The clean lines of its furniture are effectively set off by richly coloured wall coverings and elaborately swagged drapes. A carte and a regularly changing fixed-price menu offer good food, straightforward grills being served alongside fresh-flavoured crab cakes and spicy Thai-style chicken.

30 en suite (bth/shr) (1 fmly) No smoking in 4 bedrooms CTV in all bedrooms No dogs (ex guide dogs) Night porter 52P International Cuisine V meals Coffee am No smoking area in restaurant Last d 10pm

ROOMS: (incl. bkfst) s £80-£85; d £95-£100 *

MEALS: Lunch £12.50-£17.95&alc Dinner £19.55-£25.55alc*

CONF: Board 12

CARDS:

★★★ 67% **Courtyard by Marriott Coventry**

London Rd, Ryton on Dunsmore CV8 3DY (SE on A45) ☎ 01203 301585 FAX 01203 301610

The Coventry Knight is a modern hotel in a convenient location close to the airport. Bedrooms are spacious and have recently been upgraded with smart soft furnishings. Satellite TV and room service are appreciated by the corporate guests and the range of meeting rooms attracts the conference market.

49 en suite (bth/shr) (2 fmly) No smoking in 29 bedrooms CTV in all bedrooms STV No dogs (ex guide dogs) Night porter 150P Fishing Table tennis English & Continental Cuisine V meals Coffee am Tea pm No smoking area in restaurant

ROOMS: s £45-£75; d £45-£75 * **LB**

CONF: Thtr 300 Class 100 Board 24 Del from £95

CARDS:

★★★ 66% ***Hylands***

Warwick Rd CV3 6AU (on A444, close to railway station & opposite Memorial Park) ☎ 01203 501600 FAX 01203 501027

This friendly modern hotel stands close to the city centre and station overlooking an attractive park. Popular with business guests, it provides bright, well equipped bedrooms and good range of conference facilities. A good range of food is provided from carvery and set menus, with friendly service from a keen team. Extensive car parking on site.

54 en suite (bth/shr) (4 fmly) No smoking in 18 bedrooms CTV in all bedrooms STV Night porter 60P English & Continental Cuisine V meals Coffee am Tea pm Last d 9.45pm

CARDS:

★★★ 61% **Leofric**

Broadgate CV1 1LZ (opposite West Orchards Car Park) ☎ 01203 221371 FAX 01203 551352

This is a large city-centre hotel refurbished in the early nineties in a contemporary style making use of soft pastel shades to create a modern light feel. Public areas are split level, busy and open plan, the brasserie looks over the piano bar and lounge. Parking and access from West Orchards car park.

94 en suite (bth/shr) (5 fmly) No smoking in 20 bedrooms CTV in all bedrooms STV No dogs (ex guide dogs) Lift Night porter 650P

contd.

International Cuisine V meals Coffee am Tea pm No smoking area in restaurant Last d 9.45pm
ROOMS: s fr £67; d fr £75 * **LB**
OFF-PEAK: s fr £40
CARDS:

★★★61% **Novotel**

Wilsons Ln CV6 6HL (exit M6 junct 3, follow signs for B4113 towards Longford, Bedworth. Take 3rd exit on large roundabout) ☎ 01203 365000
FAX 01203 362422
The first-ever Novotel in the UK, this hotel is conveniently located by junction 3 of the M6, making it a handy stop for overnight travellers. Bedrooms have been completely upgraded recently, and there is a range of meeting rooms for small conferences. Guests can dine until midnight, either in the restaurant or their room. There is an outdoor swimming pool.
98 en suite (bth/shr) (98 fmly) No smoking in 26 bedrooms CTV in all bedrooms STV Lift Night porter Air conditioning 160P Outdoor swimming pool (heated) Petanque British & French Cuisine V meals Coffee am Tea pm No smoking area in restaurant Last d mdnt
ROOMS: s £49.50; d £49.50 * **LB**
OFF-PEAK: s £50; d £50
MEALS: Lunch £10.50-£15&alc Dinner £12.50-£17.95&alc*
CONF: Thtr 200 Class 100 Board 50 Del £80
CARDS:

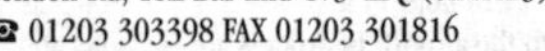

★★★60% **The Chace**

London Rd, Toll Bar End CV3 4EQ (on A423)
☎ 01203 303398 FAX 01203 301816
An attractive Victorian hotel, the Chace has a lounge bar panelled in dark oak, a balustrade staircase to the upper floors and original stained glass windows. There is a modern extension, but the style of décor and furnishings is similar. Bedrooms are well equipped but, like the public areas, are detailed for redecoration.
67 en suite (bth/shr) (20 fmly) No smoking in 20 bedrooms CTV in all bedrooms Night porter 120P Childrens play area Xmas V meals Coffee am Tea pm No smoking area in restaurant Last d 9.30pm
ROOMS: s £65-£75; d £60-£80 * **LB**
OFF-PEAK: (incl. bkfst) s £29-£45; d £58-£78
MEALS: Lunch £7.95-£12.95 Dinner £16-£18&alc*
CONF: Thtr 65 Class 40 Board 36 Del from £80
CARDS:

★★★60% **Coventry Hill**

Rye Hill, Allesley CV5 9PH (on A45)
☎ 01203 402151 FAX 01203 402235
This modern, conveniently positioned multi-storey hotel is a popular meeting place and offers a good range of conference and meeting rooms. The hotel is in the process of refurbishment with, to date, a percentage of rooms upgraded.
180 en suite (bth/shr) (19 fmly) No smoking in 84 bedrooms CTV in all bedrooms Lift Night porter 200P ch fac V meals Coffee am Tea pm No smoking area in restaurant Last d 10pm
ROOMS: s £65; d £75 * **LB**
OFF-PEAK: s £25-£55; d £45-£65
MEALS: Lunch £10.95-£14.95&alc Dinner fr £15.50&alc
CONF: Thtr 100 Class 60 Board 40 Del from £70
CARDS:

Campanile

4 Wigston Rd, Walsgrave CV2 2SD (exit 2 of M6, at 2nd roundabout turn right) ☎ 01203 622311
FAX 01203 602362
The bar and Bistro restaurant provide meals and refreshments. Bedrooms are well equipped and have en suite bathrooms. For more details about Campanile, consult the Contents page under Hotel Groups.

47 annexe en suite (bth/shr)

Campanile

Abbey Rd, Whitley CV3 4BJ (signposted from A46/A423 roundabout) ☎ 01203 639922
FAX 01203 306898

The bar and Bistro restaurant provide meals and refreshments. Bedrooms are well equipped and have en suite bathrooms. For more details about Campanile, consult the Contents page under Hotel Groups.
52 en suite (bth/shr)
ROOMS: d £36.50 *
CONF: Thtr 30 Class 35 Board 25

Forte Posthouse Coventry

Hinckley Rd, Walsgrave CV2 2HP (on A4600) ☎ 01203 613261 FAX 01203 621736
Suitable for both the business and leisure traveller, this bright hotel provides modern accommodation in well equipped bedrooms with en suite bathrooms. For more details about Forte Posthouse hotels, consult the Contents page for the section on Hotel Groups.
147 en suite (bth/shr)
ROOMS: d £69-£79 *
CONF: Thtr 450 Class 225 Board 100 Del from £99

Hilton National Coventry

Paradise Way, Walsgrave Triangle CV2 2ST (junct 2 on M6/M69 interchange) ☎ 01203 603000
FAX 01203 603011
This is a bright, modern hotel, with an informal restaurant, aimed at both the business and leisure guest. All bedrooms have en suite bathrooms and a range of modern facilities. For more information about Hilton National hotels, consult the Contents page under Hotel Groups.
172 en suite (bth/shr)
ROOMS: d £120 *
CONF: Thtr 600 Class 300 Board 20 Del from £100

Travel Inn
Rugby Rd, Binley Woods CV3 2TA (on A46 Eastern by-pass at junction with Rugby Rd)
☎ 01203 636585 FAX 01203 431178

Purpose-built accommodation, offering spacious, well equipped bedrooms, all with en suite bathrooms. Meals may be taken at the nearby family restaurant. For more information about Travel Inns, consult the Contents page under Hotel Groups.
50 en suite (bth/shr)
ROOMS: d £35.50 *

COWES See Wight, Isle of

CRANBROOK Kent Map 05 TQ73

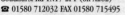

RED STAR HOTEL

★★ **Kennel Holt**
Goudhurst Rd TN17 2PT (on A262)
☎ 01580 712032 FAX 01580 715495
Many country hotels set out to be a home from home but few succeed as well as Kennel Holt, largely due to the efforts of charming proprietors Sally and Neil Chalmers. He is a talented cook in that well known British tradition of the enthusiastic amateur. She runs front of house with a keen eye for detail. The house is set in five acres of lovely gardens which come into their own in late spring and summer. Rooms are all individually furnished with tasteful decor. The public areas too have lots of charm, in particular the beautiful library with its wood panelling where a collection of Neil Chalmers' paintings is displayed.
10 en suite (bth/shr) CTV in all bedrooms No dogs 20P No coaches Croquet lawn Putting green Xmas European Cuisine V meals No smoking in restaurant Last d 9pm
ROOMS: (incl. bkfst) s fr £85; d fr £125 **LB**
MEALS: Lunch £20-£25 Dinner £20-£25*
CONF: Thtr 15 Class 15 Board 10 Del from £155
CARDS:

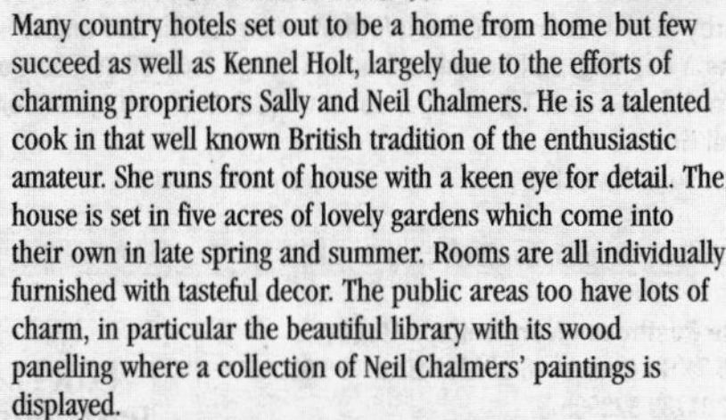

★★69% **Hartley Mount Country House**
Hartley Rd TN17 3QX (1m S on A229) ☎ 01580 712230
FAX 01580 715733
Home to Lionel and Lee Skilton, this fine Edwardian former manor house is located on the A229 two miles south of the junction with the A262. Well proportioned individually furnished bedrooms are equipped with every modern amenity and lots of thoughtful extras. There is a comfortable open-plan lounge and inner conservatory bar/breakfast room, and a candlelit and particularly well appointed dining room which features Lee Skilton's freshly prepared international à la carte cooking. Service is personally provided by the dedicated and attentive proprietors, whilst other facilities include spacious mature grounds and a croquet lawn.
6 en suite (bth/shr) (1 fmly) No smoking in all bedrooms CTV in all bedrooms No dogs (ex guide dogs) 32P No coaches Tennis (grass) Croquet lawn Pitch & putt V meals Coffee am Tea pm No smoking in restaurant Last d 9.30pm
ROOMS: (incl. bkfst) s fr £60; d £80-£100 **LB**
OFF-PEAK: (incl. bkfst) s fr £55; d £75-£95
MEALS: Lunch fr £13.95 High tea fr £4.50 Dinner fr £16.50&alc
CARDS:

CRANTOCK Cornwall & Isles of Scilly Map 02 SW76

★★67% **Crantock Bay**
West Pentire TR8 5SE (off A3075 at West Pentire Headland) ☎ 01637 830229 FAX 01637 831111

Closed Dec & Jan RS Nov & Feb
This long established family-run holiday hotel is beautifully situated on the West Pentire headland overlooking the Gannel estuary with four acres of grounds leading directly onto the beach. There are spacious and comfortable lounges for guests, as well as the well equipped leisure facilities.
34 en suite (bth/shr) (4 fmly) CTV in all bedrooms 35P No coaches Indoor swimming pool (heated) Tennis (hard) Sauna Gym Pool table Croquet lawn Putting green Jacuzzi/spa Xmas V meals Coffee am Tea pm No smoking area in restaurant Last d 8.30pm
ROOMS: (incl. bkfst & dinner) s £43-£59 **LB**
MEALS: Sunday Lunch £8.95 Dinner £14.95*
CARDS:

CRATHORNE North Yorkshire Map 08 NZ40

★★★★ 76% **Crathorne Hall**

TS15 0AR (on A67, just off A19) ☎ 01642 700398
FAX 01642 700814

Peacefully situated in 15 acres of grounds, Crathorne Hall was the last stately home to be built in the Edwardian era. It retains all its charm, with original architectural features throughout the public rooms, which include a richly decorated drawing room with a log fire and a restaurant with lovely views. Chef Phillip Pomfrey continues to offer an interesting menu which combines contemporary dishes such as Caesar salad and carpaccio with classics such as peppered beef fillet and roast saddle of venison with juniper berries. Bedrooms are all tastefully furnished and a few even have bathrooms with cast iron tubs and original tiling.

37 en suite (bth/shr) (4 fmly) No smoking in 15 bedrooms CTV in all bedrooms STV Night porter 120P Fishing Croquet lawn Jogging track, Clay pigeon shooting Xmas English & French Cuisine V meals Coffee am Tea pm Last d 10pm

ROOMS: (incl. bkfst) s £104-£140; d £140-£180 * **LB**
MEALS: Lunch fr £14&alc Dinner fr £22.75&alc*
CONF: Thtr 160 Class 100 Board 50 Del from £140
CARDS:

CRAWLEY See Gatwick Airport

CREDITON Devon Map 03 SS80

★★★ 62% **Coombe House Country Hotel**

Coleford (turn off A377 Exeter/Barnstaple road 1m N of Crediton signposted Coleford hotel 1m on left) ☎ 01363 84487
FAX 01363 84722

A Georgian manor house, situated within a mile of the stone column at Copplestone, which is the traditionally accepted as the centre of the county. A relaxing atmosphere is created by David and Patricia Jones who took over the hotel during 1995. The bedrooms are the subject of a programme of upgrading, to bring them to the expected standard. The original kitchens, with their magnificent arched brick ceiling, are now the Cellar Bar. A short fixed priced menu is offered in the hotel's restaurant.

15 en suite (bth/shr) (8 fmly) CTV in all bedrooms 70P Outdoor swimming pool (heated) Tennis (hard) Pool table Croquet lawn Xmas English, French & Italian Cuisine V meals Coffee am Tea pm No smoking in restaurant Last d 9.30pm

ROOMS: (incl. bkfst) s £39.50-£49.50; d £64.50-£79.50 * **LB**
MEALS: Lunch fr £12.50 Dinner £17.50*
CONF: Thtr 80 Class 25 Board 25 Del from £70
CARDS:

CREWE Cheshire Map 07 SJ75

★★★ 64% **Hunters Lodge**

Sydney Rd, Sydney CW1 5LU (1m from Crewe station, off A534)
☎ 01270 583440 & 588216 FAX 01270 500553

Bedrooms in this modern hotel are all contained in red brick annexe buildings and are well appointed and comfortable. There is a choice of bars and the Tudor-style restaurant offers a good selection of food.

42 en suite (bth/shr) (1 fmly) No smoking in 4 bedrooms CTV in all bedrooms STV No dogs (ex guide dogs) Night porter 240P Fishing Sauna Solarium Gym Pool table Jacuzzi/spa Games room ch fac Xmas International Cuisine V meals Coffee am No smoking area in restaurant Last d 9.30pm

ROOMS: (incl. bkfst) s £25-£50; d £42-£68 * **LB**
OFF-PEAK: (incl. bkfst) s fr £25; d fr £42
MEALS: Lunch £8.35 Dinner £13.50&alc*
CONF: Thtr 160 Class 100 Board 80 Del from £70
CARDS:

★★ 71% **White Lion**

Weston CW2 5NA (2m S A5020) ☎ 01270 587011 FAX 01270 500303
Closed Xmas & New Year

Convenient for both the M6 and Crewe Station, this extended Tudor farmhouse is located in the centre of the village of Weston. The hotel is maintained to a high standard and boasts its own lawns, beer garden and bowling green. Many of the modern bedrooms are spacious, and all offer good facilities, especially for the business traveller. A wide choice of food is available in the oak-beamed lounge bar and restaurant.

16 en suite (bth/shr) (2 fmly) No smoking in 2 bedrooms CTV in all bedrooms STV Night porter 100P No coaches Crown Green bowling English & French Cuisine V meals Coffee am Tea pm No smoking in restaurant Last d 9.30pm
(incl. bkfst)
MEALS: Dinner £16.95*
CARDS:

Travel Inn

Coppenhall Ln, Woolstanwood CW2 8SD
☎ 01270 251126 FAX 01270 256316

Purpose-built accommodation, offering spacious, well equipped bedrooms, all with en suite bathrooms. Meals may be taken at the nearby family restaurant. For more information about Travel Inns, consult the Contents page under Hotel Groups.

40 en suite (bth/shr)
ROOMS: (incl. bkfst) d £35.50 *

Travelodge

Alsager Rd, Barthomley CW2 5PT (5m E,at junc 16 M6/A500) ☎ 01270 883157 FAX 01270 883157

This modern building offers accommodation in smart, spacious and well equipped bedrooms, suitable for family use, and all with en suite bathrooms. Meals may be taken at the nearby family restaurant. For information on room rates and to make a booking, call Roomline free of charge on 0800 850950. For more details about Travelodge, consult the Contents page under Hotel Groups.

42 en suite (bth/shr)

CRICK Northamptonshire Map 04 SP57

Forte Posthouse Northampton/Rugby

NN6 7XR (at junct 18 of M1) ☎ 01788 822101
FAX 01788 823955

Suitable for both the business and leisure traveller, this bright hotel provides modern accommodation in well equipped bedrooms with en suite bathrooms. For more details about Forte Posthouse hotels, consult the Contents page for the section on Hotel Groups.

88 en suite (bth/shr)
ROOMS: d £49-£69 *
CONF: Thtr 185 Class 85 Board 60 Del from £89

CROMER Norfolk Map 09 TG24

★★ 69% **Red Lion**

Brook St NR27 9HD (from town centre take first left after church)
☎ 01263 514964 FAX 01263 512834
Closed 25 Dec

This successful Victorian hotel is tucked away in the town centre, yet within sight and sound of the sea. Public areas are popular with the local community for both food and drink, with informal dining available in the characterful Edwardian bar and adjoining flintstone-clad lounge; alternatively there is the option of formal dining, with

daily and carte menus in the pleasant Red Lion restaurant. Guests have the use of a delightful private lounge which is situated on the first floor; a snooker room, sauna and solarium are also available. Bedrooms are all individually decorated and attractive, with good use made of cheerful co-ordinated soft furnishings; each room has a good range of facilities and thoughtful extras.

12 en suite (bth/shr) (1 fmly) CTV in all bedrooms No dogs 12P No coaches Snooker Sauna Solarium Gym Pool table Discount for local leisure centre English & French Cuisine V meals Coffee am Tea pm Last d 9.30pm

ROOMS: (incl. bkfst) s fr £36; d fr £72 *
OFF-PEAK: (incl. bkfst) s fr £31; d fr £62
MEALS: Sunday Lunch fr £8.95 Dinner fr £15.95&alc*
CONF: Thtr 60 Class 50 Board 40
CARDS:

CROOKLANDS Cumbria Map 07 SD58

★★★ 65% Crooklands

LA7 7NW (on A65, 1.5m from junct 36 of M6)
☎ 015395 67432 FAX 015395 67525
Closed 24-26 Dec
(Rosette awarded for dinner only)

Located just a few minutes from the M6, this hotel provides the ideal stop-over for business and leisure travellers. Originally a farmhouse, it has been considerably extended, but much of its character remains. There are several eating options and the slate-floored Junkers Bar displays perhaps the largest collection of authentic bric-a-brac ever seen in an hotel. This theme extends upstairs to The Hayloft Restaurant where one dines amidst beams and farming memorabilia. The menu is brasserie-style and priced accordingly. Bedrooms are contained in purpose-built wings.

30 en suite (bth/shr) No smoking in 2 bedrooms CTV in all bedrooms No dogs (ex guide dogs) 150P Pool table Xmas International Cuisine V meals Coffee am No smoking area in restaurant

ROOMS: s £49.50-£55; d £49.50-£55 * **LB**
MEALS: Bar Lunch £10-£20alc
CONF: Thtr 100 Class 60 Board 50
CARDS:

CROSBY-ON-EDEN Cumbria Map 12 NY45

See also Carlisle

★★★ 73% Crosby Lodge Country House

High Crosby CA6 4QZ (leave M6 at junc 44, 3.5m from motorway off A689) ☎ 01228 573618

FAX 01228 573428
Closed 24 Dec-20 Jan RS Sun evening

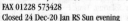

This charming mansion lies in the village of High Crosby - look out for signs leading off the A689 four miles east of Carlisle and the M6. Adorned with antiques and period furnishings it offers a quiet and relaxing atmosphere in delightful surroundings. The Sedgwick family and staff provide a high level of hospitality combined with quiet and efficient service. Freshly-made food and delicious home baking are features and the groaning dessert trolley at dinner shouldn't be ignored. The inviting bedrooms are all individual, and provide thoughtful little touches; two are in a converted courtyard building looking out onto the walled garden.

9 en suite (bth/shr) 2 annexe en suite (bth/shr) (3 fmly) CTV in all bedrooms 40P No coaches English & French Cuisine V meals Coffee am No smoking in restaurant Last d 9pm

ROOMS: (incl. bkfst) s £68-£72; d £95-£115 **LB**
OFF-PEAK: (incl. bkfst) s fr £6
MEALS: Lunch £15.50-£19.50&alc Dinner £27.50-£29.50&alc
CONF: Thtr 25 Board 12
CARDS:

CROSTHWAITE Cumbria Map 07 SD49

★★★ 61% Damson Dene

LA8 8JE (4m S A5074) ☎ 015395 68676 FAX 015395 68227

This holiday hotel lies in attractive landscaped gardens in the Lyth Valley, just west of the village on the A5074 Levens to Bowness road. Run by Methodist Holiday Hotels, the spirit of Christian fellowship is offered by way of short services of devotion in the hotel's chapel, but attendance is entirely at the discretion of guests, and the atmosphere is as friendly and outgoing as in any hotel, indeed in many cases, more so. Guests can use the facilities of the leisure complex; organised walks and tours can also be arranged. Some bedrooms are compact, but to compensate there is a foyer lounge with a log fire on cooler days, as well as a resident and diners' bar and one can also relax in the gardens, weather permitting. The dinner menu extends to five courses; at our last visit the choice was very limited, but it is hoped that this will improve.

37 en suite (bth/shr) (3 fmly) CTV in all bedrooms No dogs (ex guide dogs) 40P Indoor swimming pool (heated) Squash Snooker Sauna Solarium Gym Pool table Putting green Jacuzzi/spa table tennis Xmas English & French Cuisine V meals Coffee am Tea pm No smoking in restaurant Last d 9pm

ROOMS: (incl. bkfst) s £25-£42; d £50-£84 **LB**
OFF-PEAK: (incl. bkfst) s £23-£36; d £46-£72
MEALS: Lunch £5-£9.95 Dinner fr £15&alc*
CONF: Thtr 140 Class 60 Board 40 Del from £49
CARDS:

CROWTHORNE Berkshire Map 04 SU86

★★★ 63% Waterloo

Duke's Ride RG45 7NW ☎ 01344 777711
FAX 01344 778913

This extended Victorian red-brick building, within easy reach of Bracknell, has a friendly and cosy atmosphere. Public rooms centre on the popular bar where live fires add character and warmth to winter evenings. Bedrooms are modern, well equipped, and decorated with co-ordinating fabrics.

58 en suite (bth/shr) No smoking in 22 bedrooms CTV in all bedrooms Night porter 120P V meals Coffee am Tea pm No smoking in restaurant Last d 9.30pm

ROOMS: s £75; d £95-£110 * **LB**
OFF-PEAK: s £47; d £47-£65
MEALS: Sunday Lunch £10.95 Dinner £15-£17&alc*
CONF: Del £100
CARDS:

CROYDE Devon Map 02 SS43

Courtesy & Care Award

★★ 76% Croyde Bay House

Moor Ln, Croyde Bay EX33 1PA
☎ 01271 890270
Closed Dec-Feb

This delightful family-run hotel enjoys stunning sea views from its elevated position on the rocks overlooking Croyde Bay. The bedrooms, which share the magnificent views, have been tastefully decorated with pretty co-ordinating fabrics and soft lighting. Public areas include a comfortable panelled sitting room, a cosy bar, and a sun lounge with access to the garden. Jennifer and Alex Penny and their team of staff welcome guests,

contd.

C

and their natural warmth and friendliness plays an important part in the relaxed atmosphere which makes the hotel so special. A selection of interesting dishes make up the short daily-changing menu which emphasises fresh local produce and traditional home-cooking. Owners and staff here have won the AA Courtesy and Care Award for 1996/7.

7 en suite (bth/shr) (2 fmly) CTV in all bedrooms 8P No coaches English & French Cuisine Coffee am Tea pm No smoking in restaurant Last d 8pm
ROOMS: (incl. bkfst & dinner) s £39-£53; d £78-£106 **LB**
MEALS: Dinner £17.90*
CARDS:

★★71% **Kittiwell House**
St Mary's Rd EX33 1PG (0.5m from village in direction of Georgeham)
☎ 01271 890247 FAX 01271 890469
Closed mid Jan-mid Feb
A charming, thatched, cottage-style hotel fronted by a cobbled car park, Kittiwell House is situated behind the village. Individually designed bedrooms offer quaint and cosy accommodation in keeping with the property. Attractively beamed public areas feature real fires and a wealth of well chosen bric-à-brac.
12 en suite (bth/shr) (2 fmly) No smoking in 4 bedrooms CTV in all bedrooms 21P No coaches Xmas English & French Cuisine V meals Coffee am Tea pm No smoking in restaurant Last d 9pm
ROOMS: (incl. bkfst & dinner) s £54-£59; d £100-£108 **LB**
OFF-PEAK: (incl. bkfst & dinner) s £49-£54; d £96-£100
MEALS: Sunday Lunch £7.80-£9.25 Dinner fr £17.20&alc
CARDS:

CROYDON Greater London Map 04 TQ36

★★★★75% **Coulsdon Manor**
Coulsdon Court Rd, Coulsdon CR5 2LL
☎ 0181 668 0414 FAX 0181 668 3118
Best Western
Skilfully extended to provide a range of modern and well equipped bedrooms, this fine Victorian manor house is set within 140 acres of parkland with a professional 18 hole golf course. Attentive service and hospitality are provided by a dedicated staff who achieve high standards of customer care. Public rooms include a comfortable lounge bar with separate dining area, a formal restaurant and cocktail bar. Chef Michael Neal provides interesting a la carte and daily set priced menus (2 or 3 courses) that demonstrate a serious and dedicated approach to enjoyable cooking. There is a good range of conference and function facilities and excellent leisure facilities, which includes access to a resident golf professional, pro shop and fitness assessment.
35 en suite (bth/shr) No smoking in 2 bedrooms CTV in all bedrooms STV No dogs (ex guide dogs) Lift Night porter 200P Golf 18 Tennis (hard) Squash Sauna Solarium Gym Putting green ch fac Xmas V meals Coffee am Tea pm No smoking in restaurant Last d 9.30pm
ROOMS: (incl. bkfst) s £65-£100; d £75-£120 **LB**
MEALS: Lunch £14.95-£20&alc Dinner £19.95-£22&alc*
CONF: Thtr 180 Class 90 Board 70 Del from £135.13
CARDS:

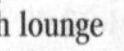

★★★★68% **Croydon Park**
7 Altyre Rd CR9 5AA (near East Croydon Station)
☎ 0181 680 9200 FAX 0181 760 0426
Best Western
Situated beside the Law Courts, this smart modern town-centre hotel offers very comfortable bedrooms all equipped to meet the demands of the corporate and leisure guest. Although lounge seating can be limited to the Gallery foyer or Whistler's bar with its large-screen satellite TV facility, Oscar's Restaurant is particularly well appointed and spacious, and offers a marvellous value for money lunch and dinner buffet. Other facilities include a large banqueting suite.
212 en suite (bth/shr) (40 fmly) No smoking in 123 bedrooms CTV in all bedrooms STV Lift Night porter Air conditioning 118P Indoor swimming pool (heated) Squash Sauna Solarium Gym Jacuzzi/spa International Cuisine V meals Coffee am Tea pm No smoking area in restaurant Last d 10.30pm
ROOMS: (incl. bkfst) d fr £95 * **LB**
OFF-PEAK: (incl. bkfst) s fr £60; d fr £80
MEALS: Lunch £14.95-£15.95&alc Dinner £15.95&alc*
CONF: Thtr 300 Class 100 Board 100 Del from £130
CARDS:

★★★★65% **Selsdon Park**
Addington Rd, Sanderstead CR2 8YA (3m SE off A2022)
☎ 0181 657 8811 FAX 0181 651 6171
Possibly one of the largest privately owned hotels in the country, Selsdon Park dates from Jacobean times and stands in over 200 acres of well kept grounds and gardens only three miles south of Croydon. It has been extended over the years to incorporate a professional 18-hole golf course and excellent leisure and conference facilities with no less than 25 meeting and syndicate rooms. Bedrooms range through standard to superior rooms overlooking the golf course and grounds. Other rooms are designated 'executive' and 'lady' and the first floor is reserved for non-smokers. There is a choice of eating options, the Phoenix Grill providing an alternative to the more formal and spacious restaurant. Chef Jean-Marie Zimmermann has introduced a new range of dishes and the cooking continues to grow in stature with some well constructed and enjoyable sauces. There are regular dinner dances on Friday and Saturday nights, along with live piano entertainment most evenings, tea dances and live jazz on the first Sunday of every month.
170 en suite (bth/shr) (7 fmly) No smoking in 120 bedrooms CTV in all bedrooms STV Lift Night porter 365P Indoor swimming pool (heated) Outdoor swimming pool (heated) Golf 18 Tennis (hard & grass) Squash Snooker Sauna Solarium Gym Pool table Croquet lawn Putting green Jacuzzi/spa Boules Jogging track Wkly live entertainment Xmas International Cuisine V meals Coffee am Tea pm No smoking area in restaurant Last d 9.30pm
ROOMS: s £88.12-£99.87; d £129.24-£188 * **LB**
OFF-PEAK: (incl. bkfst & dinner) s £79-£89; d £158-£178
MEALS: Lunch fr £18.50alc Dinner fr £25&alc*
CONF: Thtr 150 Class 80 Board 30 Del from £111.62
CARDS:

★★67% ***Windsor Castle Hotel***
415 Brighton Rd CR2 6EJ ☎ 0181 680 4559
FAX 0181 680 5121

This friendly hotel provides attractive, contemporary accommodation. It is conveniently located off the Brighton Road to the south of the centre. There is a popular locals' bar and a peaceful themed restaurant with its own bar.

29 en suite (bth/shr) (1 fmly) No smoking in 14 bedrooms CTV in all bedrooms STV No dogs (ex guide dogs) Night porter 90P Pool table V meals Coffee am Tea pm
CARDS:

★★65% Markington
9 Haling Park Rd CR2 6NG (off A235) ☎ 0181 681 6494
FAX 0181 688 6530
Personally run by the proprietors Mr and Mrs Mickelburgh for over 25 years, this hotel has a relaxed and friendly atmosphere and offers good standards of personal service from an established team of loyal and competent staff. There is a range of particularly well equipped and modern furnished bedrooms and public areas comprise a smart bar-lounge and an attractive dining room. Meals at weekends are provided by arrangement.
22 en suite (bth/shr) (3 fmly) No smoking in 4 bedrooms CTV in all bedrooms STV No dogs (ex guide dogs) 17P V meals Coffee am Tea pm No smoking in restaurant Last d 8.30pm
ROOMS: (incl. bkfst) s £49.50; d £55 **LB**
OFF-PEAK: (incl. bkfst) s £35; d £45
MEALS: Dinner £6.50-£17alc*
CONF: Thtr 30 Class 20 Board 25
CARDS:

★★64% Central
3-5 South Park Hill Rd, South Croydon CR2 7DY
☎ 0181 688 5644 & 0181 688 0840 FAX 0181 760 0861
A well established hotel located in a residential area south of the town centre offers thoughtfully designed bedrooms decorated in contemporary style and equipped with modern amenities. Public areas include a reception area bar, a pleasant lounge and a dining room where breakfast and lunch are served; bar snacks are also available at lunchtime. Friendly staff provide high standards of service, and self-catering apartments are available.
19 en suite (bth/shr) (2 fmly) CTV in all bedrooms No dogs (ex guide dogs) Night porter 15P V meals Coffee am Tea pm
CARDS:

★★60% Briarley

8 Outram Rd CR0 6XE (off A232, 0.5m W of East Croydon station) ☎ 0181 654 1000
FAX 0181 656 6084
Located in a quiet residential road less than a mile from the centre of Croydon, this small family-run hotel has been personally run by its proprietor for over 27 years. Mrs Shirley Mills and her loyal staff provide a friendly and relaxed atmosphere. There is a good range of bedrooms, including ground floor, non-smoking, brass four-poster, annexe and rooms suitable for families. Advertised room service is available until 11pm and facilities for private functions and conferences can also be provided. Meals at weekends are restricted due to a lack of demand, and are served in the bar-lounge.
18 en suite (bth/shr) 20 annexe en suite (bth) (4 fmly) CTV in all bedrooms 30P ch fac Mainly grills V meals No smoking in restaurant Last d 9.50pm
ROOMS: (incl. bkfst) s £55; d £65 **LB**
OFF-PEAK: (incl. bkfst) s £45; d £35
MEALS: Bar Lunch £3-£6alc Dinner £6.50-£18.50&alc
CONF: Thtr 20 Class 20 Board 20
CARDS:

★★59% *Norfolk House*
587 London Rd, Thornton Heath CR7 6AY ☎ 0181 689 8989
FAX 0181 689 0335
This popular hotel is well positioned for easy access to central Croydon, and has ample car parking. There are good facilities for meetings and functions with the Mural Room accommodating up to 100 persons. Bedrooms are furnished in the modern style, and there is an open-plan bar lounge, a reception area and a restaurant.
78 en suite (bth/shr) (3 fmly) CTV in all bedrooms No dogs (ex guide dogs) Night porter 154P English & French Cuisine V meals Coffee am Tea pm Last d 10pm
CARDS:

Forte Posthouse Croydon
Purley Way CR9 4LT (off A23) ☎ 0181 688 5185
FAX 0181 681 6438
Suitable for both the business and leisure traveller, this bright hotel provides modern accommodation in well equipped bedrooms with en suite bathrooms. For more details about Forte Posthouse hotels, consult the Contents page for the section on Hotel Groups.
83 en suite (bth/shr)
ROOMS: d fr £79 *
CONF: Thtr 100 Class 50 Board 40 Del from £109

Hilton National Croydon
Waddon Way, Purley Way CR9 4HH (on southbound carriageway of A23 at junc of Purley Way & Waddon Way diagonally opposite Ford dealer) ☎ 0181 680 3000 FAX 0181 681 6171
This is a bright, modern hotel, with an informal restaurant, aimed at both the business and leisure guest. All bedrooms have en suite bathrooms and a range of modern facilities. For more information about Hilton National hotels, consult the Contents page under Hotel Groups.
168 en suite (bth/shr)
ROOMS: s £102-£112; d £102-£112 *
CONF: Thtr 400 Class 240 Board 25

Travel Inn
104 Coombe Rd CR0 5RB (on A212)
☎ 0181 686 2030 FAX 0181 686 6435
Purpose-built accommodation, offering spacious, well equipped bedrooms, all with en suite bathrooms. Meals may be taken at the nearby family restaurant. For more information about Travel Inns, consult the Contents page under Hotel Groups.
39 en suite (bth/shr)
ROOMS: d £35.50 *

CUCKFIELD West Sussex Map 04 TQ32

★★★ 76% Ockenden Manor

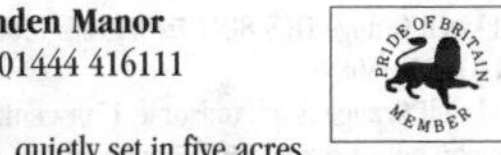

Ockenden Ln RH17 5LD ☎ 01444 416111
FAX 01444 415549
A 16th-century manor house, quietly set in five acres of mature grounds, this delightful hotel offers individually designed bedrooms in both the original building and a new wing. Most of the rooms are furnished with antiques and all are equipped to a high standard and provided with thoughtful extras. Public rooms include a panelled bar and an elegant sitting room with a log fire. The restaurant has some fine decorative features, historic stained glass and an embossed ceiling. Chef Geoff Welsh provides a consistent standard of

contd.

cooking on a fixed-price menu and carte of freshly prepared, modern English dishes. Much of the produce is local, particularly the seafood from Newhaven and game from the Balcombe estate. Full room service is available, and the friendly staff are professionally supervised by the manager Kerry Turner. Facilities for meetings, small conferences and functions can be arranged.
22 en suite (bth) CTV in all bedrooms No dogs 46P No coaches Croquet lawn Xmas V meals Coffee am Tea pm No smoking in restaurant Last d 9.30pm
ROOMS: (incl. cont bkfst) s £88-£115; d £100-£215 * LB
MEALS: Lunch £15.50-£20&alc High tea £5-£10 Dinner £29.50-£32.50&alc*
CONF: Thtr 50 Class 25 Board 25 Del from £152.75
CARDS:

CULLERCOATS Tyne & Wear Map 12 NZ37

★★63% **Bay**
Front St NE30 4QB ☎ 0191 252 3150 FAX 0191 251 4542
This commercial hotel sits looking out over the bay, a view enjoyed by most of the bedrooms, as well as the dining room and residents lounge. A good choice of sensibly priced dinner menus is available in addition to bar meals.
17 rms (11 bth/shr) (2 fmly) CTV in all bedrooms 9P Pool table Sailing Sea fishing Xmas English & French Cuisine V meals Coffee am Tea pm Last d 9pm
ROOMS: (incl. bkfst) s £20-£32; d £30-£50 *
OFF-PEAK: (incl. bkfst) s £25; d £40
MEALS: Bar Lunch £2.95-£4.50 Dinner £6-£9.95&alc
CONF: Thtr 80 Board 20
CARDS:

DARESBURY Cheshire Map 07 SJ58

★★★★65% **Lord Daresbury**

Chester Rd WA4 4BB (100yds from junc 11 of M56, on A56) ☎ 01925 267331 FAX 01925 265615
A large modern hotel in open countryside near J11 of the M56, popular with corporate and touring guests. Good modern bedrooms are in a number of wings. The public areas include a popular carvery, an open plan bar-lounge and a fine dining restaurant.
140 en suite (bth/shr) (6 fmly) No smoking in 93 bedrooms CTV in all bedrooms STV Lift Night porter 400P Indoor swimming pool (heated) Squash Snooker Sauna Solarium Gym Jacuzzi/spa Steam room Beautician Hairdresser Xmas English & French Cuisine V meals Coffee am Tea pm No smoking area in restaurant
ROOMS: (incl. bkfst) s £99-£119; d £109-£129 * LB
OFF-PEAK: (incl. bkfst) s £69-£89; d £79-£119
CONF: Thtr 400 Class 180 Board 100 Del from £105
CARDS:

DARLINGTON Co Durham Map 08 NZ21
See also Tees-Side Airport

★★★★58% ***Blackwell Grange***
Blackwell Grange DL3 8QH ☎ 01325 380888 FAX 01325 380899
Blackwell Grange is a handsome 17th-century mansion house situated in 15 acres of wooded parkland. Meeting facilities and a leisure centre make it a popular choice for conferences but equally it is well situated for exploring the Yorkshire dales and moors. An extensive refurbishment programme, currently under way, will restore this hotel to its former glory.

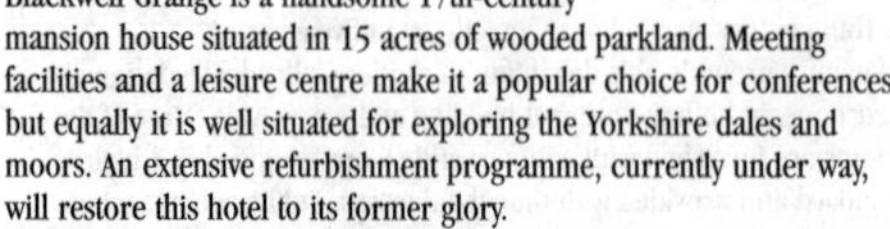

99 en suite (bth/shr) (11 fmly) No smoking in 14 bedrooms CTV in all bedrooms Lift Night porter Air conditioning 253P Indoor swimming pool (heated) Golf 18 Tennis (hard) Sauna Solarium Gym Boules Croquet International Cuisine V meals Coffee am Tea pm Last d 9.45pm
CARDS:

★★★69% **Hall Garth Golf & Country Club**
Coatham Mundeville DL1 3LU (close to A1(M) off A167) ☎ 01325 300400 FAX 01325 310083
This much extended, but delightful 16th century house which is situated in 65 acres, but just a few minutes from Junction 59 of the A1/M, offers smart well equipped accommodation. The bedrooms are divided between the main house and the original stables include a number of suites and rooms with four poster beds. Guests have the use of the extensive leisure facilities, including the excellent 9 hole golf course. The skills of head chef Kevin Hacking can be enjoyed in Hugo's restaurant where the highlight of a recent meal was brochette of deliciously fresh and accurately cooked seafood. Home cooked food is also served in Stables Country Pub.
38 en suite (bth/shr) 4 annexe en suite (bth/shr) (5 fmly) No smoking in 12 bedrooms CTV in all bedrooms STV No dogs (ex guide dogs) Night porter 150P Indoor swimming pool (heated) Golf 9 Tennis (grass) Sauna Solarium Gym Jacuzzi/spa Steam room ch fac English & French Cuisine V meals Coffee am Tea pm Last d 9.45pm
ROOMS: s £70; d £75 LB
OFF-PEAK: s fr £40; d fr £60
MEALS: Lunch £9.95-£12.95&alc Dinner £15.95-£19.95&alc*
CONF: Thtr 300 Class 120 Board 80 Del from £85
CARDS:

★★★68% **Headlam Hall**
Headlam, Gainford DL2 3HA (2m N off A67)
☎ 01325 730238 FAX 01325 730790
Closed 24-25 Dec
This Jacobean house which has immense character stands in extensive, well maintained gardens on the outskirts of the village. Bedrooms are divided between the main house and more recently built annexe, but all are comfortably furnished and well equipped. The older rooms have more character and include a splendid suite and rooms with four-poster beds. Guests can relax in the drawing room, hall or small cosy bar or for the more energetic there is a small, well equipped leisure centre. New head chef Mark Sayers is responsible for producing a short choice of simple, tasty and carefully prepared dishes.
17 en suite (bth/shr) 9 annexe en suite (bth/shr) (3 fmly) CTV in all bedrooms No dogs (ex guide dogs) Night porter 60P Indoor swimming pool (heated) Tennis (hard) Fishing Sauna Croquet lawn Clay pigeon shooting English & French Cuisine V meals Last d 9.30pm
ROOMS: (incl. bkfst) s £55-£65; d £70-£80 * LB
MEALS: Lunch £11.50 Dinner £19-£25alc*
CONF: Thtr 200 Class 40 Board 30 Del from £79
CARDS:

★★★68% **Swallow King's Head**

Priestgate DL1 1NW ☎ 01325 380222 FAX 01325 382006
There have been steady improvements at this town-centre hotel situated next to the Cornmill Shopping Centre. It now offers a sound standard of accommodation, the best bedrooms being well equipped and comfortably furnished in a contemporary style with smart modern bathrooms. Public areas include the popular Priestgate foyer lounge, open throughout the day for light snacks, and the traditional second-floor restaurant where an extensive choice of dishes is served. The hotel also has the advantage of a good secure car park.
85 en suite (bth/shr) (3 fmly) No smoking in 51 bedrooms CTV in all bedrooms STV Lift Night porter 24P Use of Dolphin Leisure Centre Xmas English, French & Italian Cuisine V meals Coffee am Tea pm Last d 9.30pm

ROOMS: (incl. bkfst) s fr £83; d fr £99 * LB
OFF-PEAK: (incl. bkfst) s fr £69; d fr £85
MEALS: Lunch £9.25-£12 Dinner £17.95-£18.50*
CONF: Thtr 250 Class 120 Board 40 Del from £90
CARDS:

★★★64% **White Horse**
Harrowgate Hill DL1 3AD (on A167 between A1(M) and town centre)
☎ 01325 382121 FAX 01325 355953
Standing on the Durham road, this large public house has a modern and well equipped bedroom extension and has been recently refurbished throughout. A good range of food is available either in the bar or the first floor restaurant, whilst service is friendly and helpful.
40 en suite (bth/shr) (3 fmly) No smoking in 20 bedrooms CTV in all bedrooms Lift Night porter 150P Pool table Mainly grills V meals Coffee am Last d 9.45pm
ROOMS: (incl. bkfst) s £44-£54.50; d £56-£66.50 * LB
MEALS: Sunday Lunch £3.95-£6.95alc Dinner fr £10.50&alc*
CONF: Thtr 70 Class 25 Board 30 Del £80
CARDS:

DARTFORD Kent Map 05 TQ57

★★★★69% **Rowhill Grange Country House Hotel**
DA2 7QH ☎ 01322 615136 FAX 01322 615137
This magnificent country house hotel nestles in 9 acres of woodland and mature gardens with its own lake - home to a pair of black swans. The bedrooms are all individually decorated to a high standard and have elegant bathrooms. Guests may eat in the Garden restaurant with its imaginative a la carte menu, or in the less formal Topiary Brasserie. All guests have membership to the hotel's new Utopia health and leisure spa, where they may enjoy the extensive facilities; the exercise pool, the therapeutic pool with its underwater massage beds and Japanese showers, the gym, sauna, steam room and hair & beauty salon.
18 en suite (bth/shr) No smoking in all bedrooms CTV in all bedrooms STV No dogs (ex guide dogs) Lift Night porter 100P No coaches Outdoor swimming pool Sauna Solarium Gym Croquet lawn Jacuzzi/spa Beauty treatment Hair salon Xmas V meals Coffee am Tea pm No smoking in restaurant Last d 9pm
ROOMS: s £79-£129; d £99-£149 * LB
MEALS: Lunch £16.95&alc Dinner £16.95-£24.95&alc*
CONF: Thtr 100 Class 70 Board 30 Del from £135
CARDS:

Campanile
Clipper Boulevard West, Edisons Park, Crossways
DA2 6QJ v 01322 278925 FAX 01322 278948
The bar and Bistro restaurant provide meals and refreshments. Bedrooms are well equipped and have en suite bathrooms. For more details about Campanile, consult the Contents page under Hotel Groups.
31 en suite (bth/shr)
ROOMS: d fr £36.50 *
CONF: Thtr 50 Class 40 Board 35 Del £57

DARTMOUTH Devon Map 03 SX85

★★★69% ***Royal Castle***
11 The Quay TQ6 9PS ☎ 01803 833033 FAX 01803 835445
A 17th-century coaching inn on the quayside features two popular bars which are full of charm and character. Individually styled bedrooms are approached from galleried landings around a covered courtyard; all are well equipped and some feature attractive period furnishings. Rooms with river views are always much in demand. The Adam Room Restaurant, which overlooks the bustling harbour from its first-floor location, offers fixed-price menus which make imaginative use of fresh local produce.
25 en suite (bth/shr) (4 fmly) CTV in all bedrooms STV Night porter 6P V meals Coffee am Tea pm Last d 9.45pm
CARDS:

★★★68% **Dart Marina**
Sandquay TQ6 9PH ☎ 01803 832580
FAX 01803 835040
FORTE Heritage
In an unrivalled position by the marina, this hotel enjoys beautiful rivers views with direct access to the water. Recent commendable upgrading has transformed the hotel's appearance and it now boasts comfortable and inviting public rooms as well as bright bedrooms each enjoying the view. The recent introduction of Malcolm Wyebrow to head the kitchen has seen a dramatic improvement in the cooking. Good use is made of quality produce, in which locally caught fish features predominantly. Imaginative starters and scrumptious home-made puddings accompany.
46 en suite (bth/shr) 4 annexe en suite (bth/shr) No smoking in 15 bedrooms CTV in all bedrooms 75P No coaches V meals Coffee am Tea pm Last d 9.30pm
MEALS: Lunch £3-£16alc Dinner £23-£28alc*
CARDS:

★★★65% **Stoke Lodge**
Stoke Fleming TQ6 0RA (2m S A379) ☎ 01803 770523
FAX 01803 770851
Stoke Fleming is located two miles south of Dartmouth, and this hotel is set in its own gardens and grounds and has been owned and run by the Mayer family for over 16 years. Bedrooms are all equipped to the same standard: south-facing rooms are particularly popular. A varied choice is offered from the restaurant's five-course table d'hÙte menu, an à la carte menu is also available.
24 en suite (bth/shr) (5 fmly) CTV in all bedrooms 50P No coaches Indoor swimming pool (heated) Outdoor swimming pool (heated) Tennis (hard) Snooker Sauna Gym Pool table Putting green Jacuzzi/spa Table tennis Xmas English & Continental Cuisine V meals Coffee am Tea pm No smoking in restaurant Last d 9pm
ROOMS: (incl. bkfst) s £43.50-£46.50; d £71-£85 * LB
MEALS: Lunch fr £10.50&alc Dinner £16.95&alc
CONF: Thtr 80 Class 60 Board 30
CARDS:

★★64% **New Endsleigh**
New Rd, Stoke Fleming TQ6 0NR (2m S A379)
☎ 01803 770381
Closed Jan
Stoke Fleming is situated two miles from Dartmouth and is designated an area of outstanding natural beauty. The hotel faces south and benefits from a large car park. Smoking is not premitted in the bedrooms, which are attractive and well equipped. Bunter's Restaurant offers an interesting blackboard menu, and there is a lively bar/lounge.
11 rms (10 bth/shr) 1 annexe en suite (shr) (1 fmly) No smoking in 11 bedrooms CTV in all bedrooms No dogs (ex guide dogs) 16P

contd.

No coaches No children 5yrs English & French Cuisine V meals Coffee am Tea pm No smoking in restaurant Last d 9pm
CARDS:

DARWEN Lancashire Map 07 SD62

★★★64% **Whitehall**

Springbank, Whitehall BB3 2JU (off A666 S of town)
☎ 01254 701595 FAX 01254 773426
This comfortable, family-owned hotel which is quietly situated in its own grounds not far from the town centre provides spacious, attractively decorated and well equipped bedrooms. Guest can relax in the comfortable lounge or in the bar and can enjoy a good choice of well prepared dishes that are served by the cheerful, friendly and helpful staff in the restaurant.
15 en suite (bth/shr) (2 fmly) CTV in all bedrooms STV 60P Indoor swimming pool (heated) Snooker Sauna Solarium Pool table English & French Cuisine V meals Coffee am Tea pm Last d 9.45pm
ROOMS: (incl. bkfst) s £45-£52; d £57-£70 * **LB**
OFF-PEAK: (incl. bkfst) s £32-£35; d £49-£57
MEALS: Lunch fr £9.50 Dinner fr £14.50*
CONF: Thtr 50 Class 50 Board 25
CARDS:

★★★63% **The Old Rosins Inn**
Pickup Bank, Hoddlesden BB3 3QD (off A666) ☎ 01254 771264 FAX 01254 873894
Set in an elevated position above Hoddlesden, this split-level 18th-century country inn is full of character, offers modern, attractively decorated and well equipped accommodation, including a room with a four-poster bed. Guests can choose to eat less formally in the bar, which being on the first floor enjoys the most fantastic views over the Lancashire moors and is also very popular with the locals, or one can dine more formally in the smart restaurant. Good function facilities are also available.
15 en suite (bth/shr) (3 fmly) CTV in all bedrooms STV No dogs (ex guide dogs) 200P English & French Cuisine V meals Coffee am Tea pm No smoking area in restaurant
ROOMS: (incl. bkfst) s £29.50-£49.50; d £39.50-£59.50 * **LB**
MEALS: Lunch £13.95&alc High tea £3.50-£7.25 Dinner £13.95&alc*
CONF: Thtr 30 Class 24 Board 70 Del from £65
CARDS:

DAVENTRY Northamptonshire Map 04 SP56

★★★69% ***Daventry***
Ashby Rd (A361) NN11 5SG ☎ 01327 301777 FAX 01327 706313
Catering predominantly for conference and business guests, this spacious modern hotel is situated on the edge of town affording easy access to the M1 and M40. It has a leisure complex including a good sized indoor pool, and a range of meeting rooms is available. A fixed-price menu with some carvery dishes is presented in the airy restaurant, and the bedrooms offer every modern comfort.
138 en suite (bth/shr) No smoking in 52 bedrooms CTV in all bedrooms STV Lift Night porter 300P Indoor swimming pool (heated) Sauna Solarium Gym Pool table Jacuzzi/spa English & French Cuisine V meals Coffee am Tea pm Last d 9.45pm
CARDS:

DAWLISH Devon Map 03 SX97

★★★65% **Langstone Cliff**
Dawlish Warren EX7 0NA (1.5m NE off A379 Exeter road) ☎ 01626 865155 FAX 01626 867166
Catering for both the leisure and business markets, this hotel has been run by the Rogers family for over 50 years. Overlooking the sea and the Exe estuary, the hotel is set in wooded grounds. Lounges and bars are spacious and comfortable, with a carvery operation in the hotel's restaurant. Bedrooms vary in size and style, and in addition to the usual facilities, satellite TV is provided. During the winter months, special cabaret weekends are arranged which attract a loyal and regular following.
64 en suite (bth/shr) 4 annexe en suite (bth/shr) (52 fmly) CTV in all bedrooms STV Lift Night porter 200P Indoor swimming pool (heated) Outdoor swimming pool (heated) Tennis (hard) Snooker Table tennis Golf practice area Wkly live entertainment ch fac Xmas V meals Coffee am Tea pm Last d 9pm
ROOMS: (incl. bkfst) s fr £49.50; d fr £84 * **LB**
OFF-PEAK: (incl. bkfst) s fr £44.50; d fr £74
MEALS: Lunch fr £11 Dinner fr £14.50
CONF: Thtr 400 Class 200 Board 80 Del from £70
CARDS:

DEDDINGTON Oxfordshire Map 04 SP43

★★★72% **Holcombe Hotel & Restaurant**

High St OX15 0SL (on the A4260 between Oxford & Banbury) ☎ 01869 338274 FAX 01869 337167
Closed early Jan
This charming hotel continues to grow in stature due to the efforts of proprietors Carole and Chedly Mahfoudh they have a gift for hospitality and their staff are always thoughtful and smiling. Bedrooms are all individually decorated and exhibit style and taste. There is a convivial atmosphere in the bar where locals gather to socialise and enjoy some informal meals. The formal restaurant is very smart and guests will enjoy relaxing in the quiet yet cosy lounge.
17 en suite (bth/shr) (3 fmly) CTV in all bedrooms 40P English & French Cuisine V meals Coffee am Tea pm No smoking area in restaurant Last d 9.45pm
MEALS: Lunch £12.95-£21.50&alc High tea £4.95 Dinner £21.50&alc
CONF: Thtr 25 Class 14 Board 18 Del from £95
CARDS:
See advertisement under BANBURY

DEDHAM Essex Map 05 TM03

RED STAR HOTEL

★★★ **Maison Talbooth**
Stratford Rd CO7 6HN (A12 towards Ipswich, 1st turning signed Dedham, follow road until nasty left hand bend, take right hand turn, hotel 1m on right) ☎ 01206 322367 FAX 01206 322752
Overlooking tranquil Dedham Vale, this pretty Georgian hotel has always offered the warmest of welcomes and attentive service. The spacious and stylish bedrooms are equipped with

many thoughtful touches, such as fruit baskets and fluffy bathrobes. The comfortable drawing room, with fresh flowers and period furniture and pictures, is the only day room in the house; here guests may take a delicious afternoon tea or snacks during the day. Excellent breakfasts are mainly served in the bedrooms, and orders are taken the night before. For dinner, Le Talbooth Restaurant is just down the road, a leisurely 15 minute walk in summer, or a courtesy car is provided. The building, situated beside the River Stour, is a delightful 16th-century timber-framed house. Here a professional team offer fine service and some very good cooking. Dishes are balanced between traditional favourites and more modern interpretations.

10 en suite (bth/shr) (1 fmly) CTV in all bedrooms No dogs (ex guide dogs) 20P Riding Croquet lawn Garden chess English & French Cuisine V meals No smoking in restaurant Last d 9.30pm

ROOMS: (incl. cont bkfst) s £85-£120; d £125-£160 **LB**

MEALS: Lunch £12-£17.50&alc Dinner £22&alc

CONF: Thtr 30 Class 20 Board 16 Del from £140

CARDS:

DENTON Greater Manchester Map 07 SJ99

★★★64% **Old Rectory Hotel**

Meadow Ln, Haughton Green M34 1GD

☎ 0161 336 7516 FAX 0161 320 3212

Complete refurbishment of this hotel, parts of which date back to the mid-19th century when it was the local rectory, has given it considerable appeal, especially to business people who seek peace and tranquillity yet desire to be within easy reach of major commercial centres. Many of the bedrooms, which have been designed mainly for the business traveller, overlook a small garden.

30 en suite (bth/shr) 6 annexe en suite (bth/shr) (1 fmly) No smoking in 4 bedrooms CTV in all bedrooms No dogs Night porter 50P Pool table Games room Xmas V meals Coffee am Tea pm No smoking area in restaurant Last d 9.30pm

ROOMS: (incl. bkfst) s £48-£65; d £55-£75 * **LB**

MEALS: Lunch £6.50-£11.95&alc Dinner £15.95&alc*

CONF: Thtr 100 Class 45 Board 50 Del from £75

CARDS:

DERBY Derbyshire Map 08 SK33

See also Draycott

★★★★ 69% **Mickleover Court**

Etwall Rd, Mickleover DE3 5XX (take first exit off A516 signposted Mickleover) ☎ 01332 521234 FAX 01332 521238

An impressive modern hotel featuring an internal glass lift which takes guests to unusual circular lounges and a colourful and informal Italian trattoria, on the top floor. The elegant Avesbury Restaurant, which features traditional and classical dishes in modern style and for which a rosette has been awarded, is situated on the ground floor. The air-conditioned bedrooms are very well appointed and each has its own private balcony. There are comprehensive banqueting and conference facilities and also an excellent leisure centre which includes a gymnasium and a spectacular swimming pool.

80 en suite (bth/shr) (20 fmly) No smoking in 20 bedrooms CTV in all bedrooms STV Lift Night porter Air conditioning 270P Indoor swimming pool (heated) Sauna Solarium Gym Jacuzzi/spa Beauty salon Steam room Wkly live entertainment Xmas English & Italian Cuisine V meals Coffee am Tea pm No smoking area in restaurant Last d 11pm

ROOMS: (incl. bkfst) s £95-£110; d £105-£120 * **LB**

MEALS: Lunch £14.50&alc Dinner £19.50-£21.50&alc*

CONF: Thtr 200 Class 80 Board 40 Del £140

CARDS:

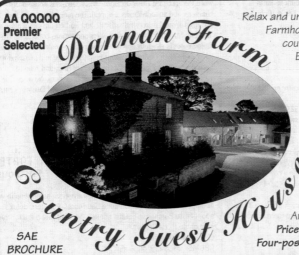

★★★★64% **Marriott Breadsall Priory**
Moor Rd DE7 6DL ☎ 01332 832235
FAX 01332 833509
(For full entry see Breadsall)

★★★70% **Midland**
Midland Rd DE1 2SQ (situated opposite Derby central railway station) ☎ 01332 345894
FAX 01332 293522
Closed 24-30 Dec & 1-2 Jan

Situated opposite the Derby Midland station, this hotel is said to be one of the oldest purpose-built railway hotels in the world. It has been sympathetically extended in recent years to provide excellent accommodation, and the new executive rooms - with their writing desks, fax/computer points and first-class bathrooms with separate shower cubicles - are particularly impressive. Public areas are being refurbished. There are a secluded garden, a secure car park (much of it covered) and numerous meeting and conference rooms.
100 en suite (bth/shr) No smoking in 3 bedrooms CTV in all bedrooms Lift Night porter 120P Wkly live entertainment English & French Cuisine V meals Coffee am Tea pm No smoking area in restaurant Last d 9.45pm
ROOMS: s £69-£84; d £74-£89 **LB**
MEALS: Lunch £7-£12alc Dinner £16-£26alc*
CONF: Thtr 150 Class 50 Board 40 Del from £92
CARDS:

★★★65% **Hotel Ristorante La Gondola**
220 Osmaston Rd DE23 8JX (on A514) ☎ 01332 332895
FAX 01332 384512
Situated between the cities inner and outer ring roads this elegant Georgian house has a well established Italian restaurant fashioned-in a contemporary style-to replicate a coliseum with intricate plaster covings and pillars. The attractively furnished bedrooms are all well equipped.
20 rms (19 bth/shr) (7 fmly) CTV in all bedrooms STV No dogs (ex guide dogs) Night porter 70P Wkly live entertainment Xmas Continental Cuisine V meals Coffee am Tea pm Last d 10pm
ROOMS: s £45-£56; d £49-£56 * **LB**
MEALS: Lunch £5.90-£7.50 Dinner £10.50-£16.50*
CONF: Thtr 80 Class 50 Board 80 Del £68
CARDS:

★★★63% **International**
Burton Rd (A5250) DE23 6AD (0.5m from city centre on A5250)
☎ 01332 369321 FAX 01332 294430
This popular hotel is ideally situated beside the A5250 and within easy reach of the city centre. Bedrooms are divided between the main building and two extensions which are immediately adjacent to the hotel. All the rooms, including a number of suites and family rooms, are attractively and comfortably furnished and well equipped; some have a personal safe and fridge, and all have ironing/pressing facilities. The public areas have a continental feel and include a comfortably furnished lounge bar and restaurant where a good choice of popular dishes is available.
41 en suite (bth/shr) 21 annexe en suite (bth/shr) (4 fmly) CTV in all bedrooms STV Lift Night porter 100P Wkly live entertainment Xmas English & Continental Cuisine V meals Coffee am Tea pm Last d 10.15pm
ROOMS: s £45-£55; d £55-£70 **LB**
OFF-PEAK: (incl. bkfst) s £32.50-£40; d £45-£65
MEALS: Lunch £6.50-£7.50&alc Dinner £7.50-£13.75&alc*
CONF: Thtr 70 Class 40 Board 30 Del from £72.50
CARDS:

★★★63% **Mackworth**
Ashbourne Rd DE22 4LY ☎ 01332 824324 FAX 01332 824692
This popular, well run and characterful hotel is conveniently situated alongside the A52 Ashbourne Road and within easy reach of the city ring road. The pleasant public areas, which retain many original features of what was once a 17th-century farmhouse, are largely dominated by the carvery and restaurant operation, but guests can easily find a quiet corner. Bedrooms, including a family room and a honeymoon suite, vary in size and are attractively decorated and well equipped.
13 en suite (bth/shr) 1 annexe en suite (bth/shr) (1 fmly) CTV in all bedrooms STV No dogs (ex guide dogs) Night porter 130P Xmas English & French Cuisine V meals Coffee am Tea pm Last d 10pm
ROOMS: (incl. bkfst) s £44.50-£47.50; d £59-£69.50 *
OFF-PEAK: (incl. bkfst) s £27.50-£30.50; d £45-£55
MEALS: Lunch £5.45-£8.95&alc Dinner £6.45-£15.95&alc
CONF: Thtr 60 Class 26 Board 24 Del from £80
CARDS:

See advertisement on opposite page

★★★63% ***Royal Stuart Hotel***
119 London Rd DE1 2QR (follow signs for Royal Infirmary)
☎ 01332 340633 FAX 01332 293502
Conveniently close to the town centre, this popular business hotel offers friendly service, a thriving bar and well-equipped, practical bedrooms.
101 en suite (bth/shr) (9 fmly) No smoking in 20 bedrooms CTV in all bedrooms STV Night porter 80P Pool table European Cuisine V meals Coffee am Tea pm Last d 9.45pm
CARDS:

★★69% **Kedleston Country House**
Kedleston Rd DE22 5JD (turn off A38 onto A52 roundabout follow signs for Kedleston Hall) ☎ 01332 559202 & 556507
FAX 01332 558822
Originally built as a coaching inn and then converted to a farmhouse, when the gentrified Georgian façade was added, this house oozes character and an individualistic appeal. The reception rooms are arranged around the central staircase and lead off through a maze of antiquity, huge displays of fresh flowers and various collectibles. The dining room is elegantly appointed with polished oak tables, sparkling silver and Crown Derby. It remains privately owned and managed with keen devotion, and the atmosphere is very friendly and relaxed.
14 en suite (bth/shr) (1 fmly) CTV in all bedrooms No dogs 70P Wkly live entertainment Xmas English & Continental Cuisine V meals Coffee am Tea pm
ROOMS: (incl. bkfst) s £42; d £55 **LB**
CONF: Thtr 80 Board 65
CARDS:

Forte Posthouse Derby/Burton
Pastures Hill, Littleover DE23 7BA (2m SW on A5250) ☎ 01332 514933 FAX 01332 518668

Suitable for both the business and leisure traveller, this bright hotel provides modern accommodation in well equipped bedrooms with en suite bathrooms. For more details about Forte Posthouse hotels, consult the Contents page for the section on Hotel Groups.
62 en suite (bth/shr)
ROOMS: d £69-£79 *
CONF: Thtr 85 Class 60 Board 25 Del from £99

Travel Inn (Derby East)
The Wyvern Business Park, Chaddesden Sidings DE21 6BF ☎ 01332 667826 FAX 01332 667827
Purpose-built accommodation, offering spacious, well equipped bedrooms, all with en suite bathrooms. Meals may be taken at the nearby family restaurant. For more information

about Travel Inns, consult the Contents page under Hotel Groups.
80 en suite (bth/shr)

Travel Inn (Derby West)

Mallard Beafeater, Uttoxeter New Rd,
RaRoR RaRk Way DE22 3NA v 01332 203003
FAX 01332 207506
Purpose-built accommodation, offering spacious, well equipped bedrooms, all with en suite bathrooms. Meals may be taken at the nearby family restaurant. For more information about Travel Inns, consult the Contents page under Hotel Groups.
40 en suite (bth/shr)
ROOMS: (incl. bkfst) d £35.50 *

European Inn

Midland Rd DE1 2SL (200yds from railway station)
☎ 01332 292000 FAX 01332 293940
A versatile and trend-setting lodge in the heart of the city, its architecture and courtyard layout is sympathetic to the area and the secure car parking is a welcome asset. The bedrooms are the equivalent of a three star hotel and are pristine. Family rooms are all along one corridor; there are ample no smoking rooms, and free ice and mineral water dispensers on each floor. The marbled reception area is continuously manned and there is a breakfast lounge and dispense bar. Antibo's pizza/steak restaurant will offer room service, though every assistance is offered to those preferring take-aways.
88 en suite (bth/shr) No smoking in 50 bedrooms CTV in all bedrooms Lift Night porter 90P
ROOMS: s fr £40.25; d fr £40.25
CONF: Thtr 100 Class 30 Board 25 Del £69.50
CARDS:

DESBOROUGH Northamptonshire Map 04 SP88

Travelodge

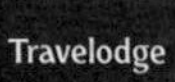

Harborough Rd NN14 2UG (on A6, southbound)
☎ 01536 762034 FAX 01536 762034
This modern building offers accommodation in smart, spacious and well equipped bedrooms, suitable for family use, and all with en suite bathrooms. Meals may be taken at the nearby family restaurant. For information on room rates and to make a booking, call Roomline free of charge on 0800 850950. For more details about Travelodge, consult the Contents page under Hotel Groups.
32 en suite (bth/shr)

DEVIZES Wiltshire Map 04 SU06

★★★61% **Bear**
Market Place SN10 1HS ☎ 01380 722444 FAX 01380 722450
Closed 25-26 Dec
Situated in the centre of this picturesque market town, this charcater inn dates back to 1550. Bedrooms vary in size and have been equipped with some thoughtful extras such as bottled water and biscuits. Public areas are traditional in style and include two bars and two eating areas.
24 en suite (bth/shr) (5 fmly) CTV in all bedrooms 25P Solarium V meals Coffee am Tea pm Last d 9.30pm
ROOMS: (incl. bkfst) s fr £50; d fr £75 * **LB**
MEALS: Lunch fr £12.50&alc Dinner fr £14.75&alc
CONF: Thtr 150 Board 50
CARDS:

DEWSBURY West Yorkshire Map 08 SE22

★★ 70% **Healds Hall**
Leeds Rd, Liversedge WF15 6JA (on A62) ☎ 01924 409112
FAX 01924 401895
Closed New Years Day
This large 18th century house stands on the A62 in the heart of West Yorkshire near Heckmondwike, convenient for the M62. It has been tastefully converted into a comfortable hotel providing well equipped modern accommodation and relaxing public rooms. A good range of well produced dishes is available on the interesting table d'hÙte menu and the carte.
25 en suite (bth/shr) (3 fmly) CTV in all bedrooms STV Night porter 80P International Cuisine V meals Coffee am Tea pm No smoking in restaurant Last d 9.30pm
ROOMS: (incl. bkfst) s £35-£53; d £45-£75 * **LB**
MEALS: Lunch £9.95-£9.75&alc Dinner £16.95&alc*
CONF: Thtr 100 Class 60 Board 80 Del £80
CARDS:

DIDCOT Oxfordshire Map 04 SU59

Travel Inn

Milton Lodge, Milton Heights, Milton OX14 4DP
☎ 01235 835168 FAX 01235 835187
Purpose-built accommodation, offering spacious, well equipped bedrooms, all with en suite bathrooms. Meals may be taken at the nearby family restaurant. For more information about Travel Inns, consult the Contents page under Hotel Groups.
40 en suite (bth/shr)
ROOMS: (incl. bkfst) d £35.50 *

The AA's professional hotel and restaurant inspectors make regular and anonymous visits to all the hotels listed in the guide. They accept no gifts or favours from hoteliers.

DONCASTER South Yorkshire Map 08 SE50

★★★65% **Doncaster Moat House**
Warmsworth DN4 9UX (2.5m SW on A630 at junc with A1) ☎ 01302 799988 FAX 01302 310197
Situated on the A630 en route to Rotherham, the Moat House was built in the grounds of Warmsworth Hall, and this Grade I listed building now houses most of the hotel's meeting rooms. Bedrooms are contained in the main hotel, the best being the most recently built executive rooms. Guests now have the option of room service in addition to a choice of menus in the restaurant. The leisure club includes a fitness studio and separate gymnasium.
100 en suite (bth/shr) (4 fmly) No smoking in 30 bedrooms CTV in all bedrooms Lift Night porter 200P Indoor swimming pool (heated) Sauna Solarium Gym Croquet lawn Jacuzzi/spa French Cuisine V meals Coffee am Tea pm Last d 10pm
ROOMS: s £83.50-£89.25; d £97-£105 * **LB**
OFF-PEAK: (incl. bkfst) s £43.95-£54; d £77.25-£82.50
MEALS: Lunch £6.95-£18.50alc Dinner £6.95-£18.50alc*
CONF: Thtr 400 Class 250 Board 40 Del from £85
CARDS:

★★★64% **Mount Pleasant**
Great North Rd DN11 0HP ☎ 01302 868696 & 868219 FAX 01302 865130
(For full entry see Rossington)

★★★62% **Danum Swallow**
High St DN1 1DN ☎ 01302 342261
FAX 01302 329034
This Edwardian town centre hotel offers spacious and comfortable public areas including an inviting ground-floor coffee lounge and attractive first-floor restaurant with small bar. Modernised bedrooms are all equipped to a similar standard but do vary in size from extremely compact singles to large doubles. There is also a full range of refurbished conference facilities and the hotel offers free overnight parking.
66 en suite (bth/shr) (3 fmly) No smoking in 15 bedrooms CTV in all bedrooms STV Lift Night porter 85P Free entry to local Leisure Centre Xmas French Cuisine V meals Coffee am Tea pm Last d 9.15pm
ROOMS: (incl. bkfst) s £48-£68; d £58-£78 * **LB**
MEALS: Lunch £8.25-£9.25 Dinner fr £16.95*
CONF: Thtr 300 Class 100 Board 100 Del from £85
CARDS:

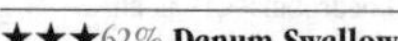

★★69% **Regent**
Regent Square DN1 2DS (on the corner of the A630 & A638, 1m from racecourse) ☎ 01302 364180 FAX 01302 322331
Closed New Year's Day RS Bank Hols
This well situated period hotel overlooks a delightfully pretty park. Enthusiastic owners, the Longworths, with the help of their cheerful and dedicated staff, create a very convivial and welcoming atmosphere. The bedrooms are furnished in a uniform style and provide the facilities of a higher classification; their sizes differ but they are priced accordingly. The reception areas are fashionably furnished in a period style and have two bars which both serve food. The Parade is furnished to imitate a library and O'Gradys is the cellar bar. Their is also a dedicated restaurant which offers an individually priced flexible menu.
50 en suite (bth/shr) (4 fmly) CTV in all bedrooms STV Lift Night porter 20P Sauna Wkly live entertainment English & French Cuisine V meals Coffee am Tea pm No smoking area in restaurant Last d 10pm
ROOMS: (incl. bkfst) s £39.50-£68; d £55-£75 **LB**
MEALS: Lunch £2-£10alc Dinner £7-£15alc*
CONF: Thtr 50 Class 30 Board 20 Del from £65
CARDS:

★★68% **Punch's**

Bawtry Rd, Bessacarr DN4 7BS ☎ 01302 370037
FAX 01302 532281

This popular and busy hotel is situated beside the A638 to the south of the town centre, convenient for the racecourse. Well equipped bedrooms are furnished with pine units and are spacious and comfortable if a little dated. Recently refurbished public areas include a choice of bars and an attractive restaurant offering a good range of dishes both at lunch and dinner. Smartly uniformed staff provide efficient and cheerful service.

24 en suite (bth/shr) (2 fmly) No smoking in 6 bedrooms CTV in all bedrooms STV Night porter 100P Pool table Wkly live entertainment V meals Coffee am No smoking area in restaurant Last d 10pm

ROOMS: (incl. bkfst) s fr £52; d fr £62 * **LB**
OFF-PEAK: (incl. bkfst) s fr £31; d fr £51
MEALS: Lunch £5-£11alc Dinner £5-£11alc*
CONF: Thtr 40 Class 30 Board 20
CARDS:

Campanile

Doncaster Leisure Park, Bawtry Rd DN4 7PD
(follow signs to Dome Leisure Centre and turn left at entrance to Dome complex) ☎ 01302 370770
FAX 01302 370813

The bar and Bistro restaurant provide meals and refreshments. Bedrooms are well equipped and have en suite bathrooms. For more details about Campanile, consult the Contents page under Hotel Groups.

50 en suite (bth/shr)

DONNINGTON See Telford

DORCHESTER-ON-THAMES Oxfordshire Map 04 SU59

★★ 67% ***White Hart***

High St OX10 7HN ☎ 01865 340074 FAX 01865 341082

An informal inn with rooms which offers good modern cooking in a fashionable Thameside village high street. The setting is a charming much favoured village of winding lanes and fashionable shops steeped with antiquity. Both the architectural character and the cooking are noteworthy. The bar and restaurant are across the courtyard and separate from the bedrooms. The style of cooking is confident and the skills assured: flavours are unfussed and natural. The atmosphere in the restaurant is relaxed, informal and animated a popular watering hole and meeting place.

19 en suite (bth/shr) (2 fmly) No smoking in 2 bedrooms CTV in 20 bedrooms No dogs (ex guide dogs) 25P No coaches V meals Coffee am Tea pm Last d 9pm

CARDS:

DORKING Surrey Map 04 TQ14

★★★★ 68% **The Burford Bridge**

FORTE Heritage

Burford Bridge, Box Hill RH5 6BX (2m NE A24)
☎ 01306 884561 FAX 01306 880386

Situated at the foot of the National Trust's Box Hill, the Burford Bridge is a charming small hotel which has always enjoyed a reputation for attentive service and a warm welcome. Bedrooms, most of which look out over the gardens, have the comforts of easy chairs and bathrobes and almost half have balconies. The lounge remains as popular as ever for light lunches and afternoon teas and in the evenings a pianist plays in the lobby.

48 en suite (bth/shr) No smoking in 17 bedrooms CTV in all bedrooms Night porter 80P Outdoor swimming pool (heated) Croquet lawn Putting green Wkly live entertainment Xmas European Cuisine V meals Coffee am Tea pm No smoking in restaurant Last d 10pm

ROOMS: d fr £100
OFF-PEAK: d fr £70
MEALS: Lunch fr £22.50&alc High tea £9-£15alc Dinner £13-£30alc*
CONF: Thtr 300 Class 100 Board 60 Del from £145
CARDS:

★★★ 62% ***The White Horse***

FORTE HOTELS

High St RH4 1BE ☎ 01306 881138
FAX 01306 887241

The focal point of this historic landmark hotel is the small bar with its guest beers. The exposed beams, creaking floors and occasional low ceilings all add to the character of the building, parts of which date back to the 15th century. Bedrooms are divided between the main building and a purpose-built annexe.

36 en suite (bth/shr) 32 annexe en suite (bth/shr) (2 fmly) No smoking in 20 bedrooms CTV in all bedrooms Night porter 73P V meals Coffee am Tea pm Last d 10pm

CARDS:

★★★ 61% **Gatton Manor Hotel Golf & Country Club**

Standon Ln GU4 7AX ☎ 01306 627555 FAX 01306 627713
(For full entry see Ockley)

Travelodge

Travelodge

Reigate Rd RH4 1QB (0.5m E, on A25)
☎ 01306 740361 FAX 01306 740361

This modern building offers accommodation in smart, spacious and well equipped bedrooms, suitable for family use, and all with en suite bathrooms. Meals may be taken at the nearby family restaurant. For information on room rates and to make a booking, call Roomline free of charge on 0800 850950. For more details about Travelodge, consult the Contents page under Hotel Groups.

54 en suite (bth/shr)

DOVER Kent Map 05 TR34

★★★70% **The Churchill**
Dover Waterfront CT17 9BP ☎ 01304 203633
FAX 01304 216320

Best Western

Completely refurbished and located on Dover's waterfront overlooking the harbour, this long established hotel forms part of an attractive terrace originally built in 1830. All the bedrooms are furnished to the same comfortable well equipped standard, and executive rooms with mini bars include some with balconies. Winston's Restaurant serves enjoyable cooking and there is a well appointed bar lounge, sun lounge and front terrace. Well groomed staff provide friendly and attentive service with professional management.

54 rms (53 bth/shr) (5 fmly) No smoking in 6 bedrooms CTV in all bedrooms STV Lift Night porter 21P Xmas English & French Cuisine V meals Coffee am Tea pm No smoking in restaurant Last d 9.15pm
ROOMS: s fr £52; d fr £72
MEALS: Lunch £12.95 High tea £5.95 Dinner £17
CONF: Thtr 90 Class 60 Board 60 Del from £82
CARDS:

See advertisement on opposite page

★★★65% ***County***
Townwall St CT16 1SZ (on A20) ☎ 01304 509955
FAX 01304 213230

County Hotels

Wide corridors and larger than average bedrooms are an unusual feature of this modern hotel which is conveniently located for the ferry ports. A small meeting room and an indoor swimming pool are useful extra amenities.

79 en suite (bth/shr) (32 fmly) No smoking in 27 bedrooms CTV in all bedrooms Lift Night porter Air conditioning 8P Indoor swimming pool (heated) ch fac English & French Cuisine V meals Coffee am Tea pm Last d 10.15pm
CARDS:

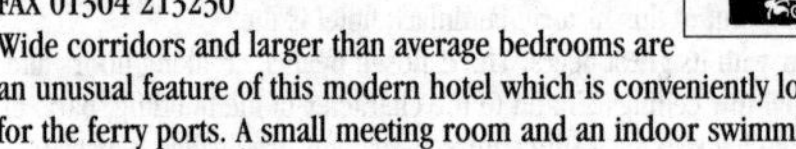

★★ 74% **Wallett's Court**
West Cliffe, St Margarets-at-Cliffe CT15 6EW
(opposite Westcliffe church) ☎ 01304 852424
FAX 01304 853430
Closed 24-28 Dec

The Oakley family create a welcoming atmosphere at this Jacobean manor house, which retains many of its original features. The accommodation is very well equipped, with traditionally furnished bedrooms in the main house, and others, more modern in style, in well converted buildings in the attractive grounds. Public rooms include a conservatory, and a comfortable lounge bar. In the restaurant Christopher Oakley provides high standards of cuisine on his monthly changing menu. Starters always include some straightforward soups, as well as hearty dishes such as the venison and pork terrine. Main courses might be a rich casserole of local game or a lighter option such a délice of wild salmon on an orange butter sauce. Desserts are equally good, with bread and butter pudding the speciality.

3 en suite (bth/shr) 9 annexe en suite (bth/shr) (2 fmly) CTV in all bedrooms No dogs (ex guide dogs) 34P No coaches Croquet lawn Coffee am Tea pm No smoking in restaurant Last d 9pm
ROOMS: (incl. bkfst) s £50-£70; d £60-£85 * **LB**
MEALS: Sunday Lunch £15.50 Dinner £22.50-£28*
CONF: Class 25 Del from £100
CARDS:

Forte Posthouse Dover
Singledge Ln, Whitfield CT16 3LF (3m outside Dover on main A2 towards London)
☎ 01304 821222 FAX 01304 825576

FORTE Posthouse

Suitable for both the business and leisure traveller, this bright hotel provides modern accommodation in well equipped bedrooms with en suite bathrooms. For more details about Forte Posthouse hotels, consult the Contents page for the section on Hotel Groups.

67 en suite (bth/shr)
ROOMS: d fr £69 *
CONF: Thtr 60 Class 18 Board 20 Del from £99

Travel Inn
Folkestone Rd CT15 7AB (on A20)
☎ 01304 213339 FAX 01304 214504

travel inn

Purpose-built accommodation, offering spacious, well equipped bedrooms, all with en suite bathrooms. Meals may be taken at the nearby family restaurant. For more information about Travel Inns, consult the Contents page under Hotel Groups.

62 en suite (bth/shr)
ROOMS: d £35.50 *

DOWNHAM MARKET Norfolk Map 05 TF60

★★65% **Castle**
High St PE38 9HF ☎ 01366 384311 FAX 01366 384311

Enthusiastic and hardworking proprietors offer a warm welcome and personal service at this old coaching inn. Bedrooms look fresh and inviting following a recent redecoration programme: the four-poster bedrooms look particularly attractive with their bold colourful soft furnishings. Public rooms also look cheerful, and the restaurant is a pleasant setting for daily and carte menus, alternatively bar snacks are available within the 'lived-in' bar.

12 rms (9 bth/shr) CTV in all bedrooms Night porter 26P Xmas French Cuisine V meals Coffee am Tea pm No smoking area in restaurant Last d 9.30pm
ROOMS: (incl. bkfst) s £32-£39; d £39-£49 * **LB**
MEALS: Lunch £9.95&alc Dinner £14.95&alc*
CONF: Thtr 60 Class 30 Board 40 Del from £52
CARDS:

★67% **Crosskeys Riverside**
Bridge St, Hilgay PE38 0LD (3m S off A10, beside bridge over river)
☎ 01366 387777

Housed in converted 17th-century buildings which stand on the river bank in the small village of Hilgay, three miles south of Downham Market, this hotel offers small, cosy public areas which include an attractive dining room with beamed ceiling and a large brick fireplace where coal fires burn in winter. Spacious bedrooms are well decorated and furnished - three of them boasting four-poster beds.

3 en suite (bth) 2 annexe en suite (bth) (1 fmly) CTV in all bedrooms 10P No coaches Fishing Croquet lawn Rowing boats Xmas English & Continental Cuisine V meals Coffee am No smoking in restaurant Last d 8pm
ROOMS: (incl. bkfst) s £33.50-£36.50; d £56-£59 * **LB**
OFF-PEAK: (incl. bkfst) s £35; d £56
MEALS: Dinner £12.50&alc
CARDS:

D

DRAYCOTT Derbyshire Map 08 SK43

★★★59% **Tudor Court**
Gypsy Ln DE72 3PB (exit M1 junct 25, take first left off A52 towards Derby. At T-junct turn left, hotel 0.5m on right) ☎ 01332 874581 FAX 01332 873133
Located between Derby and Nottingham, this mock-Tudor building stands in eight acres of woodland and is mainly geared to the conference trade, for which it offers sound facilities. Lounge space is limited and the bedrooms are cleverly planned to make the best use of space. Friendly and willing staff provide a traditional standard of service.
29 en suite (bth/shr) (8 fmly) No smoking in 6 bedrooms CTV in all bedrooms Night porter 150P Free facilities at local leisure centre V meals Coffee am Tea pm No smoking in restaurant
ROOMS: (incl. bkfst) s £49.50; d £65
CONF: Thtr 120 Class 80 Board 25
CARDS:

DRIFFIELD (GREAT) East Riding of Yorkshire Map 08 TA05

★★★69% **Bell**
46 Market Place YO25 7AN ☎ 01377 256661 FAX 01377 253228

Best Western

A focal point and meeting place of the town, this delightful 250-year-old coaching inn is particularly popular locally for the informal lunches served in its rambling bar and lounge areas. Many antique and period pieces furnish the hotel in keeping with its character. Bedrooms come in varying shapes and sizes, all with modern facilities. The friendliness of the owners Mr and Mrs Riggs and their long-serving members of staff is a great strength, as is the relaxed and informal service. The leisure, fitness and natural health centre across the courtyard is well worth the effort.
14 en suite (bth/shr) No smoking in 2 bedrooms CTV in all bedrooms Night porter 50P Indoor swimming pool (heated) Squash Snooker Sauna Solarium Gym Pool table Jacuzzi/spa Masseur No children 12yrs V meals Coffee am Tea pm No smoking in restaurant Last d 10pm
ROOMS: (incl. bkfst) s fr £65; d fr £91 * **LB**
MEALS: Sunday Lunch fr £9 Dinner £12-£20alc*
CONF: Thtr 250
CARDS:

DROITWICH Hereford & Worcester Map 03 SO86

★★★★66% **Château Impney**
WR9 0BN (on A38) ☎ 01905 774411 FAX 01905 772371
Closed Xmas
Built in the style of a French château, this beautiful and elegant hotel stands in extensive landscaped parkland. Its day rooms are classically styled and richly furnished and include a choice of dining rooms. Bedrooms are all well equipped to modern standards, and the hotel offers unrivalled facilities for conferences and exhibitions in the Impney Regency Centre which can accommodate up to 1000 delegates. There are also excellent leisure facilities. Service is professional and attentive.
67 en suite (bth/shr) (1 fmly) CTV in all bedrooms No dogs (ex guide dogs) Lift Night porter 1000P Tennis (hard) English & French Cuisine V meals Coffee am Tea pm No smoking in restaurant
CONF: Thtr 1000 Class 550 Board 160
CARDS:

★★★★61% **Raven**
Victoria Square WR9 8DU ☎ 01905 772224 FAX 01905 797100
Closed Xmas
Catering specifically for the residential conference business, this town-centre hotel offers welcoming and friendly service from a dedicated young staff. Formerly a coaching inn, the Raven is traditional in style,

with panelled public rooms and leather seating. Bedrooms vary in size but are brightly decorated and well equipped.
72 en suite (bth/shr) (1 fmly) CTV in all bedrooms Lift Night porter 250P English & French Cuisine V meals Coffee am Tea pm No smoking in restaurant
CONF: Thtr 150 Class 70 Board 40
CARDS:

Travelodge
Rashwood Hill WR9 8DA (2m N, on A38 from junc 5 at M5) ☎ 01527 861545 FAX 01527 861545

Travelodge

This modern building offers accommodation in smart, spacious and well equipped bedrooms, suitable for family use, and all with en suite bathrooms. Meals may be taken at the nearby family restaurant. For information on room rates and to make a booking, call Roomline free of charge on 0800 850950. For more details about Travelodge, consult the Contents page under Hotel Groups.
32 en suite (bth/shr)

DRONFIELD Derbyshire Map 08 SK37

★★64% **Chantry**
Church St S18 6QB (opp church with spire)
☎ 01246 413014 FAX 01246 413014
Dronfield is just south of Sheffield, and this hotel stands at its centre, behind the high stone wall of the church. The architecture of the house spans many centuries, though it is mainly Georgian and Victorian, and it is now the home of Jackie and Roy Toaduff who have entertained audiences around the world with their dancing for 38 years. Their friendliness creates a relaxed atmosphere which attracts good company - and a stay here represents value for money. Public areas all look out over a very attractive garden which is full of colour throughout the year; the restaurant is a delightful room with a green

contd.

and yellow colour scheme, furnished with quality appointments and featuring elaborate swagged drapes which frame its huge French and bay windows.
7 en suite (bth/shr) CTV in all bedrooms 28P No coaches V meals Coffee am Last d 8pm
ROOMS: (incl. bkfst) s £40-£42; d £50 *
MEALS: Bar Lunch £1.60-£4.50 Dinner fr £12*
CARDS:

D

DUDLEY West Midlands Map 07 SO99
See also Himley

★★★★66% **The Copthorne Merry Hill-Dudley**

MILLENNIUM & COPTHORNE HOTELS

The Waterfront, Level St, Brierley Hill DY5 1UR
(follow signs for Merry Hill Centre)
☎ 01384 482882 FAX 01384 482773
Part of the Merry Hill development and overlooking the canal marina, this well designed modern hotel has excellent facilities. Well proportioned bedrooms are elegantly furnished and have smart bathrooms with powerful showers. On the Connoisseur floor, where bedrooms include luxurious extras, there is a separate lounge where guests can entertain or enjoy a complimentary light breakfast. Faradays Restaurant and Bar is lively and modern and open all day for snacks, meals and cappuccinos.

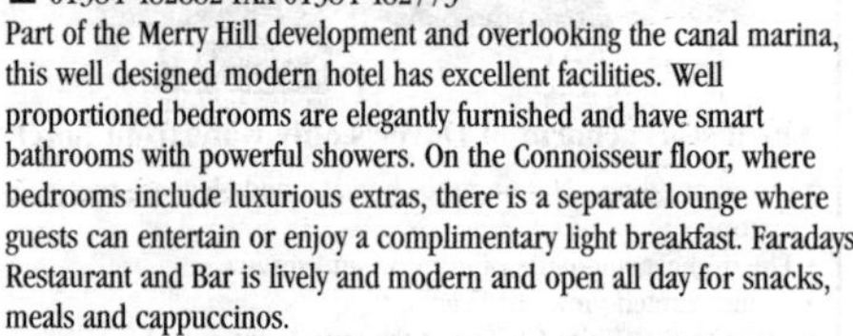

138 en suite (bth/shr) (14 fmly) No smoking in 47 bedrooms CTV in all bedrooms STV Lift Night porter 170P Indoor swimming pool (heated) Sauna Solarium Gym Jacuzzi/spa Beauty Therapist International Cuisine V meals Coffee am Tea pm No smoking area in restaurant Last d 11pm
ROOMS: s £127; d £137 * **LB**
OFF-PEAK: s £110; d £120
MEALS: Lunch £10.80-£30.05alc Dinner £10.80-£30.50alc*
CONF: Thtr 250 Class 150 Board 40 Del from £150
CARDS:

★★★58% ***Ward Arms***

REGAL
A Collection of Individual Hotels

Birmingham Rd DY1 4RN (on A461)
☎ 01384 458070 FAX 01384 457502
With easy access to the M5, and close to both the zoo and Black Country Museum, this conveniently located hotel provides well equipped bedrooms. Public rooms are a little restrictive but the bar is a popular meeting place.
72 en suite (bth/shr) No smoking in 14 bedrooms CTV in all bedrooms Night porter 150P International Cuisine V meals Coffee am Tea pm Last d 9.45pm
CARDS:

Travelodge

Travelodge

Dudley Rd, Brierley Hill DY5 1LQ (3m W, on A461)
☎ 01384 481579 FAX 01384 481579
This modern building offers accommodation in smart, spacious and well equipped bedrooms, suitable for family use, and all with en suite bathrooms. Meals may be taken at the nearby family restaurant. For information on room rates and to make a booking, call Roomline free of charge on 0800 850950. For more details about Travelodge, consult the Contents page under Hotel Groups.
32 en suite (bth/shr)

DULVERTON Somerset Map 03 SS92

★★★ 73% **Carnarvon Arms**
TA22 9AE (leave A396 at Exbridge onto B3222, hotel 1m on right)
☎ 01398 323302 FAX 01398 324022
On the Devon/Somerset border, this former railway hotel stands in its own beautiful grounds close to Exmoor National Park. Definitely a sporting establishment, it offers more than five miles of fishing on the Rivers Exe and Barle. Shooting is available, together with stabling for those who wish to bring their own horses. There are also tennis courts and an outdoor pool. Inside, public rooms are cosy and comfortable, with log fires in the lounges. The dining room has been refurbished, and offers a more formal dining option than the buttery bar. Bedrooms are attractive, with co-ordinating colour schemes and modern facilities.
25 rms (23 bth/shr) (2 fmly) CTV in all bedrooms 121P No coaches Outdoor swimming pool (heated) Tennis (hard) Fishing Snooker Croquet lawn Clay pigeon shooting Hairdressing salon Xmas V meals Coffee am Tea pm No smoking in restaurant Last d 8.30pm
ROOMS: (incl. bkfst) s £40-£55; d £70-£90 * **LB**
OFF-PEAK: (incl. bkfst) s £35-£40; d £60-£70
MEALS: Lunch fr £12.75 Dinner fr £22.75*
CONF: Thtr 100 Class 25 Board 40 Del from £55
CARDS:
See advertisement on opposite page

RED STAR HOTEL

★★ **Ashwick House**
TA22 9QD (turn left at post office, 3m NW on B3223, over two cattelgrids, signposted on left) ☎ 01398 323868
FAX 01398 323868
This delightful country house offers the perfect peaceful getaway, located in beautiful countryside on the edge of Exmoor. Proprietor Richard Sherwood ensures that guests are pampered and have every comfort. The six spacious bedrooms are attractively furnished and overlook the sweeping lawns. On arrival guests may enjoy tea and delicious home-made cakes in front of the fire or, in the summer, on the terrace. The bedrooms have lots of thoughtful touches such as fresh flowers, bathrobes and hot water bottles. The food is another enjoyable experience with irresistible home-made bread and soups, and local vegetables. The opportunity to walk in the grounds should not be missed with their wealth of flora and fauna.
6 en suite (bth) CTV in all bedrooms No dogs 27P No coaches Solarium No children 8yrs Xmas International Cuisine Coffee am Tea pm No smoking in restaurant Last d 8.30pm
ROOMS: (incl. bkfst & dinner) s £73-£79; d £126-£140 **LB**
OFF-PEAK: (incl. bkfst & dinner) s £63-£68; d £106-£120
MEALS: Sunday Lunch fr £12.75 Dinner fr £22

★★64% **Lion**
Bank Square TA22 9BU ☎ 01398 323444 FAX 01398 323980
Ideally located for exploring the Exmoor National Park, the Lion Hotel is a traditional inn of character and charm. The cosy lounge bar offers a selection of real ales and an extensive range of bar meals at lunchtime and during the evening, while in the hotel's dining room a

short a à la carte menu is available. The Tap is the locals' bar, with darts and pool, nobody minding muddy 'wellies or walking boots'. A comfortable, quiet lounge is available on the first floor adjacent to the well equipped bedrooms.
13 en suite (bth/shr) (1 fmly) CTV in all bedrooms 6P No coaches Xmas English, French & Italian Cuisine V meals Coffee am Last d 8.30pm
ROOMS: (incl. bkfst) s £28; d £56 *
MEALS: Lunch £7.50-£16.50alc Dinner £14.40-£19.50alc*
CARDS:

DUNCHURCH Warwickshire Map 04 SP47

Travelodge
London Rd, Thurlaston CV23 9LG (A45, westbound) ☎ 01788 521538 FAX 01788 521538

This modern building offers accommodation in smart, spacious and well equipped bedrooms, suitable for family use, and all with en suite bathrooms. Meals may be taken at the nearby family restaurant. For information on room rates and to make a booking, call Roomline free of charge on 0800 850950. For more details about Travelodge, consult the Contents page under Hotel Groups.
40 en suite (bth/shr)

DUNSTABLE Bedfordshire Map 04 TL02

★★★66% **Old Palace Lodge**
Church St LU5 4RT (exit M1 at junct 11 and take A505. Hotel 2m on right opposite Priory church) ☎ 01582 662201 FAX 01582 696422
The old part of this ivy-clad hotel houses reception, a restaurant and the bar that is the focal point of the public areas. A new bedroom wing extends to the rear, where there is a large car park. All bedrooms are modern and some provide extras such as mini bars and trouser presses. Staff are smartly dressed and friendly.
50 en suite (bth/shr) (4 fmly) No smoking in 3 bedrooms CTV in all bedrooms STV Lift Night porter 70P English & French Cuisine V meals Coffee am Tea pm Last d 10pm
ROOMS: s £73.50; d £83.50 **LB**
OFF-PEAK: s fr £45; d £55-£80
MEALS: Lunch £15.50-£19.25 Dinner £15.50-£19.25
CONF: Thtr 40 Class 18 Board 25 Del £97.50
CARDS: 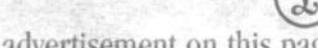

See advertisement on this page

★★65% ***Highwayman***
London Rd LU6 3DX ☎ 01582 661999 & 601122 FAX 01582 666907
Its convenient location beside the A5 south of the town, together with the standard levels of comfort in the bedrooms, makes this a popular base for commercial travellers. At the time of writing, the public areas are being completely upgraded to provide a bright bar and carvery themed restaurant.
51 en suite (bth/shr) (2 fmly) CTV in all bedrooms No dogs Night porter 60P V meals Coffee am Tea pm Last d 9.30pm
CARDS:

Travel Inn
Watling St, Kensworth LU6 3QP ☎ 01582 840509 FAX 01582 842785

Purpose-built accommodation, offering spacious, well equipped bedrooms, all with en suite bathrooms. Meals may be taken at the nearby family restaurant. For more information about Travel Inns, consult the Contents page under Hotel Groups.
40 en suite (bth/shr)
ROOMS: d £35.50 *

Travelodge

Watling St LU7 9LZ (3m N, on A5) ☎ 01525 211177 FAX 01525 211177

Travelodge

This modern building offers accommodation in smart, spacious and well equipped bedrooms, suitable for family use, and all with en suite bathrooms. Meals may be taken at the nearby family restaurant. For information on room rates and to make a booking, call Roomline free of charge on 0800 850950. For more details about Travelodge, consult the Contents page under Hotel Groups.

28 en suite (bth/shr)

DUNSTER Somerset Map 03 SS94

★★★66% **The Luttrell Arms**

High St TA24 6SG (0.5m beyond the Exmoor Visitor Centre on A396, opposite the Yarn Market) ☎ 01643 821555 FAX 01643 821567

FORTE Heritage

The Luttrell Arms dates from the 15th century and welcomes guests through a massive stone porch. The majority of bedrooms have been refurbished and are attractively decorated and well equipped. Those waiting similar good work are by comparison a little more dated. Rooms in the Latches are cottage like with narrow corridors and stairways. A choice of menus is offered in the split-level restaurant and food is also available in the Old Kitchen Bar. There is a congenial bar and comfortable beamed lounge. Friendly service is carried out by a local team.

27 en suite (bth/shr) (1 fmly) No smoking in 9 bedrooms CTV in all bedrooms 3P Xmas V meals Coffee am Tea pm No smoking in restaurant Last d 9.30pm

ROOMS: s £75; d £95-£120 * **LB**

CONF: Thtr 25 Board 15 Del from £80

CARDS:

★★69% **Exmoor House**

12 West St TA24 6SN (turn off A39 Taunton/Minehead road at A396, signed Dunster, hotel 0.5m on right beyond church) ☎ 01643 821268 FAX 01643 821268

Closed Dec & Jan

Hospitable, friendly service is provided by the resident owners and their small team of loyal, mainly local staff at this small, charming Grade 2 listed Georgian property. It is situated in one of the quieter, cobbled streets of the town, yet within easy walking distance of the main high street and the famous castle, now owned by the National Trust. Public areas are comfortable and retain much of the character and charm of the building, having a cosy atmosphere. Guests choose between the garden or Minster lounges to relax or chat with other guests. In the candlelit dining room, the short table d'hÙte menu changes daily, using fresh local ingredients.

7 en suite (bth/shr) No smoking in all bedrooms CTV in all bedrooms No children 12yrs V meals Coffee am Tea pm Last d 8pm

ROOMS: (incl. bkfst) s £27.50-£38.50; d £55-£61 **LB**

OFF-PEAK: (incl. bkfst) s £35.50

MEALS: Dinner £15.50-£16.50

CARDS:

DURHAM Co Durham Map 12 NZ24

See also Thornley

★★★★70% **Royal County**

Old Elvet DH1 3JN ☎ 0191 386 6821 FAX 0191 386 0704

SWALLOW HOTELS

This popular, long established hotel occupies buildings in three distinct styles of architecture in an enviable city-centre position overlooking the river. The comfortable bedrooms vary in size and style and are well equipped and the nicely appointed public areas include a cosy cocktail bar and a spacious foyer from which leads a magnificent carved oak staircase. Guests can either eat informally in the Brasserie which is open all day or alternatively in the County Restaurant where the service is polished and attentive and fresh flowers, sparkling silver and crisp linen set the keynote and where a pianist plays in the evening.

150 en suite (bth/shr) (4 fmly) No smoking in 49 bedrooms CTV in all bedrooms STV Lift Night porter 85P Indoor swimming pool (heated) Sauna Solarium Gym Jacuzzi/spa Steam room Plunge pool Impulse showers Wkly live entertainment Xmas International Cuisine V meals Coffee am Tea pm No smoking area in restaurant Last d 10.15pm

ROOMS: (incl. bkfst) s £85-£105; d £120-£130 * **LB**

MEALS: Lunch £10-£13.50 Dinner £17.50-£21*

CONF: Thtr 140 Class 50 Board 45 Del £120

CARDS:

See advertisement on opposite page

★★★72% **Ramside Hall**

Carrville DH1 1TD (take A690 towards Sunderland from A1M/A690 interchange, 200mtrs after going under railway bridge) ☎ 0191 386 5282 FAX 0191 386 0399

CONSORT CROWN

This impressive hotel stands in its own grounds and will have the added attraction of a golf course by the spring of 1996. Bedrooms here are delightfully furnished and very well equipped, some having four-poster beds, whilst the spacious lounge and bar areas are comfortably furnished. There are three styles of dining available, catering for all tastes, and there are plans for a leisure centre together with more bedrooms. The hotel is found on the A690 to the east of the A1.

82 en suite (bth/shr) (10 fmly) No smoking in 36 bedrooms CTV in all bedrooms STV Lift Night porter Air conditioning 500P Golf 27 Putting green Wkly live entertainment ch fac Xmas V meals Coffee am Tea pm No smoking area in restaurant Last d 9.30pm

ROOMS: (incl. bkfst) s £90-£110; d £110-£180 * **LB**

MEALS: Lunch £13.50-£18.50 High tea £4-£10 Dinner £15-£18.50&alc*

CONF: Thtr 350 Class 160 Board 40 Del from £108

CARDS:

See advertisement on opposite page

★★★70% **Three Tuns**

New Elvet DH1 3AQ (from A1 follow A690 for city. At 1st roundabout take 2nd exit then next roundabout take 1st exit) ☎ 0191 386 4326 FAX 0191 386 1406

This comfortable city centre hotel, parts of which date from the 16th Century, has been refurbished to a high standard and offers varying styles of well equipped accommodation. The characterful and inviting public areas have a Tudor theme and include a number of smart meeting rooms. The service is friendly and efficient and guests have free use of the leisure facilities at the Swallow County Hotel which is 200 yards away.

47 en suite (bth/shr) (1 fmly) No smoking in 20 bedrooms CTV in all bedrooms STV Night porter 60P Free facilities at Royal County Hotel Wkly live entertainment Xmas English & French Cuisine V meals Coffee am Tea pm No smoking area in restaurant Last d 9.30pm

ROOMS: (incl. bkfst) s £89-£95; d £109-£115 * **LB**

OFF-PEAK: (incl. bkfst) s fr £65; d fr £90

MEALS: Lunch £4.95-£10&alc Dinner £15.50-£17&alc*

CONF: Thtr 350 Class 200 Board 160 Del £102.50

CARDS:

★★★66% **Bowburn Hall**

Bowburn DH6 5NH (3m SE junc A177/A1(M)) ☎ 0191 377 0311 FAX 0191 377 3459

Standing in five acres of grounds and very convenient to the A1, this pleasantly furnished hotel provides a spacious and comfortable lounge together with richly furnished and delightfully decorated bedrooms. There is a very good range of dishes available which are served either in the lounge bar or the spacious dining room. The hotel is to be found on the edge of Bowburn and is about two miles from Durham city.

contd.

19 en suite (bth) CTV in all bedrooms No dogs 100P V meals Coffee am Tea pm Last d 9.30pm
ROOMS: (incl. bkfst) s £45-£50; d £55-£60 * **LB**
MEALS: Lunch £11.50-£14.50 Dinner £11.50-£14.50*
CONF: Thtr 100 Board 60 Del from £65
CARDS:

★★68% ***Bridge Toby***

Croxdale DH1 3SP (3 miles S of city on A167)
☎ 0191 378 0524 FAX 0191 378 9981
Conveniently situated on the A.167, just three miles south of the city, this smartly appointed former inn offers well equipped motel style accommodation situated around a pleasant courtyard. The newly refurbished and very attractive public areas include a characterful lounge bar and restaurant. The service is friendly and willing.
46 en suite (bth/shr) (4 fmly) No smoking in 16 bedrooms CTV in all bedrooms Night porter 150P Mainly grills V meals Coffee am Tea pm Last d 10.30pm
CARDS:

★★59% ***Rainton Lodge***
West Rainton DH4 6QY (4m NE on A690)
☎ 0191 512 0540 & 0191 512 0534 FAX 0191 584 1221
This motel-style hotel stands on the A690 between Durham and Sunderland and offers modern bedrooms together with a busy bar and dining room. A good range of food is available and staff are friendly and helpful.
27 en suite (bth/shr) (1 fmly) CTV in all bedrooms No dogs (ex guide dogs) Night porter 80P Riding English, French & Italian Cuisine V meals Coffee am Tea pm Last d 9.30pm
CARDS:

Roadchef Lodge

Motorway Service Area, Tursdale Rd, Bowburn DH6 5NP ☎ 0191 377 3666 FAX 0191 377 1448
Smart, spacious and well equipped bedrooms, all with en suite bathrooms, are provided by this modern hotel. Meals may be taken at a nearby family restaurant. For more information about RoadChef Lodges, consult the Contents page under Hotel Groups.
38 en suite (bth/shr)
ROOMS: d £37.95-£39.95
CONF: Thtr 20 Board 10

DUXFORD Cambridgeshire Map 05 TL44

★★★ ❀❀66% **Duxford Lodge**
Ickleton Rd CB2 4RU (junc 10 of M11 and A505)
☎ 01223 836444 FAX 01223 832271
Closed 26-30 Dec & 1 Jan RS Sat
A friendly welcome awaits guests at this small country hotel; a red brick house set in enclosed gardens in the centre of the village. The proprietors and a small team of staff provide cheerful and attentive service, and chef Chris Brooks offers menus of interesting modern French cuisine in the attractive restaurant. The meals are colourful and carefully presented, demonstrating good imagination, accomplished cooking skills and use of quality fresh produce; and a balanced wine list complements the food. The accommodation is divided between the main house and a separate building in the garden. All the rooms are attractively appointed, have colour co-ordinated schemes and offer a range of useful facilities.
11 en suite (bth/shr) 4 annexe en suite (bth/shr) CTV in all bedrooms 34P English & French Cuisine V meals Coffee am Tea pm No smoking area in restaurant Last d 9.30pm
ROOMS: (incl. bkfst) s £37-£68; d £70-£89 * **LB**
MEALS: Lunch fr £18.50 Dinner fr £18.50
CONF: Thtr 30 Class 20 Board 20 Del from £94
CARDS:

EASINGTON North Yorkshire Map 08 NZ71

★★★ ❀ 69% **Grinkle Park**

TS13 4UB (2m S off unclass road linking A174/A171) ☎ 01287 640515 FAX 01287 641278
This elegant Victorian house stands in mature and extensive parkland,and is very well furnished in all areas. The bedrooms, which are mostly spacious, are all well equuipped and furnished within the style of the house, whilst the public rooms are comfortable and inviting. A roaring log fire burns in the lounge on cooler evenings, and the staff are warm and friendly. Chef Tim Backhouse continues to provide excellent food using the best local produce available and his English/French cooking is meticulously presented.
20 en suite (bth/shr) CTV in all bedrooms 122P Tennis (hard) Fishing Snooker Croquet lawn Xmas English & French Cuisine V meals Coffee am Tea pm Last d 9pm
ROOMS: (incl. bkfst) s £65; d £85 * **LB**
OFF-PEAK: (incl. bkfst & dinner) s £66; d £98
MEALS: Lunch £9.50-£11.50 Dinner £16.50&alc*
CONF: Thtr 60 Board 25 Del £86.05
CARDS:

EASINGWOLD North Yorkshire Map 08 SE56

★★65% **George**
Market Place YO6 3AD (1m off A19 midway between York & Thirsk)
☎ 01347 821698 FAX 01347 823448
Standing in the old town centre, in the cobbled market square, this old coaching inn retains much of its original charm and character, especially in the bars. The bedrooms in the main house are superior to those at the rear whilst the dining room is attractively decorated and furnished. An extensive range of food is available either in the bar or in attractive candle lit restaurant.
14 en suite (bth/shr) (2 fmly) CTV in all bedrooms No dogs (ex guide dogs) 8P English & Continental Cuisine V meals Coffee am Tea pm Last d 9.00pm
MEALS: Lunch £10.95-£13.95&alc Dinner £13.95-£16.95&alc*
CARDS: (£)

EAST AYTON North Yorkshire Map 08 SE98

★★★63% ***East Ayton Lodge***
Moor Ln, Forge Valley YO13 9EW ☎ 01723 864227
FAX 01723 862680
Closed Jan-12 Feb
Standing in three acres of grounds close to the River Derwent, this family-owned hotel has recently been extended to include further bedrooms around the courtyard. All rooms are well equipped and pleasantly furnished; several have four-poster beds. Public rooms include a cosy television lounge and an attractive restaurant serving an extensive range of food. Service is friendly and polite.
11 en suite (bth/shr) 20 annexe en suite (bth/shr) (3 fmly) CTV in

all bedrooms 50P English & French Cuisine V meals Coffee am Last d 9pm
CARDS:

EASTBOURNE East Sussex Map 05 TV69

★★★★★ 60% **Grand**

King Edwards Pde BN21 4EQ (on seafront west of Eastbourne 1m from railway station)
☎ 01323 412345 FAX 01323 412233
This imposing Victorian hotel stands at the western end of the seafront. Its public rooms are being restored to their former elegance and bedrooms are to be considerably enhanced over the next few years. The outdoor pool is popular in summer, and there is a leisure club (available all year round) with hairdressing and beauty salons. The main dining room is traditional in style, while the Mirabelle restaurant offers a more intimate atmosphere and adventurous cooking, which has earned chef Mark Jones the award of two AA rosettes.
164 en suite (bth/shr) (20 fmly) No smoking in 4 bedrooms CTV in all bedrooms STV Lift Night porter 64P No coaches Indoor swimming pool (heated) Outdoor swimming pool (heated) Snooker Sauna Solarium Gym Jacuzzi/spa Hairdressing beauty & massage Wkly live entertainment ch fac Xmas English & French Cuisine V meals Coffee am Tea pm Last d 10pm
ROOMS: (incl. bkfst) s £95-£115; d £140-£180 *
OFF-PEAK: (incl. bkfst & dinner) s fr £60; d fr £95
CONF: Thtr 400 Class 240 Board 60 Del from £110
CARDS:

★★★★ 56% ***Cavendish***
Grand Pde BN21 4DH (follow signposts to seafront, hotel opposite the Bandstand, half way between the pier and Beachy Head cliffs)
☎ 01323 410222 FAX 01323 410941
A large inviting lounge greets visitors to this well established resort hotel. The bedrooms offer a good range of equipment and sound standards are maintained, but the decor and furnishings are dated. Public areas include a cheerfully run bar, meeting rooms and a bright front-facing restaurant where hearty meals are served.
118 en suite (bth/shr) No smoking in 30 bedrooms CTV in all bedrooms STV Lift Night porter 50P Snooker Gym Games room English & French Cuisine V meals Coffee am Tea pm Last d 9.30pm
CONF: Thtr 300 Class 180 Board 125 Del from £70
CARDS:

★★★ 76% **Lansdowne**

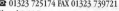

King Edward's Pde BN21 4EE (hotel situated at west end of seafront (B2103 facing western Lawns)
☎ 01323 725174 FAX 01323 739721
Closed 1-11 Jan
Enjoying one of the best locations on the promenade this long established hotel benefits from its traditional virtues of competent well groomed service and the warmth and friendliness of its loyal and well supervised staff. General Manager Jennie Hunt has recently taken over and good standards of performance continue to be maintained. There is a very good range of attractively furnished bedrooms, and with several lounges to choose from and a well appointed cocktail bar the accommodation has a lot to commend with the resplendent Devonshire restaurant complementing the facilities and featuring the enthusiastic traditional cooking of Chef George Thompson. Other facilities include two billiard rooms and lock-up garaging.
122 en suite (bth/shr) (5 fmly) CTV in all bedrooms STV Lift Night porter 23P Snooker Pool table Darts, Table tennis V meals Coffee am Tea pm Last d 8.30pm
ROOMS: (incl. bkfst) s £50-£56; d £76-£94 **LB**
MEALS: Sunday Lunch £8.50-£10.95&alc Dinner fr £14.75
CONF: Thtr 130 Class 50 Board 50 Del from £60
CARDS:

See advertisement on this page

★★★ 71% **Hydro**
Mount Rd BN20 7HZ ☎ 01323 720643 FAX 01323 641167
This long established hotel is set in an elevated position away from the hustle and bustle with impressive views of the sea and the Sussex Downs. The bedrooms have been smartly upgraded and offer modern ensuite facilities. The extensive public areas are elegant yet comfortably furnished, they include a library, cocktail bar and panelled lounges. During the summer months a lunchtime buffet is served on the garden terrace, overlooking the croquet and putting greens. There is an outdoor pool, hair and beauty salon, and several function rooms.
83 en suite (bth/shr) (1 fmly) CTV in all bedrooms Lift Night porter 50P Outdoor swimming pool (heated) Sauna Solarium Gym Croquet lawn Putting green Beauty room,Hairdressing V meals Coffee am Tea pm No smoking in restaurant Last d 8.30pm
MEALS: Lunch fr £7.50 Dinner fr £13.95*
CONF: Thtr 140 Class 90 Board 40 Del from £49
CARDS:

★★★61% Chatsworth
Grand Pde BN21 3YR (on seafront between the pier and the bandstand) ☎ 01323 411016 FAX 01323 643270
Enjoying one of the best central locations on the seafront, this splendid Edwardian hotel retains much of its original charm. Whilst being slowly upgraded and improved under new ownership, there is a choice of sea-facing or side view bedrooms; the best with the new en suite bath and shower facilities. Public rooms comprise a comfortable traditional lounge and foyer, the well appointed Devonshire Restaurant and Dukes Bar, whilst other facilities include a self-operated Victorian cage lift to all levels, a downstairs conference room and combination rooms for functions and meetings. Service is efficient and friendly with advertised room service and a duty night porter adding to the range.
46 en suite (bth/shr) (2 fmly) No smoking in 6 bedrooms CTV in all bedrooms STV Lift Night porter Wkly live entertainment Xmas V meals Coffee am Tea pm No smoking in restaurant Last d 8.30pm
ROOMS: (incl. bkfst) s £45-£60; d £80-£110 **LB**
OFF-PEAK: (incl. bkfst) s £40-£50; d £60-£80
MEALS: Sunday Lunch fr £10.75 Dinner fr £15.75
CONF: Thtr 100 Class 60 Board 30 Del from £70
CARDS:

See advertisement on opposite page

★★★60% Quality Mansion Hotel
Grand Pde BN21 3YS ☎ 01323 727411
FAX 01323 720665
This well presented, sea front hotel now has contemporary and well maintained bedrooms. There are three categories with the added advantage of the extra size due to the nature of the original design of the building. The staff are extremely friendly and make an effort to provide a welcoming environment.
95 en suite (bth/shr) (6 fmly) No smoking in 47 bedrooms CTV in all bedrooms STV Lift Night porter Air conditioning Gym Xmas English & Continental Cuisine V meals Coffee am Tea pm No smoking area in restaurant Last d 9.30pm
ROOMS: s £57.50-£67.50; d £67.50-£77.50 **LB**
MEALS: Lunch £7.50-£9.95&alc Dinner £13.50&alc
CONF: Thtr 200 Class 80 Board 40 Del from £82.50
CARDS:

★★★60% Wish Tower
King Edward's Pde BN21 4EB (opposite Martello Tower on seafront) ☎ 01323 722676
FAX 01323 721474
Open and bright public areas are a strength at this easily located hotel. Snacks and afternoon tea are served in the lounge, and meals, prepared with good intent, are served in a well maintained dining room. Bedrooms vary in size but all are gradually being renovated to a modern style.
65 en suite (bth/shr) (3 fmly) CTV in all bedrooms STV Lift Night porter 3P Nearby sports centre free to guests Xmas English & French Cuisine V meals Coffee am Tea pm No smoking in restaurant Last d 8.45pm
ROOMS: (incl. bkfst) s £35-£50; d £70-£100 *
OFF-PEAK: (incl. bkfst) s £25-£45; d £50-£90
MEALS: Bar Lunch £2.95-£5.95 Dinner £13.95&alc
CONF: Thtr 60 Class 30 Board 30 Del from £60
CARDS:

★★❀❀68% Downland Hotel & Restaurant
37 Lewes Rd BN21 2BU (on A2021, 0.5m from the town centre) ☎ 01323 732689 FAX 01323 720321
(Rosettes awarded for dinner only)
Personally run by Stephanie and Patrick Faulkner, this cosy hotel and restaurant is located on the A2021. The bedrooms are gradually being improved in the modern style. All are well equipped and might look over the rear terrace, the garden or the front main road. There is a comfortable mezzanine lounge and a small bar to complement the candlelit restaurant. Patrick's enthusiastic cooking clearly forms a major part of the enjoyment of staying here, along with Stephanie's conscientious service front of house. However, the cooking can be disconcerting, with ambitious recipes sometimes resulting in unbalanced and over-complicated results. Only the best quality ingredients are used, and the home-made breads and desserts are impressive, but some main courses fall short of the mark. Other facilities include room and laundry service and forecourt parking.
14 en suite (bth/shr) (3 fmly) CTV in all bedrooms No dogs (ex guide dogs) 10P No coaches No children 10yrs V meals Coffee am Last d 9pm
ROOMS: (incl. bkfst) s £27.50-£37.50; d £49-£75 * **LB**
MEALS: Dinner fr £17.50&alc*
CARDS:

★★67% Langham
Royal Pde BN22 7AH (follow signs for the seafront, hotel half a mile E of the pier, next to Redoubt Fortress) ☎ 01323 731451
FAX 01323 646623
Closed 15 Dec-27 Feb
A friendly family-owned and -managed hotel situated on the seafront. Brightly decorated bedrooms are comfortably furnished in modern style and equipped with many useful amenities. The public rooms are well appointed and include an adequately stocked bar and a choice of dining rooms including the attractive Portico à la carte restaurant.
87 en suite (bth/shr) (5 fmly) CTV in all bedrooms Lift Night porter 4P Pool table Wkly live entertainment European Cuisine V meals Coffee am Tea pm Last d 9pm
ROOMS: (incl. bkfst) s £23-£34; d £46-£68 * **LB**
OFF-PEAK: (incl. bkfst) s fr £23; d fr £46
MEALS: Lunch £4-£7 Dinner fr £9.50&alc*
CONF: Thtr 80 Class 40 Board 24 Del from £44.50
CARDS:

★★66% Farrar's
3-5 Wilmington Gardens BN21 4JN (turn off seafront by Wish Tower, hotel opposite Congress Theatre) ☎ 01323 723737
FAX 01323 732902
Closed 29 Dec-28 Jan
Perfectly situated opposite Devonshire Park and the theatre this family hotel has a friendly quiet and relaxing atmosphere being personally run by the proprietor Mr C Steele. There is a good range of traditionally furnished bedrooms some of which overlook the park, and public areas comprise a choice of several well furnished lounges, bar, bright well appointed dining room and lift facilities to all levels.
45 en suite (bth/shr) (3 fmly) CTV in all bedrooms Lift Night porter 26P Xmas English,French & Italian Cuisine V meals Coffee am Tea pm No smoking in restaurant Last d 8.30pm
ROOMS: (incl. bkfst) s £29-£41; d £58-£82 **LB**
OFF-PEAK: (incl. bkfst) s £25-£35
MEALS: Bar Lunch £1.95-£6 High tea 95p-£2.50 Dinner £12&alc*
CONF: Thtr 55 Class 40 Board 40 Del from £36
CARDS:

★★66% **New Wilmington**

25 Compton St BN21 4DU (A22 to Eastbourne along the seafront, turn right along promenade until Wishtower. Turn right off Promenade and Hotel is on the first left) ☎ 01323 721219 FAX 01323 728900

Closed Jan & Feb

This popular, well managed, family-run hotel is situated near the theatres and the seafront, and offers a good range of comfortable, well equipped bedrooms, including some more spacious family rooms. There is a well appointed cocktail bar-lounge and an attractively decorated double-sided non-smoking dining room. Other facilities include a separate TV lounge, readily available reception, lift, and lock-up garaging.

41 en suite (bth/shr) (8 fmly) CTV in all bedrooms Lift Night porter 2P Yes Xmas English, French & Italian Cuisine V meals Coffee am Tea pm

ROOMS: (incl. bkfst) s £31-£37; d £52-£64 * **LB**

CARDS:

★★65% **West Rocks**

Grand Pde BN21 4DL (on seafront western end) ☎ 01323 725217 FAX 01323 720421

Closed mid Nov-mid Mar

Ideally located on the seafront, this hotel is family-owned and managed and the atmosphere is relaxed and informal. Bedrooms vary in size with some spacious rooms; they continue to be upgraded to a modern style and are well equipped. The two brightly decorated lounges are comfortably appointed, and there are two sun lounges, a small cosy bar and a spacious dining room which offers a good, varied menu.

44 en suite (bth/shr) (4 fmly) CTV in all bedrooms No dogs Lift Night porter No children 3yrs English & French Cuisine V meals Coffee am Tea pm Last d 8.15pm

ROOMS: (incl. bkfst) s £30-£45; d £44-£80 **LB**

MEALS: Bar Lunch £3.25-£5.50 Dinner £10.50

CONF: Thtr 50 Class 26 Board 20

CARDS:

★★62% **Oban**

King Edward's Pde BN21 4DS (opposite Wish Tower seafront area) ☎ 01323 731581 FAX 01323 721994

The hotel occupies a delightful position on the seafront overlooking well kept lawns. The well equipped and brightly decorated bedrooms vary in size: some are spacious, many have sea views, and all are comfortably and adequately furnished. In addition there is a comfortable bar and sun lounge where snacks and afternoon tea is served. Traditional English cuisine is provided in the well appointed dining room and a choice of breakfast is offered.

31 en suite (bth/shr) (2 fmly) CTV in all bedrooms Lift Night porter Lounge bar activities Wkly live entertainment Xmas V meals Coffee am Tea pm No smoking in restaurant Last d 7.30pm

ROOMS: (incl. bkfst & dinner) s £24-£34; d £48-£72 * **LB**

OFF-PEAK: (incl. bkfst & dinner) s £20-£30; d £40-£64

MEALS: Bar Lunch £3&alc Dinner £16&alc

CARDS:

★★61% **York House**

CONSORT HOTELS

14/22 Royal Pde BN22 7AP (M25, take M23 outside Brighton take A27 towards Lewes and then Eastbourne. York House is on the sea front .25m east of the pier) ☎ 01323 412918 FAX 01323 646238

Closed 23-29 Dec

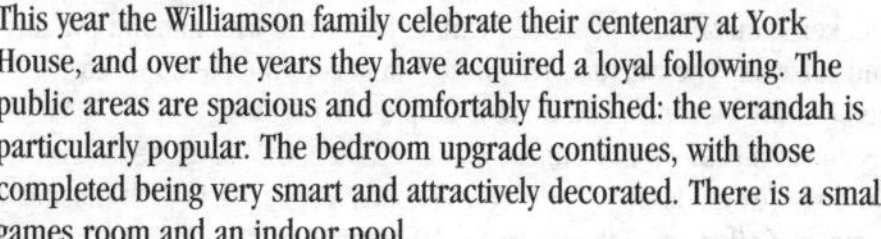

This year the Williamson family celebrate their centenary at York House, and over the years they have acquired a loyal following. The public areas are spacious and comfortably furnished: the verandah is particularly popular. The bedroom upgrade continues, with those completed being very smart and attractively decorated. There is a small games room and an indoor pool.

contd.

97 en suite (bth/shr) (8 fmly) CTV in all bedrooms STV Lift Night porter Indoor swimming pool (heated) Pool table Games room Wkly live entertainment V meals Coffee am Tea pm Last d 8pm
ROOMS: (incl. bkfst) s fr £39.50; d fr £70 **LB**
OFF-PEAK: (incl. bkfst) s £28.50-£35.50; d £57-£71
MEALS: Sunday Lunch £9 Dinner £12.50
CONF: Thtr 100 Class 30 Board 24 Del from £53
CARDS:

See advertisement on page 231

★★60% **Lathom**
4-6 Howard Square, Grand Pde BN21 4BG
☎ 01323 720985 & 641986 FAX 01323 416405
A warm friendly welcome by resident owners Fintan and Vera Tynan is assured at this much improved hotel. The atmosphere is relaxed and informal with helpful and attentive staff. The brightly decorated bedrooms do vary in size, some are small, but good use has been made of the space available, all are furnished in modern style and are suitably equipped. Evening entertainment is provided in the lounge and there is a small bar in which to enjoy a pre-dinner drink. A table d hote menu is offered at dinner, also there is a choice of breakfast, this is served in the smart dining room.
45 en suite (bth/shr) (5 fmly) CTV in all bedrooms Lift Night porter 8P Wkly live entertainment Xmas V meals Coffee am Last d 7.30pm
ROOMS: (incl. bkfst) s £25-£30; d £50-£60
MEALS: Bar Lunch £1.30-£1.50 Dinner £8.75
CARDS:

EAST DEREHAM Norfolk Map 09 TF91

★★63% **The Phoenix**
Church St NR19 1DL ☎ 01362 692276 FAX 01362 691752
This modern red-brick building sits very close to the town centre and has private car parking to the rear of the building. A small team of staff provide a polite service within the bar, restaurant and foyer lounge. Bedroom styles vary quite considerably, the newer rooms are generally more spacious and have co-ordinated colour schemes throughout their décor and soft furnishings, whilst the original rooms are dated and less spacious.
23 en suite (bth/shr) No smoking in 6 bedrooms CTV in all bedrooms 40P Xmas French & English Cuisine V meals Coffee am Tea pm No smoking in restaurant Last d 9.45pm
ROOMS: s £45-£55; d £55-£65 * **LB**
MEALS: Lunch fr £8.95 Dinner fr £12.95&alc*
CONF: Thtr 160 Class 110 Board 100
CARDS:

Remember to return your Prize Draw card for a chance to win a Romantic Weekend for two at a hotel in the Virgin Collection. See inside the front cover for the card and competition details. Remember to fill in your name and full address before posting!

EAST GRINSTEAD West Sussex Map 05 TQ33

RED STAR HOTEL

★★★ **Gravetye Manor**
RH19 4LJ (3m SW off unclass road joining B2110 & B2028) ☎ 01342 810567
FAX 01342 810080
RS 25 Dec

RELAIS & CHATEAUX. Relais Gourmands

This delightful Elizabethan stone mansion sits in a tranquil setting at the end of a long drive through Forestry Commission land. First impressions are stunning and still owe much to the work of William Robinson, the exponent of natural gardens, who lived here in 1935. Public rooms retain their original features and character, with open fires, lovely floral displays and highly polished wooden surfaces. Bedrooms are of good, comfortable proportions, and have a full range of modern amenities. A most professional service is delivered, particularly in the restaurant, where chef Mark Raffan provides interesting menus. Tian of crab followed by roast squab with a very light foie gras sausage and then hot caramel soufflé accompanied by a prune and Armagnac ice-cream to finish was the choice at a recent inspection meal.
18 en suite (bth/shr) CTV in all bedrooms No dogs 25P No coaches Fishing Croquet lawn No children 7yrs V meals Coffee am No smoking in restaurant Last d 9.45pm
ROOMS: s fr £105; d £140-£210 *
OFF-PEAK: s fr £85; d £155
MEALS: Lunch £24-£30&alc Dinner fr £30&alc*
CONF: Board 12 Del £195
CARDS:

★★★70% **Woodbury House**
Lewes Rd RH19 3UD (0.5m S of town) ☎ 01342 313657
FAX 01342 314801
An attractive 19th-century gabled house standing beside the busy A22 about a mile south-east of the town centre has been skilfully modernised to provide comfortable modern accommodation, the best rooms being in the New Wing. The bar-bistro offers an alternative to the more formal Garden Room Restaurant where a meal might comprise, for example, fresh ravioli filled with cheese and served with a basil and tomato sauce, loin of lamb filled with garlic-flavoured chicken mousse, and poached pears in Sauternes with almond praline and sabayon. The Buckmaster Room can accommodate up to 16 persons for meetings, and there is ample car parking.
13 en suite (bth/shr) 1 annexe en suite (shr) CTV in all bedrooms No dogs (ex guide dogs) 50P No coaches English & French Cuisine V meals Coffee am Tea pm Last d 10.30pm
ROOMS: (incl. bkfst) s £65-£70; d £75-£85 * **LB**

OFF-PEAK: (incl. bkfst) s fr £60; d fr £70
MEALS: Lunch £9.95-£18 High tea £2.50-£5.50 Dinner £18*
CONF: Thtr 30 Class 25 Board 30 Del from £92
CARDS:

See advertisement on this page

EAST HORNDON Essex Map 05 TQ68

Travelodge
CM13 3LL (on A127, eastbound) ☎ 01277 810819
FAX 01277 810819
This modern building offers accommodation in smart, spacious and well equipped bedrooms, suitable for family use, and all with en suite bathrooms. Meals may be taken at the nearby family restaurant. For information on room rates and to make a booking, call Roomline free of charge on 0800 850950. For more details about Travelodge, consult the Contents page under Hotel Groups.
22 en suite (bth/shr)

EASTLEIGH Hampshire Map 04 SU41

Forte Posthouse Eastleigh
Leigh Rd SO50 9PG (off A33 next to Flemming Park Leisure Centre) ☎ 01703 619700 FAX 01703 643945
Suitable for both the business and leisure traveller, this bright hotel provides modern accommodation in well equipped bedrooms with en suite bathrooms. For more details about Forte Posthouse hotels, consult the Contents page for the section on Hotel Groups.
116 en suite (bth/shr)
ROOMS: d £49-£69 *
CONF: Thtr 250 Class 90 Board 90 Del £160

Travel Inn
Leigh Rd ☎ 01582 414341 FAX 01582 400024
Purpose-built accommodation, offering spacious, well equipped bedrooms, all with en suite bathrooms. Meals may be taken at the nearby family restaurant. For more information about Travel Inns, consult the Contents page under Hotel Groups.
82 en suite (bth/shr)
ROOMS: d £35.50 *

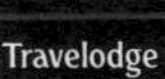

Travelodge
Twyford Rd SO50 4LF (off junct 12 on M3 on A335)
☎ 01703 616813 FAX 91703 616813
This modern building offers accommodation in smart, spacious and well equipped bedrooms, suitable for family use, and all with en suite bathrooms. Meals may be taken at the nearby family restaurant. For information on room rates and to make a booking, call Roomline free of charge on 0800 850950. For more details about Travelodge, consult the Contents page under Hotel Groups.
32 en suite (bth/shr)

EAST MIDLANDS AIRPORT Leicestershire Map 08 SK42

★★★★ 70% **Donington Thistle**
DE74 2SH (on the A453 at entrance to East Midlands Airport, just 1 mile from junction 24 and 23A of the M1 and M1/A42(M) interchange. ☎ 01332 850700
FAX 01332 850823
This modern, well designed hotel is situated at the East Midland Airport and is easily reached from the M1. Attractive public areas include a spacious foyer lounge, the Newstead Lounge, the smart Sherwood Restaurant and the Lord Byron Bar. In addition, there are comprehensive conference and function facilities and a well equipped

leisure centre with a heated swimming pool. Bedrooms are spacious and comfortable and have every modern facility.

110 en suite (bth/shr) (4 fmly) No smoking in 55 bedrooms CTV in all bedrooms STV Night porter 180P Indoor swimming pool (heated) Sauna Solarium Gym Jacuzzi/spa Steam room Wkly live entertainment Xmas International Cuisine V meals Coffee am Tea pm No smoking in restaurant Last d 10pm
ROOMS: s £90-£120; d £105-£145 * **LB**
MEALS: Lunch fr £14.50&alc High tea fr £6.75 Dinner £18.45-£19.95&alc*
CONF: Thtr 220 Class 90 Board 30
CARDS:

★★★ 63% **Yew Lodge**
33 Packington Hill DE74 2DF (off A6, close to junc 24 of M1)
☎ 01509 672518 FAX 01509 674730
Situated in the village of Kegworth and handy for both the M1 and the airport, Yew Lodge has been dramatically improved through refurbishment and extension in recent years. The reception rooms are

contd.

now light, inviting and well appointed. There is a cosy lounge and good facilities are provided in the comfortable bedrooms.
54 en suite (bth/shr) (3 fmly) CTV in all bedrooms STV Lift Night porter 150P Xmas English & French Cuisine V meals Coffee am Tea pm Last d 9.30pm
ROOMS: s £40-£72; d £50-£72 * **LB**
OFF-PEAK: s £72; d £72
MEALS: Lunch £8.75-£10&alc High tea £2.60-£5&alc Dinner £12.25&alc*
CONF: Thtr 100 Class 60 Board 36 Del from £65
CARDS: 

Hilton National East Midlands Airport
Junction 24 M1 DE74 2YW (junction 24,M1)
☎ 01509 674000 FAX 01509 672412
This is a bright, modern hotel, with an informal restaurant, aimed at both the business and leisure guest. All bedrooms have en suite bathrooms and a range of modern facilities. For more information about Hilton National hotels, consult the Contents page under Hotel Groups.
152 en suite (bth/shr)

EAST RETFORD Nottinghamshire Map 08 SK78

★★★67% **West Retford**

24 North Rd DN22 7XG (on A638)
☎ 01777 706333 FAX 01777 709951
There is an attractive setting about this well cared for Georgian house which is located on the fringes of the town on the road to Bawtry. In a separate building there are spacious and well laid out bedrooms with a few suites equipped to a very high standard. The restaurant, two bars and meeting rooms are located in the main building.
60 annexe en suite (bth/shr) (39 fmly) No smoking in 9 bedrooms CTV in all bedrooms STV Night porter 130P Croquet lawn Putting green Xmas French Cuisine V meals Coffee am Tea pm Last d 9.45pm
ROOMS: s fr £68; d fr £78 * **LB**
OFF-PEAK: (incl. bkfst) s fr £45; d fr £55
MEALS: Lunch £8.95-£16.95alc Dinner £12.95-£25alc*
CONF: Thtr 150 Class 40 Board 43 Del from £95
CARDS: 

EBCHESTER Co Durham Map 12 NZ15

★★★ 67% **The Raven**
Broomhill DH8 6RY (on B6309, overlooking village)
☎ 01207 560367 FAX 01207 560262
Spacious and well equipped bedrooms are a feature of this modern and pleasantly furnished hotel, which stands on a hillside overlooking the village. Well prepared dinners are served in the attractive conservatory restaurant and a good range of popular bar meals is available along with a range of hand pulled real ales. Friendly service is provided by a dedicated and smartly turned out staff.
28 en suite (bth/shr) (10 fmly) CTV in all bedrooms STV No dogs (ex guide dogs) Night porter Air conditioning 100P Wkly live entertainment Xmas V meals Coffee am Tea pm No smoking area in restaurant Last d 10pm
ROOMS: (incl. bkfst) s £41-£52; d £57-£69 * **LB**
OFF-PEAK: (incl. bkfst) s fr £41; d fr £57
MEALS: Lunch £5-£15&alc Dinner £17-£19&alc*
CONF: Thtr 150 Class 80 Board 40 Del £78.95
CARDS: 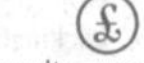

See advertisement on opposite page

EDENHALL Cumbria Map 12 NY53

★★64% ***Edenhall***
CA11 8SX ☎ 01768 881454
This long-established and traditional hotel lies in well tended gardens in a quiet village and offers friendly and attentive service. Public rooms include a spacious lounge bar and an attractive dining room, which together with some of the bright, unpretentious bedrooms, overlook the gardens.
21 en suite (bth/shr) 8 annexe en suite (bth/shr) (3 fmly) CTV in all bedrooms No dogs (ex guide dogs) 82P Fishing English, French & Italian Cuisine V meals Coffee am Tea pm Last d 9.30pm
CARDS:

EGHAM Surrey Map 04 TQ07

★★★★ 70% **Runnymede**
Windsor Rd TW20 0AG (off junc 13 of M25, on A308 towards Windsor) ☎ 01784 436171 FAX 01784 436340
Ideally located for easy access to the M25, this very successful hotel continues to grow in stature and has steadily improved in recent years. The accommodation has been completely upgraded to a standard that suits the demands of today's guests, and the River Room restaurant continues to impress with chef Laurence Curtis at the helm and live entertainment on most evenings, whilst the new Charlie Bell's café bar has added a new and very lively alternative. There are substantial facilities for functions and conferences.
171 en suite (bth/shr) (32 fmly) No smoking in 75 bedrooms CTV in all bedrooms STV Lift Night porter Air conditioning 300P Indoor swimming pool (heated) Snooker Sauna Solarium Gym Croquet lawn Putting green Steam room Beauty Salon Dance studio International Cuisine V meals Coffee am Tea pm Last d 9.45pm
MEALS: Lunch £17.95-£25.10 Dinner £22.50-£30*
CONF: Thtr 300 Class 250 Board 76 Del from £179
CARDS:

EGREMONT Cumbria Map 11 NY01

★★★58% ***Blackbeck Bridge Inn***
CA22 2NY (off A595. Follow signs 'Gosforth/Sellafield' S of Egremont, take second exit at next roundabout and hotel is 100yds on left)
☎ 01946 841661 FAX 01946 841007
A large roadside hotel with a modern extension, the Blackbeck Inn offers two styles of bedrooms, some more spacious than others. A good range of food is available in either the bar or restaurant. The hotel is convenient for Sellafield or for touring the West Lakes.
22 en suite (bth/shr) (1 fmly) CTV in all bedrooms STV 60P Pool table English & Continental Cuisine V meals Coffee am Tea pm Last d 9.30pm
CARDS:

ELLESMERE PORT Cheshire Map 07 SJ47

★★★66% **The Woodhey**

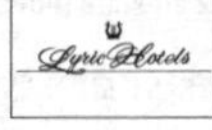

Welsh Rd, Little Sutton L66 4PS (M53 junct5 turn left at rdbt through 2 sets of traffic lights,turn right onto A550 over the hump back bridge turn left into Berwick Road) ☎ 0151 339 5121 FAX 0151 339 3214
This modern purpose-built hotel is situated on the A550 at Little Sutton, just south of Junction 5 of the M53. Bedrooms vary in size and decor, some being very spacious, and furnishings are modern. The Honeymoon Suite has a four-poster bed, and many rooms are conveniently located on the ground floor. There is a large restaurant with lounge bar adjacent. Conference, function and leisure facilities are good.
53 en suite (bth/shr) (8 fmly) No smoking in 4 bedrooms CTV in all bedrooms Night porter 200P Indoor swimming pool (heated) Sauna

Exercise equipment Wkly live entertainment Xmas V meals Coffee am Tea pm Last d 9.30pm
ROOMS: s £68-£100; d £83-£100 * LB
OFF-PEAK: (incl. bkfst & dinner) s fr £60; d fr £120
MEALS: Lunch £5.95-£7.95 Dinner £12.95-£14.95&alc*
CARDS:

★★59% **Woodcore Hotel & Restaurant**
3 Hooton Rd L66 1QU (M53 junc 5, take A41 towards Chester, first traffic lights turn right towards Willastow. Hotel 300 yards on left)
☎ 0151 327 1542 FAX 0151 328 1328
Good value for money is offered at this hotel situated in a green belt area just off the A4, two minutes west of junction 5 of the M53. Most of the bedrooms are contained in an annexe, all have en suite facilities and modern furnishings, and three are extremely large and comfortable. There are an attractive restaurant, a separate breakfast room and gardens to the rear.
7 en suite (bth/shr) 13 annexe en suite (bth/shr) (1 fmly) CTV in all bedrooms No dogs (ex guide dogs) 35P No coaches Wkly live entertainment English & Italian Cuisine V meals Coffee am Tea pm Last d 9.30pm
MEALS: Sunday Lunch £4.60-£12.50alc Dinner £13.50&alc
CARDS:

ELSTREE Hertfordshire Map 04 TQ19

★★★ 74% **Edgwarebury**
Barnet Ln WD6 3RE (on the A411 Barnet Lane, look out for concealed entrance) ☎ 0181 953 8227
FAX 0181 207 3668

This former millionaire's private neo-Tudor residence is popular with both conference and leisure guests. It is set in ten acres of mature grounds and is located within easy reach of the M1, M25 and City of London. Comfortable and modern bedrooms have been added onto the main building which has retained some original features such as stone fireplaces and oak panelling. One of the strengths of the hotel is the cooking in the kitchen, under Christopher Fisher, which makes great efforts and takes much time to produce exact tasting dishes using fresh, good quality ingredients.
47 en suite (bth/shr) (6 fmly) No smoking in 25 bedrooms CTV in all bedrooms STV Night porter 100P Tennis (hard) Jacuzzi/spa V meals Coffee am Tea pm No smoking in restaurant Last d 10pm
ROOMS: s £89-£99; d £89-£169 *
OFF-PEAK: s £59-£169; d £59-£169
MEALS: Lunch £17.50-£24.50&alc Dinner £17.50-£24&alc
CONF: Thtr 80 Class 50 Board 10 Del from £125
CARDS:

ELTERWATER Cumbria Map 07 NY30

★★★ 72% **Langdale Hotel & Country Club**
LA22 9JD (follow road into Langdale, hotel part of private estate on left in the bottom of the valley) ☎ 015394 37302 FAX 015394 37694
(Rosette awarded for dinner only)

The ideal venue for a family holiday or conference, the Langdale Hotel forms part of a country club which is set in a 35 acre estate, landscaped among water ways and woodlands on the edge of the village. Buildings are of Lakeland stone to blend with their natural surroundings and only five bedrooms are in the main hotel, most being contained in separate buildings or self-contained lodges within the grounds. They are being stylishly upgraded and are already very well equipped. The ultimate in indoor and outdoor activities are provided, the focal point being the leisure club which includes a shop and beauty salon as well as its own bar and restaurant which offer a more informal alternative to the hotel's main bar and restaurant. The estate even has its own pub within ten minutes' walking distance.

5 en suite (bth/shr) 60 annexe en suite (bth/shr) (6 fmly) CTV in all bedrooms STV No dogs Night porter 100P Indoor swimming pool (heated) Tennis (hard) Squash Snooker Sauna Solarium Gym Pool table Jacuzzi/spa ch fac Xmas International Cuisine V meals Coffee am Tea pm No smoking in restaurant Last d 9.45pm
ROOMS: (incl. bkfst & dinner) s £65-£105; d £45-£100 * LB

contd.

CONF: Thtr 100 Class 66 Board 50 Del from £85
CARDS:
See advertisement under AMBLESIDE

★★69% ***Eltermere Country House***
LA22 9HY (on unclass road between A593 & B5343)
☎ 01539 437207
Closed 25-26 Dec RS mid Nov-mid Feb
Set in landscaped gardens overlooking Elterwater Tarn, this traditional country house is well maintained throughout. Public areas include a comfortable lounge and a lounge bar leading to the dining room; both it and most of the bedrooms enjoy the fine views which help to make Eltermere ideal for a peaceful and relaxing stay.
18 rms (15 bth/shr) (4 fmly) CTV in all bedrooms No dogs (ex guide dogs) 25P No coaches Putting green ch fac English & Continental Cuisine Coffee am Last d 8.15pm

ELY Cambridgeshire Map 05 TL58

★★64% **Lamb**

2 Lynn Rd CB7 4EJ (enter Ely on A10, Hotel in centre of city near Cathedral) ☎ 01353 663574
FAX 01353 662023
This hotel is improving considerably under its new ownership, with regard to hospitality and services, and an upgrading of physical standards. Bedroom sizes vary, yet each room is pleasantly furnished and well equipped in a corporate style. Public areas include a choice of bars and eating options, with informal snacks served in the bars and lounge. A wider choice of menus is available in the restaurant.
32 en suite (bth/shr) (6 fmly) CTV in all bedrooms Night porter Xmas English & French Cuisine V meals Coffee am Tea pm No smoking area in restaurant Last d 9.30pm
ROOMS: (incl. bkfst) s fr £55; d fr £76 * **LB**
MEALS: Lunch fr £9.25&alc Dinner fr £14.95&alc*
CONF: Thtr 65 Class 28 Board 36 Del from £65
CARDS:

★62% **Nyton**
7 Barton Rd CB7 4HZ ☎ 01353 662459 FAX 01353 66619
This small family-run hotel set in two acres of attractive gardens adjoining the golf course, offers impressive views of the Cathedral and Fens. Public rooms are comfortably appointed, providing a bar and lounge area with an adjacent conservatory overlooking the gardens. Informal meals are available in the bar, and à la carte options are provided within the pleasant, wood-panelled restaurant. Bedrooms are modestly decorated and furnished.
10 en suite (bth/shr) (3 fmly) CTV in all bedrooms No dogs (ex guide dogs) Night porter 25P English & French Cuisine V meals Coffee am Tea pm Last d 8.30pm
ROOMS: (incl. bkfst) s fr £38; d fr £60 * **LB**
MEALS: Lunch fr £18 Dinner fr £15*
CARDS:

Travelodge
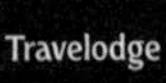
Witchford Rd CB6 3NN (at roundabout A10/A142)
☎ 01353 668499 FAX 01353 668499
This modern building offers accommodation in smart, spacious and well equipped bedrooms, suitable for family use, and all with en suite bathrooms. Meals may be taken at the nearby family restaurant. For information on room rates and to make a booking, call Roomline free of charge on 0800 850950. For more details about Travelodge, consult the Contents page under Hotel Groups.
39 en suite (bth/shr)

★ Hotels with a Red Star Award offer outstanding quality of accommodation and service within their classification. There is a full list at the front of the book.

EMPINGHAM Rutland Map 04 SK90

★★65% **The White Horse Inn**
Main St LE15 8PR (on A606, Oakham-Stamford road)
☎ 01780 460221 & 460521 FAX 01780 460521
A lovely honey-stone village inn, liberally adorned with colourful boxes, tubs and hanging baskets, the White Horse draws passers by like a magnet. It has a cosy, characterful interior with a choice of bars and a big canopied fire in the middle. Bar meals are served and there is a thriving restaurant. Appealing en suite bedrooms are located across the courtyard.
4 en suite (bth) 9 annexe en suite (bth/shr) (4 fmly) No smoking in 1 bedroom CTV in 12 bedrooms 60P Xmas English & French Cuisine V meals Coffee am Tea pm Last d 9.45pm
ROOMS: (incl. bkfst) s £48; d £58 * **LB**
MEALS: Sunday Lunch £12.95 Dinner £15.95&alc*
CARDS:

EMSWORTH Hampshire Map 04 SU70

★★★69% **Brookfield**
Havant Rd PO10 7LF (on B529) ☎ 01243 373363 & 376383
FAX 01243 376342
Closed 25 Dec-1 Jan
This popular hotel is conveniently located between Portsmouth and Chichester with good access to major routes. Personally owned and run by the Gibson family it offers friendly attentive service. The accommodation is modern and well equipped, with smart attractive decor throughout, there are some ground floor rooms. The well appointed Hermitage restaurant overlooks a pretty garden and offers a seasonally changing menu, and an award wining wine list. An ideal venue for weddings and conferences up to 140 with ample parking.
40 en suite (bth/shr) CTV in all bedrooms No dogs (ex guide dogs) Night porter 130P No coaches English & French Cuisine V meals Coffee am Tea pm Last d 9.30pm
ROOMS: (incl. bkfst) s £54-£60; d £73.50-£79.50 **LB**
MEALS: Lunch £14.95&alc High tea fr £2.50alc Dinner £14.95&alc*
CONF: Thtr 100 Class 50 Board 40 Del from £75
CARDS:

Travelodge
PO10 7RB (A27) ☎ 01243 370877 FAX 01243 370877
This modern building offers accommodation in smart, spacious and well equipped bedrooms, suitable for family use, and all with en suite bathrooms. Meals may be taken at the nearby family restaurant. For information on room rates and to make a booking, call Roomline free of charge on 0800 850950. For more details about Travelodge, consult the Contents page under Hotel Groups.
36 en suite (bth/shr)

ENFIELD Greater London Map 04 TQ39

★★★57% **Enfield**
52 Rowantree Rd EN2 8PW (1/2 mile from Enfield Chase railway station) ☎ 0181 366 3511 FAX 0181 366 2432
Quietly located in its own grounds on a leafy residential road, this informally run and well furnished hotel has a range of traditional and modern bedrooms. A wood-panelled lounge, a small bar and the Etruscan Restaurant make up the public areas.
34 en suite (bth/shr) (2 fmly) CTV in all bedrooms 20P Sauna Gym Board games in Lounge International Cuisine V meals Coffee am Tea pm No smoking area in restaurant Last d 10pm
ROOMS: (incl. bkfst) s £40-£65; d £60-£75 * **LB**
MEALS: Lunch fr £14.95 High tea fr £3.50 Dinner fr £14.95*
CONF: Thtr 60 Class 20 Board 35 Del from £75
CARDS:

★★70% **Oak Lodge**
80 Village Rd, Bush Hill Park EN1 2EU ☎ 0181 360 7082
This converted family home in Enfield's leafy suburbs is a welcome change from more impersonal hotels. Owners Mr and Mrs Brown are a charming couple who work hard to make their guests feel welcome. Bedrooms can be a little compact but all are prettily decorated and come with a wealth of nice extra touches. Good home cooking is served in the comfortable restaurant which adjoins a pretty lounge where magazines and books help create the atmosphere.
5 en suite (bth/shr) (1 fmly) CTV in all bedrooms No dogs (ex guide dogs) Night porter 4P No coaches No smoking in restaurant Last d 9pm
ROOMS: (incl. bkfst) s £59.50-£65; d £79.50-£100 *
MEALS: Dinner fr £17.50&alc*
CARDS:

EPPING Essex Map 05 TL40

Forte Posthouse Epping
High Rd, Bell Common CM16 4DG (on B1393)
☎ 01992 573137 FAX 01992 560402

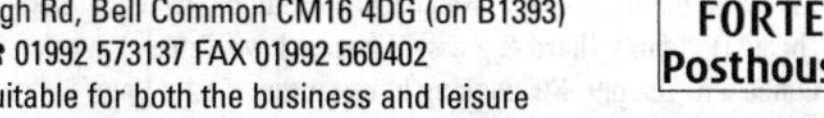

Suitable for both the business and leisure traveller, this bright hotel provides modern accommodation in well equipped bedrooms with en suite bathrooms. For more details about Forte Posthouse hotels, consult the Contents page for the section on Hotel Groups.
79 annexe en suite (bth/shr)
CONF: Thtr 85 Class 50 Board 32 Del from £99

EPSOM Surrey Map 04 TQ26

★★66% **Driftbridge**

Reigate Rd KT17 3JZ (the Hotel is in the A240 on the edge of Epsomat the crossroads) ☎ 01737 352163
FAX 01737 370477
This busy commercial and family hotel offers a friendly and informal atmosphere centred on its bars and themed restaurant. Improvements made to the public areas have added a new meeting room, and in due course similar treatment will be administered to the well equipped bedrooms.
34 en suite (bth/shr) (1 fmly) No smoking in 4 bedrooms CTV in all bedrooms STV No dogs 150P Wkly live entertainment V meals Coffee am Tea pm Last d 10.30pm
ROOMS: (incl. bkfst) s £35-£62; d £55-£72 * **LB**
MEALS: Lunch £7-£12alc Dinner £9.95-£15alc*
CONF: Thtr 150 Class 60 Board 30 Del from £95
CARDS:

★★63% **Heathside**
Brighton Rd KT20 6BW ☎ 01737 353355 FAX 01737 370857
(For full entry see Burgh Heath)

EPWORTH Lincolnshire Map 08 SE70

★★63% ***Red Lion***
Market Place DN9 1EU ☎ 01427 872208 FAX 01427 874330
This small village coaching inn is a popular venue with the locals, offering a wide range of food options together with a lively atmosphere. Bedroom sizes vary considerably, and decor is light, fresh and cheerful. Public rooms include a comfortable bar, a conservatory bar-snack area, a cosy restaurant and another, very popular bar, buzzing with young people and slightly separate from the rest of the hotel.
16 rms (5 bth 9 shr) CTV in all bedrooms No dogs (ex guide dogs) 134P Sauna Solarium Gym Steam room V meals Coffee am Tea pm Last d 10pm
CARDS:

ESCRICK North Yorkshire Map 08 SE64

★★★ 71% **Parsonage Country House**
Main St YO4 6LE (next to St Helens Church on A19) ☎ 01904 728111
FAX 01904 728151
This well furnished and very comfortable hotel stands close to the church and was in fact once the parsonage for it. The bedrooms are individually decorated and furnished and are quite delightful whilst the public rooms are very inviting, especially in the winter when a blazing log fire burns in the hearth. The well prepared Anglo-French cooking is delightfully presented and the menus are extensive and interesting.
13 en suite (bth/shr) (1 fmly) No smoking in 7 bedrooms CTV in all bedrooms No dogs (ex guide dogs) Night porter 100P No coaches Croquet lawn Putting green Xmas English & French Cuisine V meals Coffee am Tea pm No smoking in restaurant Last d 9.30pm
ROOMS: (incl. bkfst) s £70; d £105-£125 * **LB**
MEALS: Lunch £11.95 High tea £1.45-£6.50 Dinner £14.50-£19.50&alc*
CONF: Thtr 160 Class 160 Board 60 Del from £90
CARDS:
See advertisement under YORK

ESHER Surrey See LONDON SECTION plan 1 B1

★★65% **Haven**
Portsmouth Rd KT10 9AR (1m NE on A307)
☎ 0181 398 0023 FAX 0181 398 9463

CONSORT HOTELS

Conveniently situated close to Sandown racecourse, just north of the town centre on the A307, this former Edwardian house has been skilfully extended to provide a choice of several different styles of fully equipped modern bedrooms, including four recently refurbished rooms in an adjoining lodge. Room service is available daily until 11pm, and a residential licensed bar lounge complements a quiet separate lounge (sometimes reserved for private use) and an attractive dining room which offers a good range of reasonably priced food.
16 en suite (bth/shr) 4 annexe en suite (bth/shr) (3 fmly) CTV in all
contd.

bedrooms STV No dogs 21P No coaches International Cuisine V meals Coffee am Tea pm Last d 9pm
MEALS: Dinner £1.95&alc
CONF: Thtr 40 Class 48 Board 15 Del from £84.95
CARDS:

ESKDALE GREEN Cumbria Map 06 NY10

★★ 64% **Bower House Inn**
CA19 1TD (4m off A595 1/2 mile west of Eskdale Green)
☎ 019467 23244 FAX 019467 23308
Low ceilings and oak beams are a feature of this former farmhouse, situated in a largely unspoilt area of Western Lakeland, close to the main Cumbrian coast road. Many of the well equipped bedrooms are housed in converted barns, these are modern in style in contrast to those in the main building which are more traditional. The Inn has a very good reputation for food.
5 en suite (bth/shr) 19 annexe en suite (bth/shr) (3 fmly) CTV in all bedrooms No dogs 60P ch fac Xmas English & French Cuisine V meals Coffee am Tea pm No smoking in restaurant Last d 8.30pm
ROOMS: (incl. bkfst) s fr £48; d fr £64 * **LB**
OFF-PEAK: (incl. bkfst) s fr £42; d fr £60
MEALS: Lunch £12-£16 Dinner £19.50-£22*
CONF: Thtr 50 Class 50 Board 40
CARDS:

EVERCREECH Somerset Map 03 ST63

★★63% ***Pecking Mill Inn & Hotel***
BA4 6PG (on A371 1m W of village) ☎ 01749 830336
FAX 01749 831316
Closed 25-26 Dec
Situated on the A371, the Pecking Mill Inn is very conveniently located for the Bath and West Showground. The original parts of the building date back to the 16th century, these include the bar and the beamed restaurant both with open fires. The restaurant appeals to locals and visitors alike, guests having the choice from the à la carte menu or the bar meal menu. Bedrooms are neatly furnished and decorated, all are very well equipped and the best use has been made of the limited space.
6 en suite (shr) CTV in all bedrooms 26P No coaches Mainly grills V meals Coffee am Last d 9.30pm
CARDS:

EVERSHOT Dorset Map 03 ST50

RED STAR HOTEL

★★★ **Summer Lodge**
DT2 0JR (1m W of A37 halfway between Dorchester & Yeovil) ☎ 01935 83424
FAX 01935 83005

This delightful country house, set in the centre of a picturesque village in its own pretty walled garden, has been owned and run by the Corbett family for nearly 20 years. The public rooms are comfortably furnished, with log fires' water colours and abundant fresh flowers adding to the gentle elegance. The bedrooms are spacious and attractively decorated, with bathrobes, magazines, hot water bottles and fresh flowers all adding to the comforts. Chef Tim Fox presents a daily set menu and a seasonal carte offering imaginative and carefully prepared dishes. A recent meal started with a beautifully light twice-baked cheese soufflé accompanied by scallops and monkfish. A main course of medallions of venison was served with rösti potatoes and highly seasoned spinach à la crème. A mango tarte tatin completed the meal. Service by the young team is professional and attentive.

11 en suite (bth/shr) 6 annexe en suite (bth/shr) (1 fmly) CTV in all bedrooms 40P No coaches Outdoor swimming pool (heated) Tennis (hard & grass) Croquet lawn Xmas V meals Coffee am Tea pm No smoking in restaurant Last d 9pm
ROOMS: (incl. bkfst) s £110; d £140-£235 **LB**
MEALS: Lunch fr £12.50&alc High tea £5-£10alc Dinner fr £32.50&alc
CONF: Thtr 20 Board 20 Del from £137.50
CARDS:

EVESHAM Hereford & Worcester Map 04 SP04
See also Fladbury

★★★ 69% **The Evesham**
Coopers Ln, off Waterside WR11 6DA (Coopers lane is off the road alongside the River Avon) ☎ 01386 765566 & 0800 716969 (Res)
FAX 01386 765443
Closed 25 & 26 Dec
This impressive property was built in 1540, as a farmhouse, it underwent alterations in 1810, which accounts for its Georgian appearance. Set in two and a half acres of mature grounds, it is located close to the River Avon, to the south-east of the town centre, which is only a few minutes' walk away. It has been privately owned and personally run by the Jenkinson family for over 20 years, and has a well deserved reputation for hospitality and friendliness. The well equipped bedrooms, which include rooms for non-smokers and a family suite, are equally suitable for both business people and tourists. The imaginative menu provides a good and varied choice of well prepared dishes and is complemented by an extensive wine list.
40 en suite (bth/shr) (1 fmly) No smoking in 3 bedrooms CTV in all bedrooms 50P No coaches Indoor swimming pool (heated) Croquet lawn Putting green International Cuisine V meals Coffee am Tea pm Last d 9.30pm
ROOMS: (incl. bkfst) s £57-£65; d £74-£90 **LB**
MEALS: Lunch fr £6.85alc Dinner £13-£25alc
CARDS:

★★★68% **Waterside**
56 Waterside WR11 6JZ (A44/A435 junc 40yds on right alongside river) ☎ 01386 442420 FAX 01386 446272
This personally run hotel has been in the same ownership for the last 30 years, during which time it has been constantly developed and upgraded. It stands opposite the River Avon, within walking distance of the town centre. The attractive bedrooms have modern furniture, equipment and facilities and are equally suitable for tourists and business guests. Public areas include the popular 'Strollers' restaurant and bar, which has an American theme. There is also a choice of two comfortable lounges. Cream teas are served in the riverside gardens, when the weather permits.

14 en suite (bth/shr) 4 annexe en suite (bth/shr) (3 fmly) CTV in all bedrooms 30P Fishing English & American Cuisine V meals Coffee am Tea pm No smoking area in restaurant Last d 10pm
ROOMS: (incl. bkfst) s £40.60-£54.60; d £52-£75 * **LB**
MEALS: Lunch £6.95&alc Dinner £10-£15alc*
CARDS:

★★★65% **Northwick Arms**
Waterside WR11 6BT (follow A435, cross traffic lights, follow river for 0.25m hotel on right) ☎ 01386 40322 FAX 01386 41070
This large hotel overlooks the River Avon and is situated within a short walk of the town centre. It has benefited from recent improvement work, and its attractive public areas include a choice of bars. The bedrooms vary in size, but all are well furnished. One room has a four-poster bed and another - on the ground floor, with its own entrance from the pleasant patio area - has been specially designed for disabled guests. Other facilities include a self-contained function suite, a smaller conference room and a large car park.
30 en suite (bth/shr) (4 fmly) CTV in all bedrooms 100P Pool table Xmas English & Continental Cuisine V meals Coffee am Tea pm No smoking in restaurant Last d 9.30pm
ROOMS: (incl. bkfst) s £55-£60; d £68-£80 * **LB**
OFF-PEAK: (incl. bkfst) s £36-£60.50; d £60-£80
MEALS: Lunch fr £8.95 High tea fr £6.95 Dinner fr £14&alc
CONF: Thtr 240 Class 120 Board 60 Del from £75
CARDS:

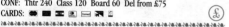

★★ 77% **The Mill at Harvington**
Anchor Ln, Harvington WR11 5NR (Harvington is found 4m NE of Evesham. The hotel is on the banks of the Avon. Reached by a bridge over the new A46)
☎ 01386 870688 FAX 01386 870688
Closed 24-27 Dec
A very attractive little hotel set in rural surroundings on the banks of the River Avon is made up of a Georgian house and a converted red-brick mill dating back to 1750; the old cast-iron bakery doors are on view in the spacious, comfortable lounge, together with many of the original wooden beams. Bedrooms with glorious views are, for the most part, well proportioned and offer thoughtful extras as well as deep armchairs and first-class beds - but prompt friendly service, warm hospitality and enjoyable food flavoured with home-grown herbs are the outstanding features of this establishment.
15 en suite (bth/shr) CTV in all bedrooms No dogs (ex guide dogs) 50P No coaches Outdoor swimming pool (heated) Fishing Croquet lawn No children 10yrs English & French Cuisine V meals No smoking in restaurant Last d 9.00pm
ROOMS: (incl. bkfst) s fr £58; d fr £92 **LB**
MEALS: Lunch £12.50-£14.25 Dinner £20.75-£29
CONF: Board 8
CARDS:

★★ 76% ***Nightingales***
Bishampton WR10 2NH ☎ 01386 462521 FAX 01386 462522
Closed 24-28 Dec
Twenty years ago the Robertson family, together with their pedigree herd of Aberdeen Angus cattle, left the Highlands of Scotland and settled on this farm in the village of Bishampton. Some 10 years ago they built a new farmhouse, and since then they have developed the property into a delightful small hotel with a popular restaurant. The bedrooms (one of them a family room) offer modern facilities, including good quality en suite bathrooms. There is a spacious lounge with a log fire, and drinks are dispensed from a small bar. In the restaurant, the Robertson's daughter Angela Morris, assisted by Peter Hornet, offers an imaginative set-price menu.
4 en suite (bth/shr) (1 fmly) CTV in all bedrooms No dogs 24P No

coaches No children 10mths English & French Cuisine V meals Coffee am Tea pm Last d 8.30pm
CARDS:

★★ 76% **Riverside**
The Parks, Offenham Rd WR11 5JP (off the A46 follow signs for Offenham. Take turning on right B4510 (Offenham) 1/2 mile turn left along private drive called The Parks to end) ☎ 01386 446200 FAX 01386 40021
RS Nov-Feb
Tucked away between Evesham and Offenham in an area of outstanding beauty, this hotel is perched above the river and boasts a superb outlook. Run very much as a restaurant with rooms, it is a friendly establishment offering comfortable, well equipped and brightly decorated bedrooms, and an inviting lounge where guests can anticipate the pleasures in store in the dining room which looks out over the river. Rosemary Willmott prepares well prepared and flavoursome dishes, based wherever possible on high quality local produce. The fixed-price menu offers a range of choice at each

contd.

course. A meal may start with a rich duck-liver and brandy pâté, to be followed by steamed fillet of bass in a crab and prawn sauce, and rounded off by rhubarb ice cream or rich chocolate truffle torte. Service is pleasing and attentive.
7 en suite (bth/shr) CTV in all bedrooms No dogs (ex guide dogs) 40P Fishing English & French Cuisine V meals Coffee am No smoking in restaurant Last d 9pm
ROOMS: (incl. bkfst) s £60; d £80 **LB**
MEALS: Lunch £16.95-£16.95 Dinner £24.95-£24.95
CARDS:

See advertisement on page 239

EWEN Gloucestershire Map 04 SU09

★★68% **Wild Duck Inn**
Drakes Island GL7 6BY (from Cirencester take A429 on reaching Kemble take left turn to Ewen keep driving to the centre of the village) ☎ 01285 770310 FAX 01285 770924
Situated in a quiet setting in the picturesque village of Ewen some 3 miles from Cirencester, the Wild Duck Inn dates back to 1563. After about 20 years the unique flying duck sign is now working again and the popular Post Horn bar is a delightful venue for residents and locals alike. A wide selection of ever-changing dishes is offered from the blackboard menus and served in the country-style restaurant. The majority of the cosy, well equipped bedrooms are located on the ground floor, with three rooms in the oldest part of the building, furnished in four-poster style. Tina and Brian Mussell are experienced hosts and, with their team of friendly staff, create a happy atmosphere.
10 en suite (bth) CTV in all bedrooms 50P No coaches water sking windsurfing English & French Cuisine V meals Coffee am Tea pm Last d 9.45pm
ROOMS: (incl. cont bkfst) s £49.50; d £69.50-£90 *
MEALS: Lunch £10-£25alc Dinner £10-£25alc*
CARDS:

See advertisement under CIRENCESTER

EXEBRIDGE Somerset Map 03 SS92

★★67% ***Anchor Inn***
TA22 9AZ (on B3222) ☎ 01398 323433
The archetypal village inn, this charming little hostelry is set in an acre of lawns beside the River Exe. Featured in Blackmore's 'Lorna Doone', it has cottagey bedrooms, brightly furnished in pine and with a good range of modern comforts. There are a congenial flagstoned bar which is popular with locals, and a quiet residents' lounge adjoining the Riverside Restaurant. The recent addition of David Lynn to head the kitchen continues the inn's reputation for freshly prepared dishes from both set and carte menus which take full advantage of local fish and game.
6 en suite (bth/shr) (2 fmly) CTV in all bedrooms STV 100P Fishing V meals Coffee am Tea pm Last d 9pm
CARDS:

EXETER Devon Map 03 SX99

★★★★67% **The Southgate**
Southernhay East EX1 1QF (on Southernhay roundabout near cathedral) ☎ 01392 412812
FAX 01392 413549

FORTE Heritage

RS Sat (restaurant closed for lunch)
This large modern hotel offers a wide range of services and amenities, designed for both the leisure and the business traveller. Bedrooms are smart, comfortable and well equipped.
110 en suite (bth/shr) (6 fmly) No smoking in 55 bedrooms CTV in all bedrooms STV Lift Night porter 115P Indoor swimming pool (heated) Sauna Solarium Gym Jacuzzi/spa Xmas International Cuisine V meals Coffee am Tea pm No smoking in restaurant Last d 10pm
ROOMS: s £69-£90; d £69-£90 * **LB**
MEALS: Lunch £12.50-£12.95&alc Dinner £19.75&alc
CONF: Thtr 100 Class 70 Board 50
CARDS:

★★★73% **Buckerell Lodge**
Topsham Rd EX2 4SQ (on B3182) ☎ 01392 52451
FAX 01392 412114

Best Western

Conveniently situated for the city centre, this privately owned hotel set in its own gardens offers comfortable accommodation and a relaxed atmosphere. The public areas include a smart cocktail bar in addition to the more informal surroundings of the Lodge Bar, where a range of snacks is available. Interesting dishes are offered on Raffles Restaurant's table d'hÙte and à la carte menus.
54 en suite (bth/shr) (2 fmly) No smoking in 12 bedrooms CTV in all bedrooms STV Night porter 100P Jacuzzi/spa Xmas International Cuisine V meals Coffee am Tea pm Last d 10.00pm
ROOMS: s £39-£89; d £79-£89 **LB**
OFF-PEAK: s £39-£89; d £79-£89
MEALS: Lunch £9.95-£12.95&alc Dinner £17.50-£20&alc
CONF: Thtr 60 Class 35 Board 30 Del from £85
CARDS:

See advertisement on opposite page

★★★72% **Barton Cross Hotel & Restaurant**
Huxham, Stoke Canon EX5 4EJ (0.5m off A396 at Stoke Canon just 3 miles north of Exeter) ☎ 01392 841245 FAX 01392 841942
Inglenook fireplaces and heavily beamed ceilings all add to the charm of this small, thatched hotel which is run in a relaxed and friendly manner. Its setting in the Exe Valley in the midst of the Devon countryside is a peaceful one, yet Exeter is only five miles away. Bedrooms are equipped with every modern creature comfort including satellite television and mini-bars. The cooking skills of Paul Bending are reliable, and he produces interesting dishes from local produce including fish and meat. The results are served in an unusual galleried restaurant from a fixed-price menu, and supported by an extensive and reasonably priced wine list.
7 en suite (bth/shr) (2 fmly) No smoking in 2 bedrooms CTV in all bedrooms STV Night porter 35P No coaches ch fac Xmas English

& French Cuisine V meals Coffee am Tea pm No smoking in restaurant Last d 10.0pm
ROOMS: (incl. bkfst) s fr £63.50; d £78.50-£85 **LB**
OFF-PEAK: (incl. bkfst) s fr £55
MEALS: Lunch £14.50-£18.50 Dinner £18.50-£22.50*
CARDS:

See advertisement on this page

★★★70% **Rougemont Thistle**
Queen St EX4 3SP (city centre opposite railway station and Royal Albert Museum) ☎ 01392 54982
FAX 01392 420928

The Rougemont is a Victorian hotel situated opposite Exeter Central Station. It has recently been refurbished to provide grand public areas, including a cocktail lounge and an elegant reception hall from which a splendid staircase rises to the upper floors. Bedrooms vary in size but all are pleasantly appointed in contemporary style. Several stylish function rooms are also available.

contd.

90 en suite (bth/shr) (5 fmly) No smoking in 13 bedrooms CTV in all bedrooms STV Lift Night porter 40P English & French Cuisine V meals Coffee am Tea pm Last d 10pm
MEALS: Lunch fr £9.75&alc Dinner £17.95*
CARDS:

★★★69% Royal Clarence
Cathedral Yard EX1 1HB (facing cathedral)
☎ 01392 58464 FAX 01392 439423
Occupying an enviable on a cobbled street overlooking the cathedral this 14th century hotel boasts enormous charm and character. The bedrooms are bright and inviting and offer elegant styles of decor and furnishings; some have the benefit of views of the cathedral. Public rooms include an intimate restaurant, busy bars and a quiet resident's lounge.
56 en suite (bth/shr) (6 fmly) No smoking in 8 bedrooms CTV in all bedrooms No dogs (ex guide dogs) Lift Night porter 15P Xmas English & French Cuisine V meals Coffee am Tea pm No smoking in restaurant Last d 9.30pm
ROOMS: s £44-£69; d £88-£109 * **LB**
MEALS: Lunch £6.95-£13 Dinner £16.50-£22*
CARDS:

★★★❀❀69% St Olaves Court
Mary Arches St EX4 3AZ (drive to City centre, follow signs to Mary Arches Parking. Hotel entrance is directly opposite car park entrance)
☎ 01392 217736 FAX 01392 413054
This lovely Georgian property, standing in its own walled garden in the centre of the city, is only 400 yards from the cathedral. Well decorated bedrooms offer a range of modern comforts and are furnished in period style. The public rooms revolve around an intimate candlelit restaurant, where handwritten menus offer a selection of interesting dishes, carefully prepared from the best of West Country ingredients by a talented team of chefs. The Wyatt family welcome guests and invite them to enjoy the relaxed atmosphere of their delightful personally-managed hotel.
11 en suite (bth) 4 annexe en suite (bth) (4 fmly) CTV in all bedrooms No dogs (ex guide dogs) 15P No coaches Jacuzzi/spa International Cuisine V meals Coffee am Tea pm No smoking in restaurant Last d 9.30pm
MEALS: Lunch £11.50-£14.50&alc Dinner £11.50-£14.50&alc
CONF: Thtr 70 Class 50 Board 35 Del from £90
CARDS:

★★★67% Devon
Exeter Bypass, Matford EX2 8XU (leave M5 at junct 30, follow signpost to Marsh Barton Ind Est A379, motel is on main A38 roundabout) (Brend) ☎ 01392 59268 FAX 01392 413142
A popular motel, the Devon provides well maintained accommodation including executive, family, standard and generous single rooms. Public areas, comprising a restaurant, carvery, bar and function rooms, are in the adjoining Georgian manor house.
41 annexe en suite (bth/shr) (3 fmly) CTV in all bedrooms STV Night porter 250P Childrens play area Wkly live entertainment ch fac English & French Cuisine V meals Coffee am Tea pm Last d 9pm
ROOMS: s £45-£50; d £55-£65 * **LB**
OFF-PEAK: s £35-£40; d £45-£55
MEALS: Lunch £10.50-£10.50 Dinner £15-£15&alc*
CARDS:

★★★❀❀67% Ebford House
Exmouth Rd EX3 0QH (1m E of Topsham on A376) ☎ 01392 877658 FAX 01392 874424
Closed 23 Dec-28 Dec
Friendly owners Samantha and Don Horton extend a sincere warm welcome and personally oversee all aspects of this classic Georgian house, conveniently situated between Exeter and Exmouth. Frisco's bistro is a popular local choice, with an informal atmosphere,

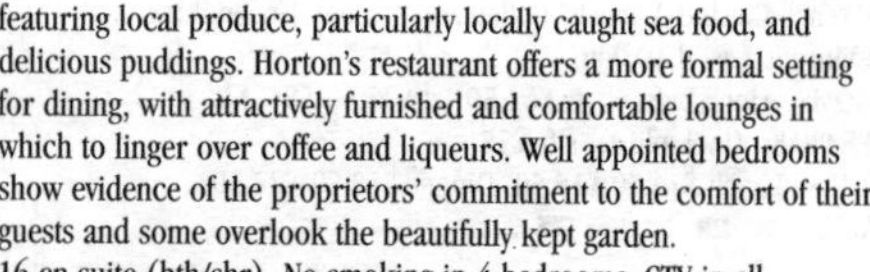

featuring local produce, particularly locally caught sea food, and delicious puddings. Horton's restaurant offers a more formal setting for dining, with attractively furnished and comfortable lounges in which to linger over coffee and liqueurs. Well appointed bedrooms show evidence of the proprietors' commitment to the comfort of their guests and some overlook the beautifully kept garden.
16 en suite (bth/shr) No smoking in 4 bedrooms CTV in all bedrooms STV No dogs (ex guide dogs) 45P Sauna Gym Jacuzzi/spa English, French & German Cuisine V meals Coffee am Tea pm No smoking in restaurant Last d 9.30pm
ROOMS: (incl. bkfst) s £62-£70; d £80-£85 **LB**
OFF-PEAK: (incl. bkfst) s fr £60; d fr £75
MEALS: Lunch £14-£16 Dinner £23.50-£26&alc*
CONF: Thtr 20 Board 14 Del from £80
CARDS:

See advertisement on opposite page

★★★63% Gipsy Hill
Gipsy Hill Ln, Monkerton EX1 3RN (3m E on B3181,leave M5 at juncn30, follow signs to Soliton Ind Est, turn right on roundabout then first left at hotel sign) ☎ 01392 465252 FAX 01392 464302
Built in the early part of this century, this friendly hotel looks out over East Devon from its elevated position in well tended gardens, close to the M5, the airport and the city. The bedrooms, some in the main house and others in a cottage annexe across the car park, vary in size but have been equipped with modern comforts. There is an attractive lounge with a bar, and a spacious restaurant where an extensive selection of dishes is available from a choice of menus.
20 en suite (bth/shr) 17 annexe en suite (bth/shr) (5 fmly) No smoking in 6 bedrooms CTV in all bedrooms Night porter 100P Wkly live entertainment ch fac English & French Cuisine V meals Coffee am Tea pm Last d 9.30pm
ROOMS: (incl. bkfst) s fr £63; d £85-£90 * **LB**
OFF-PEAK: (incl. bkfst) s fr £37.50; d fr £70
MEALS: Lunch fr £9.50&alc Dinner fr £16&alc
CONF: Thtr 140 Class 55 Board 36 Del from £83
CARDS:

See advertisement on opposite page

★★★60% Travelodge
Moor Ln, Sandygate EX2 4AR (M5 jnct 30) (Travelodge)
☎ 01392 74044 FAX 01392 410406
This purpose-built hotel, conveniently situated within the service area at junction 30 of the M5, continues to offer good value accommodation which is comfortable and practical for business and leisure use. The public areas include a small bar lounge, with an adjoining conservatory restaurant which is open all day for snacks and offers a full à la carte menu during the evening.
73 en suite (bth/shr) (22 fmly) No smoking in 24 bedrooms CTV in all bedrooms STV Night porter 100P Sunbed V meals Coffee am Tea pm
CARDS:

★★70% **St Andrews**
28 Alphington Rd EX2 8HN (M5 leave at junct31 signed Oakhampton.Follow sign for Exeter city centre/Marsh Barton along Alphington Rd.A377 A main route into City, hotel on left) ☎ 01392 276784
FAX 01392 250249
Closed 25 Dec-1 Jan
This small hotel is conveniently located within walking distance of the city centre. Bedrooms are brightly decorated and well equipped. There is a peaceful lounge with separate bar and straightforward dishes are served in the comfortable dining room using the best local meat and vegetables.
16 en suite (bth/shr) (2 fmly) No smoking in 4 bedrooms CTV in all bedrooms STV No dogs (ex guide dogs) 21P No coaches V meals Coffee am Tea pm No smoking in restaurant
ROOMS: (incl. bkfst) s fr £39; d fr £49.50 * **LB**
OFF-PEAK: (incl. bkfst) s fr £35; d fr £46
CARDS:

★★68% **Fairwinds Hotel**
EX6 7UD ☎ 01392 832911 FAX 01392 832911
(For full entry see Kennford)

★★66% ***Exeter Arms Toby***

Rydon Ln, Middlemoor PH7 4BP ☎ 01392 435353
FAX 01392 420826
Easily accessible from the M5, this purpose built complex is situated just four miles from the city centre and the airport. Bedrooms offer good standards of accommodation, and the bar and restaurant have recently been attractively refurbished.
37 en suite (bth/shr) (8 fmly) No smoking in 19 bedrooms CTV in all bedrooms No dogs (ex guide dogs) 120P V meals Coffee am Tea pm Last d 10.30pm
CARDS:

★★57% **Red House**
2 Whipton Village Rd EX4 8AR (jct 30 off M5,left before services signed Middlemoor,right at rdbt towards Pinhoe & University,in 0.75m left to Whipton/University,hotel 1m on right) ☎ 01392 56104
FAX 01392 435708
A small family run hotel on the edge of the city offers bedrooms that are well equipped with modern facilities. An extensive choice of dishes is served in a popular bar with adjacent dining area.
12 en suite (bth/shr) (2 fmly) CTV in all bedrooms 28P English & French Cuisine V meals Coffee am Tea pm Last d 9.30pm
ROOMS: (incl. bkfst) s £30-£37; d £46-£54 * **LB**
OFF-PEAK: (incl. bkfst) s £25-£30; d £40-£46
MEALS: Lunch £7.95-£11.95&alc Dinner £7.95-£11.95&alc*
CARDS: £

See advertisement on page 245

Percentage scores give you a comparison of quality within each star rating. See 'How to Use the Guide".

Travel Inn

R98 Topsham Rd, Countess Wear Roundabout, Exeter Bypass EX2 6HE (off A379) ☎ 01392 875441 FAX 01392 876174

Purpose-built accommodation, offering spacious, well equipped bedrooms, all with en suite bathrooms. Meals may be taken at the nearby family restaurant. For more information about Travel Inns, consult the Contents page under Hotel Groups.

44 en suite (bth/shr)

ROOMS: d £35.50 *

EXFORD Somerset Map 03 SS83

★★★❀❀71% **Crown**

Park St TA24 7PP (leave M5 junc25 and follow signs for Taunton. Take the A358 out of Taunton,then the B3224 via Wheddon Cross into Exford) ☎ 01643 831554 FAX 01643 831665

(Rosettes awarded for dinner only)

This is a huntin', shootin' and fishin' type hotel in this popular village in the centre of Exmoor. Service was attentive and efficient, by a young Australian who has worked here for several months and a couple of smartly uniformed waitresses. A fairly varied clientele, with locals using the bar; a range of bar meals is advertised on a blackboard, featuring modern trends of presentation and cooking skills.

17 en suite (bth) CTV in all bedrooms 30P Fishing Riding Shooting Xmas V meals Coffee am Tea pm Last d 9.30pm

ROOMS: (incl. bkfst) s £34-£42; d £84-£96 **LB**

OFF-PEAK: (incl. bkfst) s £32-£36; d £76-£80

MEALS: Bar Lunch £7.75-£16alc Dinner £18-£24&alc*

CARDS:

EXMOUTH Devon Map 03 SY08

★★★63% **The Imperial**

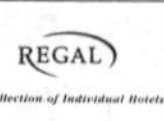

The Esplanade EX8 2SW (M5 junct30 A376 to Exmouth follow signed for seafront. Over 1st roundabout left at next, hotel at end of T junction) ☎ 01395 274761 FAX 01395 265161

Close to both the sandy beach and town centre this sea-facing, traditional hotel is pleasantly set back in gardens with tennis courts and heated outdoor pool. Over recent times the bedrooms have benefited from refurbishment and present bright, comfortable and well equipped surroundings. Many boast glorious views across Lyme Bay and all have easy access to the lift. Guests can relax in a comfortable bar lounge, and an interesting choice of dishes is served in the spacious, elegant restaurant.

57 en suite (bth/shr) (3 fmly) No smoking in 18 bedrooms CTV in all bedrooms Lift Night porter 58P Outdoor swimming pool (heated) Tennis (hard) Wkly live entertainment Xmas V meals Coffee am Tea pm No smoking in restaurant Last d 9pm

ROOMS: (incl. bkfst) s fr £52; d fr £104 * **LB**

OFF-PEAK: s fr £28; d fr £56

MEALS: Sunday Lunch £8.50-£11.05 High tea £3.15-£5.55 Dinner £16.95-£25.40*

CONF: Thtr 150 Class 80 Board 30 Del from £70

CARDS:

★★★59% **Royal Beacon**

The Beacon EX8 2AF (A376 to Exmouth from Exmouth follow seafront signs to the Beacon Hotel on left) ☎ 01395 264886 FAX 01395 268890

This Georgian hotel stands in an elevated position overlooking pleasant gardens and the Devon coastline. The hotel is beginning to show signs of age and many rooms are in need of upgrading. Public areas are relaxing and Fennels restaurant serves a range of traditional cuisine.

25 en suite (bth/shr) (2 fmly) No smoking in 4 bedrooms CTV in all bedrooms Lift 16P Xmas English & French Cuisine V meals Coffee am Tea pm Last d 9.30pm

ROOMS: s fr £42; d fr £70 * **LB**

OFF-PEAK: s fr £39; d fr £65

MEALS: Lunch fr £7.95 High tea fr £5 Dinner fr £12.75*

CONF: Thtr 120 Class 70 Board 60

CARDS: (£)

See advertisement on opposite page

★★70% **Barn**

Foxholes Hill, off Marine Dr EX8 2DF (M5 junt30 follow signs for Exmouth A376, to seafront in an easterly direction, next roundabout last exit into Foxholes Hill Hotel on right) ☎ 01395 224411 FAX 01395 224411

Closed 23rd dec - 10th Jan

Grade II listed and butterfly-shaped, this stone-built hotel overlooks the sea from an elevated position in two acres of gardens. Bedrooms are brightly decorated, spotlessly clean, and well equipped with modern facilities, and the public rooms include a comfortable and quiet lounge and a small bar. In the dining room a short daily-changing table d'hÙte menu offers a choice of freshly prepared dishes. David and Diana Palfreman extend a warm welcome to guests and, along with a small team of local staff, provide attentive service.

11 en suite (bth/shr) (4 fmly) No smoking in all bedrooms CTV in all bedrooms No dogs 24P No coaches Outdoor swimming pool Putting green European Cuisine V meals Coffee am Tea pm No smoking in restaurant Last d 8pm

ROOMS: (incl. bkfst) s £30-£34; d £60-£68 * **LB**

OFF-PEAK: (incl. bkfst) s £20-£30; d £40-£60

MEALS: Sunday Lunch £4.50-£7.95 Dinner £13-£15*

CONF: Class 40 Board 20

CARDS:

★★56% **Manor**

The Beacon EX8 2AG (M5 junct 30 take A376 to Exmouth take signs for seafront,Hotel located 300 yards from seafront by Tourist Information Office) ☎ 01395 272549 & 274477 FAX 01395 225519

Closed 1st Jan - 1st Feb

A family-run holiday hotel, the Manor is set in an elevated position between the town and seafront. Public areas include a comfortable bar-lounge and a dining room where a short and simple fixed-price menu is offered. All the bedrooms are equipped with modern facilities and some have lovely sea views.

38 en suite (bth/shr) (3 fmly) CTV in all bedrooms No dogs (ex guide dogs) Lift Night porter 15P Xmas V meals Coffee am Tea pm No smoking in restaurant Last d 8.30pm

ROOMS: (incl. bkfst) s fr £25; d fr £48 * **LB**

OFF-PEAK: (incl. bkfst) s fr £20; d £35-£40

MEALS: Bar Lunch £2-£6&alc Dinner £7.50-£8.50&alc

CONF: Thtr 100

CARDS:

★62% **Aliston House**

58 Salterton Rd EX8 2EW (on B3178) ☎ 01395 274119 & 266106

This family-run hotel, situated within walking distance of the town centre and seafront, offers a relaxed atmosphere. Bedrooms vary in size, and two are situated in a single storey building in the garden. Meals are served in an attractive dining room and there is a choice of comfortable lounges.

13 rms (2 bth 6 shr) 2 annexe en suite (shr) (2 fmly) CTV in all bedrooms 16P membership of sports club available Xmas V meals Coffee am Tea pm No smoking in restaurant Last d 8.30pm

ROOMS: (incl. bkfst) s £24-£26; d £48-£50 * **LB**

OFF-PEAK: (incl. bkfst) s £22-£24; d £44-£46

MEALS: Lunch £7-£8 High tea £3-£5 Dinner £8-£9*

CARDS: (£)

FAIRFORD Gloucestershire Map 04 SP10

★★61% **Bull Hotel**
The Market Place GL7 4AA (on the A417 in the market square adjacent to the post office) ☎ 01285 712535 712217 FAX 01285 713782
This family-run inn at the centre of the village has been the hub of the local community for many centuries and the atmosphere is one of informal friendliness. Some of the rooms have been refurbished to a high standard using attractive materials but there are still a number of rooms awaiting attention. The lively bar serves a variety of ales and food ranges from an informal snack in the bar to a full meal in the pretty restaurant. Staff are all felicitous without being intrusive.
20 rms (15 bth) CTV in all bedrooms 10P Fishing International Cuisine V meals Coffee am Tea pm Last d 9.15pm
ROOMS: (incl. bkfst) s £29.50-£49.50; d £39.50-£69.50 * **LB**
OFF-PEAK: (incl. bkfst) s £29.50; d £39.50
MEALS: Lunch £9.95&alc High tea £2.50-£4 Dinner £9.95&alc*
CONF: Thtr 60 Class 40 Board 40 Del from £53.50
CARDS:

See advertisement on this page

FAKENHAM Norfolk Map 09 TF92

★★63% **Crown**
Market Place NR21 9BP ☎ 01328 851418
FAX 01328 862433
This well established inn stands in the centre of the town; private car parking is available to the rear of the property, accessible through the archway. The public rooms have a lively atmosphere, offering a popular bar and a pleasant restaurant in which à la carte menus are offered; informal bar meals are also available. Bedrooms are quite appealing in a rustic style, generally of good comfortable proportions and well equipped with modern amenities.

contd.

11 en suite (bth/shr) CTV in all bedrooms 25P French Cuisine V meals Coffee am Tea pm No smoking area in restaurant Last d 9pm
ROOMS: (incl. bkfst) s £45; d £62 * **LB**
OFF-PEAK: (incl. bkfst) s fr £38; d fr £48
CARDS:

FALFIELD Gloucestershire Map 03 ST69

★★★ 66% **Gables Inn**
Bristol Rd GL12 8DL (on A38 just off junct 14 on M5)
☎ 01454 260502 FAX 01454 261821
This popular meeting hotel, situated conveniently close to the M5, offers a range of modern meeting rooms to suit various needs. The purpose-built bedrooms provide spacious comfort in a thoughtful layout.
32 en suite (bth/shr) (2 fmly) CTV in all bedrooms STV No dogs (ex guide dogs) Night porter 100P Sauna Solarium Gym Xmas English & Continental Cuisine V meals Coffee am Tea pm No smoking in restaurant Last d 10.30pm
ROOMS: d fr £49.50 **LB**
MEALS: Lunch £9.95 Dinner fr £16.50&alc
CONF: Thtr 150 Class 80 Board 60 Del from £89
CARDS:

FALMOUTH Cornwall & Isles of Scilly Map 02 SW83
See also Budock Water & Mawnan Smith

★★★★ 68% **Royal Duchy**
Cliff Rd TR11 4NX (Brend) ☎ 01326 313042 FAX 01326 319420
This fine period hotel is ideally situated to enjoy south-facing views across the bay, as well as being close to the beaches and within walking distance of the town centre. An extensive selection of menus offer dishes for all tastes, including a good vegetarian choice and an imaginative carte. Directions: Go through the town. At the Green Lawn Hotel turn right, at the end turn left towards seafront. Hotel is at castle end of promenade.
43 en suite (bth/shr) (6 fmly) CTV in all bedrooms STV No dogs (ex guide dogs) Lift Night porter 50P Indoor swimming pool (heated) Sauna Solarium Pool table Jacuzzi/spa Table tennis Wkly live entertainment ch fac Xmas English & French Cuisine V meals Coffee am Tea pm Last d 9pm
ROOMS: (incl. bkfst) s £50-£78; d £96-£160 * **LB**
OFF-PEAK: (incl. bkfst & dinner) s £49-£61; d £98-£164
MEALS: Lunch £9.50&alc Dinner £17.50&alc*
CONF: Thtr 50 Class 50 Board 50
CARDS:

See advertisement on opposite page

★★★ 76% **Penmere Manor**

Mongleath Rd TR11 4PN (turn right off Hillhead roundabout and follow road for approx 1m then turn left into Mongleath Road) ☎ 01326 211411
FAX 01326 317588
Closed 24-26 Dec
Set in five acres of gardens and grounds in a quiet residential area of the town, Penmere Manor has been run by the same family ownership for two generations. Elizabeth and Andrew Pope have now been at the helm for a few years and are ably assisted by manager Margaret Pennock; together with a loyal team of dedicated staff, friendly and attentive service is provided. Chef Richard Holland has recently taken over the kitchen and continues to provide interesting and imaginative dishes. The Garden Wing bedrooms are very popular, being fitted with either King-or Queen-sized beds, all being named after local gardens. The well equipped leisure club is professionally supervised and benefits from the adjacent Fountains Bar which serves light meals throughout the day and during the evening.

38 en suite (bth/shr) (15 fmly) No smoking in 29 bedrooms CTV in all bedrooms STV 50P No coaches Indoor swimming pool (heated) Outdoor swimming pool (heated) Sauna Solarium Gym Pool table Croquet lawn Jacuzzi/spa Table tennis Boules Wkly live entertainment ch fac Xmas V meals Coffee am Tea pm No smoking in restaurant Last d 9pm
ROOMS: (incl. bkfst) s £59-£91; d £85-£107 **LB**
OFF-PEAK: (incl. bkfst) s £43-£91
MEALS: Bar Lunch £8.70-£9 Dinner £19&alc*
CONF: Thtr 40 Class 30 Board 30 Del £75
CARDS:

See advertisement on opposite page

★★★ 73% **Greenbank**
Harbourside TR11 2SR ☎ 01326 312440 FAX 01326 211362
Closed 23 Dec-10 Jan
Dating back to the 18th century, Greenbanks has a long and interesting history, and has accommodated such guests as Florence Nightingale and Kenneth Graham of 'Wind in the Willows' fame. The spacious bedrooms are attractively decorated and well equipped, most have harbour views and many have balconies. The public rooms which include a sunny cocktail lounge and an elegant restaurant have a relaxed atmosphere. There is also a hairdressing salon, beauty room, sauna, solarium and gym.
61 en suite (bth/shr) (8 fmly) No smoking in 2 bedrooms CTV in all bedrooms Lift Night porter 74P Fishing Sauna Solarium Gym Pool table Hairdressing Beauty salons English & French Cuisine V meals Coffee am Tea pm Last d 9.45pm
ROOMS: (incl. bkfst) s £41.50-£66.50; d £108-£153 * **LB**
MEALS: Lunch £9-£9.50&alc Dinner £16.75&alc*
CONF: Board 20 Del from £70
CARDS:

★★★ 67% **Falmouth Beach Resort Hotel**
CONSORT HOTELS
Gyllyngvase Beach, Seafront TR11 4NA (from A39 to Falmouth follow signs to seafront & Gyllyngvase Beach, hotel opposite Gyllyngvase Beach)
☎ 01326 318084 FAX 01326 319147
This personally run beach side hotel commands lovely sea views, and many rooms have balconies to take full advantage of this. The bedrooms are all well equipped and attractively decorated with modern facilities. The public areas are comfortably furnished and a relaxed and friendly atmosphere prevails. There is an indoor pool, with sauna, solarium and fitness centre all adding to the in house facilities. The smart new carvery restaurant is particulary popular and offers a wide range of carefully prepared meals.
110 en suite (bth/shr) 7 annexe en suite (bth/shr) (26 fmly) No smoking in 95 bedrooms CTV in all bedrooms Lift Night porter 95P Indoor swimming pool (heated) Tennis (hard) Sauna Solarium Pool table Jacuzzi/spa Wkly live entertainment Xmas English & French Cuisine V meals Coffee am Tea pm No smoking in restaurant Last d 9pm
ROOMS: (incl. bkfst & dinner) s £45-£51; d £74-£86 * **LB**
MEALS: Lunch £8.45-£10.70 High tea £1.95-£4.50

contd.

Dinner £10.95-£16*
CONF: Thtr 300 Class 200 Board 150 Del from £59.50
CARDS:

★★★66% Green Lawns

Western Ter TR11 4QJ (on A39) ☎ 01326 312734
FAX 01326 211427
Closed 24-30 Dec
The leisure complex and award-winning gardens are key attractions at this conveniently situated hotel. Bedrooms vary in size, and all are comfortable and well equipped - the two honeymoon rooms have spa baths. An extensive choice of dishes is offered in the attractive split-level Garras Restaurant. Service, provided by loyal young staff, is friendly and relaxed.
40 en suite (bth/shr) (8 fmly) CTV in all bedrooms STV Night porter 69P Indoor swimming pool (heated) Tennis (hard & grass) Squash Sauna Solarium Gym Jacuzzi/spa Wkly live entertainment English & French Cuisine V meals Coffee am Tea pm Last d 10pm
ROOMS: (incl. bkfst) s £45-£80; d £80-£116 **LB**
MEALS: Lunch £5-£10&alc High tea £3-£6 Dinner £17-£19&alc*
CONF: Thtr 200 Class 80 Board 100 Del from £70
CARDS:

★★★64% Falmouth
Castle Beach TR11 4NZ (next to Pendennis Castle) ☎ 01326 312671
FAX 01326 319533
Facing the sea and set in five acres of award winning gardens, this elegant hotel retains an air of old fashioned grandeur. Bedrooms vary in size and standard and some have balconies. Public rooms are spacious and comfortable. There is a range of leisure facilities, and the restaurant offers a choice of menus.
73 en suite (bth/shr) (5 fmly) CTV in all bedrooms STV Lift Night porter 175P Indoor swimming pool (heated) Snooker Sauna Solarium Gym Pool table Croquet lawn Putting green Jacuzzi/spa Beauty salon Wkly live entertainment ch fac English, French & Italian Cuisine V meals Coffee am Tea pm No smoking area in restaurant Last d 9.30pm
ROOMS: (incl. bkfst) s £44-£84; d £66-£120 * **LB**
MEALS: Lunch £7-£8.40 Dinner £18&alc*
CONF: Thtr 200 Class 55 Board 60 Del from £49
CARDS:

★★★64% Gyllyngdune Manor
Melvill Rd TR11 4AR (from A39 follow signs for beaches and docks. Hotel 200yds beyond Pavilion and Beer Garden on right)
☎ 01326 312978 FAX 01326 211881
Closed 27 Dec-13 Jan
There are views through the trees to Falmouth Bay from this listed Georgian manor house. The attractive white-painted property, set in its own grounds, is ideally situated for easy access to the town centre and the beaches. Bedrooms vary in size, shape and design, and a programme of upgrading continues. In addition to the two lounges, there is an indoor pool and a games room with gym equipment.
30 en suite (bth/shr) (3 fmly) CTV in all bedrooms Night porter 27P Indoor swimming pool (heated) Sauna Solarium Gym Pool table Table tennis Wkly live entertainment Xmas English & Continental Cuisine V meals Coffee am Tea pm Last d 9pm
ROOMS: (incl. bkfst & dinner) s £57-£63; d £114-£126 **LB**
MEALS: Bar Lunch £7.50-£13.75alc Dinner £16&alc
CONF: Class 20 Board 20 Del from £60.50
CARDS:

★★★62% *St Michaels of Falmouth*
Gyllyngvase Beach TR11 4NB ☎ 01326 312707
FAX 01326 211772
REGAL A Collection of Individual Hotels
A popular resort hotel, is set in four acres of award winning gardens adjacent to the beach. The bedrooms vary in size, shape and style, the rooms in the Lodge being the most recently upgraded. The majority of rooms are equipped with hair dryers, wall safes and trouser presses. The public areas are spacious and comfortable, the Benson bar serving a variety of bar meals at lunch and dinner times.
57 en suite (bth/shr) 9 annexe en suite (bth/shr) (10 fmly) CTV in all bedrooms No dogs Night porter 100P Indoor swimming pool (heated) Sauna Solarium Gym Jacuzzi/spa Concessionary golf rates ch fac V meals Coffee am Tea pm Last d 9pm
CARDS:

★★65% Carthion
Cliff Rd TR11 4AP (from A39 follow signs to sea-front)
☎ 01326 313669 FAX 01326 212828
RS Nov-Feb
A Victorian property with panoramic views of Falmouth bay across the well tended sub-tropical gardens. Late in 1993, the hotel was taken over by Brian and Doreen Pewsey, who have worked hard to upgrade it, installing double glazing in seaward facing rooms. The lounge has been totally refurbished and designated a no-smoking area, and fine views can be enjoyed in the spacious sun lounge. Bedrooms are comfortable. Short set-price menus are offered in the dining room, and service is friendly.
18 en suite (bth/shr) (4 fmly) CTV in all bedrooms STV No dogs (ex guide dogs) 18P No coaches No children 10yrs English & French Cuisine V meals Coffee am Tea pm Last d 8pm
ROOMS: (incl. bkfst) d £50-£75 * **LB**
OFF-PEAK: (incl. bkfst) s £25-£38; d £40-£48
MEALS: Lunch £7.75-£12&alc Dinner £8-£12&alc*
CARDS:

★★64% Rosslyn
110 Kimberley Park Rd TR11 2JJ ☎ 01326 312699
Closed 23 Dec-1 Jan
This personally run hotel is centrally located and offers a warm welcome, the public rooms are spacious and comfortably furnished with one lounge overlooking the pretty garden. The bedrooms all have private facilities and some have sea views. There is a well stocked bar and a small games room.
25 rms (10 bth 4 shr) (3 fmly) No smoking in all bedrooms CTV in all bedrooms 20P Pool table Putting green Wkly live entertainment V meals Coffee am Tea pm Last d 9pm
ROOMS: (incl. bkfst) s £20-£22; d £38-£40 * **LB**
OFF-PEAK: (incl. bkfst) s £19-£22; d £38-£42
MEALS: Lunch £2-£6.50 High tea £2.50-£3.50 Dinner £8-£9.50*
CONF: Class 60 Del from £38

★★63% Broadmead
66-68 Kimberley Park Rd TR11 2DD (turn off A39 at traffic lights by Riders Garage, towards town centre, hotel 150yds on left)
☎ 01326 315704 & 318036 FAX 01326 311048
Closed 23 Dec-3 Jan
This informal family-run hotel is a large period house overlooking the attractive Kimberley Park. It has a comfortable no-smoking lounge, open plan with the reception, and a smaller sun lounge at the entrance. Bedrooms vary in size and outlook and are prettily decorated.
12 rms (11 bth/shr) (1 fmly) CTV in all bedrooms 8P Coffee am Tea pm No smoking in restaurant Last d 8pm
ROOMS: (incl. bkfst) s £21-£26; d £50-£56 * **LB**
OFF-PEAK: (incl. bkfst & dinner) s fr £32.50; d £65-£69
MEALS: Bar Lunch £3.25 Dinner fr £11.75*
CARDS:

★★62% Membly Hall
Sea Front TR11 4NT (from A30 turn onto A3076 for Truro then follow A39 to Falmouth.At Falmouth follow signs for seafront and beaches.Hotel located middleof seafront) ☎ 01326 312869 311115
Closed xmas week RS Dec to Feb

Set on the cliff road with wonderful sea views, this family owned hotel is very popular with coach parties. The bedrooms are bright and all have private facilities. The spacious public rooms include a bar and sun lounge which overlooks the sea.
37 en suite (bth/shr) (3 fmly) CTV in all bedrooms STV Lift Pool table Putting green Indoor short bowls,table tennis,darts Wkly live entertainment ch fac English & Continental Cuisine V meals Coffee am No smoking in restaurant Last d 7.30pm
ROOMS: (incl. bkfst & dinner) s £25-£35; d £50-£70 **LB**
OFF-PEAK: (incl. bkfst & dinner) s £23-£32; d £46-£64
MEALS: Bar Lunch £1.95-£6 Dinner £10&alc*

★★62% **Park Grove**
Kimberley Park Rd TR11 2DD (turn off A39 at traffic lights by Riders Garage, towards harbour. Hotel is 400yds on left opposite the park)
☎ 01326 313276 FAX 01326 211926
The Park Grove is a long established family-run hotel, conveniently situated opposite Kimberley Gardens. The accommodation is slowly being improved and service is relaxed and friendly. A popular bar combines with the dining room, and a four-course evening meal is featured daily. A small lounge is also provided.
19 rms (17 shr) (6 fmly) CTV in all bedrooms STV 28P Coffee am Tea pm No smoking in restaurant Last d 8pm
ROOMS: (incl. bkfst) s £21-£29; d £42-£52 **LB**
MEALS: Bar Lunch £2.50-£7.50 Dinner £12.50
CARDS: 

★★60% **Lerryn Hotel**
De Pass Rd TR11 4BJ (from A389 follow signs for Princess Pavilion and take 2nd turning on right after the Pavilion) ☎ 01326 312489
Quietly located close to the seafront, this traditional hotel is gradually being upgraded and improved by resident owners, Ann and Roy Picken. Bedrooms are all provided with TV, hair dryers and tea trays, and there is a comfortable lounge and well furnished bar. Friendly, helpful service is provided by Ann Picken, and dinner is available (only at 7 o'clock during the winter).
20 en suite (bth/shr) (2 fmly) No smoking in 10 bedrooms CTV in all bedrooms 13P Xmas English, French & Mexican Cuisine V meals Coffee am Tea pm Last d 8pm
ROOMS: (incl. bkfst & dinner) s £20.50-£31.50; d £41-£63 **LB**
MEALS: Lunch £7.75-£11 High tea £6 Dinner £7.75-£11&alc*
CONF: Class 50 Board 50 Del from £50
CARDS: 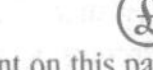

See advertisement on this page

FAREHAM Hampshire Map 04 SU50

★★★★75% **Solent**

Rookery Av, Whiteley PO15 7AJ (on Solent Business Park just off junct 9 on M27) ☎ 01489 880000
FAX 01489 880007
Despite its close proximity to the motorway and nearby business park, this modern, purpose-built hotel is peaceful; it is even secluded by fairly mature woodlands, which is the name adopted by the main restaurant. Here the kitchen produces very tasty meals, showing great effort and a promising understanding of raw ingredients. The public areas manage to convey a country house atmosphere and the bedrooms are very well thought out and well equipped. The staff are quite outstanding in their commitment to guest care and comfort.
88 en suite (bth/shr) (9 fmly) No smoking in 30 bedrooms CTV in all bedrooms STV Lift Night porter 200P Indoor swimming pool (heated) Tennis (hard) Squash Snooker Sauna Solarium Gym Jacuzzi/spa Wkly live entertainment Xmas International Cuisine V meals Coffee am Tea pm No smoking area in restaurant Last d 9.45pm
ROOMS: (incl. bkfst) s £88-£120; d £110-£140 * **LB**
OFF-PEAK: (incl. bkfst & dinner) d fr £134

contd.

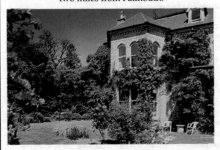

MEALS: Bar Lunch fr £10 Dinner fr £22alc*
CONF: Thtr 250 Class 120 Board 80 Del from £135
CARDS:

★★★67% **Lysses House Hotel & Conference Centre**
51 High St PO16 7BQ ☎ 01329 822622 FAX 01329 822762
Closed 25 Dec-1 Jan RS Sat, Sun & BH
This town centre hotel is well presented and offers thoughtfully equipped rooms for the business traveller; most bedrooms overlook the attractive rear garden. The public areas include a comfortable lounge and a popular bar serving a good range of snacks. The restaurant offers a more formal dining alternative with a daily set menu and an interesting carte served by friendly staff.
21 en suite (bth/shr) CTV in all bedrooms Lift Night porter 30P English & French Cuisine V meals Coffee am Tea pm No smoking in restaurant Last d 9.45pm
ROOMS: (incl. bkfst) s £55; d £70 *
OFF-PEAK: (incl. bkfst) s £35; d £54
MEALS: Lunch £11.95-£13.95&alc Dinner £16.50-£18.50&alc*
CONF: Thtr 95 Class 42 Board 28 Del from £73
CARDS:

★★★62% **Red Lion**
East St PO16 0BP ☎ 01329 822640
FAX 01329 823579
The Red Lion is a Grade Two listed coaching inn, situated in the heart of the town, which has been extended in recent years to provide additional, modern bedrooms. The original rooms are more dated and some are in need of upgrading. Public areas consist of an adjoining bar and restaurant with varied menus catering for wide-ranging tastes.
42 en suite (bth/shr) (2 fmly) CTV in all bedrooms STV No dogs (ex guide dogs) Night porter 136P Sauna Wkly live entertainment English & Continental Cuisine V meals Coffee am No smoking area in restaurant Last d 10pm
ROOMS: (incl. bkfst) s £59.50; d £75 * **LB**
OFF-PEAK: (incl. bkfst) d £45
MEALS: Lunch £12-£20&alc Dinner £12-£14.50&alc*
CONF: Thtr 80 Class 60 Board 60 Del £75
CARDS:

★★57% **Maylings Manor**
11A Highlands Rd PO16 7XJ ☎ 01329 286451 FAX 01329 822584
This Edwardian hotel is located on the edge of town and has been owned by the Burley family since 1975. The public areas include the Fleur de Lys restaurant which overlooks the large garden. The popular Raffles bar has a Country and Western theme and there are live music evenings.
24 en suite (bth/shr) (2 fmly) CTV in all bedrooms 87P English & French Cuisine V meals Coffee am Tea pm No smoking in restaurant Last d 9.30pm
ROOMS: s £32.50-£40; d £32.50-£55 * **LB**
MEALS: Lunch fr £9.50 Dinner fr £9.50*
CONF: Thtr 120 Class 60 Board 40 Del from £60
CARDS:

Forte Posthouse Fareham
Cartwright Dr, Titchfield PO15 5RJ (exit M27 at junct 9 and follow signs for A27. Continue across Segensworth roundabout following road for 1.5m, turn left at next roundabout) ☎ 01329 844644 FAX 01329 844666
Suitable for both the business and leisure traveller, this bright hotel provides modern accommodation in well equipped bedrooms with en suite bathrooms. For more details about Forte Posthouse hotels, consult the Contents page for the section on Hotel Groups.
126 en suite (bth/shr)
ROOMS: s fr £69 *
CONF: Thtr 160 Class 80 Board 50 Del £99

Travel Inn
Southampton Rd, Park Gate SO31 6AF
☎ 01489 579857 FAX 01489 577238
Purpose-built accommodation, offering spacious, well equipped bedrooms, all with en suite bathrooms. Meals may be taken at the nearby family restaurant. For more information about Travel Inns, consult the Contents page under Hotel Groups.
40 en suite (bth/shr)
ROOMS: (incl. bkfst) d £35.50 *

FARINGDON Oxfordshire Map 04 SU29

★★★69% **Sudbury House Hotel & Conference Centre**
London St SN7 8AA (off A420, signposted Folly Hill) ☎ 01367 241272 FAX 01367 242346
This handsome hotel with its colonnaded portico is set in six acres of well tended grounds. The hotel is geared up for the conference market and caters for business guests very well indeed. Bedrooms are attractive, spacious and well designed, with good desk space. The modern public areas are attractive and guests can choose to dine either in their rooms, from the bar menu or in the smart restaurant.
49 en suite (bth/shr) (2 fmly) No smoking in 17 bedrooms CTV in all bedrooms STV No dogs (ex guide dogs) Lift Night porter 85P Croquet lawn Putting green V meals Coffee am Tea pm Last d 9.30pm
ROOMS: (incl. bkfst) s £65; d £80 **LB**
OFF-PEAK: (incl. bkfst) s £55-£65; d £60-£80
MEALS: Lunch £9.95-£14.50 Dinner £17.95*
CONF: Thtr 90 Class 90 Board 40
CARDS:

★★63% **Faringdon**
1 Market Place SN7 7HL ☎ 01367 240536 FAX 01367 243250
Situated in the market place this traditional inn sits opposite the 12th-century church and can be traced back to the time of King John. The bedrooms are well equipped and have modern facilities, there is a popular lounge bar and the restaurant offers an interesting range of home-cooked dishes.
15 en suite (bth/shr) 5 annexe en suite (bth/shr) (3 fmly) CTV in all bedrooms V meals Coffee am Tea pm Last d 9pm
ROOMS: (incl. bkfst) s fr £48.50; d fr £58.50 * **LB**
OFF-PEAK: (incl. bkfst) s fr £45; d fr £55
MEALS: Lunch £6.50-£8.50&alc Dinner £8.50-£12.50&alc*
CONF: Thtr 30 Class 15 Board 20 Del from £70
CARDS:

FARNBOROUGH Hampshire Map 04 SU85

★★★64% **Falcon**
68 Farnborough Rd GU14 6TH (on A325 opposite Aerospace Centre airfield) ☎ 01252 545378 FAX 01252 522539
Closed 22-30 Dec
This hotel is conveniently placed for the town centre and access to major roads. Popular with an international business clientele, the bedrooms are modern and well equipped. There is a pleasant club-like atmosphere in the public areas, which include a small bar and open-plan lounge. The restaurant offers daily-changing and à la carte menus.
30 en suite (bth/shr) (2 fmly) CTV in all bedrooms No dogs (ex guide dogs) Night porter 30P International Cuisine V meals Coffee am Tea pm Last d 9.30pm
ROOMS: (incl. bkfst) s £67-£71 **LB**
OFF-PEAK: (incl. bkfst) s £45-£50; d £55-£65
MEALS: Lunch £12.95-£16.95&alc Dinner £15.95-£17.95&alc*

CONF: Thtr 20 Class 10 Board 16
CARDS:

Forte Posthouse Farnborough
Lynchford Rd GU14 6AZ (turn off M3 at junct 4, follow A331 and at roundabout follow A3011)
☎ 01252 545051 FAX 01252 377210
Suitable for both the business and leisure traveller, this bright hotel provides modern accommodation in well equipped bedrooms with en suite bathrooms. For more details about Forte Posthouse hotels, consult the Contents page for the section on Hotel Groups.
110 en suite (bth/shr)
ROOMS: s £99-£119; d £99-£119 *

FARNHAM Surrey Map 04 SU84

Courtesy & Care Award

★★★ 73% **Bishop's Table**
27 West St GU9 7DR ☎ 01252 710222
FAX 01252 733494
Closed 26 Dec-2 Jan
Over their 10 years of ownership, the Verjee family have lovingly restored and improved this hotel, which is full of character. The bedrooms have been individually furnished and all are well equipped with thoughtful extras. Chef Douglas Hull offers a choice of fixed-price menus in the restaurant, and although there is no lounge as such, the bar is very comfortable and efficiently run, and there is a most attractive garden to the rear of the hotel. Please ask about parking arrangements. Owners and staff here have won the AA Courtesy and Care Award for 1996/7.
9 en suite (bth/shr) 8 annexe en suite (bth/shr) (1 fmly) CTV in all bedrooms No dogs (ex guide dogs) Night porter No coaches V meals Coffee am Tea pm No smoking area in restaurant Last d 9.45pm
ROOMS: (incl. bkfst) s fr £75; d fr £85 * **LB**
OFF-PEAK: (incl. bkfst) d £60
MEALS: Lunch £9.95-£22.50&alc Dinner £20-£22.50&alc*
CONF: Thtr 26 Class 36 Board 20 Del from £85
CARDS:

See advertisement on this page

★★★ 61% **Bush**
The Borough GU9 7NN ☎ 01252 715237
FAX 01252 733530
Situated in the centre of town, this ivy-clad 17th-century coaching inn has a range of bedrooms in the original building and modern rooms in a rear extension. The lounge features splendid frescos depicting historical scenes, there is a traditional bar and a choice of dining in the Georgian-style Thackeray restaurant or the new Café-Bar-Tabac, modelled on a contemporary French bistro.
66 en suite (bth/shr) (2 fmly) No smoking in 20 bedrooms CTV in all bedrooms Night porter 80P Xmas British & French Cuisine V meals Coffee am Tea pm No smoking in restaurant Last d 10pm
ROOMS: s £90-£105; d £90-£105 * **LB**
OFF-PEAK: s £55-£65; d £55-£65
MEALS: Lunch £12-£25&alc Dinner £20-£35alc
CONF: Thtr 70 Class 40 Board 40 Del from £95
CARDS:

★★★ 60% ***Farnham House***
Alton Rd GU10 5ER (1m from town, off A31 Alton road)
☎ 01252 716908 FAX 01252 722583
This interesting property stands in five acres of mature grounds at the end of a narrow drive a mile west of the town off the A31 eastbound carriageway. The interior has some original and period features and the bedrooms have been refurbished and upgraded to a good all-round standard. Bar meals are available and a short à la carte dinner menu is served in the Oak Room restaurant. The atmosphere is informal and relaxed and the Cedar Room provides good facilities for small conferences and wedding receptions. There is also an extensive range of outdoor leisure facilities.
20 en suite (bth/shr) CTV in all bedrooms No dogs (ex guide dogs) 75P Outdoor swimming pool (heated) Tennis (hard) Croquet lawn International Cuisine V meals Coffee am Tea pm Last d 9.15pm
CARDS:

See advertisement on page 253

indicates a Town House Hotel. Please consult the section on AA Star Rating at the front of the book.

F

FARRINGTON GURNEY Somerset Map 03 ST65

★★69% **Country Ways**
Marsh Ln BS18 5TT (off A37 next to Farrington Golf Club)
☎ 01761 452449 FAX 01761 452706
Closed 24-31 Dec RS Sun
This cosy little hotel is aptly named. A warm welcome is provided by owner Janet Richards, who is also responsible for the freshly prepared and enjoyable food. Cottagey bedrooms are individually styled and cottagey, and equipped with modern facilities. The public areas are comfortable and include a small bar lounge, a conservatory sitting room, and an attractive, split-level dining room.
6 en suite (bth/shr) CTV in all bedrooms No dogs 12P No coaches Fishing V meals Coffee am Tea pm No smoking in restaurant Last d 8.45pm
ROOMS: (incl. bkfst) s £50-£60; d £60-£70 * **LB**
MEALS: Lunch £16-£22alc Dinner £16-£22alc*
CARDS:

FELIXSTOWE Suffolk Map 05 TM33

★★★68% **Orwell**
Hamilton Rd IP11 7DX (approaching on A45, straight across Dock Roundabout, straight across next roundabout, 4th exit off third roundabout) ☎ 01394 285511 FAX 01394 670687
This centrally located hotel offers a good range of comfortable day rooms, ranging from the foyer lounge to a choice of bars and dining options. The Buttery is for informal meals, whilst the restaurant offers daily changing menus and a carte at lunch and dinner. Recently refurbished bedrooms look smart with their colourful new soft furnishings and decor.
58 en suite (bth/shr) (8 fmly) No smoking in 4 bedrooms CTV in all bedrooms No dogs (ex guide dogs) Lift Night porter 70P International Cuisine V meals Coffee am Tea pm No smoking area in restaurant Last d 9.45pm
ROOMS: s £62.50; d £77.50 * **LB**
MEALS: Lunch £13.50&alc High tea £5-£10 Dinner £16.50&alc*
CONF: Thtr 200 Class 100 Board 60 Del from £85
CARDS:

★★69% **Waverley**
2 Wolsey Gardens IP11 7DF ☎ 01394 282811 FAX 01394 670185
This tall Victorian house stands on a cliff top, only a short descent from seafront and town centre. Most of the ground floor is occupied by Gladstone's Bar, where informal meals popular with a local clientele provide an alternative to the restaurant's choice of menus. Modern bedrooms are immaculately maintained.
19 en suite (bth/shr) (4 fmly) CTV in all bedrooms STV 30P Wkly live entertainment Xmas English & Italian Cuisine V meals Coffee am Tea pm No smoking area in restaurant Last d 9.30pm
ROOMS: s £52.95-£62.95; d £62.95-£72.95 * **LB**
MEALS: Lunch £7.30-£15.70&alc Dinner £15.70&alc
CONF: Thtr 85 Class 35 Board 25 Del from £69.65
CARDS: £

★★60% **Marlborough**
Sea Front IP11 8BJ (follow 'Seafront' signs) ☎ 01394 285621 FAX 01394 670724
Located facing the sea south of the pier leisure complex, this popular hotel is personally run by the Mohindra family, and comprises reception and front lobby sitting areas, the spacious and well appointed Flying Boat bar-lounge, the attractive Rattan Restaurant and L'Aperitif Bar. Bedrooms, which vary in shape and size, are furnished in a functional modern style and come well equipped with remote control satellite TV and radio. The self-contained Brackenbury Suite provides good facilities for functions and meetings accommodating up to 90 persons, and car parking is available.
47 en suite (bth/shr) (2 fmly) CTV in all bedrooms STV Lift Night porter 19P Windsurfing Xmas English & French Cuisine V meals Coffee am No smoking area in restaurant Last d 9.30pm
ROOMS: s £42.50; d £42.50-£60 * **LB**
OFF-PEAK: (incl. dinner) s £35-£39.50; d £35-£70
MEALS: Lunch £8.50-£10.50 Dinner £14.50&alc
CONF: Thtr 100 Class 60 Board 40 Del from £85
CARDS: £

FENSTANTON Cambridgeshire Map 04 TL36

Travelodge

PE18 9JG (4m SE of Huntingdon, on A14 eastbound) ☎ 01954 230919 FAX 01954 230919
This modern building offers accommodation in smart, spacious and well equipped bedrooms, suitable for family use, and all with en suite bathrooms. Meals may be taken at the nearby family restaurant. For information on room rates and to make a booking, call Roomline free of charge on 0800 850950. For more details about Travelodge, consult the Contents page under Hotel Groups.
40 en suite (bth/shr)

FERNDOWN Dorset Map 04 SU00

★★★★66% **Dormy**
DE VERE HOTELS
New Rd BH22 8ES (off A347 from Bournemouth)
☎ 01202 872121 FAX 01202 895388
This long established hotel in the leafy outskirts of Ferndown is popular with both business and leisure guests. Public rooms have a welcoming traditional feel with panelling and open fires, and a willing team of staff. Bedrooms are located in the main building and in several nearby cottage wings. There are good leisure facilities and a brasserie as well as a formal restaurant.
128 en suite (bth/shr) (15 fmly) No smoking in 28 bedrooms CTV in all bedrooms STV Lift Night porter 220P Indoor swimming pool (heated) Tennis (hard) Squash Snooker Sauna Solarium Gym Pool table Putting green Jacuzzi/spa Beauty salon Wkly live entertainment ch fac Xmas V meals Coffee am Tea pm Last d 9.30pm
ROOMS: (incl. bkfst) s £99-£199; d £125-£225 **LB**
MEALS: Lunch £12.50-£14.50 Dinner £19.50*
CARDS:

★★★63% **Bridge House**
2 Ringwood Rd, Longham BH22 9AN (on A348 towards Poole)
☎ 01202 578828 FAX 01202 572620
The Bridge House Hotel is set in a unique location in the picturesque Dorset countryside, overlooking the River Stour. In the spacious carvery bar an extensive range of good value meals is offered; guests appreciate the tables overlooking the river. In the formal dining option Thai cooking can be experienced from an à la carte menu. There is an ongoing programme of upgrading to the bedrooms; rooms are available on the ground and first floors.
37 en suite (bth/shr) (2 fmly) No smoking in 12 bedrooms CTV in all bedrooms STV Night porter 250P Fishing Wkly live entertainment Xmas English & French Cuisine V meals Coffee am Tea pm No smoking area in restaurant Last d 10.30pm
ROOMS: (incl. bkfst) s £35-£40; d £40-£60 * **LB**
OFF-PEAK: (incl. bkfst) d £40-£50
MEALS: Bar Lunch £10.50-£12.50&alc Dinner £11.50-£14.95&alc*
CONF: Thtr 120 Class 80 Board 40 Del from £40
CARDS: £

See advertisement on opposite page

★★61% **Coach House Inn**
579 Winborne Rd East, Tricketts Cross BH22 9NW
(junc A31/A348) ☎ 01202 861222
FAX 01202 894130

The accommodation at this inn is contained in 4 separate buildings in the style of a motel. The rooms are spacious and well equipped, some rooms are slightly dated but they are being steadily upgraded with smart attractive décor; there are some executive rooms available which offer more comfort and have mini bars, a trouser press and ironing boards. The popular restaurant offers a wide range of traditional dishes and grills in addition to daily specials. There are several function rooms and a weight training room.
44 annexe en suite (bth) (7 fmly) CTV in all bedrooms STV 125P Gym English & Italian Cuisine V meals Coffee am Tea pm Last d 9.30pm
ROOMS: d £35-£40 * **LB**
OFF-PEAK: d fr £33.50
MEALS: Lunch £4.50-£7.50&alc Dinner £10.25-£11&alc*
CONF: Thtr 150 Class 75 Board 40 Del from £55
CARDS:

FERRYBRIDGE SERVICE AREA West Yorkshire Map 08 SE42

Travelodge
WF11 0AF (A1/M62 jnct 33)
☎ Central Res 0800 850950

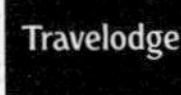

This modern building offers accommodation in smart, spacious and well equipped bedrooms, suitable for family use, and all with en suite bathrooms. Meals may be taken at the nearby family restaurant. For information on room rates and to make a booking, call Roomline free of charge on 0800 850950. For more details about Travelodge, consult the Contents page under Hotel Groups.
36 en suite (bth/shr)

FILEY North Yorkshire Map 08 TA18

★★63% ***Sea Brink***
The Beach YO14 9LA ☎ 01723 513257 FAX 01723 514139
Situated right on the seafront with superb views over Filey Bay, this family-owned hotel offers warm and friendly service. Bedrooms are well equipped and the lounge cosy and comfortable, while well produced dinners are served in a dining room overlooking the sea, and snacks and refreshments are available all day in Brinks Coffee Shop.
11 en suite (bth/shr) (5 fmly) CTV in all bedrooms STV No coaches English & French Cuisine V meals Coffee am Tea pm Last d 10pm
CARDS:

FINDON West Sussex Map 04 TQ10

★★★ 65% **Findon Manor**
High St BN14 0TA ☎ 01903 872733 FAX 01903 877473
This 16th-century former rectory stands surrounded by trees and attractive grounds in the heart of Sussex. En suite bedrooms are prettily decorated and comfortably furnished. The elegant dining room serves an interesting range of carefully prepared dishes including vegetarian options, while the popular Snooty Fox public bar offers selection of light meals and snacks. Staff are friendly and helpful.
11 en suite (bth/shr) (2 fmly) CTV in all bedrooms 28P Xmas English & French Cuisine V meals Coffee am No smoking area in restaurant Last d 9pm
ROOMS: (incl. bkfst) s fr £45; d fr £70 * **LB**
MEALS: Lunch £11.50-£16.95 Dinner fr £16.95*
CONF: Thtr 45 Class 25 Board 20 Del from £63.50
CARDS:

FIR TREE Co Durham Map 12 NZ13

★★★68% **Helme Park Hall Country House**
DL13 4NW (1m N of roundabout at A689 intersection)
☎ 01388 730970 FAX 01388 730970
A very warm and hospitable family-owned hotel which has panoramic views over the Wear Valley. The lounge bar, warmed by open fires, exploits these fine views and is extremely popular for its vast selection of bar meals. The style of furnishings and decoration is contemporary and the hotel is immaculate throughout.
13 en suite (bth/shr) (1 fmly) CTV in all bedrooms No dogs (ex guide dogs) 50P Sauna Solarium Xmas English & French Cuisine V meals Coffee am Tea pm Last d 9.30pm
ROOMS: (incl. bkfst) s £38; d £60-£91.50 * **LB**
MEALS: Lunch £8.15-£16.50&alc Dinner fr £16.50&alc
CONF: Thtr 100 Class 50 Board 120 Del £90
CARDS:

See advertisement on opposite page

★★62% ***Fir Tree Country***
Crook DL15 8DD ☎ 01388 762161
A modern single-storey inn which has extensive dining sections each with a comfortable seating area and a separate residents' lounge. Motel-style bedrooms are situated within yards of the main building.
14 en suite (bth/shr) No smoking in 4 bedrooms CTV in all bedrooms No dogs (ex guide dogs) 48P International Cuisine V meals Coffee am Tea pm Last d 10pm
CARDS:

FIVE OAKS West Sussex Map 04 TQ02

Travelodge
Staines St RH14 9AE (on A29, northbound, 1m N of Billingshurst) ☎ 01403 782711 FAX 01403 782711
This modern building offers accommodation in smart, spacious and well equipped bedrooms, suitable for family use, and all with en suite bathrooms. Meals may be taken at the nearby family restaurant. For information on room rates and to make a booking, call Roomline free of charge on 0800 850950. For more details about Travelodge, consult the Contents page under Hotel Groups.
26 en suite (bth/shr)

Travelodge

FLADBURY Hereford & Worcester Map 03 SO94

★★65% **The Chequers Inn**
Chequers Ln WR10 2PZ (off A44) ☎ 01386 860276 & 860527
FAX 01386 861286
Parts of this village inn in the centre of Fladbury, some four miles from Evesham, date from the 14th century. Much of the building's character has been retained, especially in the beamed bar, where a welcoming fire burns in colder weather. A wide range of dishes is available from both the bar meal menus and carte, and there is a carvery buffet in the traditionally furnished restaurant. Bedrooms vary in size, but all have good modern furnishings and facilities.
8 en suite (bth/shr) (1 fmly) CTV in all bedrooms STV No dogs (ex guide dogs) 25P Fishing Xmas V meals Coffee am No smoking in restaurant Last d 9.45pm
ROOMS: (incl. bkfst) s £42.50; d £55-£65 * **LB**
CARDS:

See advertisement under EVESHAM

FLAMBOROUGH East Riding of Yorkshire Map 08 TA26

★★67% **North Star**
North Marine Dr YO15 1BL (in town follow signs for 'North Landing'. Hotel 100yds from the sea) ☎ 01262 850379
This family-run hotel is found close to the famous North Landing of Flamborough Head and has been delightfully furnished throughout. The bedrooms are well equipped and have quality pine furniture together with pretty fabrics and comfortable seating. A good range of food is served in the cosy dining room and, at the time of our inspection, a new lounge was about to be added to the hotel.
7 en suite (bth/shr) CTV in all bedrooms No dogs (ex guide dogs) 30P V meals Coffee am Tea pm No smoking in restaurant Last d 9.30pm
ROOMS: (incl. bkfst) s fr £33; d fr £50 * **LB**
MEALS: Lunch fr £7.95&alc Dinner £10.50-£15&alc*
CARDS:

★64% ***Flaneburg***
North Marine Rd YO15 1LF ☎ 01262 850284 FAX 01262 850284
Mar-3rd wk Dec
This family owned hotel stands close the North Landing of Flamborough Head and is especially popular with bird watchers and golfers. It provides very adequate bedrooms with colour television; most are also en suite. The public rooms are very traditional and offer pleasant comforts whilst a good choice of food is available either in the rear bar or the nautically-themed bar. Service is friendly and informal.
13 rms (8 shr) (2 fmly) CTV in all bedrooms No dogs 20P No coaches V meals Coffee am Last d 7pm

FLEET Hampshire Map 04 SU85

★★★59% Lismoyne

Church Rd GU13 8NA (approach town on B3013, cross over railway bridge and continue to town centre. Pass through traffic lights and take first right. Hotel 0.25m on left) ☎ 01252 628555 FAX 01252 811761

Located in a quiet residential area just a short walk from the town, The Lismoyne is set in its own very attractive grounds and is popular with commercial guests. The bedrooms vary in size but are attractively decorated and furnished. Public areas include a club-style restaurant, a comfortable lounge and a bar. The hotel also has extensive function facilities.

42 en suite (bth/shr) (1 fmly) No smoking in 13 bedrooms CTV in all bedrooms Night porter 120P No coaches Xmas V meals Coffee am Tea pm No smoking in restaurant Last d 9.30pm

ROOMS: (incl. bkfst) s £65-£135; d £85-£175 * LB

OFF-PEAK: (incl. bkfst) s £55-£95; d £60-£75

MEALS: Lunch £10-£15 Dinner £12.95-£17.95&alc

CONF: Thtr 150 Class 105 Board 40 Del from £95

CARDS:

FLEET MOTORWAY SERVICE AREA (M3) Hampshire Map 04 SU75

Travelodge

Fleet Service Area RG27 8BN (between junc 4a & 5 westbound M3) ☎ 01252 815587 FAX 01252 815587

This modern building offers accommodation in smart, spacious and well equipped bedrooms, suitable for family use, and all with en suite bathrooms. Meals may be taken at the nearby family restaurant. For information on room rates and to make a booking, call Roomline free of charge on 0800 850950. For more details about Travelodge, consult the Contents page under Hotel Groups.

40 en suite (bth/shr)

FLITWICK Bedfordshire Map 04 TL03

★★★ ❀❀❀ 75% Flitwick Manor

Church Rd MK45 1AE (on A5120, 2m from M1 exit 12 towards Ampthill) ☎ 01525 712242 FAX 01525 718753

This 17th-century manor house might be miles from anywhere but it is actually only 10 minutes from the M1. The characterful building is charmingly decorated, with a comfortable lounge as a focal point. Bedrooms feature a variety of period furniture and all are superbly equipped with extras such as fresh fruit, home-made biscuits and Madeira. Staff, under the capable management of Sonia Banks, are solicitous and friendly. Chef Duncan Poyser is a talented young man whose forte is creating dishes with strong distinct flavours. A starter of home-made black pudding greatly impressed, though the texture was a little soft. A further string to Duncan's bow is his skill with pastry. Breads, canapés and petits fours are excellent and a rice pudding brulée with crème anglaise and fruit coulis proved an excellent finish to an enjoyable meal. The wine list features many carefully selected bottles but has a distinct Gallic bias.

15 en suite (bth/shr) CTV in all bedrooms 50P No coaches Tennis (hard) Croquet lawn Putting green No children 10yrs English & French Cuisine V meals Coffee am Tea pm No smoking in restaurant Last d 9.30pm

ROOMS: (incl. cont bkfst) s £100-£190; d £125-£225 * LB

MEALS: Lunch £16.95-£24.50 Dinner fr £37.50*

CONF: Thtr 40 Class 30 Board 24 Del from £160

CARDS:

See advertisement on this page

FLORE Northamptonshire Map 04 SP66

★★★70% **Courtyard by Marriott Daventry**

The High St NN7 4LP (from junct 16 on M1, follow A45 towards Daventry. Hotel 1m on right between and Upper Heyford and Flore) ☎ 01327 349022 FAX 01327 349017

Although convenient for the motorway, this modern hotel boasts rural views to the rear. Bedrooms have recently been upgraded with smart soft furnishings, so together with the good beds and power showers guests are afforded a comfortable night. Staff are also noteworthy for their attentive, caring service.

55 en suite (bth/shr) (7 fmly) No smoking in 17 bedrooms CTV in all bedrooms STV Night porter 170P Gym Wkly live entertainment Xmas V meals Coffee am Tea pm Last d 10pm

ROOMS: d £45-£65 * **LB**

OFF-PEAK: d £45

MEALS: Lunch £9.95&alc Dinner £12-£15.95alc*

CONF: Thtr 80 Class 40 Board 48 Del £98

CARDS:

FOLKESTONE Kent Map 05 TR23

★★★68% **Clifton**

The Leas CT20 2EB (from M20 junct 13, quarter mile W of town centre on A259) ☎ 01303 851231 FAX 01303 851231

Long established and enjoying a prime position overlooking the English Channel, this elegant Victorian-style hotel has gradually been improved by its dedicated owner, Mr Peter Hail. The atmosphere is very agreeable and complemented by extensive service availability. The accommodation is still slowly being upgraded; the larger principal bedrooms have the best sea views, there is a very comfortable, traditionally furnished lounge with a separate, good quality bar, a Regency-style garden restaurant and several meeting rooms. The Pleydel Suite accommodates up to 75 persons for functions. Special Weekend Breaks are available, and there is car parking close by.

80 en suite (bth/shr) (4 fmly) CTV in all bedrooms STV Lift Night porter Solarium Games room Xmas English & French Cuisine V meals Coffee am Tea pm Last d 9.15pm

ROOMS: (incl. bkfst) s £55-£71.50; d £74-£94 * **LB**

OFF-PEAK: (incl. bkfst) s £49-£52; d £65-£67

MEALS: Lunch £9.50-£10.25&alc Dinner £16-£16.50&alc*

CONF: Thtr 80 Class 72 Board 32 Del from £78

CARDS:

See advertisement on opposite page

★★❀❀❀78% **Sandgate**

8-9 Wellington Ter, The Esplanade, Sandgate CT20 3DY ☎ 01303 220444 FAX 01303 220496

Closed 2nd week Jan-mid Feb RS Sun evening & Mon

A combination of English hospitality and French flair characterise this seafront hotel and restaurant which is personally run by chef patron Samuel Gicqueau and partner Zara Jackson. Bedrooms, which are served by a lift, are comfortable and well furnished, the largest being the balcony rooms overlooking the sea. The sumptuous lounge bar has a warm open fire in the winter months, and the restaurant, La Terrasse, opens, as its name suggests, onto a terrace. Chef Gicqueau displays his flair for classic dishes, seafood, outstanding patisserie and well crafted sauces. A fine lobster ravioli with a rich lobster sauce began a recent inspection meal, the main course of supreme of pheasant stuffed with apples and chestnuts came with a classic sauce poivrade and a celeriac gratin, and the meal ended with a sinfully rich dark chocolate dessert with an almond cream and verveine ice cream.

15 en suite (bth/shr) CTV in all bedrooms STV No dogs (ex guide dogs) Lift 4P No coaches Xmas French Cuisine V meals Coffee am No smoking in restaurant Last d 9.30pm

ROOMS: (incl. bkfst) s £35; d £49-£67 *

OFF-PEAK: (incl. bkfst & dinner) d £90

MEALS: Lunch £16.50-£21.50 Dinner £16.50-£21.50*

CARDS:

See advertisement on opposite page

★★67% **Wards**

39 Earls Ave CT20 2HB ☎ 01303 245166 FAX 01303 254480

This attractively furnished family-run hotel is quietly located in the residential west end of town and features the well appointed Bistro 39 and bar lounge, offering an extensive range of dishes from around the world. Well furnished individually designed bedrooms provide good levels of comfort. Service is very relaxed and informal and other facilities include snooker room and large function room comprising the self contained Gatsby Suite accommodating up to 200 persons with a car park to the rear of the building.

10 en suite (bth/shr) (2 fmly) CTV in all bedrooms STV No dogs (ex guide dogs) 20P Snooker Jacuzzi/spa Xmas International Cuisine V meals Coffee am No smoking area in restaurant Last d 9.30pm

ROOMS: (incl. bkfst) s £52-£65; d £67-£90 *

OFF-PEAK: (incl. bkfst) s £47-£55; d £60-£85

MEALS: Lunch £5.95-£21.45alc High tea £5-£10alc Dinner £5.95-£21.45alc*

CONF: Thtr 50 Class 50 Board 20 Del from £58.50

CARDS:

Travel Inn

travel inn

Cherry Gardens Ln (M20 junct13 turn rt into Cherry Garden Ln & first rt into Travel Inn car park) ☎ 01582 414341 FAX 01582 400024

Purpose-built accommodation, offering spacious, well equipped bedrooms, all with en suite bathrooms. Meals may be taken at the nearby family restaurant. For more information about Travel Inns, consult the Contents page under Hotel Groups.

40 en suite (bth/shr)

ROOMS: d £35.50 *

FONTWELL West Sussex Map 04 SU90

Travelodge

Travelodge

BN18 0SB (on A27/A29 roundabout) ☎ 01243 543973 FAX 01243 543973

This modern building offers accommodation in smart, spacious and well equipped bedrooms, suitable for family use, and all with en suite bathrooms. Meals may be taken at the nearby family restaurant. For information on room rates and to make a booking, call Roomline free of charge on 0800 850950. For more details about Travelodge, consult the Contents page under Hotel Groups.
32 en suite (bth/shr)

FORD Wiltshire Map 03 ST87

★★ 65% ***White Hart Inn***
SN14 8RP ☎ 01249 782213 FAX 01249 783075
Set back from the A420, beside the Bybrook River, this friendly 16th-century inn offers a welcoming atmosphere, comfortable accommodation and excellent food. The well equipped bedrooms are mostly housed in converted stables, while the main building contains public areas which boast beams, inglenook fireplaces and flagstoned floors. The bar and restaurant serve generous portions of interesting home-cooked dishes which represent real value for money; robust flavours are created in dishes such as rich roast breast of pheasant with wild mushrooms and sweet shallots, and the traditional puddings are an absolute delight.
3 en suite (shr) 8 annexe en suite (bth/shr) (2 fmly) CTV in all bedrooms 80P Outdoor swimming pool (heated) V meals Coffee am
CARDS:

FORDINGBRIDGE Hampshire Map 04 SU11

★★ 67% ***Ashburn Hotel & Restaurant***
Damerham Rd SP6 1JP (on B3078)
☎ 01425 652060 FAX 01425 652150

MINOTEL Great Britain

This family run hotel is located on the edge of the village and enjoys lovely country views. The bedrooms are divided between the main house where they are spacious and well appointed, and the more modern annexe where although similarly equipped they are more simply furnished. There is a well kept garden and outdoor heated pool. The restaurant offers good carefully prepared dishes using local produce.
20 en suite (bth/shr) (3 fmly) CTV in all bedrooms 60P Outdoor swimming pool (heated) English & French Cuisine V meals Coffee am Tea pm Last d 9.30pm
CARDS: 

FOREST ROW East Sussex Map 05 TQ43

RED STAR HOTEL

★★★★ ***Ashdown Park***
Wych Cross RH18 5JR ☎ 01342 824988
FAX 01342 826206

Small Luxury Hotels of the World

This grand Victorian Gothic mansion house has seen service as a convent and a training centre before being completely refurbished in 1993 as a hotel with a high standard of spacious and elegant accommodation. Within the extensive 187 acres of attractive gardens and parkland there are fine indoor and outdoor leisure facilities and two ornamental lakes stocked with carp and golden orfe. When the weather demands it, the delightful aroma of open log fires greets guests and pervades the three splendid lounges, while the large Anderida Restaurant, where a pianist plays, is a relaxed yet formal environment for chef John McManus to display his interpretation of classical cuisine. Five grades of comfortable bedrooms, all furnished to a high standard in an understated traditional style, are on offer. The hotel's greatest strength,

contd.

however, are the charming and helpful staff.
95 en suite (bth/shr) CTV in all bedrooms STV No dogs (ex

guide dogs) Lift Night porter 149P Indoor swimming pool (heated) Golf 9 Tennis (hard) Squash Snooker Sauna Solarium Gym Croquet lawn Putting green Jacuzzi/spa Indoor golf Table tennis Beauty therapy Xmas V meals Coffee am Tea pm Last d 10pm
ROOMS: (incl. bkfst) s £99-£199; d £124-£244 * **LB**
MEALS: Lunch £18-£19.95&alc Dinner £28&alc
CONF: Thtr 150 Class 60 Board 60 Del from £178
CARDS:

See advertisement under GATWICK AIRPORT (LONDON)

FORMBY Merseyside Map 07 SD30

★★65% ***Tree Tops***
Southport Old Rd L37 0AB (off A565 Southport to Liverpool road)
☎ 017048 79651 FAX 017048 79651
Situated three miles south of Southport off the A565, this is really a restaurant and function suite with the advantage of chalet-style bedrooms in the grounds. The grounds extend to five acres and overlook a new golf course which is due to open during 1996. The restaurant has been extended by the addition of a modern conservatory and the choice of food on offer is wide ranging. A permanent marquee is used for weddings and other functions and this is completely self-contained. It is hoped to add further bedrooms shortly, which will enjoy views over the golf course.
11 en suite (bth/shr) (2 fmly) CTV in all bedrooms No dogs 100P Outdoor swimming pool (heated) English & French Cuisine V meals Coffee am Tea pm Last d 10pm
CARDS:

FORTON MOTORWAY SERVICE AREA (M6) Lancashire Map 07 SD55

Travelodge
White Carr Ln, Bay Horse LA2 9DU (between juncts 32 & 33) ☎ 01524 792227 FAX 01524 791703
This modern building offers accommodation in smart, spacious and well equipped bedrooms, suitable for family use, and all with en suite bathrooms. Meals may be taken at the nearby family restaurant. For information on room rates and to make a booking, call Roomline free of charge on 0800 850950. For more details about Travelodge, consult the Contents page under Hotel Groups.
53 en suite (bth/shr)

Travelodge

Some company-owned hotels have a central reservations telephone number. For the quick-reference list, consult the Contents page.

FOUR MARKS Hampshire Map 04 SU63

Travelodge
156 Winchester Rd GU34 5HZ (on A31, northbound) ☎ 01420 562659 FAX 01420 562659
This modern building offers accommodation in smart, spacious and well equipped bedrooms, suitable for family use, and all with en suite bathrooms. Meals may be taken at the nearby family restaurant. For information on room rates and to make a booking, call Roomline free of charge on 0800 850950. For more details about Travelodge, consult the Contents page under Hotel Groups.
31 en suite (bth/shr)

Travelodge

FOWEY Cornwall & Isles of Scilly Map 02 SX15

★★®73% **Marina**
Esplanade PL23 1HY (drive down into town down Lostwithiel Street, near bottom of hill turn right into Esplanade by Mace grocers shop)
☎ 01726 833315 FAX 01726 832779
Closed Jan & Feb
A charming Georgian residence restains the elegance of the period and offers a spectacular view from the Marina Restaurant. A range of interesting local seafood dishes are available such as pan-fried red snapper with lemon butter sauce or steak, kidney and oyster pie in a Guinness sauce. Directions: In Fowey, drive down Lostwithiel Street, turn right into the Esplanade by Mace grocers. Hotel 50yds on left.
11 en suite (bth/shr) CTV in all bedrooms No coaches Fishing Sailing Xmas English & French Cuisine V meals Coffee am No smoking in restaurant Last d 8.30pm
ROOMS: (incl. bkfst) s £43-£51; d £58-£88 * **LB**
OFF-PEAK: (incl. bkfst) s £39-£45; d £52-£80
MEALS: Dinner £15-£15&alc
CARDS:

See advertisement on opposite page

FOWNHOPE Hereford & Worcester Map 03 SO53

★★65% **Green Man Inn**
HR1 4PE (on B4224 midway between Ross-on-Wye and hereford)
☎ 01432 860243 FAX 01432 860207
This charming old village inn dates back to 1485 and has a wealth of charm and character. It provides well equipped accommodation, which includes ground-floor, family and four-poster rooms; some are housed in two separate cottage-style buildings. The hotel has two lounges, a choice of bars and a restaurant with a beamed ceiling. Other facilities include a beer garden and a play area for children.
10 en suite (bth/shr) 5 annexe en suite (bth/shr) (3 fmly) CTV in all bedrooms 75P Fishing Xmas V meals Coffee am Tea pm No smoking in restaurant Last d 9pm
ROOMS: (incl. bkfst) s £31-£32.50; d £49-£52 **LB**
MEALS: Sunday Lunch £10.20 Dinner £13.50-£15.50alc*
CONF: Thtr 40 Class 60
CARDS:

FRAMLINGHAM Suffolk Map 05 TM26

★★63% The Crown

Market Hill IP13 9AN (from A1120 take B1119. At T-junction turn right and take 3rd on left into Fore Street. Hotel on left) ☎ 01728 723521 FAX 01728 724274

This smartly painted inn is the focal point of the small market square. It has a large restaurant and a bar along with a cosy lounge area. Bedrooms, which vary in size and shape, are used by local business visitors and passing holiday-makers.

14 en suite (bth/shr) (1 fmly) No smoking in 4 bedrooms CTV in all bedrooms 10P Xmas V meals Coffee am Tea pm No smoking in restaurant Last d 9.30pm

ROOMS: s £60; d £70 * **LB**

OFF-PEAK: (incl. dinner) s £44; d £88

MEALS: Lunch £8.95-£11.95 Dinner fr £15.95*

CARDS:

FRANKLEY MOTORWAY SERVICE AREA (M5) West Midlands Map 07 SO98

Travelodge

Illey Ln B32 4AR (between junc 3 and 4 of M5) ☎ Central Res 0800 555300 FAX 01525 878451

This modern building offers accommodation in smart, spacious and well equipped bedrooms, suitable for family use, and all with en suite bathrooms. Meals may be taken at the nearby family restaurant. For information on room rates and to make a booking, call Roomline free of charge on 0800 850950. For more details about Travelodge, consult the Contents page under Hotel Groups.

61 en suite (bth/shr)

FRESHWATER See Wight, Isle of

FRINTON-ON-SEA Essex Map 05 TM21

★★63% Maplin

Esplanade CO13 9EL ☎ 01255 673832

Closed Jan

Built in 1911, this detached house has a lovely position overlooking the greensward and sea. Nick Turner and his wife Sue offer a warm welcome and attentive service. Bedrooms are traditional in style with a mixture of furniture and fabrics, and public areas have old-fashioned charm with original oak panelling.

12 rms (10 bth/shr) (2 fmly) CTV in all bedrooms 12P No coaches Outdoor swimming pool (heated) Xmas English & French Cuisine V meals Coffee am No smoking in restaurant Last d 9pm

ROOMS: (incl. bkfst) s £55-£85; d £90-£100 * **LB**

OFF-PEAK: (incl. bkfst) s £39.50-£55; d £70-£90

MEALS: Lunch fr £15.95&alc Dinner fr £18.95&alc*

CONF: Thtr 35 Class 20 Board 30 Del from £65

CARDS:

★67% Rock

The Esplanade, 1 Third Av CO13 9EQ ☎ 01255 677194 & 675173 FAX 01255 675173

Closed Jan

The hotel is set on a prominent corner overlooking the esplanade and offers bright, spacious bedrooms, many of which have sea views. Public areas comprise a lounge-cum-bar and a wood-panelled dining room. The friendly owners and their menagerie of pets create a welcoming family atmosphere.

6 en suite (shr) (2 fmly) CTV in all bedrooms 12P No coaches Sauna V meals No smoking in restaurant Last d 9pm

contd.

ROOMS: (incl. bkfst) s £49.50-£59.50; d fr £74.75 * **LB**
MEALS: Lunch £12.50-£16.50&alc Dinner £16.50&alc*
CARDS:

FRODSHAM Cheshire Map 07 SJ57

★★★66% **Forest Hill Hotel & Leisure Complex**
Bellemonte Rd, Overton Hill WA6 6HH (off B5152) ☎ 01928 735255 FAX 01928 735517
Opened in 1988, this modern hotel and leisure complex is located at the top of Overton Hill on the outskirts of Frodsham. The restaurant and most of the bedrooms have panoramic views of either the River Mersey or the Cheshire Plain. Bedrooms are mostly spacious, and the 'executive' rooms have luxury bathrooms. As well as the impressive leisure centre there are function and conference facilities.
57 en suite (bth/shr) (4 fmly) No smoking in 5 bedrooms CTV in all bedrooms STV Night porter 350P Indoor swimming pool (heated) Squash Snooker Sauna Solarium Gym Jacuzzi/spa Nightclub Wkly live entertainment Xmas International Cuisine V meals Coffee am Tea pm Last d 9.45pm
ROOMS: d £53-£78 * **LB**
MEALS: Lunch £9.95&alc Dinner £15-£26alc*
CONF: Thtr 200 Class 80 Board 48 Del from £75
CARDS:

★★64% **Heathercliffe Country House**
Manley Rd WA6 6HB (off B5152) ☎ 01928 733722 FAX 01928 735667
A mid-Victorian house, now a privately run hotel, Heathercliffe is situated in extensive wooded grounds on the top of a hill on the outskirts of Frodsham. The pleasant restaurant, with its period-style furnishings and original fireplace, has been extended by the addition of a conservatory. Here, popular dishes are served in generous portions. Bedrooms are mostly spacious and offer modern facilities, and there are three lounges, one with a welcoming fire.
9 en suite (bth/shr) CTV in all bedrooms STV Night porter 60P 8 Acre estate European Cuisine V meals Coffee am Tea pm Last d 9.30pm
ROOMS: (incl. bkfst) s fr £64; d fr £85 * **LB**
OFF-PEAK: (incl. bkfst) s fr £39; d fr £55
MEALS: Lunch £5-£11.95 Dinner fr £11.95&alc
CONF: Thtr 40 Class 20 Board 16
CARDS:

FROME Somerset Map 03 ST74

★★★62% **Mendip Lodge**

Bath Rd BA11 2HP (situated on the Bath side of Frome, on the B3090, opposite Frome College)
☎ 01373 463223 FAX 01373 463990
A busy hotel conveniently positioned on the northern edge of the town and set in attractive grounds and gardens. The motel-style bedrooms are well equipped but standards of furnishings vary. There is a friendly atmosphere created by a team of local staff.
40 en suite (bth) (12 fmly) CTV in all bedrooms STV Night porter 112P Xmas English & French Cuisine V meals Coffee am Last d 9.30pm
ROOMS: (incl. bkfst) s £50; d £50-£70 **LB**
OFF-PEAK: (incl. bkfst) s £35; d £50
MEALS: Lunch £7.95-£15.50&alc Dinner £15.50&alc*
CONF: Thtr 80 Board 50
CARDS:

★★67% **The George at Nunney**
11 Church St BA11 4LW ☎ 01373 836458 FAX 01373 836565
(For full entry see Nunney)

GAINSBOROUGH Lincolnshire Map 08 SK88

★★65% **Hickman-Hill**
Cox's Hill DN21 1HH ☎ 01427 613639 FAX 01427 677591
Once a Georgian grammar school, Hickman-Hill is now a comfortable and well furnished family-owned hotel. It stands in its own well tended grounds and is found within easy walking distance of the town centre. Bedrooms are well equipped, comfortable public rooms are inviting and the staff and owners are friendly and attentive. An extensive range of dishes is available in the dining room and small conferences can be accommodated.
8 en suite (bth/shr) (1 fmly) CTV in all bedrooms 25P No coaches Solarium Xmas V meals Coffee am Tea pm Last d 9pm
ROOMS: (incl. bkfst) s £39.50; d £51 * **LB**
MEALS: Sunday Lunch £8.50 Dinner £10.50&alc*
CONF: Thtr 24 Board 40
CARDS:

GARFORTH West Yorkshire Map 08 SE43

★★★64% **Milford Lodge**

A1 Great North Rd, Peckfield LS25 5LQ (on the southbound carriageway of the A1, E of Leeds where A63 joins A1) ☎ 01977 681800 FAX 01977 681245
Milford Lodge is situated on the A1 to the north of the M62 junction and provides modern accommodation for the travelling guest. Public areas are open plan and include a bar, lounge and restaurant which serves a very good range of food from 7am till 10pm. Service is friendly and relaxed whilst the bedrooms are well equipped and modern and conference facilities are also provided..
47 en suite (bth/shr) (10 fmly) No smoking in 19 bedrooms CTV in all bedrooms STV Night porter 76P Xmas International Cuisine V meals Coffee am Tea pm No smoking area in restaurant Last d 10pm
ROOMS: s £45; d £45 * **LB**
MEALS: Lunch £8.95-£19.45alc High tea £8.95-£19.45alc Dinner £8.95-£19.45alc*
CONF: Thtr 70 Class 35 Board 30 Del from £75
CARDS:

Hilton National Leeds/Garforth
Wakefield Rd LS25 1LH (junc A63/A642 6m E of Leeds) ☎ 0113 286 6556 FAX 0113 286 8326

HILTON

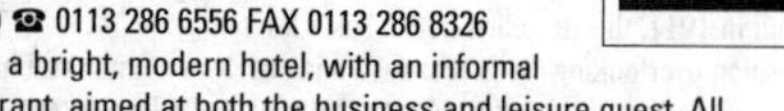

This is a bright, modern hotel, with an informal restaurant, aimed at both the business and leisure guest. All bedrooms have en suite bathrooms and a range of modern facilities. For more information about Hilton National hotels, consult the Contents page under Hotel Groups.
144 en suite (bth/shr)
ROOMS: s £65-£115; d £65-£115 *
CONF: Thtr 450 Class 150 Board 80 Del from £95

GARSTANG Lancashire Map 07 SD44

★★★65% **Crofters**
Cabus PR3 1PH (on A6, midway between junc 32 & 33 of M6)
☎ 01995 604128 FAX 01995 601646
Continual improvements are being made to this well run, family owned hotel which is conveniently situated, slightly set back from the road. The lounge, bar and restaurant have recently been refurbished to a high standard and between the bar and restaurant a good range of interesting dishes are available. Bedrooms, including executive rooms, are freshly decorated, spacious and comfortably furnished. The hotel also providesa function and banqueting suite, as well as a large car park.
19 en suite (bth/shr) (3 fmly) CTV in all bedrooms STV Night porter 200P Pool table Xmas English & French Cuisine V meals Coffee am No smoking area in restaurant Last d 10pm

ROOMS: s £40-£50; d £45-£70
MEALS: Sunday Lunch £9.85 Dinner £15-£16&alc*
CONF: Thtr 200 Class 120 Board 50 Del from £44
CARDS:

★★71% *The Pickerings*
Garstang Rd, Catterall PR3 0HD (2m S B6430)
☎ 01995 602133 FAX 01995 602100
Closed 27-28 Dec
This former rectory which is situated on the B6430 south of the village provides comfortable, well maintained accommodation. Bedrooms are situated between the main house and a small annexe and all are freshly decorated and thoughtfully equipped. The characterful public areas are enjoyable to use and guests may relax in the comfortable lounges and enjoy a good choice of well prepared dishes in the restaurant.
14 en suite (bth/shr) 2 annexe rms (1 fmly) CTV in all bedrooms 50P English & Continental Cuisine V meals Coffee am Last d 10pm
CARDS:

GATESHEAD Tyne & Wear Map 12 NZ26
See also Beamish & Whickham

★★★★65% **Newcastle Marriott**

Metro Centre NE11 9XF (follow signs for Metro Centre & then signs for Marriott Hotel)
☎ 0191 493 2233 FAX 0191 493 2030
This large modern hotel is conveniently situated on the edge of the Metro Centre and adjacent to the A1, western by-pass. Bedrooms are particularly spacious and some have interesting themes. All are very well equipped and many feature comfortable lounge areas. The public rooms are modern and include excellent conference and banqueting facilities and a very good leisure centre.
148 en suite (bth/shr) (138 fmly) No smoking in 75 bedrooms CTV in all bedrooms STV Lift Night porter Air conditioning 250P Indoor swimming pool (heated) Sauna Solarium Gym Jacuzzi/spa Health & beauty clinic Xmas International Cuisine V meals Coffee am Tea pm No smoking area in restaurant Last d 10pm
ROOMS: s £110-£125; d £125-£145 * **LB**
MEALS: Bar Lunch £2.95-£16.95 Dinner fr £16.50&alc*
CONF: Thtr 450 Class 190 Board 40 Del from £120
CARDS:

★★★68% **Swallow**

High West St NE8 1PE ☎ 0191 477 1105
FAX 0191 478 7214
This busy, modern hotel which offers varying sizes and styles of well equipped accommodation is ideally situated only one mile from Newcastle city centre; the Metro Centre is also within very easy reach. The majority of the rooms have been smartly refurbished and plans are well advanced for the remainder. The staff are very friendly and helpful, especially on arrival when your car is parked for you. Hotel manager Lucy Naismith is justifiably proud of her staff's 'Investors In People' award.
103 en suite (bth/shr) (12 fmly) No smoking in 40 bedrooms CTV in all bedrooms STV Lift Night porter 190P Indoor swimming pool (heated) Sauna Solarium Gym Jacuzzi/spa Wkly live entertainment Xmas International Cuisine V meals Coffee am Tea pm No smoking area in restaurant Last d 9.45pm
ROOMS: (incl. bkfst) s £60-£85; d £70-£95 * **LB**
MEALS: Lunch fr £8 Dinner £15-£17.50*
CONF: Thtr 350 Class 150 Board 100 Del from £99
CARDS:

★★76% **Eslington Villa**
8 Station Rd, Low Fell NE9 6DR ☎ 0191 487 6017 & 0191 420 0666
FAX 0191 420 0667
RS Sun/BHs (restricted restaurant service)
A secluded retreat, this Edwardian villa - now a stylish hotel - lies in terraced gardens in a residential area of Low Fell, overlooking the Team Valley estate. Personally run by Nick and Melanie Tulip and their dedicated staff, the atmosphere is friendly and relaxing. Public areas retain much of their original character, with fine fireplaces in the bar, lounge and restaurant. The latter also has a conservatory extension. Food features highly, and modern-style British dishes are presented in generous portions. A terrine of smoked ham with peas pudding might be followed by pan-fried monkfish on a bed of leeks with a meaux mustard sauce, with an individual lemon meringue tart completing the meal.
12 en suite (bth/shr) (2 fmly) CTV in all bedrooms Night porter 15P No coaches English & French Cuisine V meals No smoking in restaurant Last d 10pm
ROOMS: (incl. bkfst) s £49.50-£59.50; d £59.50-£69.50
OFF-PEAK: (incl. bkfst) s £44.50-£49.50; d £54.50-£59.50
MEALS: Lunch £15.95-£17.95&alc Dinner £21.95-£25.95&alc
CARDS:

GATWICK AIRPORT (LONDON) West Sussex Map 04 TQ24
See also Burgh Heath, Dorking, East Grinstead & Reigate

★★★★69% **London Gatwick Airport Hilton**

RH6 0LL ☎ 01293 518080 FAX 01293 528980

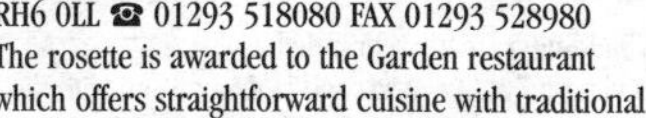

The rosette is awarded to the Garden restaurant which offers straightforward cuisine with traditional leanings; the approach is serious and the staff are both attentive and friendly. There are three other dining options, mostly off the atrium, which offer a wide choice. The hotel is linked to the south terminal by a covered walkway and also has useful amenities such as a bank, gift shop and extensive conference /banqueting facilities. The well equipped and spacious bedrooms have useful extras and are benefiting from a gradual refurbishment.
550 en suite (bth/shr) (8 fmly) No smoking in 440 bedrooms CTV in all bedrooms STV Lift Night porter Air conditioning Indoor swimming pool (heated) Sauna Solarium Gym Jacuzzi/spa Wkly live entertainment Xmas International Cuisine V meals Coffee am Tea pm No smoking area in restaurant Last d 11.30pm
ROOMS: s £145-£175; d £145-£175 * **LB**
OFF-PEAK: (incl. bkfst) s £105-£125; d £105-£125
MEALS: Lunch fr £16&alc Dinner fr £16&alc*
CONF: Thtr 500 Class 225 Board 100 Del from £115
CARDS:

★★★★65% **Copthorne London Gatwick**

Copthorne Way RH10 3PG (on A264, 2m E of A264/B2036 roundabout) ☎ 01342 714971
FAX 01342 717375
This large hotel, with 100 acres of land, is set around a well preserved 16th-century farmhouse which is now the main bar. The low-lying building sprawls over a large area containing a leisure centre, meeting rooms and two restaurants. In the Lion d'Or restaurant competently prepared and technically correct meals are served in a smart, formal setting. There are three distinct standards of bedroom with the Connoisseur rooms standing out as the best.

contd.

227 en suite (bth/shr) (10 fmly) No smoking in 98 bedrooms CTV in all bedrooms STV Lift Night porter 300P Indoor swimming pool (heated) Tennis (hard) Squash Solarium Gym Pool table Croquet lawn Putting green Jacuzzi/spa Petanque pit Wkly live entertainment English & Continental Cuisine V meals Coffee am Tea pm No smoking area in restaurant Last d 10.30pm
ROOMS: s £110-£130; d £120-£140 **LB**
MEALS: Lunch £15.95-£18.50&alc Dinner £15.95-£22.50&alc*
CONF: Thtr 110 Class 65 Board 40 Del from £145
CARDS:

★★★★64% **Copthorne Effingham Park**

West Park Rd RH4 1DW (off B2028)
☎ 01342 714994 FAX 01342 716039
There is a very good range of leisure facilities at this peacefully located hotel which is set in forty acres of grounds. It is very popular with conference organisers and week-end functions providing an excellent range of meeting rooms. The main restaurant is now the open plan brasserie near the front entrance but snacks are also available in the leisure club bar. In line with company policy there are two categories of bedroom : Connoisseur and Classic both of which are spacious and well cared for.
122 en suite (bth/shr) (6 fmly) No smoking in 36 bedrooms CTV in all bedrooms STV No dogs (ex guide dogs) Lift Night porter 500P Indoor swimming pool (heated) Golf 9 Sauna Gym Croquet lawn Putting green Jacuzzi/spa Dance studio Bowls Xmas English & Mediterranean Cuisine V meals Coffee am Tea pm No smoking area in restaurant Last d 10.30pm
ROOMS: s £105-£125; d £105-£125 * **LB**
MEALS: Lunch £16-£25 Dinner £16-£25*
CONF: Thtr 600 Class 250 Board 26 Del from £145
CARDS:

★★★★63% ***Holiday Inn Gatwick East***

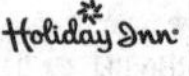

Tinsley Ln South, Three Bridges RH11 1NP
☎ 01293 561186
This stylish modern building, recently rebranded as a Holiday Inn, offers cheerful public areas and bedrooms, all with the benefit of air-conditioning. A young team of staff provide a willing service, and there are good indoor leisure facilities.

★★★★❀63% ***Holiday Inn London-Gatwick West***
Langley Dr RH11 7SX (4m S of airport from M23 junct 10 take A264 following Horsham signs hotel at junct with A23) ☎ 01293 529991 FAX 01293 515913
This is a busy and modern airport hotel located on the outskirts of Crawley and linked to the airport by a courtesy coach service. The bedrooms provide all the modern-day amenities necessary for an overnight stay. There is an all-day coffee shop and the more formal Colonnade restaurant where the kitchen concentrates on presenting honest flavours and straightforward technique.
217 en suite (bth/shr) (10 fmly) No smoking in 80 bedrooms CTV in all bedrooms Lift Night porter 180P Indoor swimming pool (heated) Snooker Sauna Solarium Gym Pool table Jacuzzi/spa Steam rooms Games room V meals Coffee am Tea pm Last d 10pm
CARDS:

★★★★62% ***Ramada***
Povey Cross Rd RH6 0BE (Ramada) ☎ 01293 820169
FAX 01293 820259
Newly refurbished public areas in this hotel have added a smart look to the ground floor. Bedrooms are well maintained and equipped with up-to-date amenities. In addition to an informal coffee shop there is the Pavilion Restaurant where the kitchen makes a keen effort at creating tasty, freshly prepared dishes.
255 en suite (bth/shr) (5 fmly) No smoking in 158 bedrooms CTV in all bedrooms Lift Night porter Air conditioning 500P Indoor swimming pool (heated) Squash Snooker Sauna Solarium Gym Pool table Jacuzzi/spa Beautician service Aerobic studio International Cuisine V meals Coffee am Tea pm Last d 10pm
CARDS:

★★★★61% **Forte Crest Gatwick**
North Terminal RH6 0PH ☎ 01293 567070
FAX 01293 567739
This large modern hotel offers a wide range of services and amenities, designed particularly for the business traveller. Bedrooms are smart, comfortable and well equipped.
456 en suite (bth/shr) (21 fmly) No smoking in 230 bedrooms CTV in all bedrooms STV Lift Night porter Air conditioning 136P Indoor swimming pool (heated) Sauna Solarium Gym Steam room Xmas British & Chinese Cuisine V meals Coffee am Tea pm No smoking area in restaurant Last d 11.30pm
ROOMS: s £90-£110; d £90-£115 * **LB**
MEALS: Lunch £15.95 Dinner £15.95*
CONF: Thtr 300 Class 200 Board 40 Del from £90
CARDS:

★★★ 68% **Stanhill Court**

Stanhill Rd, Charlwood RH6 0EP ☎ 01293 862166
FAX 01293 862773
Set in 35 acres of grounds and built in the Scottish baronial style in 1881 this fascinating hotel retains much of its original features whilst being extensively upgraded and improved. There is a wide choice of rooms most with four poster beds and good views overlooking the grounds and surrounding countryside. The accommodation has been sympathetically furnished in keeping with the hotels special ambience and spacious bedrooms all come particularly well equipped. Other facilities include a Spanish styled bodega Pavilion bar and wood panelled candlelit restaurant which features the promising cooking of Chef Steve Allen. There are also extensive facilities for meetings and functions.
12 en suite (bth/shr) (3 fmly) No smoking in 2 bedrooms CTV in all bedrooms No dogs (ex guide dogs) Night porter 100P No coaches Tennis (hard) Fishing Croquet lawn ch fac International Cuisine V meals Coffee am Tea pm No smoking in restaurant Last d 9.30pm
ROOMS: s fr £75; d £89-£120 * **LB**
OFF-PEAK: (incl. bkfst) s fr £69; d fr £89
MEALS: Lunch fr £16.95&alc High tea fr £6.50 Dinner fr £18.95&alc*
CONF: Thtr 160 Class 60 Board 60 Del from £80
CARDS:

★★★61% **Chequers Thistle**
Brighton Rd RH6 8PH (2m N, on A23)
☎ 01293 786992 FAX 01293 820625
The original inn, parts of which date back to 1537, is now open throughout the day and acts as a popular setting for all-day snacks. The building now contains several meeting rooms and contemporary bedrooms which are popular both with leisure and conference guests.

78 en suite (bth/shr) (2 fmly) No smoking in 55 bedrooms CTV in all bedrooms STV Night porter 190P Outdoor swimming pool International Cuisine V meals Coffee am Tea pm No smoking in restaurant Last d 9.30pm
ROOMS: s £85-£95; d £95-£105 * **LB**
MEALS: Lunch £12.50&alc Dinner £13.95-£17.95&alc*
CONF: Thtr 60 Class 24 Board 30 Del from £100
CARDS:

★★★58% **The George**
High St RH10 1BS ☎ 01293 524215
FAX 01293 548565

REGAL A Collection of Individual Hotels

There are several interesting historical anecdotes attached to this town centre hotel which was once a major staging post between the capital and the coast. There have been improvements over the years and the next cycle of further improvements is now due. In addition to a restaurant there is a coffee lounge where day-time snacks are served.
83 en suite (bth/shr) (3 fmly) No smoking in 43 bedrooms CTV in all bedrooms No dogs (ex guide dogs) Night porter 89P V meals Coffee am Tea pm No smoking in restaurant Last d 9.30pm
ROOMS: s £60; d £60 * **LB**
OFF-PEAK: s £45; d £45
MEALS: Sunday Lunch £6-£12alc Dinner £8-£14alc*
CONF: Thtr 50 Class 30 Board 40 Del £89.50
CARDS:

RED STAR HOTEL

★★ **Langshott Manor**
Ladbroke Rd RH6 9LN (take Ladbroke Rd, turn off the Chequers roundabout to Langshott, proceed for 0.75 miles, entrance to hotel on right) ☎ 01293 786680 FAX 01293 783905
Closed 24-30 Dec

Langshott Manor is a beautifully restored Elizabethan manor house tucked away down a quiet country lane and set amidst tranquil gardens. Family-run and personally supervised by Patricia and Geoffrey Noble with son Christopher doing the cooking, the atmosphere is in keeping with an English country house and clearly one of the hotel's strengths is the comfort of a superb range of bedrooms. The oak panelled public rooms include a cheerful morning room,a restaurant and breakfast room, and a first-floor lounge which is sometimes used for private meetings. Kit Noble's seasonal cooking is uncomplicated and straightforward and relies on good quality fresh ingredients.
8 en suite (bth/shr) No smoking in all bedrooms CTV in all bedrooms No dogs (ex guide dogs) 18P No coaches Croquet lawn Putting green Badminton English & French Cuisine No smoking area in restaurant
ROOMS: (incl. bkfst) s £95-£100; d £125-£135 **LB**
CONF: Board 12 Del from £160
CARDS:

Forte Posthouse Gatwick Airport
Povey Cross Rd RH6 0BA (at junct of A23/A217, 0.5m N of airport) ☎ 01293 771621
FAX 01293 771054

FORTE Posthouse

Suitable for both the business and leisure traveller, this bright hotel provides modern accommodation in well equipped bedrooms with en suite bathrooms. For more details about Forte Posthouse hotels, consult the Contents page for the section on Hotel Groups.
210 en suite (bth/shr)
ROOMS: s fr £79; d fr £79 *
CONF: Thtr 150 Class 70 Board 60 Del from £109

Travel Inn
North Terminal, Longbridge Way RH6 0NX
☎ 01293 568158 FAX 01293 568278

Purpose-built accommodation, offering spacious, well equipped bedrooms, all with en suite bathrooms. Meals may be taken at the nearby family restaurant. For more information about Travel Inns, consult the Contents page under Hotel Groups.
121 en suite (bth/shr)
ROOMS: d £35.50 *

Travelodge
Church Rd, Lowfield Heath, Crawley RH11 0PQ (1m S, off A23) ☎ 01293 533441 FAX 01293 535369

This modern building offers accommodation in

contd.

smart, spacious and well equipped bedrooms, suitable for family use, and all with en suite bathrooms. Meals may be taken at the nearby family restaurant. For information on room rates and to make a booking, call Roomline free of charge on 0800 850950. For more details about Travelodge, consult the Contents page under Hotel Groups.
126 en suite (bth/shr)

○ ***Gatwick Wentworth***
Crabbet Park, Turners Hill Rd, Worth RH10 4ST ☎ 01293 884806
Due to open Sep 1996
40 rms

GILLAN Cornwall & Isles of Scilly Map 02 SW72

G

★★❀❀73% **Tregildry**
TR12 6HG (from Helston join the A3083 Lizard road and take first turning left for St Keverne and follow signs for Manaccan and Gillan)
☎ 01326 231378 FAX 01326 231561
Closed Dec-Feb
Having run Quarry Garth Hotel in Windermere successfully for five years, Huw and Lynne Phillips moved southwest in late 1995. During the winter they have transformed the ground floor areas, with the use of attractive soft furnishings and imaginative décor. It is planned to carry out a programme of upgrading to the cosy bedrooms during winter 96/7. A recent meal in the stylish Herra Restaurant, and although the wine list is limited, the selection is well chosen.
10 en suite (bth/shr) (1 fmly) No smoking in all bedrooms CTV in all bedrooms 15P No coaches boat hire windsurfing Coffee am Tea pm No smoking in restaurant Last d 9pm
ROOMS: (incl. bkfst & dinner) s £50-£57.50; d £100-£115 * **LB**
OFF-PEAK: (incl. bkfst & dinner) s £45-£50; d £90-£100
MEALS: Dinner £19.50
CARDS:

GILLINGHAM Dorset Map 03 ST82

RED STAR HOTEL

★★★❀❀❀ **Stock Hill Country House**

Stock Hill SP8 5NR (3m E on B3081 off A303)
☎ 01747 823626 FAX 01747 825628
This delightful country house hotel has been gradually restored by Nita and Peter Hauser, who together have created one of the country's best hotels within its classification. Guests are greeted by Nita and her staff, who settle you in with the offer of afternoon tea and delicious Austrian pastries in the sumptuous lounge. The luxurious bedrooms are all individually styled and comfortably furnished with Nita's excellent eye for detail exhibited in the antiques and abundant ornaments. An excellent breakfast, afternoon tea and early morning tea/coffee and an imaginative dinner menu are all included in the tariff. A recent meal started with delicately flavoured smoked haddock quenelles, served with fresh tomato sauce, followed by a perfectly cooked medallion of venison wrapped in a cabbage and a herb crust and served with a richly flavoured Port sauce. The rhubarb and ginger soufflé was beautifully light and offered a good balance of flavour to complete the meal. Coffee was served with home-made petit fours in front of a roaring fire.
7 rms (6 bth/shr) 3 annexe en suite (bth/shr) CTV in all bedrooms No dogs 25P No coaches Tennis (hard) Fishing Sauna Croquet lawn Putting green No children 7yrs Xmas English, Austrian & French Cuisine V meals Coffee am Tea pm No smoking in restaurant Last d 8.45pm
ROOMS: (incl. bkfst & dinner) s £105-£145; d £230-£260 **LB**
OFF-PEAK: (incl. bkfst & dinner) d £190-£230
MEALS: Lunch £19.50-£22 Dinner £26-£30
CONF: Del from £180
CARDS:

GILLINGHAM Kent Map 05 TQ76

Travelodge
Travelodge
Rainham ME8 8PQ ☎ 01634 233343
FAX 01634 360848
(For full entry see Medway Motorway Service Area (M2))

GISBURN Lancashire Map 07 SD84

★★★❀64% **Stirk House**
BB7 4LJ (W of village, on A59) ☎ 01200 445581 FAX 01200 445744
This extended 16th-Century house stands just off the A59 one mile west of Gisburn. The majority of bedrooms are in a modern wing and purpose-built annexe; they are comfortable and well equipped, but are beginning to look somewhat dated. Spacious, well appointed public areas include an elegant restaurant serving a good choice of carefully prepared dishes from the daily-changing fixed-price menu and the ambitious carte. A typical meal might begin with a salad of smoked lamb followed by a delicious mushroom duxelle, with a brown bread and butter ice cream to finish. Other facilities include a small leisure centre with a pool, exercise room and squash courts, a large banqueting suite and a smaller conference room.
38 en suite (bth/shr) 10 annexe en suite (bth/shr) (2 fmly) CTV in all bedrooms STV Night porter 100P Indoor swimming pool (heated) Squash Sauna Solarium Gym Xmas V meals Coffee am Tea pm No smoking in restaurant Last d 9.30pm
ROOMS: (incl. bkfst) s £25-£60; d £50-£120 * **LB**
MEALS: Lunch £10-£15alc High tea £6-£10 Dinner £17&alc*
CONF: Thtr 300 Class 150 Board 50
CARDS:

GITTISHAM Devon Map 03 SY19

★★★❀❀ 70% **Combe House**

EX14 0AD (turn off A30 1m S of Honiton)
☎ 01404 42756 & 43560 FAX 01404 46004
Closed 29 Jan-13 Feb
Combe House is the home of John and Therese Boswell, and they have furnished both the bedrooms and public areas with individuality and style to properly complement the character of this stately Elizabethan mansion. Indeed, Therese is an artist and sculptor, with her work being prominently exhibited around the house. Amongst her commissions, Therese created "The Catey" sculpture which is awarded annually for excellence within the hotel and catering industry. Bedrooms are generally spacious and thoughtfully equipped to ensure

comfort. There is a choice of elegant lounges in which to relax after dinner and many fine walks through the 3,000 acre estate for the more energetic.
15 en suite (bth/shr) CTV in all bedrooms 51P No coaches Fishing Pool table Croquet lawn Shooting Riding ch fac Xmas English & French Cuisine V meals Coffee am Tea pm No smoking in restaurant Last d 9.30pm
ROOMS: (incl. bkfst) s £65-£99; d £99.50-£131 **LB**
MEALS: Lunch fr £10.25 Dinner £19.90-£23
CONF: Thtr 34 Board 24 Del £129.50
CARDS:

GLASTONBURY Somerset Map 03 ST53

★★58% **George & Pilgrims**
1 High St BA6 9DP ☎ 01458 831146
FAX 01458 832252
This 15th-century inn is steeped in history, and behind its interesting stone façade and mullion windows lie congenial surroundings. Inside there is a tiny lounge, a character bar with refectory tables and an informal brassiere/grill with a flagstone floor. Most of the bedrooms are furnished in an austere traditional style, but several are now in need of refurbishment. Staff are willing and friendly.
13 en suite (bth/shr) (1 fmly) CTV in all bedrooms V meals Coffee am Tea pm Last d 9.30pm
ROOMS: (incl. bkfst) s £35-£60; d £65-£75.50 * **LB**
MEALS: Lunch £9.50-£25alc Dinner £11-£25alc*
CONF: Thtr 80 Class 36 Board 30 Del from £70
CARDS:

GLENRIDDING Cumbria Map 11 NY31

★★★66% **Glenridding**
CA11 0PB ☎ 017684 82228 FAX 017684 82555
This friendly hotel stands in the centre of the village, with fine views of the lake. Interesting public areas include a variety of lounges - the cosy foyer one also incorporating a bar - the main dining room to the lake-side, and downstairs a lively bar and informal restaurant. Upstairs the 5-course daily-changing dinner menu presents good honest cooking with accurate flavours from fresh ingredients. Owner John Melling extends real hospitality to his guests and makes every effort to ensure that they are made to feel at home.
40 en suite (bth/shr) (4 fmly) CTV in all bedrooms Lift 40P Pool table Billiards 3/4 Snooker table Xmas V meals Coffee am Tea pm No smoking in restaurant Last d 9.45pm
ROOMS: (incl. bkfst) s £64-£66; d £88-£90 * **LB**
OFF-PEAK: (incl. bkfst) s £45-£47
MEALS: Bar Lunch £10-£15alc Dinner £25-£27.50alc
CONF: Thtr 30 Class 30 Board 20 Del from £75
CARDS:

★★★57% ***Ullswater***
CA11 0PA ☎ 017684 82444 FAX 017684 82303
Built of Lakeland slate, this large early-Victorian building is situated in the centre of the village, its 18-acre grounds leading right down to the shores of Ullswater. Spacious public rooms and well equipped lakeside bedrooms take full advantage of the views.
48 en suite (bth/shr) (4 fmly) CTV in all bedrooms Lift 200P Golf 9 Fishing Solarium Pool table ch fac English & French Cuisine V meals Coffee am Tea pm Last d 9pm
CARDS:
See advertisement under ULLSWATER

GLOSSOP Derbyshire Map 07 SK09

Courtesy & Care Award

★★76% **Wind in the Willows**

Derbyshire Level, Sheffield Rd SK13 9PT (off A57) ☎ 01457 868001 FAX 01457 853354
A charming Victorian house in its own attractive grounds, almost at the foot of the Snake Pass, personally run by Peter Marsh assisted at times by his mother Mary, who still occasionally produces the fixed dinner menu which is normally served close to 7pm. The bedrooms are very individual with many thoughtful touches and provide high standards of comfort. This year an elegant meeting room has been opened, which allows the two attractive sitting rooms, one of which contains a small dispense bar, to be available for quiet relaxation. Owners and staff here have won the AA Courtesy and Care Award for 1996/7.
12 en suite (bth/shr) CTV in all bedrooms 16P No coaches No children 10yrs English & French Cuisine Coffee am No smoking in restaurant Last d 7pm
ROOMS: (incl. bkfst) s £60-£78; d £70-£98
MEALS: Dinner fr £18.50
CONF: Thtr 35 Class 16 Board 20 Del from £102
CARDS:

GLOUCESTER Gloucestershire Map 03 SO81

★★★74% **Hatton Court**

Upton Hill, Upton St Leonards GL4 8DE (3m SE off B4073) ☎ 01452 617412 FAX 01452 612945
Set 600 feet above sea level on top of Upton Hill, just three miles from Gloucester, this manor house offers sweeping views across the Severn Valley towards the Malvern Hills. The emphasis here is on comfort, and although some of the bedrooms are a little cramped they are all elegantly furnished and equipped with many modern facilities and extras such as cuddly toys. On arrival, guests are ushered to a desk in the hall-cum-lounge area. The bar serves food and the main restaurant has a dedicated approach to cooking producing simply crafted and enjoyable meals based on seasonal ingredients.
17 en suite (bth/shr) 28 annexe en suite (bth/shr) No smoking in 2 bedrooms CTV in all bedrooms No dogs (ex guide dogs) Night porter 80P Outdoor swimming pool (heated) Sauna Solarium Gym Croquet lawn Jacuzzi/spa Xmas English & French Cuisine V meals Coffee am Tea pm No smoking in restaurant Last d 10pm
ROOMS: (incl. bkfst) s £88-£98; d £100-£135 * **LB**
MEALS: Lunch £10-£14.50&alc Dinner £18.50-£22.50&alc*

contd.

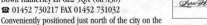

CONF: Thtr 60 Class 30 Board 30 Del from £95
CARDS:

See advertisement on opposite page

★★★ 62% **Hatherley Manor**
Down Hatherley Ln GL2 9QA (off A38)
☎ 01452 730217 FAX 01452 731032
Conveniently positioned just north of the city on the A38 Tewkesbury road with easy access to junction 11 of the M5, this 17th-century manor house has become a popular business and conference hotel. Bedrooms are modern in style, and all are well equipped, and there is a range of conference suites.
56 en suite (bth/shr) No smoking in 6 bedrooms CTV in all bedrooms STV Night porter 350P Gym ch fac English & French Cuisine V meals Coffee am Tea pm No smoking in restaurant
ROOMS: s £50-£60; d £70-£80 * LB
MEALS: Lunch £9.75-£12.50&alc
CONF: Thtr 300 Class 80 Board 50
CARDS:

★ 64% **Rotherfield House**
5 Horton Rd GL1 3PX (adjacent to Royal Hospital)
☎ 01452 410500 FAX 01452 381922
A substantial Victorian building on the road to the Royal Hospital, about a mile from the city centre, has been modernised to provide neat bedrooms of varying size and style. Hospitable owners Alan and Juliet Eacott give friendly personal service.
13 rms (8 shr) (2 fmly) CTV in all bedrooms 9P No coaches English & Continental Cuisine V meals Coffee am Tea pm No smoking in restaurant Last d 7.15pm
ROOMS: (incl. bkfst) s £19.50-£34; d £46 * LB
OFF-PEAK: (incl. bkfst) s £25; d £40
MEALS: Dinner £9.50&alc
CARDS:

Forte Posthouse Gloucester
Crest Way, Barnwood GL4 7RX (on Barnwood bypass near M5) ☎ 01452 613311
FAX 01452 371036
Suitable for both the business and leisure traveller, this bright hotel provides modern accommodation in well equipped bedrooms with en suite bathrooms. For more details about Forte Posthouse hotels, consult the Contents page for the section on Hotel Groups.
123 en suite (bth/shr)
ROOMS: s fr £79; d fr £79 *
CONF: Thtr 100 Class 50 Board 35 Del from £109

Travel Inn
Tewkesbury Rd, Longford GL2 9BE (on A38 between Longford and Gloucester)
☎ 01452 523519 FAX 01452 300924
Purpose-built accommodation, offering spacious, well equipped bedrooms, all with en suite bathrooms. Meals may be taken at the nearby family restaurant. For more information about Travel Inns, consult the Contents page under Hotel Groups.
40 en suite (bth/shr)
ROOMS: d £35.50 *

Travel Inn
Witcombe GL3 4SS (on A417 towards Cirencester)
☎ 01452 862521 FAX 01452 864926

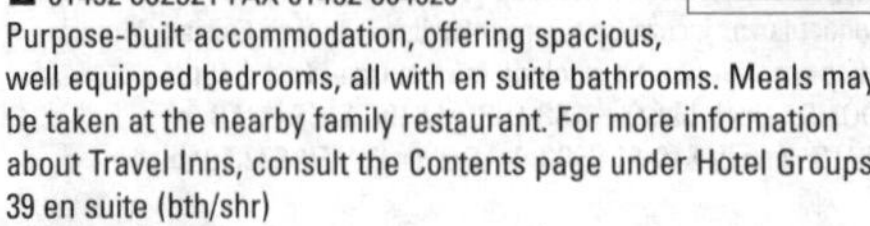

Purpose-built accommodation, offering spacious, well equipped bedrooms, all with en suite bathrooms. Meals may be taken at the nearby family restaurant. For more information about Travel Inns, consult the Contents page under Hotel Groups.
39 en suite (bth/shr)
ROOMS: d £35.50 *

GOATHLAND North Yorkshire Map 08 NZ80

★★ 71% **Mallyan Spout**
YO22 5AN (off A169) ☎ 01947 896486 FAX 01947 896327
Standing on the edge of this delightful moors village, where the sheep roam freely, this attractive stone built hotel offers a very traditional style of both service and accommodation. There are two comfortable lounges whilst the pleasant restaurant is an ideal setting for the well prepared dinners which are a highlight of any stay at the 'Mallyan'. Bedrooms are well equipped and vary in size and shape with some also enjoying superb views over the moors. Honest and friendly hospitality is provided by a keen and professional staff.
20 en suite (bth) 4 annexe en suite (bth) CTV in all bedrooms 50P English & French Cuisine V meals Coffee am Tea pm Last d 8.30pm
ROOMS: (incl. bkfst) s £45-£60; d £65-£130 * LB
MEALS: Lunch fr £13.50&alc Dinner fr £19.50&alc*
CONF: Thtr 70 Class 70 Board 40
CARDS:

See advertisement on opposite page

★★ 70% **Inn On The Moor**
YO22 5LZ (off A169 between Whitby and Pickering)
☎ 01947 896296 FAX 01947 896484
Standing in the attractive village of Goathland and near to the steam railway station of the North Yorks Moors Railway, this traditional hotel includes its own kitchen garden which supplies the hotels tables. Bedrooms are generally spacious and have quality furniture as well as good facilities. The spacious public rooms include a delightfully sunny conservatory and an elegant dining room whilst the service is both friendly and attentive.
24 en suite (bth/shr) (2 fmly) CTV in all bedrooms STV 30P Pool table Putting green ch fac V meals Coffee am Tea pm Last d 8.30pm
ROOMS: (incl. bkfst) s £30-£48; d £64 * LB
OFF-PEAK: (incl. bkfst) s fr £28; d fr £56
MEALS: Lunch fr £5alc High tea fr £2.20 Dinner fr £13.50*
CONF: Board 30 Del from £60
CARDS:

★ 70% **Whitfield House**
Darnholm YO22 5LA (from village follow signs to Darnholm for 0.75m) ☎ 01947 896215
Closed Dec & Jan
This family-owned and run hotel stands on the edge of the village and is found in a quiet lane leading to a stream and a bridge that crosses the North Yorkshire Moors Railway. The house dates back to the 17th century and was formerly an old farmhouse. It is now a comfortable small hotel offering well furnished bedrooms and two cosy lounges. A well produced four-course dinner offering a good choice is provided each evening.
8 en suite (bth/shr) (1 fmly) No smoking in all bedrooms CTV in all bedrooms 10P No coaches No children 5yrs Coffee am Tea pm No smoking in restaurant Last d 5.30pm
ROOMS: (incl. bkfst) s £28; d £56
OFF-PEAK: (incl. bkfst) s £26; d £52
MEALS: Bar Lunch £4.50-£6.50&alc Dinner £11.50&alc
CARDS:

GODALMING Surrey Map 04 SU94

★★★ 65% **Inn on the Lake**
Ockford Rd GU7 1RH (on A3) ☎ 01483 415575 FAX 01483 860445
Successfully combining the functions of a popular country inn with a serious restaurant and a hotel, this establishments is of Tudor origins with a modern extension set in two acres of landscaped gardens overlooking a lake. Bedrooms have been individually furnished and equipped with every modern amenity, the best overlooking the gardens and lake whilst those at the rear may be quieter. The inn serves a

particularly good range of bar meals, whilst the Lake View Restaurant offers more formal surroundings to enjoy the high standards of Chef Neale O'Brien's cooking. Service is quietly efficient and particularly well managed. Live piano entertainment is provided most evenings and there are very good facilities for private functions.
19 en suite (bth/shr) (1 fmly) CTV in all bedrooms STV 100P International Cuisine V meals Coffee am Tea pm Last d 10pm
ROOMS: (incl. bkfst) s £80; d £80 * **LB**
OFF-PEAK: (incl. bkfst) s £65; d £65
MEALS: Lunch £14.75-£17.50&alc Dinner £14.50-£17.50&alc*
CONF: Thtr 150 Class 60 Board 35 Del £98
CARDS:

GOLANT Cornwall & Isles of Scilly Map 02 SX15

★★ 65% **Cormorant**

PL23 1LL (from A390 Liskeard to St Austell, turn left on to B3269 Fowey and then after 2m left again)
☎ 01726 833426 FAX 01726 833426
This peaceful hotel enjoys a picturesque riverside setting on the edge of the small fishing village of Golant. Close to the towns of Fowey and St Austell, The Cormorant is positioned high above the Fowey Estuary and offers unforgettable views from full-length picture windows in the public rooms and bedrooms. In the candlelit restaurant a choice of menus offers an interesting selection of dishes, with locally caught fish being a speciality. The involvement of the resident proprietors and their small team of staff contributes to the relaxed atmosphere which attracts guests all year round.
11 en suite (bth/shr) CTV in all bedrooms 20P Indoor swimming pool (heated) Boating Xmas English & French Cuisine V meals Coffee am Tea pm No smoking area in restaurant Last d 9pm
ROOMS: (incl. bkfst) s £42-£52; d £70-£84 **LB**
OFF-PEAK: (incl. bkfst) s £35-£42; d £60-£70
MEALS: Bar Lunch £3.50-£12.50alc Dinner fr £16&alc
CARDS:

See advertisement under FOWEY

GOMERSAL West Yorkshire Map 08 SE22

★★★ 66% ***Gomersal Park***

Moor Ln BD19 4LT (off junc 26 of M62)
☎ 01274 869386 FAX 01274 861042
The main house dates back to the 19th century and the extension has been carefully designed to match the original building. The hotel provides modern and well equipped bedrooms together with comfortable public areas, whilst the excellent leisure centre is very well equipped. Service is friendly and professional and a good range of dishes is available in the restaurant with its attractive conservatory. Extensive function facilities are also provided.
52 en suite (bth/shr) (5 fmly) CTV in all bedrooms STV No dogs (ex guide dogs) Night porter 200P Indoor swimming pool (heated) Sauna Solarium Gym V meals Coffee am Tea pm Last d 10pm
CARDS:

GOODRICH Hereford & Worcester Map 03 SO51

★★61% **Ye Hostelrie**
HR9 6HX (1m off the A40, between Ross-on-Wye/Monmouth, within 100yds of Goodrich Castle) ☎ 01600 890241 FAX 01600 890838
New owners have taken on this well run hotel, parts ow which date back to the 17th century. Bedrooms are traditionally furnished and soundly maintained. Guests have the use of a pleasant bar, a spacious and comfortable lounge and a smart dining room. The hotel is situated in a small village within easy reach of Symonds Yat and other tourist attractions.
6 en suite (bth/shr) CTV in all bedrooms 32P ch fac V meals Coffee am Tea pm No smoking area in restaurant Last d 10pm
ROOMS: (incl. bkfst) s fr £27.50; d fr £40 *
MEALS: Lunch fr £16.25 High tea fr £5.50 Dinner fr £16.25&alc*
CONF: Thtr 60 Class 40 Board 30 Del from £69
CARDS:

GOODRINGTON See Paignton

GOODWOOD West Sussex Map 04 SU80

★★★★ 70% **Marriott Goodwood Park**

PO18 0QB (off the A285, 3m NE of Chichester)
☎ 01243 775537 FAX 01243 520120
Part of the Goodwood Estate, this hotel, country club and golf course has benefited in 1996 from a very significant upgrading. All the bedrooms have been smartly refurbished; Dukes Restaurant and bar have been elegantly decorated and a new marbled lobby has been created. New chef Gary Foster offers some fine cooking of dishes in a modern light and tasty vein. Leisure facilities are extensive, both outdoors and indoors, and the Waterbeach Grill provides an informal eating alternative. The hotel management is committed to a continuous improvement in standards of service.
94 en suite (bth/shr) (3 fmly) No smoking in 66 bedrooms CTV in all bedrooms STV Night porter 250P Indoor swimming pool (heated) Golf 18 Tennis (hard) Squash Sauna Solarium Gym Putting green Jacuzzi/spa Beauty salon Xmas V meals Tea pm No smoking in restaurant Last d 9.30pm
ROOMS: (incl. bkfst) s fr £93; d fr £138 * **LB**
OFF-PEAK: s fr £59; d fr £59
MEALS: Lunch £12.75-£18&alc Dinner fr £21.75&alc*
CONF: Thtr 120 Class 60 Board 60 Del from £115
CARDS:

GOOLE East Riding of Yorkshire Map 08 SE72

★★66% **Clifton**
1 Clifton Gardens, Boothferry Rd DN14 6AL
☎ 01405 761336 FAX 01405 762350
John and Dorothy Hope are delightful hosts and provide a very warm and friendly atmosphere at their predominantly commercial hotel. The public rooms have been delightfully upgraded and are a pleasure use whilst the pretty bedrooms are also very well equipped. A good choice of wholesome food is available in the

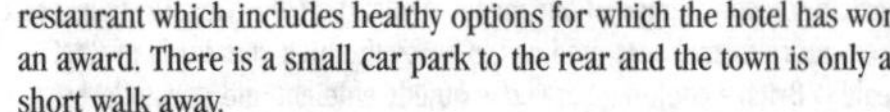

restaurant which includes healthy options for which the hotel has won an award. There is a small car park to the rear and the town is only a short walk away.
9 rms (5 bth 3 shr) (1 fmly) CTV in all bedrooms 8P English & Continental Cuisine V meals Coffee am No smoking in restaurant Last d 8.45pm
ROOMS: (incl. bkfst) s £38; d £46 * **LB**
OFF-PEAK: (incl. bkfst) s £26; d £39
MEALS: Lunch fr £4.95alc Dinner fr £6alc*
CARDS:

GORDANO MOTORWAY SERVICE AREA (M5) Somerset Map 03 ST57

Travelodge
BS20 9XG (M5 junct 19) ☎ 01275 373709
This modern building offers accommodation in smart, spacious and well equipped bedrooms, suitable for family use, and all with en suite bathrooms. Meals may be taken at the nearby family restaurant. For information on room rates and to make a booking, call Roomline free of charge on 0800 850950. For more details about Travelodge, consult the Contents page under Hotel Groups.
40 en suite (bth/shr)

GORLESTON-ON-SEA See Great Yarmouth

GOSFORTH Cumbria Map 11 NY00

★★69% **Westlakes**
CA20 1HP (junc of A595 and B5344) ☎ 019467 25221
FAX 019467 25099
Hospitality is second to none at this family-run Georgian country mansion which stands in its own grounds with an entrance just off the A595 on the edge of the village. Chris and Anne Newell are friendly and involved hosts and many business guests are regulars. The atmosphere is cosy and relaxed. There is an inviting lounge with a dispense bar at one end, and the attractive dining room comprises three rooms, one of which is ideal for private dining. Bedrooms range in size and the original master rooms are well proportioned, but the three newer rooms in the extension may hold most appeal.
9 en suite (bth/shr) (1 fmly) CTV in all bedrooms 25P No coaches English & French Cuisine V meals No smoking in restaurant Last d 9pm
ROOMS: (incl. bkfst) s £44.50-£46; d £53.50-£61.50
OFF-PEAK: (incl. bkfst) d £46.50-£54.50
MEALS: Lunch £10.70-£21.20alc Dinner £11.50-£25alc*
CARDS:

GRANGE-OVER-SANDS Cumbria Map 07 SD47

★★★ 66% **Graythwaite Manor**
Fernhill Rd LA11 7JE (follow B5277 through Grange, Fernhill Road opposite fire station behind small traffic island, hotel first left)
☎ 015395 32001 & 33755 FAX 015395 35549
Closed 5-19 Jan
This long-established family-run hotel lies in attractive landscaped gardens in an elevated position giving views of Morecambe Bay. Appealingly old-fashioned, it combines modern amenities with traditional values, and the variety of bedroom styles also follow this theme. There are three lounges, one of which has a small bar, whilst the dining room is graced by crisp white linen and sparkling silver.
21 en suite (bth/shr) (2 fmly) CTV in all bedrooms No dogs (ex guide dogs) 32P No coaches Tennis (hard) Putting green Helicopter landing area English & French Cuisine V meals Coffee am Tea pm No smoking area in restaurant Last d 8.30pm
ROOMS: (incl. bkfst) s £45-£55; d £80-£90 * **LB**
OFF-PEAK: (incl. bkfst) s £40-£50; d £60-£80

CONF: Thtr 50 Class 20 Board 25
CARDS:

See advertisement on this page

★★★65% **Netherwood**
Lindale Rd LA11 6ET (on B5277 just before the station)
☎ 015395 32552 FAX 015395 34121
This imposing stone building lies in its own grounds and terraced gardens overlooking Morecambe Bay. Tastefully extended to provide a restaurant, new bedrooms and a leisure complex, it attracts tourists, business persons, small conferences and weddings. Built in the late 1800's its public rooms feature magnificent woodwork and help create an atmosphere of relaxation. There are a variety of bedrooms, but it is worth choosing one of the premier rooms which have fine Italian furnishings and stylish modern bathrooms.
29 en suite (bth/shr) (7 fmly) No smoking in 14 bedrooms CTV in all bedrooms Lift Night porter 160P Indoor swimming pool (heated) Solarium Croquet lawn Jacuzzi/spa Beauty salon Steam room ch fac English & French Cuisine V meals Coffee am Tea pm No smoking in restaurant Last d 8.30pm
ROOMS: (incl. bkfst) s £45-£55; d £90-£110 **LB**
MEALS: Lunch £12.25-£14.25 High tea £8.75-£9.75 Dinner £21-£24
CONF: Thtr 150 Class 30 Board 40 Del from £78
CARDS:

★★★64% ***Grange***
CONSORT HOTELS
Station Square LA11 6EJ (opposite Railway Station)
☎ 015395 33666 FAX 015395 35064
Built as a hotel in the grand resort style, this imposing building lies in well tended gardens and grounds in an elevated position overlooking Morecambe Bay. The extensive public areas include conference facilities and a restaurant with an interesting and varied dinner menu. Bedrooms come in a variety of styles.
41 en suite (bth/shr) (6 fmly) CTV in all bedrooms STV Night porter 100P Sauna Solarium Gym Jacuzzi/spa English & French Cuisine V meals Coffee am Tea pm Last d 9pm
CARDS:

★★ 67% **Hampsfell House**
Hampsfell Rd LA11 6BG ☎ 015395 32567
Closed 25 & 26 Dec
Personally managed by the owners, this friendly hotel is set in its own gardens off a quiet wooded lane, but only a few minutes' drive down to the town. There are two cosy lounges served by one bar, and the well maintained bedrooms are bright and cheerful. Enjoyable home-cooked meals are offered in the comfortable dining room with its spotless table appointments.
9 en suite (bth/shr) (2 fmly) CTV in all bedrooms 20P No coaches Coffee am Tea pm No smoking in restaurant Last d 8.30pm
ROOMS: (incl. bkfst) s £25-£28; d £40-£50 * **LB**
OFF-PEAK: (incl. bkfst) d £40-£46
MEALS: Lunch £7.50-£10alc Dinner £14.50-£16.50alc*
CARDS:

★71% **Clare House**
Park Rd LA11 7HQ (turn off A590 onto B5277, through Lindale onto Grange, hotel 0.5m on left past Crown Hill/St Paul's Church)
☎ 01539 533026 & 534253
Closed Nov-Mar
This delightful country house hotel, is set in well kept gardens overlooking Morecambe Bay, just a short walk from the town centre. Bedrooms are traditionally and comfortably furnished with many modern facilities, and some have private balconies. The two lounges serve afternoon tea, and an attractive dining room offers five-course dinners.
17 rms (16 bth/shr) (1 fmly) CTV in all bedrooms No dogs (ex guide dogs) 18P No coaches Croquet lawn Putting green No children 5yrs Coffee am Tea pm No smoking in restaurant
ROOMS: (incl. bkfst & dinner) s £42.50-£44; d £85-£88 **LB**

GRANTHAM Lincolnshire Map 08 SK93

★★★73% **Swallow**

SWALLOW HOTELS
Swingbridge Rd NG31 7XT (junc of A1 southbound with A607) ☎ 01476 593000 FAX 01476 592592
This two-storey, red-brick building, conveniently located for the A1, still has the appearance of a recently built hotel. The open-plan lounge has a small outside patio area and there is a spacious restaurant which comfortably accomodates the large groups which frequently dine there. Bedrooms are also spacious, sensibly laid out and furnished to a very high standard. The staff are pleasant and well meaning in their duties.
90 en suite (bth/shr) (6 fmly) No smoking in 55 bedrooms CTV in all bedrooms STV Night porter 150P Indoor swimming pool (heated) Sauna Solarium Gym Steam room Wkly live entertainment Xmas English & French Cuisine V meals Coffee am Tea pm No smoking in restaurant Last d 9.45pm
ROOMS: (incl. bkfst) s £95; d £105 * **LB**
OFF-PEAK: (incl. bkfst) s £65; d £75
MEALS: Lunch £11-£12.95 High tea £7 Dinner £18&alc*
CONF: Thtr 200 Class 90 Board 50 Del from £98
CARDS:

★★★64% **Kings**

North Pde NG31 8AU ☎ 01476 590800
FAX 01476 590800
This much extended Georgian house, which is set back from the main road, has seen many improvements and the addition of extra facilities over recent years. The bedrooms have all been upgraded and are decorated with Sanderson wallpaper which

contd.

complements the modern light oak furniture. The Orangery which serves as a coffee shop proves popular as does the more formal Victorian restaurant. There is an open-plan lounge, separate bar and a patio which guests can enjoy in the summer.
21 en suite (bth/shr) (1 fmly) CTV in all bedrooms Night porter 36P Tennis (hard) Special rates at leisure club English & French Cuisine V meals Coffee am Tea pm No smoking in restaurant Last d 10pm
ROOMS: (incl. bkfst) s £45-£50; d £55-£60 * **LB**
OFF-PEAK: (incl. bkfst) s £35-£40; d £45-£50
MEALS: Lunch £9.50-£15 Dinner £11.95-£15
CONF: Thtr 100 Class 50 Board 40 Del from £53.75
CARDS:

★★★62% **Angel & Royal**
High St NG31 6PN ☎ 01476 65816 FAX 01476 67149

This town-centre coaching inn, reputedly the oldest inn in England, was built in the 13th century as a hostel for the the Knights Templar. Although modernised, much of the original character remains, particularly in the fascinating restaurant with its exposed stone walls and unusual windows. Bedroom standards are mixed; the best are pleasantly appointed, but others could benefit from refurbishment.
30 en suite (bth/shr) No smoking in 10 bedrooms CTV in all bedrooms 50P English & French Cuisine V meals Coffee am Tea pm No smoking in restaurant Last d 9.30pm
MEALS: Lunch £4.95-£16alc Dinner £4.95-£16alc*
CONF: Thtr 30 Class 18 Board 16 Del £79
CARDS:

Travelodge
Grantham Service Area NG32 2AB (4m N on A1)
☎ 01476 77500

This modern building offers accommodation in smart, spacious and well equipped bedrooms, suitable for family use, and all with en suite bathrooms. Meals may be taken at the nearby family restaurant. For information on room rates and to make a booking, call Roomline free of charge on 0800 850950. For more details about Travelodge, consult the Contents page under Hotel Groups.
40 en suite (bth/shr)

GRASMERE Cumbria Map 11 NY30

★★★★ 65% **Wordsworth**
LA22 9SW (in centre of village adjacent to St Oswalds church) ☎ 015394 35592 FAX 015394 35765

This tourist hotel lies close to the churchyard where William Wordsworth is buried and its landscaped gardens give it a peaceful atmosphere despite being in the centre of the village. The swimming pool and terrace lead onto the gardens where one can sit and enjoy a summer drink or afternoon tea, weather permitting. Public rooms are not grand but they are relaxing and include a comfortable drawing room and a small cocktail bar with adjoining sun lounge. The restaurant offers a blend of traditional and contemporary dishes cooked in the modern style with fish and seafood featuring strongly. Bedrooms vary in size and several are compact, but most have the benefit of good modern bathrooms and all have the expected facilities.
37 en suite (bth/shr) (3 fmly) CTV in all bedrooms No dogs (ex guide dogs) Lift Night porter 60P No coaches Indoor swimming pool (heated) Sauna Solarium Gym Pool table Croquet lawn Jacuzzi/spa Table tennis Xmas English & French Cuisine V meals Coffee am Tea pm No smoking in restaurant Last d 9pm
ROOMS: (incl. bkfst) s fr £68; d £156-£210 **LB**
MEALS: Lunch fr £18.50alc Dinner £30-£33alc
CONF: Thtr 130 Class 50 Board 40 Del from £75
CARDS:

See advertisement on opposite page

RED STAR HOTEL

★★★ **Michael's Nook Country House**
LA22 9RP (off A591) ☎ 015394 35496 FAX 015394 35645

This beautiful country house hotel takes its name from associations with Wordsworth, is set in the hills looking down on Grasmere and is run on traditional country-house lines. Staff are very friendly and willing to please, and accommodation offers every comfort. Furnishings throughout display many fine antique pieces, reflecting the former occupation of its owner. Good food has long been one of the great strengths of this hotel and a new chef, Mark Treasure from the Capital Hotel in London, took over from Kevin Mangeolles last year and is more than upholding high standards. The menu is a five-course one, with choices, and Mark cooks in a style that he describes as European and shows influences from all over the Mediterranean. Service is led by proprietor, Reg Gifford, who is very much at ease as host.
14 en suite (bth/shr) (2 fmly) CTV in all bedrooms No dogs (ex guide dogs) 20P No coaches Croquet lawn Use of facilities at Wordsworth Hotel No children 5yrs Xmas International Cuisine No smoking in restaurant Last d 8pm
ROOMS: (incl. bkfst & dinner) s £124-£136; d £156-£300 **LB**
MEALS: Lunch £28.50 Dinner £39.50-£46
CONF: Thtr 24 Board 20 Del from £135
CARDS:

★★★ 69% **Gold Rill Country House**
Red Bank Rd LA22 9PU (turn down road opposite St Oswald church) ☎ 015394 35486
FAX 015394 35486
Closed mid Dec-mid Jan

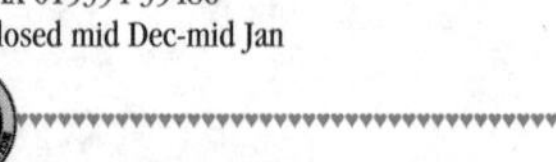

(Rosette awarded for dinner only)
You will find a friendly and relaxing atmosphere at this hotel, situated within two acres of lawned gardens in a quiet part of the village and enjoying fine open views of the lake and surrounding fells. Spotlessly clean and extremely well maintained, it boasts comfortable lounges and an attractive restaurant, where steamed puddings are an irresistible speciality. Most of the bedrooms take advantage of the impressive vista, and although they vary in size, they are all enhanced with tasteful fabrics.

25 en suite (bth/shr) (2 fmly) CTV in all bedrooms STV No dogs 35P No coaches Outdoor swimming pool (heated) Croquet lawn Putting green Xmas V meals Coffee am No smoking in restaurant
ROOMS: (incl. bkfst & dinner) s £46-£59; d £92-£118 * **LB**
OFF-PEAK: (incl. bkfst & dinner) s £36-£56; d £72-£112
MEALS: Dinner £18.50*
CARDS:

See advertisement on this page

★★★ 69% **The Swan**
LA22 9RF (on A591) ☎ 015394 35551
FAX 015394 35741

FORTE Heritage

The original part of this roadside inn is over 300 year old and was mentioned by Wordsworth in his poem "The Waggoner." Its stands on the main road between Keswick and Ambleside, a short walk from the village centre, and its attractive white facade is enhanced by summer flowers and colourful window boxes. The lounges are cosy and comfortable, again with lots of flowers and antique bric a brac and traditional afternoon tea can be taken either in the lounge or in the pretty gardens at the side of the hotel. The bedrooms are very well appointed and have every modern facility. They are tastefully decorated and furnished and one has a magnificent four-poster bed. The Waggoners Restaurant is well known for its high standard of mainly British cuisine and regular visitors to The Swan will be pleased to learn that the famous Tea Cup Trifle is still a feature of the sweet menu.

36 en suite (bth/shr) No smoking in 20 bedrooms CTV in all bedrooms 40P No coaches Croquet lawn Xmas V meals Coffee am Tea pm No smoking in restaurant Last d 9pm
ROOMS: s £75-£90; d £110-£130 **LB**
OFF-PEAK: s £50-£65; d £80-£100
MEALS: Lunch £10.35-£12.95 Dinner £18.95-£28.95
CONF: Thtr 30 Class 12 Board 16 Del from £80
CARDS:

★★★ 68% **Prince of Wales Thistle**
Keswick Rd LA22 9PR ☎ 015394 35666
FAX 015394 35565

THISTLE HOTELS

Built in the Edwardian era and in recent years restored to an elegance reminiscent of the period this hotel stands alongside the A591, with gardens leading down to the lake. The bedrooms have been tastefully furnished and decorated and many of those in the original building have views over the lake. There is also a

contd.

suite with a four-poster bed. There is ample parking and also facilities for meetings and conferences.

72 en suite (bth/shr) (8 fmly) No smoking in 13 bedrooms CTV in all bedrooms STV Night porter 100P Pool table Table tennis Rowing boats Xmas International Cuisine V meals Coffee am Tea pm No smoking in restaurant Last d 8.45pm

ROOMS: (incl. bkfst) s fr £70; d fr £88 * **LB**

MEALS: Bar Lunch £7-£10 High tea £3.45-£7.50 Dinner £19.50&alc*

CONF: Thtr 110 Class 60 Board 40

CARDS:

★★★66% **Red Lion**

Red Lion Square LA22 9SS (centre of village)

☎ 015394 35456 FAX 015394 35579

Occupying a central position in the village, this former coaching inn has been upgraded to offer modern well equipped bedrooms of varying size. There is a lively pub and buttery to complement the main restaurant and a conservatory extension to the foyer bar is planned.

34 en suite (bth) (4 fmly) CTV in all bedrooms STV Lift 38P Sauna Solarium Gym Pool table Jacuzzi/spa Hairdressing Xmas V meals Coffee am Tea pm No smoking in restaurant Last d 9pm

ROOMS: (incl. bkfst) s £41.50-£45.50; d £83-£91

OFF-PEAK: (incl. bkfst) s £32.50-£39.50; d £65-£79

MEALS: Bar Lunch £6.50-£13.50 Dinner £18.50&alc

CONF: Thtr 60 Class 30 Board 30 Del from £69.50

CARDS:

See advertisement on opposite page

★★★64% **Rothay Garden**

Broadgate LA22 9RJ ☎ 015394 35334 FAX 015394 35723

Situated on the northern approach to this well known Cumbrian village, the Rothay Garden Hotel has been considerably upgraded over the last couple of years. The bedrooms, including some with four-poster beds and whirlpool baths, are comfortable and offer all the expected amenities. Public areas include a choice of lounges and a cosy cocktail bar, as well as a bright conservatory-style restaurant which overlooks the well kept gardens which surround the hotel. The staff are friendly and professional in their approach.

26 en suite (bth/shr) (2 fmly) CTV in all bedrooms 35P No coaches Fishing Jacuzzi/spa Xmas English & French Cuisine V meals Coffee am Tea pm No smoking in restaurant Last d 9pm

ROOMS: (incl. bkfst & dinner) s £47-£67.50; d £109-£149 * **LB**

OFF-PEAK: (incl. bkfst & dinner) s £44.50-£60; d £94-£135

MEALS: Lunch £11.60-£16.40 Dinner £14.90*

CONF: Thtr 25 Class 16 Board 12 Del from £67.50

CARDS:

★★70% **Oak Bank**

Broadgate LA22 9TA (in centre of village just off A591)

☎ 015394 35217 FAX 015394 35685

Closed Jan

This friendly hotel lies in gardens close to the centre of the village, and owners Attilio and Sharon Savasi are as dedicated to the welfare of their guests today as they were when they took over in 1981. The attractive and comfortable public areas feature a stylish restaurant with a conservatory extension, and a choice of lounges with quiet corners in which to relax. Bedrooms come in different sizes, but the attractive decor and antique pine furniture compensate for the lack of space in a few. Sharon's short four-course dinner menu reflects capable Cordon Bleu cooking with a commitment to the use of fresh produce, whilst Attilio supervises proceedings with considerable flair and professionalism.

15 en suite (bth/shr) (1 fmly) CTV in 14 bedrooms 14P No coaches ch fac Xmas English & Continental Cuisine V meals Coffee am Tea pm

ROOMS: (incl. bkfst) s fr £27.50; d fr £55 * **LB**

OFF-PEAK: (incl. bkfst) s fr £25; d fr £50

MEALS: Bar Lunch £2.50-£10 High tea £5-£6 Dinner £16-£18*

CARDS:

★★68% **Grasmere**

Broadgate LA22 9TA (take A591 to from Ambleside, then second turning left into town centre. Follow road over humpbacked bridge, past playing field. Hotel on left) ☎ 015394 35277 FAX 015394 35277

Closed Jan-8 Feb

A family-run Victorian house is situated close to the centre of the village, its gardens running down to the River Rothay. Bedrooms are very well equipped bedrooms and individually appointed; two are conveniently situated on the ground floor. A modern dining room is the setting for dinner, the daily-changed four-course menu offering a choice of five main dishes based on the finest of fresh produce.

12 en suite (bth/shr) CTV in all bedrooms STV 16P No coaches Croquet lawn Putting green No children 6yrs Xmas English & French Cuisine V meals Coffee am Tea pm No smoking in restaurant Last d 8.30pm

ROOMS: (incl. bkfst) s £30-£40; d £60-£80 * **LB**

OFF-PEAK: (incl. bkfst) s fr £25; d fr £50

MEALS: High tea £5 Dinner £15*

CARDS: 

★★65% **Bridge House**

Stock Ln LA22 9SN ☎ 015394 35425 FAX 015394 35523

Closed 2 Jan-15 Feb

This well proportioned family-run hotel lies secluded in sheltered wooded gardens and is backed by the River Rothay which runs through the centre of the village. It has bright modern bedrooms, a comfortable lounge with open fire, cosy bar and a dining room serving home-cooked meals. An extension providing superior bedrooms and a new bar are planned for 1997.

12 en suite (bth/shr) No smoking in all bedrooms CTV in all bedrooms No dogs (ex guide dogs) 20P No coaches Xmas V meals Coffee am Tea pm No smoking in restaurant Last d 8.30pm

ROOMS: (incl. bkfst) s £25-£35; d £50-£70 *

MEALS: Lunch fr £1.75 High tea fr £1.75 Dinner £10-£14.50&alc*

CARDS:

RED STAR HOTEL

★ **White Moss House**

Rydal Water LA22 9SE (on A591)

☎ 015394 35295 FAX 015394 35516

Closed early Dec-mid Mar

This traditional Lakeland house sits in gardens tucked back from the main road close to Rydal Water. It was once owned by William Wordsworth but its present claim to fame is as a small

hotel with an intimate country house atmosphere. Whilst Peter Dixon's cooking and first-class wines are the reason for many guests returning regularly, they also appreciate the care and attention given by Sue Dixon and her dedicated staff. Bedrooms are all individual, and come in a variety of sizes with excellent use made of available space; they are also extremely well equipped and enhanced by attractive fabrics. For something completely different a two room suite is offered in Brockstone, a cottage situated on the hillside high above the hotel. There is no bar at White Moss, pre-dinner drinks being served in the lovely lounge, with its books and coal fire. The 5-course set dinner is served at 8pm in the cosy little cottage-style dining room. Peter Dixon combines an uncomplicated approach to cooking, with some innovative touches.
5 en suite (bth/shr) 2 annexe en suite (bth/shr) CTV in all bedrooms No dogs 10P No coaches Free use of local leisure club No children 5yrs No smoking in restaurant Last d 8pm
ROOMS: (incl. bkfst & dinner) d £120-£175 **LB**
OFF-PEAK: (incl. bkfst & dinner) d £110-£150
MEALS: Dinner £27.50
CARDS:

GRASSINGTON North Yorkshire Map 07 SE06

★★65% **Grassington House**
5 The Square BD23 5AQ (Take B6265 from Skipton, on right hand side of village square) ☎ 01756 752406 FAX 01756 752135
Gordon and Linda Elsworth and their dedicated staff continue to provide a very friendly style of service at their delightful hotel which is situated in the cobbled square. The house is attractively furnished and comfortable, whilst the cosy dining room is a good setting for the very well produced food which use mainly fresh and local produce. A good range of bar food is also available.
10 en suite (bth/shr) (1 fmly) CTV in all bedrooms 20P Xmas English & French Cuisine V meals Coffee am Tea pm
ROOMS: (incl. bkfst) s fr £26; d fr £52 * **LB**
MEALS: Lunch fr £8.95alc*
CARDS:

GRAVESEND Kent Map 05 TQ67

★★★61% **Overcliffe**
15-16 The Overcliffe DA11 0EF (outside town centre, to the west on the A226) ☎ 01474 322131 FAX 01474 536737
This well run family hotel dates from 1860 and has been skilfully converted to provide comfortable accommodation in the main house and in a Victorian lodge close by. It is personally run by the proprietors Trevor and Benita Thomas and the atmosphere is very cordial with attentive service provided by polite uniformed staff. The bedrooms are equipped with every amenity and lots of thoughtful extras. Live piano entertainment is provided most evenings in the downstairs bar-lounge and restaurant where an interesting selection of à la carte dishes is offered. The terrace can be used on warm evenings, and the freshly prepared food is complemented by a well chosen wine list. There is ample car parking and the town centre is only a few minutes walk away.
19 en suite (shr) 10 annexe en suite (bth/shr) CTV in all bedrooms STV Night porter 35P English & Continental Cuisine V meals Coffee am Tea pm
ROOMS: (incl. bkfst) s £55-£62.50; d £65-£75 *
MEALS:*
CARDS:

All AA-classified hotels now have an entry on the AA Internet site, address: http://www.theaa.co.uk/hotels The information is also available through CompuServe.

GRAYS Essex Map 05 TQ67

★★★64% **Stifford Moat House**

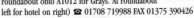

High Rd, North Stifford RM16 1UE (from M25 junct 30/31 east on A13, signed Grays, and in 1m at roundabout onto A1012 for Grays. At roundabout left for hotel on right) ☎ 01708 719988 FAX 01375 390426
RS Sat & bank holidays (restricted lunch)
This extended Georgian property is well located for its main weekday purpose of meetings and conferences. Elegant public areas include a smart restaurant and a newly refurbished bar. Bedrooms provide a good level of comfort in both sections : the main building and the more recently built garden wing.
96 en suite (bth/shr) (12 fmly) No smoking in 16 bedrooms CTV in all bedrooms Lift Night porter 130P Tennis (hard) Croquet lawn Petanque Xmas International Cuisine V meals Coffee am Tea pm No smoking area in restaurant Last d 10pm
ROOMS: s fr £78 * **LB**
MEALS: Lunch £25-£40alc Dinner £17.50&alc*
CONF: Thtr 130 Class 30 Board 36 Del £130
CARDS:

GREAT BARR West Midlands Map 07 SP09

★★★61% **Great Barr Hotel & Conference Centre**
Pear Tree Dr, Newton Rd B43 6HS (1m W of junc A34/A4041) ☎ 0121 357 1141 FAX 0121 357 7557
RS BH (restaurant may be closed)
A popular business and conference venue, this hotel is located in a quiet residential area, but has easy access to both the city and motorway. The bedroom block is located away from the hub of the public rooms. There is a good lounge, a newly refurbished oak-

contd.

panelled pub-style bar and a light airy restaurant. Car parking is extensive with part being gated and secure.
105 en suite (bth/shr) (1 fmly) CTV in all bedrooms No dogs (ex guide dogs) Night porter 175P Xmas English & Continental Cuisine V meals Coffee am Tea pm Last d 9.45pm
ROOMS: s £59.50-£62.50; d £69-£73 * **LB**
OFF-PEAK: s £33; d £40
MEALS: Lunch £8-£12.50 Dinner fr £15.75&alc*
CONF: Thtr 120 Class 50 Board 50
CARDS:
See advertisement under BIRMINGHAM

Forte Posthouse Birmingham Great Barr
Chapel Ln B43 7BG (at junction M6/A34)
☎ 0121 357 7444 FAX 0121 357 7503
FORTE Posthouse
Suitable for both the business and leisure traveller, this bright hotel provides modern accommodation in well equipped bedrooms with en suite bathrooms. For more details about Forte Posthouse hotels, consult the Contents page for the section on Hotel Groups.
192 en suite (bth/shr)
ROOMS: s £79-£95; d £79-£95
CONF: Thtr 120 Class 70 Board 50 Del from £109

GREAT CHESTERFORD Essex Map 05 TL54

★★ 66% The Crown House
CB10 1NY ☎ 01799 530515 FAX 01799 530683
This small, listed building dates from Tudor times and is conveniently situated on the B1383 within 5 minutes of Junction 9 of the M11. Bedrooms in the main house have more character than those in the courtyard building, but this is quieter. Dinner is served in the cottagey dining room where chef John Pearman has established a reputation for enjoyable home cooking: his crispy English duck with a lime and orange sauce was a success with our inspector. Breakfast is served in the bright conservatory which leads to a small patio and a garden which provides vegetables and herbs for the kitchen.
8 en suite (bth/shr) 10 annexe en suite (bth/shr) (1 fmly) CTV in all bedrooms 30P English & Continental Cuisine V meals Coffee am Tea pm No smoking in restaurant Last d 9.30pm
ROOMS: (incl. bkfst) s £51-£65; d £65-£85 * **LB**
OFF-PEAK: (incl. bkfst) s £30-£65; d £52-£85
CONF: Thtr 50 Class 40 Board 30
CARDS:

GREAT DUNMOW Essex Map 05 TL62

★★ 59% *The Saracen's Head*
High St CM6 1AG (take A120 towards Colchester turn left at roundabout, hotel 0.50m downhill)
☎ 01371 873901 FAX 01371 875743
REGAL A Collection of Individual Hotels
Situated in the centre of town, this former coaching inn retains much of its original character in the beamed public rooms. The majority of bedrooms have been refurbished to a smart, modern standard and there are 3 spacious suites with brass beds. Parking is found at the rear of the hotel.
4 en suite (bth/shr) 20 annexe en suite (bth/shr) (3 fmly) No smoking in 7 bedrooms CTV in all bedrooms 50P English & French Cuisine V meals Coffee am Tea pm Last d 9.15pm
CARDS:

GREAT LANGDALE

See Elterwater

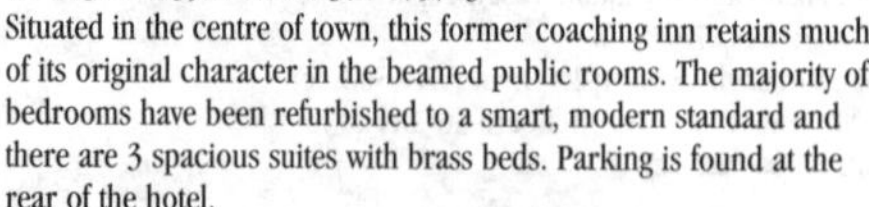
You don't have to say you love her. Just show her, with INTERFLORA. Flowers direct to your room. Freecall 0500 43 43 43.

GREAT MILTON Oxfordshire Map 04 SP60

RED STAR HOTEL

★★★★ Le Manoir Aux Quat' Saisons
OX44 7PD ☎ 01844 278881
FAX 01844 278847
RELAIS & CHATEAUX. Relais Gourmands
This fine old 15th-century manor house has been lovingly maintained and extended by the renowned Raymond Blanc to provide the highest qualities of English country house hotel style, though clearly the focus is still the restaurant, where Raymond and his head chef Clive Fretwell continue to inspire with their innovative seasonal menus that combine traditional and exotic ingredients in true harmony. The main house contains most of the well furnished and comfortable bedrooms, the three dining rooms, a meeting room and two lounges which at times have difficulty coping with the volume of business. Within the converted stables are the remaining bedrooms which are most spacious, some having their own patio overlooking the orchard. Service is attentive by immaculately white jacketed staff, with nothing being too much trouble. Additional features of the hotel are a popular cookery school held during the winter and recently a private coach service to London has been introduced.
19 en suite (bth/shr) CTV in all bedrooms STV No dogs (ex guide dogs) Night porter 60P Outdoor swimming pool (heated) Tennis (hard) Fishing Croquet lawn Xmas French Cuisine V meals Coffee am Tea pm No smoking area in restaurant Last d 10.15pm
ROOMS: d £195-£285 * **LB**
MEALS: Lunch £29.50-£69&alc Dinner fr £69&alc
CONF: Thtr 36 Board 22 Del from £190
CARDS:

GREAT WITCHINGHAM Norfolk Map 09 TG12

★★ 65% Lenwade House
Lenwade NR9 5QP ☎ 01603 872288 FAX 01603
Situated in 18 acres of grounds with its own lake and woodland, this hotel offers perfect peace just a few miles from Norwich. The bedrooms which are being upgraded are divided between the main house and a more modern extension, where they are larger. The facilities include a heated outdoor pool, grass tennis courts, a gym, a games room and conference rooms.
35 en suite (bth/shr) (5 fmly) No smoking in 14 bedrooms CTV in all bedrooms No dogs (ex guide dogs) 50P Outdoor swimming pool (heated) Tennis (grass) Fishing Squash Riding Sauna Gym Pool

contd.

table Croquet lawn Putting green Jacuzzi/spa table tennis ch fac Xmas V meals Coffee am No smoking in restaurant Last d 9.15pm
ROOMS: (incl. bkfst) s £42.50; d £62.50 * **LB**
MEALS: Lunch £13.95 Dinner £13.95&alc*
CONF: Thtr 70 Class 40 Board 30 Del from £55
CARDS:

GREAT YARMOUTH Norfolk Map 05 TG50

★★★73% *Cliff*

Gorleston NR31 6DH (2m S A12) ☎ 01493 662179
FAX 01493 653617

Best Western

The Cliff offers a warm welcome and a relaxing and comfortable environment within the smart public rooms, which include an airy restaurant, a choice of bars and a delightfully comfortable lounge. Diners have a choice of menus in the restaurant, or more informal choices of bar meals or selections from an all-day lounge menu; service is both attentive and cheerful throughout. Accommodation styles and sizes vary, and the more recently refurbished bedrooms offer well matched furniture and fabrics, enhanced by smart well lit bathrooms. Room service is available.
39 en suite (bth/shr) (5 fmly) No smoking in 2 bedrooms CTV in all bedrooms Night porter 70P V meals Coffee am Tea pm No smoking in restaurant Last d 9.30pm
CARDS:

★★★67% Regency Dolphin

Albert Square NR30 3JH (proceed along seafront and turn right at Wellington Pier, follow road round and turn left. Hotel on left hand side) ☎ 01493 855070 FAX 01493 853798
To the south of the town, set back from the beach and its pleasure attractions, this hotel offers smart modern public areas and attractive accommodation. A good level of friendly service including all-day lounge and room service is available. The bedrooms are well furnished and equipped, but sizes vary.
50 en suite (bth/shr) (4 fmly) No smoking in 5 bedrooms CTV in all bedrooms Night porter 20P Outdoor swimming pool (heated) Sauna Gym Xmas English & Continental Cuisine V meals Coffee am Tea pm No smoking area in restaurant Last d 10pm
ROOMS: (incl. bkfst) s £55-£60; d £75-£85 **LB**
MEALS: Lunch £7.95-£8.95&alc High tea £4.25 Dinner £13.50&alc
CONF: Thtr 144 Class 50 Board 60 Del £78
CARDS:

See advertisement on page 275

★★★66% Imperial

North Dr NR30 1EQ (follow signs to seafront and turn left, Hotel opposite tennis courts) ☎ 01493 851113 FAX 01493 852229
This family-managed hotel sits on the seafront on the quieter North Beach, a short walk from the bright hurly-burly of the main promenade. Professional service and good food are the strengths of the Rambouillet Restaurant, a lower ground-floor restaurant and brasserie bar which promotes a continental theme through its decor and food; fresh fish and modern French cooking are well represented. The bedrooms, each with colour coordinated soft furnishings and a good range of modern amenities, vary in size.
39 en suite (bth/shr) (4 fmly) No smoking in 12 bedrooms CTV in all bedrooms STV Lift Night porter 50P Xmas English & French Cuisine V meals Coffee am Tea pm Last d 10pm
ROOMS: (incl. bkfst) s £60; d £80 **LB**
MEALS: Lunch fr £10.50&alc Dinner fr £19.50&alc
CONF: Thtr 120 Class 30 Board 30 Del from £70
CARDS:

★★★60% Star

Hall Quay NR30 1HG ☎ 01493 842294 FAX 01493 330215
Scott Inns, who have recently acquired this well established hotel, have made careful and sympathetic improvements to it. The distinctive black and white frontage - built of brick and flint, with a timbered upper section - dates back to the late 19th-century, but some parts of the building are 200 years older. A wood-panelled lounge provides a quiet, comfortable area in which to relax, the restaurant offers various menu and carvery meal options, and there are two bars where you can enjoy a drink; the character Quay Merchants Bar, selling lunchtime bar snacks and a good range of cask beers , is a more recent addition. Bedrooms have been smartly refurbished and are all equipped to the same standard and have en suite facilities.
40 en suite (bth/shr) (3 fmly) No smoking in 3 bedrooms CTV in all bedrooms Lift Night porter 20P Xmas V meals Coffee am Tea pm No smoking area in restaurant Last d 9.30pm
ROOMS: s £49-£57; d £54-£69 * **LB**
MEALS: Lunch £4.75-£14&alc Dinner £5.95-£14&alc*
CONF: Class 40 Board 40 Del from £68.50
CARDS:

★★65% Furzedown

19-20 North Dr NR30 4EW ☎ 01493 844138 FAX 01493 844138
The Furzedown is a welcoming seafront hotel with fresh, light bedrooms in a variety of sizes. Public areas offer reasonable comfort and there is a good choice of freshly prepared evening meals on the set-price menu. Proprietors Paul and Lisa Garrod provide enthusiastic and caring personal service.
23 rms (19 bth/shr) (11 fmly) CTV in all bedrooms STV 15P English & French Cuisine V meals Coffee am Tea pm No smoking area in restaurant
ROOMS: (incl. bkfst) s £25.50-£31.50; d £40-£51 *
MEALS: Bar Lunch £1-£7*
CONF: Class 60 Board 30
CARDS:

See advertisement on opposite page

★★65% Regency

5 North Dr NR30 1ED (on sea front) ☎ 01493 843759
FAX 01493 330411
This small family run hotel sits overlooking the seafront and tennis courts at the quieter northern end of the resort. Hospitality is the strength of this small hotel, the Barnett family make every effort to create a relaxed and friendly environment. Guests can take dinner from a table d'hÙte menu in the dining room or snacks in the bar during the early evening; refreshments are available throughout the day. Some bedrooms might be compact, but they all look fresh, well maintained and are immaculately clean.
14 en suite (bth/shr) (2 fmly) CTV in all bedrooms No dogs 10P No children 7yrs Xmas V meals No smoking in restaurant Last d 8.15pm
ROOMS: (incl. bkfst) s £30-£32; d £62 * **LB**
MEALS: Bar Lunch £4.50-£10 Dinner £10.50*
CARDS:

★★64% **Burlington**
11 North Dr NR30 1EG (A12 to sea front, turn left at Britannia Pier. Hotel faces tennis courts) ☎ 01493 844568 & 842095
FAX 01493 331848
Closed Jan-Feb RS Dec (group bookings only)
A family-run hotel at the quieter northern end of town has absorbed a neighbouring building, considerably increasing the size of the public areas. These now include an indoor sun deck and swimming pool. Bedrooms vary in size and quality but are gradually being improved.
28 en suite (bth/shr) (9 fmly) No smoking in 5 bedrooms CTV in all bedrooms STV No dogs (ex guide dogs) Lift 40P Indoor swimming pool (heated) Sauna Pool table Jacuzzi/spa Turkish steam room Wkly live entertainment Xmas English & French Cuisine V meals Coffee am Tea pm No smoking in restaurant Last d 8.30pm
ROOMS: (incl. bkfst) s £45-£65; d £70-£80 * **LB**
OFF-PEAK: (incl. bkfst) s £40-£60; d £60-£70
MEALS: Lunch £9 Dinner £15-£18&alc*
CONF: Thtr 120 Class 40 Board 20 Del from £37.50
CARDS:

GREENFORD Greater London See LONDON SECTION plan 1 B4

★★★70% ***The Bridge***
Western Av UB6 8ST ☎ 0181 566 6246 FAX 0181 566 6140
Ideally situated just off the A40 Western Avenue for easy access to the M25 and central London, this Young's Brewery hotel successfully combines a lively neighbourhood pub with quality hotel accommodation and a good restaurant. Bedrooms have been particularly well designed and equipped to meet the demands of the discerning guest, including the family and the disabled. Impressive air conditioned public areas comprise a spacious wood-panelled bar-lounge which divides into three areas and features a good range of real ales, a smart à la carte restaurant, an impressive conference suite and meeting rooms. The service is friendly, conscientious and attentive.
68 en suite (bth/shr) No smoking in 44 bedrooms CTV in all bedrooms STV Lift Night porter 68P English & French Cuisine V meals Coffee am Tea pm Last d 10pm
CARDS:

GRIMSBY Lincolnshire Map 08 TA20

★★★57% **St James**
St James' Square DN31 1EP (off A180)
☎ 01472 359771 FAX 01472 241427

REGAL
A Collection of Individual Hotels

Conveniently situated for the main shopping centre, the hotel overlooks the Old Bull Ring and picturesque St James Square. Bedrooms are practical and have modern facilities. Public areas include the Chantry Restaurant and an adjoining lounge bar as well as comfortable seating in the foyer. There are also a popular public bar, meeting rooms and ample free parking for residents.

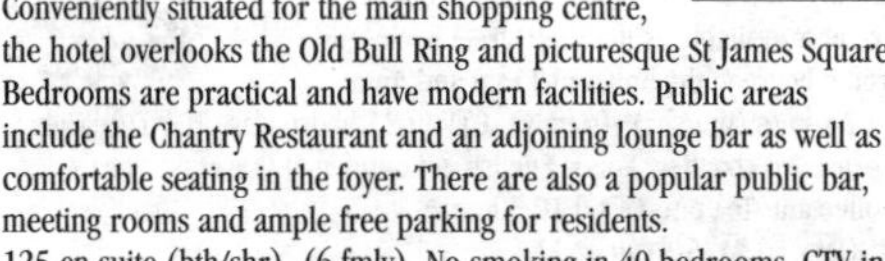

125 en suite (bth/shr) (6 fmly) No smoking in 40 bedrooms CTV in all bedrooms STV Lift Night porter 100P Sauna Pool table Min-gym Wkly live entertainment Xmas V meals Coffee am Tea pm No smoking area in restaurant Last d 10pm
ROOMS: s £55; d £55 * **LB**
OFF-PEAK: s £40
MEALS: Lunch £5-£15alc Dinner £7-£20alc*
CONF: Thtr 70 Class 30 Board 35 Del from £60
CARDS:

Forte Posthouse Grimsby
Littlecoates Rd DN34 4LX (take A1136 and then B1444) ☎ 01472 350295 FAX 01472 241354

Suitable for both the business and leisure traveller, this bright hotel provides modern accommodation in well equipped bedrooms with en suite bathrooms. For more details about Forte Posthouse hotels, consult the Contents page for the section on Hotel Groups.

52 en suite (bth/shr)
ROOMS: s £69; d £69 *
CONF: Thtr 300 Class 100 Board 60 Del from £79

GRIMSTON Norfolk Map 09 TF72

RED STAR HOTEL

★★★ **Congham Hall Country House**
Lynn Rd PE32 1AH (off A148)
☎ 01485 600250 FAX 01485 601191

PRIDE OF BRITAIN MEMBER

Standing in its own delightful grounds which include a superb herb garden, this lovely Georgian manor house is very well maintained and is richly furnished throughout. Charmingly

contd.

friendly and yet very professional service is provided by the resident owners Mr and Mrs Forecast together with their dedicated and eager team who are superbly turned out. Public rooms are elegantly furnished, richly decorated and invitingly comfortable; they include a lovely lounge together with a cosy bar. The Orangery restaurant is a perfect setting for chef Jonathan Nicholson's fine cooking; he provides an extensive menu with an interesting choice backed by a well chosen wine list. Well proportioned bedrooms have been very thoughtfully equipped and are richly furnished in the style of a country mansion. The hotel is located in the village of Grimston and is convenient for King's Lynn and the wild and beautiful north Norfolk coastline.

14 en suite (bth/shr) CTV in all bedrooms No dogs 50P No coaches Outdoor swimming pool (heated) Tennis (hard) Croquet lawn Jacuzzi/spa Cricket No children 12yrs Xmas V meals Coffee am No smoking in restaurant Last d 9.30pm

ROOMS: (incl. bkfst) s £69-£89; d £105-£135 **LB**

MEALS: Lunch £15-£25alc Dinner £24-£32alc*

CONF: Thtr 25 Class 12 Board 12 Del from £129.50

CARDS:

GRINDLEFORD Derbyshire Map 08 SK27

★★★67% **Maynard Arms**

Main Rd S30 1HP (on B6001) ☎ 01433 630321 FAX 01433 630445

The Maynard Arms is a splendid country mansion in the heart of the Peak District National Park. The style of furnishings and character within hovers somewhere between the English country house and an inn. The convivial bar serves some good bar meals, whilst the restaurant which has its own bar, and the delightful first floor drawing room are furnished in harmony with the building's period character. The bedrooms are similarly furnished according to the space available. The grounds and the views are also to be enjoyed.

11 en suite (bth/shr) CTV in all bedrooms 80P No coaches Xmas European Cuisine V meals Coffee am Tea pm No smoking in restaurant Last d 9.30pm

ROOMS: (incl. bkfst) s £49-£55; d £65-£85 * **LB**

MEALS: Lunch £10.95-£15.50 Dinner £11.50-£15.50*

CONF: Thtr 140 Class 80 Board 80 Del from £76.50

CARDS:

GRIZEDALE Cumbria Map 07 SD39

★★70% **Grizedale Lodge**

LA22 0QL (at Hawkshead take Newby Bridge Road to right turn for Forest Park Centre.) ☎ 015394 36532 FAX 015394 36572

Closed 3 Jan-8 Feb

Surrounded by meadow and woodland this former shooting lodge lies in the heart of Grizedale Forest, two miles south of Hawkshead. A small, friendly hotel, it has attractive and inviting public areas and bedrooms of varying sizes, some being well proportioned. The daily-changing dinner menu places emphasis on fresh ingredients and hearty portions.

9 en suite (bth/shr) (1 fmly) No smoking in all bedrooms CTV in all bedrooms 20P No coaches Xmas English & French Cuisine Coffee am Last d 8pm

ROOMS: (incl. bkfst & dinner) d £97-£105 * **LB**

OFF-PEAK: (incl. bkfst & dinner) s £37.50-£46.50; d £80-£105

MEALS: Dinner fr £19.95

CARDS:

GROBY Leicestershire Map 04 SK50

★★67% **Brant Inn**

Leicester Rd LE6 0DU (NW of Leicester, on A50)

☎ 0116 287 2703 FAX 0116 287 5292

A popular family pub and restaurant operation located in a mainly residential area which is easily accessed from the M1. Bedrooms and public rooms including several bars, a wicker-furnished conservatory with a flagstone floor and a rustic-style restaurant adorned with old musical instruments, have been extended and upgraded in recent years.

8 en suite (bth/shr) 2 annexe en suite (shr) No smoking in 2 bedrooms CTV in all bedrooms 200P Pool table English & French Cuisine V meals Coffee am Tea pm No smoking area in restaurant Last d 9.30pm

ROOMS: s £25-£35; d £35-£49.75 *

OFF-PEAK: (incl. bkfst) s fr £25; d fr £35

MEALS: Lunch £9.45&alc Dinner £9.45&alc*

CONF: Thtr 150 Class 120 Board 10 Del from £55

CARDS:

GUILDFORD Surrey Map 04 SU94

★★★75% **The Angel Posting House and Livery**

91 High St GU1 3DP ☎ 01483 64555 due to change to 564555 FAX 01483 33770

This charming High Street coaching inn has been welcoming travellers since the 16th century. Retaining all of its character and original features, accommodation has recently undergone a major improvement with the provision of a spacious lounge, a wood-panelled library bar and the vaulted Crypt Restaurant. More improvements to the individually furnished bedrooms are planned and several luxurious rooms are already under construction. The Jacobean fire-place and an original Parliament wall clock should not be missed, the food is well prepared and the standard of service and customer care is above average. A car parking and porter service are now available as the High street is closed to traffic between the hours of 11am and 4pm.

11 en suite (bth/shr) (4 fmly) CTV in 21 bedrooms STV Lift Night porter No coaches Xmas English & Continental Cuisine V meals Coffee am Tea pm Last d 10.30pm

ROOMS: d £135-£150 * **LB**

MEALS: Lunch £15-£16 Dinner £18.50&alc*

CONF: Thtr 80 Class 20 Board 40 Del £147

CARDS:

See advertisement on opposite page

★★★70% **The Manor**

Newlands Corner GU4 8SE (3.5m on A25 to Dorking)

☎ 01483 222624 FAX 01483 211389

Located to the south-east of Guildford on the A25 between West Clandon and Albury and secluded by nine acres of well kept grounds, this hotel is a very popular venue for local wedding receptions. The accommodation has been completely refurbished to a high standard, and bedrooms range from suites to smaller singles, all equipped with every modern amenity. There is a foyer lounge, a bar with theme nights and a Sunday jazz brunch, and a restaurant where chef Ian Penn offers a fixed-price two or three course menu, with some interesting dishes. Service is very attentive and friendly.

20 en suite (bth/shr) CTV in all bedrooms Night porter 100P No coaches Croquet lawn Wkly live entertainment English & French Cuisine V meals Coffee am Tea pm Last d 9.45pm
ROOMS: (incl. bkfst) s £70-£80; d £80-£90 * **LB**
OFF-PEAK: (incl. bkfst) s fr £52.50; d fr £62.50
MEALS: Lunch £10.95-£14.50&alc Dinner £14.25-£16.50&alc*
CONF: Thtr 120 Class 50 Board 50 Del from £115
CARDS:

Forte Posthouse Guildford

Egerton Rd GU2 5XZ (2m SW on A3 Guildford bypass) ☎ 01483 574444 FAX 01483 302960
Suitable for both the business and leisure traveller, this bright hotel provides modern accommodation in well equipped bedrooms with en suite bathrooms. For more details about Forte Posthouse hotels, consult the Contents page for the section on Hotel Groups.
111 en suite (bth/shr)
ROOMS: s £99-£109; d £99-£109 *
CONF: Thtr 200 Class 100 Board 45 Del from £135

Travel Inn

Parkway, Stoke Rd GU1 1UP ☎ 01483 304932
FAX 01483 304935
Purpose-built accommodation, offering spacious, well equipped bedrooms, all with en suite bathrooms. Meals may be taken at the nearby family restaurant. For more information about Travel Inns, consult the Contents page under Hotel Groups.
60 en suite (bth/shr)
ROOMS: d £35.50 *

GULWORTHY Devon Map 02 SX47

★★ 78% Horn of Plenty
PL19 8JD (from Tavistock take A390 W for 3m and turn right at Gulworthy Cross. After 400yds turn left and continue for a further 400yds to hotel on right) ☎ 01822 832528 FAX 01822 832528
Closed 25-26 Dec
This beautiful country house is set high above the River Tamar with stunning views across the valley. The bedrooms are bright and attractively furnished; they all overlook the pretty walled garden and have thoughtful extra touches. The public rooms are elegant yet comfortable, enhanced by personal trinkets and pictures. Elaine Gatehouse is a warmly enthusiastic host and is rightly proud of her restaurant. Chef Peter Gorton produces an interesting menu which combines 'old favourites' with more inspirational dishes. The wine list offers a good range of reasonably-priced options including some excellent first growths, European and New World selections and some half bottles.
1 en suite (bth/shr) 6 annexe en suite (bth/shr) No smoking in 2 bedrooms CTV in all bedrooms 20P No coaches No children 13yrs International Cuisine V meals No smoking in restaurant Last d 9.30pm
ROOMS: (incl. cont bkfst) s £68-£78; d £93-£98 * **LB**
OFF-PEAK: (incl. cont bkfst) s £58-£68; d £88-£93
MEALS: Lunch £10.50-£17.50 Dinner £19.50-£28.50*
CONF: Thtr 20 Class 20 Board 12
CARDS:

GUNTHORPE Nottinghamshire Map 08 SK64

★★ 66% Unicorn
Gunthorpe Bridge NG14 7FB (on A6097) ☎ 0115 966 3612
FAX 0115 966 4801
A very popular refurbished riverside inn on the banks of the Trent. The bars and restaurant are spacious, and the décor features exposed timbers and brickwork. A good range of snacks and dinners is offered throughout the day supplemented by a grill-style menu in the restaurant. Bedrooms are very good, scoring high on comfort and facilities.
16 en suite (bth/shr) (3 fmly) CTV in all bedrooms STV No dogs (ex guide dogs) 200P Fishing English & French Cuisine V meals Coffee am Tea pm No smoking area in restaurant Last d 9.30pm
ROOMS: (incl. bkfst) s £49.50; d £59.50 * **LB**
OFF-PEAK: (incl. bkfst) s £39.50; d £49.50
MEALS: Lunch £10.95-£20.20alc Dinner £11.95-£20.20alc*
CARDS:

HACKNESS North Yorkshire Map 08 SE99

★★★ 68% Hackness Grange Country

North Yorkshire National Park YO13 0JW (A64 to Scarborough and then A171 to Whitby/Scalby, follow signs to Hackness/Forge Valley National Park, through Hackness village on left hand side) ☎ 01723 882345
FAX 01723 882391
An elegant Georgian house standing in a quiet valley, Hackness Grange is surrounded by its own well tended gardens which include a lake. Tennis courts and a pitch and putt course are available outside, and indoors there is a heated pool. Richly decorated and delightfully furnished bedrooms are provided and the comfortable public rooms are delightfully relaxing and inviting. A good range of well prepared dishes is served in the elegant dining room and service is both professional and friendly.

13 en suite (bth/shr) 15 annexe en suite (bth/shr) (5 fmly) CTV in all bedrooms STV Night porter 60P No coaches Indoor swimming pool (heated) Golf 9 Tennis (hard) Croquet lawn Xmas V meals Coffee am Tea pm No smoking in restaurant Last d 9.15pm
ROOMS: (incl. bkfst) s £67.50-£73.50; d £135 * **LB**
OFF-PEAK: (incl. bkfst) s fr £40; d fr £80

contd.

H

MEALS: Lunch £11.75-£12.50 Dinner £22.50
CONF: Thtr 20 Class 10 Board 14 Del from £95
CARDS:
See advertisement under SCARBOROUGH

HADLEY WOOD Greater London Map 04 TQ29

★★★★ 69% **West Lodge Park**
Cockfosters Rd EN4 0PY (on A111, 1m S of exit 24 on M25)
☎ 0181 440 8311 FAX 0181 449 3698
Extensive parkland, including a fine Arboretum, surrounds this fine Regency-style country house hotel. The Beale family have owned West Lodge Park for three generations and the current General Manager, Andrew Beale, continues to maintain the high standards his family has set. Bedrooms are all individually decorated and feature a wealth of thoughtful extras. Executive rooms are particularly good with bathrobes, chocolates and fruit provided. The hotel is an idyllic setting for a wedding and indeed is a popular venue at weekends. Chef Peter Leggat and Restaurant Manager Alfio Carassalini work together to make the Cedar Restaurant a most enjoyable place to dine. Chef Leggat's cuisine is a modern blend of French and English influences with emphasis on classical technique. The restaurant staff are well informed and eager to please. There are some very good conference and meeting facilities and guests can have free use of high quality leisure facilities in Enfield, including a taxi there and back.
43 en suite (bth/shr) 2 annexe en suite (bth/shr) (1 fmly) No smoking in 9 bedrooms CTV in all bedrooms STV No dogs (ex guide dogs) Lift Night porter 200P No coaches Croquet lawn Putting green Fitness trail International Cuisine V meals Coffee am Tea pm No smoking in restaurant Last d 9.45pm
ROOMS: s £77.50-£185; d £110-£195 * **LB**
MEALS: Lunch £17.50-£23.95 Dinner £19.95-£27.75*
CONF: Thtr 80 Class 24 Board 30
CARDS:
See advertisement on opposite page

HAGLEY Hereford & Worcester Map 07 SO98

Travel Inn
Birmingham Rd DY9 9JS (on A456 towards Kidderminster) ☎ 01562 883120 FAX 01562 884416
Purpose-built accommodation, offering spacious, well equipped bedrooms, all with en suite bathrooms. Meals may be taken at the nearby family restaurant. For more information about Travel Inns, consult the Contents page under Hotel Groups.

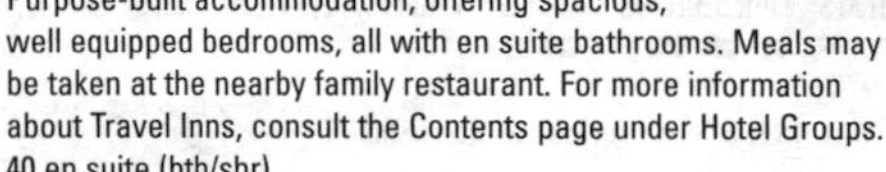

40 en suite (bth/shr)
ROOMS: d £35.50 *

HAILSHAM East Sussex Map 05 TQ50

★★★ 66% **Boship Farm**

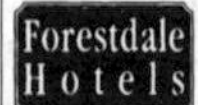

Lower Dicker BN27 4AT (on A22 at Boship roundabout, junct of A22/A267/A271)
☎ 01323 844826 FAX 01323 843945
Extended from an original farmhouse this conveniently positioned hotel offers a relaxed and congenial atmosphere. Character public areas include a cosy bar with inglenook fireplace and comfortable restaurant. Bedrooms tend to vary in size and comfort but boast a good range of modern facilities. During warmer climes the small grounds and gardens prove popular.
47 annexe en suite (bth/shr) (5 fmly) No smoking in 17 bedrooms CTV in all bedrooms Night porter 100P Outdoor swimming pool (heated) Tennis (hard) Gym Croquet lawn Jacuzzi/spa ch fac Xmas English & French Cuisine V meals Coffee am Tea pm Last d 10pm
ROOMS: (incl. bkfst) s fr £55; d £80-£90 * **LB**
OFF-PEAK: (incl. bkfst & dinner) s fr £68.50; d £106-£116
MEALS: Lunch £6.45-£12.50 Dinner fr £16.75*
CONF: Thtr 175 Class 40 Board 46 Del from £85
CARDS:

★★ 65% **The Olde Forge**
Magham Down BN27 1PN (1.5m E of Hailsham, on A271)
☎ 01323 842893 FAX 01323 842893
Closed 25 Dec-2 Jan
A comfortable small privately run hotel and restaurant, the Old Forge offers a range of well equipped bedrooms furnished in the modern style. Public rooms comprise a beamed dispense bar and lounge and a candlelit restaurant, once the original forge and now features well crafted freshly prepared food cooked by Chef Jean Daniels. Service is particularly friendly and attentive during the evening, and other facilities include a small summer terrace garden and some covered car parking.
8 rms (6 bth/shr) CTV in all bedrooms 12P No coaches English & French Cuisine V meals Coffee am Last d 9pm
ROOMS: (incl. bkfst) s £38-£40; d £45-£60 **LB**
MEALS: Sunday Lunch fr £9.95 Dinner fr £13.95&alc*
CARDS:

Travelodge
Boship Roundabout, Hellingly BN27 4DT (on A22 at Boship roundabout) ☎ 01323 844556
FAX 01323 844556
This modern building offers accommodation in smart, spacious and well equipped bedrooms, suitable for family use, and all with en suite bathrooms. Meals may be taken at the nearby family restaurant. For information on room rates and to make a booking, call Roomline free of charge on 0800 850950. For more details about Travelodge, consult the Contents page under Hotel Groups.
40 en suite (bth/shr)

HALESOWEN West Midlands Map 07 SO98

Travelodge
Illey Ln B32 4AR ☎ Central Res 0800 555300
FAX 01525 878451
(For full entry see Frankley Motorway Service Area (M5))

HALIFAX West Yorkshire Map 07 SE02

★★★ 74% **Holdsworth House**
Holmfield HX2 9TG (3m NW off A629 Keighley Road)
☎ 01422 240024 FAX 01422 245174
Once a yeoman's hall dating back to the 17th century, this hotel combines the old with the modern to great effect. Bedrooms are well furnished and have all modern amenities, whilst the public rooms are full of character and charm. The wood-panelled dining rooms make a perfect setting for chef Eric Claveau's excellent cooking which is backed by a fine wine list. Service is warm and friendly, provided by a dedicated staff.
40 en suite (bth/shr) (2 fmly) No smoking in 15 bedrooms CTV in all bedrooms Night porter 60P ch fac English & Continental Cuisine

V meals Coffee am Tea pm No smoking area in restaurant
Last d 9.30pm
ROOMS: (incl. cont bkfst) s £55-£72.50; d £75-£90 * **LB**
OFF-PEAK: (incl. cont bkfst) s £45-£72.50; d £60-£90
MEALS: Lunch £12.50-£17.50&alc Dinner £19.50&alc*
CONF: Thtr 150 Class 75 Board 50 Del from £90
CARDS:

★★69% **The Hobbit**
Hob Ln, Norland HX6 3QL ☎ 01422 832202
FAX 01422 835381
Standing high on a hillside in the hamlet of Norland and overlooking Sowerby Bridge, The Hobbit is a popular hotel providing an extensive range of food, which is served either in the Bistro bar or the delightful Rivendell Restaurant. The bedrooms are prettily decorated, well furnished and thoughtfully equipped. It is family owned and run and provides good honest Yorkshire hospitality.
17 en suite (bth/shr) 5 annexe en suite (bth/shr) (3 fmly) No smoking in 2 bedrooms CTV in all bedrooms STV No dogs (ex guide dogs) 100P Wkly live entertainment Xmas English, French & Italian Cuisine V meals Coffee am Tea pm No smoking area in restaurant
Last d 10pm
ROOMS: (incl. bkfst) s £42-£58; d £63-£73 * **LB**
OFF-PEAK: (incl. bkfst) s £29-£31; d £43-£45
MEALS: Lunch £8.95-£10.95 High tea £5.95 Dinner £10.95-£14.95&alc*
CONF: Thtr 60 Board 16 Del from £49
CARDS:

HALLAND East Sussex Map 05 TQ41

★★★63% **Halland Forge**

BN8 6PW (on A22 at junct with B2192, 4m S of Uckfield) ☎ 01825 840456 FAX 01825 840773
Conveniently located on the A22 at its junction with the B2192, this family-run hotel offers modern ground and first floor bedrooms in an adjacent annexe. The counter-service coffee shop is open daily for breakfast, meals and light refreshments until 6pm, whilst the Forge Restaurant offers an extensive choice of dishes for dinner, and has a bar-lounge with a log burning fire. There is separate small lounge, and conference facilities for up to 40 guests can be arranged.
20 annexe en suite (bth/shr) (2 fmly) CTV in all bedrooms 70P No children 5yrs English & French Cuisine V meals Coffee am Tea pm
Last d 9.30pm
ROOMS: s fr £48; d fr £61 **LB**
OFF-PEAK: d fr £36
MEALS: Lunch £11-£14.50&alc Dinner £14-£17.05&alc*
CONF: Thtr 30 Class 16 Board 20 Del from £60
CARDS:

See advertisement on this page

indicates a Country House Hotel. Please consult the section on AA Star Rating at the front of the book.

H

HAMBLETON North Yorkshire Map 08 SE53

★★66% **Owl**
Main Rd YO8 9JH (4m W on A63) (Marstons) ☎ 01757 228374
FAX 01757 228125
This busy roadside hotel offers a very extensive range of popular food which is served either in the spacious bar or one of the two attractive dining rooms. Modern and very well equipped bedrooms have trouser presses, hair dryers etc provided and have been pleasantly decorated and furnished. Service is friendly and very attentive from a well turned out and eager staff.
7 en suite (bth/shr) 6 annexe en suite (bth/shr) (1 fmly) CTV in all bedrooms STV No dogs (ex guide dogs) 101P International Cuisine V meals Coffee am Tea pm Last d 10pm
ROOMS: (incl. bkfst) s £35-£38.50; d £47-£52 *
MEALS: Lunch £3.95-£8.95 Dinner £3.95-£8.95&alc*
CONF: Thtr 80 Class 40 Board 50 Del from £52.50
CARDS:

H

HAMPSON GREEN Lancashire Map 07 SD45

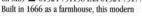

★★61% **Hampson House**
Hampson Ln LA2 0JB (4m S adjacent to junct 33 on M6) ☎ 01524 751158 FAX 01524 751779
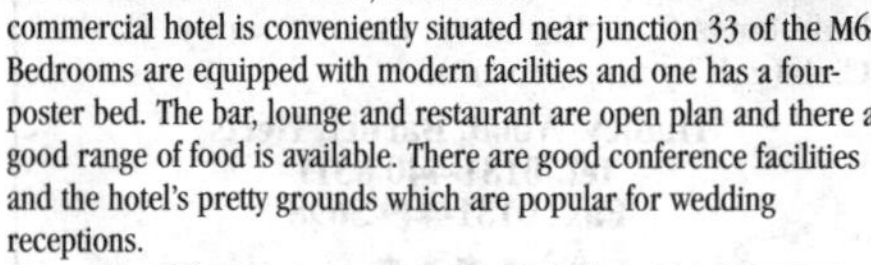
Built in 1666 as a farmhouse, this modern commercial hotel is conveniently situated near junction 33 of the M6. Bedrooms are equipped with modern facilities and one has a four-poster bed. The bar, lounge and restaurant are open plan and there a good range of food is available. There are good conference facilities and the hotel's pretty grounds which are popular for wedding receptions.
12 en suite (bth/shr) 2 annexe en suite (bth/shr) (4 fmly) CTV in all bedrooms 60P ch fac Xmas English, French & Italian Cuisine V meals Coffee am Tea pm Last d 9.30pm
ROOMS: (incl. bkfst) s fr £39.50; d fr £49.50 * **LB**
MEALS: Lunch £6.50-£10&alc Dinner £7.50-£10.50&alc*
CONF: Thtr 90 Class 40 Board 26 Del from £43
CARDS: £

HANDFORTH Map 07 SJ88 See Manchester Airport

HANSLOPE Buckinghamshire Map 04 SP84

★★★63% **Hatton Court**
Bullington End MK19 7BQ ☎ 01908 510044
FAX 01908 510945
A Victorian country house attractively set in its own grounds, this hotel appeals to both leisure guests and smaller conferences. There are bedrooms in the main house and in the converted stables. The majority are spacious, with period furnishings and ornate bathrooms, but investment is needed to keep them looking fresh.
12 en suite (bth/shr) 8 annexe en suite (bth/shr) (6 fmly) No smoking in 6 bedrooms CTV in all bedrooms STV Night porter 120P Snooker Pool table Croquet lawn Xmas V meals Coffee am Tea pm No smoking in restaurant Last d 9.30pm
ROOMS: s £80-£90; d £90-£120 * **LB**
MEALS: Lunch fr £12.95 High tea fr £6.75 Dinner fr £22.50*
CONF: Thtr 60 Class 36 Board 32 Del from £125
CARDS: £

HAREWOOD West Yorkshire Map 08 SE34

★★★63% **Harewood Arms**
Harrogate Rd LS17 9LH (on A61 at junct with A659)
☎ 0113 288 6566 FAX 0113 288 6064
Standing almost opposite Harewood House, this well maintained hotel offers good modern bedrooms together with a busy bar and restaurant, where a good range of well produced food is available. Staff are friendly and helpful and provide good Yorkshire hospitality.
13 en suite (bth/shr) 11 annexe en suite (bth/shr) (2 fmly) CTV in all bedrooms Night porter 60P Xmas English & French Cuisine V meals Coffee am Tea pm Last d 10pm
ROOMS: (incl. bkfst) s £65; d £78 *
OFF-PEAK: (incl. bkfst) s fr £45; d fr £60
CARDS:

HARLOW Essex Map 05 TL41

★★★ 74% **Churchgate Manor**

Churchgate St Village, Old Harlow CM17 0JT (on B183, E of old Harlow) ☎ 01279 420246
FAX 01279 437720
Situated in a picturesque village, north-east of Old Harlow, this Jacobean house has been developed over the years into a popular and well run hotel, with good, modern accommodation making it ideal for conferences and functions. 'Executive' rooms offer particularly high standards and extras like spa baths, minibars and safes. The elegant Manor restaurant offers good food from a reasonably priced menu, or there is a full room service. Staff are friendly and professional.
85 en suite (bth) (8 fmly) No smoking in 42 bedrooms CTV in all bedrooms STV Night porter 120P Indoor swimming pool (heated) Sauna Solarium Gym Whirlpool Xmas English & French Cuisine V meals Coffee am Tea pm No smoking in restaurant Last d 10pm
ROOMS: s £75-£105; d £89-£105 * **LB**
OFF-PEAK: s £57-£95; d £69-£95
MEALS: Lunch £14.50-£18.50&alc Dinner £14.95-£18.50&alc*
CONF: Thtr 180 Class 70 Board 40
CARDS:

★★★63% **Harlow Moat House**

Southern Way CM18 7BA (from M11 junct 7 take A414 towards Harlow. Take first exit at first roundabout and then first left) ☎ 01279 829988
FAX 01279 635094
This purpose-built 60s hotel is easily located on the southern approach to Harlow. The restaurant has undergone a transformation to create an informal atmosphere and provide food from a hot and cold buffet. Bedrooms, some with slightly dated bathrooms, are well looked after and offer those amenities expected by leisure and business users.
118 en suite (bth/shr) No smoking in 36 bedrooms CTV in all bedrooms No dogs (ex guide dogs) Night porter 180P Pool table English & French Cuisine V meals Coffee am Tea pm No smoking area in restaurant Last d 9.45pm
ROOMS: s £70-£75; d £70-£85 **LB**
OFF-PEAK: d fr £50
MEALS: Lunch £11-£18&alc Dinner £11-£18&alc
CONF: Thtr 150 Class 150 Board 50 Del from £106
CARDS:

★★★57% **Green Man**
Mulberry Green, Old Harlow CM17 0ET ☎ 01279 442521 FAX 01279 626113
This former coaching inn, parts of which date back to the 14th century, is located in a quiet area of old Harlow. Ostlers Bar is the main focus of attention in the public areas but there is also a cosy beamed restaurant with its own small bar lounge. A purpose built extension houses the bedrooms, which are a mixture of old and new in style.
55 annexe en suite (bth/shr) (1 fmly) No smoking in 27 bedrooms CTV in all bedrooms Night porter 75P Xmas International Cuisine V meals Coffee am Tea pm No smoking in restaurant Last d 9.30pm
ROOMS: s £70; d £80 * **LB**
OFF-PEAK: s £60; d £70
MEALS: Lunch £6.95-£8.15&alc Dinner £14.50&alc*

ONF: Thtr 60 Class 26 Board 30 Del from £85
ARDS:

ravel Inn
ambridge Rd CM20 2EP (just off A414)
☎ 01279 442545 FAX 01279 452169
urpose-built accommodation, offering spacious, well equipped edrooms, all with en suite bathrooms. Meals may be taken at the earby family restaurant. For more information about Travel Inns, onsult the Contents page under Hotel Groups.
3 en suite (bth/shr)
OOMS: d £35.50 *

HARLYN BAY Cornwall & Isles of Scilly Map 02 SW87

:67% **Polmark**
L28 8SB ☎ 01841 520206
osed Nov-Mar except Xmas
emote and quietly situated facing the sea, this attractive old Cornish one house stands within its own extensive grounds. Log fires in the inter enhance the relaxing and informal atmosphere of the wood anelled bar and well furnished lounges. The new wing has the best edrooms, but the older rooms are full of character. Service is rovided by the friendly proprietors David and Anita Plume.
4 rms (4 bth 5 shr) (3 fmly) CTV in 9 bedrooms 20P No coaches utdoor swimming pool (heated) English, Continental & Thai Cuisine meals Coffee am Tea pm
ARDS:

HAROME See Helmsley

HARPENDEN Hertfordshire Map 04 TL11

★★68% **Glen Eagle**
Luton Rd AL5 2PX (in town centre just beyond Oggelsby's Garage)
☎ 01582 760271 FAX 01582 460819
ocated on the northern edge of the town, this well established hotel ffers newly refurbished public rooms and comfortable ccommodation. The smart public areas look particularly striking, ith good use of cheerful bold colour schemes throughout. Guests ave the choice of informal snacks all day from the lounge menu, or ore interesting choices in the more formal surroundings of the staurant. Bedrooms are modern and well equipped: the larger oms have mini bars which are stocked upon request.
) en suite (bth/shr) (12 fmly) CTV in all bedrooms STV No dogs x guide dogs) Lift Night porter 100P English & French Cuisine V eals Coffee am Tea pm Last d 9.45pm
OOMS: d £73.50-£83.50 * **LB**
FF-PEAK: s fr £43; d fr £52
EALS: Lunch £9.99-£12.95 Dinner fr £18.50
ONF: Thtr 80 Class 30 Board 35 Del from £95
ARDS:

See advertisement on this page

★★★63% **Harpenden House**

18 Southdown Rd AL5 1PE (on A1081)
☎ 01582 449955 FAX 01582 769858
RS Bank Holidays
There is something quite grand about the restaurant at Harpenden House with its painted ceiling, show-piece chandelier and intimate alcoves. This partly compensates for the small space in the cosy bar. The bedrooms are divided between the main house and an extension of more recent construction. They vary in style but are generally large and carefully laid out. There are two apartments for long-staying guests.
18 en suite (bth/shr) 35 annexe en suite (bth/shr) (3 fmly) No smoking in 20 bedrooms CTV in all bedrooms Night porter 80P Croquet lawn Boules French Cuisine V meals Coffee am Tea pm No smoking area in restaurant Last d 10pm
ROOMS: s £91-£108; d £108-£175 * **LB**
OFF-PEAK: s fr £50; d fr £70
MEALS: Lunch £10.95-£19.95&alc Dinner £14.95-£18.95&alc*
CONF: Thtr 150 Class 60 Board 70 Del from £110
CARDS:

HARROGATE North Yorkshire Map 08 SE35
See also Knaresborough

★★★★65% **Harrogate Moat House**

Kings Rd HG1 1XX (in Harrogate follow signs to International Conference Centre, hotel adjoins)
☎ 01423 849988 FAX 01423 524435
This large modern hotel with its distinctive glass façade is situated next to the International Conference Centre and has its own car park at the rear, just a short walk away, but staff will helpfully park cars if required. Bedrooms are mainly standard throughout, although recent refurbishment has considerably improved them and those on the

contd.

upper floors have fine views over Harrogate and the distant countryside. Service is provided by a friendly and smartly uniformed staff and there are two restaurants: The Boulevard, which offers an international cuisine, and the Abbey Restaurant, which has a popular carvery menu. There is also a Workbase Business Centre with versatile banqueting and conference suites.

214 en suite (bth/shr) No smoking in 69 bedrooms CTV in all bedrooms Lift Night porter Air conditioning 130P Xmas English & French Cuisine V meals Coffee am Tea pm Last d 10pm
ROOMS: s fr £99; d fr £134 * **LB**
OFF-PEAK: (incl. bkfst) s fr £37; d fr £74
MEALS: Lunch fr £10.50&alc Dinner £11-£17*
CONF: Thtr 360 Class 220 Board 60 Del £125
CARDS:

★★★★ 63% Old Swan

Swan Rd HG1 2SR ☎ 01423 500055
FAX 01423 501154

The Old Swan has long been regarded as one of Harrogate's finest hotels and it is a pleasure to report that its new owners are in the process of restoring it to its premier position. Public areas have already been refurbished and on most evenings guests have the option of dining in either the grandeur of the Wedgwood Room or the intimacy of the Library Restauraant which has been awarded an AA rosette for dishes such as tempura of prawns with noodles and soya sauce and a glazed breast of duck with chestnuts and a red wine and truffle sauce. There are also two bars.

136 en suite (bth/shr) (5 fmly) No smoking in 12 bedrooms CTV in all bedrooms Lift Night porter 215P Croquet lawn Xmas V meals Coffee am Tea pm Last d 9.45pm
ROOMS: s £89.50; d £114 * **LB**
OFF-PEAK: (incl. bkfst) s £40; d £80
CONF: Thtr 450 Class 150 Board 100 Del from £98
CARDS:

★★★★ 59% The Majestic

FORTE Heritage

Ripon Rd HG1 2HU (N of town, on A61)
☎ 01423 568972 FAX 01423 502283

Opulent public rooms feature chandeliers, murals, paintings and beautiful wood panelling in this elegant Edwardian hotel situated in its own grounds and gardens, in an elevated position above the town. Bedrooms are traditional in style, but have all modern facilities. Those at the front, including several suites, are generally spacious whilst others are of adequate, but more modest size. There are versatile banqueting and conference facilities and also a very well equipped leisure centre with a gymnasium and good sized swimming pool.

156 en suite (bth/shr) (10 fmly) No smoking in 46 bedrooms CTV in all bedrooms STV Lift Night porter 240P Indoor swimming pool (heated) Tennis (hard) Squash Snooker Sauna Solarium Gym Jacuzzi/spa Health & fitness centre Wkly live entertainment Xmas International Cuisine V meals Coffee am Tea pm Last d 9.30pm
ROOMS: s £75-£85; d £95-£110 * **LB**
OFF-PEAK: s £50-£60; d £65-£80
MEALS: Lunch £14.95 Dinner £23.95&alc*
CONF: Thtr 400 Class 220 Board 65 Del from £109
CARDS:

★★★ 75% Boar's Head

Ripley HG3 3AY (on the A61 Harrogate/Ripon road, the hotel is in the centre of Ripley Village) ☎ 01423 771888 FAX 01423 771509

This elegant hotel stands in the delightful village of Ripley to the north of Harrogate; it is part of the Ripley Castle estate and is found in the cobbled market square. The house is furnished with many antiques and provides two lovely lounges together with an elegant restaurant where chef Steven Chesnutt produces notable cooking, with presentation being something special. Only the finest ingredients are used, whilst the wine list has been carefully chosen to please all tastes. Service is professional and very friendly, provided by a dedicated and well trained staff. The attached bar/bistro provides a pleasant alternative to the main hotel.

19 en suite (bth/shr) 6 annexe en suite (bth/shr) (2 fmly) No smoking in 5 bedrooms CTV in all bedrooms STV Night porter 63P Tennis (hard) Fishing Shooting Xmas English & French Cuisine V meals Coffee am Tea pm No smoking area in restaurant Last d 9.30pm
ROOMS: (incl. bkfst) s £80-£95; d £95-£110 * **LB**
MEALS: Lunch £13.50-£17.50 Dinner £25-£35alc*
CONF: Thtr 75 Class 28 Board 36 Del from £135
CARDS:

★★★ 73% Balmoral Hotel & Henry's Restaurant

Franklin Mount HG1 5EJ (opposite Exhibition Centre)
☎ 01423 508208 FAX 01423 530652

Although it is situated close to the town centre, this hotel has a country-house feel, and is constantly being improved. The interesting public rooms include an oriental bar and a cosy snug, while Henry's restaurant is the ideal setting for the well produced dinners. Goodies such as wild mushroom ravioli, beef fillet with smoked bacon or confit of duckling parcel may feature on the menu, which is backed by a fine wine list. Bedrooms are delightfully furnished; several have four-poster beds and all are thoughtfully equipped. Alison and Keith Hartwell and their team are always on hand to ensure guests are well cared for and comfortable.

21 en suite (bth/shr) (2 fmly) CTV in all bedrooms 12P Solarium Membership of Academy Fitness Centre Wkly live entertainment V meals Coffee am Tea pm No smoking in restaurant Last d 9.30pm
ROOMS: s fr £75; d fr £90 **LB**
OFF-PEAK: s fr £60; d fr £75
MEALS: Dinner fr £19.50&alc*
CONF: Thtr 35 Class 15 Board 30 Del from £115
CARDS:

★★★ 69% Grants

3-13 Swan Rd HG1 2SS (off A61) ☎ 01423 560666
FAX 01423 502550

This attractive Victorian hotel, situated only a short walk from the town centre, has won awards for its lovely floral garden display. The hotel is very well furnished in all areas and provides well equipped and comfortable bedrooms, all with coordinated fabrics. The recently refurbished bar, which is now air-conditioned, is the central meeting point, whilst the attractive and cosy Chimneys restaurant is the setting for the well produced dinners. Service is very friendly, and the hearty Yorkshire breakfast makes for a good start to the day.

42 en suite (bth/shr) (2 fmly) CTV in all bedrooms Lift Night porter 26P Xmas English & French Cuisine V meals Coffee am Tea pm Last d 9.30pm
ROOMS: (incl. bkfst) s £70-£102; d £80-£144 * **LB**
OFF-PEAK: (incl. bkfst) s fr £53
CONF: Thtr 70 Class 20 Board 30 Del £89
CARDS:

★★★ 68% White House

10 Park Pde HG1 5AH (off A59) ☎ 01423 501388
FAX 01423 527973

This graceful hotel overlooks the famous Stray and is proudly owned and run by the charming Mrs Forster, who is also a good cook, providing excellent dinners from imaginative menus. Bedrooms are stylishly furnished and thoughtfully equipped, in keeping with the hotel's Victorian character. Two fine lounges are available in addition to the elegant dining room.

11 en suite (bth/shr) (1 fmly) CTV in all bedrooms No dogs 10P Xmas V meals Coffee am No smoking in restaurant Last d 9pm
ROOMS: (incl. bkfst) s £88.50; d £128 **LB**
MEALS: Lunch £14.95-£16.50&alc Dinner £25-£35alc*
CARDS:

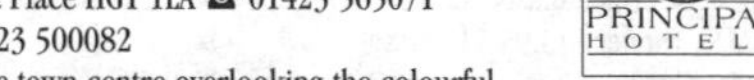

★★★64% **Imperial**
Prospect Place HG1 1LA ☎ 01423 565071
FAX 01423 500082

PRINCIPAL HOTELS

Set in the town centre overlooking the colourful flowers of the Stray, this well managed tourist and business hotel offers thoughtfully equipped bedrooms which are all due to be refurbished during 1996. Attractive public areas include a small cocktail bar, an elegant restaurant and an inviting foyer lounge where a good range of light refreshments is served during the day.

85 en suite (bth/shr) (2 fmly) No smoking in 40 bedrooms CTV in all bedrooms STV Lift Night porter 45P Xmas V meals Coffee am Tea pm No smoking in restaurant Last d 9.30pm
ROOMS: (incl. bkfst) s £85-£90; d £95-£120 * LB
OFF-PEAK: (incl. bkfst & dinner) s £42-£62; d £84-£104
MEALS: Lunch fr £8.15 Dinner £14.95&alc*
CONF: Thtr 200 Class 120 Board 36 Del from £91
CARDS:

See advertisement on this page

★★★64% **Studley**
Swan Rd HG1 2SE ☎ 01423 560425 FAX 01423 530967
Guests staying at this delightful hotel can be sure of warm and attentive service from an efficiently managed and dedicated staff. The bedrooms are modern and well equipped and the public areas although small are comfortable and inviting. Excellent cooking is provided in Le Breton room under the personal control of Michel, the head chef. The menu includes a nice mix of charcoal-grilled dishes together with more classical offerings and is very good value for money. The hotel is convenient for both the conference hall and the town centre and has a car park to the rear.

36 en suite (bth/shr) CTV in all bedrooms STV Lift Night porter 14P English & French Cuisine Coffee am Last d 10pm
ROOMS: (incl. bkfst) s £68-£88; d £85-£105 LB
OFF-PEAK: (incl. bkfst & dinner) s fr £55; d fr £110
MEALS: Lunch £8-£10.50alc Dinner £13.50-£18.80&alc*
CARDS:

★★★62% **St George Swallow**
Ripon Rd HG1 2SY (on A61 opposite Conference Centre) ☎ 01423 561431 FAX 01423 530037

Situated in the town centre close to the conference halls, this Edwardian hotel features spacious public rooms, including an ornate dining room. A programme of bedroom refurbishment is currently underway, but at present the best rooms are on the first floor. There is a leisure club in the basement and car parking is found at the rear.

93 en suite (bth/shr) (14 fmly) No smoking in 35 bedrooms CTV in all bedrooms STV Lift Night porter 60P Indoor swimming pool (heated) Sauna Solarium Gym Jacuzzi/spa Boutique Beautician Masseuse Whirlpool English & French Cuisine V meals Coffee am Tea pm Last d 9.30pm
MEALS: Dinner fr £17.50*
CONF: Thtr 200 Class 80 Board 50 Del from £98
CARDS:

★★★61% **The Crown**
Crown Place HG1 2RZ ☎ 01423 567755
FAX 01423 502284

REGAL A Collection of Individual Hotels

Originally built as a coaching inn in the 18th century, the Crown is situated in the centre of the town, next to the Royal Pump Room and within a short walk of the main shopping areas and the International Conference Centre. Recent refurbishment of many of its bedrooms and some of the public areas has brought the hotel back to life. The elegant Ripley Restaurant, with its fine wood panelling and marbled pillars, and the front lounge, where afternoon tea is served, are reminders of a bygone era. There is a splendid banqueting suite as well as other conference, syndicate and meeting rooms.

contd.

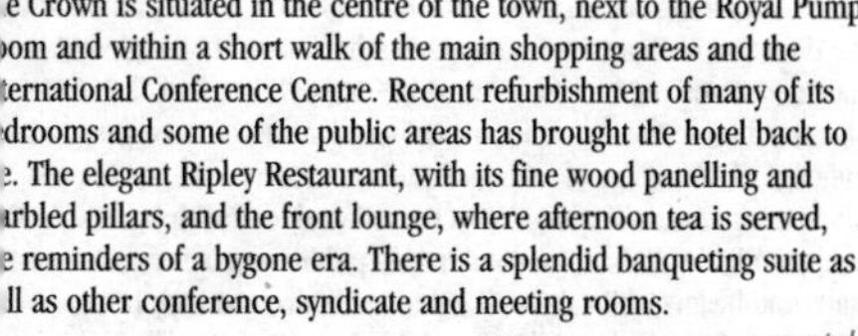

121 en suite (bth/shr) (13 fmly) No smoking in 40 bedrooms CTV in all bedrooms Lift Night porter 63P Xmas V meals Coffee am Tea pm Last d 9.30pm
ROOMS: s £20-£65; d £40-£95 * LB
CARDS:

★★★61% **Hospitality Inn**

Prospect Place, West Park HG1 1LB (on A61 close to town centre) ☎ 01423 564601 FAX 01423 507508
There is a hint of Dickens about this hotel, particularly the aptly named David Copperfield bar and the beamed Oliver Twist restaurant; but despite reference to these celebrated characters there is no suggestion of Victoriana in the modern well equipped bedrooms, or indeed in the recently opened conference and meeting room, designed to take up to 120 delegates. The hotel is only a short walk from the centre of the town and overlooks part of the famous 'stray'. It caters equally well for both leisure and business purposes and can also offer self contained apartments, ideal for family breaks or long-stay guests.
71 en suite (bth/shr) (5 fmly) No smoking in 9 bedrooms CTV in all bedrooms Lift Night porter 40P Xmas English & French Cuisine V meals Coffee am Tea pm No smoking in restaurant Last d 9.30pm
ROOMS: s £72-£79; d £82-£89 * LB
MEALS: Sunday Lunch £7.85-£8.50 Dinner £15.75&alc*
CONF: Thtr 150 Class 75 Board 58 Del from £78
CARDS:

★★70% **The Manor**
3 Clarence Dr HG1 2QE ☎ 01423 503916 FAX 01423 568709
This attractive Victorian house stands in a quiet residential area of the town and is close to the Valley Gardens and all of the town's amenities. The house has been well furnished throughout and includes well equipped bedrooms and comfortable public rooms. Interesting home cooking is provided and the service is both warm and friendly.
17 en suite (bth/shr) (1 fmly) No smoking in 4 bedrooms CTV in all bedrooms STV No dogs Lift 12P No coaches No children 12yrs English & French Cuisine V meals Coffee am Tea pm No smoking in restaurant Last d 8.45pm
ROOMS: (incl. bkfst) s £48-£65; d £68-£89 * LB
MEALS: Lunch £11-£15 Dinner £16.75-£18*
CARDS:

★★69% **Ascot House**
53 Kings Rd HG1 5HJ ☎ 01423 531005
FAX 01423 503523
MINOTEL Great Britain
Closed 28 Dec-2 Jan & 24 Jan-10 Feb
Honest and very friendly hospitality is provided at this family-owned and -run hotel which is within easy reach of the town and Conference centre. Bedrooms here are quite delightful with plenty of thoughtful extras provided and bright and fresh décor in all rooms. There is a cosy lounge and a good range of home-cooked dishes are available in the attractive dining room.
19 rms (18 bth/shr) (2 fmly) CTV in all bedrooms 14P English & Continental Cuisine V meals Coffee am Tea pm Last d 8.30pm
ROOMS: (incl. bkfst) s £44.50-£54.50; d £65-£77.50 * LB
OFF-PEAK: (incl. bkfst & dinner) s £53.50-£58; d £88-£98
MEALS: Dinner £13.95-£15.50&alc
CONF: Thtr 80 Class 36 Board 36 Del from £49.50
CARDS:

★★67% **Abbey Lodge**
29-31 Ripon Rd HG1 2JL (on the A61 just N of Harrogate centre)
☎ 01423 569712 FAX 01423 530570
Closed 24-26 Dec
This family owned and run hotel, standing on Ripon Road, provides friendly and attentive service together with modern and well equipped bedrooms. There is a pleasant front garden and parking is provided at the side of the house, which is a delightful Victorian property. A very comfortable lounge and bar is offered and a good range of well produced dishes is available from the regularly changing menu in Naylors restaurant.
19 rms (5 bth 9 shr) (3 fmly) CTV in all bedrooms 24P English & French Cuisine V meals Coffee am Last d 9pm
ROOMS: (incl. bkfst) s £28-£49; d £49-£59 LB
OFF-PEAK: (incl. bkfst) s £25-£42; d £46-£50
MEALS: Dinner fr £13.45
CARDS:

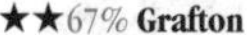

★★67% **Grafton**
1-3 Franklin Mount HG1 5EJ ☎ 01423 508491 FAX 01423 523168
Standing in a quiet side road and convenient for both the town and the Conference Centre, this friendly, family-run hotel offers good value for money. There are well equipped and bright bedrooms, together with two comfortable lounges, whilst a wide range of dishes is available in the pleasantly furnished dining room which overlooks the well tended front garden. Warm and friendly service is provided by the resident owners, Mr and Mrs Addison.
17 en suite (bth/shr) (3 fmly) CTV in all bedrooms No dogs (ex guide dogs) 3P English & Continental Cuisine V meals Coffee am Tea pm No smoking in restaurant Last d 8.30pm
ROOMS: (incl. bkfst) s £27.50-£35; d £48-£60 * LB
OFF-PEAK: (incl. bkfst) s £25-£30; d £42.50-£48
MEALS: Dinner £10.50-£11.50
CARDS:

★★67% **Green Park**
Valley Dr HG2 0JT ☎ 01423 504681 FAX 01423 530811
This traditional-style hotel is located next to the Valley Gardens and is only a short walk from the town and the Conference Centre. The bedrooms vary in size and shape and are prettily decorated and well equipped to meet today's needs and expectations. Inviting lounges are provided and a good range of well produced food is served in the cosy restaurant. Guests can expect warm and friendly service from a dedicated staff.
43 en suite (bth/shr) (2 fmly) No smoking in 14 bedrooms CTV in all bedrooms Lift Night porter 10P Xmas International Cuisine V meals Coffee am Tea pm No smoking in restaurant Last d 8.30pm
ROOMS: (incl. bkfst) s £57; d £81 LB
MEALS: Bar Lunch £1.30-£9alc Dinner £10.35-£14.75&alc
CONF: Thtr 40 Class 30 Board 24 Del £63
CARDS:

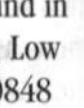

★★67% **Low Hall**
Ripon Rd, Killinghall HG3 2AY (exit Harrogate on A61 northbound in the direction of Ripon in 2m on exiting the village of Killinghall, Low Hall is 300mtrs on the right) ☎ 01423 508598 FAX 01423 560848
Standing beside the main Ripon road to the north of Harrogate and on the edge of the village of Killinghall, this attractive stone built hotel offers a very extensive range of well produced food with bar meals also being available all day. The comfortable public rooms feature stone walls and beams whilst the well equipped bedrooms have been attractively furnished and decorated Service is very friendly and is

provide by the resident owners.
7 en suite (bth/shr) No smoking in all bedrooms CTV in all bedrooms No dogs (ex guide dogs) 40P European Cuisine V meals Coffee am Tea pm No smoking in restaurant Last d 9.30pm
ROOMS: (incl. bkfst) s £39-£75; d £50-£85 *
MEALS: Lunch £12.95 Dinner £13.95*
CONF: Thtr 90 Class 70 Board 70
CARDS:

★★66% **Albany**
22-23 Harlow Moor Dr HG2 0JY ☎ 01423 565890 FAX 01423 565890
The Albany is located in a quiet residential area of Harrogate, close to the Valley Gardens and only a short walk from the town centre. The house is pleasantly furnished and offers neat, comfortable bedrooms and two lounges for guests to relax in. Well produced home cooked dinners are provided and service is very friendly and helpful.
14 en suite (shr) (3 fmly) CTV in all bedrooms No dogs (ex guide dogs) English & Continental Cuisine V meals No smoking in restaurant Last d 7.30pm
ROOMS: (incl. bkfst) s £28-£33; d £52-£62 * **LB**
OFF-PEAK: (incl. bkfst) s £28; d £52
MEALS: Dinner £14
CARDS:

★★66% **Bay Horse Inn & Motel**
Burnt Yates HG3 3EJ (W on B6165 next to village church)
☎ 01423 770230
A charming 18th century inn offering a mix of either modern or more cottagey-style bedrooms all of which are well equipped and furnished. There is a good range of freshly prepared food which may be taken either in the cosy bar or the attractive restaurant. The inn features low beams and log fires on colder days, whilst service is warm and friendly from the resident owners and their dedicated staff.
6 en suite (shr) 10 annexe en suite (shr) (2 fmly) CTV in all bedrooms No dogs (ex guide dogs) 70P English & French Cuisine V meals Coffee am Last d 9.30pm
ROOMS: (incl. bkfst) s £40; d £60 * **LB**
MEALS: Sunday Lunch £10.50 Dinner £15.95&alc*
CONF: Board 35
CARDS:

★★65% **Harrogate Brasserie Hotel & Bar**
28-30 Cheltenham Pde HG1 1DB (on A61)
☎ 01423 505041 FAX 01423 530920
This lively modern and hotel, in the centre of the town, and provides live jazz on Fridays and Sundays. A good range of interesting food is served in the French brasserie-style restaurant and the bedrooms are very modern and thoughtfully equipped. There is the added benefit of a car park to the rear of the hotel, and service is both friendly and attentive, with the owners being very much involved.
14 en suite (bth/shr) (2 fmly) CTV in all bedrooms STV 12P No coaches Wkly live entertainment Xmas English & French Cuisine V meals Coffee am Tea pm Last d 9pm
ROOMS: (incl. bkfst) s fr £40; d fr £65 *
OFF-PEAK: (incl. bkfst) s fr £37.50; d fr £55
MEALS: Lunch £15.25-£16.25&alc Dinner £15.25-£16.25&alc*
CARDS:
See advertisement on this page

★★64% **Valley**
93-95 Valley Dr HG2 0JP (overlooking the Valley Gardens)
☎ 01423 504868 FAX 04123 531940
Closed 23 Dec-2 Jan
This centrally located hotel overlooks Valley Park, a popular exhibition site. Converted from two dwellings the hotel has a good variety of similarly equipped bedrooms as well as a homely lounge bar and an attractive restaurant where home-cooked dishes are served.
16 rms (15 bth/shr) (4 fmly) CTV in all bedrooms Lift International

Cuisine V meals Coffee am Tea pm No smoking in restaurant Last d 9.45pm
ROOMS: (incl. bkfst) s £30-£40; d £50-£65 * **LB**
OFF-PEAK: (incl. bkfst) s £30-£40
CARDS:

★72% **Britannia Lodge**
16 Swan Rd HG1 2SA ☎ 01423 508482 FAX 01423 526840
Conveniently situated close to the conference centre, this friendly, family-run hotel offers good-value accommodation. Individually furnished bedrooms all have en suite facilities and are equipped with TVs and telephones. The lounge and bar are comfortable and cosy, and honest Yorkshire cooking is served.
12 en suite (bth/shr) (4 fmly) CTV in all bedrooms STV No dogs Air conditioning 7P No coaches English & French Cuisine V meals Coffee am Tea pm No smoking in restaurant Last d 8pm
ROOMS: (incl. bkfst) s £35-£50; d £55-£70 **LB**
OFF-PEAK: (incl. bkfst) s fr £32.50; d fr £48
MEALS: Lunch £8.50 High tea £8.50 Dinner £12.50
CARDS:

★70% ***Gables***
2 West Grove Rd HG1 2AD (500yds from International Conference Centre) ☎ 01423 505625 FAX 01423 561312
A corner sited hotel, the Gables is owner run and offers very good hospitality. The bedrooms are well equipped and some are very spacious. A cosy lounge is provided and good home cooking is served in the pleasant dining room. The hotel is convenient for the conference centre as well as the town.
9 en suite (bth/shr) (2 fmly) CTV in all bedrooms 9P Continental Cuisine
CARDS:

★69% **Alvera Court**
76 Kings Rd HG1 5JX (opposite Harrogate Conference Centre)
☎ 01423 505735 FAX 01423 507996
Closed 24-27 Dec
Friendly and attentive service is provided by the resident owners in this attractive and well furnished Victorian hotel. It is found close to the Conference Centre and is only a short walk from the town. Bedrooms are particularly well equipped and an inviting lounge is provided as is a small and cosy dining room.
12 en suite (bth/shr) (4 fmly) CTV in all bedrooms No dogs (ex guide dogs) 8P No coaches V meals No smoking in restaurant
ROOMS: (incl. bkfst) s £36-£42.30; d £72-£84 **LB**
OFF-PEAK: (incl. bkfst) s fr £29; d fr £58
MEALS:
CARDS:

★65% **The Croft**
42-46 Franklin Rd HG1 5EE ☎ 01423 563326
FAX 01423 530733
Warm and friendly service is provided at this pleasant hotel, located in a quiet side road, which is within easy walking distance of both the town and the conference centre. The bedrooms are thoughtfully equipped and the lounge and bar are both inviting and comfortable. Quality home-cooked food is available in the cosy dining room and there is a small car park to the rear of the house.
13 en suite (bth/shr) CTV in all bedrooms 10P Pool table ch fac English & French Cuisine V meals Coffee am Tea pm No smoking in restaurant Last d 9pm
ROOMS: (incl. bkfst) s £30-£35; d £55-£63 **LB**
OFF-PEAK: (incl. bkfst) s fr £25; d fr £48
MEALS: Dinner £12-£14alc
CONF: Class 12 Board 10 Del £60
CARDS:

★65% **The Duchy**
51 Valley Dr HG2 0JH (off A61 at Royal Baths for Valley Gardens which hotel overlooks) ☎ 01423 565818 FAX 01423 504518
Closed Xmas & New Year
An impressive stone-built house, The Duchy Hotel overlooks the Valley Gardens and is within easy walking distance of all the town's attractions. It is well furnished and provides a cosy lounge and a separate bar. All the bedrooms are well equipped and friendly service is provided by the resident owners.
9 en suite (bth/shr) (5 fmly) CTV in all bedrooms STV No dogs No coaches V meals No smoking area in restaurant Last d 7pm
ROOMS: (incl. bkfst) s £33; d £50 **LB**
MEALS: Dinner £12.50*
CARDS:

★65% ***Scotia House***
66/68 Kings Rd HG1 5JR ☎ 01423 504361 FAX 01423 526578
Standing directly opposite the conference centre, this well furnished family-run hotel offers very good value for money. The bright, fresh bedrooms are well equipped and even include telephones. A cosy lounge bar is provided and well produced home cooking is served in the attractive dining room. There is also the benefit of a small car park to the rear of the hotel.
14 rms (1 bth 9 shr) (1 fmly) No smoking in 6 bedrooms CTV in all bedrooms 7P No coaches No children 7yrs V meals Coffee am Last d 7pm
CARDS:

○ ***Rudding House***
Rudding Park, Follifoot HG3 1JH ☎ 01423 871350
Due to open 15 Apr 1997
50 rms

HARROW Greater London See LONDON SECTION plan 1 B5

★★★65% **Cumberland**
1 St Johns Rd HA1 2EF ☎ 0181 863 4111
FAX 0181 861 5668
Its location in the town centre makes this a popular hotel with locals and ideal for the corporate and leisure guest. It offers modern and well equipped bedrooms in the main house and two rear annexes. In the public areas the atmosphere is vibrant, with a lively bar featuring a good range of draught beers, whilst La Rochelle Restaurant provides more formal surroundings in which to enjoy chef Keith Arrowsmith's enterprising cooking. There are significant facilities for meetings and functions, the Garden Suite accommodating up to 110 persons.
31 en suite (bth/shr) 53 annexe en suite (bth/shr) (6 fmly) No smoking in 41 bedrooms CTV in all bedrooms STV No dogs (ex guide dogs) Night porter 57P Sauna Gym Small Fitness Room Xmas English & French Cuisine V meals Coffee am Tea pm Last d 9.30pm
ROOMS: (incl. bkfst) s £80-£90; d £90-£100 **LB**
MEALS: Lunch £9.50-£15&alc Dinner £12.50-£18.50&alc
CONF: Thtr 140 Class 50 Board 50 Del from £105
CARDS:

See advertisement on opposite page

★★69% **Harrow**
Roxborough Bridge, 12-22 Pinner Rd HA1 4HZ
(on A404) ☎ 0181 427 3435 FAX 0181 861 1370
A privately-owned hotel with ample forecourt parking is situated just a few minutes' walk from the town centre and within easy reach of the London Underground and bus stations. It has been created by the joining of a number of turn of the century houses; bedrooms are individually styled and well equipped with modern amenities.
54 en suite (bth/shr) 23 annexe en suite (bth/shr) (1 fmly) No smoking in 22 bedrooms CTV in all bedrooms Night porter 60P International Cuisine V meals Coffee am Tea pm No smoking area in restaurant Last d 9.45pm
ROOMS: (incl. bkfst) s £65-£79; d £79-£99 *
MEALS: Lunch £12.95-£17.50&alc Dinner fr £17.50&alc*

CONF: Thtr 160 Class 60 Board 60 Del from £90
CARDS:

See advertisement on opposite page

★★61% ***Northwick Park***
2-12 Northwick Park Rd HA1 2NT (off A4006) ☎ 0181 427 2899
FAX 0181 863 2314
Northwick Park offers reasonably priced accommodation both in the main house and in the new building across the large carpark. The extensive refurbishment to the public areas will be followed through in the bedrooms, which are all well equipped and of a decent size. The function room is popular for both social and business meetings.
60 en suite (bth/shr) 20 annexe en suite (bth/shr) (3 fmly) No smoking in 30 bedrooms CTV in all bedrooms STV No dogs (ex guide dogs) Night porter 65P V meals Coffee am Tea pm
CARDS:

★★59% **Lindal**
2 Hindes Rd HA1 1SJ (off A409, opposite Tesco Superstore)
☎ 0181 863 3164 FAX 0181 427 5435
The Lindal is an informal, family-run establishment with service provided mostly by members of the Plunkett family and meals being generally available by arrangement. The accommodation has been attractively furnished in the modern style and comprises a choice of bedrooms which vary in shape and size, a combined bar-lounge and dining area, and a well appointed rear breakfast room.
19 en suite (bth/shr) (3 fmly) No smoking in 5 bedrooms CTV in all bedrooms No dogs (ex guide dogs) Night porter 17P V meals Coffee am Tea pm
ROOMS: (incl. bkfst) s £40-£44.50; d £50-£55 **LB**
MEALS: Dinner fr £6&alc*
CONF: Thtr 30 Class 20 Board 20
CARDS:

£

HARTLEBURY Hereford & Worcester Map 07 SO87

Travelodge
Shorthill Nurseries DY11 6DR (A449 southbound)
☎ 01299 250553 FAX 01299 250553

Travelodge

This modern building offers accommodation in smart, spacious and well equipped bedrooms, suitable for family use, and all with en suite bathrooms. Meals may be taken at the nearby family restaurant. For information on room rates and to make a booking, call Roomline free of charge on 0800 850950. For more details about Travelodge, consult the Contents page under Hotel Groups.
32 en suite (bth/shr)

HARTLEPOOL Co Durham Map 08 NZ53

★★★62% **The Grand**
Swainson St TS24 8AA ☎ 01429 266345 FAX 01429 265217
Standing in the centre of the town, this splendid Victorian building with its impressive façade offers mainly spacious bedrooms which are also well equipped. Public rooms are extensive and include a pleasant restaurant, a spacious bar and also a large magnificent ballroom. A good range of food is available either in the bar or the restaurant.
47 en suite (bth/shr) (4 fmly) CTV in all bedrooms STV Lift Night porter 50P Pool table English & French Cuisine V meals Coffee am Tea pm Last d 9.30pm
ROOMS: (incl. bkfst) s £47.50-£65; d £60-£80 * **LB**
MEALS: Lunch £9.95-£12.95 Dinner £12.95-£14.95&alc*
CONF: Thtr 200 Class 150 Board 35 Del from £85
CARDS:

H

★★68% **Ryedale Moor**
3 Beaconsfield St, Headland TS24 0NX (access via A179) ☎ 01429 231436 FAX 01429 863787

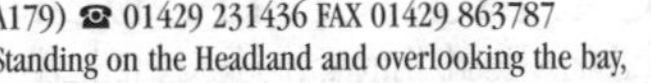

Standing on the Headland and overlooking the bay, this friendly family-run hotel offers very attentive and personal service. The bedrooms are modern in style and are well equipped, whilst the public rooms are inviting and include a separate breakfast room. A good range of dishes is available in the very pleasant dining room, and closed circuit TV is in operation.
14 en suite (bth/shr) (2 fmly) No smoking in 5 bedrooms CTV in 13 bedrooms STV No dogs 8P No children 12yrs English, French & Indian Cuisine V meals Coffee am Tea pm Last d 9.45pm
ROOMS: (incl. bkfst) s £35-£43; d £54-£60 * **LB**
OFF-PEAK: (incl. bkfst) d £48-£54
MEALS: Lunch £2.50-£6.50&alc High tea £2.50 Dinner £4.95-£6.50&alc*
CONF: Thtr 40 Class 40 Board 30 Del from £48
CARDS:

Travel Inn
Hartlepool Marina ☎ 01429 890115
FAX 01429 868674

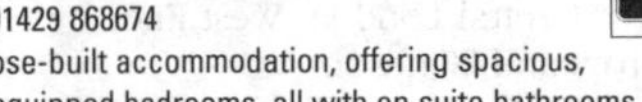

Purpose-built accommodation, offering spacious, well equipped bedrooms, all with en suite bathrooms. Meals may be taken at the nearby family restaurant. For more information about Travel Inns, consult the Contents page under Hotel Groups.
40 en suite (bth/shr)
ROOMS: (incl. bkfst) d £35.50 *

HARTSHEAD MOOR SERVICE AREA West Yorkshire Map 07 SE12

Travelodge
Clifton HD6 4JX (M62 esatbound between junct 25 & 26) ☎ 01274 851706
This modern building offers accommodation in smart, spacious and well equipped bedrooms, suitable for family use, and all with en suite bathrooms. Meals may be taken at the nearby family restaurant. For information on room rates and to make a booking, call Roomline free of charge on 0800 850950. For more details about Travelodge, consult the Contents page under Hotel Groups.
40 en suite (bth/shr)

HARVINGTON (NEAR EVESHAM) Hereford & Worcester Map 04 SP04

★★❀❀77% **The Mill at Harvington**
Anchor Ln, Harvington WR11 5NR ☎ 01386 870688
FAX 01386 870688
(For full entry see Evesham)

HARWICH Essex Map 05 TM23

★★❀72% **The Pier at Harwich**
The Quay CO12 3ER (overlooking harbour) ☎ 01255 241212
FAX 01255 551922
Closed 25-26 Dec
This handsome Victorian building on the quay looks out over the confluence of the Rivers Stour and Orwell and reflects the nautical presence in the maritime theme of the hotel's decor. The public rooms are dominated by two restaurants and a bar, which offer visitors a good choice of dining, with either informal meals served within the newly refurbished Ha'penny ground floor restaurant, or more formal dining in the first floor Pier Restaurant, which has a fine reputation for its fish dishes. Bedrooms are all attractively appointed and well equipped; many thoughtful extras give the rooms a more personal feel.
6 en suite (bth) (2 fmly) CTV in all bedrooms No dogs (ex guide dogs) Night porter 10P Wkly live entertainment English & French Cuisine V meals Last d 9.30pm
ROOMS: (incl. cont bkfst) s £45; d £70 *
MEALS: Lunch £14-£16.50&alc Dinner fr £18&alc*
CONF: Thtr 50 Class 50 Board 24
CARDS:

★★63% **Cliff**
Marine Pde, Dovercourt CO12 3RE ☎ 01255 503345 & 507373
FAX 01255 240358
RS Xmas & New Year
A traditional resort hotel stands in a central position on the cliff between Dovercourt and Harwich overlooking the sea, Harwich Harbour and the port of Felixstowe. Public rooms are modern and inviting, offering guests the choice of informal meals in the Marine Bar or more formal dining in the restaurant. Refreshments can be provided in the foyer lounge, and a new public bar is equipped with pool tables. Many of the bedrooms have benefited from recent refurbishment.
27 en suite (bth/shr) (5 fmly) No smoking in 1 bedroom CTV in all bedrooms STV Night porter 50P Pool table V meals Coffee am Tea pm No smoking area in restaurant Last d 8.45pm
ROOMS: (incl. bkfst) s fr £48; d fr £58 * **LB**
OFF-PEAK: (incl. bkfst) d fr £40
MEALS: Lunch £11.25-£11.50&alc Dinner fr £13.50&alc*
CONF: Thtr 200 Class 120 Board 60 Del from £47.50
CARDS:

HASLEMERE Surrey Map 04 SU93

★★★★❀❀72% **Lythe Hill**
Petworth Rd GU27 3BQ (1.25m E B2131) ☎ 01428 651251
FAX 01428 644131
Set in 20 acres of mature parkland and grounds, this well managed, comfortable hotel encompasses the adjoining 14th-century oak-panelled Auberge de France restaurant. There is a wonderful range of sumptuous bedrooms and suites together with some small standard doubles and luxurious garden suites. Public rooms comprise a tastefully furnished lounge, well appointed bar lounge and dining room, air-conditioned atrium conservatory and good conference facilities. Chef Roger Clarke continues to impress with his modern French professional cooking and offers both table d'hÙte and à la carte menus. Service is very attentive and particularly well managed with 24-hour room service available and a night porter.
40 en suite (bth/shr) (8 fmly) CTV in all bedrooms Night porter 200P Tennis (hard) Fishing Pool table Croquet lawn Boules Games Room Xmas English & French Cuisine V meals Coffee am Tea pm No smoking in restaurant Last d 9.15pm
ROOMS: s £84-£134; d £95-£150 * **LB**
MEALS: Lunch £14.50-£18.50&alc Dinner £18.50&alc*
CONF: Thtr 60 Class 40 Board 30 Del from £132
CARDS:

See advertisement on opposite page

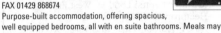

HASTINGS & ST LEONARDS East Sussex Map 05 TQ80

★★★ 72% **Beauport Park**
Battle Rd TN38 8EA (3m N off A2100)
☎ 01424 851222 FAX 01424 852465
Best Western

Set in 37 acres of peaceful and tranquil surroundings this fine c1765 Georgian manor house was once the private residence of General Sir George Murray, and whilst retaining many of its original architectural features the accommodation has been tastefully modernised to provide comfortable and well furnished rooms equipped and furnished to high standard. Chef Duncan Biggs shows his flair for modern British cooking using the best local and seasonal produce and seafood. With the staff recruited for their suitability for the job, service is particularly attentive and well managed, and the turnout in The Garden Restaurant is especially notable with waitresses dressed in their Victorian uniform.

23 en suite (bth/shr) (2 fmly) No smoking in 9 bedrooms CTV in all bedrooms STV 64P No coaches Outdoor swimming pool (heated) Golf 18 Tennis (hard) Riding Croquet lawn Putting green Wkly live entertainment ch fac Xmas International Cuisine V meals Coffee am Tea pm No smoking in restaurant Last d 9.30pm
ROOMS: (incl. bkfst) s fr £69; d fr £95 **LB**
MEALS: Lunch £16-£16.50 Dinner £18.50-£19.50
CONF: Thtr 70 Class 25 Board 30 Del from £94.50
CARDS:

See advertisement on this page

★★★ 62% **High Beech**
Battle Rd TN37 7BS (400yds from A2100 between Hastings and Battle)
☎ 01424 851383 FAX 01424 854265

Situated off the Battle Road, this privately owned hotel offers comfortable bedrooms furnished and equipped in the modern style, some with balconies and some with four-poster beds. The Wedgwood Restaurant offers a fixed-price menu and French-style à la carte, whilst the Mountbatten Bar combines with the bar-lounge and the Ambassador Suite to provide popular facilities for local functions and dinner dances. There are also good facilities for in-house conferences and an extensive range of self-catering chalets.

17 en suite (bth/shr) (3 fmly) CTV in all bedrooms STV No dogs (ex guide dogs) 65P Xmas English & Continental Cuisine V meals Coffee am Tea pm Last d 9.15pm
ROOMS: (incl. bkfst) s £40-£45; d £70-£80 * **LB**
MEALS: Sunday Lunch £11 Dinner £18.50&alc*
CONF: Thtr 250 Class 192 Board 146 Del from £55
CARDS:

See advertisement on page 293

★★★ 59% **Royal Victoria**
The Marina, St Leonards-on-Sea TN38 0BD (on western seafront off A21) ☎ 01424 445544
FAX 01424 721995

This imposing 19th-century Victorian hotel occupies a prime location

contd.

facing the sea. A marble-pillared and mirrored stairway leads up to the Piano lounge bar and Sea Terrace restaurant on the first floor, and a range of very comfortable bedrooms is available, many with sitting areas and fine views of the Channel.

50 en suite (bth/shr) (6 fmly) CTV in all bedrooms Lift Night porter 6P Xmas English & French Cuisine V meals Coffee am Tea pm Last d 9.30pm
ROOMS: (incl. bkfst) s £36-£80; d £72-£90 **LB**
OFF-PEAK: (incl. bkfst) s £33-£65; d £66-£90
MEALS: Sunday Lunch £9.95-£10.50 Dinner £15-£16&alc
CONF: Thtr 100 Class 40 Board 50 Del from £70
CARDS:

See advertisement on opposite page

HATFIELD Hertfordshire Map 04 TL20

★★★64% ***Hatfield Oak***
Roehyde Way AL10 9AF ☎ 01707 275701 FAX 01707 275701
This conference hotel is located on the A1001, parallel to, and between junctions 2 and 3 of the A1(M). Bedrooms and public rooms are modern in design and include a good range of conference and syndicate rooms. The accommodation is well equipped and thoughtfully laid out. The executive bedrooms are slightly larger and have added facilities such as a fridge and trouser press. There are several eating options: a 24-hour room service of snacks and meals, a bar/brassiere area, or more formal dining in the restaurant.
76 en suite (bth/shr) (11 fmly) No smoking in 39 bedrooms CTV in all bedrooms STV Night porter 120P V meals Coffee am Tea pm Last d 9.45pm
CARDS:

HATHERSAGE Derbyshire Map 08 SK28

★★72% **Hathersage Inn**
Main Rd S30 1BB (in village centre on A625)
☎ 01433 650259 FAX 01433 651199
This old stone-built inn situated in the centre of the village, popular with walkers and visitors to the Peaks, offers comfortable, well appointed accommodation and a warm and friendly atmosphere. Bedrooms, four of which are situated in Morley Lodge, a period house next to the main building, and include a room with a four-poster bed, are attractively decorated and thoughtfully equipped. Guests can choose to eat char-grilled dishes and drink real ale in the relaxed atmosphere of the convivial Cricketers Bar or more formally in the restaurant, relaxing afterwards in the comfortable lounge which has a roaring fire in winter.
11 en suite (bth/shr) 4 annexe en suite (bth) CTV in all bedrooms 20P Xmas V meals Coffee am Tea pm Last d 9.30pm
ROOMS: (incl. bkfst) s £49.50-£57; d £64.50-£77.50 **LB**
MEALS: Sunday Lunch £5.95-£9.90 Dinner £16.50-£17.95
CONF: Thtr 18 Class 12 Board 12 Del from £72.50
CARDS:

★★64% **George**
Main Rd S30 1BB (in village centre on A625) ☎ 01433 650436 FAX 01433 650099
Much of the original character has been retained at this 16th-century coaching inn, particularly in the public areas. A comfortable lounge adjoins an attractively appointed restaurant offering carte and fixed-price menus; bar meals are available in the George Bar. Bedrooms are modern and well equipped.
18 en suite (bth/shr) (3 fmly) No smoking in 6 bedrooms CTV in all bedrooms STV No dogs (ex guide dogs) 40P Wkly live entertainment Xmas International Cuisine V meals Coffee am Tea pm Last d 9.30pm
ROOMS: (incl. bkfst) s fr £59.50; d fr £75 * **LB**
MEALS: Lunch £9.95-£13.95&alc Dinner £11.60-£18.15alc*
CONF: Thtr 30 Class 20 Board 18 Del from £89
CARDS:

HAVANT Hampshire Map 04 SU70

★★★62% **The Bear**
East St PO9 1AA ☎ 01705 486501
FAX 01705 470551
A former coaching inn at the heart of the town offers a small cocktail bar and the Elizabethan public bar, the latter much improved in recent years. Bedrooms are gradually being upgraded, though all are fully equipped.
42 en suite (bth/shr) (3 fmly) No smoking in 11 bedrooms CTV in all bedrooms STV No dogs (ex guide dogs) Night porter 90P Xmas European Cuisine V meals Coffee am Tea pm No smoking area in restaurant Last d 10pm
ROOMS: (incl. bkfst) s £59.50; d £75 * **LB**
OFF-PEAK: (incl. bkfst) s £35; d £50-£60
MEALS: Lunch £4.95-£7.95 Dinner £12-£14.50&alc*
CONF: Thtr 120 Class 30 Board 60 Del £80
CARDS:

HAWES North Yorkshire Map 07 SD88

★★76% **Simonstone Hall**
Simonstone DL8 3LY (1.5m N on road signed to Muker and Buttertubs) ☎ 01969 667255 FAX 01969 667741
Standing high above the village, this comfortable and very well furnished country house hotel is a place to relax and unwind. The public rooms are well furnished with many antiques, whilst the elegant dining room is a perfect setting for the well produced, home-cooked dinners. Bedrooms are mainly spacious; some have antiques whilst others have more modern-style furniture, and all are well equipped and prettily decorated. Service is warm and friendly from a dedicated staff.
10 en suite (bth/shr) (2 fmly) CTV in all bedrooms 24P ch fac Xmas English & French Cuisine V meals Coffee am Tea pm Last d 8.30pm
ROOMS: (incl. bkfst) s £39.20-£61.60; d £70-£110 * **LB**
MEALS: Sunday Lunch £10-£19.50 Dinner £16-£24.75
CONF: Thtr 20 Class 20 Board 20 Del from £88
CARDS:

★★71% **Stone House**
Sedbusk DL8 3PT ☎ 01969 667571 FAX 01969 667720
Closed Jan RS mid Nov-Dec & Feb
Standing in open countryside and overlooking green fields to the north of Hawes, this lovely hotel has a delightful Edwardian charm. The public rooms are adorned with various ornaments including toy cars and teapots. The dining room serves a good selection of home-produced Yorkshire dinners and service is very friendly and informal. Bedrooms are well equipped and include three with their own individual conservatories.

15 rms (14 bth/shr) 4 annexe en suite (bth/shr) (1 fmly) CTV in all bedrooms 15P Tennis (grass) Croquet lawn Xmas V meals Coffee am No smoking in restaurant Last d 8pm
ROOMS: (incl. bkfst) s fr £32.50; d £55-£78 * **LB**
MEALS: Dinner fr £16.50
CARDS:

★★ 69% **Rookhurst Georgian Country House**
Gayle DL8 3RT (0.5m from town at Gayle, on A684)
☎ 01969 667454 FAX 01969 667454
Closed 16 Dec-Jan (ex 28 Dec-2 Jan)
This lovely Georgian country house dates back in part to 1734 and is situated in the small village of Gayle, just to the south of Hawes. It contains many items of historical interest and has beautiful drapes and oak beams as well as antique four-poster beds in the spacious bedrooms. There is a comfortable bar lounge and the elegant dining room is the ideal setting for the well produced home-cooked dinners. The house looks out on beautiful countryside and has a well tended garden.
5 en suite (bth) No smoking in all bedrooms CTV in all bedrooms No dogs (ex guide dogs) Night porter 10P No coaches No children 12yrs Coffee am Tea pm No smoking in restaurant Last d 7pm
ROOMS: (incl. bkfst) d £68-£88 * **LB**
MEALS: Dinner £15-£25*
CARDS:

★★ 61% **Fountain**
Market Place DL8 3RD (on A684 in town centre)
☎ 01969 667206 FAX 01969 667085
Closed 24-25 Dec
Standing in the centre of the market place and offering good value for money, this 17th century coaching inn also gives fine views of the surrounding hills, especially to the rear. The bedrooms are modern and are in the process of being upgraded, whilst the public rooms include a spacious bar and a rear dining room. Meals are freshly cooked and offer a good choice of dishes.
11 en suite (bth/shr) (2 fmly) No smoking in 1 bedroom CTV in all bedrooms 8P V meals Coffee am
ROOMS: (incl. bkfst) s £27; d £52
OFF-PEAK: (incl. bkfst) s £22; d £36
MEALS: Lunch £4.80*
CONF: Thtr 100 Class 50 Board 40
CARDS:

HAWKHURST Kent Map 05 TQ73

★★★ 68% **Tudor Court**
Rye Rd TN18 5DA (from A21 take A268 and continue across traffic lights. Hotel 0.5m on left)
☎ 01580 752312 FAX 01580 753966
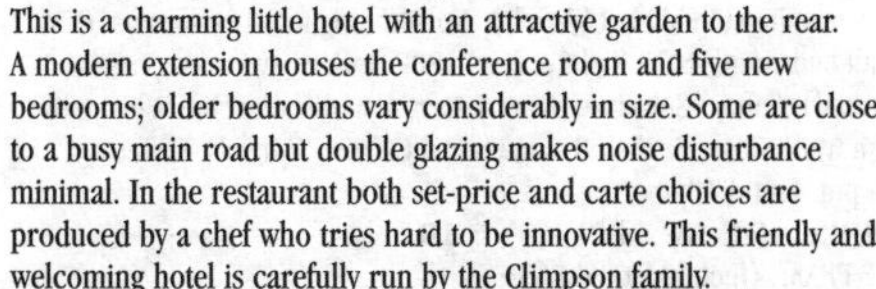
This is a charming little hotel with an attractive garden to the rear. A modern extension houses the conference room and five new bedrooms; older bedrooms vary considerably in size. Some are close to a busy main road but double glazing makes noise disturbance minimal. In the restaurant both set-price and carte choices are produced by a chef who tries hard to be innovative. This friendly and welcoming hotel is carefully run by the Climpson family.
18 en suite (bth/shr) (2 fmly) No smoking in 2 bedrooms CTV in all bedrooms No dogs (ex guide dogs) 50P Tennis (hard) Croquet lawn Putting green Clock golf Childrens play area Xmas International Cuisine V meals Coffee am Tea pm No smoking in restaurant Last d 9pm
ROOMS: (incl. bkfst) s £49; d £78-£93 * **LB**
OFF-PEAK: (incl. bkfst) s £45; d £72-£88
MEALS: Lunch £10.75-£17.50&alc Dinner £17.50&alc*
CONF: Thtr 60 Class 40 Board 32 Del from £75
CARDS:

HAWKSHEAD (NEAR AMBLESIDE) Cumbria Map 07 SD39

★★ 74% **Highfield House Country Hotel**
Hawkshead Hill LA22 0PN (on B5285 towards Coniston three quarters of a mile from Hawkshead village) ☎ 015394 36344
FAX 015394 36793
Closed 20 Dec-31 Jan
From its elevated position in its own gardens, this country house hotel enjoys one of the most stunning vistas in the Lake District, across rolling hills, valleys and mountains. Spotlessly clean and attractively maintained, it offers comfortable and thoughtfully equipped bedrooms, most of which take in the views. Similarly with public areas, where the lounge, cosy bar and bright cheery dining room are all inviting. Jim and Pauline Bennett provide a high level of attention and most of their guests prefer to dine in and enjoy the four-course home cooked dinners.
11 en suite (bth/shr) (2 fmly) CTV in all bedrooms 15P No coaches ch fac English & Continental Cuisine V meals Coffee am Tea pm No smoking in restaurant Last d 8.30pm
ROOMS: (incl. bkfst & dinner) s fr £53; d £101-£110 **LB**
MEALS: Bar Lunch fr £3.50 Dinner £16-£17
CARDS:

★★64% **Queen's Head**
Main St LA22 0NS ☎ 015394 36271 FAX 015394 36722
The Queen's Head lies in the centre of Hawkshead, a conservation village with narrow streets and historic buildings. The archetypal village inn, it boasts low beamed ceilings, brasses and memorabilia. The bar serves real ale and is very popular for its extensive bar menu, with meals tending to dominating public areas during busy periods. There is also an interesting dinner menu served in the small dining room. Bedrooms vary in size but their attractive décor and pine furnishings compensate for the lack of space in some. Three rooms are contained in a characterful cottage quietly located next door.
10 rms (1 bth 7 shr) 3 annexe en suite (bth/shr) (2 fmly) CTV in all bedrooms No dogs (ex guide dogs) Xmas English & Continental Cuisine V meals Coffee am Tea pm No smoking in restaurant Last d 9.30pm
ROOMS: (incl. bkfst) s £35-£47; d £53-£75 * **LB**
MEALS: Lunch £4.95-£20 Dinner £12-£20*
CARDS:

HAWORTH West Yorkshire Map 07 SE03

★★67% **Old White Lion**
6 West Ln BD22 8DU (on A629) ☎ 01535 642313 FAX 01535 646222
Standing at the top of the quaint cobbled street, this stone-faced inn is nearly 300 years old. Modern bedrooms, though compact, are well equipped, there is a small lounge, and both the popular beamed bars and an attractive restaurant serve a good range of food. A very friendly and obliging staff provides good Yorkshire hospitality.
15 en suite (bth/shr) (3 fmly) CTV in all bedrooms No dogs (ex guide dogs) 10P Xmas English & French Cuisine V meals Coffee am Last d 9.30pm
ROOMS: (incl. bkfst) s £38.50-£45; d £50-£60 **LB**
MEALS: Lunch fr £7 Dinner fr £12&alc*
CONF: Thtr 70 Class 40 Board 30
CARDS:

See advertisement under BRADFORD

★★64% **Three Sisters**
Brow Top Rd BD22 9PH (from A629 Keighley/Halifax road take B6144 at Flappit Corner. Hotel 0.75m on right) ☎ 01535 643458
FAX 01535 646842
Converted from a Victorian farmhouse, this stone-built hotel stands high on rugged moorland only a short distance from the village of Haworth. It is very popular for its good-value food which is served either in the bar or the cosy restaurant. The modern bedrooms are well furnished and thoughtfully equipped; a guest lounge doubles as a conference room.
9 en suite (bth/shr) (1 fmly) CTV in all bedrooms STV No dogs (ex guide dogs) 300P Wkly live entertainment Xmas English & French Cuisine V meals Coffee am Tea pm Last d 9.30pm
ROOMS: (incl. cont bkfst) s fr £35; d fr £45 * **LB**
MEALS: Lunch £6.95-£9.95&alc Dinner £13.95-£18.95alc*
CONF: Thtr 250 Class 200 Board 100
CARDS:

See advertisement on opposite page

HAYDOCK Merseyside Map 07 SJ59

★★★★62% **Haydock Thistle**
THISTLE HOTELS
Penny Ln WA11 9SG ☎ 01942 272000
FAX 01942 711092
This modern hotel with a Georgian façade is conveniently situated between Liverpool and Manchester, just off junction 23 of the M6 and is a popular rendezvous for conferences and business meetings particularly on weekdays, but at weekends it is ideal for weddings and other social functions with its terrace and courtyard gardens. Recent refurbishment of the public areas has considerably enhanced the hotel and many of its spacious and well equipped bedrooms have also been redecorated.
139 en suite (bth/shr) (13 fmly) No smoking in 30 bedrooms CTV in all bedrooms STV Night porter 180P Indoor swimming pool (heated) Sauna Solarium Gym Jacuzzi/spa Steam room Whirlpool Trim trail Xmas English & Continental Cuisine V meals Coffee am Tea pm Last d 10pm
ROOMS: s £83-£89; d £93-£99 * **LB**
OFF-PEAK: (incl. bkfst) d £65
MEALS: Lunch £8-£16 Dinner £19.50&alc*
CONF: Thtr 300 Class 180 Board 40 Del from £95
CARDS:

Forte Posthouse Haydock
FORTE Posthouse
Lodge Ln, Newton-Le-Willows WA12 0JG (adj to M6 junct 23, on A49) ☎ 01942 717878
FAX 01942 718419
Suitable for both the business and leisure traveller, this bright hotel provides modern accommodation in well equipped bedrooms with en suite bathrooms. For more details about Forte

Posthouse hotels, consult the Contents page for the section on Hotel Groups.
136 en suite (bth/shr)
ROOMS: s £79-£89; d £79-£89 *
CONF: Thtr 180 Class 100 Board 60 Del £99

Travelodge
Piele Rd WA11 9TL (2m W of junct 23 on M6, on A580 westbound) ☎ 01942 272055
FAX 01942 272055
This modern building offers accommodation in smart, spacious and well equipped bedrooms, suitable for family use, and all with en suite bathrooms. Meals may be taken at the nearby family restaurant. For information on room rates and to make a booking, call Roomline free of charge on 0800 850950. For more details about Travelodge, consult the Contents page under Hotel Groups.
40 en suite (bth/shr)

HAYES Hotels are listed under Heathrow Airport

HAYLING ISLAND Hampshire Map 04 SU70

Forte Posthouse Havant

Northney Rd PO11 0NQ (from A27 signposted Havant/Hayling Island follow A3023 across roadbridge onto Hayling Island and take sharp left on leaving bridge) ☎ 01705 465011 FAX 01705 466468
Suitable for both the business and leisure traveller, this bright hotel provides modern accommodation in well equipped bedrooms with en suite bathrooms. For more details about Forte Posthouse hotels, consult the Contents page for the section on Hotel Groups.
92 en suite (bth/shr)
ROOMS: s £30-£70; d £50-£80 *
CONF: Thtr 180 Class 80 Board 50 Del from £99

HAYTOR Devon Map 03 SX77

★★★ ❀77% **Bel Alp House**
TQ13 9XX (2.5m W of Bovey Tracey, off B3387)
☎ 01364 661217 FAX 01364 661292
Closed Dec-Feb
This chalet-style Edwardian property stands in its own beautiful gardens high up in Dartmoor National Park, with magnificent views. The family home of Roger and Sarah Curnock, it offers guests an extremely high standard of comfort and elegance. Spacious bedrooms, most benefiting from the view, are all decorated with pretty coordinating fabrics. The lounges are peaceful and relaxing and service is warm and attentive. A set five-course meal is carefully prepared by Sarah, and alternatives are always offered.
9 en suite (bth/shr) (1 fmly) CTV in all bedrooms Lift 20P No coaches Snooker Croquet lawn English & French Cuisine No smoking in restaurant Last d 8.30pm
ROOMS: (incl. bkfst) s £78-£87; d £120-£156 **LB**
MEALS: Dinner fr £30
CARDS:

★★ ❀72% **Rock Inn**
Haytor Vale TQ13 9XP ☎ 01364 661305 & 661465
FAX 01364 661242
This delightful white-painted village inn dates from the 16th-century and is situated on Dartmoor below Haytor Rocks. The bars are full of character, with exposed beams, inglenook fireplaces and flagstone floors; they offer real ales and a wide range of sophisticated bar meals. The bar snack menu and the carte include an interesting selection of fish, meat and game dishes produced with flair and imagination by chefs Philip Hurrell and Stephen Bowden. Bedrooms are comfortable and equipped with every modern creature comfort.

9 en suite (bth/shr) (2 fmly) No smoking in 2 bedrooms CTV in all bedrooms STV No dogs (ex guide dogs) 20P No coaches Xmas English & French Cuisine V meals Coffee am Tea pm
ROOMS: (incl. bkfst) s £20.95-£39.95; d £55.95 * **LB**
MEALS: Bar Lunch £5-£20 Dinner £10.95-£25*
CARDS: £

HAYWARDS HEATH West Sussex Map 05 TQ32

★★★ 60% **The Birch**
Lewes Rd RH17 7SF (0.5m E on A272 opposite Princess Royal Hospital and behind Shell Garage) ☎ 01444 451565 FAX 01444 440109
A converted Victorian house on the outskirts of the town retains much of its original wood panelling and has been carefully renovated to combine modern standards of comfort with period charm. Bedrooms are modern in style and are particularly well equipped, some of them conveniently located on the ground floor. Public areas include attractive open-plan seating next to the atmospheric Pavilion Restaurant, and The Lewes Bar with an American Pool table and a good bar menu. The Sussex Suite is av1ailable for functions, there is a good range of smaller meeting rooms, and car parking is provided.
53 en suite (bth/shr) No smoking in 15 bedrooms CTV in all bedrooms STV Night porter 65P Pool table English & French Cuisine V meals Coffee am Tea pm No smoking area in restaurant Last d 9.45pm
ROOMS: (incl. bkfst) s £30-£67.50; d £60-£95 * **LB**
MEALS: Lunch £10-£16.95 High tea £5.50-£7.50 Dinner £15.95-£17.95
CONF: Thtr 60 Class 30 Board 25 Del from £95
CARDS:

HEATHROW AIRPORT (LONDON) Greater London Map 04 TQ07
See also Hounslow and Staines

★★★★ 72% **Holiday Inn Crowne Plaza**
Stockley Rd UB7 9NA (2m N junc M4/A408)
☎ 01895 445555 FAX 01895 445122
The bedrooms are particularly comfortable and well thought out in this cosmopolitan hotel. Modern comforts include air conditioning, mini bars and 24-hour room service. The wide ranging public areas include several meeting rooms, a leisure centre and Marlowe's restaurant where a serious approach to cooking is demonstrated.
374 en suite (bth/shr) (220 fmly) No smoking in 187 bedrooms CTV in all bedrooms STV Lift Night porter Air conditioning 320P Indoor swimming pool (heated) Golf 9 Sauna Solarium Gym Jacuzzi/spa Beauty therapy room ch fac Xmas International Cuisine V meals Coffee am Tea pm No smoking area in restaurant
ROOMS: s £115; d £130 * **LB**
MEALS: Lunch £4.95-£15.95&alc Dinner £4.95-£17.50&alc*
CONF: Thtr 200 Class 120 Board 75 Del from £155
CARDS:

H

★★★★ 68% **London Heathrow Hilton**
Terminal 4, Heathrow Airport TW6 3AF
☎ 0181 759 7755 FAX 0181 759 7579

Within the concrete jungle that is Heathrow, this is a stunning architectural feature. Its modern design uses light to maximum advantage within the vast open atrium around which the bedrooms are distributed. One of the five floors of bedrooms is given over to executive rooms. The peaceful atrium houses three eating options as well as a range of convenient facilities associated with an airport hotel - it is linked to terminal four by a covered walkway.
395 en suite (bth/shr) No smoking in 252 bedrooms CTV in all bedrooms STV Lift Night porter Air conditioning 250P No coaches Indoor swimming pool (heated) Sauna Solarium Gym Aromatherapy Xmas International Cuisine V meals Coffee am Tea pm No smoking area in restaurant Last d 10.30pm
ROOMS: d £150-£155 * **LB**
MEALS: Lunch fr £18.95&alc Dinner fr £20.95&alc*
CONF: Thtr 240 Class 170 Board 80 Del from £145
CARDS:

★★★★ 67% **Forte Crest Heathrow**
Sipson Rd UB7 0JU (2m N A408) ☎ 0181 759 2323
FAX 0181 897 8659

This large modern hotel, well sited for both the airport and motorways, features a wide range of services and amenities designed to meet the needs of the business traveller. Bedrooms are smart, comfortable and well equipped. The attractive Academy Suite provides facilities for conferences, and there is a very good choice of restaurants.
569 en suite (bth/shr) (80 fmly) No smoking in 319 bedrooms CTV in all bedrooms STV No dogs (ex guide dogs) Lift Night porter Air conditioning 500P Xmas English & Meditteranean Cuisine V meals Coffee am Tea pm Last d 11pm
ROOMS: s fr £110; d fr £120 * **LB**
MEALS: Lunch £17.50&alc High tea £9.40-£15.20alc
Dinner £17.50-£26.50&alc*
CONF: Thtr 100 Class 40 Board 22 Del from £145
CARDS:

★★★★ 66% **Ramada**
Bath Rd TW6 2AQ (Ramada) ☎ 0181 897 6363 FAX 0181 897 1113
This busy conference and meeting hotel standing beside the A4 offers some of the best views of one of the airport's main runways from many of its air-conditioned bedrooms, around half of which are smart executive rooms and recently refurbished, while finishing touches to the last batch will bring the style well and truly into the 1990s. Smartly turned-out staff show excellent levels of guest care, and the brasserie restaurant, which is centred around a buffet-style operation, produces food of a high standard. The Icarus bar is a popular meeting place, and conference delegates will be impressed by the York theatre and its unique projection facilities.
640 en suite (bth/shr) (10 fmly) No smoking in 140 bedrooms CTV in all bedrooms STV No dogs (ex guide dogs) Lift Night porter Air conditioning 675P Sauna Solarium Gym Wkly live entertainment Xmas International Cuisine V meals Coffee am Tea pm No smoking area in restaurant Last d 10.30pm
ROOMS: d £105-£125 **LB**
OFF-PEAK: (incl. bkfst) d £85
MEALS: Lunch £10.50-£16.50&alc High tea £2.50-£10.75 Dinner £15.50-£19.50&alc*
CONF: Thtr 550 Class 450 Board 60 Del from £105
CARDS:

★★★★ 65% **Heathrow Marriott**
Ditton Road, Langley SL3 8PT (from junct 5 of M4/A4, follow 'Langley' signs and turn left at traffic lights into Ditton Road) ☎ 01753 544244 FAX 01753 540272

This is a busy, large hotel ideally placed for travellers, conference delegates and visitors to nearby attractions. It is conveniently located off the M4 and offers a wide range of services, a choice of eating options and an indoor leisure centre. Bedrooms are comfortable and well equipped with the executive rooms offering a little extra quality.
350 en suite (bth/shr) (117 fmly) No smoking in 174 bedrooms CTV in all bedrooms STV No dogs (ex guide dogs) Lift Night porter Air conditioning 500P Indoor swimming pool (heated) Tennis (hard) Sauna Solarium Gym Jacuzzi/spa Beautician Wkly live entertainment Xmas International Cuisine V meals Coffee am Tea pm Last d 10pm
ROOMS: d £94-£110 * **LB**
MEALS: Lunch fr £15.25 Dinner £19.95&alc*
CONF: Thtr 300 Class 150 Board 10 Del from £145
CARDS:

★★★★ 64% **The Excelsior**
Bath Rd UB7 0DU (adj M4 spur at junc with A4)
☎ 0181 759 6611 FAX 0181 759 3421
This very large modern hotel is situated only minutes from the airport. Public areas are extensive and include bars, various shops and travel offices and three places to eat. The hotel also provides good room service, lobby porterage and airport transfer coaches. The smart bedrooms are well equipped and the larger Crown Club rooms have their own lounge and air conditioning.
828 en suite (bth/shr) No smoking in 326 bedrooms CTV in all bedrooms STV Lift Night porter Air conditioning 540P Indoor swimming pool (heated) Sauna Solarium Gym Jacuzzi/spa Health & fitness centre V meals Coffee am Tea pm No smoking area in restaurant Last d 11pm
CARDS:

★★★68% **Heathrow Ambassador**
London Rd, Brands Hill SL3 8QB ☎ 01753 684001
FAX 01753 685767
(For full entry see Slough)

★★★68% **Novotel**

Junction 4 M4, Cherry Ln UB7 9HB
☎ 01895 431431 FAX 01895 431221
This modern hotel has appealing public areas housed within a bright atrium in the centre of the building. The bedrooms are all practically laid out and have recently benefited from a softening and brightening of the décor. The indoor swimming pool and small fitness room add to the appeal for both corporate and leisure users.
178 en suite (bth/shr) (29 fmly) No smoking in 56 bedrooms CTV in all bedrooms STV Lift Night porter 150P Indoor swimming pool (heated) Gym International Cuisine V meals Coffee am Tea pm Last d mndt
ROOMS: d fr £82.50 *
MEALS: Bar Lunch £5-£15alc Dinner £16.50-£30alc*
CONF: Thtr 200 Class 100 Board 50 Del from £106
CARDS:

★★★63% **Master Robert**

Great West Rd TW5 0BD ☎ 0181 570 6261
FAX 0181 569 4016
(For full entry see Hounslow)

★★★55% **Heathrow Park**

Bath Rd UB7 0EQ ☎ 0181 759 2400
FAX 0181 759 5278
Within this surprisingly quiet hotel there are extensive and sizeable meeting facilities. Free use of a nearby health centre has now been provided. There are three styles of bedroom, some of which are better maintained than others. The first-floor restaurant and bar have good views of the airport's western runway.
306 en suite (bth/shr) (55 fmly) No smoking in 70 bedrooms CTV in all bedrooms Night porter Air conditioning 500P Free use of neighbouring Health Club Continental Cuisine V meals Coffee am Tea pm No smoking area in restaurant Last d 10pm
ROOMS: s £85-£99; d £105-£125 * **LB**
OFF-PEAK: d fr £55
MEALS: Lunch fr £13.25&alc High tea £13.25-£24.50alc Dinner fr £16.25&alc*
CONF: Thtr 700 Class 500 Board 30 Del from £125
CARDS:

★★60% **Hotel Ibis**
112/114 Bath Rd UB3 5AL ☎ 0181 759 4888
FAX 0181 564 7894
Competitively priced bedrooms are offered at this large hotel, which is within easy reach of the airport. There is an open plan bar and restaurant and meeting facilities. A shuttle service (at a nominal charge) is provided to the airport.
354 en suite (bth/shr) No smoking in 134 bedrooms CTV in all bedrooms STV Lift 120P International Cuisine V meals Coffee am Tea pm No smoking area in restaurant Last d 10.30pm
ROOMS: d fr £53.50 *
MEALS: Bar Lunch £1.90-£3.95alc Dinner £6.50-£11.50alc*
CONF: Thtr 120 Class 60 Board 44 Del from £80
CARDS:

Forte Posthouse Heathrow
Bath Rd UB3 5AJ (1.5m E junc A4/A437)
☎ 0181 759 2552 FAX 0181 564 9265
Suitable for both the business and leisure traveller, this bright hotel provides modern accommodation in well equipped bedrooms with en suite bathrooms. For more details about Forte Posthouse hotels, consult the Contents page for the section on Hotel Groups.
186 en suite (bth/shr)
ROOMS: s £99; d £99 *
CONF: Thtr 50 Class 25 Board 30 Del from £87

The Radisson Edwardian
Bath Rd UB3 5AW ☎ 0181 759 6311
FAX 0181 759 4559
This stylish, period hotel offers a wide range of services and a choice of eating options for the international traveller. Bedrooms are smart and individually furnished, and are fully equipped with modern facilities.
For more informaation about Radisson Edwardian hotels, consult the Contents page under Hotel Groups.
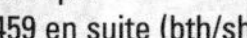
459 en suite (bth/shr)
ROOMS: s £119-£195; d £154-£225 *
CONF: Thtr 320 Class 220 Board 70

Travel Inn
362 Uxbridge Rd UB4 9HF ☎ 0181 573 7479
FAX 0181 569 1204
Purpose-built accommodation, offering spacious, well equipped bedrooms, all with en suite bathrooms. Meals may be taken at the nearby family restaurant. For more information about Travel Inns, consult the Contents page under Hotel Groups.
40 en suite (bth/shr)
ROOMS: d £35.50 *

Travelodge

M4 Service Area, Phoenix Way TW5 9NB
v Central Res 0800 850950 FAX 01384 78578
(For full entry see Heston)

HEBDEN BRIDGE West Yorkshire Map 07 SD92

★★★68% **Carlton**
Albert St HX7 8ES (turn right at cinema for hotel at top of Hope St)
☎ 01422 844400 FAX 01422 843117
This well furnished and comfortable hotel provides spacious and well equipped bedrooms and the public rooms are comfortably furnished. A good range of well produced food is available in the elegant restaurant and service is both professional and friendly.
16 en suite (bth/shr) CTV in all bedrooms STV Lift V meals Coffee am Tea pm No smoking area in restaurant Last d 9.30pm
ROOMS: (incl. bkfst) s fr £49; d £65-£75 * **LB**
MEALS: Lunch £8.95-£9.95 Dinner £9.95&alc*
CONF: Thtr 120 Class 40 Board 40 Del from £72
CARDS:

★★65% ***Hebden Lodge***
New Rd HX7 8AD ☎ 01422 845272 FAX 01422 844233
Situated opposite the Rochdale canal marina, this family-owned hotel is strong on hospitality, which is provided by Layala & Michael Hatfield, the resident owners. The bedrooms are modern and well equipped, whilst the lounge bar has been recently refurbished. A good range of value-for-money food is available in the cosy restaurant.
12 en suite (bth/shr) (1 fmly) CTV in all bedrooms English & Continental Cuisine V meals Coffee am Tea pm Last d 9pm
CARDS:

HECKFIELD Hampshire Map 04 SU76

★★68% **New Inn**
RG27 0LE ☎ 01734 326374 FAX 01734 326550
Closed 25-26 Dec
Parts of this immaculately maintained inn date from the 15th century and it now offers very comfortable bedrooms, which have been furnished and equipped to a high standard. The traditional bar boasts two roaring log fires, low beamed ceilings and a selection of well kept ales; guests have the choice of eating here, or in the cosy restaurant where a good variety of well prepared dishes is served by friendly staff.
16 en suite (bth/shr) CTV in all bedrooms 80P No coaches V meals Coffee am Tea pm No smoking in restaurant
CARDS:

HEDGE END Hampshire Map 04 SU41

★★★ 70% **Botleigh Grange**
SO30 2GA (on A334) ☎ 01489 787700
FAX 01489 788535
Best Western
Standing in well tended grounds, this attractive hotel is conveniently placed for major road links. The bedrooms in the main house include some beautifully furnished deluxe rooms. The restaurant is stylishly decorated and offers an imaginative seasonal menu specialising in some skilfully prepared game and fish dishes. There is a peaceful cocktail lounge featuring a decorative 19th-century ceiling and a bar opening on to the garden terrace.
43 en suite (bth/shr) (3 fmly) CTV in all bedrooms STV Night porter 120P Fishing Putting green Xmas English & French Cuisine V meals Coffee am Tea pm Last d 10pm
ROOMS: (incl. bkfst) s £62-£69; d £82-£92 * **LB**
MEALS: Lunch £8.50-£18.50&alc Dinner £12.50-£18.50&alc*
CONF: Thtr 200 Class 50 Board 30 Del from £70
CARDS:
See advertisement under SOUTHAMPTON

HELLIDON Northamptonshire Map 04 SP55

★★★★ 67% **Hellidon Lakes Hotel & Country Club**
NN11 6LN (signposted, off A361 between Daventry and Banbury)
☎ 01327 262550 FAX 01327 262559
This modern hotel has been built with regard for the superb scenery surrounding it. Mr and Mrs Nicoll, the owners, have landscaped the grounds creating a picturesque 27 holes of golf and, in the process have excavated 12 lakes and planted 27,000 trees. The hotel makes a superb venue for both business and pleasure, with state of the art AV equipment in the many conference rooms, excellent leisure facilities including tennis, and a comprehensive health spa. Bedrooms have recently been extended and all are furnished to a high standard. Guests can choose to dine in the club bar or in the more formal dining room.
45 en suite (bth/shr) CTV in all bedrooms STV No dogs (ex guide dogs) Night porter 140P No coaches Indoor swimming pool (heated) Golf 27 Fishing Solarium Gym Pool table Putting green Jacuzzi/spa Beautician Driving range English & French Cuisine V meals Coffee am Tea pm Last d 9.30pm
ROOMS: (incl. bkfst) s £87.50-£105; d £115-£130 * **LB**
MEALS: Lunch £17.50 High tea fr £6 Dinner £17.50*
CONF: Thtr 150 Class 70 Board 50 Del £117.50
CARDS:

HELMSLEY North Yorkshire Map 08 SE68

★★★ 76% **Black Swan**
Market Place YO6 5BJ (A170) ☎ 01439 770466
FAX 01439 770174
FORTE Heritage
Traditional standards, old fashioned courtesies and very friendly staff are the hallmarks of this long established and well known hotel, which occupies an enviable position overlooking the pretty market square. The attractively decorated bedrooms are all well equipped and reflect the character and history of the building. The more modern rooms overlooking the rear gardens are also attractive. Deep cushioned sofas, fresh flowers and open fires characterise the various lounges. The service in the dining room is professional and attentive and a good choice of dishes carefully prepared by chef Nigel Wright will please most palates.
44 en suite (bth/shr) (4 fmly) No smoking in 13 bedrooms CTV in all bedrooms Night porter 60P Croquet lawn Croquet Xmas V meals Coffee am Tea pm No smoking in restaurant Last d 9pm
ROOMS: s £90; d £115 * **LB**
MEALS: Lunch £11.75-£16 Dinner £26.50&alc
CONF: Thtr 60 Class 16 Board 22 Del from £120
CARDS:

★★★ 70% **Feversham Arms**
1 High St YO6 5AG (on B1363) ☎ 01439 770766
FAX 01439 770346
Best Western
Standing on the site of an older hostelry, this family owned and run hotel dates from 1855 when the Earl of Feversham had it rebuilt. It is now a very comfortable and well furnished hotel providing well equipped and attractive bedrooms together with pleasing public rooms. The Goya restaurant offers a wide-ranging menu, and the bar meals here are also extensive. The hotel stands in well kept grounds which include an outdoor pool and a tennis court. Service is always attentive.
18 en suite (bth/shr) (4 fmly) CTV in all bedrooms STV 30P Outdoor swimming pool (heated) Tennis (hard) English, French & Spanish Cuisine V meals Coffee am No smoking in restaurant Last d 9.30pm
ROOMS: (incl. bkfst) s £55-£65; d £70-£80 **LB**
MEALS: Lunch £12-£20&alc Dinner £20-£28&alc
CONF: Thtr 30 Class 30 Board 24 Del from £90
CARDS:

★★72% **Pheasant**
Harome YO6 5JG (2.5m SE, leave A170 after 0.25m, turn right signposted Harome for further 2m) ☎ 01439 771241
FAX 01439 771744
Closed Xmas & Jan-Feb
The rear of the hotel has a delightful patio which overlooks the duck pond and the well tended gardens. Bedrooms here are really special, being very spacious and very well equipped. A good range of English-

tyle dishes is available, whilst the lounge is warm and inviting with a ood selection of reading matter provided. The hotel is in the capable ands of the Binks family, who are delightfully friendly and caring osts. There is also the benefit of a heated indoor pool.

2 en suite (bth) 2 annexe en suite (bth) CTV in all bedrooms 20P o coaches Indoor swimming pool (heated) No children 12yrs V ıeals Coffee am No smoking in restaurant Last d 8pm
OOMS: (incl. bkfst & dinner) d £119-£130 **LB**
FF-PEAK: (incl. bkfst & dinner) d £104-£116
EALS: Bar Lunch £3.50-£12alc Dinner £19.50*

See advertisement on this page

★★68% **Carlton Lodge**
ondgate YO6 5EY (on the A170 Scarborough road)
☎ 01439 770557 FAX 01439 770623
his attractive stone house stands on the edge of the town on the ickering side featuring a large rear carpark and a function room. The edrooms, some in a modern building to the rear, are bright and esh; several have been recently upgraded to be attractive and better quipped. An interesting evening menu uses the best produce available nd is well cooked and presented. Service is both friendly and ttentive.
rms (6 shr) 4 annexe en suite (bth/shr) (1 fmly) CTV in all edrooms 45P Xmas European Cuisine V meals No smoking in estaurant Last d 9pm
OOMS: (incl. bkfst) s £29.50-£37.50; d £55-£69 * **LB**
FF-PEAK: (incl. bkfst) s £27.50-£37.50; d £52.50-£59
EALS: Lunch £12-£18.75 Dinner £12-£18.75*
ONF: Thtr 150 Class 60 Board 50 Del from £45.50
ARDS:

★68% **Crown**
arket Square YO6 5BJ (on A170) ☎ 01439 770297
his attractive 16th-century inn stands overlooking the market square nd features original beams and open fires. The well equipped edrooms are pleasantly decorated and attractively furnished. A good nge of mainly English food is available with fresh fish as a speciality. ervice is friendly and attentive.
4 rms (12 bth/shr) (1 fmly) CTV in all bedrooms 20P Xmas V eals Coffee am Tea pm Last d 8pm
OOMS: (incl. bkfst) s £30-£35; d £60-£70 **LB**
FF-PEAK: (incl. bkfst) s £28-£32; d £56-£64
EALS: Lunch £9.75-£10.95 High tea £4.95-£7.95
inner £14.95-£16.95*
ARDS:  

★61% **Feathers**
arket Place YO6 5BH ☎ 01439 770275 FAX 01439 771101
osed 23 Dec-3 Jan
is part 15th century creeper-clad hotel standing in the market place s been run by the same family for many years; bedrooms have an d world charm, while the low-beamed bars contain examples of the cal 'mouse man' furniture. This is very much a local pub, and a good nge of food is served both in the bar and a spacious rear dining

room. Service is friendly and helpful, and the hotel has its own car park.
17 rms (6 bth 7 shr) (2 fmly) CTV in all bedrooms 24P English & Continental Cuisine V meals Coffee am Last d 9pm
ROOMS: (incl. bkfst) s £35; d £60 *
OFF-PEAK: (incl. bkfst) s £30; d £50
MEALS: Sunday Lunch £6.75-£8.75 Dinner £4.95-£12alc*
CARDS:

HELSTON Cornwall & Isles of Scilly Map 02 SW62

★★ 76% **Nansloe Manor**
Meneage Rd TR13 0SB (300yds on the left from Helston/Lizard roundabout A394/A3083)

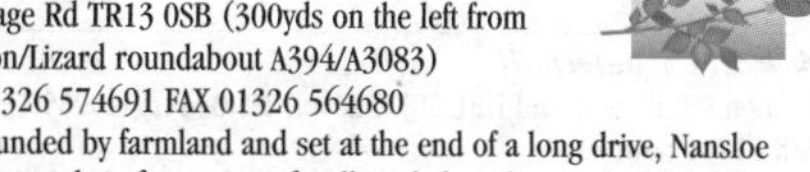

☎ 01326 574691 FAX 01326 564680
Surrounded by farmland and set at the end of a long drive, Nansloe Manor stands in four acres of well tended gardens and wooded grounds. John and Wendy Pyatt's small 18th-century manor house offers individually furnished and decorated bedrooms, each with a country or garden view and equally suited for both business and leisure users. Friendly, relaxed and efficient service is provided by the Pyatts and their team of loyal staff. In the kitchen Martin Jones continues to provide an imaginative daily-changing carte, using fresh local produce whereever possible. Dishes are carefully prepared, retaining the natural flavours and simply presented. At lunchtime a selection of daily special dishes and light meals is available.
7 rms (6 bth/shr) CTV in all bedrooms No dogs (ex guide dogs) 30P No coaches Croquet lawn No children 12yrs English & Continental Cuisine V meals Coffee am No smoking in restaurant Last d 8.30pm
ROOMS: (incl. bkfst) s £48-£60; d £96-£120 **LB**
OFF-PEAK: (incl. bkfst) s £41-£48; d £82-£106
MEALS: Lunch £11.50-£15 Dinner £20-£28alc
CARDS:

★★63% **The Gwealdues**
Falmouth Rd TR13 8JX (on A394)
☎ 01326 572808 & 573331 FAX 01326 561388
This warm, friendly hotel is popular with the commercial clientele. Situated on the outskirts of the town, the hotel has ample car parking facilities. There is an upgrading programme underway for the bedrooms, bring them into the 1990s, and each room is well equipped for the business traveller in mind. A choice of menus is offered in the small dining room, or guests may prefer to eat in the popular bar.
17 rms (15 bth/shr) (5 fmly) CTV in all bedrooms 60P No coaches V meals Coffee am Tea pm No smoking in restaurant Last d 9pm
ROOMS: (incl. bkfst) s £30-£45; d £40-£60 **LB**
MEALS: Dinner fr £12
CONF: Board 100
CARDS:

HEMEL HEMPSTEAD Hertfordshire Map 04 TL00

★★★69% **The Bobsleigh Inn**
Hempstead Rd, Bovingdon HP3 0DS (2m SW off B4505)
☎ 01442 833276 FAX 01442 832471
RS 26 Dec-5 Jan
Over recent years the Bobsleigh Inn has been developed to meet the demands of a well run modern hotel, including a splendid new reception and bar, further lounge seating, and air conditioned conference facilities. These new public rooms supplement the original and more traditionally appointed restaurant, bar and conservatory lounge. The restaurant offers daily and a la carte menus which encompass simpler and more sophisticated cooking of quality fresh ingredients, the meats being supplied locally by the family's own renowned butchers shop. Accommodation styles and sizes vary; the recently added new wing bedrooms offer light spacious rooms with colour co-ordinated soft furnishings, the original bedrooms are, by comparison, more dated but are equally well equipped. Service throughout the hotel is provided in a cheerful and professional manner.
36 en suite (bth/shr) 8 annexe en suite (bth/shr) (5 fmly) No smoking in 4 bedrooms CTV in all bedrooms STV 82P Indoor swimming pool (heated) Pool table Jacuzzi/spa International Cuisine V meals Coffee am Last d 9.30pm
ROOMS: (incl. bkfst) s £50-£80; d £75-£90
OFF-PEAK: (incl. bkfst) s £40-£65; d £55-£80
MEALS: Lunch fr £16.95&alc Dinner fr £19.95&alc
CONF: Thtr 80 Class 40 Board 40 Del from £95
CARDS:

★★★61% ***Watermill***
London Rd, Bourne End HP1 2RJ (Sarova) ☎ 01442 349955
FAX 01442 866130
This friendly hotel stands on the River Bulbourne, just a short distance from the A41 in the village of Bourne End. Accommodation is divided between three purpose-built blocks, the most recently added housing spacious, well furnished rooms with a double and single bed. The main building was created from an old water mill and contains the bar and restaurant.
61 annexe en suite (bth/shr) (4 fmly) No smoking in 20 bedrooms CTV in all bedrooms Night porter 100P Fishing Pool table Games room International Cuisine V meals Coffee am Tea pm Last d 9.45pm
CARDS:

Forte Posthouse Hemel Hempstead

Breakspear Way HP2 4UA (exit junct 8 of M1, straight over roundabout and 1st left after BP garage) ☎ 01442 251122 FAX 01442 211812
Suitable for both the business and leisure traveller, this bright hotel provides modern accommodation in well equipped bedrooms with en suite bathrooms. For more details about Forte Posthouse hotels, consult the Contents page for the section on Hotel Groups.
146 en suite (bth/shr)
ROOMS: s £89; d £89 *
CONF: Thtr 60 Class 22 Board 30 Del from £119

Travel Inn

Stoney Ln, Bourne End HP1 2SB ☎ 01442 879149
FAX 01442 879147
Purpose-built accommodation, offering spacious, well equipped bedrooms, all with en suite bathrooms. Meals may be taken at the nearby family restaurant. For more information about Travel Inns, consult the Contents page under Hotel Groups.
60 en suite (bth/shr)
ROOMS: d £35.50 *

HENLEY-ON-THAMES Oxfordshire Map 04 SU78
See also Stonor

★★★70% **Red Lion**
Hart St RG9 2AR (adjacent to Henley Bridge) ☎ 01491 572161
FAX 01491 410039
This 16th-century, red brick and ivy clad coaching in is enviably situated beside the River Thames, over looking the famous Royal Regatta Course. Family owned, and operated by a team of friendly staff the public areas, with wood panelling and flag stoned floors, are full o character and have been comfortably furnished in a style in-keeping with the old building. Bedrooms have been tastefully refurbished and equipped to a high standard; many enjoy views of the river. The attractive Regatta brasserie has introduced a more relaxed style of dining, where a short a la carte menu offers an interesting selection of freshly prepared dishes ranging from lighter snacks to more substantial main meals.
26 rms (23 bth/shr) (1 fmly) CTV in all bedrooms No dogs Night porter 25P No coaches English & French Cuisine V meals Coffee am Tea pm Last d 10pm
ROOMS: s £49-£79; d £99-£115 * **LB**
MEALS: Lunch £3.95-£25alc High tea £2-£11.50alc Dinner £3.95-£25alc*
CONF: Thtr 60 Class 20 Board 30 Del from £135
CARDS:

HEREFORD Hereford & Worcester Map 03 SO54
See also Much Birch

★★★67% **Three Counties Hotel**
Belmont Rd HR2 7BP (on A465 Abergavveny Rd) ☎ 01432 299955
FAX 01432 275114
This is a modern commercial hotel providing spacious and well furnished accommodation. Bedrooms are bright and cheery with pretty decor and matching fabrics used to good effect. Many are located in a nearby annexe building and these are equally well maintained and equipped. Good function and conference facilities are provided and spacious public rooms include an attractive foyer lounge area and a well equipped bar. Food comes by way of a fixed-price menu with many extras.
28 en suite (bth/shr) 32 annexe en suite (bth/shr) (4 fmly) No smoking in 23 bedrooms CTV in all bedrooms Night porter 250P Xmas International Cuisine V meals Coffee am Tea pm Last d 9.30pm
ROOMS: (incl. bkfst) s £52-£59.50; d £68.50-£78.50 **LB**
OFF-PEAK: (incl. bkfst & dinner) s fr £36.50; d fr £73
MEALS: Lunch fr £15.50 Dinner fr £15.50*
CONF: Thtr 300 Class 100 Board 60 Del from £75
CARDS:

★★★62% **Belmont Lodge & Golf Course**
Belmont HR2 9SA (off A465, signposted Ruckhall Lane)
☎ 01432 352666 FAX 01432 358090
This hotel and golfing complex occupies a superb location on the slopes above the River Wye. It is about a mile from the city centre via he A465 road to Abergavenny. The modern, well equipped bedrooms are located on the ground and first floors of a purpose built lodge and amily rooms are available. The restaurant and bar are located in the lubhouse, which is on the ground floor of the Grade II listed Belmont House. In addition to the golf course, sporting activities include nooker, coarse and salmon fishing, an all weather tennis court and a owling green.
30 en suite (bth/shr) (4 fmly) CTV in all bedrooms Night porter 150P Golf 18 Tennis (hard) Fishing Snooker Putting green Bowls Darts English & French Cuisine V meals Coffee am Tea pm ast d 9.30pm
ROOMS: (incl. bkfst) s £44.50; d £59.50 * **LB**
MEALS: Lunch £3-£10alc Dinner fr £13&alc*
CONF: Thtr 60 Class 14 Board 25 Del from £64.50
CARDS:

★★★62% **The Green Dragon**

FORTE Heritage

Broad St HR4 9BG (follow signs for city centre (west) and enter one-way system. Hotel situated in Broad Street on right-hand side) ☎ 01432 272506
FAX 01432 352139
This historical hotel is situated in the city centre close to the Cathedral and on market days visitors throng to its comfortable lounges for sumptuous afternoon teas. Bedrooms have recently been upgraded to a modern, but traditional style and some have four-poster beds. In summer the front of the hotel is distinguishable by its attractive hanging flower baskets. Car parking is at the rear.
87 en suite (bth/shr) No smoking in 29 bedrooms CTV in all bedrooms Lift Night porter 160P N Xmas V meals Coffee am Tea pm No smoking in restaurant Last d 9.30pm
ROOMS: s £65-£75; d £75-£85 **LB**
MEALS: Lunch £11.95-£20.95&alc Dinner £18.95-£20.95&alc*
CONF: Thtr 200 Class 80 Board 50 Del from £90
CARDS:

★★66% **Ancient Camp Inn**
HR2 9QX ☎ 01981 250449 FAX 01981 251581
(For full entry see Ruckhall)

★★64% **Merton Hotel & Governors Restaurant**
28 Commercial Rd HR1 2BD (on main A4103) ☎ 01432 265925
FAX 01432 354983
This privately-owned hotel stands on the A456 close to the city centre, is well equipped modern accommodation including a small suite on the ground floor of an annexe building. The restaurant is pleasant and the lounge and lounge bar are comfortably furnished. There is a car park, but it is difficult to find and directions should be sought before arrival.
19 en suite (bth/shr) (2 fmly) CTV in all bedrooms 25P Sauna Solarium Gym Shooting & fishing by arrangement V meals Coffee am Tea pm
ROOMS: (incl. bkfst) s £40-£45; d £60-£70 **LB**
OFF-PEAK: (incl. bkfst) s £35-£40; d £50-£55
CARDS:

★★63% **Castle Pool**
Castle St HR1 2NR (next to Cathedral) ☎ 01432 356321
FAX 01432 356321
This privately owned hotel dates back to 1850 and was once the residence of the Bishop of Hereford. It is situated close to the Cathedral but can best be located by following the signs for the General Hospital. It provides modern equipped accommodation, which includes family rooms and rooms with four-poster beds. Facilities include a room for small meetings and a pleasant garden.
26 en suite (bth/shr) (3 fmly) CTV in all bedrooms 14P International Cuisine V meals Coffee am Tea pm Last d 9.30pm
ROOMS: (incl. bkfst) s £35-£50; d £55-£70 * **LB**
MEALS: Lunch fr £8.25&alc Dinner fr £15&alc
CONF: Thtr 40 Class 30 Board 25 Del from £50
CARDS:

★★60% ***Munstone House Country***
Munstone HR1 3AH (signposted off A4103, E of A49)
☎ 01432 267122
A small friendly hotel positioned on the outskirts of the town is set back within its own grounds. It provides spacious, well equipped bedrooms and comfortable lounges, with a popular restaurant offering a good choice of food.
6 en suite (bth/shr) CTV in all bedrooms 50P No coaches V meals Coffee am Tea pm Last d 9.30pm
CARDS:

Travel Inn

Holmer Rd, Holmer HR4 9RS (on A49 towards Leominster) ☎ 01432 274853 FAX 01432 343003
Purpose-built accommodation, offering spacious, well equipped bedrooms, all with en suite bathrooms. Meals may be taken at the nearby family restaurant. For more information about Travel Inns, consult the Contents page under Hotel Groups.
40 en suite (bth/shr)
ROOMS: d £35.50 *

HERSTMONCEUX East Sussex Map 05 TQ61

★★★64% **White Friars**

Best Western

Boreham St BN27 4SE (2m E on A271)
☎ 01323 832355 FAX 01323 833882
Parts of this friendly hotel date back to the late 15th century when it is believed to have been a medieval hall. Today it is a family run establishment with some charming members of staff who provide caring levels of service. Bedrooms vary in size and they are slowly adopting a family country style and atmosphere. The restaurant produces carefully prepared meals such as chicken and asparagus mousse followed by pork fillet served with prunes and pine nuts.
12 en suite (bth/shr) 8 annexe en suite (bth) (3 fmly) CTV in all bedrooms Night porter 60P English & French Cuisine V meals Coffee am Tea pm Last d 9.30pm
MEALS: Lunch £10.50-£11.50alc Dinner fr £17.95alc*
CONF: Thtr 40 Class 25 Board 30
CARDS:

★★62% **Horse Shoe Inn**
Windmill Hill BN27 4RU (on A271) ☎ 01323 833265
FAX 01323 832001
This striking mock-Elizabethan village inn is conveniently located off the main road. Levels of comfort in the bedrooms are sound, and the hotel obviously has a lot of guests. There is a spacious restaurant and a choice of two bars as well as a large function room.
13 en suite (bth/shr) CTV in all bedrooms 100P Pool table English Cuisine V meals Coffee am Tea pm No smoking in restaurant Last d 10pm
ROOMS: s £30-£35; d £30-£35 * **LB**
OFF-PEAK: s £25; d £25
MEALS: Lunch £14-£18 High tea £7 Dinner £18
CARDS:

For the key to symbols and abbreviations, please see the bookmark inside the back cover

H

HERTFORD Hertfordshire Map 04 TL31

★★★63% **White Horse**

FORTE Heritage

Hertingfordbury SG14 2LB (1m W on A414)
☎ 01992 586791 FAX 01992 550809
Situated in the quaint and peaceful village of Hertingfordbury, on the outskirts of town, this former coaching Inn has a Georgian facade which actually belies a much older interior. Most of the bedrooms are found in the modern addition, they are generously sized and have the comforts of easy chairs and good showers. The restaurant looks onto a lovely lawn where afternoon tea and drinks can be enjoyed on fine days and the beamed lounge bar is furnished with chintzy fabrics, adding to the country atmosphere.
42 en suite (bth/shr) No smoking in 14 bedrooms CTV in all bedrooms Night porter 60P Xmas V meals Coffee am Tea pm No smoking in restaurant Last d 9.30pm
ROOMS: s £75; d £95 * **LB**
MEALS: Lunch £11.25-£16.95 Dinner £15.95-£17.95
CONF: Thtr 60 Class 30 Board 30 Del £100
CARDS:

HESLEDEN Co Durham Map 08 NZ43

★★69% ***Hardwicke Hall Manor***
TS27 4PA (NE on B1281, off A19) ☎ 01429 836326
FAX 01429 837676
This impressive mansion is now a comfortable hotel owned and run by the Bradley family. Bedrooms are especially well equipped and delightfully furnished, whilst the public rooms are very relaxing. The hotel is particularly popular for its value-for-money meals, especially at lunch times when a carvery is in operation.
11 en suite (bth/shr) (2 fmly) CTV in all bedrooms 50P English & French Cuisine V meals Coffee am Tea pm Last d 9.30pm
CARDS:

HESTON MOTORWAY SERVICE AREA (M4) Greater London
See LONDON SECTION plan 1 A3

Travelodge

M4 Service Area, Phoenix Way TW5 9NB
☎ Central Res 0800 850950 FAX 01384 78578
This modern building offers accommodation in smart, spacious and well equipped bedrooms, suitable for family use, and all with en suite bathrooms. Meals may be taken at the nearby family restaurant. For information on room rates and to make a booking, call Roomline free of charge on 0800 850950. For more details about Travelodge, consult the Contents page under Hotel Groups.
72 en suite (bth/shr)

HESWALL Merseyside Map 07 SJ28

Travel Inn

Chester Rd, Heswall L60 3SD ☎ 0151 342 1982
FAX 0151 342 8983
Purpose-built accommodation, offering spacious, well equipped bedrooms, all with en suite bathrooms. Meals may be taken at the nearby family restaurant. For more information about Travel Inns, consult the Contents page under Hotel Groups.
37 en suite (bth/shr)
ROOMS: d £35.50 *

HETHERSETT Norfolk Map 05 TG10

★★★❀70% **Park Farm**
NR9 3DL (5m S of Norwich, off A11 on B1172) ☎ 01603 810264
FAX 01603 812104
Park Farm lies in a secluded setting surrounded by pasture farmland and mature gardens; it is now a modern hotel that has evolved from the existing Georgian farmhouse. Individually-styled bedrooms are available in the main house and garden annexes; each is thoughtfully equipped and most are decorated with good use of bold rich colour schemes through co-ordinated soft furnishings and décor. The extensively redeveloped public rooms are smart and well maintained; the extensive modern health and leisure facilities prove to be very popular.
6 en suite (bth/shr) 32 annexe en suite (bth/shr) (10 fmly) No smoking in 28 bedrooms CTV in all bedrooms No dogs (ex guide dogs) Night porter 151P Indoor swimming pool (heated) Tennis (hard) Sauna Solarium Gym Croquet lawn Putting green Jacuzzi/spa Xmas English & French Cuisine V meals Coffee am Tea pm No smoking in restaurant Last d 9pm
ROOMS: (incl. bkfst) s £65-£95; d £100-£130 **LB**
OFF-PEAK: (incl. bkfst) s £60-£90
MEALS: Lunch £11.75 High tea £5.50 Dinner £16.50&alc
CONF: Thtr 120 Class 50 Board 50 Del from £97.50
CARDS:
See advertisement under NORWICH

HEVERSHAM Cumbria Map 07 SD48

★★★65% **Blue Bell**
Prince's Way LA7 7EE (1m N of Milnthorpe, on A6) ☎ 015395 62018
FAX 015395 62455
This 15th-century vicarage has the feel of an old coaching inn yet provides modern, well equipped accommodation. Public areas are traditional and include a restaurant, a lounge, and an olde worlde bar featuring a wide selection of food.
21 en suite (bth/shr) (4 fmly) CTV in all bedrooms Night porter 100P Pool table Xmas English Cuisine V meals Coffee am Tea pm No smoking in restaurant Last d 9.30pm
ROOMS: (incl. bkfst) s £39.50-£42.50; d £64-£85 **LB**
MEALS: Lunch £9.50-£11.50&alc High tea £8.95 Dinner £18.50
CONF: Thtr 85 Class 35 Board 25 Del from £65
CARDS:

HEXHAM Northumberland Map 12 NY96

★★★❀66% **Beaumont**

Best Western

Beaumont St NE46 3LT (on A69 towards Hexham)
☎ 01434 602331 FAX 01434 602331
Closed 25-26 Dec & 1 Jan
Popular with both business guests and tourists, the Beaumont overlooks the park in the town centre. Its bright cheery bedrooms are well equipped; there are two bars, a relaxing foyer lounge and a first-floor restaurant featuring well presented and innovative dishes.
23 en suite (bth/shr) (1 fmly) No smoking in 15 bedrooms CTV in all bedrooms STV No dogs Lift Night porter 8P Snooker Solarium Gym International Cuisine V meals Coffee am Tea pm No smoking in restaurant Last d 9.45pm
ROOMS: s £50-£53; d £72-£75 **LB**
MEALS: Lunch £3-£15alc Dinner £18.95&alc
CONF: Thtr 100 Class 60 Board 40
CARDS:

★★62% **County**
Priestpopple NE46 1PS (follow town centre sign from A69 and cross two bridges. Turn sharp left and follow road round in right hand loop for 0.5m) ☎ 01434 602030 FAX 01434 603202
Noticeable by its creeper-clad façade in summer, this hotel lies on the main street at the eastern end of the town. Bedrooms are well equipped and as well as a wide choice of dinner and bar menus, one can also enjoy traditional high tea.
9 en suite (bth/shr) (3 fmly) CTV in all bedrooms Night porter 2P Xmas International Cuisine V meals Coffee am Tea pm No smoking area in restaurant Last d 9pm

ROOMS: (incl. bkfst) s £42-£42; d £55-£65 * **LB**
OFF-PEAK: (incl. bkfst) s £38-£38; d £55-£55
MEALS: Lunch fr £6.95 Dinner £10.95-£12&alc
CONF: Thtr 80 Class 50 Board 60 Del from £75
CARDS:

HEYWOOD Greater Manchester Map 07 SD81

★★61% **The Albany**
87/89 Rochdale Rd East OL10 1PX ☎ 01706 369606
FAX 01706 627914
Hospitality is a strength of this popular, family-owned and run hotel, which is conveniently situated on the Rochdale road. The hotel itself consists of two separate properties, one housing reception, the other a lounge bar, cosy dining room and a function room. The neatly furnished bedrooms are divided between the two buildings.
9 rms (5 shr) 10 annexe en suite (shr) (1 fmly) CTV in all bedrooms 50P Xmas English Spanish & Italian Cuisine V meals Coffee am Tea pm Last d 10pm
ROOMS: (incl. bkfst) s £23.50-£35 *
MEALS: Lunch £6.95-£11.50&alc Dinner £6.95-£10.95&alc*
CONF: Thtr 120 Class 100 Board 80
CARDS:

HICKSTEAD West Sussex Map 04 TQ22

★★★64% ***Hickstead***
Jobs Ln, Bolney RH17 5PA (0.25m E of A23 turn off at Hickstead village towards Burgess Hill) ☎ 01444 248023 FAX 01444 245280
Convenient yet quietly located off the A23, this hotel enjoys a remote rural location and is popular for residential conferences and weekend breaks. Modern comfortable and well equipped bedrooms tend to compensate for the more restrictive public lounges. The health club has a small heated swimming pool and good car parking is available.
50 en suite (bth/shr) (8 fmly) No smoking in 5 bedrooms CTV in all bedrooms STV Night porter 150P Indoor swimming pool (heated) Fishing Sauna Solarium Gym Jacuzzi/spa English & Continental Cuisine V meals Coffee am Tea pm Last d 10pm
CARDS:

Travelodge
Travelodge
Jobs Ln RH17 5NX (A23) ☎ 01444 881377
FAX 01444 881377
This modern building offers accommodation in smart, spacious and well equipped bedrooms, suitable for family use, and all with en suite bathrooms. Meals may be taken at the nearby family restaurant. For information on room rates and to make a booking, call Roomline free of charge on 0800 850950. For more details about Travelodge, consult the Contents page under Hotel Groups.
40 en suite (bth/shr)

HIGHBRIDGE Somerset Map 03 ST34

★★63% **Sundowner**
74 Main Road, West Huntspill TA9 3QU (1m S on A38)
☎ 01278 784766 FAX 01278 784766
The friendly owners are very involved with the day to day running of this hotel. Bedrooms are simply furnished and soundly equipped, meeting the needs of both the business and the leisure traveller. The spacious open-plan bar-lounge areas have an informal atmosphere, and bar meals are readily available in addition to the extensive · la carte menu served in the popular restaurant.
8 en suite (bth/shr) (1 fmly) CTV in all bedrooms 24P English & French Cuisine V meals Coffee am Last d 8pm
ROOMS: (incl. bkfst) s £32-£36; d £42-£48 * **LB**
MEALS: Lunch £8.95-£12.45&alc Dinner £8.95-£12.45&alc*
CONF: Thtr 40 Class 24 Board 24 Del from £59.95
CARDS:

HIGHER BURWARDSLEY Cheshire Map 07 SJ55

★★66% **Pheasant Inn**

CH3 9PF (follow signs 'Cheshire Workshops')
☎ 01829 770434 FAX 01829 771097
Originally a farmhouse, this 300-year-old half-timbered sandstone building is situated on top of the Peckforton Hills. Much of the original character has been retained, enhanced by antique furniture and bric-à-brac. Most of the bedrooms are in the cleverly converted sandstone barn and include some ground-floor rooms. The inn, popular with locals for its bar meals, also has a beer garden.
2 en suite (bth/shr) 8 annexe en suite (bth/shr) (1 fmly) No smoking in 4 bedrooms CTV in all bedrooms No dogs (ex guide dogs) 60P No coaches Xmas English & French Cuisine V meals Coffee am Tea pm
ROOMS: (incl. bkfst) s £45; d £70-£80 * **LB**
MEALS: Bar Lunch £8-£15 Dinner £12.50-£15*
CARDS:

HIGH WYCOMBE Buckinghamshire Map 04 SU89

Forte Posthouse High Wycombe
FORTE Posthouse
Handy Cross HP11 1TL (intersection of M40 and A4010) ☎ 01494 442100 FAX 01494 439071
Suitable for both the business and leisure traveller, this bright hotel provides modern accommodation in well equipped bedrooms with en suite bathrooms. For more details about Forte Posthouse hotels, consult the Contents page for the section on Hotel Groups.
106 en suite (bth/shr)

Travel Inn

Thanestead Farm, London Rd, Loudwater
☎ 01582 414341 FAX 01582 400024
Purpose-built accommodation, offering spacious, well equipped bedrooms, all with en suite bathrooms. Meals may be taken at the nearby family restaurant. For more information about Travel Inns, consult the Contents page under Hotel Groups.
40 en suite (bth/shr)
ROOMS: (incl. bkfst) d £35.50 *

HILLINGDON Greater London Map 04 TQ08

★★★63% **Master Brewer**
Freezeland Way UB10 9NX ☎ 01895 251199 FAX 01895 810330
Ideally located for easy access to central London and Heathrow airport, this popular hotel is located off the A40 in the centre of Hillingdon. The modern bedrooms, overlooking a central garden, are well designed and particularly well equipped. The main hotel comprises reception, lobby lounge, busy bar, and the Barley Head Restaurant and Banqueting Suite which can accommodate up to 200 persons for all kinds of functions. There are also three additional meeting rooms.
106 en suite (bth/shr) (22 fmly) No smoking in 8 bedrooms CTV in all bedrooms STV Night porter 200P ch fac European Cuisine V meals Coffee am Tea pm No smoking area in restaurant Last d 10pm
ROOMS: s £85-£95; d £85-£95 * **LB**
OFF-PEAK: s £45; d £45
MEALS: Lunch £8.50-£20alc Dinner £8.50-£20alc*
CONF: Thtr 200 Class 100 Board 46 Del from £98.50
CARDS:

HILLINGTON Norfolk Map 09 TF72

★★67% **Ffolkes Arms**
Lynn Rd PE31 6BJ (on main A148) ☎ 01485 600210
FAX 01485 601196

contd.

An attractive coaching inn which lies beside the A148 eight miles from Kings Lynn and two miles from the Royal Estate at Sandringham, recently extended to offer enhanced reception and lounge facilities which complement a busy bar and restaurant operation. Bedrooms are housed in a modern adjacent accommodation wing; these rooms are quite spacious and well equipped.
20 annexe en suite (bth/shr) (2 fmly) CTV in all bedrooms No dogs (ex guide dogs) 200P Snooker Pool table Xmas English Italian & French Cuisine V meals Coffee am Tea pm Last d 9.45pm
ROOMS: (incl. bkfst) s £29-£32; d £45-£65 * **LB**
MEALS: Lunch £10.50-£15.95&alc High tea £5.25-£6.95 Dinner £10.50-£15.95&alc
CONF: Thtr 250 Class 80 Board 50 Del from £53
CARDS: 

HILTON PARK MOTORWAY SERVICE AREA (M6)
West Midlands Map 07 SJ90

Travelodge
Hilton Park Services (M6), Essington WV11 2DR (on M6 between juncts 10a & 11) ☎ 01922 414100 FAX 01922 701967
Travelodge
This modern building offers accommodation in smart, spacious and well equipped bedrooms, suitable for family use, and all with en suite bathrooms. Meals may be taken at the nearby family restaurant. For information on room rates and to make a booking, call Roomline free of charge on 0800 850950. For more details about Travelodge, consult the Contents page under Hotel Groups.
64 en suite (bth/shr)

HIMLEY Staffordshire Map 07 SO89

★★★60% **Himley Country Hotel**
School Rd DY3 4LG (100yds off A449)
☎ 01902 896716 FAX 01902 896668
REGAL A Collection of Individual Hotels
A modern hotel which has been built around the old village school with the schoolroom now the main restaurant. The recently refurbished lounge bar also has a school theme with old framed photographs and sporting equipment adorning the walls. Bedrooms are modern and functional and one contains a four-poster bed.
73 en suite (bth/shr) (1 fmly) No smoking in 30 bedrooms CTV in all bedrooms STV No dogs (ex guide dogs) Night porter 100P Xmas V meals Coffee am Tea pm No smoking in restaurant Last d 9.30pm
ROOMS: s £64; d £75 * **LB**
OFF-PEAK: (incl. bkfst) s fr £35; d fr £45
MEALS: Lunch £5-£20 Dinner fr £11*
CONF: Thtr 150 Class 70 Board 50 Del from £95
CARDS: 

HINCKLEY Leicestershire Map 04 SP49

★★★73% **Sketchley Grange**
Sketchley Ln, Burbage LE10 3HU (SE of town, off A5)
☎ 01455 251133 FAX 01455 631384
Best Western
In a quiet setting amongst its own landscaped gardens, this extended country house stands on the edge of the old village of Sketchley just minutes from the M69 and midlands motorway network. Bedrooms range from the luxurious to the inexpensive and offer good facilities for business people. The grange bar has the ambience of the English county pub while the atmosphere in the willow Restaurant is more formal and the perfect setting for the very competent cooking of Colin Bliss and his team.

38 en suite (bth/shr) (9 fmly) No smoking in 6 bedrooms CTV in all bedrooms STV Night porter 200P Wkly live entertainment English & French Cuisine V meals Coffee am Tea pm No smoking in restaurant

ROOMS: (incl. bkfst) s £79.50-£82.50; d £94.50-£97.50 * **LB**
OFF-PEAK: (incl. bkfst) s £37-£39; d £62-£86
CONF: Thtr 300 Class 150 Board 50 Del from £115
CARDS:
See advertisement under LEICESTER

★★69% **Kings Hotel & Restaurant**
13/19 Mount Rd LE10 1AD (follow A447 signposted to Hinckley. Under railway bridge and turn right at roundabout. First road left opposite railway station and then third right) ☎ 01455 637193 FAX 01455 636201
This hotel is quietly situated near the town centre among properties dating from the 1930s. A warm and friendly atmosphere is created by the resident proprietors who have a good sense of humour. The snug, cosy bar leads on to the striking restaurant which is both Colonial and Victorian, with fringed low lamps hanging over the tables and elaborately swagged windows; the oak fire, carved with cherubs, is a conversation piece. Bedrooms are more restrained, though equally comfortable and provided with some thoughtful extras.
7 en suite (bth/shr) No smoking in all bedrooms CTV in all bedrooms No dogs (ex guide dogs) 13P English, French & Hungarian Cuisine V meals Coffee am Last d 9.30pm
ROOMS: (incl. bkfst) s £49.50-£59.50; d £59.50-£69.50 * **LB**
MEALS: Lunch £5.90-£14.95&alc Dinner £14.90-£19.90&alc*
CONF: Thtr 40 Class 30 Board 24 Del from £65
CARDS: 

HINDON Wiltshire Map 03 ST93

★★71% **Lamb at Hindon**
SP3 6DP (1m from A303 & A350) ☎ 01747 820573 FAX 01747 820605
MINOTEL Great Britain
This stone-built free house stands in the picturesque village of Hindon, close to the A303, with easy access to Salisbury and Bath. The hotel has tradition for warm hospitality. Bedrooms retain a pleasing element of simplicity, but are comfortably furnished, with modern facilities. Public areas include popular bars full of character, a quiet residents' lounge and two attractive dining rooms. A selection of interesting dishes is offered on the fixed-price menu, and there is always a sophisticated choice of bar snacks from the blackboard menus. The food is freshly cooked, making use of local meat and game in season.
12 en suite (bth/shr) CTV in all bedrooms 26P Fishing Shooting Xmas English & French Cuisine V meals Coffee am Tea pm No smoking in restaurant Last d 9.30pm
ROOMS: (incl. bkfst) s £43-£55; d £55-£65 * **LB**
MEALS: Lunch £8.95-£20 Dinner £18.95-£18.95*
CONF: Thtr 35 Class 30 Board 20 Del from £57.50
CARDS: 

HINTLESHAM Suffolk Map 05 TM04

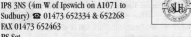

RED STAR HOTEL

★★★★ ®®® Hintlesham Hall

IP8 3NS (4m W of Ipswich on A1071 to Sudbury) ☎ 01473 652334 & 652268
FAX 01473 652463
RS Sat

Despite its Georgian façade, this is a typical Elizabethan example of a country house (built in 1578). It is set in 170 acres of parkland with recommended walking trails and a golf course. It also has a leisure centre which is linked to the club house. The hotel has magnificent public rooms including a lofty dining room, a warmly decorated book-lined library and a pine-panelled parlour which is occasionally used as a second dining room. Bedrooms, which are quietly elegant, are distributed between the main building and an adjoining converted stable block. The kitchen, under chef Alan Ford, produces resoundingly successful classical food, known for its richness and precision of execution. The game season brings out the best in the kitchen but one wonders whether some lightness could be introduced as a concession to healthier eating.

33 en suite (bth/shr) (1 fmly) CTV in all bedrooms Night porter 100P No coaches Outdoor swimming pool (heated) Golf 18 Tennis (hard) Fishing Riding Snooker Sauna Solarium Gym Croquet lawn Putting green Jacuzzi/spa Clay & game shooting Xmas English & French Cuisine V meals No smoking in restaurant Last d 9.30pm
ROOMS: (incl. cont bkfst) s £89-£105; d £110-£300 * **LB**
MEALS: Lunch fr £18.50&alc Dinner fr £24&alc*
CONF: Thtr 80 Class 50 Board 32 Del from £165
CARDS:

HINTON CHARTERHOUSE Somerset Map 03 ST75

RED STAR HOTEL

★★★ ®®® Homewood Park

BA3 6BB (between A36 & village) ☎ 01225 723731
FAX 01225 723820

A delightfully unassuming yet stylish Georgian house, Homewood Park is set in ten acres of grounds and gardens, approached by a long drive just off the A36. Owned by the Fentum family, the daily management is in the hands of daughter and son-in-law Sara and Frank Gueuning, suitably backed by a small Anglo-French team of staff. Bedrooms are attractively furnished and provided with many extra personal touches. The public rooms combine classical furnishings with a comfortable lived-in feel. Chef Stephen Morey offers well balanced, carefully prepared menus. Our inspector sampled a double-baked cheese soufflé with a ragoût of Cornish fish in a creamy sauce, followed by guinea fowl filled with chervil mousse on a port wine sauce. Dessert, a delicately flavoured butterscotch tart and a brandysnap basket full of banana ice cream, served with a rich butterscotch sauce and hot banana fritters, was the highlight of the meal.

19 en suite (bth/shr) (2 fmly) CTV in all bedrooms STV No dogs 30P No coaches Outdoor swimming pool (heated) Tennis (hard) Croquet lawn Xmas English & French Cuisine V meals Coffee am Tea pm No smoking in restaurant Last d 9.30pm
ROOMS: (incl. bkfst) s £95-£180; d £98-£190 **LB**
MEALS: Lunch fr £21&alc Dinner fr £35&alc
CONF: Thtr 35 Class 30 Board 25 Del from £155
CARDS:

HITCHIN Hertfordshire Map 04 TL12

★★★ 63% **Blakemore Thistle**

Blakemore End Rd, Little Wymondley SG4 7JJ (3m SE A602)
☎ 01438 355821 FAX 01438 742114

A range of function and meeting rooms is provided at this well established hotel, located in six acres of landscaped grounds. Bedrooms are well looked after and are sensibly laid out, and there is an informally arranged bar-lounge adjoining the dining room. The hotel has a mini-bus for local shuttles.

82 en suite (bth/shr) (6 fmly) No smoking in 23 bedrooms CTV in all bedrooms STV Lift Night porter 200P Outdoor swimming pool (heated) Croquet lawn Boule Xmas International Cuisine V meals Coffee am Tea pm Last d 9.45pm
ROOMS: s fr £75; d fr £85 * **LB**
MEALS: Lunch £15.95&alc High tea £3-£6 Dinner £18.95&alc*

contd.

CONF: Thtr 180 Class 80 Board 40
CARDS:

HOCKLEY HEATH West Midlands Map 07 SP17

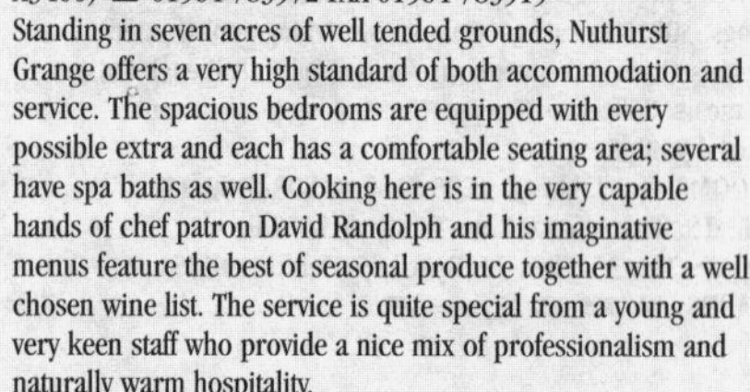

★★★ **Nuthurst Grange Country House**
Nuthurst Grange Ln B94 5NL (0.5m S on A3400) ☎ 01564 783972 FAX 01564 783919
Standing in seven acres of well tended grounds, Nuthurst Grange offers a very high standard of both accommodation and service. The spacious bedrooms are equipped with every possible extra and each has a comfortable seating area; several have spa baths as well. Cooking here is in the very capable hands of chef patron David Randolph and his imaginative menus feature the best of seasonal produce together with a well chosen wine list. The service is quite special from a young and very keen staff who provide a nice mix of professionalism and naturally warm hospitality.
15 en suite (bth/shr) (2 fmly) CTV in all bedrooms STV No dogs (ex guide dogs) Night porter 56P No coaches Croquet lawn Helipad English & French Cuisine V meals Coffee am Tea pm No smoking in restaurant Last d 9.30pm
ROOMS: (incl. cont bkfst) s fr £95; d £115-£140 * **LB**
MEALS: Lunch £16.90-£24.90 Dinner £24.90-£42.50*
CONF: Thtr 100 Class 50 Board 45 Del from £149
CARDS:

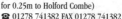

★★★59% **Aylesbury House**
Aylesbury Rd B94 6PL (turn off A3400 left just before Nags Head into Aylesbury Rd, hotel 0.50m along on left after sharp right hand bend)
☎ 01564 779207 FAX 01564 770917
This former manor house, parts of which were built at the time of the Stuarts, stands in 12 acres of grounds and gardens yet is within easy reach of the M42. Most of the bedrooms are contained in a separate building at the rear and, though not over-large, have every modern facility. Rooms in the main building are more spacious. The Mulberry Restaurant overlooks the lawn and a historically interesting beamed bar has lots of character. The hotel has its own self-contained conference centre.
6 en suite (bth/shr) 28 annexe en suite (bth/shr) (5 fmly) CTV in all bedrooms STV Night porter 50P Croquet lawn Putting green Xmas V meals Coffee am No smoking in restaurant Last d 9.30pm
ROOMS: (incl. bkfst) s fr £70; d fr £85 * **LB**
OFF-PEAK: (incl. bkfst & dinner) s fr £37.50; d fr £75
MEALS: Lunch £12.50-£19.25&alc Dinner £12.50-£19.25&alc*
CONF: Thtr 80 Class 36 Board 32 Del £95
CARDS:

HODNET Shropshire Map 07 SJ62

★★67% **Bear**
TF9 3NH ☎ 01630 685214 FAX 01630 685787
This 16th-century coaching inn is situated at the junction of the A53 and the A552 and lies in a pretty village. It has built up a fine local reputation for its food with a wide range of good-value bar meals in addition to the more formal restaurant choice. The bar features exposed timbers and also log fires in the colder weather, and staff are young and very friendly. A Baronial style function suite is available and there is large car park. Bedrooms are fresh and modern and two have four-poster beds for that special occasion.
6 en suite (bth/shr) CTV in all bedrooms No dogs (ex guide dogs) 100P Ten-pin & Skittles to order Xmas International Cuisine V meals Coffee am Tea pm No smoking area in restaurant Last d 9.45pm
ROOMS: (incl. bkfst) s £30.50-£32.50; d £50-£55 * **LB**
MEALS: Lunch £5-£18alc Dinner £10-£20alc*
CONF: Thtr 100 Class 50 Board 40
CARDS:

HOLFORD Somerset Map 03 ST14

★★ 71% **Combe House**
TA5 1RZ (from A39 in Holford take lane between garage and Plough Inn, bear left at fork and continue for 0.25m to Holford Combe)
☎ 01278 741382 FAX 01278 741382
Closed Nov-mid March
Beautifully set in three acres of mature grounds and gardens among the Quantock Hills, this converted tannery (complete with water wheel) provides traditional hospitality and accommodation in comfortable, well equipped bedrooms in a variety of sizes; there are also a choice of lounges, a cosy bar and an attractive dining room serving good home-cooked meals - whilst the more health-conscious will appreciate the useful little indoor swimming pool, sauna and solarium in the grounds.
16 en suite (bth/shr) 3 annexe rms (1 bth) (2 fmly) CTV in all bedrooms 15P No coaches Indoor swimming pool (heated) Tennis (hard) Sauna Solarium European Cuisine Coffee am Tea pm No smoking in restaurant Last d 8.30pm
ROOMS: (incl. bkfst) s £41-£61; d £82-£91 * **LB**
OFF-PEAK: (incl. bkfst) s £33-£38; d £75-£85
MEALS: Bar Lunch £2.50-£12 Dinner £15.75-£17.75
CARDS:

HOLMES CHAPEL Cheshire Map 07 SJ76

★★★ 67% **Old Vicarage**
Knutsford Rd CW4 8EF (on the A50, 1m from junct 18 on the M6)
☎ 01477 532041 FAX 01477 535728
This hotel, which is a Grade II listed building with parts that date from the 17th century, is conveniently situated beside the A50 with many rooms overlooking the open countryside. Bedrooms, most of which are in a newly added wing, are furnished with attractive limed wood fittings; they are conveniently laid out and well equipped. There are also four larger rooms in the original house, as well as family rooms and rooms on the ground floor. The public areas include an interestingly decorated bar with oak beams and an open fire, where a good range of bar meals is available. In the restaurant a wide choice of dishes is available from the frequently-changing carte menu, which is supplemented by daily specials from the blackboard.
25 en suite (bth/shr) CTV in all bedrooms STV No dogs (ex guide dogs) Night porter 70P English & French Cuisine V meals Coffee am Tea pm Last d 9.45pm
ROOMS: (incl. bkfst) s £65-£67; d £77-£80 * **LB**
OFF-PEAK: (incl. bkfst) s £33-£35; d £49.50-£52
MEALS: Lunch £15.40-£17.40alc Dinner £15.40-£18.70alc*

CONF: Thtr 36 Class 14 Board 22
CARDS:

★★★66% **Holly Lodge Hotel & Restaurant**
70 London Rd CW4 7AS (A50/A54 crossroads, from junc 18 of M6)
☎ 01477 537033 FAX 01477 535823
Built in the 19th Century, the original part of this comfortable, well run hotel has been considerably and tastefully extended. Bedrooms, some of which are located in an annexe around a small courtyard, include well appointed, newly refurbished 'executive' rooms with attractive colour co-ordinated décor and light wooden furniture. Other rooms are older, but nevertheless well equipped. A good choice of dishes is available in the smart restaurant and guests can relax in the comfy lounge. The hotel also has a number of meeting rooms.
38 en suite (bth/shr) (3 fmly) No smoking in 12 bedrooms CTV in all bedrooms STV 90P No coaches Xmas English & French Cuisine V meals Coffee am No smoking in restaurant Last d 9.30pm
ROOMS: (incl. bkfst) s £33.50-£68; d £54.50-£80 *
MEALS: Lunch £14.30 Dinner £17.95*
CONF: Thtr 120 Class 60 Board 60 Del from £50
CARDS:

HOLSWORTHY Devon

★★ 72% **Court Barn Country House**

Clawton EX22 6PS (2.5m S of Holsworthy on A388 next to Clawton church) ☎ 01409 271219
FAX 01409 271309
Closed 1-7 Jan
Set in five acres of gardens and grounds, this Victorian country house has delightful rural views. The gardens are a particular feature of the hotel, with a nine hole putting course and croquet provided for guests. The comfortable bedrooms are individually furnished and decorated, offering thoughtful extras, such as fresh flowers, books and mineral water. A four course dinner is served each evening, dishes are full of natural flavours and the cooking could be described as 'in the country house style'. In addition to the spacious restaurant, a separate breakfast room is available and two comfortable lounges, one with an open fire.
8 rms (7 bth/shr) (2 fmly) No smoking in all bedrooms CTV in all bedrooms 18P No coaches Tennis (grass) Riding Solarium Pool table Croquet lawn Putting green Outdoor badminton Xmas English & French Cuisine V meals Coffee am Tea pm No smoking in restaurant Last d 9.15pm
ROOMS: (incl. bkfst) s £32-£35; d £70-£82 **LB**
OFF-PEAK: (incl. bkfst) s fr £32; d £64-£70
MEALS: Lunch fr £12.50 Dinner £17.50-£22
CONF: Thtr 25 Board 12 Del from £75
CARDS:

HOLYWELL GREEN West Yorkshire Map 07 SE01

★★70% **Rock Inn Hotel & Churchills**
HX4 9BS (Junc 24 off M62, signs for Blackley, left at crossroads approx 1/2m on left) ☎ 01422 379721 FAX 01422 379110
This popular hotel and restaurant is pleasantly furnished in all areas, and offers a very wide choice of dishes either in the bar or Churchill's Restaurant. The bedrooms have been recently refurbished and although some are rather compact, they are all very well equipped. There are extensive bars which include a very inviting conservatory. The staff are friendly and provide attentive service.
18 en suite (bth/shr) (3 fmly) No smoking in 8 bedrooms CTV in all bedrooms STV 122P Games room ch fac Xmas English, French & Thai Cuisine V meals Coffee am Tea pm Last d 10pm
ROOMS: (incl. bkfst) s £45-£74; d £59-£82 * **LB**
MEALS: Lunch £7.50-£15&alc High tea £7.50-£11.50 Dinner £11-£15&alc*

CONF: Thtr 200 Class 100 Board 100 Del from £80
CARDS:

HONILEY Warwickshire Map 04 SP27

★★★66% **Honiley Court**

Honiley CV8 1NP (from M40 junc 15, take A4177 Solihull, at roundabout turn right approx 2m on left)
☎ 01926 484234 FAX 01926 484474
An extension of the Old Boot Inn, this modern hotel gives easy access to the M40, M42, M6, Birmingham airport and Coventry town centre. Bedrooms are spacious and have been tastefully decorated and furnished. A good selection of dishes with a choice of menu is offered in the restaurant.
62 en suite (bth/shr) (4 fmly) No smoking in 31 bedrooms CTV in all bedrooms STV Lift Night porter 250P English & French Cuisine V meals Coffee am Tea pm No smoking area in restaurant Last d 9.30pm
ROOMS: s £45-£72; d £45-£72 * **LB**
MEALS: Lunch £6.95-£15alc High tea £3.50-£5.50&alc Dinner £14-£17*
CONF: Thtr 150 Class 70 Board 70 Del from £97
CARDS:

HONITON Devon Map 03 ST10
See also Yarcombe

★★★ 65% ***Deer Park***
Weston EX14 0PG (2.5m W off A30) ☎ 01404 41266
FAX 01404 46598
This fine Georgian mansion, set in 30 acres of parkland with five miles of fishing rights on the River Otter, offers spacious and comfortable public areas. Bedrooms range from those of various sizes in the main house, to those in the Mews, situated across the garden where levels of quality are more straightforward. Service is friendly and efficient, and the hotel's restaurant offers an extensive choice of dishes from both table d'hÙte and à la carte menus.
15 en suite (bth/shr) 14 annexe en suite (bth/shr) (2 fmly) CTV in all bedrooms No dogs (ex guide dogs) Night porter 44P No coaches Outdoor swimming pool (heated) Tennis (hard) Fishing Squash Snooker Sauna Solarium Pool table Croquet lawn Putting green
contd.

Shooting Archery ch fac English & French Cuisine V meals Coffee am Tea pm Last d 10pm
CARDS:

See advertisement on opposite page

★★71% Home Farm
Wilmington E14 9JR (3m E on A35 in village of Wilmington)
☎ 01404 831278 FAX 01404 831411
This thatched former farmhouse, built in the 16th-century, is set beside the main Axminster to Honiton road, with colourful terraced gardens and a large car park. The bedrooms are warm and comfortable, now all en suite, and some are situated in a cottage across the cobbled courtyard. There is a cosy lounge, an attractive bar-lounge and an intimate beamed restaurant where a choice of interesting dishes is offered from various menus. The atmosphere is relaxed and a warm welcome is assured from the resident proprietors.
6 en suite (bth) 7 annexe en suite (bth/shr) (3 fmly) CTV in all bedrooms 25P use of local leisure centre English, French & Italian Cuisine V meals Coffee am Tea pm No smoking in restaurant Last d 9.30pm
ROOMS: (incl. bkfst) s fr £30; d fr £56 **LB**
MEALS: Lunch fr £12&alc Dinner fr £12&alc
CARDS:

★★64% Monkton Court
Monkton EX14 9QH (2m E of Honiton on A30 towards Illminster)
☎ 01404 42309 FAX 01404 46861
A former manor house, believed to date from the 17th-century, this hotel is located on the edge of the Blackdown Hills in a small village a mile from Honiton. It retains much of its historic character, and the comfortable oak-beamed lounge bar is dominated by a large central fireplace; traditional ales and a wide selection of wines and spirits are stocked. An extensive range of bar meals is offered, while in the restaurant a well balanced carte is available. The bedrooms are well equipped and have recently been refurbished. Guests are requested not to smoke in the restaurant or breakfast room.
8 rms (2 bth 4 shr) (2 fmly) CTV in all bedrooms No dogs (ex guide dogs) 60P Xmas English & French Cuisine V meals Coffee am No smoking in restaurant Last d 9.30pm
ROOMS: (incl. bkfst) s £27.50-£37.50; d £45-£55 **LB**
MEALS: Lunch £8.95&alc Dinner £12.50&alc
CONF: Thtr 30 Class 30 Board 20 Del from £40
CARDS:

★★61% Honiton Motel
Turks Head Corner, Exeter Rd EX14 8BL (off A35) ☎ 01404 43440 FAX 01404 47767
This personally run motel is ideally located for the major routes and offers value for money. The bedrooms are neat and well presented with modern en suite facilities. The public areas include a popular bar serving a wide range of snacks and a more extensive menu is offered in the restaurant.
15 annexe en suite (bth/shr) (3 fmly) CTV in all bedrooms 50P Pool table V meals Coffee am Tea pm Last d 9pm
ROOMS: (incl. bkfst) s £30-£32; d £48-£49.50
MEALS: Lunch fr £8.50&alc Dinner fr £8.50&alc*
CONF: Thtr 150 Class 100 Board 50
CARDS:

See advertisement on opposite page

HOOK Hampshire Map 04 SU75

★★69% Hook House
London Rd RG27 9EQ (1m E of Hook on A30)
☎ 01256 762630 FAX 01256 760232
Closed Xmas
This attractive family-run hotel is set in several acres of gardens, and conveniently located for both Reading and Basingstoke. The bedrooms, although compact, are well equipped and have modern en suite shower rooms. Public areas are elegant and comfortable, and the restaurant serves good home-cooked food with imaginative flourishes.
13 en suite (shr) CTV in all bedrooms No dogs 20P No coaches Croquet lawn V meals Last d 9pm
ROOMS: (incl. bkfst) s £49.50; d £59.50 *
OFF-PEAK: (incl. bkfst) s £45; d £55
MEALS: Dinner £12-£15alc*
CONF: Thtr 20 Class 20 Board 20
CARDS:

★★68% *Raven*
Station Rd RG27 9HS (0.75m N of M3 junc 5 on B3349) ☎ 01256 762541 FAX 01256 768677
Situated in the town centre adjacent to the railway station, the Raven is a well run hotel which centres around the busy public bar. The restaurant offers a popular grill option supplemented by daily specials. Bedrooms are all practical to use and well equipped for the business traveller.

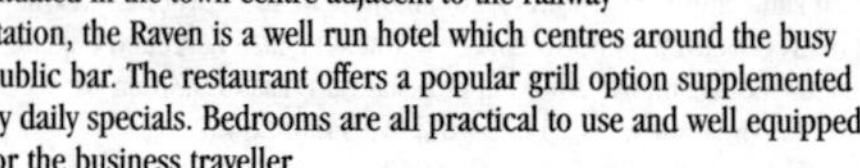

38 en suite (bth/shr) (5 fmly) No smoking in 6 bedrooms CTV in all bedrooms STV No dogs (ex guide dogs) Night porter 100P Sauna Wkly live entertainment European Cuisine V meals Coffee am Last d 10pm
CARDS:

HOPE COVE Devon Map 03 SX64

★★67% Cottage
TQ7 3HJ (from Kingsbridge A381 towards Salcombe, it is suggested you take 2nd right at village of Marlborough continue & turn left for Inner Hope) ☎ 01548 561555 FAX 01548 561455
Closed 3-30 Jan
Set in two acres of grounds with glorious views of the coastline, the hotel has been owned and managed by the Ireland family for nearly 20 years. The de luxe bedrooms have balconies, while others are more simply furnished. The intimate Herzogin Cecile Cabin was built from the timbers of the famous ship wrecked along the coast nearly 50 years ago and the restaurant, where an extensive choice is offered, has views over the Bolt Tail and the harbour.
35 rms (25 bth/shr) (5 fmly) CTV in 29 bedrooms STV 50P No coaches Xmas V meals Coffee am Tea pm
ROOMS: (incl. bkfst & dinner) s £51.50-£64.75; d £82-£109.50 * **LB**
OFF-PEAK: (incl. bkfst & dinner) s £34.75-£42.50; d £69-£85
CONF: Thtr 50 Board 24

★★64% Lantern Lodge
TQ7 3HE (turn right off A381 Kingsbridge-Salcombe road, take first right after passing Hope Cove sign then first left along Grand View Rd)
☎ 01548 561280 FAX 01548 561736
Closed Dec-Feb
Overlooking the fishing village, with a view extending from Bolt Head to Plymouth Sound, this hotel has improved greatly during the past few years. Bedrooms are prettily decorated, with Victorian and Edwardian furniture, and public areas include several cosy sitting areas and an intimate dining room.
14 en suite (bth/shr) (1 fmly) CTV in all bedrooms No dogs (ex guide dogs) 15P No coaches Indoor swimming pool (heated) Sauna Solarium Putting green Multi-gym No children 10yrs Coffee am Tea pm No smoking in restaurant Last d 8.30pm
ROOMS: (incl. bkfst & dinner) s £46.75-£63.25; d £85-£115 * **LB**
MEALS: Bar Lunch £2.40-£5.50 Dinner £14.50*
CARDS:

★★61% Sun Bay
Inner Hope Cove TQ7 3HH ☎ 01548 561371 FAX 01548 561371
Closed 1st 2 wks Dec & Jan
Overlooking the unspoilt harbour of Inner Hope Bay from its setting

on the edge of the village, this family-run hotel has a relaxed, informal atmosphere. Bedrooms, whilst compact, are brightly decorated and have modern furnishings. Refreshments are served on the sun terrace in summer.
14 en suite (bth/shr) (4 fmly) CTV in all bedrooms 14P No coaches Xmas V meals Coffee am Tea pm No smoking in restaurant Last d 8.30pm
ROOMS: (incl. bkfst & dinner) s £25-£70; d £50-£80 * **LB**
MEALS: Lunch £1.70-£6.95 Dinner fr £7.95&alc*
CARDS:

HORLEY Hotels are listed under Gatwick Airport

HORNCASTLE Lincolnshire Map 08 TF26

★★65% **Admiral Rodney**
North St LN9 5DX (off A153) ☎ 01507 523131 FAX 01507 523104
Thoroughly modern and very friendly, this popular inn is situated in the town centre. The ground floor is open plan with the bar and restaurant, arranged in a crescent. To one side an area leading out to a pretty courtyard is set aside as lounge and is furnished with old Chesterfields and big plants. The bedrooms are excellent - very spacious and furnished with polished period mahogany-style desks and drawers and offset by more contemporary fabrics and décor.
31 en suite (bth/shr) (3 fmly) No smoking in 4 bedrooms CTV in all bedrooms STV Lift Night porter 70P Xmas V meals Coffee am Tea pm Last d 9.30pm
ROOMS: (incl. bkfst) s £45-£50; d £62-£72 * **LB**
OFF-PEAK: (incl. bkfst) s £38-£43; d £50-£60
MEALS: Bar Lunch £3.95-£4.95 Dinner fr £11.95&alc*
CONF: Thtr 140 Class 80 Board 80 Del £59
CARDS:

HORNCHURCH Essex Map 05 TQ58

★★★61% **Palms**
Southend Arterial Rd RM11 3UJ (on A127) (Hilton)
☎ 01708 346789 FAX 01708 341719
There are comfortable bedrooms at this roadside hotel which is ideally placed for meetings. There is a night club atmosphere to the open-plan bar and restaurant area which is enthusiastically run. Occasional live light music in the evening adds a certain character.
137 en suite (bth/shr) (6 fmly) No smoking in 30 bedrooms CTV in all bedrooms Night porter 250P Wkly live entertainment International Cuisine V meals Coffee am Tea pm Last d 10pm
ROOMS: s £84; d £84 *
MEALS: Lunch £13.50-£19&alc Dinner £19&alc*
CONF: Thtr 300 Class 100 Board 80 Del £99
CARDS:

HORNING Norfolk Map 09 TG31

★★★65% **Petersfield House**
Lower St NR12 8PF (from Wroxham take A1062 follow for two and a half miles then turn right into Horning Village, hotel in centre of village on left) ☎ 01692 630741 FAX 01692 630745
This quiet family managed hotel sits amid well kept gardens, adjacent to the banks of the River Bure and a few minutes walk from the centre of the village. A friendly environment is enhanced by traditional services in the public rooms, which include a comfortable lounge area and a light airy restaurant overlooking the rear gardens. Bedroom sizes are variable, ranging from cosy through to spacious. Most rooms have garden views and all are well maintained and suitably equipped.
18 en suite (bth/shr) (1 fmly) CTV in all bedrooms 70P No coaches Fishing Putting green Wkly live entertainment Xmas English & Continental Cuisine V meals Coffee am Tea pm Last d 9.30pm

contd.

ROOMS: (incl. bkfst) s fr £58; d fr £72 * **LB**
MEALS: Lunch £10.50-£13.50&alc High tea £3.75 Dinner £15.50&alc
CONF: Thtr 50 Class 40 Board 30 Del from £75.50
CARDS:

HORRABRIDGE Devon Map 02 SX57

★★ 67% ***Overcombe***
PL20 7RN (off A386) ☎ 01822 853501
Two Edwardian semi detached houses were joined to create this small hotel which looks across Walkham Valley to the high granite tors of Dartmoor from its setting on the edge of the village only a hundred yards from open moorland. Individually furnished and decorated bedrooms include two on the ground floor, one of which is specifically designed to meet the needs of disabled guests. The short but imaginative fixed-price menu served at dinner features good local produce. A main course of breast of duck, cooked in the modern style and served sliced in a pool of sweet plum sauce flavoured with rum, was delicious; local granary bread and a selection of cheeses were also very tasty. The hotel appeals to both business and leisure guests and has many visitors who return regularly.
11 rms (10 bth/shr) (2 fmly) CTV in all bedrooms 10P No coaches Croquet lawn V meals Last d 7.15pm
CARDS:

See advertisement on opposite page

HORSHAM West Sussex Map 04 TQ13

★★★★ 76% **South Lodge**
Brighton Rd RH13 6PS ☎ 01403 891711 FAX 01403 891253
(For full entry see Lower Beeding)

★★★ 72% **Random Hall**
Stane St, Slinfold RH13 7QX (on A290 0.5m from village of Slinfold)
☎ 01403 790558 FAX 01403 791046
This fine hotel dates back to the late 16th century and retains much of its historic farmhouse character. Low oak beams, inglenook fireplaces and flagstone floors set the tone. Bedrooms are sympathetically furnished and range from quiet singles to the spacious first-floor rooms which include one with a four-poster; many ground-floor rooms retain their original oak beams and panelled walls. The candlelit Tudor-style restaurant is home to the imaginative modern British cooking of Chef Jonathan Gettings who offers a three-course fixed-price menu along with suggested wines. There is a dining club for regular guests which offers Master Classes and tutored wine tastings.
15 en suite (bth/shr) (2 fmly) CTV in all bedrooms No dogs 50P No coaches Xmas V meals Coffee am Tea pm No smoking area in restaurant Last d 10pm
ROOMS: s fr £57.50; d fr £57.50 * **LB**
MEALS: Lunch £5.50-£10.50 Dinner £11.95-£17.95
CONF: Thtr 16 Class 8 Board 12 Del from £89.75
CARDS:

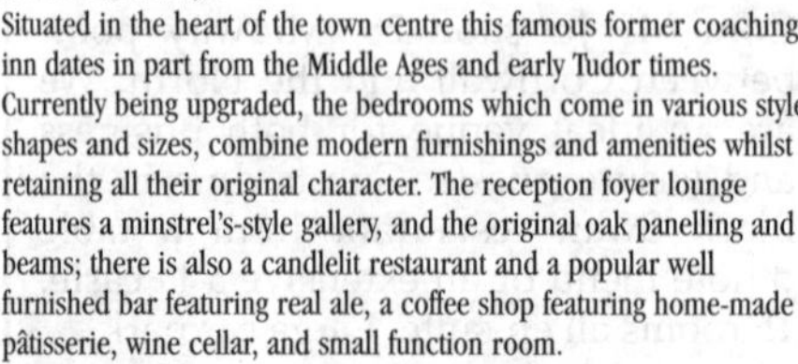

★★ 67% **Ye Olde King's Head**
Carfax RH12 1EG (close to town hall, 0.5m from railway station) ☎ 01403 253126
FAX 01403 242291
Situated in the heart of the town centre this famous former coaching inn dates in part from the Middle Ages and early Tudor times. Currently being upgraded, the bedrooms which come in various styles, shapes and sizes, combine modern furnishings and amenities whilst retaining all their original character. The reception foyer lounge features a minstrel's-style gallery, and the original oak panelling and beams; there is also a candlelit restaurant and a popular well furnished bar featuring real ale, a coffee shop featuring home-made pâtisserie, wine cellar, and small function room.
42 rms (41 bth/shr) (1 fmly) CTV in all bedrooms 40P English & French Cuisine V meals Coffee am Tea pm No smoking area in restaurant Last d 10pm
ROOMS: (incl. bkfst) s £58-£68; d £68-£88 * **LB**
MEALS: Lunch £5.95-£25 Dinner £16.50-£25*
CONF: Thtr 45 Class 40 Board 30
CARDS:

Travel Inn
57 North St RH12 1RB (opposite railway station)
☎ 01403 250141 FAX 01403 270797
Purpose-built accommodation, offering spacious, well equipped bedrooms, all with en suite bathrooms. Meals may be taken at the nearby family restaurant. For more information about Travel Inns, consult the Contents page under Hotel Groups.
40 en suite (bth/shr)
ROOMS: d £35.50 *

HORTON-CUM-STUDLEY Oxfordshire Map 04 SP51

★★★ 68% **Studley Priory**
OX33 1AZ (2.5m off B4027) ☎ 01865 351203
FAX 01865 351613
Only six miles from the centre of Oxford, Studley Priory belongs in another, less hectic, age. This former Benedictine nunnery was founded in the 12th-century but was extended by the Croke family who acquired the property when Henry VIII dissolved the monasteries. A friendly professional welcome awaits guests at this special property, and new chef Trevor Bosch's imaginative cuisine makes dining a special treat too. Bedrooms are undergoing refurbishment and those rooms which have been upgraded are very smart indeed. There are facilities for conferences and extensive pretty grounds.
19 en suite (bth/shr) No smoking in 4 bedrooms CTV in all bedrooms STV No dogs Night porter 101P Golf 18 Tennis (hard & grass) Croquet lawn Putting green Clay pigeon shooting Xmas English & French Cuisine V meals Coffee am Tea pm No smoking in restaurant Last d 9pm
ROOMS: (incl. cont bkfst) s £95-£130; d £105-£225 * **LB**
MEALS: Lunch £22.50-£35.25alc Dinner £22.50-£35.25alc*
CONF: Thtr 40 Class 25 Board 25 Del from £135
CARDS:

HORWICH Greater Manchester Map 07 SD61

★★ 64% ***Swallowfield***
Chorley New Rd BL6 6HN (on A673, off junc 6 of M61)
☎ 01204 697914 FAX 01204 68900
Located on the outskirts of Horwich, this friendly, informal hotel has ample car parking and its own small garden. Bedrooms - several of which are on the ground floor - are all modern and well equipped, many of them also being spacious. The hotel has a loyal following of regular visitors.
31 en suite (bth/shr) (6 fmly) CTV in all bedrooms 35P No coaches Coffee am Tea pm Last d 8.30pm
CARDS:

HOUGHTON-LE-SPRING Tyne & Wear Map 12 NZ34

★★ 58% **Chilton Lodge**
Black Boy Rd, Chilton Moor, Fencehouses DH4 6PY
☎ 0191 385 2694 FAX 0191 385 2694
Set in open countryside near the village of Fencehouses, this business has evolved from original farm cottages to a complex providing modern but functional bedrooms, a country pub and a spacious ballroom catering for functions and weddings. Menus offer a wide choice of bar and dining room meals.
18 en suite (bth/shr) CTV in all bedrooms No dogs (ex guide dogs) Night porter 100P V meals Coffee am Last d 9.45pm

ROOMS: (incl. bkfst) s £29.50-£34.50; d £40-£45 * **LB**
MEALS: Lunch £12.95 Dinner £12.95&alc*
CONF: Del from £55
CARDS:

HOUNSLOW Greater London See LONDON SECTION plan 1 B2
See also Heathrow Airport

★★★ 63% Master Robert
Great West Rd TW5 0BD (A4) ☎ 0181 570 6261
FAX 0181 569 4016

Best Western

This easily located hotel is three-and-a-half miles to the east of Heathrow airport. The well equipped bedrooms are housed in separate buildings with plenty of motel-style parking space. There is a restaurant and bars serving meals.
94 en suite (bth/shr) (8 fmly) No smoking in 33 bedrooms CTV in all bedrooms STV No dogs (ex guide dogs) Night porter 135P Continental Cuisine V meals Coffee am Tea pm
ROOMS: s £75-£82; d £75-£82 * **LB**
OFF-PEAK: s £43-£46; d £43-£46
CONF: Thtr 130 Class 48 Board 134
CARDS:

HOVE See Brighton & Hove

HOVINGHAM North Yorkshire Map 08 SE67

★★★ 70% Worsley Arms
YO6 4LA (on B1257) ☎ 01653 628234 FAX 01653 628130
An impressive building standing in the centre of the village and offering very comfortable public rooms together with attractive bedrooms, some of which are sited in a large house over the road. Chef Andrew Jones provides a very high standard of cooking in the restaurant, whilst there is an alternative food operation in the Cricketers bar/bistro. Service is friendly and professional from a dedicated staff.
11 en suite (bth/shr) 8 annexe en suite (bth/shr) No smoking in all bedrooms CTV in all bedrooms Night porter 52P Tennis (hard) Squash Shooting Xmas V meals Coffee am Tea pm No smoking in restaurant Last d 9.30pm
ROOMS: (incl. bkfst) s fr £55; d fr £75 * **LB**
MEALS: Lunch fr £15alc Dinner fr £23.50alc*
CONF: Thtr 40 Class 40 Board 30 Del from £85
CARDS: £

HOW CAPLE Hereford & Worcester Map 03 SO63

★★ 63% How Caple Grange
HR1 4TF (adj B4224 between Hereford & Ross-on-Wye)
☎ 01989 740208 & 740668 FAX 01989 740301
This large stone-built property dates back to 1730. It stands in its own extensive grounds and gardens, on the B4224, between Ross-on-Wye and Hereford. The majority of the bedrooms have either antique or period furniture, but all have modern equipment and all but one have en-suite facilities. Rooms with four-poster beds and family rooms are both available. Other facilities include a comfortable lounge, a choice of bars, a function room, an outdoor swimming pool and a fitness suite with sauna, plunge bath, solarium and fitness equipment.
26 rms (18 bth) CTV in all bedrooms 100P Outdoor swimming pool Sauna Solarium Gym Putting green Jacuzzi/spa Xmas Coffee am Tea pm Last d 8.30pm
ROOMS: (incl. bkfst) s £25-£32.50; d £50-£55 **LB**
MEALS: Bar Lunch fr £4 High tea fr £4 Dinner fr £10*
CONF: Thtr 100 Class 40 Board 40 Del from £50

AA Members can use the Hotel Guide Discount Card at the back of the book for discounts at hotels displaying the £ symbol by their entry.

HOWTOWN (NEAR POOLEY BRIDGE) Cumbria Map 12 NY41

RED STAR HOTEL

★★★ Sharrow Bay Country House
Sharrow Bay CA10 2LZ (at Pooley Bridge take right hand fork by church to Howtown. At cross road turn right and follow Lakeside Road for 2m.)
☎ 017684 86301 & 86483 FAX 017684 86349

RELAIS & CHATEAUX. Relais Gourmands

Closed late Nov-late Feb
The Peter Pan of British hotels, reputed to have been the first true country house hotel, Sharrow Bay enchants one with its magical air and it is easy to see why it continues to command a world-wide reputation. The house lies right on the north-east

contd.

shores of Lake Ullswater and its style and location are reminiscent of a villa by the Italian Lakes. Public rooms combine a gracious style with comfort and relaxation, there being a choice of lounges and dining rooms, adorned with antiques, flowers, ornaments and beautiful furnishings. Bedrooms are a delight, and whilst not all are en suite, they are all individual and equipped with a host of thoughtful extras. Uniquely, many are contained outwith the hotel, in the grounds, in far-off cottages, and in a magnificent Elizabethan farm house, complete with its own lounges and breakfast room, set high above the lake about a mile away. Whatever the location, all are of similar standard and indeed some excel even those in the main house, in terms of charm. Dinner at Sharrow is an occasion, the six course meal being served around 8pm by a smart and attentive team. The mainly British dishes are presented in a contemporary manner and one really is spoilt for choice, particularly with starters, which alone may feature various seafood, terrines and game.
Breakfasts are equally memorable, not to mention the superb and popular afternoon teas.
11 rms (7 bth/shr) 17 annexe en suite (bth/shr) CTV in all bedrooms No dogs 30P No coaches No children 13yrs English & French Cuisine Coffee am Tea pm No smoking in restaurant Last d 8.45pm
ROOMS: (incl. bkfst & dinner) s £100-£180; d £270-£340
MEALS: Lunch £32 Dinner £42
CONF: Board 12

HUDDERSFIELD West Yorkshire Map 07 SE11
See also Marsden

★★★69% **Bagden Hall**
Wakefield Rd, Scissett HD8 9LE (on A636, between Scissett and Denby Dale) ☎ 01484 865330 FAX 01484 861001
This well furnished house is set in forty acres of grounds which incorporate a golf course. Bedrooms vary in size, but all are well equipped and pleasantly appointed. Extensive public areas comprise a cosy bar, a sunny conservatory, lounges and conference room. A pleasant mix of English and French cuisine is served in the elegant restaurant and staff are helpful at all times.
17 en suite (bth/shr) (3 fmly) No smoking in 2 bedrooms CTV in all bedrooms No dogs (ex guide dogs) Night porter 96P Golf 9 Putting green Xmas English & French Cuisine V meals Coffee am Tea pm No smoking area in restaurant Last d 9.30pm
ROOMS: (incl. bkfst) s £60-£100; d £80-£100 * LB
OFF-PEAK: (incl. bkfst & dinner) s £39.95-£49.95; d £79.90-£99.90
MEALS: Lunch £8.95-£11.95 High tea fr £2.95 Dinner fr £15.95&alc*
CONF: Thtr 80 Class 40 Board 30 Del from £87
CARDS:

★★★69% **Old Golf House Hotel**
New Hey Rd, Outlane HD3 3YP (M62 Junc 24 or 23) ☎ 01422 379311 FAX 01422 372694
COUNTRY CLUB Hotel Group
Conveniently positioned beside the M62 this stone-built hotel offers a very convivial atmosphere with genuine hospitality provided by willing staff. Public rooms centre around a popular lounge bar where a good range of snacks and lighter meals is served as an alternative to the restaurant. Bedrooms are bright and inviting with a good range of modern facilities. Some boast extra spaciousness with comfortable sitting areas.
50 en suite (bth/shr) (4 fmly) No smoking in 24 bedrooms CTV in all bedrooms STV Night porter 100P Sauna Solarium Gym 5 Hole pitch & putt V meals Coffee am Tea pm Last d 10pm

ROOMS: s £45-£65; d £65-£75 * **LB**
MEALS: Lunch £9.95&alc High tea £1.95-£5.95 Dinner £14.95-£16.95&alc*
CONF: Thtr 100 Class 50 Board 40 Del from £95
CARDS:

★★★65% **George**
St George's Square HD1 1JA (M62 Junc 24 follow signs Huddersfield Town Centre) ☎ 01484 515444 FAX 01484 435056
PRINCIPAL HOTELS
Well appointed and equipped accommodation is provided at this sympathetically restored Victorian hotel, which is ideally situated next to the station. It is perfectly located for both business and private guests who have the choice of eating less formally in the characterful lounge bar, in the smartly appointed restaurant or from room service. The hotel has a number of well equipped meeting rooms and there are many attractions such as the Bronte parsonage within a few minutes drive.
60 en suite (bth/shr) (1 fmly) No smoking in 8 bedrooms CTV in all bedrooms STV Lift Night porter 23P Xmas International Cuisine V meals Coffee am Tea pm No smoking in restaurant Last d 9.30pm
ROOMS: (incl. bkfst) s fr £79; d fr £89 * LB
OFF-PEAK: (incl. bkfst) s fr £49; d fr £60
MEALS: Lunch £6.95-£7.95&alc High tea £4.50 Dinner £14.95&alc
CONF: Thtr 200 Class 60 Board 60 Del from £85
CARDS:

★★★62% **Briar Court**
Halifax Rd, Birchencliffe HD3 3NT (on A629, 300yds S of junc 24 on M62) ☎ 01484 519902 FAX 01484 431812
This modern hotel is convenient to the M62 motorway to the south of junction 24. The bedrooms are modern and well furnished though fairly compact, and public rooms comprise an open plan lounge, bar and reception. Guests may choose to eat in the hotel's dining room or the popular Italian restaurant, where a wide range of dishes is available.
47 en suite (bth/shr) (3 fmly) No smoking in 20 bedrooms CTV in all bedrooms STV No dogs (ex guide dogs) Night porter 140P English & Italian Cuisine V meals Coffee am No smoking in restaurant Last d 9.15pm
ROOMS: (incl. bkfst) s £63; d £73
OFF-PEAK: (incl. bkfst) s fr £45; d fr £55
MEALS: Lunch £6.95-£12.95&alc Dinner £13.95-£14.95&alc*
CONF: Thtr 150 Class 50 Board 60 Del from £80
CARDS:

★★73% **Lodge**
48 Birkby Lodge Rd, Birkby HD2 2BG (junc 24 of M62, then exit A629 for Birkby. Turn right at Nuffield Hospital down Birkby Lodge Road, hotel 200yds on left) ☎ 01484 431001 FAX 01484 421590
Closed 25-27 Dec
Situated in a leafy part of Huddersfield and run along country house lines, this inviting hotel is well furnished throughout and is a perfect retreat. Bedrooms are bright, fresh and well equipped, including lots of little extras, whilst the public rooms are both warm and inviting.

There is a most unusual ceiling in the main lounge which adds to the character. Cooking is in the hands of the owner together with a dedicated team who use only the best produce for the essentially British dishes. Staff provide friendly service at all times.
11 en suite (bth/shr) (2 fmly) No smoking in all bedrooms CTV in all bedrooms 41P No coaches English & Continental Cuisine V meals Coffee am Tea pm No smoking in restaurant Last d 9.45pm
ROOMS: (incl. bkfst) s £59.95-£75; d £68-£75 **LB**
OFF-PEAK: (incl. bkfst) s fr £55; d fr £60
MEALS: Lunch £12.95-£16 Dinner £22.95-£24.70*
CONF: Thtr 45 Class 24 Board 24 Del from £90
CARDS:

★★67% **Huddersfield**
33-47 Kirkgate HD1 1QT (on A62 ring road) ☎ 01484 512111
FAX 01484 435262
Situated right in the centre of the town and having the benefit of secure parking, this busy hotel offers a wide range of facilities. Bedrooms vary in size but are all very well equipped, and public areas include a bistro, all-day brasserie, night club and small leisure suite.
46 en suite (bth/shr) (6 fmly) CTV in all bedrooms STV Lift Night porter 60P Sauna Pool table Wkly live entertainment Xmas V meals Coffee am Tea pm Last d 10pm
ROOMS: (incl. bkfst) s fr £47.50; d fr £64
OFF-PEAK: (incl. bkfst) s fr £35; d fr £44
MEALS: Lunch £5.50-£9alc High tea £5.50-£9alc
Dinner £12-£15&alc
CARDS:

★67% **Elm Crest**

2 Queens Rd, Edgerton HD2 2AG (take A629 out of Huddersfield to the lights at Blacker Rd take 1st turning right after lights, hotel 50yds on left)
☎ 01484 530990 FAX 01484 516227
A few minutes' drive from the motorway network, Elm Crest is well placed and very accessible. It is a well preserved period residence spanning four floors. Home from home comforts and a friendly atmosphere prevail. The dining room, where tasty fresh dishes are served from a short but appealing menu, is in the basement and adjacent to the cosy lounge. Mementoes and family treasures provide the finishing touches.
8 rms (5 shr) (1 fmly) No smoking in all bedrooms CTV in all bedrooms No dogs 12P No coaches English & French Cuisine V meals Coffee am Tea pm No smoking in restaurant
ROOMS: (incl. bkfst) s £25-£32; d £45-£57 * **LB**
OFF-PEAK: (incl. bkfst) s £22-£30; d £40-£50
MEALS: Lunch £10-£15&alc High tea £10-£12 Dinner £14-£20&alc*
CONF: Class 15 Board 12 Del from £40
CARDS:

Hilton National Huddersfield/Halifax

Ainley Top HD3 3RH (500yds from exit 24 on M62)
☎ 01422 375431 FAX 01422 310067
This is a bright, modern hotel, with an informal restaurant, aimed at both the business and leisure guest. All bedrooms have en suite bathrooms and a range of modern facilities. For more information about Hilton National hotels, consult the Contents page under Hotel Groups.
114 en suite (bth/shr)
ROOMS: s £89; d £89 *
CONF: Thtr 400 Class 150 Board 50 Del from £125

HULL East Riding of Yorkshire Map 08 TA02
See also Little Weighton

★★★70% **Grange Park**

Main St HU10 6EA ☎ 01482 656488
FAX 01482 655848
(For full entry see Willerby)

★★★69% **Willerby Manor**
Well Ln HU10 6ER ☎ 01482 652616 FAX 01482 653901
(For full entry see Willerby)

★★★66% **Quality Royal**

Ferensway HU1 3UF (follow signs for Railway Station)
☎ 01482 325087 FAX 01482 323172
This former Victorian railway hotel has been completely renovated following a disastrous fire in the early nineties and now provides modern, well appointed bedrooms and spacious, comfortable public rooms. The ornate ceilings and archways of the originl building have been retained and the façade restored to its former grandeur. Banqueting and conference facilities and a leisure centre are two major amenities and there is also free parking. Service is provided by friendly, helpful and smartly dressed staff.
155 en suite (bth/shr) No smoking in 85 bedrooms CTV in all bedrooms STV Lift Night porter 130P Indoor swimming pool (heated) Sauna Solarium Gym Pool table Spa pool Steamroom Xmas English & Continental Cuisine V meals Coffee am Tea pm No smoking area in restaurant Last d 9.30pm
ROOMS: s £67.50; d £87.50 **LB**
MEALS: Lunch £7.95-£9.95&alc Dinner £13.50&alc*
CONF: Thtr 450 Class 200 Board 65 Del from £82.50
CARDS:

★★★65% **Rowley Manor**

Rowley Rd HU20 3XR ☎ 01482 848248
FAX 01482 849900
(For full entry see Little Weighton)

★★65% **Fox & Coney Inn**
Market Place HU15 2AT ☎ 01430 422275 FAX 01430 421552
(For full entry see South Cave)

★★64% **Pearson Park**

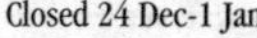
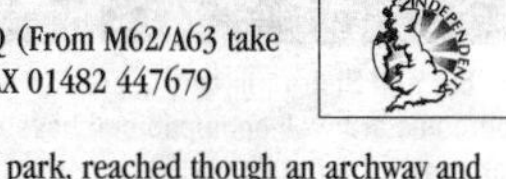

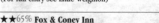

70-72 Pearson Park HU5 2TQ (From M62/A63 take A1079) ☎ 01482 343043 FAX 01482 447679
Closed 24 Dec-1 Jan
Situated in a delightful public park, reached though an archway and about one mile from the city centre, this family-run hotel provides variously shaped bedrooms which are all modern and well equipped. Light refreshments are served in the coffee shop whilst more extensive meals are in the pleasant dining room.
32 en suite (bth/shr) (2 fmly) CTV in all bedrooms Night porter
contd.

30P English & French Cuisine V meals Coffee am Tea pm No smoking in restaurant Last d 9pm
ROOMS: (incl. bkfst) s £45; d £60 * **LB**
OFF-PEAK: (incl. bkfst) s £35; d £45
MEALS: Lunch fr £7.50&alc Dinner fr £10.95&alc
CONF: Thtr 82 Class 20 Board 26
CARDS:

See advertisement on opposite page

★★ 59% **Comfort Friendly Inn**

11 Anlaby Rd HU1 2PJ (turn off A63 onto A1079)
☎ 01482 323299 FAX 01482 214730
A mainly commercial hotel, previously known as Valiant House, offers value for money accommodation and a cheerful informal atmosphere. The first floor public areas include a lounge bar overlooking the city and various function/meeting rooms. There is parking to the front of the hotel and a private car park to the rear.
59 en suite (bth/shr) (5 fmly) No smoking in 29 bedrooms CTV in all bedrooms STV Night porter 100P Xmas English & Continental Cuisine V meals Coffee am Tea pm No smoking area in restaurant Last d 9.30pm
ROOMS: s £38.50-£49.50; d £38.50-£49.50 **LB**
MEALS: Lunch £7.50-£9.95&alc Dinner £9.75&alc*
CONF: Thtr 140 Class 80 Board 60 Del from £65
CARDS:

Campanile

Beverley Rd, Freetown Way HU2 9AN (pass station and first right after crossroads)
☎ 01482 325530 FAX 01482 587538

The bar and Bistro restaurant provide meals and refreshments. Bedrooms are well equipped and have en suite bathrooms. For more details about Campanile, consult the Contents page under Hotel Groups.
47 annexe en suite (bth/shr)
CONF: Thtr 35 Class 20 Board 23 Del £57

Forte Posthouse Hull
Ferriby High Rd HU14 3LG ☎ 01482 645212
FAX 01482 643332
(For full entry see North Ferriby)

FORTE Posthouse

Forte Posthouse Hull Marina
The Marina, Castle St HU1 2BX ☎ 01482 225221
FAX 01482 213299
Suitable for both the business and leisure traveller, this bright hotel provides modern accommodation in well equipped bedrooms with en suite bathrooms. For more details about Forte Posthouse hotels, consult the Contents page for the section on Hotel Groups.
99 en suite (bth/shr)
ROOMS: s £59-£89; d £59-£89 *
CONF: Thtr 150 Class 60 Board 50

FORTE Posthouse

Travel Inn

Ferriby Rd, Hessle HU13 0JA ☎ 01482 645285
FAX 01482 645299
Purpose-built accommodation, offering spacious, well equipped bedrooms, all with en suite bathrooms. Meals may be taken at the nearby family restaurant. For more information about Travel Inns, consult the Contents page under Hotel Groups.
40 en suite (bth/shr)
ROOMS: d £35.50 *

Travelodge
Beacon Service Area HU15 1RZ ☎ 01430 424455
FAX 01430 424455
(For full entry see South Cave)

Travelodge

HUNGERFORD Berkshire Map 04 SU36

★★ 64% **Three Swans**
117 High St RG17 0DL ☎ 01488 682721
FAX 01488 681708
This lovely, quality inn is furnished in an attractive contempory style with rich wall coverings and a wealth of oak panelling. Bedrooms are furnished and equipped to a high standard, and staff are friendly and informal.
15 en suite (bth/shr) (2 fmly) No smoking in 2 bedrooms CTV in all bedrooms 50P European Cuisine V meals Coffee am Tea pm No smoking area in restaurant Last d 9.30pm
ROOMS: (incl. bkfst) s £55; d £70 * **LB**
OFF-PEAK: (incl. bkfst) s £30; d £60
MEALS: Lunch £8.50-£10.50&alc Dinner £6.50-£35alc*
CONF: Thtr 60 Class 40 Board 36 Del from £75
CARDS:

HUNSTANTON Norfolk Map 09 TF64

★★★ 64% ***Le Strange Arms***
Golf Course Rd, Old Hunstanton PE36 6JJ (turn off A149 1m of town. Road bends sharp right and access road to hotel on bend) ☎ 01485 534411
FAX 01485 534724
Le Strange Arms is located in Old Hunstanton and sits right on the coast line with lawns that sweep down to sandy beaches. The public rooms offer good comfort and a range of eating options, with informal fare served in the Ancient Mariners pub, which sits adjacent to the main hotel building, or alternatively the main restaurant offers a good choice form A la carte and daily menus. Bedroom styles and sizes are varied, the original main house rooms are cottagey with period furnishings, whilst the new wing rooms offer good contemporary style bedrooms, all rooms are equipped with a range of modern amenities.
36 en suite (bth/shr) (4 fmly) CTV in all bedrooms Night porter

CONSORT HOTELS

30P Tennis (grass) Snooker ch fac V meals Coffee am Tea pm Last d 9pm
CARDS:

See advertisement on this page

★★69% ***Caley Hall***
Old Hunstanton Rd PE36 6HH (1 mile from Hunstanton, on A149)
☎ 01485 533486 FAX 01485 533348
Closed Jan-Feb
The bar and restaurant are in the main building of this informal hotel, while the comfortably proportioned bedrooms are located in a series of converted outbuildings.
33 annexe en suite (bth) (5 fmly) CTV in all bedrooms STV 70P Snooker International Cuisine V meals Coffee am Last d 9pm
CARDS:

★★64% **The Lodge Hotel & Restaurant**
Old Hunstanton Rd PE36 6HX (1m E on A149) ☎ 01485 532896 FAX 01485 535007
Further improvements have been made to this popular family-run hotel which is situated within easy reach of the beach and the town centre. Bedrooms have modern furnishings and facilities, most are cheerfully decorated and have co-ordinated soft furnishings; a four-poster bedroom and an executive ground floor suite are also available. Public rooms include a comfortable lounge area, spacious restaurant and a newly refurbished bar, where informal meals are readily available.
16 en suite (bth/shr) (3 fmly) CTV in all bedrooms 70P Snooker Pool table Games room ch fac Xmas English, French & Italian Cuisine V meals Coffee am Tea pm No smoking in restaurant Last d 9.15pm
ROOMS: (incl. bkfst) s £30-£44; d £60-£76 **LB**
OFF-PEAK: (incl. bkfst) s £25-£44; d £50-£76
MEALS: Lunch £17.95&alc Dinner £17.95*
CONF: Class 50
CARDS:

HUNSTRETE Somerset Map 03 ST66

★★★ **Hunstrete House**
BS18 4NS (From Bath A4 to Bristol, take A39 through Marksbury, A368 turn off Hunstrete Village) ☎ 01761 490490 FAX 01761 490732

Set in 92 acres of deer park at the edge of the Mendip Hills, Hunstrete is a beautiful 18th-century house which successfully combines the ambience of a private country house with the attentive and personal service of a first-rate hotel. A series of day rooms are elegantly furnished with the finest fabrics and

contd.

antique furniture; oil paintings decorate the walls and there are lovely floral displays throughout. Bedrooms are similarly luxurious, each one having its own individual style and character; thick robes, decanters of sherry and reading material help guests to unwind. In the kitchen Robert Clayton and his small brigade cook from short but interesting menus which might include a memorable boudin of chicken with Madeira and creamed leeks, and fillet of seabass with vanilla sauce and basil mash.
12 en suite (bth/shr) 11 annexe en suite (bth/shr) CTV in all bedrooms No dogs (ex guide dogs) Night porter 40P No coaches Outdoor swimming pool (heated) Tennis (hard) Croquet lawn Xmas English & French Cuisine V meals Coffee am Tea pm No smoking in restaurant Last d 9.30pm
ROOMS: (incl. bkfst) s £120-£140; d £160-£180 * **LB**
MEALS: Lunch fr £20 Dinner fr £34
CONF: Thtr 40 Class 24 Board 24 Del from £165
CARDS:

H

HUNTINGDON Cambridgeshire Map 04 TL27

★★★73% **The Old Bridge**
PE18 6TQ (off A1 near junct with A1-M1 link and A604/M11)
☎ 01480 452681 FAX 01480 411017
A handsome ivy-clad 18th-century house standing on the banks of the River Ouse, close to the town centre, will appeal to business and leisure visitors alike. Attractively appointed public areas include a well stocked bar and a comfortable lounge which is a popular local rendezvous, while eating options range from the panelled restaurant's imaginative carte - supported by an outstanding wine list - to an informal terrace meal. Bedrooms in a variety of sizes offer mixed modern appointments and all the expected amenities.
26 en suite (bth/shr) (3 fmly) CTV in all bedrooms STV Night porter 50P Fishing Private mooring for boats Xmas English & Mediterranean Cuisine V meals Coffee am Tea pm Last d 10.30pm
ROOMS: (incl. bkfst) s £69.50-£89.50; d £89.50-£120 * **LB**
OFF-PEAK: (incl. bkfst & dinner) s £67.50-£77.50; d £135-£145
MEALS: Lunch £6.96-£17.95alc Dinner £6.96-£17.95alc*
CONF: Thtr 50 Class 20 Board 24 Del from £127.50
CARDS:

★★★62% **The George**
George St PE18 6AB ☎ 01480 432444
FAX 01480 453130
This historic former coaching inn is situated in the centre of town and can be easily reached from the ring road. The majority of the bedrooms are attractively appointed and equipped with every modern amenity. The hotel was built in early Stuart times and was once home to Oliver Cromwell's grandfather. Shakespearean plays are staged in the courtyard each year by a local theatre group.
24 en suite (bth/shr) (3 fmly) No smoking in 7 bedrooms CTV in all bedrooms Night porter 71P Xmas International Cuisine V meals Coffee am Tea pm No smoking in restaurant Last d 9.30pm
ROOMS: s fr £62.50; d fr £75 * **LB**
MEALS: Bar Lunch £1.95-£11.50 High tea £1.20-£2.95 Dinner £13.95-£16.95
CONF: Thtr 150 Class 100 Board 50
CARDS:

★★65% **The George Coaching Inn**
Great North Rd, Buckden PE18 9XA (2m S A14/A1) ☎ 01480 810307
FAX 01480 811274
This old coaching inn has undergone considerable change throughout the public areas, which now offer a larger lounge bar to complement the adjoining restaurant, a small foyer seating area and a couple of small meeting rooms. There are plans to gradually upgrade the accommodation during 1996. Currently bedroom styles vary with a mix of modern and traditional appointments, and the majority of rooms have en suite facilities. The enthusiastic proprietors are committed to providing a warm welcome and friendly service. The young kitchen brigade offer a good choice of interesting meals through daily and à la carte menus, along with a well chosen wine list.
16 en suite (bth/shr) (2 fmly) CTV in all bedrooms 50P Xmas V meals Coffee am Tea pm No smoking area in restaurant Last d 9.45pm
ROOMS: (incl. bkfst) s £56; d £72-£79 * **LB**
OFF-PEAK: (incl. bkfst) s £39; d £54
MEALS: Sunday Lunch £11-£15 High tea £5-£15 Dinner £12-£25*
CONF: Thtr 70 Board 20 Del from £85
CARDS:

★★64% **Grange**
115 High St, Brampton PE18 8RA ☎ 01480 459516
FAX 01480 459391
This small family-run hotel is situated close to the centre of Brampton village in reasonably quiet residential surroundings. Sound levels of accommodation are provided and the lounge bar is the heart of the public area operation, a popular meeting point for the locals who enjoy the relaxed informal environment. A good selection of food is available, from à la carte restaurant dining or bar snack choices supplemented by daily blackboard specials.
9 rms (1 bth 7 shr) (1 fmly) CTV in all bedrooms No dogs 40P English & Continental Cuisine V meals Coffee am Last d 9.45pm
ROOMS: (incl. bkfst) s £25-£49; d £55-£59 *
MEALS: Sunday Lunch £10-£15alc Dinner fr £14.95&alc*
CONF: Thtr 30 Class 24 Board 20
CARDS:

HURSTBOURNE TARRANT Hampshire Map 04 SU35

★★★67% **Esseborne Manor**
SP11 0ER (7m N Andover on A343)
☎ 01264 736444 FAX 01264 736725
Built at the end of the last century, this attractive manor house is set in its own grounds amid the North Wessex Downs. The house has a comfortable welcoming feel, and the young, friendly staff provide a relaxed service. The pretty bedrooms are individually decorated and have lots of extra touches, and there is a comfortable guests' lounge overlooking the garden. Chef Nicholas Watson provides an interesting menu using quality local ingredients; during the summer months there is a special garden menu.
The extensive wine list is largely French, but offers a good range of New World choices.
6 en suite (bth/shr) 4 annexe en suite (bth/shr) CTV in all bedrooms No dogs (ex guide dogs) 50P No coaches Tennis (hard) Croquet lawn Putting green Golf practice net No children 7yrs English & French Cuisine V meals Coffee am Tea pm Last d 9.30pm
ROOMS: (incl. bkfst) s £84-£95; d £95-£135 **LB**
MEALS: Lunch £12-£15&alc High tea £8-£12 Dinner £15-£20&alc
CONF: Board 25 Del from £129
CARDS:

HURST GREEN Lancashire Map 07 SD63

★★68% **Shireburn Arms**
BB7 9QJ (off B6243) ☎ 01254 826518
FAX 01254 826208
This characterful, family owned inn is beautifully situated in the heart of the Ribble Valley. Bedrooms, one with a four-poster bed, are attractively decorated and well equipped. Fine views across the valley can be enjoyed from the spacious restaurant where a good range of dishes is served, and there is a cosy lounge where a welcoming coal fire burns in the winter. The hotel also benefits from a

unction room and a popular tea shop which serves lighter snacks and lelicious cakes.
16 en suite (bth/shr) (3 fmly) CTV in all bedrooms 71P Xmas
English & French Cuisine V meals Coffee am Tea pm
ROOMS: (incl. bkfst) s £39; d £54 * **LB**
CONF: Thtr 100 Class 50 Board 50
CARDS:

HYTHE Kent Map 05 TR13

★★★★ 75% **The Hythe Imperial**
Princes Pde CT21 6AE (M20,junc11 take A261)
☎ 01303 267441 FAX 01303 264610

This prestigious and professionally managed hotel faces the sea in an extensive 52 acre estate, which includes a golf course and formal gardens. The accommodation is furnished in a traditional style with many bedrooms now upgraded with good quality co-ordinated decor and period furniture. Service is most courteous and attentive, and the public areas include several bars, a comfortable lounge, and the attractive and well appointed Princes Restaurant; informal dining is available throughout the day in the newly created Churchill's bistro and bar. Extensive indoor leisure facilities offer a smart new swimming pool, a refurbished and extended hi-tech gym and there is a noteworthy provision for families with children.
100 en suite (bth/shr) (5 fmly) CTV in all bedrooms STV No dogs (ex guide dogs) Lift Night porter 201P Indoor swimming pool (heated) Golf 9 Tennis (hard & grass) Squash Snooker Sauna Solarium Gym Croquet lawn Putting green Jacuzzi/spa Beauty salon Fitness assessments ch fac Xmas V meals Coffee am Tea pm No smoking in restaurant Last d 9pm
ROOMS: (incl. bkfst) s £90-£110; d £115-£155 * **LB**
MEALS: Lunch £15-£20&alc Dinner £21-£23&alc*
CONF: Thtr 220 Class 100 Board 60
CARDS:

★★★ 72% **Stade Court**
West Pde CT21 6DT (M20, junc 11 on A261)
☎ 01303 268263 FAX 01303 261803
Stade Court stands on the seafront, just yards from a shingle beach, a popular hotel that offers very good levels of hospitality and service; the cheerful young team provide a caring and courteous service. Bedrooms are furnished in a modern style, some are unique with split levels providing additional sitting areas or bedrooms, and each room is thoughtfully equipped with a good range of facilities. The public rooms offer a comfortable first floor lounge, a convivial bar and a smartly appointed restaurant, in which chef Kevin Lea provides a good range of interesting dishes which are both tasty and decorative. There are good facilities for private meetings, and all the indoor leisure and golf facilities at the sister Hythe Imperial Hotel are also available for resident guests.
42 en suite (bth/shr) (5 fmly) No smoking in 7 bedrooms CTV in all bedrooms STV Lift 14P Indoor swimming pool (heated) Golf 9 Tennis (hard & grass) Squash Snooker Sauna Solarium Gym Croquet lawn Putting green Jacuzzi/spa All leisure facilities at sister hotel Xmas English & Continental Cuisine V meals Coffee am Tea pm No smoking area in restaurant Last d 9pm
ROOMS: (incl. bkfst) s fr £61.50; d fr £85 * **LB**
MEALS: Lunch £12.50-£15&alc Dinner £16.50-£19&alc*
CONF: Thtr 60 Class 50 Board 30 Del from £80
CARDS:

ILFORD Greater London See LONDON SECTION plan 1 H5

Travel Inn
Redbridge Ln East IG4 5BG ☎ 0181 550 7909
FAX 0181 550 6214

Purpose-built accommodation, offering spacious, well equipped bedrooms, all with en suite bathrooms. Meals may be taken at the nearby family restaurant. For more information about Travel Inns, consult the Contents page under Hotel Groups.
43 en suite (bth/shr)
ROOMS: d £35.50 *

Travelodge
Beehive Ln, Gants Hill IG4 5DR ☎ 0181 550 4248
FAX 0181 550 4248
This modern building offers accommodation in smart, spacious and well equipped bedrooms, suitable for family use, and all with en suite bathrooms. Meals may be taken at the nearby family restaurant. For information on room rates and to make a booking, call Roomline free of charge on 0800 850950. For more details about Travelodge, consult the Contents page under Hotel Groups.
32 en suite (bth/shr)

ILFRACOMBE Devon Map 02 SS54

★★ 69% **Elmfield**
Torrs Park EX34 8AZ (take A361 to Ilfracombe left at 1st traffic lights, left again at 2nd traffic lights, after 10yds left again hotel near top of hill on left) ☎ 01271 863377 FAX 01271 866828
Closed Dec-end Mar (ex Xmas)
A detached Victorian house in pleasant terraced gardens, the Elmfield is a quiet hotel which provides neat bedrooms with many modern facilities. In the dining room a short menu of good home cooking is offered, but guests must either order in advance or choose from a short carte of more convenience-style food.
11 en suite (bth/shr) 2 annexe en suite (bth/shr) CTV in all bedrooms No dogs 14P No coaches Indoor swimming pool (heated) Sauna Solarium Gym Pool table Jacuzzi/spa Darts No children 8yrs Xmas English & Continental Cuisine V meals No smoking in restaurant Last d 7.30pm
ROOMS: (incl. bkfst & dinner) s £39-£42; d £78-£84 * **LB**
OFF-PEAK: (incl. bkfst & dinner) s £35-£38; d £70-£76
MEALS: Bar Lunch £5-£10 Dinner £13-£14&alc
CARDS:

★★ 65% **Ilfracombe Carlton**
Runnacleave Rd EX34 8AR (take A361 to Ilfracombe left at traffic lights, left at next lights follow brown sign 'tunnels, beaches') ☎ 01271 862446 & 863711
FAX 01271 865379
Closed 3-31 Jan RS Feb
A popular choice for holidays, this hotel is well positioned for the attractions of the town. It is personally managed and the loyal staff create a cheerful, friendly atmosphere. The accommodation is pleasantly decorated and well equipped, with good modern facilities. Public areas are spacious and comfortable, and entertainment is provided most evenings. In the dining room a daily changing menu of traditional fare is offered.
48 en suite (bth/shr) (8 fmly) CTV in all bedrooms STV No dogs

contd.

(ex guide dogs) Lift Night porter 25P Wkly live entertainment Xmas Coffee am Tea pm No smoking in restaurant Last d 8.30pm
ROOMS: (incl. bkfst) s fr £29.50; d fr £50 * **LB**
OFF-PEAK: (incl. bkfst) s fr £27.50; d fr £50
MEALS: Bar Lunch £1.50-£3.50 Dinner £12.50*
CONF: Thtr 50 Class 50 Board 50 Del from £44.50
CARDS:

See advertisement on opposite page

★★63% **St Helier**
Hillsborough Rd EX34 9QQ (leave M5 junc27 onto A361 continue to Ilfracombe, then take Combe Martin road through High St hotel opposite 'Old Thatched Inn') ☎ 01271 864906 FAX 01271 864906
Closed Oct-Mar
Bright, fresh bedrooms with modern furnishings are provided at this family-run hotel which overlooks the harbour and is a convenient distance from the golf course. The reception area has a small TV lounge, and there are facilities for families, a choice of bars and a well tended garden.
16 rms (12 bth 1 shr) (6 fmly) CTV in all bedrooms STV 29P No coaches Pool table Darts English & Continental Cuisine V meals Coffee am Tea pm Last d 7.30pm
ROOMS: (incl. bkfst) s £23-£25; d £42-£46 * **LB**
MEALS: Dinner £8-£9
CARDS:

★★63% ***Tracy House***
Belmont Rd EX34 8DR ☎ 01271 863933 & 868979
RS Oct-Mar
The Watts family offer a warm welcome at this detached Victorian house conveniently located for the town centre. Bedrooms are simply furnished but bright and spacious, many having views over the town towards the sea. Public rooms include a bar and a traditionally furnished lounge.
11 rms (9 bth/shr) (2 fmly) CTV in all bedrooms 12P No coaches Solarium Putting green English & Continental Cuisine Coffee am Tea pm Last d 8pm
CARDS:

★58% **Torrs**
Torrs Park EX34 8AY ☎ 01271 862334
Closed Nov-Feb
A friendly, informal atmosphere and good standards of hospitality are provided by the resident owners of this hotel near the town centre and seafront. Public areas are comfortable if not luxurious, and tables are well spaced in a dining room where the dinner menu offers a choice of uncomplicated main dishes followed by some interesting desserts. Bedrooms are comfortable and reasonably equipped.
14 en suite (bth/shr) (5 fmly) CTV in all bedrooms 14P No children 5yrs V meals Coffee am Tea pm No smoking in restaurant Last d 7.30pm
ROOMS: (incl. bkfst & dinner) s fr £29.50; d fr £59 **LB**
OFF-PEAK: (incl. bkfst & dinner) s fr £26.50; d fr £53
MEALS: Lunch fr £7 Dinner fr £7.50&alc
CARDS:

ILKLEY West Yorkshire Map 07 SE14

★★★56% **Cow & Calf**
Moor Top LS29 8BT (1m off A65, signposted Cow & Calf rocks) ☎ 01943 607335 FAX 01943 816022

Closed Xmas
Located on the moors, high above the town, this family-owned and run hotel is close to the Cow and Calf rocks from which it takes its name. There are splendid views from the public rooms, which include a spacious dining room serving a satisfying range of dishes. The bedrooms are well equipped and are due to be upgraded shortly. There is a well tended garden for guests to enjoy.
20 en suite (bth/shr) (1 fmly) No smoking in 3 bedrooms CTV in all bedrooms 100P No coaches English & French Cuisine V meals Coffee am No smoking area in restaurant Last d 9pm
ROOMS: (incl. bkfst) s £45-£55; d £70-£80 * **LB**
MEALS: Lunch £5.75-£9.50 Dinner £13.75&alc
CONF: Thtr 40 Class 25 Board 25 Del from £60
CARDS:

★★74% **Rombalds**
11 West View, Wells Rd LS29 9JG (follow signs for Ilkley Moor from A65 turn right between Midland Bank & Dacre Son & Hartley)
☎ 01943 603201 FAX 01943 816586
Standing between the moors and the town, this Georgian terraced house is very attractive and has a pleasant front garden. It provides comfortable bedrooms which have been thoughtfully equipped whilst the elegant lounges are a delight to occupy. The young team are very caring and friendly and also very professional in their approach. The charming restaurant is the perfect setting for the well produced lunches and dinners prepared along classical lines.
15 en suite (bth/shr) No smoking in 1 bedroom CTV in all bedrooms 28P Xmas English & French Cuisine V meals Coffee am Tea pm No smoking in restaurant Last d 9.30pm
ROOMS: (incl. bkfst) s £65-£95; d £80-£110 * **LB**
OFF-PEAK: (incl. bkfst) s £50-£75; d £70-£90
MEALS: Lunch £6.95-£12.95&alc Dinner £8.75-£15.75&alc*
CONF: Thtr 70 Class 40 Board 25 Del from £75
CARDS:

★70% **Grove**
66 The Grove LS29 9PA ☎ 01943 600298 FAX 01943 600298
Closed 24 Dec-2 Jan
In a fine position overlooking the town gardens and convenient for the shops, the Grove is an attractive semidetached Victorian villa which is run as a small hotel by friendly proprietors Mr and Mrs Emslie. Dinners are prepared by request, and guests have use of a comfortable lounge and small, fully stocked bar. En suite bedrooms are mostly of a generous size and they are well looked after.
6 en suite (bth/shr) (2 fmly) CTV in all bedrooms 5P No coaches No smoking in restaurant Last d 7.30pm
ROOMS: (incl. bkfst) s £39-£42; d £52-£54 **LB**
OFF-PEAK: (incl. bkfst) s £30-£38; d £38-£48
MEALS: Lunch £9-£12&alc Dinner £13-£16&alc
CARDS:

★64% **Moorview**
104 Skipton Rd LS29 9HE (travelling west on A65 through Ilkley hotel on right just after 40mph sign on western side of town)
☎ 01943 600156
Roger and Christine Head, owners of this large Victorian house on the Skipton road, make every effort to ensure their guests are well looked after. The atmosphere is informal and nothing is too much trouble. Bedrooms vary in size, and whilst not all en suite, are nicely furnished and good use of modern wallpapers and fabrics is made. There is also a comfortable lounge which is warmed by a real fire in winter, and a small dining room where a very good set dinner is available.
13 rms (9 shr) (3 fmly) CTV in all bedrooms 15P V meals No smoking in restaurant Last d 7.30pm
ROOMS: (incl. bkfst) s £28-£38; d £40-£50 *
OFF-PEAK: (incl. bkfst) s £25-£38; d £38-£48
MEALS: Dinner £11-£12.50*
CARDS:

See advertisement on opposite page

ILMINSTER Somerset Map 03 ST31

★★★68% **Pheasant Hotel & Restaurant**
Water St, Seavington St Mary TA19 0QH (3m E of Ilminster, off B3168)
☎ 01460 240502 FAX 01460 242388

Closed 24 Dec-5 Jan
This delightful part thatched former farmhouse, surrounded by its own well tended gardens, is situated near the border of Somerset and is therefore also close to the counties of Dorset and Devon. The sympathetic decor and furnishings complement the character of the bar and restaurant, with their oak-beamed ceilings and splendid inglenook fireplaces. Individually styled bedrooms, some in cottages around the main house, have been equipped with modern facilities, and thoughtful extras such as sparkling wine, bottled waters and peanuts. An interesting menu offers a wide selection of dishes, which like the extensive wine list, shows a strong Italian influence. A pasta starter was accompanied by a sauce of garlic and mushrooms, flavoured with dry Martini and served with lashings of fresh parmesan, and was followed by a succulent rack of lamb in another creamy sauce, flavoured with grain mustard. Desserts are enticingly displayed on a trolley and included various meringues, tirimisu and a compote of fruits.
2 en suite (bth/shr) 6 annexe en suite (bth/shr) (2 fmly) CTV in all bedrooms STV No dogs (ex guide dogs) 50P No coaches ch fac International Cuisine V meals No smoking area in restaurant
ROOMS: (incl. bkfst) s fr £60; d fr £80 **LB**
MEALS:*
CARDS:

★★66% **Shrubbery**

CONSORT HOTELS

TA19 9AR (half a mile from A303 towards Ilminster town centre) ☎ 01460 52108 FAX 01460 53660
Situated on the western outskirts of the town, this extended Victorian property is set in attractive gardens with a swimming pool. The public areas are spacious and comfortable with many period features. Guests have the option of eating formally in the restaurant which offers both a fixed-price and à la carte menu, or in the bar which is more relaxed. Bedrooms in the main building are spacious, while those in the Garden Wing are more compact, all offer facilities beyond those expected in a hotel of this classification.
14 en suite (bth/shr) (3 fmly) CTV in all bedrooms STV 100P Outdoor swimming pool (heated) Tennis (grass) V meals Coffee am Tea pm Last d 9.30pm
ROOMS: (incl. bkfst) s £50-£65; d £80-£100 * **LB**
OFF-PEAK: (incl. bkfst) s £45; d £60-£70
MEALS: Lunch £6-£14&alc High tea £5.50-£7.50 Dinner £19.50*
CONF: Thtr 250 Class 100 Board 60 Del from £90
CARDS:

Travelodge

Travelodge

Horton Cross TA19 9PT (on A303) ☎ 01460 53748
FAX 01460 53748
This modern building offers accommodation in smart, spacious and well equipped bedrooms, suitable for family use, and all with en suite bathrooms. Meals may be taken at the nearby family restaurant. For information on room rates and to make a booking, call Roomline free of charge on 0800 850950. For more details about Travelodge, consult the Contents page under Hotel Groups.
32 en suite (bth/shr)

IMMINGHAM Lincolnshire Map 08 TA11

★★63% ***Old Chapel Hotel & Restaurant***
50 Station Rd DN40 3AY ☎ 01469 572377 FAX 01469 577883
A 19th-century Methodist chapel on the edge of the village has been converted into a well furnished value-for-money hotel. Bedrooms, though not generously proportioned, are well equipped and maintained, while the bar and restaurant provide a good choice of food and friendly service.
14 en suite (bth/shr) CTV in all bedrooms STV No dogs (ex guide dogs) 28P ch fac V meals Coffee am Tea pm Last d 10pm
CARDS:

I

INGATESTONE Essex Map 05 TQ69

★★★64% **The Heybridge**
Roman Rd CM4 9AB (on B1002) ☎ 01277 355355
FAX 01277 353288
Parts of this hotel date back to the 15th century, and in the original building there are a beamed cocktail bar and a restaurant which offers a lengthy traditional carte and live music at weekends. The hotel also has one of the largest banqueting suites in Essex. The comfortable chalet-style bedrooms have recently been upgraded and have attractive soft furnishings. A bowl of fresh fruit in every room is a welcome extra.
22 en suite (bth/shr) (3 fmly) No smoking in 2 bedrooms CTV in all bedrooms STV No dogs Night porter 220P Wkly live entertainment Xmas International Cuisine V meals Coffee am Tea pm Last d 10.15pm
ROOMS: s £78.50-£88.50; d £88.50-£115 *
MEALS: Lunch £13&alc Dinner £13&alc*
CONF: Thtr 600 Class 400 Board 10 Del from £116.60
CARDS:

INSTOW Devon Map 02 SS43

★★★69% **Commodore**
Marine Pde EX39 4JN (leave M5 junc27 follow N Devon link road to Bideford. Turn right before bridge to Instow hotel 3m from bridge) ☎ 01271 860347 FAX 01271 861233
Closed 24-26 Dec
Across the road from a sandy beach on the River Torridge, this attractive, purpose-built hotel commands glorious views. Bedrooms are individually styled, and those at the front have rooftop balconies. Public areas provide a bar-lounge, a no-smoking lounge, a large function suite and a restaurant serving enjoyable food from both carte and fixed-price menus.
20 en suite (bth/shr) CTV in all bedrooms No dogs Night porter 200P Xmas English & Continental Cuisine V meals Coffee am Tea pm No smoking area in restaurant Last d 9.15pm
ROOMS: (incl. bkfst & dinner) s £50-£60; d £95-£120 * **LB**
OFF-PEAK: (incl. bkfst & dinner) s £50-£60; d £86-£96
MEALS: Lunch £11-£14&alc Dinner £15-£19*
CONF: Thtr 250 Class 250 Board 80 Del from £65.50
CARDS:

See advertisement on opposite page

IPPLEPEN Devon Map 03 SX86

★★63% **Old Church House Inn**
Torbryan TQ12 5UR (take A381 from Newton Abbot after 5m turn right into Ipplepen continue a further one & a quarter miles to Torbryan hotel opposite the church) ☎ 01803 812372 FAX 01803 812180

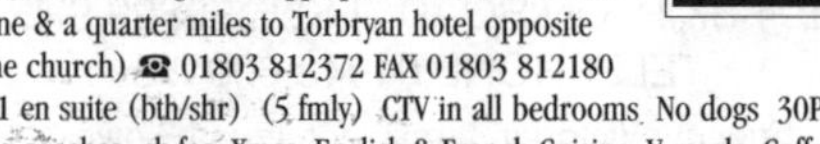

11 en suite (bth/shr) (5 fmly) CTV in all bedrooms No dogs 30P No coaches ch fac Xmas English & French Cuisine V meals Coffee am Tea pm Last d 10pm
ROOMS: s £35-£45; d £50-£65 * **LB**
MEALS: Lunch £8-£12&alc Dinner £12.50&alc*
CARDS:

IPSWICH Suffolk Map 05 TM14

★★★★ **Hintlesham Hall**
IP8 3NS ☎ 01473 652334 & 652268
FAX 01473 652463
(For full entry see Hintlesham)

★★★76% **Belstead Brook**
Belstead Brook Park, Belstead Rd IP2 9HB (take A1214 from A12/A14 interchange rdbt & follow signs to Belstead. Over bridge & 1st left into Belstead Rd then 1st left into hotel) ☎ 01473 684241 FAX 01473 681249

The hotel stands in eight acres of grounds on the edge of a residential area south of Ipswich. Friendly, attentive service is provided by an enthusiastic and professional team of staff. The modern and comfortable bedrooms include five purpose-built suites, ladies' rooms and no-smoking bedrooms. Public rooms include a small, intimate wood-panelled cocktail bar, a lounge bar and a restaurant which offers good formal dining. Chef John Gear and his brigade provide menus of English and rural French recipes which are presented in a modern style; diabetic, gluten-free and vegetarian menus are available.
76 en suite (bth/shr) (2 fmly) No smoking in 32 bedrooms CTV in all bedrooms STV Lift Night porter 120P Indoor swimming pool (heated) Sauna Solarium Gym Wkly live entertainment Xmas English & French Cuisine V meals Coffee am Tea pm No smoking area in restaurant Last d 10pm
ROOMS: s £75-£85; d £75-£115 **LB**
OFF-PEAK: s £65-£75; d £65-£115
MEALS: Lunch £19.50&alc High tea £12 Dinner £19.50&alc
CONF: Thtr 200 Class 45 Board 50 Del £110
CARDS:

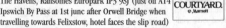

★★★72% **Marlborough**
Henley Rd IP1 3SP (take A1156 from A14 or A1214 from A12 turn right at Henley Rd/ A1214 x-rds) ☎ 01473 257677 FAX 01473 226927

This well run hotel is located north of the town centre in quiet residential surroundings with a good size attractive garden as a bonus. Personally managed by Robert and Karen Gough the service throughout is very friendly and attentive with a strong commitment to the needs of the individual customer being provided. Chef Simon Barker continues to provide a tempting range of interesting dishes together with some eclectic combinations all produced from fresh good quality ingredients and professional standards of skill. There are two styles of bedrooms; the main house and the new wing, but all furnished and equipped to the same high standard with attractive co-ordinated decor and fabrics. Public areas provide a very comfortable reception lobby lounge, an intimate and contemporary bar and a very attractive and well appointed restaurant overlooking the illuminated gardens.
22 en suite (bth/shr) (3 fmly) CTV in all bedrooms Night porter 60P Xmas English & French Cuisine V meals Coffee am Tea pm No smoking in restaurant Last d 9.30pm
ROOMS: (incl. bkfst) s £68-£72; d £78-£95 * **LB**
MEALS: Lunch £10-£14 Dinner fr £17.15&alc*
CARDS:

★★★69% **Courtyard by Marriott Ipswich**
The Havens, Ransomes Europark IP3 9SJ (just off A14 Ipswich By Pass at 1st junc after Orwell Bridge when travelling towards Felixstow, hotel faces the slip road) ☎ 01473 272244 FAX 01473 272484

This is a modern purpose built hotel situated in a business park on the outskirts of town. The interior has been designed with some style and bedrooms are well furnished and spacious.

60 en suite (bth/shr) (2 fmly) No smoking in 45 bedrooms CTV in all bedrooms STV No dogs (ex guide dogs) Lift Night porter 150P Sauna Solarium Gym Pool table Xmas International Cuisine V meals Coffee am Tea pm No smoking area in restaurant Last d 10pm
ROOMS: s £40-£65; d £55-£65 * **LB**
OFF-PEAK: s £45; d £45
MEALS: Lunch £12.95&alc Dinner £12.95-£16.95&alc*
CARDS:

★★★64% Ipswich Moat House

London Rd, Copdock IP8 3JD (2m S of A12/A14 interchange follow signs for Copdock/Washbrook, hotel 1m on left on old A12) ☎ 01473 209988
FAX 01473 730801
This hotel is a popular venue for conferences and its facilities have recently been improved with a state-of-the-art meeting room and a business centre. Bedrooms are all similarly furnished in a modern style. There is a carvery restaurant and an all-day menu is available in the lounge or from room service in the bedrooms. The small leisure club is unsupervised.
73 en suite (bth/shr) (2 fmly) No smoking in 20 bedrooms CTV in all bedrooms Lift Night porter 400P Indoor swimming pool (heated) Snooker Sauna Solarium Gym Jacuzzi/spa Xmas English & Continental Cuisine V meals Coffee am Tea pm No smoking in restaurant Last d 9.50pm
ROOMS: s £65-£85; d £65-£95 * **LB**
OFF-PEAK: s £50-£85; d £50-£95
MEALS: Lunch fr £13.50 Dinner fr £13.50*
CARDS:

★★★62% Novotel

Greyfriars Rd IP1 1UP (from A14 towards Felixstowe turn left onto A137 & follow for 2m into centre of town, hotel on double rdbt by Stoke Bridge)
☎ 01473 232400 FAX 01473 232414
This modern purpose-built hotel is located in the heart of the city, fairly close to the docks. It has extensive meeting and conference facilities to cater for its main function. The bedrooms are almost all identical and provide the standards of comfort expected from this group of hotels.
101 en suite (bth/shr) (6 fmly) No smoking in 62 bedrooms CTV in all bedrooms STV Lift Night porter Air conditioning 50P bar billiards Wkly live entertainment ch fac International Cuisine V meals Coffee am Tea pm No smoking area in restaurant Last d midnight
ROOMS: s £61; d £61 * **LB**
MEALS: Lunch £13.50&alc High tea £4.95 Dinner £11.65-£25alc*
CONF: Thtr 200 Class 80 Board 75 Del £90
CARDS:

★★65% Claydon Country House
16-18 Ipswich Rd, Claydon IP6 0AR (take A45 to Ipswich 4m before Ipswich take Great Blakenham road turn left off B113 to Claydon, hotel on left) ☎ 01473 830382 FAX 01473 832476
Standing in the village of Claydon, this pleasant house offers modern and well equipped bedrooms which are well equipped for today's traveller. A very good range of dishes are available in the charming restaurant whilst service is attentive and friendly. A cosy bar is found on the lower ground floor and comfortably furnished.
14 en suite (bth/shr) (2 fmly) CTV in all bedrooms STV No dogs (ex guide dogs) Night porter 60P No coaches ch fac Xmas English & French Cuisine V meals Coffee am Tea pm Last d 9.30pm
ROOMS: (incl. bkfst) s £40-£45; d £44-£53 * **LB**
OFF-PEAK: (incl. bkfst) s fr £30; d fr £30
MEALS: Lunch £6.50-£30 High tea £5 Dinner £8-£30
CONF: Thtr 40 Class 30 Board 20 Del £72
CARDS:

Forte Posthouse Ipswich
FORTE Posthouse
London Rd IP2 0UA (off A1214, from A12/A45)
☎ 01473 690313 FAX 01473 680412
Suitable for both the business and leisure traveller, this bright hotel provides modern accommodation in well equipped bedrooms with en suite bathrooms. For more details about Forte Posthouse hotels, consult the Contents page for the section on Hotel Groups.
109 en suite (bth/shr)
CONF: Thtr 120 Class 50 Board 40

Travel Inn

Mockbeggars Hall Farm, Claydon
☎ 01473 833125 FAX 01473 833127
Purpose-built accommodation, offering spacious, well equipped bedrooms, all with en suite bathrooms. Meals may be taken at the nearby family restaurant. For more information about Travel Inns, consult the Contents page under Hotel Groups.
61 en suite (bth/shr)
ROOMS: (incl. bkfst) d £35.50 *

Travelodge

Capel St Mary IP9 2JP ☎ 01473 312157
FAX 01473 312157
This modern building offers accommodation in smart, spacious and well equipped bedrooms, suitable for family use, and all with en suite bathrooms. Meals may be taken at the nearby family restaurant. For information on room rates and to make a booking, call Roomline free of charge on 0800 850950. For more details about Travelodge, consult the Contents page under Hotel Groups.
32 en suite (bth/shr)

ISLE OF Places incorporating the words 'Isle of' or 'Isle' will be found under the actual name - eg Isle of Wight is listed under Wight, Isle of.

IVYBRIDGE Devon Map 02 SX65

★★ 74% ***Glazebrook House Hotel & Restaurant***
TQ10 9SE (off A38) ☎ 01364 73322 FAX 01364 72350
This delightful mid-Victorian house stands in four acres of beautiful grounds and gardens on the southern edge of the Dartmoor National Park. Individually styled bedrooms are attractively furnished and co-ordinated, the hall and lounge/bar are comfortable and a short carte and fixed-price menu are available in either the spacious main dining room or a more intimate one reserved for residents. Chef David Merriman produces imaginative and interesting dishes using only the best local produce; a starter of duck liver pâté flavoured with Grand Marnier and served with a home-made chutney was particularly appealing. The hotel is also popular for residential and day conferences.
10 en suite (bth/shr) No smoking in 1 bedroom CTV in all bedrooms No dogs 50P No coaches English & French Cuisine V meals Coffee am Tea pm Last d 9pm
CARDS:

★★61% ***Sportsmans Inn Hotel & Restaurant***
Exeter Rd PL21 0BQ ☎ 01752 892280 FAX 01752 690714
11 rms (2 bth 7 shr) No smoking in all bedrooms CTV in all bedrooms No dogs (ex guide dogs) P Last d 9.30pm
CARDS:

KEGWORTH Leicestershire Map 08 SK42

★★64% **Kegworth**
Packington Hill DE74 2DF (0.5m from junct 24 of the M1 on the A6 towards Loughborough) ☎ 01509 672427 FAX 01509 674664
This modern hotel has been converted from a squash club and there are still many hints as to its former use. An impressive leisure centre includes gymnasium and pool and of course there are still squash courts. Bedrooms are all well equipped and comfortable. There is an attractive open plan lounge and bar and the restaurant serves carvery style meals supplemented by a popular carte. One major advantage is the proximity to the M1, the hotel is about 400 yards from an exit.
52 en suite (bth/shr) (3 fmly) No smoking in 24 bedrooms CTV in all bedrooms STV Night porter 150P No coaches Indoor swimming pool (heated) Squash Sauna Solarium Gym Jacuzzi/spa V meals Coffee am Tea pm Last d 9.30pm
ROOMS: s £50; d £50-£65 *
MEALS: Lunch £11.50 Dinner £11.50&alc*
CONF: Thtr 200 Class 70 Board 40 Del from £77
CARDS:

KEIGHLEY West Yorkshire Map 07 SE04

★★68% ***Beeches***
Bradford Rd BD21 4BB ☎ 01535 610611
Closed Xmas

TOBY

Located just half a mile from the town centre, this attractive stone building stands on a leafy corner of the A650. Modern bedrooms are well equipped and the informal restaurant serves a good range of dishes including classic steaks, chicken and fish dishes. Conference facilities and ample car parking are also available and service is friendly and efficient.

43 en suite (bth/shr) CTV in all bedrooms Night porter 120P
CARDS:

★★66% **Dalesgate**
406 Skipton Rd, Utley BD20 6HP (2m NW A629)
☎ 01535 664930 FAX 01535 611253
This well furnished and thoughtfully equipped hotel is found in the village of Utley and offers modern accommodation and very good value. There is a cosy bar and a good range of well produced food is served in the cottage dining room.
20 en suite (bth/shr) CTV in all bedrooms 25P ch fac French Cuisine V meals Coffee am Tea pm No smoking area in restaurant Last d 9pm
ROOMS: (incl. bkfst) s £30-£42; d £50-£60 * **LB**
MEALS: Dinner £10.50-£10.95&alc
CARDS:

KELLING Norfolk Map 09 TG04

★★67% **The Pheasant**
Coast Rd NR25 7EG (on A419 coast road, mid-way between Sheringham & Blakeney) ☎ 01263 588382 FAX 01263 588101
This delightfully peaceful hotel is set back from the coast road, shielded by several towering pine trees. The bedrooms are modern, spacious and well maintained and there is an open-plan bar and lounge area as well as a large restaurant offering a wide choice of dishes. The owners are actively involved in the day-to-day running of the hotel.
29 en suite (bth/shr) (1 fmly) No smoking in 16 bedrooms CTV in all bedrooms STV 100P Solarium V meals Coffee am Tea pm No smoking in restaurant Last d 9pm
ROOMS: (incl. bkfst) s £31-£41; d £50-£70 * **LB**
MEALS: Bar Lunch £2-£15alc Dinner £5-£20alc*
CONF: Thtr 40 Class 30 Board 20
CARDS:

KENDAL Cumbria Map 07 SD59
See also Crooklands

★★71% **Garden House**
Fowl-ing Ln LA9 6PH (leave M6 junc36 follow signs for A6 north & turn right at Duke of Cumberland after 200yds turn right inti lane near Burmah Garage) ☎ 01539 731131 FAX 01539 740064
RS 26-30 Dec
Set in several acres of pretty gardens and lawns, this fine Regency house is located in a quiet residential area but is also convenient for the town centre. Bedrooms are decorated with pretty papers and rich fabrics, and trouser presses and other modern facilities are provided. Canopied and four-poster beds are available and one room is located at ground-floor level. It is family run and services are friendly and informal.
10 en suite (bth/shr) (2 fmly) No smoking in 8 bedrooms CTV in all bedrooms 40P English & French Cuisine V meals Coffee am Last d 9pm
ROOMS: (incl. bkfst) s £45-£52.50; d £70-£80 * **LB**

Prices shown in the directory are meant as a guide only and are subject to change without warning. Please check before you book.

FF-PEAK: (incl. bkfst) d £65-£75
EALS: Lunch £4-£12 Dinner £14.95-£17.95&alc*
)NF: Thtr 30 Class 20 Board 20 Del from £80
ARDS:

KENILWORTH Warwickshire Map 04 SP27

★★65% **Chesford Grange**

esford Bridge CV8 2LD (0.5m SE Jct A46/A452 at bt take right exit signed Leamington Spa. After prox 250yds at x-rds turn right hotel on left)
☎ 01926 859331 FAX 01926 859075
nveniently located on the outskirts of the town with good access to ajor link roads, this popular business and conference hotel has an tensive range of facilities including the Periquito night club. With mply styled but well equipped bedrooms, it also offers a good range bars, meeting rooms and a restaurant offering a carvery in addition set menus. Extensive car parking is available on site.
3 en suite (bth/shr) 111 annexe en suite (bth/shr) (12 fmly) No noking in 55 bedrooms CTV in all bedrooms STV Lift Night porter 50P Gym Xmas V meals Coffee am Tea pm Last d 9.30pm
OOMS: (incl. bkfst) s fr £85; d fr £95 **LB**
EALS: Lunch fr £13 High tea £3-£8 Dinner £15.50-£20
)NF: Thtr 860 Class 300 Board 50 Del £110
ARDS:

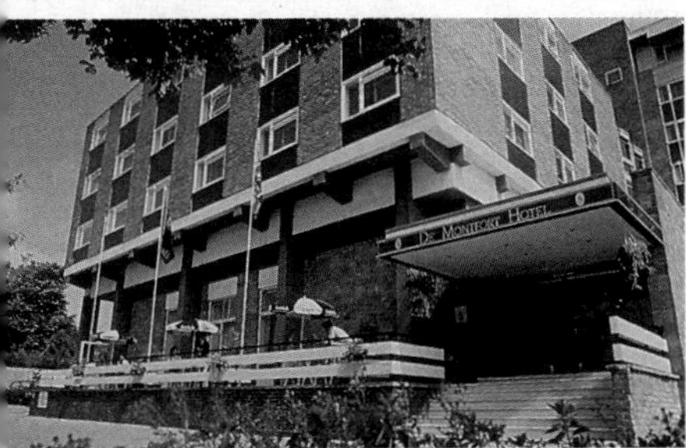

★★64% **De Montfort**
he Square CV8 1ED (take A452 into Kenilworth, hotel at top end of ain street by rdbt) ☎ 01926 855944 FAX 01926 857830
his multi-story hotel, built in the early 1970's has seen recent furbishment with attractively decorated bedrooms providing a good ray of equipment and modern facilities. Public rooms are detailed r similar good work and include a choice of bars, and a coffee shop hich is open to residents and the public until late evening.
06 en suite (bth/shr) (6 fmly) No smoking in 40 bedrooms CTV in l bedrooms STV Lift Night porter 85P Pool table Xmas V meals offee am Tea pm No smoking in restaurant Last d 9.30pm
OOMS: s fr £79; d fr £85 * **LB**
FF-PEAK: (incl. bkfst) s fr £55; d fr £65
EALS: Lunch £10 Dinner £18.95&alc*
ONF: Thtr 300 Class 120 Board 60 Del from £120
ARDS:

★★64% **Clarendon House**
ld High St CV8 1LZ ☎ 01926 857668 Cen. Res. 0800 616883
AX 01926 850669
his old tavern, dating from 1430, is situated in the centre of the enilworth conservation area, and old world ambience is one of the otel's charms. Bedrooms vary in size and are practically designed ith a good range of equipment. The carte is supplemented by a ackboard selection of daily specials.
) en suite (bth/shr) CTV in all bedrooms 20P V meals Coffee am ea pm Last d 9.30pm
OOMS: (incl. bkfst) s £49.50-£65; d fr £75 * **LB**

MEALS: Sunday Lunch £11.50 Dinner £12.25-£19alc*
CONF: Thtr 200 Class 50 Board 60 Del from £65
CARDS:

KENNFORD Devon Map 03 SX98

★★68% **Fairwinds**
EX6 7UD (4m from Exeter, off A38) ☎ 01392 832911
FAX 01392 832911
Closed Dec
This small no-smoking hotel offers a relaxed atmosphere and friendly, informal service. The comfortable modern bedrooms have been well equipped, and public areas include a reception lounge and a bar-lounge, adjacent to the attractive restaurant. Here, a selection of home-cooked dishes make up the interesting menu.
8 rms (6 bth/shr) (1 fmly) No smoking in all bedrooms CTV in all bedrooms STV No dogs 8P No coaches V meals No smoking in restaurant Last d 8pm
ROOMS: (incl. bkfst) s £24-£35; d £46-£47 * **LB**
OFF-PEAK: (incl. bkfst) s £23-£33; d £42-£46
MEALS: Dinner £10.95-£13.60&alc
CARDS:

KENTON Greater London See LONDON SECTION plan 1 C5

Travel Inn

Kenton Rd HA3 8AT (on A4006 between Harrow and Wembley) ☎ 0181 907 4069 FAX 0181 909 1604
Purpose-built accommodation, offering spacious, well equipped bedrooms, all with en suite bathrooms. Meals may be taken at the nearby family restaurant. For more information about Travel Inns, consult the Contents page under Hotel Groups.
44 en suite (bth/shr)
ROOMS: d £35.50 *

K

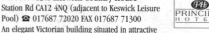

KESWICK Cumbria Map 11 NY22
See also Thornthwaite

★★★★62% **Keswick Country House**

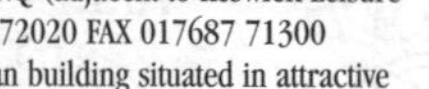

Station Rd CA12 4NQ (adjacent to Keswick Leisure Pool) ☎ 017687 72020 FAX 017687 71300

An elegant Victorian building situated in attractive grounds and gardens overlooking the town and adjoining the old railway station. Recent refurbishment has considerably enhanced the public rooms which include a Victorian Conservatory complete with its own grape-vine. Bedrooms are rather compact, but well equipped and many have fine views of the surrounding mountains and fells. Facilities are available for business meetings and conferences and the location is ideal for wedding receptions.

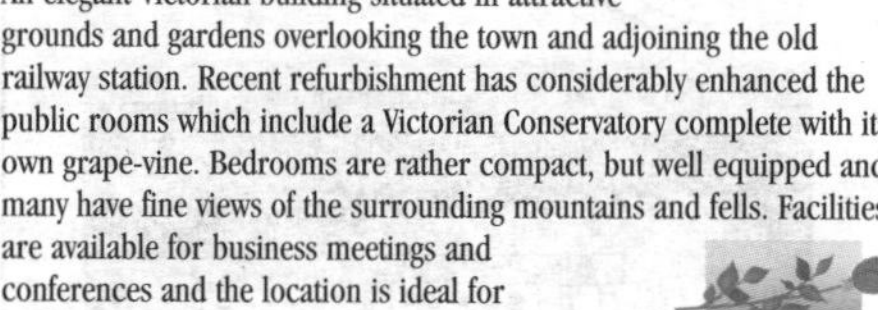

66 en suite (bth/shr) (6 fmly) CTV in all bedrooms STV Lift Night porter 55P Pool table Croquet lawn Putting green Pitch & putt Xmas V meals Coffee am Tea pm No smoking in restaurant Last d 9.15pm
ROOMS: (incl. bkfst) s £42-£80; d £84-£96 **LB**
OFF-PEAK: (incl. bkfst) s £30-£80; d £50-£96
MEALS: Sunday Lunch £9.95 Dinner £14.95&alc*
CONF: Thtr 60 Class 35 Board 35 Del from £70
CARDS:

See advertisement under WINDERMERE

★★★67% **Derwentwater**

Portinscale CA12 5RE (off A66 turn into village of Portinscale, follow signs) ☎ 017687 72538
FAX 017687 71002

Geared wholly to the needs of the leisure market, this hotel lies in the village of Portinscale, just a mile from Keswick on the western shores of Derwentwater. Its gardens stretch down to the lake and many of the bedrooms have a fine outlook to the distant fells. Splendid views are also enjoyed from the conservatory, where afternoon teas and after-dinner coffees are served. The hotel shop offers gifts, local produce and tourist information.

44 en suite (bth/shr) (2 fmly) CTV in all bedrooms Lift Night porter 120P Fishing Pool table Putting green Wkly live entertainment ch fac Xmas English & French Cuisine V meals Coffee am Tea pm No smoking area in restaurant Last d 9.15pm
ROOMS: (incl. bkfst) s £69-£85; d £110-£168 * **LB**
MEALS: Bar Lunch £2.75-£15&alc Dinner £19.95&alc
CARDS:

See advertisement on opposite page

★★★63% **Skiddaw**

Main St CA12 5BN (in the Market Square in heart of the town)
☎ 017687 72071 FAX 017687 74850

Set in the town square and with a small car park to the rear, this hotel offers a lively little restaurant, along with bedrooms in a range of sizes. Its bar is a popular rendezvous for morning coffees and daily snacks, but is less busy in the evenings and there is also a quiet upstairs lounge for residents.

40 en suite (bth/shr) (7 fmly) CTV in all bedrooms STV Lift 12P Sauna Solarium Free use of out of town leisure fac Xmas English & French Cuisine V meals Coffee am Tea pm No smoking in restaurant Last d 9.30pm
ROOMS: (incl. bkfst) s £34-£38; d £62-£75 **LB**
MEALS: Lunch £5.50-£11.50alc High tea fr £5.95alc Dinner £14-£15&alc
CONF: Thtr 70 Class 60 Board 40 Del from £59
CARDS:

See advertisement on page 32

★★ 76% **Dale Head Hall Lakeside**

Lake Thirlmere CA12 4TN (mid-way between Keswick & Grasmere, off A591, onto private drive to shores of Lake Thirlmere)
☎ 017687 72478 & 0800 454166 FAX 017687 71070
(Rosette awarded for dinner only)

This fine country house lies secluded in extensive woodland and gardens overlooking Thirlmere. The Lowe family offer the utmost in hospitality which makes for a friendly and relaxing atmosphere. A house of two period styles, the rear - including the dining room and several bedrooms - retains its 16th-century character, with oak beams original woodwork and natural stone, whilst the front - with most of the bedrooms and two lovely lounges - are of a later period. The house is also graced with beautiful pieces of furniture crafted by Alan Lowe. Dinner features good British cooking, along with a serious wine list and whilst the menu choice is small it runs to five courses.

9 en suite (bth/shr) (1 fmly) No smoking in all bedrooms No dogs 22P No coaches Tennis (grass) Fishing Croquet lawn Xmas V meals Coffee am Tea pm No smoking in restaurant Last d 8.30pm
ROOMS: (incl. bkfst) s £60-£65; d £70-£80 * **LB**
OFF-PEAK: (incl. bkfst) s £55-£60; d £60-£75
MEALS: Dinner £24.50*
CARDS:

See advertisement on page 32

★★ 75% **Grange Country House**

Manor Brow, Ambleside Rd CA12 4BA (take A66 into Keswick then left onto A591 to Windermere for half a mile, take first right, hotel on right) ☎ 017687 72500
Closed 5 Nov-7 Mar

This elegant lakeland house sits in its own gardens high above the town and enjoys superb views of the surrounding fells. Duncan and Jane Miller are enthusiastic hosts whose cheery outgoing manner creates a friendly and relaxing atmosphere. Spotlessly clean and attractively maintained throughout, public rooms give a choice of lounges including the lounge bar with a log fire and a dining room which takes full advantage of the views. The same can be said of the bedrooms, all of which are individual, some furnished in contemporary style and others with period pieces, the upper rooms having beamed ceilings. The daily-changing dinner menu offers a short choice but it does run to five courses, featuring good honest British cooking.

10 en suite (bth/shr) No smoking in all bedrooms CTV in all

contd

bedrooms 13P No coaches No children 7yrs V meals Coffee am Tea pm No smoking in restaurant Last d 8pm
ROOMS: (incl. bkfst & dinner) d £91-£105 **LB**
MEALS: Dinner £19
CARDS:

★★ 72% **Lyzzick Hall Country House**
Under Skiddaw CA12 4PY (do not enter town keep to Keswick by-pass then take 3rd exit off rdbt onto A591 towards Carlisle hotel is one & a half miles on right) ☎ 017687 72277 FAX 017687 72278
Closed 24-26 Dec & Feb
This fine country house lies in an elevated position under Skiddaw, two miles northwest of Keswick and enjoying superb views across the valley. Owners Alfredo and Dorothy Fernandez and their staff provide a friendly, hospitable atmosphere in which families are very welcome. There are two lounges, a small bar area and a spacious restaurant. Bedrooms vary in size but are all well equipped. There is a choice of three dinner menus to satisfy everyone's palate and pocket.
24 en suite (bth/shr) 1 annexe en suite (bth/shr) (3 fmly) CTV in all bedrooms No dogs 40P No coaches Indoor swimming pool (heated) ch fac International Cuisine V meals Coffee am No smoking in restaurant Last d 9.30pm
ROOMS: (incl. bkfst) s £37-£39; d £74-£78 **LB**
OFF-PEAK: (incl. bkfst) s fr £35; d fr £70
MEALS: Lunch £9-£16alc Dinner £19.50-£20&alc
CARDS:

★★68% **Chaucer House**

Derwentwater Place CA12 4DR (Turn right off A591 into Manor Brow, continue down hill, past Castlerigg Catholic Training Centre and sharp double bend, hotel on right) ☎ 017687 72318 & 73223 FAX 017687 75551
Closed Dec-Jan
Attractive, comfortable public areas and efficient service by smart, well groomed staff are features of this well maintained hotel which lies just off the town centre and has a car park to the rear. Dinner offers a wide range of dishes, with a carte augmenting the fixed-price four-course menu.
35 rms (28 bth/shr) (4 fmly) No smoking in 6 bedrooms CTV in all bedrooms STV Lift 25P English & French Cuisine V meals Coffee am No smoking in restaurant Last d 9pm
ROOMS: (incl. bkfst) s £24.50-£38; d £40.95-£83 * **LB**
OFF-PEAK: (incl. bkfst & dinner) s £31-£41; d £58-£88
MEALS: Dinner £6.95-£16.50&alc*
CARDS:

★★68% **Lairbeck**
Vicarage Hill CA12 5QB (follow A66 to rdbt with A591 turn left then immediately right onto Vicarage Hill, hotel 150 yds on right)
☎ 017687 73373
Closed Jan & Feb RS 22-31 Dec
This fine Victorian country house lies secluded in its own gardens, yet is convenient for the A66/A591 Keswick by-pass and within walking distance of the town. Quietly run by Colin and Kathleen Lisle, the atmosphere is peaceful and relaxed and will appeal particularly to the more mature guest. The house retains much of its original character, but has been sympathetically modernised over the years, being attractively furnished, very well maintained and above all spotlessly clean. Bedrooms come in a variety of sizes, several being particularly well proportioned, but each is individual and named after its original use when the house was a private residence. There is a cosy residents' bar with a magnificent marble fireplace, and an attractive dining room with views of the garden.
14 en suite (bth/shr) (1 fmly) No smoking in all bedrooms CTV in all bedrooms No dogs (ex guide dogs) 20P No coaches Croquet lawn No children 5yrs Xmas English & French Cuisine V meals No smoking in restaurant Last d 8pm
ROOMS: (incl. bkfst & dinner) s £47; d £94 **LB**
OFF-PEAK: (incl. bkfst & dinner) s £40; d £80
MEALS: Dinner £14*
CARDS:

★★67% **Highfield**
The Heads CA12 5ER (approaching from A66 take 2nd exit at rdbt, turn left follow road to t-junc left again & right at mini rdbt, The Heads is 4th turning on right) ☎ 01768 772508
Fronted by gardens and overlooking the park with a vista of mountains beyond, this friendly hotel has bedrooms in a variety of sizes, with some well proportioned ones to the front, two having their own balcony. There is a choice of lounges and two cosy dining rooms with dinner menus offering a good selection of home-cooked dishes.
19 rms (15 bth/shr) (3 fmly) CTV in 15 bedrooms 19P No coaches No children 5yrs Xmas V meals Coffee am Tea pm No smoking in restaurant Last d 8pm
ROOMS: (incl. bkfst) s £20-£29; d £48-£58
OFF-PEAK: (incl. bkfst) d £40-£50
MEALS: Dinner £12-£14&alc
CARDS:

★★ 66% **Applethwaite Country House Hotel**
Applethwaite, Underskiddaw CA12 4PL ☎ 017687 72413
FAX 017687 75706
Closed 10 Dec-1 Feb
This small welcoming family-run country house hotel, a former Victorian residence built of local stone, is situated about 1.5 miles north of Keswick and stands in its own well tended grounds on a hillside under the shadow of Skiddaw. Relaxing public rooms enjoying splendid views over the Borrowdale Valley include a choice of comfortable non-smoking sitting rooms, and enjoyable home cooking is served in the attractive dining room. Bedrooms are smartly decorated and offer both traditional and modern furnishings.
12 en suite (bth/shr) (3 fmly) No smoking in all bedrooms CTV in all bedrooms No dogs (ex guide dogs) 10P No coaches Croquet lawn Putting green bowling green No children 7yrs V meals No smoking in restaurant Last d 6.50pm
ROOMS: (incl. bkfst) s £27.15-£31; d £54.30-£62 * **LB**
OFF-PEAK: (incl. bkfst) s £27.15-£29; d £54-£58
MEALS: Dinner £16*
CARDS:

See advertisement on opposite page

★★65% **Queen's**
Main St CA12 5JF (From A66 take Keswick turn off & Hotel is in the Market Sq near The Moot Hall)
☎ 017687 73333 FAX 017687 71144
Closed 24-26 Dec
This large hotel lies right in the town's market place and has the benefit of a small covered garage to the rear. Well proportioned public areas include a foyer lounge and conservatory, and the well equipped bedrooms, although varying in style, offer good value for money.

contd.

K

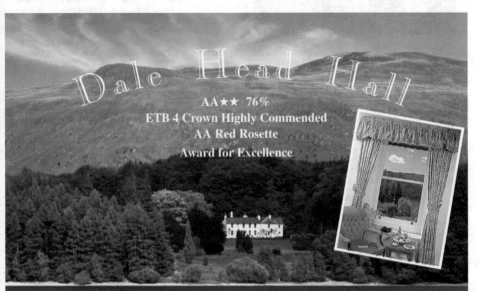

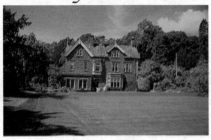

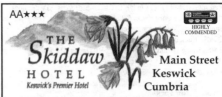

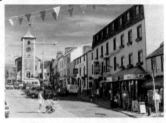

37 en suite (bth/shr) (15 fmly) CTV in all bedrooms STV No dogs Lift 8P English French Italian & Indian Cuisine V meals Coffee am Tea pm No smoking in restaurant Last d 9.30pm
ROOMS: (incl. bkfst) s £22.50-£30; d £45-£60 * **LB**
MEALS: Lunch £8.50&alc High tea £7.50 Dinner £12.50&alc*
CONF: Thtr 60 Class 30 Board 30
CARDS:

★★64% **Crow Park**
The Heads CA12 5ER ☎ 017687 72208 FAX 017687 74776
This family-run hotel lies in a splendid Victorian crescent enjoying fine views down the Borrowdale Valley, yet within walking distance of the town centre. Attractive and comfortable public areas feature an interesting display of historic local photographs.
27 rms (14 bth 12 shr) (1 fmly) No smoking in 1 bedroom CTV in all bedrooms STV 27P Xmas English & Continental Cuisine V meals Coffee am No smoking in restaurant Last d 8pm
ROOMS: (incl. bkfst) s £21.50-£28.50; d £43-£57 **LB**
OFF-PEAK: (incl. bkfst) s £20.50-£21.50; d £41-£43
MEALS: Dinner £10-£14*
CARDS:

RED STAR HOTEL

★ **Swinside Lodge**
Newlands CA12 5UE (off A66 turn left at Portinscale & follow road to Grange for 2m. Ignore signs to Swinside & Newlands Valley)
☎ 01768 772948 FAX 01768 772948
Closed Dec-mid Feb
This Victorian Lakeland house enjoys a picture postcard setting, lying in its own gardens at the foot of Catbells and surrounded by fields and meadows, with Derwentwater a five minute stroll away. Tastefully converted to an hotel by Graham Taylor, this little gem is immaculately maintained, with modern well equipped bedrooms and delightful public areas comprising a choice of lovely lounges with lots of interesting books, and a cosy candle-lit dining room. Hospitality is second-to-none. Graham Taylor is the perfect host and is assisted by Lisa, both providing friendly and spontaneous attention, but in an unobtrusive manner. The house is not licensed but one is welcome to bring ones own wine and other drinks, although a complimentary sherry is served prior to dinner, which is at 7.30pm. The five-course meal offers no choice except for desserts. Chris Asteley gets the best from his ingredients without recourse to fussiness, and a red pepper souffle and a bitter chocolate tart served just warm, reflected his skills. A main course of baked Borrowdale trout with a lemon-scented watercress stuffing and chervil butter sauce, was a perfectly balanced dish. There's always a soup course, accompanied by delicious home-baked bread and rolls.
7 en suite (bth/shr) No smoking in 9 bedrooms CTV in all bedrooms No dogs (ex guide dogs) 10P No coaches No children 12yrs Xmas English & French Cuisine Coffee am Tea pm No smoking in restaurant Last d 7.30pm
ROOMS: (incl. bkfst & dinner) s £69-£78; d £122-£152 **LB**
MEALS: Dinner £25-£29

★69% **Edwardene**
26 Southey St CA12 4EF (take A591 towards Keswick town centre at pedestrian traffic lights turn left into Southey St) ☎ 017687 73586 FAX 017687 73824
Built in the traditional Lakeland style of stone and slate, this charming Victorian building has been converted from two adjacent houses. Its exterior is a myriad of colour from shrubs, baskets and tubs; the interior is well maintained and thoughtfully furnished. Further attractions are the friendly atmosphere and a position just around the corner from the shops.
11 en suite (bth/shr) (1 fmly) No smoking in all bedrooms CTV in all bedrooms No dogs (ex guide dogs) No coaches Xmas Coffee am No smoking in restaurant Last d 6.30pm
ROOMS: (incl. bkfst) s £21-£23; d £42-£46
MEALS: Dinner £11.50
CARDS:

★68% **Linnett Hill**
4 Penrith Rd CA12 4HF (from A66 west after 17m take left fork into Keswick, hotel is facing river & park, just before town centre, on left)
☎ 017687 73109
This friendly little family-run hotel lies on the main road leading into the town from the south and east and has the benefit of a car park at the rear, as well as being only a few minutes walk from the centre of Keswick. Well maintained throughout, it has cheery bedrooms, an attractive lounge and a cosy residents' bar, whilst dinner offers tasty home cooking from a short four-course menu. Guests are asked to choose dinner and breakfast dishes beforehand.
10 en suite (bth/shr) No smoking in all bedrooms CTV in all bedrooms No dogs (ex guide dogs) 12P No children 5yrs Xmas V meals Coffee am Tea pm No smoking in restaurant Last d 6.30pm
ROOMS: (incl. bkfst) s £24-£30; d £45 * **LB**
OFF-PEAK: (incl. bkfst) d £40
MEALS: Dinner fr £13&alc*
CARDS:

KETTERING Northamptonshire Map 04 SP87

★★★★ 71% **Kettering Park**
SHIRE INNS
Kettering Parkway NN15 6XT (just off junct 9 of A14, M1 to A1 link road, on the Kettering Venture Park)
☎ 01536 416666 FAX 01536 416171
There are excellent levels of comfort and good quality furnishings in the spacious and thoughtfully laid out bedrooms in this modern, purpose-built hotel, located just off junction 9 of the A14. It caters mainly for conferences and meetings but readily adapts to leisure and individual users. There is a smart and attentive team of staff in Langberry's Restaurant where the menu shows thought and imagination.
88 en suite (bth/shr) (28 fmly) No smoking in 40 bedrooms CTV in all bedrooms STV Lift Night porter 200P Indoor swimming pool (heated) Squash Snooker Sauna Solarium Gym Jacuzzi/spa Steam rooms Wkly live entertainment Xmas International Cuisine V meals Coffee am Tea pm Last d 9.45pm
ROOMS: (incl. bkfst) s £88-£128; d £108-£148 * **LB**
OFF-PEAK: (incl. bkfst & dinner) s fr £49; d fr £124
MEALS: Bar Lunch fr £10 Dinner fr £22alc*
CONF: Thtr 260 Class 120 Board 40 Del from £135
CARDS:

Travel Inn

Rothwell Rd NN16 8XF (on A14 linking A1 & M1. Off junct7 of the A14 near Telford Way Industrial Estate) ☎ 01536 310082 FAX 01536 310104

Purpose-built accommodation, offering spacious, well equipped bedrooms, all with en suite bathrooms. Meals may be taken at the nearby family restaurant. For more information about Travel Inns, consult the Contents page under Hotel Groups.

39 en suite (bth/shr)

ROOMS: (incl. bkfst) d £35.50 *

KEYNSHAM Somerset Map 03 ST66

★★66% Grasmere Court

22-24 Bath Rd BS18 1SN (on Main A4 Bath Road, midway between Bristol & Bath) ☎ 0117 986 2662 FAX 0117 986 2762

Conveniently located midway between Bath and Bristol city centres, this recently renovated hotel is run by the Llewellin family. The well stocked cocktail bar is the ideal place for guests to socialise and unwind after a busy day. While a home cooked, table d'hote menu is available on Monday-Thursday, a range of bar meals are offered over the weekend. The bedrooms are spacious and comfortable, ranging from standard rooms, to superior and the four poster room, all being priced accordingly.

16 en suite (bth/shr) (2 fmly) No smoking in all bedrooms CTV in all bedrooms STV No dogs 17P No coaches V meals Coffee am Tea pm No smoking in restaurant Last d 7.30pm

ROOMS: (incl. bkfst) s £43; d £58 * **LB**

OFF-PEAK: (incl. bkfst) s £34; d £48

MEALS: Bar Lunch £2-£6 Dinner £7-£12*

CARDS:

★★62% Grange

42 Bath Rd BS18 1SN ☎ 0117 986 9181 FAX 0117 986 6373

Ideally situated between the cities of Bath and Bristol, this small hotel offers comfortable accommodation and a relaxed atmosphere. Bedrooms are equipped with modern comforts and the public areas include a choice of lounges; one with a bar, and an informal restaurant.

11 en suite (bth/shr) 18 annexe en suite (bth/shr) (4 fmly) No smoking in 11 bedrooms CTV in all bedrooms No dogs (ex guide dogs) 25P Gym English & French Cuisine V meals Coffee am Tea pm Last d 9pm

ROOMS: (incl. bkfst) s £44.50-£69; d £59.50-£78 **LB**

OFF-PEAK: (incl. bkfst) s £37; d £52

MEALS: Lunch £9.25-£10.25alc Dinner £10.25-£14.05alc*

CONF: Thtr 20 Class 20 Board 16

CARDS:

KIDDERMINSTER Hereford & Worcester Map 07 SO87

★★★★59% Stone Manor

Stone DY10 4PJ (2m SE on A448) ☎ 01562 777555 FAX 01562 777834

This mock Tudor property dates back to 1926. It stands in 25 acres of impressive grounds and gardens, 2 miles east of Kidderminster on the A448. Facilities include extensive function and conference facilities and the hotel is understandably a popular venue for business conferences and wedding receptions. The accommodation is graded into four categories, which range from economy to de-lux. Rooms with four-poster beds are available. At the time of our last inspection, work to upgrade many bedrooms was due to commence.

52 en suite (bth/shr) (8 fmly) No smoking in 6 bedrooms CTV in all bedrooms STV Night porter 400P Outdoor swimming pool Tennis (hard) Pool table Croquet lawn Putting green Xmas International Cuisine V meals Coffee am Tea pm Last d 10pm

contd.

K

ROOMS: s £49.50-£75; d £49.50-£75 * **LB**
MEALS: Lunch £11.50-£13.25&alc Dinner £15.50-£16.95&alc*
CONF: Thtr 150 Class 48 Board 60 Del from £99.50
CARDS:

KILLINGTON LAKE MOTORWAY SERVICE AREA Cumbria
Map 07 SD59

Roadchef Lodge

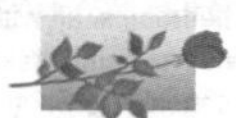

Killington Lake Motorway Servi, M6 Southbound, Killington LA8 0NW (1m S of junc37 M6)
☎ 01539 621666 FAX 01539 621660
Smart, spacious and well equipped bedrooms, all with en suite bathrooms, are provided by this modern hotel. Meals may be taken at a nearby family restaurant. For more information about RoadChef Lodges, consult the Contents page under Hotel Groups.
36 en suite (bth/shr)
ROOMS: s £39.95; d £39.95
CONF: Board 8

KINGHAM Oxfordshire Map 04 SP22

★★★71% **Mill House Hotel & Restaurant**
OX7 6UH (turn off A44 at either Chipping Norton or Stow on the Wold onto B4450, hotel is on outskirts of Kingham village)
☎ 01608 658188 FAX 01608 658492
This charming Cotswold stone hotel is set in extensive, well manicured grounds bordered by a trout stream. General Manager Simon Ellis leads from the front and personally welcomes each guest and the friendly staff follow his example creating a warm and relaxing atmosphere. Each bedroom is individually furnished and thoughtfully equipped with many extras. There is a comfortable lounge and bar, and the restaurant serves carefully prepared food. The Mill House is an attractive base from which to explore the surrounding countryside.
21 en suite (bth/shr) 2 annexe rms (1 fmly) CTV in all bedrooms 62P No coaches Fishing Croquet lawn No children 5yrs Xmas English & French Cuisine V meals Coffee am Tea pm No smoking in restaurant Last d 9.15pm
ROOMS: (incl. bkfst) s £55-£65; d £90-£110 * **LB**
MEALS: Lunch fr £12.95&alc Dinner fr £19.95&alc
CONF: Thtr 30 Class 24 Board 20 Del from £110
CARDS:

KINGSBRIDGE Devon Map 03 SX74

★★★77% **Buckland-Tout-Saints**

Goveton TQ7 2DS (2.5m N of Kingsbridge on A381)
☎ 01548 853055 FAX 01548 856261
This beautifully proportioned Queen Anne manor house stands in seven acres of grounds in a sheltered position with far-reaching views of rolling Devon countryside. The bedrooms are individually furnished and equipped with modern comforts. Wood panelled public areas have been tastefully furnished in keeping with the elegance of the building and include a small meeeting room and a choice of comfortable lounges, one with a bar. Dinner is served in an intimate restaurant where the chef incorporates fresh local produce into an imaginative short menu. At a recent inspection meal a tagliatelle starter was served with succulent pieces of smoked chicken and a creamy pepper-based sauce. The main course of sea bass was cooked to perfection and delicately flavoured, though the accompanying white wine sauce was a little overpowering. The Taylor family and their team of friendly staff welcome guests and provide attentive services.
12 en suite (bth/shr) CTV in all bedrooms 16P No coaches Croquet lawn Putting green Xmas English & French Cuisine V meals Coffee am Tea pm Last d 9.30pm
ROOMS: (incl. bkfst & dinner) s £60-£75; d £120-£170 * **LB**
MEALS: Lunch £14.50 Dinner £27.50*
CARDS:

See advertisement on opposite page

★★73% **White House**

TQ7 2JX (on the A379 at the eastern end of the village) ☎ 01548 580580 FAX 01548 581124
Closed 29 Dec-Etr
Situated between Kingsbridge and Dartmouth, the White House Hotel is set in an acre of well tended gardens. The public areas have recently been extended with the addition of the Garden Room Restaurant, which has been built in keeping with the rest of the Grade 2 building. There are ample lounge areas including the spacious drawing room and the cosy Brockington Room, both of which are no-smoking areas. In addition, there is the Normandy bar-lounge, where a welcoming log fire burns on cooler evenings. The table d'hÙte menu offers a limited choice of dishes, all of which are freshly prepared by one of the partners, David Alford. At a recent test meal herb-filled mushrooms were followed by medallions of beef with a piquant peppercorn sauce accompanied by some delicious fresh vegetables. A frangipane pear tart was taken for dessert and the meal was completed by a small selection of local cheeses. Michael Roberts, the other partner in the business, attends to guests' needs with a small team of attentive staff.
8 en suite (bth/shr) (1 fmly) CTV in all bedrooms 12P No coaches Croquet lawn Badminton Xmas English, French & Italian Cuisine V meals Coffee am Tea pm No smoking in restaurant Last d 8.05pm
ROOMS: (incl. bkfst) d £72-£92 * **LB**
OFF-PEAK: (incl. bkfst) d £66-£84
MEALS: Dinner £8.75-£15
CARDS:

★★65% **Kings Arms**

93 Fore St TQ7 1AB (adjacent to Town Hall and the Shambles) ☎ 01548 852071 FAX 01548 852977
Centrally situated in the town, the Kings Arms has been welcoming guests since 1775. John and Janet Cocklin with their team of loyal staff create a relaxed and informal atmosphere for guests, whether staying on holiday or joining locals drinking in the bar. The split-level restaurant serves a varied à la carte menu, featuring English and continental cuisine. At lunchtime and during the evening a range of bar meals is also available. The bedrooms are the subject of an upgrading programme.
11 rms (9 bth/shr) (2 fmly) CTV in all bedrooms STV 25P No coaches Indoor swimming pool (heated) Wkly live entertainment Xmas English & French Cuisine V meals Coffee am No smoking area in restaurant Last d 9.30pm
ROOMS: (incl. bkfst) s £35-£40; d £60-£70 * **LB**
MEALS: Lunch £10-£12.50alc Dinner £14.50-£18alc*
CONF: Thtr 160 Class 60 Board 12
CARDS:

KING'S LYNN Norfolk Map 09 TF62

★★★ **Congham Hall Country House**

Lynn Rd PE32 1AH ☎ 01485 600250
FAX 01485 601191
(For full entry see Grimston)

★★★69% **Knights Hill**

Knights Hill Village, South Wootton PE30 3HQ (junct A148/A149) ☎ 01553 675566 FAX 01553 675568
This hotel complex offers a wide range of facilities which makes it equally popular with both corporate and leisure guests. The conference and banqueting centre and the modern indoor leisure centre are housed in converted 17th-century farm buildings, as is the Farmers Arms village pub. The accommodation is mainly located in extensions to the 16th-century hunting lodge. These bedrooms are well

appointed and quite spacious. By comparison the courtyard annexe bedrooms are more varied in size and of a simpler style. Dining options include formal meals in the Garden Restaurant in the main hotel, or informal choices in the Farmers Arms.

38 en suite (bth/shr) 16 annexe en suite (bth/shr) No smoking in 14 bedrooms CTV in all bedrooms STV Night porter 350P Indoor swimming pool (heated) Tennis (hard) Sauna Solarium Gym Croquet lawn Jacuzzi/spa Heli-pad International Cuisine V meals Coffee am Tea pm Last d 9.30pm

ROOMS: s £70-£80; d £80-£90 * **LB**

MEALS: Sunday Lunch fr £10.95 Dinner fr £16.95&alc

CONF: Thtr 350 Class 150 Board 30 Del from £65

CARDS:

★★★66% **Butterfly**

Beveridge Way, Hardwick Narrows PE30 4NB (Situated on A10/A47 roundabout, take exit for Hardwick Narrows Industrial Estate)

☎ 01553 771707 FAX 01553 768027

A modern, purpose-built hotel, the Butterfly is located off the major roundabout to the south-east of the town centre. Friendly, smartly dressed staff are much in evidence in open-plan public areas, which stretch from the reception to the restaurant. Bedrooms are spacious and provide good levels of comfort, reflecting the simple and successful policy of the owning company.

50 en suite (bth/shr) (2 fmly) No smoking in 10 bedrooms CTV in all bedrooms STV No dogs (ex guide dogs) Night porter 70P European & Oriental Cuisine V meals Coffee am Tea pm No smoking area in restaurant Last d 10pm

ROOMS: s fr £55; d fr £55 * **LB**

OFF-PEAK: s fr £45; d fr £45

MEALS: Lunch fr £9.75&alc Dinner fr £12.25&alc*

CONF: Thtr 40 Class 21 Board 22 Del from £62.50

CARDS:

See advertisement under BURY ST EDMUNDS

★★★65% **The Duke's Head**

Tuesday Market Pl PE30 1JS ☎ 01553 774996

FAX 01553 763556

An attractive Georgian building is situated in the market square of the old town, opposite the Customs House. The older part of the hotel is very traditional in style, but the accommodation is modern both in the main house and in a new wing at the rear. Public areas comprise a comfortable lounge, a lounge bar, a public bar and a buttery. Meeting/conference facilities and private car parking are also available.

71 en suite (bth/shr) (2 fmly) No smoking in 33 bedrooms CTV in all bedrooms Lift Night porter 41P Xmas English & French Cuisine V meals Coffee am Tea pm Last d 9.45pm

ROOMS: s £60; d £70 * **LB**

OFF-PEAK: s £60; d £60

MEALS: Lunch £8-£10&alc Dinner £15-£18&alc*

CONF: Thtr 240 Class 120 Board 60 Del from £70

CARDS:

★★69% **Russet House**

53 Goodwins Rd PE30 5PE (follow town centre signs along Hardwick Rd at small rdbt just before Southgates turn right into Vancouver Av after short drive hotel on left) ☎ 01553 773098 FAX 01553 773098

Closed 22 Dec-1 Jan

This large, late Victorian house stands in spacious gardens within easy reach of both the town centre and the A47 bypass. It is privately owned and personally run by Barry and Rae Muddle, who have been here 17 years. During that time, they have considerably extended and upgraded the accommodation. The modern furnished and equipped bedrooms are soundly maintained and include family rooms, rooms on ground floor level and a room with a four-poster bed. There is a comfortable lounge, a pleasant bar and an elegant dining room which is becoming increasingly popular with locals.

13 en suite (bth/shr) (2 fmly) No smoking in 1 bedroom CTV in all bedrooms 14P No coaches V meals Coffee am No smoking in restaurant Last d 8pm

ROOMS: (incl. bkfst) s £35-£46; d £48-£68 *

MEALS: Dinner fr £14.50&alc*

CARDS:

★★66% **Stuart House**

35 Goodwins Rd PE30 5QX (from A47/A10 follow signs for town centre continue to mini-rdbt (Southgates) take 3rd exit after half a mile turn left into Goodwins Rd) ☎ 01553 772169

FAX 01553 774788

This hotel is under new ownership, and at the time of our Inspectors' visit in summer 1996 there were major alterations and refurbishment taking place to most of the accommodation. Public rooms had just undergone considerable change too, the restaurant has been refurbished and a new bar has been created, this room is richly decorated and has a stripped wooden floor; informal bar meals are served here, whilst in the restaurant a daily and a la carte menus are generally available.

17 rms (15 bth/shr) 2 annexe en suite (bth/shr) (2 fmly) No smoking in 6 bedrooms CTV in all bedrooms STV 30P Jacuzzi/spa Wkly live entertainment Xmas International Cuisine V meals Coffee am Tea pm Last d 9.30pm

ROOMS: (incl. bkfst) s fr £35; d £55-£80 * **LB**

OFF-PEAK: (incl. bkfst) s fr £30; d £45-£80

MEALS: Lunch £5-£20&alc High tea £4-£6&alc Dinner £10-£18&alc*

CONF: Class 60

CARDS:

★★65% **Grange**
Willow Park, South Wootton Ln PE30 3BP (take A148 towards King's Lynn for 1.5m at traffic lights turn left into Wootton Rd 400yds on right South Wootton Ln hotel 1st on left) ☎ 01553 673777 & 671222 FAX 01553 673777
Closed 24-31 Dec
This large Edwardian house sits in a quiet residential area surrounded by well tended gardens and ample private car parking. The inviting public rooms are very well maintained, and the wood panelled lobby and wide stairwell are particularly appealing. Bedrooms are available in the main house and an adjacent garden annexe, offering spotlessly clean accommodation.
5 en suite (bth/shr) 4 annexe en suite (bth) CTV in all bedrooms 16P No coaches V meals Coffee am Tea pm No smoking in restaurant
ROOMS: (incl. bkfst) s £36.50-£38; d £48-£52 * **LB**
MEALS: Lunch £8.75-£10.55alc
CONF: Thtr 20 Class 15 Board 12 Del from £110.50
CARDS:

★★63% **The Tudor Rose**
St Nicholas St, off Tuesday Market Place PE30 1LR
☎ 01553 762824 FAX 01553 764894
This personally-run 15th-century inn retains much of its original character and charm and the first floor restaurant is particularly striking with its exposed beams and whitewashed walls. The public rooms also include two bars, where real ale beers and informal bar meals are served. Bedroom styles and sizes vary, all are well maintained and the more recently redecorated rooms look cheerful with their co-ordinated colour schemes.
13 rms (4 bth 7 shr) CTV in all bedrooms English & French Cuisine V meals Coffee am Tea pm No smoking in restaurant Last d 9pm
ROOMS: (incl. bkfst) s £38.50; d £50 * **LB**
MEALS: Lunch £1.60-£7.95alc Dinner £11.50-£18.10alc*
CARDS:

KINGSTON UPON THAMES Greater London
See LONDON SECTION plan 1 C1

★★★68% **Kingston Lodge**
Kingston Hill KT2 7NP (on the A308)
☎ 0181 541 4481 FAX 0181 547 1013
FORTE Heritage
The location of this friendly hotel and the quality of many of the bedrooms contribute to its week day popularity. Under a new manager, the staff are showing signs of increased guest care. The Courtyard Restaurant, which overlooks an enclosed small garden and patio area, serves food which shows promise.
62 en suite (bth/shr) No smoking in 20 bedrooms CTV in all bedrooms Night porter 74P Wkly live entertainment Xmas Continental Cuisine V meals Coffee am Tea pm No smoking in restaurant Last d 10pm
ROOMS: s £120; d £130 **LB**
MEALS: Lunch £18&alc Dinner £19.50&alc*
CONF: Thtr 80 Class 50 Board 35 Del £140
CARDS:

★70% **Chase Lodge**
10 Park Rd, Hampton Wick KT1 4AS ☎ 0181 943 1862 FAX 0181 943 9363
This attractive property, situated in a quiet residential area just minutes from the centre of Kingston is ideally placed for access to the M3. The en suite bedrooms are individually decorated and well equipped. A comfortable guests' lounge operates a snack menu throughout the day and the conservatory restaurant offers a good range of dishes. Parking permits are provided as this is a restricted parking area.
6 en suite (bth/shr) 4 annexe en suite (bth/shr) (1 fmly) CTV in all bedrooms Night porter 20P No coaches Xmas V meals Coffee am Tea pm No smoking in restaurant Last d 9.30pm
ROOMS: (incl. bkfst) s £48-£62; d £62-£107
OFF-PEAK: (incl. bkfst) s £42-£53; d £55-£107
CARDS:

KINGTON Hereford & Worcester Map 03 SO25

★★65% **Burton**
Mill St HR5 3BQ (at rdbt of A44/A411 interchange take road signed town centre) ☎ 01544 230323 FAX 01544 230323
This small friendly hotel is situated in the town centre. It provides well equipped accommodation, which includes family bedded rooms. In addition to the bright and pleasant restaurant, there is an attractive lounge bar and a cosy lounge. Other facilities include a meeting room and a large ballroom.
15 en suite (bth/shr) (3 fmly) CTV in all bedrooms 50P Xmas International Cuisine V meals Coffee am Tea pm Last d 9.30pm
ROOMS: (incl. bkfst) s £40-£48; d £55-£65 **LB**
MEALS: Lunch £14.50 Dinner fr £14.50
CONF: Thtr 150 Class 100 Board 20 Del from £47
CARDS:

KIRBY MISPERTON North Yorkshire Map 08 SE77

★★63% ***Beansheaf Restaurant Motel***
Malton Rd YO17 0UE (S of Pickering, on A169)
☎ 01653 668614 & 668488 FAX 01653 668370
This modern roadside hotel offers 2 styles of dining, although the Italian restaurant may only be available at weekends, depending on demand. The bedrooms are well equipped and service is friendly and provided mainly by the resident owners Michele and Elizabeth Sardone.
20 en suite (bth/shr) (2 fmly) CTV in all bedrooms 60P Sauna ch fac English & Continental Cuisine V meals Coffee am Tea pm Last d 9.30pm
CARDS:

KIRBY MUXLOE Leicestershire Map 04 SK50

★★65% **Castle Hotel & Restaurant**
Main St LE9 2AP (M1 at J21A or new bypass A46 or A47 Hinckley Road to B5380) ☎ 0116 239 5337 FAX 0116 238 7868
This attractive creeper-clad hotel was once a 16th-century farmhouse built with timbers and bricks taken from the nearby castle. Many original features remain with a wealth of timbers throughout and several inglenook fireplaces. Bedrooms are very well equipped with modern facilities and several are located in nearby outbuildings. Staff are friendly and attentive and there is a relaxing atmosphere throughout.
6 en suite (bth/shr) 8 annexe en suite (bth/shr) (1 fmly) No smoking in 5 bedrooms CTV in all bedrooms No dogs (ex guide dogs) 70P English & French Cuisine V meals Coffee am Tea pm No smoking in restaurant Last d 9.30pm
ROOMS: (incl. bkfst) s £45-£50; d £50-£70 * **LB**
OFF-PEAK: (incl. bkfst) s £35-£40; d £45-£50

MEALS: Lunch £16.95&alc Dinner £16.95&alc
CONF: Thtr 100 Class 70 Board 60 Del £79.50
CARDS:

See advertisement under LEICESTER

KIRKBURTON West Yorkshire Map 07 SE11

★★★70% **Springfield Park**
Penistone Rd HD8 0PE (3m S, on A629, close to M1 and M62)
☎ 01484 607788 FAX 01484 607961
This attractive modern hotel is built on the site of an old mill to the south of Huddesfield on the Sheffield road, and provides comfortable and well furnished bedrooms. The open-plan lounge foyer is comfortable, the restaurant offers a good choice of dishes, and service is friendly and attentive.
46 en suite (bth/shr) (5 fmly) No smoking in 10 bedrooms CTV in all bedrooms STV Night porter 120P No coaches Pool table International Cuisine V meals Coffee am Tea pm Last d 9.45pm
ROOMS: (incl. bkfst) s £62.50-£75; d £72.50-£85 **LB**
OFF-PEAK: (incl. bkfst) s fr £30; d fr £60
MEALS: Sunday Lunch £8.50-£10 Dinner £15-£19&alc
CONF: Thtr 154 Class 40 Board 40 Del from £80
CARDS:

KIRKBY LONSDALE Cumbria Map 07 SD67

★★68% **Whoop Hall Inn**
LA6 2HP (1m SE on A65) ☎ 015242 71284
FAX 015242 72154

MINOTEL Great Britain

This busy roadside inn has been extended and altered over recent years and now provides sound modern accommodation. Bedrooms are very well equipped and every room even has its own video with a small supply of films Family and four-poster rooms are also available. Public areas are quite extensive with several eating areas in addition to the bar. Food is available all day with a restaurant as well as a buttery. A recent addition is a large function suite that caters for weddings and other local events.
22 en suite (bth/shr) (3 fmly) No smoking in 11 bedrooms CTV in all bedrooms STV Night porter 120P Pool table Jacuzzi/spa Wkly live entertainment Xmas English & Continental Cuisine V meals Coffee am Tea pm Last d 10pm
ROOMS: (incl. bkfst) s £47.50-£57.50; d £64-£74 * **LB**
MEALS: Lunch £3.50-£6.50&alc Dinner £8.50-£18.50alc
CONF: Thtr 80 Class 80 Board 60 Del from £70
CARDS:

★★67% **Pheasant Inn**
LA6 2RX (leave M6 junc36 onto A65, turn left at A683 1m onwards in centre of village) ☎ 015242 71230 FAX 015242 71230
Closed 6-12 Jan
This traditional country inn and restaurant lies in a quiet village one mile north of Kirkby Lonsdale on the A683. Public areas are full of character and one can eat well in either the beamed bar with its open fire in cooler weather, or the restaurant; menus offer a tremendous variety which includes an impressive choice of fish. There is a quiet and comfortable lounge for residents upstairs.
10 en suite (bth/shr) CTV in all bedrooms 40P V meals Coffee am No smoking in restaurant Last d 9pm
ROOMS: (incl. bkfst) s £35-£37.50; d £60-£64 *
MEALS: Bar Lunch £2.25-£20alc Dinner £15-£22alc*
CARDS:

★★63% **Plough Hotel**
Cow Brow LA6 1PJ (turn off junc 36 M6, head for Skipton/Kirkby Lonsdale, 1m from M6) ☎ 015395 67227 FAX 015395 67848
Situated on the A65 and convenient to the M6 at junction 36, this well furnished hotel stands in open countryside close the town of Kirkby Lonsdale. It provides modern and well equipped bedrooms together

with an extensive range of food which is served either in the bar or the pleasant restaurant. There is also a good conference and banqueting suite, and service is friendly.
12 en suite (bth/shr) (2 fmly) CTV in all bedrooms STV 72P Fishing ch fac Xmas English & French Cuisine V meals Coffee am Tea pm Last d 9.30pm
ROOMS: (incl. bkfst) s £32; d £49.50 * **LB**
OFF-PEAK: (incl. bkfst) s £30; d £45
MEALS: Lunch £5.95-£9.95&alc High tea £6-£8&alc Dinner £5.95-£12.95&alc*
CARDS:

KIRKBYMOORSIDE North Yorkshire Map 08 SE68

★★70% **George & Dragon**
17 Market Place YO6 6AA (off A170 between Thirsk/Scarborough, in centre of market town) ☎ 01751 433334 FAX 01751 433334
This 17th-century hotel is found in the centre of the town and has been pleasantly upgraded by the caring owners, Stephen and Francis Colling. The popular bar is full of character, having an interesting cricket theme, whilst a pleasant lounge is also provided for those guests looking for peace and quiet. Bar meals and excellent restaurant dinners are available and the hotel boasts an award-winning wine list. The comfortable bedrooms, located in buildings to the rear, are well furnished and service here is warm, friendly and natural.
12 en suite (bth/shr) 7 annexe en suite (bth/shr) (3 fmly) No smoking in 5 bedrooms CTV in all bedrooms 20P ch fac Xmas V meals Coffee am No smoking in restaurant Last d 9.15pm
ROOMS: (incl. bkfst) s fr £49; d £75-£85 * **LB**
MEALS: Bar Lunch £11.50-£17alc Dinner £11.50-£17alc*
CONF: Thtr 50 Class 20 Board 20 Del from £89
CARDS:

KIRKBY STEPHEN See Advertisement

KNARESBOROUGH North Yorkshire Map 08 SE35

★★★ 70% Dower House

Bond End HG5 9AL (on A59, 3m from International Conference Centre, follow signs for Mother Shipton's Cave) ☎ 01423 863302 FAX 01423 867665

This Grade II listed building is convenient for both the town and the River Nidd and is only three miles from Harrogate. The house is delightfully furnished and offers well equipped bedrooms and inviting public rooms. The Terrace Restaurant is a perfect setting for the quality British cooking, which is prepared with both skill and flair. Conferences and business meetings are well catered for and there is also an excellent leisure and health club available.

28 en suite (bth/shr) 4 annexe en suite (bth/shr) (2 fmly) No smoking in 9 bedrooms CTV in all bedrooms No dogs (ex guide dogs) Night porter 80P Indoor swimming pool (heated) Sauna Solarium Gym Jacuzzi/spa Xmas English & French Cuisine V meals Coffee am Tea pm No smoking in restaurant Last d 9.30pm

ROOMS: (incl. bkfst) s £50-£65; d £70-£90 * **LB**

MEALS: Sunday Lunch £9.75 Dinner £18.50-£19.50&alc

CONF: Thtr 65 Class 35 Board 40 Del from £80

CARDS:

★★★ 62% General Tarleton Inn

Boroughbridge Rd, Ferrensby HG5 0QB (on A6055, on cross road in Ferrensby) ☎ 01423 340284 FAX 01423 340288

This pleasant hotel stands on the edge of the village of Ferrensby and is two miles from Knaresborough. It is family-owned and run and mixes the old and new to great effect. The well furnished bedrooms are modern, whilst the bar and restaurant are set in the 18th-century part of the complex. A good range of food is available, served either in the bar or the Granary Restaurant, and service is attentive and friendly.

15 en suite (bth/shr) CTV in all bedrooms 60P V meals Coffee am No smoking in restaurant Last d 9.30pm

MEALS: Lunch £8.95 Dinner £9.95-£17.50*

CONF: Thtr 40 Class 25 Board 25 Del from £30

CARDS:

KNUTSFORD Cheshire Map 07 SJ77

★★★★ 68% Cottons

SHIRE INNS

Manchester Rd WA16 0SU (on A50 1m from junc19 of M6) ☎ 01565 650333 FAX 01565 755351

Within easy reach of the M6 this hotel continues to benefit from major changes. The bedrooms are now all modern and very well equipped and following the opening of a brand new leisure centre, the rest of the public areas are being altered to allow for more space and increased comfort. The kitchen shows care and attention to detail in a menu which has a noticeable Cajun influence. A sample meal might be crab cakes with a pepper sauce, roast loin of lamb with lentils and a raisin and apple creme brulee.

99 en suite (bth/shr) (4 fmly) No smoking in 44 bedrooms CTV in all bedrooms STV Lift Night porter 180P Indoor swimming pool (heated) Tennis (hard) Squash Sauna Solarium Gym Jacuzzi/spa Fitness and beauty rooms Xmas English & French Cuisine V meals Coffee am Tea pm No smoking area in restaurant Last d 9.45pm

ROOMS: (incl. bkfst) s £99-£129; d £120-£150 * **LB**

OFF-PEAK: (incl. bkfst & dinner) d fr £116

MEALS: Bar Lunch fr £10 Dinner fr £22alc*

CONF: Thtr 200 Class 120 Board 30 Del from £130

CARDS:

★★★ 65% Cottage Restaurant & Lodge

London Rd, Allostock WA16 9LU (on A50 between Holmes Chapel and Knutsford) ☎ 01565 722470 FAX 01565 722479

This attractive Cheshire brick building is well situated at Allostock on the A50 between Holmes Chapel and Knutsford, within easy reach of the M6. The open-plan public areas include a conservatory lounge, comfortably furnished lounge bar, spacious restaurant and small function room, all of which have been decorated with real character. The bedrooms, reached from outside the main building and including some ground floor rooms, are spacious, attractively decorated and well equipped. A good choice of dishes carefully prepared by head chef Brian Joy and brigade is offered on the ambitious, good value fixed-price menu which boasts a number of 'speciality' dishes. First courses may include a deliciously light and well cooked boudin of chicken and apricots on a tomato sauce or a tartlet of smoked haddock with sun-dried tomatoes and spinach. Main courses such as sea bass on a bed of spinach with garlic and a mustard and herb grain sauce are equally interesting, and a pudding of chocolate mousse in a tuille basket finished off an enjoyable meal.

12 en suite (bth/shr) (4 fmly) No smoking in 4 bedrooms CTV in all bedrooms Air conditioning 60P Xmas French Cuisine V meals Coffee am Tea pm Last d 9.30pm

ROOMS: (incl. bkfst) s £61; d £70 *

OFF-PEAK: (incl. bkfst) s £25; d £50

MEALS: Lunch £9-£10.95 Dinner £9-£10.95&alc*

CONF: Thtr 40 Class 40 Board 40

CARDS:

★★ 71% The Longview Hotel & Restaurant

55 Manchester Rd WA16 0LX (NW on A50) ☎ 01565 632119 FAX 01565 652402

Closed 24 Dec-3 Jan

Owned and energetically run by Pauline and Stephen West, this hotel has a Victorian theme throughout. Bedrooms are fully en suite and thoughtfully equipped, and public areas include a cellar lounge bar and an elegant restaurant with an extensive menu. Dishes might include spicy home-made sausages to start, followed by the fish of the day; puddings, such as steamed ginger sponge, are traditional in style.

13 en suite (bth/shr) 10 annexe en suite (bth/shr) (1 fmly) CTV in all bedrooms 26P No coaches English & Continental Cuisine V meals Coffee am Last d 21.00

ROOMS: (incl. bkfst) s £55-£70; d £70-£80 * **LB**

OFF-PEAK: (incl. bkfst) s £39-£55; d £58-£75

MEALS: Dinner £16.50-£18.50&alc*

CARDS:

See advertisement on opposite page

★★ 68% The Toft

Toft Rd WA16 9EH (1m S on A50) ☎ 01565 633470 & 634443 FAX 01565 632603

Closed Xmas & New Year

Cleverly converted 16th century former farmhouse situated in spacious gardens, on the A50, south of Knutsford. The bedrooms are cosy and have modern furnishings and equipment and other facilities include a pleasant lounge and bar. A good range of imaginative dishes is offered from the entirely vegetarian menu at Dock Willett's, the hotel restaurant.

11 en suite (bth/shr) No smoking in all bedrooms CTV in all bedrooms No dogs (ex guide dogs) 35P No coaches No children

10yrs Vegetarian Cuisine V meals No smoking in restaurant
Last d 9.30pm
ROOMS: (incl. bkfst) s fr £49.50; d fr £60
MEALS: Dinner fr £18.50alc*
CARDS:

Travelodge
Chester Rd, Tabley WA16 0PP (on A556, northbound just E of junct 19 on M6)
☎ 01565 652187 FAX 01565 652187
This modern building offers accommodation in smart, spacious and well equipped bedrooms, suitable for family use, and all with en suite bathrooms. Meals may be taken at the nearby family restaurant. For information on room rates and to make a booking, call Roomline free of charge on 0800 850950. For more details about Travelodge, consult the Contents page under Hotel Groups.
32 en suite (bth/shr)

LACEBY Lincolnshire Map 08 TA20

★★★63% **The Oaklands**
Barton St DN37 7LF (from Humberside Airport 8m on A18 to roundabout, straight over and hotel 75yds on right) ☎ 01472 872248 FAX 01472 878143
An extended Victorian house is situated in five acres of grounds and gardens close to the junction of the A46 and A18, five miles west of Grimsby. The comfortable bedrooms are split between the main building and a modern wing; the honeymoon suite has a four-poster bed. Spacious public areas comprise The Garden Restaurant with crisp linen cloths and fresh flowers, a guest lounge with antique furniture and an open fire, and The Saxon Arms bar and conservatory which has good facilities for children and a lounge bar. Other attractions include an indoor heated swimming pool, a gymnasium, a driving range and meeting/conference facilities.
46 en suite (bth/shr) (1 fmly) No smoking in 10 bedrooms CTV in all bedrooms Night porter 200P Indoor swimming pool (heated) Sauna Solarium Gym Golf driving range ch fac English & French Cuisine V meals Coffee am Tea pm No smoking in restaurant Last d 9.15pm
MEALS: Lunch £6.50-£8.50 High tea £5-£6 Dinner £15.40-£17&alc
CONF: Thtr 200 Class 80 Board 45 Del from £79
CARDS:

LANCASTER Lancashire Map 07 SD46
See also Hampson Green

★★★★69% **Lancaster House**
Green Ln, Ellel LA1 4GJ (M6 junct. 33 north towards Lancaster. through Calgate village, turn right onto Green LaneHotel just before University entrance)
☎ 01524 844822 FAX 01524 844766
This modern hotel, built in the style of a country house, is situated in open countryside next to Lancaster University and on clear days glimpses of Morecambe Bay can be seen from some of the comfortable and very well equipped bedrooms. A log fire burns in the foyer lounge on chilly days reflecting also the warmth and hospitality provided by the helpful and willing staff. The Gressingham Restaurant offers an extensive à la carte menu of mainly British dishes cooked and presented in modern style with much emphasis on the use of good fresh ingredients. There is also an excellent leisure club and a comprehensive business training centre.
80 en suite (bth/shr) (10 fmly) No smoking in 36 bedrooms CTV in all bedrooms STV Night porter 100P Indoor swimming pool (heated) Sauna Solarium Gym Jacuzzi/spa Childrens pool,Activity centre 1 mile Wkly live entertainment Xmas V meals Coffee am Tea pm No smoking in restaurant Last d 9.30pm
ROOMS: s £79-£84; d £79-£84 **LB**
OFF-PEAK: s £59-£65; d £59-£65

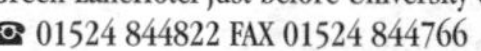

MEALS: Lunch £11.95-£12.95 High tea £3.85-£15.95alc Dinner £18.50-£32.50alc
CONF: Thtr 180 Class 50 Board 60 Del from £88.13
CARDS:
See advertisement under WINDERMERE

★★★61% **Royal Kings Arms**
Market St LA1 1HP (follow 'City Centre' signs from M6, then 'Castle & Railway Station', turn off before traffic lights next to Waterstones bookshop)
☎ 01524 32451 FAX 01524 841698
Situated in the centre of the town this hotel was established in 1625 and rebuilt in 1879. Although modernised more recently, it still possesses several of its 19th century features such as lofty ceilings and an interesting, galleried restaurant on the first floor. Bedrooms vary in size but are contemporary in style and equipped with a full range of modern facilities. There is a small car park to the rear and staff are generally friendly and helpful.
55 en suite (bth/shr) (2 fmly) No smoking in 15 bedrooms CTV in
contd.

all bedrooms STV Lift Night porter 20P Wkly live entertainment Xmas European Cuisine V meals Coffee am Tea pm No smoking in restaurant Last d 9.30pm
ROOMS: s £49.50-£60; d £49.50-£80 * **LB**
OFF-PEAK: s £35-£45; d £35-£65
MEALS: Sunday Lunch £8.95-£17.50alc Dinner £12.50-£25alc
CARDS:

Forte Posthouse Lancaster

Waterside Park, Caton Rd LA1 3RA (close to junc 34 M6) ☎ 01524 65999 FAX 01524 841265
Suitable for both the business and leisure traveller, this bright hotel provides modern accommodation in well equipped bedrooms with en suite bathrooms. For more details about Forte Posthouse hotels, consult the Contents page for the section on Hotel Groups.
115 en suite (bth/shr)

LANCING West Sussex Map 04 TQ10

★★ 72% **Sussex Pad**
Old Shoreham Rd BN15 0RH (situated on the main A27 oposite Shoreham Airport and by Lancing College) ☎ 01273 454647 FAX 01273 453010
Conveniently located on the eastbound carriageway of the A27 directly opposite Shoreham Airport this well run inn has been extensively upgraded in recent years by its caring and dedicated owner Mr Wally J Pack. Bedrooms and bathrooms are being upgraded. The spacious conservatory lounge/bar/breakfast room is a very popular local rendezvous as it is open throughout the day for meals and a good range of light refreshments. Ladywells Restaurant offers a fixed-price menu and allows partner and chef Paul Hornsby to demonstrate his flair with some interesting recipes such as crab bisque with lemon grass and mild chillies, and two cuts of rabbit sautéed in cider with shallot and coarse grain mustard. Service is attentive and efficient.
19 en suite (bth/shr) CTV in all bedrooms STV 60P Xmas English & French Cuisine V meals Coffee am Tea pm No smoking in restaurant Last d 10pm
ROOMS: (incl. bkfst) s £52-£60; d £66-£80 *
MEALS: Lunch £16-£19&alc Dinner £16-£19&alc*
CARDS:

LANDCROSS Devon Map 02 SS42

★★ 63% ***Beaconside***
EX39 5JL (1m SW on A388) ☎ 01237 477205
The Tucker family continues to offer genuine Devonshire hospitality at this relaxing hotel near Bideford. Most of the bedrooms have been upgraded with attractive co-ordinated fabrics, and generous portions of good home cooking are provided in the dining room. The grounds include a trail through 23 acres of woodland, which includes a Japanese garden.
8 rms (6 bth/shr) (2 fmly) CTV in all bedrooms No dogs (ex guide dogs) 16P Outdoor swimming pool (heated) Tennis (grass) Coffee am Tea pm Last d 7.30pm

LAND'S END See Sennen

LANGAR Nottinghamshire Map 08 SK73

★★ 71% **Langar Hall**
NG13 9HG (accessible via Bingham on the A52 or Cropwell Bishop from the A46, both signposted, the house adjoins the church) ☎ 01949 860559 FAX 01949 861045
Closed Xmas day
Hidden behind the village church this Victorian mansion is full of charm and antiquity. It stands perched on the edge of the Vale of Belvoir and surveying the network of canals and mediaeval fish ponds below. The comforts and facilities of a modern hotel combine with the hospitality of a country home, bedrooms (some of which are four-poster) being individually furnished and filled with books and fine paintings. The cooking is fairly straightforward with some personal creations featuring fresh ingredients and clear flavours.
11 en suite (bth/shr) (1 fmly) No smoking in 10 bedrooms CTV in all bedrooms Night porter 20P No coaches Fishing Croquet lawn ch fac V meals Coffee am Tea pm Last d 9.30pm
ROOMS: (incl. bkfst) s £60-£85; d £85-£135 * **LB**
OFF-PEAK: (incl. bkfst) s £50-£85; d £75-£105
MEALS: Lunch £12.50-£21.50&alc Dinner £17.50-£35&alc*
CONF: Thtr 20 Class 20 Board 20 Del £135
CARDS:

LANGHO Lancashire Map 07 SD73

★★★ 72% **Northcote Manor**
Northcote Rd BB6 8BE (M6 junt.31, 8 miles to Northcote,follow signsto Clitheroe, Hotel is set back on the left just before the roundabout) ☎ 01254 240555 FAX 01254 246568
Probably more famous for its restaurant, this very comfortable, characterful hotel is superbly situated in the Ribble Valley, yet close to the M6. The large bedrooms, where effective use has been made of very pretty and in some cases quite striking soft furnishings, are very thoughtfully equipped and offer very good levels of comfort indeed. Guests can enjoy a drink in one of the comfortable lounges whilst browsing over the tempting menus created by chef patron Nigel Haworth and his head chef Jonathan Baron. The wine list is interesting and the service is friendly and attentive.
14 en suite (bth/shr) CTV in all bedrooms STV No dogs (ex guide dogs) 50P No coaches Croquet lawn Xmas International Cuisine V meals Coffee am Tea pm
ROOMS: (incl. bkfst) s fr £75; d £95-£115 **LB**
MEALS: Lunch fr £13.50&alc
CONF: Thtr 40 Class 20 Board 26
CARDS:

★★★ 65% **Mytton Fold Hotel & Golf Complex**
Whalley Rd BB6 8AB (off A59 between Langho & Whalley)
☎ 01254 240662 FAX 01254 248119
RS Xmas wk
This lovely stone-built farm has been sympathetically extended and developed by the Hargreaves family. It is located close to the A59 on the outskirts of the village. Bedrooms are spacious and offer good amenities, while the public areas include a lounge bar with a cast iron range, several conference rooms and an 18 hole golf course.
27 en suite (bth/shr) CTV in all bedrooms No dogs (ex guide dogs) 150P Golf 18 Pool table Putting green V meals Coffee am Tea pm No smoking in restaurant Last d 9.30pm
ROOMS: (incl. bkfst) s £37-£47; d £60-£72 * **LB**
MEALS: Sunday Lunch £9 Dinner £11.50-£14&alc*
CONF: Thtr 300 Class 100 Board 100 Del from £62
CARDS:

LANGTOFT East Riding of Yorkshire Map 08 TA06

★★ 68% **Old Mill Hotel & Restaurant**
Mill Ln YO25 0BQ ☎ 01377 267284 FAX 01377 267383
A rural modernised inn which offers high standards of comfort. The public rooms are mainly divided between a well appointed restaurant and the comfortable open-plan lounge bar which includes a dining area for bar meals, the reception and the bar. The cuisine is good, the locally sourced ingredients range from fresh char-grilled tuna and saddle of hare to Thai chicken. The atmosphere is friendly and the services provided competent.
8 en suite (bth/shr) (1 fmly) No smoking in 2 bedrooms CTV in all

bedrooms 30P Xmas English & Continental Cuisine V meals Coffee am No smoking area in restaurant
ROOMS: (incl. bkfst) s fr £42.50; d fr £55 **LB**
OFF-PEAK: (incl. bkfst) s fr £40; d fr £52.50
MEALS: Bar Lunch £9-£18&alc Dinner £10-£20&alc
CONF: Thtr 40 Class 20 Board 20
CARDS:

LARKFIELD Kent Map 05 TQ65

★★★64% **Larkfield Priory**
London Rd ME20 6HJ (1.50miles from M20 Junction 4,situated on the A20) ☎ 01732 846858
FAX 01732 846786

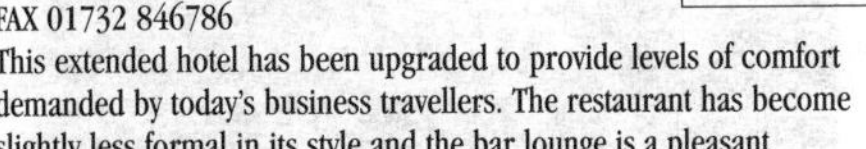

This extended hotel has been upgraded to provide levels of comfort demanded by today's business travellers. The restaurant has become slightly less formal in its style and the bar lounge is a pleasant alternative for lighter meals and snacks.
52 rms (51 bth/shr) No smoking in 24 bedrooms CTV in 51 bedrooms Night porter 80P Xmas International Cuisine V meals Coffee am No smoking in restaurant Last d 9.30pm
ROOMS: s fr £63; d fr £63 * **LB**
OFF-PEAK: s fr £47; d fr £47
MEALS: Lunch £12 Dinner fr £16.95&alc*
CONF: Thtr 70 Class 30 Board 30 Del from £90
CARDS:

LASTINGHAM North Yorkshire Map 08 SE79

★★★ 69% **Lastingham Grange**
YO6 6TH (2miles east on A170 towards Scarborough, onto Lastingham, in village turn left uphill towards Moors. Hotel can be found on right)
☎ 01751 417345 & 417402
Closed mid Dec-Feb
Standing in ten acres of very well tended gardens and on the edge of the North Yorkshire moors, this family-owned hotel provides excellent hospitality for which guests return year after year. The lounge is a sheer delight being very comfortable and inviting. The traditional bedrooms are prettily decorated and carefully furnished and have been thoughtfully equipped to include all of today's expected needs and comforts. The five-course dinner is well prepared.
12 en suite (bth) (2 fmly) CTV in all bedrooms 32P No coaches Large adventure playground ch fac V meals Coffee am Tea pm No smoking in restaurant Last d 8.30pm
ROOMS: (incl. bkfst) s £64.50-£70.50; d £119.75-£131.25 * **LB**
MEALS: Lunch fr £14.75 Dinner £25.50-£25.50*

LAUNCESTON Cornwall & Isles of Scilly Map 02 SX38
See also Lifton

★★ 76% **Penhallow Manor Country House**
PL15 7SJ LAUNCESTON ☎ 01566 86206
FAX 01566 86179

(For full entry see Altarnun)

See advertisement on page 339

★★60% ***Eagle House***
Castle St PL15 8BA ☎ 01566 772036
Ask for directions to this attractive red brick Georgian hotel, situated next to the town's castle. Bedrooms vary in design, some being in the original hotel and some at garden level overlooking the countryside; the restaurant also benefits from this view. A limited choice is offered on the fixed-price menu, and simple bar meals are also available. Service is informal and relaxed.
14 en suite (bth/shr) (1 fmly) CTV in all bedrooms STV No dogs (ex guide dogs) 100P No coaches V meals Coffee am Tea pm Last d 9pm
CARDS:

L

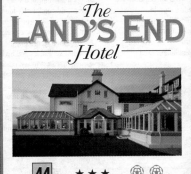

LAVENHAM Suffolk Map 05 TL94

★★★ 76% **The Swan**

FORTE Heritage

High St CO10 9QA (in centre of village of Lavenham on the A134 Road Bury St Edmunds/Hadleigh)
☎ 01787 247477 FAX 01787 248286

This truly delightful hotel is one of the attractions in this quintessentially picturesque English town. The building fairly hums with polished levels of service and friendly staff. Bedrooms are smart and being gradually up-dated, and the public areas invite relaxing moments taking tea, a drink in one of two bars or a meal in the pleasant restaurant, complete with minstrels' gallery. In the evening there is a choice of two menus using seasonal, fresh ingredients put together with precision by the kitchen. A sober but competent style of cooking is suited to this locality : a recent meal consisted of oyster mushroom soup with tarragon, guinea fowl breast with cider and caramelised apple and a summer pudding.

46 en suite (bth/shr) No smoking in 15 bedrooms CTV in all bedrooms Night porter 60P Croquet lawn Wkly live entertainment Xmas V meals Coffee am Tea pm No smoking in restaurant Last d 9.30pm
ROOMS: s £80-£50; d £125-£140 **LB**
MEALS: Lunch fr £15.95&alc High tea fr £7.95 Dinner fr £25.95&alc
CONF: Thtr 60 Class 35 Board 25 Del from £120
CARDS:

★ 73% **Angel**

Market Place CO10 9QZ (from A14 take Bury East/Sunbury turn off A143, after 4miles take A1141 to Lavenham, Angel is off the High Street)
☎ 01787 247388 FAX 01787 248344

This quaint 15th-century inn sits in the heart of the medieval town, overlooking the market place and the famous Guildhall. Enthusiastic proprietors and staff ensure diners and guests feel at ease within the friendly and relaxed environment of the cosy public rooms. The ground floor is taken up with a wide bar and dining areas, where good home cooking of English and French country cuisine is offered from a daily-changing menu that includes tasty home-made soups, pies, casseroles and seasonal game dishes. Bedrooms are all comfortably appointed and have a range of facilities and thoughtful extras.

8 en suite (bth/shr) (1 fmly) CTV in all bedrooms 5P No coaches Wkly live entertainment V meals Coffee am No smoking area in restaurant
ROOMS: (incl. bkfst) s £37.50-£47.50; d £60-£70 **LB**
MEALS: Lunch £10-£17.50alc
CARDS:

LEA MARSTON Warwickshire Map 04 SP29

★★★69% **Lea Marston Hotel & Leisure Complex**

CONSORT HOTELS

Haunch Ln B76 0BY (off A4097, close to junc 9 of M42) ☎ 01675 470468 FAX 01675 470871

This modern, purpose-built hotel, leisure and conference complex is located in a quiet setting yet only 1.5 miles from the M42 motorway. The building is well maintained and houses spacious, well equipped bedrooms. There is a choice of eating options, the range of informal meals served in the bar area providing an alternative to the main restaurant's more serious cuisine.

49 en suite (bth/shr) (2 fmly) CTV in all bedrooms STV No dogs (ex guide dogs) Night porter 165P Indoor swimming pool (heated) Golf 9 Tennis (hard) Sauna Solarium Gym Pool table Croquet lawn Putting green Jacuzzi/spa Wkly live entertainment ch fac Xmas English & French Cuisine V meals Coffee am Tea pm No smoking in restaurant Last d 9.30pm
ROOMS: (incl. bkfst) s £88; d £98 * **LB**
OFF-PEAK: (incl. bkfst) s £45-£62; d £50-£67
MEALS: Lunch £10.95-£13.95 Dinner £16.95&alc*
CONF: Thtr 110 Class 60 Board 40 Del from £98
CARDS:

£

LEAMINGTON SPA (ROYAL) Warwickshire Map 04 SP36

RED STAR HOTEL

★★★ *Mallory Court*

RELAIS & CHATEAUX. Relais Gourmands

Harbury Ln, Bishop's Tachbrook CV33 9QB (2m S off B4087 towards Harbury)
☎ 01926 330214 FAX 01926 451714
Closed 2-11 Jan

A visit to Mallory Court is memorable for many reasons. The beautifully restored house is a fine example of period architecture, dating back to the 1920s, and set in 10 acres of landscaped grounds and formal gardens, which contain a croquet lawn, all weather tennis courts, and for the very hardy, an open air, unheated swimming pool. Day rooms include two elegant and comfortable lounges and an impressive panelled restaurant, which provides an ideal setting in which to enjoy the light, innovative cuisine of Head Chef Steven Shore and his highly skilled team. Only the best fresh produce is used, including vegetables and herbs grown in the hotel's own garden. Needless to say, canapés, and petits fours are all home made and the breads are baked on the premises. There is no bar, but drinks service in the lounge is readily forthcoming, as one would expect in an informal country house style of operation. The tastefully decorated bedrooms are individual in style, and all have a good array of modern equipment and facilities, as well as numerous thoughtful and welcoming extra touches. Some of the original Art Deco bathrooms are still in use.

10 en suite (bth/shr) (1 fmly) CTV in all bedrooms No dogs 52P No coaches Outdoor swimming pool Tennis (hard) Squash Croquet lawn No children 9yrs French Cuisine V meals Coffee am Tea pm Last d 9.45pm
CARDS:

★★★ 76% *Regent*

Best Western

77 The Parade CV32 4AX ☎ 01926 427231
FAX 01926 450728

When opened in 1819, the Regent was the largest hotel in the world with 100 bedrooms. In many ways the spirit of traditional hotel keeping remains strong here: hospitality levels are truly exceptional and the care provided through excellent service is an example to many modern establishments. Though the ambience may be traditional bedrooms are modern and feature dramatic bold fabrics

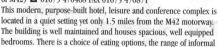

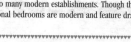

and every convenience including in-house TV. The extensive public areas include two restaurants, a relaxing lounge and the Phoenix bar with its feature mural. The Cridlan family, manager John Biesok and all their staff uphold the traditions of fine hotel keeping and contribute to making a stay at this 'grand old lady' very special.
80 en suite (bth/shr) (7 fmly) CTV in all bedrooms Lift Night porter 100P Pool table Table tennis English, French & Italian Cuisine V meals Coffee am Tea pm Last d 10.45pm
CARDS:

★★★66% **The Leamington Hotel & Bistro**

64 Upper Holly Walk CV32 4JL ☎ 01926 883777
FAX 01926 330467
Formerly the Inchfield hotel this Regency hotel has been greatly upgraded by new owners Frank Nixey and Hilary Ashover. Bedrooms are spacious and smart with a thoughtful range of equipment provided for guests. The residents lounge is a relaxing room with a lovely high ceiling and some ornate plasterwork. The restaurant is delightful with dark wood predominating and a lovely range of paintings and prints Cuisine is classic with a modern twist.
22 en suite (bth/shr) (6 fmly) No smoking in 4 bedrooms CTV in all bedrooms No dogs (ex guide dogs) 22P No coaches Xmas English & French Cuisine V meals Coffee am Tea pm Last d 10pm
ROOMS: (incl. cont bkfst) s fr £60; d £70-£85 * **LB**
MEALS: Lunch £5.95-£11.75 High tea fr £6.50
Dinner £10.95-£15.95*
CONF: Thtr 45 Class 32 Board 24 Del from £85
CARDS:

★★★63% **Angel**
143 Regent St CV32 4NZ (in the town centre of Royal Leamington Spa on junction of Regent Street and Holly Walk) ☎ 01926 881296
FAX 01926 881296
This well established hotel comes in two parts now that a new extension has been grafted on to the existing shell. There are two styles of bedroom, one of which is contemporary and well thought out, the other style more traditional. Meals are provided in the informal bar as well as a smart restaurant.
50 en suite (bth/shr) (3 fmly) CTV in all bedrooms STV Lift Night porter 38P Xmas English & French Cuisine V meals Coffee am Tea pm Last d 9.30pm
ROOMS: (incl. bkfst) s £30-£49.50; d £45-£59 * **LB**
MEALS: Lunch fr £8.95&alc Dinner fr £12.50&alc
CONF: Thtr 70 Class 40 Board 40 Del from £50
CARDS:

★★★63% ***Courtyard by Marriott Leamington Spa***

Olympus Av, Tachbrook Park CV34 6RJ
☎ 01926 425522 FAX 01926 881322
Located on the edge of a business park and within easy reach of the M40 this modern hotel provides a good standard of accommodation. Bedrooms are furnished and equipped with all amenities and although the public rooms are not overlarge they are stylishly appointed. A good

range of items, including grills and international dishes is offered in the attractive, informal restaurant.
94 en suite (bth/shr) (12 fmly) No smoking in 40 bedrooms CTV in all bedrooms STV Lift Night porter 120P European Cuisine V meals Coffee am Tea pm Last d 10pm
CARDS:

★★★61% **Falstaff**
16-20 Warwick New Rd CV32 5JQ (on A4099)
☎ 01926 312044 FAX 01926 450574
Bedrooms at The Falstaff come in a variety of styles and sizes but all are reasonably well equipped and attractive. The recently refurbished restaurant is very smart and there are extensive conference and banqueting facilities.
63 en suite (bth/shr) (2 fmly) No smoking in 5 bedrooms CTV in all bedrooms No dogs (ex guide dogs) Night porter 80P English & Continental Cuisine V meals Coffee am Tea pm No smoking area in restaurant Last d 9.45pm
MEALS: Lunch fr £9.50&alc Dinner fr £16&alc*
CONF: Thtr 50 Class 40 Board 28 Del from £75
CARDS:

★★★61% **Manor House**

REGAL
A Collection of Individual Hotels

Avenue Rd CV31 3NJ ☎ 01926 423251
FAX 01926 425933
Conveniently positioned close to the town centre, this large early-Victorian property promotes a traditional atmosphere in its spacious and comfortably appointed lounges, bar and character restaurant. Bedrooms tend to vary in size and spaciousness; many having been refurbished to a good standard.
53 en suite (bth/shr) (2 fmly) No smoking in 19 bedrooms CTV in

contd.

all bedrooms Lift Night porter 130P Boardgames V meals Coffee am Tea pm No smoking in restaurant Last d 9.30pm
MEALS: Lunch £9.95-£11.25 High tea £2.95-£4.95 Dinner £17.95-£23.95&alc
CONF: Thtr 120 Class 46 Board 40 Del from £75
CARDS:

★★70% **Adams**
22 Avenue Rd CV31 3PQ ☎ 01926 450742
FAX 01926 313110
This impeccably maintained Georgian house just to the south of the town centre has been run for the last eight years by Mr and Mrs Van der Ende. They are both rightly proud of their small hotel and this is reflected in the spotless bedrooms. The fabrics and furnishings are of excellent quality and Mrs Van der Ende has a keen eye for detail. There is a comfortable lounge and smart bar, and home cooked meals can be enjoyed in the attractive dining room.
14 en suite (bth/shr) CTV in all bedrooms STV No dogs 14P No coaches Xmas V meals Coffee am Tea pm No smoking in restaurant Last d 8.00pm
ROOMS: (incl. bkfst) s £45.50-£54; d £52-£64.50 * **LB**
OFF-PEAK: (incl. bkfst) s fr £38; d fr £52
MEALS: Bar Lunch £6.50-£10&alc Dinner £17.50-£20&alc
CARDS:

★★62% **Beech Lodge**
Warwick New Rd CV32 5JJ (off A445, opposite Mid-Warwickshire College) ☎ 01926 422227 FAX 01926 435288
Closed 16 Dec-3 Jan
Personal service is provided by friendly resident owners who are making gradual changes to this hotel. Simply furnished bedrooms, some of them compact, offer a range of modern facilities, while the bar and lounge have been filled with personal items ans this adds a certain character.
14 rms (12 bth/shr) CTV in all bedrooms 16P No coaches English & French Cuisine V meals Last d 8pm
ROOMS: (incl. bkfst) s £36-£44; d £47-£60 **LB**
OFF-PEAK: (incl. bkfst) s £25-£35; d £40-£50
CARDS:

RED STAR HOTEL

★ **Lansdowne**
87 Clarendon St CV32 4PF (town centre at junct of Clarendon St & Warwick St)
☎ 01926 450505 FAX 01926 421313
RS 26 Dec-2 Jan
Proprietors David and Gillian Allen have been providing consistently high levels of hospitality, food and service at this delightful hotel for almost 20 years. The Regency property is conveniently located close to the town centre and the accommodation is equally suitable for both business people and tourists. The attractively decorated and tastefully appointed bedrooms are well equipped; a family room plus bedrooms on ground floor level are both available. The public areas are furnished in period style and include a comfortable lounge, a small but cosy bar and a pleasant dining room, where guests have the choice of either two or three courses from Lucinda Robinson's sensibly balanced set-price menu. Using only fresh ingredients, her dishes, which are neither too elaborate or over ambitious, are skilfully prepared and refreshingly honest.
15 rms (12 bth/shr) (1 fmly) CTV in 12 bedrooms No dogs (ex guide dogs) 11P No coaches No children 5yrs English, French & Italian Cuisine V meals Coffee am No smoking in restaurant Last d 8.30pm
ROOMS: (incl. bkfst) s £49.95-£56.95; d £59.90-£69.90 **LB**
MEALS: Dinner £14.95-£18.95&alc
CARDS:

★68% **Milverton House**
1 Milverton Ter CV32 5BE (200 yards from Leamington Spa Fire Station) ☎ 01926 428335 FAX 01926 428335
An attractive Victorian property located in a mainly residential area, Milverton House is personally run by friendly proprietors Mr and Mrs Kinzett. There are ten comfortable bedrooms, all of which are individually furnished. There is no bar but drinks can be served in the relaxing lounge and Mr Kinzett offers good home-cooked meals in the stylish dining room.
10 rms (7 bth/shr) (1 fmly) CTV in all bedrooms 6P No coaches V meals Coffee am Tea pm No smoking in restaurant Last d 7pm
ROOMS: (incl. bkfst) s £20-£36; d £36-£54 * **LB**
OFF-PEAK: (incl. bkfst) s £18-£32; d £32-£42
MEALS: Dinner £6.50-£14*
CARDS:

LEATHERHEAD Surrey Map 04 TQ15

★★67% **Bookham Grange**
Little Bookham Common, Bookham KT23 3HS (off A246 first right after Bookham Railway station)
☎ 01372 452742 FAX 01372 450080
MINOTEL Great Britain
Quietly situated in two-and-a-half acres, this friendly family-run hotel has all the style and charm of an English country house. Improvements continue, with more bedrooms currently being upgraded to a higher standard and all are well equipped. As well as two popular function and meeting rooms, there is a beamed bar, central sitting area and the small cosy Polesden Restaurant where chef Lionel Jouanet continues to provide enterprising and very enthusiastic standards of cooking. Service is attentive and friendly and personally supervised by the proprietors Mr and Mrs Perry. The hotel is located close to Bookham railway station which provides quick access to London and all the local attractions. Weekend and 'flexi-breaks' offer good value for money and are well worth an enquiry.
18 en suite (bth/shr) (2 fmly) CTV in all bedrooms 100P International Cuisine V meals Coffee am Tea pm No smoking in restaurant Last d 9.30pm
ROOMS: (incl. bkfst) s fr £60; d fr £75 * **LB**
MEALS: Lunch fr £13&alc Dinner fr £13*
CONF: Thtr 80 Class 24 Board 24
CARDS:

LEDBURY Hereford & Worcester Map 03 SO73

★★★66% **Feathers**
High St HR8 1DS (south from Worcester A449,east from HerefordA438,north from Gloucester A417,Hotel is situated in the High Street) ☎ 01531 635266 FAX 01531 632001
This 16th-century coaching inn is a distinctive landmark in the High Street with its whitewashed and black-timbered front colourfully adorned with hanging baskets of flowers. Bedrooms are quaint and well equipped, and care has been taken to preserve the character of the building. Imaginative dishes, created from good quality ingredients and competently prepared sauces, are served both in the restaurant and in the popular bar which has a bistro-style seating area. Any self-indulgence can be rectified on the hotel's squash courts. There is a parking area behind the building.
11 en suite (bth/shr) (2 fmly) CTV in all bedrooms Night porter 16P Squash Wkly live entertainment Xmas English & French Cuisine V meals Coffee am Tea pm Last d 9.30pm
ROOMS: (incl. bkfst) s £49.50-£65; d £65-£95 * **LB**
CONF: Thtr 100 Class 100 Board 80 Del from £89.95
CARDS:

★★71% **Hope End Country House**
Hope End HR8 1JQ (2m N of Ledbury just beyond the Wellington Hotel) ☎ 01531 633613 FAX 01531 636366
Closed mid Dec-early Feb
Peace and tranquillity are assured at this delightful refuge: a semi-Gothic house set within a walled garden and two courtyards in 40 acres of natural parkland. Well proportioned bedrooms, nicely finished in country furnishings, offer excellent beds, crisp linen and comfortable armchairs, giving a relaxed rustic atmosphere. The heart of the hotel is in the kitchen, where owner Patricia Hegerty uses organically grown produce from husband John's walled garden in old-fashioned honest English cooking. A recent inspection meal included confit of duck with chicory and orange salad, then lightly baked fillet of turbot followed by tempting home-made puddings. Breakfasts are an equal treat.
6 en suite (bth/shr) 2 annexe en suite (bth/shr) CTV in 1 bedroom No dogs 10P No coaches Listed Georgian Park No children 12yrs V meals No smoking in restaurant
ROOMS: (incl. bkfst) s £85-£108; d £120-£140 * **LB**
MEALS:*
CARDS:

★★66% **The Verzons Country House**
Trumpet HR8 2PZ (3m W of Ledbury A438) ☎ 01531 670381 FAX 07531 670830
Closed 24-26 Dec
A country house dating from 1790, situated on the A438 three miles from Ledbury, this family-run hotel stands in pretty gardens extending to four acres. The bedrooms are quite large and many have fine views of the Malvern Hills. Armchairs and sofas are provided in some rooms, and one has a four-poster bed. There is a cheerful log fire in the bar, and good-value meals are served in a small restaurant (the main restaurant opening on demand). The comfortable lounge is equipped with books and games, and another room is available for small conferences and functions.
9 en suite (bth/shr) (2 fmly) CTV in all bedrooms 60P English & French Cuisine V meals Coffee am Last d 9.30pm
ROOMS: (incl. bkfst) s £45-£55; d £65-£75 **LB**
CARDS:

LEEDS West Yorkshire Map 08 SE33
See also Garforth & Shipley

★★★★★70% **Oulton Hall**
DE VERE HOTELS
Rothwell Ln, Oulton LS26 8HN (M62 junct.30 A639 2 miles from this junction on the left hand side)
☎ 0113 282 1000 FAX 0113 282 8066
Surrounded by formal gardens and a championship standard golf course, this splendid mansion has been tastefully restored to create an impressive hotel. The majority of the attractive and well furnished bedrooms are housed in a modern wing, although the luxurious suites are in the original house. Day rooms are spacious and suitably grand although service does not always live up to the surroundings. There is a fine leisure centre with its own food outlet and extensive state-of-the-art function and conference facilities.
152 en suite (bth/shr) No smoking in 128 bedrooms CTV in all bedrooms STV Lift Night porter 260P Indoor swimming pool (heated) Golf 18 Squash Snooker Sauna Solarium Gym Croquet lawn Putting green Jacuzzi/spa Beauty therapy Aerobics ch fac English & French Cuisine V meals Coffee am Tea pm No smoking in restaurant Last d 9.30pm
MEALS: Lunch fr £13 Dinner fr £21.50&alc*
CONF: Thtr 350 Class 150 Board 40 Del from £150
CARDS:

See advertisement on page 341

★★★★73% **Leeds Marriott**
Marriott HOTELS·RESORTS·SUITES
4 Trevelyan Square, Boar Ln LS1 6ET (from M1 or M62 follow signs to City Centre turn into Sovereign St,left at lights right into NCP car park adjacent to the hotel) ☎ 0113 236 6366 FAX 0113 236 6367
This large modern hotel has a carefully restored Victorian façade and although centrally situated has a peaceful location overlooking an attractive city square. The bedrooms are spacious, modern and very comfortably furnished. Several are designated as executive rooms, others are designed for disabled guests and some have been nominated as non-smoking rooms; there are also eight suites with separate lounges. The hotel features two restaurants, Dysons, named after one of the country's foremost jewellers who once occupied the site and which contains much original memorabilia and John T's where more informal meals are served. There is an excellent leisure club and also comprehensive conference and banqueting facilities.
244 en suite (bth/shr) (85 fmly) No smoking in 152 bedrooms CTV in all bedrooms STV Lift Night porter Air conditioning Indoor swimming pool (heated) Sauna Solarium Gym Whirlpool Xmas International Cuisine V meals Coffee am Tea pm No smoking area in restaurant Last d 10.30pm
ROOMS: (incl. bkfst) s £85-£110; d £85-£110 * **LB**
OFF-PEAK: (incl. bkfst) s £54-£99; d £54-£99
MEALS: Lunch £12.95&alc Dinner £15.95&alc*
CONF: Thtr 300 Class 150 Board 25 Del from £135
CARDS:

★★★★69% **Holiday Inn Crowne Plaza**
Holiday Inn CROWNE PLAZA
Wellington St LS1 4DL (from M1 follow signs to City Centre, at city square left into Wellington Street)
☎ 0113 244 2200 FAX 0113 244 0460
An impressive modern hotel situated conveniently close to the city centre offers comfortably furnished, well equipped bedrooms - some of them designed specifically for the wheelchair user. Guests also have

access to a marbled reception lobby, a formal restaurant, an Italian restaurant/bar and a leisure centre.
125 en suite (bth/shr) (48 fmly) No smoking in 56 bedrooms CTV in all bedrooms STV No dogs (ex guide dogs) Lift Night porter Air conditioning 125P Indoor swimming pool (heated) Snooker Sauna Solarium Gym Jacuzzi/spa Steam room Xmas International Cuisine V meals Coffee am Tea pm Last d 10.30pm
ROOMS: s £115; d £115 * **LB**
OFF-PEAK: (incl. bkfst) s fr £72; d fr £72
MEALS: Lunch fr £9.95 Dinner fr £16.95*
CONF: Thtr 200 Class 100 Board 60 Del from £125
CARDS:

★★★★68% **The Queen's**

City Square LS1 1PL (follow signs for Leeds and city centre,hotel adjacent to the railway station in City Square) ☎ 0113 243 1323 FAX 0113 242 5154
This former 1930s railway hotel has been restored recently to much of its former splendour and now offers the facilities demanded by today's traveller. The public rooms are particularly impressive, including the elegant Palm Court Lounge, stylish Harewood Restaurant and popular Ridings Roast Room. Much of the traditional bedroom furniture dates back to the time when the hotel was established. There is a valet service for car parking.
190 en suite (bth/shr) No smoking in 72 bedrooms CTV in all bedrooms STV Lift Night porter 88P International Cuisine V meals Coffee am Tea pm No smoking area in restaurant Last d 10pm
MEALS: Lunch £12-£12.50&alc High tea £5.95-£9.95 Dinner £14.95-£17.50&alc*
CONF: Thtr 600 Class 160 Board 40 Del from £79
CARDS:

★★★ 79% **Haley's Hotel & Restaurant**

Shire Oak Rd, Headingley LS6 2DE (from City Centre follow local signs to University, 1.5m turn right in Headinley between Midland and Yorkshire Banks)
☎ 0113 278 4446 FAX 0113 275 3342
Closed 26-30 Dec
Haley's is an imposing Victorian house located in a quiet tree lined cul-de-sac. It combines the elegance and style of the country house genre with the quality and range of services required of the modern city hotel. Individually styled bedrooms and reception rooms are richly decorated and furnished with fine antiques. Private meeting rooms are air-conditioned, and the staff are courteous and dedicated. The cuisine, which is essentially modern British, demonstrates both flair and competence. JCB cards are accepted as well as the usual credit cards.
22 en suite (bth/shr) No smoking in 6 bedrooms CTV in all bedrooms STV No dogs (ex guide dogs) Night porter 18P No coaches V meals Coffee am No smoking in restaurant Last d 9.45pm
ROOMS: (incl. bkfst) s £55-£95; d £75-£112 * **LB**
MEALS: Sunday Lunch £14 Dinner £18-£26alc*
CONF: Thtr 30 Class 20 Board 25
CARDS:

★★★69% **Merrion Thistle**

Merrion Centre LS2 8NH (from the M1/M62/A61 join city loop road to junct 7, the Hotel is situated on Wade road adjoining to the Merrion Centre)
☎ 0113 243 9191 FAX 0113 242 3527
Situated adjacent to the Merrion Centre, this hotel has recently been refurbished to a very high standard. Bedrooms are mainly compact singles and are carefully laid out. Two bars are provided for guests' enjoyment - the Box Office which features live music and entertainment several evenings a week, and a quieter cocktail bar. Free parking is available in the centre's car park between 4pm and 9.30am.
109 en suite (bth/shr) No smoking in 76 bedrooms CTV in all bedrooms STV Lift Night porter P Xmas English & French Cuisine V meals Coffee am Tea pm No smoking in restaurant Last d 10.30pm

contd.

Some company-owned hotels have a central reservations telephone number. For the quick-reference list, consult the Contents page.

ROOMS: s £85-£95; d £95-£105 * LB
OFF-PEAK: (incl. bkfst) s £39.50-£49.50; d £57-£67.50
MEALS: Lunch £3-£8 Dinner £14.75&alc*
CONF: Thtr 80 Class 25 Board 25 Del from £115
CARDS:

★★★64% **Golden Lion**

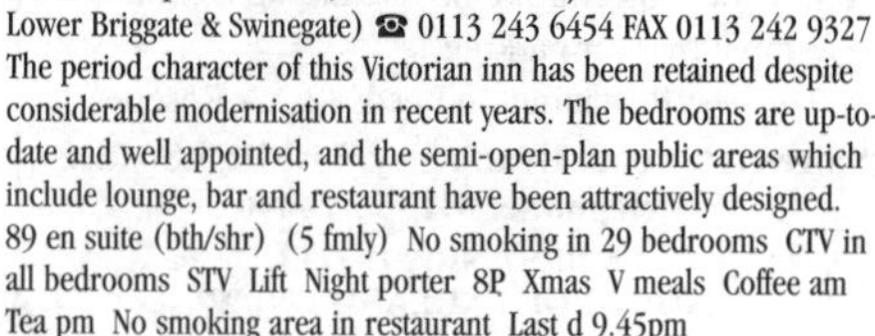

Lower Briggate LS1 4AE (2 mins from Leeds Rail Station, M1 & M6 junct 47 1.5 miles, Leeds - Bradford Airport 10 miles, Hotel situated on junct of Lower Briggate & Swinegate) ☎ 0113 243 6454 FAX 0113 242 9327
The period character of this Victorian inn has been retained despite considerable modernisation in recent years. The bedrooms are up-to-date and well appointed, and the semi-open-plan public areas which include lounge, bar and restaurant have been attractively designed.
89 en suite (bth/shr) (5 fmly) No smoking in 29 bedrooms CTV in all bedrooms STV Lift Night porter 8P Xmas V meals Coffee am Tea pm No smoking area in restaurant Last d 9.45pm
ROOMS: (incl. bkfst) s £79-£89; d £85-£95 * LB
MEALS: Dinner £13.95-£15.15&alc*
CONF: Thtr 120 Class 65 Board 45 Del from £97
CARDS:

★★★60% **Metropole**

King St LS1 2HQ (from M1/M62/M621 follow signs for City Centre.Take A65 Airport into Wellington St, at first traffic Island turn right into King St Hotel on right) ☎ 0113 245 0841 FAX 0113 242 5156
RS 26-30 Dec
This Victorian hotel with its distinctive terracotta façade retains many of its original art deco features. Accommodation continues to be improved, and the refurbished bedrooms offer a good range of modern facilities and smart bathrooms. Public areas are spacious, and the friendly staff provides willing service. The hotel is centrally situated close to the station.
105 en suite (bth/shr) No smoking in 20 bedrooms CTV in all bedrooms STV Lift Night porter 40P Xmas V meals Coffee am Tea pm Last d 9.30pm
ROOMS: s fr £79; d fr £105 * LB
OFF-PEAK: (incl. bkfst) s fr £45; d fr £70
MEALS: Lunch fr £9.95 Dinner fr £14.95&alc*
CONF: Thtr 300 Class 100 Board 80
CARDS:

★63% **Aragon**

250 Stainbeck Ln LS7 2PS (off A61 2m from city centre) ☎ 0113 275 9306 FAX 0113 275 7166
Closed 24 Dec-2 Jan
Built by a mill owner in 1893 and converted to a hotel in the 1970s, this pleasant family-owned hotel offers good value for money together with comfortable and very clean accommodation. It stands in a quiet leafy area of north Leeds in well tended gardens.
13 rms (9 bth 2 shr) (1 fmly) No smoking in 1 bedroom CTV in all bedrooms 25P No coaches V meals Coffee am Tea pm Last d 9pm
ROOMS: (incl. bkfst) s £26.50-£39.95; d £40-£48.52 LB
OFF-PEAK: (incl. bkfst) s £35.50; d £45.50
MEALS: Bar Lunch £3.50-£14alc Dinner £10.50&alc
CONF: Thtr 24 Board 12
CARDS:

TOWN HOUSE HOTEL

42 The Calls

LS2 7EW ☎ 0113 244 0099 FAX 0113 234 4100
Closed 5 days Xmas
This very well furnished town house hotel has been carefully converted from its previous life as a warehouse. It stands on the banks of the canal at the heart of the city. Superb quality and care are apparent throughout. The luxury bedrooms are furnished to meet every conceivable need of the modern traveller, including CD players, mini-bars and large desks. Breakfast can be served in the bedrooms or can be enjoyed in the pleasant breakfast room overlooking the canal. There is a wide choice of restaurants close by - among them the stylish Brasserie 44 next door.
41 en suite (bth/shr) No smoking in 6 bedrooms CTV in all bedrooms STV Lift Night porter 28P No coaches Fishing V meals Coffee am Tea pm
ROOMS: s £95-£140; d £125-£145 LB
OFF-PEAK: s £65-£75
CONF: Thtr 55 Class 40 Board 42 Del from £120.50
CARDS:

Forte Posthouse Leeds/Selby

LS25 5LF ☎ 01977 682711 FAX 01977 685462
(For full entry see Lumby)

Hilton National Leeds City

Neville St LS1 4BX (from M1/M62/M621 follow city centre signs) ☎ 0113 244 2000 FAX 0113 243 3577
This is a bright, modern hotel, with an informal restaurant, aimed at both the business and leisure guest. All bedrooms have en suite bathrooms and a range of modern facilities. For more information about Hilton National hotels, consult the Contents page under Hotel Groups.
206 en suite (bth/shr)
ROOMS: s £105-£125; d £105-£125 *

Travel Inn

Wellington St ☎ 01132 428104 FAX 01132 428105
Purpose-built accommodation, offering spacious, well equipped bedrooms, all with en suite bathrooms. Meals may be taken at the nearby family restaurant. For more information about Travel Inns, consult the Contents page under Hotel Groups.
84 en suite (bth/shr)
ROOMS: (incl. bkfst) d £35.50 *

Travel Inn (Leeds Airport)

Victoria Av, Yeadon LS19 7AW ☎ 01132 504284 FAX 01132 505838
Purpose-built accommodation, offering spacious, well equipped bedrooms, all with en suite bathrooms. Meals may be taken at the nearby family restaurant. For more information about Travel Inns, consult the Contents page under Hotel Groups.
40 en suite (bth/shr)
ROOMS: (incl. bkfst) d £35.50 *

LEEK Staffordshire Map 07 SJ95

★★64% ***Bank End Farm Motel***
Leek Old Rd ST9 9QJ ☎ 01538 383638
Closed Xmas week
This small, motel-style hotel, where the atmosphere is very informal and relaxed, is still very much part of a working farm. Lcated just off the A53 two miles from the town centre, it has been in the Robinson family for many years. Mrs Robinson is a very hospitable host and takes charge in the kitchen, where she prepares a good range of home-made dishes which are served in the small dining room with the most wonderful views of the valley beyond. Guests also have the use of a small, comfortable lounge bar, and the bedrooms, including a suite and family rooms, are attractively decorated, well equipped and located around the farm's yard.
10 rms (9 bth/shr) (2 fmly) No smoking in 1 bedroom CTV in all bedrooms 25P No coaches Indoor swimming pool (heated) Fishing ch fac English & French Cuisine V meals
CARDS:

LEEMING BAR North Yorkshire Map 08 SE28

★★62% **Motel Leeming**
The Great North Rd DL8 1DT ☎ 01677 422122
FAX 01677 424507
(For full entry see Bedale)

★★60% **White Rose**
Bedale Rd DL7 9AY (on A684, E of A1 junc)
☎ 01677 422707 & 424941 FAX 01677 425123
Situated in a convenient location for the A1, this mainly business-style hotel provides modern bedrooms which are also well equipped. A very good range of reasonably-priced food is available either in the bar or the friendly restaurant.
18 en suite (bth/shr) (2 fmly) CTV in all bedrooms 50P Pool table V meals Coffee am Tea pm No smoking area in restaurant
Last d 9.30pm
ROOMS: (incl. bkfst) s £31; d £45 *
OFF-PEAK: (incl. bkfst) s fr £22; d fr £35
MEALS: Lunch £7.95 High tea £7.75 Dinner £11.95&alc
CARDS:

LEE-ON-THE-SOLENT Hampshire Map 04 SU50

★★★60% **Belle Vue**
39 Marine Pde East PO13 9BW ☎ 01705 550258 FAX 01705 552624
Closed 25 & 26 Dec RS 24 Dec
Situated right on the seafront, this popular hotel has splendid views over the Solent. The bedrooms are smartly decorated and well equipped; many have sea views and some have balconies. The Seasons Restaurant offers an interesting and varied menu, and the Promenade Bar offers regular nightly entertainment such as live bands, karaoke and discos.
24 en suite (bth/shr) 3 annexe en suite (bth/shr) (4 fmly) CTV in all bedrooms STV Night porter 55P Wkly live entertainment V meals Coffee am No smoking area in restaurant Last d 9.45pm
ROOMS: d £39.50-£59.50 * **LB**
OFF-PEAK: d £37.50-£55
MEALS: Lunch £8.75-£22.90alc Dinner £11.45-£22.90alc*
CONF: Thtr 150 Class 60 Board 40 Del from £70
CARDS:

LEICESTER Leicestershire Map 04 SK50

★★★★61% **Holiday Inn**
St Nicholas Circle LE1 5LX (from junct 21 off M1/M69 take A5460 to city centre for approx 3.5m)
☎ 0116 253 1161 FAX 0116 251 3169

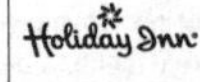

This purpose-built hotel in the city centre has seen recent, substantial refurbishment and offers spacious bedrooms, all with air-conditioning, mini bars, a pay movie channel and satellite TV. Executive bedrooms offer that little extra depth in comfort. A smart lobby leads to the lounge bar and the informal Hayloft Restaurant. Overnight guests can park free in the adjacent multi-story car park.
188 en suite (bth/shr) (99 fmly) No smoking in 106 bedrooms CTV in all bedrooms STV Lift Night porter Air conditioning Indoor swimming pool (heated) Sauna Solarium Gym Jacuzzi/spa Health bar International Cuisine V meals Coffee am Tea pm
Last d 10.15pm
ROOMS: s £80-£99; d £90-£109 * **LB**
OFF-PEAK: s £59-£99; d £59-£99
MEALS: Lunch fr £12.95&alc High tea £2.55-£12 Dinner fr £18.25&alc
CONF: Thtr 300 Class 140 Board 35 Del from £97
CARDS:

★★★72% **Belmont House**
De Montfort St LE1 7GR (from A6 in S direction, take first right after BR station, 200yds on right)
☎ 0116 254 4773 FAX 0116 247 0804
Closed 25-28 Dec
At the end of a mile long leafy promenade which stretches from Victoria Park, this well established family-owned hotel is only a short walk from the town centre. The extensive public areas are comfortable and arranged as small areas with a cosy, welcoming feel to them. The bedrooms are thoughtfully designed for the business user, providing a good desk with extra telephone points and swivel, office-style chairs in which to work. The Bistro provides informal meals, and there is also the Cherry Restaurant for those who want to dine in style.

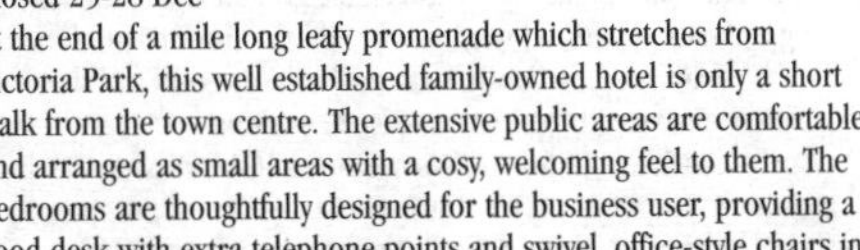

44 en suite (bth/shr) 21 annexe en suite (bth/shr)

contd.

(7 fmly) No smoking in 15 bedrooms CTV in all bedrooms Lift Night porter 60P English & French Cuisine V meals Coffee am Tea pm Last d 10pm
ROOMS: s £68-£78; d £76-£86 * **LB**
OFF-PEAK: (incl. bkfst) s £40-£55; d £55-£65
MEALS: Lunch £11.50-£12.95&alc Dinner fr £17.50&alc*
CONF: Thtr 120 Class 60 Board 50 Del from £80
CARDS:

See advertisement on opposite page

★★★66% **Stage**
Leicester Rd (A50), Wigston Fields LE18 1JW (S on A50) ☎ 0116 288 6161 FAX 0116 281 1874
Located about three miles south of the city centre, this is a busy commercial hotel offering well equipped modern bedrooms and spacious public areas. Conferences, weddings and other functions are catered for and the hotel has its own fully equipped leisure centre. Food options are extensive with a good selection of bar meals and more formal restaurant dining.
79 en suite (bth/shr) (10 fmly) No smoking in 6 bedrooms CTV in all bedrooms No dogs (ex guide dogs) Night porter 200P Indoor swimming pool (heated) Sauna Solarium Gym Jacuzzi/spa Wkly live entertainment Xmas International Cuisine V meals Coffee am Tea pm Last d 9.45pm
ROOMS: (incl. bkfst) s £75; d £85 * **LB**
MEALS: Sunday Lunch £8.95-£10 Dinner £14.95-£25*
CONF: Thtr 250 Class 100 Board 100 Del from £95
CARDS:

★★★ 65% **Time Out Hotel & Leisure**

Enderby Rd, Blaby LE8 4GD (M1 junct.21, A46 towards Leicester take 4th exit at 1st roundabout, ahead at 2nd, left at3rd follow signs to Blaby,over 4th roundabout Hotel on left) ☎ 0116 278 7898 FAX 0116 278 1974
A modern hotel adjacent to the link road on the outskirts of the city which provides bright, comfortable and well equipped bedrooms. Public rooms are cosy and welcoming with a choice of restaurants and commendable food standards. The hotel offers friendly service from a keen local team and boasts conscientious standards of cleanliness.
25 en suite (bth/shr) No smoking in 3 bedrooms CTV in all bedrooms STV 102P No coaches Indoor swimming pool (heated) Riding Sauna Solarium Gym Croquet lawn Jacuzzi/spa English & French Cuisine V meals Coffee am Tea pm No smoking area in restaurant Last d 10pm
ROOMS: (incl. bkfst) s £49.50-£65; d £65-£70 * **LB**
OFF-PEAK: (incl. bkfst) s £17.50-£45; d £27.50-£50
MEALS: Sunday Lunch £6.50-£9.50 Dinner £9.95-£15.95&alc*
CONF: Thtr 25 Class 40 Board 25 Del from £85
CARDS:

★★★64% **Hermitage**

Wigston Rd, Oadby LE2 5QE ☎ 0116 256 9955 FAX 0116 272 0559
This modern company hotel is located in a residential area close to Oadby centre and approximately 3 miles south of Leicester. Bedrooms are well equipped and comfortable. Public areas are light and inviting, split between the ground and first floor, offering a choice of bars, a foyer lounge and a good selection of food within the restaurant. The business guest is well served by the choice of conference/meeting rooms and ample car parking.
57 en suite (bth/shr) (4 fmly) No smoking in 16 bedrooms CTV in all bedrooms Lift Night porter 160P Pool table Xmas European Cuisine V meals Coffee am Tea pm No smoking in restaurant Last d 9.30pm
ROOMS: s £57.50-£72; d £57.50-£81 * **LB**
OFF-PEAK: (incl. bkfst) s £30-£40; d £60
MEALS: Lunch £4.95-£9.96 Dinner fr £13.50&alc*
CONF: Thtr 250 Class 100 Board 60 Del from £70
CARDS:

★★★64% **Regency**
360 London Rd LE2 2PL (on the A6 London Road 1.5m from the city centre, near outer ring road which leads to the M1 & M9 approx 4m away) ☎ 0116 270 9634 FAX 0116 2701375
Originally a convent this busy commercial hotel has been completely modernised over recent years and now provides bright and well-equipped accommodation. Bedrooms are attractively decorated with rich fabrics and matching wallpapers and all are furnished with modern fitted units. Several are suitable for families and there are four honeymoon suites. Live entertainment is regularly held and specially themed dinners are held which can include murder mysteries and Caribbean nights. A choice of eating options is provided with the Scandals Cafe serving inexpensive meals and the Regency Restaurant offering more formal dining. A large function suite is available and the mostly young staff are friendly and attentive.
32 en suite (bth/shr) (4 fmly) CTV in all bedrooms No dogs (ex guide dogs) Night porter 40P Xmas English & French Cuisine V meals Coffee am Last d 10pm
ROOMS: (incl. bkfst) s £39.50-£45; d £55 *
OFF-PEAK: (incl. bkfst) s £30; d £40
MEALS: Lunch £6-£12 High tea £5 Dinner £12.75&alc*
CONF: Thtr 90 Class 50 Board 25 Del from £61
CARDS:

★★★58% **Saint James**
Abbey St LE1 3TE (turn right after St Margaret's bus station) ☎ 0116 251 0666 FAX 0116 251 5183
Set astride the multi-storey car park next to St Margaret's bus station, this hotel provides free monitored parking for residents. The interior is modern in style, guests having the use of a comfortable open-plan lounge area, a small bar and a galleried restaurant which has views out over the city skyline. Light bedrooms with fitted wood furniture offer a good range of up-to-date facilities.
73 en suite (bth/shr) (3 fmly) CTV in all bedrooms Lift Night porter English & French Cuisine V meals Coffee am Tea pm Last d 9.30pm
ROOMS: (incl. bkfst) s £49-£52.50; d £57-£62 * **LB**
OFF-PEAK: (incl. bkfst) s £40-£42.50; d £45-£50
MEALS: Dinner £12.50-£13.50&alc*
CONF: Thtr 200 Class 120 Board 35 Del from £75
CARDS:

★★69% **Red Cow**
Hinckley Rd, Leicester Forest East LE3 3PG (4m W on A47) ☎ 0116 238 7878 FAX 0116 238 6539
A cottage-style, friendly family inn, The Red Cow has a cosy restaurant and a superb neighbouring bedroom wing furnished to a high standard throughout.
31 en suite (bth/shr) (26 fmly) No smoking in 23 bedrooms CTV in all bedrooms No dogs (ex guide dogs) 120P English & French Cuisine V meals Coffee am Tea pm Last d 10pm
ROOMS: s £39.50; d £39.50 *
OFF-PEAK: s £28.50; d £28.50
MEALS: Bar Lunch 1p&alc Dinner £9-£17alc
CARDS:

See advertisement on opposite page

★★62% **Old Tudor Rectory**
Main St, Glenfield LE3 8DG ☎ 0116 2915678 FAX 0116 2911416
Closed 24 Dec-1 Jan
This popular commercial hotel is situated west of Leicester in the village of Glenfield. Bedrooms have pretty wallpapers and fabrics are used to good effect and many extra facilities are provided. The lounge bar is cosy and comfortable and food comes by way of a small fixed-price menu. A beauty salon is among the facilities available.

contd.

15 en suite (bth/shr) 1 annexe en suite (bth/shr) (2 fmly) CTV in all bedrooms 37P Solarium Gym Jacuzzi/spa Beauty salon V meals Coffee am Tea pm Last d 9.30pm
ROOMS: (incl. bkfst) s £38-£42; d £53-£60 **LB**
OFF-PEAK: (incl. bkfst) s £30.40-£35; d £40-£42.40
CONF: Thtr 20 Class 20 Board 20 Del from £45
CARDS:

See advertisement on opposite page

★★58% **Gables**

368 London Rd LE2 2PN (.50mile city side of junction A563 (South East) and A6) ☎ 0116 270 6969
FAX 0116 270 6969
This commercial hotel is located south of the city centre near the university. Many bathrooms have been modernised recently and a programme of redecoration is planned for bedrooms. The lounge bar is cosy and comfortable and an adjoining room serves as a popular venue for business meetings and local functions.
30 en suite (bth/shr) (9 fmly) CTV in all bedrooms No dogs (ex guide dogs) 29P No coaches English & French Cuisine V meals Coffee am No smoking in restaurant Last d 9.30pm
ROOMS: (incl. bkfst) s £39-£45; d £55
OFF-PEAK: (incl. bkfst) s £32; d £45
MEALS: Lunch £9.76&alc Dinner £13.50-£16&alc
CONF: Thtr 60 Class 12 Board 28
CARDS:

Forte Posthouse Leicester

Braunstone Ln East LE3 2FW (on A46 approach from junc 21 of M1/M69) ☎ 0116 263 0500
FAX 0116 282 3623
Suitable for both the business and leisure traveller, this bright hotel provides modern accommodation in well equipped bedrooms with en suite bathrooms. For more details about Forte Posthouse hotels, consult the Contents page for the section on Hotel Groups.
164 en suite (bth/shr)
ROOMS: s fr £69; d fr £69 *
CONF: Thtr 85 Class 54 Board 45 Del from £89

Travel Inn

Forest Park, Hinckley Rd, Leicester Forest East LE3 3GD (Join outer ring rd A563. At rdbt turn left onto A47 signed Hinckley. Situated half a mile on left) ☎ 0116 2394677 FAX 0116 2393429
Purpose-built accommodation, offering spacious, well equipped bedrooms, all with en suite bathrooms. Meals may be taken at the nearby family restaurant. For more information about Travel Inns, consult the Contents page under Hotel Groups.
40 en suite (bth/shr)
ROOMS: (incl. bkfst) d £35.50 *

LEIGH DELAMERE MOTORWAY SERVICE AREA (M4) Wiltshire Map 03 ST87

Travelodge

M4 Service Area SN14 6LB
☎ Central Res 0800 850950 FAX 01666 837112
This modern building offers accommodation in smart, spacious and well equipped bedrooms, suitable for family use, and all with en suite bathrooms. Meals may be taken at the nearby family restaurant. For information on room rates and to make a booking, call Roomline free of charge on 0800 850950. For more details about Travelodge, consult the Contents page under Hotel Groups.
51 en suite (bth/shr)

LEIGHTON BUZZARD Bedfordshire Map 04 SP92

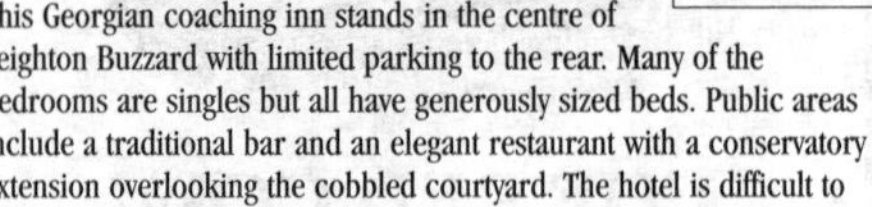

★★★58% **Swan**
High St LU7 7EA (opposite market cross in the Town Centre) ☎ 01525 372148 FAX 01525 370444
This Georgian coaching inn stands in the centre of Leighton Buzzard with limited parking to the rear. Many of the bedrooms are singles but all have generously sized beds. Public areas include a traditional bar and an elegant restaurant with a conservatory extension overlooking the cobbled courtyard. The hotel is difficult to find, so it is wise to ask for directions.
38 en suite (bth/shr) (1 fmly) CTV in all bedrooms STV Night porter 10P Xmas European Cuisine V meals Coffee am Tea pm Last d 9pm
ROOMS: s £49.50-£55; d £58.50-£65 **LB**
OFF-PEAK: (incl. bkfst) s £40-£45; d £56-£60
MEALS: Lunch £7.95-£9.95 Dinner £13.95-£14.50&alc*
CONF: Thtr 50 Class 25 Board 25 Del from £80
CARDS:

LEISTON Suffolk Map 05 TM46

★65% **White Horse**
Station Rd IP16 4HD (on B1119, signposted Leiston, 4m to hotel)
☎ 01728 830694 FAX 01728 833105
This inn owes much of its popularity to its proximity to the town centre and Sizewell. The bedrooms are well equipped, if somewhat tight for space in some cases. There are two bars, a restaurant and a large beer garden with attractions for children. The first-floor lounge can also be used for functions.
10 rms (1 bth 7 shr) 3 annexe en suite (shr) (1 fmly) CTV in all bedrooms 17P Pool table ch fac Xmas English & French Cuisine V meals Coffee am Tea pm Last d 9.30pm
ROOMS: (incl. bkfst) d £25-£33.50 * **LB**
OFF-PEAK: (incl. bkfst) d £45-£52
MEALS: Bar Lunch fr £2 Dinner £7-£15alc
CARDS:

LENHAM Kent Map 05 TQ85

★★60% **Dog & Bear**
The Square ME17 2PG (turn off M20 from Maidstone/London direction, proceed S on A20 past Leeds Castle,turn right at Lenham Village and enter village square) ☎ 01622 858219 FAX 01622 859415
Dating from around 1602, this former coaching inn is attractively positioned in the market square, within the sound of the bells of the village church. It provides comfortable, well equipped bedrooms, some of which are housed in the converted stable block across the courtyard. The beamed bar is full of character and features a range of real ales, bar meals and blackboard specials, whilst the dining room offers an interesting carte and grills.
24 en suite (bth/shr) (3 fmly) No smoking in 9 bedrooms CTV in all bedrooms 40P English & French Cuisine V meals Coffee am Tea pm No smoking area in restaurant Last d 9.30pm
ROOMS: (incl. bkfst) s £38.50-£40; d £49.50-£52 * **LB**
MEALS: Lunch £10-£15alc Dinner fr £15.20alc
CONF: Thtr 60 Class 40 Board 40 Del from £60
CARDS:

LEOMINSTER Hereford & Worcester Map 03 SO45

★★65% **Talbot**
West St HR6 8EP (approach either from A49, A44 or A4112, the Hotel can be found at the centre of the town) ☎ 01568 616347 FAX 01568 614880
This former coaching inn is situated in the town centre. It dates back to the 15th century and original features, such as exposed ceiling beams, plus real fires and antique furniture in the two bars, help to

enhance the olde worlde character. Privately owned and personally run, it provides a variety of bedroom styles and sizes, some of which were being refurbished, at the time of our last inspection. Facilities include rooms for private functions and conferences.
20 en suite (bth/shr) (3 fmly) CTV in all bedrooms 20P Xmas English & French Cuisine V meals Coffee am Tea pm Last d 9.30pm
ROOMS: (incl. bkfst) s fr £45; d fr £64 * **LB**
OFF-PEAK: (incl. bkfst) s fr £38; d fr £50
MEALS: Lunch fr £10.50&alc Dinner fr £16&alc
CARDS:

★★57% **Royal Oak**

MINOTEL Great Britain

South St HR6 8JA (junct A44/A49)
☎ 01568 612610 FAX 01568 612710
This hotel - a large white building which is quite a landmark in the centre of town - offers modestly furnished but fairly well equipped accommodation. Staff provide cheerful service, and locals are drawn to the bar and restaurant, where well prepared food is ceremoniously wheeled to the tables. There are also a high-ceilinged banqueting room, a cavernous dance-cum-conference hall and a cellar bar.
17 en suite (bth/shr) 1 annexe en suite (bth/shr) (2 fmly) No smoking in 2 bedrooms CTV in all bedrooms 25P V meals Coffee am Last d 9.30pm
ROOMS: (incl. bkfst) s £31.50-£35; d £45-£55 * **LB**
MEALS: Lunch £6.50 Dinner £10.25*
CONF: Thtr 220 Class 100 Board 50
CARDS:

RED STAR HOTEL

★❀❀ **Marsh Country**
Eyton HR6 0AG (leave B4361 signposted Eyton & Lucton, continue along lane until the common, hotel on the right)
☎ 01568 613952
Jacqueline and Martin Gilleland's delightful little country house hotel is in a rural location just outside Leominster. It comprises three buildings in one, the oldest part being a 14th-century timbered dwelling. The hospitable owners run the place almost on their own, Jacqueline in the kitchen and Martin front of house. Bedrooms are mostly small but tastefully decorated and provided with lots of thoughtful extras. A barn with a flagstone floor and a high arched and beamed ceiling has been converted into a comfortable lounge adjacent to the cosy bar/lounge. The attractive country dining room is the setting for some enjoyable British cooking based on quality produce from the kitchen garden or local suppliers. Smoking is permitted only in the lounges.

contd.

5 rms (4 bth/shr) No smoking in 4 bedrooms CTV in 4 bedrooms No dogs (ex guide dogs) 15P No coaches Croquet lawn No children 12yrs Last d 9pm
MEALS: Sunday Lunch fr £19.95 Dinner fr £22.50*
CARDS:

LETCHWORTH Hertfordshire Map 04 TL23

★★64% **Broadway**

The Broadway SG6 3NZ (from junct 9 A1 M follow signs to Letchworth Town Centre, Hotel is on Broadway oposite main post office)
☎ 01462 480111 FAX 01462 481563
This well established hotel is located in the centre of town. It has two bars and a large, attractive, traditional-style conference room which is ideal for commercial and social functions. The bedrooms are well looked after and will be benefiting from gradual improvements.
35 en suite (bth/shr) No smoking in 13 bedrooms CTV in all bedrooms STV No dogs (ex guide dogs) Lift Night porter 40P Wkly live entertainment V meals Coffee am Tea pm
ROOMS: (incl. bkfst) s £31-£54.95; d £53-£64.95 **LB**
CONF: Thtr 200 Class 120 Board 160 Del from £69.50
CARDS:

LEWDOWN Devon Map 02 SX48

RED STAR HOTEL

★★ **Lewtrenchard Manor**

EX20 4PN (from A30 from Exeter turn on to Plymouth/Tavistock road. At T junct turn right and immediately left on to Old A30 signposted Lewdown) ☎ 01566 783256 & 783222 FAX 01566 783332
This delightful Jacobean Manor House nestles in the heart of beautiful Devon countryside. Personally run by James and Sue Murray, Lewtrenchard offers high standards of comfort but retains the atmosphere of a family home. The bedrooms, all with lovely views, are individually decorated and have lots of thoughtful extras. The elegant public rooms boast large open fireplaces and attractive family antiques, with many comfortable corners in which to enjoy the tranquillity of the house. The oak panelled restaurant is the perfect setting to enjoy chef Jason Buck's skilfully prepared food served by a young friendly staff headed by Kate.
8 rms (7 bth/shr) CTV in all bedrooms 50P No coaches Fishing Croquet lawn Clay pigeon shooting No children 7yrs Xmas English & French Cuisine V meals Coffee am Tea pm No smoking in restaurant Last d 9.30pm
ROOMS: (incl. bkfst) d fr £100 * **LB**
OFF-PEAK: (incl. bkfst) s fr £75; d fr £75
MEALS: Lunch £16 Dinner £28*
CONF: Thtr 50 Class 40 Board 30 Del from £115
CARDS:

LEWES East Sussex Map 05 TQ41

★★★76% **Shelleys Hotel**

THISTLE HOTELS

High St BN7 1XS ☎ 01273 472361
FAX 01273 483152
A recent total refurbishment of the bedrooms at Shelleys has created deep levels of comfort and individual character with good quality furnishings. The building itself dates back to the 16th century and has preserved some interesting architectural features from its history. It also has a peaceful rear lawn and gardens overlooked by the restaurant, where dishes created by the kitchen team show extra thought and a keenness to please.
Day rooms have a gentle, peaceful atmosphere, with true town-house elegance.
19 en suite (bth/shr) (2 fmly) CTV in all bedrooms STV Night porter 25P Xmas European Cuisine V meals Coffee am Tea pm No smoking in restaurant Last d 9.15pm
ROOMS: s £95-£120; d £120-£170 * **LB**
OFF-PEAK: (incl. bkfst & dinner) s £72-£117; d £144-£164
MEALS: Lunch £11.50-£15&alc Dinner fr £24&alc*
CONF: Thtr 50 Class 20 Board 28 Del from £140
CARDS:

See advertisement on opposite page

★★★68% **White Hart**

Best Western

55 High St BN7 1XE (opposite County Court)
☎ 01273 476694 FAX 01273 476695
This 16th-century coaching inn stands in the High Street and offers an attractive range of public rooms, including a Coffee Shop, the Conservatory Restaurant and carvery, a foyer lounge with log burning fire, a traditional front bar serving real ale, a sun terrace on the roof, a new Hearts bar lounge, meeting rooms and a well equipped leisure centre. The oak beamed and wood panelled interior retains much of its original architectural character and some bedrooms in the original inn offer four poster beds. Most of the

bedrooms, however, are in a spacious modern extension facing the South Downs. Service is very friendly and the atmosphere is relaxed and informal.

23 rms (19 bth/shr) 29 annexe en suite (bth/shr) (3 fmly) CTV in all bedrooms STV Night porter 40P Indoor swimming pool (heated) Sauna Solarium Gym Jacuzzi/spa Wkly live entertainment Xmas V meals Coffee am Tea pm Last d 10.15pm

ROOMS: (incl. bkfst) s £54; d £76 * **LB**

MEALS: Lunch £10.50&alc Dinner £10.50&alc*

CONF: Thtr 250 Class 120 Board 90

CARDS:

See advertisement on this page

LEYBURN North Yorkshire Map 07 SE19

★61% **Golden Lion**

Market Place DL8 5AS (set on the A684 in Market square of Leyburn)

☎ 01969 22161 FAX 01969 23836

Closed 25 & 26 Dec

This popular inn and hotel stands in the market square and dates back to 1765. It offers well equipped bedrooms which include telephones and, in most cases en suite facilities. A good range of food is provided in either the bar or the attractive rear restaurant. The bar serves its own house beer, called Oliver John, and there is an interesting collection of beer bottles around the walls.

16 rms (11 bth 2 shr) (5 fmly) CTV in all bedrooms Lift No coaches English & Continental Cuisine V meals Coffee am Tea pm Last d 9.30pm

ROOMS: (incl. bkfst) s £20-£28; d £40-£56 * **LB**

MEALS: Lunch £7.95-£8.50 High tea fr £5.95 Dinner £8.50-£14.50&alc

CARDS:

LICHFIELD Staffordshire Map 07 SK10

★★★65% **Little Barrow**
Beacon St WS13 7AR (200 yds from cathedral on right)
☎ 01543 414500 FAX 01543 415734
Conveniently situated for the city centre, the cathedral and Beacon Park, this friendly hotel offers modern, attractively decorated and well equipped accommodation. The emphasis throughout the hotel is on hospitality and service; early morning tea can be delivered to your room and your shoes cleaned. A good range of well prepared dishes, including daily-changing 'specials' are offered, in addition to a wide range of bar meals. The hotel also has a good-sized conference and banqueting facility.
24 en suite (bth/shr) (2 fmly) CTV in all bedrooms No dogs (ex guide dogs) Night porter 70P International Cuisine V meals Coffee am Tea pm Last d 9.30pm
MEALS: Lunch £8-£15&alc Dinner fr £13.50&alc
CONF: Thtr 100 Class 70 Board 70
CARDS:

★★67% **The Olde Corner House**
Walsall Rd, Muckley Corner WS14 0BG (at junct of A5/A461)
☎ 01543 372182 FAX 01543 372211
This characterful hotel, part of which dates from 1683 and was originally a coaching inn, is run by Brian and Pam Higgins who have recently added a new wing of smart bedrooms. Both the existing and new rooms however, including two with four-poster beds, are attractively decorated and well equipped. The atmosphere is informal and relaxed, and a very good range of tasty, well prepared dishes is available in either of the two restaurants, or the bar.
23 en suite (bth/shr) No smoking in all bedrooms CTV in all bedrooms No dogs 65P No coaches Pool table Xmas International Cuisine V meals Coffee am Tea pm Last d 10pm
ROOMS: (incl. bkfst) s fr £39; d £55-£65 * **LB**
OFF-PEAK: (incl. bkfst) s fr £35; d fr £45
MEALS: Dinner £10.95
CARDS:

★★66% **Swan**
Bird St WS13 6PT (from A5127,A461,A51 at the Bowling Green Island take City Centre exit to next Island, turn left into Swan Road, Hotel at end on right) ☎ 01543 414777 FAX 01543 411277
This 18th-century former coaching inn is full of character, ideally located in the city, and close to the cathedral and Beacon Park. It offers freshly decorated and well equipped accommodation, with some ground floor rooms situated immediately adjacent to the main building. Guests can relax in the comfortable lounge and have the choice of eating in the restaurant, or in the pub across the courtyard, where a good selection of real ales and bar meals is served.
11 en suite (bth/shr) 8 annexe en suite (bth) CTV in all bedrooms STV Night porter 80P Pool table English & French Cuisine V meals Coffee am Tea pm Last d 9.45pm
ROOMS: (incl. bkfst) s £50; d £64.50 *
OFF-PEAK: (incl. bkfst) s £40; d £52
MEALS: Lunch £7.75-£8.95&alc Dinner £12.95&alc
CONF: Thtr 120 Class 100 Board 40 Del £80
CARDS:

See advertisement on opposite page

★★62% **Angel Croft**
Beacon St WS13 7AA (situated opposite main west gate entrance to Lichfield Cathedral) ☎ 01543 258737 FAX 01543 415605
Closed 25 & 26 Dec RS Sun evenings
This traditional hotel, which has been owned and personally run by the Hilpert family for the last 24 years, is ideally located close to the cathedral, within easy walking distance of the city centre. The comfortable and well equipped bedrooms, including a four-poster and family rooms, are divided between the main hotel and an adjacent Georgian townhouse. The hotel's long established staff provide friendly and attentive service.
10 rms (3 bth 5 shr) 8 annexe en suite (bth/shr) (1 fmly) CTV in all bedrooms No dogs (ex guide dogs) Night porter 60P V meals Coffee am Tea pm No smoking in restaurant Last d 8.45pm
ROOMS: (incl. bkfst) s £38.50-£54.50; d £45-£66.50 *
MEALS: Lunch £10.50-£14 Dinner £11-£18*
CARDS:

LIFTON Devon Map 02 SX38

★★★❀❀❀73% **Arundell Arms**
PL16 0AA (off A30) ☎ 01566 784666
FAX 01566 784494
Closed 3 days Xmas
This delightful 18th-century coaching inn, situated in a peaceful village halfway between Bodmin and Dartmoor, is popular for sporting holidays and boasts 20 miles of fishing waters. Log fires blaze in the sitting room and bar on cooler evenings, and the combination of flagstone floors, fresh flowers and personal treasures emphasises the relaxed and friendly atmosphere that pervades the hotel. Bedrooms have been tastefully decorated with restful colour schemes and practically furnished for both business and leisure use. Almost all the staff are local, and the Arundell Arms has been owned and personally managed by Anne Voss-Bark since 1961. Another of the hotel's great strengths is the vibrant cooking of chef Philip Burgess. A most enjoyable, inspection meal started with a risotto of woodland mushrooms, followed by delicately flavoured scallops served with creamed puy lentils. The fillet of beef chosen as the main course beautifully matched the high quality of the meat with the sweetness of puréed parsnips and the contrast of a sharp, rich peppercorn sauce. Pudding was a tangy lemon tart with sufficient citrus flavour to cut through the cream.
24 en suite (bth/shr) 5 annexe en suite (bth/shr) CTV in all bedrooms STV 80P No coaches Fishing Skittle alley Games room English & French Cuisine V meals Coffee am Tea pm No smoking in restaurant Last d 9.30pm
ROOMS: (incl. bkfst) s £40-£64; d £80-£102 **LB**
OFF-PEAK: (incl. bkfst) s £39-£61; d £78-£97
MEALS: Lunch £18-£26 Dinner £26-£30
CONF: Thtr 100 Class 36 Board 46 Del from £80
CARDS:

See advertisement on opposite page

★★❀❀75% ***Lifton Hall Country House***
PL16 0DR (off A30) ☎ 01566 784863 & 784263 FAX 01566 784770
Since acquiring Lifton Hall at the end of 1993, Mary and Gary Dodds have transformed it into a small luxury hotel in traditional English style. Bedrooms are attractively furnished and have character and charm. Dan's Bar maintains the atmosphere of a village inn and serves good bar meals. There is also a separate restaurant, where chef Christopher Hope produces some imaginative cooking in dishes often enlivened with Eastern flavours. Residents have the use of an elegant

drawing room in which to relax in peace, and service throughout is both friendly and efficient.

11 en suite (bth/shr) (4 fmly) CTV in all bedrooms 30P Fishing Falconry & hawking International Cuisine V meals Last d 9pm
CARDS:

★★68% **Thatched Cottage**
Sprytown PL16 0AY (leave A30 dual Carriageway at Stowford Cross,turn south for 2 miles until Sprytown Cross is reached, straight across cross roads hotel on right) ☎ 01566 784224 FAX 01566 784334
The Thatched Cottage dates back to the 16th-century and nestles in 2.5 acres of landscaped gardens with an elevated patio, ponds, lawns and ample car parking. Comfortable bedrooms are located in a converted stable block a short distance from the main hotel. The cottage houses a cosy lounge with an inglenook fireplace, two small beamed dining areas and a compact bar. Imaginative fixed-price menus are offered, featuring home-cooked dishes based on local produce. Morning coffee and afternoon tea are a speciality.
5 annexe en suite (bth/shr) CTV in all bedrooms 12P No coaches No children 12yrs International Cuisine V meals Coffee am Tea pm Last d 9.30pm
ROOMS: (incl. bkfst) s £38.50-£49.50; d £77-£90 **LB**
MEALS: Lunch £1.95-£10.50alc Dinner £18.50-£21.50
CONF: Thtr 20 Board 16
CARDS:  

£

LINCOLN Lincolnshire Map 08 SK97

★★★★63% **The White Hart**

FORTE Heritage

Bailgate LN1 3AR (from A15 rdbt on north side of city follow historic Lincoln signs go through Newport Arch continue along Bailgate, hotel on corner at bend of road) ☎ 01522 526222 FAX 01522 531798
This centrally located hotel has a delightful location between the castle and the imposing cathedral. Secure car parking is provided and there are attentive levels of service. There is an informal eating option in the Orangery in addition to the quietly elegant dining room.
48 en suite (bth) (4 fmly) No smoking in 18 bedrooms CTV in all bedrooms Lift Night porter 95P Wkly live entertainment Xmas English & Continental Cuisine V meals Coffee am Tea pm Last d 10pm
ROOMS: s £80-£95; d £100-£115 * **LB**
MEALS: Lunch fr £10.95 High tea fr £9 Dinner fr £22.50*
CONF: Thtr 90 Class 40 Board 30 Del from £130
CARDS:

★★★67% **Courtyard by Marriott Lincoln**

COURTYARD Marriott

Brayford Wharf North LN1 1YW (A46 Ring Road,take A57 to Lincoln Central, past the Grandstand, after Tanvics, turn right Hotel will be found on left hand side) ☎ 01522 544244 FAX 01522 560805
This modern, purpose-built hotel is located beside Brayford pool. It has spacious and well equipped bedrooms which have been properly

contd.

L

looked after. On the ground floor there are meeting and conference facilities, a fitness room as well as an informal bar which lies below the main restaurant.

95 en suite (bth/shr) (20 fmly) No smoking in 40 bedrooms CTV in all bedrooms STV Lift Night porter Air conditioning 100P Gym International Cuisine V meals Coffee am Tea pm Last d 10.30pm
ROOMS: s £49-£62; d fr £49 * **LB**
MEALS: Lunch fr £9.95&alc Dinner fr £11.95&alc*
CONF: Thtr 30 Class 20 Board 20 Del from £92.50
CARDS:

★★★ 63% Washingborough Hall Country House

MINOTEL Great Britain

Church Hill, Washingborough LN4 1BE (from B1188 onto B1190 Church Hill, 2 miles turn right opposite Methodist Church) ☎ 01522 790340 FAX 01522 792936
Washingborough Hall is a charming Georgian manor house quietly situated on the edge of a sleepy village next to the church and just a short distance away from Lincoln. Guests are received in a warm manner by the resident proprietors Brian and Mary Shillaker. Each of the bedrooms has its own character, some with four-poster beds and spa baths. In the aptly named Wedgwood dining room there is a wide selection of freshly cooked and appetising dishes.The hotel is set in three acres of carefully tended grounds which include a small swimming pool.
14 en suite (bth/shr) No smoking in 2 bedrooms CTV in all bedrooms 50P No coaches Outdoor swimming pool (heated) Croquet lawn International Cuisine V meals Coffee am Tea pm No smoking in restaurant Last d 8.30pm
ROOMS: (incl. bkfst) s fr £55; d fr £75 * **LB**
MEALS: Sunday Lunch £7.50 Dinner £16-£22.50alc
CONF: Thtr 50 Board 24 Del from £69.50
CARDS:

★★★ 62% Moor Lodge

CONSORT HOTELS

Sleaford Rd LN4 1HU ☎ 01522 791366 FAX 01522 794389
(For full entry see Branston)

★★ 69% Hillcrest

15 Lindum Ter LN2 5RT (from S of town take Wragby Road, pass Adam & Eve public house on right take first right upper Lindum street, Down to end turn left in Lindum Terrace) ☎ 01522 510182 FAX 01522 510182
Closed 23 Dec-3 Jan
The hospitality displayed by owner Jenni Bennett and her small team of staff is the undoubted strength of this small, privately owned hotel. Although the layout of he building is not particularly conventional, guests can enjoy the most wonderful views across the park from the comfortably furnished lounge bar and restaurant. Quite a wide choice of simple but interesting dishes is available in addition to a good range of bar snacks or packed lunches. Bedrooms vary in size, but all are en suite and comfortably furnished.
17 en suite (bth/shr) (4 fmly) No smoking in 6 bedrooms CTV in all bedrooms 8P International Cuisine V meals Coffee am Tea pm No smoking in restaurant Last d 8.45pm
ROOMS: (incl. bkfst) s £37-£47; d £62.50-£65 **LB**
MEALS: Bar Lunch £5-£8alc Dinner £12-£15alc
CONF: Thtr 25 Class 12 Board 12 Del £75
CARDS:

★★ 66% Castle

Westgate LN1 3AS (follow signs for 'Historic Lincoln' Hotel is at North East corner of the Castle) ☎ 01522 538801 FAX 01522 575457
This friendly owner-run hotel stands in the heart of historic Lincoln only yards away from the castle and within walking distance of the city centre. The bedrooms have been attractively upgraded whilst the public areas contain a combined bar/restaurant where a good range of well prepared dishes is served. Service is very friendly and attentive.
15 en suite (bth/shr) 4 annexe en suite (shr) (1 fmly) CTV in all bedrooms 21P Xmas Continental Cuisine V meals Coffee am Tea pm No smoking area in restaurant Last d 9.30pm
ROOMS: (incl. bkfst) s fr £50; d fr £65 **LB**
MEALS: Lunch £6.75&alc Dinner £11.40-£22.05alc*
CONF: Thtr 50 Class 18 Board 22
CARDS:

See advertisement on opposite page

★★ 64% Loudor

37 Newark Rd, North Hykeham LN6 8RB (3m SW A1434)
☎ 01522 680333 & 500474 FAX 01522 680403
This friendly, family owned and run hotel, standing beside the Newark Road about three miles from the city centre, is very well cared for by resident owners Mr & Mrs Faulkner. Modern bedrooms are well equipped and the public rooms cosy and comfortable. It is very popular with commercial guests and provides substantial evening meals in the pleasant dining room.
9 en suite (bth/shr) 1 annexe en suite (shr) (1 fmly) CTV in all bedrooms STV No dogs 12P No coaches English & French Cuisine Coffee am
ROOMS: (incl. bkfst) s £30-£33; d £38-£40 *
MEALS: High tea £11-£14alc*
CARDS:

Forte Posthouse Lincoln

FORTE Posthouse

Eastgate LN2 1PN (adjacent to cathedral)
☎ 01522 520341 FAX 01522 510780
Suitable for both the business and leisure traveller, this bright hotel provides modern accommodation in well equipped bedrooms with en suite bathrooms. For more details about Forte Posthouse hotels, consult the Contents page for the section on Hotel Groups.
70 en suite (bth/shr)
ROOMS: s £69; d £69 *

Travel Inn

travel inn

Lincoln Rd, Cantwick Hill LN4 2RF (on the junc of B1188 to Branston and B1131/A607 to Bracebridge Heath) ☎ 01522 525216 FAX 01522 542521
Purpose-built accommodation, offering spacious, well equipped bedrooms, all with en suite bathrooms. Meals may be taken at the nearby family restaurant. For more information about Travel Inns, consult the Contents page under Hotel Groups.
41 en suite (bth/shr)
ROOMS: d £35.50 *

LIPHOOK Hampshire Map 04 SU83

★★★ 76% Old Thorns Golf Course Hotel & Restaurant

Longmoor Rd, Griggs Green GU30 7PE (A3 Guildford to Portsmouth, take Griggs Green exit

(first after Liphook). Signposted)
☎ 01428 724555 FAX 01428 725036
This smartly presented hotel offers something for everyone; set in beautiful countryside there is an 18-hole golf course and golf shop. The indoor pool also has a sauna and solarium and the grounds are impressive. The bedrooms are all spacious and well equipped with comfortable furnishings and balconies. Guests may dine in the European restaurant with its extensive carte, or experience authentic Japanese cuisine in the Nipon Kan Restaurant, where the friendly staff will guide you through the menu.
28 en suite (bth/shr) 5 annexe en suite (shr) CTV in all bedrooms STV No dogs (ex guide dogs) Night porter 80P No coaches Indoor swimming pool (heated) Golf 18 Tennis (hard) Sauna Solarium Pool table Putting green European & Japanese Cuisine V meals Coffee am Tea pm Last d 9pm
ROOMS: (incl. bkfst) s fr £79.50; d fr £99.50 * **LB**
CONF: Thtr 100 Class 50 Board 30
CARDS:

See advertisement on this page

Travelodge

☎ 0800 850950
This modern building offers accommodation in smart, spacious and well equipped bedrooms, suitable for family use, and all with en suite bathrooms. Meals may be taken at the nearby family restaurant. For information on room rates and to make a booking, call Roomline free of charge on 0800 850950. For more details about Travelodge, consult the Contents page under Hotel Groups.
40 en suite (bth/shr)

For the key to symbols and abbreviations, please see the bookmark inside the back cover

LISKEARD Cornwall & Isles of Scilly Map 02 SX26

RED STAR HOTEL

★★ ❀❀❀ **Well House**
St Keyne PL14 4RN ☎ 01579 342001
FAX 01579 343891

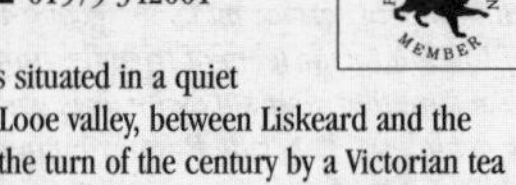

This country house is situated in a quiet secluded lane in the Looe valley, between Liskeard and the coast. It was built at the turn of the century by a Victorian tea planter and has three acres of interesting grounds that include a tennis court, swimming pool and lily ponds. Now owned and run by Nick Wainford and Ione Nurdin, the house has been creatively updated to provide an elegant and comfortable environment for guests occupying the seven bedrooms to enjoy. Chef Wayne Pearson continues to provide very sound standards of cooking that make excellent use of freshly caught fish from Looe as well as other local produce.

7 en suite (bth/shr) (1 fmly) CTV in all bedrooms 30P No coaches Outdoor swimming pool (heated) Tennis (hard) Croquet lawn V meals Last d 8.45pm
ROOMS: (incl. cont bkfst) s £60; d £90-£105 * **LB**
OFF-PEAK: (incl. cont bkfst) s £60; d £72-£84
MEALS: Lunch £19.95-£29.70 Dinner £19.95-£29.70*
CARDS:

★★ ❀ 66% **Pencubitt Country House Hotel**
Station Rd PL14 4EB (on arriving in Liskeard town centre follow the signs for "Park & Ride for Looe" The Hotel can be found on the B3254 past the railway station) ☎ 01579 342694
6 Jan-24 Dec
New owners Michael and Claire Kent have reverted to calling this former wool merchant's house by its original name. Peacefully situated on the southern edge of the town, the hotel is set in two acres of gardens and grounds. Having completely redecorated and refurnished the public areas, the Kents have started on a programme of upgrading the bedrooms. The five course dinner menu offers an imaginative choice of dishes, using carefully prepared, fresh local ingredients.
8 en suite (bth/shr) (1 fmly) CTV in all bedrooms 50P No coaches English & French Cuisine Coffee am Tea pm No smoking in restaurant Last d 8.30pm
ROOMS: (incl. bkfst) s £30; d £60 **LB**
OFF-PEAK: (incl. bkfst) s £25-£30; d £50-£60
MEALS: Dinner £18
CARDS:

★★ 59% **Lord Eliot**
Castle St PL14 3AU (take A38 into Liskeard, hotel 0.5m on left past St Martins Church) ☎ 01579 342717 FAX 01579 347593
Bedrooms in this personally run hotel are modestly furnished and decorated. There are a panelled restaurant serving a varied choice of dishes, a function room which is popular locally, and a traditionally styled bar and lounge.
15 rms (14 bth/shr) (1 fmly) No smoking in 2 bedrooms CTV in all bedrooms Night porter 60P Xmas English & French Cuisine V meals Coffee am Tea pm Last d 9pm
ROOMS: (incl. bkfst) s £34.07-£44.65; d £47-£63.45 * **LB**
OFF-PEAK: (incl. bkfst) s £30.55; d £54.05
MEALS: Lunch £11.95-£13.95 Dinner £11.95-£13.95&alc*
CONF: Thtr 180 Class 180 Board 180 Del from £50
CARDS:

LITTLEBOURNE Kent Map 05 TR25

★★ ❀ 67% **Bow Window Inn**
50 High St CT3 1ST ☎ 01227 721264 FAX 01227 721250
The Bow Window Inn is a 300 year-old country cottage situated in the small village of Littlebourne. It offers warm and comfortable accommodation; all bedrooms are furnished in keeping with the house and have many facilities. Public areas are limited, but the restaurant offers an opportunity to dine in excellent surroundings that include exposed oak beams and a large Kentish fireplace which help to create a traditional ambience. An interesting menu is available, and dishes are carefully prepared by chef/patron Rolf Steinmetz.
8 en suite (bth/shr) (1 fmly) CTV in all bedrooms No dogs (ex guide dogs) 16P No coaches English & Continental Cuisine V meals Coffee am Tea pm Last d 9.30pm
MEALS: Lunch £13.75-£18alc Dinner £15-£19alc*
CARDS:

LITTLE HALLINGBURY See Bishop's Stortford

LITTLE LANGDALE Cumbria Map 07 NY30

★★ 65% **Three Shires Inn**
LA22 9NZ (turn off A593, 2.5m from Ambleside at 2nd junct signposted for the Langdales. Hotel 1m along lane) ☎ 015394 37215
Closed Jan (ex New Year) RS Dec
This country hotel and inn lies in a small village amidst fine mountain scenery in an area popular with walkers. One can eat well in either the dining room or the bar and there are tables outside, with a small stream running by. There is a cosy foyer lounge with a log fire on cooler days, as well as a TV lounge, there being TVs in only the three superior rooms.
10 en suite (bth/shr) (1 fmly) CTV in 4 bedrooms No dogs 22P No coaches Xmas British & Continental Cuisine V meals Coffee am Tea pm No smoking in restaurant Last d 8.30pm
ROOMS: (incl. bkfst) s £32-£40; d £64-£80 * **LB**
OFF-PEAK: (incl. bkfst) s fr £29.50; d fr £59
MEALS: Bar Lunch £6.95-£13alc Dinner fr £17.95&alc

LITTLE WEIGHTON East Riding of Yorkshire Map 08 SE93

★★★ 65% **Rowley Manor**
Rowley Rd HU20 3XR (9m NW of Hull, west of A164 Beverley to Hessle road) ☎ 01482 848248
FAX 01482 849900

This peaceful Georgian house stands in open countryside just out of Little Weighton, on the road to Rowley. Set in 34 acres of parkland, lawns and rose gardens, it offers a quiet relaxing environment in which resident proprietors oversee the provision of genuinely friendly service. Country house traditions like croquet in summer and roaring log fires in winter are maintained, and spacious public areas display an increasingly good mix of period pieces; most of the fresh, inviting

and individually designed bedrooms are similarly furnished in a style befitting the house's original character.
16 en suite (bth/shr) CTV in all bedrooms STV Night porter 80P Riding Solarium Croquet lawn ch fac Xmas International Cuisine V meals Coffee am Tea pm Last d 10pm
ROOMS: (incl. bkfst) s fr £60; d fr £70 * **LB**
MEALS: Lunch £19.95-£24.90alc Dinner £19.95-£24.90alc
CONF: Thtr 90 Class 30 Board 50 Del from £85
CARDS:

LIVERPOOL Merseyside Map 07 SJ39
See also Blundellsands

★★★★57% **Liverpool Moat House**

Paradise St L1 8JD ☎ 0151 471 9988
FAX 0151 709 2706
This hotel is situated close to the Albert Dock and also the city centre and although at the time of writing was somewhat dated in style a programme of refurbishment should reflect a much higher standard of furnishing and decoration in 1997. In addition to two eating options, there is also a well equipped leisure centre and a variety of modern meeting and conference rooms. The bedrooms are all spacious and many have views towards the River Mersey and the rejuvenated docks.
251 en suite (bth/shr) (202 fmly) No smoking in 130 bedrooms CTV in all bedrooms Lift Night porter Air conditioning Indoor swimming pool (heated) Sauna Solarium Gym Whirlpool/Stream Room Xmas English & French Cuisine V meals Coffee am Tea pm Last d 10.pm
ROOMS: s £98-£99.50; d £115-£120 * **LB**
OFF-PEAK: (incl. bkfst) s fr £55; d fr £75
MEALS: Sunday Lunch £7.95-£10.95 Dinner £16.25&alc*
CONF: Thtr 450 Class 210 Board 152 Del from £105
CARDS:

★★★★55% **Atlantic Tower Thistle**

Chapel St L3 9RE (follow signs for the City Centre, Pier Head then Atlantic Tower Hotel. Situated opposite St Nicholas Church on Chapel Street)
☎ 0151 227 4444 FAX 0151 236 3973
A distinctive modern hotel, built to resemble a ship's bow, situated in a prime position overlooking the River Mersey. The accommodation is gradually being upgraded and although double bedrooms are compact the single rooms provide more space and are well equipped. There are ten luxury suites all differently themed and many have fine views over the river. The formal Stateroom Restaurant also commands fine views towards Birkenhead and in contrast less formal meals can be enjoyed in the Clubcar Carver, a 'pullman carriage', noted for its roast joints. Conference and banqueting facilities are available and there are car parks adjacent to the hotel.
226 en suite (bth/shr) (6 fmly) No smoking in 48 bedrooms CTV in all bedrooms STV Lift Night porter Air conditioning 60P Xmas European Cuisine V meals Coffee am Tea pm Last d 10.15pm
ROOMS: s £83-£93; d £93-£103 * **LB**

MEALS: Lunch £7.50-£15&alc Dinner £16.50-£20&alc*
CONF: Thtr 110 Class 70 Board 30 Del from £95
CARDS:

★★★61% **The Royal**
Marine Ter, Waterloo L22 5PR (6.50m NW of city centre)
☎ 0151 928 2332 FAX 0151 949 0320
A listed Georgian building situated at Waterloo, ten minutes by car from Liverpool city centre, the Royal Hotel looks out over Liverpool Bay. The bedrooms are modern in style and designed mainly for the business person, though there are rooms suitable for family use. Both carte and fixed price menus are offered in the ornate Marine View restaurant, and a comprehensive range of bar meals is served in the spacious lounge bar.
25 en suite (bth/shr) (3 fmly) CTV in all bedrooms STV No dogs (ex guide dogs) Night porter 25P No coaches English & French Cuisine V meals Coffee am Tea pm Last d 9.30pm
ROOMS: (incl. bkfst) s fr £41.50; d fr £62.50 * **LB**
OFF-PEAK: (incl. bkfst) s £34.50-£38; d £48.50-£58
MEALS: Lunch £8.95 Dinner £12.95-£17&alc
CONF: Thtr 120 Class 70 Board 40 Del from £65
CARDS:

★★58% **Green Park**
4/6 Greenbank Dr L17 1AN ☎ 0151 733 3382 FAX 0151 734 1161
Two gabled, red-brick Victorian houses have been converted to create this hotel close to Sefton Park, about three miles from the city centre. It has some dated bedrooms and others more modern in style with up-to-date facilities. Public areas include a lounge bar that is particularly popular with both locals and residents.
23 rms (21 bth/shr) (3 fmly) CTV in all bedrooms Night porter Air conditioning 25P V meals Coffee am Tea pm Last d 9pm
contd.

L

ROOMS: (incl. bkfst) s £24-£28; d £36-£40 *
MEALS: Lunch fr £6.25&alc High tea fr £4&alc Dinner fr £5.75&alc*
CONF: Thtr 60 Class 40 Board 20
CARDS:

Campanile
Chaloner St, Queens Dock L3 4AJ (follow brown tourist signs marked "Albert Dock" Hotel is situated south on the waterfront)
☎ 0151 709 8104 FAX 0151 709 8725

The bar and Bistro restaurant provide meals and refreshments. Bedrooms are well equipped and have en suite bathrooms. For more details about Campanile, consult the Contents page under Hotel Groups.
78 en suite (bth/shr)
CONF: Thtr 30 Class 20 Board 25 Del £57

Travel Inn
Queens Dr, West Derby L13 0DL (on A5058)
☎ 0151 228 4724 FAX 0151 220 7610

Purpose-built accommodation, offering spacious, well equipped bedrooms, all with en suite bathrooms. Meals may be taken at the nearby family restaurant. For more information about Travel Inns, consult the Contents page under Hotel Groups.
40 en suite (bth/shr)
ROOMS: d £35.50 *

Travel Inn
Wilson Rd, Tarbock L36 6AD (on intersection of M62/M57, from junc6 M62 take A5080 towards Huyton then first right into Wilson Rd)
☎ 0151 480 9614 FAX 0151 480 9361

Purpose-built accommodation, offering spacious, well equipped bedrooms, all with en suite bathrooms. Meals may be taken at the nearby family restaurant. For more information about Travel Inns, consult the Contents page under Hotel Groups.
40 en suite (bth/shr)

Travel Inn (Liverpool North)
North Perimiter Rd L30 7PT ☎ 0151 531 1497
FAX 0151 520 1842

Purpose-built accommodation, offering spacious, well equipped bedrooms, all with en suite bathrooms. Meals may be taken at the nearby family restaurant. For more information about Travel Inns, consult the Contents page under Hotel Groups.
43 en suite (bth/shr)
ROOMS: (incl. bkfst) d £35.50 *

LIZARD, THE Cornwall & Isles of Scilly Map 02 SW71

★★69% **Housel Bay**
Housel Cove TR12 7PG (follow A39/A394 to Helston, take the A3083 to the Lizard, at Lizard sign bear left, at school turn left and proceed down Lane to Hotel) ☎ 01326 290417 & 290917 FAX 01326 290359

For over 100 years guests have stayed at The Housel Bay Hotel and admired the superb views over the sea from its clifftop position. Friendly attentive service is provided by proprietors who have owned and run the hotel for many years. Along with the lounge and bar, the majority of the comfortable bedrooms benefit from the stunning location.
21 en suite (bth/shr) (1 fmly) No smoking in 2 bedrooms CTV in all bedrooms STV Lift 29P Xmas International Cuisine V meals Coffee am Tea pm No smoking in restaurant Last d 8.45pm
ROOMS: (incl. bkfst) s £28-£44; d £56-£88 * **LB**
OFF-PEAK: (incl. bkfst) s £22-£34; d £44-£68
MEALS: Sunday Lunch £8 Dinner £16-£22&alc*
CARDS:

LOCKINGTON Hotels are listed under East Midlands Airport

LOLWORTH Cambridgeshire Map 05 TL36

Travelodge
Huntingdon Rd CB3 8DR (on A14 northbound, 3m N of junct 14 on M11) ☎ 01954 781335
FAX 01954 781335

This modern building offers accommodation in smart, spacious and well equipped bedrooms, suitable for family use, and all with en suite bathrooms. Meals may be taken at the nearby family restaurant. For information on room rates and to make a booking, call Roomline free of charge on 0800 850950. For more details about Travelodge, consult the Contents page under Hotel Groups.
20 en suite (bth/shr)

Index of London Hotels

Page no.	Hotel name & postal dist.	Plan no. & grid ref
397	Abbey Court (W2)	Plan 2 A1
400	Academy (WC1)	Plan 3 C4
390	Athenaeum (W1)	Plan 4 G5
386	Baileys (SW7)	Plan 4 C2
376	Bardon Lodge (SE£)	Plan 1 G3
384	Barkston Gardens (SW5)	Plan 4 A2
382	Basil Street Hotel (SW3)	Plan 4 F4
382	Beaufort (SW3)	Plan 4 E3
378	Berkeley (SW1)	Plan 4 F4
395	Berkshire (W1)	Plan 2 G2
401	Blooms (WC1)	Plan 3 C4
401	Bloomsbury Park (WC1)	Plan 3 D4
400	Bonnington in Bloomsbury (WC1)	Plan 3 D4
391	Britannia Inter-Continental (W1)	Plan 2 G1
390	Brown's (W1)	Plan 3 A1
386	Cannizaro House (SW19)	Plan 1 D1
382	Capital (SW3)	Plan 4 F4
397	Carnarvon (W5)	Plan 1 C3/C4
380	Cavendish (SW1)	Plan 5 B6
396	Central Park (W2)	Plan 2 B1
375	Charles Bernard (NW3)	Plan 1 E4/E5
380	Chelsea (SW1)	Plan 4 F4
392	Chesterfield (W1)	Plan 4 H6
389	Churchill Inter-Continental (W1)	Plan 2 F3
376	Clarendon (SE3)	Plan 1 G3
387	Claridge's (W1)	Plan 2 G2
392	Clifton-Ford (W1)	Plan 2 G3
384	Comfort Inn (SW5)	Plan4 A2
387	Connaught (W1)	Plan 2 G1
386	Conrad International London (SW10)	Plan1 E3
398	Copthorne Tara (W8)	Plan 4 A4
392	Cumberland (W1)	Plan 2 F2
397	Delmere (W2)	Plan 2 D3
387	Dorchester (W1)	Plan 4 G6
402	Drury Lane Moat House (WC2)	Plan 3 D3
384	Earls Court International (SW6)	Plan1 D3
401	Forte Posthouse Bloomsbury (WC1)	Plan 3 C5

LONDON

LONDON

Page no.	Hotel name & postal dist.	Plan no. & grid ref
395	Metropolitan (W1)	Plan 4 G5
391	Montcalm (W1)	Plan 2 F3
394	Mostyn (W1)	Plan 2 F2
403	Mountbatten (WC2)	Plan 3 C2
393	Mount Royal (W1)	Plan 2 F2
373	New Barbican (EC1)	Plan 3 H6
388	Novotel London Waterloo (SE1)	Plan 5 E3
398	Novotel London Hammersmith (W6)	Plan 1 D3
396	Park Court (W2)	Plan 2 C1
391	Park Lane (W1)	Plan 4 H5
394	Parkes (SW3)	Plan4 E3
403	Pastoria (WC2)	Plan 3 C1
397	Pembridge Court (W2)	Plan 2 A1397
	Plaza on Hyde Park (W2)	Plan 2 C2
381	Quality Eccleston (SW1)	Plan 5 A2
391	Radisson SAS Portman(W1)	Plan 2 F3
374	Raglan Hall (N10)	Plan 1 E6
394	Regent Palace (W1)	Plan 3 B2
394	Regent's Park Marriott (NW3)	Plan 1 E4/E5
385	Rembrandt (SW7)	Plan 4 D3
373	Ridgeway (E4)	Plan 1 G6
388	Ritz (W1)	Plan 5 A6
398	Royal Garden (W8)	Plan 1 D3
381	Royal Horseguards Thistle (SW1)	Plan 5 D5
396	Royal Lancaster (W2)	Plan 2 C2
401	Royal Scot (WC1)	Plan 3 E6
402	Royal Trafalgar Thistle (WC2)	Plan 3 C1
380	Royal Westminster Thistle (SW1)	Plan 4 H3
381	Rubens (SW1)	Plan 5 A4
400	Russell (WC1)	Plan 3 C4
393	St George's (W1)	Plan 3 A3
401/2	Savoy (WC2)	Plan 3 D1
395	Savoy Court (W1)	Plan 2 F2
393	Selfridge Thistle (W1)	Plan 2 F2
379	Sheraton Park Tower (SW1)	Plan 4 F4
393	Sherlock Holmes (W1)	Plan 2 F4
380	Stafford (SW1)	Plan 5 A5
402	Strand Palace (WC2)	Plan 3 D2
383	Swallow International (SW5)	Plan 4 B2
373	Tower Thistle (E1)	Plan 6 D3
373	Travel Inn (E6)	Plan 1 H4
376	Travelodge (NW7)	Plan 1 D6
382	22 Jermyn Street (SW1)	Plan 3 B1
386	Vanderbilt (SW7)	Plan 4 C3
402	Waldorf Meridien (WC2)	Plan 3 D2
391	Washington (W1)	Plan 4 H6
391	Westbury (W1)	Plan 3 A2
374	White House (NW1)	Plan 2 H5
395	Whites (W2)	Plan 2 C1
383	Windmill on Common (SW4)	Plan 1 E2

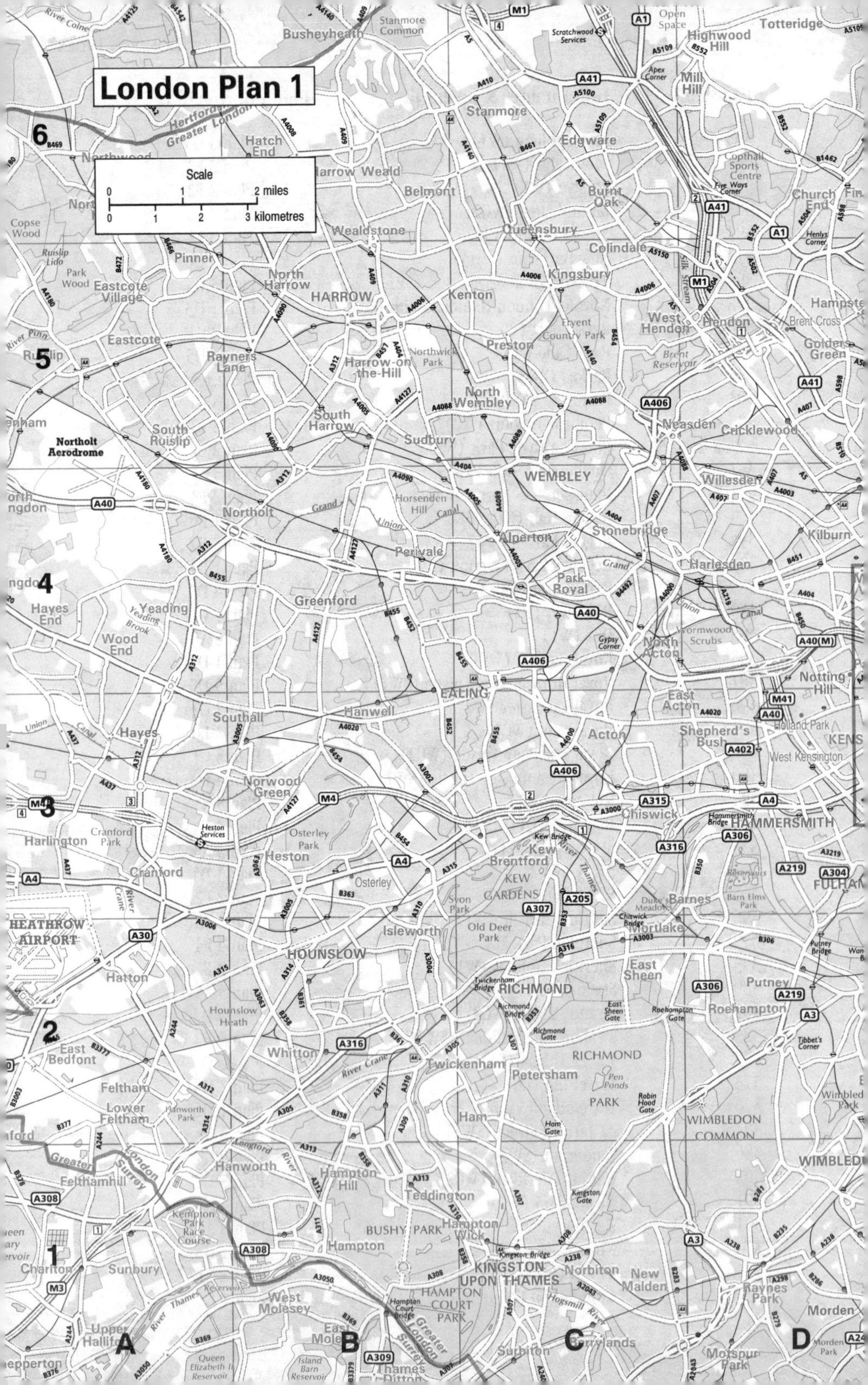

London Plan 1
Scale
0
1
2 miles
0
1
2
3 kilometres
Busheyheath
Stanmore Common
Open Space
Totteridge
Highwood Hill
Scratchwood Services
Apex Corner
Mill Hill
Stanmore
Edgware
Hatch End
Northwood
Harrow Weald
Belmont
Burnt Oak
Copthall Sports Centre
Fire Ways Corner
Church End
Henlys Corner
Copse Wood
Ruislip Lido
Park Wood
Pinner
Eastcote Village
Wealdstone
Queensbury
Colindale
North Harrow
HARROW
Kenton
Kingsbury
Fryent Country Park
West Hendon
Hendon
Brent Cross
Golders Green
Brent Reservoir
Silk Stream
River Pinn
Ruislip
Eastcote
Rayners Lane
Harrow-on-the-Hill
Northwick Park
Preston
North Wembley
Neasden
Cricklewood
South Ruislip
Northolt Aerodrome
South Harrow
Sudbury
WEMBLEY
Willesden
Northolt
Horsenden Hill
Grand Union Canal
Alperton
Stonebridge
Kilburn
Perivale
Harlesden
Park Royal
Hayes End
Yeading
Yeading Brook
Greenford
Wood End
Gypsy Corner
North Acton
Wormwood Scrubs
Notting Hill
EALING
East Acton
Southall
Hanwell
Hayes
Acton
Shepherd's Bush
Holland Park
West Kensington
Norwood Green
Chiswick
HAMMERSMITH
Hammersmith Bridge
Harlington
Cranford Park
Heston Services
Osterley Park
Heston
Kew Bridge
Kew
River Thames
Brentford
KEW GARDENS
Cranford
River Crane
Osterley
Syon Park
Duke's Meadows
Barnes
Barn Elms Park
FULHAM
HEATHROW AIRPORT
Isleworth
Old Deer Park
Chiswick Bridge
Mortlake
Putney Bridge
HOUNSLOW
East Sheen
Putney
Hatton
Twickenham Bridge
RICHMOND
Hounslow Heath
Richmond Bridge
Richmond Gate
East Sheen Gate
Roehampton Gate
Roehampton
Tibbet's Corner
East Bedfont
Whitton
Twickenham
Petersham
RICHMOND PARK
Pen Ponds
Robin Hood Gate
Feltham
Hanworth Park
Lower Feltham
Ham
Ham Gate
WIMBLEDON COMMON
Wimbledon Park
Longford River
Hanworth
Hampton Hill
WIMBLEDON
Felthamhill
Teddington
Kingston Gate
Kempton Park Race Course
BUSHY PARK
Hampton Wick
Hampton
Kingston Bridge
Charlton
Sunbury
KINGSTON UPON THAMES
Norbiton
New Malden
Raynes Park
HAMPTON COURT PARK
Hampton Court Bridge
Hogsmill River
West Molesey
Morden
Upper Halliford
East Molesey
Berrylands
Morden Park
Surbiton
Motspur Park
Queen Elizabeth II Reservoir
Island Barn Reservoir
Thames Ditton
Hertfordshire
Greater London
Surrey
A
B
C
D
1
2
3
4
5
6
M1
A1
A41
M4
M3
A40
A406
A4
A30
A316
A3
A308
A309
A315
A306
A219
A205
A307
A402
M41
A40(M)
A304

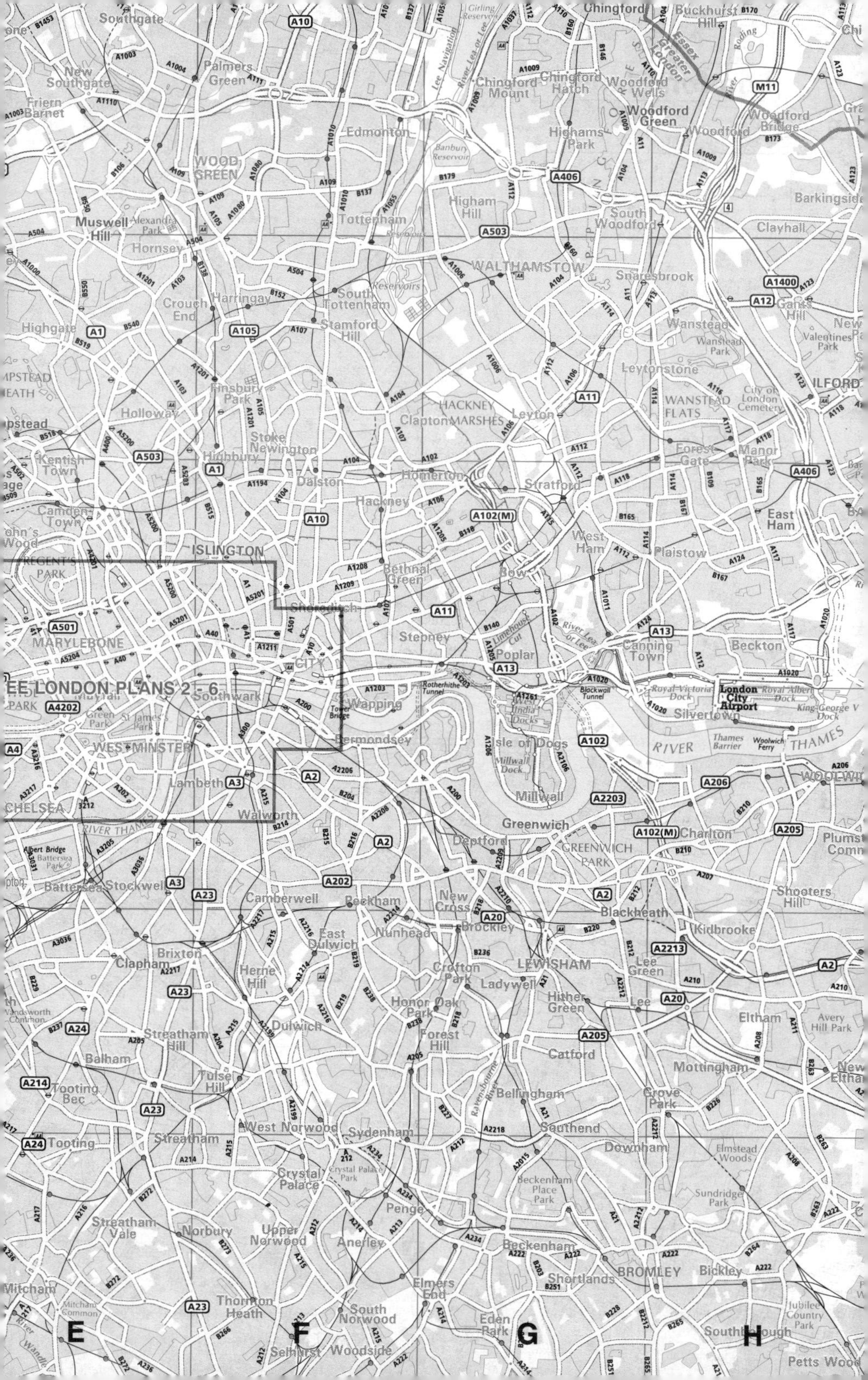
Southgate
Chingford
Buckhurst Hill
Palmers Green
New Southgate
Friern Barnet
Chingford Mount
Chingford Hatch
Woodford Wells
Woodford Green
Woodford
Woodford Bridge
Edmonton
Highams Park
Banbury Reservoir
WOOD GREEN
Muswell Hill
Alexandra Park
Tottenham
Higham Hill
South Woodford
Barkingside
Clayhall
Hornsey
WALTHAMSTOW
Snaresbrook
Crouch End
Harringay
South Tottenham
Reservoirs
Gants Hill
Highgate
Stamford Hill
Wanstead
Wanstead Park
Valentines Park
Leytonstone
Finsbury Park
HACKNEY MARSHES
Clapton
Leyton
WANSTEAD FLATS
City of London Cemetery
ILFORD
Holloway
Stoke Newington
Forest Gate
Manor Park
Kentish Town
Highbury
Dalston
Homerton
Stratford
Camden Town
Hackney
East Ham
West Ham
Plaistow
ISLINGTON
REGENT'S PARK
Bethnal Green
Bow
Shoreditch
MARYLEBONE
Stepney
Limehouse Cut
River Lea or Lee
Canning Town
Beckton
Poplar
CITY
SEE LONDON PLANS 2 - 6
Southwark
Wapping
Rotherhithe Tunnel
Blackwall Tunnel
Royal Victoria Dock
Royal Albert Dock
London City Airport
Silvertown
King George V Dock
Green Park
St James's Park
Tower Bridge
West India Docks
WESTMINSTER
Bermondsey
Isle of Dogs
Millwall Dock
RIVER THAMES
Thames Barrier
Woolwich Ferry
Lambeth
Millwall
CHELSEA
Walworth
Greenwich
Charlton
Albert Bridge
Battersea Park
Deptford
GREENWICH PARK
Battersea
Stockwell
Camberwell
Peckham
New Cross
Blackheath
Shooters Hill
Nunhead
Brockley
Kidbrooke
East Dulwich
Clapham
Brixton
Herne Hill
Crofton Park
LEWISHAM
Lee Green
Ladywell
Honor Oak Park
Hither Green
Lee
Eltham
Avery Hill Park
Dulwich
Streatham Hill
Forest Hill
Balham
Catford
Mottingham
Tooting Bec
Tulse Hill
Bellingham
Grove Park
West Norwood
Sydenham
Southend
Tooting
Streatham
Downham
Elmstead Woods
Crystal Palace
Crystal Palace Park
Beckenham Place Park
Sundridge Park
Penge
Streatham Vale
Norbury
Upper Norwood
Anerley
Beckenham
Mitcham
Mitcham Common
Shortlands
BROMLEY
Bickley
Thornton Heath
Elmers End
Jubilee Country Park
South Norwood
Eden Park
River Wandle
Selhurst
Woodside
Southborough
Petts Wood
E
F
G
H

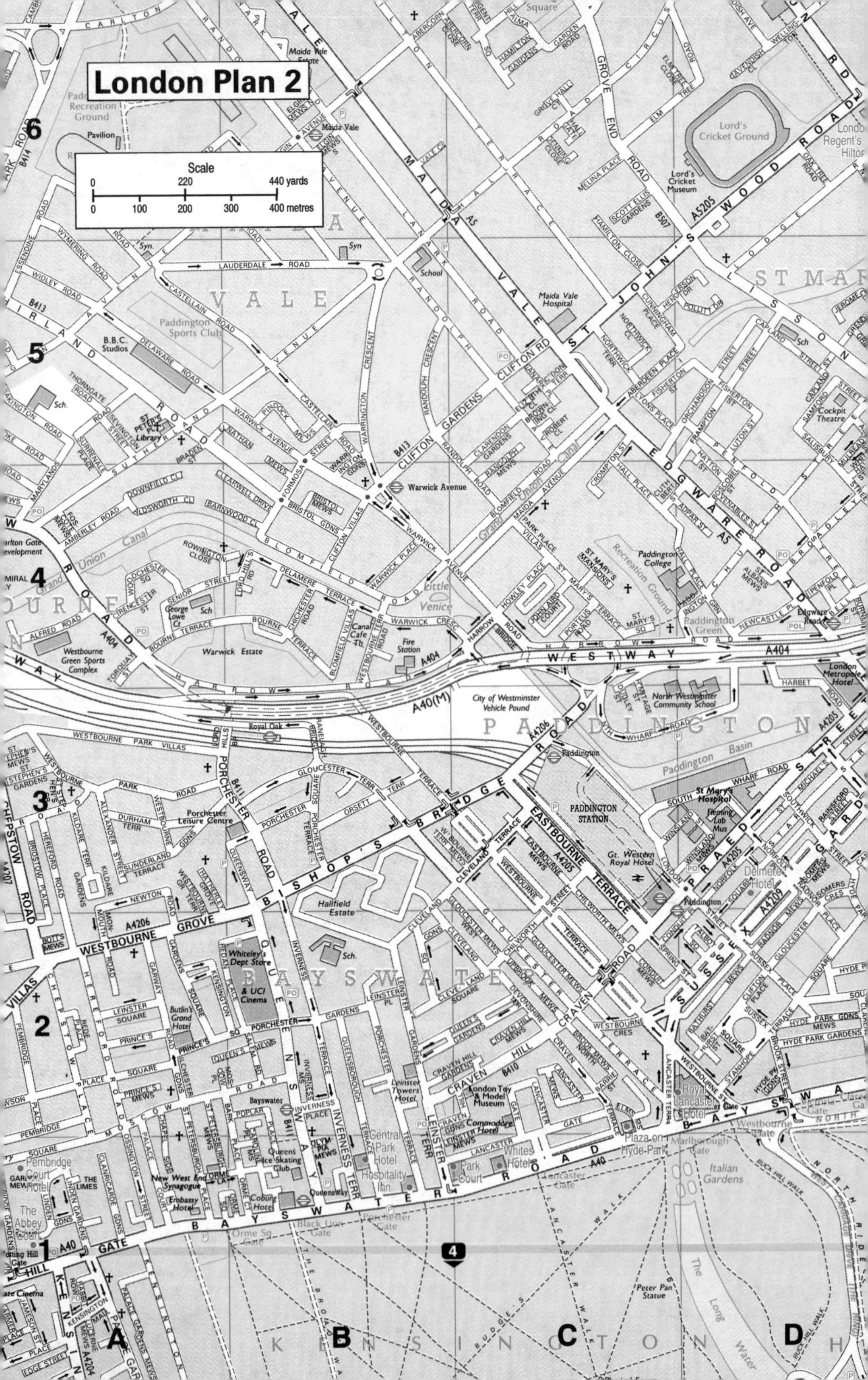

London Plan 2
Scale
0
220
440 yards
0
100
200
300
400 metres
6
5
4
3
2
1
A
B
C
D
4
Paddington Recreation Ground
Pavilion
Maida Vale Estate
Maida Vale
MAIDA VALE
A5
VALE
Lord's Cricket Ground
Lord's Cricket Museum
ST JOHN'S WOOD ROAD
A5205
B507
GROVE END ROAD
Maida Vale Hospital
School
Syn
Syn.
LAUDERDALE ROAD
CASTELLAIN ROAD
Paddington Sports Club
B.B.C. Studios
DELAWARE ROAD
SHIRLAND ROAD
B413
ELGIN AVENUE
RANDOLPH AVENUE
WARRINGTON CRESCENT
RANDOLPH CRESCENT
CLIFTON GARDENS
CLIFTON RD
WARWICK AVENUE
Warwick Avenue
FORMOSA STREET
BRISTOL GDNS
CLIFTON VILLAS
BLOMFIELD ROAD
Grand Union Canal
Little Venice
WARWICK CRESC
DELAMERE TERRACE
Canal Cafe Th.
Fire Station
St Peter's Pl.
Library
Sch.
Sch
George Lowe Ct
BOURNE TERRACE
Warwick Estate
Westbourne Green Sports Complex
ALFRED ROAD
HARROW ROAD
A404
WESTWAY
A40(M)
City of Westminster Vehicle Pound
Royal Oak
PADDINGTON
Paddington
Paddington Basin
PADDINGTON STATION
Gt. Western Royal Hotel
St Mary's Hospital
Fleming Lab Mus
Paddington College
Recreation Ground
Paddington Green
Edgware Road
EDGWARE ROAD
North Westminster Community School
London Metropole Hotel
Cockpit Theatre
ST MARY'S TERRACE
PRAED STREET
A4205
A4206
EASTBOURNE TERRACE
BISHOP'S BRIDGE ROAD
WESTBOURNE TERRACE
PORCHESTER ROAD
B411
Porchester Leisure Centre
Hallfield Estate
WESTBOURNE GROVE
BAYSWATER
Whiteley's Dept Store & UCI Cinema
Butlin's Grand Hotel
QUEENSWAY
Bayswater
Queensway
Queens Ice Skating Club
New West End Synagogue
Embassy Hotel
Coburg Hotel
Central Park Hotel
Hospitality Inn
Leinster Towers Hotel
London Toy & Model Museum
Commodore Hotel
Park Court
Whites Hotel
Plaza on Hyde Park
Royal Lancaster Hotel
Delmere Hotel
CRAVEN HILL
CRAVEN ROAD
B410
SUSSEX GARDENS
A4209
HYDE PARK GARDENS
BAYSWATER ROAD
A40
NOTTING HILL GATE
Pembridge Court Hotel
The Abbey Court
Gate Cinema
KENSINGTON
Orme Sq Gate
Black Lion Gate
Porchester Gate
Lancaster Gate
Marlborough Gate
Westbourne Gate
Italian Gardens
Peter Pan Statue
The Long Water
THE BROAD WALK
LANCASTER WALK
BUCK HILL WALK
NORTH RIDE
WEST CARRIAGE DRIVE
KENSINGTON

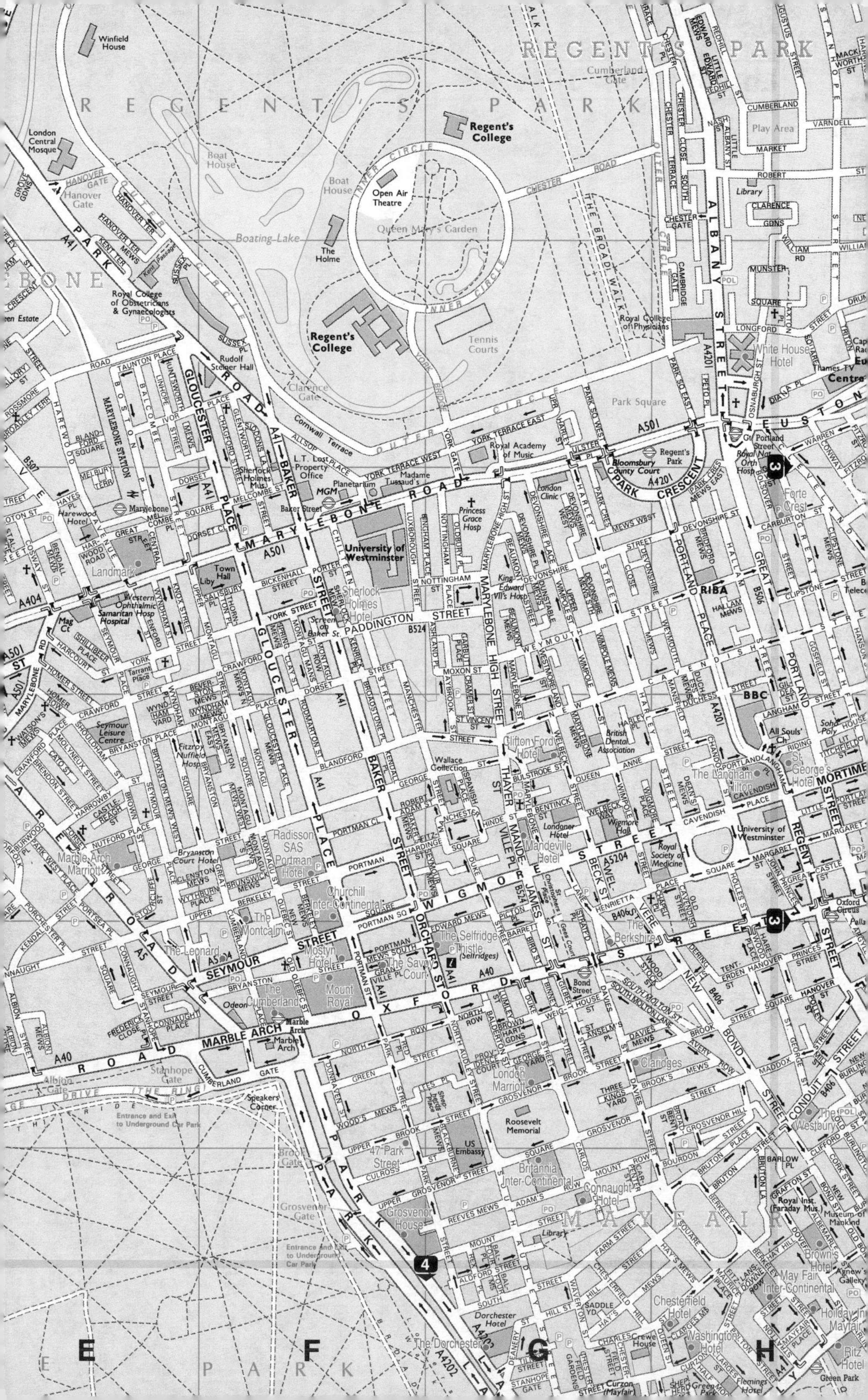
REGENTS PARK
Winfield House
London Central Mosque
Hanover Gate
Boat House
Boating Lake
Open Air Theatre
Queen Mary's Garden
The Holme
Regent's College
Tennis Courts
Inner Circle
Outer Circle
Chester Road
The Broad Walk
Cumberland Gate
Play Area
Library
Royal College of Obstetricians & Gynaecologists
Royal College of Physicians
White House Hotel
Thames TV Centre
Rudolf Steiner Hall
Clarence Gate
Park Square
Cornwall Terrace
York Terrace East
York Terrace West
Royal Academy of Music
Regent's Park
Bloomsbury County Court
Park Crescent
Great Portland Street
Royal Nat Orth Hosp
L.T. Lost Property Office
Planetarium
Madame Tussaud's
Baker Street
Sherlock Holmes Mus.
Marylebone
Marylebone Station
Harewood Hotel
Landmark
Town Hall
Liby
Western Ophthalmic
Samaritan Hosp Hospital
Princess Grace Hosp
University of Westminster
London Clinic
King Edward VII's Hosp
Sherlock Holmes Hotel
Screen on Baker St.
Forte Crest
RIBA
BBC
All Souls' Ch
Seymour Leisure Centre
Fitzroy Nuffield Hosp
Wallace Collection
Clifton Ford Hotel
British Dental Association
The Langham Hilton
St. George's Hotel
University of Westminster
Royal Society of Medicine
Londoner Hotel
Wigmore Hall
Mandeville Hotel
Marble Arch Marriott
Bryanston Court Hotel
Radisson SAS Portman Hotel
Churchill Inter-Continental
The Montcalm
The Leonard
Mostyn Hotel
The Savoy Court
The Selfridge Thistle
(Selfridges)
Bond Street
The Berkshire
Oxford Circus
Odeon
The Cumberland
Marble Arch
Stanhope Gate
Albion Gate
Speakers Corner
Entrance and Exit to Underground Car Park
Brook Gate
Grosvenor Gate
London Marriott
Claridges
Roosevelt Memorial
US Embassy
47 Park Street
Britannia Inter-Continental
Connaught Hotel
The Westbury
Royal Inst. (Faraday Mus.)
Museum of Mankind
Grosvenor House
Brown's Hotel
Agnew's Gallery
May Fair Inter-Continental
Chesterfield Hotel
Crewe House
Washington Hotel
Holiday Inn Mayfair
Ritz Hotel
Green Park
Dorchester Hotel
The Dorchester
Curzon (Mayfair)
MAYFAIR
OXFORD STREET
WIGMORE STREET
MARYLEBONE ROAD
EUSTON ROAD
PARK LANE
MARBLE ARCH
BAKER STREET
GLOUCESTER PLACE
PORTLAND PLACE
REGENT STREET
NEW BOND STREET
MARYLEBONE HIGH STREET
PADDINGTON STREET
SEYMOUR STREET
EDGWARE ROAD
BAYSWATER ROAD
PARK ROAD
ALBANY STREET
A41
A501
A4201
A5204
A40
A404
A4202
B524
B506
B406
3
4
E
F
G
H
PARK

London Plan 3
6
5
4
3
2
1
A
B
C
D
SOMERS TOWN
ST PANCRAS
BLOOMSBURY
SOHO
ST GILES
ST JAMES'S
British Library (under construction)
St Pancras Station
King's Cross St Pancras
Euston Station
Euston Road
Kennedy Hotel
National Temperance Hospital
Camden Town Hall & St Pancras Liby
Elizabeth Garrett Anderson Hosp.
Shaw Th. & Library
Ibis Euston
Friends House
Wellcome Inst
New Ambassadors Hotel
County Hotel
Scandic Crown Hotel
British Medical Assoc
White House Hotel
Capital Radio
Euston Tower
Thames TV Centre
University College
University College Hosp.
Bloomsbury Theatre
Percival David Foundation of Chinese Arts
Tavistock Hotel
Royal National Hotel
University of London
Thomas Coram Foundation
Coram's Fields Playground
Brunswick Housing & Shopping Centre
Forte Crest
Renoir Cinema
Russell Square
Hotel Russell
President Hotel
National Hosp.
Hospital for Sick Children
Royal London Homeopathic Hospital
Imperial Hotel
Waverley House Hotel
Bedford Hotel
Bloomsbury Park
The Bonnington in Bloomsbury
British Telecom Tower
Middlesex Hospital
Pollock's Toy Museum
Drill Hall
The Academy
R.A.D.A.
Vanbrugh Th.
British Museum and Library
Blooms Hotel
Building Centre
Bedford Corner Hotel
Goodge Street
Rathbone Hotel
BBC
RIBA
All Souls' Ch
St George's Hotel
The Langham Hilton
University of Westminster
Oxford Circus
Palladium
Berners Park Plaza Hotel
Tottenham Court Road
Astoria
Centre Pt.
St Giles Circus
Dominion
YMCA
The Kenilworth
The Marlborough
Congress Ho (TUC)
The Kingsley Thistle
Holborn Town Hall
Shaftesbury Hotel
Oasis Sports Centre
Drury Lane Moat House
New London Theatre
Freemason's Hall
House of St Barnabas
Marshall Street Leisure Centre
St. Anne's Court
Phoenix Th & Curzon Cin
Shaftesbury Hosp
Contemp Applied Arts
Donmar
The Mountbatten
Cambridge Th.
Royal Opera House
Covent Garden
Jubilee Mkt
Theatre Mus
London Transport Mus
Rubber Works
Africa Centre
St Paul's
Strand Palace
Vaudeville
Adelphi Th.
Savoy Th.
Prince Edward Th
Palace Th
Curzon (West End)
St Martin's Th
Fire Sta
Arts Th
Photo Gall
Gielgud Th
Queens Th
Apollo
Lyric Th
Prince Charles Th
Hippodrome
Warner
Leicester Square
County Ct
St Peter's Hosp.
Albery Th
Wyndhams Th
The Duke of York Th
The Hampshire
Garrick Th
Coliseum
The Pastoria
Odeon
Empire
MGM
St John's Hosp
Trocadero Centre (MGM & Metro)
Regent Palace
Le Meridien Piccadilly
London Pavilion
Piccadilly Circus
Criterion Th
Prince of Wales Th
Design Cen
Comedy Th
Royal Trafalgar Thistle Hotel
National Portrait Gallery
National Gallery
St Martin-in-the-Fields
Charing Cross Hotel
Charing Cross
Royal Society of Arts
York Water Gate
Trafalgar Square
Nelson's Column
S Africa House
Canada Ho
Her Majesty's Th
Haymarket
Royal Haymarket Th
British Travel Centre
22 Jermyn Street
St James's Church
The Cavendish
Royal Academy of Arts
Museum of Mankind
Royal Inst. (Faraday Mus.)
Brown's Hotel
May Fair Inter-Continental
Holiday Inn Mayfair
Ritz Hotel
Washington Hotel
Green Park
The Westbury
Agnew's Gallery
Admiralty Arch
Mall Gallery
Government Offices
Min of Agriculture
Northumberland Avenue
Embankment
Victoria Embankment Gardens
Piccadilly
Oxford Street
New Oxford Street
Regent Street
Tottenham Court Road
Gower Street
Shaftesbury Avenue
Charing Cross Road
Great Portland Street
Southampton Row
Kingsway
Long Acre
Strand
High Holborn
Haymarket

Scale
0
220
440 yards
0
100
200
300
400 metres
PENTONVILLE
FINSBURY
CLERKENWELL
ST LUKE'S
PENTON RISE
Kingsway College
Royal Scot Hotel
Royal Scot Magistrates Court
London Ryan
Holiday Inn
Mount Pleasant (Postal Sorting Office)
Sadlers Wells Theatre
Lilian Baylis Theatre
Town Hall
London Records Office
House of Detention
Kingsway College
St Mark's Hospital
New Barbican
Finsbury Leisure Complex
CITY ROAD
GOSWELL ROAD
ALDERSGATE STREET
OLD STREET
LEVER STREET
PERCIVAL STREET
SKINNER STREET
ROSEBERY AVENUE
FARRINGDON ROAD
CLERKENWELL ROAD
GRAY'S INN ROAD
Clerkenwell Heritage Centre
Museum of the Order of St John
St Bartholomew's Medical School
Charterhouse
Farringdon
Barbican
The Barbican
Barbican Centre
Guildhall School of Music & Drama
St Giles
Exhibition Halls
BEECH STREET
CHISWELL
Gray's Inn
St Alban's
St Etheldreda's Ch
Central Markets (Smithfield)
Founders Hall
St Bart the Great
Butcher's Hall
Ironmongers Hall
Barber Surgeons' Hall
Mus of London
Salters' Hall
Roman Wall Remains
LONDON WALL
State House
HMSO
Chancery Lane
HOLBORN
HOLBORN CIRCUS
HOLBORN VIADUCT
Staple Inn
London Silver Vaults
Daily Mirror Offices
Patent Office
Science Ref. Lib.
Lincoln's Inn
Lincoln's Inn Fields
St Andrew's
City Temple
Holy Sepulchre
St Bartholomew's Hospital
National Postal Museum
St Botolph's
St Anne & St Agnes Ch
Plaisterers' Hall
Pewterers' Hall
Brewers' Hall
Girdlers' Hall
Clock Museum
Guildhall
Haberdashers' Hall
British Telecom Centre
Goldsmiths' Hall
Waxchandlers' Hall
Saddlers Hall
St Lawrence Jewry
Public Record Office
Old Curiosity Shop
Dr Johnson's House
City (Thameslink) Station
Central Criminal Court
Cutlers' Hall
NEWGATE STREET
St Paul's
PATERNOSTER SQUARE
St Paul's Cathedral
Stationers Hall
St Martin's
CHEAPSIDE
Bank of England Extension
St Mary le Bow
St Mary Aldermary
Mercers Hall
POULTRY
Royal Courts of Justice
London School of Economics
FLEET STREET
LUDGATE CIRCUS
LUDGATE HILL
St Brides
Prince Henry's Room
Temple Church
Inns of Court and Chancery
Middle Temple Hall
Inner Temple
Australia House
St Clement Danes
Bush House (B.B.C.)
St Mary-le-Strand
Courtauld Institute Galleries
Roman Bath
Howard Hotel
King's College
STRAND
ALDWYCH
Temple
VICTORIA EMBANKMENT
H.M.S. President
H.Q.S. Wellington (Master Mariners)
Thames Police Station
Blackfriars
BLACKFRIARS STATION
BLACKFRIARS BRIDGE
QUEEN VICTORIA STREET
Apothecaries' Hall
Youth Hostel
Faraday Building
College of Arms
Telecom Technology Showcase
Mermaid Theatre
St Benet's
City of London School
UPPER THAMES STREET
CANNON STREET
Temple of Mithras
Mansion House
Painters' Hall
Vintners Hall
Innholders' Hall
Livery Halls
Queenhithe Stairs
Southwark Br. Stairs
RIVER
SOUTHWARK BRIDGE
Old Barge House Stairs
Oxo Tower Wharf
Bankside Gallery
Bankside Power Station (under development)
Globe Theatre Site
Shakespeare Globe Mus.
The London Television Centre (LWT)
Royal National Theatre
National Film Th.
Queen Elizabeth Hall
Purcell Room
Mus of the Moving Image
London Nautical Sch
WATERLOO BRIDGE
STAMFORD STREET
SOUTHWARK STREET
SUMNER STREET
E
F
G
H
5
6

London Plan 4
KENSINGTON GARDENS
Kensington Palace
Round Pond
Albert Memorial
Royal Albert Hall
Royal College of Art
Royal College of Music
Royal Geographical Society
Imperial College
Science Museum
Natural History Museum
Victoria & Albert Museum
Serpentine Gallery
Serpentine Bridge
Peter Pan Statue
Physical Energy Statue
Italian Gardens
The Long Water
Kensington & Chelsea Town Hall
High Street Kensington
South Kensington
Gloucester Road
Earls Court
West Brompton
KENSINGTON ROAD
KENSINGTON CHURCH STREET
CROMWELL ROAD
OLD BROMPTON ROAD
FULHAM ROAD
EARL'S COURT ROAD
GLOUCESTER ROAD
QUEEN'S GATE
BAYSWATER ROAD
SOUTH KENSINGTON
Scale
0 220 440 yards
0 100 200 300 400 metres
A B C D
1 2 3 4 5 6

MAYFAIR
PARK LANE
A4202
Grosvenor House
Grosvenor Gate
Brook Gate
US Embassy
Britannia Inter-Continental
Connaught Hotel
47 Park Street
Entrance and Exit to Underground Car Park
Dorchester Hotel
The Dorchester
Chesterfield Hotel
Washington Hotel
May Fair Inter-Continental
Brown's Hotel
Holiday Inn Mayfair
Ritz Hotel
Green Park
Royal Inst. (Faraday Mus.)
Museum of Mankind
Agnew's Gallery
Crewe House
Curzon (Mayfair)
Green Park Hotel
Flemings Hotel
London Mews Hilton
London Hilton on Park Lane
Park Lane Hotel
Athenaeum Hotel
Four Seasons Hotel
Inter-Continental Hotel
The Metropolitan
PICCADILLY
GREEN PARK
Apsley House (Wellington Mus)
Hyde Park Corner
Wellington Arch
CONSTITUTION HILL (CLOSED TO TRAFFIC ON SUNDAYS)
Buckingham Palace
Buckingham Palace Gardens
Queen's Gallery
The Royal Mews
Rubens Hotel
Goring Hotel
Royal Westminster Thistle
Victoria Palace
Westminster Th.
Victoria
Grosvenor Thistle (Victoria)
Apollo Victoria
VICTORIA STATION
Victoria Place Shopping Centre
Victoria Rail/Air Terminal
The Collonades Shopping Centre
Quality Eccleston Hotel
London Tourist Board & Convention Bureau
Ebury Court Hotel
Coach Sta Arrivals
Victoria Coach Sta.
BELGRAVIA
BELGRAVE SQUARE
GROSVENOR PL
A302
Lanesborough
The Berkeley
The Halkin Hotel
Halkin Hotel
The Lowndes
Hyatt Carlton Tower Hotel
Sheraton Park Tower
Hyde Park Hotel
Knightsbridge Barracks
Bowater House
KNIGHTSBRIDGE
A315
A4
Basil Street Hotel
The Chelsea Hotel
Capital Hotel
Knightsbridge Fire Sta
Harrods Store
Knightsbridge Crown Ct
The Parkes Hotel
The Beaufort
BROMPTON ROAD
BROMPTON
SLOANE STREET
A3216
Cadogan Hotel
St Columba's Ch
Wilbraham Hotel
Royal Ct Hotel
Royal Court Th
Sloane Square
KING'S ROAD
A3217
Duke of York's H.Q.
Guinness Trust Estate
School
Chelsea Cinema
Chelsea Old Town Hall
PIMLICO ROAD
A3214
Chelsea Barracks
CHELSEA BRIDGE ROAD
Burtons Court
Museum
Ranelagh Gardens
Royal Hospital
National Army Museum
Lister Hosp
B302
B313
B324
Abbots Manor Estate
EBURY BRIDGE
A3212
GROSVENOR ROAD
Churchill Gardens
SERPENTINE
SERPENTINE ROAD
ROTTEN ROW
SOUTH CARRIAGE DRIVE
Albert Gate
Edinburgh Gate
Boat House
Pier
Norwegian/British Monument
E PARK
E
F
G
H
2
5

London Plan 5
PICCADILLY
Green Park
GREEN PARK
ST JAMES'S
ST JAMES'S PARK
St James's Park Lake
Duck Island
Queen Victoria Memorial
Buckingham Palace
Queen's Gallery
The Royal Mews
Wellington Barracks
Guards' Chapel & Museum
Home Office
BIRDCAGE WALK
THE MALL
PALL MALL
HAYMARKET
REGENT ST
Piccadilly Circus
TRAFALGAR SQUARE
National Gallery
Nelson's Column
Charing Cross
CHARING CROSS STA.
NORTHUMBERLAND AVE
WHITEHALL
Old Admiralty
Horse Guards Parade
Ministry of Defence
Banqueting House
Foreign & Commonwealth Office
Treasury
Cenotaph
Norman Shaw Building (MPs Offices)
WESTMINSTER BRIDGE
Big Ben
Houses of Parliament
Westminster Abbey
Westminster School
Jewel Tower
Victoria Tower Gardens
PARLIAMENT SQUARE
Queen Elizabeth II Conf. Centre
Central Hall
BROAD SANCTUARY
BROADWAY
New Scotland Yard
Dept. of Trade and Industry
VICTORIA STREET
Westminster City Hall
Westminster Cathedral
VICTORIA STATION
Victoria Place Shopping Centre
VAUXHALL BRIDGE ROAD
HORSEFERRY ROAD
LAMBETH BRIDGE
MILLBANK
Thames House
Millbank Tower
Tate Gallery
Millbank Estate
Royal Army Medical College
Westminster School Playing Field
WESTMINSTER
Lillington Gardens Estate
Pimlico
PIMLICO
BELGRAVE ROAD
WARWICK WAY
GROSVENOR ROAD
Churchill Gardens
Pimlico Gardens
VAUXHALL BRIDGE
VAUXHALL STATION
ALBERT EMBANKMENT
VICTORIA EMBANKMENT
Fire Brigade Headquarters
Hungerford
Hispaniola
Abbots Manor Estate
Sch
Library
A
B
C
D
1
2
3
4
5
6

H.Q.S. Wellington (Master Mariners)
Thames Police Station
Queenhithe Stairs
Southwark Br. Stairs
RIVER
Old Barge House Stairs
Oxo Tower Wharf
Riverside Walk
BLACKFRIARS BRIDGE
A201
Bankside Gallery
Bankside Power Station (under development)
Globe Theatre Site
Shakespeare Globe Mus.
Clink Exhibition
Southwark Heritage Centre
The London Television Centre (LWT)
Royal National Theatre
National Film Th
Queen Elizabeth Hall
Purcell Room
Hayward Gallery
Mus of the Moving Image
Schiller International University
London Nautical Sch
WATERLOO BRIDGE
WATERLOO ROAD
STAMFORD STREET
SOUTHWARK STREET
BLACKFRIARS ROAD
UNION STREET
SOUTHWARK BRIDGE ROAD
NORTH SOUTHWARK
Shell Centre
International Rail Terminal
WATERLOO STATION
Waterloo
Waterloo (East) Station
Young Vic Theatre
Southwark College
Old Vic Theatre
THE CUT
County Hall
YORK ROAD
Crown Court at the Borough
Fire Brigade Mus
Fire Sta
Southwark Th
Borough
BOROUGH HIGH STREET
GREAT DOVER STREET
BOROUGH ROAD
WESTMINSTER BRIDGE ROAD
Lambeth North
St George's Cathedral
ST GEORGE'S CIRCUS
South Bank University
Inner London Sessions House (Crown Court)
Newington Gardens
Mathieson Court
LAMBETH ROAD
KENNINGTON ROAD
Archbishop's Park
Imperial War Museum
Geraldine Mary Harmsworth Park
Imperial War Museum Annexe
ST GEORGE'S ROAD
LONDON ROAD
NEWINGTON CAUSEWAY
Elephant & Castle
London College of Printing
Metropolitan Tabernacle
Recreation Centre
Shopping Centre
Elephant and Castle
Coronet Film Centre
NEW KENT ROAD
Heygate Estate
SOUTHWARK
London Park Hotel
NEWINGTON BUTTS
Draper Estate
Walworth Town Hall
The Cuming Museum
John Smith House
WALWORTH ROAD
NEWINGTON
Lambeth Walk Open Space
Ethelred Estate
Cotton Gardens Estate
KENNINGTON LANE
KENNINGTON PARK ROAD
Kennington
Lambeth County Court
Kennings Estate
Art School
College
KENNINGTON
LAMBETH
Scale
0 220 440 yards
0 100 200 300 400 metres
E
F
G
H

London Plan 6
Scale
0
220
440 yards
0
100
200
300
400 metres
A
B
C
D
1
2
3
4
5
6
The Barbican
Barbican Centre
Guildhall School of Music & Drama
Mus of London
Moorgate
Broadgate
Liverpool Street Station
Exchange Square
Spitalfields Market Hall
Christ Church
London Guildhall University
Guildhall
Clock Museum
Bank of England (& Mus)
Bank of England Extension
Stock Exchange
Royal Exchange
Mansion House
Temple of Mithras
Lloyd's
Leadenhall Market
Nat. West Tower
Monument
Cannon Street Sta
Fenchurch Street Station
Custom House
Tower of London
Tower Hill Pageant
All Hallows by-the-Tower
World Trade Centre
London Commodity Exchange
St. Katharine Dock
Tower Thistle
H.M.S. Belfast
London Bridge City Pier
Tower Pier
Tower Stairs
Swan Lane Pier
Queenhithe Stairs
Southwark Br Stairs
Shakespeare Globe Mus.
Globe Theatre Site
Clink Exhibition
Southwark Heritage Centre
Southwark Cathedral
Schooner Kathleen & May
Glaziers/Scientific Instrument Makers Hall
London Bridge Hosp.
Hays Galleria
Southwark Crown Court
Area Under Development
London Bridge Station
London Dungeon
Britain at War Museum
Borough Market
St.Thomas' Hosp Op. Th.
George Inn
Guy's Hospital
Greenwood Th
Tower Bridge Museum
Lambeth College
London City Mission
St. John's Estate
St. Saviour's Estate
Arnold Estate
Leathermarket Gardens
Fire Brigade Mus
Southwark Th
Inner London Sessions House (Crown Court)
Caledonian Market
NORTH SOUTHWARK
RIVER THAMES
LONDON BRIDGE
SOUTHWARK BRIDGE
TOWER BRIDGE
TOWER BRIDGE APPROACH
LONDON WALL
CHEAPSIDE
POULTRY
CORNHILL
LEADENHALL STREET
FENCHURCH STREET
THREADNEEDLE STREET
KING WILLIAM STREET
CANNON STREET
QUEEN VICTORIA STREET
THAMES STREET
LWR THAMES STREET
EASTCHEAPE
BISHOPSGATE
HOUNDSDITCH
WHITECHAPEL
MINORIES
ALDGATE HIGH ST
BYWARD ST
TOWER HILL
CHISWELL STREET
FINSBURY SQUARE
WORSHIP STREET
COMMERCIAL STREET
ALDERSGATE STREET
TOOLEY STREET
BOROUGH HIGH STREET
ST THOMAS ST
BERMONDSEY STREET
DRUID STREET
LONG LANE
SOUTHWARK STREET
UNION STREET
GREAT DOVER STREET
ABBEY STREET
SNOWSFIELDS
BORO ROAD

LONDON Greater London Plans 1-5, pages 362-372. (Small scale maps 4 & 5 at back of book.) Hotels are listed below in postal district order, commencing East, then North, South and West, with a brief indication of the area covered. Detailed plans 2-5 show the locations of AA-appointed hotels within the Central London postal districts. If you do not know the postal district of the hotel you want, please refer to the index preceding the street plans for the entry and map pages.

E1 STEPNEY AND EAST OF THE TOWER OF LONDON

★★★★ 67% **Tower Thistle**

St Katharine's Way E1 9LD (adjacent to Tower Bridge on North side of River Thames) ☎ 0171 481 2575 FAX 0171 488 4106

No longer on the fringes of the hotel scene, this large well-run hotel is truly coming into its own. The bedrooms must offer some of the best views in London, also exploited by the clever siting of some of the food and drink outlets. Foremost among them is the resurrected Princes Restaurant which has developed a serious team of staff preparing and serving meals using good ingredients and based on classical techniques. Over half the bedrooms have been refurbished and the others are earmarked for similar treatment over the coming years.

803 en suite (bth/shr) (24 fmly) No smoking in 320 bedrooms CTV in all bedrooms STV No dogs Lift Night porter Air conditioning 252P Gym Wkly live entertainment Xmas International Cuisine V meals Coffee am Tea pm

ROOMS: s £134-£159; d £155-£195 * **LB**

MEALS: Lunch £16.95*

CONF: Thtr 375 Class 225 Board 98 Del from £160

CARDS:

E4 CHINGFORD See LONDON plan 1 G6

★★ 58% **Ridgeway**

115/117 The Ridgeway, North Chingford E4 6QU (on B169, leave M25 at junc25/ M11 at junc 4) ☎ 0181 529 1964 FAX 0181 524 9130

Informal and very relaxed family run commercial hotel with particularly good quality furnished and well equipped range of bedrooms, There is a combined reception, bar lounge and smart restaurant that offers Greek speciality cuisine. Restaurant meals and service are restricted at weekends and the standard of service can be rather uncoordinated at times. Ideally located for easy access to the M25 and North Circular Road there is also ample forecourt car parking.

20 en suite (bth/shr) (4 fmly) CTV in all bedrooms No dogs (ex guide dogs) Night porter 9P No coaches English & Continental Cuisine Last d 10pm

MEALS: Lunch £7-£10alc High tea £3.50-£5.50alc Dinner £7-£12alc*

CONF: Thtr 60 Class 65 Board 65

CARDS:

See advertisement on this page

E6 EAST HAM See LONDON plan 1 H4

Travel Inn

1 Woolwich Manor Way, Beckton E6 4NT (from A13 take A117, Woolwich Manor Way, towards City Airport, hotel on left after first rdbt)

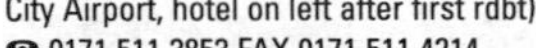

☎ 0171 511 3853 FAX 0171 511 4214

Purpose-built accommodation, offering spacious, well equipped bedrooms, all with en suite bathrooms. Meals may be taken at the nearby family restaurant. For more information about Travel Inns, consult the Contents page under Hotel Groups.

40 en suite (bth/shr)

ROOMS: (incl. bkfst) d £35.50 *

EC1 CITY OF LONDON

★★★ 65% **New Barbican**

Central St, Clerkenwell EC1V 8DS ☎ 0171 251 1565 FAX 0171 253 1005

This modern hotel is very popular with both tourists

contd.

and corporate guests. It is about a ten minute walk from the Barbican and a courtesy bus is provided in the mornings. Bedrooms are similarly appointed, and there are a number of executive rooms. Services are geared towards the city centre guest with luggage handling, additional room service and extended restaurant meal times.
302 en suite (bth/shr) 167 annexe en suite (bth/shr) (57 fmly) No smoking in 30 bedrooms CTV in all bedrooms No dogs (ex guide dogs) Lift Night porter 12P V meals Coffee am Tea pm No smoking area in restaurant
ROOMS: s £90-£100; d £100-£110 * **LB**
MEALS: Lunch fr £12.95*
CONF: Thtr 160 Class 60 Board 50 Del from £130
CARDS:

N1 ISLINGTON See LONDON plan 1 F4

★★★64% **Great Northern**
Kings Cross N1 9AN (entrance faces side of Kings Cross station)
☎ 0171 837 5454 FAX 0171 278 5270
If you are en route for Europe through the Channel Tunnel this hotel will be ideally placed once the International Rail Link Terminal has been built. The accommodation is spacious and comfortable and currently being refurbished and upgraded, offering a good level of facilities to leisure and business clientele. The coffee house is open throughout the day for all meals and light refreshments and a lively bar features an extensive range of real ale, while other facilities include a non-smoking lounge, porters desk, same-day laundry service, 24-hour room service and an extensive range of meeting rooms, with the self-contained purpose-built air-conditioned Hertford Suite catering for all types of function. Car parking can also be arranged.
78 en suite (bth/shr) (16 fmly) No smoking in 22 bedrooms CTV in all bedrooms STV No dogs (ex guide dogs) Lift Night porter 12P English Cuisine V meals Coffee am Tea pm No smoking area in restaurant
ROOMS: (incl. bkfst) s £88; d £94 **LB**
CONF: Thtr 100 Class 80 Board 45
CARDS:

N10 MUSWELL HILL See LONDON plan 1 E6

★★★67% **Raglan Hall**
8-12 Queens Ave, Muswell Hill N10 3NR
☎ 0181 883 9836 FAX 0181 883 5002
Best Western
Service and hospitality are the hallmarks at Raglan Hall an attractively fronted hotel on the tree lined Queens Avenue in Muswell Hill. Staff really try hard to make their guests feel welcome. Bedrooms vary in size but all are well equipped and are appreciated by both business and leisure guests alike. Public areas centre round a relaxing bar and meals are carefully prepared by a talented young chef.
46 en suite (bth/shr) (8 fmly) No smoking in 6 bedrooms CTV in all bedrooms STV No dogs (ex guide dogs) Night porter 7P V meals Coffee am Tea pm Last d 9.45pm
ROOMS: s £85-£90; d £90-£95 *
MEALS: Bar Lunch £3.50-£5 Dinner £15.50-£16.50
CONF: Thtr 120 Class 20 Board 50 Del from £110
CARDS:

Some well known brand-name hotels share a uniform identity and offer the same facilities throughout Britain. The brand standard is accepted by the AA and they therefore have no star rating. See the section on Hotel Groups at the front of the book.

NW1 REGENT'S PARK See LONDON plan 1 E4

RED STAR HOTEL

★★★★★ ❀❀ ***Landmark***
222 Marylebone Rd NW1 6TQ
☎ 0171 631 8000 FAX 0171 631 8080
This Victorian building was totally renovated and transformed early in the 1990s into a magnificent hotel. At its heart is the spectacular Winter Garden, an eight-storey atrium fringed with high palm trees: here a pianist plays and delicious afternoon teas, drinks and light meals are served. There are two further eating options: the panelled Cellars and the main Dining Room, where a new team in the kitchen produces a modern menu, with interesting oriental influences. Bedrooms are a very good size, with especially fine marble bathrooms, with deep tubs and separate shower cubicles. Equipment levels range from multi-lingual TV channels and three phone lines to a handy umbrella and jogging map. The high standards of friendly service from the young staff have always been noteworthy, and so they remain.
309 en suite (bth/shr) CTV in all bedrooms STV No dogs Lift Night porter Air conditioning 90P Indoor swimming pool (heated) Sauna Gym Health club Massage Turkish bath Italian Cuisine V meals Coffee am Tea pm Last d 10.30
CARDS:

★★★★❀69% **The White House**
Albany St NW1 3UP (opposite Gt Portland St Underground and set slightly back from Marylebone & Euston Rd) ☎ 0171 387 1200 FAX 0171 388 0091
The White House is one of London's best kept secrets just off Marylebone Road at its junction with Great Portland Street the hotel is superbly located for the attractions of the West End. This imposing building opened as an apartment building in 1936 and has been transformed into a charming hotel where the promised emphasis on hospitality and comfort is met with aplomb. The facilities offered include 4 food outlets including the popular Wine Press which is frequently let privately. Bedrooms are comfortable and are equipped with all the comforts one would expect in an operation of this scale. Reserve floor bedrooms come with the use of a dedicated lounge which is a convenient refuge from the hustle and bustle of London life. Formal dining takes place in the restaurant where solicitous staff serve food from an imaginative menu which has been prepared with thought and skill.
584 en suite (bth/shr) (2 fmly) No smoking in 82 bedrooms CTV in all bedrooms STV No dogs (ex guide dogs) Lift Night porter 7P Sauna Gym Xmas V meals Coffee am Tea pm No smoking area in restaurant Last d 11.15pm
ROOMS: s £139-£163; d £145-£175

MEALS: Lunch fr £18.75&alc Dinner fr £22.75&alc*
CONF: Thtr 120 Class 45 Board 40 Del from £170
CARDS:

★★★63% **Kennedy**

Cardington St NW1 2LP (A40 to Euston,then A501to Euston Stn,turn left before Stn into Melton St,then into Cardington St,hotel is on left 200yds from traffic lights) ☎ 0171 387 4400 FAX 0171 387 5122
The Kennedy is a modern hotel located close to Euston Station. Both standard and superior rooms are available, the latter being more spacious and fitted with mini bars. Public areas include a lounge bar with satellite TV and all day snacks, Spires restaurant which has a broad appeal and a range of smart meeting rooms.
360 en suite (bth/shr) (25 fmly) No smoking in 44 bedrooms CTV in all bedrooms No dogs (ex guide dogs) Lift Night porter Air conditioning 24P English & French Cuisine V meals Coffee am Tea pm Last d 10.30pm
ROOMS: s fr £85; d fr £95 * **LB**
MEALS: Lunch £14.50&alc Dinner £14.50&alc*
CONF: Thtr 100 Class 45 Board 50 Del £125
CARDS:

★★62% **Hotel Ibis Euston**

3 Cardington St NW1 2LW (near Euston Railway Stn)
☎ 0171 388 7777 FAX 0171 388 0001
Conveniently situated adjacent to Euston Station and having the advantage of a large secure basement car park, this popular and busy hotel offers good-value budget accommodation. Bedrooms are practically furnished in a functional style but have colourful fabrics and queen-size beds. Public areas are semi open-plan and include an informal restaurant and all-day bar serving light snacks. Breakfast is a simple self-service affair.
300 en suite (bth/shr) No smoking in 150 bedrooms CTV in all bedrooms STV Lift 100P English & French Cuisine V meals Coffee am Tea pm
ROOMS: s fr £56; d fr £56 *
MEALS: Bar Lunch £1.90-£4.50 Dinner £6.50-£11.50*
CONF: Thtr 140 Class 70 Board 60 Del £80
CARDS:

NW2 BRENT CROSS See LONDON plan 1 D5

★★★63% **Holiday Inn Garden Court**

Tilling Rd, Brent Cross NW2 1LP (at the foot of the M1 Motorway,Tilling Rd is 2nd exit off the M1 roundabout.The hotel is off the A5 & A41 on the A406(North Circular) ☎ 0181 455 4777 Res & 0181 201 8686 FAX 0181 455 4660
Situated beside Brent Cross Shopping Centre, this newly built hotel is conveniently placed for the M1 and the North Circular Road which leads to Wembley; it also has good parking. Bedrooms are furnished in a contemporary style, with both sound proofing and air-conditioning ensuring a restful night. Executive rooms have now been introduced, complete with corner desk, office chair and fax. This particular Holiday Inn has won the company's own Worldwide Torchbearer Award for quality of service. Only 33 hotels out of more than 2000 in the group hold this award.
153 en suite (bth/shr) (32 fmly) No smoking in 82 bedrooms CTV in all bedrooms STV Lift Night porter Air conditioning 155P Pool table V meals Coffee am Tea pm No smoking area in restaurant Last d 9.45pm
ROOMS: s £105; d £105 **LB**
MEALS: Bar Lunch £3.75-£6.85 Dinner £9.95-£11.95&alc*
CONF: Thtr 50 Class 24 Board 26
CARDS:

NW3 HAMPSTEAD AND SWISS COTTAGE
See LONDON plan 1 E5/E4

★★★★69% **Regents Park Marriott**

128 King Henry's Rd NW3 3ST (near Swiss Cottage Underground Station) ☎ 0171 722 7711
FAX 0171 586 5822
Situated at Swiss Cottage, this large modern hotel has undergone considerable refurbishment. The spacious bedrooms all have large beds and the executive rooms have the benefit of a dedicated club lounge. Smart public areas comprise an open plan marbled lobby and bar-lounge. Additionally, there is indoor leisure, free parking and a shop.
303 en suite (bth/shr) (157 fmly) No smoking in 102 bedrooms CTV in all bedrooms STV No dogs (ex guide dogs) Lift Night porter Air conditioning 150P Indoor swimming pool (heated) Sauna Solarium Gym Hair & Beauty salon Xmas International Cuisine V meals Coffee am Tea pm Last d 10.30pm
ROOMS: s fr £165; d fr £185 * **LB**
OFF-PEAK: (incl. bkfst) s £95-£105; d £110-£130
MEALS: Lunch fr £18.95 Dinner fr £15.95*
CONF: Thtr 400 Class 220 Board 105 Del from £163.50
CARDS:

★★★59% **Charles Bernard**
5-7 Frognal, Hampstead NW3 6AL (A406 North Circular Rd,follow signs for West End & A41,cont until Tower Hill Garage,turn right onto

contd.

LONDON

Finchley Rd,hotel approx 1 mile)
☎ 0171 794 0101 FAX 0171 794 0100
This friendly hotel is popular with foreign visitors to the capital and is conveniently located close to Finchley Road. Bedrooms are currently undergoing refurbishment, and the newly decorated rooms are most attractive and thoughtfully equipped. There is a busy restaurant with service provided by smiling staff.
57 en suite (bth/shr) CTV in all bedrooms STV No dogs Lift Night porter 15P English & French Cuisine Coffee am Tea pm Last d 9.15pm
ROOMS: (incl. bkfst) s £60-£65; d £71-£75 *
MEALS: Lunch £11.50-£18.50alc High tea £4.50-£6.50alc Dinner £11.75-£20alc
CARDS:

See advertisement on opposite page

Forte Posthouse Hampstead
215 Haverstock Hill NW3 4RB (take A41 to Swiss Cottage just before this junction take feeder road left into Buckland Cres onto Belsize Av left into Haverstock Hill) ☎ 0171 794 8121 FAX 0171 435 5586
Suitable for both the business and leisure traveller, this bright hotel provides modern accommodation in well equipped bedrooms with en suite bathrooms. For more details about Forte Posthouse hotels, consult the Contents page for the section on Hotel Groups.
140 en suite (bth/shr)
ROOMS: s £99-£109; d £99-£109 *
CONF: Thtr 30 Class 20 Board 20 Del £129

NW7 MILL HILL See LONDON plan 1 D6

Travelodge
M1 Scratchwood Service Area, Mill Hill NW7 3HB (access from Motorway only) ☎ 0181 906 0611
FAX 0181 906 3654

This modern building offers accommodation in smart, spacious and well equipped bedrooms, suitable for family use, and all with en suite bathrooms. Meals may be taken at the nearby family restaurant. For information on room rates and to make a booking, call Roomline free of charge on 0800 850950. For more details about Travelodge, consult the Contents page under Hotel Groups.
100 en suite (bth/shr)

NW8 REGENT'S PARK See LONDON plan 1 E4

★★★★65% **London Regents Park Hilton**
18 Lodge Rd NW8 7JT (from the end of M1 take A41 to central London,at Swiss Cottage take A41 Finchley Rd past Lords Cricket ground,Hotel in front)
☎ 0171 722 7722 FAX 0171 483 2408

Some of the bedrooms have prime views over Lords cricket ground. There is a light-hearted cricket theme in the lounge bar which serves food and drink all through the day. In addition to the principal restaurant, Minsky's, with its 'international deli' theme, there is a Japanese restaurant as well as full room service. Bedrooms, many of which have been refurbished, provide spacious and well kept modern comforts.
377 en suite (bth/shr) (4 fmly) No smoking in 50 bedrooms CTV in all bedrooms STV No dogs (ex guide dogs) Lift Night porter Air conditioning 82P Wkly live entertainment Xmas International Cuisine V meals Coffee am Tea pm No smoking area in restaurant Last d 10.30pm
ROOMS: s £120-£135; d £135-£155 * **LB**
MEALS: Lunch £18.95&alc High tea £3.95-£20alc Dinner £18.95&alc*
CONF: Thtr 150 Class 75 Board 50 Del from £130
CARDS:

SE1 SOUTHWARK AND WATERLOO

★★★68% ***Novotel London Waterloo***
113 Lambeth Rd SE1 7LS ☎ 0171 793 1010
FAX 0171 793 0202

Just a short walk from the Houses of Parliament and convenient for Waterloo International station, this newly built Novotel has a striking, modern interior. The spacious lobby leads to the traditionally styled Flag and Whistle pub, and the Garden Brasserie which offers a buffet breakfast and a range of popular dishes. There is also a small shop. In the basement there is a small leisure facility and secure car parking, priced competitively for residents. Bedrooms can sleep up to four people and are fitted with the latest technology: a voice messaging system and television that allow you to access a number of services, including viewing your bill and ordering room service.
187 rms (183 bth/shr) (40 fmly) No smoking in 147 bedrooms CTV in all bedrooms Lift Air conditioning 46P Sauna Gym Jacuzzi/spa Wkly live entertainment International Cuisine V meals Coffee am Tea pm Last d midnight
CARDS:

See advertisement on opposite page

SE3 BLACKHEATH See LONDON plan 1 G3

★★67% ***Bardon Lodge***
Stratheden Rd SE3 7TH ☎ 0181 853 4051
FAX 0181 858 7387

This friendly small hotel, under the supervision of manager Roger Hayes, offers a range of compact but attractive, well equipped bedrooms. The hotel sometimes uses well appointed accommodation in the neighbouring Vanburgh Hotel. The Lamplight restaurant is a popular spot for locals dining out, and facilities for meetings are available.
32 rms (27 bth/shr) (3 fmly) CTV in all bedrooms No dogs (ex guide dogs) Night porter 16P English & Continental Cuisine V meals Coffee am Last d 9.30pm
CARDS:

★★56% **Clarendon**
8-16 Montpelier Row, Blackheath SE3 0RW ☎ 0181 318 4321
FAX 0181 318 4378
Located in one of the last remaining villages in London, by the side of Blackheath Common and in the shadow of Greenwich Park, the Clarendon is a busy, popular hotel. Bedrooms are in the process of refurbishment but are well equipped and cosy. There is a spacious restaurant and a smart bar with a nautical theme.
193 rms (164 bth/shr) (37 fmly) CTV in all bedrooms Lift Night porter 80P Free use of local leisure centre Wkly live entertainment Xmas English, French & Italian Cuisine V meals Coffee am Tea pm No smoking area in restaurant Last d 9.45pm
ROOMS: s fr £43.50; d £60-£100 * **LB**
MEALS: Lunch £11.95-£12&alc Dinner fr £12&alc*
CONF: Thtr 200 Class 50 Board 120 Del from £72
CARDS:

See advertisement on opposite page

LONDON

SE10 GREENWICH See LONDON plan 1 G3

★★60% **Hotel Ibis**

30 Stockwell St SE10 9JN ☎ 0181 305 1177

FAX 0181 858 7139

Part of the European Hotel Group Accor, this modern hotel is found in the heart of Greenwich, next to the multi-screen cinema. Public areas are open-plan; there is a self service buffet breakfast and the bar is open all day for drinks and snacks. Bedrooms are practical and economical.

82 en suite (bth/shr) No smoking in 17 bedrooms CTV in all bedrooms STV Lift 30P Coffee am No smoking area in restaurant

ROOMS: d £48 *

CARDS:

SW1 WESTMINSTER

RED STAR HOTEL

★★★★★ **The Berkeley**

Wilton Place, Knightsbridge SW1X 7RL

(Leading Hotels) ☎ 0171 235 6000

FAX 0171 235 4330

Occupying a prestigious position both in its location, looking out over Hyde Park, and in the hearts of its loyal clientele, this fine hotel has a reputation for providing modern amenities while retaining the style of a bygone era. Cultivating a discreet 'home from home' atmosphere, both comforting and serene, the Berkeley retains a commanding position as one of London's top venues. The current programme of refurbishment has resulted in a redesign of the ground floor to provide a choice of two restaurants, the Lutyens writing room and the cocktail lounge. Leisure facilities are hi-tech, and the Roman swimming pool at roof level becomes positively Mediterranean in the summer when the roof is open. Bedrooms range from standard singles, through deluxe twins and doubles, to a range of suites, with rooms on the 6th and 7th floors having their own balcony. Each bedroom has an individually made 'armoire' which houses the latest technology - TV, video, etc. Of the two restaurants, Vong's, with its south-east Asian inspiration, is currently the most fashionable, whilst the Berkeley Room features the modern Anglo-French cooking of chef Andrew Turner.

159 en suite (bth/shr) No smoking in 28 bedrooms CTV in all bedrooms STV No dogs (ex guide dogs) Lift Night porter Air conditioning 50P No coaches Indoor swimming pool (heated) Sauna Solarium Gym Cinema Tennis at Vanderbilt Club Wkly live entertainment Xmas International Cuisine V meals Coffee am Tea pm Last d 10.45pm

ROOMS: s £229-£264; d £311-£335 * **LB**

MEALS: Lunch £22.50&alc High tea fr £12 Dinner £24-£27.50&alc*

CONF: Thtr 220 Class 70 Board 50

CARDS:

RED STAR HOTEL

★★★★★ **The Hyde Park**

66 Knightsbridge SW1X 7LA (opposite Harvey Nichols) ☎ 0171 235 2000

FAX 0171 235 4552

This former Edwardian gentleman's club enjoys an enviable situation in the heart of bustling Knightsbridge yet also enjoys views over Hyde Park. Refurbishment of the day rooms has resulted in a totally new and elegant lounge in addition to an inviting light wood-panelled bar with contemporary furnishings. The On the Park Restaurant has also been re-styled in soft coffee and cream and continues to offer reliable Italian based cuisine as an alternative to the exalted five rosette Restaurant of Marco Pierre White. The individually decorated bedrooms are traditionally furnished with good armchairs, large beds and quality co-ordinated fabrics, and most now have smart modern marble bathrooms with first-class toiletries.

185 en suite (bth/shr) No smoking in 22 bedrooms CTV in all bedrooms STV No dogs (ex guide dogs) Lift Night porter Air conditioning P No coaches Gym Fitness centre Wkly live entertainment Xmas English, French & Italian Cuisine V meals Coffee am Tea pm Last d 11pm

ROOMS: s fr £250; d fr £280 **LB**

OFF-PEAK: s fr £205; d fr £225

MEALS: Lunch £25-£29 Dinner £34-£36*

CONF: Thtr 250 Class 130 Board 60

CARDS:

RED STAR HOTEL

★★★★★ **Lanesborough**

Hyde Park Corner SW1X 7TA ☎ 0171 259 5599

FAX 0171 259 5606

There is nothing clinical about the conversion of this former hospital to luxury hotel except for the precision with which the decorators have made their mark. The fabrics and furnishings are sumptuous and the levels of comfort are all that one would expect at a hotel of this calibre. Efficient room service from a personal butler, available 24 hours a day, underlines the hotel's

concern to offer its guests the highest levels of care, and bedrooms are extremely well equipped. A focal point of the ground floor is the conservatory-style restaurant with its arched glass ceiling, Chinese lanterns and huge urns bursting with plants. This is the relaxed setting for the menus prepared by head chef, Paul Gayler, which feature a wonderful array of really fresh-tasting seafood. His recognised forte is meatless dishes, which have a separate heading on the uncomplicated carte. For those wanting to relax after shopping, or meet friends, afternoon tea also represents good value for money.
95 en suite (bth/shr) No smoking in 24 bedrooms CTV in all bedrooms STV Lift Night porter Air conditioning 38P No coaches Gym Jacuzzi/spa Fitness studio Wkly live entertainment Xmas International Cuisine V meals Coffee am

Tea pm Last d mdnt
ROOMS: s £230-£282; d £335-£440 **LB**
OFF-PEAK: (incl. cont bkfst) d fr £282
MEALS: Lunch £23.50-£26.50&alc Dinner £28.50&alc*
CONF: Thtr 90 Class 48 Board 40
CARDS:

★★★★★ 74% **Hyatt Carlton Tower**
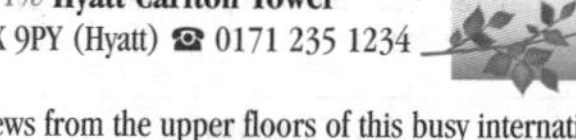
Cadogan Place SW1X 9PY (Hyatt) ☎ 0171 235 1234
FAX 0171 235 9129
There are superb views from the upper floors of this busy international hotel, situated in the heart of Knightsbridge overlooking Cadogan Gardens. The Chinoiserie Lounge is the first point of contact for guests, and here all manner of light meals and refreshments are served. A good choice of food is available elsewhere too: the Rib Room with its highly popular cocktail bar serves straightforward dishes featuring prime cuts of beef, and upstairs the Chelsea Room offers more flamboyant cooking in the French style, prepared by Chef Bernard Gaume who cooks with top class ingredients. Bedrooms, while not particularly spacious, are well equipped and maintained, and there is a glitzy health spa.
220 en suite (bth/shr) No smoking in 46 bedrooms CTV in all bedrooms STV No dogs (ex guide dogs) Lift Night porter Air conditioning 40P No coaches Indoor swimming pool (heated) Tennis (hard) Sauna Solarium Gym Beauty treatment Hair salon Health club Wkly live entertainment English & French Cuisine V meals Coffee am Tea pm Last d 11.15pm
ROOMS: s fr £220.50; d fr £270 **LB**
MEALS: Lunch £19.50-£24.50 Dinner £30.50&alc*
CONF: Thtr 400 Class 250 Board 80
CARDS:

★★★★★ 71% **Sheraton Park Tower**
101 Knightsbridge SW1X 7RN ☎ 0171 235 8050 & 235 3368
Res FAX 0171 235 3368
The Sheraton Park Tower boasts an impeccable address in the heart of Knightsbridge. The unique circular modern hotel has bedrooms all of the same good size, with higher tariffs bringing a more lofty view and a greater array of facilities, up to a full butler service. Public areas are not extensive but have a lively atmosphere; there is the main bar off the lobby and afternoon tea can be taken in The Rotunda Lounge accompanied by a harpist. Newly developed Restaurant 101 is now the showpiece of chef Pascal Proyart, whose cuisine de la mer has great flair and skill. A sound array of five star services are offered by a friendly team of staff.
289 en suite (bth/shr) (289 fmly) No smoking in 60 bedrooms CTV in all bedrooms STV Lift Night porter Air conditioning 90P Health facilities at affiliated club Xmas French Cuisine V meals Coffee am Tea pm No smoking area in restaurant Last d 11pm
ROOMS: s £220-£310; d £240-£330 *
OFF-PEAK: s £175-£255; d £175-£255
MEALS: Lunch £17.50-£21.50&alc Dinner £32&alc*
CONF: Thtr 60 Class 50 Board 35 Del from £296.63
CARDS:

RED STAR HOTEL

★★★★ **Goring**
PRIDE OF BRITAIN MEMBER
Beeston Place, Grosvenor Gardens SW1W 0JW (behind Buckingham Palace, right off Lower Grosvenor Place, just prior to the Royal Mews on the left) ☎ 0171 396 9000 FAX 0171 834 4393
This bastion of English tradition has been owned by the Goring family since 1910 and continues to maintain the highest standards of service under the watchful supervision of General Manager William Cowpe and his friendly team. The comfortable bedrooms are constantly being improved, and over half now have air-conditioning. The elegant public areas include an attractive lounge and cocktail bar overlooking the pretty gardens; and a grand restaurant. A recent inspection meal started with a skate and caper salad, followed by breast of guinea fowl with foie gras; a delicious apricot and apple tatin finished on the right note. All were served by an attentive and professional restaurant team.
76 en suite (bth/shr) CTV in all bedrooms STV No dogs Lift Night porter 8P No coaches Free membership of nearby Health Club Wkly live entertainment Xmas English & French Cuisine V meals Coffee am Tea pm Last d 10.30pm
ROOMS: s £174; d £200 **LB**
OFF-PEAK: s £145; d £176
MEALS: Lunch £21-£24 Dinner £30
CONF: Thtr 60 Class 30 Board 30 Del £260
CARDS:

LONDON

Red Star Hotel

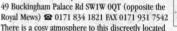

★★★★ Halkin

Halkin St, Belgravia SW1X 7DJ ☎ 0171 333 1000 FAX 0171 333 1100

Although just a stone's throw from Hyde Park corner, this splendid ultra-modern hotel set in the heart of Belgravia is a haven of peace and tranquillity. The elegantly cool marble and granite-floored foyer sets the tone for the intimate public areas which feature a small lounge and bar and an immaculately appointed restaurant which overlooks a small rear garden. High-tech Italian design is evident throughout, but particularly in the splendid bedrooms with their sophisticated lighting and air-conditioning systems. Furnished to superlative standards, rooms feature the finest linens, sumptuous pillows, and many thoughtful extras such as personal fax lines, while the spacious marbled bathrooms have deep tubs and large walk-in showers. Staff are very friendly and attentive yet discreet and professional and acknowledge all their guests by name. The kitchens, under the direction of Stefano Cavallini, go from strength to strength. The short but interesting carte offers exciting modern interpretations of Milanese dishes and is matched by an equally enterprising list of Italian wines.

41 en suite (bth/shr) No smoking in 9 bedrooms CTV in all bedrooms STV No dogs (ex guide dogs) Lift Night porter Air conditioning P No coaches Italian Cuisine V meals Coffee am Tea pm Last d 11pm

ROOMS: d £258.50-£323 * **LB**

OFF-PEAK: d £176.50-£215

MEALS: Lunch fr £24.50&alc Dinner £37.50-£48alc*

CONF: Thtr 42 Class 29 Board 26

CARDS:

★★★★ 76% **Stafford**

16-18 St James's Place SW1A 1NJ ☎ 0171 493 0111 FAX 0171 493 7121

Discreetly situated in a cul-de-sac in St James, this elegant hotel has a club like but unstuffy atmosphere. The lounges and restaurant have been delightfully refurbished without changing the style, and the American Bar with its collection of ties and photographs is a famous rendezvous. The cooking has been brought to life with the arrival of well known chef Chris Oakes, whose menus skilfully blend old favourites with some newer ideas. The charming bedrooms have also been redecorated and the opportunity has been taken to add air-conditioning and some vigorous showers. Carriage House bedrooms in a separate wing are larger and very popular. New management, under the direction of Terry Holmes, have ambitions to restore this small jewel back to the top echelon of London hotels.

80 en suite (bth/shr) CTV in all bedrooms STV No dogs Lift Night porter Air conditioning No coaches Membership of Fitness Club available Xmas English & French Cuisine V meals Coffee am Tea pm Last d 10.30pm

ROOMS: s fr £170; d £185-£360 * **LB**

MEALS: Lunch £19.50-£22.50 Dinner £19.95-£25*

CARDS:

★★★★ 69% **Royal Westminster Thistle**

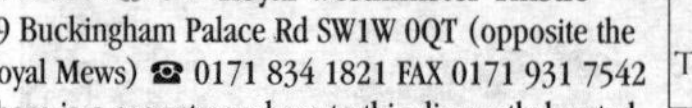

49 Buckingham Palace Rd SW1W 0QT (opposite the Royal Mews) ☎ 0171 834 1821 FAX 0171 931 7542

THISTLE HOTELS

There is a cosy atmosphere to this discreetly located hotel with a prominently placed bar and brasserie. One of its strengths is the size of the bedrooms which are spacious by London standards, and the staff are generally very helpful and willing. The smart restaurant provides an imaginative menu in elegant style which delivers full flavoured dishes.

134 en suite (bth/shr) (69 fmly) No smoking in 67 bedrooms CTV in all bedrooms STV No dogs (ex guide dogs) Lift Night porter Air conditioning Xmas English & French Cuisine V meals Coffee am Tea pm No smoking area in restaurant Last d 11pm

ROOMS: s £128-£145; d £135-£165 * **LB**

OFF-PEAK: s £67-£130; d £134

MEALS: Lunch £10.95-£12.95 Dinner £18.95-£21.95&alc

CONF: Thtr 180 Class 60 Board 14 Del from £185

CARDS:

★★★★ 68% **The Cavendish**

81 Jermyn St SW1Y 6JF ☎ 0171 930 2111 FAX 0171 839 2125

This large, modern and very popular hotel offers a wide range of services and amenities, which are particularly appreciated by the corporate guest. Bedrooms are smart, comfortable and well equipped.

255 en suite (bth/shr) No smoking in 195 bedrooms CTV in all bedrooms STV Lift Night porter 85P Wkly live entertainment Xmas European Cuisine V meals Coffee am Tea pm No smoking area in restaurant Last d 10.45pm

ROOMS: s fr £150; d fr £175 * **LB**

MEALS: Lunch £12.50-£17.50alc High tea £9.50 Dinner £12.50-£30alc*

CONF: Thtr 80 Class 45 Board 14 Del from £145

CARDS:

★★★★ 68% **The Chelsea**

17 Sloane St, Knightsbridge SW1X 9NU ☎ 0171 235 4377 FAX 0171 235 3705

MILLENNIUM & COPTHORNE HOTELS

Surrounded by a wealth of exclusive designer houses, with the world famous Harrods and Harvey Nichols stores nearby, the Chelsea is a stylish modern hotel fitting in with its neighbourhood. From the marble lobby, a glass and chrome staircase leads up to the First Floor Restaurant and bar where a striking glass atrium creates an airy setting in which to enjoy an eclectic menu. Extensive refurbishment of the bedrooms was well under way at our last visit, with elegant furniture imported from Dubai.

224 en suite (bth/shr) No smoking in 57 bedrooms CTV in all bedrooms STV No dogs (ex guide dogs) Lift Night porter Air conditioning 10P No coaches Wkly live entertainment Xmas English & Mediterranean Cuisine V meals Coffee am Tea pm No smoking area in restaurant Last d 10pm
ROOMS: s £155-£170; d £165-£190 *
OFF-PEAK: s £110; d £110-£145
MEALS: Lunch £17.50&alc High tea £9.50 Dinner £20-£30alc*
CONF: Thtr 120 Class 60 Board 40 Del from £119
CARDS:

★★★★ 67% ***The Lowndes***

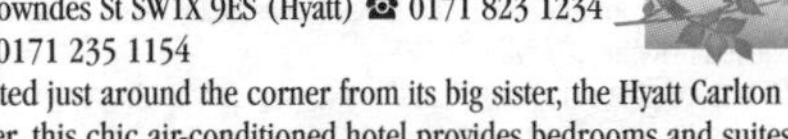

21 Lowndes St SW1X 9ES (Hyatt) ☎ 0171 823 1234
FAX 0171 235 1154
Located just around the corner from its big sister, the Hyatt Carlton Tower, this chic air-conditioned hotel provides bedrooms and suites with every modern facility. Many rooms have balconies, and service meets the demands of the discerning international traveller. Public rooms are limited to a smart marbled and wood-panelled lobby, a sitting area, and all-day dining in the Lowndes Brasserie 21. Tempting in-room dining and 24-hour room service is provided along with very efficient concierge and car parking arrangements. The friendly and discreet town house atmosphere is enhanced by chef Schilo van Coevorden's high standard of cooking.
78 en suite (bth/shr) No smoking in 31 bedrooms CTV in all bedrooms STV No dogs (ex guide dogs) Lift Night porter Air conditioning No coaches Tennis (hard) European Cuisine V meals Coffee am Tea pm Last d 11.15pm
CARDS:

★★★★ 61% **Royal Horseguards Thistle**

Whitehall Court SW1A 2EJ ☎ 0171 839 3400
FAX 0171 925 2263
The flamboyant exterior stands in stark contrast to the rather austere style of neighbouring government buildings. Proximity to major tourist sights and the Thames are a bonus of this hotel which has some striking public areas. Bedroom standards vary but the company has ambitious plans to turn the bulk of them into modern, attractive and contemporary rooms.
377 en suite (bth/shr) No smoking in 135 bedrooms CTV in all bedrooms STV No dogs Lift Night porter International Cuisine V meals Coffee am Tea pm Last d 10.30pm
ROOMS: s £125-£160; d £135-£190 **LB**
MEALS: Lunch £22.50&alc Dinner £22.50&alc*
CONF: Thtr 60 Class 30 Board 24
CARDS:

★★★★ 57% **Grosvenor Thistle**

Buckingham Palace Rd, Victoria SW1W 0SJ (adjacent to Victoria railway station) ☎ 0171 834 9494
FAX 0171 630 1978
This Victorian landmark has had a facelift to its public areas which has resulted in a clean façade and a remodelled reception foyer. It is now looking resplendent as in its earlier days of glory. Close proximity to the stations (bus and train) make this an understandably popular base with tourists and day-trippers alike. An advantage to this hotel is the size of the bedrooms, many of which have double-height ceilings.

366 en suite (bth/shr) (35 fmly) No smoking in 131 bedrooms CTV in all bedrooms STV No dogs (ex guide dogs) Lift Night porter Xmas V meals Coffee am Tea pm No smoking area in restaurant Last d 10.30pm
ROOMS: s £108; d £137 * **LB**
MEALS: Lunch £16.35&alc High tea £7-£10.95alc Dinner £16.35&alc*
CONF: Thtr 200 Class 85 Board 85
CARDS:

★★★ 70% **Rubens**
Buckingham Palace Rd SW1W 0PS (opposite the Royal Mews) (Sarova) ☎ 0171 834 6600 FAX 0171 828 5401
The Rubens opened in 1912 as a hostel for debutantes visiting Buckingham Palace; during the war years it became the headquarters of the Polish forces, but it is now once again a charming and elegant hotel, balancing traditional style with constant modernisation. Lounges have deep seating and look out over the royal mews to the palace where the state carriages are kept. The Old Master restaurant offers an international menu which includes a particularly good roast. Staff are friendly and well trained.
180 en suite (bth) (10 fmly) No smoking in 44 bedrooms CTV in all bedrooms STV No dogs (ex guide dogs) Lift Night porter Jacuzzi/spa Xmas V meals Coffee am Tea pm No smoking area in restaurant Last d 10pm
ROOMS: s fr £110; d fr £135 * **LB**
OFF-PEAK: (incl. bkfst) s fr £95; d fr £120
MEALS: Lunch fr £14.50alc Dinner £10.95-£15.95&alc*
CONF: Thtr 75 Class 30 Board 40 Del from £155
CARDS:

★★★ 61% ***Quality Eccleston***

Eccleston Square SW1V 1PS ☎ 0171 834 8042
FAX 0171 630 8942
Quietly situated overlooking the square, this well managed, good-value hotel has recently been refurbished and

contd.

upgraded. Bedrooms are all furnished in the modern style, Premier Plus rooms providing additional facilities and lots of little extras. The Restaurant D'Amigo specialises in Italian cooking and there are a foyer coffee shop area and a small bar with comfortable lobby seating. The function room will accommodate over 150 people, and there are lots of smaller rooms for Board Meetings, etc. Service is friendly and helpful and parking meters are available close by.
114 en suite (bth/shr) No smoking in 30 bedrooms CTV in all bedrooms STV Lift Night porter Mini-gym English & Continental Cuisine V meals Coffee am No smoking area in restaurant Last d 9.30pm
CONF: Thtr 150 Class 65 Board 60 Del from £105
CARDS:

TOWN HOUSE HOTEL

22 Jermyn Street

22 Jermyn St, St James's SW1Y 6HL
☎ 0171 734 2353 FAX 0171 734 0750
Located in one of the most fashionable streets in the heart of London's West End, this elegant town house offers a standard of privacy and comfort that one would expect at a fine country house. All its suites and studio rooms are individually furnished with antique pieces, set off by designer fabrics. Personally managed by Annette Foster, the dedicated team of staff work well together and provide the highest levels of service to ensure guests' well being. All modern amenities are provided in the rooms, and there are also valet, dry-cleaning and laundry services. The concierge provides an invaluable fund of information and help. Temporary membership of a nearby health club can be arranged, as can valet parking by prior agreement.
18 en suite (bth/shr) (13 fmly) CTV in all bedrooms STV Lift Night porter P No coaches Membership of nearby Health Club V meals Coffee am
ROOMS: d fr £222
CARDS:

See advertisement on opposite page

SW3 CHELSEA, BROMPTON

RED STAR HOTEL

★★★★ *Capital*

Basil St, Knightsbridge SW3 1AT
☎ 0171 589 5171 FAX 0171 225 0011
An exclusive hotel in the heart of Knightsbridge, The Capital provides high standards of personal attention and attracts a loyal clientele, who appreciate the 48 individually designed bedrooms with their fine furniture and stylish decorative themes. In 1995 there was major work on the façade, which is now more in keeping with the buildings around it. At the same time the restaurant was re-styled, with wonderful etched glass and burr walnut inlaid shutters designed by David Linley, stunning mirrors and paintings. The restful new colour scheme allows one to focus on Philip Britten's superb cooking. An appetiser of mussel broth set the scene for an inspection meal, followed by a well flavoured duo of jellied consommés. A delicate tuile filled with sliced artichoke and topped by a thick cream with six herbs, set on a tastily dressed salad atop a tomato coulis, was excellent, but the real pièce de résistance was the salad of two foie gras, grilled with a grape and lime confit and a boudin marinated in Sauternes, with a slice of light toasted brioche.
48 en suite (bth/shr) CTV in all bedrooms Lift Night porter Air conditioning 15P No coaches French Cuisine V meals Coffee am Tea pm Last d 11.15pm
CARDS:

★★★ 71% Basil Street

Basil St, Knightsbridge SW3 1AH ☎ 0171 581 3311
FAX 0171 581 3693
The Basil Street Hotel is one of the grand dames of London hotels which ignores the vagaries of fashion and continues to make her stately progress maintaining the standards of discreet excellence of years past. All the bedrooms are spacious, well equipped and decorated with individual style. The large restaurant is rather under-used which is a shame as chef James Peake produces a tasty range of both modern dishes and traditional favourites including some delicious beef.
89 rms (76 bth/shr) (4 fmly) CTV in all bedrooms Lift Night porter No coaches Wkly live entertainment International Cuisine V meals Coffee am Tea pm Last d 10pm
ROOMS: s £70-£130; d £110-£185 * **LB**
MEALS: Lunch £8.50-£16.50 Dinner £17-£22*
CONF: Thtr 70 Class 32 Board 32 Del from £179
CARDS:

TOWN HOUSE HOTEL

The Beaufort

33 Beaufort Gardens SW3 1PP ☎ 0171 584 5252 FAX 0171 589 2834
Discreet and elegantly furnished, this hotel is quietly situated in a peaceful tree-lined square a short distance from Harrods. Individually styled, comfortable bedrooms have remote control TV and video playback facilities, radios, direct-dial telephones and such thoughtful extras as bath robes and umbrellas; drinks from the drawing room bar are included in the price of the room, as is room service of continental breakfast and light refreshments (the latter available throughout the day). Guests can also obtain complimentary membership of a nearby Health Club for the duration of their stay. Service is particularly helpful and, with few extras to pay for, the hotel represents exceptional value for money. Parking can be difficult, but some meters are usually available and there is an NPC nearby.
28 en suite (bth/shr) (7 fmly) No smoking in 6 bedrooms CTV in all bedrooms STV No dogs (ex guide dogs) Lift Night porter Air conditioning No coaches
ROOMS: s £129.25-£282; d £176.25-£282 *
CARDS:

See advertisement on opposite page

TOWN HOUSE HOTEL

Parkes
41 Beaufort Gardens, Knightsbridge SW3 1PW (off Brompton Road, 150yds from Harrods) ☎ 0171 581 9944 FAX 0171 581 1999
Within walking distance of Harrods and all the other delights of fashionable Knightsbridge, Parkes Hotel also benefits from its location in a peaceful, tree-lined square. Accommodation consists of beautifully appointed bedrooms and suites, furnished in English country-house style, some of which have their own kitchen and veranda. There are a quiet lounge and fine breakfast room downstairs, and snacks can be served to the rooms on request. Reception includes concierge and chauffeur services, and the friendly team of staff are ably led by assistant manager Julie Capps.
33 en suite (bth/shr) (16 fmly) CTV in all bedrooms STV No dogs (ex guide dogs) Lift Night porter No coaches
ROOMS: (incl. bkfst) d £135-£294 *
CARDS:

SW4 CLAPHAM See LONDON plan 1 E2

★★★ 67% **The Windmill on The Common**
Southside, Clapham Common SW4 9DE ☎ 0181 673 4578
FAX 0181 675 1486
Having already enjoyed a fine history as a public house since 1729, this popular neighbourhood establishment has been skilfully extended to provide smart bedrooms equipped with every modern amenity. The pub with its three spacious and traditionally furnished bars and bistro counter forms the main part, featuring an extensive range of award-winning Young and Co real ales, whilst the small wood-panelled and air conditioned restaurant features the enthusiastic cooking of chef Louise Griffiths. Service is friendly and helpful, particularly efficient in the restaurant, and the limited room service and duty night porter add to the range. There is also a small lounge and good car parking.
29 en suite (bth/shr) No smoking in 15 bedrooms CTV in all bedrooms STV Night porter 16P European Cuisine V meals Coffee am Tea pm Last d 10pm
ROOMS: (incl. bkfst) s fr £80; d fr £90 * **LB**
OFF-PEAK: (incl. bkfst) s fr £60; d fr £68
MEALS: Lunch fr £13.50 Dinner £13.95-£20&alc*
CONF: Thtr 40 Class 25 Board 20
CARDS:

SW5 EARL'S COURT

★★★★ 63% **Swallow International**

Cromwell Rd SW5 0TH ☎ 0171 973 1000
FAX 0171 244 8194
Closed 22-27 Dec
This large hotel is convenient for both Earls Court and Olympia. It is also popular with overseas tour groups. It has modern, if a little compact, bedrooms which are well looked after. In addition to an all-day eating option, there is the more formal Blayneys restaurant where some effort is made to produce interesting dishes. The hotel has the added advantage of parking (limited spaces) and an indoor leisure facility.
417 en suite (bth/shr) (36 fmly) No smoking in 40 bedrooms CTV in all bedrooms STV Lift Night porter Air conditioning 80P Indoor swimming pool (heated) Sauna Solarium Gym Whirlpool spa Turkish Steamroom Wkly live entertainment International Cuisine V meals Coffee am Tea pm No smoking area in restaurant Last d 10.30pm
ROOMS: s £110-£125; d £125-£140 * **LB**
MEALS: Lunch £14.50-£17.95 Dinner £14.50-£22.50&alc*
CONF: Thtr 200 Class 100 Board 24 Del from £149.50
CARDS:

LONDON

★★★ 72% **Hogarth**
33 Hogarth Rd, Kensington SW5 0QQ
☎ 0171 370 6831 FAX 0171 373 6179
Genuinely friendly and helpful staff make a stay at this modern hotel a particular pleasure, with service personally supervised by manager Geoff Breese. Situated off the Earls Court Road, near the Exhibition Centre and London Underground, this purpose built hotel offers good accommodation, including top-floor rooms with balconies. Attractive public areas inlcude a small bar, reception lounge area and a good restaurant. Limited room service is available, and in the restaurant the quality of the cooking is noteworthy. The hotel also benefits from having its own car park.
85 en suite (bth/shr) (12 fmly) No smoking in 18 bedrooms CTV in all bedrooms STV Lift Night porter 20P English & French Cuisine V meals Coffee am Tea pm No smoking in restaurant Last d 9.30pm
ROOMS: (incl. bkfst) s £79-£85; d £95-£100 * **LB**
MEALS: Lunch £12-£17&alc Dinner £13.50-£17&alc*
CONF: Thtr 50 Class 20 Board 24 Del from £96
CARDS:

★★★ 63% **Barkston Gardens**
34-44 Barkston Gardens SW5 0EW ☎ 0171 373 7851
FAX 0171 370 6570
Ideally located close to the Exhibition Centre and for easy access to the West End, this popular hotel has been completely refurbished and offers a range of modern bedrooms all furnished and equipped to the same standard. The Bistro Bistrot and bar is open throughout the day for light refreshments, with an interesting and varied menu for breakfast, lunch and dinner. Advertised room service is available, night porter, and there is a lift to all levels and extensive facilities for conferences. Car parking can be a little difficult during the daytime.
82 en suite (bth/shr) (11 fmly) No smoking in 22 bedrooms CTV in all bedrooms STV No dogs (ex guide dogs) Lift Night porter French Cuisine V meals Coffee am Tea pm No smoking area in restaurant Last d 9.30pm
MEALS: Lunch £2.50-£6.75 High tea £2.50-£6.75 Dinner £4.75-£9.75&alc*
CARDS:

See advertisement on opposite page

★★ 67% **Comfort Inn**
22-32 West Cromwell Rd, Kensington SW5 9QJ
☎ 0171 373 3300 FAX 0171 835 2040

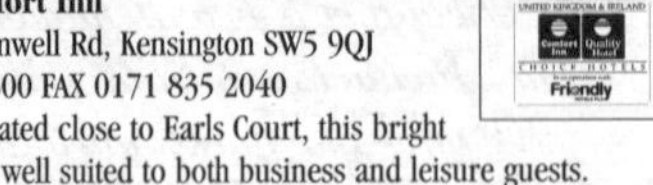

Conveniently located close to Earls Court, this bright modern hotel is well suited to both business and leisure guests. Bedrooms vary in size but all provide a full range of modern facilities including air conditioning. The cosy public areas include a straightforward restaurant and a useful, spacious meeting room.
125 en suite (bth/shr) (6 fmly) No smoking in 62 bedrooms CTV in all bedrooms STV Lift Night porter mini gym Xmas English & Continental Cuisine V meals Coffee am Tea pm No smoking area in restaurant Last d 9.45pm
ROOMS: s £69-£79.50; d £79.50-£92.50 **LB**
MEALS: Lunch £7.50-£9.95&alc Dinner £13.50&alc*
CONF: Thtr 100 Class 60 Board 40 Del from £105
CARDS:

SW6 FULHAM See LONDON plan 1 D3

★★★ 62% **Earls Court International**
47 Lillie Rd SW6 1UQ (A4 to central London,0.5m after Hammersmith flyover turn right at traffic lights into North End Rd follow for 0.5m to mini rdbt left into Lillie Rd) ☎ 0171 385 1255 FAX 0171 381 0215
There are vast conference facilities at this well established tourist hotel. An ongoing refurbishment programme to the bedrooms is bringing them right up to the late 1990s in decor and style. There are 2 restaurants and the added advantage of secure car parking facilities.
501 en suite (bth/shr) No smoking in 96 bedrooms CTV in all bedrooms STV Lift Night porter 130P International Cuisine V meals Coffee am Tea pm No smoking area in restaurant Last d 10.30pm
ROOMS: s £89; d £99 * **LB**
MEALS: Lunch £13.50 Dinner £13.50&alc*
CONF: Thtr 1750 Class 900 Del from £122
CARDS:

SW7 SOUTH KENSINGTON

★★★★ 73% **The Gloucester**
4-18 Harrington Gardens SW7 4LH
☎ 0171 373 6030 FAX 0171 373 0409
A major all-round refurbishment, now virtually complete, has consolidated the Gloucester's reputation as the top international hotel in South Kensington. Bedrooms have been furnished in a contemporary style, marbled bathrooms and air conditioning systems are featured in all rooms and guests who opt for a Club room have use of the Club lounge which serves a complimentary, express breakfast, and cocktails in the evening. The elegant lobby leads to Humphrey's Bar and the stylish South West Seven restaurant, serving enjoyable modern cuisine, whilst a separate entrance takes guests to the informal setting of Bugis Street Café and Bar which has an Oriental theme. Underground parking is competitively priced for residents.
548 en suite (bth/shr) (2 fmly) No smoking in 232 bedrooms CTV in all bedrooms STV Lift Night porter Air conditioning 100P Gym Wkly live entertainment Xmas English & Continental Cuisine V meals Coffee am Tea pm No smoking area in restaurant
ROOMS: s £176.25-£199.75; d £193.88-£217.38 * **LB**
MEALS: Lunch fr £9.99&alc Dinner £7.95-£13.50alc*
CONF: Thtr 440 Class 280 Board 120 Del from £215
CARDS:

★★★★ 70% **Harrington Hall**
5-25 Harrington Gardens SW7 4JW ☎ 0171 396 9696
FAX 0171 396 9090
Although it lies behind an original facade, this is an entirely new modern air conditioned hotel. Well designed along classical lines it comprises a very smart marbled reception foyer, tastefully furnished

lounge bar, and spacious well appointed candlelit Wetherbys restaurant which features a hot buffet, good range of dishes and wines plus an interesting à la carte menu and occasional live entertainment. The quality of the bedrooms is impressive, all being furnished to the same high standard with marbled bathrooms and lots of additional facilities designed to suit the needs of the discerning corporate and leisure guest.

200 en suite (bth/shr) No smoking in 81 bedrooms CTV in all bedrooms STV No dogs (ex guide dogs) Lift Night porter Air conditioning Sauna Gym Xmas European Cuisine V meals Coffee am Tea pm Last d 10.30pm

ROOMS: d £140-£175 * **LB**

OFF-PEAK: (incl. cont bkfst) d £125-£165

MEALS: Lunch £19.75 Dinner fr £19.75*

CONF: Thtr 260 Class 150 Board 50 Del from £155

CARDS:

See advertisement on this page

★★★★66% **Jurys**

109 - 113 Queensgate, South Kensington SW7 5LR (Jurys)

☎ 0171 589 6300 FAX 0171 581 1492

Closed 23-27 Dec

Stylish South Ken. has more than it's fare share of restaurants and hotels but there is certainly room for this fine hotel. Jurys promises a warm Irish welcome and certainly the friendliness here is not easily forgotten. Bedrooms are smart and modern and the recently refurbished restaurant and foyer make good use of bold colours and attractive furnishings. Kavanagh's bar is an oasis of charm with the "craic" flowing as easily as the Guinness. Copplestones restaurant is a convenient feeding stop for those unwilling to experiment with the many local restaurants. There are some well equipped conference facilities and both business and leisure guests are bound to feel at home quickly, our inspector certainly looks forward to returning soon.

173 en suite (bth/shr) (4 fmly) No smoking in 45 bedrooms CTV in all bedrooms STV No dogs (ex guide dogs) Lift Night porter Wkly live entertainment Xmas European Cuisine V meals Coffee am Tea pm No smoking area in restaurant Last d 10pm

ROOMS: s £135-£160; d £135-£160 **LB**

MEALS: Lunch £15-£20 Dinner £10.85-£13.50alc*

CONF: Thtr 80 Class 42 Board 40 Del from £148

CARDS:

★★★★64% **Rembrandt**

11 Thurloe Place SW7 2RS (opp Victoria & Albert Museum) (Sarova)

☎ 0171 589 8100 FAX 0171 225 3363

Commissioned as luxury suites for Harrods in 1900, this ornate building is situated only a few minutes' walk from the famous store. Stylish public areas include a conservatory lounge serving snacks, teas and cocktails all day and the Masters Restaurant which offers both a carvery menu and carte. The Aquilla health and fitness centre has a Roman theme and boasts a beautiful pool, sauna/steam rooms and a poolside terrace serving refreshments. Bedrooms vary from the recently refurbished executive class to standard rooms which are gradually being upgraded.

195 en suite (bth/shr) (25 fmly) No smoking in 28 bedrooms CTV in all bedrooms STV No dogs (ex guide dogs) Lift Night porter Indoor swimming pool (heated) Sauna Solarium Gym Health & Fitness centre Xmas International Cuisine V meals Coffee am Tea pm No smoking area in restaurant Last d 10pm

ROOMS: s fr £115; d fr £140 * **LB**

OFF-PEAK: (incl. bkfst) s fr £100; d fr £130

MEALS: Lunch £13.75-£15.95&alc Dinner fr £15.95&alc*

CONF: Thtr 250 Class 95 Board 80 Del from £155

CARDS:

★★★★62% ***Forum***
97 Cromwell Rd SW7 4DN (Inter-Continent) ☎ 0171 370 5757
FAX 0171 373 1448
Conveniently located for both the tourist and business guest, this functional modern hotel is the tallest in London and enjoys panoramic views over the capital. Bedrooms are generally compact though well equipped while public areas feature a number of food and beverage outlets such as the popular Gloucester Road Deli where drinks, snacks and a comprehensive international menu is available throughout the day. Service is relaxed and staff friendly.
910 en suite (bth/shr) (36 fmly) No smoking in 31 bedrooms CTV in all bedrooms STV No dogs (ex guide dogs) Lift Night porter 75P Gym International Cuisine V meals Coffee am Tea pm
Last d 11.45pm
CARDS:

★★★★61% **Holiday Inn Kensington**

100 Cromwell Rd SW7 4ER (close to Gloucester Rd tube station) ☎ 0171 373 2222 FAX 0171 373 0559
Behind the period façade of this Holiday Inn there is a modern hotel. Bedrooms vary from duplex suites with spiral staircases to executive and standard rooms, all smartly equipped, air-conditioned and triple glazed. There is a popular bar with direct access to the street and a more sedate bar and restaurant-Oliver's.
162 en suite (bth/shr) (96 fmly) No smoking in 60 bedrooms CTV in all bedrooms STV No dogs (ex guide dogs) Lift Night porter Air conditioning 5P Sauna Gym Pool table Jacuzzi/spa Whirlpool Steam room Xmas International Cuisine V meals Coffee am Tea pm No smoking area in restaurant Last d 10pm
ROOMS: s fr £155; d fr £175 **LB**
MEALS: Lunch £15&alc High tea £3.25-£7.50 Dinner £15&alc*
CONF: Thtr 130 Class 60 Board 54 Del £170
CARDS:

The Vanderbilt - A Radisson Edwardian Hotel
68/86 Cromwell Rd SW7 5BT ☎ 0171 589 2424
FAX 0171 225 2293
This stylish, period hotel offers a wide range of services and a choice of eating options for the international traveller. Bedrooms are smart and individually furnished, and are fully equipped with modern facilities. For more informaation about Radisson Edwardian hotels, consult the Contents page under Hotel Groups.
223 en suite (bth/shr)
ROOMS: s £85-£109; d £110-£142 *
CONF: Thtr 110 Class 36 Board 40

○ **Baileys Hotel**

140 Gloucester Rd SW7 4QH ☎ 0171 373 6000
FAX 0171 370 3760
As we went to print, new owners of this delightful period building are in the process of making significant refurbishments to the entire hotel and introducing improved service standards. The hotel is likely to be a highly rated four-star property, with bedrooms varying in size but all smart and air-conditioned.
213 en suite (bth/shr) No smoking in 86 bedrooms CTV in all bedrooms Lift Night porter 95P Fitness room Xmas French Cuisine V meals Coffee am Tea pm
ROOMS: (incl. bkfst) s £110-£176.25; d £120-£193.88 *
OFF-PEAK: (incl. bkfst) s £110; d £120
MEALS: High tea £1-£18alc*
CARDS:

★ *Hotels with a Red Star Award offer outstanding quality of accommodation and service within their classification. There is a full list at the front of the book.*

SW10 WEST BROMPTON See LONDON plan 1 E3

★★★★★72% **Conrad International London**
Chelsea Harbour SW10 0XG ☎ 0171 823 3000 FAX 0171 351 6525
Modern both architecturally and aesthetically, this smart hotel is unique for being Europe's first purpose-built all suite hotel. Each suite is thoughtfully laid out and exceptionally well equipped; Penthouse suites and those with balconies have spectacular views and are much sought after. Most of the public rooms look out onto a vista of yachts and cruisers in the marina, particularly so in the newly refurbished restaurant; like the building the menu here is modern, offering a short but varied selection of dishes, with an emphasis on healthier and lighter sauced recipes. There is an impressive range of ultra modern conference suites and meeting rooms with their own support staff, whilst the fitness health club also has trained personnel to oversee a range of modern gyms, beauty treatments and a splendid 17 metre swimming pool.
160 en suite (bth/shr) (27 fmly) No smoking in 22 bedrooms CTV in all bedrooms STV Lift Night porter Air conditioning No coaches Indoor swimming pool (heated) Sauna Solarium Gym Steam room Massage therapist Xmas International Cuisine V meals Coffee am Tea pm Last d 10.30pm
ROOMS: s £205.62-£271; d £225.62-£291 * **LB**
OFF-PEAK: s £152.75-£271; d £172.75-£291
MEALS: Lunch £10-£20alc Dinner £22.50-£24.50*
CONF: Thtr 200 Class 140 Board 40 Del from £229
CARDS:

SW19 WIMBLEDON See LONDON plan 1 D1

Courtesy & Care Award

★★★★76% **Cannizaro House**

West Side, Wimbledon Common SW19 4UF (Approaching from M25 follow A219 signed Wimbledon into Parkside and past old fountain sharp right then 2nd on left) ☎ 0181 879 1464
FAX 0181 879 7338
Situated on the western edge of Wimbledon Common, this elegant Georgian building offers sumptuous day rooms including a central drawing room with its original fireplace, painted ceiling and fresh flower displays. The restaurant is equally fine with its crystal chandeliers, oil paintings, gilt mirrors and well spaced tables while several of the other rooms overlooking Cannizaro Park are used for private meetings or dinners. Bedrooms have all been attractively refurbished in tasteful country house style and guests are provided with home comforts such as towelling robes and home-made biscuits. At dinner, the chef offers a fixed price menu as well as an

interesting carte featuring a good range of fish dishes and some vegetarian options. Management and staff here have won the AA Courtesy and Care Award for 1996/7.
46 en suite (bth/shr) No smoking in 6 bedrooms CTV in all bedrooms STV No dogs (ex guide dogs) Lift Night porter 60P No coaches No children 8yrs English & French Cuisine V meals Coffee am Tea pm No smoking area in restaurant Last d 10.30pm
ROOMS: s £125-£150; d £145-£200 * **LB**
MEALS: Lunch £21.50-£25.75 Dinner £21.50-£25.75*
CONF: Thtr 80 Class 34 Board 40 Del from £170
CARDS:

W1 WEST END

RED STAR HOTEL

★★★★★ **Claridge's**
Brook St W1A 2JQ (Leading Hotels)
☎ 0171 629 8860 FAX 0171 499 2210
Set in the heart of London's Mayfair, this fine hotel has welcomed visiting royalty, heads of state and some of the world's most illustrious families for close on 100 years. It retains all of its original architectural features, including a stunning black and white marble front hall foyer and reading room, where the Hungarian Quartet entertains guests at lunch and dinner. The atmosphere is regal and formal service reflects the hotel's motto 'we strive for excellence'. Currently undergoing a complete program of refurbishment, with new top floor penthouses, suites and a health club being added, bedrooms range from the spectacular royal suites to spacious single rooms, all featuring stunning bathrooms, original Art Deco fixtures and fittings, new air conditioning, the finest linens, bell pushes to summon the maid, waiter, or valet, and the very latest in technology. To satisfy the whims of wealthy clients, food may be flown in from anywhere in the world, but high quality British produce also features in the restaurant. More informal dining is offered in the Causerie where there is a daily Smorgasbord.
192 en suite (bth/shr) CTV in all bedrooms STV No dogs (ex guide dogs) Lift Night porter Air conditioning No coaches Sauna Gym Tennis at the Vanderbilt Club Wkly live entertainment Xmas International Cuisine V meals Coffee am Tea pm Last d 11pm
ROOMS: s £205-£235; d £255-£310 * **LB**
MEALS: Lunch £29&alc High tea £16.50 Dinner £38-£40&alc*
CONF: Thtr 260 Class 110 Board 50 Del from £120
CARDS:

RED STAR HOTEL

★★★★★ **Connaught**
Carlos Place W1Y 5AE (Leading Hotels)
☎ 0171 499 7070 FAX 0171 495 3262
The Connaught, situated in the heart of Mayfair, is regarded by many as one of the world's most exclusive hotels. It has never compromised its inimitable standards. The professionalism of the senior personnel is exemplary, and the well groomed staff provide the highest degree of customer care. Suites and bedrooms are individually furnished, many with antiques and all with supremely comfortable beds, fine linen, and new air-conditioning. There is a bell system to summon maid, valet or waiter, and each floor has its own service section. Public rooms are not on the grand scale but their quality is irreproachable. They include a drawing room, double-sided American bar, the restaurant and separate grill room. Maitre chef de cuisine Michel Bourdin has given a decade of service and offers a range of impeccably cooked classic French dishes, supplemented by a range of regular and popular lunch items and table d'hÙte alternatives.
90 en suite (bth/shr) CTV in all bedrooms No dogs Lift Night porter 3P No coaches English & French Cuisine Tea pm Last d 10.45pm
ROOMS: s fr £233; d fr £335 * **LB**
MEALS: Lunch £25-£30&alc Dinner £34-£55&alc*
CARDS:

RED STAR HOTEL

★★★★★ **The Dorchester**
Park Ln W1A 2HJ (opposite Hyde Park) (Leading Hotels) ☎ 0171 629 8888
FAX 0171 409 0114
Overlooking the delightful expanses of Hyde Park, The Dorchester is undoubtedly one of the world's finest hotels. The management and staff provide exceptional standards of service throughout (although there is scope for improvements to the quality of the room service) whilst retaining a reserved level of friendliness and decorum. The promenade leading off the foyer provides the perfect rendezvous for watching the world go by whilst enjoying one of the best afternoon teas with delicious patisserie and formal service. The bar, which specialises in light Italian dishes, also features jazz entertainment every Wednesday and Saturday night, and has long been famous for its cocktails.

contd.

Opposite, the richly decorated Spanish-style Grill Room serves traditional food from the finest of British ingredients, and with The Terrace now being used exclusively as a private room, there are plans to create a more innovative repertoire. The Oriental Restaurant continues to offer Cantonese dishes of a similarly high quality.

244 en suite (bth/shr) No smoking in 34 bedrooms CTV in all bedrooms STV No dogs (ex guide dogs) Lift Night porter Air conditioning 25P No coaches Sauna Solarium Gym Jacuzzi/spa Health club Wkly live entertainment Xmas English, Cantonese & Italian Cuisine V meals Coffee am Tea pm Last d 11pm
ROOMS: s £225-£250; d £250-£280 * **LB**
MEALS: Lunch fr £25.50&alc High tea fr £26 Dinner £34-£77*
CONF: Thtr 550 Class 250 Board 42
CARDS:

RED STAR HOTEL

★★★★★ **Four Seasons**
Hamilton Place, Park Ln W1A 1AZ (Leading Hotels)
☎ 0171 499 0888 FAX 0171 493 6629
This finely tuned modern hotel just off Park Lane provides the high standards in all areas of its operation expected by today's international traveller, not in the grand style but in a friendly, polished and efficient fashion. Bedrooms, some of which have been refurbished, are elegant in an understated manner without skimping on quality. Meals are provided to the bedrooms and the room service menu is extensive. Useful facilities abound, including multi-language TV channels, in-room video player and bar. Some rooms have the added bonus of views over the south-eastern edge of Hyde Park. Jogging Maps are considerately provided and there is a state-of-the art fitness room. There is an in-house 'alternative' eating option that provides healthy balanced dishes, served either in the bedrooms or Lanes Restaurant, which is also one of the main restaurants. Although he has recently left The Four Seasons restaurant, this is where chef de cuisine, Jean-Christophe Novelli, built a fine reputation for his innovative style of cooking.
227 en suite (bth/shr) (227 fmly) No smoking in 72 bedrooms CTV in all bedrooms STV No dogs (ex guide dogs) Lift Night porter Air conditioning 50P No coaches Gym Wkly live entertainment Xmas International Cuisine V meals Coffee am Tea pm No smoking area in restaurant Last d 11pm
ROOMS: s £240-£270; d £285-£295 * **LB**
MEALS: Lunch £25-£32.50 Dinner £28&alc*
CONF: Thtr 500 Class 200 Board 90
CARDS:

★★★★★ 78% **Ritz**
150 Piccadilly W1V 9DG ☎ 0171 493 8181
FAX 0171 493 2687

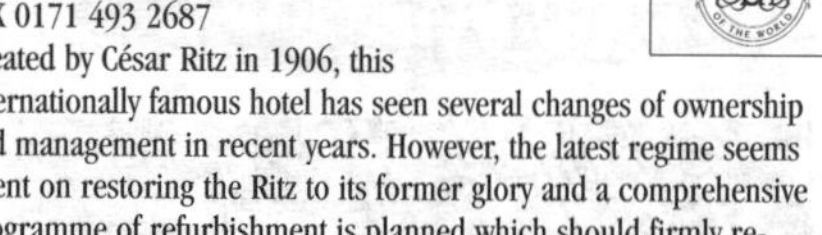

Created by César Ritz in 1906, this internationally famous hotel has seen several changes of ownership and management in recent years. However, the latest regime seems intent on restoring the Ritz to its former glory and a comprehensive programme of refurbishment is planned which should firmly re-establish it as one of the best hotels in the capital. Traditionally appointed bedrooms offer high levels of comfort (although not all as yet have air-conditioning), are furnished in Louis XVI-style and have fine marble bathrooms, many with separate shower cabinets. The elegant public areas, graced with floral displays, include the ever popular Palm Court where the afternoon tea ritual attracts hundreds of visitors every day, and the sumptuous restaurant with its fabulous trompe l'oeil ceiling and gold chandeliers. This is a perfect setting in which to sample the equally exciting cooking of chef David Nicholls. He insists on top quality produce and selects his ingredients on the basis of flavour, frequently changing the menus to reflect what is at its peak. Consequently, the highlight of an excellent meal in late February was a memorable risotto of fresh black and white truffle topped with grated pecorino cheese. High calibre staff ensure that guests receive friendly, attentive and professional service throughout every department of the hotel.
130 en suite (bth/shr) CTV in all bedrooms STV No dogs (ex guide dogs) Lift Night porter P No coaches Wkly live entertainment Xmas International Cuisine V meals Coffee am Tea pm Last d 11.30pm
ROOMS: d £215 *
MEALS: Lunch fr £28 Dinner £36.50-£43*
CONF: Thtr 70 Class 25 Board 30
CARDS:

STOP PRESS! *AA Members can book accommodation at many hotels in this guide through the AA Booking Service, usually at attractive discounts. See page 5 for details or telephone 0990 050505*

★★★★★❀❀❀74% ***Hotel Inter-Continental***

1 Hamilton Pl, Hyde Park Corner W1V 0QY
☎ 0171 409 3131 FAX 0171 493 3476

Situated on Hyde Park Corner and enjoying excellent views (at least from the upper floors) over the park and Knightsbridge, this hotel is popular with the international traveller and offers a comprehensive range of services and facilities. Bedrooms vary from inner court rooms to spacious suites, but a programme of continual refurbishment ensures that all are kept in good condition. The smart marble foyer includes an attractive lounge where a harpist accompanies afternoon tea. Also on the ground floor is the all-day Coffee House restaurant, but for serious dining, the aptly named Le Soufflé Restaurant holds the AA's accolade of three rosettes. Service here is reassuringly traditional, despite the modern decor, and long-serving chef Peter Kromberg is responsible for creating some delicious menus which focus on soufflés, both savoury and sweet.

467 en suite (bth/shr) No smoking in 58 bedrooms CTV in all bedrooms No dogs (ex guide dogs) Lift Night porter Air conditioning 100P No coaches Sauna Gym Health centre English, French, Italian & Oriental Cuisine V meals Coffee am Tea pm
CARDS:

★★★★★❀❀73% ***Churchill Inter-Continental***

30 Portman Square W1A 4ZX ☎ 0171 486 5800
FAX 0171 486 1255

Looking out over Portman Square, this modern hotel provides accommodation in the English country-house style, but with such amenities as dual voltage plugs, modem and fax lines. Club Rooms on the eighth floor entitle occupants to a dedicated lounge and reception, breakfast, cocktails and clothes-pressing services. Public areas display a wealth of marble, pillars and chandeliers and in the comfortable Terrace Lounge afternoon tea and other light refreshments are served. Clementine's Restaurant, all light and air in contrast to the gentleman's club atmosphere of the Churchill Bar, is an attractive setting for the Mediterranean-inspired cooking of Idras Caldora, whose menus might include a terrine of duck served on a bed of frisée with a wild mushroom dressing, or a lobster and scallop raviolo with a morel and shellfish sauce. Staff are friendly and obliging and the hotel boasts a business centre.

448 en suite (bth/shr) No smoking in 66 bedrooms CTV in all bedrooms STV Lift Night porter Air conditioning No coaches Tennis (hard) Mediterranean Cuisine V meals Coffee am Tea pm
CARDS:

★★★★★❀❀❀❀❀73% **Grosvenor House**

FORTE HOTELS

Park Ln W1A 3AA ☎ 0171 499 6363
FAX 0171 493 3341

Internationally recognised, this splendid hotel is majestically positioned on Park Lane, fronted by an impressive Lutyens' façade. Bedrooms tend to vary in size and style but the refurbishment programme is now well in hand and those completed boast commendable standards. There is also a wing of fully serviced apartments, complete with lounge and kitchen. One of the strengths of the hotel however is the impressive banqueting, function and private dining rooms. The Great Room in particular seats 1500 guests in grand surroundings. Other facilities include leisure, shops, comfy lounges and bars. An excellent range of eating options is available, notably Nico at Ninety with its incomparable food and service.

454 en suite (bth/shr) No smoking in 70 bedrooms CTV in all bedrooms STV No dogs (ex guide dogs) Lift Night porter Air conditioning 120P Indoor swimming pool (heated) Sauna Solarium Gym Jacuzzi/spa Health & Fitness centre Wkly live entertainment Xmas English, French & Italian Cuisine V meals Coffee am Tea pm No smoking area in restaurant Last d 10.30pm
ROOMS: s £246.75-£297.50; d £264.38-£340.75 * **LB**
MEALS: Lunch £21-£26alc High tea £11.50-£16.50alc Dinner £25-£35alc*
CONF: Thtr 1200 Class 600 Board 60
CARDS:

★★★★★❀❀❀73% **Le Meridien Piccadilly**

Le MERIDIEN

21 Piccadilly W1V 0BH ☎ 0171 734 8000
FAX 0171 437 3574

This well established hotel could justifiably lay claim to be the closest to the centre of the capital, being located within whistling distance of Piccadilly Circus. It has comfortable bedrooms, all with a similar style of decor and a range of amenities expected at this classification. There is appropriate musical entertainment to accompany afternoon tea in the lounge, and also in the bar and Oak Room retaurant in the evening. Here, Pascal Villain produces modern French cuisine, and there is a second restaurant, the Terrace, which, under the direction of Paul Merret, is evolving a more modern London style of menu.

266 en suite (bth/shr) No smoking in 90 bedrooms CTV in all bedrooms STV No dogs (ex guide dogs) Lift Night porter Air conditioning P No coaches Indoor swimming pool (heated) Squash Snooker Sauna Solarium Gym Pool table Jacuzzi/spa Health & Leisure club Wkly live entertainment Xmas French Cuisine V meals Coffee am Tea pm No smoking area in restaurant Last d 10.15pm
ROOMS: s £230-£250; d £250-£270 * **LB**
MEALS: Lunch £19.50-£24.50&alc Dinner £28-£49&alc*
CONF: Thtr 250 Class 160 Board 80
CARDS:

★★★★★❀❀❀70% **The London Hilton on Park Lane**

HILTON INTERNATIONAL

22 Park Ln W1A 2HH ☎ 0171 493 8000
FAX 0171 493 4957

The London Hilton is noted for its panoramic views over Hyde Park and the city, and where better to enjoy them than from Windows Restaurant on the 28th floor. Live music plays nightly in the bar and intimate lighting sets the scene for a romantic evening. Menus created by Jacques Rolancey combine a classic training with modern influences and other options for dining include Trader Vic's, legendary for its cocktails and Polynesian cuisine, the Brasserie and St George's Bar with its pub atmosphere. Large windows are a feature of all bedrooms and executive rooms have personal faxes.

447 en suite (bth/shr) No smoking in 140 bedrooms CTV in 446 bedrooms STV No dogs (ex guide dogs) Lift Night porter Air conditioning P Gym Wkly live entertainment Xmas European Cuisine V meals Coffee am Tea pm Last d 1.30am
ROOMS: s £258.50-£335; d £258.50-£335 * **LB**
MEALS: Lunch £11.50-£35.95&alc High tea £12.75-£27.50&alc Dinner £11.50-£33.50&alc*
CONF: Thtr 1250 Class 520 Board 160
CARDS:

★★★★★❀❀67% **May Fair Inter-Continental**

INTER·CONTINENTAL. HOTELS AND RESORTS

Stratton St W1A 2AN ☎ 0171 629 7777
FAX 0171 629 1459

Popular with showbiz celebrities, this friendly and well managed hotel has an intimate atmosphere but offers a wide range of amenities,

contd.

LONDON

including a varied choice of eating outlets, two bars, a shop, business centre, its own theatre and a smart leisure club which, unusually for London has a pool. Comfortably furnished, air-conditioned bedrooms continue to be upgraded and feature some sumptuously refurbished suites. The stylish new Le Chateau Restaurant offers Michael Croaker's modern British cuisine with specialities such as fish cakes with Pommery mustard sauce, grilled calves, liver with bacon and cheese mash, and bread and butter pudding.

287 en suite (bth/shr) (14 fmly) No smoking in 37 bedrooms CTV in all bedrooms STV No dogs (ex guide dogs) Lift Night porter Air conditioning No coaches Indoor swimming pool (heated) Sauna Solarium Gym Hair & beauty salon Wkly live entertainment Xmas English & French Cuisine V meals Coffee am Tea pm No smoking area in restaurant Last d 11pm

ROOMS: s £205-£235; d £235-£265 *

MEALS: Lunch £11-£20&alc High tea £6.50-£11 Dinner £23-£29.50&alc*

CONF: Thtr 290 Class 108 Board 70

CARDS:

★★★★★66% **The Langham Hilton, London**

1 Portland Place, Regent St W1N 4JA

☎ 0171 636 1000 FAX 0171 323 2340

When it opened in 1865 this hotel laid claim to being the first 'grand' hotel in London. There are signs in the architecture of this grand style and the themed food and drink outlets hark back to grander times. There is the bright, airy, 'Victorian' style of the Palm Court where afternoon tea and snacks are served; the Chukka bar with its polo memorabilia and a touch of the continent in the Tsar's bar with its choice of over 60 Vodkas. A modern and easy approach to cooking is adopted in the main restaurant, Memories, where meals are often accompanied by live harp music. Bedrooms are furnished in a straightforward, functional style with an eye on providing well maintained and clean facilities. There are some better category bedrooms which have been specifically designed with the business traveller in mind.

379 en suite (bth/shr) No smoking in 120 bedrooms CTV in all bedrooms STV Lift Night porter Air conditioning No coaches Tennis (hard) Sauna Solarium Gym Beauty salon Hairdressing Wkly live entertainment Xmas International Cuisine V meals Coffee am Tea pm No smoking area in restaurant Last d 11.45pm

ROOMS: s £195-£270; d £220-£290 * **LB**

MEALS: Lunch £23-£30.50 High tea fr £14.50 Dinner £25-£29.25&alc*

CONF: Thtr 300 Class 190 Board 100

CARDS:

RED STAR HOTEL

★★★★❀❀ **Athenaeum**

116 Piccadilly W1V 0BJ (overlooking Green Park) ☎ 0171 499 3464 FAX 0171 493 1860

Extensively refurbished and upgraded in recent years, this fine establishment remains one of the most popular and friendly of the Piccadilly hotels in its prime position overlooking Green Park. Regular guests will be pleased to see familiar faces still but a change in general manager has brought even higher standards of performance from most members of staff. Chef David Marshall continues to provide a sensibly sized and realistically priced menu in Bulloch's Restaurant, whilst the Windsor lounge is a quiet and very comfortable setting for lighter snacks or meals. A new Health Spa has been provided for the exclusive use of residents, and the exclusive bedrooms and bathrooms have been equipped to the highest standards. Car parking service can be arranged.

156 en suite (bth/shr) No smoking in 58 bedrooms CTV in all bedrooms STV Lift Night porter Air conditioning No coaches Sauna Gym Jacuzzi/spa Steam room Massage & treatment rooms Wkly live entertainment International Cuisine V meals Coffee am Tea pm No smoking area in restaurant Last d 11pm

ROOMS: s £240.88-£317.25; d £264.38-£340.75 **LB**

MEALS: Lunch £24.50-£31.50&alc Dinner £24.50-£31.50&alc*

CONF: Thtr 55 Class 35 Board 36

CARDS:

RED STAR HOTEL

★★★★❀❀ **Brown's**

FORTE HOTELS

Albemarle St, Dover St W1X 4BP (turn left from Green Park Underground, 3rd road on left is Albemarle St) ☎ 0171 493 6020 FAX 0171 493 9381

Located in the heart of Mayfair, this exclusive hotel perhaps owes its unique atmosphere to the fact that it occupies 11 townhouses sandwiched between two streets. Its public rooms have a lovely country house feeling which accounts for the popularity of its afternoon tea. Traditional fare, with some modern notes, is served in the restaurant with dishes such as lobster tagliatelle and roast pheasant with celeriac gratin. The bedrooms, individual in size and style, are in excellent condition having recently undergone a major refurbishment.

116 en suite (bth/shr) (15 fmly) No smoking in 16 bedrooms CTV in all bedrooms STV No dogs (ex guide dogs) Lift Night

porter No coaches Xmas English & French Cuisine V meals Coffee am Tea pm No smoking area in restaurant Last d 10.45pm
ROOMS: s £246.75-£334.88; d £276.13-£763.75 * **LB**
MEALS: Lunch fr £18alc Dinner fr £30alc*
CONF: Thtr 80 Class 40 Board 30
CARDS:

★★★★❀❀78% **Park Lane**
Piccadilly W1Y 8BX (opposite Green Park) ☎ 0171 499 6321
FAX 0171 499 1965
A thorough refurbishment programme to the bedrooms had just been completed at the time of our last visit to this fine hotel in Piccadilly. A choice of dining is offered in the French-style Brasserie on the Park or the the more formal Bracewells Restaurant. There is a well appointed cocktail bar adjoining the latter, and breakfast is served in the Garden Room. Room service is provided 24 hours, including valet and evening maid service. The Palm Court lounge, which provides access from Piccadilly to the main entrance of the hotel in Brick Street, has been completely redecorated in art deco style. It is the ideal rendezvous for afternoon tea, with live piano entertainment. The hotel has numerous meeting and function rooms - the Ballroom accommodates up to 600 guests - and other facilities include hairdressing, aromatherapy, fitness gym, business centre and garage.
310 en suite (bth/shr) (20 fmly) No smoking in 80 bedrooms CTV in all bedrooms STV Lift Night porter 180P Gym Wkly live entertainment Xmas English & French Cuisine V meals Coffee am Tea pm No smoking area in restaurant Last d 10.30pm
ROOMS: s £211.50-£282; d £235-£282 * **LB**
MEALS: Lunch £18-£25&alc Dinner £30-£50alc*
CARDS:

★★★★❀76% **The Montcalm-Hotel Nico London**
Great Cumberland Place W1A 2LF ☎ 0171 402 4288
FAX 0171 724 9180
Discreetly located close to Marble Arch and Oxford Street, this mid-crescent Georgian town house was named after an 18th-century general, The Marquis de Montcalm, who was celebrated for his dignity and style. Today the hotel exemplifies these rare and welcome qualities with conscientious and competent standards of customer care. It has recently been refurbished to a high standard, and there is a good range of bedrooms including penthouses, junior suites and split-level duplex rooms. Bedrooms are equipped with every modern amenity such as international satellite TV, mini-bars and marbled bathrooms. The particularly well appointed Crescent Restaurant features the robust and imaginative cooking of chef Gary Robinson and uncomplicated 1/2/3 course menus which offer wonderful value for money, especially at lunchtime. Service is very willing, and available 24 hours, along with extensive advertised room service and concierge.
120 en suite (bth/shr) No smoking in 28 bedrooms CTV in all bedrooms STV No dogs (ex guide dogs) Lift Night porter Air conditioning 10P No coaches V meals Coffee am Tea pm No smoking area in restaurant
ROOMS: s £217.37-£240.87; d £240.87-£258.50 **LB**
CONF: Thtr 80 Class 36 Board 36 Del from £250
CARDS:

★★★★❀75% **Britannia Inter-Continental**
Grosvenor Square W1A 3AN ☎ 0171 629 9400
FAX 0171 629 7736
INTER·CONTINENTAL HOTELS AND RESORTS
An extensive range of facilities is offered at this professionally managed hotel in the heart of Mayfair. Bedrooms vary from compact standards to more comfortable deluxe rooms, but all are smartly appointed. Public areas include a cocktail bar, piano bar and English pub as well as a choice of three restaurants. The hotel also offers a well equipped business centre, an unattended fitness room and a parade of shops. A good level of services is provided, including valet and 24-hour room service.
318 en suite (bth/shr) No smoking in 60 bedrooms CTV in all bedrooms STV No dogs (ex guide dogs) Lift Night porter Air conditioning 15P Solarium Gym Hairdresser Fitness centre Beauty Salon Wkly live entertainment Xmas English, American, French, Italian & Japanese Cuisine V meals Coffee am Tea pm Last d 10.30pm
ROOMS: s fr £180; d fr £180 * **LB**
OFF-PEAK: s fr £149; d fr £149
MEALS: Lunch £20-£23 Dinner £20-£23&alc*
CONF: Thtr 100 Class 54 Board 55 Del from £150
CARDS:

★★★★74% **Radisson SAS Portman**
22 Portman Square W1H 9FL ☎ 0171 208 6000 FAX 0171 208 6001
Ideally located within walking distance of Oxford Street and Park Lane this modern corporate international hotel has undergone a complete programme of refurbishment and now offers a range of comfortable air-conditioned theme bedrooms, all equipped to a high standard. Spacious and comfortable air-conditioned open-plan public rooms include a lobby lounge, cocktail bar and the Portman Corner Restaurant which features all day dining and an interesting modern popular menu with some spicy Asian influences. Traditional afternoon teas are served in the lobby lounge and extensive 24-hour room service is provided. Other facilities include a shop, extensive self contained-facilities for conferences and functions, business centre, separate airline check-in, and car parking.
279 en suite (bth/shr) No smoking in 117 bedrooms CTV in all bedrooms STV No dogs (ex guide dogs) Lift Night porter Air conditioning 400P Tennis (hard) Sauna Solarium Gym Xmas International Cuisine V meals Coffee am Tea pm No smoking area in restaurant Last d 11pm
ROOMS: d £210 * **LB**
OFF-PEAK: (incl. bkfst) s fr £120; d fr £150
MEALS: Lunch £16.50-£17.50alc Dinner fr £18.50alc*
CONF: Thtr 380 Class 220 Board 65 Del from £212
CARDS:

★★★★❀74% ***The Westbury***
Bond St, Conduit St W1A 4UH ☎ 0171 629 7755
FAX 0171 495 1163
FORTE HOTELS
This distinctive hotel is ideally positioned in London's classiest shopping district, and has benefited from substantial recent upgrading. Bedrooms are particularly attractive and now reflect a truly international de luxe standard. Busy public rooms include a popular lounge and the well-known Polo bar, together with La Méditerranée restaurant which features a lively modern Italian menu. An extra effort is made to provide traditional services at the Westbury.
244 en suite (bth/shr) (6 fmly) No smoking in 76 bedrooms CTV in all bedrooms STV No dogs (ex guide dogs) Lift Night porter Air conditioning 20P Complimentary access to Health Club Wkly live entertainment V meals Coffee am Tea pm Last d 10.30pm
CARDS:

★★★★❀73% **The Washington**
5-7 Curzon St, Mayfair W1Y 8DT (Sarova) ☎ 0171 499 7000
FAX 0171 495 6172
Situated in the heart of fashionable Mayfair close to Piccadilly and Bond Street this smart well appointed air conditioned modern hotel has been completely refurbished and upgraded to a very high standard. Bedrooms furnished in burred oak range from state rooms and suites with Jacuzzi to equally comfortable twins and doubles all equipped with every modern amenity to meet the demands of today's discerning traveller. The marbled and wood panelled public areas are very comfortable, and as well as efficient 24 hour room service Madison's bar lounge provides all day dining between 11am and 11pm with

contd.

LONDON

enterprising and reliable standards of pre-theatre, flambe, and a la carte cooking featured in the adjoining restaurant every evening. There is a good range of business services including several private conference and board rooms. Full concierge is provided including car parking when possible, and well turned out staff are friendly, helpful, conscientious, competent and particularly well managed.
173 en suite (bth/shr) No smoking in 44 bedrooms CTV in all bedrooms STV No dogs (ex guide dogs) Lift Night porter Air conditioning Xmas International Cuisine V meals Coffee am Tea pm No smoking area in restaurant Last d 10pm
ROOMS: s £175; d £195 * **LB**
OFF-PEAK: (incl. bkfst) s £125; d £160
MEALS: Lunch fr £25alc Dinner fr £19.95&alc*
CONF: Thtr 80 Class 35 Board 36 Del from £211.95
CARDS:

★★★★ 72% **Clifton-Ford**
47 Welbeck St W1M 8DN ☎ 0171 486 6600 FAX 0171 486 7492
Extensive and good quality improvements during the past few years have positioned this well managed, friendly hotel into the forefront of a very successful corporate and leisure market. The accommodation had been particularly well furnished and equipped, and public areas include a sumptuous lounge, a marble reception lobby, a well appointed cocktail bar and Doyles brasserie style restaurant. The staff are attentive and friendly and there is well supervised 24-hour service. Additional facilities include a hotel garage, and The Marylebone Suite which can accommodate up to 150 guests for meetings and functions.
200 en suite (bth/shr) (7 fmly) CTV in all bedrooms STV Lift Night porter 20P European Cuisine V meals Coffee am Tea pm Last d 10pm
ROOMS: s £176.25; d £193.87 *
MEALS: Lunch £21-£30alc Dinner £21-£30alc*
CONF: Thtr 150 Class 80 Board 40
CARDS:

★★★★ 72% **London Marriott**
Grosvenor Square W1A 4AW (Marriott) ☎ 0171 493 1232
FAX 0171 491 3201
Situated in the heart of Mayfair, this popular hotel offers a comfortable standard of accommodation. There are several sizes and styles of bedroom (so check on reservation), and all have had a recent soft refurbishment. Air conditioning is a useful facility; bathrooms are on the compact side. Public areas are smart but limited in extent. Snacks and drinks are served all day in the Regent Lounge, and sound modern cooking is offered in the Diplomat Restaurant. The staff provide a cheerful and willing service.
221 en suite (bth/shr) (26 fmly) No smoking in 120 bedrooms CTV in all bedrooms STV No dogs (ex guide dogs) Lift Night porter Air conditioning 80P No coaches Gym Exercise & fitness centre Xmas V meals Coffee am Tea pm No smoking area in restaurant Last d 10.30pm
ROOMS: s £189-£215; d £189-£215 * **LB**
MEALS: Lunch £19.50-£24.50&alc Dinner £9.95&alc*
CONF: Thtr 800 Class 450 Board 60
CARDS:

★★★★ 71% **Marble Arch Marriott**

134 George St W1H 6DN (from Marble Arch turn into the Edgeware Road then take 4th turning on right)
☎ 0171 723 1277 FAX 0171 402 0666
Situated just off the Edgware Road, this modern hotel offers stylish and comfortable accommodation. Generously sized bedrooms are well equipped, and furnished with good quality furniture and marbled bathrooms. Executive rooms have their own lounge on the top floor, where a complimentary breakfast and speedy checkout is available. Public areas are relatively limited, but there is a good leisure centre and car parking.

240 en suite (bth/shr) (95 fmly) No smoking in 120 bedrooms CTV in all bedrooms STV No dogs (ex guide dogs) Lift Night porter Air conditioning 60P Indoor swimming pool (heated) Sauna Solarium Gym Jacuzzi/spa Whirlpool Wkly live entertainment Xmas English & American Cuisine V meals Coffee am Tea pm No smoking area in restaurant Last d 10.15pm
ROOMS: s £140-£190; d £140-£190 * **LB**
OFF-PEAK: (incl. cont bkfst) s £140-£190; d £140-£190
MEALS: Lunch £22-£24&alc Dinner £22.50-£25&alc*
CONF: Thtr 150 Class 75 Board 60 Del from £210
CARDS:

★★★★ 68% **The Chesterfield**
35 Charles St, Mayfair W1X 8LX ☎ 0171 491 2622
FAX 0171 491 4793
This privately owned hotel at the heart of Mayfair retains an exclusive, intimate ambience. There is a charming oak-panelled library lounge for afternoon tea, and the clubby bar and adjoining terrace serve light meals throughout the day; Butlers Restaurant is professionally run, and chef David Needes has introduced both a new seasonal carte and an exciting style of modern cooking with a strong Mediterranean influence. Innovative combinations of flavour and texture result in very enjoyable meals, such as the one our inspector singled out for special praise. He chose home-made spinach fettucine tossed with pancetta, olives and tomatoes, following this by very tender and pink calves' liver with red onions, horseradish mash and a very tasty Marsala gravy; sticky toffee pudding was served with vanilla ice cream. A new wine list is currently being selected, and service remains extremely attentive and helpful. A very good value conservatory buffet luncheon is available Monday-Friday.
110 en suite (bth/shr) (4 fmly) No smoking in 16 bedrooms CTV in all bedrooms STV No dogs (ex guide dogs) Lift Night porter No coaches Wkly live entertainment Xmas English European & American Cuisine V meals Coffee am Tea pm No smoking area in restaurant Last d 10pm
ROOMS: s £135-£170 * **LB**
OFF-PEAK: s £175-£220
MEALS: Lunch £8.50&alc Dinner £22.50&alc*
CONF: Thtr 130 Class 60 Board 60 Del from £200
CARDS:

★★★★ 68% ***The Cumberland***
FORTE HOTELS
Marble Arch W1A 4RF ☎ 0171 262 1234
FAX 0171 724 4621
Conveniently for both the Capital's shopping area and the greenery of Hyde Park, Cumberland's position is unrivalled. The extent of the public rooms is vast, with cafés, oriental dining and the perennial Carvery, shops and all the usual services. There are excellent business facilities and a well trained staff and management. Bedrooms are comfortably furnished and up to date.
890 en suite (bth/shr) (21 fmly) No smoking in 242 bedrooms CTV in all bedrooms STV No dogs (ex guide dogs) Lift Night porter English Japanese & Chinese Cuisine V meals Coffee am Tea pm Last d midnt
CARDS:

LONDON

★★★★ ❀❀ 68% The Selfridge Thistle

THISTLE HOTELS

Orchard St W1H 0JS (behind Selfridges Department store) ☎ 0171 408 2080 FAX 0171 409 2295

The upgrading and refurbishment of this justifiably popular hotel continues. Most of the bedrooms have been refurbished and although on the small side they are elegantly decorated, modern and well equipped. The first floor is a wonderful retreat from the bustle: a sedate lounge and rustic-themed bar. In Fletchers restaurant, head chef Mark Page and his kitchen team produce enjoyable, imaginative and well crafted dishes firmly based on classical training.

295 en suite (bth/shr) CTV in all bedrooms STV No dogs (ex guide dogs) Lift Night porter Air conditioning P Xmas European Cuisine V meals Coffee am Tea pm No smoking area in restaurant Last d 11pm

ROOMS: s £155-£170; d £180-£199 * **LB**

OFF-PEAK: (incl. bkfst) s £73-£143; d fr £146

MEALS: Lunch £9.95-£24.50&alc Dinner £9.50-£24.50*

CONF: Thtr 200 Class 120 Board 36 Del from £160

CARDS:

★★★★ ❀❀❀ 67% St George's

FORTE HOTELS

Langham Place W1N 8QS ☎ 0171 580 0111 FAX 0171 436 7997

St George's is situated within Henry Wood House which is shared by the BBC. It is a unique set-up with the reception lobby at ground level and no further public areas until you reach the top of the building on the fifteenth floor. It is here that guests can enjoy the marvellous views over the city within the stylish surroundings of the Heights restaurant and bar. A new kitchen brigade is headed by Nick Evenden, formerly of the Café Royal and the imaginative cooking shows great potential for the future. Typical dishes include a lasagne of lobster and rocket, chump of lamb with pancetta, thyme and sweetbreads and monkfish with herb risotto and tomato confit. There is a range of suites but otherwise all the bedrooms are similarly furnished in a practical style.

86 en suite (bth/shr) (8 fmly) No smoking in 16 bedrooms CTV in all bedrooms STV Lift Night porter 2P Xmas V meals Coffee am Tea pm No smoking area in restaurant Last d 10pm

ROOMS: s £150-£160; d £160-£170 **LB**

MEALS: Lunch fr £23&alc Dinner £28-£35alc*

CONF: Thtr 35 Class 20 Board 24 Del from £175

CARDS:

★★★★ ❀ 65% Holiday Inn Mayfair

Holiday Inn

3 Berkeley St W1X 6NE ☎ 0171 493 8282 FAX 0171 629 2827

A modern hotel situated between Piccadilly and Berkeley Square, this Holiday Inn has limited public areas. The ambience, however is both elegant and intimate, created by smart furnishings, clever lighting and live piano music in the evenings. Full room service is available, and the restaurant offers a choice of ambitious menus, presented by chef Barry Brewington. Bedrooms are located on seven floors, and half of the rooms have been refurbished to executive standard. The remainder are still pleasant, comfortable and well equipped.

185 en suite (bth/shr) (67 fmly) No smoking in 56 bedrooms CTV in all bedrooms No dogs (ex guide dogs) Lift Night porter Air conditioning No coaches Wkly live entertainment Xmas International Cuisine V meals Coffee am Tea pm No smoking area in restaurant Last d 10.30pm

ROOMS: s £160-£200; d £160-£200 * **LB**

OFF-PEAK: (incl. bkfst) s £130-£160; d £130-£160

MEALS: Lunch fr £11alc Dinner fr £20alc*

CONF: Thtr 60 Class 35 Board 30 Del from £165

CARDS:

★★★★ 62% Mount Royal

THISTLE HOTELS

Bryanston St, Marble Arch W1A 4UR (off Oxford Street) ☎ 0171 629 8040 FAX 0171 499 7792

Massive investment in recent years has totally transformed this very large hotel, and its excellent range of facilities attract a wide clientele as well as some tour groups. Almost half the bedrooms can honestly be described as de luxe in style and quality, and they have effective air conditioning. The standard rooms are less glamorous, but this is reflected in the rate. The impressive public areas situated at first-floor level are reached by an escalator and include an attractive cocktail bar and brasserie restaurant. Smartly uniformed staff are friendly and comprehensive concierge services are also offered.

689 en suite (bth/shr) (12 fmly) No smoking in 331 bedrooms CTV in all bedrooms STV No dogs (ex guide dogs) Lift Night porter P Xmas International Cuisine V meals Coffee am Tea pm No smoking area in restaurant Last d 1.45pm

ROOMS: s £140-£155; d £165-£180 **LB**

MEALS: Lunch fr £16.95&alc High tea fr £8.50 Dinner fr £16.95&alc*

CONF: Thtr 300 Class 160 Board 80 Del £195

CARDS:

★★★ 63% Sherlock Holmes

108 Baker St W1M 2LJ (from Marylebone Flyover onto Marylebone Rd and at Baker St turn right for hotel on lt) (Hilton) ☎ 0171 486 6161 FAX 0171 486 0884

This is a comfortable hotel which also houses memorabilia associated with the famous detective character. Bedrooms are fairly uniform and suited to both leisure and tourist users. Completely refurbished public areas include a bar-lounge area and a restaurant.

125 en suite (bth/shr) No smoking in 34 bedrooms CTV in all bedrooms No dogs (ex guide dogs) Lift Night porter Xmas English & French Cuisine V meals Coffee am Tea pm No smoking area in restaurant Last d 10pm

ROOMS: s £108-£129; d £130-£140 *

OFF-PEAK: s £88; d £88

MEALS: Lunch £11.75-£13.75 Dinner £14.95-£17.95&alc*

CONF: Thtr 80 Class 20 Board 25 Del from £130

CARDS:

LONDON

★★★62% **Mandeville**
Mandeville Place W1M 6BE (off Oxford Street) ☎ 0171 935 5599
FAX 0171 935 9588
This popular, centrally located hotel is within easy walking distance of Oxford Street and offers well equipped bedrooms. The public areas include a coffee-shop style 'Orangery' and a more formal restaurant - 'Baboons' -with its own cocktail bar. There is also the lively Boswell's Bar which attracts a good local trade.
165 en suite (bth/shr) No smoking in 30 bedrooms CTV in all bedrooms STV No dogs (ex guide dogs) Lift Night porter International Cuisine V meals Coffee am Tea pm Last d 10.30pm
ROOMS: (incl. cont bkfst) s £75-£100; d £90-£130
MEALS: Lunch £14.50-£15.95 Dinner £14.50-£15.95*
CARDS:

See advertisement on opposite page

★★★61% **Mostyn**
4 Bryanston St W1H 8DE ☎ 0171 935 2361 FAX 0171 487 2759
Improvements still continue at this attractive Georgian hotel conveniently located close to Oxford Street, Marble Arch and Park Lane. Bedrooms are furnished in the modern style, all come with marbled bathrooms and the 1st and 4th floor air conditioned rooms add to the quality. Other facilities include a smart reception lobby, open plan lounge and bar, and a downstairs Tio Taberna and Tapas Bar restaurant featuring Spanish cuisine and continental and cooked English breakfast. 24 hour room service is also available.
121 en suite (bth/shr) (15 fmly) No smoking in 54 bedrooms CTV in all bedrooms STV No dogs (ex guide dogs) Lift Night porter Spanish Brasserie Cuisine V meals Coffee am Tea pm No smoking area in restaurant
ROOMS: (incl. bkfst) s £98-£105; d £124-£135 *
CONF: Thtr 140 Class 80 Board 60 Del from £105
CARDS:

★★54% ***Regent Palace***
FORTE HOTELS
Glasshouse St, Piccadilly W1A 4BZ
☎ 0171 734 7000 FAX 0171 734 6435
This vast and popular hotel is conveniently located just off Piccadilly Circus. Bedrooms are comfortable and well equipped. The busy ground floor area comprises a traditional carvery restaurant with Art Deco splendour, two bars, a brasserie and a few useful shops.
950 rms (41 fmly) No smoking in 336 bedrooms CTV in all bedrooms Lift Night porter V meals Coffee am Tea pm Last d 9.15pm
CARDS:

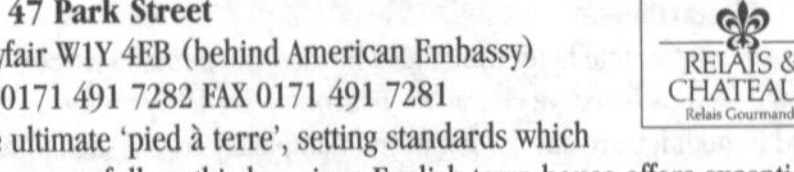

47 Park Street
RELAIS & CHATEAUX. Relais Gourmands
Mayfair W1Y 4EB (behind American Embassy)
☎ 0171 491 7282 FAX 0171 491 7281
The ultimate 'pied à terre', setting standards which others now follow, this luxurious English town house offers exceptional quality both in standards of performance and in the accommodation. The suites which all provide a separate kitchen facility range from standard, studio, two bedroom, de luxe and superior, and all come exquisitely and individually furnished to the highest standards meeting the demands of today's discerning international guest. Service is refined and competent, performed by conscientious and enthusiastic professional French and British staff who, under the direction of hotel general manager Ian Merrick, provide the guests with a very discreet and highly skilled standard of customer care. With all the food prepared in the adjoining kitchens of Le Gavroche the quality of the cooking speaks for itself and clearly adds a further excellent dimension to staying at an exclusive address in the heart of London's Mayfair.
52 en suite (bth/shr) (48 fmly) CTV in all bedrooms STV No dogs (ex guide dogs) Lift Night porter Air conditioning P No coaches French Cuisine
ROOMS: s £293.75-£540.50; d £293.75-£540.50 *
CONF: Thtr 20 Class 20 Board 20
CARDS:

TOWN HOUSE HOTEL

The Leonard

15 Seymour St W1H 5AA ☎ 0171 935 2010
FAX 0171 935 6700
Located off stylish Portman Square, The Leonard offers a luxurious oasis from the hubbub of the city. The bedrooms are all individually decorated with every conceivable comfort for the business or leisure guest. All rooms are equipped with fax/modem link, satellite TV, CD player, video, mini-bar and air conditioning. There is a small exercise room and the lounge and bar are tastefully furnished with antique pieces and fresh flowers. The friendly staff provide a relaxed and attentive service 24 hours a day ensuring guests' well being.
28 en suite (bth/shr) CTV in all bedrooms STV No dogs (ex guide dogs) Lift Night porter Air conditioning No coaches Gym English & Italian Cuisine V meals Coffee am Tea pm
ROOMS: s fr £129.25; d £176.25-£376 * **LB**
CONF: Thtr 40 Class 25 Board 30
CARDS:

See advertisement on opposite page

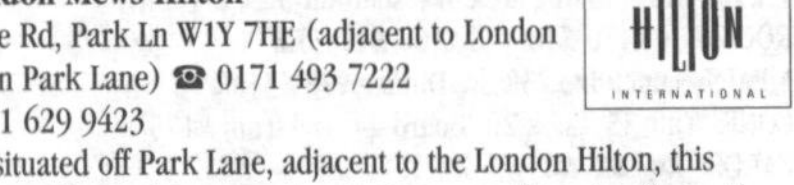

London Mews Hilton
HILTON INTERNATIONAL
Stanhope Rd, Park Ln W1Y 7HE (adjacent to London Hilton on Park Lane) ☎ 0171 493 7222
FAX 0171 629 9423
Quietly situated off Park Lane, adjacent to the London Hilton, this townhouse offers a discreet and exclusive atmosphere, together with the benefits of being affiliated to its five-star neighbour. Bedroom refurbishment is underway; more than half have already been completed with stylish fabrics and marble bathrooms. The drawing room has been elegantly furnished in country house style, and light meals are served throughout the day as well as a traditional afternoon tea. Otherwise residents can dine in the small but sunny dining room, or from room service.
72 en suite (bth/shr) No smoking in 11 bedrooms CTV in all bedrooms STV Lift Night porter Air conditioning 8P No coaches European Cuisine V meals Coffee am Tea pm Last d 9.30pm
ROOMS: s £145-£175; d £165-£195 *
OFF-PEAK: (incl. bkfst) s £124; d £144

MEALS: Bar Lunch fr £4.50alc Dinner fr £20alc*
CONF: Thtr 55 Class 25 Board 30 Del from £185
CARDS:

The Berkshire - A Radisson Edwardian Hotel
Oxford St W1N 0BY (opposite Bond Street Underground Station) ☎ 0171 629 7474
FAX 0171 629 8156

This stylish, period hotel offers a wide range of services and a choice of eating options for the international traveller. Bedrooms are smart and individually furnished, and are fully equipped with modern facilities. For more informaation about Radisson Edwardian hotels, consult the Contents page under Hotel Groups.

147 en suite (bth/shr)
ROOMS: s £129-£185; d £154-£245 *
CONF: Thtr 45 Class 20 Board 26

Forte Posthouse Regents Park
Carburton St, Regents Park W1P 8EE
☎ 0171 388 2300 FAX 0171 387 2806

Suitable for both the business and leisure traveller, this bright hotel provides modern accommodation in well equipped bedrooms with en suite bathrooms. For more details about Forte Posthouse hotels, consult the Contents page for the section on Hotel Groups.
317 en suite (bth/shr)
ROOMS: s £125; d £140 *
CONF: Thtr 320 Class 160 Board 50 Del from £160

The Grafton - A Radisson Edwardian Hotel
130 Tottenham Court Rd W1P 9HP (next to Warren Street station) ☎ 0171 388 4131 FAX 0171 387 7394

This stylish, period hotel offers a wide range of services and a choice of eating options for the international traveller. Bedrooms are smart and individually furnished, and are fully equipped with modern facilities. For more informaation about Radisson Edwardian hotels, consult the Contents page under Hotel Groups.
324 en suite (bth/shr)
ROOMS: s £89-£145; d £114-£175 *
CONF: Thtr 100 Class 40 Board 36

The Savoy Court - A Radisson Edwardian Hotel
Granville Place W1H 0EH (off Oxford Street)
☎ 0171 408 0130 FAX 0171 493 2070
This stylish, period hotel offers a wide range of services and a choice of eating options for the international traveller. Bedrooms are smart and individually furnished, and are fully equipped with modern facilities. For more informaation about Radisson Edwardian hotels, consult the Contents page under Hotel Groups.
95 en suite (bth/shr)
ROOMS: s £73-£130; d £98-£147 *

○ ***The Metropolitan***
18-19 Old Park Ln W1Y 4LB ☎ 0171 447 1000
157 rms

W2 BAYSWATER, PADDINGTON

★★★★70% **White's**
Lancaster Gate W2 3NR (off Bayswater Rd)
☎ 0171 262 2711 FAX 0171 262 2147

There are wonderful views over Hyde Park from this hotel, an elegant Victorian glass-canopied mansion where spacious, attractively furnished bedrooms are equipped with such extras as safes and mini bars; deluxe rooms have a sitting room area and, in many cases, private balconies, while the third floor is reserved for non-

contd.

LONDON

smokers. The bright lounge overlooks the park and is elegantly furnished with leather chairs, period prints and fresh flowers. A restaurant featuring an ornate ceiling, chandeliers and oil paintings offers a traditional menu in a club-like formal setting and an efficient, unpretentious staff provides willing and enthusiastic service.

54 en suite (bth) No smoking in 10 bedrooms CTV in all bedrooms STV No dogs (ex guide dogs) Lift Night porter Air conditioning 25P No coaches Xmas English & French Cuisine V meals Coffee am Tea pm No smoking area in restaurant Last d 10.30pm
ROOMS: s £155-£170; d £190-£245 * **LB**
OFF-PEAK: (incl. bkfst) s fr £80; d fr £160
MEALS: Lunch fr £16&alc Dinner fr £19.50&alc*
CONF: Thtr 25 Class 20 Board 20 Del from £190
CARDS:

★★★★ 68% Royal Lancaster
Lancaster Ter W2 2TY (directly above Lancaster Gate Underground Station) ☎ 0171 262 6737 FAX 0171 724 3191
This 18-storey hotel has splendid views of Kensington Gardens as well as the city from its higher floors. Currently undergoing a programme of complete refurbishment the bedrooms which all have mini-bars and satellite TV are slowly being improved, with the Club rooms offering the most space and comfort. Public areas are impressive, located on ground and first floors and comprise a comfortable lounge and bar, shops, hairdressing, and concierge. There are three dining options with a newly opened Nipa Thai restaurant offering exotic and authentic speciality cuisine from Thailand in contrast to The Park Restaurant which features fine pâtisserie, and the capable cooking skills of chef Nigel Blatchford; The Pavement Café on the ground floor is an ideal rendezvous and is open throughout the day.
418 en suite (bth/shr) (10 fmly) No smoking in 28 bedrooms CTV in all bedrooms STV No dogs (ex guide dogs) Lift Night porter Air conditioning 100P Wkly live entertainment V meals Coffee am Tea pm No smoking area in restaurant Last d 10.30pm
ROOMS: s £175-£195; d £195-£215 **LB**
MEALS: Lunch £19.50-£23.50 Dinner £19.50-£23.50*
CONF: Thtr 1500 Class 650 Board 40 Del from £185
CARDS:

★★★ 65% Park Court
75 Lancaster Gate, Hyde Park W2 3NN (off Bayswater Road) ☎ 0171 402 4272 FAX 0171 706 4156
Fronted by its own pleasant gardens, this recently refurbished hotel with its elegant 19th century façade overlooks the expanse of Kensington Gardens. While it remains a busy tourist hotel, the new, attractively appointed executive bedrooms are proving popular with the business person and offer comfortable surroundings including air-conditioning, personal safes and well lit modern bathrooms. Smart, marble-floored public areas contain a foyer bar and an all-day brasserie in addition to a shop and range of conference rooms.

390 en suite (bth/shr) (25 fmly) No smoking in 219 bedrooms CTV in all bedrooms STV Lift Night porter Xmas V meals Coffee am Tea pm Last d 11pm
ROOMS: s £90-£100; d £100-£120 * **LB**
OFF-PEAK: (incl. bkfst) s fr £94; d fr £108
MEALS: Lunch fr £14.75 Dinner fr £14.75*
CONF: Thtr 120 Class 50 Board 40 Del from £90
CARDS:

★★★ 60% Hospitality Inn

104/105 Bayswater Rd W2 3HL (Corner of Bayswater Rd and Porchester Ter) ☎ 0171 262 4461
FAX 0171 706 4560
Refurbishment of the public areas of this popular hotel has resulted in the introduction of colourful decor and soft furnishings. Some of the bedrooms enjoy excellent views over Hyde Park and many have been upgraded with modern furnishings; others are older in style, but all are comfortable and well equipped. Free parking is available to guests.
175 en suite (bth/shr) No smoking in 66 bedrooms CTV in all bedrooms STV Lift Night porter Air conditioning 60P International Cuisine V meals Coffee am Tea pm No smoking area in restaurant Last d 10.30pm
ROOMS: s £90-£105; d £110-£120 **LB**
MEALS: Lunch £12.95-£20.95alc Dinner £12.95-£20.95alc*
CONF: Thtr 60 Class 22 Board 36 Del £130
CARDS:

★★★ 59% Central Park
Queensborough Ter W2 3SS ☎ 0171 229 2424 FAX 0171 229 2904
Central Park, a popular hotel offering good value for money, is situated just off the Bayswater Road. Its main strength is the warm and friendly welcome offered by staff. A bedroom refurbishment plan is in progress. Public areas are spacious with a shop and leisure centre adding to the facilities available.
251 rms (210 bth 31 shr) (10 fmly) CTV in all bedrooms Lift Night porter 30P Sauna Solarium Gym International Cuisine V meals Coffee am Tea pm Last d 10pm
CARDS:

See advertisement on opposite page

★★★58% **Plaza on Hyde Park**
Lancaster Gate W2 3LG (200yds from Lancaster Gate Underground Station) (Hilton) ☎ 0171 262 5022 FAX 0171 724 8666
A large busy hotel opposite Hyde Park and only a few minutes' walk from Marble Arch offers modern accommodation in a variety of bedrooms, the best of them being the smart Viceroy rooms. The bar and informal café-restaurant serve food all day.
402 en suite (bth/shr) No smoking in 120 bedrooms CTV in all bedrooms No dogs (ex guide dogs) Lift Night porter Wkly live entertainment International Cuisine V meals Coffee am Tea pm No smoking area in restaurant Last d 10.30pm
ROOMS: s £90-£95; d £103-£110 * **LB**
MEALS: Lunch £12-£25alc Dinner £12-£25alc*
CONF: Thtr 32 Class 20 Board 16 Del £120
CARDS:

★★68% **Delmere**
130 Sussex Gardens, Hyde Park W2 1UB
☎ 0171 706 3344 FAX 071-262 1863

This is a charming and friendly hotel with much to commend it. The well turned out team of staff are keen and eager to please. La Perla restaurant shows a conscientious effort at cooking with fresh ingredients, and the cosy bar is themed around classical and contemporary jazz. Bedrooms vary in shape and size, but have a good level of facilities.
38 en suite (bth/shr) (3 fmly) CTV in all bedrooms Lift Night porter 2P No coaches Italian & Continental Cuisine V meals Last d 10.30pm
ROOMS: (incl. cont bkfst) s £59.50-£78; d £79.50-£96 **LB**
MEALS: Dinner £10-£16&alc
CARDS:

TOWN HOUSE HOTEL

The Abbey Court
20 Pembridge Gardens, Kensington W2 4DU
☎ 0171 221 7518 FAX 0171 792 0858
This elegant, five-storey, Victorian town house stands in a quiet residential area a short distance from the hubbub of Notting Hill High Street. Now skilfully renovated, it offers a range of individually designed bedrooms which have been charmingly furnished with antiques and provided with such thoughtful extras as home-made shortbread and a personal safe; each of the Italian marbled bathrooms has a jacuzzi, and both bathrobes and quality toiletries are supplied. Huge floral arrangements bring colour and scent to public rooms, and the pretty conservatory (where breakfast, afternoon tea and drinks are served) has patio doors opening on to a tiny flower-filled paved area which is delightful in summer. A friendly, helpful staff cares well for guests.
22 en suite (bth/shr) (1 fmly) CTV in all bedrooms STV No dogs (ex guide dogs) Night porter No coaches V meals Coffee am Tea pm
CARDS:

TOWN HOUSE HOTEL

Pembridge Court
34 Pembridge Gardens W2 4DX ☎ 0171 229 9977
FAX 0171 727 4982
Under new ownership but still privately owned and carrying on in the same tradition of providing personal care and attention for its International clientele with Manager Valerie Gilliat still at the helm. This fine 19th-century Victorian town house has been lovingly restored and sympathetically furnished to provide a range of well appointed bedrooms including deluxe doubles and twins, four poster and the

Holland Room taking pride of place. All rooms come particularly well equipped with every modern amenity and although there are no in-room facilities for making hot beverages a 24 hour room service is provided along with a night porter, very efficient and friendly management and long time serving members of helpful staff. With Caps Restaurant now closed to the general public it still provides an added but limited bar and meal dining facility for residents between 4pm and 11pm. Car parking can be rather difficult at times but meter spaces can usually be found around the square.
20 en suite (bth/shr) (3 fmly) CTV in all bedrooms STV Lift Night porter 2P No coaches Membership of local Health Club English & French Cuisine V meals Coffee am Tea pm No smoking area in restaurant
ROOMS: (incl. bkfst) s £105-£130; d £125-£165 *
CARDS:

W5 EALING See LONDON plan 1 C3/C4

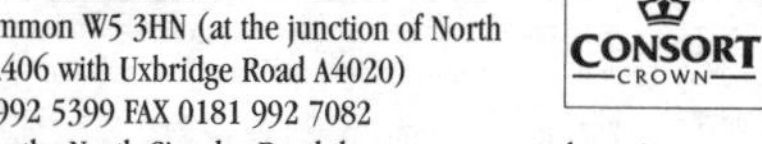

★★★69% **Carnarvon**
Ealing Common W5 3HN (at the junction of North Circular A406 with Uxbridge Road A4020)
☎ 0181 992 5399 FAX 0181 992 7082

CONSORT CROWN

Located on the North Circular Road the easy access and spacious parking make the Carnarvon an excellent choice for the business guest who will appreciate the thoughtfully equipped bedrooms with spacious desk provision. The foyer, bar and restaurant have been recently refurbished and are very attractive. Staff are helpful and make every effort to provide efficient service to their guests.
145 en suite (bth/shr) No smoking in 30 bedrooms CTV in all bedrooms STV No dogs (ex guide dogs) Lift Night porter 150P European Cuisine V meals Coffee am Tea pm No smoking area in restaurant Last d 9.30pm

contd.

ROOMS: s £95-£105; d £110-£120 * **LB**
OFF-PEAK: (incl. cont bkfst) s £65-£75; d £75-£85
MEALS: Lunch £12.50-£18&alc Dinner £16-£18&alc*
CONF: Thtr 200 Class 80 Board 50 Del from £120
CARDS:

W6 HAMMERSMITH See LONDON plan 1 D3

★★★67% ***Novotel***
Hammersmith Int. Centre, 1 Shortlands W6 7DR
☎ 0181 741 1555 FAX 0181 741 2120

NOVOTEL

This large purpose-built hotel, situated close to the centre of London, and to Hammersmith Tube Station, is easily accessible from the M4 and Heathrow Airport, and benefits from its own car park. The accommodation,all of which has been upgraded, comprises well designed bedrooms equipped with a wide range of modern facilities, and the open-plan public areas include an informal restaurant, a choice of bars, a shop and a range of conference and function rooms.
635 en suite (bth/shr) No smoking in 231 bedrooms CTV in all bedrooms STV Lift Air conditioning 230P English & French Cuisine V meals Coffee am Tea pm Last d mdnt
CARDS:
See advertisement on opposite page

W8 KENSINGTON See LONDON plan 1 D3

★★★★★ 69% **Royal Garden Hotel**
2-24 Kensington High St W8 4PT ☎ 0171 937 8000
FAX 0171 361 1991
The Royal Garden, after almost two years of closure and refurbishment, is back with a bang! The paintwork had hardly dried when our inspector visited, but it was already evident that the hotel's reputation as a relaxed, fun, five star was being maintained by the new management and helpful staff. Extensive public areas offer guests a range of environments for eating and drinking, from the traditionally styled Bertie's bar with its balcony overlooking the smart foyer, to the stunning views of Hyde Park from the funky top floor restaurant, The Tenth. There's also a sunny ground floor brasserie and plans for a Cantonese restaurant. Bedrooms have been restyled and reshaped, and offer a choice of suites, excellent split-level park view rooms, more functional standard accommodation, and cheaper, popular Trader's rooms.
401 en suite (bth/shr) (4 fmly) No smoking in 85 bedrooms CTV in all bedrooms STV Lift Night porter Air conditioning Health & fitness centre opening Oct'96 Xmas International Cuisine V meals Coffee am Tea pm Last d 11.30pm
ROOMS: s £170-£240; d £230-£265 *
MEALS: Lunch fr £16&alc Dinner fr £24.50&alc*
CONF: Thtr 750 Class 400 Board 36 Del from £259
CARDS:

★★★★ 69% **Kensington Park Thistle**
16-32 De Vere Gardens, Kensington W8 5AG
☎ 0171 937 8080 FAX 0171 937 7616

Attractive public areas are a feature of this bright modern hotel which has extensive meeting room facilities. In addition to Monique's all day brasserie, there is an elegant restaurant, the Cairngorm, where creative and cleverly crafted dishes are served. Bedrooms vary in size but all are well presented and some are very quiet.
332 en suite (bth/shr) (14 fmly) No smoking in 90 bedrooms CTV in all bedrooms STV No dogs (ex guide dogs) Lift Night porter Xmas International Cuisine V meals Coffee am Tea pm No smoking area in restaurant Last d 11pm
ROOMS: s £129-£145; d £149-£165 * **LB**
MEALS: Lunch £13.95&alc Dinner £13.95-£22.50&alc*
CONF: Thtr 125 Class 75 Board 50 Del £165
CARDS:

★★★★ 67% **Copthorne Tara**
Scarsdale Place,off Wrights Ln W8 5SR
☎ 0171 937 7211 FAX 0171 937 7100

MILLENNIUM & COPTHORNE HOTELS

The Tara is one of London's larger hotels; it is a modern building which is conveniently situated in a quiet cul-de-sac off Kensington High street. Eating and drinking options are numerous: a lively Brasserie and adjoining bar, the recently re-themed Dublin bar or there is the more sedate surroundings of the Cafe Mozart and Jerome's restaurant. Bedrooms feature modern technology including electronic lighting and an effective fresh air climatisation system. For a hotel of this size, it is commendable that the service is well managed and welcoming.
825 en suite (bth/shr) No smoking in 200 bedrooms CTV in all bedrooms STV No dogs (ex guide dogs) Lift Night porter Air conditioning 110P Xmas Continental Cuisine V meals Coffee am Tea pm Last d 11pm
ROOMS: s £150-£185; d £165-£200 **LB**
MEALS: Lunch £17.50-£21&alc Dinner £17.50-£21&alc
CONF: Thtr 360 Class 150 Board 92 Del from £190
CARDS:

★★★★54% **Kensington Palace Thistle**
De Vere Gardens W8 5AF (opposite Kensington Park)
☎ 0171 937 8121 FAX 0171 937 2816

THISTLE HOTELS

Directly overlooking Kensington Gardens, this hotel is popular with tour groups. Public areas are limited to Fox and Henderson's, an all day brasserie, and to the Tavern on the Park bar.

Guests looking for more facilities are able to use the adjacent sister hotel. Bedrooms are scheduled for refurbishment during 1996.
298 en suite (bth/shr) (27 fmly) No smoking in 112 bedrooms CTV in all bedrooms STV No dogs (ex guide dogs) Lift Night porter Xmas International Cuisine V meals Coffee am Tea pm Last d 11.30pm
ROOMS: s £99-£125; d £110-£145 * **LB**
OFF-PEAK: (incl. bkfst) s £56-£66; d £112-£122
MEALS: Lunch £11.55-£13.95&alc High tea £4.50-£5.45alc Dinner £16.95&alc*
CONF: Thtr 200 Class 110 Board 70 Del from £112
CARDS:

★★★68% **Kensington Close**

Wright's Ln, Kensington W8 5SP (off Kensington High Street) ☎ 0171 937 8170 FAX 0171 937 8289
Just a minute's walk from the shops of Kensington High Street, this large friendly hotel offers extensive facilities for both the tourist and business person. These include a choice of restaurants, a fully equipped health and fitness centre, underground car parking and the air-conditioned, high-tech Academy Training Suite. Standard bedrooms are generally compact but well equipped while executive rooms offer a higher level of comfort and walk-in showers.
542 en suite (bth/shr) No smoking in 150 bedrooms CTV in all bedrooms STV Lift Night porter 100P Indoor swimming pool (heated) Squash Sauna Solarium Gym Pool table Health & Fitness centre with Beauty room Xmas English & Italian Cuisine V meals Coffee am Tea pm No smoking area in restaurant Last d 11pm
ROOMS: s £129; d £150 * **LB**
OFF-PEAK: (incl. bkfst) s fr £54; d fr £108
MEALS: Lunch fr £15.95 Dinner fr £15.95
CONF: Thtr 180 Class 80 Board 60 Del £149
CARDS:

W11 HOLLAND PARK, NOTTING HILL
See LONDON plan 1 D3/D4

★★★★ 77% **Halcyon**
81 Holland Park W11 3RZ ☎ 0171 727 7288 FAX 0171 229 8516
Situated on Holland Park Avenue, this hotel is essentially a large townhouse. The elegant foyer gives a splendid first impression with fresh flowers, fine pictures, antique furniture and a welcoming and efficient reception and concierge team. Bedrooms are individually decorated and mostly very spacious, with good comfortable seating, quality appointments and good-sized marble bathrooms. The lower ground floor has a small lounge bar, which can be popular from nearby media businesses, and an elegant modern restaurant, The Room, where chef Martin Haddon prepares some very capable and imaginative modern cooking. The friendly restaurant team and the short but serious wine list add to the pleasures of a visit here.
43 en suite (bth/shr) CTV in all bedrooms STV No dogs (ex guide dogs) Lift Night porter Air conditioning P No coaches English & French Cuisine V meals Coffee am Tea pm Last d 10.30pm
ROOMS: s £185; d £265-£570
MEALS: Lunch £23-£35alc Dinner £29-£35alc*
CONF: Class 20 Board 14
CARDS:

★★★★64% **London Kensington Hilton**
Holland Park Av W11 4UL ☎ 0171 603 3355
FAX 0171 602 9397
This modern hotel offers a good range of facilities, including two restaurants, all-day lounge service, a business centre, a shop and good car parking. The air-conditioned bedrooms offer every modern convenience, and there is a choice of bath or shower. Some floors have been refurbished recently, so check your requirements on booking.
603 en suite (bth/shr) No smoking in 100 bedrooms CTV in all bedrooms STV Lift Night porter Air conditioning 120P Xmas International Cuisine V meals Coffee am Tea pm No smoking area in restaurant Last d 10.30pm
ROOMS: s £120-£170; d £140-£190 * **LB**
MEALS: Lunch fr £15.95&alc Dinner £3.50-£19alc*
CONF: Thtr 300 Class 150 Board 60 Del from £150
CARDS:

W14 WEST KENSINGTON See LONDON plan 1 D3

Hilton National London, Olympia

380 Kensington High St W14 8NL ☎ 0171 603 3333
FAX 0171 603 4846
This is a bright, modern hotel, with an informal restaurant, aimed at both the business and leisure guest. All bedrooms have en suite bathrooms and a range of modern facilities. For more information about Hilton National hotels, consult the Contents page under Hotel Groups.
405 en suite (bth/shr)

WC1 BLOOMSBURY, HOLBORN

★★★★66% **Holiday Inn**

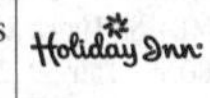

1 Kings Cross Rd WC1X 9HX (0.50m from Kings Cross station on the corner of King Cross Rd and Calthorpe St) ☎ 0171 833 3900 FAX 0171 917 6163
This smart, modern hotel is conveniently placed for Kings Cross station and the City. Its bedrooms have been fitted to a high standard, each one with air conditioning, fridge and power shower and there is the option of ladies', no-smoking and executive rooms. The marbled lobby leads to a range of attractively furnished public rooms including an intimate cocktail bar, comfortable lounge where a light breakfast and snacks can be taken throughout the day, and Carriages restaurant

contd.

LONDON

which serves both carvery and à la carte meals. A small car park operates on a first-come-first served basis.
405 en suite (bth/shr) (163 fmly) No smoking in 160 bedrooms CTV in all bedrooms STV Lift Night porter Air conditioning 14P Indoor swimming pool (heated) Squash Sauna Solarium Gym Jacuzzi/spa Hair & Beauty salon Xmas International Cuisine V meals Coffee am Tea pm No smoking area in restaurant Last d 10pm
ROOMS: s £140-£160; d £150-£170 * **LB**
MEALS: Lunch fr £15&alc Dinner fr £18&alc*
CONF: Thtr 220 Class 110 Board 25 Del from £139.50
CARDS:

★★★★60% **Hotel Russell**
Russell Square WC1B 5BE ☎ 0171 837 6470
FAX 0171 837 2857

FORTE HOTELS

What the bedrooms might lack in contemporary comforts and design the public areas make up for with their wonderful character. There is a range of bars, restaurants and lounges where locals and tourists alike can wind down or conduct business. The facade of the building is a striking feature of the surrounding area.
329 en suite (bth/shr) (1 fmly) No smoking in 23 bedrooms CTV in all bedrooms STV Lift Night porter Xmas V meals Coffee am Tea pm
ROOMS: s £130-£145; d £145-£160 * **LB**
MEALS: Lunch fr £17.50 Dinner fr £17.50*
CONF: Thtr 400 Class 200 Board 30
CARDS:

★★★69% **The Kingsley Thistle**
Bloomsbury Way WC1A 2SD ☎ 0171 242 5881
FAX 0171 831 0225

This unobtrusive hotel, within close walking distance of the British Museum, provides comfortable, well maintained bedrooms which have all been recently refurbished and in some cases completely rebuilt. Cosy public areas (some earmarked for further development) round off the hotel's amenities. An effort is made to promote the restaurant which relies mainly on a carvery buffet. There is a friendly atmosphere.
130 en suite (bth/shr) (19 fmly) No smoking in 42 bedrooms CTV in all bedrooms STV Lift Night porter Jacuzzi/spa V meals Coffee am Tea pm Last d 10pm
ROOMS: s £99-£120; d £115-£140 * **LB**
OFF-PEAK: (incl. bkfst) d fr £118
MEALS: Lunch £8.95-£15.25&alc Dinner £8.95-£15.25&alc*
CONF: Thtr 90 Class 40 Board 35 Del from £134
CARDS:

★★★69% **The Bonnington in Bloomsbury**
92 Southampton Row WC1B 4BH ☎ 0171 242 2828
FAX 0171 831 9170

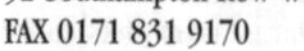

Centrally situated with easy access to the West End theatres, this well established late Edwardian hotel maintains traditional standards in comfortable modern surroundings. Bedrooms vary in shape and size and are equipped with every modern amenity. Some are suitable for families and others are designated for non-smokers. The air-conditioned Waterfalls Restaurant offers a good choice of menu, fresh ingredients, home-made desserts and freshly brewed coffee, whilst a popular bar with feature large screen TV provides an additional eating option with the bar buffet. Public areas include a comfortable lobby lounge, formal reception and concierge facilities and 2 lifts. There are good facilities for meetings and functions, the Derby Suite accommodating up to 250 persons. Twenty four-hour room service and an ironing room are also available.
215 en suite (bth) (16 fmly) No smoking in 85 bedrooms CTV in all bedrooms STV Lift Night porter English & French Cuisine V meals Coffee am Tea pm Last d 10.30pm
ROOMS: (incl. bkfst) s fr £93; d fr £118 * **LB**
OFF-PEAK: (incl. bkfst) s fr £64; d fr £98
MEALS: Lunch fr £11&alc High tea £3-£6alc Dinner fr £18.50&alc
CONF: Thtr 250 Class 70 Board 50 Del from £90
CARDS:

★★★64% **London Ryan**
Gwynne Place, Kings Cross Rd WC1X 9QN
☎ 0171 278 2480 FAX 0171 837 3776

Mount Charlotte Hotels MH

There has been considerable investment in the London Ryan during recent years which has resulted in comfortable and well furnished bedrooms, with a choice between standard, executive and family rooms available. A pleasant ground-floor lounge leads to a small bar and the Casablanca restaurant where all meals are served - but room service is also available. A small car park at the rear is a bonus for corporate guests.
211 en suite (bth/shr) (18 fmly) No smoking in 65 bedrooms CTV in all bedrooms No dogs (ex guide dogs) Lift Night porter 34P arrangement with nearby Health Club English & Continental Cuisine V meals Coffee am Tea pm No smoking area in restaurant
ROOMS: s £75-£80; d £85-£90 * **LB**
MEALS: Lunch £7.25-£12.50*
CONF: Thtr 15 Class 16 Board 28
CARDS:

★★★61% **Academy**
17-21 Gower St WC1E 6HG ☎ 0171 631 4115
FAX 0171 636 3442

This centrally located hotel is a good base from which to explore London, with shopping, theatres and tourist attractions within a short distance. The hotel is being extended and its new rooms will be spacious and well equipped. Public areas include a smart restaurant and bar offering imaginative modern food, and a tiny library overlooking a small walled courtyard, which guests can enjoy in summer.
40 rms (36 bth/shr) (5 fmly) CTV in all bedrooms STV No dogs (ex guide dogs) No coaches Xmas English & French Cuisine V meals Coffee am Last d 11pm
ROOMS: s £90-£100; d £115-£160 *
MEALS: Lunch £14.95 Dinner £16.95*
CONF: Thtr 16 Class 12 Board 16 Del from £120
CARDS:

★★★58% **Royal Scot**
100 Kings Cross Rd WC1X 9DT ☎ 0171 278 2434
FAX 0171 8330798

Well positioned for both Kings Cross and St Pancras stations, this large modern hotel offers compact, well equipped bedrooms with air-cooling units and fridges - a welcome feature in summer - and a programme of refurbishment is under way. The best rooms are on the sixth floor. All-day dining is available in the ground floor restaurant and more formal dinners are served in Bugatti's restaurant upstairs. There is also a small inner car park and meeting facilities.

351 en suite (bth/shr) (22 fmly) No smoking in 18 bedrooms CTV in all bedrooms STV No dogs (ex guide dogs) Lift Night porter Air conditioning 35P English & French Cuisine V meals Coffee am Tea pm Last d 9.45pm
ROOMS: s £75-£85; d £85-£95 *
MEALS: Lunch £10.95-£14.50&alc High tea fr £4.75 Dinner £10.95-£14.50&alc*
CONF: Thtr 170 Class 60 Board 50 Del from £96
CARDS:

★★★57% **Bloomsbury Park**
126 Southampton Row WC1B 5AD
☎ 0171 430 0434 FAX 0171 242 0665

Located midway along Southampton Row, this snug hotel caters to all markets. Bedrooms vary in size and shape, with some overlooking the road, and are mostly well looked after. Public areas are quite compact; there is a small dining area with its own bar and an additional bar, Pete's, with direct access off the street.

95 en suite (bth/shr) No smoking in 13 bedrooms CTV in all bedrooms STV No dogs (ex guide dogs) Lift Night porter International Cuisine V meals Coffee am Tea pm Last d 9.30pm
ROOMS: s £85-£95; d £95-£105 * **LB**
MEALS: Bar Lunch £3.25-£4.50alc Dinner £16.50&alc*
CONF: Thtr 30 Class 10 Board 20 Del from £99
CARDS:

All AA-classified hotels now have an entry on the AA Internet site, address: http://www.theaa.co.uk/hotels The information is also available through CompuServe.

TOWN HOUSE HOTEL

Blooms
7 Montague St WC1B 5BP (off Russell Square)
☎ 0171 323 1717 FAX 0171 636 6498

This elegant 18th-century townhouse is in a side street near the British Museum and Bloomsbury. It has now been beautifully restored and comfortably furnished. The bedrooms are individually furnished and well provided with modern amenities, thoughtful little extras and 24-hour room service. The public areas are decorated with antiques and fine art. There is a quiet breakfast room and lounge/bar, a rear garden terrace, smart lobby and a lift to all floors.

27 en suite (bth/shr) CTV in all bedrooms STV No dogs (ex guide dogs) Lift Night porter No coaches European Cuisine V meals Coffee am Tea pm
ROOMS: (incl. bkfst) s £100-£120; d £150-£180 *
CARDS:

Forte Posthouse Bloomsbury
Coram St WC1N 1HT (off Upper Woburn Place)
☎ 0171 837 1200 FAX 0171 837 5374

Suitable for both the business and leisure traveller, this bright hotel provides modern accommodation in well equipped bedrooms with en suite bathrooms. For more details about Forte Posthouse hotels, consult the Contents page for the section on Hotel Groups.

284 en suite (bth/shr)
ROOMS: s fr £130; d fr £145 *
CONF: Thtr 750 Class 300 Board 22 Del from £160

The Kenilworth - A Radisson Edwardian Hotel
Great Russell St WC1B 3LB (opposite British Museum) ☎ 0171 637 3477 FAX 0171 631 3133

This stylish, period hotel offers a wide range of services and a choice of eating options for the international traveller. Bedrooms are smart and individually furnished, and are fully equipped with modern facilities. For more informaation about Radisson Edwardian hotels, consult the Contents page under Hotel Groups.

192 en suite (bth/shr)
ROOMS: s £89-£145; d £114-£175 *
CONF: Thtr 150 Class 70 Board 50

The Marlborough - A Radisson Edwardian Hotel
Bloomsbury St WC1B 3QD ☎ 0171 636 5601
FAX 0171 636 0532

This stylish, period hotel offers a wide range of services and a choice of eating options for the international traveller. Bedrooms are smart and individually furnished, and are fully equipped with modern facilities. For more informaation about Radisson Edwardian hotels, consult the Contents page under Hotel Groups.

172 en suite (bth/shr)
ROOMS: s £112-£160; d £137-£226 *
CONF: Thtr 250 Class 90 Board 50

WC2 SOHO, STRAND

RED STAR HOTEL

★★★★★ **The Savoy**
Strand WC2R 0EU (Leading Hotels)
☎ 0171 836 4343 FAX 0171 240 6040

contd.

LONDON

(Rosettes awarded for Savoy Restaurant)
The Savoy's many devotees will be aware of the changes effected since the hotel's well publicised change of management two years ago. Improvement works to include new air conditioning are now all but finished and the accommodation has been refurbished to a high standard, taking care to preserve the famous Art Deco design features and the push-button bell system for summoning maid, valet and waiter. The American bar has had a facelift, as have the main lobby and the banqueting rooms. Executive suites are also being built on the 8th floor. The new marble bathrooms, with their celebrated thunderstorm showers, are superb. In addition to the dignified room service, there are three notable restaurants, which, under the skilled direction of Anton Edelman, play their part in enhancing the Savoy's pre-eminent reputation: the Grill Room, popular for its daily roasts, Upstairs, for snacks with a seafood bias and the River Room, with its views of the Thames, where a dance band plays in the evenings. Outstanding facilities for private functions and meetings are available.

202 en suite (bth/shr) No smoking in 30 bedrooms CTV in all bedrooms STV No dogs (ex guide dogs) Lift Night porter 58P No coaches Indoor swimming pool (heated) Sauna Gym Tennis at the Vanderbilt Club Wkly live entertainment Xmas English & French Cuisine V meals Coffee am Tea pm Last d 11.15pm
ROOMS: s £205-£225; d £250-£330 * **LB**
MEALS: Lunch £24.50-£27.50&alc High tea £16.50 Dinner £29.75-£41.50&alc*
CONF: Thtr 500 Class 200 Board 32 Del from £342.50
CARDS:

★★★★★ 68% **The Waldorf Meridien**
Aldwych WC2B 4DD ☎ 0171 836 2400
FAX 0171 836 7244

Le MERIDIEN

This famous hotel has benefited from a multi-million pound refurbishment and an injection of enthusiastic and committed management. The stylish Palm Court Lounge remains the centrepiece, with weekend afternoon tea dances as popular as ever, and the more elegant surroundings of the cocktail bar is a busy meeting place for pre-theatre drinks. Bedrooms have been tastefully styled, and whilst several are not particularly spacious, all are well equipped and air-conditioned. A more recent arrival on the team is Philippe Pichon as chef de cuisine for The Waldorf Restaurant. Philippe's French upbringing is clearly reflected in his style of cooking. The menus make exciting reading and the vibrant flavours and quality of ingredients similarly stimulate the palate.

292 en suite (bth/shr) No smoking in 109 bedrooms CTV in all bedrooms STV No dogs (ex guide dogs) Lift Night porter Air conditioning Hairdressing salon Wkly live entertainment International Cuisine V meals Coffee am Tea pm No smoking area in restaurant Last d 11pm

ROOMS: s fr £205.63; d £217.38-£258.50 * **LB**
MEALS: Lunch £25&alc High tea £22-£25 Dinner fr £31&alc*
CONF: Thtr 300 Class 150 Board 40 Del from £230
CARDS:

★★★★ 62% **Drury Lane Moat House**
10 Drury Ln WC2B 5RE (on the corner of Drury Lane & High Holborn, car park access from High Holborn)
☎ 0171 208 9988 FAX 0171 831 1548

MOAT HOUSE

Conveniently located for the Opera House, theatreland and Covent Garden Market, the Moat House has recently benefited from extensive refurbishment to its bedrooms, bringing them up to a smart, modern standard. Public areas include a comfortable lobby lounge, bar and an informal Bistro which is open all day and offers anything from a salad to a duck cassoulet. A mini-gym and car park are useful facilities.
163 en suite (bth/shr) (15 fmly) No smoking in 40 bedrooms CTV in all bedrooms Lift Night porter Air conditioning P Solarium Gym Xmas French Cuisine V meals Coffee am Tea pm No smoking area in restaurant Last d 10pm
ROOMS: s £125; d £139 * **LB**
OFF-PEAK: s £85-£125; d £115-£139
MEALS: Lunch £3.50-£10.50alc Dinner fr £15.85alc*
CONF: Thtr 60 Class 40 Board 40 Del £160
CARDS:

★★★ 65% **Royal Trafalgar Thistle**
Whitcomb St WC2H 7HG ☎ 0171 930 4477
FAX 0171 925 2149

THISTLE HOTELS

Tucked away in a side street adjacent to the National Gallery and convenient for many of the West End theatres, this popular hotel offers a sound standard of accommodation. Bedrooms are well maintained and equipped but the majority are rather compact. Public areas include a pleasant foyer lounge, split-level brasserie open from 7.30am until late and a lively traditional pub.
108 en suite (bth/shr) No smoking in 36 bedrooms CTV in all bedrooms STV No dogs (ex guide dogs) Lift Night porter English & French Cuisine V meals Coffee am Tea pm No smoking area in restaurant Last d 11.30pm
ROOMS: s £110-£120; d £135-£145 * **LB**
OFF-PEAK: (incl. bkfst) s £64-£114; d £128
MEALS: Lunch £12-£18alc Dinner £12-£18alc*
CARDS:

★★★ 64% **Strand Palace**
Strand WC2R 0JJ ☎ 0171 836 8080
FAX 0171 836 2077

FORTE HOTELS

This conveniently situated hotel continues to improve with the further upgrading of bedrooms and public areas. Though some rooms are rather compact, all well equipped with such facilities as trouser presses and hair dryers. Dining options include an Italian restaurant, a buffet and a bar brasserie. The old ballroom has been converted into a modern conference room with all the latest equipment.
783 en suite (bth/shr) No smoking in 224 bedrooms CTV in all

LONDON

bedrooms STV Lift Night porter Discount at nearby Health Club Xmas International Cuisine V meals Coffee am Tea pm Last d mdnt
ROOMS: s £118; d £133 * **LB**
MEALS: Lunch £16.95&alc High tea fr £7.50 Dinner £16.95&alc
CONF: Thtr 160 Class 85 Board 40 Del £145
CARDS:

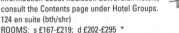

The Hampshire - A Radisson Edwardian Hotel

Leicester Square WC2H 7LH v 0171 839 9399
FAX 0171 960 8122
This stylish, period hotel offers a wide range of services and a choice of eating options for the international traveller. Bedrooms are smart and individually furnished, and are fully equipped with modern facilities. For more informaation about Radisson Edwardian hotels, consult the Contents page under Hotel Groups.

124 en suite (bth/shr)
ROOMS: s £167-£219; d £202-£295 *
CONF: Thtr 80 Class 60 Board 24

The Mountbatten - A Radisson Edwardian Hotel

Monmouth St, Seven Dials, Covent Garden WC2H 9HD (just off Shaftesbury Av, on the corner of Seven Dials rdbt) ☎ 0171 836 4300
FAX 0171 240 3540
This stylish, period hotel offers a wide range of services and a choice of eating options for the international traveller. Bedrooms are smart and individually furnished, and are fully equipped with modern facilities. For more informaation about Radisson Edwardian hotels, consult the Contents page under Hotel Groups.
127 en suite (bth/shr)
ROOMS: s £125-£185; d £160-£235 *
CONF: Thtr 90 Class 45 Board 32

The Pastoria - A Radisson Edwardian Hotel

3-6 St Martins St WC2H 7HL (off Leicester Square) ☎ 0171 930 8641 FAX 0171 925 0551
This stylish, period hotel offers a wide range of services and a choice of eating options for the international traveller. Bedrooms are smart and individually furnished, and are fully equipped with modern facilities. For more informaation about Radisson Edwardian hotels, consult the Contents page under Hotel Groups.
58 en suite (bth/shr)
ROOMS: s £99-£142; d £119-£189 *

LONDON AIRPORTS
See under Gatwick & Heathrow

STOP PRESS! *AA Members can book accommodation at many hotels in this guide through the AA Booking Service, usually at attractive discounts. See page 5 for details or telephone 0990 050505*

LONDON

LONG EATON Derbyshire Map 08 SK43
See also Sandiacre

★★★61% **Novotel**

Bostock Ln NG10 4EP ☎ 0115 946 5111
FAX 0115 946 5900
This modern hotel is well placed for junction 25 of the M1 and the cities of Derby and Nottingham. Bedrooms are standardised throughout, spacious but functional. Public areas are open plan and the range of meeting rooms makes this a popular choice for conferences.
105 en suite (bth/shr) (20 fmly) No smoking in 58 bedrooms CTV in all bedrooms STV Lift 180P Outdoor swimming pool (heated) English & French Cuisine V meals Coffee am Tea pm No smoking area in restaurant Last d mdnt
ROOMS: d £49.50 *
OFF-PEAK: (incl. bkfst) s £45; d £50
MEALS: Lunch £12-£14&alc Dinner £12-£14&alc*
CONF: Thtr 220 Class 120 Board 80 Del from £83
CARDS:

★★62% **Europa**
20 Derby Rd NG10 1LW (on A6005) ☎ 0115 972 8481
FAX 0115 946 0229
The Europa is a predominantly commercial hotel located close to the town centre. It has a relaxed atmosphere and informal style of service, with the owners actively involved. Public rooms are somewhat limited but there is a conservatory lounge area where light refreshments and snacks are available during the day; home-cooked fare is served at dinner in a pleasant dining room adjacent to the small bar. Bedrooms are light and neat, though more modestly furnished.
15 en suite (bth/shr) (2 fmly) CTV in all bedrooms No dogs (ex guide dogs) Night porter 27P V meals Coffee am Tea pm Last d 9pm
ROOMS: (incl. bkfst) s £34-£36; d £40-£42 **LB**
OFF-PEAK: (incl. bkfst) s £31-£33; d £38-£40
MEALS: Lunch £4-£8 High tea £3-£5 Dinner £8-£15*
CONF: Thtr 30 Class 25 Board 25
CARDS:

LONGHORSLEY Northumberland Map 12 NZ19

★★★★ 71% **Linden Hall**
NE65 8XF (1m N off A697) ☎ 01670 516611 FAX 01670 788544
This magnificent Georgian country house stands in more than 400 acres of woodland and gardens off the A697, one mile north of Longhorsley. Elegant public areas - reached through a grand inner hall - comprise an opulent drawing room, the Dobson restaurant (where chef Keith Marshall offers a range of dishes in modern style), a comfortable cocktail bar and a small coffee shop in the former cellars; individually furnished and decorated bedrooms make effective use of soft, elegant fabrics and some also have four-poster beds. Excellent leisure facilities include a swimming pool and fitness centre, extensive banqueting and function facilities are available, and an adjacent granary has been converted into a country pub with a lively but relaxed atmosphere.
50 en suite (bth/shr) (4 fmly) CTV in all bedrooms STV Lift Night porter 260P Indoor swimming pool (heated) Tennis (hard) Snooker Sauna Solarium Gym Pool table Croquet lawn Putting green Jacuzzi/spa Hairdressing Health & beauty spa Xmas English & French Cuisine V meals Coffee am Tea pm No smoking in restaurant Last d 9.45pm
ROOMS: (incl. bkfst) s £97.50; d £125 * **LB**
MEALS: Lunch £13.95-£16.95 Dinner £25-£30*
CONF: Thtr 325 Class 150 Board 40 Del from £95
CARDS:

LONG MELFORD Suffolk Map 05 TL84

★★★64% **The Bull**
FORTE Heritage
Hall St CO10 9JG (take A134 to Sudbury, village of Long Melford signed off to the right hotel half way along main street) ☎ 01787 378494
FAX 01787 880307
Built in the 15th century, this is a good example of a white and black timbered building which also has, as a feature, a large Elizabethan fireplace in one of its lounges. Bedrooms provide modern comforts and meals are served in a large and spacious dining room.
25 en suite (bth/shr) (3 fmly) No smoking in 11 bedrooms CTV in all bedrooms 20P Xmas V meals Coffee am Tea pm No smoking in restaurant Last d 9.30pm
ROOMS: s fr £65; d fr £85 * **LB**
OFF-PEAK: (incl. bkfst & dinner) s fr £59; d fr £118
MEALS: Lunch £14.95-£17.95&alc Dinner £18.95-£24.95&alc
CONF: Thtr 60 Class 30 Board 35 Del from £80
CARDS:

★★ 73% **Countrymen Restaurant At The Black Lion Hotel**
The Green CO10 9DN (at junct of A134/A1092)
☎ 01787 312356 FAX 01787 374557
Closed 23 Dec-3 Jan RS Sun eve & Mon
This family-run coaching inn near the 15th-century church offers individually decorated bedrooms and inviting public rooms centred on a restaurant where the chef/proprietor presents a seasonally changing menu of robust, straightforward dishes based on fresh produce.
9 en suite (bth/shr) (5 fmly) CTV in all bedrooms 9P No coaches International Cuisine V meals Coffee am Last d 9.30pm
CARDS:

LONG SUTTON Lincolnshire Map 09 TF42

Travelodge
Travelodge
Wisbech Rd PE12 9AG (on junc A17/B1359)
☎ 01406 362230 FAX 01406 362230
This modern building offers accommodation in smart, spacious and well equipped bedrooms, suitable for family use, and all with en suite bathrooms. Meals may be taken at the nearby family restaurant. For information on room rates and to make a booking, call Roomline free of charge on 0800 850950. For more details about Travelodge, consult the Contents page under Hotel Groups.
40 en suite (bth/shr)

LOOE Cornwall & Isles of Scilly Map 02 SX25

★★70% **Fieldhead**
MINOTEL Great Britain
Portuan Rd PL13 2DR ☎ 01503 262689
FAX 01503 264114
Closed Jan
Colour co-ordinated and equipped with every modern comfort, many of the bedrooms and public rooms in this attractive turn-of-the-century house also enjoy glorious coastal views. The lounge and a dining room offer an extensive choice of dishes on carte and set-price menus. Guests can take their ease in a well tended garden with outdoor heated pool and sun terrace.
14 en suite (bth/shr) (2 fmly) CTV in all bedrooms No dogs (ex guide dogs) 14P Outdoor swimming pool (heated) No children 5yrs Xmas V meals Coffee am Tea pm
ROOMS: (incl. bkfst) s £37.50; d £60-£78 * **LB**
MEALS: Bar Lunch £3.50-£7.50alc*
CARDS:

See advertisement on opposite page

★★68% **Commonwood Manor**
St Martin's Rd PL13 1LP (on B3253) ☎ 01503 262929
FAX 01503 262632
Closed 22-31 Dec
This tastefully furnished hotel stands in an elevated positionin in three acres of grounds overlooking the East Looe River and with panoramic woodland and town views. There are a dining room and bar, and a separate traditional lounge offers relaxation. There is also an attractive terraced garden.
11 en suite (bth/shr) (1 fmly) CTV in all bedrooms STV 20P No coaches Outdoor swimming pool (heated) English & Continental Cuisine V meals Coffee am Tea pm No smoking in restaurant Last d 8pm
ROOMS: (incl. bkfst) s £32-£37; d £64-£74 **LB**
OFF-PEAK: (incl. bkfst) s £29-£33; d £58-£66
MEALS: Bar Lunch £2.50-£12 Dinner £12-£16
CARDS:

LOSTWITHIEL Cornwall & Isles of Scilly Map 02 SX15

★★★65% **Restormel Lodge**

Hillside Gardens PL22 0DD (on A390)
☎ 01208 872223 FAX 01208 873568
Owned and personally supervised by the Hanson Family for over thirty years, Restormel Lodge benefits from a character bar and lounge area and modern, well equipped bedrooms. In the restaurant, which overlooks the outdoor pool, a varied selection of dishes is offered. The friendly and relaxing atmosphere appeals to both the leisure and business user.
21 en suite (bth/shr) 12 annexe en suite (bth) (3 fmly) CTV in all bedrooms STV 40P Outdoor swimming pool (heated) Xmas V meals Coffee am Tea pm No smoking in restaurant Last d 9.30pm
ROOMS: s £40-£42; d £60-£62 * **LB**
OFF-PEAK: (incl. bkfst & dinner) s £40-£60; d £70-£84
MEALS: Bar Lunch £1-£9.60alc Dinner £15-£17&alc*
CONF: Thtr 100 Class 80 Board 60 Del from £50
CARDS:

★★66% **Lostwithiel Golf & Country Club**
Lower Polscoe PL22 0HQ (off A390) ☎ 01208 873550
FAX 01208 873479
Amongst rolling hills and on the edge of town, this Golf and Country Club is now established as a sporting and leisure resort in its own right. Original Cornish stone barns have been converted to provide comfortable, well equipped modern bedrooms, situated round a central courtyard. In addition to the challenging 18-hole golf course, the energetic can enjoy the indoor swimming pool, all weather tennis courts andfloodlit driving range. The Sportsman's bar is open for lunches and snacks and the Black Prince restaurant has lovely open views onto the surrounding countryside.
18 en suite (bth/shr) CTV in all bedrooms 120P Indoor swimming pool (heated) Golf 18 Tennis (hard) Fishing Snooker Gym Putting green Undercover floodlit driving range English, French & Italian Cuisine V meals Coffee am Tea pm
ROOMS: (incl. bkfst) s £38; d £76 * **LB**
OFF-PEAK: (incl. bkfst) s £31; d £62
MEALS: Lunch £15.95*
CONF: Thtr 200 Class 30 Board 25 Del £64.95
CARDS:

See advertisement on this page

LOUGHBOROUGH Leicestershire Map 08 SK51

★★★65% **Quality Friendly Hotel**

New Ashby Rd LE11 0EX ☎ 01509 211800
FAX 01509 211868
Conveniently situated within a mile of junction 23 of

contd.

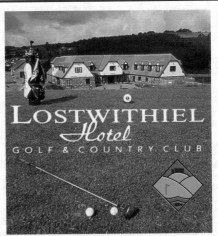

the M1, this popular modern hotel offers comfortable and well equipped accommodation which meets the needs of both the business traveller and leisure guest. All the practically furnished bedrooms offer a spacious work area while some rooms have small lounges and kitchenettes, ideal for the longer stay or families. There is a small leisure centre and comprehensive banqueting and conference facilities.

94 en suite (bth/shr) (5 fmly) No smoking in 47 bedrooms CTV in all bedrooms STV Night porter Air conditioning 125P Indoor swimming pool (heated) Sauna Solarium Gym Jacuzzi/spa Xmas English & Continental Cuisine V meals Coffee am Tea pm No smoking area in restaurant Last d 9.30pm
ROOMS: s £67.50; d £87 **LB**
MEALS: Lunch £7.50-£9.95&alc Dinner £13.50&alc
CONF: Thtr 225 Class 120 Board 120 Del from £90
CARDS:

★★56% **Great Central**
Great Central Rd LE11 1RW (from town centre take A60 towards Nottingham then first right. Hotel on left) ☎ 01509 263405 FAX 01509 264130
The Great Central, a large period building, stands beside the steam-hauled railway of the same name; this runs from Loughborough to Leicester at weekends, filling the hotel with enthusiasts. Its high-ceilinged bar, furnished with contemporary Victoriana, has a convivial atmosphere and offers a good range of ales and bar meals. Bedrooms are located on two upper floors, and these are cleanly decorated and furnished with contrasting fabrics.
20 en suite (bth/shr) (3 fmly) CTV in all bedrooms STV 40P Xmas International Cuisine V meals Coffee am No smoking area in restaurant Last d 9.30pm
ROOMS: (incl. bkfst) s £25-£30; d £35-£40 **LB**
MEALS: Sunday Lunch £5-£7 Dinner £5-£7
CONF: Thtr 100 Class 100 Board 40
CARDS:

LOUTH Lincolnshire Map 08 TF38

★★★73% **Kenwick Park**
Kenwick Park LN11 8NR ☎ 01507 608806 FAX 01507 608027
Overlooking Kenwick Park golf course, this elegant Georgian-style house stands to the south of the town in the 500 acre Kenwick Park Estate. Bedrooms are large and comfortable, with every modern facility and the fine public rooms include the Fairway Restaurant where Head Chef Robert Morley and his team produce imaginative à la carte and set menus. There is also a separate and well stocked bar overlooking the golf course. Leisure facilities are excellent.
24 en suite (bth/shr) (16 fmly) CTV in all bedrooms STV Night porter 50P Indoor swimming pool (heated) Golf 18 Tennis (hard) Squash Snooker Sauna Solarium Gym Pool table Putting green Jacuzzi/spa Xmas V meals Coffee am Tea pm No smoking in restaurant Last d 9.30pm
ROOMS: (incl. bkfst) s £79.50; d £98 * **LB**
MEALS: Lunch £11.95-£19.95&alc Dinner £13.95-£19.95&alc*
CONF: Thtr 120 Class 40 Board 40 Del £120
CARDS:

★★★62% **Beaumont**
66 Victoria Rd LN11 0BX ☎ 01507 605005 FAX 01507 607768
A family-run hotel is located near the swimming pool and Cordeaux High School. Bedrooms range from spacious suites to singles, but each room is well equipped. Public areas are all comfortable and tastefully decorated. Service by a small team of neatly uniformed staff is both courteous and attentive throughout.
16 en suite (bth/shr) (2 fmly) CTV in all bedrooms STV Lift 70P Xmas English & Italian Cuisine V meals Coffee am Tea pm No smoking area in restaurant Last d 9.30pm
ROOMS: (incl. bkfst) s £40-£50; d £60-£75 * **LB**
MEALS: Lunch £10.50-£24alc Dinner £10.50-£24alc*
CONF: Thtr 112 Class 50 Board 46
CARDS:

LOWER BEEDING West Sussex Map 04 TQ22

★★★★76% **South Lodge**
Brighton Rd RH13 6PS (off A281)
☎ 01403 891711 FAX 01403 891253

This beautifully restored Victorian mansion house stands in 90 acres of gardens which contain over 260 varieties of camellia and rhododendron. This peaceful setting is further accentuated by quietly located bedrooms, each individually furnished with care and provided with modern comforts. Another pleasant feature of the hotel is the attentive level of service shown by the staff. The kitchen, under Tim Neal, produces excellent side items such as scones and pastries but sometimes allows flights of fancy to overreach what could be very enjoyable meals.
39 en suite (bth) CTV in all bedrooms STV No dogs (ex guide dogs) Night porter 80P No coaches Tennis (hard) Fishing Croquet lawn Golf-driving net Shooting Petanque Wkly live entertainment Xmas V meals Coffee am Tea pm No smoking in restaurant Last d 10.30pm
ROOMS: s fr £120; d fr £145 **LB**
MEALS: Lunch £16.50-£18.50 Dinner £25-£32*
CONF: Thtr 85 Class 40 Board 30
CARDS:

LOWER SLAUGHTER Gloucestershire Map 04 SP12

RED STAR HOTEL

★★★ **Lower Slaughter Manor**
GL54 2HP (off A429 signposted "The Slaughters", the manor is 0.5m on right entering village) ☎ 01451 820456 FAX 01451 822150

Closed 2-9 Jan
Standing in mature, immaculately maintained gardens, with a croquet lawn, putting greens and tennis court, this impressive 17th-century Grade II listed manor is the home of Audrey and Peter Marks. Public rooms feature ornate interior architecture, set off by deep, comfortable seating, antique furniture and beautiful fresh flowers. Bedrooms, divided between the nearby coach house and the main building, are all attractively furnished; several rooms have 4-poster beds and private suites are available. There is also an indoor swimming pool. Attentive service is professionally carried out by a team of well trained staff and attention to detail remains of paramount importance. An interesting selection of dishes offered from the menu continues to excite. The emphasis throughout a carefully prepared meal was on the quality and flavour of the ingredients. A well balanced wine list provides an extensive selection of fine wines from around the world, and help is always at hand to make just the right choice.
10 en suite (bth/shr) 4 annexe en suite (bth/shr) CTV in all bedrooms No dogs (ex guide dogs) 35P No coaches Indoor swimming pool (heated) Tennis (hard) Sauna Croquet lawn Putting green No children 10yrs Xmas French Cuisine V meals Coffee am Tea pm No smoking in restaurant Last d 9.30pm
ROOMS: (incl. bkfst & dinner) s £145-£240; d £190-£320 * **LB**
MEALS: Lunch £19.95-£23.95&alc Dinner £32.50-£36&alc
CONF: Thtr 30 Board 14 Del £165
CARDS:

★★★❀❀❀76% **Washbourne Court**
GL54 2HS (turn off A429 at signpost 'The Slaughters', between Stow-on-the-Wold and Bourton-on-the-Water. Hotel is in the centre of village)
☎ 01451 822143 FAX 01451 821045
This magnificent 17th-century hotel, standing in four acres of grounds alongside the River Eye in the centre of the village, is independently owned and managed by the Pender family. Bedrooms range from self-contained cottage suites with their own lounge and cooking facilities to newer rooms in the coach house, while the five rooms in the main house vary in size but are similarly well equipped. Patrick Robert, a native of Brittany who has worked at several highly regarded hotels and restaurants in this country and was formerly the sous-chef here, has taken over in the restaurant and will be providing menus integrating classical French cuisine with imaginative modern British cooking.
5 en suite (bth/shr) 13 annexe en suite (bth/shr) (4 fmly) CTV in all bedrooms 67P No coaches Tennis (hard) Jacuzzi/spa Xmas V meals Coffee am Tea pm
ROOMS: (incl. bkfst) s £85; d £95-£185 * **LB**
MEALS: Lunch £13.95 Dinner £25.95*
CONF: Thtr 20 Class 20 Board 14 Del £105
CARDS:

LOWESTOFT Suffolk Map 05 TM59

★★★64% **Hotel Hatfield**

The Esplanade NR33 0QP (from town centre follow signs for 'South Beach' (A12 Ipswich). Hotel 200yds on left) ☎ 01502 565337 FAX 01502 511885
The Hotel Hatfield sits on the seafront overlooking the south beach and has its own private car park, which is located across the road, directly opposite the hotel. Public areas include two bars, one with a terrace, and a restaurant where a simple menu is based on steak and other staple favourites. There are several conference and function rooms available for seminars and meetings. Bedrooms are generally of good comfortable proportions, although there are a few compact single bedrooms, each room is furnished with dark varnished wooden furniture and lighter colour co-ordinated fabrics and they have the latest in modern amenities.
33 en suite (bth/shr) (1 fmly) CTV in all bedrooms STV No dogs (ex guide dogs) Lift Night porter 26P Xmas English & French Cuisine V meals Coffee am Tea pm Last d 10pm
ROOMS: (incl. bkfst) s £45-£55; d £68-£73 * **LB**
OFF-PEAK: (incl. bkfst) s £50; d £63-£68
MEALS: Lunch £5.95-£12.50&alc High tea £2.50-£4.50 Dinner £12.50&alc*
CONF: Thtr 100 Class 50 Board 40 Del £25
CARDS:

Travel Inn

249 Yarmouth Rd NR32 4AA ☎ 01502 572441
FAX 01502 581223
Purpose-built accommodation, offering spacious, well equipped bedrooms, all with en suite bathrooms. Meals may be taken at the nearby family restaurant. For more information about Travel Inns, consult the Contents page under Hotel Groups.
40 en suite (bth/shr)
ROOMS: (incl. bkfst) d £35.50 *

LOWESWATER Cumbria Map 11 NY12

★67% **Grange Country House**
CA13 0SU ☎ 01946 861211 & 861570
Closed 17-27 Dec RS Jan-Feb
This family-run country hotel lies in a lovely valley at the north-western end of Loweswater. It has a friendly and relaxed atmosphere and cosy public areas. There is a small bar, a residents' lounge and an attractive dining room. The well equipped bedrooms all have en suite bathrooms and the traditional furnishings combine with several four-poster beds.
8 rms (7 bth/shr) 2 annexe en suite (bth) (2 fmly) CTV in all bedrooms 22P No coaches National Trust boats & fishing V meals Coffee am Tea pm No smoking in restaurant Last d 8pm
ROOMS: (incl. bkfst) s fr £32; d fr £64
OFF-PEAK: (incl. bkfst) s fr £30; d fr £60
MEALS: Lunch £2-£13 High tea £5-£10 Dinner £7.50-£13*

LUDLOW Shropshire Map 07 SO57

★★★❀70% **The Feathers at Ludlow**

Bull Ring SY8 1AA (in the town centre)
☎ 01584 875261 FAX 01584 876030
This historic, long-established hotel dating back to the 17th century features exposed timbers, ornate ceilings and oak panelling. Spacious and comfortable modern bedrooms are equipped such facilities as mini-bars and trouser presses, and most en suite bathrooms are fitted with bidets. Public rooms include two bars, a lounge and a reading room, and the Prince of Wales function suite is situated on the first floor. A widely-priced range of food is offered on good English menus. The enclosed car park is locked at night.
39 en suite (bth/shr) (3 fmly) No smoking in 5 bedrooms CTV in all bedrooms Lift Night porter 37P Snooker Jacuzzi/spa Xmas V meals Coffee am Tea pm No smoking in restaurant Last d 9pm
ROOMS: (incl. bkfst) s £65-£85; d £88-£140 **LB**
OFF-PEAK: (incl. bkfst) s £60-£80
MEALS: Lunch £12.50-£18.50&alc Dinner £20-£27alc
CONF: Thtr 80 Class 40 Board 10 Del from £80
CARDS:

★★★❀❀69% **Dinham Hall**
By the Castle SY8 1EJ (on A49) ☎ 01584 876464
FAX 01584 876019
Located opposite the castle, this hotel dates back to the 18th century. It lies in well maintained and landscaped lawns and

contd.

gardens and is a short walk from the town centre. Bedrooms are equipped with many extra facilities such as trouser presses and mini-bars, some are suitable for families and others have four-poster beds for that special occasion. Public rooms are elegantly furnished and staff are smart, efficient and friendly. Food is a particularly enjoyable experience and, as well as a carte choice, there is a special gourmet menu offering five courses.
11 en suite (bth/shr) (1 fmly) CTV in all bedrooms 16P No coaches Sauna Gym Xmas International Cuisine V meals Coffee am Tea pm No smoking in restaurant Last d 9pm
ROOMS: (incl. bkfst) s £62-£72; d £89-£120 **LB**
MEALS: Lunch fr £13.50&alc Dinner fr £23.50&alc*
CONF: Thtr 28 Class 28 Board 24 Del from £88
CARDS:

★★★ 69% Overton Grange

Hereford Rd SY8 4AD (on B4361)
☎ 01584 873500 FAX 01584 873524
Located a short distance from the bypass, this fine Edwardian mansion lies in attractive grounds and is popular for local weddings. Bedrooms are decorated with pretty papers and fabrics and many beds have attractive canopies. Public areas include a panelled restaurant and entrance hall as well as a smart cocktail bar with adjacent lounge. Adrian Jones, who heads the kitchen brigade, is responsible for the provision of enjoyable food and this has already been recognised in our rosette award.
16 rms (14 bth/shr) (2 fmly) No smoking in 2 bedrooms CTV in all bedrooms No dogs (ex guide dogs) Night porter 80P Croquet lawn Xmas V meals Coffee am Tea pm No smoking in restaurant Last d 9.45pm
ROOMS: (incl. bkfst) s £35-£55; d £60-£80 **LB**
MEALS: Lunch £13.50-£15.50 High tea £8.25 Dinner £19.50*
CONF: Thtr 160 Class 80 Board 50
CARDS:

★★ 65% Dinham Weir
Dinham Bridge SY8 1EH ☎ 01584 874431
Closed Jan
Located at the edge of the River Teme and its weir, the agreeable sound of gently rushing water permeates the atmosphere throughout the hotel. The restaurant and its adjoining bar reaches down to the riverside and there are also pleasant lawns and gardens where guests may sit. Bedrooms are cosy and well decorated and all are equipped with modern amenities.
8 en suite (bth/shr) CTV in all bedrooms No dogs 10P No children 5yrs Xmas V meals Coffee am Tea pm No smoking in restaurant Last d 8.30pm
ROOMS: (incl. bkfst) s £50-£55; d £65-£80 **LB**
MEALS: Lunch £8.95-£12.50&alc Dinner £12.50&alc*
CARDS:

★★ 63% Cliffe
Dinham SY8 2JE (from centre of town turn left into Dinham by the castle. Cross river and bear right) ☎ 01584 872063
Standing in a pleasant and peaceful part of the town with good views of the castle, this friendly small hotel offers modern bedrooms and attractive public areas. The hotel stands in its own grounds and provides a good range of home-cooked food. It is also popular for the live jazz that is usually played at weekends.
9 en suite (bth/shr) CTV in all bedrooms 50P No coaches No children 10yrs V meals Coffee am No smoking in restaurant Last d 8.30pm
ROOMS: (incl. bkfst) s £30-£35; d £52-£58 **LB**
MEALS: Sunday Lunch £7.95 Dinner £12.95*
CARDS:

Travelodge
Travelodge
Woofferton SY8 4AL (on A49 at junct A456/B4362)
☎ 01584 711695 FAX 01584 711695
This modern building offers accommodation in smart, spacious and well equipped bedrooms, suitable for family use, and all with en suite bathrooms. Meals may be taken at the nearby family restaurant. For information on room rates and to make a booking, call Roomline free of charge on 0800 850950. For more details about Travelodge, consult the Contents page under Hotel Groups.
32 en suite (bth/shr)

LUDWELL Wiltshire Map 03 ST92

★★ 68% Grove House
SP7 9ND (2m E of Shaftesbury on A30) ☎ 01747 828365 FAX 01747 828365
This comfortable and friendly family-run hotel is situated on the edge of Cranborne Chase, just three miles from the ancient Saxon hilltop town of Shaftesbury. Most of the bedrooms are at the rear of the building and enjoy views of the pretty garden. The public areas include a choice of lounges and a spacious dining room where a selection of dishes make up the fixed-priced menu. Many guests return regularly, but the most loyal are the badgers who come each evening to feed.
10 rms (4 bth 5 shr) (1 fmly) CTV in all bedrooms 12P No coaches Xmas English & Continental Cuisine V meals Coffee am Tea pm No smoking in restaurant Last d 9pm
ROOMS: (incl. bkfst) s £29.50; d £59 **LB**
MEALS: Dinner fr £17.50
CARDS:

LULWORTH COVE See West Lulworth

LUMBY North Yorkshire Map 08 SE43

Forte Posthouse Leeds/Selby
FORTE Posthouse
LS25 5LF (leave A1 at A63 signposted Selby, hotel on A63) ☎ 01977 682711 FAX 01977 685462
Suitable for both the business and leisure traveller, this bright hotel provides modern accommodation in well equipped bedrooms with en suite bathrooms. For more details about Forte Posthouse hotels, consult the Contents page for the section on Hotel Groups.
95 en suite (bth/shr)
ROOMS: s fr £69; d fr £69 *

LUTON Bedfordshire Map 04 TL02

★★★ 71% Strathmore Thistle
THISTLE HOTELS
Arndale Centre LU1 2TR (from M1 junct 10 take signs to Luton town centre.In St Mary's Rd drive across traffic lights,turn left at mini rdbt into Guildford St, hotel on left) ☎ 01582 34199 FAX 01582 402528
Comfortable, modern standards of accommodation and friendly, professional service are provided by this modern, purpose built hotel

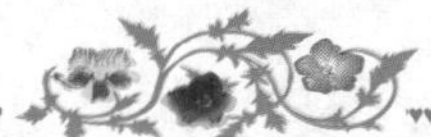

situated next to the Arndale shopping centre in the town centre. Attractively furnished bedrooms offer an extensive range of facilities, (though their bathrooms are rather small and functional), with some extras in the executive rooms. Public rooms include a stylish lobby lounge and small cocktail bar as well as two eating options; Angelines - a formal restaurant, the other a congenial, relaxed café bar. Guests arriving by car should collect a token from reception before entering the adjacent multi-story car park, (manned throughout the night).
150 en suite (bth/shr) (7 fmly) No smoking in 55 bedrooms CTV in all bedrooms STV Lift Night porter 44P International Cuisine V meals Coffee am Tea pm No smoking area in restaurant Last d 9.45pm
ROOMS: s £79-£95; d £95-£110 * **LB**
MEALS: Lunch £5.95-£17.25&alc High tea £4.95-£5.25 Dinner fr £17.25&alc*
CONF: Thtr 300 Class 150 Del from £105
CARDS:

★★★62% **The Chiltern**

Waller Av, Dunstable Rd LU4 9RU (from junct 11 on M1 take A505 to Luton and turn off into Waller Avenue after passing Lex Vauxhall Garage)
☎ 01582 575911 FAX 01582 581859
Conveniently positioned close to the M1 this modern hotel is geared towards the business guest with its good range of conference and meeting rooms. Bedrooms on the first and second floors have recently been upgraded, while those on the third are more dated. Room service is available twenty-four hours, a lounge menu is displayed throughout the day, and the restaurant caters for all tastes and most diets.
91 en suite (bth/shr) No smoking in 27 bedrooms CTV in all bedrooms STV Lift Night porter 150P Xmas European Cuisine V meals Coffee am Last d 10pm
ROOMS: d £75 * **LB**
OFF-PEAK: d £45
MEALS: Lunch £8.95 Dinner £14.95&alc*
CONF: Thtr 250 Class 180 Board 40 Del £75
CARDS:

★★★60% **The Luton Gateway**

641 Dunstable Rd LU4 8RQ (from M1 junc11 travel towards Luton, hotel on right within 100yds)
☎ 01582 575955 FAX 01582 490065
Easily accessible from the junction of the A505 and M1, this hotel boasts a dedicated business centre for conferences and meetings. Bedrooms can be a little dated but are well maintained and there is a congenial bar and restaurant.
109 en suite (bth/shr) No smoking in 48 bedrooms CTV in all bedrooms No dogs (ex guide dogs) Lift Night porter 90P Snooker Pool table Xmas English & French Cuisine V meals Coffee am Tea pm
ROOMS: d fr £60 * **LB**
OFF-PEAK: (incl. bkfst) s fr £35; d fr £45
MEALS: Lunch £4.95-£9.95&alc*
CONF: Thtr 80 Class 40 Board 30 Del from £60
CARDS:

LUTON AIRPORT Bedfordshire Map 04 TL12

★★60% **Hotel Ibis**

Spittlesea Rd LU2 9NZ (from junct 10 on M1 follow signs to Airport) ☎ 01582 424488
FAX 01582 455511
Part of a budget European chain, this modern purpose-built hotel is the only hotel within the airport complex. Every bedroom is identically decorated and furnished in a modest, no frills style; however new quilted bedspreads have lifted the rooms a little. All have en suite bathrooms with bath as well as shower. The bar and restaurant are open all day, and breakfast, not included in the competitive room charge, is entirely self-service.
98 en suite (bth/shr) (6 fmly) No smoking in 30 bedrooms CTV in all bedrooms STV Lift Night porter Air conditioning 150P Xmas English & French Cuisine V meals Coffee am Tea pm No smoking area in restaurant Last d 10.30pm
ROOMS: d £39.50 *
MEALS: Lunch £6.50-£11.50 Dinner £6.50-£11.50*
CONF: Thtr 100 Class 55 Board 45 Del from £65
CARDS:

LUTTERWORTH Leicestershire Map 04 SP58

★★★64% **Denbigh Arms**

High St LE17 4AD (exit M1 junct 20 and turn right at traffic lights, over bridge and past Fox Inn)
☎ 01455 553537 FAX 01455 556627
A converted Georgian coaching inn, this hotel is located on the southern edge of town, convenient for junction 20 of the M1. The restaurant now offers a more informal atmosphere and casual dining, with daily blackboard specials supplementing the menus. There is a quiet foyer lounge area and a good-sized lounge bar across the courtyard. Bedrooms are mostly spacious, are comfortably furnished in pine, and have modern amenities.
31 en suite (bth/shr) (3 fmly) No smoking in 2 bedrooms CTV in all bedrooms STV Night porter 30P Pool table Xmas English & French Cuisine V meals Coffee am Tea pm Last d 9.30pm
ROOMS: (incl. bkfst) s £60; d £70 * **LB**
OFF-PEAK: (incl. bkfst) s £54.50; d £64.50
CONF: Thtr 60 Class 29 Board 30
CARDS:

★★★62% **Fernie Lodge Restaurant & Hotel**
2 Berridges Ln, Husbands Bosworth LE17 6LE ☎ 01858 880551
FAX 01858 880014
Enjoying a good position off the A471, handy for the M1 but in a peaceful country location, this much extended Geogian manor house offers generously sized bedrooms with good quality furniture, large TVs with a satellite channel and spacious bathrooms. Public areas include a large bar and a good range of conference, meeting and banqueting rooms.
18 en suite (bth/shr) (4 fmly) No smoking in 5 bedrooms CTV in all bedrooms STV Night porter 40P Wkly live entertainment Xmas French Cuisine V meals Coffee am Tea pm No smoking in restaurant Last d 10pm
ROOMS: s £40-£67; d £45-£67 * **LB**
OFF-PEAK: s £45-£67; d £30-£67
MEALS: Lunch £8.95-£11.95 Dinner £19.95-£22.95*
CARDS:

LYDFORD Devon Map 02 SX58

★★73% **Lydford House**

EX20 4AU (turn off A386 halfway between Okehampton and Tavistock, signpost Lydford, 500yds on right hand side) ☎ 01822 820347
FAX 01822 820442
This impressive Victorian country house is set in eight acres of gardens (look out for the 'secret garden') and also has the benefit of a riding stables on the premises which are right on the edge of Dartmoor, within the National Park. There is a pleasing charm about the restaurant, where you will be offered freshly prepared food, changing daily according to where the best quality lies. The new conservatory provides a relaxing setting in which to take a pre-dinner drink or to relax over coffee.
13 rms (11 bth/shr) (2 fmly) No smoking in 1 bedroom CTV in all bedrooms 30P No coaches Riding Free use of Tavistock Leisure

contd.

L

Centre No children 5yrs V meals Coffee am Tea pm No smoking in restaurant Last d 8pm
ROOMS: (incl. bkfst) s £35; d £70 LB
MEALS: Sunday Lunch £8 Dinner £15*
CARDS:

LYME REGIS Dorset Map 03 SY39
See also Rousdon

★★★69% **Alexandra**
Pound St DT7 3HZ (on the B3052) ☎ 01297 442010
FAX 01297 443229
Closed Xmas & New Year
This family run hotel boasts a prime location high above the Cob Hamlet which featured in 'Persuasion' and 'French Lieutenant's Woman'. The bedrooms are individually decorated with pretty chintz fabrics and attractive furniture. The elegant restaurant offers range of French and English cuisine and takes advantage of the view. A bright south facing conservatory opens in into the pretty gardens and can be appreciated all year, and there is also a cosy lounge with log fires in the winter months.
27 en suite (bth/shr) (8 fmly) CTV in 26 bedrooms Night porter 25P No coaches English & French Cuisine V meals Coffee am Tea pm Last d 9pm
ROOMS: (incl. bkfst & dinner) s £65; d £80-£110 LB
OFF-PEAK: (incl. bkfst & dinner) s £40-£50
MEALS: Lunch £12.50-£13.50&alc High tea £5 Dinner £18.50-£21&alc
CARDS:

★★★67% **Dower House**
Rousdon DT7 3RB ☎ 01297 21047 FAX 01297 24748
(For full entry see Rousdon)

★★❀69% **Kersbrook**

Pound Rd DT7 3HX ☎ 01297 442596
FAX 01297 442596
RS 7 Jan-& Feb
A warm relaxed atmosphere is created in this charming thatched building by proprietors Mr and Mrs Stephenson. The bedrooms retain a lot of their original features, and although not large are comfortably furnished and attractively decorated. There is a cosy bar, a bright sunny lounge, and the restaurant offers a choice of a daily-changing menu and an extensive carte, where the chef makes full use of local fresh produce.
10 en suite (bth/shr) No smoking in all bedrooms CTV in all bedrooms 14P Xmas English, French & Italian Cuisine V meals Coffee am Tea pm Last d 8.50pm
ROOMS: (incl. bkfst) s £50-£55; d £65-£77 LB
OFF-PEAK: (incl. bkfst) s £40-£50; d £50-£65
MEALS: Lunch £4.50-£8.95 Dinner £16.50&alc
CARDS:

★★68% **Buena Vista**
Pound St DT7 3HZ (W on A3052) ☎ 01297 442494
Closed Dec-Jan
This personally-run hotel is situated overlooking the harbour and Cobb in a third of an acre of attractive gardens with a private path leading down to the sea. Many of the bedrooms have balconies to take advantage of the views and all have en suite facilities. There are two comfortable lounges and a delightful south facing sun terrace.
18 rms (17 bth/shr) (1 fmly) CTV in all bedrooms 20P No coaches V meals Coffee am Tea pm No smoking in restaurant Last d 8pm
ROOMS: (incl. bkfst) s £38-£42; d £64-£98 LB
MEALS: Dinner £12-£15.50
CARDS:

★★66% **Royal Lion**
Broad St DT7 3QF ☎ 01297 445622 FAX 01297 445859
Closed 3 days Xmas
This popular town centre hotel, dating from 1601, has retained a lot of its original character. The bedrooms in the main house are traditionally furnished and have sloping floors, beamed ceilings and fireplaces; those in the more recently built wing, are more spacious and some have balconies with sea views and others a private terrace. There is an attractive leisure suite with heated pool, jacuzzi and steam room; also a play area for children with table tennis and snooker.
30 en suite (bth/shr) (4 fmly) CTV in all bedrooms 36P No coaches Indoor swimming pool (heated) Snooker Sauna Gym Pool table Jacuzzi/spa Games room Coffee am Tea pm Last d 9pm
ROOMS: (incl. bkfst) s fr £34; d fr £68 * LB
CARDS:

★★62% **Bay**
Marine Pde DT7 3JQ ☎ 01297 442059
Closed Dec-Feb
This family-run hotel is set right on the seafront and offers simple friendly accommodation. The bedrooms vary in size and have reasonable facilities, some have sea views. There is a large lounge and a smart dining room where a fixed-price dinner and breakfasts are served.
21 rms (12 bth/shr) (3 fmly) CTV in 20 bedrooms 20P No coaches Snooker Sauna Solarium Gym Pool table English & French Cuisine V meals Coffee am Tea pm Last d 8pm
ROOMS: (incl. bkfst) s fr £29; d fr £53 * LB
OFF-PEAK: (incl. bkfst) d fr £58
MEALS: Lunch fr £6.50 Dinner fr £17.50
CARDS:

★62% **Tudor House**
Church St DT7 3BU ☎ 01297 442472
Closed Oct-end Mar
This 16th century town centre hotel is being given a new lease of life by its new owners. Bedrooms vary in size and shape due to the age of the building; all have low beamed ceilings and sloping floors, some have been redecorated and have ensuite facilities. The public areas include a carvery restaurant, tow lounges and a flag-stoned basement bar which houses the original 'town well'.
17 en suite (bth/shr) (10 fmly) CTV in 8 bedrooms No dogs (ex guide dogs) 20P Coffee am Tea pm Last d 7.30pm
ROOMS: (incl. bkfst) s £16-£17.50; d £37-£55 *
OFF-PEAK: (incl. bkfst) s £16; d £32
CARDS:

LYMINGTON Hampshire Map 04 SZ39

★★★73% **Passford House**
Mount Pleasant Ln SO41 8LS (from A337 at Lymington turn right at mini roundabout, then first right at Tollhouse public house, then right into Mount Pleasant Lane) ☎ 01590 682398 FAX 01590 683494
Located on the edge of the town in its own grounds, Passford House
contd.

offers peace and tranquillity. The bedrooms vary in size and style but are all comfortable and well equipped. There is an attractive wood-panelled lounge where a log fire burns in the winter months, and guests may relax here with a cream tea. The restaurant offers an extensive menu which makes full use of local produce, and there is a leisure suite with an indoor pool for the energetic.
53 en suite (bth/shr) 2 annexe en suite (bth/shr) (4 fmly) CTV in all bedrooms Night porter 104P Indoor swimming pool (heated) Outdoor swimming pool (heated) Tennis (hard) Sauna Solarium Gym Pool table Croquet lawn Putting green Jacuzzi/spa Petanque Table tennis ch fac Xmas English & French Cuisine V meals Coffee am Tea pm No smoking in restaurant Last d 9pm
ROOMS: (incl. bkfst) s £65-£100; d £110-£140 **LB**
OFF-PEAK: (incl. bkfst) s fr £60; d fr £80
MEALS: Lunch £13.50-£25 High tea fr £9.50 Dinner £19.50-£30
CONF: Thtr 80 Class 45 Board 40 Del from £100
CARDS:

See advertisement on page 411

★★★68% **Stanwell House**
High St SO41 9AA (A337 to town centre, on right hand side of High St before it descends to quay) ☎ 01590 677123 FAX 01590 677756
This popular high street hotel has been transformed in the last few months and now has a lot more style and panache. The public areas include a bright airy conservatory lounge area where coffee, teas and smacks are served throughout the day. There is a pleasant bistro and a more formal restaurant offering a set menu and an interesting carte. The bedrooms have been refurbished and those in the main house, although of varying sizes have been individually decorated with rich fabrics and furnishings in jewel colours.
29 en suite (bth/shr) (1 fmly) No smoking in 4 bedrooms CTV in all bedrooms Night porter Xmas English & French Cuisine V meals Coffee am Tea pm Last d 10pm
ROOMS: (incl. bkfst) s £55-£72; d £85-£119 *
MEALS: Lunch £10.50-£13.50&alc Dinner £17&alc*
CONF: Thtr 30 Class 20 Board 22
CARDS:

See advertisement on opposite page

RED STAR HOTEL

★★ **Gordleton Mill**
Silver St, Hordle SO41 6DJ (2m NW on Hordle road)
☎ 01590 682219 FAX 01590 683073
Closed 2-16 Jan & first 2 wks Nov RS Sun evening/Mon (restaurant closed)
This delightful 17th-century watermill is set on the banks of the River Avon in picturesque grounds. The bedrooms are attractively decorated and luxuriously equipped with whirlpool baths, fresh fruit and flowers, bathrobes and champagne. The public rooms have lots of character and take full advantage of the lovely views, particularly the restaurant. Chef manager Toby Hill has established an enviable reputation for his excellent food and his seasonally changing menu fully exploits the high quality local produce. A recent meal started with an appetiser of light yellow pepper mousse wrapped in fine slices of smoked duck. The fish soup was rich but quite delicately flavoured and lightly perfumed with orange. A pig's trotter was filled with sweetbreads and served on a bed of creamy potato, with a richly flavoured sauce of morels. Breads and pastries, particularly at breakfast, are truly memorable.
7 en suite (bth/shr) (1 fmly) No smoking in 4 bedrooms CTV in all bedrooms 60P No coaches Fishing No children 7yrs Xmas French Cuisine V meals Coffee am Tea pm No smoking in restaurant Last d 9.30pm
ROOMS: (incl. bkfst) s £97; d £112-£136 * **LB**
OFF-PEAK: (incl. bkfst) d £103-£129
MEALS: Lunch fr £26alc Dinner £40&alc*
CONF: Board 16 Del from £130
CARDS:

★★75% **String of Horses**
Mead End Rd SO41 6EH ☎ 01590 682631
FAX 01590 682631
(For full entry see Sway)

LYMM Cheshire Map 07 SJ68

★★★61% ***Lymm***
Whitbarrow Rd WA13 9AQ ☎ 01925 752233 FAX 01925 756035
RS New Year
Quietly situated near the centre of the village, the Lymm hotel is an attractive extended Inn with the majority of the bedrooms found in a modern wing. Within the main building there is the restaurant and a comfortable lounge bar which offers live music at weekends. On a recent visit staff were most helpful with warm smiles.
22 en suite (bth/shr) 47 annexe en suite (bth/shr) (1 fmly) CTV in all bedrooms Night porter 120P English & French Cuisine V meals Coffee am Tea pm Last d 9.45pm
CARDS:

LYMPSHAM Somerset Map 03 ST35

★★65% **Batch Country House Hotel**
BS24 0EX (off A370) ☎ 01934 750371 FAX 01934 750501
Closed Xmas
A friendly and relaxed atmosphere is created by Mr and Mrs Brown in this long white building which stands in its own grounds in a quiet location mid-way between Weston-Super-Mare and Burnham-on-Sea. The spacious lounges overlook the gardens an in the beamed dining room an extensive range of dishes is offered.
8 en suite (bth) (4 fmly) No smoking in 2 bedrooms CTV in all

bedrooms No dogs 70P No coaches Fishing English & Continental Cuisine V meals Coffee am Tea pm No smoking in restaurant Last d 8.30pm
ROOMS: (incl. bkfst) s £37-£41; d £56-£62 **LB**
MEALS: Lunch £11.50 Dinner £12-£14&alc
CONF: Thtr 70 Class 60 Board 40 Del from £64
CARDS:
See advertisement under WESTON-SUPER-MARE

LYNDHURST Hampshire Map 04 SU30

★★★  78% **Parkhill**

Beaulieu Rd SO43 7FZ (off B3056 to Beaulieu)
☎ 01703 282944 FAX 01703 283268

Be careful not to miss the turn off to Parkhill: it is easy to be distracted by the New Forest scenery and its abundant wild life. The hotel was built in the 18th century and owners Mr and Mrs Topham have restored it to an excellent standard. The elegant public rooms feature open log fires and have many small nooks where guests can seek peace and privacy. Bedrooms are equipped with almost every extra imaginable including fans to cool the summer heat. Dining is also a pleasure and chef Richard Turner presents a menu of English classics, some with a continental twist.

15 en suite (bth/shr) 5 annexe en suite (bth/shr) (2 fmly) CTV in all bedrooms Night porter 77P Outdoor swimming pool (heated) Fishing Croquet lawn Putting green Outdoor chess Xmas English & French Cuisine V meals Coffee am Tea pm No smoking in restaurant Last d 9.30pm
ROOMS: (incl. bkfst) s £50-£70; d £100-£140 **LB**
MEALS: Lunch fr £15&alc High tea fr £2.25 Dinner fr £25.50&alc*
CONF: Thtr 60 Class 40 Board 35 Del £82.50
CARDS:

See advertisement on this page

★★★❀71% **Crown**
High St SO43 7NF (in the centre of the village, opposite the church) ☎ 01703 282922
FAX 01703 282751

There has been an inn on this site since the 1600s and the present property dates back to 1897. The rooms all have their own character with handsome pieces of furniture and attractive fabrics. The two comfortable lounges have a relaxed atmosphere and there is a popular panelled bar. The restaurant overlooks the small garden, and offers a daily changing menu of carefully prepared seasonal dishes; the home-made soups are especially good.
39 en suite (bth/shr) (8 fmly) CTV in all bedrooms STV Lift 60P Xmas European Cuisine V meals Coffee am Tea pm
ROOMS: (incl. bkfst) s £63.50-£65.50; d £97-£99 * **LB**
CONF: Thtr 70 Class 30 Board 45
CARDS:

See advertisement on opposite page

★★★65% **Forest Lodge**
Pikes Hill, Romsey Rd SO43 7AS (exit M27 at junct 1 and join A337 towards Lyndhurst. On approaching village, police station/courts on right, take first right into Pikes Hill)
☎ 01703 283677 FAX 01703 283719
Situated on the edge of Lyndhurst and the New Forest, this small privately owned hotel offers smart accommodation in well equipped bedrooms. The public areas include two traditionally furnished lounges, a well presented restaurant and a swimming pool.
23 en suite (bth/shr) (3 fmly) CTV in all bedrooms 50P Indoor swimming pool (heated) ch fac Xmas V meals Coffee am Tea pm No smoking in restaurant Last d 8.45pm
ROOMS: (incl. bkfst) s £50; d £79-£89 * **LB**
MEALS: Dinner £17.50*
CONF: Thtr 100 Class 70 Board 50 Del from £75
CARDS:

★★★63% **Lyndhurst Park**
High St SO43 7NL ☎ 01703 283923
FAX 01703 283019

Forestdale Hotels

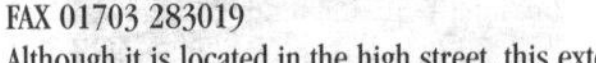

Although it is located in the high street, this extended Georgian house also boasts a setting of five acres of mature grounds, good car parking, and outdoor leisure facilities. There are two bars and a cosy oak-panelled restaurant with a conservatory addition which is used during warmer climes. Bedrooms are slowly being upgraded and tend to vary in styles and sizes.
59 en suite (bth/shr) (3 fmly) No smoking in 3 bedrooms CTV in all bedrooms Lift Night porter 100P Outdoor swimming pool (heated) Tennis (hard) Snooker Sauna Table tennis ch fac Xmas English & Continental Cuisine V meals Coffee am Tea pm Last d 10pm
ROOMS: (incl. bkfst) s fr £65.95; d £85-£90 * **LB**
OFF-PEAK: (incl. bkfst & dinner) s fr £78.50; d £112-£122
MEALS: Lunch fr £11.45 High tea fr £5.95 Dinner fr £16.95*
CONF: Thtr 300 Class 120 Board 80 Del from £75
CARDS:

★71% **Knightwood Lodge**
Southampton Rd SO43 7BU (on A35)
☎ 01703 282502 FAX 01703 283730
Closed 25 Dec

MINOTEL Great Britain

Conveniently located on the Southampton to Lyndhurst road, this personally run hotel offers good value for money. The bedrooms are comfortable and well equipped, with modern en suite facilities. There is also a very attractive leisure complex with pool, sauna, steam room and solarium. The restaurant offers a good variety of home-cooked meals and there is a well stocked bar.
14 en suite (bth/shr) 4 annexe en suite (bth/shr) (2 fmly) CTV in all bedrooms STV 15P No coaches Indoor swimming pool (heated) Sauna Solarium Gym Jacuzzi/spa Steam room V meals No smoking in restaurant
ROOMS: (incl. bkfst) s £30-£40; d £55-£75 * **LB**
MEALS: Dinner fr £14.95*
CARDS:

LYNMOUTH Devon Map 03 SS74

See also Lynton

★★★60% **Tors**
EX35 6NA ☎ 01598 753236 FAX 01598 752544
Closed 4-31 Jan RS Feb (wknds only)
Tors hotel stands in an elevated position overlooking the bay. Public areas are comfortably appointed and include a light and airy dining room offering set-price, carte and vegetarian menus. The bedrooms vary in size and quality and include some comfortable rooms with good sea views.
35 rms (33 bth/shr) (5 fmly) CTV in all bedrooms Lift 40P Outdoor swimming pool (heated) Pool table Table tennis Xmas English & French Cuisine V meals Coffee am Tea pm No smoking in restaurant Last d 8.45pm
ROOMS: (incl. bkfst) s £37-£77; d £64-£94 * **LB**
MEALS: Lunch £11&alc Dinner £18-£24&alc*
CONF: Thtr 60 Class 40 Board 25 Del from £59
CARDS:

★★❀❀70% **Rising Sun**
Harbourside EX35 6EQ ☎ 01598 753223 FAX 01598 753480
The Rising Sun Hotel is an historic 14th-century thatched smugglers inn, overlooking the small, picturesque harbour and the East Lyn salmon river. The building is steeped in history, with an oak panelled dining room and bar, crooked ceilings, thick walls and uneven oak floors. Hugo Jeune and his small team of friendly young staff provide an attentive, style of service in a relaxed atmosphere. The bedrooms are comfortable and well equipped, and some are being further upgraded using attractive soft furnishings. The reputation of the restaurant is well known, the chef specialises in Exmoor game and seafood, preparing dishes with care and presenting them in a modern style, with stunning results.
11 en suite (bth/shr) 5 annexe en suite (bth/shr) (2 fmly) No smoking in 6 bedrooms CTV in all bedrooms No dogs (ex guide dogs) No coaches Fishing No children 7yrs Xmas English & French Cuisine V meals Coffee am No smoking in restaurant Last d 9pm
ROOMS: (incl. bkfst) s £47.50; d £79-£99 * **LB**
MEALS: Lunch fr £15&alc Dinner fr £23.50&alc*
CARDS:

See advertisement on opposite page

★★69% **Bath**
Sea Front EX35 6EL ☎ 01598 752238 FAX 01598 752544
Closed Nov-Feb RS Mar (wknds only)
Owned by the same family since the early 50s, this friendly, traditional hotel stands in the centre of the village near the harbour. The bedrooms vary in size but all have modern en suite facilities. Five rooms with sea views, classed as Grade A, are well worth the supplement. Cream teas are served in the sun lounge and an extensive

range of bar meals is available at lunch time. The hotel's restaurant offers an imaginative choice from a daily-changing menu, including local salmon and lobster in summer.
24 en suite (bth/shr) (9 fmly) CTV in all bedrooms 15P Pool table English & French Cuisine V meals Coffee am Tea pm No smoking in restaurant Last d 8.30pm
ROOMS: (incl. bkfst) s £27-£37; d £54-£74 **LB**
MEALS: Lunch £5-£10 Dinner £16-£21
CARDS:

LYNTON Devon Map 03 SS74
See also Lynmouth

★★★70% ***Lynton Cottage***
North Walk EX35 6ED (take turning next to St Mary's church and first right.) ☎ 01598 752342 FAX 01598 752597
Closed Jan
Situated at the end of a private drive, this hotel enjoys stunning views of the Lyn Valley and Lynmouth Bay. Dating back to the 17th-century, it combines period charm with modern facilities which, when added to the relaxed and friendly atmosphere created by resident proprietors John and Maisie Jones, results in a delightful, and very comfortable place to stay. Individually-styled bedrooms vary in size and the public areas include two lounges (one with a bar) and an attractive restaurant. The interesting fixed-priced menu presents a well balanced selection of freshly prepared dishes, and the dessert trolley offers a choice of delicious hot and cold puddings.
17 en suite (bth/shr) CTV in all bedrooms 26P No coaches No children 14yrs French Cuisine V meals Coffee am Tea pm Last d 8.45pm
CARDS:

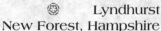

★★70% Hewitts

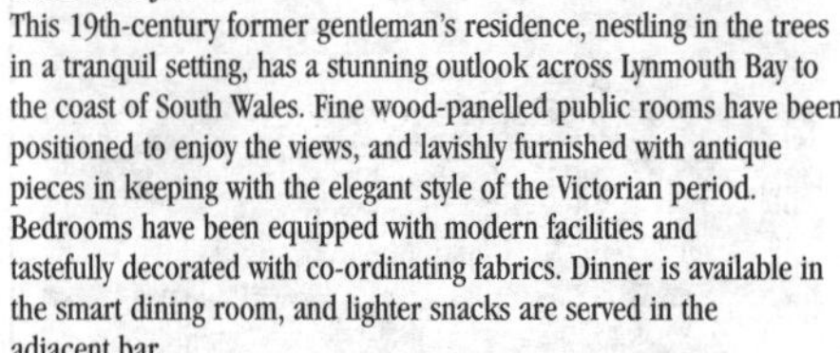

North Walk EX35 6HJ ☎ 01598 752293
FAX 01598 752489
Closed Dec-Jan

This 19th-century former gentleman's residence, nestling in the trees in a tranquil setting, has a stunning outlook across Lynmouth Bay to the coast of South Wales. Fine wood-panelled public rooms have been positioned to enjoy the views, and lavishly furnished with antique pieces in keeping with the elegant style of the Victorian period. Bedrooms have been equipped with modern facilities and tastefully decorated with co-ordinating fabrics. Dinner is available in the smart dining room, and lighter snacks are served in the adjacent bar.

10 en suite (bth/shr) (1 fmly) No smoking in all bedrooms CTV in all bedrooms 13P No coaches Jacuzzi/spa European Cuisine V meals Coffee am Tea pm No smoking in restaurant Last d 7pm
ROOMS: (incl. bkfst) s £30; d £64-£78 * **LB**
MEALS: Dinner £15*
CONF: Board 12
CARDS:

★★62% *Crown*

Sinai Hill EX35 6AG ☎ 01598 752253 FAX 01598 753311

Situated in the heart of the old part of Lynton, The Crown is a popular hotel with tourists and attracts locals in the bar for the convivial atmosphere. Bedrooms are undergoing a plan of reburbished. In the restaurant a value-for-money table d'hote menu is offered together with an a la carte menu featuring sizzling platters and some Chinese dishes. Amanda King and Beth Ring are friendly and involved proprietors.

15 en suite (bth/shr) (3 fmly) CTV in all bedrooms 25P No coaches Darts V meals Coffee am Last d 8.30pm
CARDS:

★★62% Sandrock

Longmead EX35 6DH ☎ 01598 753307 FAX 01598 752665
Closed Dec-Jan

Located close to the Valley of the Rocks, this personally managed hotel has a number of regularly returning guests. The bedrooms are well presented and the lounge is cosy and traditional. There are a bar area and a neat, bright dining room where home-cooked evening meals are offered. The hotel is in a charming area close to many lovely tourist spots.

9 rms (5 bth 2 shr) (3 fmly) CTV in all bedrooms 9P No coaches Pool table V meals Coffee am Tea pm Last d 7.30pm
ROOMS: (incl. bkfst) s £19.50-£21.50; d £39-£48 **LB**
MEALS: Bar Lunch £2-£8 Dinner fr £11.50*
CARDS:

RED STAR HOTEL

★ Highcliffe House

Sinai Hill EX35 6AR ☎ 01598 752235 FAX 01598 752235

Over the last year, John Bishop and Steven Phillips have worked hard to sympathetically restore this former Victorian gentleman's residence and they have succeeded in creating a small, luxurious hotel which pampers its guests. Set some 800 feet above the bay, the hotel has spectacular views over Lynton and the surrounding coastline and beautiful Exmoor countryside. There is a choice of comfortable lounges, each furnished in keeping with the period of the house. In the candlelit dining room imaginative dinners are served, using the freshest of local ingredients. Each bedroom is individually decorated and lovingly furnished with antique pieces; all rooms are equipped with the expected creature comforts.

6 en suite (bth/shr) No smoking in all bedrooms CTV in all bedrooms No dogs 10P No coaches No children Xmas English & Continental Cuisine V meals No smoking in restaurant Last d 7pm
ROOMS: (incl. bkfst) s £45; d £70-£76 **LB**
MEALS: Dinner £18.50
CARDS:

★ 74% Combe Park

Hillsford Bridge EX35 6LE (0.25m from junct of A39/B3223 at Hillsford Bridge) ☎ 01598 752356
Closed Nov-mid Mar

This former hunting lodge stands in a picturesque location of wooded countryside, with Hoar Oak Water tumbling by at the end of the lawn. There are two comfortable lounges and a small bar. Dinner offers a choice of starters and desserts around a set main course, all prepared with great care by Shirley Barnes. Bedrooms are restfully furnished in traditional style. Dogs are welcome.

9 en suite (bth/shr) 11P No coaches No children 12yrs Coffee am Tea pm No smoking in restaurant
ROOMS: (incl. bkfst & dinner) s £66; d £92-£99 * **LB**
MEALS: Dinner fr £19.50*

★ 69% Chough's Nest

North Walk EX35 6HJ ☎ 01598 753315
Closed Dec-Feb RS Mar (wknds only)

There are spectacular panoramic views over Lynmouth Bay towards Countisbury headland from this beautiful stone hotel, built a century ago by a Dutch millionaire as a private residence. The enthusiastic new owners pride themselves on providing a relaxed and friendly atmosphere for guests to enjoy, and there is a comfortable, inviting feel to the public rooms. Well equipped bedrooms are furnished in a variety of styles, and a short set menu is offered in the dining room by

talented young chef/patron Andy Collier, whose experience of cooking from various parts of the world helps him to produce an eclectic array of dishes, especially from Indonesia. Vegetarian options are always available.
12 en suite (bth/shr) (2 fmly) No smoking in all bedrooms CTV in all bedrooms No dogs 10P No coaches International Cuisine V meals Coffee am Tea pm No smoking in restaurant Last d 8pm
ROOMS: (incl. bkfst & dinner) s fr £39.50; d fr £79 *
MEALS: Lunch £10.50 Dinner fr £16.50*
CARDS:

★69% **Seawood**
North Walk EX35 6HJ ☎ 01598 752272
Closed Nov-Etr
Warm hospitality is the keynote of this small, homely hotel. Further upgrading has provided attractively decorated bedrooms with co-ordinating soft furnishings, while public areas, though limited, include a comfortable sitting room, a cosy bar and a well appointed dining room which offers a number of vegetarian choices on its set menu of sound, freshly prepared dishes.
12 en suite (bth/shr) (1 fmly) CTV in all bedrooms 10P No coaches No children 10yrs V meals No smoking in restaurant Last d 6.30pm
ROOMS: (incl. bkfst) s £25-£29; d £50-£58
MEALS: Dinner £10-£14

★68% **North Cliff**
North Walk EX35 6HJ (off A39, approx 100yds from St Mary's church)
☎ 01598 752357
Closed Dec-Jan
Mr and Mrs Irlam offer a warm welcome at this friendly little hotel which commands spectacular views over the bay. Bedrooms are spacious and comfortable with cosy eiderdowns on the beds. Public areas include a small bar and a comfortable lounge where guests can relax after one of Mrs Irlam's enjoyable home-cooked dinners.
14 en suite (bth/shr) (2 fmly) No smoking in 6 bedrooms CTV in all bedrooms 15P No coaches Pool table Table tennis No smoking in restaurant Last d 6pm
ROOMS: (incl. bkfst) s £24-£25; d £48-£50 *
MEALS: Dinner £11
CARDS:

★60% **Fairholme**
North Walk EX35 6ED ☎ 01598 752263 FAX 01598 752263
Closed Oct-Apr
Superb views over Lynmouth and friendly service from resident proprietors feature among the attractions of a hotel offering neat, well tended bedrooms, a comfortable lounge and dining room, and a separate tea shop.
11 rms (8 bth) (2 fmly) CTV in all bedrooms No dogs 12P No coaches Indoor swimming pool (heated) Sauna No children 10yrs Coffee am Tea pm No smoking in restaurant Last d 7.30pm
ROOMS: (incl. bkfst) s £23-£25; d £46-£50 *
MEALS: Dinner fr £10

LYTHAM ST ANNES Lancashire Map 07 SD32

★★★★61% **Clifton Arms**
West Beach, Lytham FY8 5QJ (on the A584 along the seafront)
☎ 01253 739898 FAX 01253 730657
Improvements continue to be made at this privately owned hotel, which is situated on the seafront, overlooking the Ribble estuary. Afternoon tea can be enjoyed in the newly refurbished lounge, with its deep cushioned sofas and raised open fire. A good range of well prepared dishes is offered in the spacious restaurant or from room service. Bedrooms currently vary in quality and comfort, although the majority have been completely refurbished. The staff are friendly and cheerful, especially the porters who on an inspection visit proved to be very helpful. The hotel also benefits from a large car park and a number of well equipped conference/banqueting suites.
44 en suite (bth/shr) No smoking in 4 bedrooms CTV in all bedrooms STV No dogs (ex guide dogs) Lift Night porter 50P Xmas V meals Coffee am Tea pm No smoking area in restaurant Last d 9.45pm
ROOMS: (incl. bkfst) s £79-£86; d £91-£99 * **LB**
OFF-PEAK: (incl. bkfst) s £40-£50; d £80-£90
MEALS: Lunch £13.50-£17 Dinner £17.50-£21&alc*
CONF: Thtr 300 Class 200 Board 100 Del from £90
CARDS:

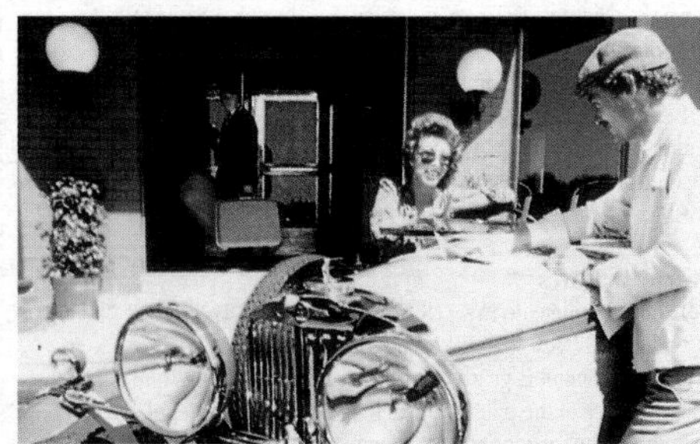

★★★67% **Chadwick**
South Promenade FY8 1NP ☎ 01253 720061 FAX 01253 714455
Ideally situated on the promenade, this family owned hotel with its friendly staff continues to be popular with its regular guests. Bedrooms are bright, freshly decorated and well equipped, some having spa baths. The spacious public areas include the newly refurbished restaurant, where a good choice of tasty dishes can be chosen from either the table d'hÙte or gourmet menu. For late arrivals an extensive 24-lounge

contd.

lounge and room service MENU is available. An immaculately maintained indoor pool, sauna and solarium are also available.
72 en suite (bth/shr) (24 fmly) CTV in all bedrooms STV No dogs (ex guide dogs) Lift Night porter 40P No coaches Indoor swimming pool (heated) Sauna Solarium Gym Pool table Jacuzzi/spa Turkish bath Games room Wkly live entertainment ch fac Xmas International Cuisine V meals Coffee am Tea pm No smoking in restaurant Last d 8.30pm
ROOMS: (incl. bkfst) s £35-£39.50; d £46-£52 * **LB**
OFF-PEAK: (incl. bkfst) s £35-£38; d £46-£48
MEALS: Lunch £6.90-£8 High tea £5.50-£6.90 Dinner £15-£15.80
CONF: Thtr 72 Class 24 Board 28 Del from £52
CARDS:

See advertisement on page 417

★★★65% **Bedford**
307-311 Clifton Dr South FY8 1HN ☎ 01253 724636
FAX 01253 729244
This friendly, family-run hotel is conveniently situated close to the town centre and the promenade. Bedrooms vary in size, but are attractively decorated, well equipped and include extras such as bathrobes. A good choice of home-made dishes is available in an attractively furnished dining room and there is also a small coffee shop which is open all day. The hotel also has a conference and banqueting suite, leisure facilities, and a sizeable car park at the front.
36 en suite (bth/shr) (6 fmly) CTV in all bedrooms STV Lift Night porter 20P Sauna Solarium Gym Jacuzzi/spa Steam room Wkly live entertainment Xmas English & Continental Cuisine V meals Coffee am Tea pm No smoking in restaurant Last d 8.30pm
ROOMS: (incl. bkfst) s £32.50-£35; d £50-£59 * **LB**
OFF-PEAK: (incl. bkfst) s £30; d £50
MEALS: Lunch £5.95&alc High tea £5.95 Dinner £15&alc
CONF: Thtr 150 Class 100 Board 40 Del from £40
CARDS: £

★★67% ***Glendower***

North Promenade FY8 2NQ ☎ 01253 723241
FAX 01253 723241
A friendly privately-owned hotel situated on the North Promenade only a short walk from the centre of St Anne's. In recent years the hotel has been totally refurbished and provides well appointed accommodation with many modern features. Two rooms have four-poster beds and several have been designed for families and have separate bedrooms. There are comfortable lounges, an attractive restaurant and banqueting and conference facilities as well as a private car park. There is also a small leisure centre with a heated pool, sauna and solarium.
60 en suite (bth) (17 fmly) CTV in all bedrooms Lift Night porter 45P Indoor swimming pool (heated) Sauna Solarium Pool table Badminton Table tennis Fitness room V meals Coffee am Last d 8.15pm
CARDS:

★★65% **St Ives**
7-9 South Promenade FY8 1LS ☎ 01253 720011 FAX 01253 722873
Closed 24-26 Dec
This friendly hotel is geared very much towards families and is ideally situated close to the pier. The spacious public areas include a swimming pool, games and TV rooms and plenty of lounge areas as well as a crèche and purpose-built soft play area. A good range of popular dishes are served in the spacious restaurant. The modern bedrooms vary in size and many have been redecorated with pretty, colour co-ordinated wallpapers and fabrics.
70 rms (60 bth 3 shr) (44 fmly) CTV in all bedrooms STV Night porter Air conditioning 100P Indoor swimming pool (heated) Sauna Solarium Gym Pool table Crazy golf Cycle hire ch fac Xmas English & French Cuisine V meals Coffee am Tea pm Last d 8.30pm
ROOMS: (incl. bkfst) s £19.50-£32.50; d £59 * **LB**
OFF-PEAK: (incl. bkfst) d £32.50
MEALS: Lunch £5 Dinner £14.50*
CONF: Thtr 100 Class 100 Board 50 Del £50
CARDS:

★71% **Lindum**

63-67 South Promenade FY8 1LZ (opposite the putting green) ☎ 01253 721534 & 722516
FAX 01253 721364
Situated on the promenade at St Annes, within a short walk of the town centre, this popular resort hotel features well equipped modern bedrooms with en suite bath or shower rooms. Public rooms are spaciously comfortable, and live entertainment is put on regularly throughout the season. The daily menu offers good value for money, friendly staff provide helpful service and the hotel has its own forecourt car park.
80 en suite (bth/shr) (25 fmly) No smoking in 4 bedrooms CTV in all bedrooms Lift Night porter Air conditioning 20P Sauna Solarium Jacuzzi/spa Xmas British & Continental Cuisine V meals Coffee am Tea pm No smoking in restaurant Last d 6.45pm
ROOMS: (incl. bkfst) s £26-£35; d £52-£60 **LB**
OFF-PEAK: (incl. bkfst) s fr £24.50; d fr £40
MEALS: Sunday Lunch fr £8.50 Dinner fr £11.50
CONF: Thtr 80 Class 30 Board 25 Del from £40
CARDS: £

★65% ***Ennes Court***
107 South Prom FY8 1NP ☎ 01253 723731
This popular, privately owned and personally run hotel is ideally situated on the promenade. The atmosphere is informal and relaxed and nothing is too much trouble for owners Mr and Mrs Traynor, who are extremely friendly and helpful. All bar one of the rooms is en suite, and all are comfortably furnished, some enjoying the most marvellous views. Guests can relax in the little sun lounge, the larger more formal lounge or the cosy bar. A good range of simple, but well prepared dishes is available in the dining room.
10 en suite (bth/shr) (2 fmly) CTV in all bedrooms No dogs (ex guide dogs) 9P No coaches No children 3yrs

MACCLESFIELD Cheshire Map 07 SJ97
See also Pott Shrigley

★★★63% **Belgrade Hotel & Restaurant**

Jackson Ln, Kerridge, Bollington SK10 5BG (off A523, 2m along B5090) ☎ 01625 573246
FAX 01625 574791
Surrounded by pleasant grounds, this listed Victorian building stands between the villages of Bollington and Kerridge and enjoys pleasant country views. Courtesy transport is provided to Manchester airport which is only 25 minutes away. The hotel also provides modern and comfortable bedrooms which are well equipped and now include satellite TV and trouser presses. There is an impressive hall with a delightful mosaic and this leads to the comfortable public rooms which includes a cosy bar and lounge. A very good range of food is available in the spacious restaurant and the conservatory is a pleasant place in which to take afternoon tea.
54 en suite (bth/shr) (2 fmly) CTV in all bedrooms STV No dogs (ex guide dogs) Night porter 200P Pool table Xmas International Cuisine V meals Coffee am Tea pm Last d 9.30pm
ROOMS: (incl. bkfst) s £49.50; d £59.50 *
OFF-PEAK: (incl. bkfst) s £40; d £49.50
MEALS: Lunch £6.95-£9.95 Dinner £13.95*
CONF: Thtr 80 Class 50 Board 50
CARDS: £

❀ Rosette symbols denote the quality of food in hotel restaurants on a rising scale of 1-5.

MADELEY Staffordshire Map 07 SJ74

★★61% ***Crewe Arms***
Wharf St, Madeley Heath CW3 9LP (Off A525, near junct with A531)
☎ 01782 750392
The atmosphere is informal and relaxed at this privately owned hotel, which is ideally situated just 15 minutes from the M6. The spacious bedrooms are all furnished in a similar style, conveniently laid out and well equipped. Guests have the choice of eating informally in the characterful bar, where a good range of lighter meals are served, or more formally in the panelled restaurant. Families are also welcomed, there is a pool table and a games area for children.
10 en suite (bth) (2 fmly) CTV in all bedrooms No dogs (ex guide dogs) 50P Pool table V meals Coffee am Tea pm
CARDS:

MAIDENCOMBE See Torquay

MAIDENHEAD Berkshire Map 04 SU88
See also Bray

★★★★ ❀❀❀ 78% **Fredrick's**

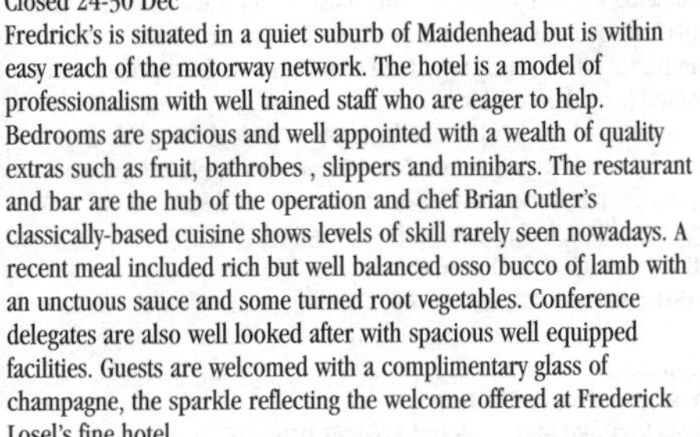

Shoppenhangers Rd SL6 2PZ ☎ 01628 35934
FAX 01628 771054
Closed 24-30 Dec
Fredrick's is situated in a quiet suburb of Maidenhead but is within easy reach of the motorway network. The hotel is a model of professionalism with well trained staff who are eager to help. Bedrooms are spacious and well appointed with a wealth of quality extras such as fruit, bathrobes , slippers and minibars. The restaurant and bar are the hub of the operation and chef Brian Cutler's classically-based cuisine shows levels of skill rarely seen nowadays. A recent meal included rich but well balanced osso bucco of lamb with an unctuous sauce and some turned root vegetables. Conference delegates are also well looked after with spacious well equipped facilities. Guests are welcomed with a complimentary glass of champagne, the sparkle reflecting the welcome offered at Frederick Losel's fine hotel.
37 en suite (bth/shr) CTV in all bedrooms STV No dogs Night porter 90P No coaches Croquet lawn English & French Cuisine V meals Coffee am Last d 9.45pm
ROOMS: (incl. bkfst) s £148-£158; d £178-£188 *
MEALS: Lunch £21.50-£25.50&alc Dinner £31.50&alc*
CONF: Thtr 120 Class 80 Board 60 Del from £195
CARDS:

★★★★58% **Holiday Inn Maidenhead/Windsor**

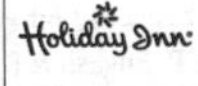

Manor Ln SL6 2RA (once in Shoppenhanger Road go straight across two mini-roundabouts, hotel on right behind Esso Garage) ☎ 01628 23444
FAX 01628 770035
On the outskirts of the town with good access to the M4 this modern hotel is popular during the week with business people. Some bedrooms have been refurbished but most are compact although with all the expected facilities, including 24-hour room service.
189 en suite (bth/shr) (20 fmly) No smoking in 40 bedrooms CTV in all bedrooms STV No dogs (ex guide dogs) Lift Night porter 400P Indoor swimming pool (heated) Squash Snooker Sauna Solarium Gym Pool table Jacuzzi/spa International Cuisine V meals Coffee am Tea pm No smoking in restaurant Last d 9.30pm
ROOMS: d £120-£135 *
OFF-PEAK: (incl. bkfst) d £95-£130
MEALS: Lunch £7.95-£16.50 Dinner £19.50*
CONF: Thtr 400 Class 200 Board 30 Del from £148
CARDS:

★★★66% **Walton Cottage**
Marlow Rd SL6 7LT ☎ 01628 24394 FAX 01628 773851
Closed 25 Dec-3 Jan
This family-run hotel provides excellent accommodation close to the centre of town with some special rooms featuring sitting rooms and kitchenettes. Other rooms are smaller but all are well equipped and immaculately clean. The restaurant is useful through the week but restricted service applies at weekends when meals are only available by prior arrangement. Staff are willing and friendly.
25 en suite (bth/shr) 32 annexe en suite (bth/shr) CTV in all bedrooms STV No dogs (ex guide dogs) Lift Night porter 60P International Cuisine V meals Coffee am Tea pm No smoking in restaurant Last d 9.30pm
ROOMS: (incl. bkfst) s £69-£105; d £79-£130 *
MEALS: Bar Lunch £5-£8 Dinner fr £15.75*
CONF: Thtr 70 Class 40 Board 30
CARDS:

★★★66% **Ye Olde Bell Hotel**
Hurley SL6 5LX (take A4130 to Henley look for East Arms public house, High St is on the right just before the pub) ☎ 01628 825881
FAX 01628 825939
The main part of the hotel is full of old world character in keeping with the gentle nature of its peaceful setting. Most of the well equipped bedrooms are housed nearby in a series of converted outbuildings. There is a small cosy bar and an inviting restaurant which overlooks the rear lawns. Some of the meeting rooms are in a striking country house style.
11 en suite (bth/shr) 25 annexe en suite (bth/shr) (3 fmly) No smoking in 5 bedrooms CTV in 35 bedrooms STV Night porter 85P No coaches Croquet lawn Badminton Petanque Xmas V meals Coffee am Tea pm No smoking area in restaurant Last d 9.30pm

contd.

M

ROOMS: s £95-£110; d £110-£135 * **LB**
OFF-PEAK: (incl. bkfst & dinner) s fr £62.50; d fr £125
MEALS: Lunch fr £15.95 Dinner fr £19.50*
CONF: Thtr 140 Class 60 Board 40 Del from £145
CARDS:

★★★65% **Thames Riviera**
At the Bridge SL6 8DW ☎ 01628 74057 FAX 01628 776586
Closed 26-30 Dec
A substantial, well established, family-owned Victorian hotel, located beside the River Thames on the A4 leading out to Slough. Bedrooms are divided between the main building and the attractive Waterside Lodge across the car park; they vary in size but are all well equipped. The formal split-level restaurant enjoys river views, and there is a small coffee shop as well as 24-hour room service. Staff are pleasant and willing to please.
34 en suite (bth/shr) 18 annexe en suite (bth/shr) (1 fmly) No smoking in 4 bedrooms CTV in all bedrooms STV No dogs (ex guide dogs) Night porter 60P No coaches Wkly live entertainment International Cuisine V meals Coffee am Tea pm Last d 9.45pm
ROOMS: s £40-£80; d £80-£90 * **LB**
OFF-PEAK: (incl. bkfst) s £40; d £80
MEALS: Lunch £3-£13.95 Dinner fr £18.50&alc
CONF: Thtr 50 Class 30 Board 20 Del from £85
CARDS:

MAIDSTONE Kent Map 05 TQ75

★★★★61% **Marriott Tudor Park**

Ashford Rd, Bearsted ME14 4NQ (2m E, heading towards Ashford) ☎ 01622 734334
FAX 01622 735360
Built in the late 80s, this modern hotel has recently benefited from extensive refurbishment. Bedrooms now offer generously sized beds, striking fabrics and mini-bars, and an excellent new cardiovascular gym has been added to the already extensive leisure and golf facilities. Dining options include the informal Long Weekend Restaurant whilst Fairviews attracts guests looking for a fine dining experience.
118 en suite (bth/shr) (47 fmly) No smoking in 65 bedrooms CTV in all bedrooms STV Lift Night porter 250P Indoor swimming pool (heated) Golf 18 Tennis (hard) Sauna Solarium Gym Putting green Jacuzzi/spa Driving range Beauty salon Steam room ch fac Xmas V meals Coffee am Tea pm No smoking in restaurant Last d 10pm
ROOMS: (incl. bkfst) s fr £65; d fr £71 *
MEALS: Lunch £14.95-£16.95 Dinner fr £18&alc*
CONF: Thtr 250 Class 120 Board 60 Del from £115
CARDS:

★★★64% **Larkfield Priory**

London Rd ME20 6HJ ☎ 01732 846858
FAX 01732 846786
(For full entry see Larkfield)

★★ 74% **Tanyard**
Wierton Hill, Boughton Monchelsea ME17 4JT (from B2163 at Boughton Monchelsea, turn down Park Lane opposite Cock pub, first right down Wierton Road, fork right down Wierton Hill, hotel on left)
☎ 01622 744705 FAX 01622 741998
Closed Xmas & 1st wk Jan
Peacefully set in ten acres of landscaped hillside and gardens with a pond and lovely country views, this medieval country house provides accommodation of the highest standard. The spacious bedrooms are individually furnished, and while they retain their original character they also provide every modern facility. There are a cosy sitting room with a log fire and a small bar with a feature fireplace and stone floor. This leads into the new candlelit 30-cover restaurant, where proprietor Jan Davies offers a daily two, three or four-course fixed-price menu of enjoyable modern cooking.
6 en suite (bth/shr) CTV in all bedrooms No dogs (ex guide dogs) 20P No coaches Jacuzzi/spa No children 6yrs English & French Cuisine V meals No smoking in restaurant Last d 9pm
ROOMS: (incl. bkfst) s £60-£125; d £90-£125
MEALS: Lunch £20 Dinner £25*
CARDS:
See advertisement on opposite page

★★64% **Grange Moor**
St Michael's Rd ME16 8BS (off A26) ☎ 01622 677623
FAX 01622 678246
Closed last week Dec
A friendly family run mock Tudor hotel situated just off the A26 Tonbridge Road. There is a good range of well equipped bedrooms some with four poster in the main building, and newer rooms (without a direct dial telephone) further down the road. The bar is very popular with the locals and serves a comprehensive choice of popular bar meals and snacks. There are several dining and function rooms, and a small well furnished lounge. Ample car parking space is provided.
47 rms (12 bth 33 shr) (6 fmly) CTV in all bedrooms Night porter 60P English & French Cuisine V meals Coffee am Tea pm Last d 10pm
ROOMS: (incl. bkfst) s £38-£47; d £52 * **LB**
OFF-PEAK: (incl. bkfst) s £35-£46; d £45
MEALS: Bar Lunch £8.50-£12.50alc Dinner fr £12.50alc*
CONF: Thtr 100 Class 50 Board 50
CARDS:

★★64% **Russell**

CONSORT HOTELS

136 Boxley Rd ME14 2AE ☎ 01622 692221
FAX 01622 762084
This attractive Victorian house is set in two acres of grounds, on the edge of Maidstone only minutes from the major routes. The bedrooms which are being steadily upgraded are well equipped and have modern facilities. The attractive restaurant offers good home-cooked food and has a good local following. There are several function rooms and the hotel is a popular venue for wedding receptions.
42 en suite (bth/shr) (4 fmly) CTV in all bedrooms No dogs (ex guide dogs) Night porter 100P Jacuzzi/spa ch fac Xmas French

Cuisine V meals Coffee am Tea pm No smoking area in restaurant Last d 9.30pm
ROOMS: (incl. bkfst) s £45-£65; d £60-£85 * **LB**
OFF-PEAK: (incl. bkfst) s £45; d £50-£60
MEALS: Lunch fr £13.95&alc Dinner fr £13.95&alc
CONF: Thtr 300 Class 100 Board 90 Del from £75
CARDS:

★★61% **Boxley House**

The Street, Boxley ME14 3DZ (3m N between A249 & A229, follow signs to Boxley hotel next to church)
☎ 01622 692269 FAX 01622 683536
RS Sun
A 17th century former manor house set in 20 acres of parkland and conveniently located for access for M20 Jct 6. Modestly furnished accommodation has been modernised and is provided in both the main house and in adjacent annexe buildings, while public rooms compromise a front bar, an attractive wood panelled and galleried dining area combining the Garden function room, and a first floor breakfast room and lounge. Popular for local functions, wedding receptions and live club and disco entertainment on Friday nights the atmosphere is informal, and friendly, and the hotel is well managed by Peter and Jackie Quilty. Other facilities include an adjacent conference room and ample car parking.
11 en suite (bth/shr) 7 annexe en suite (bth/shr) (3 fmly) CTV in all bedrooms STV 102P Outdoor swimming pool (heated) V meals Coffee am Tea pm Last d 9pm
MEALS: Lunch £9.50-£11.75 Dinner £15-£25alc*
CONF: Thtr 90 Class 50 Board 20
CARDS:

Travel Inn

London Rd ME16 0HG (leave M20 junct5 take London Rd and head towards Maidstone. Half a mile from junc5. ☎ 01622 752515 FAX 01622 672469
Purpose-built accommodation, offering spacious, well equipped bedrooms, all with en suite bathrooms. Meals may be taken at the nearby family restaurant. For more information about Travel Inns, consult the Contents page under Hotel Groups.
40 en suite (bth/shr)
ROOMS: d £35.50 *

MALDON Essex Map 05 TL80
See also Tolleshunt Knights

★★64% ***The Blue Boar***

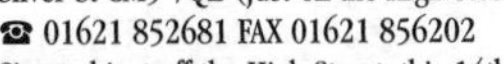

Silver St CM9 7QE (just off the High Street)
☎ 01621 852681 FAX 01621 856202
Situated just off the High Street, this 14th-century coaching inn offers guests the choice of three bars which are full of character. Most of the bedrooms are furnished to an excellent standard with mahogany furniture and floral fabrics, and planned refurbishment will take care of the remaining few.
21 en suite (bth/shr) 8 annexe en suite (bth/shr) (1 fmly) No smoking in 17 bedrooms CTV in all bedrooms 40P V meals Coffee am Tea pm Last d 9.30pm
CARDS:

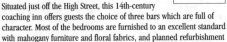

MALHAM North Yorkshire Map 07 SD96

★★65% **The Buck Inn**
BD23 4DA ☎ 01729 830317
In the heart of the village overlooking the beck, this stone built inn offers warm and friendly service. A good range of food is available either in the newly refurbished dining room or one of the two characterful bars. Bedrooms are well equipped and all are now en suite and the hotel offers very good value for money.
10 en suite (bth/shr) (2 fmly) CTV in all bedrooms No dogs (ex

guide dogs) 20P Xmas V meals Coffee am Last d 9pm
ROOMS: (incl. bkfst) s £26-£31; d £52 * **LB**
OFF-PEAK: (incl. bkfst) d £46
MEALS: Lunch fr £10.30alc Dinner £6.85-£18.95alc*
CARDS:

MALMESBURY Wiltshire Map 03 ST98

★★★ 76% **Old Bell**
Abbey Row SN16 0AG (on A429)
☎ 01666 822344 FAX 01666 825145
Said to be England's oldest hotel, this Grade I listed property with its own garden and ample parking is located next to the abbey in the centre of historic Malmesbury. Modern facilities have been provided in recent years which, carefully combined with the many original features of the building, result in an extremely comfortable hotel of enormous character. Some of the bedrooms are contained in a newer wing while others form part of the main house and may have views of the church or main street. A choice of fixed-price menus is available in the most attractive Edwardian dining room; all dishes are skilfully prepared from fresh ingredients, and aptly supported by a selection of fine wines from around the World.

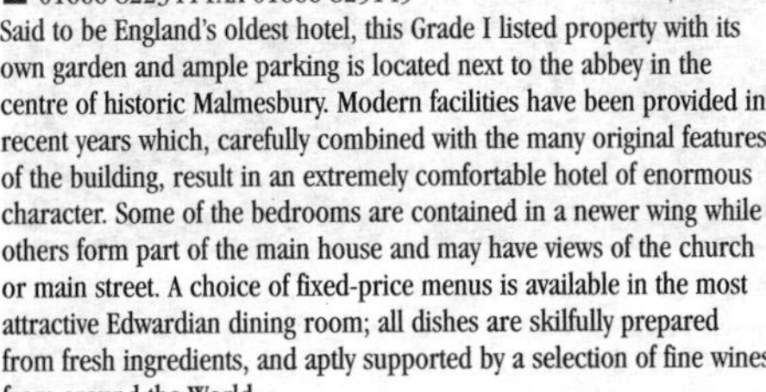

31 en suite (bth/shr) (1 fmly) CTV in all bedrooms STV Night porter 30P Xmas V meals Coffee am Tea pm Last d 9.30pm
ROOMS: (incl. bkfst) s £60-£70; d £85-£150 * **LB**
MEALS: Lunch fr £15 Dinner £18.50-£24*
CONF: Thtr 40 Class 20 Board 26 Del from £115
CARDS:

★★★ 75% **Whatley Manor**
Easton Grey SN16 0RB (3m W on B4040)
☎ 01666 822888 FAX 01666 826120
Set in mature, extensive and well kept gardens and grounds, this

contd.

impressive mellow stone-built manor house offers the ideal haven for both the leisure and business traveller. The outdoor heated swimming pool is available during the summer months, a tennis court is also provided. Indoor leisure facilities include snooker, table tennis, jacuzzi, sauna and solarium which are all situated in the former stable yard. Public areas include a spacious wood-panelled drawing room with a welcoming open fire. Bedrooms are generally spacious and comfortable, especially rooms in the Manor, Tudor and Terrace wings, while rooms in the Court House are more functional, which is reflected in the tariff. In the restaurant an interesting table d'h'te menu is available. A friendly team of staff provide an efficient style of service in a relaxed manner.

18 en suite (bth) 11 annexe en suite (bth) (3 fmly) CTV in all bedrooms Night porter 60P No coaches Outdoor swimming pool (heated) Tennis (hard) Fishing Sauna Solarium Croquet lawn Jacuzzi/spa Table tennis Xmas English & Continental Cuisine V meals Coffee am Tea pm Last d 9pm
ROOMS: (incl. bkfst) s £70-£80; d £82-£114 * **LB**
OFF-PEAK: (incl. bkfst) d £72-£100
MEALS: Lunch £14-£15 High tea fr £7 Dinner fr £28*
CONF: Thtr 50 Class 30 Board 30 Del £125
CARDS:

See advertisement on opposite page

★★★66% **Knoll House**
Swindon Rd SN16 9LU (on B4042)
☎ 01666 823114 FAX 01666 823897

MINOTEL Great Britain

Within 5 miles of junction 17 of the M4 and 25 minutes of the M5, this hotel is ideally situated on the outskirts of England's oldest borough of Malmesbury. Formerly a Victorian family home, The Knoll House now offers comfortable accommodation and a relaxed atmosphere. Bedrooms range from those in the main house which tend to be more spacious, to those in the annexe which are more cosy; all are equipped with a range of modern facilities. The Cedar Room Restaurant provides formal surrounding in which to dine from an interesting fixed priced menu, while lighter meals and snacks are available from the blackboard in the bar.
12 en suite (bth/shr) 10 annexe en suite (bth/shr) (1 fmly) CTV in all bedrooms 40P Outdoor swimming pool (heated) Croquet lawn Xmas English & French Cuisine V meals Coffee am Tea pm No smoking in restaurant Last d 9.30pm
ROOMS: (incl. bkfst) s £50-£60; d £65-£80 * **LB**
MEALS: Sunday Lunch £2.95 Dinner £15-£24*
CONF: Thtr 50 Board 30 Del from £85
CARDS:

See advertisement on opposite page

★★69% **Mayfield House**
SN16 9EW (3m N on A429) ☎ 01666 577409 & 577198
FAX 01666 577977
Mayfield House is a friendly hotel in a small village setting three miles from Malmesbury. The atmosphere is relaxed and the resident proprietors are naturally hospitable. Bedrooms, including some on the ground floor, come in a variety of shapes and sizes and are gradually being refurbished. There is a comfortable foyer lounge, and Pettifers Bar offers a range of meals which provide an alternative to the more imaginative menu available in an attractive restaurant which - under the direction of keen young head chef Mark Bullows - has now been awarded a rosette.
20 en suite (bth/shr) (1 fmly) CTV in all bedrooms 50P Xmas English & French Cuisine V meals Coffee am Tea pm No smoking in restaurant Last d 9pm
ROOMS: (incl. bkfst) s £42; d £62 **LB**
MEALS: Sunday Lunch fr £10.95 Dinner fr £15.95
CONF: Thtr 40 Class 30 Board 25
CARDS:

See advertisement on opposite page

MALTON North Yorkshire Map 08 SE77

★★★70% **Burythorpe House**
Burythorpe YO17 9LB (4m S) ☎ 01653 658200
FAX 01653 658204

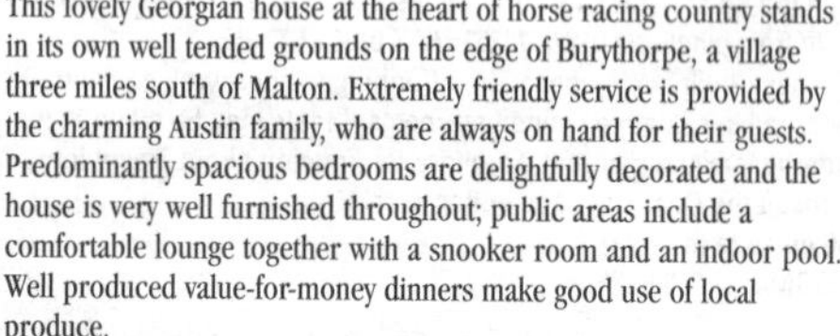

This lovely Georgian house at the heart of horse racing country stands in its own well tended grounds on the edge of Burythorpe, a village three miles south of Malton. Extremely friendly service is provided by the charming Austin family, who are always on hand for their guests. Predominantly spacious bedrooms are delightfully decorated and the house is very well furnished throughout; public areas include a comfortable lounge together with a snooker room and an indoor pool. Well produced value-for-money dinners make good use of local produce.
11 en suite (bth/shr) (2 fmly) CTV in all bedrooms No dogs (ex guide dogs) 50P No coaches Indoor swimming pool (heated) Tennis (hard) Snooker Sauna Solarium Gym Xmas International Cuisine V meals Coffee am Last d 9.30pm
ROOMS: (incl. bkfst) s fr £43.50; d £53-£80 *
CARDS:

★★★65% ***Green Man***
15 Market St YO17 0LY (from A64 follow signs fo Malton town centre, turn left into Market St, hotel on left) ☎ 01653 600370
FAX 01653 696006
Standing in the centre of the market town, this well furnished hotel has been recently refurbished and is very much the town's meeting place. The bedrooms are well equipped and have been attractively furnished whilst the public rooms are comfortable and inviting. A good range of food is provided and service from a dedicated young staff is attentive and friendly.
24 en suite (bth/shr) (4 fmly) CTV in all bedrooms Night porter 40P V meals Coffee am Tea pm Last d 10pm
CARDS:

See advertisement on opposite page

★★64% **Talbot**
Yorkersgate YO17 0AA (off A64) ☎ 01653 694031
FAX 01653 693355

contd.

Situated on the western approach to the market town, this well established ivy-clad hotel overlooks the River Derwent and some open countryside. A major refurbishment has recently been completed to upgrade facilities, yet many traditional architectural features are still retained..
31 en suite (bth/shr) (3 fmly) CTV in all bedrooms Night porter 36P Xmas V meals Coffee am Tea pm Last d 9pm
ROOMS: (incl. bkfst) s £37.50-£52.50; d £75-£105 **LB**
MEALS: Lunch £10.50-£11.50 Dinner fr £16.50
CONF: Thtr 80 Class 40 Board 40 Del from £55
CARDS:

See advertisement on opposite page

★ 72% **Newstead Grange**

Beverley Rd, Norton YO17 9PJ (on the B1248 at junct with Settrington road) ☎ 01653 692502
FAX 01653 696951
Closed mid-Nov-mid Feb
Owners Pat and Paul Williams look after their guests personally in this dignified Georgian country house. Prettily decorated bedrooms contain good quality beds and some fine antiques, while the lounge with its open fire provides a popular meeting place. The four-course dinner is all home-cooked.
8 en suite (bth/shr) No smoking in all bedrooms CTV in all bedrooms No dogs (ex guide dogs) 15P No coaches A non-smoking establishment No children 10yrs English & French Cuisine V meals No smoking in restaurant Last d 7pm
ROOMS: (incl. bkfst) s £40-£45; d £66-£75 * **LB**
OFF-PEAK: (incl. bkfst) s £36.50-£40; d £62-£66
CARDS:

★ 62% **Wentworth Arms**
Town St, Old Malton YO17 0HD (turn off A64 onto A169 to Malton. Hotel 400yds on right) ☎ 01653 692618 FAX 01653 692618
Closed 25 Dec
This former coaching inn at Old Malton is a mile from the town, just off the by-pass at the A169 junction. A friendly, family-owned and run hotel, it offers very good value for money and is renowned for its hearty home-cooked meals which are served in the beamed and stone walled dining room.
5 rms (4 shr) CTV in all bedrooms No dogs 30P No coaches No children 6yrs Coffee am Tea pm Last d 9pm
ROOMS: (incl. bkfst) s fr £23; d fr £46 *
MEALS: Lunch £3.75-£6.75alc High tea fr £4.50alc Dinner fr £6.75alc
CARDS:

MALVERN Hereford & Worcester Map 03 SO74

Courtesy & Care Award

★★★ 70% **Cottage in the Wood**

CONSORT CROWN

Holywell Rd, Malvern Wells WR14 4LG
(3m S off A449 opposite Gulf/Rover petrol station. Signposted from main road)
☎ 01684 575859 FAX 01684 560662
Nestling on a wooded hillside and enjoying spectacular views, this one time home of Sir Edward Elgar is now a family-run hotel with a warm and welcoming atmosphere. Cosy bedrooms, contained in a cluster of 3 separate buildings, are packed with personalised touches and thoughtful extras such as a pair of binoculars and of course Malvern water, the local brew. Day rooms have recently been attractively refurbished and the stylish dining room provides a fitting setting for the imaginative cooking of Kathryn Young. Good use is made of seasonal produce and the highlight of a recent meal was some accurately cooked cod set on a potato and fennel salad with tartar dressing. Owners and staff here have won the AA Courtesy and Care Award for 1996/7.

8 en suite (bth/shr) 12 annexe en suite (bth/shr) CTV in all bedrooms 40P No coaches Xmas V meals Coffee am Tea pm No smoking in restaurant Last d 9pm
ROOMS: (incl. bkfst) s £68-£74; d £89-£135 * **LB**
MEALS: Sunday Lunch £10.95-£13.95&alc Dinner £23-£27alc*
CONF: Thtr 20 Board 14 Del £110
CARDS:

See advertisement on opposite page

★★★ 65% **Abbey**

DE VERE HOTELS

Abbey Rd WR14 3ET (opposite Winter Gardens)
☎ 01684 892332 FAX 01684 892662
Right in the heart of the historic town, the large, popular hotel is positioned directly adjacent to the Benedictine Priory. Over recent times it has benefited from a major upgrading programme and extensive public areas include several conference and function rooms as well as comfortable bars and lounges. Bedrooms vary in size and location but are fitted with modern furnishings and a good range of equipment. The restaurant serves a daily fixed-price menu with good vegetarian choice and a carte with popular dishes. Guests have free use of the nearby swimming pool and large car park.
107 en suite (bth/shr) (5 fmly) No smoking in 16 bedrooms CTV in all bedrooms Lift Night porter 120P Wkly live entertainment Xmas V meals Coffee am Tea pm No smoking in restaurant Last d 9pm
ROOMS: (incl. bkfst) s £75; d £85 * **LB**
MEALS: Lunch £9 Dinner fr £16.50*
CONF: Thtr 350 Class 160 Board 68 Del £102.50
CARDS:

★★★ 65% **Colwall Park**
Walwyn Rd, Colwall WR13 6QG (3m SW on B4218)
☎ 01684 540206 FAX 01684 540847
Colwall Park is a part red brick and part black-timbered and white washed hotel set in the centre of the village of Colwall. There is a warm atmosphere in the panelled bar and lounge, and for functions there is a ballroom opening on to the garden. The simply kept but smart bedrooms are reached via a wide staircase. A new chef with a solid London training has settled in and adapted to the style of the region. The daily fixed-price menu offers well crafted dishes such as poached haddock with Welsh rarebit, and roast breast of chicken with a rich cream sauce and grapes.
23 en suite (bth/shr) (6 fmly) No smoking in 2 bedrooms CTV in all bedrooms Night porter 40P No coaches Croquet lawn Boule Wkly

live entertainment Xmas V meals Coffee am Tea pm No smoking in restaurant Last d 9pm
ROOMS: (incl. bkfst) s £49.50-£59.50; d £75-£89.50 **LB**
MEALS: Lunch £11.50&alc Dinner £20-£22.50&alc
CONF: Thtr 120 Class 80 Board 50 Del £82.50
CARDS:

★★★64% **Foley Arms**

14 Worcester Rd WR14 4QS (M5 exit 7 north or 8 south, M50 exit 2, proceed to Great Malvern on A449) ☎ 01684 573397 FAX 01684 569665

Reputed to be Malvern's oldest hotel, the Foley Arms dates back to the 19th century. It stands in the town centre and is being continually improved by its friendly owners. Bedrooms vary in size and style; most have period-style furniture and all have a good array of modern equipment. Family and four-poster rooms are also available. Public areas include a period-style bar, a bright restaurant overlooking the terrace and a choice of smoking and non-smoking lounges. Other

contd.

facilities include a small conference room, a large self-contained function suite and a private car park.
28 en suite (bth/shr) (2 fmly) No smoking in 5 bedrooms CTV in all bedrooms STV 42P Discount at Leisure Centre Xmas English & French Cuisine V meals Coffee am Tea pm No smoking in restaurant Last d 9.30pm
ROOMS: (incl. bkfst) s £65-£82; d £83-£105 * **LB**
MEALS: Lunch £9.25-£9.75 Dinner £17.50&alc*
CONF: Thtr 150 Class 40 Board 45 Del from £88
CARDS:

See advertisement on page 425

★★❀ 74% **Holdfast Cottage**

Little Malvern WR13 6NA (on A4104 midway between Welland and Little Malvern) ☎ 01684 310288
FAX 01684 311117
Set in two acres of gardens, this charming hotel is run in a very friendly manner by Jane and Stephen Knowles. Attractive bedrooms are really comfortable and lots of personal touches are provided. Day rooms have a wealth of charm and the restaurant enjoys a high reputation for its cuisine.
8 en suite (bth/shr) (1 fmly) No smoking in all bedrooms CTV in all bedrooms 15P No coaches Croquet lawn Xmas Coffee am Tea pm No smoking in restaurant Last d 9pm
ROOMS: (incl. bkfst) s £42-£44; d £74-£84 **LB**
OFF-PEAK: (incl. bkfst) d £74-£80
MEALS: Dinner £18
CONF: Thtr 20 Board 14 Del from £90
CARDS:

See advertisement on opposite page

★★66% **Mount Pleasant**

Belle Vue Ter WR14 4PZ (on A449, 0.5m from Great Malvern station) ☎ 01684 561837
FAX 01684 569968 Closed 25 & 26 Dec
This attractive Georgian property is centrally situated and commands impressive views of the Severn Valley. The extensive terraced gardens lead directly onto the Malvern Hills. Personally run, it provides accommodation that is all similarly well equipped, and most bedrooms are furnished in period style. Public areas include the popular "Cafe El Sol", which serves as a coffee shop during the day and a restaurant at night. A wide choice of dishes is provided, including several Spanish specialities. In addition to the lounge bar and quiet resident's lounge, the hotel also has two function or conference rooms.
15 rms (14 bth/shr) CTV in all bedrooms No dogs (ex guide dogs) 20P English & Spanish Cuisine V meals Coffee am Tea pm No smoking area in restaurant Last d 9.30pm
ROOMS: (incl. bkfst) s £48-£52.50; d £65-£77.50 * **LB**
MEALS: Lunch £7.50-£12.50 Dinner £14.95-£15.95&alc
CONF: Thtr 80 Class 40 Board 45 Del from £67.50
CARDS:

See advertisement on opposite page

★★64% **Great Malvern**
Graham Rd WR14 2HN (from Worcester on A449, turn left just beyond the fire station into Graham Rd. Hotel is at the end of Graham Rd on the right) ☎ 01684 563411 FAX 01684 560514
Closed 24-26 Dec
Improvements continue at this 18th-century hotel in the town centre. Bedrooms are generally spacious and comfortable, with mixed furnishings. There is a popular bar and a congenial bistro with more formal dining.
14 rms (13 bth/shr) (2 fmly) CTV in all bedrooms No dogs (ex guide dogs) Lift 9P European Cuisine V meals Coffee am Tea pm No smoking area in restaurant Last d 9pm
ROOMS: (incl. bkfst) s £45-£50; d £60-£70 * **LB**
MEALS: Bar Lunch £8.50-£19.50alc Dinner £9.50-£20.50alc
CONF: Thtr 60 Class 20 Board 30 Del from £70
CARDS:

★★63% **Cotford**
51 Graham Rd WR14 2HU ☎ 01684 574680 & 574642
FAX 01684 572952
Closed 24 Dec-5 Jan
Dating from the 19th century and conveniently located within a few minutes' walk of the town centre, this large stone-built house stands in mature grounds with its own private car park. Some of the recently refurbished modern bedrooms are suitable for family occupation, and other facilities include a small bar and a comfortable lounge.
16 rms (15 bth/shr) (4 fmly) CTV in all bedrooms 18P Pool table V meals Coffee am Tea pm No smoking in restaurant Last d 9pm
ROOMS: (incl. bkfst) s £35-£42; d £58-£63 **LB**
MEALS: Dinner £12-£20*
CONF: Thtr 26 Class 26 Del from £60
CARDS:

★★63% **Malvern Hills**
Wynds Point WR13 6DW (4m S, at junct of A449 with B4232)
☎ 01684 540237 & 540690 FAX 01684 540327
Located on the A449, west of Malvern, this family-run hotel is an ideal place for ramblers; the location is noteworthy for the nearby ancient earthworks from which there are stunning views. The hotel has a popular bar, a restaurant offering good cooking and accommodation which provides sound comfort.

17 rms (16 bth/shr) (1 fmly) No smoking in 12 bedrooms CTV in all bedrooms 35P No coaches Xmas English & French Cuisine V meals Coffee am Tea pm Last d 9pm
ROOMS: (incl. bkfst) s £35-£40; d £60-£65 * **LB**
OFF-PEAK: (incl. bkfst) s £30-£40
MEALS: Lunch £8-£13.50 Dinner £15.50-£17.50*
CONF: Thtr 40 Class 40 Board 30 Del from £69
CARDS:

★★62% ***Essington***
Holywell Rd, Malvern Wells WR14 4LQ (3m S A449)
☎ 01684 561177 FAX 01684 561177
From its elevated position on the side of the Malvern Hills, this large 19th-century property set in two acres of terraced gardens commands views across the Severn Valley to the Cotswolds. Traditionally furnished and well equipped bedrooms include one with a four-poster bed, welcoming fires are lit in the lounge bar and there is an attractive dining room with period-style furnishings.
9 en suite (bth/shr) CTV in all bedrooms 30P No coaches Coffee am Last d 8.15pm
CARDS:

★★62% **Thornbury House**
Avenue Rd, Great Malvern WR14 3AE (close to the Railway Station)
☎ 01684 572278 FAX 01684 577042
A large, detached Victorian property, this personally run hotel situated close to the city centre, a few minutes from the railway station, provides soundly maintained accommodation which is equally suitable for tourists and commercial visitors. Some bedrooms have period-style furniture while others are more modern and most have en suite facilities. Public rooms include an attractive dining room and a cosy bar, and there are mature gardens to the rear.
15 rms (11 shr) (1 fmly) No smoking in 4 bedrooms CTV in all bedrooms 12P No coaches V meals No smoking in restaurant Last d 9pm
ROOMS: (incl. bkfst) s £38; d £58 * **LB**
MEALS: Dinner £9.95-£18&alc
CARDS:

MANCHESTER Greater Manchester Map 07 SJ89
See also Manchester Airport & Salford

★★★★❀❀76% **Victoria & Albert**

Water St M60 9EA (Granada) ☎ 0161 832 1188
FAX 0161 834 2484
Situated opposite the Granada Studios and on the banks of the River Irwell, this modern hotel has been imaginatively created from former warehouses, reminders of which are evident in the exposed brick walls, wooden beams and iron pillars which are features of the well equipped bedrooms and stylish public areas. The latter includes a conservatory lounge, a Victorian themed bar-lounge and all day French style brasserie. Our award of two rosettes is for the Sherlock Holmes Restaurant, where chef John Benson-Smith and his team offer from menus written in an entertaining style, imaginative cuisine, underpinned by sound classical technique. The staff and management offer a dedicated and cheerful service.
156 en suite (bth/shr) (2 fmly) No smoking in 24 bedrooms CTV in all bedrooms STV No dogs (ex guide dogs) Lift Night porter Air conditioning 97P Snooker Sauna Solarium Gym Wkly live entertainment ch fac Xmas V meals Coffee am Tea pm No smoking area in restaurant Last d 9.30pm
ROOMS: s £135-£165; d £135-£250 * **LB**
OFF-PEAK: (incl. bkfst) s £85-£115; d £95-£115
MEALS: Lunch £17.95&alc Dinner £30-£40alc*
CARDS:

See advertisement on page 429

M

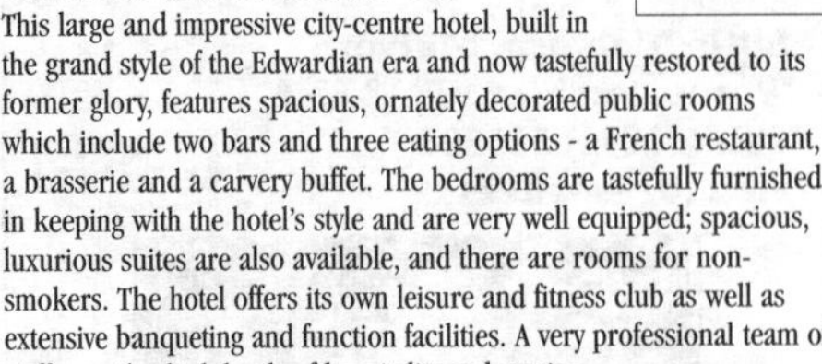

★★★★ 71% **Holiday Inn Crowne Plaza**
Peter St M60 2DS (close to G-Mex Centre)
☎ 0161 236 3333 FAX 0161 932 4100
This large and impressive city-centre hotel, built in the grand style of the Edwardian era and now tastefully restored to its former glory, features spacious, ornately decorated public rooms which include two bars and three eating options - a French restaurant, a brasserie and a carvery buffet. The bedrooms are tastefully furnished in keeping with the hotel's style and are very well equipped; spacious, luxurious suites are also available, and there are rooms for non-smokers. The hotel offers its own leisure and fitness club as well as extensive banqueting and function facilities. A very professional team of staff provides high levels of hospitality and service.
303 en suite (bth/shr) (63 fmly) No smoking in 120 bedrooms CTV in all bedrooms STV No dogs (ex guide dogs) Lift Night porter Air conditioning Indoor swimming pool (heated) Squash Sauna Solarium Gym Jacuzzi/spa Hairdressing Beauty salon Wkly live entertainment Xmas International Cuisine V meals Coffee am Tea pm Last d 10.30pm
ROOMS: d £125-£145 **LB**
MEALS: Lunch £14.95-£20.95&alc Dinner £18.95-£32.50&alc
CONF: Thtr 650 Class 250 Board 120 Del from £99
CARDS:

★★★★ 68% **Palace**
Oxford St M60 7HA ☎ 0161 236 9999
FAX 0161 236 0674
This elegant hotel with a striking terracotta façade and famous clock tower, was built in 1895 as the Head Office of the Refuge Assurance Company and its opulent, lofty public rooms with decoratively tiled pillars portray the flamboyant style of the period. A remarkable marble staircase is also a feature. Bedrooms and suites are of a very high standard and several retain original panelling and Victorian tiling. Many of the bathrooms have original parquet floors. The main restaurant has been named after the architect, Alfred Waterhouse, and forms part of the large and very comfortable lounge area. More informal meals can be enjoyed in the colourful Mongolian Restaurant on the lower ground floor. Service by friendly and helpful staff is efficient and professional.
135 en suite (bth/shr) (130 fmly) No smoking in 17 bedrooms CTV in all bedrooms STV Lift Night porter English & Continental Cuisine V meals Coffee am Tea pm Last d 9.30pm
ROOMS: s £95-£250; d £120-£250 * **LB**
OFF-PEAK: (incl. bkfst) d £80-£140
MEALS: Lunch £14.95&alc Dinner £14.95&alc*
CONF: Thtr 850 Class 400 Board 100 Del £140
CARDS:

M

★★★★ 62% **Copthorne Manchester**
Clippers Quay, Salford Quays M5 2XP (close to M602)
☎ 0161 873 7321 FAX 0161 873 7318
This modern hotel occupies a waterfront location overlooking a marina and is part of the Salford Quays development. The bedrooms, which have recently been refurbished, have been well designed and include rooms for non-smokers and disabled persons and also more luxurious Connoisseur Rooms with many extras. Dining facilities include the formal Chandlers Restaurant providing French cuisine from an a la carte menu or Clippers with its international menu. There is a well equipped leisure centre and also versatile conference and banqueting facilities
166 en suite (bth/shr) (6 fmly) No smoking in 56 bedrooms CTV in all bedrooms STV No dogs (ex guide dogs) Lift Night porter 120P Indoor swimming pool (heated) Sauna Gym Jacuzzi/spa Steam room Wkly live entertainment English & French Cuisine V meals Coffee am Tea pm No smoking area in restaurant Last d 10.15pm
ROOMS: s £120-£140; d £135-£155 **LB**
MEALS: Lunch fr £19.50&alc Dinner fr £20.50&alc
CONF: Thtr 150 Class 70 Board 70 Del from £138
CARDS:

★★★★ 57% **Portland Thistle**
3/5 Portland St, Piccadilly Gdns M1 6DP (in city centre, overlooking Piccadilly Gardens)
☎ 0161 228 3400 FAX 0161 228 6347
Since last year there have been a few improvements to this centrally situated hotel overlooking Piccadilly Gardens. Although bedrooms generally remain compact, new carpeting and bedspreads have brightened many of them, while the small foyer lounge has been redecorated and refurbished. Facilities on offer include a choice of restaurants and bars and there is also a well equipped leisure centre. A comprehensive range of services includes valet parking.
205 en suite (bth/shr) (6 fmly) No smoking in 51 bedrooms CTV in all bedrooms STV Lift Night porter 25P Indoor swimming pool (heated) Sauna Solarium Gym Jacuzzi/spa Xmas International Cuisine V meals Coffee am Tea pm No smoking area in restaurant Last d 10.30pm
ROOMS: s £95-£105; d £120-£130 * **LB**
MEALS: Lunch £14.95-£16.45&alc Dinner £20.45*
CONF: Thtr 300 Class 120 Board 40 Del from £129
CARDS:

★★★ 64% **Novotel**
Worsley Brow M28 4YA ☎ 0161 799 3535
FAX 0161 703 8207
(For full entry see Worsley)

★★★ 62% ***Waterside***
Wilmslow Rd, Didsbury M20 5WZ ☎ 0161 445 0225
FAX 0161 446 2090
This modern hotel and leisure complex stands in spacious grounds between Cheadle and Didsbury. Well equipped modern accommodation includes ground-floor, family and no-smoking rooms. Public areas are extensive, with a lounge, lounge bar, restaurant, games room with pool and snooker tables and a play room for young children. In addition, there are a swimming pool, gym, sports hall, sauna and steam room.
46 en suite (bth/shr) (1 fmly) No smoking in 10 bedrooms CTV in all bedrooms Night porter 200P Indoor swimming pool (heated) Tennis (hard) Snooker Sauna Solarium Gym Jacuzzi/spa Badminton Table tennis ch fac English & French Cuisine V meals Coffee am Tea pm Last d 9.45pm
CARDS:

★★★ 61% **Willow Bank**
340-342 Wilmslow Rd, Fallowfield M14 6AF (on B5093)
☎ 0161 224 0461 FAX 0161 257 2561
This long established, privately owned hotel is conveniently situated three miles from the city centre and is within easy reach of the airport. The restaurant offers an extensive range of well prepared dishes, and has a loyal following of regular diners. The traditionally furnished bedrooms, whilst they vary in size and style, are well equipped. The

hotel also benefits from conference facilities and plenty of parking.
116 en suite (bth/shr) (2 fmly) CTV in all bedrooms No dogs (ex guide dogs) Night porter 100P Xmas English & Continental Cuisine V meals Coffee am Tea pm No smoking area in restaurant
Last d 10.15pm
ROOMS: (incl. bkfst) s fr £48; d fr £55 * **LB**
OFF-PEAK: (incl. bkfst) s fr £36; d fr £45
MEALS: Lunch £7-£10&alc High tea fr £6 Dinner fr £10&alc*
CONF: Thtr 50 Class 28 Board 28 Del from £65
CARDS:

★★67% ***Crescent Gate***
Park Crescent, Victoria Park, Rusholme MI4 5RE (off B5117)
☎ 0161 224 0672 FAX 0161 257 2822
Closed Xmas
This friendly, privately owned hotel is ideally situated just off the Wilmslow Road and is within easy reach of both the city centre and the airport. Bedrooms, two of which have external access, are all freshly decorated and thoughtfully equipped. The long serving staff in the

contd.

dining room, together with the owners of the hotel Mr and Mrs Hughes, make sure guests are well looked after.
14 rms (9 bth/shr) 11 annexe en suite (bth/shr) (1 fmly) CTV in all bedrooms STV 18P No coaches V meals Coffee am Tea pm Last d 8pm
CARDS:

See advertisement on page 429

★★65% **Elm Grange**
Wilmslow Rd, Withington M20 4GJ (4m from city centre on B5093) ☎ 0161 445 3336
FAX 0161 445 3336
Closed 23 Dec-4 Jan
Pleasantly situated in a residential area of south Manchester, this family-run hotel is convenient for both city-centre and airport. Bedrooms are well equipped and furnished and decorated to a high standard, and guests can relax in a conservatory lounge or welcoming bar before dining in the nicely appointed restaurant.
31 rms (16 bth/shr) (1 fmly) No smoking in 12 bedrooms CTV in all bedrooms No dogs 42P English & French Cuisine V meals Coffee am Tea pm Last d 9pm
ROOMS: (incl. bkfst) s £27-£39.50; d £42-£56 * **LB**
OFF-PEAK: (incl. bkfst) s £24.50-£34.50; d £36-£46
MEALS: Dinner £9.50&alc*
CARDS:

★★64% **Comfort Friendly Inn**

Hyde Rd, Birch St, West Gorton M12 5NT (3m SE on A57) ☎ 0161 220 8700 FAX 0161 220 8848
This purpose-built hotel was constructed for a French company and the decor is rather austere, though all the bedrooms are en suite and well equipped and the room rates are competitive. There are also a small but neatly appointed restaurant, a lounge bar and facilities for meetings and conferences. The large car park, which includes reserved spaces for disabled drivers, is surrounded by a security fence.
90 en suite (bth/shr) (5 fmly) No smoking in 45 bedrooms CTV in all bedrooms STV Night porter 70P Gym Xmas English & Continental Cuisine V meals Coffee am Tea pm Last d 9.30pm
ROOMS: d £38.50-£49.50 **LB**
MEALS: Lunch £7.50-£9.95 Dinner £9.75&alc
CONF: Thtr 100 Class 50 Board 40 Del from £65
CARDS:

★★63% **Mitre**
Cathedral Gates M3 1SW (next to Cathedral)
☎ 0161 834 4128 FAX 0161 839 1646
Situated in the oldest part of Manchester, next to the cathedral, this hotel dates from 1815 and was known as the Old Church Tavern. Much modernised in recent years, it now provides comfortable and well equipped accommodation. The public areas include a lounge, a cosy residents' bar, a nicely appointed dining room and two meeting rooms.
28 rms (23 bth/shr) CTV in all bedrooms No dogs (ex guide dogs) Night porter English & French Cuisine V meals Coffee am Tea pm Last d 9pm
ROOMS: (incl. bkfst) s £39-£49; d £50-£57 * **LB**
OFF-PEAK: (incl. bkfst) s £30-£37; d £39-£46
MEALS: Lunch £3.50-£7.50&alc Dinner £3.50-£7.50&alc*
CONF: Thtr 40 Class 30 Board 20 Del from £60
CARDS:

★★62% **Royals**
Altrincham Rd M22 4BJ ☎ 0161 998 9011
FAX 0161 998 4641
A gabled mock Tudor building conveniently situated for both the city of Manchester and the International Airport. Most bedrooms and public areas have recently been refurbished and offer a good standard of accommodation at competitive rates. One room contains a four-poster bed. There are also conference and banqueting facilities, a garden and one large area in the lower ground floor has been equipped as a children's play area.
32 en suite (bth/shr) (6 fmly) No smoking in 6 bedrooms CTV in all bedrooms No dogs (ex guide dogs) Night porter 150P No coaches Xmas International Cuisine V meals Coffee am Tea pm No smoking area in restaurant
ROOMS: (incl. bkfst) s £60-£72; d £72-£90 *
OFF-PEAK: (incl. bkfst) s £56-£66; d £66-£79
MEALS: Lunch £1.85-£16alc High tea £4.50-£10alc*
CONF: Thtr 100 Class 50 Board 40 Del from £75
CARDS:

★★60% **Montana**
59 Palatine Rd, Withington M20 3LJ ☎ 0161 445 6427
FAX 0161 448 9458
Cheerful, friendly staff offer relaxed and informal service at an hotel that offers sound standards of comfort in a home-like atmosphere. Bedrooms are well equipped and day rooms, including two lounges, one for non-smokers, made welcoming by the use of plants, prints and ornaments. The spacious restaurant, with its separate bar, has a Spanish feel to its decor, and also serves tapas as well as more tradional dishes.
21 rms (17 bth/shr) 3 annexe en suite (bth) (2 fmly) CTV in 21 bedrooms STV 40P No smoking area in restaurant Last d 8pm
ROOMS: (incl. cont bkfst) s £25-£30; d £45-£50 * **LB**
OFF-PEAK: (incl. cont bkfst) s £23-£28; d £42-£48
CONF: Class 50 Board 30 Del from £50
CARDS:

Campanile

55 Ordsall Ln, Salford M5 4RS ☎ 0181 569 6969
The bar and Bistro restaurant provide meals and refreshments. Bedrooms are well equipped and have en suite bathrooms. For more details about Campanile, consult the Contents page under Hotel Groups.

Forte Posthouse Manchester

FORTE Posthouse

Palatine Rd, Northenden M22 4FH (beside B5167)
☎ 0161 998 7090 FAX 0161 946 0139

Suitable for both the business and leisure traveller, this bright hotel provides modern accommodation in well equipped bedrooms with en suite bathrooms. For more details about Forte Posthouse hotels, consult the Contents page for the section on Hotel Groups.

190 en suite (bth/shr)
ROOMS: d £69 *
CONF: Thtr 150 Class 80 Board 80 Del from £65

MANCHESTER AIRPORT Greater Manchester Map 07 SJ88

★★★★68% **Pinewood Thistle**

180 Wilmslow Rd, Handforth SK9 3LG (3m from junct 5 of M56 turn off A34 onto B5358 towards Wilmslow. Hotel on left before Handforth Station)
☎ 01625 529211 FAX 01625 536812

This modern hotel, situated a short distance from Manchester International Airport, has retained high standards since recent refurbishment and although bedrooms could be described as compact they are very tastefully furnished and decorated and have every modern facility. There is a very comfortable foyer lounge and a first-floor cocktail bar and restaurant in which head chef Ian Mitchell's cooking can be enjoyed in opulent surroundings overlooking the gardens.

58 en suite (bth/shr) (3 fmly) No smoking in 20 bedrooms CTV in all bedrooms STV No dogs (ex guide dogs) Lift Night porter 200P Xmas International Cuisine V meals Coffee am Tea pm Last d 9.45pm
ROOMS: s £85-£90; d £95-£100 * **LB**
OFF-PEAK: (incl. bkfst) s fr £35; d fr £80
MEALS: Lunch £11-£12.50 High tea fr £6.50 Dinner fr £17&alc
CONF: Thtr 200 Class 100 Board 60 Del from £95
CARDS:

★★★★64% **Manchester Airport Hilton**

Outwood Ln, Ringway M90 4WP (900yds from junct 5 of M56) ☎ 0161 435 3000
FAX 0161 499 2399
RS Sat

A busy modern hotel is conveniently situated in the airport complex, easily reached from the M56. The sound-proofed bedrooms are well appointed, and while the executive rooms offer extra comfort, all rooms are shortly to be upgraded to a high standard. A stream and shrubbery separate the foyer and the lounge bar; other facilities include two restaurants, a leisure centre with a plunge pool and a gymnasium, meeting/conference rooms and a business centre. There are good car parking facilities and a courtesy transport service to the airport terminals.

222 en suite (bth/shr) (6 fmly) No smoking in 40 bedrooms CTV in all bedrooms STV Lift Night porter 220P Indoor swimming pool (heated) Sauna Gym Jacuzzi/spa Steam room Wkly live entertainment Xmas International Cuisine V meals Coffee am Tea pm No smoking area in restaurant Last d 10.30pm
ROOMS: s £120-£140; d £145-£165 * **LB**
OFF-PEAK: s £93-£103; d £103-£123
MEALS: Lunch £18-£25 Dinner £18-£25&alc*
CONF: Thtr 300 Class 120 Board 60 Del from £145
CARDS:

★★★★62% **Belfry**

Stanley Rd SK9 3LD (off A34, approx 4m S of junct 10 M63)
☎ 0161 437 0511 FAX 0161 499 0597
Closed 26 Dec & 1 Jan RS 25 Dec

This modern hotel, which has been owned and run by the Beech family for nearly 30 years, is conveniently situated for Manchester and especially the airport. The comfortable bedrooms, including executive rooms and suites, are traditionally furnished. The public areas include a smart cocktail bar and a striking split-level restaurant, where service from the mostly long-standing staff is both attentive and helpful. The hotel also has a large function room called the Mirabelle Suite, which is popular for dinner dances, in addition to a number of smaller meeting and dining rooms.

80 en suite (bth/shr) (2 fmly) No smoking in 40 bedrooms CTV in all bedrooms STV No dogs (ex guide dogs) Lift Night porter 150P Wkly live entertainment Xmas International Cuisine V meals Coffee am Tea pm Last d 10pm
ROOMS: (incl. bkfst) s £82-£95; d £95-£110 **LB**
OFF-PEAK: (incl. bkfst) s fr £35; d fr £70
MEALS: Lunch £15.50-£16&alc Dinner £17.50&alc*
CONF: Thtr 120 Class 70 Board 50 Del £115
CARDS:

★★★68% **Etrop Grange**

Thorley Ln M90 4EG ☎ 0161 499 0500
FAX 0161 499 0790

A former Georgian mansion situated in semi-rural surroundings yet within sight of Manchester International Airport still manages to retain the aura of a country house and successfully combines Georgian and modern styles throughout its public areas and bedrooms. Several of the latter have four-poster beds and all offer every modern facility. The Coach House Restaurant is renowned for its high standard of cuisine at both lunch and dinner, but guests can also be served lighter meals in the attractive Conservatory if they wish. A free chauffeur driven car takes guests to the Airport terminal.

39 en suite (bth/shr) No smoking in 7 bedrooms CTV in all bedrooms STV Night porter 100P No coaches Wkly live entertainment English & French Cuisine V meals Coffee am Tea pm Last d 10pm
ROOMS: s £99-£135; d £104-£140 * **LB**
OFF-PEAK: d £65-£99.50
MEALS: Lunch £12.95-£16.50 Dinner £22.50-£33.50*
CONF: Thtr 60 Class 20 Board 24 Del from £110
CARDS:

★★★67% ***Manchester Airport Moat House***

MOAT HOUSE

Altrincham Rd SK9 4LR ☎ 01625 529201
FAX 01625 531876

Despite its convenient position on the A538, north of Wilmslow, this hotel is situated in a semi-rural location overlooking a Country Park. A major refurbishment programme was about to commence as the guide went to print, to include all the bedrooms and re-scheming of the public areas. To the rear of the hotel there is an excellent Country Club with lounge bar and terrace overlooking the pool, and a night-club opens three evenings a week. Its proximity to the airport and the fact that long-term parking is included in the room rate make this a popular choice for travellers.

125 en suite (bth/shr) (23 fmly) No smoking in 18 bedrooms CTV in all bedrooms Lift Night porter 400P Indoor swimming pool (heated) Squash Sauna Solarium Gym Pool table Jacuzzi/spa

contd.

Steam room Beauty therapy International Cuisine V meals Coffee am Tea pm Last d 10.30pm
CARDS:

Forte Posthouse Manchester Airport
Ringway Rd, Wythenshawe M90 3NS
☎ 0161 437 5811 FAX 0161 436 2340
Suitable for both the business and leisure traveller, this bright hotel provides modern accommodation in well equipped bedrooms with en suite bathrooms. For more details about Forte Posthouse hotels, consult the Contents page for the section on Hotel Groups.
285 en suite (bth/shr)
ROOMS: d £89-£99 *
CONF: Thtr 80 Class 26 Board 30 Del £120

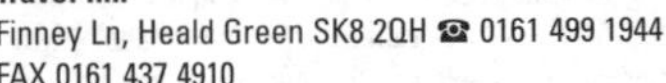

Travel Inn

Finney Ln, Heald Green SK8 2QH ☎ 0161 499 1944
FAX 0161 437 4910
Purpose-built accommodation, offering spacious, well equipped bedrooms, all with en suite bathrooms. Meals may be taken at the nearby family restaurant. For more information about Travel Inns, consult the Contents page under Hotel Groups.
41 en suite (bth/shr)
ROOMS: d £35.50 *

MANSFIELD Nottinghamshire Map 08 SK56

★★65% **Pine Lodge**
281-283 Nottingham Rd NG18 4SE (on A60 Nottingham to Mansfield road) ☎ 01623 22308 FAX 01623 656819
This privately owned and personally run hotel, where the emphasis is very much on making guests feel at home, has been developed from two Victorian villas and is conveniently situated on the edge of the town alongside the A60 Nottingham road. The en suite bedrooms, including family rooms, are soundly furnished and equipped with the usual facilities. Guests can choose from a good range of well prepared dishes in the restaurant and there is a small lounge bar. The hotel also benefits from a sauna room, a good sized meeting and banqueting facility, as well as ample parking.
20 en suite (bth/shr) (2 fmly) CTV in all bedrooms STV No dogs 40P No coaches Sauna Solarium English & Italian Cuisine V meals Coffee am Tea pm Last d 8.45pm
ROOMS: (incl. bkfst) s £39.95-£55; d £59.95-£65 **LB**
OFF-PEAK: (incl. bkfst) s £25-£40; d £40-£50
MEALS: Dinner £12.95-£14.95&alc*
CONF: Thtr 50 Class 30 Board 35 Del from £55
CARDS: £

MARAZION Cornwall & Isles of Scilly Map 02 SW53

★★❀70% **Mount Haven**

Turnpike Rd TR17 0DQ (from A30 follow signs for 'Marazion' and 'St Michael's Mount'. Continue through village to hotel on right)
☎ 01736 710249 FAX 01736 711658
Closed 20-27 Dec RS Oct-May
Personally run by dedicated owners, John and Delyth James, this former coaching house is located on a hillside, overlooking Mounts Bay and the National Trust's St Michael's Mount. Front facing rooms have balconies and enjoy the stunning views, while all rooms continue to be improved. In the split level restaurant both a fixed price and carte are offered, menus based on fresh local produce including fish from Newlyn.
17 en suite (bth/shr) (5 fmly) CTV in all bedrooms 30P No coaches V meals Coffee am Tea pm No smoking in restaurant Last d 9pm
ROOMS: (incl. bkfst) s £36-£44; d £67-£75 **LB**
OFF-PEAK: (incl. bkfst) d £56-£64
MEALS: Sunday Lunch fr £9 Dinner £18.50&alc*
CARDS:

MARCH Cambridgeshire Map 05 TL49

★★66% **Olde Griffin**
High St PE15 9EJ ☎ 01354 652517
FAX 01354 650086
This former coaching inn continues to prove popular with tourist and commercial travellers for its value-for-money food and accommodation. Bedroom styles and sizes are variable, but each has en suite facilities and a range of modern amenities; guests will certainly welcome the fact that the town square clock chimes have now been silenced during the hours of darkness. The public rooms offer a choice of eating and drinking areas; informal meals can be taken in the lounge or bar areas, or more formal dining is available in the newly refurbished restaurant. Services throughout are friendly and helpful.
20 rms (19 bth/shr) (1 fmly) CTV in all bedrooms No dogs (ex guide dogs) 50P International Cuisine V meals Coffee am Tea pm No smoking area in restaurant Last d 9.30pm
ROOMS: (incl. bkfst) s £32.50-£38.50; d £47.50-£55 * **LB**
MEALS: Sunday Lunch fr £11.95 Dinner fr £12.50&alc
CONF: Thtr 100 Class 50 Board 36 Del from £62.45
CARDS: £

MARKET DRAYTON Shropshire Map 07 SJ63

★★★❀❀ 70% **Goldstone Hall**
Goldstone TF9 2NA (4m S, signposted from A529)
☎ 01630 661202 & 661487 FAX 01630 661585
This fine seventeenth-century country house hotel was for many years the seat of Shropshire squires. Set in superbly maintained gardens and mature woodland, it is reached off the A529 by following the signs for Goldstone Hall Gardens. Beams, exposed timbers and open fires abound, and many rooms have original panelled walls. The bedrooms, though furnished in period style in keeping with the character of the building, are also fitted with a wide range of modern amenities. The daily-changing carte offered in the dining room is always prepared from fresh produce, and Simon Smith, who has recently taken over in the kitchens, continues to deliver good results.
8 en suite (bth/shr) CTV in all bedrooms No dogs (ex guide dogs) 60P Fishing Snooker V meals Coffee am Tea pm Last d 10.30pm
ROOMS: (incl. bkfst) s fr £59.50; d £83.50-£93.50 **LB**
MEALS: Lunch £15-£30alc Dinner £20-£30alc*
CONF: Thtr 50 Board 30 Del from £89
CARDS:

★★65% **Rosehill Manor**
Rosehill TF9 2JF (SW, on A41) ☎ 01630 638532 FAX 01630 638532
Run by the friendly Eardley family, this is a small hotel which is situated in its own pleasant grounds. Pretty bedrooms are provided and some are suitable for families. There is a comfortable lounge for residents and the olde worlde bar features oak beams and a wood-burning stove for the colder weather. There is a carte menu with a

good range of popular meals available.
7 en suite (bth/shr) CTV in all bedrooms STV 50P No coaches English & French Cuisine V meals Coffee am Tea pm No smoking in restaurant Last d 9.30pm
ROOMS: (incl. bkfst) s £39; d £50.60 *
MEALS: Lunch fr £11.95 Dinner £16.50-£18.50alc*
CARDS:

MARKET HARBOROUGH Leicestershire Map 04 SP78

★★★68% Three Swans
21 High St LE16 7NJ ☎ 01858 466644
FAX 01858 433101
A former coaching inn in the centre of an attractive and popular market town has been much extended and completely renovated to make a welcoming hotel with a convivial public bar, much used as a meeting place and for its bar meals. It also boasts a select cocktail bar and a formal restaurant serving good food. The bedrooms, like the public areas, are furnished in character and offer an unusually high standard of comfort.
20 en suite (bth/shr) 16 annexe en suite (bth/shr) (3 fmly) No smoking in 4 bedrooms CTV in all bedrooms STV No dogs (ex guide dogs) Night porter 58P International Cuisine V meals Coffee am Tea pm Last d 10pm
ROOMS: (incl. bkfst) s £69-£77; d £79-£89 * **LB**
OFF-PEAK: (incl. bkfst) s fr £60; d fr £67
MEALS: Lunch £12.95-£18.95 Dinner fr £18.95*
CONF: Thtr 100 Class 60 Board 50 Del from £95
CARDS:

★★★60% Angel
37 High St LE16 7NL (on A6)
☎ 01858 462702 FAX 01858 410464
A convivial former coaching inn, The Angel stands on the town's main street. Completely renovated, it has a good dining room and a comfortably furnished bar lounge where substantial bar meals are served. The bedrooms have character and good facilities.
30 en suite (bth/shr) CTV in all bedrooms 30P Jacuzzi/spa Xmas English & Continental Cuisine V meals Coffee am Tea pm No smoking in restaurant Last d 9.30pm
ROOMS: s £49.50-£60; d £49.50-£80 * **LB**
OFF-PEAK: s £35-£45; d £35-£65
MEALS: Lunch £8.95-£17.50alc Dinner £12.50-£25alc
CONF: Thtr 110 Class 45 Board 50 Del from £69.50
CARDS:

MARKFIELD Leicestershire Map 08 SK41

★★★65% Field Head
Markfield Ln LE6 0PS (access via B5327, off roundabout junct with the A50, 1m from junct 22 of the M1) ☎ 01530 245454 FAX 01530 243740
This former farmhouse dating back to 1672 has been considerably extended in recent years, but the restaurant still retains exposed timbers and open fireplaces. Bedrooms are attractively decorated and modern, and one has a four-poster bed. The bar and lounge areas are interestingly furnished, and there is farm bric-à-brac in one of the conference suites.
28 en suite (bth/shr) (2 fmly) No smoking in 6 bedrooms CTV in all bedrooms STV No dogs (ex guide dogs) Night porter 85P European Cuisine V meals Coffee am Tea pm No smoking area in restaurant Last d 9.45pm
ROOMS: (incl. bkfst) s £55; d £65-£75 * **LB**
OFF-PEAK: (incl. bkfst) s £30; d £40-£50
MEALS: Lunch £4.95-£12 Dinner £14-£15.95&alc*
CONF: Thtr 50 Class 30 Board 30 Del £85
CARDS:

Travelodge
Little Shaw Ln LE6 0PP (on A50 junct with M1 motorway) ☎ Central Res 0800 850950
This modern building offers accommodation in smart, spacious and well equipped bedrooms, suitable for family use, and all with en suite bathrooms. Meals may be taken at the nearby family restaurant. For information on room rates and to make a booking, call Roomline free of charge on 0800 850950. For more details about Travelodge, consult the Contents page under Hotel Groups.
40 en suite (bth/shr)

MARKHAM MOOR Nottinghamshire Map 08 SK77

Travelodge
DN22 0QU (on A1 northbound) ☎ 01777 838091
FAX 01777 838091
This modern building offers accommodation in smart, spacious and well equipped bedrooms, suitable for family use, and all with en suite bathrooms. Meals may be taken at the nearby family restaurant. For information on room rates and to make a booking, call Roomline free of charge on 0800 850950. For more details about Travelodge, consult the Contents page under Hotel Groups.
40 en suite (bth/shr)

MARKINGTON North Yorkshire Map 08 SE26

★★★ 76% Hob Green
HG3 3PJ (exit A61 4m after Harrogate and turn right at Wormald Green) ☎ 01423 770031
FAX 01423 771589
Set in 800 acres of beautiful countryside and yet very convenient for Harrogate, this charming country house offers tranquillity and comfort and is the perfect place in which to relax and unwind. The elegant public rooms include delightful lounges with open fires, together with a charming restaurant. The cooking remains as good as ever with an emphasis on quality local produce and is backed by a well balanced wine list.

contd.

The staff here are very caring and are naturally friendly and helpful. 12 en suite (bth/shr) CTV in all bedrooms 40P No coaches Croquet lawn English & French Cuisine V meals Coffee am Tea pm Last d 9.30pm
CARDS:

See advertisement under HARROGATE

MARLBOROUGH Wiltshire Map 04 SU16

★★★73% Ivy House Hotel & Garden Restaurant

High St SN8 1HJ ☎ 01672 515333 FAX 01672 515338
Starting life in 1707 as the Marlborough Academy for boys, this attractive Grade II property is now a comfortable, personally run hotel, conveniently situated overlooking the High Street. Bedrooms are tastefully decorated and furnished, each equipped with every modern facility. There is a smart reception lounge and another quieter lounge on the first floor. The elegant restaurant offers interesting dishes at reasonable prices from a choice of menus, and a bistro off the courtyard provides an informal alternative.
28 en suite (bth/shr) (2 fmly) No smoking in 8 bedrooms CTV in all bedrooms STV 36P Xmas International Cuisine V meals Coffee am Tea pm No smoking area in restaurant Last d 9.30pm
ROOMS: (incl. bkfst) s £58.50-£69.50; d £68-£85 * **LB**
MEALS: Lunch £8.95-£12.50&alc Dinner fr £18&alc
CONF: Thtr 100 Class 40 Board 30 Del from £95
CARDS:

See advertisement on opposite page

M

★★★59% The Castle & Ball

FORTE Heritage

High St SN8 1LZ ☎ 01672 515201
FAX 01672 515895
This traditional town centre coaching inn has an open-plan lounge bar which is a popular meeting place for locals, especially on market days. Meeting rooms have recently been upgraded and bedrooms are next on the schedule.
34 en suite (bth/shr) (1 fmly) No smoking in 13 bedrooms CTV in all bedrooms 48P Xmas V meals Coffee am Tea pm Last d 9.30pm
ROOMS: s £75-£80; d £90-£95 * **LB**
MEALS: Lunch £11.25-£12.25&alc Dinner fr £18.95&alc*
CONF: Thtr 45 Class 20 Board 30
CARDS:

MARLOW Buckinghamshire Map 04 SU88

★★★★74% Danesfield House

Henley Rd SL7 2EY (approx 2m from Marlow on A404) ☎ 01628 891010 FAX 01628 890408
Built in Victorian times but in an Italian renaissance style, and with its formal gardens and outlook across the Thames, this is a very impressive hotel indeed. Previous owners had lavished a small fortune on its restoration and now the present incumbents are carrying out the further improvements that will enable Danesfield House to take its place in the top flight of British hotels. Amongst other additions, a new leisure spa and conference centre are planned for 1997. Public rooms including the magnificent Great Hall are sumptuous, and bedrooms are well proportioned. Giles Thompson, previously number two at the Connaught, is the chef who hopes to achieve acclaim for the Oak Room restaurant, and certainly there are early indications that success is not too far away.

87 en suite (bth/shr) (3 fmly) No smoking in 5 bedrooms CTV in all bedrooms STV No dogs (ex guide dogs) Lift Night porter 100P Outdoor swimming pool (heated) Tennis (hard) Croquet lawn Putting green Jacuzzi/spa Wkly live entertainment Xmas English & French Cuisine V meals Coffee am Tea pm No smoking in restaurant Last d 9.45pm
ROOMS: (incl. bkfst) s £130; d £155-£185 * **LB**
OFF-PEAK: (incl. bkfst & dinner) s £97.50; d £195
MEALS: Lunch £24.50&alc Dinner £34.50&alc*
CONF: Thtr 80 Class 60 Board 65 Del from £200
CARDS:

★★★★72% The Compleat Angler

FORTE Heritage

Marlow Bridge SL7 1RG (by Marlow bridge)
☎ 01628 484444 FAX 01628 486388
Enjoying an enviable position right beside the River Thames this internationally famous hotel offers a traditional and civilised atmosphere. Bedrooms are all furnished in country-house style and many feature splendid bathrooms with separate showers. The best rooms are in a modern wing and have balconies overlooking the rushing weir. Public areas are comfortably furnished and guests have the choice of a small lounge, panelled bar or riverside conservatory. The popular restaurant has splendid river views.
62 en suite (bth/shr) (20 fmly) No smoking in 16 bedrooms CTV in all bedrooms STV Lift Night porter 100P Tennis (hard) Fishing Croquet lawn Boating Xmas English & French Cuisine V meals Coffee am Tea pm No smoking in restaurant Last d 10pm
ROOMS: s £135-£180; d £160-£199 **LB**
MEALS: Lunch £24.50-£32.50&alc Dinner fr £34.50&alc*
CONF: Thtr 120 Class 50 Board 40 Del from £195
CARDS:

MARPLE Greater Manchester Map 07 SJ98

★74% Springfield

Station Rd SK6 6PA (beside A626) ☎ 0161 449 0721
This charming, well maintained hotel is situated on the edge of the Peak District close to Stockport, the M63 and the rest of the motorway network. The en suite bedrooms are comfortable, attractively furnished and well equipped. Public areas have been decorated with character and include a cosy lounge bar and a homely restaurant serving a small choice of well prepared, home-cooked dishes with an Italian theme. The hotel has a friendly and relaxed atmosphere, and enthusiastic owners, Mr and Mrs Giannecchini, make every effort to ensure their guests are well looked after.
6 en suite (bth/shr) No smoking in 1 bedroom CTV in all bedrooms STV No dogs (ex guide dogs) 10P No coaches French & Italian Cuisine V meals Coffee am Tea pm No smoking area in restaurant Last d 7.45pm
ROOMS: (incl. bkfst) s fr £40; d fr £50 * **LB**
OFF-PEAK: (incl. bkfst) s fr £35; d fr £45
MEALS: Bar Lunch fr £3 Dinner fr £14.50*
CARDS:

MARSDEN West Yorkshire Map 07 SE01

★★★64% Hey Green Country House

Waters Rd HD7 6NG (off A62) ☎ 01484 844235 FAX 01484 847605
Standing in its own well tended grounds which include a lake, this family-owned hotel offers comfortable bedrooms which are well equipped and pleasantly furnished. Public rooms are spacious and a good range of food is available either in the elegant restaurant or the traditional-style bar. It is located at the end of a long lane reached by way of the village of Marsden.
10 en suite (bth/shr) (2 fmly) CTV in all bedrooms 70P Fishing Orienteering course V meals Coffee am Tea pm Last d 9pm
ROOMS: s £49; d £60-£70 * **LB**
OFF-PEAK: (incl. bkfst) s fr £45; d £60-£70
MEALS: Lunch £10.95-£21.25&alc Dinner £19.50-£21.25&alc*
CONF: Thtr 130 Class 80 Board 60 Del from £75.50
CARDS:

Percentage scores give you a comparison of quality within each star rating. See 'How to Use the Guide".

MARSTON MORETAINE Bedfordshire Map 04 SP94

Travelodge
Beancroft Rd Junction MK43 0PZ (on A421, northbound) ☎ 01234 766755 FAX 01234 766755
This modern building offers accommodation in smart, spacious and well equipped bedrooms, suitable for family use, and all with en suite bathrooms. Meals may be taken at the nearby family restaurant. For information on room rates and to make a booking, call Roomline free of charge on 0800 850950. For more details about Travelodge, consult the Contents page under Hotel Groups.
32 en suite (bth/shr)

MARSTON TRUSSELL Northamptonshire Map 04 SP68

★★63% **The Sun Inn**
Main St LE16 9TY (off A4304, between villages of Lubenham and Theddingworth) ☎ 01858 465531
FAX 01858 433155
Recent improvements have enhanced the enjoyment of a stay at the Sun Inn. Bedrooms are attractive and well furnished and the cosy bar has a firm local following. There is a well equipped function room and guests have the option of dining in the bar or in the more formal restaurant, where frequent themed evenings showcase the talents of chef Robert Junkin.
19 en suite (bth/shr) (3 fmly) CTV in all bedrooms 60P Fishing V meals Coffee am Tea pm Last d 9.30pm
ROOMS: (incl. bkfst) s £39.50-£45; d £50-£60 * **LB**
OFF-PEAK: (incl. bkfst) s £39.50; d £50
MEALS: Lunch £11.95-£23.95alc Dinner £15.95-£23.95alc
CONF: Thtr 60 Class 40 Board 28
CARDS:

MARTINHOE Devon Map 03 SS64

★★72% **Old Rectory**
EX31 4QT ☎ 01598 763368 FAX 01598 763567
Closed 7 Nov-Etr
The Bradbury family's hotel is set in three acres of gardens some five hundred yards from the North Devon Coastal Footpath. It is furnished with period pieces interspersed with the work of Daniel Bradbury, the proprietors' talented son, and patchwork quilts are a feature of the comfortable bedrooms. Suzanne Bradbury is an accomplished cook and offers stylish fresh food (in contrast to the simple menu descriptions). Guests are asked not to smoke in the dining room, drawing room or bedrooms. Two luxurious self-catering cottages are also available.
8 en suite (bth/shr) CTV in all bedrooms No dogs (ex guide dogs) 14P No coaches No children 14yrs English & French Cuisine Coffee am Tea pm No smoking in restaurant Last d 6.30pm
ROOMS: (incl. bkfst & dinner) d fr £120 *
MEALS: Dinner £24

MARTOCK Somerset Map 03 ST41

★★★70% **The Hollies**
Bower Hinton TA12 6LG (on B3165 S of town centre just off A303)
☎ 01935 822232 FAX 01935 822249
The bar and restaurant of the Hollies are located in the former farmhouse, an attractive stone-built property dating back some 300 years. In addition to the carte, a range of bar meals is available for less formal dining. Bedrooms are in a modern annexe, the majority looking out on to a grassy courtyard. The rooms are generally spacious and well equipped, and a further 15 have recently been added.
30 annexe en suite (bth/shr) (2 fmly) No smoking in 4 bedrooms CTV in all bedrooms STV No dogs (ex guide dogs) 80P ch fac V meals Last d 9pm

ROOMS: (incl. bkfst) s £49.50-£75; d £62-£90 * **LB**
MEALS: Lunch £8.95-£18alc Dinner £14-£20alc*
CONF: Thtr 150 Class 80 Board 60 Del from £67.50
CARDS:

MARYPORT Cumbria Map 11 NY03

★55% ***Waverley***
Curzon St CA15 6LW ☎ 01900 812115 FAX 01900 817734
This friendly and informal commercial hotel lies in the town centre and provides bright functional accommodation of a standard commensurate with its modest prices.
20 rms (4 bth/shr) (2 fmly) CTV in all bedrooms Pool table English & Continental Cuisine V meals Coffee am Tea pm Last d 9pm
CARDS:

MATLOCK Derbyshire Map 08 SK36

★★★72% **Riber Hall**
DE4 5JU (1m off A615 at Tansley)
☎ 01629 582795 FAX 01629 580475
Riber Hall is a listed Elizabethan Manor House which dates in part from the 1400s. The walled gardens extend through rose covered arbours from the conservatories, lounges and dining room and beyond to the orchard house, and contain some exotic species. Inside the house the style of architecture and the richness of the furnishings and fabric are redolent of a bygone era, though every modern amenity is provided. The recent award winning restaurant extension is built within the original framework and its period architecture is replicated seamlessly. The bedrooms are highly individual with glorious carved oak four-posters and deep cushioned armchairs. The cuisine is improving under Russell Archer who mixes classic and modern styles together with great success. Sauces are particularly fine. A summer

contd.

lunch started with a smooth liver pâté and toasted brioche, followed by a really plump tender supreme of chicken in a light butter sauce, and ended with a strawberry parfait.
11 annexe en suite (bth/shr) No smoking in 4 bedrooms CTV in all bedrooms STV 50P No coaches Tennis (hard) Croquet lawn No children 10yrs English & French Cuisine V meals Coffee am Tea pm No smoking area in restaurant Last d 9.30pm
ROOMS: (incl. cont bkfst) s £85-£99; d £105-£150 * **LB**
OFF-PEAK: (incl. cont bkfst) s fr £80; d fr £95
MEALS: Lunch £11.75-£14.75 Dinner fr £25.25*
CONF: Thtr 20 Class 20 Board 20 Del from £135
CARDS:

★★★66% The New Bath
New Bath Rd DE4 3PX ☎ 01629 583275
FAX 01629 580268

FORTE Heritage

This long-established, traditional and comfortable hotel is, in some areas, beginning to show the ravages of time, but gradual upgrading is beginning to restore much of its fabric and it still retains considerable character and charm for which it has been renowned for many years. One of the features of the hotel is its indoor plunge pool and sauna fed by a natural spring and there is also a very large outdoor pool surrounded by well tended lawns and gardens. A relaxing hotel with friendly and willing staff.
55 en suite (bth/shr) (5 fmly) No smoking in 11 bedrooms CTV in all bedrooms Night porter 200P Indoor swimming pool (heated) Outdoor swimming pool Tennis (hard) Sauna Solarium Xmas V meals Coffee am Tea pm No smoking in restaurant Last d 9.30pm
ROOMS: s fr £70; d fr £85 * **LB**
MEALS: Lunch £10.95-£11.95 Dinner £18.95&alc*
CONF: Thtr 180 Class 60 Board 50 Del £95
CARDS:

★★ 72% Red House
Old Rd, Darley Dale DE4 2ER (just off A6, 2.5m north of Matlock)
☎ 01629 734854 FAX 01629 734854
A fine, carefully preserved late 19th-century house stands just off the A6 on the edge of the village. Some bedrooms are very spacious and all are thoughtfully furnished with a mix of period and contemporary pieces and distinctive wall coverings. The reception rooms with their magnificent pillared fire surrounds are both elegant and comfortable with fine views over the lawns and topiary-edged terraces. Roasts and other home-cooked dishes are served in a well appointed dining room. Willing staff create a relaxed atmosphere throughout.
7 en suite (bth/shr) 2 annexe en suite (bth/shr) CTV in all bedrooms 16P No coaches English & French Cuisine V meals Last d 8.30pm
ROOMS: (incl. bkfst) s £48-£55; d £76-£80 * **LB**
MEALS: Lunch £11.95-£13.95 Dinner £18.50
CARDS:

★★66% Temple
Temple Walk, Matlock Bath DE4 3PG (turn left on A6 after church)
☎ 01629 583911 FAX 01629 580851
This attractive hotel is perched high on the hill above the resort with great views of the valley and hills beyond. Guests can choose between a carvery and a more formal restaurant offering a range of dishes which includes Austrian specialities. Bedrooms are thoughtfully furnished and their modern en suites fully tiled.
14 en suite (bth/shr) CTV in all bedrooms No dogs Night porter 32P Xmas English, French & Austrian Cuisine V meals Coffee am Tea pm No smoking in restaurant Last d 9pm
ROOMS: (incl. bkfst) s £39; d £61-£66 * **LB**
MEALS: Dinner £13-£18alc*
CONF: Thtr 60 Class 60 Board 40
CARDS:

MAWGAN PORTH Cornwall & Isles of Scilly Map 02 SW86

★★66% Tredragon
TR8 4DQ ☎ 01637 860213 FAX 01637 860269

Set high above the bay with coastal views, this family-run hotel offers exceptional levels of hospitality and service. Bedrooms are modern in decor and furnishings, and the restaurant offers a dinner menu with a limited choice at each course, supplemented by an extra fish course and a cold salad table. There are organised activity holidays featuring quilting, fishing and painting.
27 en suite (bth/shr) (12 fmly) CTV in all bedrooms 30P Indoor swimming pool (heated) Sauna Solarium Pool table ch fac Xmas English & French Cuisine V meals Coffee am Tea pm No smoking in restaurant Last d 8pm
ROOMS: (incl. bkfst) s £25-£35; d £50-£60 **LB**
MEALS: Bar Lunch £1.75-£10 Dinner £16.50-£18.50
CONF: Thtr 50 Class 40 Board 30
CARDS:

★★63% Thorncliff
Trenance, Mawgan Porth TR8 4DA ☎ 01637 860898
FAX 01637 860893
Closed Nov RS Dec, Jan & Feb
Set in an elevated position with splendid views of Mawgan Porth beach, the hotel has recently undergone total refurbishment. Bedrooms are all comfortable although some are compact. The spacious bar lounge opens onto a small verandah which faces due south on-to the beach. A short fixed-price menu is offered in the dining room.
17 en suite (bth/shr) (5 fmly) No smoking in 2 bedrooms CTV in all bedrooms 18P Pool table Xmas English & Continental Cuisine V meals Coffee am No smoking area in restaurant Last d 8pm
ROOMS: (incl. bkfst) s £23-£27; d £46-£54 * **LB**
MEALS: Dinner £12*
CARDS:

MAWNAN SMITH Cornwall & Isles of Scilly Map 02 SW72

★★★ 74% Meudon
TR11 5HT ☎ 01326 250541 FAX 01326 250543
Closed 6 Nov-Feb

THE Virgin HOTEL COLLECTION

Standing in a tranquil setting, surrounded by National Trust land, this late-Victorian mansion with a modern wing has been in the same family for over 20 years and offers high standards of service and hospitality. Bedrooms are of a good size, well furnished and, like the smart public areas, have views across the wonderful sub-tropical gardens that run down a sheltered valley to the sea.
29 en suite (bth/shr) (1 fmly) CTV in all bedrooms Night porter 52P No coaches Fishing Riding Private beach Hair salon ch fac Xmas International Cuisine V meals Coffee am Tea pm Last d 9pm
ROOMS: (incl. bkfst & dinner) s £80-£100; d £140-£176 * **LB**
MEALS: Lunch £15 Dinner £25&alc*
CONF: Thtr 50 Class 30 Board 30 Del £115
CARDS:

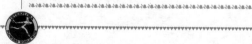

★★★73% **Budock Vean**
TR11 5LG ☎ 01326 250288 & 250230 FAX 01326 250892
Closed 2 Jan-10 Feb
Located in an area of outstanding beauty, set in 65 acres of mature grounds, with a private foreshore to the Helford River, this attractive hotel has its own nine-hole parkland golf course. Bedrooms vary in standard and size, the majority having views over the course or the valley. The lounges are comfortable and spacious, and there is a cocktail bar as well as the golfers' bar. Service is relaxed, informal and efficient, and many guests return year after year.
58 en suite (bth/shr) (6 fmly) CTV in all bedrooms Lift Night porter 100P No coaches Indoor swimming pool (heated) Golf 9 Tennis (hard) Fishing Snooker Pool table Croquet lawn Putting green Wkly live entertainment ch fac Xmas English & French Cuisine V meals Coffee am Tea pm No smoking in restaurant Last d 9pm
ROOMS: (incl. bkfst & dinner) s £47-£80; d £94-£160 **LB**
MEALS: Lunch £12 High tea £10 Dinner £19&alc*
CONF: Thtr 80 Class 100 Board 40 Del from £65
CARDS:

★★★ 65% ***Trelawne***
TR11 5HS ☎ 01326 250226 FAX 01326 250909
Closed 29 Dec-12 Feb
Set in attractive gardens with viewsover the rugged coastline, Trelawne Hotel has been ably run by the Gibbons family for many years. Their chefs Grant Mather and Nigel Woodland produce a range of interesting dishes like smoked haddock with spinach, coated with a light cheese sauce, best end of lamb with provençale vegetables and a memorable strawberry mille feuilles.
14 en suite (bth/shr) (2 fmly) CTV in all bedrooms 20P No coaches Indoor swimming pool (heated) English & French Cuisine Coffee am Tea pm Last d 8.30pm
CARDS:
See advertisement under FALMOUTH

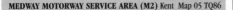

MEALSGATE Cumbria Map 11 NY24

★★68% **Kelsey**
CA5 1JP ☎ 016973 71229 & 71372 FAX 016973 71372
This cosy little roadside hotel is well maintained by owners Les and Sue Cluskey who, along with their staff, provide warm and friendly service. Public areas are attractive and one can eat well in either the lounge bar (where the emphasis is on food) or in the dining room. Bedrooms are nicely decorated, well equipped and thoughtfully laid out.
6 en suite (bth/shr) (2 fmly) CTV in all bedrooms 21P English & French Cuisine V meals No smoking area in restaurant
CARDS:

MEDWAY MOTORWAY SERVICE AREA (M2) Kent Map 05 TQ86

Travelodge
Rainham ME8 8PQ (between juncts 4 & 5 M2)
☎ 01634 233343 FAX 01634 360848

Travelodge

This modern building offers accommodation in smart, spacious and well equipped bedrooms, suitable for family use, and all with en suite bathrooms. Meals may be taken at the nearby family restaurant. For information on room rates and to make a booking, call Roomline free of charge on 0800 850950. For more details about Travelodge, consult the Contents page under Hotel Groups.
58 en suite (bth/shr)

MELKSHAM Wiltshire Map 03 ST96

★★★ 67% ***Beechfield House***

Beanacre SN12 7PU (1m N via A350)
☎ 01225 703700 FAX 01225 790118
A character Victorian hotel built of Bath stone, Beechfield House has a relaxing, friendly atmosphere and stands in eight acres of mature grounds and gardens. Bedrooms tend to vary in size with those in the new wing being more spacious. The fixed-price menu offered at lunch and dinner features home grown fruit and vegetables from the hotel's garden.
24 en suite (bth/shr) No smoking in 4 bedrooms CTV in all bedrooms Night porter 40P Outdoor swimming pool (heated) Tennis (grass) croquet ch fac V meals Coffee am Tea pm Last d 9.30pm
CARDS:

★★ 68% **Shaw Country**
Bath Rd, Shaw SN12 8EF (2m NW A365)
☎ 01225 702836 & 790321 FAX 01225 790275
Closed 26-27 Dec
This friendly hotel, situated on the outskirts of the town within easy reach of Bath, the M4 and the M5, is run by the Lewis family. The creeper-clad house, situated with its own garden, is said to date from the late 16th century. The accommodation has been sympathetically upgraded and now provides comfortable bedrooms with modern facilities. Downstairs there is a cosy bar, and a separate lounge where guests can relax in peace and quiet. Fresh ingredients are used in the production of the interesting dishes offered from a choice of menus in the Mulberry Restaurant.
13 en suite (bth/shr) (2 fmly) CTV in all bedrooms 30P No coaches Jacuzzi/spa English & French Cuisine V meals Coffee am Tea pm No smoking in restaurant Last d 9pm
ROOMS: (incl. bkfst) s £40; d £59-£80 * **LB**
MEALS: Lunch fr £10&alc Dinner £13-£14&alc*
CONF: Thtr 30 Class 20 Board 30
CARDS:
See advertisement under BATH

★★64% **Kings Arms**
Market Place SN12 6EX (in town centre opposite Lloyds Bank)
☎ 01225 707272 FAX 01225 702085
A former coaching inn built from Bath stone is set in the Market Place with a delightful cobbled courtyard. Owners David and Helen Dodd have retained the character and charm of their period home over the
contd.

years, and bedrooms are well equipped. The bar attracts a busy local trade, and an extensive range of bar meals is offered; a no-smoking area is available at lunchtime. The spacious restaurant offers a well balanced menu and good breakfasts are served, such as that enjoyed by our inspector - freshly made scrambled eggs with chopped ham.
13 rms (10 bth/shr) CTV in all bedrooms 30P No coaches V meals Coffee am Tea pm Last d 9pm
ROOMS: (incl. bkfst) s £35-£45; d £49 * **LB**
MEALS: Lunch £7.50-£11.50&alc Dinner £11.50&alc
CARDS:

MELLING Lancashire Map 07 SD57

★★63% ***Melling Hall***

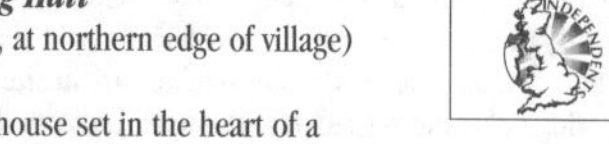

LA6 2RA (on A683, at northern edge of village)
☎ 01524 221298
A gracious period house set in the heart of a picturesque Lune Valley village which enjoys distant views to the LAKELAND fells. It remains a spaciously appointed house to which many improvements have been made over the years. The public areas include a convivial public bar, which is popular with locals, a lounge bar and the restaurant.
14 rms (7 bth 3 shr) (1 fmly) CTV in all bedrooms STV 40P English & French Cuisine V meals Coffee am Last d 9.30pm
CARDS:

MELTON MOWBRAY Leicestershire Map 08 SK71
See also Upper Broughton

RED STAR HOTEL

★★★★❀❀ **Stapleford Park**

Stapleford LE14 2EF (off B676 towards Colsterworth) ☎ 01572 787522
FAX 01572 787651
This stately home, set in a 500-acre estate, with its own fishing lake, stables, church, and gardens originally laid out by Capability Brown, is the epitome of English country living and is run more as a country house than a hotel by the friendly and efficient staff. Each of the splendid bedrooms has been designed by a company or an individual - such as Turnbull and Asser, Lindka Cierach and David Hicks in the main house and IBM, Coca-Cola, MGM and Land-Rover in the cottage in the grounds. Whimsical paintings are hung cheek to cheek with works of art, and elaborate floral displays abound. The public rooms are varied and spacious with splendid polished dark mahogany panelling much in evidence; breakfast is served in the magnificent former vaulted kitchens - on Beatrix Potter china. The surroundings are opulent but, intentionally, the atmosphere is relaxed. Cooking by Malcolm Jessop is interesting with a blend of light styles and interesting ingredients.
44 en suite (bth/shr) 7 annexe en suite (bth/shr) CTV in all bedrooms STV Lift Night porter 120P No coaches Indoor swimming pool (heated) Tennis (hard) Fishing Riding Sauna Solarium Gym Pool table Croquet lawn Putting green Jacuzzi/spa Shooting Falconry Off road driving Wkly live entertainment Xmas European Cuisine V meals Coffee am Tea pm No smoking in restaurant Last high tea 5.30pm
ROOMS: (incl. cont bkfst) s £145; d £145 * **LB**
MEALS: Lunch £12.50-£22.50 High tea £7.50*
CONF: Thtr 200 Class 150 Board 80 Del from £175
CARDS:

★★68% **Quorn Lodge**
46 Asfordby Rd LE13 0HR (from town centre take A6006, hotel 300 yds from junct of A606/A607 on right) ☎ 01664 66660 & 62590
FAX 01664 480660
Originally a hunting lodge, just off the town centre with its bustling market place, this hotel is deservedly popular and its atmosphere is very friendly. The owners continue to upgrade and extend the existing range of public areas and bedrooms. Each bedroom is individual in its colour scheme and all are thoughtfully designed and equipped. The restaurant is elegant and the bar-cum-lounge is most comfortable.
19 en suite (bth/shr) (2 fmly) No smoking in 11 bedrooms CTV in all bedrooms STV 33P V meals Coffee am Tea pm No smoking in restaurant Last d 9.30pm
ROOMS: (incl. bkfst) s £45.50-£47.50; d £55-£65 * **LB**
OFF-PEAK: (incl. bkfst) s fr £37.50; d £50-£65
MEALS: Lunch £9.50-£12.50&alc Dinner £9.50-£12.50&alc
CONF: Thtr 90 Class 60 Board 85 Del from £72.50
CARDS:

★★68% **Sysonby Knoll**
Asfordby Rd LE13 0HP (0.5m from town centre beside A6006)
☎ 01664 63563 FAX 01664 410364
Closed 25 Dec-1 Jan
Behind the hotel's contemporary facade lies a fine, though much extended, Edwardian residence. It remains true to this original period at the rear, where it has a commanding raised position above the knoll and the River Eye beyond. The public areas are furnished in Bubinga wood, and now extend into the garden with the recent addition of a conservatory where refreshments and lighter, more informal meals will be served. The staff are long-serving and very professional, displaying a high level of attentiveness and commitment to their customers. In view of the facilities provided, this hotel offers good value for money.
23 en suite (bth/shr) 1 annexe en suite (bth/shr) (2 fmly) CTV in all bedrooms STV 50P Outdoor swimming pool English & French Cuisine V meals Coffee am Tea pm No smoking area in restaurant Last d 9pm
ROOMS: (incl. bkfst) s £35-£54; d £49-£57 * **LB**
MEALS: Lunch fr £8.95 Dinner £10.50-£11.50&alc*
CONF: Thtr 30 Class 16 Board 24 Del from £70
CARDS:

See advertisement on opposite page

MEMBURY MOTORWAY SERVICE AREA (M4) Berkshire
Map 04 SU37

Travelodge

Travelodge

Membury Service Area RG16 7TU (M4 between junct 14 & 15 westbound) ☎ 01488 72336 FAX Y
This modern building offers accommodation in smart, spacious and well equipped bedrooms, suitable for family use, and all with en suite bathrooms. Meals may be taken at the nearby family restaurant. For information on room rates and to make a booking, call Roomline free of charge on 0800 850950. For

more details about Travelodge, consult the Contents page under Hotel Groups.
40 en suite (bth/shr)

MERE Wiltshire Map 03 ST83

★63% **The Talbot**
The Square BA12 6DR (turn off A303 onto B3095/3092, 1m to centre of village) ☎ 01747 860427
Dating from 1580, the Talbot hotel enjoys a central situation in the country town of Mere, just one mile from the A303, midway between Exeter and London. Bedrooms have been equipped with modern comforts yet retain the character of the old building. A cosy residents' lounge is available upstairs and a choice of popular ground floor bars serve a range of bar meals. The Cavalier Restaurant offers a more formal dining operation.
7 en suite (bth/shr) (3 fmly) CTV in all bedrooms 25P English & Continental Cuisine V meals Coffee am No smoking in restaurant
ROOMS: (incl. bkfst) s £25-£32.50; d £40-£53 * **LB**
OFF-PEAK: (incl. bkfst) s fr £20
CARDS:

MERIDEN West Midlands Map 04 SP28

★★★★68% **Marriott Forest of Arden**
Maxstoke Ln CV7 7HR (off A45 towards Coventry)
☎ 01676 522335 FAX 01676 523711

Marriott
HOTELS · RESORTS · SUITES

Within easy reach of both the M6 and M42, this impressive modern hotel enjoys a rural location surrounded by lakes, gardens and two golf courses, yet is equally convenient for the NEC and Birmingham. Very popular with conference and holiday guests, it offers an extensive range of sporting and leisure activities including an attractive pool area with the Poolside Grill open all day. There is a large, comfortable cocktail lounge and a split-level restaurant. Bedrooms are spacious and boast an extensive range of facilities.

154 en suite (bth/shr) (4 fmly) No smoking in 125 bedrooms CTV in all bedrooms STV Lift Night porter Air conditioning 300P Indoor swimming pool (heated) Golf 18 Tennis (hard) Fishing Snooker Sauna Solarium Gym Putting green Jacuzzi/spa Health & Beauty salon Xmas English & French Cuisine V meals Coffee am Tea pm No smoking in restaurant Last d 9.45pm
ROOMS: s £95-£150; d £95-£150 *
MEALS: Lunch £9.95-£16.50 Dinner £19.50*
CONF: Thtr 150 Class 120 Board 35 Del from £125
CARDS:

★★★68% **Manor**
Main Rd CV7 7NH ☎ 01676 522735 FAX 01676 522186
Originally a Georgian manor, sympathetically extended and now a comfortable modern hotel, very conveniently situated in a quiet village location, only a short distance from Birmingham Airport and the National Exhibition Centre. The recently re-furbished Regency

contd.

M

Restaurant provides a high standard of cuisine and fully justifies the award of a rosette. Less formal meals are available in the Triumph Bar and Buttery which is open all day.
74 en suite (bth/shr) No smoking in 34 bedrooms CTV in all bedrooms STV Night porter 200P Xmas English & French Cuisine V meals Coffee am Tea pm No smoking in restaurant Last d 9.45pm
ROOMS: (incl. bkfst) s £60-£110; d £60-£130 * **LB**
MEALS: Lunch £13.95-£17.50&alc Dinner £13.95-£17.50&alc
CONF: Thtr 250 Class 150 Board 60 Del from £110
CARDS:

MEVAGISSEY Cornwall & Isles of Scilly Map 02 SX04

★★67% **Sharksfin**
The Quay PL26 6QU ☎ 01726 843241 FAX 01726 842552
Closed Jan-Feb
The best bedrooms of this quayside hotel have been equipped with modern facilities, and its unrivalled position guarantees them a superb outlook. There are also fine views of the harbour from the attractive bar and spacious restaurant on the ground floor, the latter offering carte and fixed-price menus on which local fish features prominently; the Quay Hole serves as a breakfast room (in addition to being open all day for the service of light refreshments) and there is a comfortable residents' lounge on the first floor.
11 rms (8 shr) (1 fmly) CTV in all bedrooms No dogs (ex guide dogs) No coaches V meals Coffee am Tea pm
ROOMS: (incl. bkfst) s £32; d £64-£70 * **LB**
MEALS: Bar Lunch £4-£15&alc*
CARDS:

M

★★64% ***Tremarne***
Polkirt PL26 6UY ☎ 01726 842213
Closed 11 Nov-1 Mar
Peter and Mary O'Connor are the friendly owners of this small holiday hotel. Guests are advised to ask for details on how to find the hotel, as it is located on the far side of Mevagissey, in a private road at the top of Polkirt Hill. Bedrooms are attractively co-ordinated, well equipped and some benefit from fine views of Chapel Point. Guests can relax in the two lounges or enjoy a drink in the cosy bar. In the dining room Mary's home cooking can be enjoyed, she uses local produce where ever possible and a selection of West Country cheeses are always available.
14 en suite (bth/shr) (2 fmly) CTV in all bedrooms 14P No coaches Outdoor swimming pool (heated) No children 3yrs Coffee am Tea pm Last d 6pm
CARDS:

MICHAEL WOOD MOTORWAY SERVICE AREA (M5)
Gloucestershire Map 03 ST79

Travelodge
Lower Wick GL11 6DD (M5 northbound between junct 13 & 14) ☎ 01454 261513
This modern building offers accommodation in smart, spacious and well equipped bedrooms, suitable for family use, and all with en suite bathrooms. Meals may be taken at the nearby family restaurant. For information on room rates and to make a booking, call Roomline free of charge on 0800 850950. For more details about Travelodge, consult the Contents page under Hotel Groups.
40 en suite (bth/shr)

MIDDLEHAM North Yorkshire Map 07 SE18

★★ 75% **Millers House**
DL8 4NR ☎ 01969 622630 FAX 01969 623570
Closed Jan
This delightful hotel stands just off the cobbled market square of this historic village. It has been carefully restored by the very friendly Sunderland family and provides comfortable accommodation in peaceful surroundings. Rich fabrics and co-ordinating wallpapers are used to good effect and, particularly impressive, is the four-poster room with its ornate ceiling. Food continues to be enjoyable and the conservatory extension to the restaurant looks out onto pretty walled gardens. The area is famous for its racing stables and special Racing Weekends are held together with Wine Tasting and other themed events.
7 rms (6 bth/shr) CTV in all bedrooms No dogs (ex guide dogs) 8P No children 10yrs Xmas English & French Cuisine V meals No smoking in restaurant
ROOMS: (incl. bkfst) s £36.50; d £73-£90 * **LB**
MEALS: Dinner £19.50
CONF: Class 15 Board 15 Del from £68
CARDS:

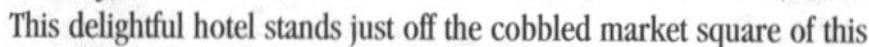

MIDDLESBROUGH North Yorkshire Map 08 NZ42

★★62% **Marton Way Toby**
Marton Rd TS4 3BS (S, off A172 opposite South Cleveland Hospital complex) ☎ 01642 817651
FAX 01642 829409

RS 24-26 Dec & 1 Jan (no meals)
This is a modern hotel situated on the outskirts of the town on the A172, opposite South Cleveland Hospital. Despite its contemporary structure the bedrooms, although well equipped, are compact and dated, but were scheduled for total upgrading during 1996, together with the public areas. The Toby Carving Room provides a relaxed setting in which to enjoy daily roasts or dishes from the varied and popular menu or alternatively light meals can be served in the lounge. The residents' car park is in a courtyard which is surrounded by the ground and first floor bedrooms.
53 en suite (bth/shr) (4 fmly) No smoking in 18 bedrooms CTV in all bedrooms STV Night porter 500P Pool table British & Continental Cuisine V meals Coffee am Tea pm No smoking in restaurant Last d 10pm
ROOMS: (incl. bkfst) s £28.50-£41.50; d £44.50-£51.50 * **LB**
MEALS: Lunch £12.50&alc Dinner £12.50&alc*
CONF: Thtr 85 Class 50 Board 40 Del from £66
CARDS:

★68% **The Grey House**
79 Cambridge Rd, Linthorpe TS5 5NL ☎ 01642 817485
FAX 01642 817485
Standing in its own rose garden in a quiet residential area of Middlesbrough, this attractive Victorian house is well furnished throughout and provides guests with thoughtfully equipped and mainly spacious bedrooms. There is a comfortable residents' lounge and a set evening meal is available in the newly refurbished dining room. Service is homely, provided by the resident owners Mr and Mrs Wattis.
9 en suite (bth/shr) (1 fmly) CTV in all bedrooms 10P No coaches
ROOMS: (incl. bkfst) s £30-£35; d £44-£50 *
CARDS:

MIDLETON-IN-TEESDALE Co Durham Map 12 NY92

★★ 63% Teesdale
Market Place DL12 0QG ☎ 01833 640264 FAX 01833 640651
The Teesdale is a pleasant stone-built hotel standing in the centre of the market place. It is family owned and run and offers prettily decorated modern bedrooms. The comfortable lounge has recently been refurbished, and a good range of home-cooked dishes is available in either the intimate restaurant or the inviting bars.
13 rms (10 bth/shr) (1 fmly) CTV in all bedrooms 14P No coaches Xmas English, French, German & Italian Cuisine V meals Coffee am Tea pm Last d 8.30pm
ROOMS: (incl. bkfst) s fr £42.50; d £50-£60.50 * **LB**
OFF-PEAK: (incl. bkfst) s fr £38.50; d fr £45
MEALS: Lunch fr £10.50 Dinner fr £18.95
CARDS:

MIDDLETON STONEY Oxfordshire Map 04 SP52

★★ 68% Jersey Arms

OX6 8SE (on the B430 10m N of Oxford, between junct 9 & 10 of M40) ☎ 01869 343234 & 343505
FAX 01869 343565
There is a well cared for charm about this coaching inn which stands at a fairly busy junction a short distance from the M40 motorway. The spacious courtyard bedrooms are more secluded than those in the main building and they are all well looked after. In addition to bar meals, there is an imaginative choice of dishes in the wood-panelled dining room. Though the kitchen might occasionally slip up technically, it makes that extra effort to create fresh tasting meals.
6 en suite (bth) 10 annexe en suite (bth) (3 fmly) CTV in all bedrooms No dogs (ex guide dogs) 55P No coaches Xmas English & French Cuisine V meals Coffee am Tea pm No smoking in restaurant Last d 9.30pm
ROOMS: (incl. bkfst) s fr £65; d fr £79.50 * **LB**
MEALS: Lunch £19.50-£25alc Dinner £19.50-£25alc*
CONF: Board 12 Del £89.50
CARDS:

MIDDLE WALLOP Hampshire Map 04 SU23

★★ 75% Fifehead Manor

SO20 8EG (situated on A343 between Andover and Salisbury, 2m S of Middle Wallop Army camp)
☎ 01264 781565 FAX 01264 781400
This charming Manor House dating from the 11th century, is ideally located for Winchester, Andover and Salisbury. Now under new ownership the hotel is undergoing a refurbishment programme, and several rooms have already been upgraded and individually decorated. The public rooms include a comfortable lounge and bar, and an intimate restaurant serving a seasonally changing menu using quality local ingredients.
10 en suite (bth) 5 annexe en suite (bth) CTV in all bedrooms 50P No coaches Croquet lawn English & French Cuisine V meals Coffee am Tea pm No smoking in restaurant
ROOMS: (incl. bkfst) s £60; d £80-£110 * **LB**
MEALS: Lunch fr £15*
CONF: Thtr 20 Class 20 Board 15 Del £80
CARDS:

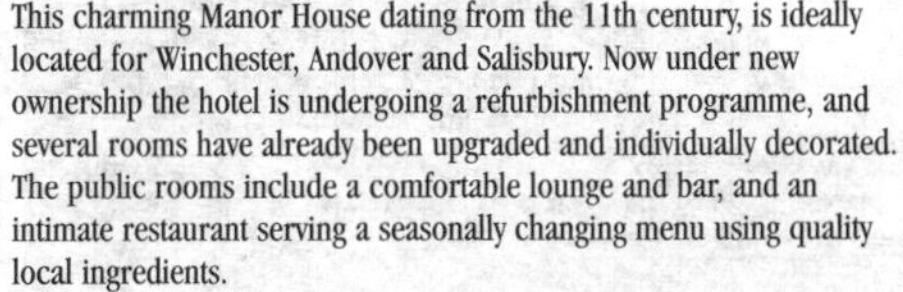

MIDHURST West Sussex Map 04 SU82

★★★ 77% Angel

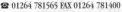

North St GU29 9DN ☎ 01730 812421
FAX 01730 815928
Once a coaching inn on the London to Portsmouth route, this 16th-century building provides plenty of good cheer, fine levels of comfort and excellent standards of food. The focal point is the brasserie which adjoins the popular bar. There is also an elegant restaurant which is an apt showcase for chef Andrew Stephenson's dishes which are notable for their flavour and honesty. A sample meal might be smoked salmon tartare with cucumber relish, local fallow deer saddle with root vegetable gratin, and crème brûlée layered with plums. Canapés and cakes are also noteworthy. Modern comforts are found in the various sized bedrooms which now include some additional spacious bedrooms with plush fabrics.
21 en suite (bth/shr) 4 annexe en suite (bth/shr) (2 fmly) No smoking in 2 bedrooms CTV in all bedrooms No dogs (ex guide dogs) 40P Wkly live entertainment Xmas English, French, Italian & Caribbean Cuisine V meals Coffee am Tea pm Last d 10pm
ROOMS: (incl. bkfst) s £75; d £80-£140 * **LB**
MEALS: Lunch £14.50-£17.95 Dinner £17.50*
CONF: Thtr 60 Class 40 Board 40 Del £110
CARDS:

★★★ 73% Spread Eagle

South St GU29 9NH (on A286)
☎ 01730 816911 FAX 01730 815668
This former coaching inn, parts of which date back to 1430, is full of character : oak beams, smoky inglenook fireplaces, sloping floors and wood panelling. The well looked after bedrooms are individually furnished and each has its own quite different character. The restaurant, with customers' Christmas puddings hanging from its beams, provides a smart setting for the kitchen's technically skilful food. A recent meal produced well crafted chicken quenelles with a mushroom sauce, monkfish with braised wild rice and chocolate cheesecake with an orange sauce anglaise.
37 en suite (bth/shr) 4 annexe en suite (shr) CTV in all bedrooms Night porter 70P No coaches Xmas English & French Cuisine V meals Coffee am Tea pm No smoking in restaurant Last d 9.15pm
ROOMS: (incl. cont bkfst) s fr £77; d £110-£175 * **LB**
MEALS: Lunch £12.95-£16.95 Dinner £26-£37*
CONF: Thtr 70 Class 40 Board 35 Del from £115
CARDS:

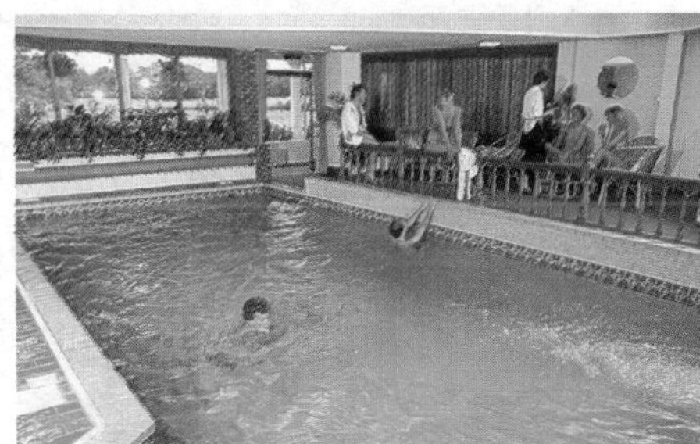

★★★ 72% Southdowns

Trotton GU31 5JN (on A272, after town turn left at Keepers Arms) ☎ 01730 821521 FAX 01730 821790
This attractive privately owned hotel and restaurant nestles in the Sussex countryside; set in spacious grounds if offers quiet and peaceful surroundings and good facilities for conferences and wedding receptions. Two styles of bedrooms, original main house and the new wing, are attractively furnished and especially well equipped, whilst the beamed Tudor bar, smart residents lounge and spacious Country Restaurant adds a further very good dimension. Chef Peter Broomhead offers a seasonal carte as well as a market menu and recommendations this year have included a notable Traditional Yorkshire Pudding with foie gras and onion gravy, Confit of Duck with cabbage onions bean sprouts, a delicious plum sauce and perfectly cooked field fresh vegetables. Service is very attentive and friendly and personally supervised by hosts Dominic Vedovato and Richard Lion.

contd.

20 en suite (bth/shr) (3 fmly) No smoking in 4 bedrooms CTV in all bedrooms No dogs 70P Indoor swimming pool (heated) Tennis (hard) Fishing Sauna Solarium Croquet lawn Exercise equipment Xmas European Cuisine V meals Coffee am Tea pm No smoking area in restaurant Last d 9.30pm
ROOMS: (incl. bkfst) s £60-£90; d £70-£120 * **LB**
MEALS: Lunch £12.95-£17.95&alc High tea fr £5.95 Dinner fr £19.95&alc
CONF: Thtr 120 Class 30 Board 30 Del from £99
CARDS:

MIDSOMER NORTON Somerset Map 03 ST65

★★★66% **Centurion**
Charlton Ln BA3 4BD (off A367, 10m S of Bath)
☎ 01761 417711 FAX 01761 418357
Closed 24-26 Dec
This modern family-run hotel, situated between the cities of Bath and Wells, incorporates the adjacent Fosseway Country Club with its golf course and other leisure amenities. Comfortable bedrooms are furnished to a high standard with co-ordinating fabrics, and the public areas include a choice of bars, an attractive lounge and a range of meeting and function rooms. Table d'hÙte and à la carte menus provide an extensive selection of dishes available in the smart restaurant overlooking the garden.
44 en suite (bth/shr) (4 fmly) CTV in all bedrooms No dogs (ex guide dogs) Night porter 100P Indoor swimming pool (heated) Golf 9 Squash Bowling green Sports field English & Continental Cuisine V meals Coffee am Tea pm No smoking area in restaurant Last d 9.30pm
ROOMS: (incl. bkfst) s £50-£60; d £60-£80 * **LB**
MEALS: Lunch £7.90-£12.50&alc High tea £2-£7 Dinner £15.50-£17.50&alc*
CONF: Thtr 180 Class 70 Board 50 Del from £87
CARDS:

See advertisement under BATH

MILDENHALL Suffolk Map 05 TL77

★★★65% **Riverside**
Mill St IP28 7DP (taking A1101 into town, left at mini roundabout along High St, hotel is last building on left before bridge)
☎ 01638 717274 FAX 01638 715997
This imposing 18th-century, red-brick property sits in a delightful position on the banks of the River Lark on the outskirts of the attractive market town. The recently refurbished public rooms offer a quiet lounge area, choice of two bars and a delightful conservatory terrace restaurant which looks out over the rear gardens to the river. Bedroom styles and sizes are quite variable, the more recently refurbished rooms offer light and cheerful appointments; there are three separate cottage bedrooms which provide useful ground-floor accommodation.
20 en suite (bth/shr) (4 fmly) CTV in all bedrooms Lift 50P Fishing Croquet lawn Private boats Xmas International Cuisine V meals Coffee am Tea pm No smoking area in restaurant
ROOMS: (incl. bkfst) s £52-£60; d fr £80 * **LB**
MEALS: Lunch £6-£16 High tea fr £5 Dinner fr £17&alc*
CONF: Thtr 50 Class 40 Board 30 Del from £90
CARDS:

★★★64% **Smoke House Inn**
Beck Row IP28 8DH (A1101 into Mildenhall, follow Beck Row signs. Hotel located immediately after mini-roundabout through Beck Row on right-hand side)
CONSORT HOTELS
☎ 01638 713223 & 0800 507050 (reservations-free)
FAX 01638 712202
This large hotel complex is two miles from Mildenhall, adjacent to the air force base, and comprises a small shopping mall, conference centre and hotel. Parts of the original building date back to the 16th century, and the open log fires, exposed beams and brickwork give character to the public rooms, which offer a choice of bars and dining options. The bedrooms are generally of comfortable proportions and have a sound level of appointments - each has the added feature of a video.
94 en suite (bth/shr) 10 annexe en suite (bth/shr) (20 fmly) CTV in all bedrooms No dogs (ex guide dogs) Night porter 200P Tennis (hard) Pool table Heliport Radio controlled model cars Wkly live entertainment V meals Coffee am Tea pm No smoking in restaurant
CONF: Thtr 120 Class 80 Board 50
CARDS:

See advertisement on opposite page

MILFORD ON SEA Hampshire Map 04 SZ29

★★★ 74% **South Lawn**
Lymington Rd SO41 0RF (on B3058) ☎ 01590 643911
FAX 01590 644820
Closed 20 Dec-18 Jan
This former dower house is located on the edge of the New Forest, close to the sea in four acres of well tended grounds. The hotel offers perfect tranquillity and Mrs and Mrs Barton create a relaxed and friendly atmosphere. The bedrooms are spacious and attractively decorated, and the large lounge offers a comfortable area in which to relax whilst enjoying the gardens. The bright dining room serves a good range of local produce prepared with care by Ernst Barton and his team.

24 en suite (bth/shr) CTV in all bedrooms No dogs Lift 60P No children 7yrs English, French & German Cuisine V meals Coffee am Tea pm No smoking in restaurant Last d 8.30pm
ROOMS: (incl. bkfst) s £47.50-£52; d £84-£95 * **LB**
MEALS: Lunch fr £11 Dinner £17.50-£19.50&alc*
CARDS:

See advertisement under LYMINGTON

★★★ 69% **Westover Hall**
Park Ln SO41 0PT (take main road 3m through village, hotel last building on left) ☎ 01590 643044 FAX 01590 644490
This handsome Victorian House was built for the Siemens family and commands spectacular views out to the Isle of Wight. The public areas retain all their period character and are being sympathetically restored by the new owners. There is a beautiful galleried hall with original wood panelling, and the public rooms include a sunny bar and day room overlooking the garden, a comfortably furnished lounge and a small sun lounge. Chef Roberto Musetti provides fresh, interesting menus with influences from his native Italy. The owners are involved in every area of the day to day running and create a relaxed and friendly atmosphere.
15 en suite (bth/shr) (4 fmly) CTV in all bedrooms 50P No coaches Xmas European Cuisine V meals Coffee am Tea pm No smoking in restaurant Last d 9pm
ROOMS: (incl. bkfst) s £40-£65; d £100-£130 * **LB**
OFF-PEAK: (incl. bkfst) s £40-£50; d £90-£120
MEALS: Lunch £16.50-£18.50 High tea fr £5 Dinner £16.50-£18.50
CONF: Thtr 50 Class 30 Board 25 Del from £100
CARDS:
See advertisement under LYMINGTON

MILTON COMMON Oxfordshire Map 04 SP60

★★★ 68% **Belfry**
Brimpton Grange OX9 2JW (on A40, between junc 7 & 8)
☎ 01844 279381 FAX 01844 279624
Closed 24-30 Dec RS Sat (snack lunches only)
This smart modern hotel with a mock-Tudor creeper-clad façade specialises in the conference market, with excellent meeting facilities and an attractive leisure suite clear benefits. Bedrooms are spacious with good desk space and an excellent range of facilities including satellite TV. Meals are served in the attractive pastel-coloured restaurant by a team of young attentive staff ably led by manager Mr Barber.
75 en suite (bth/shr) CTV in all bedrooms STV Night porter 200P Indoor swimming pool (heated) Sauna Solarium Gym Pool table Wkly live entertainment English & Continental Cuisine V meals Coffee am Tea pm Last d 9.30pm
ROOMS: (incl. bkfst) s £75-£97.50; d £95-£115 * **LB**
MEALS: Lunch fr £15.50&alc Dinner fr £19.75&alc*
CONF: Thtr 250 Class 100 Board 50 Del from £115
CARDS:
See advertisement under THAME

MILTON KEYNES Buckinghamshire Map 04 SP83
See also Aspley Guise, Hanslope & Woburn

★★★ 70% **Courtyard by Marriott Milton Keynes**

London Rd, Newport Pagnell MK16 0JA (1m from junct 14 of M1 on the A509) ☎ 01908 613688 FAX 01908 617335

contd.

Designed around a handsome three-storey Georgian house and a pretty courtyard, the Coach House offers welcoming public areas and modern bedrooms. Quality fabrics and generously sized bathrooms are a feature throughout and staff are well trained and personable.
49 en suite (bth/shr) (1 fmly) No smoking in 26 bedrooms CTV in all bedrooms STV No dogs (ex guide dogs) Night porter 160P Sauna Solarium Gym International Cuisine V meals Coffee am Tea pm No smoking in restaurant Last d 10pm
ROOMS: s £79; d £79 * **LB**
OFF-PEAK: s £45; d £45
MEALS: Lunch £9.95-£14 Dinner £14-£20*
CONF: Thtr 200 Del from £100
CARDS:

★★★62% **Quality Friendly Hotel**
Monks Way, Two Mile Ash MK8 8LY (junct A5/A422)
☎ 01908 561666 FAX 01908 568303

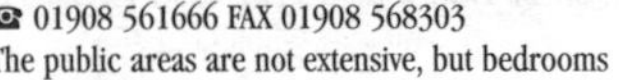

The public areas are not extensive, but bedrooms are spacious and well laid out, and include thoughtful extras to ensure that guests have a comfortable stay. The mainly young staff are freindly and helpful.
88 en suite (bth/shr) (15 fmly) No smoking in 44 bedrooms CTV in all bedrooms STV Night porter Air conditioning 200P Indoor swimming pool (heated) Sauna Solarium Gym Jacuzzi/spa Steam room Whirlpool spa Xmas English & Continental Cuisine V meals Coffee am Tea pm No smoking in restaurant Last d 9.30pm
ROOMS: s £67.50; d £87.50 **LB**
MEALS: Lunch £7.50-£9.95&alc Dinner £13.50&alc
CONF: Thtr 130 Class 60 Board 45 Del from £105
CARDS:

★★71% ***Shenley Church Inn***
Burchard Crescent, Shenley Church End MK5 6HQ
☎ 01908 505467 FAX 01908 502308
RS 25 Dec
Dark wood and muted colours have been used to create a warm atmosphere in the public areas of this recently built hotel. The bedrooms are very well looked after and provide good modern comforts. The restaurant is a themed Toby Grill.
50 en suite (bth/shr) (12 fmly) No smoking in 14 bedrooms CTV in all bedrooms STV No dogs (ex guide dogs) Lift Night porter 200P Wkly live entertainment V meals Coffee am Tea pm
CARDS:

★★67% **Peartree Bridge Inn**
Waterside, Peartree Bridge MK6 3PE ☎ 01908 691515 FAX 01908 690274

This modern purpose-built hotel stands just five minutes' drive from junction 14 of the M1 in a green site next to the marina and the Grand Union Canal. Bedrooms are well maintained and comprehensively equipped; the restaurant is a themed Toby Grill.
39 en suite (bth/shr) No smoking in 10 bedrooms CTV in all bedrooms STV No dogs (ex guide dogs) Night porter 100P Wkly live entertainment V meals Coffee am Tea pm No smoking in restaurant Last d 10pm
ROOMS: (incl. bkfst) s fr £62.50; d fr £72.50 *
OFF-PEAK: (incl. bkfst) s fr £31; d fr £53
MEALS: Lunch £4.99-£11 Dinner £4.99-£11*
CARDS:

★★66% **Different Drummer**
94 High St, Stony Stratford MK11 1AH
☎ 01908 564733 FAX 01908 260646
Originally known as the Swan, this small town-centre hotel dates from the 15th-century. Modern bedrooms are well equipped and a spacious guests' lounge features a bar and plenty of reading material. The hotel also contains a popular Italian restaurant serving well prepared food in a pleasant atmosphere. Staff throughout are friendly and attentive.
8 en suite (bth/shr) 4 annexe en suite (shr) (2 fmly) CTV in all bedrooms No dogs (ex guide dogs) No coaches English & Italian Cuisine V meals Last d 10pm
ROOMS: (incl. bkfst) s £55-£65; d £66-£75 *
OFF-PEAK: (incl. bkfst) s £40; d £50
MEALS: Lunch £10-£20&alc High tea fr £3.95 Dinner fr £19.50&alc*
CARDS:

See advertisement on opposite page

★★64% **Swan Revived**
High St, Newport Pagnell MK16 8AR (on B526)
☎ 01908 610565 FAX 01908 210995

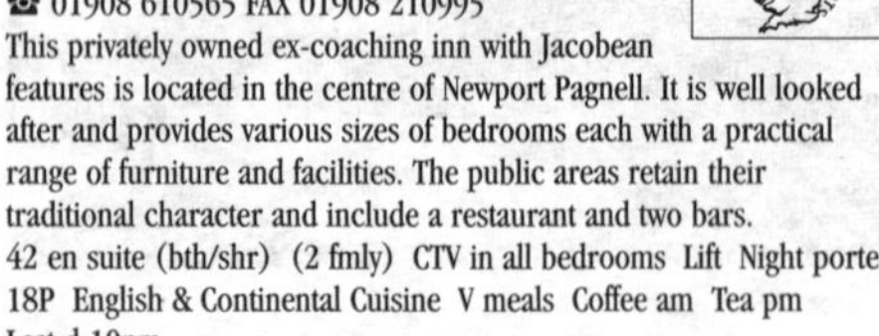

This privately owned ex-coaching inn with Jacobean features is located in the centre of Newport Pagnell. It is well looked after and provides various sizes of bedrooms each with a practical range of furniture and facilities. The public areas retain their traditional character and include a restaurant and two bars.
42 en suite (bth/shr) (2 fmly) CTV in all bedrooms Lift Night porter 18P English & Continental Cuisine V meals Coffee am Tea pm Last d 10pm
ROOMS: (incl. bkfst) s £39.50-£62.50; d £55-£65 * **LB**
MEALS: Lunch £9.75 Dinner £8.75-£20alc
CONF: Thtr 70 Class 30 Board 28 Del from £85
CARDS:

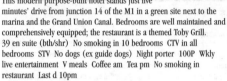

Forte Posthouse Milton Keynes

500 Saxon Gate West MK9 2HQ ☎ 01908 667722
FAX 01908 674714
Suitable for both the business and leisure traveller, this bright hotel provides modern accommodation in well equipped bedrooms with en suite bathrooms. For more details about Forte Posthouse hotels, consult the Contents page for the section on Hotel Groups.
150 en suite (bth/shr)
ROOMS: d £89-£99
CONF: Thtr 150 Class 85 Board 35 Del from £125

Hilton National

Timbold Dr, Kents Hill MK7 6HL ☎ 01908 694433
FAX 01908 695533
This is a bright, modern hotel, with an informal restaurant, aimed at both the business and leisure guest. All bedrooms have en suite bathrooms and a range of modern facilities. For more information about Hilton National hotels, consult the Contents page under Hotel Groups.
138 en suite (bth/shr)
ROOMS: s £97.50-£125; d £97.50-£125 *
CONF: Thtr 300 Class 120 Board 30 Del from £140

Travel Inn

Secklow Gate West MK9 3BZ (follow H6 route)
☎ 01908 663388 FAX 01908 607481
Purpose-built accommodation, offering spacious, well equipped bedrooms, all with en suite bathrooms. Meals may be taken at the nearby family restaurant. For more information about Travel Inns, consult the Contents page under Hotel Groups.
38 en suite (bth/shr)
ROOMS: d £35.50 *

MINEHEAD Somerset Map 03 SS94

★★★71% **Benares**

Northfield Rd TA24 5PT (along sea front 75yds before harbour turn left into Blenheim Rd then right into Northfield Rd) ☎ 01643 704911 FAX 01643 706373
Closed 9 Nov-25 Mar (ex Xmas)
An extended Edwardian house set in an acre and a half of beautifully maintained gardens in a quiet residential area yet only a short walk from the seafront. Italian fireplaces and stained glass windows are two of the original features in the spacious and comfortable public areas. Each evening a short fixed-price, 5-course dinner is served with a good choice of home-made puddings. Peter Maskrey and his small loyal team of staff provide a friendly and relaxed style of service.
19 en suite (bth/shr) (3 fmly) CTV in all bedrooms 22P No coaches ch fac Xmas English, French & Italian Cuisine V meals Coffee am Tea pm No smoking in restaurant Last d 8.30pm
ROOMS: (incl. bkfst) s £44.50; d £83 * **LB**

contd.

M

MEALS: Bar Lunch £2-£15alc Dinner £18
CARDS:

See advertisement on page 445

★★★68% **Northfield**
Northfield Rd TA24 5PU ☎ 01643 705155
FAX 01643 707715
Set in beautifully maintained gardens on the lower slopes of North Hill, the hotel is within easy walking distance of the town centre and the seafront. Public areas are spacious and comfortable and the leisure facilities are freely available to hotel guests. Each evening in the wood-panelled dining rooms, a fixed-price menu is offered, plus a limited à la carte selection. Bedrooms vary in size and style, all are well equipped and the soft furnishings are attractively co-ordinated. Many of the guests return year after year and are recognised by the loyal team of mainly local staff.
25 en suite (bth/shr) (7 fmly) CTV in 24 bedrooms Lift 44P No coaches Indoor swimming pool (heated) Solarium Gym Putting green Jacuzzi/spa Steam room Xmas V meals Coffee am Tea pm No smoking area in restaurant
ROOMS: (incl. bkfst) s £44-£52; d £80-£104 **LB**
OFF-PEAK: (incl. bkfst) s fr £35; d fr £60
CONF: Thtr 70 Class 45 Board 30
CARDS:

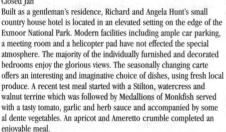

★★ 76% **Periton Park**
Middlecombe TA24 8SW ☎ 01643 706885
FAX 01643 706885
Closed Jan

Built as a gentleman's residence, Richard and Angela Hunt's small country house hotel is located in an elevated setting on the edge of the Exmoor National Park. Modern facilities including ample car parking, a meeting room and a helicopter pad have not effected the special atmosphere. The majority of the individually furnished and decorated bedrooms enjoy the glorious views. The seasonally changing carte offers an interesting and imaginative choice of dishes, using fresh local produce. A recent test meal started with a Stilton, watercress and walnut terrine which was followed by Medallions of Monkfish served with a tasty tomato, garlic and herb sauce and accompanied by some al dente vegetables. An apricot and Ameretto crumble completed an enjoyable meal.
8 en suite (bth/shr) No smoking in 3 bedrooms CTV in all bedrooms 12P No coaches Riding Croquet lawn No children 12yrs Xmas English & French Cuisine V meals No smoking in restaurant
ROOMS: (incl. bkfst) s £50-£56; d £80-£92 * **LB**
MEALS:
CONF: Thtr 24 Board 16 Del £86
CARDS:

MONK FRYSTON North Yorkshire Map 08 SE52

★★★ 68% **Monk Fryston Hall**

LS25 5DU (on A63 towards Selby)
☎ 01977 682369 FAX 01977 683544
This very traditional hotel stands its own well tended grounds in the centre of the village, and parts of the house date back to the Middle Ages. Much of the old charm is retained both in the well equipped and generally spacious bedrooms and also in the comfortable and inviting public areas. Good British cooking is provided in the elegant restaurant which overlooks the terrace whilst service is very attentive and naturally friendly.
28 en suite (bth/shr) (2 fmly) CTV in all bedrooms Night porter 60P No coaches Putting green Xmas V meals Coffee am Tea pm No smoking area in restaurant Last d 9.30pm
ROOMS: (incl. bkfst) s £68.50-£72; d £95-£102 **LB**
MEALS: Lunch £13.75-£15.75&alc Dinner £20-£24&alc
CONF: Thtr 50 Class 40 Board 30 Del from £108
CARDS:

MONTACUTE Somerset Map 03 ST41

★★ 71% **Kings Arms Inn**
Bishopstow TA15 6UU (turn off A303 at A3088 roundabout signposted Montacute. Inn by church in centre of village) ☎ 01935 822513
FAX 01935 826549
Closed 26 Dec-8 Jan
A 16th-century Hamstone Inn situated in the centre of one of Somerset's most picturesque and unspoilt villages, near the historic Montacute House, offers comfortable bedrooms (including a four-poster and a half tester room) which are well decorated and thoughtfully furnished. A varied selection of bar meals is available in the convivial Pickwick Bar, while in the Abbey Room an interesting choice of dishes is offered from the carte on Monday-Saturday evenings, complimented by a wine list which specialises in examples from the New World.
13 en suite (bth/shr) (2 fmly) No smoking in 4 bedrooms CTV in all bedrooms No dogs (ex guide dogs) 15P English & French Cuisine V meals Coffee am Tea pm No smoking in restaurant Last d 9pm
ROOMS: (incl. bkfst) s £49.50-£56; d £69-£85 * **LB**
OFF-PEAK: (incl. bkfst) s £49-£56; d £69-£85
MEALS: Lunch £9.50-£11.50 Dinner £17-£22alc*
CARDS:

MORCOTT Rutland Map 04 SK90

Travelodge
Uppingham LE15 9DL (on A47, eastbound)
☎ 01572 747719 FAX 01572 747719
This modern building offers accommodation in smart, spacious and well equipped bedrooms, suitable for family use, and all with en suite bathrooms. Meals may be taken at the nearby family restaurant. For information on room rates and to make a booking, call Roomline free of charge on 0800 850950. For more details about Travelodge, consult the Contents page under Hotel Groups.
40 en suite (bth/shr)

MORDEN Greater London See LONDON SECTION plan 1 D1

Travelodge
Epsom Rd SM4 5PH (on A24) ☎ 0181 640 8227
FAX 0181 640 8227
This modern building offers accommodation in smart, spacious and well equipped bedrooms, suitable for family use, and all with en suite bathrooms. Meals may be taken at the nearby family restaurant. For information on room rates and to make a booking, call Roomline free of charge on 0800 850950. For more details about Travelodge, consult the Contents page under Hotel Groups.
32 en suite (bth/shr)

MORECAMBE Lancashire Map 07 SD46

★★★66% **Elms**
Bare Village LA4 6DD ☎ 01524 411501 FAX 01524 831979
This popular, well run hotel stands in its own gardens just off the promenade at Bare. The well maintained and equipped bedrooms have pretty soft furnishings and include a number of rooms with four-poster beds. Guests can relax in the newly decorated lounge bar and enjoy well prepared meals in the restaurant, where the service is attentive and prompt. The hotel also owns The Owl's Nest pub, close to the main building, where bar meals are served at lunchtime and guests can enjoy a quiet drink in the evening.
40 en suite (bth/shr) (3 fmly) CTV in all bedrooms Lift Night porter 80P Pool table Xmas English & French Cuisine V meals Coffee am Tea pm Last d 9pm

ROOMS: (incl. bkfst) s £54-£60; d £78-£84 * **LB**
OFF-PEAK: (incl. bkfst) s £35-£54; d £50-£78
MEALS: Lunch fr £9.95 Dinner fr £14.95&alc*
CONF: Thtr 200 Class 72 Board 60 Del from £64
CARDS:

★★★65% **Strathmore**
East Promenade LA4 5AP ☎ 01524 421234
FAX 01524 414242

This friendly family owned hotel is situated in an excellent position on the sea front and has unrivalled views over the bay towards the hills of the Lake District. The bedrooms are slightly dated, but are nevertheless well equipped with modern facilities. The hotel was named after the liner "Strathmore", which was launched at Barrow-in-Furness and a historical record of the ship can be found in the main entrance hall. The hotel has its own car park and there is also parking on the sea front.
51 en suite (bth/shr) (6 fmly) CTV in all bedrooms STV No dogs (ex guide dogs) Lift Night porter 42P Wkly live entertainment Xmas English & French Cuisine V meals Coffee am Tea pm No smoking area in restaurant Last d 9.45pm
ROOMS: (incl. bkfst) s £59-£64; d £78-£88 * **LB**
MEALS: Lunch £7.95-£9.95 Dinner £8.95-£16.95&alc*
CONF: Thtr 200 Class 100 Board 70 Del from £74
CARDS:

★★★59% ***Headway***
Marine Rd East LA4 5AW ☎ 01524 412525 FAX 01524 832630
RS Nov-Apr
Fine views over Morecambe Bay and the hills of the Lake District beyond can be enjoyed from many of the bedrooms of this large hotel which is quietly situated on the east promenade. The bedrooms themselves are freshly decorated, neatly furnished, and include family rooms and a very pretty room with a four-poster bed. The public areas include a comfortable sun lounge and a spacious restaurant, where friendly staff serve a good range of tasty dishes. The hotel also benefits from an attractive function room which proves very popular for weddings.
51 en suite (bth/shr) (4 fmly) CTV in all bedrooms No dogs (ex guide dogs) Lift Night porter 20P V meals Coffee am Tea pm Last d 8pm
CARDS:

★★59% **Clarendon**
Marine Rd West, West End Promenade LA4 4EP
☎ 01524 410180 FAX 01524 421616
This long-established hotel is located on the promenade with good sea views from the lounge and many of the bedrooms. The rooms have modern facilities and there are several family rooms. Both the bar and the restaurant offer a good range of value-for-money food.
31 rms (28 bth/shr) (2 fmly) CTV in all bedrooms Lift Night porter Pool table Xmas V meals Coffee am Tea pm Last d 9pm
ROOMS: (incl. bkfst) s £29-£36; d £46-£49 * **LB**
MEALS: Lunch £4.50-£7.50 High tea £5 Dinner £8.50-£12.50*
CONF: Thtr 60 Class 50 Board 50
CARDS:

MORETON Merseyside Map 07 SJ28

★★★66% ***Leasowe Castle***
Leasowe Rd L46 3RF ☎ 0151 606 9191 FAX 0151 678 5551
Leasowe Castle, which is situated near the local golf course, was built nearly 400 years ago and still retains some impressive features. The Star Chamber sitting room is particularly special and its ornately carved wall panels and ceiling came from the Palace of Westminster. Bedrooms are well equipped and comfortable and include several suitable for families and some with four-poster beds. Extensive function facilities are provided and the hotel is licensed to hold civil marriages. The Stables Bistro provides an alternative to the more formal main restaurant and a wide range of options is on offer. A fully equipped mini-gymnasium is now available.
47 en suite (bth/shr) (3 fmly) No smoking in 3 bedrooms CTV in all bedrooms No dogs (ex guide dogs) Lift Night porter 200P Sauna Gym ch fac English & Continental Cuisine V meals Coffee am Tea pm Last d 10pm
CARDS:

MORETONHAMPSTEAD Devon Map 03 SX78

★★★★63% **Manor House**
TQ13 8RE (on B3212) ☎ 01647 440355
FAX 01647 440961
This substantial Victorian property boats an enviable position within acres of quiet grounds which include a golf course and commanding rural views. The upgrading programme continues with enthusiasm with the new courtyard bedrooms being bright and inviting. Public rooms display many period features, especially ornate oak panelling, are spacious and comfortably styled.
89 en suite (bth/shr) (5 fmly) CTV in all bedrooms STV Lift Night porter 100P Golf 18 Tennis (hard) Fishing Riding Snooker Croquet lawn Putting green Xmas English & French Cuisine V meals Coffee am Tea pm No smoking in restaurant Last d 9.30pm
ROOMS: (incl. bkfst) s £72.50-£82.50; d £100-£130 * **LB**
MEALS: Lunch £7.95-£9.95 High tea £3.75-£6.95 Dinner £18.95-£24.50&alc*
CONF: Thtr 100 Class 50 Board 40 Del £115
CARDS:

See advertisement on this page

★★73% The White Hart
The Square TQ13 8NF (at junct of A382/B3212)
☎ 01647 440406 FAX 01647 440565
Closed 25-26 Dec
A warm welcome is assured at this privately owned and personally managed Georgian Post House. The original charm of the building has been carefully retained, and bedrooms are comfortable and well equipped, with many thoughtful extras. The traditional dining room offers an extensive selection of dishes.
20 en suite (bth/shr) (3 fmly) No smoking in 10 bedrooms CTV in all bedrooms STV 12P No children 10yrs Xmas International Cuisine V meals Coffee am Tea pm No smoking in restaurant Last d 8.30pm
ROOMS: (incl. bkfst) s £43-£48; d £65-£73 **LB**
MEALS: Sunday Lunch fr £5.95alc Dinner £12.50-£19.25&alc*
CONF: Thtr 80 Class 50 Board 30 Del from £65
CARDS:

MINOTEL Great Britain

See advertisement on opposite page

★77% Blackaller Hotel
North Bovey TQ13 8QY ☎ 01647 440322 FAX 01647 440322
North Bovey is a charming village about 3 miles from Moretonhampstead, with Blackaller hidden away on the banks of the River Bovey. Peter Hunt and Hazel Phillips run the hotel on very relaxed and friendly lines, remembering the small individual touches that making staying at a hotel special. Public areas are spacious and comfortable, including a relaxing drawing room, well stocked bar and cosy dining room. Mrs Phillips uses fresh, locally-produced ingredients in the short, daily-changing dinner menu. At breakfast the home-produced honey must not be missed. Although the individually furnished bedrooms are not over-spacious, they are comfortable and equipped with modern facilities.
5 en suite (bth/shr) 1 annexe en suite (bth) CTV in all bedrooms P No coaches Xmas V meals Coffee am Tea pm No smoking in restaurant Last d 8.30pm
ROOMS: (incl. bkfst) s £28-£29; d £66-£70 * **LB**
OFF-PEAK: (incl. bkfst) s £28; d £66
MEALS: Dinner £19-£50alc*

MORETON-IN-MARSH Gloucestershire Map 04 SP23

★★★66% Manor House Hotel
High St GL56 0LJ (off A429 at south end of the town)
☎ 01608 650501 FAX 01608 651481
Still a hotel of two halves, the Manor House has some smart modern bedrooms and others that are showing their age, although refurbishment is making inroads. Public areas include a cosy lounge, a bar and a restaurant where simple dishes are turned out by proficient and well trained chefs.
39 rms (35 bth 3 shr) (1 fmly) CTV in all bedrooms No dogs (ex guide dogs) Lift Night porter 25P No coaches Indoor swimming pool (heated) Sauna Putting green Jacuzzi/spa Xmas English & French Cuisine V meals Coffee am Tea pm No smoking in restaurant Last d 9.30pm
ROOMS: (incl. bkfst) s £55-£75; d £85-£135 * **LB**
OFF-PEAK: (incl. bkfst & dinner) s £55-£65; d £115-£170
MEALS: Lunch £10.95-£12.50&alc Dinner £21.90-£24.50&alc*
CONF: Thtr 100 Class 55 Board 50 Del from £95
CARDS:

★★61% The White Hart Royal
High St GL56 0BA (on Fosse Way (A429)) ☎ 01608 650731
FAX 01608 650880
A former inn, dating from the 17th century, this hotel once provided refuge for Charles I. The bedrooms are slowly being upgraded and public areas maintain their appeal for regulars - flagstone floors and a cobbled entrance hall adding to the atmosphere.
20 en suite (bth/shr) (4 fmly) CTV in all bedrooms 7P Xmas V meals Coffee am Tea pm No smoking in restaurant Last d 9pm
ROOMS: (incl. bkfst) s £45-£55; d £65-£80 * **LB**
OFF-PEAK: (incl. bkfst) s £35-£45; d fr £55
MEALS: Sunday Lunch fr £10.25 High tea £4.50-£8.50 Dinner £15.50-£18.50&alc
CONF: Thtr 60 Class 20 Board 20 Del from £65
CARDS:

MORPETH Northumberland Map 12 NZ28

★★★★71% Linden Hall
NE65 8XF ☎ 01670 516611 FAX 01670 788544
(For full entry see Longhorsley)

★★★★66% Longhirst Hall
Longhirst NE61 3LL (on A197/B1337 Pegswood/Widdrington road)
☎ 01670 791348 FAX 01670 791385
This hotel is situated west of Morpeth and is part of an extensive complex which includes university accommodation and conserved acres of grounds and woodland. The former stately home offers modern accommodation and high standards of service, making it ideal for conferences or the business traveller. There is a choice of three bars, but the lounge is somewhat limited in space and can be congested at dinner times. An imaginative menu and award-winning wine list feature in the restaurant, where the fine cuisine has earned one rosette.
75 en suite (bth/shr) No smoking in 40 bedrooms CTV in all bedrooms STV Lift Night porter 350P Tennis (hard & grass) Sauna Gym Pool table Croquet lawn Putting green Jacuzzi/spa Golf course due to open Apr 1997 Xmas V meals Coffee am Tea pm No smoking area in restaurant Last d 9.45pm
ROOMS: (incl. bkfst) s £35-£75; d £70-£82.50 * **LB**
MEALS: Lunch £6.50-£11.95 Dinner £15&alc*
CONF: Thtr 80 Class 48 Board 36 Del from £82.50
CARDS:

See advertisement on opposite page

MORTEHOE See Woolacombe

MOULSFORD Oxfordshire Map 04 SU58

★★76% Beetle & Wedge
Ferry Ln OX10 9JF ☎ 01491 651381 FAX 01491 651376
RS 25 Dec (restaurant closed)
This fine Thames-side hotel, once the home of Jerome K Jerome, is a collection of historic buildings which have been brought together to create a synchronous whole. Experienced hoteliers Kate and Richard Smith set standards of excellence many hotels aspire to but which only a select few reach. Bedrooms are individually decorated with great taste and style and are geared towards the leisure user. Bathrooms all feature huge enamelled baths with claw feet and excellent toiletries. All rooms bar one overlook the Thames as do the comfortable public areas. The two restaurants on site vary in style with the dining room traditionally elegant and the Boathouse a more informal cosy operation. Richard Smith serves the same high standards of cuisine in both, only the style varies. A recent Boathouse meal started with a gutsy smoked Toulouse sausage served with lentils. A main course of John Dory came with some lemon scented cous-cous and a fine ratatouille. The ever popular choux beignets soufflé came with a piquant lemon curd. The wine list is worth exploring, particularly the special recommendations; since diners are not obliged to drink a whole bottle, a dipstick system operates.
6 en suite (bth/shr) 4 annexe en suite (bth/shr) No smoking in 6 bedrooms CTV in all bedrooms 44P Fishing Wkly live entertainment V meals Coffee am No smoking area in restaurant Last d 10pm
ROOMS: (incl. bkfst) s £80-£100; d £95-£125 * **LB**
MEALS: Lunch £17.50-£27.50 Dinner £35&alc*
CONF: Thtr 50 Class 30 Board 25 Del from £125
CARDS:

M

MOUNT HAWKE Cornwall & Isles of Scilly Map 02 SW74

★ 75% **Tregarthen Country Cottage**
Banns Rd TR4 8BW (from the A30 turn off at Three Burrows roundabout onto the B3277 St Agnes road, take first left and follow signs to Mount Hawke approx 2m) ☎ 01209 890399
FAX 01209 891041
Situated in pleasant rural surroundings on the edge of the village, this delightful cottage-style hotel provides a warm welcome to guests, many of whom return on a regular basis. Guests enjoy the comfort of the lounge, with its deep armchairs and roaring log fire. In the well appointed dining room, traditional home cooked dishes are chosen from a set menu.
6 en suite (bth/shr) No smoking in all bedrooms No dogs (ex guide dogs) 12P No coaches No smoking in restaurant
ROOMS: (incl. bkfst) s £27.50; d £55 **LB**
OFF-PEAK: (incl. bkfst) s £25; d £50

MOUSEHOLE Cornwall & Isles of Scilly Map 02 SW42

★★68% **Lobster Pot**
South Cliff TR19 6QX ☎ 01736 731251 FAX 01736 731140
Closed last 3 wks Jan
This delightful harbourside hotel and restaurant - originally built as fishermen's cottages - now offers services and facilities generally associated with establishments of a higher classification. Literally overhanging the harbour wall, the cottagey bedrooms are small but pleasant and well equipped. A good range of fresh dishes (in which local fish predominate) is served in the restaurant, which has a splendid sea view.
13 en suite (bth/shr) 12 annexe rms (9 bth/shr) (5 fmly) CTV in all bedrooms No dogs (ex guide dogs) Xmas English & French Cuisine V meals Coffee am Tea pm No smoking in restaurant
ROOMS: (incl. bkfst) s £33-£63; d £66-£126 * **LB**
MEALS: Lunch £7.50 High tea £6 Dinner £15.95&alc*
CARDS:

★★59% **Carn Du**
Raginnis Hill TR19 6SS (through village, up hill towards bird hospital, house on right overlooking harbour) ☎ 01736 731233
From its vantage point, Carn Du commands magnificent views of Mount's Bay sweeping round to the Lizard Point. A small quiet hotel, personally run by Andrew and Sigrid Field, with a relaxing atmosphere. Each evening a short fixed price menu is served with the emphasis home cooked food especially using local fish. Bedrooms vary in size, mostly they are compact and soundly furnished.
7 en suite (bth/shr) CTV in all bedrooms No dogs 12P No coaches English & German Cuisine V meals Coffee am No smoking in restaurant Last d 8.30pm
ROOMS: (incl. bkfst) s £30; d £60-£70 **LB**
OFF-PEAK: (incl. bkfst) s £25; d £50
MEALS: Bar Lunch £2.50-£8 Dinner fr £14.95
CARDS:

MUCH BIRCH Hereford & Worcester Map 03 SO53

★★★63% **Pilgrim**
Ross Rd HR2 8HJ (off A49) ☎ 01981 540742
FAX 01981 540620
This family-run, modernised red brick rectory is set back from the A49 between Hereford and Ross-on-Wye, surrounded by four acres of grounds. The bedrooms are spacious and well maintained and there is a cosy lounge as well as a popular bar. A good choice of meals is offered in the restaurant.
20 en suite (bth/shr) (3 fmly) No smoking in 5 bedrooms CTV in all bedrooms 40P No coaches Croquet lawn Putting green Pitch & putt
contd.

Badminton Xmas English & French Cuisine V meals Coffee am Tea pm Last high tea 6pm
ROOMS: (incl. bkfst) s £39.50-£49.50; d £39-£59.50 * **LB**
MEALS: Lunch £8.75 High tea £4.95
CONF: Thtr 45 Class 45 Board 25
CARDS:

MUCH WENLOCK Shropshire Map 07 SO69

★★★70% ***Raven***
30 Barrow St TF13 6EN ☎ 01952 727251 FAX 01952 728416
This old coaching inn dates back to 1700 with parts of it going even further back to the 15th century. An interesting item from its history is the fact that the first modern Olympic Games was plotted within its walls. It is now a thriving and modern hotel with comfortable bedrooms and public areas. Bedrooms have been allowed to retain their original shapes and layouts and this has proved to be an attractive feature. A conservatory and separate restaurant have recently been added and the new team of chefs are making a determined effort to provide attractive dishes and enjoyable food; the menu changes regularly according to market supplies. There is a central courtyard where guests may sit out during better weather, and a large car park is provided.
8 en suite (bth/shr) CTV in all bedrooms STV No dogs (ex guide dogs) 30P No coaches International Cuisine V meals Coffee am Tea pm Last d 9.30pm
CARDS:

★★68% ***Wheatland Fox***
TF13 6AD ☎ 01952 727292
The main structure of this half-timbered hotel dates back to 1669 although the Georgian frontage was added later. Bedrooms are smart and modern, two are located in a converted outbuilding and all are well equipped. A full menu is available in the restaurant and a good range of bar food is also served. The hotel lies near Telford and Ironbridge and is a good base for tourists to the area.
3 en suite (bth/shr) 2 annexe en suite (bth/shr) CTV in all bedrooms No dogs (ex guide dogs) 12P No coaches English & French Cuisine V meals Coffee am Tea pm Last d 9pm
CARDS:

★★62% **Gaskell Arms**
Bourton Rd TF13 6AQ (on A458) ☎ 01952 727212
FAX 01952 727736
This 17th-century inn stands in the shelter of Wenlock Edge. Bars and the attractive restaurant still feature exposed beams and timbers and log fires burn during colder weather. Bedrooms are well maintained and some are suitable for families. Ironbridge and Telford are a short drive away.
11 rms (6 bth/shr) (2 fmly) CTV in all bedrooms No dogs 31P ch fac V meals Coffee am No smoking area in restaurant Last d 9.30pm
ROOMS: (incl. bkfst) s £29-£39; d £48-£58 * **LB**
MEALS: Lunch £10.50-£12.95 Dinner £12.95&alc
CARDS:

MUDDIFORD Devon Map 02 SS53

★★64% **Broomhill Country House Hotel**
EX31 4EX ☎ 01271 850262 FAX 01271 850575
Three miles from the centre of Barnstaple, this attractive country house overlooks a wooded valley from an elevated position in its own grounds, which include a tennis court and swimming pool. Bedrooms have been equipped with modern facilities, and there is a comfortable lounge and bar. A short, fixed-price menu offers an interesting selection of carefully prepared dishes, available in the elegant dining room.
8 en suite (shr) No smoking in all bedrooms CTV in all bedrooms No dogs (ex guide dogs) 30P No coaches Outdoor swimming pool (heated) Tennis (hard) Fishing Pool table No children 7yrs Xmas French Cuisine V meals Last d 10pm
ROOMS: (incl. bkfst) s fr £35; d fr £63 * **LB**
OFF-PEAK: (incl. bkfst) s fr £37; d fr £59
MEALS: Lunch fr £13.95alc Dinner fr £13.50&alc
CARDS:

MUDEFORD See Christchurch

MULLION Cornwall & Isles of Scilly Map 02 SW61

★★★74% **Polurrian**
TR12 7EN ☎ 01326 240421 FAX 01326 240083
Closed Jan-Feb
Superbly positioned overlooking Polurrian Cove, amid dramatic coastal scenery, this whitewashed Edwardian hotel is professionally run and its loyal staff provide high standards of service. Many of the attractively decorated bedrooms have sea views, and the public areas are comfortable and smartly furnished. The Leisure Club features a crèche and separate teenage area.
39 en suite (bth/shr) (22 fmly) CTV in all bedrooms STV Night porter 80P Indoor swimming pool (heated) Outdoor swimming pool (heated) Tennis (hard) Squash Snooker Sauna Solarium Gym Croquet lawn Putting green Jacuzzi/spa Cricket net Whirlpool ch fac English & French Cuisine V meals Coffee am Tea pm No smoking area in restaurant Last d 9pm
MEALS: Lunch £8.50-£12.50 High tea £10 Dinner £18&alc*
CONF: Thtr 100 Class 60 Board 20
CARDS:

See advertisement on opposite page

MUNGRISDALE Cumbria Map 11 NY33

★76% **The Mill**
CA11 0XR (exit M6 at junct 40, 2m N of A66)
☎ 01768 779659 FAX 01768 779155
Closed Dec & Jan
Formerly a mill cottage dating from 1651, this charming little hotel and restaurant lies beside a stream and provides a retreat of great character, with cosy lounges, low ceilings and a wealth of antiques, paintings and period pieces. Whilst many guests come for Eleanor Quinlan's cooking, this is more than just a restaurant with rooms and Richard Quinlan is happy to impart his knowledge of the area. Dinner however is the lynchpin of the evening; the menu is short, but extends to five courses and will satisfy the heartiest of lakeland appetites. Of the two main course dishes, one is invariably vegetarian, whilst sweet tooths will consider the pudding trolley to be the highlight, but do leave room for the cheese board.
7 rms (5 bth/shr) CTV in all bedrooms 15P No coaches Fishing Games room English & French Cuisine V meals Coffee am Tea pm No smoking in restaurant Last d 8pm
ROOMS: (incl. bkfst) s £28-£35; d £50-£70 *
MEALS: Dinner £23

NAILSWORTH Gloucestershire Map 03 ST89

★★66% **Egypt Mill**
GL6 0AE (on A46) ☎ 01453 833449 FAX 01453 836098
The water wheels are still turning in this former flour mill and can be seen from the ground floor bar where light meals and snacks are also served. The split level restaurant above offers good value, fixed price menus and a carte. Bedrooms are in the miller's house and a former storage barn which has been skilfully converted to provide modern facilities.
8 en suite (bth/shr) 8 annexe en suite (bth/shr) (1 fmly) CTV in all bedrooms STV No dogs (ex guide dogs) 120P Wkly live entertainment ch fac Xmas English & French Cuisine V meals Coffee am Tea pm Last d 9.45pm

ROOMS: (incl. bkfst) s fr £42.50; d fr £65 * **LB**
MEALS: Lunch £8.45-£10.50&alc Dinner fr £15.75&alc*
CONF: Thtr 100 Class 80 Del from £70
CARDS:

NANTWICH Cheshire Map 07 SJ65

RED STAR HOTEL

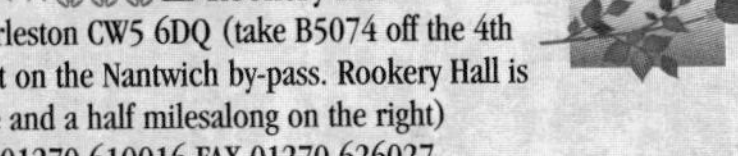

★★★ **Rookery Hall**
Worleston CW5 6DQ (take B5074 off the 4th rdbt on the Nantwich by-pass. Rookery Hall is one and a half milesalong on the right)
☎ 01270 610016 FAX 01270 626027
This imposing Regency mansion house enjoys an enviable position in 200 acres of gardens and parkland and has been sympathetically extended over the years. Retaining much of its period charm and elegance, the hotel has nevertheless been modernised to appeal to both the corporate and leisure markets. Bedrooms are particularly spacious, each with a sumptuous bathroom, and a range of thoughtful extras such as mineral water, ice and fresh fruit. Well proportioned public rooms feature an impressive hall and attractive drawing room. There are several conference rooms, and in the mahogany-panelled dining room guests may choose from a range of dishes, complemented by a wine list that includes several by the glass. Management and staff make every effort to ensure that guests are well looked after.
30 en suite (bth/shr) 15 annexe en suite (bth/shr) No smoking in 12 bedrooms CTV in all bedrooms No dogs (ex guide dogs) Lift Night porter 150P Tennis (hard) Fishing Croquet lawn Clay pigeon shooting Archery Falconry Xmas European Cuisine V meals Coffee am Tea pm No smoking in restaurant
ROOMS: (incl. bkfst) s £98.50-£180; d £180-£250 * **LB**
MEALS: Lunch £12.50-£17.50alc*
CONF: Thtr 90 Class 40 Board 40
CARDS:

★★68% **Crown**
High St CW5 5AS (take A52 to Nantwich hotel in centre of town) ☎ 01270 625283
FAX 01270 628047
Closed 25 Dec
This 400-year-old half-timbered building, situated in the pedestrianised High Street, was once a coaching inn on the route between London and Chester and the older parts of the hotel have considerable character and charm with uneven floors, steep staircases and much timber framing. The bedrooms in the original areas vary in shape and size because of the age of the building, but all have modern facilities as

do those in the newer part, which are rather more compact. The main restaurant serves Italian food, but also offers a more conventional menu for resident guests. Staff throughout are helpful and friendly and the popular bar provides a good standard of food at lunch times.
18 en suite (bth/shr) (2 fmly) CTV in all bedrooms STV Night porter 18P English & Italian Cuisine V meals Coffee am Tea pm Last d 10pm
ROOMS: (incl. bkfst) s fr £59.50; d fr £69 **LB**
MEALS: Lunch fr £5alc Dinner £15.95-£17.50&alc*
CONF: Thtr 200 Class 150 Board 70 Del from £80
CARDS:

NARBOROUGH Leicestershire Map 04 SP59

★★63% ***Charnwood***
48 Leicester Rd LE9 5DF ☎ 0116 286 2218 FAX 0116 275 0119
Closed 1 wk from 25 Dec RS Sun
This busy hotel is situated just two miles from the M1/M69 interchange. It provides well equipped, modern bedrooms and many of these are decorated with pretty papers and fabrics. There is a combined bar and lounge area and the restaurant provides well cooked food from either the extensive carte menu or the special gourmet selection. Staff are friendly and eager to please and the hotel is a popular venue for local weddings.
20 en suite (bth/shr) CTV in all bedrooms 50P No coaches English & French Cuisine V meals Coffee am Tea pm Last d 9pm
CARDS:

NEEDHAM MARKET Suffolk Map 05 TM05

Travelodge
Beacon Hill IP6 8NY (A14/A140) ☎ 01449 721640
FAX 01449 721640

contd.

This modern building offers accommodation in smart, spacious and well equipped bedrooms, suitable for family use, and all with en suite bathrooms. Meals may be taken at the nearby family restaurant. For information on room rates and to make a booking, call Roomline free of charge on 0800 850950. For more details about Travelodge, consult the Contents page under Hotel Groups.
40 en suite (bth/shr)

NESSCLIFFE Shropshire Map 07 SJ31

★★69% **Nesscliffe**
Nesscliffe SY4 1DB (on A5 between Shrewsbury/Oswestry)
☎ 01743 741430 FAX 01743 741104
This hotel is located north-west of the town alongside the A5 in the village of Nesscliffe. It has recently undergone complete refurbishment and now provides comfortable accommodation. Bedrooms are pine furnished, several are quite spacious and two have four-poster beds. Public rooms are set out in the open plan mode with a small restaurant and two bar sections. Blackboard specials supplement the carte menu and there is also a range of bar food available. The hotel is surrounded by walking country and clay pigeon shooting and fishing can be arranged for guests.
8 en suite (bth/shr) (1 fmly) CTV in all bedrooms STV Night porter 50P V meals Coffee am Tea pm Last d 10pm
ROOMS: (incl. bkfst) s fr £45; d fr £55 *
MEALS: Lunch £4.95-£7&alc Dinner £6-£14alc*
CARDS:

NETHER STOWEY Somerset Map 03 ST13

★★63% **Apple Tree Inn**

Keenthorne TA5 1HZ (on A39) ☎ 01278 733238
FAX 01278 732693
Having run successful restaurants on the continent for many years, Mr and Mrs Carins took over the hotel during October 1995. Many improvements have taken place during the winter to bring the hotel to a good standard. There are two types of bedroom, those in the main building are cosier and have more character than those in the new wing which are very suitable for the business traveller. Public areas are spacious and the conservatory is an ideal location for the service of breakfast and the bistro menu. The hotel is situated on the A39 within easy access of Bridgwater.
15 en suite (bth/shr) (1 fmly) No smoking in 3 bedrooms CTV in all bedrooms No dogs (ex guide dogs) 60P ch fac European Cuisine V meals Coffee am Tea pm No smoking in restaurant Last d 9.30pm
ROOMS: (incl. bkfst) s £35; d £45-£50 * **LB**
MEALS: Dinner £14.25-£16.75&alc
CARDS:

NEWARK-ON-TRENT Nottinghamshire Map 08 SK75

★★71% **Grange**
73 London Rd NG24 1RZ (outskirts of town off southern approach road to A1) ☎ 01636 703399 FAX 01636 702328
Closed 24 Dec-2 Jan
Although it is located on one of the A1 access roads south of this historic town, the hotel is quietly situated in a residential area. It is family-owned and managed with a keen devotion, with high standards of housekeeping and maintenance. Recent improvements have extended the lounge bar and upgraded the restaurant which serves both a table d'hÙte and a good à la carte menu.
10 en suite (bth/shr) 5 annexe en suite (bth/shr) (2 fmly) No smoking in 2 bedrooms CTV in all bedrooms No dogs 19P V meals No smoking in restaurant Last d 9pm
ROOMS: (incl. bkfst) s £49.50-£55; d £59.50-£69.50 * **LB**
MEALS: Sunday Lunch £10-£12.50 Dinner fr £14&alc
CARDS:

★★67% **South Parade**
117-119 Baldertongate NG24 1RY (from B6326 follow Newark signs drive into Newark turn right at lights on x-rds then right again hotel on left opposite Fountain Gardens) ☎ 01636 703008 FAX 01636 605593
This enthusiastically run hotel offers a blend of professionalism and friendliness. Bedrooms are furnished in a mixture of styles; some are quite small, but all provide the expected facilities. Pleasant reception rooms feature a relaxing lounge overlooking the street, a bar and a dining room. Recent refurbishment and redecoration have substantially improved the appearance of the establishment.
14 rms (11 bth/shr) (2 fmly) CTV in all bedrooms Night porter 12P No coaches V meals Last d 8.45pm
MEALS: Sunday Lunch £9.50-£12.50alc Dinner £9.50-£12.50alc*
CARDS:

NEWBURY Berkshire Map 04 SU46

Courtesy & Care Award

★★★★ 77% **Donnington Valley**
Old Oxford Rd, Donnington RG16 9AG (exit M4 junct 13, take A34 southbound and exit at Donnington Castle. Turn right over bridge then left hotel is 1m on right) ☎ 01635 551199
FAX 01635 551123
This popular hotel has over recent times gained an enviable reputation not only in terms of comfort and facilities, but more importantly hospitality and natural friendliness of the staff, whose willing and good natured approaches cannot fail to set guests at their ease. Physically the hotel also goes from strength to strength; public areas and bedrooms exude that little extra in charm and sense of quality and are bright and inviting. The kitchen works hard at producing imaginative dishes, without deviating too far from classical roots, with intense, honest flavours and textures. Management and staff here have won the AA Courtesy and Care Award for 1996/7.
58 en suite (bth/shr) (11 fmly) No smoking in 20 bedrooms CTV in all bedrooms STV Lift Night porter 160P Golf 18 Putting green Wkly live entertainment Xmas English & French Cuisine V meals Coffee am Tea pm No smoking in restaurant Last d 10pm
ROOMS: s £89.50-£109.50; d £104.50-£124.50 **LB**
OFF-PEAK: (incl. bkfst) s £65-£85; d £45-£55
MEALS: Lunch £17.25&alc Dinner £20&alc
CONF: Thtr 140 Class 80 Board 50
CARDS:

See advertisement on page 455

★★★★ 72% **Regency Park**
Bowling Green Rd, Thatcham RG18 3RP (take A4 signed Thatcham/Reading at 4th set of traffic lights turn left into Northfield Rd then 3rd left into Bowling Green Rd, hotel on right)
☎ 01635 871555 FAX 01635 871571
The lack of distractions in its quiet setting makes this a useful and popular conference hotel. It has a dedicated business centre and well planned facilities. Bedrooms, while spacious and practical for conference guests, are just as suitable for informal visits. The staff stand out for their natural friendliness and alert levels of service. Chef Martin Jeavons takes pride in his menu compilation which provides well worked dishes which might include a trout mousse with langoustine followed by jambonette of chicken in a thick reduction sauce.
50 en suite (bth/shr) (12 fmly) CTV in all bedrooms STV Lift Night porter 120P No coaches Tennis (hard) Xmas English & Continental Cuisine V meals Coffee am Tea pm Last d 10.30pm
ROOMS: (incl. bkfst) s £94.50-£102; d £113-£124 * **LB**
MEALS: Lunch £14.95&alc High tea £5.75 Dinner £19.50-£21.50&alc
CONF: Thtr 170 Class 100 Board 60 Del £145
CARDS:

See advertisement on page 453

★★★★ 62% **Foley Lodge**
Stockcross RG20 8JU (two and a half miles west of Newbury on B4000 north of the A4 Newbury to Hungerford road) ☎ 01635 528770
FAX 01635 528398
This erstwhile banqueting venue is now a well established conference and social function hotel. In the recent past, a modern purpose built block of well furnished bedrooms was added onto the main Victorian building. Staff are friendly and the keen kitchen brigade are well geared to the needs of the function clientele. Bistro-style meals are served in the Café Jardin and more elaborate modern dishes are available in the formal Wellingtonia restaurant.
68 en suite (bth/shr) (5 fmly) No smoking in 17 bedrooms CTV in all bedrooms STV Lift Night porter 160P Indoor swimming pool (heated) Pool table Croquet lawn Putting green Short tennis Xmas English & French Cuisine V meals Coffee am Tea pm Last d 9.30pm
ROOMS: (incl. bkfst) s £95-£135; d £110-£150 * **LB**
OFF-PEAK: (incl. bkfst) s £55-£95; d £80-£120
MEALS: Lunch £9.95-£12.50 Dinner £14-£17.50&alc*
CONF: Thtr 240 Class 90 Board 60 Del from £145
CARDS:

★★★ **Hollington Country House**
Woolton Hill RG20 9XA (take A343 from Newbury towards Andover, after 3m turn right & follow signs to Woolton Hill & Hollington Herb Garden) ☎ 01635 255100 FAX 01635 255075

John and Penny Guy have really found their feet at Hollington and this most impressive hotel continues to go from strength to strength. The atmosphere is that of a country house, and the attitude of the staff helps to emphasise this. Bedrooms are decorated with real taste and panache, each with its individual style. The range of thoughtful facilities provided is really superb and getting lost in one of the spa baths is a pleasure worth getting weary for. The excellent cuisine of chef David Lake, however, will tempt the guest downstairs to sample cooking in the light modern style, but not devoid of classical luxuries. A seared piece of foie gras which accompanied a rich pork and duck rillete dish was heavenly, and this was from the table d'hÙte menu; further treats are in store on the à la carte. John and Penny are Australian and their wine list is truly spectacular and strong in fine products of their own country.
20 en suite (bth/shr) (1 fmly) No smoking in 2 bedrooms CTV in all bedrooms No dogs (ex guide dogs) Lift Night porter 39P No coaches Outdoor swimming pool (heated) Tennis (hard) Snooker Croquet lawn Putting green Xmas English & French Cuisine V meals Coffee am Tea pm Last d 9.30pm
ROOMS: (incl. bkfst) s £95-£165; d £135-£375 **LB**
MEALS: Lunch £14.50-£17.50&alc Dinner fr £30&alc
CONF: Thtr 60 Class 25 Board 25 Del from £195
CARDS:

★★★ 62% **The Chequers**
Oxford St RG14 1JB ☎ 01635 38000
FAX 01635 37170
RS Sat

REGAL
A Collection of Individual Hotels

This traditional town-centre hotel stands at the northern end of the main shopping street and and has a small, attractive garden. Soundly equipped bedrooms vary in size, outlook and location; most are in the original building but some are in an extension around the car park. Public areas include a spacious, comfortable lounge and a popular bar.
45 en suite (bth/shr) 11 annexe en suite (bth/shr) (3 fmly) No smoking in 19 bedrooms CTV in all bedrooms Night porter 60P V meals Coffee am Tea pm Last d 9.45pm
CARDS:

★★★ 61% **Millwaters**
London Rd RG14 2BY (take A34 S to Newbury. At end of dual carriageway take A4 at roundabout towards Reading. Hotel 1m on right nearly opposite Swan public house.)
☎ 01635 528838 FAX 01635 523406
Easily accessible from the M4 via the A34, Millwaters is set in quiet grounds on the outskirts of town. The bedrooms are built round a pretty pond and waterfall and the rivers Kennet and Lambourn run through the grounds. The property is Georgian in origin but the decor is modern in design with many interesting ethnic features. Bedrooms are largely spacious and well equipped, and the airy Oasis restaurant

serves a popular brasserie-style menu.
30 en suite (bth/shr) CTV in all bedrooms Night porter 50P No coaches Fishing Jacuzzi/spa English & French Cuisine V meals Coffee am Tea pm Last d 9.30pm
ROOMS: (incl. bkfst) s fr £68; d fr £78 *
MEALS: Lunch £9.95-£14.50 Dinner fr £14.50*
CONF: Thtr 50 Class 30 Board 22 Del from £120
CARDS:

Hilton National Newbury
Pinchington Ln RG14 7HL (leave M4 junc13 follow A34 southbound through Robin Hood Rdbt

straight across next rdbt at next rdbt follow signs for hotel & Tesco superstore) ☎ 01635 529000 FAX 01635 529337
This is a bright, modern hotel, with an informal restaurant, aimed at both the business and leisure guest. All bedrooms have en suite bathrooms and a range of modern facilities. For more information about Hilton National hotels, consult the Contents page under Hotel Groups.
109 en suite (bth/shr)
ROOMS: s £98; d £90 *
CONF: Thtr 200 Class 100 Board 100 Del £140

Travelodge
☎ 0800 850950
This modern building offers accommodation in smart, spacious and well equipped bedrooms, suitable for family use, and all with en suite bathrooms. Meals may be taken at the nearby family restaurant. For information on room rates and to make a booking, call Roomline free of charge on 0800 850950. For more details about Travelodge, consult the Contents page under Hotel Groups.

NEWBY BRIDGE Cumbria Map 07 SD38

★★★★ 68% **Lakeside**
LA12 8AT ☎ 015395 31207 FAX 015395 31699
Beautifully located beside the southern shore of Lake Windermere and next to the steamer terminal and the steam railway terminus, this spacious and well furnished hotel provides good all-round comforts. There is a delightful conservatory lounge, whilst the elegant restaurant is the perfect location to enjoy the well produced modern British and European cooking. Ruskins Brasserie provides a more informal style of dining. Bedrooms are mainly spacious and have been very thoughtfully equipped and are delightfully furnished. Guests can expect very friendly and attentive service together with a high standard of professionalism.
72 en suite (bth/shr) (7 fmly) No smoking in 34 bedrooms CTV in all bedrooms STV Lift Night porter 200P Indoor swimming pool (heated) Fishing Pool table Croquet lawn Jacuzzi/spa Private jetty Use of Health club Xmas English & French Cuisine V meals Coffee am Tea pm No smoking in restaurant Last d 9.30pm
ROOMS: (incl. bkfst) s £80-£100; d £120-£160.50 * **LB**
MEALS: Lunch £7-£15alc Dinner fr £25alc*
CARDS: £

★★★ 69% **Whitewater**
The Lakeland Village LA12 8PX (leave M6 junc36 follow signs for A590 Barrow 1m through Newby Bridge, turn right at signpost for Lakeland Village, hotel on left) ☎ 015395 31133 FAX 015395 31881
Converted from what was a centuries-old mill and former soap powder factory, this modern business, conference and leisure hotel commands a spectacular position right on the banks of the rushing River Leven, one mile west of Newby Bridge. Exposed natural stonework is a feature and there is an upper floor connection to an extensive leisure complex built adjacent. The hotel has spacious, well equipped bedrooms, two bars, a restaurant and a stylish lounge.

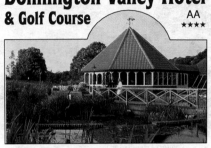

35 en suite (bth/shr) (10 fmly) CTV in all bedrooms STV No dogs (ex guide dogs) Lift Night porter 50P Indoor swimming pool (heated) Tennis (hard) Squash Sauna Solarium Gym Pool table Putting green Jacuzzi/spa Beauty treatment spa Xmas European Cuisine V meals Coffee am Tea pm Last d 9pm
ROOMS: (incl. bkfst) s £65-£75; d £95-£105 * **LB**
MEALS: Sunday Lunch £5.50-£15alc Dinner £12.55-£25alc*
CONF: Thtr 80 Class 32 Board 40 Del from £95
CARDS: £

★★★ 68% **The Swan**
LA12 8NB (leave M6 junc36 follw A590 sinposted Barrow for 16m, hotel on right of the old 5 arch bridge, in Newby Bridge)
☎ 015395 31681 FAX 015395 31917
This long-established hotel has a picturesque setting on the banks of the River Leven at the southern end of Lake Windermere, with riverside walks past all the moorings. The main restaurant has a high lofted ceiling and natural stone walls, with a comfortable cocktail lounge adjoining. There is a second, less formal, restaurant and lounge bar at ground floor level. Bedrooms come in a variety of styles, are well equipped and include some excellent family units. The hotel is well managed and staff are willing and helpful.
36 en suite (bth/shr) (6 fmly) CTV in all bedrooms STV No dogs (ex guide dogs) Night porter 104P No coaches Fishing Croquet lawn Boules golf swing practice net Wkly live entertainment ch fac Xmas English & French Cuisine V meals Coffee am Tea pm No smoking in restaurant Last d 9.30pm
ROOMS: (incl. bkfst) s £60-£87.50; d £90-£135 **LB**
MEALS: Sunday Lunch £11.50-£12.50 Dinner £18.95-£19.50&alc
CONF: Thtr 65 Class 18 Board 28 Del from £82
CARDS:

NEWCASTLE-UNDER-LYME Staffordshire Map 07 SJ84

★★63% **Comfort Friendly Inn**

Liverpool Rd ST5 9DX (on A34) ☎ 01782 717000 FAX 01782 713669

Value-for-money accommodation is offered at this conveniently located hotel to the north of the town, within easy reach of the M6. The bedrooms - which include some suitable for families - are well equipped, all en suite, and divided between the main house and an annexe to the rear. The main building also houses a spacious restaurant and lounge bar.

43 en suite (bth/shr) 24 annexe en suite (bth/shr) (5 fmly) No smoking in 25 bedrooms CTV in all bedrooms Night porter 160P Gym Xmas English & Continental Cuisine V meals Coffee am Tea pm No smoking area in restaurant Last d 9.30pm

ROOMS: d £38.50-£49.50 **LB**

MEALS: Lunch £7.50-£9.95&alc Dinner £9.75&alc*

CONF: Thtr 180 Class 80 Board 30 Del from £65

CARDS:

Forte Posthouse Newcastle under Lyme

Clayton Rd ST5 4DL (on A519 at junct 15 of M6) ☎ 01782 717171 FAX 01782 717138

Suitable for both the business and leisure traveller, this bright hotel provides modern accommodation in well equipped bedrooms with en suite bathrooms. For more details about Forte Posthouse hotels, consult the Contents page for the section on Hotel Groups.

119 en suite (bth/shr)

ROOMS: d £79-£89 *

CONF: Thtr 70 Class 40 Board 34 Del from £109

NEWCASTLE UPON TYNE Tyne & Wear Map 12 NZ26

See also Seaton Burn & Whickham

Courtesy & Care Award

★★★★ 77% **Vermont**

Castle Garth NE1 1RQ (city centre by the high level bridge & Castle Keep) (Taz) ☎ 0191 233 1010 FAX 0191 233 1234

Opened in 1994, and still one of the city's newest hotels, The Vermont was previously County Hall, an imposing building in the city centre next to the Castle and with fine views across the River Tyne. It offers an impressive range of services as well as three bars and two restaurants. The Brasserie provides meals throughout the day and evening, but for fine dining in a classical setting and with service to match, The Blue Room is the place to enjoy a standard of cooking that has earned two AA rosettes for its quality. Bedrooms, including six suites, are smartly furnished and thoughtfully equipped. However the hotel's true strength lies in its delightful staff. They and the management have won the AA's Courtesy and Care Award for 1996/7.

101 en suite (bth/shr) (12 fmly) No smoking in 20 bedrooms CTV in all bedrooms STV Lift Night porter Air conditioning 50P No coaches Solarium Gym Beauty salon Xmas International Cuisine V meals Coffee am Tea pm Last d 11pm

ROOMS: s £110; d £125 * **LB**

OFF-PEAK: (incl. bkfst) s £79; d £89

MEALS: Lunch £13.50&alc Dinner £15.50&alc*

CONF: Thtr 210 Class 60 Board 36 Del from £125

CARDS:

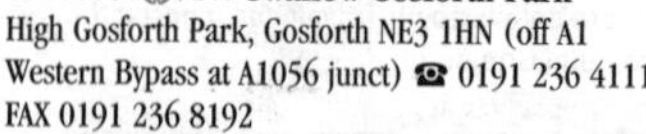

★★★★ 71% **Swallow Gosforth Park**

High Gosforth Park, Gosforth NE3 1HN (off A1 Western Bypass at A1056 junct) ☎ 0191 236 4111 FAX 0191 236 8192

A large modern hotel situated in 12 acres of parkland, just off the A1 north of Newcastle and close to the racecourse. It is also conveniently placed for the International Airport. Recent refurbishment of bedrooms and public areas has considerably enhanced the hotel which also provides excellent conference, banqueting and leisure facilities. The elegant Brandling Restaurant has now been awarded a rosette for its high standard of international cuisine, but as an alternative the attractive Conservatory restaurant offers a less formal eating option. The smartly uniformed staff are friendly and professional and service is helpful and spontaneous. The hotel also has beauty and hair dressing salons and a small souvenir shop.

178 en suite (bth/shr) (7 fmly) No smoking in 99 bedrooms CTV in all bedrooms STV Lift Night porter 300P Indoor swimming pool (heated) Tennis (hard) Squash Sauna Solarium Gym Jacuzzi/spa Steam room Xmas International Cuisine V meals Coffee am Tea pm No smoking area in restaurant Last d 11pm

ROOMS: (incl. bkfst) s £85-£125; d £100-£125 * **LB**

OFF-PEAK: (incl. bkfst) s fr £55; d fr £70

MEALS: Lunch £16-£17&alc High tea fr £10 Dinner fr £18.50*

CONF: Thtr 600 Class 350 Board 50 Del from £98

CARDS:

★★★★ 70% **Copthorne Newcastle**

The Close, Quayside NE1 3RT (east of A189 off B1600) ☎ 0191 222 0333 FAX 0191 230 1111

Situated on the banks of the Tyne in the heart of the city, the Copthorne has been uniquely designed to allow all bedrooms to benefit from a river view. The rooms are also spacious and attractively furnished in contemporary style; first floor rooms have balconies. There is a choice of two restaurants; Boaters, decorated in sunny yellow shades, is informal, whilst Le Rivage has a darker, more intimate colour scheme and a fine carte with dishes such as a warm salad of pigeon with mushrooms.

156 en suite (bth/shr) (15 fmly) No smoking in 28 bedrooms CTV in all bedrooms STV Lift Night porter Air conditioning 186P Indoor

swimming pool (heated) Sauna Solarium Gym Jacuzzi/spa Steam room Xmas International Cuisine V meals Coffee am Tea pm Last d 10.15pm
ROOMS: s £115-£135; d £128-£148 * **LB**
OFF-PEAK: (incl. bkfst) s fr £79; d fr £89
MEALS: Lunch £12.95&alc Dinner £16.50&alc*
CONF: Thtr 250 Class 150 Board 80 Del from £125
CARDS:

★★★★58% **Holiday Inn**
Great North Rd NE13 6BF
☎ 0191 201 9988 FAX 0191 236 8091
(For full entry see Seaton Burn)

★★★68% **Imperial Swallow**
Jesmond Rd NE2 1PR (on A1058)
☎ 0191 281 5511 FAX 0191 281 8472
This busy hotel is situated in the suburb of Jesmond within, easy reach of the city centre and provides every modern comfort in its attractive and tastefully designed bedrooms. It offers more amenities than are usually found in similar establishments including a Coffee Shop, in addition to the more formal Chapters Restaurant, a Leisure Club complete with a heated swimming pool and gymnasium, conference and meeting facilities and free parking for more than 100 cars. The smartly dressed staff, obviously proud of their hotel, are courteous and helpful.
122 en suite (bth/shr) (6 fmly) No smoking in 90 bedrooms CTV in all bedrooms STV Lift Night porter Air conditioning 125P Indoor swimming pool (heated) Sauna Solarium Gym Jacuzzi/spa Steam room Xmas V meals Coffee am Tea pm Last d 9.45pm
ROOMS: (incl. bkfst) s £80-£85; d £90-£100 **LB**
OFF-PEAK: (incl. bkfst) d fr £78
MEALS: Lunch £8.50-£9.50 Dinner fr £16*
CONF: Thtr 150 Class 60 Board 50 Del from £97.50
CARDS:

★★★68% **Swallow Hotel-Gateshead**
High West St NE8 1PE ☎ 0191 477 1105
FAX 0191 478 7214
(For full entry see Gateshead)

★★★67% **Washington Moat House**
Stone Cellar Rd, District 12, High Usworth NE37 1PH
☎ 0191 402 9988 FAX 0191 415 1166
(For full entry see Washington)

★★★64% ***Novotel***
Ponteland Rd, Kenton NE3 3HZ (off A1 (M) NW of city) ☎ 0191 214 0303 FAX 0191 214 0633
Built at the beginning of this decade, the Novotel is a bright, modern hotel offering spacious accommodation of a reliable standard at a competitive price. The Garden Brasserie is open all day for snacks and meals; a small, residents-only leisure club, a range of meeting rooms and good parking are also available.
126 en suite (bth/shr) (126 fmly) No smoking in 51 bedrooms CTV in all bedrooms STV Lift 260P Indoor swimming pool (heated) Sauna Exercise equipment English & French Cuisine V meals Coffee am Tea pm
CARDS:

★★★❀64% **Swallow**
Newgate St]E1 5SX ☎ 0191 232 5025
AX 0191 232 8428
Situated in the centre of the city, this modern high-rise hotel offers somewhat functional accommodation. Bedrooms, however, are well equipped and the upper two floors are expected to be refurbished by the end of 1995. Public areas are limited to a comfortable sixth-floor cocktail bar and air-conditioned restaurant which enjoys panoramic views over the city. Enjoyable meals are offered on both the daily-changing menu and more extensive carte, the highlight of a recent visit being a tender shank of lamb which was full of flavour and accompanied by a garlic and mint jus. Dinner dances are held monthly and the hotel has the advantage of its own extensive car park.
93 en suite (bth/shr) No smoking in 41 bedrooms CTV in all bedrooms STV Lift Night porter 120P Use of gym at nearby fitness centre Xmas English & French Cuisine V meals Coffee am Tea pm No smoking area in restaurant Last d 9.30pm
ROOMS: (incl. bkfst) s £48-£75; d £55-£85 * **LB**
MEALS: Lunch £7.25-£10.95&alc Dinner £13.50-£17.25*
CONF: Thtr 100 Class 40 Board 36 Del from £68
CARDS:

★★★62% **County Thistle**
Neville St NE99 1AH (opposite Central Station)
☎ 0191 232 2471 FAX 0191 232 1285
Ideally situated opposite Central Station and with its own car park, this long-established hotel is close to the main shopping areas, and Newcastle Arena is only ten minutes' walk away. Bedrooms vary in size and style, but all are well equipped. The public areas include an elegant wood-panelled restaurant where a good choice of popular dishes is served. The hotel also has a number of smart meeting rooms.
115 en suite (bth/shr) (4 fmly) No smoking in 32 bedrooms CTV in all bedrooms STV Lift Night porter 28P International Cuisine V meals Coffee am Tea pm No smoking area in restaurant Last d 10pm
ROOMS: s £80-£90; d £90-£100 * **LB**
MEALS: Lunch £10.50 High tea £6.50 Dinner £16.95-£17.95&alc*
CONF: Thtr 130 Class 80 Board 60 Del from £85
CARDS:

★★★62% **New Kent Hotel**
127 Osborne Rd NE2 2TB (beside B1600, opposite St Georges Church) ☎ 0191 281 1083
FAX 0191 281 3369
This modern business hotel offers attractive, well equipped bedrooms, a lounge bar and a restaurant providing good-value meals.
32 en suite (bth/shr) (4 fmly) CTV in all bedrooms STV Night porter 22P No coaches Xmas International Cuisine V meals Coffee am Last d 9.30pm
ROOMS: (incl. bkfst) s £55; d £65 **LB**
OFF-PEAK: (incl. bkfst) s £39.50; d £60
CONF: Thtr 90 Class 50 Board 24 Del from £80
CARDS:

★★★61% **Hospitality Inn**
64 Osborne Rd, Jesmond NE2 2AT (take B1318 through Gosforth to large rdbt turn left onto A189 to 2nd set of lights B1600/A1058 turn right hotel beyond St George's Church) ☎ 0191 281 7881 FAX 0191 281 6241
Well equipped bedrooms which are gradually being upgraded are the

contd.

main feature of this hotel, but there is also an all-day Coffee House which provides tasty snacks as well as full meals. More formal meals can be taken in the sister hotel, The Northumbria, opposite. There are also a banqueting suite and a number of smaller function and meeting rooms. A private car park is available at the rear.

89 en suite (bth/shr) (6 fmly) No smoking in 17 bedrooms CTV in all bedrooms Lift Night porter 52P Xmas European Cuisine V meals Coffee am Tea pm Last d 10.30pm
ROOMS: (incl. bkfst) s £72-£82; d £82-£92 * LB
OFF-PEAK: (incl. bkfst) s £37-£47; d £74-£84
MEALS: Lunch £11.15-£20.05alc High tea £5-£10 Dinner £10-£11&alc*
CONF: Thtr 100 Class 60 Board 46 Del from £95
CARDS:

★★76% Eslington Villa
8 Station Rd, Low Fell NE9 6DR ☎ 0191 487 6017 & 0191 420 0666
FAX 0191 420 0667
(For full entry see Gateshead)

N

★★72% *Bank Top*
TOBY
Ponteland Rd, Kenton NE3 3TY ☎ 0191 214 0877
FAX 0191 214 0095
Situated just off the western by-pass and convenient for the airport, this recently refurbished hotel was built in colonial style and offers a very good standard of accommodation at reasonable rates. Bedrooms are well maintained and comfortably furnished with modern facilities; the attractively decorated public areas include a choice of characterful bars and a smart Toby Grill. Staff are friendly and efficient.
30 en suite (bth/shr) No smoking in 10 bedrooms CTV in all bedrooms STV No dogs Night porter Air conditioning 140P Pool table V meals Coffee am Tea pm Last d 10.30pm
CARDS:

★★64% Cairn
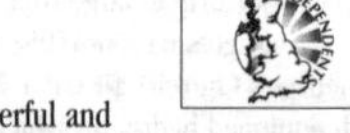
97/103 Osborne Rd, Jesmond NE2 2TJ
☎ 0191 281 1358 FAX 0191 281 9031
This commercial hotel offers bright, cheerful and well equipped bedrooms, whilst smart attractive public rooms feature a split-level dining room and two lively bar areas.
50 en suite (bth/shr) (2 fmly) CTV in all bedrooms STV Night porter 22P none Xmas V meals Coffee am Tea pm No smoking area in restaurant Last d 9.15pm
ROOMS: (incl. bkfst) s £45-£57; d £50-£70 LB
OFF-PEAK: (incl. bkfst) s £45-£50; d £50-£60
MEALS: Lunch £7.50-£10 Dinner £11-£13.75&alc*
CONF: Thtr 150 Class 110 Board 100 Del from £80
CARDS:

See advertisement on opposite page

★★61% *Whites*
38-40 Osborne Rd, Jesmond NE2 2AL (1m N)
☎ 0191 281 5126 FAX 0191 281 9953
A commercial hotel, Whites has modern well equipped bedrooms, a cosy bar and a restaurant offering modestly priced meals.
40 rms (36 bth/shr) (4 fmly) CTV in all bedrooms No dogs Night porter No coaches V meals Coffee am
CARDS:

See advertisement on opposite page

Forte Posthouse Newcastle upon Tyne
FORTE Posthouse
New Bridge St NE1 8BS ☎ 0191 232 6191
FAX 0191 261 8529
Suitable for both the business and leisure traveller, this bright hotel provides modern accommodation in well equipped bedrooms with en suite bathrooms. For more details about Forte Posthouse hotels, consult the Contents page for the section on Hotel Groups.
166 en suite (bth/shr)
ROOMS: d fr £79 *
CONF: Thtr 600 Class 350 Board 50 Del from £65

Forte Posthouse Washington
FORTE Posthouse
Emerson District 5 NE37 1LB
☎ 0191 416 2264 FAX 0191 415 3371
(For full entry see Washington)

NEWCASTLE UPON TYNE AIRPORT Tyne & Wear Map 12 NZ17

★★★64% Newcastle Airport Moat House

Woolsington NE13 8DJ (from the A1 onto the A696 following signs for Newcastle International Airport)
☎ 0191 401 9988 FAX 01661 860157
This modern hotel is situated within the airport complex and many areas have recently been upgraded, including reception, the lounge, the large ballroom and several of the older-style bedrooms. The Old Rangoon Restaurant, which provides a wide range of dishes from around the world, is interestingly themed and contains lots of old photographs, colonial headgear and other paraphernalia from various corners of the globe. The hotel is pleasantly situated in semi-rural surroundings and its location is very convenient for all major roads and Newcastle city centre, which is only six miles away.
100 en suite (bth/shr) No smoking in 30 bedrooms CTV in all bedrooms STV Lift Night porter 200P International Cuisine V meals Coffee am Tea pm Last d 10.30pm
ROOMS: s £40-£79; d £80-£105 * LB
MEALS: Lunch £11.35-£20alc High tea £3-£4.50alc
Dinner £11.35-£20alc*
CARDS:

NEWENT Gloucestershire Map 03 SO72

★59% George
Church St GL18 1PU (located in town centre) ☎ 01531 820203
Situated in the ancient market town, near the Welsh border, this 17th-century former coaching inn has retained its original character and

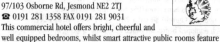

charm. The heart of the inn is the spacious bar, attracting locals and residents alike, serving a selection of real ales and a wide choice of bar meals. In the hotel's dining room an interesting carte is offered. Bedrooms are simply furnished and decorated.
9 rms (2 bth/shr) (2 fmly) No smoking in all bedrooms CTV in all bedrooms 12P V meals Coffee am No smoking area in restaurant
ROOMS: (incl. bkfst) s £18-£25; d £30-£37 *
MEALS: Lunch £9.95-£14.95*
CONF: Thtr 100 Class 100 Board 30
CARDS:

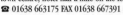

NEWMARKET Suffolk Map 05 TL66

★★★71% ***Bedford Lodge***

Bury Rd CB8 7BX (take Bury St Edmunds road from town centre, hotel half a mile on the left)
☎ 01638 663175 FAX 01638 667391

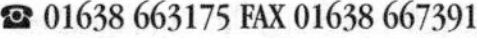

The original Georgian hunting lodge has been greatly extended to provide tastefully appointed accommodation and modern conference facilities. The public rooms offer a choice of comfortable lounge areas, a recently refurbished bar and an appealing restaurant. Bedrooms are split between modern purpose-built rooms of comfortable proportions and those in the old house which offer more individuality. All the rooms are well equipped and thoughtfully designed, and there is also a good choice of suites. Service is both professional and friendly throughout, the availability of room and lounge service is a bonus. A superb modern leisure centre with hair and beauty salons has proved to be a very successful addition to the hotel.
56 en suite (bth/shr) (7 fmly) CTV in all bedrooms Lift Night porter 90P Indoor swimming pool (heated) Sauna Solarium Gym Jacuzzi/spa Steam room Hair & beauty salon International Cuisine V meals Coffee am Tea pm Last d 9.30pm
CARDS:

★★★67% **Heath Court**
Moulton Rd CB8 8DY (from A14 leave at Newmarket/Ely exit (A142) follow town centre signs through mini-rdbt at clocktower turn immediately left into Moulton Rd)
☎ 01638 667171 FAX 01638 666533
This modern red-brick building is located to the east of the town centre, overlooking one of the main horse training grounds. The bedrooms are generously proportioned and sensibly designed. The well run kitchen puts a lot of hard work into providing an excellent selection of meals in the bar and restaurant, based on fresh seasonal ingredients.
41 en suite (bth/shr) (2 fmly) No smoking in 6 bedrooms CTV in all bedrooms STV Lift Night porter 60P Xmas V meals Coffee am Tea pm No smoking area in restaurant Last d 9.45pm
ROOMS: (incl. bkfst) s £55-£65; d £70-£80 * **LB**
MEALS: Lunch £16.25-£24alc High tea £1.35-£6.70alc Dinner £16.25-£24alc
CONF: Thtr 150 Class 40 Board 40 Del from £60
CARDS:

NEW MILTON Hampshire Map 04 SZ29

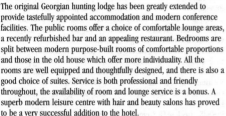

RED STAR HOTEL

★★★★★ **Chewton Glen**
Christchurch Rd BH25 6QS ☎ 01425 275341
FAX 01425 272310

Since owners Martin and Brigitte Skan opened their now well established hotel in its 70 acres of grounds over

contd.

30 years ago it has been greatly extended and now comprises, as well as the original house, two garden wings and some courtyard duplex suites. Bedrooms vary in style, and improvements are always underway, so, for example, in the last year some bedrooms in the main house were refurbished to include splendid bathrooms, and garden wing rooms have been reduced in number to allow for separate sitting rooms. The high standards of appointment are supplemented by many thoughtful touches and first-class housekeeping. In the Marryat Restaurant, the well established chef Pierre Chevillard continues to provide superior standards of cooking. The menu style has changed, with an extensive-choice, three-course table d'hÙte being offered at both lunch and dinner, with supplements, as well as a lighter alternative at lunch. This is backed by an excellent wine list that demonstrates the care and attention that would be expected of such a fine hotel.

51 en suite (bth/shr) 2 annexe en suite (bth/shr) CTV in all bedrooms STV No dogs (ex guide dogs) Night porter 100P Indoor swimming pool (heated) Outdoor swimming pool Golf 9 Tennis (hard) Snooker Sauna Solarium Gym Croquet lawn Putting green Jacuzzi/spa Steam room Treatment rooms Hairdresser No children 7yrs Xmas French Cuisine V meals Coffee am Tea pm No smoking in restaurant Last d 9.30pm
ROOMS: s £195-£395; d £195-£395 * **LB**
MEALS: Lunch £23.50 Dinner £42*
CONF: Thtr 110 Class 65 Board 40 Del from £210
CARDS:

NEWPORT PAGNELL Buckinghamshire Map 04 SP84

Travelodge
Newport Pagnell Service Area MK16 8DS (M1 northbound between junct 14 & 15)
☎ 01908 610878
This modern building offers accommodation in smart, spacious and well equipped bedrooms, suitable for family use, and all with en suite bathrooms. Meals may be taken at the nearby family restaurant. For information on room rates and to make a booking, call Roomline free of charge on 0800 850950. For more details about Travelodge, consult the Contents page under Hotel Groups.
92 en suite (bth/shr)

NEWQUAY Cornwall & Isles of Scilly Map 02 SW86

★★★ 69% **Hotel Bristol**
Narrowcliff TR7 2PQ ☎ 01637 875181
FAX 01637 879347
A long-established, family-run hotel celebrates its 75th anniversary in 1997. The Young family have been involved in the management from day one. Public areas are spacious and comfortable, appealing to both the leisure user and those on business in the area. In the restaurant a short fixed-price menu changes daily. Bedrooms are well equipped and comfortable.
74 en suite (bth/shr) (23 fmly) CTV in all bedrooms Lift Night porter 105P Indoor swimming pool (heated) Snooker Sauna Solarium Pool table Table tennis Xmas English & French Cuisine V meals Coffee am Tea pm Last d 8.45pm
ROOMS: (incl. bkfst) s £49-£54; d £78-£88 **LB**
MEALS: Lunch fr £11&alc Dinner fr £17.50&alc*
CONF: Thtr 200 Class 80 Board 20 Del from £60
CARDS:

★★★65% **Barrowfield**
Hilgrove Rd TR7 2QY (take A3058 to Newquay towards Quintrell Downs, turn right at rdbt continue into town and turn left at Shell garage) ☎ 01637 878878 FAX 01637 879490
This popular holiday hotel is conveniently situated just a short walk from both the town centre and the cliff tops overlooking two beaches. Recently refurbished bedrooms are well equipped and designed with guest comfort in mind, whilst a selection of national and international dishes is offered in the air-conditioned restaurant. Entertainment is provided each evening during the season.
81 en suite (bth/shr) 2 annexe en suite (bth/shr) (18 fmly) CTV in 81 bedrooms STV Lift Night porter 70P Indoor swimming pool (heated) Outdoor swimming pool (heated) Snooker Sauna Solarium Gym Pool table Jacuzzi/spa Games room Xmas French Cuisine V meals Coffee am Tea pm No smoking in restaurant Last d 9pm
ROOMS: (incl. bkfst & dinner) s £27-£53; d £54-£108 **LB**
MEALS: Bar Lunch £3-£5 Dinner £13&alc*
CONF: Thtr 150 Class 60 Board 40
CARDS:

★★★65% **Headland**
Fistral Beach TR7 1EW (turn off A30 onto A392 at Indian Queens, on approaching Newquay follw signs for Fistral Beach) ☎ 01637 872211
FAX 01637 872212
Closed Xmas & Jan
Overlooking the sea on three sides, this impressive hotel is situated on Towan Head peninsula and is conveniently located for the golf course. Owners John and Carolyn Armstrong pride themselves in the hotel's efficient standards of service, whilst continuing to upgrade the fabric of this period hotel. Special features of the hotel include a Toddlers play room, Surf shop and coffee shop, which doubles as an informal dining option in the evening. The bedrooms vary in size and standard, being priced accordingly.
99 en suite (bth/shr) (56 fmly) CTV in all bedrooms Lift Night porter 400P Indoor swimming pool (heated) Outdoor swimming pool (heated) Golf 9 Tennis (hard) Snooker Sauna Solarium Pool table Croquet lawn Putting green Surfing playareas hot air balloons Wkly live entertainment ch fac English & French Cuisine V meals Coffee am Tea pm Last d 9pm
ROOMS: (incl. cont bkfst) s £37-£55; d £70-£100 **LB**
OFF-PEAK: (incl. cont bkfst) s £37-£45; d £70-£85
MEALS: Bar Lunch £2.75-£10.75alc High tea £4.50&alc Dinner £13-£17&alc
CONF: Thtr 250 Class 120 Board 50 Del from £69
CARDS:

★★★64% **Trebarwith**
Island Estate TR7 1BZ ☎ 01637 872288 FAX 01637 875431
Closed Jan-Mar & 30 Oct-Dec
In an elevated position with superb sea and coastal views, this holiday hotel has been in the Tarrant family for over 30 years, the day to day running of the hotel now in the capable hands of Nigel and Jane Tarrant. The bedrooms are constantly being improved and upgraded. The public areas are spacious and comfortable and even include a

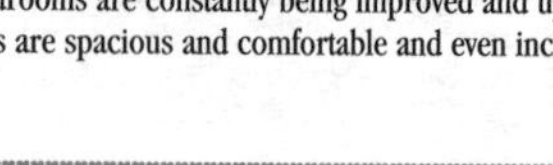

small video film theatre. Smart casual dress is requested for those dining in the Wedgwood Restaurant.
41 en suite (bth/shr) (8 fmly) CTV in all bedrooms No dogs (ex guide dogs) Night porter 40P Indoor swimming pool (heated) Fishing Snooker Sauna Solarium Pool table Jacuzzi/spa Video theatre Games room Wkly live entertainment V meals Coffee am Tea pm No smoking in restaurant Last d 8.30pm
ROOMS: (incl. bkfst & dinner) s £42-£47; d £76-£94 * **LB**
OFF-PEAK: (incl. bkfst & dinner) s £36-£39; d £50-£60
MEALS: Bar Lunch £1-£6 Dinner £14
CARDS:

★★★61% **Glendorgal**
Lusty Glaze Rd, Porth TR7 3AB (from A392 at Quintrell Downs rdbt turn right towards the sea do not turn towards Porth, drive to bottom of road & turn right at Hotel Riviera) ☎ 01637 874937
FAX 01637 851341
The Glendorgal Hotel is situated in a quiet, private location just outside the town and also benefits from separate access to the beach. As might be expected from this elevated location, views out to sea from public areas and front facing bedrooms are most impressive. Bedrooms are generally spacious if quite straightforward in design. New indoor leisure facilities are now open whilst, for the less energetic, entertainment is provided in the bar. Freshly prepared meals are served in the adjacent conservatory restaurant.
38 en suite (bth/shr) CTV in all bedrooms STV Night porter 60P Outdoor swimming pool (heated) Tennis (hard) Snooker Sauna Solarium Gym Pool table Jacuzzi/spa Wkly live entertainment ch fac Xmas V meals Coffee am Tea pm No smoking in restaurant Last d 9pm
ROOMS: (incl. bkfst & dinner) s £35-£45; d £70-£90 **LB**
MEALS: Sunday Lunch £6.50-£8.50 High tea £3.50-£5 Dinner £12.50-£15*

CONF: Thtr 40 Class 48 Board 25 Del from £60
CARDS:

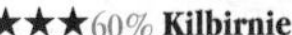

★★★60% **Kilbirnie**
Narrowcliff TR7 2RS (on A392) ☎ 01637 875155
FAX 01637 850769

This family owned and run popular hotel is equally suited to both the holiday and business clientele that it attracts. Overlooking the Barrowfields and the Atlantic, it is conveniently located for easy access to the town centre and the seafront. The bedrooms, though not overly spacious, are well equipped; a continual programme of upgrading is in progress. The spacious public areas include a large ballroom, a cosy cocktail bar and an attractive dining room where a limited choice fixed-price menu is served.
66 en suite (bth/shr) (3 fmly) CTV in all bedrooms STV Lift Night porter Air conditioning 68P Indoor swimming pool (heated) Outdoor swimming pool (heated) Snooker Sauna Solarium Pool table Jacuzzi/spa Table tennis Xmas Coffee am Tea pm Last d 8.30pm
ROOMS: (incl. bkfst & dinner) s £34-£44; d £68-£88 * **LB**
MEALS: Bar Lunch £2.50-£5.85 Dinner fr £12.50*
CONF: Thtr 80 Class 40 Board 20 Del from £46
CARDS:
See advertisement on this page

★★✿70% **Whipsiderry**
Trevelgue Road, Porth TR7 3LY (turn right onto Padstow road B3276 out of Newquay, in half a mile turn right at Trevelgue Rd)
☎ 01637 874777 FAX 01637 874777
Closed Nov-Etr (ex Xmas)
For 23 years, Dick and Ann Drackford have run this popular holiday hotel and this year they have been joined by their daughter and son-in-law. In the restaurant a short fixed-price menu is offered, with
contd.

N

imaginative dishes produced using fresh local ingredients. The neatly decorated bedrooms are comfortable, and a programme of upgrading is underway. Badgers can sometimes be seen feeding on the lawns at dusk.
24 rms (5 bth 14 shr) (5 fmly) CTV in all bedrooms 30P Outdoor swimming pool (heated) Sauna Pool table Putting green Xmas English & Continental Cuisine V meals Coffee am Tea pm No smoking in restaurant Last d 8pm
ROOMS: (incl. bkfst & dinner) s £30-£42; d £60-£84 **LB**
MEALS: Bar Lunch £2.50-£6.50 Dinner £12.95-£16.95
CARDS:

See advertisement on opposite page

★★64% **Corisande Manor**
Riverside Av, Pentire TR7 1PL (from A392 Newquay road follow signs for Pentire) ☎ 01637 872042
Closed 12 Oct-5 May
David and Anne Painter have owned and run this delightfully positioned hotel for over 28 years. Overlooking the Gannel estuary and set in terraced gardens, this house was built in 1900 for an Austrian Count. The dining room ceiling was constructed using timbers from a Spanish schooner which sank in the bay some 300 years ago. The majority bedrooms benefit from excellent views.
19 rms (5 bth 11 shr) (3 fmly) CTV in all bedrooms 19P No coaches Solarium Croquet lawn Putting green Outdoor chess Rowing boats No children 3yrs English, French & Italian Cuisine V meals Coffee am Tea pm No smoking in restaurant Last d 7.30pm
ROOMS: (incl. bkfst) s £24-£26; d £48-£52 **LB**
OFF-PEAK: (incl. bkfst) s £18-£20; d £36-£40
MEALS: Bar Lunch £3.60-£7.80 Dinner £12.50
CARDS:

★★63% **Philema**
1 Esplanade Rd, Pentire TR7 1PY (from A30 follow A392 signs then signs for Fistral Beach & Pentire, turn left at rdbt for Pentire. Hotel at bottom of Pentire Rd) ☎ 01637 872571 FAX 01637 873188
Closed Nov-Mar
This friendly, family holiday hotel benefits from panoramic views across Fistral Bay. Modern bedrooms are comfortably furnished and well equipped and some like the public rooms overlook the sea. In the dining room a simple set-price menu is offered, considered to be value for money.
29 en suite (bth/shr) (16 fmly) CTV in all bedrooms STV 37P Indoor swimming pool (heated) Snooker Sauna Solarium Pool table Jacuzzi/spa Table tennis English & Continental Cuisine V meals Coffee am Tea pm No smoking area in restaurant Last d 7.30pm
ROOMS: (incl. bkfst) s £22-£35; d £44-£70 **LB**
MEALS: Bar Lunch £1.50-£3.50 High tea £3-£10 Dinner £7.50-£15&alc
CARDS:

★★62% **Beachcroft**
Cliff Rd TR7 1SW (turn off A30 towards St Mawgan RAF camp then onto Newquay opposite railway station)
☎ 01637 873022 FAX 01637 873022
Closed early Oct-early Apr
This popular, centrally located, family-run hotel features a private path to the beach below. It has been in the same family ownership of the Price and Chester families since 1966. The well equipped bedrooms are neatly decorated and traditionally furnished, some benefiting from splendid sea views. The public areas are spacious and comfortable and include a well run dining room and cosy coffee shop.
69 en suite (bth/shr) (13 fmly) CTV in all bedrooms Lift Night porter 80P Indoor swimming pool (heated) Outdoor swimming pool (heated) Tennis (hard) Sauna Solarium Pool table Putting green Games room Table tennis Wkly live entertainment ch fac V meals Coffee am Tea pm Last d 8pm
ROOMS: (incl. bkfst) s £19-£25; d £38-£50 *
OFF-PEAK: (incl. bkfst) s fr £17.50; d fr £35
MEALS: Dinner £7.50-£9.50
CARDS:

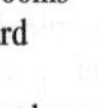

★★61% **Cedars**
Mount Wise TR7 2BA (enter Newquay via Narrowcliff follow one way system into Berry Rd & Mountwise approx 500yds on right from Mountwise public car park) ☎ 01637 874225
Closed Nov-Mar (ex New Year)
This privately owned, family run hotel attracts a holiday clientele, many in groups. The public areas are spacious and comfortable and include a bar lounge with entertainment on certain evenings during the season. In the dining room a simple style of cooking is available, served by a friendly and efficient staff. The bedrooms range from superior rooms with seating areas and balconies to reasonably furnished standard rooms.
36 rms (15 bth 16 shr) (8 fmly) CTV in all bedrooms 42P Outdoor swimming pool (heated) Sauna Solarium Gym Pool table Jacuzzi/spa Wkly live entertainment Xmas Coffee am Tea pm Last d 7.30pm
ROOMS: (incl. bkfst) s £19-£30; d £38-£58 * **LB**
OFF-PEAK: (incl. bkfst) s £18-£22.50; d £36-£50
MEALS: Dinner fr £6.75
CARDS:

★★61% **Porth Veor Manor Hotel & Restaurant**
Porth Way TR7 3LW (on B3276 quarter of a mile from junc with A3058) ☎ 01637 873274
FAX 01637 851690
A 19th-century stone-built house with grounds overlooking Porth beach offers accommodation in bedrooms which are simply furnished but comfortable. A balanced, fixed-price menu supplements the dinner carte.
16 en suite (bth/shr) (3 fmly) CTV in all bedrooms 40P Croquet lawn Putting green Xmas International Cuisine V meals Coffee am Tea pm No smoking in restaurant Last d 8.30pm
ROOMS: (incl. bkfst & dinner) s £35-£45; d £70-£90 **LB**
MEALS: Sunday Lunch £6.95-£8.95 Dinner £10.95-£13.95&alc
CARDS:

★★58% **Tremont**
Pentire Av TR7 1PB ☎ 01637 872984 FAX 01637 851984
This privately owned holiday hotel overlooks the Fistral Beach, famed for its surfing. There is a choice of bedrooms, all well equipped, which are being steadily upgraded. The public areas are spacious, and live entertainment is provided on certain evenings. The extensive leisure facilities include a squash court, an indoor pool, sauna, solarium and a mini gym. In the dining room, a helpful team of staff serve the wholesome fare.
57 rms (54 bth/shr) 7 annexe en suite (bth/shr) (26 fmly) CTV in all bedrooms Lift 60P Indoor swimming pool (heated) Tennis (hard) Squash Sauna Solarium Gym Putting green Table tennis Wkly live entertainment English & French Cuisine Coffee am Tea pm No smoking area in restaurant Last d 7.30pm
CONF: Thtr 160
CARDS:

★64% **Trevone**
Mount Wise TR7 2BP ☎ 01637 873039 FAX 01637 851334
Closed Nov-March RS Apr & Oct
The Chegwin family have owned and run this hotel since 1924, with Miss Pam being in control at the present time. A comfortable lounge and bar are available, with home-cooked meals in the dining room. The bedrooms are generally compact and simply furnished. Special interest holidays are a feature of this friendly hotel.
32 rms (27 bth/shr) (3 fmly) No dogs (ex guide dogs) 20P Pool table Games room table tennis Wkly live entertainment English French & Italian Cuisine Coffee am No smoking in restaurant

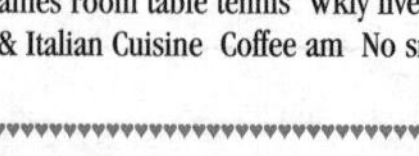

Last d 7.30pm
ROOMS: (incl. bkfst) s £15-£22.50; d £30-£45 * **LB**
MEALS: Dinner £8*

NEWTON ABBOT Devon Map 03 SX87

★★★71% ***Passage House***
Hackney Ln, Kingsteignton TQ12 3QH (leave the A380 for the A381 and follow racecourse signs) ☎ 01626 55515 FAX 01626 63336
This modern, purpose-built hotel is located overlooking the Teign estuary. The comfortable bedrooms are very well equipped with extras such as trouser presses, hair dryers, mini bars and satellite tv, and Penthouse rooms have balconies overlooking the estuary. The Health and Leisure Club offers a beautifully maintained swimming pool and other facilities. A choice of menus is available in the restaurant, while adjacent to the hotel stands the 18th-century Passage House Inn which provides a less formal atmosphere.
39 en suite (bth/shr) (32 fmly) No smoking in 3 bedrooms CTV in all bedrooms STV Lift Night porter 300P Indoor swimming pool (heated) Sauna Solarium Gym Jacuzzi/spa V meals Coffee am Tea pm Last d 9.30pm
CARDS:

★★★69% **The Ilsington Country**

Ilsington TQ13 9RR (take A38 after 12 miles exit for Newton Abbot take the 3rd turning at rdbt towards Ilsington pass Ilsington Post Office)
☎ 01364 661452 FAX 01364 661307
This hotel is only 13 miles from Exeter but appears to belong to a different world. Approached by a winding single track road, the hotel is set in extensive grounds - an ideal location for a traditional Devon cream tea. The hotel provides a venue for business meetings with a dedicated conference suite, and leisure guests are also catered for in the fully-staffed fitness centre. Bedrooms are bright and attractive with many personal touches such as quality toiletries. Most rooms have recently been refurbished to a high standard and all are individually styled. Public areas are smart and spacious and the pretty lounge has some superb views over the Dartmoor countryside.
25 en suite (bth/shr) (2 fmly) CTV in all bedrooms STV Lift 100P Indoor swimming pool (heated) Tennis (hard) Sauna Solarium Gym Pool table Croquet lawn Jacuzzi/spa Sports injury re-hab available Xmas English & French Cuisine V meals Coffee am Tea pm No smoking in restaurant Last d 9pm
ROOMS: (incl. bkfst) s fr £55; d fr £80 **LB**
MEALS: Sunday Lunch £9.95-£12.50 High tea £2.95 Dinner £18.50
CONF: Thtr 35 Class 30 Board 30 Del from £85
CARDS:

★★63% **Queens**

CONSORT HOTELS

Queen St TQ12 2EZ (Opposite the railway station, beside Courtenay Park)
☎ 01626 63133 & 54106 FAX 01626 64922
Popular with business clientele during the week for accommodation, and local people in the bars, this friendly traditional hotel stands near the town centre. Guests have the option of either dining in the formal Regency Restaurant, having a lighter meal in the bar or choosing from the extensive room service menu. A recent addition to the hotel's facilities is Azarats, a lively wine bar offering wines and designer beers. Bedrooms are being upgraded.
22 rms (20 bth/shr) (3 fmly) CTV in all bedrooms 8P No coaches English & French Cuisine V meals Coffee am Tea pm No smoking area in restaurant Last d 8.45pm
ROOMS: (incl. bkfst) s fr £45; d fr £66 * **LB**
OFF-PEAK: (incl. bkfst) s fr £35; d fr £56
MEALS: Bar Lunch fr £1.45 Dinner fr £13.25&alc*
CONF: Thtr 120 Class 60 Board 50 Del from £65
CARDS:

★66% **Hazelwood**
33A Torquay Rd TQ12 2LW ☎ 01626 66130 FAX 01626 65021
Situated in a residential area, only five minutes' level walk to the town centre and the railway station, this small private hotel is personally run by owners Les and Valerie Newnham. The majority of the bedrooms have been attractively refurbished and all are well equipped, with modern facilities; two rooms are available on the ground floor. In the small dining room, a short fixed-price menu is offered; a comfortable bar/lounge is also available.
8 rms (6 bth/shr) CTV in all bedrooms 10P No coaches V meals Coffee am No smoking in restaurant Last d 7.15pm
ROOMS: (incl. bkfst) s fr £35; d fr £49 * **LB**
OFF-PEAK: (incl. bkfst) s fr £30; d fr £40
MEALS: Dinner £6.30-£7.30*
CARDS:

NEWTON-LE-WILLOWS Merseyside Map 07 SJ59

★★65% ***Kirkfield***
2/4 Church St WA12 9SU (on A49) ☎ 01925 228196
FAX 01925 291540
Well equipped bedrooms are provided at this fully modernised hotel, which stands opposite St Peter's church. Weddings and other functions are well catered for and facilities also exist for business meetings. Eating options are wide ranging and the hotel is popular for its value-for-money meals. Staff are friendly and there is a relaxing and informal atmosphere.
14 en suite (bth/shr) (1 fmly) CTV in all bedrooms No dogs (ex guide dogs) 50P International Cuisine V meals Coffee am
Last d 9.30pm
CARDS:

NEWTOWN LINFORD Leicestershire Map 04 SK50

★★63% ***Johnscliffe Hotel & Restaurant***
73 Main St LE6 OAF (turn left off A50 at Field Head Restaurant and after 0.5m at T-junct turn left. Hotel on right hand side after 50yds)
☎ 01530 242228 FAX 01530 244460
Closed 26 Dec-2 Jan
This relaxing, family-run hotel is located in a pretty village just a few minutes from both Leicester city centre and junction 22 of the M1. It lies above the River Lyn and there are superb views over the valley. An attractive sun lounge opens out on to the gardens and this has proved a popular venue for weddings and other local functions. Bedrooms are equipped with modern facilities and several have four-poster beds.
15 rms (14 bth/shr) (1 fmly) CTV in all bedrooms 54P V meals Coffee am Tea pm Last d 9.30pm
CARDS:

NORMAN CROSS Cambridgeshire Map 04 TL19

Forte Posthouse Peterborough
Great North Rd PE7 3TB (on southbound A1 at junct with A15) ☎ 01733 240209 FAX 01733 244455

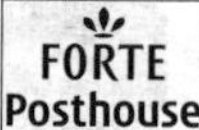

Suitable for both the business and leisure traveller, this bright hotel provides modern accommodation in well equipped bedrooms with en suite bathrooms. For more details about Forte Posthouse hotels, consult the Contents page for the section on Hotel Groups.
93 en suite (bth/shr)
ROOMS: d £69 *
CONF: Thtr 50 Class 16 Board 24 Del from £89

NORMANTON Rutland Map 04 SK90

★★★ 70% **Normanton Park**
Oakham, Rutland LE15 8RP (1m E unclass road)
☎ 01780 720315 FAX 01780 721086
Normanton Park is a recently restored Georgian stable block - all that remains of the original Hall and its vast estate. It is a contemporary and pleasing conversion on the waters edge, a haven for boating and fishing enthusiasts. The newer wing of bedrooms and restaurant take advantage of the magnificent views. Diners can enjoy the evening sun as it sets over the water and casts a warm glow over the Orangery. The cuisine is predominantly modern British and the dishes are tasty and wholesome. The sailing bar, and courtyard patio, offers a more convivial and informal alternative.
23 rms (22 bth/shr) (5 fmly) CTV in all bedrooms Night porter 80P Cycle hire, Fishing ch fac Xmas V meals Coffee am Tea pm Last d 9.45pm
ROOMS: (incl. bkfst) s £55-£65; d £75-£85 **LB**
MEALS: Lunch £15-£25alc Dinner £15-£25
CONF: Thtr 60 Class 40 Board 30
CARDS:
See advertisement under OAKHAM

NORTHALLERTON North Yorkshire Map 08 SE39

★★★ 69% **Solberge Hall**
Newby Wiske DL7 9ER (3.25m S off A167)
☎ 01609 779191 FAX 01609 780472
Standing in its own extensive grounds, with fine views over the countryside, this attractive Victorian hotel provides well equipped bedrooms for the modern traveller. Public rooms are comfortable and a good choice of food is available in the elegant Garden Room restaurant. Staff are professional, friendly and pleasantly enthusiastic.
25 en suite (bth/shr) (2 fmly) CTV in all bedrooms 100P Snooker Croquet lawn Xmas English & French Cuisine V meals Coffee am Tea pm No smoking in restaurant Last d 9.30pm
ROOMS: (incl. bkfst) s fr £60; d fr £80 * **LB**
MEALS: Lunch £6.95 High tea £6.95 Dinner £21&alc*
CONF: Thtr 100 Class 50 Board 40 Del from £76.96
CARDS:

★★67% **The Golden Lion**
High St DL7 8PP (take A684 travel approx 5m onto A167 through built-up area 3rd exit at next rdbt to town centre at 3rd rdbt turn left into High St)
☎ 01609 777411 FAX 01609 773250
A former coaching inn with an attractive Georgian façade and a porticoed entrance, in the centre of the town with a large car park at the rear. The bedrooms, which vary in shape and size, have been tastefully furnished and decorated and careful modernisation has preserved the character, charm and atmosphere of this old established hotel. The cosy Chaucers Restaurant provides a very sound standard of cooking and prides itself on traditional English roasts as well as more adventurous dishes. All the staff are friendly and helpful.
26 rms (21 bth/shr) No smoking in 12 bedrooms CTV in all bedrooms 100P Xmas V meals Coffee am Tea pm No smoking in restaurant Last d 9pm
ROOMS: s £50-£55; d £60-£65 * **LB**
OFF-PEAK: (incl. dinner) s £29-£49; d £58-£98
MEALS: Sunday Lunch £6.95 Dinner £11.95-£13.75*
CONF: Thtr 150 Class 80 Board 40 Del from £60
CARDS:

NORTHAMPTON Northamptonshire Map 04 SP76
See also Flore

★★★★67% **Swallow**
Eagle Dr NN4 7HW (off A45, between A428 & A508)
☎ 01604 768700 FAX 01604 769011
This hotel is custom-made for conferences and even has on site a self-contained management development centre. Nearly all the bedrooms have had cosmetic changes which has softened the décor and added a further degree of comfort in addition to the wide wide range of modern day facilities. There is a choice of two restaurants, one Italian and the other more formal, which demonstrate a serious approach to decent food.
120 en suite (bth/shr) (12 fmly) No smoking in 55 bedrooms CTV in all bedrooms STV Night porter 187P Indoor swimming pool (heated) Sauna Solarium Gym Jacuzzi/spa Steam room Wkly live entertainment Xmas English, French & Italian Cuisine V meals Coffee am Tea pm Last d 10.30pm
ROOMS: (incl. bkfst) s £98; d £108 * **LB**
OFF-PEAK: (incl. bkfst) s £40; d £70
MEALS: Lunch fr £13.75 Dinner fr £19.75&alc*
CONF: Thtr 220 Class 100 Board 36 Del £132
CARDS:

★★★67% **Courtyard by Marriott Northampton**
Bedford Rd NN4 7YF (follow A508 towards Northampton after 2m exit for A428 at rdbt take last exit onto A428 signposted Bedford) ☎ 01604 22777
FAX 01604 35454
Situated beside the A427 Bedford road to the southeast of town, this modern purpose-built hotel offers a good standard of well maintained accommodation. The bedrooms are spacious with smart new bathrooms. On the ground floor there is a friendly, informal restaurant with a bar lounge extension.
104 en suite (bth/shr) (55 fmly) No smoking in 50 bedrooms CTV in all bedrooms STV Lift Night porter Air conditioning 150P Gym European Cuisine V meals Coffee am Tea pm Last d 10.30pm

ROOMS: s £62.50-£86; d £62.50-£86 * **LB**
OFF-PEAK: s £43-£86; d £43-£86
MEALS: Lunch £4-£13.95&alc Dinner £13.95&alc*
CONF: Thtr 40 Board 26 Del from £99
CARDS:

★★★63% Northampton Moat House
MOAT HOUSE
Silver St NN1 2TA ☎ 01604 739988
FAX 01604 230614
Smart, spacious and modern, this multi-storey hotel close to the city centre offers a contemporary style of decor and furnishings. Catering particularly for the business user, it has a good range of conference and training rooms, a choice of bars and an all-day light meal and snack menu which is served to bedrooms or in the lounge.
141 en suite (bth/shr) (4 fmly) No smoking in 63 bedrooms CTV in all bedrooms Lift Night porter 150P Sauna Solarium Gym Pool table Steam room International Cuisine V meals Coffee am Tea pm Last d 10pm
ROOMS: s £75-£85; d £90-£110 *
OFF-PEAK: (incl. bkfst) s £34-£37.50; d £68-£75
MEALS: Lunch £15-£25alc Dinner £15-£25alc*
CONF: Thtr 600 Class 300 Board 160 Del from £75
CARDS:

★★72% Lime Trees
8 Langham Place, Barrack Rd NN2 6AA (from city centre follow sign A508 Leicester near racecourse park & cathedral) ☎ 01604 32188
FAX 01604 233012
RS 27 Dec-New Year

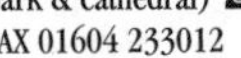

This lovely hotel has been built up to it's present very high standards by the hard work of proprietor Bob Elkin and his partner. Bedrooms and public areas have been upgraded to an excellent standard and this work is ongoing. The smart conference room is popular with both business and social functions and the meetings facilities are up to the minute. Staff are particularly charming and housekeeping is immaculate. A super small hotel.
25 rms (23 bth/shr) (3 fmly) CTV in all bedrooms No dogs (ex guide dogs) Night porter 23P No coaches English & Continental Cuisine V meals Coffee am Tea pm Last d 9pm
ROOMS: (incl. bkfst) s £49.50-£55; d £60-£67 **LB**
OFF-PEAK: (incl. bkfst) s £37.50-£39.50; d £49.50-£55
MEALS: Lunch £12-£14&alc Dinner £16.50-£18.50&alc*
CONF: Thtr 50 Class 50 Board 30
CARDS:

★★68% *Midway*
TOBY
London Rd, Wootoon NN4 0TG ☎ 01604 769676
FAX 01604 769523
Closed 23-26 Dec
Spacious and comfortable accommodation is available at a friendly hotel located close to junction 14 of the M1. Guests have use of lounge bar and a busy Toby Grill restaurant.

31 en suite (bth/shr) (4 fmly) No smoking in 13 bedrooms CTV in all bedrooms Night porter 150P Pool table Wkly live entertainment V meals Coffee am Tea pm Last d 10pm
CARDS:

★★66% *Thorplands Toby*
TOBY
Talavera Way, Round Spinney NN3 4RN
☎ 01604 494241 FAX 01604 790532
Closed 25,26 Dec & 1 Jan
This friendly establishment stands by the A43 at Round Spinney, totally surrounded by trees. Bedrooms are contained in a purpose-built block and are spacious, comfortable and well equipped. The popular restaurant offers a good range of dishes in a jovial atmosphere.
31 en suite (bth/shr) (4 fmly) No smoking in 15 bedrooms CTV in all bedrooms No dogs (ex guide dogs) Night porter 200P Wkly live entertainment V meals Coffee am Tea pm Last d 10.30pm
CARDS:

Travel Inn
travel inn
Harpole Turn, Weedon Rd, Harpole NN7 4DD (on A45) ☎ 01604 832340 FAX 01604 831807
Purpose-built accommodation, offering spacious, well equipped bedrooms, all with en suite bathrooms. Meals may be taken at the nearby family restaurant. For more information about Travel Inns, consult the Contents page under Hotel Groups.
51 en suite (bth/shr)
ROOMS: d £35.50 *

Travelodge
Travelodge
Upton Way NN5 6EG (A45, towards M1 junct 16)
☎ 01604 758395 FAX 01604 758395
This modern building offers accommodation in smart, spacious and well equipped bedrooms, suitable for family use, and all with en suite bathrooms. Meals may be taken at the nearby family restaurant. For information on room rates and to make a booking, call Roomline free of charge on 0800 850950. For more details about Travelodge, consult the Contents page under Hotel Groups.
40 en suite (bth/shr)

○ ***Grand***
Gold St NN1 1RE ☎ 01604 250511 FAX 01604 234534
Conveniently located in the centre of Northampton, the Grand is a popular hotel with businessmen who appreciate the spacious, well equipped rooms.
57 rms (2 fmly) CTV in 62 bedrooms Lift Night porter 90P V meals Coffee am Tea pm Last d 9.15pm
CARDS:

NORTH FERRIBY East Riding of Yorkshire Map 08 SE92

Forte Posthouse Hull
Ferriby High Rd HU14 3LG (on A63, W of Hull)
☎ 01482 645212 FAX 01482 643332
FORTE Posthouse
Suitable for both the business and leisure traveller, this bright hotel provides modern accommodation in well equipped bedrooms with en suite bathrooms. For more details about Forte Posthouse hotels, consult the Contents page for the section on Hotel Groups.
96 en suite (bth/shr)
ROOMS: d £49-£69 *
CONF: Thtr 100 Class 40 Board 40 Del from £65

NORTHLEACH Gloucestershire Map 04 SP11

★★64% **Wheatsheaf**
GL54 3EZ (junct A4/A429) ☎ 01451 860244 FAX 01451 861037
In the heart of the village, this attractive ivy-clad inn offers bright individually styled bedrooms with a good range of facilities, many of them overlooking the garden at the rear. There are congenial bars and a pretty little restaurant with crisp linen and attractive table settings.
9 en suite (bth/shr) CTV in all bedrooms No dogs 18P No coaches No children 5yrs V meals Coffee am No smoking area in restaurant Last d 9pm
ROOMS: (incl. bkfst) s £39 * **LB**
OFF-PEAK: (incl. bkfst) s £39; d £55-£85
MEALS: Lunch £12-£28alc Dinner fr £15.50&alc*
CARDS:

NORTH MUSKHAM Nottinghamshire Map 08 SK75

Travelodge
NG23 6HT (3m N, on A1 southbound)
☎ 01636 703635 FAX 01636 703635
Travelodge
This modern building offers accommodation in smart, spacious and well equipped bedrooms, suitable for family use, and all with en suite bathrooms. Meals may be taken at the nearby family restaurant. For information on room rates and to make a booking, call Roomline free of charge on 0800 850950. For more details about Travelodge, consult the Contents page under Hotel Groups.
30 en suite (bth/shr)

NORTH WALSHAM Norfolk Map 09 TG23

★★59% **Kings Arms**
Kings Arms St NR28 9JX (in centre of town next to Midland Bank & visible from the market cross, a one-way system takes all traffic into the town centre) ☎ 01692 403054 FAX 01692 500095
8 en suite (bth/shr) CTV in all bedrooms No dogs (ex guide dogs) 20P Pool table English & Thai Cuisine V meals Coffee am Last d 9pm *contd.*

ROOMS: (incl. bkfst) s £27.50; d £44 **LB**
MEALS: Lunch £5-£10alc Dinner £5-£10alc*
CARDS:
See advertisement on opposite page

NORTH WALTHAM Hampshire Map 04 SU54

★★★56% **Wheatsheaf**
RG25 2BB (on A30 one & a half miles from junc7 M3 follow signs for Basingstoke, then Kings Worthy & Popham)
☎ 01256 398282 FAX 01256 398253
This former roadside coaching inn stands beside the A30 a few miles to the southwest of Basingstoke. Public areas are limited to a traditional-style bar and the oak-beamed restaurant serving a range of popular dishes. In contrast, bedrooms are more contemporary in style and are equipped to a good standard.
28 en suite (bth/shr) (1 fmly) No smoking in 5 bedrooms CTV in all bedrooms STV Night porter 70P Pool table Childrens play area Xmas Continental Cuisine V meals Coffee am Tea pm No smoking area in restaurant Last d 10pm
ROOMS: (incl. bkfst) s fr £59.50; d fr £72 * **LB**
OFF-PEAK: (incl. bkfst) s fr £58; d fr £62
MEALS: Lunch £9.95-£14.50&alc High tea fr £5.50alc Dinner £10.50-£14.50&alc*
CONF: Thtr 80 Class 30 Board 35 Del from £85
CARDS:

NORTHWICH Cheshire Map 07 SJ67

★★62% ***Wincham Hall***
Hall Ln, Wincham CW9 6DG (on A559)
☎ 01606 43453 FAX 01606 40128
This privately owned and personally run hotel, which dates from the 12th century, offers comfortable accommodation and a good standard of food. The bedrooms vary in size, but all have modern furnishings and equipment. Public areas include a small restaurant, a comfortably furnished lounge with a wood burning stove, which is in the oldest part of the building, and a lounge bar - off which leads a good-sized function room.
10 rms (9 bth/shr) (1 fmly) CTV in 9 bedrooms 200P Croquet lawn English & Continental Cuisine V meals Coffee am Tea pm Last d 9.45pm
CARDS:

NORTHWOLD Norfolk Map 05 TL79

★★67% **Woodland Comfort Inn**
Thetford Rd IP26 5LQ ☎ 01366 728888
FAX 01366 727121
Friendly
This attractive cluster of buildings, with its bedrooms set around a courtyard, is situated in a delightful rural location about 12 miles north of Thetford. The large bedrooms are ideal for families and several have beds in alcoved areas for this purpose; disabled persons will also find the ground floor rooms convenient. The beamed

old world Woodland Inn combines its role as a country public house and the hotel restaurant.
34 en suite (bth/shr) (5 fmly) No smoking in 17 bedrooms CTV in all bedrooms STV Night porter Air conditioning 250P Gym Xmas English & Continental Cuisine V meals Coffee am Tea pm No smoking area in restaurant Last d 9.30pm

ROOMS: d £38.50-£49.50 **LB**
MEALS: Lunch £7.50-£9.95&alc Dinner £9.75&alc
CONF: Thtr 150 Class 60 Board 40 Del from £65
CARDS:

NORTON Shropshire Map 07 SJ70

★★74% **Hundred House**
Bridgnorth Rd TF11 9EE (on A442 6m N of Bridgnorth)
☎ 01952 730353 FAX 01952 730355
This is an impressive Georgian inn with traditional bars and several intimate dining areas. Exposed timbers feature as do original brick walls, stained-glass windows and cheerful log fires when needed. Bedrooms are individually decorated and fitted with appropriate period furnishings. Many have brass beds and some are even fitted with romantic ceiling swings. The carte restaurant is now supplemented with a Brasserie style menu which is served throughout the bar areas and food continues to enjoy a large local following.
10 en suite (bth) (5 fmly) CTV in all bedrooms 40P English & French Cuisine V meals Coffee am Last d 10pm
ROOMS: (incl. bkfst) s £65-£79; d £79-£90 * **LB**
MEALS: Lunch £19.50-£27alc Dinner £19.50-£27alc*
CARDS:

NORWICH Norfolk Map 05 TG20
See also South Walsham

★★★★77% **Sprowston Manor**

Sprowston Park, Wroxham Road, Sprowston NR7 8RP (2m NE A1151) ☎ 01603 410871
FAX 01603 423911
Sprowston Manor sits within ten acres of parkland and adjacent to the local golf course, on the outskirts of the city. This 19th-century manor house offers smart modern lobby areas, an elegant restaurant and bar, extensive conference and leisure facilities which include the newly developed and luxurious La Fontana Health Spa. Accommodation is very good, offering well proportioned and comfortable bedrooms that have a full range of facilities and come in a range of styles, which include family and four poster rooms, junior and full suites. Services throughout the hotel are both professional and friendly, service is particularly attentive in the Manor restaurant where chef John Curtis provides interesting daily and carte menus of modern European cooking; vegetarian menus are readily available.
87 en suite (bth/shr) (12 fmly) No smoking in 29 bedrooms CTV in all bedrooms STV No dogs (ex guide dogs) Lift Night porter 120P Indoor swimming pool (heated) Golf 18 Sauna Solarium Gym Jacuzzi/spa Beauty salon Health spa Xmas English & French Cuisine V meals Coffee am Tea pm No smoking in restaurant Last d 10pm

ROOMS: s £87; d £93 **LB**
MEALS: Lunch £12.50-£22.50&alc Dinner £22.50-£24&alc
CONF: Thtr 100 Class 45 Board 50 Del £135
CARDS:

★★★68% **Hotel Nelson**
Prince of Wales Rd NR1 1DX (follow signs for city centre & football ground ☎ 01603 760260 FAX 01603 620008
Over recent years the public areas of this modern hotel have been extended and refurbished, the most recent and final phase of refurbishment included the reception, foyer lounge, restaurant and lounge bar. The good use of bold rich colour schemes throughout these areas has given the hotel a most welcoming feel. Bedrooms are also modern in style, comfortable and well appointed. A smart leisure complex and a range of conference suites makes this hotel a popular choice with both leisure and corporate markets.
132 en suite (bth/shr) (15 fmly) CTV in all bedrooms No dogs (ex guide dogs) Lift Night porter 210P Indoor swimming pool (heated) Sauna Solarium Gym Steam room Beauty & hair salon Xmas European Cuisine V meals Coffee am Tea pm No smoking area in restaurant Last d 9.45pm
ROOMS: (incl. bkfst) s £77.50-£80; d £89.50-£92 **LB**
MEALS: Sunday Lunch £11.50 Dinner fr £14.95
CONF: Thtr 90 Board 44 Del from £99.50
CARDS:

★★★68% **Hotel Norwich**

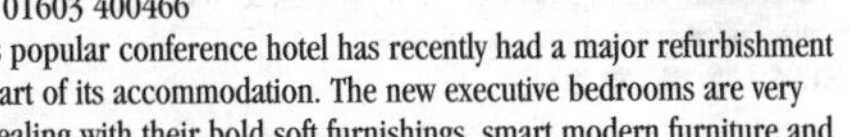

121-131 Boundary Rd NR3 2BA (1.5m NW, between A1067 & A140 intersections) ☎ 01603 787260
FAX 01603 400466
This popular conference hotel has recently had a major refurbishment to part of its accommodation. The new executive bedrooms are very appealing with their bold soft furnishings, smart modern furniture and

contd.

good range of amenities. Family and standard bedrooms are to have the same treatment during 1996. Public rooms also have more appeal, as the bar has been upgraded to a smart modern standard, comparable to that of the lounge, small business centre and the conference and banqueting suites.
107 en suite (bth/shr) (15 fmly) No smoking in 37 bedrooms CTV in all bedrooms STV No dogs (ex guide dogs) Night porter 225P Indoor swimming pool (heated) Sauna Solarium Gym Jacuzzi/spa Steam room Xmas International Cuisine V meals Coffee am Tea pm Last d 10pm
ROOMS: (incl. bkfst) s £69.50-£89.50; d £79.50-£99.50 * **LB**
MEALS: Lunch £9-£16alc Dinner fr £14.50*
CONF: Thtr 300 Class 150 Board 60 Del from £86.50
CARDS:

★★★65% **Quality Friendly Hotel**
2 Barnard Rd, Bowthorpe NR5 9JB (1st roundabout on A1074 from Swaffham) ☎ 01603 741161
FAX 01603 741500

This modern hotel provides a good standard of accommodation and bedrooms have all the usual facilities with the Premium Plus rooms offering extras such as mini bars, hairdryers, trouser presses and teletext; several rooms have also been designed for disabled persons. One of the features of the hotel is its very good leisure centre which includes a gymnasium and a heated swimming pool. Conference and banqueting facilities are also available.
80 en suite (bth/shr) (5 fmly) No smoking in 40 bedrooms CTV in all bedrooms STV Night porter 140P Indoor swimming pool (heated) Sauna Solarium Gym Jacuzzi/spa Xmas English & Continental Cuisine V meals Coffee am Tea pm No smoking area in restaurant Last d 9.30pm
ROOMS: s £67.50; d £87.50 **LB**
MEALS: Lunch £7.95-£9.95&alc Dinner £13.50&alc
CONF: Thtr 200 Class 75 Board 60 Del from £82.50
CARDS:
See advertisement under NORTHWICH

★★★64% ***Maids Head***
Tombland NR3 1LB (hotel opposite cathedral)
☎ 01603 209955 FAX 01603 613688
A historic hotel, parts of which are over 700 years old, is situated in the heart of the city close to the impressive Norman Cathedral. The Courtyard Restaurant where coach and horses once drove through, the cosy, beamed and panelled Jacobean bar and many of the oak beamed bedrooms - particularly in the Cathedral Wing - are reminiscent of its earlier days. The bedrooms have every modern facility and there is a private car park at the side of the building.
81 en suite (bth/shr) (2 fmly) No smoking in 30 bedrooms CTV in all bedrooms Lift Night porter 100P English & French Cuisine V meals Coffee am Tea pm Last d 10pm
CARDS:

★★★64% **Norwich Sport Village & Hotel in Broadland**
Drayton High Rd, Hellesdon NR6 5DU (at junct of A47 Ring Road and A1067 to Fakenham) ☎ 01603 789469 FAX 01603 406845
This functional modern hotel forms part of an impressively equipped sports and leisure complex which includes an aqua-park and is ideal for business use. Public areas do tend to mingle with sports facilities but not inconveniently so, and the bedroom accommodation is separate and secure.
55 en suite (bth/shr) (2 fmly) CTV in all bedrooms STV No dogs (ex guide dogs) Lift Night porter 800P Indoor swimming pool (heated) Tennis (hard) Squash Snooker Sauna Solarium Gym Pool table Jacuzzi/spa Badminton Table tennis Beauty salon Xmas International Cuisine V meals Coffee am Tea pm Last d 9.30pm
ROOMS: (incl. bkfst) s £59.50-£62; d £74-£77 * **LB**
OFF-PEAK: (incl. bkfst) s £52-£56; d £62-£66
MEALS: Bar Lunch fr £3 Dinner £15.95*
CONF: Thtr 180 Class 46 Board 80 Del from £79
CARDS:
See advertisement on opposite page

★★74% **The Old Rectory**
103 Yarmouth Rd, Thorpe St Andrew NR7 0HF
☎ 01603 700772 FAX 01603 700772
The Old Rectory is the Georgian home of Chris and Sally Entwistle, an enthusiastic young couple who provide a warm welcome and an attentive personal service within a country house environment. The delightful lounge is particularly relaxing, an elegantly appointed room with deep comfortable sofas and an open log fire. A good-value four-course daily menu is served within the restaurant, providing freshly cooked meals prepared from local produce. Bedrooms are divided between the main house and the adjacent Coach House; individually styled and tastefully furnished, the rooms are well proportioned with many thoughtful extras.
5 en suite (bth/shr) 3 annexe en suite (bth/shr) No smoking in all bedrooms CTV in all bedrooms STV No dogs (ex guide dogs) 17P No coaches Outdoor swimming pool (heated) English & French Cuisine V meals Coffee am Tea pm No smoking in restaurant Last d 9pm
ROOMS: (incl. bkfst) s £49.50; d £65 * **LB**
MEALS: Dinner £14.50-£15*
CONF: Thtr 25 Class 18 Board 18 Del from £82.50
CARDS:
See advertisement on opposite page

★★73% **Annesley House**
6 Newmarket Rd NR2 2LA (on A11 half a mile before city centre) ☎ 01603 624553 FAX 01603 621577
RS Xmas

Annesley Hotel comprises 3 Georgian houses, 2 of which are linked by a conservatory that houses a well established grape vine. The remaining public areas include a small lounge bar and a well appointed restaurant where fixed-price and à la carte menus feature a range of uncomplicated dishes based on quality fresh produce. The accommodation is spotlessly kept, offering attractively appointed bedrooms with co-ordinated soft furnishings and smart modern furniture. A friendly atmosphere is encouraged by the enthusiastic proprietors, Jill and David Reynolds, who ensure that a caring professional service is provided at all times.
17 en suite (bth/shr) 8 annexe en suite (bth/shr) (3 fmly) CTV in all bedrooms STV No dogs (ex guide dogs) 25P No coaches English & French Cuisine V meals Coffee am Tea pm No smoking in restaurant Last d 9pm
ROOMS: (incl. bkfst) s £57.50-£67.50; d £67.50-£77.50 * **LB**
MEALS: Lunch £15.50 Dinner £16.50&alc*
CARDS:

★★ 69% Cumberland
212-216 Thorpe Rd NR1 1TJ (on A1247, 1m from railway station)
☎ 01603 434550 & 434560 FAX 01603 433355
Closed 26 Dec-2 Jan
Whilst the exterior of this small privately-owned hotel might be considered rather uninspiring, inside you will find a welcoming environment which is complemented by the enthusiastic and cheerful young staff, who provide a helpful, personal service. Chef Craig Robinson offers interesting choices of English and French cooking from daily and à la carte menus in the cheerful restaurant, which is themed on South African vineyards and appointed with Cape Dutch furniture. A new bar is planned for mid-1996 and guests also have the use of a small comfortable lounge with satellite TV. Bedroom styles and sizes vary, all are individually decorated and the soft furnishings in the adjacent Cottage rooms are particularly cheerful and bold.
23 en suite (bth/shr) 4 annexe en suite (bth/shr) (2 fmly) CTV in all bedrooms No dogs (ex guide dogs) Night porter 63P English & French Cuisine V meals Coffee am Tea pm No smoking in restaurant Last d 9.30pm
ROOMS: (incl. bkfst) s £37.50-£55; d £50-£65 * **LB**
MEALS: Lunch fr £9.95 Dinner fr £16.95&alc*
CONF: Thtr 120 Class 80 Board 60 Del from £55
CARDS:

★★ 65% The Townhouse
18-22 Yarmouth Rd, Thorpe St Andrew NR7 0EF (turn off A1042 towards Thorpe St Andrew heading for city centre The Town House is situated on the left) ☎ 01603 700600 FAX 01603 31786
Parts of this red-brick building date back to 1740 and the location, on the banks of the River Yare, adds to the character of this successful budget hotel. The newly refurbished public rooms are dominated by the Beefeater restaurant which offers informal dining that has broad appeal. Light attractive bedrooms are furnished in a modern style with a good range of modern amenities.
18 en suite (bth/shr) (3 fmly) CTV in all bedrooms No dogs (ex guide dogs) 20P No coaches V meals Coffee am Tea pm No smoking area in restaurant Last d 10.30pm
ROOMS: s fr £35; d fr £35 *
MEALS: Lunch £6.15-£12alc Dinner £6.15-£12alc*
CARDS:

See advertisement on opposite page

★★ 63% Beeches Hotel & Victorian Gardens
4-6 Earlham Rd NR2 3DB (on B1108, behind St Johns RC Cathedral just off inner ring road)
☎ 01603 621167 FAX 01603 620151
Closed 22 Dec-2 Jan
The Beeches is a privately-owned hotel, which sits about a ten minute walk from the city centre, comprising two well maintained detached houses and a sunken Victorian garden. The accommodation styles and sizes vary: the most recently refurbished bedrooms in the Plantation House annexe are very well appointed, with modern limed oak furniture and colour co-ordinated décor and soft furnishings. Whilst public areas are currently restricted to a bistro-style restaurant and a small reception foyer lounge, there are plans for major alterations during early 1996 to create a bar and a new reception, which should offer greater flexibility and choice for guests.
17 en suite (bth/shr) 9 annexe en suite (bth/shr) (1 fmly) No smoking in 23 bedrooms CTV in all bedrooms STV No dogs (ex guide dogs) 24P English & French Cuisine V meals Coffee am Tea pm No smoking in restaurant Last d 8.30pm
ROOMS: (incl. bkfst) s fr £49; d fr £65 * **LB**
OFF-PEAK: (incl. bkfst) s fr £46; d fr £59
MEALS: Dinner fr £10&alc*
CONF: Class 30
CARDS:

See advertisement on opposite page

★★ 60% The Georgian House
32-34 Unthank Rd NR2 2RB (follow A11 into city centre at Co-op rdbt turn left at next rdbt turn left at 3rd rdbt turn left hotel 20yds on left opposite RC Cathedral) ☎ 01603 615655 FAX 01603 765689
This friendly hotel, located close to the Roman Catholic cathedral, consists of two linked Victorian buildings. New resident owners are hoping to gradually improve the restaurant operation and upgrade public areas. There are eight spacious bedrooms in a new wing, and all are well equipped.
27 en suite (bth/shr) (4 fmly) No smoking in 4 bedrooms CTV in all bedrooms No dogs 40P No coaches ch fac English & French Cuisine V meals Coffee am Tea pm Last d 8.30pm
ROOMS: (incl. bkfst) s fr £42.50; d fr £55 * **LB**
MEALS: Dinner fr £12.50*
CONF: Class 20
CARDS:

See advertisement on opposite page

Forte Posthouse Norwich
Ipswich Rd NR4 6EP (take A47, southern bypass, until sign for A140, then turn N into Norwich. Hotel 0.5m on right) ☎ 01603 456431 FAX 01603 506400
Suitable for both the business and leisure traveller, this bright hotel provides modern accommodation in well equipped bedrooms with en suite bathrooms. For more details about Forte Posthouse hotels, consult the Contents page for the section on Hotel Groups.
116 en suite (bth/shr)
ROOMS: d £69 *
CONF: Thtr 100 Class 48 Board 40 Del from £74

Travelodge
Thickthorn Service Area, Norwich Southern Bypass NR9 3AU (A11/A47 interchange)
☎ 01603 457549 FAX 01603 457549
This modern building offers accommodation in smart, spacious and well equipped bedrooms, suitable for family use, and all with en suite bathrooms. Meals may be taken at the nearby family restaurant. For information on room rates and to make a booking, call Roomline free of charge on 0800 850950. For more details about Travelodge, consult the Contents page under Hotel Groups.
40 en suite (bth/shr)

NOTTINGHAM Nottinghamshire Map 08 SK54
See also Langar

★★★★ 64% Nottingham Royal Moat House
Wollaton St NG1 5RH (take A52 towards Nottingham follow signs for Royal Centre & into Wollaton St, hotel is on the left & car park is just before hotel)
☎ 0115 936 9988 FAX 0115 947 5888
This city-centre hotel features a covered arcade with tropical trees and plants, several bars and a choice of four restaurants. The Penthouse

contd.

Bar on the top floor has panoramic views of the city and serves snacks at lunch time. Some of the single bedrooms are compact, but all are comprehensively equipped and well maintained. There is free parking for guests in the on-site car park.
201 en suite (bth/shr) (20 fmly) No smoking in 124 bedrooms CTV in all bedrooms Lift Night porter Air conditioning 605P Gym Wkly live entertainment Xmas Inetrnational Cuisine V meals Coffee am Tea pm No smoking area in restaurant Last d 10.45pm
ROOMS: s fr £95; d fr £115 * **LB**
MEALS: Lunch fr £6.95&alc Dinner fr £6.95&alc*
CONF: Thtr 600 Class 300 Board 50 Del from £95
CARDS:

★★★67% ***Nottingham Moat House***

Mansfield Rd NG5 2BT ☎ 0115 935 9988
FAX 0115 969 1506
Closed 28-30 Dec
This large modern hotel is conveniently situated on the A60, north of the city. Its light, airy bedrooms have every modern facility, and spacious public areas offer a choice of bars and restaurants which includes the refined Club Bar - its atmosphere similar to that of a gentleman's club. There is comprehensive provision for functions and banquets, staff throughout are friendly and helpful, and good car parking facilities are available.
172 en suite (bth/shr) No smoking in 89 bedrooms CTV in all bedrooms Lift Night porter 340P Pool table V meals Coffee am Tea pm Last d 11pm
CARDS:

★★★65% **Holiday Inn Garden Court**

Castle Marina Park NG7 1GX (on A453 at Castle Marina) ☎ 0115 950 0600 FAX 0115 950 0433
Situated within the Castle Marina Business and Retail Park, this attractive modern hotel offers good-value accommodation in excellent bedrooms. Public areas and services are limited to keep costs down, but the staff are welcoming and helpful.
100 en suite (bth/shr) (43 fmly) No smoking in 50 bedrooms CTV in all bedrooms STV Lift Night porter 100P V meals Coffee am Tea pm Last d 10pm
ROOMS: s £69.50; d £69.50 * **LB**
MEALS: Dinner £12.95&alc*
CONF: Thtr 50 Board 25 Del £95
CARDS:

★★★65% **Nottingham Gateway**
Nuthall Rd, Cinderhill NG8 6AZ (take A610 from junct 26 of M1)
☎ 0115 979 4949 FAX 0115 979 4744
Located in an easterly suburb this modern purpose-built hotel is ideally placed for both the motorway and the city. It has the full range of facilities and services expected of a hotel of its class, and in addition there is a speciality Thai restaurant, overlooking a fountained semi-moat, which is also popular with locals and residents alike. The lobby is marbled and light and features a glass-walled elevator.
108 en suite (bth) (8 fmly) No smoking in 54 bedrooms CTV in all bedrooms STV No dogs (ex guide dogs) Lift Night porter Air conditioning 250P English, French & Thai Cuisine V meals Coffee am Tea pm No smoking area in restaurant Last d 10.30pm
ROOMS: s £30-£60; d £42-£70 **LB**
OFF-PEAK: s £30-£50; d £42-£60
MEALS: Lunch £6-£8 High tea £3.75-£9.25 Dinner £11.95-£14.50&alc
CONF: Thtr 300 Class 100 Board 50 Del from £89
CARDS:

See advertisement on opposite page

★★★65% **Westminster Hotel**
312 Mansfield Rd, Carrington NG5 2EF
(on A60 1m N of town centre) ☎ 0115 952 3023
FAX 0115 952 0156
Closed 25 Dec-2 Jan
Situated just on the northern fringe of the city centre, the Westminster is a very friendly and notably well kept family-run hotel with a relaxed atmosphere which has a strong appeal to the business guest. The bedrooms are similarly furnished and decorated, but are of different shapes and sizes to suit the Victorian origins of the hotel. The restaurant caters for traditional tastes, whilst bar meals are offered on Sunday evenings in the comfortable bar.
62 en suite (bth/shr) No smoking in 30 bedrooms CTV in all bedrooms STV No dogs (ex guide dogs) Lift Night porter 50P English & Continental Cuisine V meals Coffee am Tea pm Last d 9.15pm
ROOMS: s £58-£68; d £70-£80 **LB**
OFF-PEAK: s £25; d £50
MEALS: Bar Lunch £3-£8 Dinner £13-£18*
CONF: Thtr 60 Class 30 Board 30
CARDS:

See advertisement on opposite page

★★★63% **Rutland Square**
St James St NG1 6FJ (on entering the city follow brown signs to the castle, hotel on right 50 yds on from the castle) ☎ 0115 941 1114
FAX 0115 941 0014
An elegant conversion of redundant industrial buildings, this hotel is situated in the heart of the city and its tourist attractions. Behind its Regency facade the hotel is modern and comfortable with particularly good business facilities, both in the bedrooms and in the business and conference centre on the opposite side of the square.
105 en suite (bth/shr) (3 fmly) No smoking in 38 bedrooms CTV in all bedrooms STV Lift Night porter 25P Discount at local leisure centre Xmas English & French Cuisine V meals Coffee am Tea pm Last d 9.30pm
ROOMS: s £35-£68; d £56-£80 **LB**
MEALS: Lunch £6.95-£12&alc Dinner £11.95&alc*
CONF: Thtr 200 Class 70 Board 45 Del from £90
CARDS:

See advertisement on opposite page

★★★63% **Swans Hotel & Restaurant**

84-90 Radcliffe Rd, West Bridgford NG2 5HH (on A6011 approached from either A60 or A52)
☎ 0115 981 4042 FAX 0115 945 5745
Just a short stroll from the Trent Bridge cricket ground, the Swans is a composite of several houses connected over recent years. From the roadside, the reception area presents a cosy and inviting picture; on the inside it provides comfortable accommodation with plain emulsioned walls prettily decorated with stencilling. Service is friendly and efficient.
30 en suite (bth/shr) (3 fmly) CTV in all bedrooms STV No dogs (ex guide dogs) Lift Night porter 31P Xmas English & French Cuisine V meals Coffee am Tea pm No smoking area in restaurant Last d 10pm

contd.

N

ROOMS: (incl. bkfst) s £45-£55; d £55-£65 * **LB**
OFF-PEAK: (incl. bkfst) s £32.50; d £45
MEALS: Lunch £9.95&alc Dinner £9.95&alc
CONF: Thtr 50 Class 20 Board 30 Del from £64
CARDS:

See advertisement on opposite page

★★★62% The Strathdon Thistle

Derby Rd NG1 5FT (follow A52 to city centre to Wollaton St after last set of traffic lights, hotel on right just after Jet petrol station) ☎ 0115 941 8501 FAX 0115 948 3725
Situated close to the city centre, this popular hotel provides comfortable modern accommodation for a predominantly business clientele. Public areas include a reception lounge, the Boston Bean bar, Bobbins restaurant, a comfortable cocktail bar and a conservatory lounge. Numerous meeting/conference rooms, including a modern boardroom, are available.
68 en suite (bth/shr) No smoking in 22 bedrooms CTV in all bedrooms STV Lift Night porter 10P International Cuisine V meals Coffee am Tea pm No smoking area in restaurant Last d 10pm
ROOMS: s £60-£78; d £78-£98 * **LB**
MEALS: Lunch £14.60&alc High tea fr £6.50 Dinner £16.30&alc*
CONF: Thtr 150 Class 65 Board 40 Del from £80
CARDS:

★★★61% Bestwood Lodge

Bestwood Country Park, Arnold NG5 8NF (3m N off A60) ☎ 0115 920 3011 FAX 0115 967 0409
Standing in its own parklands and surrounded by beautiful trees, Bestwood Lodge is a turreted house with a central spire which combines the vernacular of a stately home and the comfort and modern facilities of today's hotel. The internal architecture is outstanding, with some Gothic features such as the high vaulted ceilings in the lounge bar and the gallery above. Bedrooms are contemporary in their furnishings and comfortable, enjoying the splendid countryside views. The restaurant offers a carvery as well as the more formal à la carte. The hotel is a very popular wedding and conference venue.
40 en suite (bth/shr) (2 fmly) CTV in all bedrooms Night porter 100P Riding V meals Coffee am Tea pm Last d 10pm
ROOMS: (incl. bkfst) s £45-£49.50; d £56-£65 * **LB**
OFF-PEAK: (incl. bkfst) s £29; d £50-£55
MEALS: Lunch £12-£25&alc High tea £4-£8 Dinner £7-£13.95&alc*
CONF: Thtr 200 Class 65 Board 50 Del from £56
CARDS:

★★70% Priory

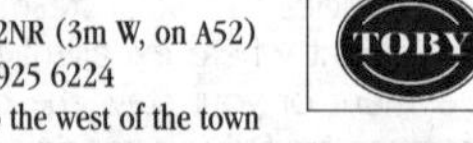

Derby Rd, Wollaton Vale NG8 2NR (3m W, on A52) ☎ 0115 922 1691 FAX 0115 925 6224
Standing in its own grounds to the west of the town centre, this well managed hotel offers a very good standard of accommodation. Bedrooms are comfortably furnished, equipped with modern amenities and particularly well maintained. Public areas offer a choice of bars and an attractively themed restaurant where a good range of dishes is available at lunch time and in the evening. Smartly uniformed staff provide friendly and attentive service.

31 en suite (bth/shr) (4 fmly) No smoking in 12 bedrooms CTV in all bedrooms STV No dogs (ex guide dogs) Night porter 200P Wkly live entertainment V meals Coffee am Tea pm No smoking in restaurant Last d 10.30pm
ROOMS: (incl. bkfst) s fr £62; d fr £73 * **LB**
OFF-PEAK: (incl. bkfst) s fr £32; d fr £57
MEALS: Lunch £6.75-£17.50alc Dinner £8.25-£17.50alc*
CONF: Thtr 60 Class 40 Board 30 Del from £85
CARDS:

★★67% Hotel Des Clos
Old Lenton Ln NG7 2SA ☎ 0115 986 6566 FAX 0115 986 0343
A comfortable riverside hotel which comes well recommended for its tranquil and friendly atmosphere, good cooking and fine wines. The location next to a main arterial route is handy for both the city and Central TV studios-it is rather tricky to find so get directions.
4 en suite (bth/shr) 5 annexe en suite (bth/shr) CTV in all bedrooms 24P No coaches Jacuzzi/spa No children 12yrs French Cuisine V meals Coffee am Tea pm Last d 9pm
ROOMS: s £75-£120; d £90-£120
OFF-PEAK: (incl. bkfst & dinner) d £54-£69
MEALS: Lunch fr £16.95&alc Dinner fr £21.50&alc
CONF: Thtr 16 Class 16 Board 16 Del from £110
CARDS: 

★★65% Rufford
53 Melton Road,West Bridgford NG2 7NE (on A606, near junct A60 Loughborough Road) ☎ 0115 981 4202 FAX 0115 945 5801
Closed Xmas
A small proprietor-managed hotel located in a good residential area half a mile south of Trent Bridge. Its popularity with business guests particularly is due to the friendly atmosphere and the convivial and inviting small conservatory bar and dining room. The bedrooms are very well equipped, thoughtfully designed and well kept.
35 en suite (shr) CTV in all bedrooms STV No dogs (ex guide dogs) Night porter 35P Pool table V meals Coffee am Tea pm Last d 8pm

ROOMS: (incl. bkfst) s £30.55-£39.95; d £45-£54.05 *
MEALS: Dinner £5.95-£10.95alc*
CARDS:

See advertisement on this page

★★64% **The Stage**

Gregory Boulevard NG7 6LB (on A6130, opposite Forest Park) ☎ 0115 960 3261 FAX 0115 969 1040

This modern commercial hotel is situated a mile north of the town centre, overlooking the Forest Sports and Recreation fields - home to 'Goose Fair', Europe's oldest and largest annual fun fair. Spacious public areas include a public bar, a restaurant and several meeting rooms. The reasonably priced accommodation is well equipped and tastefully appointed in two distinct styles. Secure car parking is available.

52 en suite (bth/shr) (5 fmly) No smoking in 4 bedrooms CTV in all bedrooms No dogs (ex guide dogs) Night porter 80P Xmas International Cuisine Coffee am Tea pm Last d 9pm
ROOMS: (incl. bkfst) s £35-£39.50; d £42-£49.50 * **LB**
MEALS: Lunch £10.95-£14 High tea £1.95 Dinner £10.95-£14
CONF: Thtr 100 Class 50 Board 35 Del from £52.50
CARDS:

★★63% **Balmoral**

55-57 Loughborough Rd, West Bridgford NG2 7LA (beside A60 Loughborough Road) ☎ 0115 945 5020 & 955 2992 FAX 0115 955 2991

Located in a good residential suburb near Trent Bridge, the Balmoral is a popular family-run hotel which provides good even standards of accommodation throughout. Predominantly good value grill menus are served in a friendly and informal manner.

31 en suite (bth/shr) CTV in all bedrooms No dogs (ex guide dogs) 30P No coaches Pool table V meals

contd.

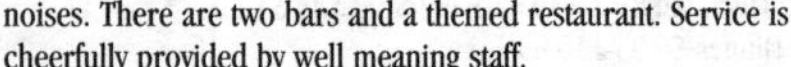

ROOMS: (incl. bkfst) s £24.50-£35; d £39.50-£45 *
CARDS:

Forte Posthouse Nottingham

Saint James's St NG1 6BN ☎ 0115 947 0131
FAX 0115 948 4366
Suitable for both the business and leisure traveller, this bright hotel provides modern accommodation in well equipped bedrooms with en suite bathrooms. For more details about Forte Posthouse hotels, consult the Contents page for the section on Hotel Groups.
130 en suite (bth/shr)
ROOMS: d £79 *
CONF: Thtr 600 Class 350 Board 120 Del from £77

Travel Inn

The Pheonix Centre, Millennium Way West NG8 6AS ☎ 0115 951 9971 FAX 0115 977 0113
Purpose-built accommodation, offering spacious, well equipped bedrooms, all with en suite bathrooms. Meals may be taken at the nearby family restaurant. For more information about Travel Inns, consult the Contents page under Hotel Groups.
60 en suite (bth/shr)
ROOMS: d £35.50 *

NUNEATON Warwickshire Map 04 SP39

★★★64% **Weston Hall**

Weston Ln, Weston in Arden, Bulkington CV12 9RU (leave M6 junc2 follow B4065 through Ansty turn left in Shilton, follow Nuneaton signs out of Bulkington, turn into Wseton Ln at 30mph sign)
☎ 01203 312989 FAX 01203 312989
Set in seven acres of land, this impressive grey stone Elizabethan manor house is located near the town of Bulkington, within easy reach of the M6 and M69. Some original features have been retained in the main building, but the bedrooms are housed in a more contemporary extension to the rear. Extensive function facilities are also available.
36 en suite (bth/shr) (7 fmly) CTV in all bedrooms 300P Fishing Sauna Solarium Gym Croquet lawn Jacuzzi/spa Xmas International Cuisine V meals Coffee am Tea pm Last d 9.30pm
ROOMS: (incl. bkfst) s £55; d £75 * **LB**
OFF-PEAK: (incl. bkfst) d fr £65
CONF: Thtr 200 Class 100 Board 30 Del £90
CARDS:
See advertisement under COVENTRY

★★67% ***Longshoot Toby***

TOBY

Watling St CV11 6JH ☎ 01203 329711
FAX 01203 344570
Closed 24 Dec-4 Jan
This traditional looking building is prominently located at the junction of two busy roads. The accommodation is housed in a motel-style building behind the main hotel which cuts out most of the roadside noises. There are two bars and a themed restaurant. Service is cheerfully provided by well meaning staff.
47 annexe en suite (bth/shr) CTV in all bedrooms No dogs (ex guide dogs) Night porter 120P Pool table V meals Coffee am Last d 10pm
CARDS:

Travel Inn

Coventry Rd CV10 7PJ (S of town near A444/B4113 junct) ☎ 01203 343584 FAX 01203 327156
Purpose-built accommodation, offering spacious, well equipped bedrooms, all with en suite bathrooms. Meals may be taken at the nearby family restaurant. For more information about Travel Inns, consult the Contents page under Hotel Groups.
48 en suite (bth/shr)
ROOMS: d £35.50 *

Travelodge

Bedworth CV10 7TF (2m S, on A444)
☎ 01203 382541 FAX 01203 382541
This modern building offers accommodation in smart, spacious and well equipped bedrooms, suitable for family use, and all with en suite bathrooms. Meals may be taken at the nearby family restaurant. For information on room rates and to make a booking, call Roomline free of charge on 0800 850950. For more details about Travelodge, consult the Contents page under Hotel Groups.
40 en suite (bth/shr)

Travelodge

St Nicholas Park Dr CV11 6EN (on A47)
☎ 01203 353885 FAX 01203 353885
This modern building offers accommodation in smart, spacious and well equipped bedrooms, suitable for family use, and all with en suite bathrooms. Meals may be taken at the nearby family restaurant. For information on room rates and to make a booking, call Roomline free of charge on 0800 850950. For more details about Travelodge, consult the Contents page under Hotel Groups.
28 en suite (bth/shr)

NUNNEY Somerset Map 03 ST74

★★67% **The George at Nunney**
11 Church St BA11 4LW (0.5m N off A361 Frome/Shepton Mallet)
☎ 01373 836458 FAX 01373 836565
The George at Nunney is a 17th-century inn located in the centre of the Saxon village opposite the castle. The various bars reflect the character of the period, and an extensive range of meals is served, together with a commendable selection of whiskies and real ales. Bedrooms are cosy, neatly decorated and equipped beyond expectation.
9 en suite (bth/shr) (2 fmly) CTV in all bedrooms No dogs (ex guide dogs) 30P No coaches Pool table Xmas English & French Cuisine V meals Coffee am Last d 9.30pm
ROOMS: (incl. bkfst) s £42-£49; d £58-£69 **LB**
OFF-PEAK: (incl. bkfst) s £35-£42; d £45-£49
MEALS: Lunch £5.50-£7.50&alc Dinner £5.50-£9.90&alc*
CARDS:

See advertisement under BATH

NUTFIELD Surrey Map 04 TQ35

★★★74% **Nutfield Priory**

ARCADIAN HOTELS

RH1 4EN (1 mile east of Redhill on A25)
☎ 01737 822066 FAX 01737 823321
Closed 26-30 Dec
An extravagant folly built in 1872, this gothic-style country house is situated high on Nutfield Ridge with spectacular views over the Sussex and Surrey countryside. Individually decorated bedrooms are generally spacious and thoughtfully equipped, while day rooms include a foyer

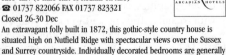

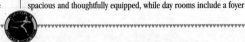

lounge complete with original pipe organ, an oak-panelled library, a bar and the unusual Cloisters Restaurant.

60 en suite (bth/shr) (4 fmly) No smoking in 12 bedrooms CTV in all bedrooms STV Lift Night porter 130P No coaches Indoor swimming pool (heated) Squash Snooker Sauna Solarium Gym Jacuzzi/spa Badminton Steam room Creche V meals Coffee am Tea pm No smoking in restaurant Last d 10pm
ROOMS: s £110-£130; d £140-£220 * **LB**
MEALS: Lunch £14-£18 Dinner £24&alc
CONF: Thtr 80 Class 45 Board 40 Del £185
CARDS:

OAKHAM Rutland Map 04 SK80

RED STAR HOTEL

★★★ **Hambleton Hall**
Hambleton LE15 8TH (3m E off A606)
☎ 01572 756991 FAX 01572 724721

RELAIS & CHATEAUX. Relais Gourmands

Set in a pretty village on the shores of Rutland Water, this fine Victorian house has a prominent position on the peninsula, giving unrivalled views over landscaped lawns and terraces. The staff, many of them French, are smartly dressed and carefully trained in the art of customer care. The comfortable bedrooms were originally designed by Nina Campbell and offer a range of sizes and styles. The lovely marble-tiled bathrooms are particularly worthy of note. Public areas share the same impeccable aesthetic quality, featuring some stunning floral arrangements. Chef Aaron Patterson continues to delight the discerning palate with compositions aimed at the perfect balance of taste, texture and colour.

15 en suite (bth/shr) CTV in all bedrooms Lift 40P No coaches Outdoor swimming pool (heated) Tennis (hard) Xmas V meals Coffee am Tea pm Last d 9.30pm
ROOMS: (incl. cont bkfst) s fr £125; d fr £150 * **LB**
OFF-PEAK: (incl. cont bkfst) s fr £110; d fr £115
MEALS: Lunch £19.50-£31.50&alc Dinner £29.50-£35&alc*
CONF: Thtr 30 Class 25 Board 20 Del from £185
CARDS:

★★★ 70% **Barnsdale Lodge**
The Avenue, Rutland Water LE15 8AH (2m E on A606)
☎ 01572 724678 FAX 01572 724961
A very popular roadside farmhouse built in attractively mellowed local stone which overlooks Rutland Water. Bedrooms and public areas surround a very large and colourfully planted courtyard. The decorative theme is genuine and some reproduction Edwardian, blending well with the stone walls and flagged floors. Bedrooms are comfortable with really good beds on iron bedsteads and contemporary, stylish soft furnishings. The lounge is contained within the bar area and is adjacent to a conservatory buttery which opens all day. The restaurant; a series of three intimate dining rooms offers a good range of internationally appealing, freshly cooked, flavoursome dishes.
29 en suite (bth/shr) (4 fmly) No smoking in 12 bedrooms CTV in all bedrooms Night porter 200P Fishing Shooting arranged ch fac Xmas V meals Coffee am Tea pm
ROOMS: (incl. bkfst) s £55-£65; d £75-£85 * **LB**
MEALS: Lunch £13.95-£30&alc*
CONF: Thtr 330 Class 120 Board 76 Del £82.50
CARDS:

See advertisement on page 479

★★★ 70% **Normanton Park**
Oakham, Rutland LE15 8RP OAKHAM ☎ 01780 720315
FAX 01780 721086
(For full entry see Normanton)

★★★ 65% **The Boultons Country House**
4 Catmose St LE15 6HW ☎ 01572 722844
FAX 01572 724473

CONSORT HOTELS

Standing next to the Rutland museum, this attractive house was originally a cottage and has since been carefully extended to include a reception area and a rear bedroom block. The bedrooms are prettily decorated and have mainly pine furniture and are also thoughtfully equipped. A very good range of well prepared food is available in two restaurants whilst the bar retains an old world charm. The service is very attentive and is naturally friendly and there is a car park to the rear of the hotel.
25 en suite (bth/shr) (2 fmly) CTV in all bedrooms 15P Xmas English & French Cuisine V meals Coffee am Tea pm No smoking in restaurant Last d 10pm
ROOMS: (incl. bkfst) s £60; d £70 **LB**
MEALS: Lunch £10.50-£12.50 Dinner £12.50-£15&alc
CONF: Thtr 60 Class 40 Board 30 Del from £80
CARDS:

★★★ 61% ***Whipper-in Hotel***
Market Place LE15 6DT ☎ 01572 756971 FAX 01572 757759
A well established market town coaching inn which was fashionably refurbished a number of years ago in the English country house mode. The bedrooms remain of good quality both for their comfort and for their furnishings. The candlelit restaurant is equally appealing and decorative, furnished in a contemporary style, and freshly cooked modern English dishes are offered. An open fire warms the lounge bar - a room popular as a local meeting place.
24 en suite (bth/shr) CTV in all bedrooms Night porter V meals Coffee am Tea pm Last d 9.30pm
CARDS:

See advertisement on page 479

OCKLEY Surrey Map 04 TQ14

★★★ 61% **Gatton Manor Hotel Golf & Country Club**
Standon Ln GU4 7AX (off A29 at Ockley turn into Cat Hill Lane, signposted for 2m hotel entrance on the right)
☎ 01306 627555 FAX 01306 627713
Having been considerably upgraded over the past two years, this popular golf and country club offers a range of well proportioned modern bedrooms linked by an overhead corridor to the main club bar, small restaurant and a combination of function rooms. Other facilities include a comfortable drawing room, new health club and well equipped gymnasium, and an 18-hole professional golf course.
14 en suite (bth/shr) (2 fmly) CTV in all bedrooms No dogs (ex guide dogs) 250P No coaches Golf 18 Fishing Sauna Solarium

contd.

O

Gym Pool table Putting green Jacuzzi/spa Bowling green Xmas English & Continental Cuisine V meals Coffee am Tea pm Last d 9pm
ROOMS: (incl. bkfst) s fr £50; d fr £80 * **LB**
MEALS: Lunch £9.75-£12&alc Dinner £9.75-£12&alc*
CONF: Thtr 66 Class 60 Board 30 Del from £99
CARDS:

ODIHAM Hampshire Map 04 SU75

★★66% **George**
High St RG29 1LP (1m from junct 5 of M3)
☎ 01256 702081 FAX 01256 704213
This historic 15th century inn has been sympathetically restored and retains many original features. The bedrooms in the main house have lots of character with original beams and individual furnishings, while those in the coach house are more modern. There are two cosy bars, popular with the locals, offering an extensive range of dishes.
9 en suite (bth/shr) 9 annexe en suite (bth/shr) (1 fmly) No smoking in 5 bedrooms CTV in all bedrooms STV 20P No coaches English & French Cuisine V meals Coffee am Tea pm Last d 10pm
ROOMS: (incl. bkfst) s fr £65; d £75-£90 * **LB**
OFF-PEAK: (incl. bkfst) s fr £45; d £65-£90
MEALS: Lunch fr £13.95&alc Dinner £18-£25alc*
CONF: Board 10
CARDS:

OKEHAMPTON Devon Map 02 SX59

★★60% **White Hart**
Fore St EX20 1HD (located in town centre, adjacent to the only town traffic lights, car park at rear of hotel)
☎ 01837 52730 & 54514 FAX 01837 53979
The White Hart, a 17th-century coaching inn, enjoys a prominent position in the centre of the small town of Okehampton and allows easy access to the A30 for touring Devon and Cornwall. Bedrooms have been equipped with modern facilities and the public areas include a choice of character bars and a beamed restaurant.
19 en suite (bth/shr) (2 fmly) No smoking in 4 bedrooms CTV in all bedrooms No dogs (ex guide dogs) 22P Games room Skittle alley Xmas European Cuisine V meals Coffee am Tea pm No smoking area in restaurant Last d 9pm
ROOMS: (incl. bkfst) s £32.50-£35; d £40 *
MEALS: Lunch £9.95&alc Dinner £9.95&alc*
CONF: Thtr 100 Class 80 Board 40 Del from £55.50
CARDS:

Travelodge
Widdon Down EX20 2QT ☎ 01647 231626
FAX 01647 231626
Travelodge
This modern building offers accommodation in smart, spacious and well equipped bedrooms, suitable for family use, and all with en suite bathrooms. Meals may be taken at the nearby family restaurant. For information on room rates and to make a booking, call Roomline free of charge on 0800 850950. For more details about Travelodge, consult the Contents page under Hotel Groups.
40 en suite (bth/shr)

OLDBURY West Midlands Map 07 SO98

★★★❀73% **Jonathans'**
16-24 Wolverhampton Rd, Oldbury B68 0LH (junct with A456/A4123, 1m from junct 2 or 3 of M5)
☎ 0121 429 3757 FAX 0121 434 3107
The modern red brick exterior of this hotel gives no indication of the extraordinary evocation of the Victorian era within, created by the two Jonathons, Bedford and Baker. The style is authentic and even absurd in places, but definitely fun for those who appreciate such an ambience. The brasserie and bar has most recently received a facelift - a startling even stunning collection of vibrant coloured glassware matches the decor. A maze of corridors and staircases connects the various lounges, drawing rooms, bars, restaurants and bedrooms, and a cuisine characterised by much hyperbole offers plentiful amounts of traditional old fashioned English cooking.
45 en suite (bth) No smoking in 2 bedrooms CTV in all bedrooms No dogs (ex guide dogs) Night porter 75P No coaches Xmas English & Continental Cuisine V meals Coffee am Tea pm No smoking area in restaurant Last d 10.30pm
ROOMS: (incl. bkfst) s £75-£98; d £90-£155 * **LB**
OFF-PEAK: (incl. bkfst) d fr £45
MEALS: Lunch fr £14.50 Dinner £16-£30*
CONF: Thtr 80 Class 65 Board 60 Del from £105
CARDS:

Travelodge
Wolverhampton Rd B69 2BH (on A4123, northbound off junct 2 of M5)
☎ 0121 552 2967 FAX 0121 552 2967
Travelodge
This modern building offers accommodation in smart, spacious and well equipped bedrooms, suitable for family use, and all with en suite bathrooms. Meals may be taken at the nearby family restaurant. For information on room rates and to make a booking, call Roomline free of charge on 0800 850950. For more details about Travelodge, consult the Contents page under Hotel Groups.
33 en suite (bth/shr)

OLDHAM Greater Manchester Map 07 SD90

★★★❀70% **Hotel Smokies Park**
CONSORT CROWN
Ashton Rd, Bardsley OL8 3HX (on A627 between Oldham and Ashton-under-Lyne) ☎ 0161 624 3405
FAX 0161 627 5262
This modern hotel is situated midway between Ashton-under-Lyne and Oldham and although its comfortable bedrooms have been designed with the business person in mind leisure guests will also find the facilities convenient. The hotel is also renowned for its nightclub, which is open on Fridays and Saturdays and also its distinctive restaurant, which has been awarded a rosette for the first time this year. Head chef Kevin Amesbury's international à la carte menu provides a wide range of both British and continental dishes and the table d'hÙte menu is particularly good value.
47 en suite (bth/shr) (2 fmly) No smoking in 10 bedrooms CTV in all bedrooms STV No dogs (ex guide dogs) Night porter 120P Sauna Solarium Gym Wkly live entertainment English & French Cuisine V meals Coffee am Tea pm Last d 10pm
ROOMS: (incl. bkfst) s £58-£75; d £66-£85 * **LB**
OFF-PEAK: (incl. bkfst) s £35-£50; d £50-£70
MEALS: Lunch £14.50-£25alc Dinner £14.50-£14.95&alc*
CONF: Thtr 300 Class 125 Board 50 Del from £75
CARDS:

★★★65% **Avant**
Windsor Rd, Manchester St OL8 4AS (W on A62)
☎ 0161 627 5500 FAX 0161 627 5896

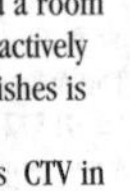

This modern, purpose built hotel, enjoys panoramic views over the town from its elevated position just off the A62 offers attractive, well equipped accommodation. Bedrooms are mostly identical but well laid out, and include a number of suites and a room for disabled guests. The extensive public areas include an attractively decorated restaurant where a good choice of well prepared dishes is available.
103 en suite (bth/shr) (2 fmly) No smoking in 16 bedrooms CTV in all bedrooms STV Lift Night porter 120P Xmas English & Lancashire Cuisine V meals Coffee am Tea pm No smoking area in restaurant Last d 9.30pm

ROOMS: (incl. bkfst) s £65-£75; d £75-£85 **LB**
OFF-PEAK: (incl. bkfst & dinner) s £75-£85; d £120-£130
MEALS: Sunday Lunch fr £9.95 High tea £4.95-£9.95
Dinner £16.50-£19.50&alc
CONF: Thtr 200 Class 100 Board 60 Del from £85
CARDS:

★★★64% **Pennine Way Hotel**
Manchester St OL8 1UZ ☎ 0161 624 0555 FAX 0161 627 2301
Conveniently positioned in the town centre yet with easy access to the M62, this purpose-built hotel has a popular conference and corporate business following. Bedrooms are uncluttered but well equipped and there is a lively bar and restaurant. Extensive function facilities include a ballroom.
130 en suite (bth/shr) (50 fmly) No smoking in 26 bedrooms CTV in all bedrooms STV Lift Night porter 250P Gym Pool table Xmas European Cuisine V meals Coffee am Tea pm No smoking in restaurant Last d 10pm
ROOMS: (incl. bkfst) s £65-£75; d £76.50 * **LB**
OFF-PEAK: (incl. bkfst) s £48.50; d £55
MEALS: Sunday Lunch fr £8.95 Dinner £15.50&alc*
CONF: Thtr 320 Class 70 Board 70 Del from £50
CARDS:

★★★61% **The Bower**
Hollinwood Av, Chadderton OL9 8DE (2.25m SW A6104)
☎ 0161 682 7254 FAX 0161 683 4605
RS 25-31 Dec
A former family home known locally as Henshaw House was converted some years ago into a mainly business hotel and a modern bedroom wing was added. It has an enclosed garden, ideal for wedding photographs, as well as a range of banqueting and conference facilities. Bedrooms are not overlarge, but have every modern facility

contd.

and several have recently been upgraded. There is a spacious lounge bar in which bar meals are served and an attractively appointed restaurant for the more formal occasion.

63 en suite (bth/shr) (1 fmly) No smoking in 19 bedrooms CTV in all bedrooms Night porter 140P Wkly live entertainment Continental Cuisine V meals Coffee am Tea pm No smoking in restaurant Last d 9.45pm
ROOMS: s fr £67.50; d fr £77.50 * **LB**
MEALS: Lunch £7-£11.95 Dinner £17.50-£20&alc*
CONF: Thtr 220 Class 60 Board 60 Del from £90
CARDS:

★★66% **High Point**
64 Napier St East OL8 1TR (SW of town, near A62)
☎ 0161 624 4130 FAX 0161 627 2757
Considerable improvements have been made by the new owners of this long established hotel which enjoys the most marvellous views of the Pennines and is just 10 minutes from the M.62. Being personally run, hospitality is a strength and the small team of staff are both enthusiastic and friendly. Whilst the freshly decorated bedrooms vary in size, all are well equipped. The smartly decorated public areas include a conservatory restaurant which has quickly gained a very good reputation locally.
17 en suite (bth/shr) (2 fmly) CTV in all bedrooms 44P Riding by arrangement Wkly live entertainment English & French Cuisine V meals Coffee am Tea pm Last d 9.30pm
ROOMS: (incl. bkfst) s fr £40; d fr £50 * **LB**
OFF-PEAK: (incl. bkfst) s fr £35; d fr £40
MEALS: Lunch £7.95-£8.50 Dinner £10.95-£13.95*
CONF: Thtr 40 Class 25 Board 25 Del from £65
CARDS:

OLD SODBURY Gloucestershire Map 03 ST78

★★61% **Cross Hands**
BS17 6RJ ☎ 01454 313000 FAX 01454 324409
This former posting house stands beside the A46, just one and a half miles from Junction 18 of the M4 and within easy reach of both Bath and Bristol. Bedrooms vary in size, some being in need of refurbishment, but all offer a good range of facilities. The busy public areas include a character bar, an adjacent function suite in a converted barn, and a spacious split-level restaurant, where a selection of interesting dishes is available from a detailed menu.
24 rms (3 bth 17 shr) CTV in all bedrooms STV Night porter 200P Xmas European Cuisine V meals Coffee am Tea pm Last d 10.30pm
ROOMS: (incl. cont bkfst) s £52.50-£60.50; d £67.50-£79.50 * **LB**
OFF-PEAK: (incl. bkfst) s £35-£49.50; d £47.50-£65.50
MEALS: Sunday Lunch £8.95-£10.95&alc Dinner £14.50-£25alc*
CONF: Thtr 70 Class 35 Board 45 Del from £80.50
CARDS:

⌂ indicates a Town House Hotel. Please consult the section on AA Star Rating at the front of the book.

OLLERTON Nottinghamshire Map 08 SK66

★★65% **Hop Pole**
Main St NG22 9AD ☎ 01623 822573
A village inn in the old part of Ollerton, close to the River Maun, the Hop Pole is popular with locals for its carvery food operation and traditional ales. Bedrooms vary in size but all are fresh in appearance and well appointed with light wood fixtures and a good range of facilities. Each has a modern bathroom.
11 rms (10 bth/shr) (1 fmly) CTV in all bedrooms No dogs (ex guide dogs) 30P Pool table Darts V meals Coffee am Tea pm
ROOMS: (incl. bkfst) s £32; d £45 * **LB**
OFF-PEAK: (incl. bkfst) s fr £30
MEALS: Lunch £7.95*
CARDS:

ONNELEY Staffordshire Map 07 SJ74

★★69% ***Wheatsheaf Inn at Onneley***
Barhill Rd CW3 9QF (beside A525)
☎ 01782 751581 FAX 01782 751499
Mr and Mrs Bittner and family, the owners of this well maintained 18th-century inn, are very much involved in the day to day running of the hotel, together with their friendly staff. All the bedrooms have modern en suite shower facilities, are attractively decorated and well equipped. Thoughtful touches such as a bowl of fruit and mineral water and plenty of magazines are also provided. Guests have the choice of eating informally in the bar, where a good range of Tapas is available in addition to other more traditional dishes, or slightly more formally in the restaurant which again offers Spanish dishes.
5 en suite (shr) CTV in all bedrooms STV 150P Golf 9 Pool table English & Spanish Cuisine V meals Coffee am Tea pm Last d 9.30pm
CARDS:

ORFORD (NEAR WOODBRIDGE) Suffolk Map 05 TM44

★★65% ***The Crown & Castle***
IP12 2LJ (turn right from B1084 on entering village)
☎ 01394 450205 FAX 01394 450176
There are wonderful views of the surrounding area, including the castle, from this welcoming hotel which has a black and white timbered façade. The ground-floor public areas have been completely refurbished to provide a higher standard of comfort. Bedrooms in the main building have also been improved, but the Garden Studio rooms remain more spacious and easily accessible.
10 rms (1 bth 5 shr) 10 annexe en suite (bth/shr) (10 fmly) CTV in all bedrooms 20P European Cuisine V meals Coffee am Tea pm Last d 8.45pm
CARDS:

ORMSKIRK Lancashire Map 07 SD40

★★★64% **Beaufort**
High Ln, Burscough L40 7SN (1m N, on A59)
☎ 01704 892655 FAX 01704 895135
This modern purpose-built hotel offers well furnished bedrooms. The beamed restaurant serves enjoyable meals and there are two bars. Staff are professional and helpful.
21 en suite (bth/shr) CTV in all bedrooms STV Night porter 126P Xmas International Cuisine V meals Coffee am Tea pm No smoking in restaurant Last d 9.30pm

MENZIES HOTELS

ROOMS: s £49.50-£60; d £49.50-£80 * **LB**
OFF-PEAK: s £35-£45; d £35-£65
MEALS: Lunch £8.95-£17.50alc Dinner £12.50-£25alc
CONF: Thtr 40 Class 20 Board 25 Del from £69.50
CARDS:

OSTERLEY Greater London See LONDON SECTION plan 1 B3

★★63% **Osterley**
764 Great West Rd TW7 5NA ☎ 0181 568 9981
FAX 0181 569 7819
Situated beside the A4 east bound carriageway convenient for the airport and west London, this Tudor-style pub has been skilfully extended to provide a good range of well equipped bedrooms most of which are in an adjoining modern purpose-built extention. Gulpers Pub is a popular venue for locals and offers a good range of real ales and keg beers, whilst the restaurant offers à la carte menu dining in modern surroundings. Service is friendly and helpful with full reception facilities provided. There are also extensive facilities for conferences and all types of functions.
57 en suite (bth/shr) 5 annexe rms (9 fmly) CTV in all bedrooms Night porter 143P V meals Coffee am Tea pm Last d 10pm
MEALS: Lunch £9.95-£16 Dinner £6.95-£13&alc*
CARDS:

OSWESTRY Shropshire Map 07 SJ22
See also Whittington

★★★❀❀70% **Wynnstay**
Church St SY11 2SZ (centre of town, opposite parish church)
☎ 01691 655261 FAX 01691 670606
This long-established hotel is well positioned in the centre of the historic market town. The house is Georgian and has both a 200-year-old walled Crown Bowling Green and a new leisure centre with a large pool and sixteen station gymnasium. Bedrooms, which include a number of suites and rooms with four-poster beds, are well equipped and attractively decorated with quality furnishings. The public areas include the elegant Camellia Restaurant, where the service is professional and attentive and dishes such as tender cannon of lamb wrapped in light filo pastry on a bed of celeriac purée and a mint beurre blanc can be enjoyed. The wine list is fun and offers a short selection of popular wines. The hotel also has a large conference and banqueting suite and with a good car park.
27 en suite (bth/shr) (4 fmly) No smoking in 12 bedrooms CTV in all bedrooms 70P Indoor swimming pool (heated) Sauna Solarium Gym Jacuzzi/spa Crown green bowling Beauty suite French Cuisine V meals Coffee am Tea pm Last d 9.30pm
MEALS: Lunch fr £12.50 Dinner £16.95-£19.95&alc
CONF: Thtr 290 Class 150 Board 50
CARDS:

★★68% **Pen-y-Dyffryn Hall Country Hotel**
Rhydycroesau SY10 7JT (from A5 into Oswestry town centre, follow signs to Llansilin on B4580, hotel is 3m W of Oswestry just before Rhydycroesau village) ☎ 01691 653700 FAX 01691 653700
Situated just inside England, this delightful small hotel has lovely views of the Welsh hills. Bedrooms are attractively decorated and furnished, and all have modern en suite facilities. Trouser presses and hairdryers are provided and one room has a four-poster bed. There are a cosy sitting room with a cheerful log fire, a small bar and an adjacent dining room; a larger lounge and restaurant come into use when the house is full. A fixed-price menu is offered, along with daily specials, and the food is wholesome and enjoyable.
8 en suite (bth/shr) (1 fmly) CTV in all bedrooms 30P No coaches Fishing Guided walks ch fac Xmas English & Continental Cuisine V meals No smoking in restaurant Last d 8.30pm
ROOMS: (incl. bkfst) s £42-£47; d £60-£70 **LB**
MEALS: Dinner £14.50-£15.50&alc
CARDS:

Travelodge
Mile End Service Area SY11 4JA (junct A5/A483)
☎ 01691 658178 FAX 01691 658178
This modern building offers accommodation in smart, spacious and well equipped bedrooms, suitable for family use, and all with en suite bathrooms. Meals may be taken at the nearby family restaurant. For information on room rates and to make a booking, call Roomline free of charge on 0800 850950. For more details about Travelodge, consult the Contents page under Hotel Groups.
40 en suite (bth/shr)

OTLEY West Yorkshire Map 08 SE24

★★★66% **Chevin Lodge Country Park**
Yorkgate LS21 3NU (signed from A658 Bradford to Harrogate road) ☎ 01943 467818
FAX 01943 850335
This unique hotel which claims to be the largest log building in Britain, is set in several acres of private woodland and also has its own small lake. The bedrooms are either in the main part of the hotel or in log cabins dotted around the woodland. All are very well equipped, warm and cosy. The public rooms are equally inviting, and an interesting range of food is provided, including plain dishes and some more unusual ingredients. A leisure club is due to open during the spring of 1996.
27 en suite (bth/shr) 23 annexe en suite (bth/shr) (4 fmly) CTV in all bedrooms Night porter 100P Indoor swimming pool (heated) Tennis (hard) Fishing Sauna Solarium Gym Jacuzzi/spa Mountain bikes, jogging trails Xmas English & French Cuisine V meals Coffee am No smoking in restaurant Last d 7.30pm
ROOMS: (incl. bkfst) s £87-£97; d £87-£107
OFF-PEAK: (incl. bkfst) s £60-£70; d £87-£107
MEALS: Lunch £11.50-£11.50 Dinner £16-£18.25&alc
CONF: Thtr 150 Class 85 Board 60 Del from £95
CARDS:

OTTERY ST MARY Devon Map 03 SY19

★★68% ***Tumbling Weir Hotel & Restaurant***
EX11 1AQ ☎ 01404 812752 FAX 01404 812752
This thatched 17th-century cottage stands between the River Otter and its millstream, approached by a well-lit path from a public car park. The en suite bedrooms are cosy and well equipped, while original beams and fireplaces can be seen in the relaxing public areas. A candlelit restaurant offers an interesting selection of dishes.
12 en suite (bth/shr) CTV in all bedrooms STV 10P Fishing English & French Cuisine V meals Coffee am Tea pm Last d 9pm
CARDS:

OUNDLE Northamptonshire Map 04 TL08

★★★67% **The Talbot**
New St PE8 4EA ☎ 01832 273621
FAX 01832 274545
There is a naturally friendly atmosphere in this characterful town-centre hotel which dates back to 1626. Bedrooms are spacious and quiet; some are located in the main building. The bar and lounge are combined to create a cosy area and good levels of service are provided in the smartly-kept restaurant.
39 en suite (bth/shr) (4 fmly) No smoking in 15 bedrooms CTV in all bedrooms Night porter 60P Xmas Contemporary British Cuisine V meals Coffee am Tea pm No smoking in restaurant Last d 9.30pm
ROOMS: s £70; d £80 * **LB**
MEALS: Lunch £11.95-£12.95 Dinner £17.95&alc*
CONF: Thtr 120 Class 50 Board 50 Del £105
CARDS:

OXFORD Oxfordshire Map 04 SP50
See also Milton Common

★★★★ **Le Manoir Aux Quat' Saisons**
OX44 7PD ☎ 01844 278881 FAX 01844 278847
(For full entry see Great Milton)

★★★★68% **The Randolph**
Beaumont St OX1 2LN ☎ 01865 247481
FAX 01865 791678
This fine hotel is situated right in the centre of the city and has now been almost completely refurbished. Smart bedrooms are on three floors, sizes varying and those at the top having views of the spires. The drawing room for afternoon tea is a popular Oxford rendezvous. New chef, Geoff Balharrie and his team produce dishes showing great promise in a style involving traditional and modern ideas.
109 en suite (bth/shr) No smoking in 43 bedrooms CTV in all bedrooms STV Lift Night porter 60P International Cuisine V meals Coffee am Tea pm No smoking area in restaurant Last d 10pm
ROOMS: s fr £135; d fr £155 * **LB**
MEALS: Lunch £14.50-£19.50 Dinner £25-£30*
CONF: Thtr 300 Class 120 Board 35 Del from £150
CARDS:

★★★68% **Studley Priory**
OX33 1AZ ☎ 01865 351203 FAX 01865 351613
(For full entry see Horton-cum-Studley)

★★★64% **Eastgate**
The High, Merton St OX1 4BE ☎ 01865 248244
FAX 01865 791681
A relaxing hotel almost like an English country house yet situated in the city centre amongst many buildings of historic and architectural interest and also close to the River Thames and Magdalen Bridge. Bedrooms are comfortably furnished and have every modern facility, some overlook the famous Examination Hall others, the enclosed hotel car park at the rear.
43 en suite (bth/shr) (18 fmly) No smoking in 17 bedrooms CTV in all bedrooms Lift Night porter 27P Wkly live entertainment Xmas British classical Cuisine V meals Coffee am Tea pm No smoking in restaurant Last d 9.30pm
ROOMS: s £95; d £110 * **LB**
MEALS: Lunch £11.50-£17.50 Dinner £16.95-£19.95&alc*
CARDS:

★★★63% **Oxford Moat House**
Godstow Rd, Wolvercote Roundabout OX2 8AL
(adjacent to A34/A40, 2m from city centre)
☎ 01865 59933 FAX 01865 310259
Closed 27-30 Dec
A contemporary hotel situated on the northern edge of the city offers modern, well appointed bedrooms, many of which have recently been upgraded. The hotel has a variety of conference and banqueting suites and also a well equipped leisure centre. The location is ideal for business persons or tourists visiting the area.
155 en suite (bth/shr) (17 fmly) No smoking in 31 bedrooms CTV in all bedrooms STV Night porter 250P Indoor swimming pool (heated) Squash Snooker Sauna Solarium Gym Whirlpool 9 Hole mini golf Xmas English & French Cuisine V meals Coffee am Tea pm No smoking area in restaurant Last d 9.45pm
ROOMS: s £85-£120 * **LB**
MEALS: Lunch £10-£16alc Dinner £13.50-£20alc*
CONF: Thtr 150 Class 60 Board 40 Del from £80
CARDS:

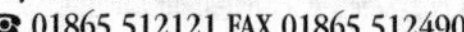

★★★62% ***Cotswold Lodge***
66A Banbury Rd OX2 6JP (turn off the A40 Oxford ring road onto the A4165, Banbury Road - signposted City centre/Summertown. Hotel 1.5m on left)
☎ 01865 512121 FAX 01865 512490
Closed 26 Dec-2 Jan
This family run hotel is located just a short walk from the city centre. The Victorian building has been extended round a pretty patio area. The hotel is popular with business guests and also caters for conference and banquet trade. Bedrooms are generally spacious and well equipped though some are beginning to look a little tired. The restaurant serves some well prepared imaginative cuisine.
50 en suite (bth/shr) (2 fmly) CTV in all bedrooms Night porter 60P English & French Cuisine V meals Coffee am Tea pm Last d 10pm
CARDS:

★★★62% **Linton Lodge**
Linton Rd OX2 6UJ (Hilton) ☎ 01865 53461 FAX 01865 310365
This hotel is situated in a quiet residential area north of the city centre and offers modern and comfortable accommodation in pleasant surroundings. The main part of the hotel comprises a conversion of Edwardian houses - the panelled Library Restaurant, an adjacent lounge and the Dragon Bar all being located in this area, together with many of the bedrooms. Other rooms are in a modern extension which adjoins the main building at the rear. The restaurant offers a buffet-style breakfast, a carvery lunch and a dinner menu, with attentive service.
71 en suite (bth/shr) (2 fmly) No smoking in 20 bedrooms CTV in all bedrooms Lift Night porter 40P Croquet lawn English & French Cuisine V meals Coffee am Tea pm No smoking area in restaurant Last d 9.30pm
ROOMS: s £99; d £119 **LB**
OFF-PEAK: s £70; d £90
MEALS: Lunch £10.25 Dinner £8.95-£17.25
CONF: Thtr 120 Class 50 Board 35 Del from £95
CARDS:

★★64% ***Palace***
250 Iffley Rd OX4 1SE (on A4158) ☎ 01865 727627
FAX 01865 200478
This handsome well kept Victorian house on the Iffley Road is personally run by Mr and Mrs Parojcic who take pride in both their attractive hotel and the warm welcome they extend to guests. Bedrooms are prettily appointed. Taditional British home cooking and also some of the Parojcic's native dishes are served in the pleasant dining room.

8 en suite (bth/shr) (2 fmly) CTV in all bedrooms No dogs 6P V meals Coffee am Tea pm Last d 9pm
CARDS:

★★60% Victoria
180 Abingdon Rd OX1 4RA 1 ☎ 01865 724536 FAX 01865 794909
The Victoria is a friendly hotel run by its hospitable owners, Mr and Mrs Parojcic. Accommodation offers sound standards of comfort.
17 rms (11 bth/shr) 5 annexe en suite (bth) (2 fmly) No smoking in 3 bedrooms CTV in all bedrooms 17P Italian & Yugoslav Cuisine V meals Coffee am Tea pm
ROOMS: (incl. bkfst) s fr £37.50; d £55.50-£72.50 * **LB**
CONF: Class 20 Del from £95
CARDS:

★62% River
17 Botley Rd OX2 0AA (1m along Botley Road from ring road west exit, beside Osney Bridge) ☎ 01865 243475 FAX 01865 724306
Closed 21 Dec-4 Jan RS winter weekends
The River Hotel overlooks the Thames at Osney Bridge, and is within walking distance of the city centre. Bedrooms are simply furnished and well equipped, some in an annexe across the road. The restaurant, where smoking is discouraged, has river views.
14 rms (5 bth 7 shr) 8 annexe rms (3 bth 3 shr) (5 fmly) CTV in all bedrooms No dogs (ex guide dogs) 25P No coaches Fishing Coffee am Tea pm No smoking in restaurant Last d 8pm
ROOMS: (incl. bkfst) s £39-£57; d £64-£70 *
MEALS: Bar Lunch fr £3 Dinner £7-£10
CONF: Thtr 50 Class 24 Board 20
CARDS:

Travel Inn

Oxford Businees Park, Garsington Rd OX4 2JZ
☎ 01865 779230 FAX 01865 775887

Purpose-built accommodation, offering spacious, well equipped bedrooms, all with en suite bathrooms. Meals may be taken at the nearby family restaurant. For more information about Travel Inns, consult the Contents page under Hotel Groups.
60 en suite (bth/shr)
ROOMS: d £35.50 *

Travelodge

Peartree Roundabout OX2 8JZ (junc A34/A43)
☎ 01865 54301 FAX 01865 513474
This modern building offers accommodation in smart, spacious and well equipped bedrooms, suitable for family use, and all with en suite bathrooms. Meals may be taken at the nearby family restaurant. For information on room rates and to make a booking, call Roomline free of charge on 0800 850950. For more details about Travelodge, consult the Contents page under Hotel Groups.
100 en suite (bth/shr)

Travelodge

London Rd, Wheatley OX33 1JH (off A40)
☎ 01865 875705 FAX 01865 875705
This modern building offers accommodation in smart, spacious and well equipped bedrooms, suitable for family use, and all with en suite bathrooms. Meals may be taken at the nearby family restaurant. For information on room rates and to make a booking, call Roomline free of charge on 0800 850950. For more details about Travelodge, consult the Contents page under Hotel Groups.
24 en suite (bth/shr)

***STOP PRESS!** AA Members can book accommodation at many hotels in this guide through the AA Booking Service, usually at attractive discounts. See page 5 for details or telephone 0990 050505*

English Tourist Board
HIGHLY COMMENDED
1994 Cèsar Award
Good Hotel Guide
77% ★★★
Treglos Hotel
Constantine Bay, Nr Padstow, Cornwall PL28 8JH
Telephone: (01841) 520727 Fax: (01841) 521163
Guests return year after year to enjoy the personal attention, high standard of service, the superb restaurant and luxurious comfort. Specializing in local seafood, vegetables from the hotel garden and home made desserts with cornish cream. Short stroll to beautiful sandy beach.
Write to owner managers Jim and Rose Barlow for colour brochure.
See gazetteer under Constantine Bay.

PADSTOW Cornwall & Isles of Scilly Map 02 SW97
See also Constantine Bay

★★★65% Old Custom House Inn
South Quay PL28 8ED (St Austell Brewery)
☎ 01841 532359 FAX 01841 533372
In an idyllic harbour-side setting this busy pub-style hotel offers a choice of eating in either the spacious and popular public bar or the restaurant, where competently cooked traditional dishes include fishy main courses such as fresh marlin steak and seafood creole.
27 en suite (bth) CTV in all bedrooms STV 9P Pool table Xmas English & French Cuisine V meals Coffee am Tea pm Last d 9pm
ROOMS: (incl. bkfst) s £46-£67; d £56-£90 * **LB**
MEALS: Bar Lunch £1.75-£6.95 Dinner £11.85-£23.60alc*
CONF: Board 85
CARDS:

★★★62% The Metropole
Station Rd PL28 8DB ☎ 01841 532486
FAX 01841 532867

FORTE Heritage

The Metropole which is in a superb location with glorious views across the Camel Estuary provides friendly services by local staff in traditional surroundings. Bedrooms are generally of a reasonable size but vary in style, some having been recently refurbished to a smart standard while other remain dated. Recent upgrading has improved the Veranda Bar and Lounge where afternoon tea can be taken.
44 en suite (bth/shr) (5 fmly) No smoking in 19 bedrooms CTV in all bedrooms Lift 38P Outdoor swimming pool (heated) Xmas V meals Coffee am Tea pm No smoking in restaurant Last d 9pm
ROOMS: s fr £70; d fr £90 *
MEALS: Lunch £11.95 Dinner £18.95*
CARDS:

★★ 75% Seafood Restaurant
Riverside PL28 8BY ☎ 01841 532485 FAX 01841 533344
Closed 21-28 Dec
People come from far and wide to visit Rick and Jill Stein's celebrated seafood restaurant which has now been established for over 20 years. Bedrooms were added a decade ago in response to the demand from travellers who wished to wake up to the wonderful harbour views as well as enjoying the days catch accompanied by one of the fine bottles of wine. Bedrooms are all individually priced and furnished in a fresh, contemporary style; the most popular are the two rooms which share a spacious roof terrace. Residents and diners can enjoy drinks in a sunny conservatory and the restaurant itself has a bright and summery feel created by decorative mirrors, colourful prints, crisp linen and wicker chairs. Menus change twice daily, with the more imaginative dishes available at dinner. Classics such as fish soup and skate beurre noire are first class but equally a dish of John Dory with aubergine, pesto and a mixed salad with preserved lemon displayed Rick's careful handling of ingredients.
10 en suite (bth/shr) CTV in all bedrooms 12P No coaches International Cuisine Last d 10pm
ROOMS: (incl. bkfst) s £40.90-£79.20; d £62-£120 * **LB**
MEALS: Lunch fr £23 Dinner fr £31.50*
CARDS:

★★ 65% Green Waves
Trevone Bay PL28 8RD ☎ 01841 520114
Apr-Oct
19 en suite (bth/shr) CTV in all bedrooms 18P No coaches Half size snooker table Coffee am No smoking in restaurant
ROOMS: (incl. bkfst & dinner) s £24-£37; d £48-£74 * **LB**
CARDS:

See advertisement on opposite page

PAIGNTON Devon Map 03 SX86

★★★ 68% Redcliffe

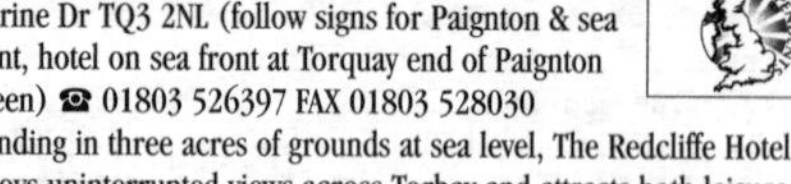

Marine Dr TQ3 2NL (follow signs for Paignton & sea front, hotel on sea front at Torquay end of Paignton Green) ☎ 01803 526397 FAX 01803 528030
Standing in three acres of grounds at sea level, The Redcliffe Hotel enjoys uninterrupted views across Torbay and attracts both leisure and corporate markets. Bedrooms vary in size and style, those with sea views being particularly popular. The professionally supervised leisure centre is available to the local membership in addition to hotel residents. The loyal staff are commended for their friendliness and attentive service.
59 en suite (bth/shr) (8 fmly) CTV in all bedrooms STV No dogs (ex guide dogs) Lift Night porter 80P Indoor swimming pool (heated) Outdoor swimming pool (heated) Fishing Sauna Solarium Gym Pool table Putting green Jacuzzi/spa Table tennis Wkly live entertainment Xmas English & French Cuisine V meals Coffee am Tea pm Last d 8.30pm
ROOMS: (incl. bkfst) s £46-£50; d £96-£100 * **LB**
OFF-PEAK: (incl. bkfst) s £38-£42; d £76-£84
MEALS: Sunday Lunch £9.25-£9.95 Dinner £14.75-£15.75&alc
CONF: Thtr 150 Class 50 Board 50 Del from £44
CARDS:

See advertisement on opposite page

★★★ 59% The Palace

Esplanade Rd TQ4 6BJ (opposite Paignton pier)
☎ 01803 555121 FAX 01803 527974
In a commanding sea front position with good views across the bay this traditional hotel offers plenty of car parking space as well as spacious public areas. Accommodation ranges from somewhat dated rooms to those that have been attractively refurbished. A few carte choices supplement the Paris Restaurant's simple fixed-price menu. Friendly services from a keen young team.
52 en suite (bth/shr) (1 fmly) No smoking in 4 bedrooms CTV in all bedrooms Lift Night porter 60P Outdoor swimming pool (heated) Tennis (hard) Sauna Pool table Jacuzzi/spa Xmas V meals Coffee am Tea pm No smoking in restaurant Last d 9pm
ROOMS: s fr £55; d fr £75 * **LB**
MEALS: Lunch £6.95-£7.95&alc Dinner £9.95&alc*
CONF: Thtr 45 Class 15 Board 20 Del from £75
CARDS:

★★ 67% Preston Sands
10/12 Marine Pde TQ3 2NU ☎ 01803 558718 FAX 01803 527345
This friendly hotel is personally run by owners Eric and Susan Mitchell who create a relaxed atmosphere. Located in a quiet cul-de-sac on the sea front, it is just a few yards from the safe, sandy beach. Many of the bedrooms and the public rooms benefit from the views across the bay, and in the summer months guests may enjoy cream tea on the balcony. The bedrooms are bright and well equipped with pretty co-ordinated decor.
31 en suite (bth/shr) (3 fmly) CTV in all bedrooms STV 24P No children 8yrs Xmas V meals Coffee am Tea pm No smoking in restaurant Last d 7.30pm
ROOMS: (incl. bkfst) s £23-£26; d £44-£50 **LB**
OFF-PEAK: (incl. bkfst) s £21; d £42
MEALS: Sunday Lunch £10-£13 Dinner £10-£13&alc*
CARDS:

★★ 64% Sunhill
Alta Vista Rd TQ4 6DA ☎ 01803 557532 FAX 01803 663850
Sunhill enjoys wonderful views from its elevated position above the bay. The en suite bedrooms are well proportioned and many open onto the balcony. Public areas include a bright dining room and a sun terrace, there is also a bar where there is live entertainment throughout the season. There is a lift to most floors and a lower-ground floor snooker room.
30 en suite (bth/shr) (3 fmly) CTV in all bedrooms Lift 31P Xmas English & French Cuisine V meals Coffee am Tea pm No smoking in restaurant Last d 8.30pm
ROOMS: (incl. bkfst) s £21.50-£33; d £43-£66 * **LB**
OFF-PEAK: (incl. bkfst) s £20-£30; d £40-£60
MEALS: Lunch £5-£6 Dinner £6.50-£7.50&alc*
CONF: Thtr 25 Board 10 Del from £30
CARDS:

★★ 63% Dainton
95 Dartmouth Rd, Three Beaches, Goodrington TQ4 6NA (located on the A379 at Goodrington) ☎ 01803 550067 FAX 01803 666339
An attractive Tudor-style property situated at Goodrington, about a mile from Paignton and within easy walking distance of the beach and leisure park, provides accommodation in bedrooms which are attractively decorated and well equipped - though in some cases compact. The popular beamed restaurant offers residents a good-value fixed-price meal at 6.30pm, and a carte is also available; in addition, a range of bar meals is served both at lunch time and during the evening. Smoking is not permitted in the bedrooms or restaurant.
11 en suite (bth/shr) (3 fmly) CTV in all bedrooms Night porter

20P No coaches Solarium Wkly live entertainment Xmas English & Continental Cuisine V meals Coffee am Tea pm No smoking in restaurant Last d 9.30pm
ROOMS: (incl. bkfst) s fr £28; d fr £52 * LB
MEALS: Lunch fr £7.50 Dinner fr £9*
CARDS:

★★63% **Tor Sands**
8 Sands Rd TQ4 6EH ☎ 01803 559695 FAX 01803 526786
Closed Jan
Tor Sands Hotel is conveniently located, being only a short, level walk to the famous Paignton sands and harbour and within easy reach of all the local amenities. Brother and sister partnership Sally and Andrew Linskey recently took over the hotel from their parents who had successfully run it for over 20 years. Bedrooms are cosy, and although they lack telephones at present, are well equipped. The bar/lounge is spacious and guests enjoy the entertainment provided on most evenings. In the dining room the meals are wholesome and home cooked, with a choice at each course. The hotel specialises in 'Turkey and Tinsel' short breaks, both before and after Christmas, which are extremely popular.
29 rms (15 bth 11 shr) 5 annexe en suite (bth/shr) CTV in all bedrooms Night porter 15P Wkly live entertainment Xmas V meals Coffee am Tea pm No smoking area in restaurant Last d 7pm
ROOMS: (incl. bkfst & dinner) s £20-£25; d £40-£50 LB

★★62% **Torbay Holiday Motel**
Totnes Rd TQ4 7PP (on A385 Totnes/Paignton road, 2.5m from Paignton) ☎ 01803 558226 FAX 01803 663375
Closed 24-31 Dec
This contemporary establishment offers spacious, well equipped bedrooms; some are located on the ground floor, and self catering or luxury suites are also available. The Rally Bar serves a wide range of

contd.

food, while the Spinnaker restaurant offers both carte and fixed-price menus. An indoor pool is kept at 80°F throughout the year.
16 en suite (bth/shr) CTV in all bedrooms STV 150P No coaches Indoor swimming pool (heated) Outdoor swimming pool (heated) Sauna Solarium Gym Pool table Crazy golf Adventure playground English & French Cuisine V meals Coffee am Last d 9pm
ROOMS: (incl. bkfst) s £29.50-£32.50; d £47-£53 *
MEALS: Bar Lunch £4.55-£10.55alc Dinner £8.95*
CARDS:

See advertisement on page 485

★61% **South Sands**
Alta Vista Rd TQ4 6BZ ☎ 01803 557231 & 529947
FAX 01803 529947
Closed Nov-Mar RS 24-28 Dec
Ideally located for the beach, this family run hotel overlooks Goodrington Sands and the Bay. The bedrooms are bright and simply furnished most with ensuite facilities. Cecile Cahill offers a good range of home cooked evening meals.
19 en suite (bth/shr) (14 fmly) CTV in all bedrooms 17P Pool table Wkly live entertainment Xmas International Cuisine V meals No smoking in restaurant Last d 7pm
ROOMS: (incl. bkfst) s £20-£28; d £40-£56 * **LB**
MEALS: Bar Lunch £1.50-£5 Dinner £9.50
CARDS:

PAINSWICK Gloucestershire Map 03 SO80

★★★76% **Painswick**

Kemps Ln GL6 6YB (off A46, in centre of village, 2nd road behind church off Tibbiwell)
☎ 01452 812160 FAX 01452 814059
In the centre of the architectural gem of Painswick, a Cotswold village surrounded by valleys and beautiful rural countryside, is The Painswick Hotel; once the home of wealthy rectors of the village, built mainly in 1790 and now a delightful personally managed hotel. More recently modern facilities have been introduced yet care has been taken to retain all the character and charm of the Palladian style. The public rooms have been furnished with antiques and the walls adorned with fine pictures which, together with open fires, enhance the grace and elegance of the ages in which they were built. Bedrooms range from those that enjoy the interesting qualities of the building to those more recent rooms in a wing overlooking the garden, most have fabulous country views. A committed team of friendly staff care for guests and enhance the relaxed atmosphere which makes this hotel special. The menu is interesting and the style of cooking excels with fresh ingredients prepared in an uncomplicated manner.
19 en suite (bth/shr) (4 fmly) CTV in all bedrooms 25P Croquet lawn Xmas V meals Coffee am Tea pm No smoking area in restaurant
ROOMS: (incl. bkfst) s £70-£110; d £105-£145 **LB**
MEALS: Lunch £14.75&alc High tea £22-£25alc Dinner £18.50-£27.50&alc*
CONF: Thtr 40 Class 20 Board 20 Del from £90
CARDS:

PANGBOURNE Berkshire Map 04 SU67

★★★75% **The Copper Inn**
Church Rd RG8 7AR (next to Pangbourne parish church) ☎ 0118 9842244 FAX 0118 9845542
After a near total refurbishment the standards at the Copper Inn have been restored to the levels of years past. Partners Michel Rosso and Roy Tudor Hughes have returned to the hotel after running it in the 1980s. Bedrooms are spacious, well maintained and equipped with a wealth of extras. Bathrooms in particular are very stylish. The guest lounge is amply provided with comfortable sofas and adjoins a smart restaurant where chef Michel Perron cooks with great flair in Provencal style. Menu staples include an intense bouillabaisse and a melting confit of duck with canellini beans.
There is a public bar which is popular with locals and some dedicated conference facilities.
14 en suite (bth/shr) 8 annexe en suite (bth/shr) (1 fmly) CTV in all bedrooms STV 20P Xmas English & French Cuisine V meals Coffee am Tea pm No smoking area in restaurant
ROOMS: s £75-£80; d £85-£95 **LB**
OFF-PEAK: s £60-£70; d £70-£80
CONF: Thtr 60 Class 24 Board 30
CARDS:

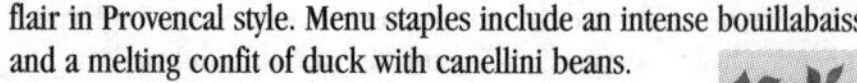

★★61% ***George Hotel***
The Square RG8 7AJ ☎ 0118 9842237
FAX 017357 5396
There has been a building on this site in the centre of the village since 1295. The hotel has a popular regulars' bar to the front of the building and to the back there are pleasantly decorated bedrooms, a few with character features. There is a spacious lounge adjoining Lord's Restaurant which strives to serve elaborate dishes.
8 en suite (bth/shr) CTV in all bedrooms 25P English & French Cuisine V meals Coffee am Tea pm Last d 10pm
CARDS:

PAPWORTH EVERARD Cambridgeshire Map 04 TL26

★★59% **Papworth**
Ermine St South CB3 8PB (on A428/A1198)
☎ 01954 718851 FAX 01954 718069
This modern brick, one-storey building is on the A1198, approximately a mile south of the town and Papworth hospital. The accommodation is functional in style and accessible from the courtyard. Public rooms include an open plan restaurant and bar, where a menu of predominantly Greek dishes is offered. There is ample car parking around the hotel.
20 en suite (bth/shr) (1 fmly) CTV in all bedrooms No dogs (ex guide dogs) 50P Xmas French & Greek Cuisine V meals Coffee am Tea pm Last d 10pm
ROOMS: (incl. bkfst) s £30-£35; d £40-£50 * **LB**
MEALS: Lunch £7-£10&alc Dinner £7-£10&alc*
CONF: Thtr 30 Class 30 Board 20
CARDS:

PARBOLD Lancashire Map 07 SD41

★★63% **Lindley**
Lancaster Ln WN8 7AB (exit M6 at junct 27 and take A5209 signposted Burscough. Turn right onto B5246, signposted Rufford, 500yds right hand side) ☎ 01257 462804 FAX 01257 464628
Once a comfortable Victorian dwelling, this house is now a popular hotel. Bedrooms are quite large, public areas are semi-open-plan and the restaurant looks out over the garden. A good range of food is served - grills are a speciality.
8 en suite (bth/shr) (1 fmly) CTV in all bedrooms 46P English & Continental Cuisine V meals Coffee am Tea pm Last d 9.30pm
ROOMS: (incl. bkfst) s £33; d £42 * **LB**
MEALS: Lunch £7.45-£11.15alc Dinner £11.40-£21.70alc*
CARDS:

PARKHAM Devon Map 02 SS32

★★★74% **Penhaven Country House**
EX39 5PL (turn off A39 at Horns Cross and follow signs to Parkham, turn left after church) ☎ 01237 451388 & 451388
FAX 01237 451878
This 17th-century rectory stands in 11 acres of mature gardens and woodlands on the edge of the village, surrounded by beautiful countryside yet only a short drive from the coast. Now a small privately

owned hotel, the Manor offers comfortable accommodation with modern facilities. The spacious bedrooms have been decorated and furnished in quiet colours and equipped with thoughtful extras such as home-made biscuits and reading material. There are two lounges, one with a bar, and there is a smart conservatory dining room. A daily-changing fixed-price menu, usually included in the price of accommodation, offers an interesting choice of dishes and is supported by a more extensive carte. The best of fresh ingredients are used featuring locally caught fish and vegetables and herbs from the hotel's garden. Vegetarian food is a house speciality.
12 en suite (bth/shr) CTV in all bedrooms 50P No coaches No children 10yrs Xmas English & French Cuisine V meals Coffee am Tea pm No smoking in restaurant Last d 9pm
ROOMS: (incl. bkfst & dinner) s £65.95-£70; d £131.90-£140 * **LB**
OFF-PEAK: (incl. bkfst & dinner) s £54.95-£59.95; d £109.90-£120
MEALS: Lunch £9.50&alc Dinner £13.95&alc
CARDS: 

PATELEY BRIDGE North Yorkshire Map 07 SE16

★★ 65% **Grassfields Country House**
Low Wath Rd HG3 5HL (turn off A59 onto B6451 and turn left at Summerbridge onto B6165. Cross bridge and take first right at petrol pumps) ☎ 01423 711412
Closed Dec-Jan
An elegant Georgian house which stands in its own well tended gardens and which is only a short walk from the town centre. There is a delightfully comfortable drawing room with a marble fireplace and a small bar is also provided. A set 3 course dinner is available each evening and uses the best available produce. A very friendly atmosphere prevails around the hotel which is family owned and run. Bedrooms are mainly spacious and are prettily decorated and there are several antiques around.. It offers very good value for money.
9 en suite (bth/shr) (3 fmly) CTV in all bedrooms No coaches V meals Coffee am Tea pm No smoking in restaurant
ROOMS: (incl. bkfst) s £25-£29; d £40-£55 * **LB**
OFF-PEAK: (incl. bkfst) s £20-£25; d £40-£45
MEALS: Dinner £12*

PATTERDALE Cumbria Map 11 NY31

★★57% **Patterdale**
CA11 0NN ☎ 017684 82231 FAX 017684 82440
Closed Jan-Feb
This roadside hotel lies at the southern end of Ullswater and enjoys fine views of the valley and fells. Its core business is tours and it offers practical and functional standards.
57 en suite (bth/shr) (4 fmly) CTV in all bedrooms 31P Tennis (hard) Fishing Xmas V meals Coffee am No smoking in restaurant Last d 8pm
ROOMS: (incl. bkfst) s £27.50-£30; d £55-£60 * **LB**
OFF-PEAK: (incl. bkfst) s £25-£27.50; d £50-£55
MEALS: Lunch fr £7.50 Dinner fr £15
CONF: Class 20 Del from £50
CARDS:

PATTINGHAM Staffordshire Map 07 SO89

★★★66% **Patshull Park Hotel Golf & Country Club**
Patshull Park WV6 7HR (1.5m W of Pattingham) ☎ 01902 700100 FAX 01902 700874
Set in 280 acres of attractive parkland designed by Capability Brown, this hotel has a championship golf course, a well equipped leisure complex and 80 acres of fishing lakes; trout and pike fishing can be arranged for guests, in addition to the wide range of other sporting activities on offer. There are two bedroom styles, the newer wing rooms being more modern and spacious. As well as the more formal Lakeside restaurant, there is an all-day coffee shop for lighter meals. Conferences, weddings and others functions are well catered for and golfing parties are welcome.

49 en suite (bth/shr) (2 fmly) CTV in all bedrooms STV Night porter 200P Indoor swimming pool (heated) Golf 18 Fishing Sauna Solarium Gym Putting green Jacuzzi/spa Beauty therapist Xmas V meals Coffee am Tea pm No smoking in restaurant Last d 9.30pm
ROOMS: (incl. bkfst) s £59-£69; d £59-£69 **LB**
MEALS: Lunch £10.50 High tea £3-£6alc Dinner £16.95&alc*
CONF: Thtr 160 Class 75 Board 44 Del £85
CARDS:
See advertisement under WOLVERHAMPTON

PEASMARSH East Sussex Map 05 TQ82

★★★ 74% **Flackley Ash**
TN31 6YH (3m from Rye, beside A268)
☎ 01797 230651 FAX 01797 230510

Best Western

A skilfully extended Georgian country house set in attractive and well kept grounds and gardens. There is a good range of individually furnished bedrooms including more spacious executive rooms, all equipped to a high standard. A spacious restaurant features the enjoyable traditional cuisine of chef Dale Skinner, whose specialities include local seafood and seasonal fresh vegetables. Other facilities include conference and banqueting facilities for up to 100 guests, and a fully equipped indoor leisure suite. Service is very friendly and helpful and room service can be provided until 10.30pm. The Special Events diary is also well worth an enquiry.
32 en suite (bth/shr) (3 fmly) CTV in all bedrooms 70P Indoor swimming pool (heated) Sauna Solarium Gym Pool table Croquet lawn Putting green Jacuzzi/spa Float tank Beautician Hairdresser Xmas English & French Cuisine V meals Coffee am Tea pm No smoking in restaurant Last d 9.45pm
ROOMS: (incl. bkfst) s £69-£85; d £108-£124 * **LB**
MEALS: Lunch £11.95-£13.95 High tea £4.25-£7.50 Dinner £22-£30*
CONF: Thtr 100 Class 50 Board 40 Del from £95
CARDS: 
See advertisement under RYE

PELYNT Cornwall & Isles of Scilly Map 02 SX25

★★61% **Jubilee Inn**
PL13 2JZ ☎ 01503 220312 FAX 01503 220920
The Jubilee is a free-house village inn, parts of which date from the 16th century. The focal point is the beamed double-sided bar, with its flagstone floor, old world charm, real ale and good bar food. The dining room also opens for lunch and dinner and a first-floor lounge is provided. Bedrooms are individually furnished, mostly with antiques. The majority are in the main building and a further three are in the proprietors' lodge next door.
9 en suite (bth/shr) (2 fmly) CTV in all bedrooms 86P Pool table ch fac Xmas English & Continental Cuisine V meals Coffee am Last d 9pm
ROOMS: (incl. bkfst) s fr £33; d fr £56 * **LB**
MEALS: Lunch fr £9.50&alc Dinner fr £8alc*
CARDS:

PENCRAIG Hereford & Worcester Map 03 SO52

★★66% **Pencraig Court**
HR9 6HR (off A40, 4m S of Ross-on-Wye)
☎ 01989 770306 FAX 01989 770040
Closed Xmas
This large Georgian house stands in four acres of grounds and gardens on the A40, between Ross-on-Wye and Symonds Yat and boasts impressive views across the River Wye. Friendly new owners, who took over in October 1995 had, at the time of our visit, already made several improvements and the work was continuing. Bedrooms are all traditionally furnished, but have modern equipment and en-suite facilities. Family rooms and a room with a four-poster bed are available. Public rooms include a choice of two comfortable lounges and a pleasant restaurant with period furnishings. There is no bar, but service of drinks is readily provided in the lounges.
11 en suite (bth) (2 fmly) CTV in all bedrooms 20P Riding Croquet lawn V meals Coffee am Tea pm No smoking area in restaurant Last d 9pm
ROOMS: (incl. bkfst) s fr £45; d fr £60 * **LB**
OFF-PEAK: (incl. bkfst) s fr £39.50; d fr £50
MEALS: Lunch fr £12.50 High tea fr £5 Dinner fr £15.50*
CONF: Board 20 Del from £60
CARDS:

See advertisement under ROSS-ON-WYE

PENRITH Cumbria Map 12 NY53
See also Edenhall, Shap & Temple Sowerby

★★★★64% **North Lakes**

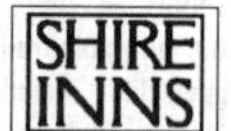

Ullswater Rd CA11 8QT (M6 junct 40 at intersection with A66) ☎ 01768 868111 FAX 01768 868291
This modern hotel, which is located off junction 40 of the M6, is well placed for both business and leisure users. There are two types of bedroom, both providing modern comforts with the higher category offering extra personal touches. There are two bars and a restaurant with a varied and interesting menu.
84 en suite (bth/shr) (6 fmly) No smoking in 25 bedrooms CTV in all bedrooms STV Lift Night porter 150P Indoor swimming pool (heated) Squash Sauna Solarium Gym Jacuzzi/spa Spa pool Childrens pool Wkly live entertainment Xmas English & French Cuisine V meals Coffee am Tea pm No smoking area in restaurant Last d 9.45pm
ROOMS: (incl. bkfst) s £92-£112; d £114-£134 * **LB**
OFF-PEAK: (incl. bkfst & dinner) s £74; d fr £138
MEALS: Bar Lunch fr £10 Dinner fr £22alc*
CONF: Thtr 200 Class 140 Board 24 Del from £125
CARDS:

★★★65% **Tebay Mountain Lodge**
Orton CA10 3SB (Westmorland) ☎ 015396 24351 FAX 015396 24354
(For full entry see Tebay)

★★68% **George**

Devonshire St CA11 7SU ☎ 01768 862696
FAX 01768 868223
Closed 25-26 Dec & 1 Jan
Efficient service by friendly and obliging staff is offered at this long-established town centre hotel which retains much of its original character and tradition, featuring lovely old woodwork, brass and antiques. The foyer lounge serves morning coffees and home-made afternoon teas, and along with the lounge bar, enjoys an open fire on cold days. Bedrooms are more contemporary and include a reasonably-priced suite.
31 en suite (bth/shr) (1 fmly) CTV in all bedrooms Night porter 30P English & French Cuisine Coffee am Tea pm Last d 9pm
ROOMS: (incl. bkfst) s fr £40.75; d fr £54 * **LB**
MEALS: Lunch fr £5.75 Dinner fr £13.50*
CONF: Thtr 60 Class 60 Board 140
CARDS:

★★66% **Brantwood Country Hotel**
Stainton CA11 0EP (From M6 junct 40 join A66 Keswick road and in 0.5 mile turn left then right signposted Stainton) ☎ 01768 862748
FAX 01768 890164
The Brantwood is located in the centre of the quiet village of Stainton, with spacious gardens through the arched courtyard to its rear. The variously sized bedrooms are cheerily decorated and sensibly furnished with modern fitted units; five are located across the courtyard in a period conversion. Other amenities include a restaurant and bar, both serving hearty, good-value meals.
6 en suite (shr) 5 annexe en suite (bth/shr) (3 fmly) CTV in all bedrooms No dogs 35P No coaches English & Continental Cuisine V meals Coffee am Tea pm No smoking in restaurant Last d 8.45pm
ROOMS: (incl. bkfst) s £37-£45; d £54-£68 **LB**
OFF-PEAK: (incl. bkfst) s £32-£38; d £50-£60
MEALS: Sunday Lunch £9.75 Dinner £16&alc
CONF: Thtr 60 Class 30 Board 30
CARDS:

See advertisement on opposite page

★★62% ***Clifton Hill***
Clifton CA10 2EJ ☎ 01768 862717 FAX 01768 867182
A large family owned and run hotel stands in neat gardens in an elevated position, set back from the A6, three miles south of Penrith. The hotel specialises in coach tours, which it organises itself, and is conveniently situated not far from junction 40 of the M6. Bedrooms vary in size and several of them are located on the ground floor, while spacious public areas include an attractive conservatory.
59 en suite (bth/shr) (3 fmly) CTV in 62 bedrooms Night porter 200P Games room Indoor bowling V meals Coffee am Tea pm Last d 8.30pm

See advertisement on opposite page

Travelodge
Travelodge
Redhills CA11 0DT (on A66) ☎ 01768 866958
FAX 01768 866958
This modern building offers accommodation in smart, spacious and well equipped bedrooms, suitable for family use, and all with en suite bathrooms. Meals may be taken at the nearby family restaurant. For information on room rates and to make a booking, call Roomline free of charge on 0800 850950. For more details about Travelodge, consult the Contents page under Hotel Groups.
32 en suite (bth/shr)

PENZANCE Cornwall & Isles of Scilly Map 02 SW43 Telephone numbers are due to change during the currency of this guide.

★★★ 64% **Higher Faugan**
Newlyn TR18 5NS (off B3115, 0.75m from Newlyn crossroads)
☎ 01736 362076 FAX 01736 351648
RS Nov-Mar
Built in the early 1900's for the Newlyn artist Stanhope Forbes, Higher Faugan is set in 10 acres of gardens and grounds, in an elevated position with commanding coastal and rural views. The bedrooms are individually furnished and decorated, the majority having views over the garden and several available on the ground floor. A varied choice of dishes is offered on the daily changing fixed price menu. In addition to the spacious lounge a cosy bar is provided for guests.
11 en suite (bth/shr) (2 fmly) CTV in all bedrooms 20P Outdoor swimming pool (heated) Tennis (hard) Snooker Solarium Gym Pool table Croquet lawn Putting green English, French & Italian Cuisine Coffee am Tea pm No smoking in restaurant Last d 8.30pm
ROOMS: (incl. bkfst) s £49-£55; d £80-£106 **LB**
MEALS: Lunch fr £7.95 Dinner fr £17.75
CARDS:

P

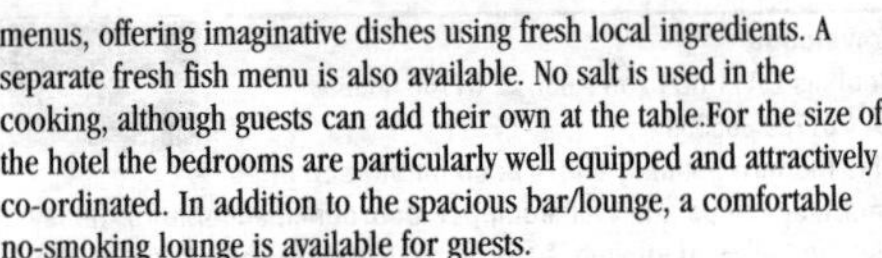

★★★60% **Mount Prospect**

Britons Hill TR18 3AE (approach on A30 pass heliport straight on to next rdbt,bear left direction of town take 3rd turning on the right,hotel is on right hand side) ☎ 01736 63117 FAX 01736 50970
Closed Xmas & New Year
Two semidetached Victorian villas were joined together to create this friendly family-run hotel, which offers panoramic views across Penzance to Mounts Bay. The rooms vary in outlook, some are no smoking and a gradual upgrading programme is in progress.
24 en suite (bth/shr) (2 fmly) No smoking in 9 bedrooms CTV in all bedrooms STV Night porter 14P Outdoor swimming pool (heated) Pool table English & Continental Cuisine Coffee am Tea pm Last d 8.45pm
ROOMS: (incl. bkfst) s £43-£45; d £60-£70 * **LB**
OFF-PEAK: (incl. bkfst) s £39-£43; d £58-£68
MEALS: Bar Lunch £3-£8.50 Dinner £11-£15&alc*
CONF: Thtr 60 Class 70
CARDS:

★★★57% **Queen's**
The Promenade TR18 4HG ☎ 01736 62371 FAX 01736 50033
Located on the busy promenade, this traditional resort hotel benefits from extensive views overlooking Mount's Bay. The fine sweeping staircase is a particularly fine feature of the public areas, with its extensive collection of pictures. Bedrooms vary in size and standard, an upgrading programme is planned to be carried out. At lunch time a range of bar meals is served and a set price meal is served during the evening.
71 en suite (bth/shr) (9 fmly) CTV in all bedrooms STV Lift Night porter 50P Snooker Sauna Solarium Gym Xmas English & French Cuisine V meals Coffee am Tea pm No smoking in restaurant Last d 8.45pm
ROOMS: (incl. bkfst) s £44-£49; d £76-£96 * **LB**
OFF-PEAK: (incl. bkfst) s £39-£44; d £62-£72
MEALS: Lunch fr £10.70 Dinner fr £14.95*
CONF: Thtr 200 Class 100 Board 80 Del from £62.80
CARDS:

★★59% **Sea & Horses**

6 Alexandra Ter TR18 4NX (enter town on A30, stay on seafront follow signs Newlyn/Mousehole for approx 1m, hotel set back off main road)
☎ 01736 61961 FAX 01736 330499
Set back from the promenade, this small hotel is part of a terrace with superb views over Mounts Bay. Brian and Marion Holden took over from the previous, long established owners early in 1995 and have begun a programme of improvements which includes modernising the bedrooms. There is a comfortable lounge and bar and enjoyable meals are served in the dining room.
11 rms (2 bth 6 shr) (4 fmly) No smoking in 1 bedroom CTV in all bedrooms 12P Xmas V meals Coffee am Tea pm No smoking in restaurant Last d 8pm
ROOMS: (incl. bkfst) s £28-£35; d £56-£70 **LB**
OFF-PEAK: (incl. bkfst) s fr £25; d fr £50
MEALS: Lunch £11.50 High tea £2-£10 Dinner fr £11.50*
CARDS:

★72% **Tarbert**

11-12 Clarence St TR18 2NU (take Land's End turning at town approach. At 2nd roundabout turn left, continue past next mini rdbt - 100yds turn right into Clarence St) ☎ 01736 63758 & 64317 FAX 01736 331336
Closed 23 Dec-30 Jan
Originally built as a sea captain's residence in 1830, the Tarbert is now a friendly small hotel personally run by Patti and Julian Evans. The small restaurant offers both carte and value for money fixed price menus, offering imaginative dishes using fresh local ingredients. A separate fresh fish menu is also available. No salt is used in the cooking, although guests can add their own at the table.For the size of the hotel the bedrooms are particularly well equipped and attractively co-ordinated. In addition to the spacious bar/lounge, a comfortable no-smoking lounge is available for guests.
12 en suite (bth/shr) CTV in all bedrooms No dogs 5P No coaches English & French Cuisine V meals Coffee am Tea pm No smoking in restaurant Last d 8.30pm
ROOMS: (incl. bkfst) s £25.50-£29.50; d £46-£59 **LB**
MEALS: Dinner £14-£16&alc
CARDS:

★71% **Estoril**
46 Morrab Rd TR18 4EX ☎ 01736 62468 & 67471 FAX 01736 67471
Closed Jan
The Estoril Hotel is quietly located, midway between the seafront and the town centre. Over the years it has been carefully modernised and provides good standards of accommodation. Bedrooms are neatly present, well equipped and provide many thoughtful extras. In the dining room, the short table d'hÙte menu uses local produce wherever possible.
10 en suite (bth/shr) (2 fmly) No smoking in all bedrooms CTV in all bedrooms No dogs 4P No coaches V meals
ROOMS: (incl. bkfst) s £24-£26; d £48-£52 * **LB**
MEALS: Dinner £12*
CARDS:

PERRANPORTH Cornwall & Isles of Scilly Map 02 SW75

★★63% **Beach Dunes**
Ramoth Way, Reen Sands TR6 0BY (turn off A30 onto B3075 at Goonhavern continue onto B3285 at 30mph sign private road on right Ramoen Way, Beach Dunes at end of road)
☎ 01872 572263 FAX 01872 573824
Closed Nov & Dec
Owners Keith and Margaret Wooldridge provide a friendly, relaxed atmosphere at this hotel which enjoys an elevated position overlooking Perran Bay and the local countryside. It is located at the end of a private road and adjoins the 18-hole Perranporth Golf Course. There is a comfortable bar-lounge for guests, and a choice of menu is offered in the dining room; both rooms are no-smoking areas. Bedrooms are neatly furnished and decorated.
6 rms (5 bth/shr) 3 annexe en suite (bth/shr) (2 fmly) CTV in all bedrooms 15P No coaches Indoor swimming pool (heated) Golf 18 Squash No children 3yrs V meals Coffee am Tea pm No smoking in restaurant Last d 8pm
ROOMS: (incl. bkfst) s £25.50-£28.50; d £51-£57 * **LB**
MEALS: Bar Lunch £2.50-£8.50 Dinner fr £14.50
CARDS:

PERSHORE Hereford & Worcester Map 03 SO94

★★★60% **Angel Inn & Posting House**
High St WR10 1AF ☎ 01386 552046 FAX 01386 552581
This established hotel sits at the heart of the town in grounds which stretch down to the banks of the river Avon. Most bedrooms are spacious and well thought-out, while popular meals and more formal dining are available in the bar and wood-panelled dining room.
15 en suite (bth/shr) CTV in all bedrooms 51P Fishing English, Spanish & Italian Cuisine V meals Coffee am Tea pm Last d 9.45pm
ROOMS: (incl. bkfst) s £45-£47; d £59.95-£65 * **LB**
OFF-PEAK: (incl. bkfst) s fr £36.50; d fr £52
CARDS:

PETERBOROUGH Cambridgeshire Map 04 TL19
See also Alwalton & Stilton

★★★★65% **Swallow**

Peterborough Business Park, Lynchwood PE2 6GB
☎ 01733 371111 FAX 01733 236725
(For full entry see Alwalton)

★★★68% **Orton Hall**

Orton Longueville PE2 7DN (off A605 (East) opposite Orton Mere) ☎ 01733 391111 FAX 01733 231912
Closed 26-30 Dec
This rambling and historic country house is situated in 20 acres of mature parkland. Despite its conversion into a hotel many of its original features have been retained, including the Huntly restaurant with fine oak panelling, the Grand Hall (now used for banquets) and an elegant Conservatory with 16th Century terracotta floors. There are several quiet lounges for guests use and across the courtyard lies the Old Ramblewood Inn, a clever conversion of stables into a character English pub. Bedrooms are generally spacious, comfortably furnished and have every modern convenience.

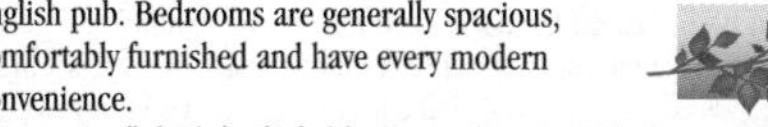

49 en suite (bth/shr) (2 fmly) No smoking in 27 bedrooms CTV in all bedrooms Night porter 200P Three quarter size snooker table International Cuisine V meals Coffee am Tea pm No smoking in restaurant
ROOMS: s £60-£95; d £90-£115 * **LB**
MEALS: Lunch fr £11.95 Dinner fr £16.95*
CONF: Thtr 120 Class 48 Board 30 Del from £90
CARDS:

★★★67% **Peterborough Moat House**

Thorpe Wood PE3 6SG (on A1260, overlooking the golf course) ☎ 01733 289988 FAX 01733 262737
This modern hotel stands close to Thorpe Wood Golf Course and Nene Country Park, only two miles from the city centre. With extensive conference and banqueting facilities, the hotel is geared for business people, but a small leisure club and other nearby leisure facilities make it an ideal venue for weekend breaks as well. The bedrooms are very well equipped, light and airy; four have their own sitting rooms.
125 en suite (bth/shr) No smoking in 45 bedrooms CTV in all bedrooms Lift Night porter 230P Indoor swimming pool (heated) Sauna Solarium Gym Jacuzzi/spa Spa pool International Cuisine V meals Coffee am Tea pm No smoking area in restaurant Last d 10pm
ROOMS: s fr £75; d fr £95 **LB**
OFF-PEAK: (incl. bkfst) s fr £34; d fr £68
MEALS: Lunch fr £15.95&alc Dinner fr £16.50&alc*
CONF: Thtr 400 Class 150 Board 50 Del from £105
CARDS:

★★★66% **Butterfly**
Thorpe Meadows, Off Longthorpe Parkway PE3 6GA (from A1179 take exit for Thorpe Meadows and city centre, turn right at next two roundabouts) ☎ 01733 64240 FAX 01733 65538
The Butterfly Hotel is located next to the international rowing course in Thorpe Meadows, offering parkland, lake and river walks and access to the steam railway. There is a friendly, relaxed atmosphere throughout the public areas, which are dominated by Walt's Restaurant, an informal operation with elements of self-service in the hors d'oeuvre and sweet selections. Bedrooms are modern in style and include ground floor, studio and ladies' rooms; new this year are the pay movie channels to remote-controlled TVs.

contd.

70 en suite (bth/shr) (2 fmly) No smoking in 10 bedrooms CTV in all bedrooms STV No dogs (ex guide dogs) Night porter 85P European Cuisine V meals Coffee am Tea pm Last d 10pm
ROOMS: s fr £59.50; d fr £59.50 * **LB**
OFF-PEAK: s fr £45; d fr £45
MEALS: Lunch fr £9.76&alc Dinner fr £12.25&alc*
CONF: Thtr 80 Class 50 Board 50 Del from £85
CARDS:
See advertisement under BURY ST EDMUNDS

★★★65% **Bull**
Westgate PE1 1RB (turn off A1 follow signs to city centre, hotel in heart of city opposite Queensgate shopping centre)
☎ 01733 61364 FAX 01733 557304
Work undertaken in recent years has brought greatly improved accommodation and ultra-modern meeting and conference rooms to this city-centre hotel. Public areas are pleasantly colour-coordinated and a comfortable no-smoking lounge supplements the foyer lounge and bar. Improved access to the secure rear car park is now also complete.
103 en suite (bth) (3 fmly) CTV in all bedrooms Night porter 100P English & French Cuisine V meals Coffee am Tea pm Last d 10.30pm
ROOMS: (incl. bkfst) s £68.70; d £79 * **LB**
OFF-PEAK: (incl. bkfst & dinner) s £42.50; d £85
MEALS: Lunch £13.50&alc Dinner £13.50&alc*
CONF: Thtr 200 Class 80 Board 60 Del £89.50
CARDS:

Forte Posthouse Peterborough
Great North Rd PE7 3TB ☎ 01733 240209
FAX 01733 244455
(For full entry see Norman Cross)

Travel Inn
Ham Ln, Orton Meadows, Nene Park PE2 0UU
(take A605 & follow signs to Nene Park)
☎ 01733 235794 FAX 01733 391055
Purpose-built accommodation, offering spacious, well equipped bedrooms, all with en suite bathrooms. Meals may be taken at the nearby family restaurant. For more information about Travel Inns, consult the Contents page under Hotel Groups.
40 en suite (bth/shr)
ROOMS: d £35.50 *

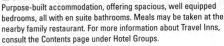

Travelodge
Great North Rd PE7 3UR ☎ 01733 231109
FAX 01733 231109
(For full entry see Alwalton)

PETTY FRANCE Gloucestershire Map 03 ST78

★★★69% **Petty France**
GL9 1AF (on A46 S of junct with A433)
☎ 01454 238361 FAX 01454 238768
This former dower house, set in its own delightful grounds, offers a friendly atmosphere and comfortable surroundings. Bedrooms in the main house tend to be more spacious whilst those in the converted stables are modern and cottagey. Attractive public areas include a lounge with log fires in the winter and flowers from the garden, and an elegant restaurant where an interesting menu is complemented by an extensive selection of wines. All dishes are prepared from fresh ingredients, some purchased locally and others from international markets.
8 en suite (bth/shr) 12 annexe en suite (bth/shr) (1 fmly) No smoking in 2 bedrooms CTV in all bedrooms 50P Croquet lawn International Cuisine V meals Coffee am Tea pm No smoking in restaurant Last d 9.30pm
CONF: Thtr 55 Class 20 Board 24 Del from £85
CARDS:

PEVENSEY East Sussex Map 05 TQ60

★★64% **Priory Court**
Castle Rd BN24 5LG ☎ 01323 763150 FAX 01323 769030
Situated opposite the castle, this 17th-century former vicarage set in its own grounds is personally run by the proprietor Mrs Lisa Murrow. Bedrooms are furnished in the traditional style some with antiques, trouser press and clack radio alarm. The beamed public areas are full of character with a log burning fire, separate comfortable lounge, and a popular bar offering a good range of real ales, extensive bar meals, along with an a la carte menu in the dining room.
9 rms (7 bth/shr) (1 fmly) CTV in all bedrooms 60P No coaches Xmas English & French Cuisine V meals Coffee am Tea pm Last d 9.30pm
ROOMS: (incl. bkfst) s £25-£35; d £39-£49 * **LB**
MEALS: Lunch £9.95 High tea £1.95 Dinner £9.95&alc
CARDS:
See advertisement on opposite page

PICKERING North Yorkshire Map 08 SE78

★★72% **Forest & Vale**
Malton Rd YO18 7DL Hotel is at junction of A169 & A170 in town of Pickering, just off the roundabout
☎ 01751 472722 FAX 01751 472972
Dating back in part to the 18th century, this family-owned hotel offers very good hospitality together with professional and friendly service. The public rooms are inviting and comfortable whilst the bedrooms have been prettily decorated and equipped with much thought. Only the best available produce is used in the excellent cooking which offers a wide choice of dishes together with good presentation.
12 en suite (bth/shr) 5 annexe en suite (bth/shr) (3 fmly) CTV in all bedrooms 70P English & French Cuisine V meals Coffee am No smoking in restaurant Last d 9pm
ROOMS: (incl. bkfst) s £46-£58; d £68-£80 **LB**
OFF-PEAK: (incl. bkfst) s £42-£54; d £64-£76
MEALS: Lunch £8.95-£8.95&alc Dinner £16.25-£16.25&alc
CARDS:

★★71% **The Sinnington Country Hotel**
Main St, Sinnington YO6 6SQ (3m west of town, off A170)
☎ 01751 431577 FAX 01751 432791
Closed 1-17 Jan
This charming grade II listed inn stands in the peaceful and very English village of Sinnington and is only a short way from the main A170. It lies in the lea of the beautiful North York Moors and is convenient for Pickering and the North York Moors steam railway. It has recently been completely refurbished to a high standard and has retained its old charm with beams, antiques and wood panelling adding to the delightful scene. There are well equipped bedrooms available and a cosy and comfortable residents' lounge is also provided. A good range of food is available and is served either in the

pleasant bars or the spacious beamed restaurant. Nigel & Liz Bradley are enthusiastic hosts and are backed by a dedicated and friendly team.
7 en suite (bth/shr) 6 annexe en suite (bth/shr) (2 fmly) No smoking in all bedrooms CTV in all bedrooms No dogs (ex guide dogs) Night porter 40P No coaches Pool table Xmas V meals Coffee am Tea pm No smoking in restaurant Last d 9.30pm
ROOMS: (incl. bkfst) s fr £40; d fr £58 * **LB**
OFF-PEAK: (incl. bkfst) s fr £34; d fr £48
MEALS: Sunday Lunch £8.75-£10.95alc Dinner fr £18.50alc*
CONF: Class 24 Board 18
CARDS:

£

★★66% **Cottage Leas Country**
Nova Ln, Middleton YO18 8PN (2m E, take A170 towards Thirsk, in Middleton turn right between pub & church, hotel 1.50m along single track lane) ☎ 01751 472129 FAX 01751 474 930
This lovely 18th-century farmhouse stands in open countryside with pleasant views overlooking the valley. The house is warm and inviting, and provides a comfortable lounge with plenty of reading matter, whilst the restaurant is a delightful setting for the extensive range of home-cooked food. The bedrooms are attractive and have been thoughtfully equipped. A relaxed style of service is provided by Mr and Mrs Ireland and their friendly staff.
11 en suite (bth/shr) 1 annexe en suite (bth) (2 fmly) CTV in all bedrooms 60P Tennis (hard) Croquet lawn Badminton Xmas English & French Cuisine V meals Coffee am Tea pm
ROOMS: (incl. bkfst) s £39-£40; d fr £68 * **LB**
MEALS: Lunch £9.50-£10.50 Dinner £14.75-£16.75&alc
CARDS: 

£

★★64% **White Swan**

Market Place YO18 7AA (in the market place between the Church and the Steam Railway Station)
☎ 01751 472288 FAX 01751 472288
This cosy hotel is full of character and stands in the centre of the town. It has a most interesting bar as well as a delightful dining room where a good range of well cooked food is provided. Bedrooms are attractive and furnished to a good standard and a separate residents' lounge is also provided. Service is very friendly from a keen and eager staff.
12 en suite (bth/shr) (1 fmly) No smoking in 4 bedrooms CTV in all bedrooms 35P Motorised Treasure Hunt Xmas V meals Coffee am Last d 9.45pm
ROOMS: (incl. bkfst) s £55-£65; d £76-£98 * **LB**
OFF-PEAK: (incl. bkfst) s fr £45; d fr £60
MEALS: Lunch £6.95-£10.95 Dinner £14.50-£18.50
CONF: Thtr 15 Class 12 Board 20 Del from £55
CARDS:

PICKHILL North Yorkshire Map 08 SE38

★★65% **Nags Head Country Inn**
YO7 4JG (6m SE of Leeming Bar) ☎ 01845 567391 & 567570 FAX 01845 567212
Standing in the centre of the village, convenient for the A1, this country inn offers an extensive range of food and modern accommodation. It is owned and run by brothers Raymond and Edward Boynton, and service is friendly and attentive. The bars are full of character and includes an extensive collection of ties.
8 en suite (bth/shr) 7 annexe en suite (bth/shr) CTV in all bedrooms 50P ch fac International Cuisine V meals Coffee am Tea pm No smoking in restaurant Last d 9.30pm
ROOMS: (incl. bkfst) s £34; d £48 * **LB**
MEALS: Lunch £10-£12&alc Dinner £15-£18&alc*
CONF: Thtr 36 Class 18 Board 24 Del from £40
CARDS:

PLYMOUTH Devon Map 02 SX45

★★★★62% ***Copthorne Plymouth***
MILLENNIUM & COPTHORNE HOTELS
Armada Way PL1 1AR (from town centre follow signs for railway station and ferryport) ☎ 01752 224161 FAX 01752 670688
A gradual programme of refurbishment is underway at this centrally situated modern hotel. The best bedrooms are currently on the third and fourth floors; public areas (spread over two floors) include a choice of restaurants and a small leisure centre. Staff are generally friendly and willing.
135 en suite (bth/shr) (29 fmly) No smoking in 18 bedrooms CTV in all bedrooms Lift Night porter 50P Indoor swimming pool (heated) Sauna Solarium Gym Pool table International Cuisine V meals Coffee am Tea pm Last d 10pm
CARDS:

★★★★60% ***Hoe Moat House***

Armada Way PL1 2HJ (A374 city centre then follow signs for Barbican & Hoe B3240) ☎ 01752 639988 FAX 01752 673816
In a prime position overlooking the Hoe, this high rise hotel offers a good range of facilities including a leisure club, an all day Sports Bar with satellite television, children's play area, business centre and a restaurant and bar on the eleventh floor which offers panoramic views of the city and the sea. Many of the bedrooms offer fine views, all are spacious but bathrooms can be functional; executive rooms are available.
212 en suite (bth/shr) (102 fmly) No smoking in 84 bedrooms CTV in all bedrooms STV Lift Night porter Air conditioning 180P Indoor swimming pool (heated) Sauna Solarium Gym Pool table Steam room Table tennis International Cuisine V meals Coffee am Tea pm Last d 10.30pm
CARDS:

P

★★★69% **Duke of Cornwall**

Millbay Rd PL1 3LG (follow signs to city centre then to Plymouth Pavilions Conference & Leisure Centre which leads you past hotel)

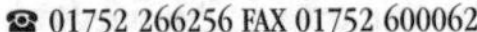

☎ 01752 266256 FAX 01752 600062

This impressive Victorian Gothic Hotel is conveniently located for easy access to the city centre, Barbican and the ferry port. The professional management and staff provided a quietly efficient standard of service throughout the hotel. In the Devonshire Restaurant an imaginative table d'hote menu is offered using fresh local ingredients, prepared with care. Bedrooms are individually furnished and decorated, several featuring original four poster beds.

70 en suite (bth/shr) (6 fmly) No smoking in 20 bedrooms CTV in all bedrooms Lift Night porter 50P Pool table Games room Xmas English & French Cuisine V meals Coffee am Tea pm Last d 10pm

ROOMS: (incl. bkfst) s fr £69.50; d £79.50-£89.50 * **LB**

OFF-PEAK: (incl. bkfst) s fr £59.50; d £69.50-£79.50

MEALS: Lunch £17.95-£23.15 Dinner £17.95-£23.15*

CONF: Thtr 300 Class 125 Board 84 Del from £60

CARDS:

★★★68% **Boringdon Hall**

Colebrook, Plympton PL7 4DP (A38 at Marsh Mills rdbt follow signs for Plympton along dual carriageway to small island turn left over bridge and follow brown tourist signs)

☎ 01752 344455 FAX 01752 346578

Situated on the outskirts of Plymouth with good main route access, this attractive Grade I listed property stands in 10 acres of mature grounds and gardens . The majority of the bedrooms are set around the central garden, and these are well furnished and offer a good range of modern facilities. The older part of the building dates back to the 900s, and the rooms are furnished in appropriate style - some with four-poster beds. Meals are available in the Gallery Restaurant, overlooking the Great Hall, and the popular Admiral's Carvery, which is open on Sundays. There is also a range of meeting and function rooms, plus a small leisure complex.

41 en suite (bth/shr) (5 fmly) No smoking in 8 bedrooms CTV in all bedrooms STV Night porter 150P Indoor swimming pool (heated) Tennis (hard) Sauna Gym Putting green pitch & putt 9 hole Xmas English & French Cuisine V meals Coffee am Tea pm No smoking in restaurant Last d 9.30pm

ROOMS: (incl. bkfst) s £35.50-£65; d £71-£85 * **LB**

MEALS: Lunch £9.50-£17.95 Dinner fr £17.95&alc*

CONF: Thtr 120 Class 40 Board 50 Del from £75

CARDS:

★★★68% **Elfordleigh**

Colebrook, Plympton PL7 5EB ☎ 01752 336428 FAX 01752 344581

Set amidst attractive wooded countryside, the Elfordleigh has views of the beautiful Plym Valley and is situated within its own golf course. Churchill's Restaurant provides a fixed price menu and the formal dining option, while the Country Pantry offers a more informal style of dining. Bedrooms are comfortable and well equipped. Extensive leisure are available to residents and the club's members.

18 en suite (bth/shr) (3 fmly) No smoking in 10 bedrooms CTV in all bedrooms STV Night porter 250P No coaches Indoor swimming pool (heated) Outdoor swimming pool (heated) Golf 9 Tennis (hard) Squash Snooker Sauna Solarium Gym Pool table Croquet lawn Putting green Jacuzzi/spa Beauty therapy Steam room Xmas European Cuisine V meals Coffee am Tea pm No smoking in restaurant Last d 9.15pm

ROOMS: s fr £67.50; d fr £67.50 * **LB**

MEALS: Lunch fr £8.95 High tea fr £5.50 Dinner fr £19.50

CONF: Thtr 80 Class 35 Board 40 Del from £99

CARDS:

★★★68% **New Continental**

Millbay Rd PL1 3LD (from the city centre follow signs for the Pavilions which are adjacent to hotel) ☎ 01752 220782 FAX 01752 227013

Closed 24 Dec-2 Jan

Situated within a minutes walk of the Pavilions and the city centre, The New Continental Hotel attracts both the leisure and business user. Bedrooms are all well equipped but fall into two categories, executive and standard, each priced accordingly. Located near the hotel's leisure facility, the Cafe Continental serves light meals throughout the day. The Executive Restaurant serves a fixed price menu and provides a formal style of dining.

99 en suite (bth/shr) (20 fmly) No smoking in 28 bedrooms CTV in all bedrooms STV Lift Night porter 100P Indoor swimming pool (heated) Sauna Solarium Gym Steam Room Beautician English, French & Greek Cuisine V meals Coffee am Tea pm Last d 10pm

ROOMS: (incl. bkfst) s £65-£70; d £75-£120 * **LB**

OFF-PEAK: (incl. bkfst) s fr £50; d fr £60

MEALS: Lunch fr £8.95 Dinner fr £14.50&alc*

CONF: Thtr 400 Class 100 Board 70 Del from £60

CARDS:

★★★65% **Grand**

Elliot St, The Hoe PL1 2PT ☎ 01752 661195 FAX 01752 600653

In an enviable position with superb views over the Hoe, this hotel has an attractive traditional interior. Recent upgrading has enhanced the comfortable public rooms, a congenial restaurant and a small range of meeting rooms. Bedrooms vary in size and those on the front have balconies.

77 en suite (bth/shr) (6 fmly) No smoking in 20 bedrooms CTV in all bedrooms STV Lift Night porter 70P Wkly live entertainment Xmas International Cuisine V meals Coffee am Tea pm No smoking in restaurant Last d 9.45pm

ROOMS: (incl. bkfst) s £72-£112; d fr £84 * **LB**

OFF-PEAK: (incl. bkfst) s fr £35; d £45

MEALS: Lunch £5-£10&alc High tea fr £6.50 Dinner £16.50*

CONF: Thtr 70 Class 45 Board 25

CARDS:

See advertisement on opposite page

★★★61% **Strathmore**

Elliot St, The Hoe PL1 2PR ☎ 01752 662101 FAX 01752 223690

The Strathmore is located in a Victorian terrace adjacent to Plymouth's famous Hoe, convenient for the city centre and the Barbican. All the uniformly furnished bedrooms have satellite TV, and a popular medieval-themed restaurant serves a fixed-price menu and a carte. There is a circular bar and a night club which remains open until late some evenings.

54 en suite (bth/shr) (6 fmly) CTV in all bedrooms STV Lift Night porter Xmas English & Continental Cuisine V meals Coffee am Last d 9.30pm

ROOMS: (incl. bkfst) s £35-£45; d £45-£55 *

OFF-PEAK: (incl. bkfst) s fr £35; d fr £45

MEALS: Lunch £7.50 Dinner £12.50*

CONF: Thtr 60 Class 40 Board 20 Del from £59

CARDS:

★★★60% **Novotel**

Marsh Mills Roundabout, 270 Plymouth Rd PL6 8NH (take 1st exit off A38 Plymouth/Kingsbridge, onto Marsh Mills roundabout, follow signs forPlymouth the Hotel is straight ahead) ☎ 01752 221422 FAX 01752 221422

Situated on the outskirts of town, this modern hotel offers good value accommodation. All rooms sleep a minimum of three making them ideal for families and businessmen who enjoy the comfort of a double bed. Public areas are open plan and meals are available throughout the day in either the Garden Brasserie, bar or in your room. The outdoor swimming pool is a welcome addition during the summer.

100 en suite (bth/shr) (15 fmly) No smoking in 38 bedrooms CTV

in all bedrooms STV Lift Night porter 140P Outdoor swimming pool (heated) ch fac Xmas French Cuisine V meals Coffee am Tea pm No smoking area in restaurant Last d mdnt
ROOMS: s £49.50; d £49.50 * **LB**
OFF-PEAK: s £32.50-£45; d £32.50-£45
MEALS: Lunch £12.50-£14.50&alc Dinner £12.50-£14.50&alc
CONF: Thtr 300 Class 120 Board 100 Del from £74.95
CARDS:

★★67% Invicta
11-12 Osborne Place, Lockyer Street, The Hoe PL1 2PU
☎ 01752 664997 FAX 01752 664994
Closed 24 Dec-3 Jan
Situated opposite the famous bowling green and within easy walking distance of the city centre and the Barbican, The Invicta Hotel has a friendly, family atmosphere. In the dining room both fixed-price and à la carte menus are available, featuring mainly grills and speciality dishes at value for money prices. Bedrooms are attractively co-ordinated, thoughtfully equipped and well maintained.
23 rms (21 bth/shr) (6 fmly) CTV in all bedrooms STV Night porter 10P Mainly grills No smoking in restaurant Last d 9pm
ROOMS: (incl. bkfst) s £39-£42; d £49-£52 * **LB**
OFF-PEAK: (incl. bkfst) s £36-£39; d £46-£50
MEALS: Dinner £8.50-£9.50&alc*
CONF: Thtr 35 Class 40 Board 60 Del from £42
CARDS:

★★66% Camelot

5 Elliot St, The Hoe PL1 2PP (from the A38 follow signs fot the city centre, The Hoe, Citadel Rd and then onto Elliot St) ☎ 01752 221255 & 669667
FAX 01752 603660

contd.

Situated within easy walking distance of Plymouth's famous Hoe, the city centre and the Barbican, the Camelot Hotel has a friendly, relaxed atmosphere. Bedrooms are comfortable, and each is equipped with modern facilities. There is a well stocked bar and separate lounge for guests. In the restaurant both fixed-price and à la carte menus are offered.
17 en suite (bth/shr) (4 fmly) CTV in all bedrooms No dogs (ex guide dogs) No coaches English & French Cuisine V meals Coffee am Tea pm No smoking in restaurant Last d 8.30pm
ROOMS: (incl. bkfst) s fr £39; d fr £50 * **LB**
MEALS: Lunch £13 High tea £6 Dinner £13&alc
CONF: Thtr 60 Class 40 Board 20 Del £60
CARDS:

★★65% **Langdon Court**
Down Thomas PL9 0DY (follow H.M.S. Cambridge signs from Elburton) ☎ 01752 862358 FAX 01752 863428
Langdon Court is a historic manor house, set in seven acres of gardens, grounds and woodland, located about six miles from the city centre. Over the last few years, the Barnes/Cox partnership has continued to upgrade and improve the facilities provided. The bar is a popular venue for tourists and locals alike, for value for money and interesting bar food, while in the restaurant a short carte is offered. Bedrooms vary in size and quality, and all rooms are well equipped.
16 en suite (bth/shr) (4 fmly) CTV in all bedrooms 100P No children 4yrs French Cuisine V meals Coffee am Tea pm Last d 9.30pm
ROOMS: (incl. bkfst) s £36-£46; d £58-£69 * **LB**
MEALS: Sunday Lunch £9.95 Dinner £14.95&alc
CONF: Thtr 30 Class 15 Board 15 Del £66
CARDS:

★★60% **Grosvenor**
9 Elliot St, The Hoe PL1 2PP ☎ 01752 260411 FAX 01752 668878
Closed 24 Dec-1 Jan
Created from two adjoining Victorian properties, this friendly and relaxed hotel is conveniently situated between the Hoe and the city centre. In addition to the usual facilities, bedrooms are equipped with Sky TV. In the dining room, a choice of dishes is offered, allowing guests to choose anything from a light snack to a three-course meal.
28 en suite (bth/shr) (1 fmly) CTV in all bedrooms STV 3P No coaches V meals Last d 9pm
ROOMS: (incl. bkfst) s fr £26; d fr £33 * **LB**
OFF-PEAK: (incl. bkfst) s fr £25; d fr £30
MEALS: Dinner £8-£14alc
CARDS:

★69% **Victoria Court**
62/64 North Rd East PL4 6AL (from A38 follow signs for city centre, past railway station follow North Rd for approx 200yds hotel on left) ☎ 01752 668133 FAX 01752 668133
Closed 22 Dec-1 Jan
This small family-run hotel, occupying two terraced Victorian houses, is within walking distance of the city centre and train station. Bedrooms are comfortable and nicely decorated and the public areas retain much of the original character of the building. There is an attractive lounge and a separate bar. The dining room, situated on the lower ground floor, offers a choice of popular dishes.
13 rms (10 shr) (4 fmly) CTV in all bedrooms No dogs 6P No coaches European Cuisine V meals Coffee am Tea pm Last d 8pm
ROOMS: (incl. bkfst) s £29-£42; d £42-£52 **LB**
MEALS: Dinner fr £12.50
CARDS:

★66% **Imperial**
Lockyer Street, The Hoe PL1 2QD ☎ 01752 227311
FAX 01752 674986
Closed 25-31 Dec
This Grade II listed building is conveniently located for the city centre, the Hoe and the Barbican. All the comfortable, well equipped bedrooms are neatly furnished and decorated, the dining room offers a wide choice of dishes at dinner, and guests can relax in a spacious sitting room or the cosy wood-panelled Worcester Bar. On-site car parking is available to the front and rear of the house.
22 rms (16 bth/shr) (4 fmly) CTV in all bedrooms No dogs (ex guide dogs) 14P V meals Coffee am Tea pm No smoking area in restaurant Last d 8.15pm
ROOMS: (incl. bkfst) s £30-£45; d £40-£56 **LB**
OFF-PEAK: (incl. bkfst) s £25-£44; d £38-£48
MEALS: Bar Lunch £2-£5 Dinner £12.95
CONF: Thtr 25 Class 25 Board 16
CARDS:

★64% **Drake**
1 & 2 Windsor Villas, Lockyer Street, The Hoe PL1 2QD (follow City Centre signs, left at Theatre Royal, last left, first right) ☎ 01752 229730
FAX 01752 255092
Closed Xmas
The Drake was created by the linking of two Victorian town houses which stand between the famous bowling green and the city centre. Most bedrooms have been upgraded to a good standard; the rest are currently being improved. The comfortable lounge has a well stocked bar and a separate dining room offers a well balanced fixed-price menu. Service is friendly, relaxed and attentive.
36 rms (28 bth/shr) (3 fmly) CTV in all bedrooms No dogs (ex guide dogs) 25P Pool table European Cuisine V meals Coffee am Last d 9pm
ROOMS: (incl. bkfst) s £35-£45; d £48-£54 * **LB**
OFF-PEAK: (incl. bkfst) s £30-£45; d £44-£54
MEALS: Lunch £7-£12 Dinner £7-£12*
CONF: Class 25 Board 20
CARDS:

Campanile
Marsh Mills, Longbridge Rd PL6 8LD (from Exeter take the A38 towards Plymouth, continue over the fly over take the slip road to the roundabout, the Hotel is on the 4th exit) ☎ 01752 601087 FAX 01752 223213

The bar and Bistro restaurant provide meals and refreshments. Bedrooms are well equipped and have en suite bathrooms. For more details about Campanile, consult the Contents page under Hotel Groups.
51 en suite (bth/shr)
ROOMS: s £29.95-£36.50; d £29.95-£36.50 *
CONF: Thtr 30 Class 24 Board 24 Del £57

Forte Posthouse Plymouth
Cliff Rd, The Hoe PL1 3DL (turn off A38 at Plymouth follow signs for City Centre, then follow signs for Hoe, the Hotel is situated on Cliff Road West Hoe) ☎ 01752 662828 FAX 01752 660974

Suitable for both the business and leisure traveller, this bright hotel provides modern accommodation in well equipped bedrooms with en suite bathrooms. For more details about Forte Posthouse hotels, consult the Contents page for the section on Hotel Groups.
106 en suite (bth/shr)
ROOMS: s fr £69; d fr £76.50 *
CONF: Thtr 120 Class 60 Board 40 Del £99

Travel Inn

300 Plymouth Rd, Crabtree, Marsh Mills PL3 6RW
☎ 01752 600660 FAX 01752 600112
Purpose-built accommodation, offering spacious, well equipped bedrooms, all with en suite bathrooms. Meals may be taken at the nearby family restaurant. For more information about Travel Inns, consult the Contents page under Hotel Groups.
40 en suite (bth/shr)
ROOMS: (incl. bkfst) d £35.50 *

○ **Kitley**
The Kitley Estate, Yealmpton PL8 2NW ☎ 01752 881555
20 rms

POCKLINGTON East Riding of Yorkshire Map 08 SE84

★67% ***Yorkway Motel***
South Moor, Hull Rd YO4 2NX (between Beverley & York on the A1079 with the junc of B1247) ☎ 01759 303071 & 304852
Closed 25 Dec-1 Jan
Proprietors Philip and Linda Lemon have created a multi-service facility comprising a small motel and tearoom in this white-washed building beside the A1079 at the Pocklington junction.
Accommodation, in an extention, offers neat bedrooms with light wood furniture, a range of modern facilities and en suite shower rooms. Public rooms have recently been rearranged and the restaurant cheerfully refurbished. There is an L-shaped open-plan area, with a lounge to one side of a small bar and another seating/informal dining area and TV to the other.
10 rms (9 shr) (1 fmly) CTV in all bedrooms No dogs (ex guide dogs) 30P No coaches Coffee am Tea pm Last d 8.30pm
CARDS:

PODIMORE Somerset Map 03 ST52

Travelodge
BA22 8JG (on A303, near junct with A37)
☎ 01935 840074 FAX 01935 840074
This modern building offers accommodation in smart, spacious and well equipped bedrooms, suitable for family use, and all with en suite bathrooms. Meals may be taken at the nearby family restaurant. For information on room rates and to make a booking, call Roomline free of charge on 0800 850950. For more details about Travelodge, consult the Contents page under Hotel Groups.
31 en suite (bth/shr)

POLPERRO Cornwall & Isles of Scilly Map 02 SX25

★❀68% **Claremont**
Fore St PL13 2RG (on Polperro's main street)
☎ 01503 272241 FAX 01503 272241
RS 1 Oct-31 Mar
A relaxed small hotel in the centre of a lovely fishing village offers French cuisine concentrating largely on seafood. Starters include Scallops Normande, scallops in their shell with a white wine sauce, and to follow red mullet chargrilled Mediterranean style.
10 en suite (bth/shr) (3 fmly) CTV in all bedrooms STV 16P No coaches Xmas French Cuisine V meals Coffee am Tea pm Last d 8pm
ROOMS: (incl. bkfst) s £28-£38; d £38-£56 **LB**
OFF-PEAK: (incl. bkfst) s £19-£28; d £35-£40
MEALS: Bar Lunch £3-£6alc Dinner £12-£15&alc
CARDS:

POLZEATH Cornwall & Isles of Scilly Map 02 SW97

★★❀❀72% **The Cornish Cottage Hotel & Restaurant**
PL27 6US (off B3314) ☎ 01208 862213 FAX 01208 862259
Closed 3 Jan-5 Feb
Clive and Christine Mason welcome guests to their small, well run hotel on the road leading down to Sandy Bay. Bedrooms are well furnished and include a few easy access rooms in the garden wing. There is a spacious conservatory lounge adjacent to the cosy bar, and in the soundly appointed restaurant a daily fixed price menu is offered together with a short carte of chef Tim Rogers' speciality dishes. Tim's serious approach to cooking is reflected in his choice of dishes, using good quality, local ingredients wherever possible. It was pleasing to see straightforward dishes, tasting of what they were supposed to. The chicken liver parfait was a delight, though the pickled vegetables were rather harsh. Spinach and snowpea soup had a delicate flavour of both vegetables. The roast fillet of lamb was a picture, the baby vegetables being served as an integral part of the dish. The redcurrant jus flavoured with mint really complemented the 'just pink' lamb. To complete the meal, the 15-minute wait for the black cherry soufflé was truly justified, it appeared well risen, moist and delicately flavoured.
14 rms (1 bth 10 shr) CTV in all bedrooms 20P No coaches Outdoor swimming pool (heated) No children 12yrs Xmas English & French Cuisine V meals Coffee am Tea pm Last d 9pm
ROOMS: (incl. bkfst) s £47; d £94 **LB**
MEALS: Sunday Lunch £15-£16.50 Dinner £25*
CARDS:

PONTEFRACT West Yorkshire Map 08 SE42

★★★62% ***Parkside***
Park Rd WF8 4QD (follow signs for racecourse hotel opposite racecourse) ☎ 01977 709911
FAX 01977 701602
Conveniently situated both for the M62 and the racecourse, this modern hotel provides well equipped bedrooms together with extensive conference facilities. A wide range of food is available in either the bar or the charming restaurant, and staff are friendly and helpful.
16 en suite (bth/shr) 12 annexe en suite (bth/shr) (1 fmly) CTV in all bedrooms STV No dogs (ex guide dogs) Night porter 200P outdoor childrens play area beer garden Wkly live entertainment European Cuisine V meals Coffee am Tea pm Last d 10pm
CARDS:

POOLE Dorset Map 04 SZ09
See also Bournemouth

★★★★❀❀70% **Haven**
Banks Rd, Sandbanks BH13 7QL (take the B3965 towards Poole Bay, turn left onto the Peninsula, the Hotel can be found 1.5 miles on the left next to the Swanage Toll Ferry point) ☎ 01202 707333 FAX 01202 708796
This attractive hotel overlooks Poole Bay and has enviable views of Brownsea Island and the Purbeck Hills. The bedrooms, many with balconies, are attractively decorated and well equipped. There are two restaurants offering a choice of menus from chef Heinz Karl Nagler's kitchens where enjoyable dishes are skilfully prepared. The public areas include a sea-facing conservatory and well equipped leisure facilities.

contd.

96 en suite (bth/shr) (6 fmly) CTV in 94 bedrooms STV No dogs (ex guide dogs) Lift Night porter 150P No coaches Indoor swimming pool (heated) Outdoor swimming pool (heated) Tennis (hard) Fishing Squash Sauna Solarium Gym Jacuzzi/spa steam room spa pool Xmas English & French Cuisine V meals Coffee am Tea pm No smoking in restaurant Last d 9.30pm
ROOMS: (incl. bkfst) s £75-£85; d £130-£180 * **LB**
MEALS: Lunch £15 Dinner £23*
CONF: Thtr 160 Class 70 Board 50 Del from £86
CARDS:

See advertisement under BOURNEMOUTH

★★★★63% **Quay Thistle**

The Quay BH15 1HD (take A350 into Poole town centre, hotel signposted from here approx 0.50m) ☎ 01202 666800 FAX 01202 684470
Situated on the quay, this modern hotel enjoys uninterrupted views across the large natural harbour to the Purbeck Hills. Recently refurbished throughout, it offers a smart standard of accommodation. Bedrooms are small but thoughtfully designed and most have good en suite bathrooms. Public areas are mostly located on the first floor and include a pleasant cocktail bar and an octagonal restaurant specialising in freshly caught local seafood.
68 en suite (bth/shr) (4 fmly) No smoking in 22 bedrooms CTV in all bedrooms STV Lift Night porter 150P Wkly live entertainment Xmas French Cuisine V meals Coffee am Tea pm Last d 10pm
ROOMS: s £85-£90; d £95-£100 * **LB**
OFF-PEAK: (incl. bkfst) s £85-£90; d £90-£95
MEALS: Lunch £17&alc High tea fr £7.50 Dinner £19-£21&alc*
CONF: Thtr 60 Class 20 Board 30 Del from £89
CARDS:

★★★81% **Salterns**

38 Salterns Way, Lilliput BH14 8JR (From Poole follow B3369 Sandbanks road. In one mile at Lilliput shops turn into Salterns Way) ☎ 01202 707321 FAX 01202 707488
Situated right beside Poole Marina, this hotel enjoys glorious views across the harbour to Brownsea Island. Owners Beverley and John Smith offer a warm welcome and with their dedicated staff ensure guests' comfort. The bedrooms are very comfortably furnished and have pretty décor and smart bathrooms, together with thoughtful extras. Chef Nigel Popplewell heads the kitchen and produces an interesting menu; dishes make good use of local game and fish, recent meals of turbot with mussels, and scallops were very enjoyable. The wine list is quite extensive and ranges from fair-priced house wines to Grand Crus.
20 en suite (bth/shr) (4 fmly) No smoking in 2 bedrooms CTV in all bedrooms STV Night porter 300P No coaches Fishing Snooker ch fac Xmas English & French Cuisine V meals Coffee am Last d 9.30pm
ROOMS: s £66; d £86 * **LB**
MEALS: Lunch £15&alc Dinner £21-£25&alc*
CONF: Thtr 100 Class 50 Board 50 Del from £106
CARDS:

See advertisement on opposite page

★★★79% **Mansion House**
Thames St BH15 1JN (off The Quay, opposite St James Church) ☎ 01202 685666 FAX 01202 665709
A historic building, set close to the Old Quay and St James' Church, this very friendly hotel boasts an attractive entrance and imposing staircase. The older part of the building, with its beamed ceilings and flagstoned floors, has been skilfully extended. All its bedrooms are indvidually decorated, on different themes, with many little extra personal touches to add comfort. The hotel has a popular dining club, where Gerry Godden's imaginative and skilfully prepared food can be enjoyed, as our inspector found when she dined off salmon fishcakes with an excellent champagne sauce, followed by breast of duck with a delicate jasmine-scented sauce and poached sultanas, and finished with a deliciously light textured but richly flavoured chocolate pudding. Guests who want a lighter meal will find the informal bistro caters admirably.
28 en suite (bth/shr) (2 fmly) CTV in all bedrooms STV Night porter 40P No coaches Xmas English & French Cuisine V meals Coffee am Tea pm Last d 9.30pm
ROOMS: (incl. bkfst) s £52-£75; d £85-£112 * **LB**
MEALS: Lunch £10.50-£12 Dinner £20.75-£23.75alc*
CONF: Thtr 40 Class 18 Board 20 Del from £85
CARDS:

See advertisement on opposite page

★★★73% **Sandbanks**
15 Banks Rd, Sandbanks BH13 7PS (take the A338 through Bournemouth, follow signs for Sandbanks Peninsula, Hotel is on left 300 yds down Peninsula) ☎ 01202 707377 FAX 01202 708885
This large hotel is popular with both the leisure and business guest, it has direct access to Sandbanks beach and superb views across the Poole Harbour. The rooms are well equipped and many have balconies, there are also family rooms. The hotel provides special facilities for children including a special supervised restaurant. There are conference rooms, an indoor pool and leisure suite. The main restaurant overlooks the sea and offers a varied menu of interesting dishes using local produce.

105 en suite (bth/shr) (27 fmly) No smoking in 10 bedrooms CTV in all bedrooms STV No dogs (ex guide dogs) Lift Night porter 200P Indoor swimming pool (heated) Sauna Solarium Gym Pool table Putting green Jacuzzi/spa Hobie Cat Sailing Mountain bike hire Wkly live entertainment ch fac Xmas International Cuisine V meals Coffee am Tea pm No smoking in restaurant Last d 9pm

ROOMS: (incl. bkfst & dinner) s £56-£85; d £112-£170 **LB**

OFF-PEAK: (incl. bkfst & dinner) s £49.75-£56; d £99.50-£112

MEALS: Lunch £6.50-£14.50 High tea £4.50-£7 Dinner £13-£18.50&alc

CONF: Thtr 150 Class 60 Board 50 Del from £77

CARDS:

See advertisement under BOURNEMOUTH

★★★ 68% **Harbour Heights**

73 Haven Rd, Sandbanks BH13 7LW ☎ 01202 707272

FAX 01202 708594

From its hill-top location, this personally run hotel commands spectacular views across the harbour to Brownsea Island and Studland Bay. The modern bedrooms are spacious and smartly furnished; most

contd.

have sea views. The extensive hot and cold lunchtime buffet is popular with local residents, while the Harbour View restaurant offers an interesting carte and a daily set menu, including vegetarian options.
48 en suite (bth/shr) (5 fmly) CTV in all bedrooms STV Lift Night porter 84P ch fac English, French, Italian & Oriental Cuisine V meals Coffee am Tea pm No smoking area in restaurant Last d 9.30pm
ROOMS: (incl. bkfst) s fr £43; d fr £70 * **LB**
OFF-PEAK: (incl. bkfst) s fr £43; d fr £70
MEALS: Lunch £10.95-£11.50 High tea £5 Dinner £16.50-£18*
CONF: Thtr 60 Class 60 Board 24 Del from £70
CARDS:

★★69% **Arndale Court**
62/66 Wimborne Rd BH15 2BY (on th A349 close to Town Centre, opposite Poole Stadium entrance) ☎ 01202 683746
FAX 01202 668838
This smart hotel situated just minutes from Poole centre and the Old Quay, is very popular with business guests in the week, and is quieter at weekends, when it makes a good base for breaks. The bedrooms vary in size but are very well equipped with mini bars, irons, trouser presses and satellite televisions. The public areas are bright and relaxed, there is a restaurant and a wide range of snacks are served in the bar.
32 en suite (bth/shr) (7 fmly) CTV in all bedrooms STV Night porter English & French Cuisine V meals Coffee am Last d 9pm
ROOMS: (incl. bkfst) s £51; d £59.50 *
OFF-PEAK: (incl. bkfst) s £40; d £55
MEALS: Sunday Lunch £9.50-£12.50alc Dinner £12-£20alc*
CARDS:

★★63% **Norfolk Lodge**

1 Flaghead Rd, Canford Cliffs BH13 7JL (between Poole & Bournemouth hotel on corner of Haven & Flaghead Rd) ☎ 01202 708614 & 708661
FAX 01202 708614
This attractive Victorian Property is located in a quiet residential area just a few minutes' walk from the beach. The bedrooms are well presented with modern en suite facilities and the Martin family offer a warm welcome and friendly service. Good home-cooked evening meals are served in the restaurant, which overlooks the garden with its aviaries full of exotic birds.
19 rms (17 bth/shr) (4 fmly) CTV in all bedrooms 16P No coaches Last d 8pm
ROOMS: (incl. bkfst) s £35-£40; d £54-£56 **LB**
OFF-PEAK: (incl. bkfst) s £34; d £54
MEALS: Lunch £7.50-£9 Dinner £9-£12
CARDS:

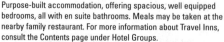

Travel Inn

Ringwood Rd, Tricketts Cross, Ferndown BH22 9BB (off A348) ☎ 01202 874210
FAX 01202 897794
Purpose-built accommodation, offering spacious, well equipped bedrooms, all with en suite bathrooms. Meals may be taken at the nearby family restaurant. For more information about Travel Inns, consult the Contents page under Hotel Groups.
32 en suite (bth/shr)
ROOMS: d £35.50 *

PORLOCK Somerset Map 03 SS84

★★★64% **Anchor & Ship**
Porlock Harbour TA24 8PB (From A39 take the B3225 Porlock Weir road) ☎ 01643 862753 FAX 01643 862843
RS Jan
Overlooking the harbour, this long-established family hotel offers comfortable accommodation. There are two styles of bedroom; those in the main building are more spacious than the rooms in the adjacent Ship Inn, which have more character. Throughout the public areas there is a relaxed, informal atmosphere. In the Harbour Restaurant, both fixed-price and à la carte menus are offered, with local seafood being a speciality; the wine list provides good value for money. Meanwhile in the Ship Inn an extensive range of bar meals is available, along with a range of real ales. Ample parking is available opposite the hotel.
20 rms (14 bth/shr) (2 fmly) CTV in all bedrooms Xmas English & Continental Cuisine V meals Coffee am Tea pm No smoking in restaurant Last d 9-9.15pm
ROOMS: (incl. bkfst) s £47.75-£62.75; d £79.50-£107.50 **LB**
OFF-PEAK: (incl. bkfst) s £42.75-£56.75; d £69.50-£95.50
MEALS: Bar Lunch £3.75-£6.45 Dinner £19.75-£19.75&alc
CARDS:

RED STAR HOTEL

★★ **The Oaks**
TA24 8ES ☎ 01643 862265 FAX 01643 862265
Closed 2 Jan-Feb
An elegant Victorian house stands in a well tended garden in an elevated position overlooking the pretty village of Porlock. The comfortable bedrooms are well equipped and individually appointed with good quality furnishings. An entrance hall has an open fire and leads to an attractive sitting room and a cosy bar. The refurbished restaurant serves a short five-course set-price menu offering an imaginative choice including creamy watercress soup, monkfish cooked in lime, fillet of pork with a walnut filling served with a herbed hollondaise sauce and a traditional sherry trifle. The wine list offers a varied choice to suite all tastes.
9 en suite (bth/shr) (2 fmly) No smoking in all bedrooms CTV in all bedrooms 12P No coaches No children 8yrs Xmas No smoking in restaurant Last d 8.30pm
ROOMS: (incl. bkfst) s £50; d £80 * **LB**
MEALS: Dinner fr £24
CARDS:

PORTESHAM Dorset Map 03 SY68

★★64% **Millmead Country**
MINOTEL Great Britain
Goose Hill DT3 4HE ☎ 01305 871432
FAX 01305 871432
This small personally-run hotel is in a village setting close to Abbottsbury and the sea. The bedrooms are attractively decorated with co-ordinated fabrics, modern en suite facilities and pretty finishing touches. There is a spacious lounge and a well appointed restaurant overlooking the garden and patio. The hotel also caters for weddings and conferences in a marquee.
6 en suite (bth/shr) CTV in all bedrooms 40P No children 10 Xmas

Coffee am Tea pm No smoking in restaurant Last d 8.30pm
ROOMS: (incl. bkfst) s £40.50; d £68 * **LB**
OFF-PEAK: (incl. bkfst) s £37.50; d £60
MEALS: Dinner fr £14.50*
CARDS:

PORT GAVERNE Cornwall & Isles of Scilly Map 02 SX08

★★ 69% ***Port Gaverne***
PL29 3SQ (signposted from B3314) ☎ 01208 880244
FAX 01208 880151
Closed 6 Jan-17 Feb
Situated on the county's north coast, this 17th-century Cornish Inn has retained considerable character and charm. Its restaurant specialises in fresh seafood.
16 en suite (bth/shr) 3 annexe en suite (bth/shr) (5 fmly) CTV in 18 bedrooms 30P No coaches International Cuisine V meals Coffee am
CARDS:

★★ 67% ***Headlands***

MINOTEL Great Britain

PL29 3SH (on cliff top, 0.50m E of Port Isaac)
☎ 01208 880260 FAX 01208 880885
This cliff-top hotel with sweeping views of the coast provides personal service. Individually styled bedrooms are furnished to modern standards and there is a traditional lounge, small bar and restaurant featuring fresh local produce.
11 en suite (bth/shr) (1 fmly) CTV in all bedrooms 40P No coaches Sauna International Cuisine V meals Coffee am Tea pm
Last d 9.30pm
CARDS:

See advertisement on this page

PORTHLEVEN Cornwall & Isles of Scilly Map 02 SW62

★★ 64% ***Harbour***
Commercial Rd TR13 9JB (turn left at roundabout off Helston ring road. After approx 3m Commercial Road is to left of harbour)
(St Austell Brewery) ☎ 01326 573876
Bedrooms are comfortable and well equipped, the majority having en suite facilities, at this inn which overlooks the harbour from a setting on the east side of the village. A wide range of value-for-money meals is available in its good-sized family restaurant, with the option of lighter snacks at lunchtime, and the spacious public bar attracts locals and tourists alike.
10 rms (8 bth/shr) (1 fmly) CTV in all bedrooms No dogs 10P No coaches Sea fishing arranged V meals Coffee am Tea pm
CARDS:

PORT ISAAC Cornwall & Isles of Scilly Map 02 SW98
See also Port Gaverne

★★ 63% **Castle Rock**
4 New Rd PL29 3SB ☎ 01208 880300 FAX 01208 880219
This privately-owned hotel is situated on the cliffs at the top of the village, enjoying impressive views of the sea and coastline. Bedrooms, some on the ground floor, are furnished and equipped in a modern style, the majority offering fine sea views. The lounge bar and bright, pleasant restaurant both feature picture windows with sea views, and a choice of dishes is offered on the restaurant's fixed-price menu.
14 rms (9 bth 4 shr) (1 fmly) CTV in all bedrooms 20P No children 5yrs Xmas International Cuisine V meals Coffee am Tea pm No smoking in restaurant Last d 9.30pm
ROOMS: (incl. bkfst) s £32-£34; d £64-£74 * **LB**
MEALS: Sunday Lunch £7.95 Dinner £13&alc
CARDS:

See advertisement on this page

PORTLAND Dorset Map 03 SY67

★★★65% **Portland Heights**

Yeates Corner DT5 2EN (from A354 follow signs for Portland Bill, the hotel is on the summit of the island) ☎ 01305 821361 FAX 01305 860081

This friendly popular hotel is being continually improved and offers smart modern public areas. The first floor bar and restaurant command spectacular panoramic views across Portland Bay and Chesil Beach. The bedrooms are modern and have pretty co-ordinated decor. There is an outdoor pool and a leisure suite including sauna, solarium, fitness room and squash court.

65 en suite (bth/shr) (8 fmly) No smoking in 2 bedrooms CTV in all bedrooms Night porter 160P Outdoor swimming pool (heated) Squash Sauna Solarium Gym Pool table Steam room, games room ch fac Xmas International Cuisine V meals Coffee am Tea pm No smoking area in restaurant Last d 9.15pm

ROOMS: (incl. bkfst) s £49.50-£52; d £59.50-£62 * **LB**

OFF-PEAK: (incl. bkfst) s £44.50-£47; d £54.50-£57

MEALS: Lunch £6-£18.50 Dinner £16.50&alc

CONF: Thtr 200 Class 120 Board 80 Del from £60

CARDS:

PORTSCATHO Cornwall & Isles of Scilly Map 02 SW83

★★★61% **Rosevine**

Porthcurnick Beach TR2 5EW ☎ 01872 580206 & 580230 FAX 01872 580230

Closed Nov-Etr

Authentic international additions bring variety to the traditional British fare featured on three and five-course fixed-price menus in the spacious modern restaurant of this hotel, a Georgian country house quietly set in three and a half acres of mature sub-tropical gardens overlooking Porthcurnick Beach.

14 en suite (bth/shr) 1 annexe en suite (bth/shr) (2 fmly) CTV in all bedrooms Night porter 40P No coaches International Cuisine Coffee am Tea pm No smoking area in restaurant Last d 8.30pm

ROOMS: (incl. bkfst & dinner) s £46-£70; d £92-£140 **LB**

OFF-PEAK: (incl. bkfst & dinner) s £44-£48; d £88-£132

MEALS: Bar Lunch £6-£10alc Dinner £16.75-£20.50

CARDS:

★★73% **Gerrans Bay**

Gerrans TR2 5ED (turn off A3078 at Trewithian follow signs for Gerrans Hotel past church on road to St Anthony Head)

☎ 01872 580338 FAX 01872 580250

Closed Nov-Mar

The Gerrans Bay Hotel is situated in the heart of the Roseland Peninsula, and its location is one of the hotel's strengths, but certainly not the only one. Ann and Brian Greaves are continually making improvements and are on hand to ensure an efficient service in all areas; in our inspectors' experience, as well as catering for guests' needs, they will also be on hand to have a chat after dinner. Ann Greaves uses local produce whenever possible and provides first class cooking. Bedrooms are attractively and comfortably furnished.

14 rms (12 bth/shr) (2 fmly) CTV in all bedrooms 16P No coaches Xmas Coffee am Tea pm No smoking in restaurant Last d 8pm

ROOMS: (incl. bkfst & dinner) s £43.50-£52.25; d £83-£104.50 **LB**

MEALS: Sunday Lunch £9 Dinner £19-£21.50

CARDS:

See advertisement on opposite page

★★67% ***Roseland House***

Rosevine TR2 5EW (A3078 for St Mawes. Pass through Ruan-High-Lanes and signposted after 2m)

☎ 01872 580644 FAX 01872 580801

This hotel sits on a cliff top looking over magnificent views. The chef/proprietor Carolyn Hindley offers a set five-course dinner including home-made soup followed by dill-cured salmon. The main course might be fillet of sea-bass with a wine cream and herb sauce.

15 en suite (bth) (5 fmly) No smoking in all bedrooms CTV in all bedrooms No dogs (ex guide dogs) 28P No coaches Fishing Private beach V meals Coffee am Tea pm Last d 8.30pm

CARDS:

PORTSMOUTH & SOUTHSEA Hampshire Map 04 SZ69

★★★★64% **Portsmouth Marriott**

North Harbour PO6 4SH (at the juct of A27/A3)

☎ 01705 383151 FAX 01705 388701

This large, busy and well maintained hotel is ideal for both leisure and business guests. It offers a wide range of services and a choice of eating options located on the open-plan ground floor. There is also a shop and extensive leisure facilities. Comfortable bedrooms are equipped with up-to-date modern amenities.

170 en suite (bth/shr) (76 fmly) No smoking in 86 bedrooms CTV in all bedrooms STV Lift Night porter Air conditioning 300P Indoor swimming pool (heated) Squash Snooker Sauna Solarium Gym Jacuzzi/spa Whirlpool Health & beauty room Xmas English & French Cuisine V meals Coffee am Tea pm No smoking area in restaurant Last d 10.30pm

ROOMS: (incl. bkfst) s £71-£101; d £86-£109 * **LB**

MEALS: Lunch fr £16.95 High tea fr £3.95 Dinner fr £17&alc*

CONF: Thtr 400 Class 250 Board 50 Del from £120

CARDS:

★★★65% **Hospitality Inn**

St Helens Pde PO4 0RN ☎ 01705 731281 FAX 01705 817572

A large, popular seafront hotel is situated directly opposite Southsea Pier. Bedrooms vary in size but are modern and well equipped; front-facing rooms have good sea views across the Solent to the Isle of Wight. Public areas include a spacious reception foyer, a bar/lounge and the Ark Royal Restaurant, which offers both a daily fixed-price menu and a carte. Service is well supervised and friendly, and room service is also available between 7.00pm and 9.30pm daily. The Invincible Suite offers very good conference/banqueting facilities and there is a range of smaller meeting and banqueting rooms.

115 en suite (bth/shr) (6 fmly) No smoking in 25 bedrooms CTV in all bedrooms Lift Night porter 62P Xmas English & French Cuisine V meals Coffee am No smoking in restaurant Last d 10pm
ROOMS: (incl. bkfst) s £69; d £79 * **LB**
MEALS: Bar Lunch £3-£7.50 Dinner fr £15&alc*
CONF: Thtr 250 Class 160 Board 30 Del from £84
CARDS:

★★71% **The Beaufort**
71 Festing Rd PO4 0NQ (follow signs for seafront at South Parade Pier take left fork, Festing Rd is fourth turning on left) ☎ 01705 823707 FAX 01705 870270
This friendly, well run hotel is located in a residential area, close to the town and seafront. The bedrooms are attractively decorated, with co-ordinated fabrics and modern en suite facilities. The public areas include a comfortable lounge and a well presented dining room offering good home-cooked fare.
19 en suite (bth/shr) (3 fmly) No smoking in 8 bedrooms CTV in all bedrooms STV No dogs 10P Xmas English & French Cuisine V meals No smoking in restaurant Last d 8.30pm
ROOMS: (incl. bkfst) s £35-£48; d £48-£68 * **LB**
OFF-PEAK: (incl. bkfst) s £35-£38; d £45-£55
MEALS: Dinner £12.90-£13.90&alc*
CONF: Class 20 Del from £55
CARDS:

See advertisement on this page

★★70% **Westfield Hall**
65 Festing Rd PO4 0NQ (follow signs Seafront, bear left at South Parade Pier then 3rd turning left)
☎ 01705 826971 FAX 01705 870200
This attractive family-run hotel offers a warm welcome and is conveniently located for the seafront and the town. There are now seven very smart new rooms which are for non-smokers, as well as a separate lounge. All rooms are well equipped with modern ensuite facilities including trouser presses and satellite TV. The dining room is located on the lower floor and offers good traditional home cooking. The forecourt car park has closed circuit TV.
16 en suite (bth/shr) 7 annexe en suite (bth/shr) (5 fmly)

contd.

No smoking in 9 bedrooms CTV in all bedrooms STV No dogs 18P Xmas V meals No smoking in restaurant Last d 8.30pm
ROOMS: (incl. bkfst) s £38-£45; d £50-£65 * **LB**
OFF-PEAK: (incl. bkfst) s £35-£40; d £48-£58
MEALS: Dinner £10.95-£12.95&alc*
CARDS:

See advertisement on opposite page

★★69% ***Green Farm Hotel***

Copnor Rd, Hilsea PO3 5HS ☎ 01705 654645
Green Farm was restored two years ago, and parts of the building date back to the 17th century. The rooms are spacious and well equipped with modern en suite facilities, colour televisions with satellite, trouser press and hair dryer. The restaurant is attractively decorated in a country house theme, and offers an interesting and varied menu, in addition to extensive bar snacks. There is a comfortable lounge area available to residents during bar opening times.
30 en suite (bth/shr) (6 fmly) No smoking in 10 bedrooms CTV in all bedrooms STV Night porter P ch fac
CARDS:

★★68% **Seacrest**

11/12 South Pde PO5 2JB (from M27 follow signs for Southsea seafront. Hotel opposite Rock Gardens)
☎ 01705 733192 FAX 01705 832523
This fine Victorian house is set on the edge of the Rock Gardens and enjoys impressive views over the Solent. The bedrooms vary in size but are all attractively decorated, with modern en suite facilities. The public areas include a comfortably furnished lounge with leather chesterfields and popular well stocked bar. The friendly staff create a relaxed atmosphere.
28 en suite (bth/shr) (3 fmly) CTV in all bedrooms STV Lift 12P Xmas V meals Coffee am Tea pm No smoking in restaurant Last d 8pm
ROOMS: (incl. bkfst) s £38-£48; d £42-£60 * **LB**
MEALS: Dinner £12.95&alc*
CARDS:

See advertisement on opposite page

★★61% **Sandringham**
Osborne Rd, Clarence Pde PO5 3LR (facing Southsea Common)
☎ 01705 822914 & 826969 FAX 01705 822330
This popular hotel commands wonderful views over the Solent and Southsea Common. Pleasantly furnished bedrooms offer modern en suite facilities and there are two comfortable lounges (one with a large-screen TV) and a lounge bar. The beamed dining room offers generous portions of traditional home-cooked food.
There is no parking, but a free car park lies directly opposite the hotel.
45 en suite (bth/shr) (7 fmly) CTV in all bedrooms No dogs (ex guide dogs) Lift Bingo Dancing lessons Wkly live entertainment ch fac Xmas English & French Cuisine V meals Coffee am Tea pm Last d 9pm
ROOMS: (incl. bkfst) s £25-£40; d £40-£45 * **LB**
OFF-PEAK: (incl. bkfst) s £25-£34; d £38-£48
MEALS: Lunch £5-£12 Dinner £12&alc*
CARDS:

★★60% ***Hotel Ibis***

Winston Churchill Av PO1 2LX ☎ 01705 640000
FAX 01705 641000
This modern hotel is centrally located and has the added advantage of secure parking. The bedrooms are furnished to the company standard with modern amenities. On the ground floor there are bright meeting rooms and an open-plan bar, lounge and restaurant.
144 en suite (shr) CTV in all bedrooms STV Lift Night porter 50P English & French Cuisine V meals Coffee am Last d 10.30pm
CARDS:

★★59% **Keppels Head**

PO1 3DT (opp Harbour Railway Station)
☎ 01705 833231 FAX 01705 838688
Located just 200yds from the historic dockyard, this traditional hotel has comfortable modern bedrooms with good facilities. There is an attractive carvery-style restaurant and a bar lounge. Service, under the management of Dieter Schlieben, is friendly and helpful.
27 en suite (bth/shr) (6 fmly) No smoking in 8 bedrooms CTV in all bedrooms Lift Night porter 18P V meals Coffee am Tea pm Last d 9pm
ROOMS: s £40-£45; d £50-£65 * **LB**
OFF-PEAK: (incl. bkfst) s £30-£39; d £40-£59
MEALS: Lunch £10-£15 Dinner £14.75-£20&alc*
CONF: Thtr 60 Class 30 Board 24 Del from £80
CARDS:

Forte Posthouse Portsmouth

FORTE Posthouse

Pembroke Rd PO1 2TA (from M275, follow signs for Southsea and I.O.W Hovercroft for 1 mile, at Southsea Common the Hotel can be found on the right) ☎ 01705 827651 FAX 01705 756715
Suitable for both the business and leisure traveller, this bright hotel provides modern accommodation in well equipped bedrooms with en suite bathrooms. For more details about Forte Posthouse hotels, consult the Contents page for the section on Hotel Groups.
163 en suite (bth/shr)
ROOMS: s £69-£79; d £69-£79 *
CONF: Thtr 220 Class 120 Board 80 Del from £89

Hilton National Portsmouth

Eastern Rd, Farlington PO6 1UN (on junct of A27/A2030, NE of city centre) ☎ 01705 219111
FAX 01705 201762
This is a bright, modern hotel, with an informal restaurant, aimed at both the business and leisure guest. All bedrooms have en suite bathrooms and a range of modern facilities. For more

information about Hilton National hotels, consult the Contents page under Hotel Groups.
116 en suite (bth/shr)

Travel Inn

Southampton Rd, North Harbour, Cosham
PO6 4SA ☎ 01705 321122 FAX 01705 324895
Purpose-built accommodation, offering spacious, well equipped bedrooms, all with en suite bathrooms. Meals may be taken at the nearby family restaurant. For more information about Travel Inns, consult the Contents page under Hotel Groups.
40 en suite (bth/shr)
ROOMS: d £35.50 *

POTT SHRIGLEY Cheshire Map 07 SJ97

★★★★61% **Shrigley Hall Golf & Country Club**
Shrigley Park SK10 5SB ☎ 01625 575757 FAX 01625 573323
Set in 260 acres of parkland above Macclesfield, on the edge of the Peak District National Park, but within easy reach of Manchester, this former Silesian Monastery has been converted into an hotel with impressive leisure, conference and banqueting facilities. The original Georgian house, with its magnificent entrance hall, has been considerably extended to include an inner courtyard around which most of the bedrooms are situated. The bedrooms themselves vary in size and quality, from smaller rooms to larger and more luxurious rooms. The informal pool cafe offers light snacks whilst the carte and table d'hÙte menus in the Oakridge restaurant offer a good selection of traditional dishes.
156 en suite (bth/shr) (5 fmly) No smoking in 20 bedrooms CTV in all bedrooms STV Lift Night porter 300P No coaches Indoor swimming pool (heated) Golf 18 Tennis (hard) Fishing Snooker Sauna Solarium Gym Putting green Jacuzzi/spa Beauty salon Steam

contd.

P

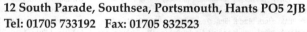

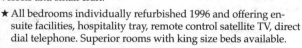

spa Wkly live entertainment Xmas International Cuisine V meals Coffee am Tea pm No smoking in restaurant Last d 9.45pm
ROOMS: (incl. bkfst) s £98; d £125 * LB
MEALS: Lunch fr £12 Dinner £19-£28&alc*
CONF: Thtr 280 Class 140 Board 50 Del £140
CARDS:

POWBURN Northumberland Map 12 NU01

RED STAR HOTEL

★★ **Breamish House**
NE66 4LL ☎ 01665 578266 & 578544
FAX 01665 578500
Closed 31 Dec-14 Feb

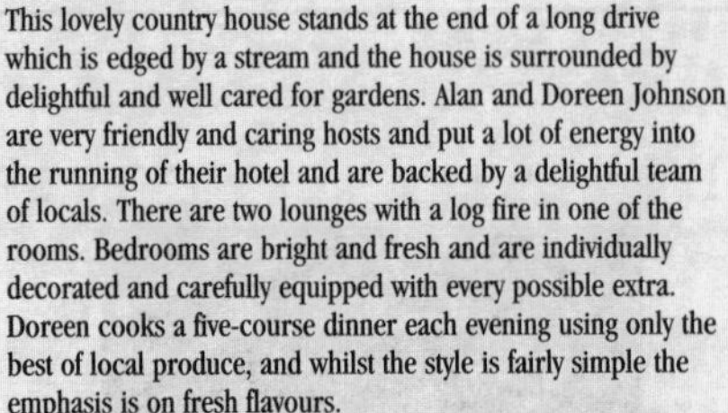

This lovely country house stands at the end of a long drive which is edged by a stream and the house is surrounded by delightful and well cared for gardens. Alan and Doreen Johnson are very friendly and caring hosts and put a lot of energy into the running of their hotel and are backed by a delightful team of locals. There are two lounges with a log fire in one of the rooms. Bedrooms are bright and fresh and are individually decorated and carefully equipped with every possible extra. Doreen cooks a five-course dinner each evening using only the best of local produce, and whilst the style is fairly simple the emphasis is on fresh flavours.
10 rms (9 bth/shr) 1 annexe en suite (bth/shr) CTV in all bedrooms 30P No coaches Croquet lawn No children 12yrs Xmas Coffee am Tea pm No smoking in restaurant Last d 8pm
ROOMS: (incl. bkfst & dinner) s £77; d £120-£152 * LB
OFF-PEAK: (incl. bkfst & dinner) s £69.50; d £103-£131
MEALS: Sunday Lunch fr £13.50 Dinner fr £23.50*
CARDS:

PRESTBURY Cheshire Map 07 SJ97

★★★69% **Bridge**
The Village SK10 4DQ (off A538 through village, hotel next to church)
☎ 01625 829326 FAX 01625 827557
This delightful, privately owned hotel, parts of which date from the 17th century, is quietly tucked away between the church and the River Bollin and yet is within easy reach of Manchester and the airport. The comfortable, well equipped bedrooms are divided between the main building and an adjoining wing, which is built of Cheshire brick and overlooks the well tended gardens. Service from the mainly long standing staff is professional and attentive.
23 en suite (bth/shr) (4 fmly) CTV in all bedrooms No dogs (ex guide dogs) Night porter 52P Wkly live entertainment V meals Coffee am Tea pm Last d 9.45pm
ROOMS: s £72-£77; d £78-£88 * LB
MEALS: Lunch £9.75-£10.95 Dinner £11.95-£13.15*
CONF: Thtr 100 Class 56 Board 48 Del £95
CARDS:

TOWN HOUSE HOTEL

White House Manor
New Rd SK10 4HP (on the A538 Macclesfield Road)
☎ 01625 829376 FAX 01625 828627
Quietly situated, a few minutes walk from the centre of the picturesque village, this delightful Georgian house provides beautifully appointed bedrooms. Effective use has been made of co-ordinating soft furnishings to create highly individual bedrooms, all of which are supremely comfortable, with many thoughtful extras, some even having their own steam rooms. Carefully prepared dishes are available from room service and breakfast can be taken in the delightful orangery. The White House restaurant, under the same ownership, is a couple of minutes' walk away.
9 en suite (bth/shr) CTV in all bedrooms STV No dogs (ex guide dogs) 9P No coaches Jacuzzi/spa No children 10yrs V meals Last d 10pm
ROOMS: s £65-£90; d £95 *
OFF-PEAK: (incl. bkfst) s £40-£65; d £65-£95
MEALS: Lunch £12.50-£14.50&alc Dinner £13.95-£16.95&alc
CONF: Thtr 60 Class 40 Board 26 Del from £85
CARDS:

PRESTON Lancashire Map 07 SD52
See also Barton

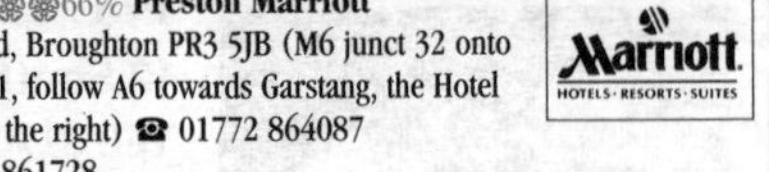

★★★★ 66% **Preston Marriott**
Garstang Rd, Broughton PR3 5JB (M6 junct 32 onto M55 junct 1, follow A6 towards Garstang, the Hotel in .05m on the right) ☎ 01772 864087
FAX 01772 861728
An extended Victorian country house set in well tended gardens, this hotel has benefited from recent and substantial refurbishment. Many bedrooms have been upgraded and although some of the standard rooms are small, they are attractively appointed. Public rooms have seen similar good work; there is a large lounge bar on three levels and a charming restaurant where guests receive attentive personal service. Food is still a major strength and the cooking of Neil McKevitt and his team shows both care and skill. Guests also have use of a leisure club with its own coffee shop serving light meals.
98 en suite (bth/shr) (10 fmly) No smoking in 50 bedrooms CTV in all bedrooms STV No dogs (ex guide dogs) Lift Night porter 220P Indoor swimming pool (heated) Sauna Solarium Gym Pool table Jacuzzi/spa Steam room Beauty salon Xmas English & French Cuisine V meals Coffee am Tea pm No smoking in restaurant Last d 9.30pm
ROOMS: (incl. bkfst) s £72-£85; d fr £79 * LB
MEALS: Lunch fr £13.50 Dinner fr £18.95&alc*
CONF: Thtr 200 Class 120 Board 40 Del from £110
CARDS:

★★★67% **Swallow**

Preston New Rd, Samlesbury PR5 0UL (1m from M6, on A59/A677 junct) ☎ 01772 877351
FAX 01772 877424

The recent creation of a comfortable lounge and lounge bar has certainly enhanced the public areas of this busy hotel and the re-siting and enlargement of the attractively appointed restaurant has augmented the facilities. It is a hotel which caters equally for business and leisure markets with good conference and banqueting facilities and an excellent leisure centre. Bedrooms are a little dated but nevertheless well equipped and staff throughout the hotel are both helpful and friendly.

78 en suite (bth/shr) No smoking in 16 bedrooms CTV in all bedrooms STV Lift Night porter 300P Indoor swimming pool (heated) Squash Sauna Solarium Gym Jacuzzi/spa Steam room Wkly live entertainment Xmas International Cuisine V meals Coffee am Tea pm No smoking in restaurant Last d 9.30pm

ROOMS: (incl. bkfst) s £78; d £95 * **LB**

MEALS: Lunch £8.95-£9.95 Dinner fr £16.50&alc*

CONF: Thtr 250 Class 100 Board 60 Del from £97.50

CARDS:

★★★66% **Tickled Trout**

Macdonald Hotels

Preston New Rd, Samlesbury PR5 0UJ (close to M6 junct 31) ☎ 01772 877671 FAX 01772 877463

Considerable upgrading has recently been carried out at this riverside hotel, which is also adjacent to the M6 motorway, and the public areas in particular have been much improved. The well equipped bedrooms, although compact, are agreeably furnished and decorated and several have views over the River Ribble. The hotel also has a leisure suite and facilities for conferences and meetings as well as ample car parking.

72 en suite (bth/shr) (56 fmly) No smoking in 10 bedrooms CTV in all bedrooms Night porter 156P Fishing Sauna Solarium Wave pool Steam room Wkly live entertainment ch fac Xmas International Cuisine V meals Coffee am Tea pm No smoking in restaurant Last d 9.45pm

ROOMS: s £78-£81; d £98-£101 * **LB**

OFF-PEAK: (incl. bkfst) s £45-£48; d £65-£68

MEALS: Lunch £9.95-£10.50 Dinner £18.45-£19&alc*

CONF: Thtr 100 Class 40 Board 4

CARDS:

★★★65% **Novotel**

Reedfield Place, Walton Summit PR5 6AB (M6 junct 29 M61 junct 9,then A6 Preston RoadHotel is next to Bamber Bridge roundabout) ☎ 01772 313331
FAX 01772 627868

This modern hotel, which is conveniently situated for both the M6 and M61 motorways, has recently been re-decorated and is fresh, clean and bright. Bedrooms are spacious if austere, and have every modern convenience. Bathrooms have separate toilets and two rooms have facilities for disabled guests. There is a comfortable lounge, a small restaurant, meeting and function rooms and a compact outdoor swimming pool, as well as ample parking.

98 en suite (bth/shr) (98 fmly) No smoking in 35 bedrooms CTV in all bedrooms STV Lift Night porter 140P Outdoor swimming pool (heated) Pool table Continental Cuisine V meals Coffee am Tea pm No smoking area in restaurant Last d midnt

ROOMS: s fr £44.50; d fr £44.50 * **LB**

OFF-PEAK: (incl. bkfst) s fr £44.50; d fr £44.50

MEALS: Lunch £5.95-£14 Dinner £5.95-£16*

CONF: Thtr 180 Class 80 Board 52 Del £80

CARDS:

★★65% **Claremont**

516 Blackpool Rd, Ashton-on-Ribble PR2 1HY (on A538)
☎ 01772 729738 FAX 01772 726274

This well maintained, private hotel is situated on the Blackpool road, convenient for the M55 and M6 motorways. Bedrooms are bright, attractively decorated and well equipped; some have hairdryers and trouser presses. The public areas include a cosy reception lounge, a comfortable lounge bar and a restaurant where a good choice of dishes is available. The hotel also benefits from a self-contained function room and pleasant gardens.

14 en suite (bth/shr) CTV in all bedrooms No dogs (ex guide dogs) 27P No coaches V meals Coffee am Tea pm No smoking in restaurant Last d 8.30pm

ROOMS: (incl. bkfst) s fr £37.50; d fr £51 *

MEALS: Lunch fr £8.95 Dinner fr £11.95&alc

CONF: Thtr 85 Class 45 Board 50 Del from £57.45

CARDS:

Forte Posthouse Preston

Ringway PR1 3AU (M6 junct 31 follow signs for the Town Centre right at T junct, Forte Posthouse is on the left) ☎ 01772 259411 FAX 01772 201923

contd.

Suitable for both the business and leisure traveller, this bright hotel provides modern accommodation in well equipped bedrooms with en suite bathrooms. For more details about Forte Posthouse hotels, consult the Contents page for the section on Hotel Groups.
121 en suite (bth/shr)
ROOMS: s fr £69; d fr £69 *
CONF: Thtr 120 Class 50 Board 40 Del from £99

Travel Inn

Blackpool Rd, Lea PR4 0XB (off A583) ☎ 01772 720476 FAX 01772 729971
Purpose-built accommodation, offering spacious, well equipped bedrooms, all with en suite bathrooms. Meals may be taken at the nearby family restaurant. For more information about Travel Inns, consult the Contents page under Hotel Groups.
38 en suite (bth/shr)
ROOMS: d £35.50 *

PRESTWICH Greater Manchester Map 07 SD80

Travel Inn

Bury New Rd M25 3AJ (junct 17 M62)
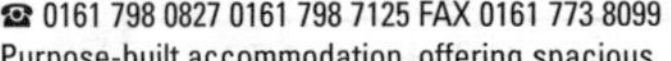
☎ 0161 798 0827 0161 798 7125 FAX 0161 773 8099
Purpose-built accommodation, offering spacious, well equipped bedrooms, all with en suite bathrooms. Meals may be taken at the nearby family restaurant. For more information about Travel Inns, consult the Contents page under Hotel Groups.
60 en suite (bth/shr)
ROOMS: d £35.50 *

PUCKERIDGE Hertfordshire Map 05 TL32

★★★ 61% **Vintage Court**
Vintage Corner SG11 1SA Turn off A10 onto A120-turn left 100 yards off roundabout, the hotel is 200 yards on the right
☎ 01920 822722 FAX 01920 822877
Closed 26 Dec-2 Jan
This hotel at the A10/A120 junction caters well for conferences, offering separate syndicate and meeting rooms and a private bar and lounge area as well as a dedicated conference help desk. Spacious accommodation is equipped with modern facilities.
25 en suite (bth/shr) No smoking in 13 bedrooms CTV in all bedrooms 80P Snooker Darts English & French Cuisine V meals Coffee am Tea pm Last d 9.15pm
ROOMS: (incl. bkfst) s £54.95-£69.95; d £62.90-£77.90 **LB**
OFF-PEAK: (incl. bkfst) s £54.95; d £62.90
MEALS: Lunch £16.85&alc Dinner £13.85-£16.85&alc
CARDS:

PUDDINGTON Cheshire Map 07 SJ37

★★★ ❀❀ 68% **Craxton Wood**
Parkgate Rd L66 9PB (leave M6 take M56 direction North Wales, take A5117, A540 direction Hoylake, Hotel is 200 yards past the traffic lights) ☎ 0151 339 4717 FAX 0151 339 1740
Closed Sun, BH, last 2 wks Aug & 1st wk Jan
This interesting hotel, run by the Petranca family for nearly 30 years is peacefully situated in its own grounds close to both the M56 and M53. The spacious bedrooms, including one or two on the ground floor and a large suite, are attractively decorated, comfortably furnished and well equipped. Service from long standing members of staff in the restaurant is professional and attentive and the cooking of Scotsman James Minnis continues to please. A good range of dishes can be chosen from the regularly changing carte, supported by daily specials. At an inspection meal our inspector plumped for a light terrine of woodland mushrooms bound with chicken, to start. The accompanying trio of sweet pepper purées was somewhat insipid compared to the full favour of the mushrooms and the chicken. The main course, poached salmon with spinach and a good full-flavoured lobster sauce, was very enjoyable. Puddings were a triumph, including traditional crème brûlée served with a bowl of summer fruits. After dinner guests can retire to the bar, the traditionally furnished lounge or, in the summer, the terrace.
14 en suite (bth/shr) CTV in all bedrooms STV No dogs (ex guide dogs) 40P No coaches French Cuisine V meals Last d 10pm
ROOMS: (incl. bkfst) s £49.50-£87.50; d £101.85-£118.50 **LB**
OFF-PEAK: (incl. bkfst & dinner) d £123-£155
MEALS: Lunch £19.85&alc Dinner £18.95-£19.85&alc*
CONF: Thtr 30 Board 20 Del from £98.85
CARDS:

PULBOROUGH West Sussex Map 04 TQ01

★★ ❀ 73% **Chequers**
Church Place RH20 1AD (off A29, opposite the church) ☎ 01798 872486 FAX 01798 872715
This delightful Queen Anne hotel stands opposite the church, overlooking the Pulborough Wild Brooks, the Arun Valley and the Sussex Downs. There is a good range of individually furnished bedrooms, well equipped with modern facilities and thoughtful extras, including some on the ground floor and one with a four-poster bed. Public areas include an elegant and comfortable lounge, conservatory coffee shop overlooking the patio and gardens which serves light meals from morning to the end of the afternoon, whilst the double-sided, stylish restaurant serves well prepared menus for dinner in more formal surroundings.
11 en suite (bth/shr) (3 fmly) No smoking in 2 bedrooms CTV in all bedrooms 16P No coaches Xmas V meals Coffee am Tea pm No smoking in restaurant Last d 8.45pm
ROOMS: (incl. bkfst) s £49.50-£54.50; d £77-£87 * **LB**
MEALS: Sunday Lunch £6-£10 High tea £4.75-£6.75 Dinner fr £16.95*
CONF: Thtr 30 Class 30 Board 20 Del from £55
CARDS:

PURFLEET Essex Map 05 TQ57

Travel Inn

High St RM16 1QA ☎ 01708 865432
FAX 01708 860852
Purpose-built accommodation, offering spacious, well equipped bedrooms, all with en suite bathrooms. Meals may be taken at the nearby family restaurant. For more information about Travel Inns, consult the Contents page under Hotel Groups.
30 en suite (bth/shr)
ROOMS: d £35.50 *

PURTON Wiltshire Map 04 SU08

★★★ ❀❀ 78% **The Pear Tree at Purton**
Church End SN5 9ED (from junct 16 of M4 follow signs to Purton, at Spar grocers turn right hotel is 0.25m on left)
☎ 01793 772100 FAX 01793 772369
An impressive former vicarage built of Cotswold stone stands in its own grounds with a landscaped Victorian garden and croquet lawn. Its situation, whilst very rural, is within five miles of the centre of Swindon and Jnc 16 of the M4. Proprietors Francis and Anne Young are totally involved in the day-to-day running of their delightful hotel and along with a team of well trained staff, offer friendly attentive service. Bedrooms are individually decorated and are given names of various characters from the village. Each room has been carefully planned to emphasise comfort and is equipped with many thoughtful extras including Sherry decanters, fresh fruit, flowers, books and magazines. There is an attractive lounge with adjoining bar area. Dinner is served in the smart conservatory restaurant, and guests can enjoy the best

local meat, poultry and fish delivered daily from a short list of imaginative dishes prepared by chef Janet Pichel-Juan.
18 en suite (bth/shr) (2 fmly) CTV in all bedrooms STV 60P No coaches Croquet lawn V meals Coffee am Tea pm Last d 9.15pm
MEALS: Lunch £17.50 Dinner £27.50
CONF: Thtr 70 Class 30 Board 30 Del from £135
CARDS:

QUORN Leicestershire Map 08 SK51

★★★★71% **Quorn Country**

Charnwood House, Leicester Rd LE12 8BB (opposite the police station) ☎ 01509 415050
FAX 01509 415557
RS 26 Dec & New Year
Set in the heart of rural Leicestershire with four acres of landscaped gardens sweeping down to the river's edge, the hotel has the character of the quintessential English country house. Behind the stone and whitewashed walls of the exterior, a magnificent reception hall with a Minster fireplace, panelled walls, mahogany staircase, oil paintings and fine antiques awaits guests seeking high levels of comfort and natural hospitality. Whilst the Orangery restaurant offers its own distinctive and contemporary style of cuisine, the Shires is more traditional. The food here though modern and imaginative is underpinned by classical techniques. The ingredients used are fresh and of good quality. A dish of salmon, brill and halibut comes variously topped with either a pastry lid or herb crust nestling in a light tomato and basil dressing. The hotel has its own smokery and duck appears regularly both as a signature main course crisply oven roasted or finely sliced with an apricot and walnut oil dressing.
20 en suite (bth/shr) (1 fmly) No smoking in 3 bedrooms CTV in all bedrooms STV Night porter Air conditioning 100P Fishing English & Continental Cuisine V meals Coffee am Tea pm Last d 9.30pm
ROOMS: s £64-£84; d £76-£96 **LB**
MEALS: Lunch £11.95-£13.90&alc Dinner £18.95-£20.90&alc
CONF: Thtr 100 Class 32 Board 26 Del from £105
CARDS:
See advertisement under LEICESTER

★★★70% **Quorn Grange**
88 Wood Ln LE12 8DB (turn off old A6 onto Wood Lane toward Swithland, hotel approx 800yds on the left)
☎ 01509 412167 FAX 01509 415621
RS 24-28 Dec
Quorn Grange is a gracious country house set peacefully amid its own extensive grounds. Hospitality is the cornerstone of the hotel together with its cuisine, which puts locally sourced ingredients to good use. Public areas have recently been refurbished and the bedrooms, most of which look out over the gardens, are individually styled and thoughtfully furnished.
15 en suite (bth/shr) CTV in all bedrooms Night porter 119P English & French Cuisine V meals Coffee am Tea pm Last d 10pm
ROOMS: s £72; d £88 * **LB**
OFF-PEAK: (incl. cont bkfst) s £50; d £64
MEALS: Lunch £8.50-£12.35&alc Dinner £17.95&alc*
CONF: Thtr 100 Class 50 Board 30 Del from £110
CARDS:

RAINHILL Merseyside Map 07 SJ49
See also St Helens

★59% **Rockland**
View Rd L35 0LG (leave M62 junc 7, take A57 towards Rainhill,after 1m turn left into View Rd, hotel 0.25m on left)
☎ 0151 426 4603 FAX 0151 426 0107
This long-established hotel, lying in pleasant lawns and gardens in a very peaceful area, has been under the same family ownership for nearly sixty years. Local groups and societies regularly use the hotel for meetings and lunches. The bedrooms are modestly appointed, but all have modern en suite or private bathrooms. Self-catering chalets are also available in the grounds, and there is ample parking.
11 rms (9 bth 1 shr) (2 fmly) CTV in all bedrooms 30P V meals Coffee am Tea pm Last d 8.15pm
ROOMS: (incl. bkfst) s £25-£33.50; d £35-£44 * **LB**
MEALS: Sunday Lunch £5.50-£8.50 Dinner £10.75&alc
CARDS:

RAMSBOTTOM Greater Manchester Map 07 SD71

★★★63% **Old Mill**
Springwood BL0 9DS ☎ 01706 822991 FAX 01706 822291
Further improvements are being made to this long established, privately owned hotel, which enjoys the most marvellous views from its elevated position above the town. The older bedrooms have been refurbished and have new bathrooms and the more modern rooms have been redecorated. All the bedrooms, however, are quite compact, but well equipped. Guests have the choice of two restaurants, one less formal than the other and relaxing afterwards in the first floor lounge, bar, or, for the more energetic, working off the calories in the leisure centre. Recent additions to the hotel include a honeymoon suite and a couple of new meeting rooms.
36 en suite (bth) (3 fmly) CTV in all bedrooms No dogs Night porter 85P Indoor swimming pool (heated) Sauna Solarium Gym Xmas French & Italian Cuisine V meals Coffee am Tea pm
ROOMS: (incl. bkfst) s £31.50-£45.50; d £46-£65 * **LB**
CONF: Thtr 75 Class 24 Board 36 Del from £43.50
CARDS:
See advertisement under MANCHESTER

RAMSGATE Kent Map 05 TR36

★★★65% **San Clu**
Victoria Pde, East Cliff CT11 8DT (opposite Granville Theatre)
☎ 01843 592345 FAX 01843 580157
Enjoying a quiet location overlooking the sea not far from the Sally Ferry Terminal, this Victorian hotel featuring balconies has been completely refurbished and upgraded to provide comfortable well furnished and well equipped bedrooms. A popular bar-lounge offers a good range of real ales and bar meals, whilst an attractively decorated

contd.

R

restaurant provides relaxing and well appointed surroundings for dining. The hotel is also geared up for business with a good range of meeting rooms, and facilities for wedding receptions. Service is friendly, informal and well managed.
44 en suite (bth/shr) (14 fmly) CTV in all bedrooms Lift Night porter 16P Xmas International Cuisine V meals Coffee am Tea pm Last d 9.15pm
ROOMS: (incl. bkfst) s £40-£70; d £60-£130 * **LB**
OFF-PEAK: (incl. bkfst) s £37-£70; d £50-£130
MEALS: Sunday Lunch fr £10.50 High tea fr £10 Dinner £9.50-£12.50&alc*
CONF: Thtr 180 Class 100 Board 100 Del from £55
CARDS:

See advertisement on opposite page

RAMSGILL North Yorkshire Map 07 SE17

★★71% **Yorke Arms**
HG3 5RL (turn off A61 at Ripley onto B6165 to Pateley Bridge. Turn right at Nidderdale Motors) ☎ 01423 755243 FAX 01423 755243
RS 25 Dec
This creeper-clad hotel situated in Upper Nidderdale, close to the beautiful Gouthwaite reservoir, offers elegantly comfortable public areas and mainly modern bedrooms which are all well equipped and delightfully furnished. Carefully prepared dinners are served in an attractive restaurant where the emphasis is on local produce.
13 en suite (bth/shr) (2 fmly) CTV in all bedrooms No dogs (ex guide dogs) 20P Xmas English & Continental Cuisine V meals Coffee am Tea pm No smoking in restaurant Last d 9pm
ROOMS: (incl. bkfst) s £40-£50; d £60-£100 * **LB**
MEALS: Lunch £12.25-£15 Dinner £19.25-£21.25*
CONF: Thtr 10 Class 10 Del from £85
CARDS:

RANGEWORTHY Gloucestershire Map 03 ST68

★★74% **Rangeworthy Court**
Church Ln, Wotton Rd BS17 5ND (signposted off B4058)
☎ 01454 228347 FAX 01454 228945
There is a welcoming atmosphere at this impressive creeper-clad manor house, which is set in its own well tended gardens with an outdoor swimming pool. Conscientious and friendly owners Mervyn and Lucia Gillett have created a comfortable hotel of enormous character and charm, and along with a team of willing staff provide attentive services and good food. There is a choice of cosy lounges with log fires, and many original features such as mullioned windows, solid oak beams and flag-stone floors have been retained throughout the building. Bedrooms are well proportioned and have been equipped with modern facilities. Chef Peter Knight provides a choice of menus, offering interesting dishes with honest textures and flavours, prepared from local produce.
14 en suite (bth/shr) (4 fmly) CTV in all bedrooms STV 40P No coaches Outdoor swimming pool (heated) Xmas V meals Coffee am No smoking area in restaurant Last d 9pm
ROOMS: (incl. bkfst) s £53-£60; d £68-£82 * **LB**
OFF-PEAK: (incl. bkfst) s fr £45; d fr £58
MEALS: Lunch £10.95-£15alc Dinner fr £18alc
CONF: Thtr 22 Class 16 Board 16 Del from £88
CARDS:

See advertisement under BRISTOL

RAVENSCAR North Yorkshire Map 08 NZ90

★★★60% ***Raven Hall***
YO13 0ET ☎ 01723 870353 FAX 01723 870072
Occupying one of the most dramatic locations on England's coastline, this impressive hotel stands in 100 acres of grounds and gardens some 600 feet above sea level and enjoys superb views towards Robin Hood's Bay. The bedrooms are traditional in style as is the dining room where a satisfactory range of food is available. Public areas are also in keeping with a country mansion.
53 en suite (bth/shr) (22 fmly) No smoking in 1 bedroom CTV in all bedrooms No dogs Night porter 203P Indoor swimming pool (heated) Outdoor swimming pool Golf 9 Tennis (hard) Snooker Sauna Croquet lawn Putting green Crown green bowls Giant chess Wkly live entertainment V meals Coffee am Tea pm Last d 8.45pm
CARDS:

See advertisement under SCARBOROUGH

RAVENSTONEDALE Cumbria Map 07 NY70

★★70% **Black Swan**
CA17 4NG ☎ 015396 23204 FAX 015396 23604
This friendly hotel is the focal point of a picturesque village only ten minutes drive from the M6. Known for its good food and real ales, one can dine either in the attractive little dining room with its antique furniture and sparkling table appointments, or in the cosy bar where a log fire burns on cooler nights. Bedrooms are well equipped and come in a variety of sizes, including three ground floor chalet-style rooms with their own front doors.
14 rms (11 bth/shr) 4 annexe en suite (bth/shr) (1 fmly) CTV in all bedrooms 30P No coaches Tennis (hard) Fishing Xmas V meals Coffee am Tea pm No smoking in restaurant Last d 9.15pm
ROOMS: (incl. bkfst) s £30-£45; d £50-£70 * **LB**
OFF-PEAK: (incl. bkfst) s £25-£45; d £40-£70
MEALS: Lunch £9.75&alc High tea £6.50 Dinner £23&alc*
CARDS:

See advertisement under KIRKBY STEPHEN

★★65% **The Fat Lamb**
Crossbank CA17 4LL (on A683) ☎ 01539 623242 FAX 01539 623285
Dating from the 17th century and originally a farmhouse, the Fat Lamb is now a roadside country inn in a moorland setting high above the village. It retains its traditional character: the bar features an old range whose fire is still lit on cold days, whilst paintings of the area, along with old prints, adorn the walls. Bedrooms are contained in both the original house and a ground-floor extension. TVs can be provided on request. An extensive bar menu, plus blackboard specials, complement the fixed-price dinner menu.
12 en suite (bth/shr) (4 fmly) No smoking in all bedrooms CTV in all bedrooms 60P Fishing Private 5 acre nature reserve Xmas V meals Coffee am Tea pm No smoking in restaurant Last d 9pm
ROOMS: (incl. bkfst) s £30-£33; d £52-£56 * **LB**
MEALS: Lunch £10.50-£11.50 Dinner £17*

READING Berkshire Map 04 SU77

Telephone numbers are likely to change during the currency of this guide. See also Wokingham

★★★★61% **Holiday Inn**

Caversham Bridge, Richfield Av RG1 8BD (M4 junct 10/A329M to Reading. Join A4 follow signs to Caversham) ☎ 0118 9259988 FAX 0118 9391665

This modern hotel by Caversham Bridge offers attractive views of the Thames from many of its rooms. A high canopied ceiling emphasises the spaciousness of the open-plan lobby, restaurant and bar, and there is a separate pub-bar. Well equipped bedrooms are all in a practical modern style.
111 en suite (bth/shr) No smoking in 15 bedrooms CTV in all bedrooms STV Lift Night porter 200P Indoor swimming pool (heated) Sauna Solarium Gym Aromatherapy Beauty treatment Xmas International Cuisine V meals Coffee am Tea pm No smoking area in restaurant Last d 10pm
ROOMS: d fr £106 * **LB**
OFF-PEAK: (incl. bkfst) d fr £62
MEALS: Lunch £9.95-£11.95&alc High tea fr £6.75 Dinner fr £17.95&alc*
CONF: Thtr 200 Class 160 Board 76 Del £146
CARDS:

★★★69% **Courtyard by Marriott Reading**
Bath Rd, Padworth RG7 5HT (leave the M4 at junct 12 and follow A4 towards Newbury, hotel is 3.5m on left) ☎ 01734 714411 FAX 01734 714442

This modern purpose built hotel allows easy access to the M4, Reading and Newbury. Bedrooms are comfortably furnished, air-conditioned and boast a comprehensive range of modern amenities. The reception area features an attractive galleried lounge. A selection of dishes offered on the carte is supplemented by a small choice of daily specials.
50 en suite (bth/shr) No smoking in 14 bedrooms CTV in all bedrooms STV No dogs (ex guide dogs) Night porter Air conditioning 200P Sauna Solarium V meals Coffee am No smoking in restaurant Last d 9.45pm
ROOMS: d fr £75 * **LB**
OFF-PEAK: d fr £47
MEALS: Lunch fr £9.95 Dinner fr £14&alc*
CONF: Thtr 200 Class 100 Board 50 Del £120
CARDS:

★★★62% **Euro International**
648-654 Oxford Rd RG30 1EH ☎ 01734 500541 FAX 01734 567220
This purpose-built modern hotel is within easy reach of the city centre and is an excellent choice for the business traveller. Bedrooms are bright, spacious and well equipped with plenty of desk space. The comfortable lounge bar is furnished with leather sofas and is a relaxing place to have a drink. Whilst the current kitchen operation is rather limited plans are afoot to improve this aspect of the hotel.
80 en suite (bth/shr) (6 fmly) No smoking in 17 bedrooms CTV in all bedrooms Night porter 200P International Cuisine V meals Coffee am Tea pm Last d 9.30pm
ROOMS: (incl. bkfst) s £55-£65; d £75-£85 *
OFF-PEAK: (incl. bkfst) s fr £55; d £65-£75
MEALS: Lunch £12.95-£15&alc Dinner £12.95-£15&alc
CONF: Thtr 100 Class 60 Board 40 Del £89
CARDS:

R

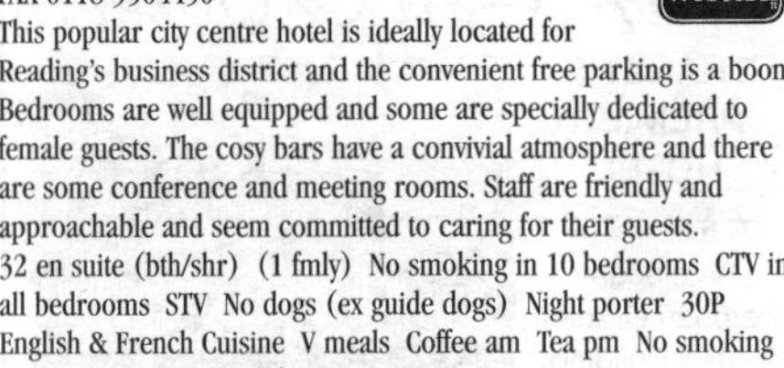

★★★61% **Ship**
4-8 Duke St RG1 4RY ☎ 0118 9583455
FAX 0118 9504450
This popular city centre hotel is ideally located for Reading's business district and the convenient free parking is a boon. Bedrooms are well equipped and some are specially dedicated to female guests. The cosy bars have a convivial atmosphere and there are some conference and meeting rooms. Staff are friendly and approachable and seem committed to caring for their guests.
32 en suite (bth/shr) (1 fmly) No smoking in 10 bedrooms CTV in all bedrooms STV No dogs (ex guide dogs) Night porter 30P English & French Cuisine V meals Coffee am Tea pm No smoking area in restaurant Last d 9.30pm
ROOMS: s fr £77; d fr £87 * **LB**
OFF-PEAK: (incl. bkfst) s fr £30; d fr £60
CONF: Thtr 50 Class 30 Board 30 Del from £75
CARDS:

★★65% **Rainbow Corner**
132-138 Caversham Rd RG1 8AY (from junct 11 of M4 take A327 to town centre then follow signs to Caversham) ☎ 01734 588140
FAX 01734 586500
Located to the north of the city centre, with its own private parking area, this establishment is made up of three terraced houses knocked together to create a cosy hotel with modern comforts. Its enduring popularity is due, in part, to the genuinely friendly nature of most of the staff and the relaxed and informal atmosphere.
22 en suite (bth/shr) (1 fmly) CTV in all bedrooms STV Night porter 15P No coaches V meals Coffee am Tea pm Last d 9.30pm
ROOMS: s £38-£54; d £46-£59 * **LB**
MEALS: Lunch £9.95-£12.95&alc High tea £6.50&alc Dinner £12.95&alc*
CONF: Thtr 30 Class 30 Board 20
CARDS:

See advertisement on page 511

Forte Posthouse Reading

Basingstoke Rd RG2 0SL (from junct 11 on M4 follow A33 towards Reading. Hotel 0.5m on left)
☎ 01734 875485 FAX 01734 311958
Suitable for both the business and leisure traveller, this bright hotel provides modern accommodation in well equipped bedrooms with en suite bathrooms. For more details about Forte Posthouse hotels, consult the Contents page for the section on Hotel Groups.
138 en suite (bth/shr)
ROOMS: d £89 *
CONF: Thtr 100 Class 50 Board 45 Del from £119

Travelodge

387 Basingstoke Rd RG2 0JE (on A33, southbound)
☎ 01734 750618 FAX 01734 750618
This modern building offers accommodation in smart, spacious and well equipped bedrooms, suitable for family use, and all with en suite bathrooms. Meals may be taken at the nearby family restaurant. For information on room rates and to make a booking, call Roomline free of charge on 0800 850950. For more details about Travelodge, consult the Contents page under Hotel Groups.
36 en suite (bth/shr)

Travelodge
Reading Service Area RG30 3UQ
☎ Central Res 0800 850950 FAX 01734 595444
This modern building offers accommodation in smart, spacious and well equipped bedrooms, suitable for family use, and all with en suite bathrooms. Meals may be taken at the nearby family restaurant. For information on room rates and to make a booking, call Roomline free of charge on 0800 850950. For more details about Travelodge, consult the Contents page under Hotel Groups.
40 en suite (bth/shr)

REDDITCH Hereford & Worcester Map 07 SP06

★★★62% **Southcrest**
Pool Bank, Southcrest B97 4JS (follow signs to hotel, 2nd on right after B & Q DIY store) ☎ 01527 541511 FAX 01527 402600
Closed 24 Dec-2 Jan & BH's RS Sun evenings
This large, privately owned hotel is set in extensive wooded grounds just south of the town centre and is reached by following the signs to 'Other Redditch Districts' and then 'Southcrest'. Originally a country house dating back to the beginning of the century, it has been considerably extended over the last 25 years. Bedrooms in the main house are spacious and two have four-poster beds; the majority of them (including some on the ground floor) are located in a new wing, and they are all soundly maintained and well equipped. As well as a small traditionally furnished bar and an attractive restaurant, there are function suites and meeting rooms which are much in demand by local businesses.
58 en suite (bth/shr) (2 fmly) CTV in all bedrooms STV Night porter 100P French Cuisine V meals Coffee am Last d 9.15pm
ROOMS: (incl. bkfst) s fr £63; d fr £70 * **LB**
OFF-PEAK: (incl. bkfst) s fr £35; d fr £42
CONF: Thtr 90 Class 30 Board 40 Del £75
CARDS:

★★63% ***Hotel Montyville***
101 Mount Pleasant, Southcrest B97 4JE ☎ 01527 544411 & 402566
FAX 01527 544341
This privately owned hotel is situated less than half a mile from the town centre and is located in the Southcrest district of Redditch. It provides modern furnished and equipped accommodation, catering mainly for business people, but it is equally suitable for other visitors. Public areas include the pleasant 'Granny's' restaurant which is decorated and furnished in Victorian style and has an abundance of period bric-a-brac. A similarly themed lounge bar is adjacent.
16 en suite (bth/shr) (2 fmly) No smoking in 5 bedrooms CTV in all bedrooms 12P No coaches Use of nearby sports & fitness centre International Cuisine V meals Coffee am Last d 10pm
CARDS:

Campanile

Far Moor Ln, Winyates Green B98 0SD (A435 towards Redditch, then A4023 Redditch/Bromsgrove) ☎ 01527 510710
FAX 01527 517269

The bar and Bistro restaurant provide meals and refreshments. Bedrooms are well equipped and have en suite bathrooms. For more details about Campanile, consult the Contents page under Hotel Groups.
50 annexe en suite (bth/shr)
CONF: Thtr 40 Class 25 Board 25

REDHILL Surrey Map 04 TQ25
See also Nutfield

★★67% **Lakers**
2 Redstone Hill RH1 4BL ☎ 01737 768434
FAX 01737 768828

Closed 25 Dec-1 Jan
This former coaching inn has modern bedrooms and is located close to the town centre. The restaurant, which has recently undergone a major refurbishment, serves Toby's popular range of meals.
33 en suite (bth/shr) 4 annexe en suite (bth/shr) (4 fmly) No smoking in 17 bedrooms CTV in all bedrooms STV No dogs (ex guide dogs) Night porter Pool table V meals Coffee am Tea pm Last d 10pm
MEALS: Lunch £6.95-£15 Dinner £6.95-£15alc*
CONF: Thtr 50 Board 25 Del from £65
CARDS:

Redhill Travel Inn
Brighton Rd, Salfords RH1 5BT ☎ 01737 767277
FAX 01737 778099

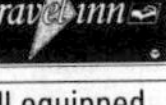

Purpose-built accommodation, offering spacious, well equipped bedrooms, all with en suite bathrooms. Meals may be taken at the nearby family restaurant. For more information about Travel Inns, consult the Contents page under Hotel Groups.
49 en suite (bth/shr)
ROOMS: d £35.50 *

REDRUTH Cornwall & Isles of Scilly Map 02 SW64

★★★66% ***Penventon***
TR15 1TE ☎ 01209 214141 FAX 01209 219164
The Pascoe family have owned this fine Georgian manor house, set in its own extensive grounds, for a quarter of century, but time has hardly stood still when it comes to guest comfort. Public areas are lavishly furnished and a range of French, Italian and English dishes, over a hundred in total, is offered in The Dining Galleries. Also, the new Spice of Life bar, adjacent to the hotel, provides a more informal atmosphere. Bedrooms are more simply designed whilst still enjoying the required facilities and levels of comfort.
50 en suite (bth/shr) (3 fmly) CTV in all bedrooms Night porter 100P Indoor swimming pool (heated) Snooker Sauna Solarium Gym Pool table Jacuzzi/spa Leisure spa Masseuse Steam bath Wkly live entertainment ch fac English French & Italian Cuisine V meals Coffee am Tea pm Last d 9.30pm
CARDS:

★★69% **Aviary Court**
Mary's Well, Illogan TR16 4QZ (off A3047)
☎ 01209 842256 FAX 01209 843744

A charming period property, situated between Redruth and Portreath, Aviary Court is set in well tended gardens on the edge of Illogan Woods. The Studley family work well as a team to provide friendly and attentive service. Each bedrooms is individually furnished and decorated, and there are thoughtful extras such as fresh fruit, bottled mineral water and fresh flowers. Public areas are comfortable and cosy, while in the attractive restaurant Mrs Studley makes use of quality Cornish produce in the generous meals.
6 en suite (bth/shr) (1 fmly) CTV in all bedrooms No dogs 25P No coaches No children 3yrs English & French Cuisine No smoking in restaurant Last d 8.45pm
ROOMS: (incl. bkfst) s £38-£42; d £54-£58 *
MEALS: Sunday Lunch £8.50 Dinner fr £13&alc*
CONF: Thtr 20 Class 20 Board 20
CARDS:

★★68% **Crossroads**
Scorrier TR16 5BP (off A30) ☎ 01209 820551 FAX 01209 820392
Conveniently situated at Scorrier, some 2miles north of Redruth with easy access off the A30, this modern, purpose built hotel is equally suited to both the business and leisure user. The bedrooms fall into two categories, standard and executive rooms, the latter being larger and furnished in a more modern style. All rooms are well equipped. A feature of the hotel is the high level of room service provided. In the restaurant guests have the option of dining from the value for money fixed price menu or from the carte which features a wide range of interesting dishes.
35 en suite (bth/shr) (4 fmly) No smoking in 2 bedrooms CTV in all bedrooms Lift 140P English & French Cuisine V meals Coffee am Tea pm Last d 9.30pm
ROOMS: (incl. bkfst) s £31-£47.50; d £40-£58 * **LB**
MEALS: Lunch £8.50-£10&alc Dinner £11-£13&alc
CONF: Thtr 100 Class 30 Board 30
CARDS:

REDWORTH Co Durham Map 08 NZ22

★★★★72% **Redworth Hall Hotel & Country Club**
DL5 6NL (off A6072) ☎ 01388 772442 FAX 01388 775112
A very impressive Jacobean mansion has been carefully extended and furnished to provide this very comfortable and inviting hotel. Lounges are spacious and two restaurants are available - the Conservatory Room offering more traditional meals (including a carvery option), while the Blue Room allows the chef scope to display his skill in the preparation of a range of dishes which are a delight to the eye as well as the palate. Caring, attentive service is well supervised by a professional management team. The hotel already has an excellent leisure centre, and a golf course is planned for the future.
100 en suite (bth/shr) (10 fmly) No smoking in 30 bedrooms CTV in all bedrooms STV Lift Night porter Air conditioning 200P Indoor swimming pool (heated) Tennis (hard) Squash Snooker Sauna Solarium Gym Croquet lawn Spa pool Xmas English & Continental Cuisine V meals Coffee am Tea pm No smoking area in restaurant Last d 9.45pm
ROOMS: (incl. bkfst) s £103-£112; d £120-£155 * **LB**
OFF-PEAK: (incl. bkfst) s fr £57; d fr £114
MEALS: Lunch £11.50-£12.50 Dinner £18.50-£29.95&alc*
CONF: Thtr 300 Class 150 Board 40 Del from £85
CARDS:

REIGATE Surrey Map 04 TQ25

★★★65% **Reigate Manor Hotel**
Reigate Hill RH2 9PF (on A217, 1m S of junct 8 on M25) ☎ 01737 240125 FAX 01737 223883
This well established and steadily improving hotel is located on the A217 fairly close to the M25. It is a popular venue for meetings, conferences and social functions. Bedrooms are spacious and well maintained and the hotel also has leisure facilities as well as a large car park. Fresh-tasting meals are served in Friths restaurant which is overseen by pleasant staff.

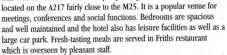

contd.

50 en suite (bth/shr) (1 fmly) No smoking in 18 bedrooms CTV in all bedrooms STV No dogs (ex guide dogs) Night porter 130P Sauna Solarium Gym English & French Cuisine V meals Coffee am Tea pm Last d 10pm
ROOMS: (incl. bkfst) s £76-£80; d £90-£99 * **LB**
OFF-PEAK: (incl. bkfst) s £45-£50; d £60-£65
MEALS: Lunch £10.95-£16&alc Dinner £18.50-£19.50&alc*
CONF: Thtr 200 Class 80 Board 50 Del from £100
CARDS:

★★★63% **Bridge House**
Reigate Hill RH2 9RP (on A217 between M25 and Reigate)
☎ 01737 246801 & 244821 FAX 01737 223756
RS BH
This very popular hotel and restaurant commands panoramic views over the surrounding countryside from its setting on top of Reigate Hill. Spacious front-facing bedrooms with a furnished balcony come equipped with modern amenities and good-size bathrooms. The restaurant, which features live entertainment and dancing four nights a week, forms a major part of the hotel's success with Chef David Dunn maintaining traditional standards of professional cookery, including gueridon and flambé, à la carte and table d'hÙte choices. Restaurant service is rather formal but attentive and friendly. Conferences and functions are catered for in the Calder and Kingswood Suites.
40 en suite (bth/shr) (3 fmly) CTV in all bedrooms No dogs Night porter 110P Wkly live entertainment Xmas English, French & Italian Cuisine V meals Coffee am Last d 10pm
ROOMS: s £40-£62; d £60-£70 *
MEALS: Lunch £8.75-£14.50&alc Dinner £16.75-£21.75&alc*
CONF: Thtr 100 Class 70 Board 60 Del from £86.50
CARDS:

RENISHAW Derbyshire Map 08 SK47

★★★58% **Sitwell Arms**
Station Rd S31 9WF (on A616 W of junct 30 of M1) ☎ 01246 435226 FAX 01246 433915
Whilst technically in Derbyshire the hotel lies a few miles east of Sheffield just off Junction 30 of the M1. It is a well equipped hotel, the public areas furnished in a contemporary Inn design with plenty of exposed timbers and comfortable lounging areas. Bedrooms are spacious and comfortable.
30 en suite (bth/shr) No smoking in 10 bedrooms CTV in all bedrooms No dogs (ex guide dogs) Night porter 150P Xmas V meals Coffee am Tea pm No smoking area in restaurant Last d 9.45pm
ROOMS: (incl. bkfst) s £29.95-£49.50; d £49.50-£59.50 * **LB**
OFF-PEAK: (incl. bkfst) s £21-£29.95; d £42-£45
MEALS: Lunch £6.75-£7.95&alc Dinner £9.95-£17.50alc*
CONF: Thtr 160 Class 60 Board 60
CARDS:
See advertisement under SHEFFIELD

RICHMOND North Yorkshire Map 07 NZ10

★★68% **King's Head**
Market Place DL10 4HS (in Richmond Market Place, 5m from A1/A66 at Scotch Corner on the A6108)
CONSORT HOTELS
☎ 01748 850220 FAX 01748 850635
The historic King's Head Hotel stands in the old cobbled market square and has a delightful Georgian facade. There are spacious and inviting lounges featuring a collection of old clocks and also contains many interesting antiques. The bedrooms are well equipped and pleasantly decorated and many of the rooms also have antique furniture. A good range of interesting dishes is served in the first floor restaurant and bar meals are also available.
24 en suite (bth/shr) 4 annexe en suite (bth/shr) (1 fmly) No smoking in 11 bedrooms CTV in all bedrooms Night porter 25P Xmas International Cuisine V meals Coffee am Tea pm No smoking in restaurant Last d 9.15pm
ROOMS: (incl. bkfst) s £45-£53; d £70-£97 * **LB**
OFF-PEAK: (incl. bkfst & dinner) s £55.50-£63.50; d £91-£118
MEALS: Sunday Lunch £6.95-£9.50 Dinner fr £14.95&alc*
CONF: Thtr 180 Class 80 Board 50 Del from £75
CARDS:

★★60% **Frenchgate**
59-61 Frenchgate DL10 7AE (turn left at mini-roundabout by Methodist Church, take next left into Frenchgate)
☎ 01748 822087 & 823596 FAX 01748 823596
Closed 26 Dec-Jan
This attractive Georgian house is located in a quiet cobbled street by one of the historic gates to the town. The bedrooms are simply furnished but are equipped with modern facilities, whilst the public rooms feature a Mousey Thompson fireplace in the comfortable upstairs lounge. A good range of food is available in the attractive and cosy dining room and service is attentive and friendly. A delightful garden is to be found at the rear of the hotel.
13 rms (3 bth 4 shr) No smoking in 2 bedrooms CTV in all bedrooms 6P No coaches No children 7yrs V meals Last d 8pm
ROOMS: (incl. bkfst) s £28-£37; d £53-£60 * **LB**
CARDS:

RICHMOND UPON THAMES Greater London
See LONDON SECTION plan 1 C2

★★★★74% **Richmond Gate**
Richmond Hill TW10 6RP ☎ 0181 940 0061 FAX 0181 332 0354
This Georgian country house is situated on the crest of Richmond Hill, close to the Royal Park and Terrace, and has distant views down towards the River Thames. There is a particularly good range of stylish bedrooms, all equipped to a very high standard, including luxury doubles and suites, smaller garden wing rooms, and several four-posters. The best rooms,furnished with antiques, are located in the main house. There is a choice of restaurants: the informal Victorian conservatory bistro and the candlelit Gates on the Park restaurant. The spectacular new Cedars health and leisure club is now fully open and is equipped with every high quality facility, including a swimming pool and coffee bar. Other features are the extensive private rooms for functions and meetings, 24-hour room service, night porter, cocktail bar and several lounges. Service is well managed, attentive and helpful.
66 en suite (bth/shr) (2 fmly) No smoking in 12 bedrooms CTV in all bedrooms STV No dogs (ex guide dogs) Night porter 50P Indoor swimming pool (heated) Squash Sauna Solarium Gym Croquet lawn Jacuzzi/spa Wkly live entertainment Xmas International Cuisine V meals Coffee am Tea pm No smoking in restaurant Last d 10pm
ROOMS: (incl. bkfst) s £105; d £125 * **LB**
OFF-PEAK: (incl. bkfst) s £80; d £100

CONF: Thtr 50 Class 25 Board 30 Del from £139.50
CARDS:

★★★70% **Richmond Hill**

Richmond Hill TW10 6RW (located at the top of Richmond Hill on B321) ☎ 0181 940 2247 & 0181 940 5466 FAX 0181 940 5424

The Georgian Manor at the heart of this popular hotel was built in about 1726, but has been considerably extended in recent years to provide a good range of modern bedrooms equipped with every amenity. The original bedrooms have now been completely refurbished to include suites, large singles, four-poster and family rooms. The smart restaurant features the enthusiastic and enterprising cooking of chef Jean Claude Seraille. There is an impressive healh club and good facilities for meetings.

127 en suite (bth/shr) (9 fmly) No smoking in 31 bedrooms CTV in all bedrooms STV Lift Night porter 150P Indoor swimming pool (heated) Squash Sauna Solarium Gym Jacuzzi/spa Wkly live entertainment Xmas English & French Cuisine V meals Coffee am Tea pm No smoking area in restaurant Last d 9.30pm
ROOMS: (incl. bkfst) s £100-£110; d £120-£130 * **LB**
MEALS: Lunch £14-£16&alc Dinner £19.50-£21.50&alc*
CONF: Thtr 200 Class 150 Board 50 Del from £145
CARDS:

RINGWOOD Hampshire Map 04 SU10

★★★ 69% **Tyrrells Ford Country House**

Avon BH23 7BH (turn off A31 to Ringwood. Follow B3347, Hotel 3m S on left at Avon)
☎ 01425 672646 FAX 01425 672262

This family owned country house hotel is situated in ten acres of woodland and gardens on the B3347 out of Ringwood. The staff are friendly and capable, making it a popular choice for business and leisure guests alike. The wood-panelled restaurant offers a daily changing menu in addition to a small carte of traditional and modern dishes. The bedrooms are comfortably furnished and well equipped with modern en suite facilities; the hotel also has conference facilities and is a popular venue for wedding receptions.

16 en suite (bth/shr) CTV in all bedrooms No dogs (ex guide dogs) 100P Xmas English & French Cuisine V meals Coffee am No smoking in restaurant Last d 9.30pm
ROOMS: (incl. bkfst) s £60-£75; d £80-£100 * **LB**
OFF-PEAK: (incl. bkfst) s £55-£65
MEALS: Lunch £12.95-£14.95 Dinner £18.95*
CONF: Thtr 40 Class 40 Board 30 Del from £100
CARDS:
See advertisement under CHRISTCHURCH

★★ 73% **Moortown Lodge Hotel**

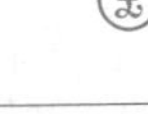

244 Christchurch Rd BH24 3AS (off A31 onto B3347. Hotel 1.5m S on right) ☎ 01425 471404
FAX 01425 476052

Closed 24 Dec-mid Jan

This delightful little hotel is personally run by Jilly and Bob Burrows-Jones, who provide a warm welcome to their guests. The bedrooms are cosy and attractively decorated with modern en suite shower facilities and extra home comforts. Jilly is the chef and produces an excellent set menu every night. A favourite starter is a beautifully light floating cheese island. The main courses include some locally sourced game and fish prepared in a traditional way with good clean flavours. The wine list places an emphasis on France but includes some New World and European listings, and there is a good range of half bottles.

6 rms (2 bth 3 shr) (1 fmly) No smoking in 3 bedrooms CTV in all bedrooms No dogs 8P No coaches British & French Cuisine V meals No smoking in restaurant Last d 8.30pm
ROOMS: (incl. bkfst) s £38-£45; d £50-£80 * **LB**
MEALS: Dinner £16.95-£18.95&alc
CARDS:

★★59% **Candlesticks Inn**

136 Christchurch Rd BH24 3AP (from M27/A31, take B3347 towards Christchurch) ☎ 01425 472587 FAX 01425 472587

This charming 15th-century cottage is handily placed for visiting both the New Forest and the coast. Bedrooms are spacious and comfortably furnished, and all have en suite showers, colour television and telephones. The cosy restaurant has low-beamed ceilings, open fires and plenty of old world charm, and a good variety of traditional and French dishes are served there. A range of snacks is also available in the conservatory bar, which is very popular in the summer.

8 en suite (shr) (4 fmly) CTV in all bedrooms No dogs 45P Jacuzzi planned for Oct 1996 English & French Cuisine V meals Coffee am No smoking area in restaurant Last d 9pm
ROOMS: (incl. bkfst) s £27.50-£31.50; d £45-£48 * **LB**
MEALS: Lunch £2.25-£6.95 Dinner £9.95&alc
CARDS:

RIPON North Yorkshire Map 08 SE37

★★★67% **Ripon Spa**

Park St HG4 2BU (on B6265 Pateley Bridge road)
☎ 01765 602172 FAX 01765 690770

This long-established hotel provides traditional services in modern surroundings. The grounds are particularly attractive and croquet is played on the lawns during summer months. Two bars are available, a cocktail bar serves diners and residents and the Turf Bar is available for snacks and less formal meals. The impressive restaurant serves from a daily menu and a carte choice of popular dishes. Bedrooms are mostly spacious and modern facilities are provided. Weddings and other functions are popular locally and regular Jazz and Bridge events are held.

40 en suite (bth/shr) (5 fmly) CTV in all bedrooms STV Lift Night porter 80P V meals Coffee am Tea pm
CONF: Thtr 150 Class 80 Board 100
CARDS:

★★61% **Unicorn**

Market Place HG4 1BP (on south east corner of Market Place)
☎ 01765 602202 FAX 01765 690734
Closed 24-25 Dec

A historic inn, standing in the market square, which continues to improve. It offers pleasantly furnished bedrooms and is continuing to improve its standards. The public rooms include a popular bar and a cosy rear dining room where a good range of dishes is available. There is car parking to the rear which is to be found via the supermarket car park.

33 en suite (bth/shr) (4 fmly) CTV in all bedrooms Night porter 20P English & French Cuisine V meals Coffee am Last d 9pm
ROOMS: (incl. bkfst) s £45-£55; d £59-£67 * **LB**
MEALS: Lunch £4.95-£6.75alc Dinner £12-£15&alc*
CONF: Thtr 60 Class 10 Board 26 Del from £65
CARDS:

RISLEY Derbyshire Map 08 SK43

★★★70% **Risley Hall**
Derby Rd DE72 3SS (off junct 25 on M1, Sandiacre exit, left at T junct, 0.5m on left) ☎ 01159 399000 FAX 01159 397766
RS Sun
This magnificent fairly new hotel, built in the early part of the 18th century but with parts that date from 1524, is set amongst beautiful, well tended gardens. It is conveniently situated midway between Nottingham and Derby on the A52 intersection of the M1 (Junction 25). The well equipped bedrooms, which are individually decorated and furnished with interesting fabrics and soft furnishings, exude quality and comfort. Public areas include a comfortably furnished morning room, a choice of bars, a couple of meeting rooms and the most magnificent baronial hall, which is an ideal venue for weddings and banqueting functions. Food is of a high standard, and service is professional and attentive.
16 en suite (bth/shr) (8 fmly) CTV in all bedrooms STV No dogs (ex guide dogs) Lift Night porter Air conditioning 100P Indoor swimming pool (heated) Snooker Gym Pool table Croquet lawn Jacuzzi/spa Archery Xmas European Cuisine V meals Coffee am Tea pm No smoking in restaurant Last d 9pm
ROOMS: (incl. bkfst) s £50-£85; d £60-£95 * **LB**
MEALS: Lunch £10.95-£14.95 High tea £2.95-£6.95 Dinner £15.95-£16.95*
CARDS:
See advertisement under DERBY

ROBIN HOOD'S BAY North Yorkshire Map 08 NZ90

★62% **Grosvenor**
Station Rd YO22 4RA ☎ 01947 880320
Standing in the upper part of the village and opposite the tennis courts, this family-owned hotel provides functional bedrooms which are well equipped, whilst the public rooms are comfortable and include two lounges and a separate bar. A good range of dishes is available both in the dining room and the bar, and service is friendly and attentive.
12 rms (5 bth/shr) (2 fmly) CTV in 6 bedrooms No dogs (ex guide dogs) No coaches Coffee am Last d 9pm
ROOMS: (incl. bkfst) s £21-£23.50; d £42-£47 *
CARDS:

ROCHDALE Greater Manchester Map 07 SD81

★★★66% **Norton Grange**
Macdonald Hotels
Manchester Rd, Castleton OL11 2XZ (beside A664)
☎ 01706 30788 FAX 01706 49313
A much extended Victorian property, Norton Grange is set in nine acres of landscaped gardens. Bedrooms are equipped to a modern standard and include ground-floor, no-smoking and family rooms, plus a full suite. Public areas offer a choice of bars and extensive conference and banqueting facilities.
51 en suite (bth/shr) (28 fmly) No smoking in 25 bedrooms CTV in all bedrooms Lift Night porter 150P International Cuisine V meals Coffee am Tea pm No smoking in restaurant
ROOMS: s fr £92; d fr £114 * **LB**
CONF: Thtr 180 Class 80 Board 60
CARDS:

★★57% **Midway**

Manchester Rd, Castleton OL11 2XX (off M62 junct 20, A627, then A664, 0.5m on right) ☎ 01706 32881
FAX 01706 53522
This medium-sized hotel, made up of two older houses with a modern extension between them, is conveniently situated just outside the town on the A664. Some improvements have been made and more are planned, but in the meantime the majority of the bedrooms are limited in terms of their quality and comfort. In the original part of the house there are a number of more recently refurbished rooms, including a suite. A good range of popular dishes is available in the attractively decorated restaurant, next to which is a comfortable lounge-bar. The hotel, which also has an ample car park, a couple of meeting rooms, and a large function suite/ballroom where regular entertainment is provided, is a very popular venue for wedding receptions.
24 en suite (bth/shr) CTV in all bedrooms No dogs (ex guide dogs) Night porter 100P Xmas English & French Cuisine V meals Coffee am Tea pm Last d 7.45pm
ROOMS: (incl. bkfst) s £19.50-£35.95; d £39.50-£49 * **LB**
CONF: Thtr 200 Class 100 Board 150
CARDS:

Travel Inn

Newhey Rd, Milnrow ☎ 01706 299999
FAX 01706 299074
Purpose-built accommodation, offering spacious, well equipped bedrooms, all with en suite bathrooms. Meals may be taken at the nearby family restaurant. For more information about Travel Inns, consult the Contents page under Hotel Groups.
ROOMS: d £35.50 *

ROCHESTER Kent Map 05 TQ76

★★★★ 76% ***Bridgewood Manor Hotel***

Bridgewood Roundabout, Maidstone Rd ME5 9AX
(adjacent to roundabout on A229) ☎ 01634 201333
FAX 01634 201330
Well placed for easy access to the motorways this modern hotel provides quality accommodation equipped with every modern amenity. Air conditioned public areas are comprised of a smartly furnished lobby lounge, a wood panelled bar and an elegant modern restaurant, with a further dining option in the Terrace bar. Chef Michael Rieder has already made his mark with his Signature menu, Seasonal Specialities, and fixed price menus. Service is personally supervised by a management team who are dedicated to high standards of customer care. An extensive range of leisure amenities includes a hi-tech gym, swimming pool, children's adventure play ground and beauty salon.
100 en suite (bth/shr) (12 fmly) No smoking in 25 bedrooms CTV in all bedrooms STV Lift Night porter 178P Indoor swimming pool (heated) Tennis (hard) Snooker Sauna Solarium Gym Putting green Jacuzzi/spa Hairdressing ch fac English & French Cuisine V meals Coffee am Tea pm Last d 10pm
CARDS:

★★61% **Royal Victoria & Bull Hotel**
16-18 High St ME1 1PX (opposite Guildhall Museum)
☎ 01634 846266 FAX 01634 832312
Once visited by Queen Victoria and mentioned in some of Charles Dickens' novels, this historic former coaching inn is located at the top end of a fashionable high street and is ideal for tourist and business clientele. A new Giannino's Italian Restaurant features popular pizza, pasta and grills whilst the refurbished Rochester Bar adds a contemporary aspect for the younger generation. Bedrooms vary but

come very well equipped and some have four-poster beds. The car park is also a bonus.
28 rms (21 bth/shr) (2 fmly) CTV in all bedrooms Night porter 25P Jacuzzi/spa Italian/International Cuisine V meals Coffee am Tea pm No smoking area in restaurant Last d 10.30pm
ROOMS: (incl. bkfst) s £45; d £55 **LB**
MEALS: Lunch £5-£15alc Dinner £5-£15alc
CONF: Thtr 100 Class 60 Board 40 Del from £59.50
CARDS:

Forte Posthouse Rochester
Maidstone Rd ME5 9SF (on A229 1m N of M2 jnct 3) ☎ 01634 687111 FAX 01634 684512
FORTE Posthouse
Suitable for both the business and leisure traveller, this bright hotel provides modern accommodation in well equipped bedrooms with en suite bathrooms. For more details about Forte Posthouse hotels, consult the Contents page for the section on Hotel Groups.
105 en suite (bth/shr)
ROOMS: d £69-£79 *
CONF: Thtr 110 Class 48 Board 40 Del from £109

ROCHFORD Essex Map 05 TQ89

★★★66% **Hotel Renouf**
Bradley Way SS4 1BU (turn off A127 onto B1013 to Rochford, at 3rd mini roundabout turn right & keep right)
☎ 01702 541334 FAX 01702 549563
Closed 26-30 Dec
A smart, red-brick establishment within Rochford town centre, this family-run hotel provides modern accommodation and a relaxed, friendly atmosphere. There is a small foyer seating area, a comfortable bar and an attractive French restaurant; it is here that chef patron Derek Renouf offers imaginative set-price and à la carte menus. The bedrooms are modern in style and decorative, with limed oak furniture, coordinated decor and matching soft furnishings.
24 en suite (bth/shr) (2 fmly) CTV in all bedrooms STV Night porter 25P No coaches French Cuisine V meals Last d 9.45pm
ROOMS: (incl. bkfst) s fr £59.50; d fr £79.50 *
OFF-PEAK: (incl. bkfst) s fr £49.50; d fr £69.50
MEALS: Lunch £12.50-£17.50&alc Dinner £15.50-£17.50&alc
CONF: Thtr 30 Class 30 Board 20
CARDS:

ROMALDKIRK Co Durham Map 12 NY92

★★73% **Rose & Crown**
DL12 9EB (6m NW from Barnard Castle on B6277)
☎ 01833 650213 FAX 01833 650828
Closed 25 & 26 Dec
A charming Dales country village inn full of rustic and historic charm with old oak beams, panelling and open log fires, together with an elegant stylish dining room and lounge. Main house rooms are cosy and traditionally furnished but with sympathetic contemporary soft furnishings; the other newer rooms are more comfortable for the business guest. Chef and proprietor Chris Davy is capable and conscientious, offering a mixture of traditional and modern dishes. The menu is centred around a repertoire of the faithful and the favourites and changes with the seasons.
7 en suite (bth/shr) 5 annexe en suite (bth/shr) (1 fmly) CTV in all bedrooms 40P English & French Cuisine Coffee am Tea pm No smoking in restaurant Last d 9pm
ROOMS: (incl. bkfst) s £58; d £79 **LB**
MEALS: Sunday Lunch £12.25 Dinner £23.50
CARDS:

ROMFORD Greater London

Travel Inn
Mercury Gardens RM1 3PB ☎ 01708 760548
FAX 01708 760456

Purpose-built accommodation, offering spacious, well equipped bedrooms, all with en suite bathrooms. Meals may be taken at the nearby family restaurant. For more information about Travel Inns, consult the Contents page under Hotel Groups.
47 en suite (bth/shr)

ROMSEY Hampshire Map 04 SU32
See also Ampfield

★★★70% **Potters Heron**
Winchester Rd SO51 9ZF ☎ 01703 266611
FAX 01703 251359
(For full entry see Ampfield)
COUNTRY CLUB Hotel Group

★★★62% **New Forest Heathlands**
Romsey Rd, Ower SO51 6ZJ ☎ 01703 814333
FAX 01703 812123

Closed 25 Dec RS Sat
The hotel is located in Ower on the edge of the New Forest, convenient for major road links. The open-plan public areas are spacious and the rooms are located in purpose-built wings overlooking the fields. The public bar - The Vine Inn - has a good local trade and offers a friendly atmosphere.
52 en suite (bth/shr) (2 fmly) CTV in all bedrooms STV Night porter 150P Sauna Solarium Gym Croquet lawn Jacuzzi/spa International Cuisine V meals Coffee am Tea pm No smoking in restaurant Last d 9pm
ROOMS: (incl. bkfst) s £57-£77; d £77-£97 * **LB**
MEALS: Lunch £7.75-£8.95&alc Dinner fr £16.75&alc*
CONF: Thtr 200 Class 100 Board 70 Del from £60
CARDS:

★★★62% **The White Horse**
Market Place SO51 8ZJ ☎ 01794 512431
FAX 01794 517485
FORTE Heritage
In the centre of this quaint Hampshire town, the White Horse dates back to Elizabethan times although it has a Georgian façade and a more recent extension to the rear. There is a cosy lounge which features original frescos and is a popular meeting place for morning coffee and afternoon tea. Bedrooms vary from attractively furnished beamed rooms, to spacious Coach House rooms with their own entrance, and modern rooms which are scheduled for upgrading.
33 en suite (bth/shr) (7 fmly) No smoking in 11 bedrooms CTV in all bedrooms Night porter 60P Free use of nearby leisure facilities Xmas V meals Coffee am Tea pm Last d 9pm
ROOMS: s fr £65; d fr £85 * **LB**
MEALS: Sunday Lunch £8.50-£11.95 Dinner £17.95*
CONF: Thtr 40 Class 20 Board 20 Del £90
CARDS:

ROSEDALE ABBEY North Yorkshire Map 08 SE79

★★72% **Milburn Arms**
YO18 8RA (7m N of A170 from Wrelton village)
☎ 01751 417312 FAX 01751 417312
RS 23-27 Dec
This delightful hotel is set in the centre of the pretty village which is right at the heart of the North York Moors National Park. The very well equipped bedrooms are a pleasure to stay in, and the public areas include a charming and comfortable lounge with a welcoming open fire and a good choice of reading material. The bars are very popular, a high

contd.

standard of cooking using only the best local produce available is served in the split-level restaurant. Owners Joan and Terry Bradley are friendly hosts.

3 en suite (bth/shr) 8 annexe en suite (bth/shr) (2 fmly) CTV in all bedrooms 35P Xmas English & French Cuisine V meals Coffee am No smoking in restaurant Last d 9.30pm

ROOMS: (incl. bkfst) s £42.50-£44.50; d £70-£74 **LB**

OFF-PEAK: (incl. bkfst) s fr £32.50; d fr £50

MEALS: Sunday Lunch £8.75-£10.95 Dinner £18.50-£27alc

CARDS:

★★65% **White Horse Farm**

MINOTEL Great Britain

YO18 8SE ☎ 01751 417239 FAX 01751 417781

Closed 25 Dec

White Horse Farm is a delightful hotel which overlooks the village and enjoys lovely views towards the moors. There is a relaxing, peaceful lounge in addition to the more active bar where a very good range of bar meals is served alongside hand-pulled real ales. The pleasant restaurant features a dinner menu offering a varied choice of dishes based on quality local produce. The bedrooms are well furnished and restful, while service throughout is friendly and attentive.

11 en suite (bth/shr) 4 annexe en suite (bth/shr) (2 fmly) CTV in all bedrooms 50P No coaches Xmas English & Continental Cuisine V meals Last d 8.45pm

ROOMS: (incl. bkfst) s £44; d £68 * **LB**

OFF-PEAK: (incl. bkfst) s £30-£35; d £60

MEALS: Sunday Lunch £6.95-£9.30 Dinner £15-£18*

CONF: Thtr 30 Class 30 Board 30 Del from £60

CARDS:

ROSSINGTON South Yorkshire Map 08 SK69

★★★64% **Mount Pleasant**

CONSORT HOTELS

Great North Rd DN11 0HP (on A638 Great North Rd 1.5m E of village) ☎ 01302 868696 & 868219 FAX 01302 865130

Closed 25 Dec

Dating back to the 18th century, this was originally the estate house to Rossington Hall and stands within 100 acres of wooded parklands midway between Bawtry and Doncaster. The hotel has a homely atmosphere and each of the bedrooms - many of which are on the ground floor - are individually designed and furnished. The reception areas comprise of a series of small comfortable lounges where refreshments and drinks are served and an equally comfortable restaurant. The staff are very efficient.

29 en suite (bth/shr) (2 fmly) No smoking in 20 bedrooms CTV in all bedrooms STV No dogs (ex guide dogs) Night porter 100P No coaches Solarium Gym English & French Cuisine V meals Coffee am Tea pm No smoking in restaurant Last d 9.30pm

ROOMS: (incl. bkfst) s £48; d £73 * **LB**

MEALS: Lunch £10-£15 High tea £5-£10 Dinner £16-£20*

CONF: Thtr 45 Class 30 Board 30 Del from £89

CARDS:

ROSS-ON-WYE Hereford & Worcester Map 03 SO62

See also Goodrich, Pencraig and Symonds Yat

★★★❀❀ 74% **Pengethley Manor**

Best Western

Pengethley Park HR9 6LL (4m N on A49 Hereford rd) ☎ 01989 730211 FAX 01989 730238

This fine Georgian mansion is set in extensive grounds and gardens which contain two commercial vineyards to the north of Ross-on-Wye. The hotel provides a high level of professional and friendly service and has a well deserved reputation for its cuisine. The accommodation is tastefully appointed and there is a wide variety of bedroom styles, all similarly well equipped. Half are in separate buildings across a courtyard. Rooms on ground-floor level and rooms with four-poster beds are available. The elegant public rooms are furnished in a style sympathetic to the character of the house.

11 en suite (bth/shr) 14 annexe en suite (bth/shr) (3 fmly) CTV in all bedrooms 70P Outdoor swimming pool (heated) Fishing Snooker Croquet lawn Golf improvement course Xmas English & French Cuisine V meals Coffee am Tea pm Last d 9.30pm

ROOMS: (incl. bkfst) s £70-£115; d £100-£160 * **LB**

MEALS: Lunch £13.50-£16 Dinner £24&alc

CONF: Thtr 50 Class 25 Board 28 Del £111.65

CARDS:

See advertisement on opposite page

★★★❀❀70% **Chase**

Gloucester Rd HR9 5LH (E side of town, on B4260) ☎ 01989 763161 FAX 01989 768330

This large Regency Mansion is surrounded by extensive grounds and gardens, but is only a few minutes walk from the town centre. A high level of professional service is provided by the dedicated team of friendly staff, under the leadership of Manager John Lewis. The modern furnished and equipped accommodation provides a variety of bedroom sizes and styles, which includes rooms with four-poster beds. Public areas are tastefully furnished and the attractive restaurant provides an ideal setting in which to enjoy the creations of Chef Ken Tait and his talented team. His set price menu contains an imaginative and interesting selection of classical dishes with a modern interpretation. The flavours are very distinctive and powerful. Other facilities at the hotel include a large function suite and conference rooms.

39 en suite (bth/shr) (1 fmly) CTV in all bedrooms STV No dogs (ex guide dogs) Night porter 200P V meals Coffee am Tea pm Last high tea 6pm

ROOMS: (incl. bkfst) s £65; d £80 * **LB**

MEALS: Lunch £12.50 High tea £6*

CONF: Thtr 300 Class 150 Board 50 Del £110

CARDS:

See advertisement on opposite page

★★★❀64% **Royal**

Palace Pound HR9 5HZ (close to St Marys Church) ☎ 01989 565105 FAX 01989 768058

From its elevated position this character hotel boasts commanding views out over the River Wye and an expanse of countryside beyond. Public rooms include a cosy lounge, small bar and spacious restaurant. The majority of bedrooms have benefited from recent upgrading and are comfortable and inviting. Unfortunately those awaiting similar good work now look tired and dated. We are pleased to report, however, that the recent introduction of chef Paul Bradey has seen significant improvements with enjoyable and imaginative cooking.
40 en suite (bth/shr) (4 fmly) No smoking in 11 bedrooms CTV in all bedrooms Night porter 70P Fishing Xmas English & French Cuisine V meals Coffee am Tea pm No smoking in restaurant Last d 9.30pm
ROOMS: s £65; d £65-£70 * **LB**
MEALS: Sunday Lunch £12.50 Dinner £19.75*
CONF: Thtr 80 Class 50 Board 30 Del from £95
CARDS:

★★ 75% Peterstow Country House
Peterstow HR9 6LB (3m NE, off A49 next to St Peter's Church)
☎ 01989 562826 FAX 01989 567264
Closed 1st two wks in Jan
It was back in 1987 that Jeanne and Mike Denne fell in love with this former rectory standing in 28 acres of woodland and pastures, next to St Peter's Church, and by 1989, after carrying out considerable restoration work, they opened it as a hotel. It offers accommodation in a variety of bedrooms, some of them huge, and all furnished and equipped to a high standard. There are rooms at ground-floor level and some with half-tester beds. Public areas are furnished in period style and, at the time of our last inspection, a conservatory extension to the elegant restaurant was being built. Head chef Andrew Poole maintains the hotel's reputation for fine cuisine, with his imaginative set price menu, which takes full advantage of good local produce. A recently opened bistro in a converted barn, gives diners the alternative of lighter dishes in an informal setting.
9 en suite (bth/shr) (3 fmly) CTV in all bedrooms No dogs (ex guide dogs) 45P No coaches Fishing Clay pigeon shooting No children 7yrs Xmas V meals Coffee am Tea pm No smoking in restaurant Last d 9pm
ROOMS: (incl. bkfst) s £42.50-£76; d £55-£99 * **LB**
MEALS: Lunch £13.50&alc Dinner £24.50-£26.50&alc
CARDS:

See advertisement on page 521

★★ 73% Glewstone Court
Glewstone HR9 6AW ☎ 01989 770367 FAX 01989 770282
Closed 25-27 Dec
This lovely old house is quietly set in three acres of mature grounds, just off the A40 between Ross-on-Wye and Symonds Yat. It is run in a relaxed and informal manner by Bill and Christine Reeve-Tucker and family, who provide willing service and friendly hospitality. Christine is an accomplished cook and the hotel has a well deserved reputation for its food. The bedrooms vary in style, but all have modern equipment and facilities, while the public rooms are comfortably furnished in a style befitting the Georgian character of the house, and the place abounds with objets d'art which have been enthusiastically collected over the years. In addition to the main dining room, there is also a bistro for more informal meals.
7 en suite (bth/shr) (2 fmly) CTV in all bedrooms 25P No coaches Croquet lawn V meals Coffee am Last d 9.30pm
ROOMS: (incl. bkfst) s £40-£70; d £85-£100 **LB**
MEALS: Lunch £15-£23 Dinner £24
CONF: Thtr 35 Board 16 Del from £90
CARDS:

★★ 70% *Rocks Place*
Yatton HR9 7RD (300yds off A449 between Ross-on-Wye/Ledbury)
☎ 01531 660218

contd.

This 16th-century barn has been very carefully converted by Peter and Mollie Cotton into a delightful country hotel. Many of the original timbers remain and these adorn the walls and ceilings. Bedrooms, which are fitted with period furnishings in keeping with the building, all have modern en suite bath or shower rooms and one has a four-poster bed. There is a comfortable lounge, a cosy bar and food comes by way of a fixed price menu. Mollie looks after the kitchen and Peter supervises the bar and other public areas. There are pretty grounds and a peaceful and relaxing atmosphere prevails. The hotel is located 300 yards off the A449, four miles north of its junction with the M50.
7 en suite (bth/shr) (1 fmly) No smoking in all bedrooms CTV in all bedrooms No dogs (ex guide dogs) 40P Croquet lawn Putting green V meals Coffee am Tea pm Last d 8.45pm
CARDS:

★★68% Hunsdon Manor
Gloucester Rd, Weston-Under-Penyard HR9 7PE Two miles east of M50 on the A40 road to Gloucester ☎ 01989 562748 & 563376
FAX 01989 768348
This beautifully preserved old manor house is set in two and a half acres of lovely gardens. It stands on the A40, in the village of Weston-under-Penyard, some 2 miles east of Ross-on-Wye. Privately-owned and personally-run, it provides a variety of styles and sizes of bedrooms, all similarly well equipped; rooms with four-poster beds, family-bedded rooms and rooms on ground floor level are all available. Most of the latter are located in cleverly converted outbuildings, overlooking the rear garden. Public rooms include a new and very attractively appointed restaurant.
13 en suite (bth/shr) 12 annexe en suite (bth/shr) (3 fmly) CTV in all bedrooms 55P No coaches Sauna English & Continental Cuisine V meals Coffee am Tea pm No smoking area in restaurant
Last d 9.30pm
ROOMS: (incl. bkfst) s £38; d £55 **LB**
MEALS: Dinner £16-£18&alc
CARDS: £

See advertisement on opposite page

★★65% Bridge House
Wilton HR9 6AA ☎ 01989 562655
This 250-year-old property is situated at Wilton, just off the A40, near its junction with the A49. Now a small privately-owned and personally-run hotel, it has been in the same family since 1979. It provides quite spacious accommodation, which includes a family bedded room and a room with a four-poster bed. In addition to the cottage-style restaurant, there is a cosy bar and a comfortable lounge with a conservatory extension. Other facilities include a private car park and a very pleasant garden, which extends to the bank of the River Wye.
8 en suite (bth/shr) CTV in all bedrooms No dogs 14P No coaches No children 10yrs Xmas English & French Cuisine V meals No smoking in restaurant Last d 10.30pm
ROOMS: (incl. bkfst) s £32.50-£35; d £52-£55 * **LB**
OFF-PEAK: (incl. bkfst) d fr £45
MEALS: Dinner £13.95-£14.95&alc
CARDS:

★★65% King's Head
8 High St HR9 5HL ☎ 01989 763174 FAX 01989 769578
Closed 24-26 Dec
A former coaching inn dating from the 14th century, this town-centre hotel with exposed beams and wall timbers offers a wealth of charm and character. Public areas include a cosy dining room, a spacious lounge and an old world bar. Bedrooms, however, offer modern equipment and facilities; several are located in a converted stable block to the rear of the main building, and some of these are on the ground floor. Family rooms are also available.
14 en suite (bth) 9 annexe en suite (bth) (6 fmly) CTV in all bedrooms 20P No coaches Xmas V meals Coffee am Tea pm No smoking in restaurant Last d 9pm
ROOMS: (incl. bkfst) s fr £38; d fr £65 * **LB**
MEALS: Sunday Lunch £7-£13 High tea £4 Dinner £14
CARDS: £

★★64% Chasedale
Walford Rd HR9 5PQ (from Ross-on-Wye town centre head south on B4234, hotel 0.5m on left) ☎ 01989 562423
This impressive Victorian country house stands in its own extensive, mature grounds and offers warm and friendly hospitality from private owners. Bedrooms include a range of family and ground-floor accommodation with a variety of furniture styles, and all come with en suite facilities and modern equipment. A pleasant split-level restaurant serves a good selection of popular dishes, and there is a spacious lounge.
10 en suite (bth) (3 fmly) No smoking in 1 bedroom CTV in all bedrooms 14P No coaches Xmas English & French Cuisine V meals Coffee am Tea pm No smoking in restaurant Last d 9pm
ROOMS: (incl. bkfst) s £29.50-£30; d £59-£60 **LB**
OFF-PEAK: (incl. bkfst) s £27.50-£30; d £55-£60
MEALS: Lunch £9.20-£10.20 Dinner £12.50-£12.75&alc
CONF: Thtr 40 Class 30 Board 25 Del from £40.50
CARDS: £

★★64% Orles Barn
Wilton HR9 6AE (off junct A40/A49) ☎ 01989 562155
FAX 01989 768470
Closed Nov
This family-run former farmhouse stands in attractive grounds. Most of the neat well maintained bedrooms have modern bathrooms and there is a cosy lounge bar leading to the restaurant, both of which offer a range of food.
9 rms (7 bth/shr) (2 fmly) CTV in all bedrooms Night porter 20P Outdoor swimming pool (heated) ch fac English, French & Spanish Cuisine V meals Coffee am Tea pm No smoking in restaurant Last d 9.15pm
ROOMS: (incl. bkfst) s £35-£45; d £50-£60 * **LB**
OFF-PEAK: (incl. bkfst) s £30-£40; d £40-£50
MEALS: Lunch £7.95-£10.75&alc High tea £3.50-£6.50&alc Dinner £11.75-£14.75&alc*
CARDS: £

Travel Inn
Ledbury Rd HR9 7QJ ☎ 01989 563861
FAX 01989 566124
travelinn
Purpose-built accommodation, offering spacious, well equipped bedrooms, all with en suite bathrooms. Meals may be taken at the nearby family restaurant. For more information about Travel Inns, consult the Contents page under Hotel Groups.
40 en suite (bth/shr)
ROOMS: (incl. bkfst) d £35.50 *

ROSTHWAITE Cumbria Map 11 NY21
See also Borrowdale

★★★60% *Scafell*
CA12 5XB (6m S of Keswick on B5289) ☎ 017687 77208
FAX 017687 77280
Closed 2 Jan-2 Feb
Lying in gardens by the roadside and backed by a fast-flowing mountain river in the beautiful Borrowdale valley, this long-established hotel is run in traditional style by a friendly and helpful team. One can have dinner in the spacious dining room, supper in the cocktail bar, or eat even less formally in the hotel's pub.

contd.

indicates a Country House Hotel. Please consult the section on AA Star Rating at the front of the book.

R

24 en suite (bth/shr) (3 fmly) CTV in all bedrooms 50P No coaches International Cuisine V meals Coffee am Tea pm
CARDS:

See advertisement on opposite page

ROTHERHAM South Yorkshire Map 08 SK49

★★★★66% **Hellaby Hall**
Old Hellaby Ln, Hellaby S66 8SN ☎ 01709 702701 FAX 01709 700979
We are proud to welcome Hellaby Hall to our guide. Its architecture is unique: 17th century and distinctively Flemish. The reception rooms have the feel and proportions of a baronial hall. In the reception lobby the high ceilings are exposed to the rafters with staircases leading off on one side to the conference and function suites and on the other to a network of oak panelled lounges and a quiet bar adjacent to the restaurant. Here the decorative style is both contemporary and bold using the same rich jewel colours of the deep cushioned sofas of the lobby, but with harlequin designs reflected by a wall of mirrors. The cuisine is modern British -good ingredients and freshly cooked. The wine list is usefully annotated and sorted by grape variety. The service is relaxed, friendly and attentive but deliberately unstuffy. The bedrooms are mainly uniform in their design but spacious and decorative. The hotel was designed with disabled access as a priority.
52 en suite (bth/shr) (4 fmly) No smoking in 12 bedrooms CTV in all bedrooms STV Lift Night porter 235P Croquet lawn Putting green Petanque Outdoor skittles Wkly live entertainment Xmas English & French Cuisine V meals Coffee am Tea pm Last d 10pm
ROOMS: (incl. bkfst) s fr £78; d fr £88 * **LB**
OFF-PEAK: (incl. bkfst) s fr £50; d fr £70
MEALS: Lunch £7.95-£12.50&alc Dinner fr £19.50&alc*
CONF: Thtr 140 Class 70 Board 60 Del from £90
CARDS:

★★★68% **Elton**
Main St, Bramley S66 0SF (3m E A631)
☎ 01709 545681 FAX 01709 549100
A truly friendly and exceptionally well managed hotel in the centre of Bramley village. The main building, where the public rooms are situated, has recently been extended to include a conservatory and a covered walkway to the new wing, which houses the spacious, well equipped bedrooms. The owners Mr and Mrs Keary are intimately involved with the hotel and have an equally committed and enthusiastic staff.
13 en suite (bth/shr) 16 annexe en suite (bth/shr) (4 fmly) No smoking in 5 bedrooms CTV in all bedrooms STV Night porter 44P English & French Cuisine V meals Coffee am Tea pm No smoking area in restaurant Last d 9.30pm
ROOMS: s £48-£60; d £65-£70 **LB**
OFF-PEAK: s £38; d £48-£50
MEALS: Lunch £10.50-£11.50&alc Dinner £19.25-£19.50&alc
CONF: Thtr 30 Class 24 Board 24 Del from £80.85
CARDS:

★★★67% **Consort**
Brampton Rd, Thurcroft S66 9JA ☎ 01709 530022
FAX 01709 531529
Located close to the joining of the M1 and M18 the hotel is ideally placed for the counties industrial heartland, as a stopover as well as for touring the Derbyshire Peaks. It has excellent conference facilities modern, purpose built and comfortable accommodation as well as a convivial bar and restaurant. The hotel is efficiently managed by the proprietor and the atmosphere is very friendly and relaxed.
18 en suite (bth/shr) (1 fmly) CTV in all bedrooms STV No dogs (ex guide dogs) Night porter 90P V meals Coffee am Tea pm
ROOMS: (incl. bkfst) s £30-£60; d £45-£70 * **LB**
CONF: Thtr 300 Class 120 Board 50 Del £80
CARDS:

★★★67% **Swallow**
West Bawtry Rd S60 4NA (from junct 33 of the M1 take A630 towards Rotherham, hotel is approx 0.5m on right hand side) ☎ 01709 830630
FAX 01709 830549

A large modern hotel with excellent leisure facilities, the Swallow is ideal for both business and leisure purposes. Bedrooms are spacious and well equipped and a number of family rooms are also available. There is a choice of conference and meeting rooms and good, secure car parking facilities. Pride of place however goes to Holly's Restaurant which offers both à la carte and table d'hÛte menus with English regional and classical dishes.
100 en suite (bth/shr) (2 fmly) No smoking in 44 bedrooms CTV in all bedrooms STV Lift Night porter 222P Indoor swimming pool (heated) Solarium Gym Jacuzzi/spa Steam room Sunbeds Childrens pool Xmas English & Continental Cuisine V meals Coffee am Tea pm No smoking area in restaurant Last d 9.45pm
ROOMS: (incl. bkfst) s fr £82; d fr £96 * **LB**
OFF-PEAK: (incl. bkfst) s fr £60; d fr £72
MEALS: Lunch £9.95-£12.95 Dinner £17.75-£27*
CONF: Thtr 300 Class 120 Board 40 Del from £100
CARDS:

★★★66% **Carlton Park**
102/104 Moorgate Rd S60 2BG ☎ 01709 849955
FAX 01709 368960

Recent bedroom refurbishment has considerably improved the accommodation at this modern hotel, which also offers a variety of conference and meeting rooms. The hotel restaurant provides a selection of international dishes and the popular Carlton Bar has a wide choice of bar meals. Lounge service is also available. There is a small fitness centre but no swimming pool.
75 en suite (bth/shr) (6 fmly) No smoking in 22 bedrooms CTV in all bedrooms STV Lift Night porter 95P Sauna Solarium Gym Jacuzzi/spa Wkly live entertainment Xmas International Cuisine V meals Coffee am Tea pm No smoking area in restaurant
ROOMS: s £34-£59.50; d £68-£69.50 * **LB**
MEALS: Lunch £14.95&alc*
CONF: Thtr 250 Class 160 Board 60
CARDS:

★★66% **Brentwood**
Moorgate Rd S60 2TY ☎ 01709 382772 FAX 01709 820289
Closed 26 & 27 Dec RS BH's
This Victorian house is set back from the road with neatly tended gardens and ample car parking. Most of the public areas have been sympathetically decorated to complement original features of the house, the restaurant being particularly attractive. The set-price menu and the carte offer a good choice of dishes. Accommodation styles and sizes vary considerably; bedrooms in the new wing are generally more spacious and have more modern appointments.
33 en suite (bth/shr) 10 annexe en suite (bth/shr) (4 fmly) CTV in

all bedrooms Night porter 60P ch fac English & Continental Cuisine V meals Coffee am Last d 9.30pm
ROOMS: (incl. bkfst) s £35-£54; d £68 * **LB**
OFF-PEAK: (incl. bkfst) s £25; d £40
MEALS: Lunch £10.95-£17&alc Dinner £11-£17&alc*
CONF: Thtr 60 Class 20 Board 20
CARDS:

Campanile

Hellaby Industrial Estate, Lowton Way, Off Denby Way S66 8RY (junct 1 of M18. Follow directions to Maltby off roundabout. At traffic lights turn left and take 2nd road on left) ☎ 01709 700255 FAX 01709 545169

The bar and Bistro restaurant provide meals and refreshments. Bedrooms are well equipped and have en suite bathrooms. For more details about Campanile, consult the Contents page under Hotel Groups.
50 en suite (bth/shr)
ROOMS: d fr £36.50 *
CONF: Thtr 34 Class 20 Board 25 Del from £42.80

Travel Inn

Bawtry Rd S65 3JB (on A631 towards Wickersley) ☎ 01709 543216 FAX 01709 531546
Purpose-built accommodation, offering spacious, well equipped bedrooms, all with en suite bathrooms. Meals may be taken at the nearby family restaurant. For more information about Travel Inns, consult the Contents page under Hotel Groups.
37 en suite (bth/shr)
ROOMS: d £35.50 *

ROTHERWICK Hampshire Map 04 SU75

RED STAR HOTEL

★★★★ 🏵🏵 **Tylney Hall**

RG27 9AZ (take B3349 towards Hook, follow signs for Rotherwick, at end of village after pond turn left, hotel in 1m) ☎ 01256 764881 FAX 01256 768141
Set in 66 acres of delightful parkland and gardens originally laid out by Gertrude Jekyll with lakes and ornamental fountains, this Victorian country house offers spacious and comfortable accommodation. Day rooms feature log fires, fresh flower displays and fine ceilings and include a choice of lounges and a library bar in addition to numerous meeting and function rooms - such as a magnificent baronial style suite complete with stage and minstrels' gallery. Traditionally furnished bedrooms range from the spacious to the huge, and offer good toiletries and linen, towelling robes and mineral water. The splendid Oak Room is the setting for Stephen Hine's cooking which is modern in style and based on good quality ingredients. Typical of the menu are dishes like marinated scallops with courgette and aubergine chutney, grilled breast of duck with celeriac r^sti and orange marmalade, or asparagus with parmesan and sweet pepper mousse. Service is personable and friendly.

35 en suite (bth/shr) 56 annexe en suite (bth/shr) (1 fmly) CTV in all bedrooms No dogs (ex guide dogs) Lift Night porter 120P No coaches Indoor swimming pool (heated) Outdoor swimming pool (heated) Tennis (hard) Snooker Sauna Gym Croquet lawn Clay pigeon shooting Archery ch fac Xmas English & French Cuisine V meals Coffee am Tea pm No smoking in restaurant Last d 9.30pm
ROOMS: (incl. bkfst) s £104-£114; d £124-£134 * **LB**
MEALS: Lunch £19.95&alc Dinner £30&alc*
CONF: Thtr 120 Class 70 Board 40 Del from £190
CARDS:

See advertisement under BASINGSTOKE

ROTHLEY Leicestershire Map 08 SK51

★★★ 63% **Rothley Court**

FORTE Heritage

Westfield Ln LE7 7LG (on B5328) ☎ 0116 237 4141
FAX 0116 237 4483

This splendid 11th century manor house with its own chapel stands in six acres of gardens edged by the river and rolling hills. Much of the original character has been retained in the public rooms which feature period stained glass windows, oak panelling and fine fireplaces. Accommodation id offered in traditionally furnished bedrooms in the main house or more modern contemporary country house style garden bedrooms. There is a relaxed ambience about the hotel and Wayne Leadon's cooking makes good use of quality ingredients with more imaginative British cuisine.

13 en suite (bth/shr) 21 annexe en suite (bth/shr) No smoking in 14 bedrooms CTV in all bedrooms Night porter 100P Xmas V meals Coffee am Tea pm No smoking in restaurant Last d 9.30pm

ROOMS: s fr £80; d fr £90 * **LB**

OFF-PEAK: d fr £80

MEALS: Lunch £13.95-£14.95&alc High tea £3.50-£8.50 Dinner fr £21.50&alc*

CONF: Thtr 100 Class 35 Board 35 Del from £110

CARDS:

★★ 70% **The Limes**

35 Mountsorrel Ln LE7 7PS (turn of old A6, Hotel off village green)
☎ 0116 230 2531

Closed 23 Dec-2 Jan

A popular owner managed hotel, The Limes offers a surprisingly good range of facilities for a hotel of its classification and is excellent value for money. Throughout the hotel good standards are maintained and guests are received in a friendly manner. The car park is noteworthy for its security and safety.

11 en suite (bth/shr) CTV in all bedrooms STV No dogs (ex guide dogs) Air conditioning 15P No coaches No children 14 English Cuisine V meals No smoking in restaurant

ROOMS: (incl. bkfst) s fr £42.50; d fr £55 *

CARDS:

R

ROUSDON Devon Map 03 SY29

★★★ 67% **Dower House**

Rousdon DT7 3RB (A3052, 3m from Lyme Regis) ☎ 01297 21047
FAX 01297 24748

Closed Dec-Jan

This small family-run hotel is located on the edge of Lyme Regis and offers friendly, comfortable accommodation. The bedrooms are attractively decorated and well equipped with modern en suite facilities. There is a popular well stocked bar and the restaurant offers a daily-changing menu. The lounge has a cosy atmosphere to it and there is also a heated pool and sauna.

9 en suite (bth/shr) (2 fmly) CTV in all bedrooms 30P No coaches Indoor swimming pool (heated) Sauna Xmas V meals Coffee am Tea pm No smoking in restaurant Last d 9pm

ROOMS: (incl. bkfst) s £38-£48; d £60-£80 * **LB**

MEALS: Lunch £10.50-£17.50&alc Dinner £17.50*

CARDS:

★★ 63% **Orchard Country**

DT7 3XW (off A3052 between Lyme Regis & Seaton, opposite Allhallows College Rousdon) ☎ 01297 442972

Closed Nov-Mar

Ideally situated for touring the East Devon and Dorset coastline, this cottage-style property is set in its own pretty gardens, back from the Seaton to Lyme Regis road. The bedrooms are neatly furnished and decorated and provide the essential facilities. There is a comfortable lounge with a bar, and a small lounge with television. In the dining room, a choice of dishes is offered from a set-price menu.

12 en suite (bth/shr) CTV in all bedrooms 30P No children 8yrs V meals Coffee am Tea pm No smoking in restaurant Last d 8.15pm

ROOMS: (incl. bkfst) s £36; d £60 * **LB**

MEALS: Dinner £12&alc*

CARDS:

ROWNHAMS MOTORWAY SERVICE AREA Hampshire Map 04 SU31

Roadchef Lodge

Rownhams Service Area, M27 Westbound SO16 8AP (M27 1m E of junct 3) ☎ 01703 741144
FAX 01703 740204

Smart, spacious and well equipped bedrooms, all with en suite bathrooms, are provided by this modern hotel. Meals may be taken at a nearby family restaurant. For more information about RoadChef Lodges, consult the Contents page under Hotel Groups.

39 en suite (bth/shr)

CONF: Board 15

ROWSLEY Derbyshire Map 08 SK26

★★★ 70% **East Lodge Country House**

DE4 2EF (A6, Rowsley Village, 5m from Bakewell, 3m from Matlock) ☎ 01629 734474

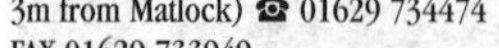

FAX 01629 733949

The seasonal display of rhododendrons is particularly colourful at this time of year at this country house hotel, which is set back from the main road. The lawns, where teas are served in favourable weather, lead down to a lovely spring-fed ornamental pond which is home to a family of ducks. The house, formerly part of the Haddon Hall estate has been carefully renovated and refurbished to retain its architecture and character. The furnishings and decoration are of the fashionable country house genre, the hospitality is superb.

14 en suite (bth/shr) (1 fmly) CTV in all bedrooms No dogs 30P Croquet lawn Xmas International Cuisine V meals Coffee am Tea pm No smoking in restaurant Last d 9.30pm

ROOMS: (incl. bkfst) s fr £60; d £78-£94 * **LB**

OFF-PEAK: (incl. bkfst) s fr £48; d fr £55

MEALS: Lunch £9.50-£14.50 High tea fr £6.25 Dinner £18.50-£29.50*

CONF: Thtr 60 Board 20 Del from £85

CARDS:

See advertisement under BAKEWELL

RUAN HIGH LANES Cornwall & Isles of Scilly Map 02 SW93

★★ 75% **Hundred House**

TR2 5JR (from A390, 4m W of St Austell turn left onto B3287 to Tregony/St Mawes, turn left onto A3078 to St Mawes, hotel 4m along on right)
☎ 01872 501336 FAX 01872 501151

Closed Nov-Feb

Parts of Mike and Kitty Eccles' small hotel date back to the 1790's, though the main building is Edwardian. Set in the heart of the Roseland Peninsular, surrounded by unspoilt countryside and within a mile of the sea, The Hundred House Hotel has very comfortable and spacious public areas, furnished with quality and beautifully decorated throughout. The individually furnished and decorated bedrooms vary in style and shape but each is well equipped and has lovely country or garden views. Kitty Eccles is an accomplished and imaginative cook, and the daily-changing menu offers a choice of starters and sweets, the main course being fixed unless by prior arrangement. Essentially English in style, dishes are based on the best of Cornish produce. To accompany the meals, Mike Eccles has chosen an interesting selection of wines from around the world.

10 en suite (bth/shr) (2 fmly) CTV in all bedrooms 15P No coaches

Croquet lawn English Cuisine Coffee am Tea pm No smoking in restaurant
ROOMS: (incl. bkfst) s £36-£38.50; d £72-£77 **LB**
MEALS: Bar Lunch fr £2.50 Dinner fr £22.50
CARDS:

RUCKHALL Hereford & Worcester Map 03 SO43

★★ 66% Ancient Camp Inn

HR2 9QX (A465, turn right to Belmont Abbey, 2.5m to hotel) ☎ 01981 250449 FAX 01981 251581
RS Mon
This delightful inn, once a cider house and named after a nearby Iron Age settlement, is remotely located in beautiful countryside overlooking the River Wye. Approach roads are narrow but the journey is well worth it. The ground floor areas are made up of a cosy bar and several eating areas. Flagged floors, exposed beams and log fires feature and there is a warm and relaxing atmosphere. Food is a pleasant experience with a blackboard selection offering fresh market produce. Venison, teal, sea bass and turbot are usually available and the rack of Welsh lamb is a must. Bedrooms are modern and well decorated.
5 en suite (bth/shr) CTV in all bedrooms No dogs (ex guide dogs) 30P No coaches Fishing No children 16 Xmas International Cuisine V meals Coffee am Tea pm No smoking area in restaurant
Last d 9pm
ROOMS: (incl. bkfst) s £35-£45; d £48-£58 *
MEALS: Lunch £10-£15alc High tea fr £10alc Dinner fr £20alc
CARDS:

RUGBY Warwickshire Map 04 SP57

★★★ 66% *Whitefields Hotel & Golf Complex*

Coventry Rd, Thurlaston CV23 9JR (4m SW close to junc 1 M45)
☎ 01788 521800 & 522393 FAX 01788 521695
Closed 25 Dec
This modern, purpose-built building is centred around its newly constructed 18-hole golf course. It has a large club bar next to a restaurant which serves tasty, imaginative dishes; straightforward levels of comfort are provided in the good-sized bedrooms.
16 en suite (bth/shr) (2 fmly) CTV in all bedrooms STV No dogs (ex guide dogs) Night porter 150P Golf 18 Fishing Putting green International Cuisine V meals Coffee am Tea pm Last d 9.30pm
CARDS:

★★★ 61% Brownsover Hall

Brownsover Ln, Old Brownsover CV21 1HU 1.5m N A426) ☎ 01788 546100 FAX 01788 579241
An attractive mock-Gothic hall, surrounded by seven acres of lovely grounds but just a few minutes' drive from the motorway, offering a peaceful setting for small conferences and short breaks. Bedrooms in the main house are all furnished to a good standard, whilst the four in the coach house are the most recently refurbished. Meals are served in the former chapel, an impressive room with mullioned windows.
27 en suite (bth/shr) 4 annexe en suite (bth/shr) (1 fmly) No smoking in 11 bedrooms CTV in all bedrooms STV Night porter 60P Tennis (hard) V meals Coffee am Tea pm Last d 9.30pm
CARDS:

★★★ 60% Grosvenor

Clifton Rd CV21 3QQ ☎ 01788 535686 FAX 01788 541297
The Grosvenor, made up of four buildings on a corner plot, stands within five minutes' walk of the town centre. Bedrooms vary in size and character, but all are attractively furnished - as, too, are the public rooms. An indoor swimming pool and other leisure facilities are available for guests' use.
21 en suite (bth/shr) (1 fmly) CTV in all bedrooms Night porter 33P No coaches Indoor swimming pool (heated) Sauna Solarium Gym Jacuzzi/spa Aromatherapy V meals Coffee am Tea pm Last d 10pm
ROOMS: (incl. bkfst) s £60-£69.50; d £70-£79.50 * **LB**
OFF-PEAK: (incl. bkfst) s £30-£43.50; d £50-£58
MEALS: Lunch £7.95-£9.95&alc Dinner £15-£25alc*
CONF: Thtr 30 Class 15 Board 20 Del from £97.50
CARDS:

★★ 64% Hillmorton Manor

78 High St, Hillmorton CV21 4EE (2m SE off A428)
☎ 01788 565533 & 572403 FAX 01788 540027
Standing on the outskirts of Rugby and personally run by the owner, this Victorian manor house with cosy public rooms features a distinguished restaurant. Bedrooms are bright and well equipped.
11 en suite (bth/shr) (1 fmly) CTV in all bedrooms 40P English & French Cuisine V meals Coffee am Tea pm No smoking in restaurant
Last d 10pm
ROOMS: (incl. bkfst) s fr £45; d fr £58 *
OFF-PEAK: (incl. bkfst) s fr £36; d fr £45
MEALS: Lunch £6-£15 High tea fr £6 Dinner £16.25&alc*
CARDS:

Forte Posthouse Northampton/Rugby

NN6 7XR ☎ 01788 822101 FAX 01788 823955
(For full entry see Crick)

FORTE Posthouse

RUGELEY Staffordshire Map 07 SK01

Travelodge

Travelodge

Western Springs Rd WS15 2AS (on A51/B5013)
☎ 01889 570096 FAX 01889 570096
This modern building offers accommodation in smart, spacious and well equipped bedrooms, suitable for family use, and all with en suite bathrooms. Meals may be taken at the nearby family restaurant. For information on room rates and to make a booking, call Roomline free of charge on 0800 850950. For more details about Travelodge, consult the Contents page under Hotel Groups.
32 en suite (bth/shr)

RUNCORN Cheshire Map 07 SJ58

Campanile

Lowlands Rd WA7 5TP ☎ 01928 581771
FAX 01928 581730

The bar and Bistro restaurant provide meals and refreshments. Bedrooms are well equipped and have en suite bathrooms. For more details about Campanile, consult the Contents page under Hotel Groups.
53 en suite (bth/shr)
ROOMS: d £36.50 *
CONF: Thtr 25 Class 16 Board 25 Del £57

Forte Posthouse Warrington/Runcorn
Wood Ln, Beechwood WA7 3HA (off M56 junc 2, turn left at roundabout then 100 yards on left turn into Halton Station Road under a railway bridge and continue into Wood Lane) ☎ 01928 714000 FAX 01928 714611
Suitable for both the business and leisure traveller, this bright hotel provides modern accommodation in well equipped bedrooms with en suite bathrooms. For more details about Forte Posthouse hotels, consult the Contents page for the section on Hotel Groups.
135 en suite (bth/shr)
ROOMS: d £69 *
CONF: Thtr 500 Class 60 Board 36 Del from £99

Travel Inn
Chester Rd, Preston Brook (1m from M56 junct 11 or 12) ☎ 01928 716829 FAX 01928 719852
Purpose-built accommodation, offering spacious, well equipped bedrooms, all with en suite bathrooms. Meals may be taken at the nearby family restaurant. For more information about Travel Inns, consult the Contents page under Hotel Groups.
ROOMS: (incl. bkfst) d £35.50 *

RUSHDEN Northamptonshire Map 04 SP96

Travelodge
Saunders Lodge NN10 9AP (on A45, eastbound) ☎ 01933 57008 FAX 01933 57008
This modern building offers accommodation in smart, spacious and well equipped bedrooms, suitable for family use, and all with en suite bathrooms. Meals may be taken at the nearby family restaurant. For information on room rates and to make a booking, call Roomline free of charge on 0800 850950. For more details about Travelodge, consult the Contents page under Hotel Groups.
40 en suite (bth/shr)

RUSHYFORD Co Durham Map 08 NZ22

★★★ 68% **Eden Arms Swallow**
DL17 0LL (on A167) ☎ 01388 720541
FAX 01388 721871
Improvements continue to be made at this distinctive 17th-century coaching inn, where the staff are helpful and friendly. Bedrooms are all being upgraded to the same standard, and the best are comfortably and attractively furnished. The recently refurbished public areas include a pleasant lounge bar and a restaurant, and there is also a well equipped leisure centre with an adjoining coffee lounge. Typical of the style of the hotel's new chef, Steven Caldwell, are dishes like roast monkfish tails on a ragout of caramelised onions and peppers, and roast codling on a risotto of barley with a tomato and chive jus.
46 en suite (bth/shr) (4 fmly) No smoking in 20 bedrooms CTV in all bedrooms STV Night porter 200P Indoor swimming pool (heated) Sauna Solarium Gym Pool table Jacuzzi/spa Steam room Xmas English & French Cuisine V meals Coffee am Tea pm Last d 10pm
ROOMS: (incl. bkfst) s £78; d £92 * **LB**
OFF-PEAK: (incl. bkfst) s £65; d £80
MEALS: Lunch £5.95-£11.50 High tea £1.90-£7.15 Dinner £9.50-£17.50&alc
CONF: Thtr 100 Class 40 Board 50 Del from £95
CARDS:

RUSTINGTON West Sussex Map 04 TQ00

Travelodge
Worthing Rd BN17 6JN (on A259, 1m E of Littlehampton) ☎ 01903 733150 FAX 01903 733150
This modern building offers accommodation in smart, spacious and well equipped bedrooms, suitable for family use, and all with en suite bathrooms. Meals may be taken at the nearby family restaurant. For information on room rates and to make a booking, call Roomline free of charge on 0800 850950. For more details about Travelodge, consult the Contents page under Hotel Groups.
36 en suite (bth/shr)

RYDE See Wight, Isle of

RYE East Sussex Map 05 TQ92

★★★ 66% **Mermaid Inn**
Mermaid St TN31 7EU ☎ 01797 223065 & 223788
FAX 01797 225069
Reputedly one of England's oldest inns, the Mermaid is appropriately situated on a picturesque cobbled street. It caters for those who appreciate tradition and charm but value modern facilities. Roaring log fires are provided in cool weather, and the panelled walls of the cosy bar are adorned with relics of the past. There are two comfortable lounges and thoughtfully furnished bedrooms with many fine period pieces. Set-price and à la carte menus are offered in the charming restaurant.
28 rms (24 bth/shr) (5 fmly) CTV in all bedrooms No dogs Night porter 25P Xmas V meals Coffee am Tea pm Last d 9.30pm
ROOMS: (incl. bkfst) s £58-£73; d £121-£145 **LB**
OFF-PEAK: (incl. bkfst) s £58-£73; d £121-£145
MEALS: Lunch £13.50-£16.95&alc Dinner £23-£25&alc
CONF: Thtr 80 Class 50 Board 40 Del from £95
CARDS:

★★★ 63% **The George**
High St TN31 7JP ☎ 01797 222114
FAX 01797 224065
There is much historic character in this personally run and friendly hotel. Bedrooms and bathrooms are more contemporary in style and provide cosy levels of comfort. The busy restaurant makes a point of using fresh seafood from the nearby coast, served in an uncomplicated style.
22 en suite (bth/shr) (2 fmly) No smoking in 6 bedrooms CTV in all bedrooms 7P Xmas V meals Coffee am Tea pm No smoking in restaurant Last d 9pm
ROOMS: s £70-£75; d £80-£100 * **LB**
MEALS: Sunday Lunch £11.95-£12.95 Dinner £13.95-£21.95*
CONF: Thtr 80 Class 40 Board 30 Del from £80
CARDS:

★★ 71% ***Broomhill Lodge***
Rye Foreign TN31 7UN (1.5m N on A268)
☎ 01797 280421 FAX 01797 280402
Built in the 1820's and set in its own grounds of three acres and within easy reach of the historic Cinque Ports Town of Rye. Bedrooms are individually decorated in an attractive style and comfortably furnished, all are well equipped with many modern amenities. There are two elegant and tastefully appointed lounges for relaxing and a spacious brightly decorated restaurant, where a choice of menu is offered at dinner.
12 en suite (bth/shr) CTV in all bedrooms 20P Snooker Sauna English & French Cuisine V meals Coffee am Tea pm Last d 10pm
CARDS:

SAFFRON WALDEN Essex Map 05 TL53

★★❀65% **Saffron**
10-12 High St CB10 1AY (on leaving M11: from the South junct 9, from North junct 10, follow signs to Saffron Walden)
☎ 01799 522676 FAX 01799 513979
A sympathetically refurbished 16th-century building, this small, privately owned hotel is located in the High Street of the town. The conservatory restaurant offers a daily fixed-price menu and carte of imaginative cooking from chef Nigel Few, though simpler grills and vegetarian options are also available. Service, though polite and smiling, is a little rushed at times. Bedrooms vary in size, and some of the modern shower rooms are rather small. The executive and four-poster rooms are tastefully appointed and have more luxurious bathrooms.
17 en suite (bth/shr) (1 fmly) No smoking in 4 bedrooms CTV in all bedrooms 12P Xmas English Cuisine V meals Coffee am Tea pm No smoking area in restaurant
ROOMS: (incl. bkfst) s £45-£60; d £65-£85 * **LB**
CONF: Thtr 100 Class 50 Board 40 Del from £89.50
CARDS:

See advertisement on this page

ST AGNES Cornwall & Isles of Scilly Map 02 SW75

★★★64% **Rose in Vale Country House**
Rose in Vale, Mithian TR5 0QD ☎ 01872 552202 FAX 01872 552700
Hidden away in its own wooded valley, this friendly family-run hotel - a lovely Georgian house just outside the picturesque village of Mithian - offers lunchtime bar snacks and an evening choice of carte or fixed-price menus.
19 en suite (bth/shr) (4 fmly) CTV in all bedrooms 40P No coaches Outdoor swimming pool (heated) Solarium Croquet lawn Badminton Table tennis Billiards Xmas English & Continental Cuisine V meals Coffee am Tea pm No smoking in restaurant Last d 8.30pm
ROOMS: (incl. bkfst) s £42.50; d £75 * **LB**
MEALS: Lunch £9.25 Dinner £18.95&alc*
CARDS:

★★66% **Rosemundy House**
Rosemundy TR5 0UF (turn off A30 to St Agnes continue for approx 3m, on entering village take turning on the right signposted Rosemundy, hotel is at foot of the hill) ☎ 01872 552101
FAX 01872 552101
Closed Nov-Mar
This family-run hotel offers warm hospitality and comfortable accommodation. The bedrooms, which vary in size, are fresh and pleasantly furnished and a new lounge has been added to the existing public areas. The cuisine on offer in the large dining room is uncomplicated.
44 en suite (bth/shr) (12 fmly) CTV in all bedrooms 40P Outdoor swimming pool (heated) Pool table Croquet lawn Putting green Badminton Games room Coffee am No smoking in restaurant Last d 8pm
ROOMS: (incl. bkfst & dinner) s fr £28; d fr £56
MEALS: Dinner £12*
CARDS:

★65% **Sunholme**
Goonvrea Rd TR5 0NW (on B3277, leisure park on right, museum on left. Turn left after 150 yds.) ☎ 01872 552318
Closed Nov-25Mar
Situated on the southern slopes of St Agnes Beacon, Sunholme Hotel has spectacular views from its extensive grounds. David and Jill Llewellyn took over the hotel in 1994 and have set about generally upgrading the property. Bedrooms are cosy and well equipped, new furnishings having been installed in some rooms. The three inter-

contd.

connecting lounges benefit from the views, each area is well furnished and comfortable. A cosy bar is also available. In the dining room, a varied choice of dishes is offered, all of which are home made, using local produce. The Llewellyn's relaxed, friendly approach to guests, creates a delightful atmosphere.
10 en suite (shr) (3 fmly) CTV in all bedrooms 12P No coaches Coffee am Tea pm No smoking in restaurant Last d 7.30pm
ROOMS: (incl. bkfst) s £27-£30; d £54-£60 **LB**
OFF-PEAK: (incl. bkfst) s £25-£28; d £50-£56
MEALS: Bar Lunch £2-£2.50alc Dinner £12&alc*
CARDS:

ST ALBANS Hertfordshire Map 04 TL10

★★★★ 76% Sopwell House Hotel & Country Club
Cottonmill Ln, Sopwell AL1 2HQ (follow St Albans sign to M10 rbt then take A414, first left and follow Sopwell signs) ☎ 01727 864477 FAX 01727 844741/845636
The grace, colour and style of architecture reflect the time when the building and surrounding land was owned by the Mountbatten family. Public areas have recently been refurbished and extended, the new conservatory lounge bar gives added flexibility to an already good range of public rooms. The Library lounge is tastefully furnished and appealing with its bold colour schemes, it here that pre-dinner drinks are often offered prior to dining in the Magnolia Conservatory restaurant, where Chef Steven Wheeler presents interesting menus and enjoyable meals. Alternatively, diners have the option of informal dining in the Brasserie or snacks and refreshments from lounge or room service menus. All the bedrooms are attractively decorated in colour-co-ordinated styles and many are furnished with custom built wooden furniture with in-laid hotel logo; four poster beds are an additional feature in many rooms. In addition to well managed and impressive indoor leisure facilities there are a range of health, beauty and fitness treats available. The modern conference centre is a very popular with large and small meetings and functions.
92 en suite (bth/shr) (6 fmly) CTV in all bedrooms STV Lift Night porter 200P Indoor swimming pool (heated) Snooker Sauna Solarium Gym Jacuzzi/spa Health & beauty spa Hairdressing salon Xmas English & French Cuisine V meals Coffee am Tea pm Last d 10pm
ROOMS: s £69.50-£99.75; d £94.75-£129.75 * **LB**
MEALS: Lunch £16.95 Dinner £21.75-£23.75*
CONF: Thtr 400 Class 220 Board 90 Del from £139.50
CARDS:

See advertisement on opposite page

★★★★ 65% Noke Thistle
Watford Rd AL2 3DS (2.75m S at junct A405/B4630) ☎ 01727 854252 FAX 01727 841906
THISTLE HOTELS
Committed management and a loyal team of staff ensure that service at the Noke remains as attentive, friendly and professional as ever. Executive rooms are more spacious and comfortable than the Club rooms but all have attractive fabrics and co-ordinated decor. Public rooms are elegant but compact and Berties restaurant has a good local reputation; chef Andrew Stickings has recently taken over at the helm and has managed to retain the rosette award. The Baltimore Bean Company offers more informal dining, American style.

111 en suite (bth/shr) (4 fmly) No smoking in 40 bedrooms CTV in all bedrooms STV Night porter 150P Gym Membership of local Health Club English & French Cuisine V meals Coffee am Tea pm Last d 9.45pm
ROOMS: s £93-£95; d £103-£105 **LB**
OFF-PEAK: (incl. bkfst) s £42.50-£45; d £68-£70
MEALS: Lunch £18.50&alc Dinner £22&alc*
CONF: Thtr 60 Class 26 Board 26 Del from £130
CARDS:

★★★ 66% The Manor St Michael's Village
Fishpool St AL3 4RY (from St Albans Abbey follow Fishpool Street toward St Michael's village. Hotel located 0.5m on left hand side) ☎ 01727 864444 FAX 01727 848909
St Michael's Manor is set in five acres of award-winning gardens overlooking the river and lake of an adjoining park. The property dates back to the 16th century but incorporates a number of architectural styles. Guests have a choice of lounges when the hotel is not busy with conferences, and there are a small cocktail bar and a well appointed restaurant. Service is attentive and traditions such as porterage, shoe cleaning and early morning tea are upheld. Major refurbishment of half the bedrooms has recently been completed - the new-style bedrooms being individually designed and attractively furnished, while old-style rooms look quite dated by comparison.
23 en suite (bth/shr) No smoking in 3 bedrooms CTV in all bedrooms No dogs (ex guide dogs) Night porter 70P No coaches Croquet lawn Xmas V meals Coffee am Tea pm Last d 9.30pm
ROOMS: (incl. bkfst) s £95-£110; d £105-£165 **LB**
MEALS: Lunch £14.50-£18.50&alc Dinner fr £19.50&alc*
CONF: Thtr 30 Class 18 Board 20 Del £135
CARDS:

★★★ 64% Hertfordshire Moat House

London Rd, Markyate AL3 8HH (exit M1 junct 9 north towards Dunstable/Whipsnade hotel is 1m from motorway on right) ☎ 01582 449988 FAX 01582 842282
Conveniently located for the motorway and Luton airport, this modern hotel offers bedrooms with practical furniture where pay movies and room service can be enjoyed. Public areas are attractively styled and include a carvery restaurant. The meeting rooms, business centre and small gym make this a popular choice of meetings and conferences.
89 en suite (bth/shr) (16 fmly) No smoking in 44 bedrooms CTV in all bedrooms Night porter 350P Solarium Gym Pool table International Cuisine V meals Coffee am Tea pm No smoking area in restaurant Last d 10pm
ROOMS: s £75-£100; d £80-£120 * **LB**
OFF-PEAK: s £30-£50; d £40-£80
MEALS: Lunch £12-£16.95&alc High tea £5.70 Dinner £16.95&alc*

CONF: Thtr 350 Class 130 Board 60 Del from £105
CARDS: 

★★65% Lake

234 London Rd AL1 1JQ (junct 22 off M25 follow A1081 to St Albans, after Colney rdbt hotel is 1m on left) ☎ 01727 840904 FAX 01727 862750

CONSORT HOTELS

Located a short distance to the south of the centre, this hotel has a well-meaning team of staff. The bar, lounge and restaurant are often sited in one area which creates atmosphere which sometimes can be quite close. The bedrooms are well looked after and nearly all have modern bathrooms.

43 en suite (bth/shr) (2 fmly) No smoking in 12 bedrooms CTV in all bedrooms No dogs (ex guide dogs) 70P International Cuisine V meals Coffee am Last d 9.30pm
ROOMS: (incl. bkfst) s £49.50-£54.50; d £74.50 *
OFF-PEAK: (incl. bkfst) s £29.50-£35; d £54.50
MEALS: Bar Lunch £2.50-£6.50 Dinner £9.95-£14.45*
CONF: Thtr 200 Class 60 Board 50 Del from £69
CARDS: 

★★56% Avalon

260 London Rd AL1 1TJ ☎ 01727 856757 FAX 01727 856750

A friendly small hotel, the Avalon is set back from the A1081 about a mile from the centre of town. Bedrooms are well furnished in the modern style with pine furniture, and there is now a bar-cum-lounge adjoining the themed restaurant which serves northwest Indian cuisine.

14 en suite (bth/shr) (2 fmly) CTV in all bedrooms No dogs 14P English, Italian & Oriental Cuisine Coffee am
ROOMS: (incl. bkfst) s fr £49; d fr £55 * **LB**
OFF-PEAK: (incl. bkfst) s fr £39; d fr £45
CONF: Class 35 Board 30
CARDS:

ST ANNES See Lytham St Annes

ST AUSTELL Cornwall & Isles of Scilly Map 02 SX05

HOTEL *of the* YEAR

★★★★ 73% Carlyon Bay

Sea Rd, Carlyon Bay PL25 3RD (Brend)
☎ 01726 812304 FAX 01726 814938

Enjoying a dramatic cliff-top location with stunning Cornish views, this welcoming hotel is surrounded by 250 acres of grounds including a championship golf course and extensive leisure facilities. Attractive public areas include several small meeting rooms, a spacious lounge and a comfortable cocktail

contd.

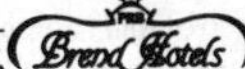

bar; bedrooms are comfortable and well equipped. The grand Bay View Restaurant offers a wide selection of dishes on the carte, fixed-price and vegetarian menus, with local fish a speciality. A less formal lunch and dining operation is featured in the recently refurbished golf clubhouse. Our inspectors have nominated Carlyon Bay as AA Hotel of the Year for England for 1996/7.
73 en suite (bth/shr) (14 fmly) CTV in all bedrooms STV No dogs (ex guide dogs) Lift Night porter 101P No coaches Indoor swimming pool (heated) Outdoor swimming pool (heated) Golf 18 Tennis (hard) Snooker Sauna Solarium Putting green Jacuzzi/spa Table tennis/9-hole approach course Wkly live entertainment ch fac Xmas English & French Cuisine V meals Coffee am Tea pm Last d 9pm
ROOMS: (incl. bkfst) s £64-£79; d £122-£182 * **LB**
MEALS: Lunch £9.50-£10.50&alc Dinner £22.50&alc*
CONF: Thtr 100
CARDS:

See advertisement on page 529

★★★65% Porth Avallen
Sea Rd, Carlyon Bay PL25 3SG ☎ 01726 812802 FAX 01726 817097
Closed 26 Dec-4 Jan
This long-established traditional hotel, set in its own grounds overlooking Carlyon Bay, offers bedrooms in a range of styles, all equipped with modern facilities. There are a comfortable oak-panelled lounge with a terrace, a bar and dining room.
24 en suite (bth/shr) (4 fmly) CTV in all bedrooms STV No dogs (ex guide dogs) Night porter 50P English & French Cuisine V meals Coffee am Tea pm No smoking in restaurant Last d 9pm
ROOMS: (incl. bkfst) s £51-£59.90; d £72-£85 * **LB**
MEALS: Lunch fr £8.25&alc High tea fr £4.50 Dinner fr £15&alc*
CONF: Thtr 100 Class 50 Board 30 Del from £59
CARDS:

★★★63% Cliff Head
Sea Rd, Carlyon Bay PL25 3RB (2m E off A390)
☎ 01726 812345 FAX 01726 815511
Bedrooms at the front of this hotel enjoy fine views over the bay and surrounding cliffs, providing a fitting backdrop to the relaxing and welcoming atmosphere that can be found within. A choice of lounges is offered, together with an outdoor swimming pool for the more adventurous. Entertainment is also provided after dinner.
44 en suite (bth/shr) (5 fmly) CTV in all bedrooms Night porter 60P Outdoor swimming pool (heated) Sauna Solarium Gym Pool table British Cuisine V meals Coffee am Tea pm Last d 9.30pm
ROOMS: (incl. bkfst) s £35-£45; d £65-£75 **LB**
MEALS: Lunch £4.95-£7.95&alc Dinner fr £14.95&alc
CONF: Thtr 100 Class 80 Board 60 Del from £60
CARDS:

See advertisement on opposite page

★★ 78% Boscundle Manor
Tregrehan PL25 3RL (2m E off A390)
☎ 01726 813557 FAX 01726 814997
Closed end Oct-Mar
This handsome 18th-century stone-built manor house, situated in its own secluded grounds, is run along the lines of a private house by the resident proprietors Andrew and Mary Flint. Boscundle is lovingly furnished with antiques, creating an atmosphere of quality and quiet elegance. Public rooms include an attractive lounge with a log fire, a bar-lounge, a conservatory breakfast room and a delightful dining room where guests can enjoy Mary Flint's cooking. The menu offers a short choice of local fish and meat, in fact all the dishes are based on the best of fresh produce, and home-made desserts are served with Cornish clotted cream. Bedrooms are spacious and comfortable, all have been equipped with modern facilities and some are located in cottages in the garden.
7 en suite (bth/shr) 3 annexe en suite (bth/shr) CTV in all bedrooms 15P No coaches Outdoor swimming pool (heated) Gym Croquet lawn Golf practice area T/tennis Badminton International Cuisine No smoking in restaurant Last d 8pm
ROOMS: (incl. bkfst) s £60-£70; d £110-£130 *
OFF-PEAK: (incl. bkfst) s £55; d £90
MEALS: Dinner £15-£22.50
CARDS:

★★66% Pier House
Harbour Front, Charlestown PL25 3NJ (follow A390 to St Austell,Mt Charles r'aboutturn left down Charlestown Road)
☎ 01726 67955 FAX 01726 69246
Pleasantly situated overlooking the quayside and harbour, this free house has been extended to provide comfortable well equipped bedrooms, some with glorious views, and a spacious tiered restaurant with an additional bar lounge. The original Harbour Inn bar offers real ale and popular meals from the blackboard, while the restaurant is open throughout the day for light refreshments and cream teas, as well as lunch and dinner. There is also a cosy residents' lounge with exposed stone walls and beams.
25 en suite (bth/shr) (4 fmly) CTV in all bedrooms No dogs (ex guide dogs) 56P English Cuisine V meals Coffee am Tea pm Last d 9.30pm
ROOMS: (incl. bkfst) s £30-£38; d £50-£62 * **LB**
OFF-PEAK: (incl. bkfst) s fr £27; d £45-£55.80
MEALS: Lunch £6.85-£11.75alc Dinner £13.25-£27.25alc*
CONF: Class 20
CARDS:

★★63% White Hart
Church St PL25 4AT (St Austell Brewery)
☎ 01726 72100 FAX 01726 74705
Closed 25 & 26 Dec
This stone-built inn at the centre of the town offers a relaxed atmosphere and well equipped bedrooms. Busy bars are popular with non-residents for lunches and snacks, while a more formal operation is available in the comfortable restaurant.
18 en suite (bth/shr) CTV in all bedrooms No dogs (ex guide dogs) V meals Coffee am Tea pm Last d 9pm
CONF: Thtr 50
CARDS:

★61% Selwood House
60 Alexandra Rd PL25 4QN ☎ 01726 65707 FAX 01726 68951
This friendly business hotel stands on the approach road to the town centre. Bedrooms are equipped with modern facilities and public areas include a comfortable lounge, a small bar and a bright dining room. Parking is available at the rear of the building.
11 en suite (bth/shr) (2 fmly) CTV in all bedrooms 14P No children 12yrs V meals Coffee am Tea pm No smoking in restaurant Last d 7pm
ROOMS: (incl. bkfst) s £32; d £59
OFF-PEAK: (incl. bkfst) d £45
MEALS: Dinner £10*
CONF: Board 15 Del from £47.50
CARDS:

ST HELENS Merseyside Map 07 SJ59
See also Rainhill

★★★★ 65% Chalon Court
Chalon Way, Linkway West WA10 1NG
☎ 01744 453444 FAX 01744 454655

The impressive glass pyramids and the predominantly glass façade of Chalon Court reflect the importance of glass to this

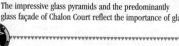

town. The hotel is ultra-modern and provides spacious and comfortable accommodation. Bedrooms include several suites and no-smoking and lady rooms are also available. As well as a fully equipped leisure club, extensive facilities are provided for functions and business meetings. Lighter meals are served in the Café Bar and the more formal Renaissance restaurant offers high culinary standards. Market fish specials and steak choices augment a good à la carte menu.
84 en suite (bth/shr) (16 fmly) No smoking in 44 bedrooms CTV in all bedrooms STV Lift Night porter Air conditioning 140P Indoor swimming pool (heated) Sauna Solarium Gym Jacuzzi/spa Steam room Wkly live entertainment Xmas English Modern Cuisine V meals Coffee am Tea pm No smoking in restaurant Last d 9.45pm
ROOMS: s £49.50-£79.50; d £49.50-£79.50 *
MEALS: Lunch £9.95&alc Dinner £15.95-£19.95&alc*
CONF: Thtr 220 Class 120 Board 60 Del from £75
CARDS:

Forte Posthouse Haydock
Lodge Ln, Newton-Le-Willows WA12 OJG
☎ 01942 717878 FAX 01942 718419
(For full entry see Haydock)

ST IVES Cambridgeshire Map 04 TL37

★★★66% **Olivers Lodge**
Needingworth Rd PE17 4JP ☎ 01480 463252
FAX 01480 461150
Situated just off the inner ring road in a peaceful residential area, this small hotel offers comfortable accommodation and helpful service. Main house and annexe bedrooms all have modern appointments and a good range of facilities; a lounge bar and air-conditioned restaurant are also available.
11 en suite (bth/shr) 5 annexe en suite (bth/shr) (3 fmly) No smoking in 1 bedroom CTV in all bedrooms STV 30P Croquet lawn Motor cruiser Xmas International & Traditional English Cuisine V meals Coffee am Tea pm Last d 9.30pm
ROOMS: (incl. bkfst) s £57-£65; d £65-£75 **LB**
OFF-PEAK: (incl. bkfst) s £45-£60; d £55-£60
MEALS: Lunch £11.50-£12.50&alc Dinner £14.50-£18.50&alc*
CONF: Thtr 75 Class 45 Board 40 Del from £70.70
CARDS:

★★★64% **Dolphin**
London Rd PE17 4EP (on B1040) ☎ 01480 466966 & 497497
FAX 01480 495597
RS 25-31 Dec
There are some delightful views of the River Ouse from the public areas within this modern hotel, which sits beside the ancient stone bridge that links it to the town centre. The mostly open-plan public rooms include a choice of bars and a pleasant restaurant, where an interesting selection of dishes is offered from daily and à la carte menus. The modern accommodation is divided between the main hotel and an adjacent annexe; the original bedrooms have recently been refurbished: these rooms are now more cheerful with colour co-ordinated décor and soft furnishings. Secure car parking and modern conference/function suites are popular attractions to both the local community and corporate guests.
31 en suite (bth/shr) 16 annexe en suite (bth/shr) (2 fmly) CTV in all bedrooms No dogs (ex guide dogs) Night porter 300P Fishing Pool table English & Continental Cuisine V meals Coffee am Tea pm Last d 9.30pm
ROOMS: (incl. bkfst) s £62-£70; d £80-£95 **LB**
MEALS: Lunch £11.95-£17 Dinner £15.50-£17&alc*
CONF: Thtr 150 Class 80 Board 50 Del from £95
CARDS:

★★★64% **Slepe Hall**
Ramsey Rd PE17 4RB (leave A604 & follow by-pass signed Huntingdon towards St Ives, turn into Ramsey Rd at only set of traffic lights in the area) ☎ 01480 463122 FAX 01480 300706
Closed 25-27 Dec
Service at this small, privately run hotel is both polite and friendly, which helps create a relaxed atmosphere throughout the cosy public areas. Diners have a good choice, with interesting menus offered in the pleasant surroundings of the restaurant or informal meals available within the bar area. Bedroom styles and sizes vary, the original house rooms displaying cheerful floral patterns, whilst the more modern accommodation in the new wing tending to be of a lighter style.
16 rms (15 bth/shr) (1 fmly) CTV in all bedrooms STV 70P No coaches English and Continental Cuisine V meals Coffee am Tea pm Last d 9.30pm
ROOMS: (incl. bkfst) s £57-£65; d £70-£80 **LB**
MEALS: Lunch £10.95-£13.95&alc Dinner £13.95-£15.95&alc*
CONF: Thtr 200 Class 80 Board 60 Del from £77.95
CARDS:

ST IVES Cornwall & Isles of Scilly Map 02 SW54

★★★72% **Porthminster**
The Terrace TR26 2BN (on A3074)
☎ 01736 795221 FAX 01736 797043
From its enviable position, overlooking the sandy beach, the Porthminster Hotel continues to make alterations and improvements. Trevor Richards assisted by his loyal team of staff, many of whom have worked at the hotel for over twenty years, welcome back guests, some who holiday at the hotel on a very regular basis. Bedrooms are comfortable, all having been upgraded and modernised to meet the demands of the 1990's. The public rooms are spacious, all benefiting from the spectacular views over St Ives Bay. In the

contd.

restaurant, a traditional style of cuisine is served under the watchful eye of Elizabeth Hodson, the charming restaurant manager.
47 en suite (bth/shr) (14 fmly) CTV in all bedrooms Lift Night porter 43P Indoor swimming pool (heated) Outdoor swimming pool (heated) Sauna Solarium Gym Pool table Jacuzzi/spa ch fac Xmas English & French Cuisine V meals Coffee am Last d 8.30pm
ROOMS: (incl. bkfst) s £56-£62; d £112-£124 **LB**
OFF-PEAK: (incl. bkfst) s £48-£58; d £96-£116
MEALS: Lunch £7.50-£25alc Dinner £19.50&alc*
CONF: Thtr 90 Board 24
CARDS:

See advertisement on opposite page

★★★69% **Carbis Bay**
Carbis Bay TR26 2NP ☎ 01736 795311 FAX 01736 797677
Closed Jan-Mar
This long-established, family-run hotel actually owns Carbis Bay beach and clearly benefits from its fine seaside location. The accommodation is very comfortable and has modern bedrooms, two lounges (one non-smoking), a restaurant and bar. Service is particularly helpful and friendly, supervised by the proprietor's family.
30 en suite (bth/shr) (9 fmly) No smoking in 5 bedrooms CTV in all bedrooms 206P Outdoor swimming pool (heated) Fishing Snooker Pool table Private beach ch fac Xmas English & Continental Cuisine V meals Coffee am Tea pm No smoking in restaurant Last d 8.30pm
ROOMS: (incl. bkfst) s £64-£100; d £90-£134 **LB**
OFF-PEAK: (incl. bkfst) s £45-£90; d £70-£134
MEALS: Lunch £5 Dinner £10-£30*
CARDS: 

See advertisement under CARBIS BAY

★★★65% **Garrack**
Higher Ayr TR26 3AA (follow signs for 'Porthmeor Beach and Car Parks') ☎ 01736 796199 FAX 01736 798955
Standing in two acres of grounds with fine views over Porthmeor beach, this hotel has been operated by the same family for over 30 years. Bedrooms vary from rooms in a modern wing to those in the original building; the latter at the time of the last visit due to be upgraded. Room 10, adjacent to reception, is especially designed for disabled guests. The small leisure complex is combined with an all day coffee shop operation. In the restaurant both fixed price and carte menus are available. The dishes are enjoyable, the kitchen using quality local produce, including seafood and lobsters.
17 en suite (bth/shr) 2 annexe rms (3 fmly) CTV in all bedrooms 30P No coaches Indoor swimming pool (heated) Sauna Solarium Gym Xmas English & French Cuisine V meals Coffee am Tea pm Last d 8.30pm
ROOMS: (incl. bkfst) s £64; d £128 * **LB**
OFF-PEAK: (incl. bkfst) s fr £61; d fr £88
MEALS: Sunday Lunch fr £10.50 Dinner fr £17.50&alc
CARDS:

See advertisement on opposite page

★★68% ***Boskerris***
Boskerris Rd, Carbis Bay TR26 2NQ (upon entering Carbis Bay take 3rd turning right after garage) ☎ 01736 795295 FAX 01736 798632
Closed Nov-Xmas & 29 Dec-Etr RS Xmas
Situated in an acre and a half of grounds overlooking Carbis Bay, with magnificent views across St Ives harbour and Godrevy Head. The hotel is personally run by Marie Monk and her son Spencer, and continues to attract a regular clientele. Bedrooms are well decorated and equipped, lounge areas are comfortable and the dining room is attractively presented. Leisure facilities include an outdoor heated pool and a games room with table tennis.
13 rms (11 bth/shr) 5 annexe en suite (bth/shr) (4 fmly) CTV in all bedrooms 20P Outdoor swimming pool (heated) Putting green Games room English & French Cuisine V meals Coffee am Tea pm Last d 8.30pm
CARDS:

★★68% ***Pedn-Olva***
The Warren TR26 2EA ☎ 01736 796222 FAX 01736 797710
This charming, privately owned holiday hotel stands at the water's edge, at the end of a labyrinth of narrow, winding streets. Many of the neat bedrooms have glorious views across the bay, and the public areas also take full advantage of the location with their vast picture windows. Staff are friendly and helpful, and among many loyal guests are some who have been visiting for nearly 30 years.
28 en suite (bth/shr) 7 annexe rms (4 bth/shr) (5 fmly) CTV in all bedrooms Night porter 21P Outdoor swimming pool (heated) English & French Cuisine V meals Coffee am Tea pm Last d 9.15pm
CARDS:

★★67% **Skidden House**
Skidden Hill TR26 2DU ☎ 01736 796899
FAX 01736 798619
Skidden House, situated in the centre of the town, dates back many centuries and is said to be the oldest hotel in St Ives. It has cosy bedrooms equipped with modern facilities. In the intimate dining room both fixed-price and à la carte menus are offered, using fresh local produce wherever possible. A tasty cream of potato and herb soup began a test meal, followed by a crab and avocado salad. Pork fillet and prunes with a cream and brandy sauce was accompanied by new and Dauphanois potatoes, carrots and mange-touts. To complete the meal an underside down apple pie was served with double cream.
7 en suite (shr) No smoking in 2 bedrooms CTV in all bedrooms 7P No coaches Xmas English & French Cuisine V meals Coffee am Last d 8.45pm
ROOMS: (incl. bkfst) s £40-£52; d £70-£90 * **LB**
MEALS: Dinner £19.50-£22.50&alc*
CARDS: 

★★66% **Chy-an-Dour**
Trelyon Av TR26 2AD (turn off A30 onto A3074, hotel on the right just past garage) ☎ 01736 796436 FAX 01736 795772
Built in 1890 as a gentleman's residence, the hotel has an uninterrupted panoramic view over St Ives, the harbour and

Porthminster Beach. Owners David and Renee Watson welcome guests to their comfortable hotel. David Watson is the chef and provides well prepared, honest cooking in the restaurant at both dinner and breakfast. The 4-course dinner menu changes daily, using fresh local produce wherever possible. Most of the bedrooms enjoy the splendid views; all the rooms are well equipped and many have been attractively refurbished.
23 en suite (bth/shr) (2 fmly) No smoking in 9 bedrooms CTV in all bedrooms No dogs (ex guide dogs) Lift 23P No children 5yrs English & Continental Cuisine V meals Coffee am No smoking in restaurant Last d 8pm
ROOMS: (incl. bkfst) s £27-£38; d £54-£76 * **LB**
MEALS: Bar Lunch £2.75-£5 Dinner £14.75-£16.75*
CARDS:

★★65% **Cornwallis**
Headland Rd, Carbis Bay TR26 2NR ☎ 01736 795294
This friendly, family-run holiday hotel enjoys a quiet and peaceful location, and has an unrestricted view across Carbis bay. Personally run by dedicated and enthusiastic owners Peter and Karen Finch, the accommodation is being gradually upgraded, recent improvements including a new reception, foyer and well furnished bar. Bedrooms are well appointed and come in a variety of sizes, most with a good sea view. The terraced patio has a heated swimming pool, and there is access to the coastal path and scenic railway from the hotel.
12 rms (10 bth/shr) (3 fmly) CTV in all bedrooms No dogs 12P No coaches Outdoor swimming pool (heated) Pool table Table Tennis Xmas Traditional English Cuisine V meals Coffee am Tea pm Last d 7.30pm
ROOMS: (incl. bkfst) s £25-£34; d £50-£68 * **LB**
OFF-PEAK: (incl. bkfst) s £18-£22; d £36-£44
MEALS: Dinner £10-£14*
CARDS:

★★63% ***Chy-an-Drea***
The Terrace TR26 2BP ☎ 01736 795076 FAX 01736 793957
Closed 18 Oct-1 Apr
With superb views over St Ives Bay, this hotel has been run by the Boss family for many years and has a friendly and relaxed atmosphere. The public areas are bright and comfortably furnished, and the pretty dining room offers a daily-changing set-price menu of traditional cuisine. Bedrooms vary in size, and the front-facing singles are compact, though they do have superb views and small balconies.
33 en suite (bth/shr) (2 fmly) CTV in all bedrooms 25P Solarium Jacuzzi/spa No children 5yrs V meals Coffee am Last d 8pm
CARDS:

★★62% ***Chy-an-Albany***
Albany Ter TR26 2BS ☎ 01736 796759 FAX 01736 795584
A friendly resort hotel within leisurely walking distance of the centre of the town. The comfortable public areas are pleasantly appointed, and on certain nights during the season there is entertainment provided. In the attractive dining room a short set-price menu is available. The bedrooms vary in size; the front-facing rooms are always popular.
34 rms (9 bth 18 shr) (14 fmly) CTV in all bedrooms No dogs (ex guide dogs) 37P English & Continental Cuisine V meals Coffee am Tea pm Last d 8pm
CARDS:

★★60% **St Eia**
Trelyon Av TR26 2AA ☎ 01736 795531 FAX 01736 793591
A relaxed and friendly, hotel with views overlooking St Ives, the harbour and Porthminster Beach. The neat bedrooms are comfortable and furnished to make the best use of space. In the attractive dining room, guests have the choice of a fixed-price menu and a short à la carte are offered. Guests can relax in the cosy lounge or watch the boats from the bar window.

contd.

19 en suite (bth/shr) (4 fmly) CTV in all bedrooms No dogs (ex guide dogs) 20P Xmas Traditional English Cuisine V meals Coffee am No smoking in restaurant Last d 9pm
ROOMS: (incl. bkfst) s £27.50-£35; d £55-£70 * **LB**
OFF-PEAK: (incl. bkfst) s £25-£30; d £50-£60
MEALS: Dinner £9.50-£15&alc*
CARDS:

★66% **Hotel Rotorua**
Trencrom Ln, Carbis Bay TR26 2TD ☎ 01736 795419
FAX 01736 795419
Closed Nov-Etr
In a leafy lane a short distance from Carbis Bay, this purpose-built hotel stands in well tended gardens. Bedrooms are of a good size and have modern furniture and attractive fabrics. Public areas are spacious and include a comfortable lounge, a separate bar lounge and a pine-furnished dining room. Friendly and attentive service is provided by the owners and their staff.
13 en suite (bth/shr) (10 fmly) CTV in all bedrooms 10P No coaches Outdoor swimming pool (heated) Pool table ch fac Coffee am Last d 7pm
ROOMS: (incl. bkfst) s £18-£26; d £36-£52 *
MEALS: Bar Lunch £4-£5 Dinner £7.50

★58% **Dunmar**
Pednolver Ter TR26 2EL (take A3074 and fork left at the Porthminster Hotel into Albert Road. Hotel is 200yds along at junction of Pednolver and Porthminster Terrace) ☎ 01736 796117 Freephone 0500 131218 FAX 01736 796117
A small, informal, family-run holiday hotel, the Dunmar stands close to the town centre and beaches in an elevated position with views over St Ives Bay. Bedrooms are nicely furnished, many with modern facilities, and the cosy dining room offers traditional dishes from a set menu.
17 rms (4 bth 9 shr) (7 fmly) CTV in all bedrooms 20P Xmas English Cuisine V meals Coffee am Tea pm No smoking in restaurant
ROOMS: (incl. bkfst) s £17.50-£29; d £35-£58 * **LB**
CARDS:

ST KEYNE Cornwall & Isles of Scilly Map 02 SX26

★★ 67% **Old Rectory House**

PL14 4RL ☎ 01579 342617
Closed Xmas
The Old Rectory enjoys a peaceful and secluded setting in its own three acres of grounds surrounded by farmland, with beautiful views of the countryside. Pat and John Minifie welcome guests to their small hotel, which is run in a relaxed and friendly manner. Bedrooms are individually furnished and decorated, one room is available on the ground floor. Each evening a short table d'hote menu is offered, using fresh local ingredients, cooked with care and simply presented.
8 en suite (bth/shr) (2 fmly) No smoking in 4 bedrooms CTV in all bedrooms 30P No coaches English & French Cuisine V meals No smoking in restaurant Last d 8pm
ROOMS: (incl. bkfst) s £35; d £50-£70 **LB**
MEALS: Lunch £16-£17&alc Dinner £16-£17&alc*
CONF: Board 30
CARDS:

ST LAWRENCE See Wight, Isle of

ST LEONARDS Dorset Map 04 SU10

★★★66% **St Leonards Hotel**
BH24 2NP (1.5m from Ringwood on the A31 between Ferndown and Ashley Heath) ☎ 01425 471220
FAX 01425 480274
Conveniently located near Ringwood, this hotel has been considerably developed since its days as a roadside inn. Bedrooms are all similarly furnished in a bright modern style and several look onto the attractive grounds at the rear. Open plan public areas feature a lively bar and restaurant, with a popular grill menu and live jazz on Friday evenings.
33 en suite (bth/shr) (4 fmly) No smoking in 8 bedrooms CTV in all bedrooms STV No dogs Night porter 250P Sauna Gym Wkly live entertainment ch fac European Cuisine V meals Coffee am Tea pm Last d 10pm
ROOMS: (incl. bkfst) s £49.50-£55; d £49.50-£65 * **LB**
OFF-PEAK: (incl. bkfst) s £45
MEALS: Lunch £6-£12.50 Dinner £12-£14.50&alc*
CONF: Thtr 100 Class 50 Board 40 Del £85
CARDS:

ST LEONARDS-ON-SEA See Hastings & St Leonards

ST MARTIN'S See Scilly, Isles of

ST MARY CHURCH See Torquay

ST MARY'S See Scilly, Isles of

ST MAWES Cornwall & Isles of Scilly Map 02 SW83

★★★ 73% **Idle Rocks**
Harbour Side TR2 5AN (off A3078) ☎ 01326 270771
FAX 01326 270062
This fine hotel enjoys a superb situation on the water's edge, overlooking the sheltered harbour. Most of the tastefully decorated, well equipped bedrooms have outstanding views, those in the Bohella House wing tending to be larger. The public areas include a smart and restful no-smoking lounge for residents and an attractive bar with access to the waterside patio, all positioned to enjoy the magnificent view. In a restaurant specialising in local fish, fixed-priced menus offer imaginative dishes prepared from the best of ingredients under the careful supervision of head chef Alan Vickops. A recent inspection meal started with a smooth duck paté served with home-made herb bread. This was followed by a grilled fillet of turbot on a bed of sliced potato with an oil-based sauce flavoured with sun-dried tomatoes. Lemon tart, chosen from the list of mouthwatering desserts, was pleasantly tart and served with a less intense lemon jus. A courteous team of staff provides attentive services, and the relaxed atmosphere is in keeping with the peaceful surroundings of this delightful fishing village.
17 en suite (bth/shr) 7 annexe en suite (bth/shr) (2 fmly) CTV in all bedrooms Jacuzzi/spa Xmas English & French Cuisine Coffee am Tea pm No smoking in restaurant Last d 9.15pm
ROOMS: (incl. bkfst & dinner) s £55-£73; d £110-£146 **LB**
OFF-PEAK: (incl. bkfst & dinner) s £45-£63; d £90-£126
MEALS: Bar Lunch £3.25-£6.80alc High tea £1-£4.95alc Dinner £22.50-£24.95
CONF: Thtr 30 Class 20 Board 20
CARDS:

See advertisement on opposite page

★★ 72% **Rising Sun**
TR2 5DJ (from A39 take A3078 signposted St Mawes, hotel is in centre of village) (St Austell Brewery) ☎ 01326 270233
The Rising Sun benefits from a location close to the waterfront in this delightful fishing village. Major works have been carried out recently to provide stylish and comfortable bedrooms, individually furnished and including a number of water-colours and drawings specially commissioned from local artists. The bar retains the character of the village inn and is much frequented by locals, whilst locally caught fish features strongly in the imaginative dishes served in the new Brasserie.
9 en suite (bth/shr) CTV in all bedrooms STV 2P No coaches English, French & Italian Cuisine V meals Coffee am Tea pm No smoking area in restaurant Last d 9.30pm
ROOMS: (incl. bkfst) s fr £35; d fr £59 * **LB**

OFF-PEAK: (incl. bkfst) d fr £50
MEALS: Sunday Lunch £2.50-£7.95alc Dinner £5.95-£14.95alc*
CARDS:

★★ 65% St Mawes
The Seafront TR2 5DW (opposite the quay in the centre of the village)
☎ 01326 270266
Closed Dec & Jan
This distinctive 17th-century house is situated on the seafront overlooking the harbour. The simple selection of freshly cooked English and French dishes offered in the cosy restaurant makes good use of the local seafood, including Cornish lobster. The home-made desserts are not to be missed.
7 rms (5 bth/shr) CTV in all bedrooms No coaches No children 5yrs English & French Cuisine V meals Coffee am No smoking in restaurant Last d 8.15pm
ROOMS: (incl. bkfst & dinner) s £55-£66; d £96-£108 * **LB**
MEALS: Bar Lunch £4.50-£12alc Dinner £17-£26
CARDS:

ST MELLION Cornwall & Isles of Scilly Map 02 SX36

★★★ 73% St Mellion Hotel Golf & Country Club
St Mellion Golf & County Club PL12 6SD (St Mellion is on the A388 approx 4m N of Saltash) ☎ 01579 351351 FAX 01579 350116
In the middle of a 450 acre estate, surrounded by the rolling grassland of two 18-hole golf courses, lies the St Mellion Golf and Country Club, with its superb range of leisure facilities. Most of the bedrooms, in a dedicated building, offer views over the course, as does the first-floor lounge bar. Dinner is served in the aptly named Garden Room restaurant whilst the brasserie offers a less formal dining atmosphere.
38 annexe en suite (bth/shr) (14 fmly) No smoking in 12 bedrooms CTV in all bedrooms No dogs (ex guide dogs) Lift Night porter 400P Indoor swimming pool (heated) Golf 36 Tennis (hard) Squash Snooker Sauna Solarium Gym Pool table Putting green Jacuzzi/spa Badminton ch fac Xmas International Cuisine V meals Coffee am Tea pm Last d 10pm
ROOMS: s £51-£79; d £52-£102 * **LB**
OFF-PEAK: s £45-£64; d £38-£52
MEALS: Lunch £6.50-£12.50&alc Dinner £10.50-£15.50&alc
CONF: Thtr 150 Class 80 Board 26 Del from £90
CARDS:

ST NEOTS Cambridgeshire Map 04 TL16

★★ 65% Abbotsley Golf
Potton Rd, Eynesbury Hardwicke PE19 4XN (leave A1 at junct with A428 to Cambridge. take 1st left at second roundabout and then last exit at next roundabout. Left after 300 yds and 1st right)
☎ 01480 474000 FAX 01480 471018
This purpose built hotel is located within the heart of a 36-hole golf complex, to the southeast of St Neots, off the B1046; the Abbotsley is also home to the famous Vivien Saunders golf school. The service is both friendly and informal within the bar and restaurant, and guests have the benefit of a recently extended lounge area and a separate informal dining area overlooking the adjacent golf course. Bedrooms have been cleverly converted from old farm buildings, situated around the award-winning courtyard garden and putting green.
17 en suite (bth/shr) (2 fmly) CTV in 15 bedrooms 120P Golf 36 Squash Putting green Xmas International Cuisine V meals Coffee am Tea pm Last d 9.30pm
ROOMS: (incl. bkfst) s £36-£51; d £64-£80 * **LB**
MEALS: Lunch fr £14.50 Dinner fr £14.50*
CONF: Thtr 80 Class 46 Board 32 Del from £62
CARDS:

SALCOMBE Devon Map 03 SX73
See also Hope Cove, Kingsbridge & Thurlestone

★★★ 79% Tides Reach

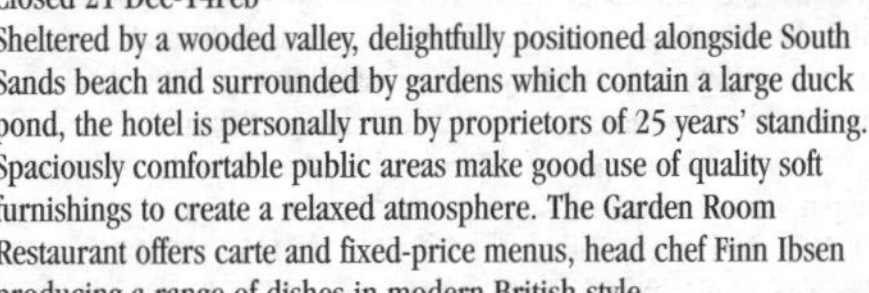

South Sands TQ8 8LJ ☎ 01548 843466
FAX 01548 843954
Closed 21 Dec-14Feb
Sheltered by a wooded valley, delightfully positioned alongside South Sands beach and surrounded by gardens which contain a large duck pond, the hotel is personally run by proprietors of 25 years' standing. Spaciously comfortable public areas make good use of quality soft furnishings to create a relaxed atmosphere. The Garden Room Restaurant offers carte and fixed-price menus, head chef Finn Ibsen producing a range of dishes in modern British style
38 en suite (bth/shr) (5 fmly) CTV in all bedrooms Lift Night porter 100P No coaches Indoor swimming pool (heated) Squash Snooker Sauna Solarium Gym Jacuzzi/spa Windsurfing Dingy sailing Water skiing No children 8yrs English & Continental Cuisine V meals Coffee am Tea pm No smoking in restaurant Last d 9.30pm
ROOMS: (incl. bkfst & dinner) s £75-£91; d fr £130 **LB**

contd.

MEALS: Bar Lunch £4.25-£9.50 Dinner fr £26.50&alc
CARDS:

See advertisement on opposite page

★★★ 77% **Soar Mill Cove**
Soar Mill Cove, Malborough TQ7 3DS (3m W of town off A381 at Malborough. Follow signs 'Soar') ☎ 01548 561566
FAX 01548 561223
Closed Nov-8 Feb
Overlooking one of the prettiest bays in the country, Soar Mill Cove is the perfect place to relax and enjoy the scenery. All the spacious and well equipped bedrooms enjoy the magnificent views and have their own balcony. The kitchen is run by Keith Makepeace who has developed his own style, using local produce with fish and shellfish a speciality. The staff are attentive and friendly ensuring a comfortable stay.
19 en suite (bth) (2 fmly) CTV in all bedrooms 30P No coaches Indoor swimming pool (heated) Outdoor swimming pool (heated) Tennis (grass) Putting green Table tennis ch fac International Cuisine Coffee am Tea pm Last d 8.30pm
ROOMS: (incl. bkfst) s £92-£122; d £130-£163 **LB**
OFF-PEAK: (incl. bkfst) s £70-£92; d £122-£142
MEALS: Lunch £12-£25alc High tea £7-£15alc Dinner £34-£44alc*
CARDS:

★★★ 74% **Bolt Head**
TQ8 8LL (follow signs to South Sands)
☎ 01548 843751 FAX 01548 843060
Closed 09 Nov-mid Mar
Bolt Head was built of wood at the turn of the century, and enjoys magnificent views over the Salcombe estuary. Bedrooms fall into two categories, superior and standard, and may have views of the estuary, the countryside or the swimming pool at the rear of the hotel. A four-course menu is offered each evening, using fresh local produce wherever possible. A test meal featured crisply fried mushrooms with garlic mayonnaise, and home-made celery soup followed by turkey escalopes with sage and Parma ham. Strawberry trifle, from the laden dessert trolley, was chosen to finish. The breakfast buffet is also worthy of note, with fresh fruits, yoghurts, cereals, juices and a selection of cold meats and salads.
28 en suite (bth/shr) (6 fmly) CTV in all bedrooms STV 30P No coaches Outdoor swimming pool (heated) Pool table Boule court English & French Cuisine V meals Coffee am Tea pm Last d 9pm
ROOMS: (incl. bkfst & dinner) s £52-£72; d £104-£164 * **LB**
MEALS: Lunch £1.75-£15 Dinner £24-£38.50*
CARDS:

See advertisement on opposite page

★★★ 66% **South Sands**
South Sands TQ8 8LL ☎ 01548 843741 FAX 01548 842112
Closed Nov-March
With direct access to safe sands, and just a mile from the ferry to Salcombe, this hotel offers comfortable accommodation in well equipped bedrooms. Public areas are on two levels and include a spacious reception lounge with a well stocked bar and a separate public bar. The bright, modern restaurant overlooks the sea.
30 en suite (bth/shr) (10 fmly) CTV in all bedrooms 50P No coaches Indoor swimming pool (heated) Sauna Solarium Jacuzzi/spa ch fac English & Continental Cuisine V meals Coffee am Tea pm No smoking in restaurant Last d 9pm
ROOMS: (incl. bkfst & dinner) s £65-£85; d £115-£165 **LB**
OFF-PEAK: (incl. bkfst & dinner) s £53-£63; d £92-£116
MEALS: Bar Lunch £5.50-£9.50 Dinner fr £21&alc
CARDS:

★★ 68% **Grafton Towers**
Moult Rd, South Sands TQ8 8LG (approach Salcombe from Kingsbridge,follow signs for South Sands,look for Hotel sign)
☎ 01548 842882
Closed mid Oct-Mar
Superbly placed for spectacular coastal walks and panoramic views of the estuary, this Victorian mansion is peacefully set in well kept lawns. The unhurried atmosphere and warm welcome are very relaxing, and recently upgraded, tastefully decorated public areas include a restaurant with a fixed-price menu and an interesting choice of home-cooked dishes. Bedrooms have bright co-ordinating colour schemes and are well equipped.
13 rms (9 bth 3 shr) CTV in all bedrooms 13P No coaches English and French Cuisine V meals Coffee am No smoking in restaurant
ROOMS: (incl. bkfst) s £31-£45; d £62-£69 * **LB**
MEALS: High tea £15-£19*
CARDS:

★ 68% **Woodgrange Hotel**
Devon Rd TQ8 8HJ (on A381) ☎ 01548 842439 FAX 01548 842006
Closed Nov-Etr
This small personally run hotel is set high above the estuary with lovely views. The bedrooms are comfortable and well equipped, with en suite facilities. There is a cosy guest lounge which faces South as well as a well stocked bar. A traditional set priced menu is served in the dining room.
7 en suite (bth/shr) (1 fmly) CTV in all bedrooms 12P No coaches Coffee am Tea pm No smoking in restaurant Last d 5pm
ROOMS: (incl. bkfst) s £20-£25; d £40-£50 **LB**
MEALS: Bar Lunch £3-£5 Dinner £15-£17*
CARDS:

★ 67% **Sunny Cliff**
Cliff Rd TQ8 8JX ☎ 01548 842207
Closed Nov-Feb
Enjoying a glorious position overlooking the estuary right on the water's edge, this small hotel has a friendly, relaxed atmosphere. Bedrooms are compact but brightly furnished and decorated. All public rooms enjoy the views, and in the attractive dining room well balanced short fixed-price menus are offered.
14 rms (9 bth/shr) 4 annexe en suite (bth/shr) (3 fmly) CTV in all bedrooms 18P Outdoor swimming pool (heated) Fishing Moorings and Landing stage English Cuisine Coffee am Tea pm No smoking in restaurant Last d 8pm
ROOMS: (incl. bkfst) s £31.50-£80; d £63-£160 **LB**
MEALS: Bar Lunch £1.60-£4.75 Dinner £14.50&alc
CARDS:

SALE Greater Manchester Map 07 SD79

Travel Inn

Carrington Ln, Ashton-Upon-Mersey (from M63 junct6 take A6144(M) towards Carrington. Hotel on left) ☎ 0161 962 8113 FAX 0161 905 1742
Purpose-built accommodation, offering spacious, well equipped bedrooms, all with en suite bathrooms. Meals may be taken at the nearby family restaurant. For more information about Travel Inns, consult the Contents page under Hotel Groups.
ROOMS: d £35.50 *

SALFORD Greater Manchester Map 07 SJ89
See also Manchester

★ 64% **Beaucliffe**
254 Eccles Old Rd, Pendleton M6 8ES (leave M602 at junction 2, onto A576, hotel a quarter of a mile from motorway) ☎ 0161 789 5092
FAX 0161 787 7739
Huge improvements continue to be made by the Betts family who recently bought the hotel and are working hard to upgrade its facilities. The neatly furnished bedrooms are in the process of being refurbished, as are the public areas which include a comfortable

contd.

S

lounge, cosy bar and attractively decorated restaurant, where the standard of food is high and has gained a good reputation locally. Mr and Mrs Betts and their two sons are very hospitable and will do their utmost to ensure that guests are well looked after and comfortable.
21 rms (2 bth 15 shr) (2 fmly) CTV in all bedrooms 25P Snooker ch fac European/French Cuisine V meals Coffee am Tea pm No smoking in restaurant Last d 8.45pm
ROOMS: (incl. bkfst) s £32-£39; d £40-£52 **LB**
OFF-PEAK: (incl. bkfst) s £25-£28; d £36-£40
MEALS: Dinner fr £12.95
CARDS:

Travel Inn

Basin 8 The Quays, Salford Quays M5 4SQ
☎ 0161 872 4026 FAX 0161 876 0094
Purpose-built accommodation, offering spacious, well equipped bedrooms, all with en suite bathrooms. Meals may be taken at the nearby family restaurant. For more information about Travel Inns, consult the Contents page under Hotel Groups.
52 en suite (bth/shr)
ROOMS: d £35.50 *

SALISBURY Wiltshire Map 04 SU12

★★★ 74% **Milford Hall**
206 Castle St SP1 3TE ☎ 01722 417411 FAX 01722 419444
Within easy walking distance of the city centre, this family-run hotel in its own grounds features a thoughtful mix of old and new. The recently extended Georgian mansion now offers comfortable accommodation and a relaxed atmosphere. Bedrooms are large, equipped with modern facilities and are spotless. There are various bars and lounges and a smart restaurant where freshly prepared, interesting dishes are served. At a recent inspection meal, a delicately flavoured smoked salmon parfait starter was followed by a tender lamb steak, served with a garlic and rosemary flavoured sauce. The chocolate and hazelnut terrine chosen for dessert was rich and delicious!
35 en suite (bth/shr) (1 fmly) No smoking in 5 bedrooms CTV in all bedrooms Night porter 80P free facilities at local leisure centre Xmas English & French Cuisine V meals Coffee am Tea pm No smoking in restaurant Last d 9.30pm
ROOMS: (incl. bkfst) s £42.50-£52.50; d £57.50-£70 * **LB**
MEALS: Lunch £4.50-£9.50 High tea £2.50-£4.50 Dinner £10-£16&alc
CARDS:

See advertisement on opposite page

★★★ 73% **The White Hart**

St John St SP1 2SD ☎ 01722 327476
FAX 01722 412761
Dating in part from the 16th century, this refurbished hotel is conveniently set opposite the cathedral precinct with its own car parking. Due to the architecture bedrooms tend to vary id size but all are tastefully decorated and boast bright, modern bathrooms. The comfortable bar and lounge are popular, especially for afternoon teas, and the smart restaurant overlooks a pretty inner courtyard. Chef David Heyward cooks with imagination and flair making good use of quality ingredients.
68 en suite (bth/shr) (3 fmly) No smoking in 28 bedrooms CTV in all bedrooms Night porter 90P Xmas V meals Coffee am Tea pm No smoking in restaurant Last d 9.30pm
ROOMS: s £86; d £102 * **LB**
MEALS: Lunch £12.95-£13.95 Dinner £12.95-£26alc
CONF: Thtr 80 Class 40 Board 40 Del from £95
CARDS:

★★★ 68% ***Rose & Crown***

Harnham Rd, Harnham SP2 8JQ ☎ 01722 327908
FAX 01722 339816
This charming 13th-century hotel stands in one of the finest positions in the town; set in its own rose garden on the banks of the river Avon and overlooking the cathedral, which is just a short walk away. Bedrooms in the original building include one four-poster room; others in the new wing are well designed and smartly furnished; all have good bathrooms and most boast pretty views. Public rooms are equally attractive and roaring fires burn in both bars. One bar is particularly popular with locals.
28 en suite (bth/shr) (6 fmly) No smoking in 14 bedrooms CTV in all bedrooms STV Night porter 40P English & French Cuisine V meals Coffee am Tea pm Last d 10pm
CARDS:

★★★ 67% **Red Lion**
Milford St SP1 2AN (in city centre off Market Sq)
☎ 01722 323334 FAX 01722 325756
This famous old coaching inn, situated in the heart of the city, dates back to the 13th century and is constructed around a charming creeper-clad courtyard where drinks and snacks are served during warmer months. The Red Lion has been owned by 3 generations of the Maidment family and a friendly family atmosphere pervades the establishment. Individually designed bedrooms have been refurbished with smart fabrics and modern bathrooms, and the public areas enjoy all the character of an historic building.
54 en suite (bth/shr) (4 fmly) CTV in all bedrooms No dogs (ex guide dogs) Lift Night porter 10P Xmas V meals Coffee am Tea pm No smoking in restaurant Last d 9pm
ROOMS: s £69.50-£75; d £89.50-£95 * **LB**
MEALS: Lunch £10.25-£12.75 Dinner fr £17.50&alc
CONF: Thtr 100 Class 50 Board 40 Del from £80
CARDS:

See advertisement on opposite page

★★★ 66% ***Grasmere House***

Harnhan Rd SP2 8JN (on the S side of Salisbury, follow the ring road route and local signs for the A3094 Harnham, next to All Saints Church)
☎ 01722 338388 FAX 01722 333710
This attractive Victorian house has been sympathetically extended to provide spacious and well equipped bedrooms. The house is set in one and a half acres of mature grounds stretching down to the River

Nadder. The public rooms include a comfortable lounge, and a conservatory restaurant which leads onto the terrace and enjoys beautiful views across the water meadows to the cathedral. The daily-changing menu offers good fresh local produce prepared with imagination and thought; the home made soups and desserts are a speciality.
4 en suite (bth/shr) 16 annexe en suite (bth/shr) (1 fmly) No smoking in 6 bedrooms CTV in all bedrooms 36P Croquet lawn International Cuisine V meals Coffee am Tea pm Last d 9.30pm
CARDS:

See advertisement on this page

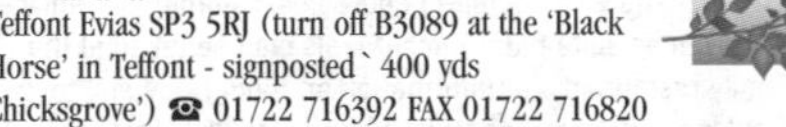

★★ 78% **Howard's House**
Teffont Evias SP3 5RJ (turn off B3089 at the 'Black Horse' in Teffont - signposted ` 400 yds Chicksgrove') ☎ 01722 716392 FAX 01722 716820
Howard's House is set in two acres of colourful gardens in one of Wiltshire's prettiest villages. Bedrooms on the first and second floors have been remodelled to create spacious rooms, each with its own seating area. Day rooms include a sitting room where a welcoming fire burns on cooler days. Since its restoration in 1989, the hotel has gained a loyal following for chef partner Paul Firmin's imaginative menus. An inspection meal started with a light twice baked soufflé flavoured with Shropshire blue cheese and served with a well balanced cheese and mustard sauce. Fillet of lamb was cooked in puff pastry with pistachios and pickled walnuts and served with a reduction of port and Madeira. An old favourite, steamed apple and cinnamon sponge, presented with a modern apricot sauce and cinnamon ice cream, completed the meal. Breakfast, including freshly squeezed orange juice and a pastry case filled with mushrooms, poached egg and hollandaise sauce, deserves more than a passing mention.
9 en suite (bth/shr) CTV in all bedrooms 23P No coaches Croquet

contd.

lawn Xmas Modern British Cuisine V meals No smoking in restaurant Last d 9.30pm
ROOMS: (incl. bkfst) s £95; d £115 * **LB**
MEALS: Sunday Lunch £18.50-£26.50 Dinner £26.50
CONF: Class 20 Board 12 Del from £135
CARDS:

★★68% King's Arms
9-11 St John's St SP1 2SB ☎ 01722 327629 FAX 01722 414246
The King's Arms, situated in the heart of this picturesque city, is within walking distance of the many attractions of Salisbury and easily accessible to the beautiful countryside of Wiltshire. Many original features such as oak beams, exposed fireplaces, slanting staircases and sloping floors enhance the character of this delightful old building, now privately owned and personally managed by Ron and Barbara Stokes. Bedrooms have been equipped with every modern comfort; four-poster suites and family rooms are available. Pippins Restaurant combines informality in a relaxed atmosphere with home-cooked food and excellent wines. There is a choice of bars, and a quiet lounge in a separate building across the courtyard.
12 en suite (bth/shr) 3 annexe en suite (bth/shr) (1 fmly) No smoking in 3 bedrooms CTV in all bedrooms Pool table Games room Bar billiards Xmas English & Continental Cuisine V meals Coffee am Tea pm Last d 9.30pm
ROOMS: (incl. bkfst) s £45-£55; d £58-£78 * **LB**
MEALS: Bar Lunch £3.95-£6&alc Dinner fr £12.95&alc*
CARDS:

★★65% The Old Mill
Town Path, West Harnham SP2 8EU
☎ 01722 327517 & 322364 FAX 01722 333367
Beautifully situated on the River Nadder, this historic mill dates back to 1135. In 1550 the river was diverted through the building to drive three water wheels for Wiltshire's first paper mill, and the water continues to cascade through the restaurant to this day. There is a cosy beamed bar which is popular with the locals and the restaurant offers a wide range of traditional and modern dishes. The bedrooms are individually decorated, comfortably furnished and well equipped with full en suite facilities.
10 en suite (bth/shr) (3 fmly) CTV in all bedrooms No dogs (ex guide dogs) Night porter 15P Fishing Xmas English Cuisine V meals Coffee am
ROOMS: (incl. bkfst) s £40; d £65 * **LB**
MEALS: Lunch £2.50-£12.50alc*
CARDS:

★★56% The Trafalgar

33 Milford St SP1 2AP (1m from A36,Hotel is situated in City Centre,on the left prior to Culver Street Multi-story car park) ☎ 01722 338686 FAX 01722 414496
This former coaching inn dates back in parts to the 15th century and is convenient for the city centre. Its bistro restaurant offers a good range of dishes. Bedrooms are well equipped.
18 en suite (bth/shr) (1 fmly) CTV in all bedrooms No coaches Traditional English Cuisine V meals Coffee am Tea pm No smoking in restaurant Last d 10pm
ROOMS: (incl. bkfst) s £39.50-£50; d £49.50-£65 * **LB**
MEALS: Lunch £11.25&alc Dinner £11.25&alc*
CARDS:

SALTASH Cornwall & Isles of Scilly Map 02 SX45

Travelodge
Callington Rd, Carkeel PL12 6LF (on A38 Saltash By-Pass - 1 mile from Tamar Bridge)
☎ Central Res 0800 850950 FAX 01752 849028
This modern building offers accommodation in smart, spacious and well equipped bedrooms, suitable for family use, and all with en suite bathrooms. Meals may be taken at the nearby family restaurant. For information on room rates and to make a booking, call Roomline free of charge on 0800 850950. For more details about Travelodge, consult the Contents page under Hotel Groups.
32 en suite (bth/shr)
CONF: Thtr 25 Class 15 Board 12

SAMPFORD PEVERELL Devon Map 03 ST01

Travelodge
Sampford Peverell Service Area EX16 7HD (junc 27, M5) ☎ 01884 821087
This modern building offers accommodation in smart, spacious and well equipped bedrooms, suitable for family use, and all with en suite bathrooms. Meals may be taken at the nearby family restaurant. For information on room rates and to make a booking, call Roomline free of charge on 0800 850950. For more details about Travelodge, consult the Contents page under Hotel Groups.
40 en suite (bth/shr)

SANDBACH Cheshire Map 07 SJ76

★★★66% *Chimney House*

Congleton Rd CW11 0ST (on A534, 1m from M6 junct 17 heading for Congleton) ☎ 01270 764141 FAX 01270 768916
Chimney House is an attractive Tudor-style hotel set in eight acres of woodland. It is particularly appealing in the summer when the façade is enhanced by a wonderful display of hanging baskets and planters. Bedrooms offer a good level of comfort and the open-plan public areas have a warm ambience.
48 en suite (bth/shr) (6 fmly) No smoking in 33 bedrooms CTV in all bedrooms STV No dogs (ex guide dogs) Night porter 110P Sauna Solarium Putting green English & French Cuisine V meals Coffee am Tea pm Last d 10pm
CARDS:

★★★65% Old Hall Hotel
High St CW11 0AL (from M6 junct 17 take ring rd to traffic lights turn right hotel on left) ☎ 01270 761221 FAX 01270 762551
This distinctive black and white timber framed building, built in 1656 and which boasts a priest hole, a left hand spiral staircase and even an underground passage to the local parish church, now offers characterful, well equipped accommodation. There is a cosy panelled lounge where a fire is lit on cooler days and in the restaurant, where the service is attentive and friendly, a good choice of well prepared dishes are offered. The hotel is conveniently located within walking distance of the town centre and one mile from Junction 17 of the M6.
14 en suite (bth/shr) CTV in all bedrooms 50P Jacuzzi/spa ch fac English & Continental Cuisine V meals Coffee am Tea pm No smoking in restaurant Last d 9.15pm
ROOMS: (incl. bkfst) s fr £65; d fr £78 * **LB**
OFF-PEAK: (incl. bkfst) s fr £50; d fr £70
MEALS: Lunch fr £11.50 Dinner fr £16.50&alc*

CONF: Thtr 40 Class 16 Board 18 Del from £105
CARDS:

★★★63% **Saxon Cross**
Holmes Chapel Rd CW11 9SE (on A5022 towards Holmes Chapel)
☎ 01270 763281 FAX 01270 768723
Comfortable, modern and well equipped bedrooms are a feature of this motel-style establishment, which is located close to junction 17 of the M6, convenient for Manchester and the airport. It is a good venue for business meetings and conferences.
52 en suite (bth/shr) (2 fmly) No smoking in 3 bedrooms CTV in all bedrooms STV Night porter 150P English & French Cuisine V meals Coffee am Tea pm Last d 9.30pm
ROOMS: (incl. bkfst) s £36-£59.50; d £49-£69 * **LB**
OFF-PEAK: (incl. bkfst) s £46; d £58
MEALS: Lunch £8.60-£15 Dinner £15&alc*
CONF: Thtr 150 Class 200 Board 80 Del from £80
CARDS:

SANDBANKS See Poole

SANDIACRE Derbyshire Map 08 SK43
See also Long Eaton

Forte Posthouse Nottingham/Derby
Bostocks Ln NGIO 5NJ (N of M1 junc 25)
☎ 0115 9397800 FAX 0115 9490469

Suitable for both the business and leisure traveller, this bright hotel provides modern accommodation in well equipped bedrooms with en suite bathrooms. For more details about Forte Posthouse hotels, consult the Contents page for the section on Hotel Groups.
91 en suite (bth/shr)
CONF: Thtr 60 Class 26 Board 28 Del from £77

SANDIWAY Cheshire Map 07 SJ67

RED STAR HOTEL

★★★ **Nunsmere Hall Country House**
Tarporley Rd, Oakmere CW8 2ES ☎ 01606 889100 FAX 01606 889055

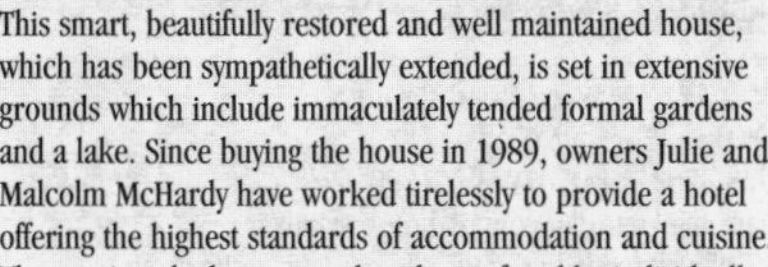

This smart, beautifully restored and well maintained house, which has been sympathetically extended, is set in extensive grounds which include immaculately tended formal gardens and a lake. Since buying the house in 1989, owners Julie and Malcolm McHardy have worked tirelessly to provide a hotel offering the highest standards of accommodation and cuisine. The spacious bedrooms are hugely comfortable, individually decorated and furnished and very thoughtfully equipped. Guests can relax in the drawing room, the elegant oak panelled cocktail bar or the library. The colourful dining room is where the competently prepared dishes of new head chef Stephen Williams can be enjoyed, and service is professional and attentive. The hotel also has a number of conference suites, and activities such as falconry and archery can easily be arranged.
32 en suite (bth/shr) No smoking in 8 bedrooms CTV in all bedrooms STV No dogs (ex guide dogs) Lift Night porter 80P No coaches Snooker Croquet lawn Putting green Archery,Air Rifle Shooting,Falconry Xmas French Cuisine V meals Coffee am Tea pm No smoking in restaurant Last d 10pm
ROOMS: s £105-£125; d £140-£165 * **LB**
MEALS: Lunch £19.50-£22.75 Dinner £30-£45alc*
CONF: Thtr 50 Class 24 Board 32 Del from £165
CARDS:

SANDY Bedfordshire Map 04 TL14

★★★62% **Holiday Inn Garden Court**
Girtford Bridge, London Rd SG19 1DH (located on the A1 at the rdbt to Bedford) ☎ 01767 692220
FAX 01767 680452

This modern hotel with a separate conference and meeting centre is conveniently located just off the A1. It has spacious and well equipped bedrooms, most with extra seating space. There is a small bar and a cosy restaurant where straightforward meals are served in a friendly atmosphere.
57 en suite (bth/shr) No smoking in 37 bedrooms CTV in all bedrooms STV No dogs (ex guide dogs) 150P Fishing Xmas V meals Tea pm No smoking area in restaurant Last d 10pm

contd.

S

ROOMS: s £45; d £45 *
OFF-PEAK: s £35; d £35
MEALS: High tea £1-£2.50alc Dinner £15-£25alc*
CONF: Thtr 150 Class 125 Board 125 Del from £70
CARDS:

SARRE Kent Map 05 TR26

★★61% **Crown Inn**
Ramsgate Rd CT7 0LF (on A28.In the centre of the village)
☎ 01843 847808 FAX 01843 847914
Better known as the Cherry Brandy House , this historic inn lies half way between Canterbury and Margate and has a colourful history dating back to C1500; arriving guests will be offered a glass of the liqueur in question - first made here by French Huguenots in the 17th century and still made locally today. An attractive well decorated candlelit restaurant and three cosy bars serving good traditional ales and enterprising standards of cooking make up the public areas along with a small conference room on the first floor, whilst a modern extension has increased the number of well furnished comfortable and particularly well equipped bedrooms.
12 en suite (bth/shr) (1 fmly) CTV in all bedrooms 25P V meals Coffee am Tea pm Last d 9.30pm
ROOMS: (incl. bkfst) s fr £43.50; d fr £56.50 **LB**
MEALS: Lunch £6-£15alc Dinner £15-£20alc*
CONF: Board 12 Del from £60
CARDS: £

SAUNDERTON Buckinghamshire Map 04 SP70

★★62% **Rose & Crown**

Wycombe Rd HP27 9NP (on A4010, 0.6 miles from Exit4 M40) ☎ 01844 345299 FAX 01844 343140
Closed 25-30 Dec
This charming old roadside inn is focused around a cosy bar which has a friendly atmosphere and a convivial clientele. Bedrooms are compact but are well equipped and furnished. Meals are available in either the bar or in a smart restaurant.
17 rms (14 bth/shr) CTV in all bedrooms No dogs (ex guide dogs) 50P No coaches No children 5 English & French Cuisine Coffee am Tea pm No smoking area in restaurant Last d 9.15pm
ROOMS: (incl. bkfst) s £57.95-£62.95; d £68.95-£72.95 * **LB**
OFF-PEAK: (incl. bkfst) s fr £45; d fr £59.95
MEALS: Lunch £11.95-£31.50alc Dinner £17.25-£31.50alc*
CONF: Thtr 30 Board 15
CARDS:

SAUNTON Devon Map 02 SS43

★★★★69% **Saunton Sands**
EX33 1LQ (turn off A361 at Braunton, signposted Croyde B3231 hotel 2m on left hand side) (Brend) ☎ 01271 890212 FAX 01271 890145
This modern hotel enjoys an enviable elevated position with far-reaching views across the bay and direct access to five miles of sandy beach. Saunton Sands is one of ten Brend Hotels, well known in the South West for their friendliness and traditional service. Bedrooms vary in size, many have separate but integral children's accommodation and several feature balconies and glorious views. The smart public areas include a choice of comfortable lounges and a commendable range of leisure facilities ideal for both families and business guests.
92 en suite (bth/shr) (39 fmly) CTV in all bedrooms STV No dogs (ex guide dogs) Lift Night porter 142P No coaches Indoor swimming pool (heated) Outdoor swimming pool (heated) Tennis (hard) Squash Snooker Sauna Solarium Pool table Putting green Jacuzzi/spa Table tennis Wkly live entertainment ch fac Xmas English & French Cuisine V meals Coffee am Tea pm Last d 9pm
ROOMS: (incl. bkfst) s £60-£82; d £116-£180 * **LB**
OFF-PEAK: (incl. bkfst) s £50-£78; d £100-£176
MEALS: Lunch £10.50&alc Dinner £22.50&alc*
CONF: Thtr 150
CARDS: £

See advertisement on opposite page

★★66% **Preston House**
EX33 1LG ☎ 01271 890472 FAX 01271 890555
This Victorian hotel faces south, overlooking the ten-mile sweep of Barnstaple Bay, with direct access to the beach. The majority of the bedrooms benefit from the magnificent position. Each room is individually furnished and decorated to a good standard and all are well equipped. Public areas are spacious and include an elegant lounge, a cosy TV room and a small bar. In the restaurant, a short fixed-price menu is offered. Breakfast is served on the glassed-in verandah.
15 en suite (bth/shr) (1 fmly) CTV in all bedrooms No dogs 20P No coaches Outdoor swimming pool (heated) Tennis (hard) Sauna Solarium Jacuzzi/spa Clay pigeon shooting,Horse Riding No children 12yrs English & Continental Cuisine V meals Coffee am Tea pm Last d 8.30pm
ROOMS: (incl. bkfst) s £35-£70; d £65-£85 * **LB**
OFF-PEAK: (incl. bkfst) s £27.50-£60; d £55-£75
MEALS: Lunch fr £8.50 Dinner £15-£25*
CARDS: £

SAWLEY Lancashire Map 07 SD74

★★64% **Spread Eagle**
BB7 4NH (off A59, on the banks of the River Ribble)
☎ 01200 441202 FAX 01200 441973
This characterful village inn is conveniently situated, just off the A59 north of Clitheroe. The modern bedrooms, all of which are en suite and equipped with trouser presses and hairdryers, are situated in a cleverly converted outbuilding, immediately adjacent to the main building. Well prepared food is available in the restaurant from which guests can enjoy the most marvellous views across the Ribble valley. There is also a cosy lounge bar where a fire is lit in winter.
10 en suite (bth/shr) (2 fmly) CTV in all bedrooms No dogs (ex guide dogs) 100P English & French Cuisine V meals Coffee am Tea pm No smoking area in restaurant Last d 9pm
ROOMS: (incl. bkfst) s £45-£50; d £55-£60 * **LB**
MEALS: Lunch £10.95-£13.95 Dinner £16.95-£19.95&alc
CONF: Thtr 50 Class 50 Board 20 Del from £70
CARDS: £

SAXMUNDHAM Suffolk Map 05 TM36

★65% **Bell**
High St IP17 1AF (off A12) ☎ 01728 602331 FAX 01728 833105
This large Georgian building in the centre of the town provides well cared for bedrooms with direct dial telephone facilities; some bedrooms which are without en suite toilets nevertheless have shower cubicles. Public areas include a first-floor meeting room as well as two bars and a freshly decorated restaurant.
14 rms (8 bth/shr) (2 fmly) CTV in all bedrooms 30P Xmas English & Italian Cuisine V meals Coffee am Tea pm Last d 9.30pm
ROOMS: (incl. bkfst) s £25-£33.50; d £45-£52 * **LB**
MEALS: Sunday Lunch fr £6.95&alc Dinner £7-£15alc*
CARDS: £

SCARBOROUGH North Yorkshire Map 08 TA08

★★★ 68% **Wrea Head Country**

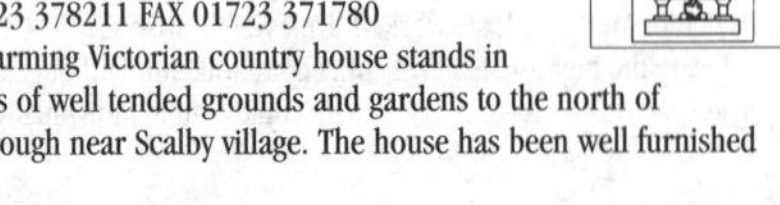

Scalby YO13 0PB (3m NW off A171)
☎ 01723 378211 FAX 01723 371780
This charming Victorian country house stands in 14 acres of well tended grounds and gardens to the north of Scarborough near Scalby village. The house has been well furnished

S

throughout and delightful day rooms include a library and a comfortable bar whilst the elegant dining room is the perfect setting for the carefully produced dinner. Bedrooms vary in size and have all been thoughtfully equipped. Service is both professional and friendly from smartly turned out staff.

21 en suite (bth/shr) (2 fmly) CTV in all bedrooms Night porter 50P No coaches Croquet lawn Putting green Xmas European Cuisine V meals Coffee am Tea pm No smoking in restaurant Last d 9.30pm

ROOMS: (incl. bkfst) s £49.50-£67.50; d £90-£155 **LB**

OFF-PEAK: (incl. bkfst) s fr £40; d fr £80

MEALS: Lunch £12.50-£15.50&alc Dinner fr £22.50&alc

CONF: Thtr 30 Class 16 Board 20 Del from £95

CARDS:

See advertisement on page 545

★★★66% **Crown**

Esplanade YO11 2AG ☎ 01723 373491

FAX 01723 362271

Situated in a commanding position overlooking the South Bay and harbour this historic hotel has just celebrated its 150th birthday, and in the 1920's was described by the AA as Scarborough's leading Hotel. In recent years it has undergone considerable refurbishment to provide modern, comfortable accommodation with bedrooms at the front of the hotel enjoying excellent views over the sea. The staff are friendly and helpful and a good standard of mainly British cooking can be enjoyed in the elegant, recently redecorated restaurant.

78 en suite (bth/shr) (7 fmly) No smoking in 9 bedrooms CTV in all bedrooms Lift Night porter Snooker V meals Coffee am Tea pm No smoking in restaurant Last d 9pm

MEALS: Lunch £5.50-£25 Dinner £16.95&alc*

CONF: Thtr 160 Class 60 Board 70

CARDS:

★★★63% **Esplanade**

Belmont Rd YO11 2AA ☎ 01723 360382

FAX 01723 376137

Standing in a commanding position overlooking the South Bay and harbour, this imposing Victorian hotel is very traditional in style and operation. Bedrooms are modern and comfortable and the lounges well furnished and inviting. The spacious modern Landau restaurant has an oriel window which enjoys excellent sea views. Staff are friendly, attentive and helpful and there is a small car park available.

73 en suite (bth/shr) (9 fmly) CTV in all bedrooms Lift Night porter 24P Pool table Darts Table tennis Xmas English & French Cuisine V meals Coffee am Tea pm No smoking in restaurant Last d 9pm

ROOMS: (incl. bkfst) s £42.50; d £78-£86 * **LB**

OFF-PEAK: (incl. bkfst & dinner) s £29; d £58

MEALS: Dinner £15.50-£22.50*

CARDS: 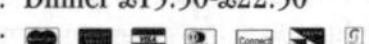 

★★★63% **Palm Court**

Nicholas Cliff YO11 2ES (opposite the Information Centre)

☎ 01723 368161 FAX 01723 371547

The Palm Court meets the needs of both holiday makers and the conference trade to good effect and also combines the modern and traditional. It is close to the town centre and has the benefit of its own undercover parking whilst guests also have the added attraction of an indoor pool. Public rooms are spacious and comfortable and the bedrooms, which are modern and well equipped, are generally also spacious. Traditional menus are provided in the attractive restaurant and service is both attentive and professional.

46 en suite (bth/shr) (7 fmly) CTV in all bedrooms No dogs (ex guide dogs) Lift Night porter 80P Indoor swimming pool (heated) Sauna Table tennis Wkly live entertainment Xmas English French & Italian Cuisine V meals Coffee am Tea pm No smoking area in restaurant Last d 9pm

ROOMS: (incl. bkfst) s £37-£47; d £68-£78 * **LB**

OFF-PEAK: (incl. bkfst) s £27-£32; d £60-£70

MEALS: Lunch fr £9.25 Dinner £13&alc*

CONF: Thtr 200 Class 100 Board 60 Del from £48

CARDS: 

★★★62% **Ambassador**

Centre of the Esplanade YO11 2AY ☎ 01723 362841 FAX 362841

The Ambassador stands in a prime position on the South Cliff and has excellent views over the bay towards the harbour and castle. The bedrooms, which are generally spacious, are comfortable and well equipped, whilst the public rooms are well furnished and inviting. The hotel provides live entertainment during the season, and the service is both friendly and attentive.

59 en suite (bth/shr) (10 fmly) CTV in all bedrooms STV Lift Night porter Indoor swimming pool (heated) Sauna Solarium Jacuzzi/spa Xmas V meals Coffee am Tea pm No smoking in restaurant Last d 8.30pm

ROOMS: (incl. bkfst) s fr £27; d fr £54 * **LB**

MEALS: Bar Lunch £1.75-£7.95 Dinner £11.50-£14.50*

CONF: Thtr 140 Class 90 Board 60 Del from £60

CARDS:

★★★61% **Hotel St Nicholas**

St Nicholas Cliff YO11 2EU ☎ 01723 364101

FAX 01723 500538

Overlooking South Bay this large hotel caters for both the tourist and business person. Contemporary bedrooms vary in size but all are well equipped with modern amenities while the spacious public areas include a choice of bars and eating options in addition to a basement leisure centre.

contd.

144 en suite (bth/shr) (17 fmly) CTV in all bedrooms STV Lift Night porter 30P Indoor swimming pool (heated) Snooker Sauna Solarium Gym Pool table Children's games room ch fac Xmas English Cuisine V meals Coffee am Tea pm No smoking in restaurant Last d 9.15pm
ROOMS: (incl. bkfst & dinner) d £75-£90 * **LB**
OFF-PEAK: (incl. bkfst & dinner) s £35-£55
MEALS: Sunday Lunch £8.95 High tea £2-£8 Dinner £12.25&alc
CONF: Thtr 400 Class 220 Board 60 Del from £70
CARDS:

★★★57% **Clifton**
Queens Pde, North Cliff YO12 7HX ☎ 01723 375691
FAX 01723 364203
This large resort hotel enjoys an elevated position on the cliff, high above the beach; most bedrooms have superb views over the North Bay. Dinner is usually taken in the ballroom except when entertainment is provided for the benefit of tours when alternative arrangements are made.
68 en suite (bth/shr) (11 fmly) CTV in all bedrooms Lift Night porter 45P Sauna Solarium Pool table V meals Coffee am Tea pm No smoking in restaurant Last d 9pm
MEALS: Lunch £10.50-£12.50 High tea £4.50-£7.50 Dinner £17-£20
CONF: Thtr 120 Class 50 Board 50 Del from £75
CARDS: Connect

See advertisement on opposite page

★★71% **Gridley's Crescent**
The Crescent YO11 2PP (on entering Scarborough travel towards railway station then follow signs to Brunswick Pavilion, at traffic lights turn into Crescent) ☎ 01723 360929 FAX 01723 354126
A distinctive listed building of character which has been carefully refurbished by the resident owners, Mr & Mrs Gridley. The hotel stands overlooking a small park and is close to the town centre and the bay. Bedrooms have been delightfully furnished as well as being thoughtfully equipped. There are two dining styles here with an elegant restaurant serving a set price menu and a carte whilst the other is less formal and provides carvery style dishes. A comfortable lounge together with a good conference room is available and service is very friendly and attentive.
20 en suite (bth/shr) No smoking in 7 bedrooms CTV in all bedrooms No dogs (ex guide dogs) Lift Night porter No coaches No children 6yrs V meals Coffee am No smoking in restaurant Last d 9.30pm
ROOMS: (incl. bkfst) s £41.50; d £72.50 * **LB**
MEALS: Lunch fr £9.95 Dinner fr £15&alc*
CARDS:

★★69% ***The Mount***
Cliff Bridge Ter, Saint Nicholas Cliff YO11 2HA
☎ 01723 360961 FAX 01723 360961
Closed Jan-mid Mar
Overlooking the sea and enjoying superb views of the coastline, this elegant Regency hotel is personally owned and run to high standard. The richly furnished public rooms are comfortable and inviting whilst the well equipped bedrooms have been carefully decorated and are a delight to occupy. Service is friendly and attentive and car parking is available opposite the hotel.
50 en suite (bth/shr) (5 fmly) No smoking in 2 bedrooms CTV in all bedrooms Lift Night porter V meals Coffee am Tea pm
CARDS:

See advertisement on page 547

★★64% ***Bradley Court***
7-9 Filey Rd, South Cliff YO11 2SE
☎ 01723 360476 FAX 01723 376661
This mainly modern hotel is situated on the Filey road and is only a short walk from both the town centre and the South Cliff. Bedrooms are well equipped and there are spacious public rooms which include a bar lounge and a large function room.
40 en suite (bth/shr) (4 fmly) No smoking in 2 bedrooms CTV in all bedrooms No dogs (ex guide dogs) Lift Night porter 40P European Cuisine V meals Coffee am Tea pm Last d 8.30pm
CARDS:

See advertisement on opposite page

★★64% **Red Lea**
Prince of Wales Ter YO11 2AJ ☎ 01723 362431 FAX 01723 371230
A family-owned hotel providing very good value for money and which is well situated on the South cliff. It comprises an attractive row of Victorian houses and offers well equipped bedrooms together with adequate public areas, with the added facility of an indoor pool. A good value five-course dinner is served in the spacious dining room.
67 en suite (bth/shr) (7 fmly) CTV in all bedrooms No dogs (ex guide dogs) Lift Night porter Indoor swimming pool (heated) Sauna Solarium Gym Pool table Xmas International Cuisine Coffee am Tea pm No smoking in restaurant Last d 8.30pm
ROOMS: (incl. bkfst) s £32-£33; d £62-£66 *
OFF-PEAK: (incl. bkfst) s £31-£33; d £62-£64
MEALS: Lunch fr £8.50 Dinner fr £12*
CONF: Thtr 40 Class 25 Board 25 Del from £53
CARDS:

★★62% **Southlands**
15 West St, South Cliff YO11 2QW ☎ 01723 361461
FAX 01723 376035
Closed Jan-20 Feb
A family-owned and run hotel which offers good all round standards of both comfort and service. The bedrooms are very traditional in style and are bright and freshly decorated and have every modern convenience provided. There is a spacious lounge, and during the season dances are held in the ballroom. Service is warm and friendly.
58 en suite (bth/shr) (8 fmly) CTV in all bedrooms STV Lift Night porter 45P Pool table Xmas Traditional English Cuisine V meals Coffee am Tea pm Last d 8.30pm
ROOMS: (incl. bkfst) s £21-£31; d £36-£56 *
MEALS: Bar Lunch £1.50-£4.25 Dinner £13&alc*
CONF: Thtr 100 Class 60 Board 40 Del £60
CARDS:

★★59% **Brooklands**
Esplanade Gardens, South Cliff YO11 2AW
☎ 01723 376576 FAX 01723 376576
Closed Jan-Feb
The Brooklands is a traditional seaside resort hotel offering good value for money. It stands on the South Cliff and has ample lounges and serves adequate dinners each evening. Several bedrooms have been recently upgraded and staff are friendly and provide a down to earth style of service.
61 rms (53 bth 5 shr) (11 fmly) CTV in all bedrooms No dogs (ex guide dogs) Lift 1P Riding Pool table Wkly live entertainment Xmas English Cuisine V meals Coffee am Tea pm No smoking in restaurant Last d 7.30pm
ROOMS: (incl. bkfst) s £31; d £62-£67 * **LB**
OFF-PEAK: (incl. bkfst) s £20; d £40
MEALS: Lunch £5 High tea £2-£3 Dinner £10*
CARDS:

SCILLY, ISLES OF Map 02

BRYHER

○ **Hell Bay Hotel**
☎ 01720 422947
12 en suite (bth/shr)

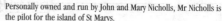

ST MARTIN'S Map 02

RED STAR HOTEL

★★★ ❀❀❀ **St Martin's on the Isle**

Lower Town TR25 0QW ☎ 01720 422092
FAX 01720 422298
Closed Nov-Feb

Designed in the eighties from a cluster of cottages nestling in the hillside, this island hideaway provides the ideal opportunity for guests searching for peace and tranquillity. With it's own beach, jetty, and yacht, the hotel enjoys a breathtaking panorama of the sea and surrounding islands. Individually decorated and furnished bedrooms have been named after local legends, places, and events, and most have sea views Public rooms have been cleverly designed with stone floors, split levels, and refreshingly bold decor, there's additional leisure facilities, including a snooker room, and snacks and refreshments can be enjoyed on the lawn. In the Tean Restaurant, new chef Patrick Tweedie has made a significant impact, and the standard of food here is now exceptional. Under the personal management of Keith Bradford, staff provide a blend of highly polished service and warm hospitality.

24 en suite (bth) (4 fmly) CTV in all bedrooms STV No coaches Indoor swimming pool (heated) Fishing Snooker Solarium Sailing on own boat Clay pigeon shooting ch fac French Cuisine V meals Coffee am Tea pm No smoking in restaurant Last d 10.30pm

ROOMS: (incl. bkfst) s £55-£90; d £110-£180 * **LB**
OFF-PEAK: (incl. bkfst) s £50-£55; d £100-£110
MEALS: Bar Lunch £3.75-£12 High tea fr £9.50 Dinner fr £29.50*
CONF: Thtr 50 Class 50 Board 50 Del from £115
CARDS:

ST MARY'S Map 02

★★★68% ***Star Castle***
The Garrison TR21 0JA
☎ 01720 422317 & 423342 FAX 01720 422343
Closed end Oct-mid Mar

Commanding magnificent views in every direction, Star Castle dates back to 1593, being built to defend the island. Bedrooms fall into two categories, those in the castle, having all the character and charm expected of a building of this age, while the Garden Apartments are more modern; sea facing rooms having French windows opening onto verandas with superb views of the off-islands. Each evening in the restaurant an imaginative fixed price menu is served, guests thoroughly enjoying either a pre or post dinner drink in the Dungeon Bar. Personally owned and run by John and Mary Nicholls, Mr Nicholls is the pilot for the island of St Marys.

9 en suite (bth/shr) 21 annexe en suite (bth/shr) (13 fmly) CTV in all bedrooms 6P No coaches Indoor swimming pool (heated) Pool table games room V meals Coffee am Tea pm Last d 8.45pm
CARDS:

★★74% **Tregarthens**
Hugh Town TR21 0PP (100yds from the quay)
☎ 01720 422540 FAX 01720 422089
Closed late Oct-mid Mar

Best Western

First opened as a hotel in 1848 by Captain Tregarthen, a famous steam packet owner; Tregarthens Hotel overlooks St Mary's harbour and the islands of Tresco, Bryher and Samson. The professional staff offer a warm welcome, in a naturally friendly manner. The majority of the bedrooms benefit from superb views out to sea, all are well equipped and neatly furnished. Traditional cuisine is served in the restaurant which has a lovely picture window. The receptionists efficiently handle any travel arrangements that are required by guests.

32 en suite (bth/shr) 1 annexe en suite (bth/shr) (5 fmly) CTV in all bedrooms No dogs English & French Cuisine V meals Coffee am Tea pm No smoking in restaurant

ROOMS: (incl. bkfst & dinner) s £61-£69; d £122-£138 * **LB**
OFF-PEAK: (incl. bkfst & dinner) s £53-£61; d £106-£122
MEALS: Dinner fr £20*
CARDS:

See advertisement on opposite page

TRESCO Map 02

RED STAR HOTEL

★★★ ❀❀ **The Island**

TR24 0PU (helicopter service Penzance to Tresco, hotel on north east side of island)
☎ 01720 422883 FAX 01720 423008
Closed Nov-Feb

It's magnificent island setting, stunning gardens, and idyllic surroundings are only the first impressions for visitors to this splendid hotel. Guests are met at the heliport or pier and transported by tractor and trailer past the private beach to receive the warmest of welcomes from management and staff. Sunny public rooms include a very popular lounge and bar, together with a quiet library for residents, and bedroom accommodation has been designed to make the best of the sea views. The Flower Wing rooms are spacious and comfortable, offering the best choice for discerning guests, while the Garden Wing rooms are more compact. Local fish and shellfish are staples on the enticing daily changing menus.

40 en suite (bth/shr) (19 fmly) CTV in all bedrooms No dogs

(ex guide dogs) No coaches Outdoor swimming pool (heated) Tennis (hard) Fishing Pool table Croquet lawn Putting green Boating Table tennis Bowls ch fac V meals Coffee am Tea pm Last d 9.30pm
ROOMS: (incl. bkfst & dinner) s £70-£160; d £140-£320 * LB
MEALS: Bar Lunch £1.95-£20 Dinner £30*
CARDS:

★★ 71% **New Inn**

TR24 0QQ (by New Grimsby Quay)
☎ 01720 422844 FAX 01720 423200
A warm welcome awaits guests at this well run hostelry which, with all year opening, has firmly established itself as a vital part of life on Tresco. Sue Shone and her bubbly staff provide attentive service, and visitors will be helped with travel arrangements and met at the pier. Accommodation is brightly appointed, with pretty fabrics and thoughtful extras, and the bar, with furnishings fashioned from wrecked wood, has bags of appeal. Graham Shone's cooking adds an extra dimension, with good use of local ingredients, including, of course, the freshest of fish.
12 rms (10 bth/shr) CTV in all bedrooms No dogs (ex guide dogs) No coaches Outdoor swimming pool (heated) Pool table Sea fishing Xmas English & French Cuisine V meals Coffee am No smoking in restaurant Last d 8.45pm
ROOMS: (incl. bkfst & dinner) s £52-£62; d £104-£150 * LB
MEALS: Bar Lunch £8-£16alc Dinner £16.50-£21.50*
CARDS:

AA Members can use the Hotel Guide Discount Card at the back of the book for discounts at hotels displaying the £ symbol by their entry.

SCOTCH CORNER (NEAR RICHMOND) North Yorkshire
Map 08 NZ20

★★★65% **Quality Scotch Corner**

DL10 6NR (at A1/A66 junct) ☎ 01748 850900
FAX 01748 855417
Conveniently placed for weary travellers, this hotel offers modern accommodation in both the original 1930's building and the more recent extension. Premier rooms incur a small extra charge but guests have the benefit of additional facilities and more space. Public areas include two lounges, one designated no-smoking and there is extensive lounge service throughout the day. An excellent new leisure club boasts the latest fitness equipment, a generously sized pool, lounge bar and beauty salon.
90 en suite (bth/shr) (5 fmly) No smoking in 45 bedrooms CTV in all bedrooms STV Lift Night porter 200P Indoor swimming pool (heated) Sauna Solarium Gym Jacuzzi/spa Beauty therapist Golf simulator Xmas V meals Coffee am Tea pm Last d 9.30pm
ROOMS: s £57.50-£67.50; d £67.50-£87.50 **LB**
MEALS: Lunch £7.50-£9.95&alc Dinner £13.50&alc
CONF: Thtr 280 Class 110 Board 40 Del from £82.50
CARDS:

Travelodge

Travelodge

Skeeby DL10 5EQ (0.5m S on A1) ☎ 01748 823768
FAX 01748 823768
This modern building offers accommodation in smart, spacious and well equipped bedrooms, suitable for family use, and all with en suite bathrooms. Meals may be taken at the nearby family restaurant. For information on room rates and to make a booking, call Roomline free of charge on 0800 850950. For more details about Travelodge, consult the Contents page under Hotel Groups.
40 en suite (bth/shr)

Travelodge

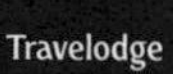

A1/A66, Middleton Tyas Ln DL10 6PQ
☎ 01325 377177 FAX 01325 377890
This modern building offers accommodation in smart, spacious and well equipped bedrooms, suitable for family use, and all with en suite bathrooms. Meals may be taken at the nearby family restaurant. For information on room rates and to make a booking, call Roomline free of charge on 0800 850950. For more details about Travelodge, consult the Contents page under Hotel Groups.
50 en suite (bth)

SCUNTHORPE Lincolnshire Map 08 SE81

★★★68% **Briggate Lodge Inn**
Ermine St, Broughton DN20 0NQ (200yds from junct 4 on the M180, on the Brigg-Scunthorpe roundabout) ☎ 01652 650770
FAX 01652 650495
A modern red brick building surrounded by wooded grounds and an attractive garden, the Briggate Lodge has inviting public areas with a good choice of bars and food options. An all-day menu is available in the buttery, while the more formal restaurant offers a wide selection of international dishes. Accommodation is modern, and the newer wing provides deluxe bedrooms, two suites and a four-poster room. The main golf course was due to open in 1996.
50 en suite (bth/shr) No smoking in 15 bedrooms CTV in all bedrooms STV No dogs (ex guide dogs) Lift Night porter 250P Golf 27 Putting green Golf practice nets Driving range Wkly live entertainment ch fac Xmas International Cuisine V meals Coffee am Tea pm Last d 10pm
ROOMS: (incl. bkfst) s £69-£76; d £78-£84 * **LB**
OFF-PEAK: (incl. bkfst) s fr £51.70; d fr £62.70
MEALS: Lunch £11.50-£15.70 Dinner £16.50&alc*
CONF: Thtr 100 Class 60 Board 50 Del from £103
CARDS:

★★★65% **Wortley House**
Rowland Rd DN16 1SU ☎ 01724 842223 FAX 01724 280646
Catering mainly for the commercial trade, this town centre hotel is located near the railway station on the southern edge of the town. It provides spacious public rooms which have been recently upgraded whilst the modern bedrooms are very well equipped to include both hair dryers and trouser presses. A good range of well produced food is available either in the bar or the bistro-style dining room. There is a flexible range of function and conference facilities available, as well as good car parking.
38 en suite (bth/shr) (2 fmly) No smoking in 4 bedrooms CTV in all bedrooms STV Night porter 100P Xmas English & French Cuisine V meals Coffee am Tea pm No smoking area in restaurant Last d 9.30pm
ROOMS: (incl. bkfst) d £67.50-£70 * **LB**
MEALS: Lunch £8.75-£14 Dinner £12.50-£14&alc
CONF: Thtr 300 Class 120 Board 80 Del from £65
CARDS:

★★★62% **Royal**

MENZIES HOTELS

Doncaster Rd DN15 7DE ☎ 01724 282233
FAX 01724 281826
Standing on the Doncaster road and about a mile from the town centre this modern and comfortable hotel has recently received an upgrade to the public rooms. It provides modern and well equipped bedrooms and a good range of food is available.
33 en suite (bth/shr) (1 fmly) No smoking in 10 bedrooms CTV in all bedrooms Night porter 33P Xmas European Cuisine V meals Coffee am Tea pm No smoking in restaurant Last d 9.30pm
ROOMS: d fr £59.50 * **LB**
OFF-PEAK: d fr £35
MEALS: Lunch fr £9.95&alc Dinner £12.50-£25alc*
CONF: Thtr 240 Class 200 Board 100 Del from £75
CARDS:

SEAHOUSES Northumberland Map 12 NU23

★★72% **Olde Ship**

NE68 7RD (lower end of main street above harbour)
☎ 01665 720200 FAX 01665 721383

Closed Dec-Jan
Lying just a stone's throw from the harbour, this friendly family-run hotel has tremendous character with its cosy public areas and corridors adorned with nautical and period memorabilia which are of great interest. The salon bar is typical of an English village pub, with an atmosphere second to none and tip-top real ale to boot. Apart from two rooms with four-posters, bedrooms are not large, but they are thoughtfully equipped and most have been stylishly upgraded to a very good standard.
12 en suite (bth/shr) 4 annexe en suite (bth/shr) CTV in all bedrooms STV No dogs 16P No coaches Putting green No children 10yrs V meals Coffee am Tea pm Last d 8.15pm
ROOMS: (incl. bkfst) s £29.50-£35; d £59-£70 **LB**
MEALS: Lunch £8-£8.75 Dinner £12.50-£13.50*
CARDS:

★★71% **Bamburgh Castle**
NE68 7SQ (from A1 follow signs for Seahouses) ☎ 01665 720283 FAX 01665 720283
Enthusiastically run by Paul and June Hopper, this large but friendly hotel enjoys a picture postcard setting overlooking the harbour, with views of Bamburgh Castle, the Farne Islands and Holy Island. One can watch the fishing boats from the attractive restaurant and relax in one of the several lounges. Bedrooms come in a variety of sizes, all being well equipped and having comfortable chairs.
20 en suite (bth/shr) (2 fmly) No smoking in 5 bedrooms CTV in all bedrooms STV 30P Putting green Small exercise room,outdoor table tennis V meals Coffee am Tea pm No smoking area in restaurant Last d 8.30pm
ROOMS: (incl. bkfst) s £33.95-£39.95; d £61.90-£71.90 * **LB**
OFF-PEAK: (incl. bkfst) s £33.95
MEALS: Sunday Lunch £7.50 Dinner £18.95*
CONF: Thtr 40 Class 20 Board 25 Del from £39.95

★★70% ***Beach House***
Sea Front NE68 7SR ☎ 01665 720337 FAX 01665 720921
Closed Nov-Mar
This family-run tourist hotel lies well back from the road and enjoys fine views out to sea towards the Farne Islands. The atmosphere is friendly and relaxed - there is no bar but guests can have drinks in the lounge. The dinner menu offers a short choice but extends to four courses, with good honest home cooking featuring local produce. The thoughtfully equipped bedrooms are bright and cheery, the more spacious being located on the ground floor.
14 en suite (bth/shr) (3 fmly) CTV in all bedrooms 16P No coaches Jacuzzi/spa Games table V meals Coffee am Last d 8.30pm
CARDS:

SEATON BURN Tyne & Wear Map 12 NZ27

★★★★58% **Holiday Inn**

Great North Rd NE13 6BF (3m W of Tyne Tunnel towards Morpeth) ☎ 0191 201 9988 FAX 0191 236 8091
A good range of facilities, such as a well equipped leisure centre and spacious bedrooms are features of this modern hotel, situated close to the junction of the A1 and A19 roads, about 6 miles north of the city centre. Some of the bedrooms are less contemporary in style, but most have two double beds and all have modern facilities. Its convenient location is ideal for both leisure and business purposes and it is also within easy reach of Newcastle International Airport.
150 en suite (bth/shr) (77 fmly) No smoking in 74 bedrooms CTV in all bedrooms Night porter Air conditioning 300P Indoor swimming pool (heated) Sauna Solarium Gym Pool table Putting green Jacuzzi/spa Games room Wkly live entertainment Xmas International Cuisine V meals Coffee am Tea pm No smoking area in restaurant Last d 10pm
ROOMS: s £79-£103.50; d £89-£113.50 * **LB**
OFF-PEAK: s £55-£79; d £59-£89
MEALS: Lunch £5-£18 Dinner £14-£17&alc*
CONF: Thtr 400 Class 200 Board 100 Del from £110
CARDS:

SEAVIEW See Wight, Isle of

SEDGEFIELD Co Durham Map 08 NZ32

★★★64% **Hardwick Hall**
TS21 2EH (on A177) ☎ 01740 620253 FAX 01740 622771
A splendid country house-style hotel set in the peaceful seclusion of parkland. The bedrooms are thoughtfully furnished and equipped and a strong feature of the hotel. Otherwise there is a choice of bars and dining arrangements which range from bar meals to an à la carte in the elegant gilded restaurant.
17 en suite (bth/shr) (2 fmly) CTV in all bedrooms No dogs (ex guide dogs) 200P ch fac English & French Cuisine V meals Coffee am Tea pm Last d 9.30pm
ROOMS: (incl. bkfst) s £50-£60; d £60-£75 * **LB**
OFF-PEAK: (incl. bkfst) s £40-£50; d £55-£65
MEALS: Lunch £9.85-£12.95 High tea £3.95-£4.95 Dinner £16.95-£18.95*
CONF: Thtr 80 Class 30 Board 40 Del from £80
CARDS:

★★66% **Crosshill**
1 The Square TS21 2AB (access via A689, overlooking church) ☎ 01740 620153 FAX 01740 621206
A cheerful and friendly family-owned village inn, next to the lovely old church. Bedrooms are thoughtfully furnished and their bathrooms modern. The range of bar meals and restaurant dishes is good.
8 en suite (bth/shr) (2 fmly) CTV in all bedrooms Night porter 9P Xmas English & Continental Cuisine V meals Coffee am Tea pm Last d 9.45pm
ROOMS: s £35-£38; d £38-£45 * **LB**
OFF-PEAK: s £33-£36; d £36-£42
MEALS: Lunch £7.50-£20&alc Dinner £11.50-£20&alc
CONF: Thtr 20 Class 30 Board 40
CARDS:

Travelodge
Travelodge
TS21 2LH (on A689, 3m E of junct A1M) ☎ 01740 623399 FAX 01740 623399
This modern building offers accommodation in smart, spacious and well equipped bedrooms, suitable for family use, and all with en suite bathrooms. Meals may be taken at the nearby family restaurant. For information on room rates and to make a booking, call Roomline free of charge on 0800 850950. For more details about Travelodge, consult the Contents page under Hotel Groups.
40 en suite (bth/shr)

SEDGEMOOR MOTORWAY SERVICE AREA (M5) Somerset Map 03 ST35

Travelodge

Welcome Break Service Area BS24 0JL (between junct 22 & 23 M5 northbound) ☎ 01934 750831
This modern building offers accommodation in smart, spacious and well equipped bedrooms, suitable for family use, and all with en suite bathrooms. Meals may be taken at the nearby family restaurant. For information on room rates and to make a booking, call Roomline free of charge on 0800 850950. For more details about Travelodge, consult the Contents page under Hotel Groups.
40 en suite (bth/shr)

SEDLESCOMBE East Sussex Map 05 TQ71

★★★62% **Brickwall**
The Green TN33 0QA (off A21 on B2244 at top of Sedlescombe Green)
☎ 01424 870253 FAX 01424 870785
Overlooking the village green and dating from C1597, the original and more interesting part of the house retains much of its Tudor character whilst skilfully combining the more functional modern garden wing bedroom extension. The wood panelled, oak beamed restaurant and bar-lounge is particularly attractive and well furnished and chef Waters has built up a reputation locally for good value reliable standards of cooking. The atmosphere is very cordial and friendly with a loyal team of professional staff who are personally supervised by the charismatic Italian proprietor Mr Peppe Pollio. Plans for a new leisure club and more bedrooms were in hand as we went to print.
23 en suite (bth/shr) (2 fmly) CTV in all bedrooms STV 25P No coaches Outdoor swimming pool (heated) Xmas English, French & Italian Cuisine V meals Coffee am Last d 9pm
ROOMS: (incl. bkfst) s £40-£45; d £60-£70 * **LB**
OFF-PEAK: (incl. bkfst) s £35; d £55
MEALS: Lunch £13.50-£15 Dinner £17-£19*
CARDS:

SELBY North Yorkshire Map 08 SE63

★★66% **Owl**
Main Rd YO8 9JH (Marstons) ☎ 01757 228374 FAX 01757 228125
(For full entry see Hambleton (4m W A63))

★★63% ***Park View***
20 Main St, Riccall YO4 6PX (follow road through village on left)
☎ 01757 248458
Located just off the A19 in the village of Riccall, this family-owned hotel offers well equipped bedrooms together with a cosy bar and pleasant dining room. A good range of value-for-money dishes is available. Service from the resident owners is personal and friendly.
7 en suite (bth/shr) 2 annexe en suite (bth/shr) (3 fmly) CTV in all bedrooms 26P Snooker V meals Coffee am Tea pm Last d 10pm
CARDS:

SENNEN Cornwall & Isles of Scilly Map 02 SW32

★★★66% **The Land's End Hotel**
TR19 7AA ☎ 01736 871844 FAX 01736 871599

CONSORT HOTELS

At the very tip of South West England, situated right on the cliff top, the hotel has splendid views out to sea, the Longships lighthouse and the Isles of Scilly beyond. The Atlantic Restaurant has the sea as a backdrop, a fixed price menu is served, using fresh local ingredients, in a conservatory atmosphere. Bedrooms are attractive, with co-ordinating soft furnishings, though some are compact.
33 en suite (bth/shr) (2 fmly) CTV in all bedrooms Night porter 1000P Y Wkly live entertainment Xmas Traditional English Cuisine V meals Coffee am Tea pm No smoking in restaurant Last d 9.30pm
ROOMS: (incl. bkfst) s £28.50-£72; d £79-£144 * **LB**
MEALS: Lunch £4.50-£8.95 High tea £3.50-£6 Dinner £18.95*
CONF: Thtr 200 Class 100 Board 50 Del £59.50
CARDS:
See advertisement under LAND'S END

★★66% **Old Success Inn**

Sennen Cove TR19 7DG (turn right off the A30 approx 1mile before Land's End, signposted Sennen Cove. The Hotrel is situated on the left at the bottom of the hill) ☎ 01736 871232 FAX 01736 871457
Situated in Sennen Cove, the Old Success is a delightful 17th-century fisherman's inn, which has been carefully modernised to retain its original features. Two honeymoon suites are available; rooms on the second floor feature four-poster beds and spectacular sea views; many of the remaining rooms also benefit from the views. Charlie's Bar attracts locals and visitors alike, with its good selection of real ales and tempting array of snacks and meals. The Cove Carvery offers guests a more formal dining option.
12 rms (1 fmly) CTV in all bedrooms STV 12P Wkly live entertainment Xmas V meals Coffee am Tea pm No smoking in restaurant
ROOMS: (incl. bkfst) s £25-£40; d £32-£80 * **LB**
OFF-PEAK: (incl. bkfst) s £20-£30; d £40-£80
MEALS: Sunday Lunch £5.50-£9.95 Dinner £13.50&alc
CARDS:

SETTLE North Yorkshire Map 07 SD86

★★★64% **Falcon Manor**

Skipton Rd BD24 9BD (turn off A65 on roundabout at southern end of Settle by-pass, continue for 0.50m) ☎ 01729 823814 FAX 01729 822087
This impressive, stone-built early Victorian hotel stands to the south of the town and enjoys beautiful views of the surrounding hills. It retains many of the original features and offers well equipped and attractively furnished bedrooms, together with pleasant public areas. A good range of well prepared food is available, either in the bar or the elegant restaurant.
15 en suite (bth/shr) 5 annexe en suite (bth/shr) (3 fmly) CTV in all bedrooms 85P Croquet lawn Bowling green Xmas English & Continental Cuisine V meals Coffee am Tea pm No smoking in restaurant Last d 9.30pm
ROOMS: (incl. bkfst) s £55; d fr £80 * **LB**
OFF-PEAK: (incl. bkfst) s fr £45
MEALS: Lunch fr £11.95 High tea fr £6.50 Dinner fr £19.50*
CONF: Thtr 45 Board 20 Del from £75
CARDS:

SEVENOAKS Kent Map 05 TQ55

★★★65% **Royal Oak**
Upper High St TN13 1HY (on A225, opp Sevenoaks School)
☎ 01732 451109 FAX 01732 740187
This well established hotel has been an inn since the 17th century and has been skilfully extended and improved to provide a range of individually furnished bedrooms. Those in the main house vary in shape and size but the majority of the rooms are in the adjoining modern annexe. Bedroom refurbishment is underway and the annexe bedrooms were already completed as we went to press. The public areas are given over to a popular bar bistro and the more formal restaurant where chef James Butterfill offers a blend of professionally produced English and French cuisine. Advertised room service is available until 10pm, (including hot meals during restaurant opening times and other facilities include a small conservatory lounge and two modern conference rooms.
21 en suite (bth/shr) 16 annexe en suite (bth/shr) CTV in all bedrooms Night porter 50P Tennis (hard) Xmas English & French Cuisine V meals Coffee am Tea pm Last d 9.30pm

ROOMS: s £65; d £75 * **LB**
MEALS: Lunch £15.95-£17.95&alc High tea fr £5.25 Dinner fr £17.95&alc*
CONF: Thtr 35 Board 25
CARDS:

See advertisement on this page

SEVERN STOKE Hereford & Worcester Map 03 SO84

★★★ 70% **Old School House**

WR8 9JA (midway beween Worcester and Tewkesbury - just off the A38) ☎ 01905 371368 & 371464 FAX 01905 371591
This black and white-timber framed property is situated on the edge of the village of Severn Stoke; it was originally a farmhouse and in more recent times, until 1964, served as the local school and school house. The bedrooms are all individually styled and tastefully decorated and furnished; all have good modern facilities. No-smoking rooms, bedrooms on ground floor level, a family room and a room with a four-poster bed are all available. The public areas are cosy and have a wealth of charm. The attractive restaurant overlooks the surrounding countryside, with the Malvern hills in the background. It has a well deserved reputation for its food.
13 en suite (bth/shr) (1 fmly) No smoking in 3 bedrooms CTV in all bedrooms 80P Outdoor swimming pool (heated) Fishing Boat for charter Clay pigeon shooting Xmas V meals Coffee am No smoking in restaurant Last d 9.30pm
ROOMS: (incl. bkfst) s £37.50-£55; d £55-£80 **LB**
MEALS: Lunch £9.95-£15 Dinner £15.50-£17.50&alc
CONF: Thtr 100 Class 40 Board 40 Del £75
CARDS:
See advertisement under WORCESTER

SEVERN VIEW MOTORWAY SERVICE AREA (M4)
Gloucestershire Map 03 ST58

Travelodge
M4 Motorway (junc 21) BS12 3BJ (junct 21)
☎ 0800 850950 FAX 01454 632482
This modern building offers accommodation in smart, spacious and well equipped bedrooms, suitable for family use, and all with en suite bathrooms. Meals may be taken at the nearby family restaurant. For information on room rates and to make a booking, call Roomline free of charge on 0800 850950. For more details about Travelodge, consult the Contents page under Hotel Groups.
51 en suite (bth/shr)

SHAFTESBURY Dorset Map 03 ST82
See also Ludwell

★★★ 69% **Royal Chase**

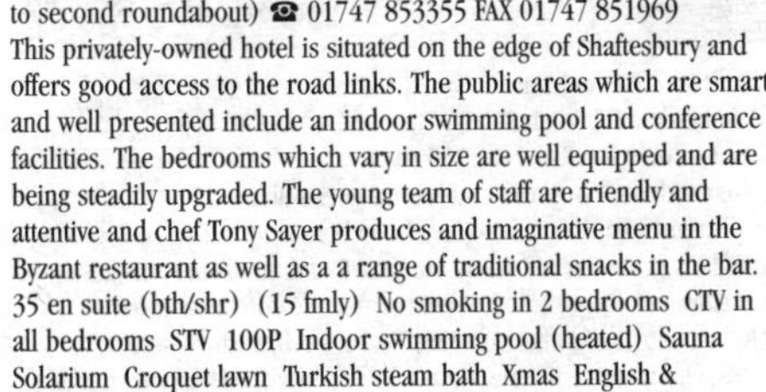

Royal Chase Roundabout SP7 8DB (take A303 to within 7m of town and then A350 signposted Blandford Forum. Avoid town centre and follow road to second roundabout) ☎ 01747 853355 FAX 01747 851969
This privately-owned hotel is situated on the edge of Shaftesbury and offers good access to the road links. The public areas which are smart and well presented include an indoor swimming pool and conference facilities. The bedrooms which vary in size are well equipped and are being steadily upgraded. The young team of staff are friendly and attentive and chef Tony Sayer produces and imaginative menu in the Byzant restaurant as well as a a range of traditional snacks in the bar.
35 en suite (bth/shr) (15 fmly) No smoking in 2 bedrooms CTV in all bedrooms STV 100P Indoor swimming pool (heated) Sauna Solarium Croquet lawn Turkish steam bath Xmas English & Continental Cuisine V meals Coffee am Tea pm No smoking in restaurant Last d 9.30pm

ROOMS: s £71-£81; d £87-£97 **LB**
OFF-PEAK: (incl. bkfst) s £49.50-£59.50; d £60-£70
MEALS: Lunch £9.95-£16.50&alc High tea £2-£6.50 Dinner £16.50&alc
CONF: Thtr 140 Class 90 Board 50 Del from £77
CARDS:

★★★ 59% **The Grosvenor**

The Commons SP7 8JA (at junct of A30 & A350 in centre of town) ☎ 01747 852282
FAX 01747 854755
Once a coaching inn, this hotel at the heart of the market town is slowly being upgraded to modern standard - though a truly magnificent antique carved sideboard remains the pride of the first floor lounge. Bedrooms tend to vary is size and style and although well equipped still exhibit older, more functional bathrooms. There is a popular local bar and a pretty restaurant across the courtyard features local dishes as well as a roast of the day. There is some on-street parking available outside the hotel and in nearby streets, although the free overnight car park is a reasonable walk away.
35 en suite (bth/shr) (4 fmly) No smoking in 16 bedrooms CTV in all bedrooms Xmas V meals Coffee am Tea pm No smoking in restaurant Last d 9.00pm
ROOMS: (incl. bkfst) s £33-£38; d £66-£76 * **LB**
OFF-PEAK: (incl. bkfst & dinner) s fr £29; d fr £58
MEALS: Sunday Lunch £11.95 High tea £4-£10 Dinner £14.95&alc
CONF: Thtr 150 Class 85 Board 80 Del from £65
CARDS:

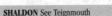

SHALDON See Teignmouth

SHANKLIN See Wight, Isle of

SHAP Cumbria Map 12 NY51

★★★63% **Shap Wells**

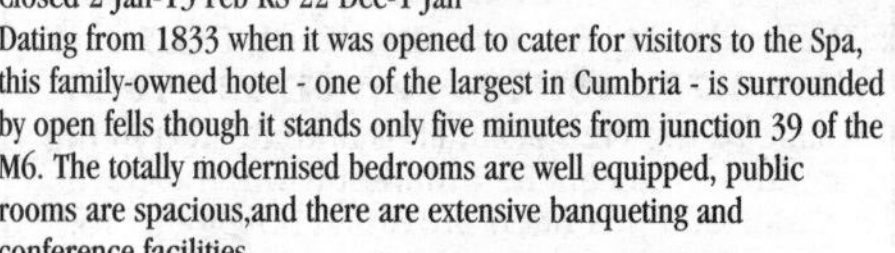

CA10 3QU (situated 3m SW of Shap Village off A6)
☎ 01931 716628 FAX 01931 716377
Closed 2 Jan-13 Feb RS 22 Dec-1 Jan
Dating from 1833 when it was opened to cater for visitors to the Spa, this family-owned hotel - one of the largest in Cumbria - is surrounded by open fells though it stands only five minutes from junction 39 of the M6. The totally modernised bedrooms are well equipped, public rooms are spacious,and there are extensive banqueting and conference facilities.
89 en suite (bth/shr) (11 fmly) CTV in all bedrooms STV 200P Tennis (hard) Snooker Pool table Games room Wkly live entertainment English & French Cuisine V meals Coffee am Last d 8.30pm
ROOMS: (incl. bkfst) s fr £45; d fr £70 * **LB**
MEALS: Lunch fr £7.50 Dinner fr £13.50&alc*
CONF: Thtr 200 Class 100 Board 50
CARDS:
See advertisement under KENDAL

SHARDLOW Derbyshire Map 08 SK43

★★60% **The Lady In Grey**
Wilne Ln DE72 2HA (7m SE of Derby, off A6)
☎ 01332 792331 FAX 01332 792331
Adjacent to the canal, this small family owned and run hotel stands in its own mature grounds. It provides adequate bedrooms together with open plan public rooms which include a small bar, a lounge and a traditional style dining room which provides a large range of dishes from the two menus.
9 en suite (bth/shr) (2 fmly) CTV in all bedrooms No dogs 30P No coaches International Cuisine V meals No smoking in restaurant Last d 9.30pm
MEALS: Sunday Lunch £5.95-£8.75&alc Dinner £9.95-£12.90&alc*
CARDS:

SHEDFIELD Hampshire Map 04 SU51

★★★64% **Meon Valley Hotel**

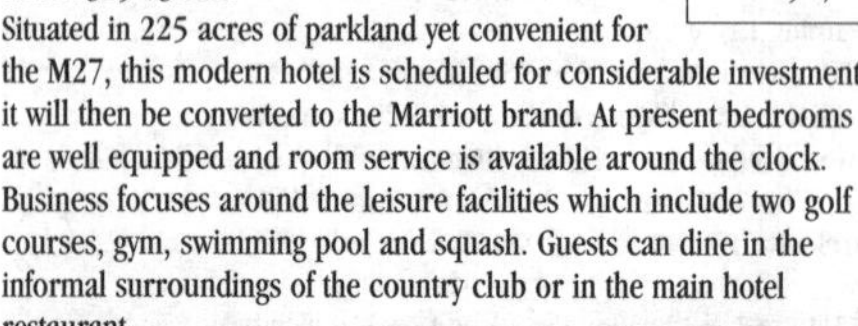

Sandy Ln SO3 2HQ ☎ 01329 833455
FAX 01329 834411
Situated in 225 acres of parkland yet convenient for the M27, this modern hotel is scheduled for considerable investment; it will then be converted to the Marriott brand. At present bedrooms are well equipped and room service is available around the clock. Business focuses around the leisure facilities which include two golf courses, gym, swimming pool and squash. Guests can dine in the informal surroundings of the country club or in the main hotel restaurant.
83 en suite (bth/shr) No smoking in 40 bedrooms CTV in all bedrooms STV No dogs (ex guide dogs) Night porter 300P Indoor swimming pool (heated) Golf 18 Tennis (hard) Squash Snooker Sauna Solarium Gym Pool table Health & beauty salon Dance studio ch fac Xmas English & French Cuisine V meals Coffee am Tea pm Last d 9.45pm

ROOMS: (incl. bkfst) s £65-£85; d £75-£95 * **LB**
OFF-PEAK: (incl. bkfst) s £65-£75; d £75-£85
MEALS: Lunch £8.25-£15 Dinner £21&alc*
CONF: Thtr 110 Class 60 Board 40 Del from £95
CARDS:

SHEFFIELD South Yorkshire Map 08 SK38

★★★★63% **Sheffield Moat House**
Chesterfield Rd South S8 8BW (on A61)
☎ 0114 282 9988 FAX 0114 237 8140
MOAT HOUSE
Modern, well equipped accommodation is provided at this easily accessible, purpose-built hotel, where the friendly staff make genuine efforts to ensure that guests are well looked after. Facilities include extensive conference and banqueting suites including a state of the art meeting room and a business centre, as well as a secure car park.
95 en suite (bth/shr) (9 fmly) No smoking in 40 bedrooms CTV in all bedrooms Lift Night porter 260P Indoor swimming pool (heated) Sauna Solarium Gym Pool table Jacuzzi/spa Health & beauty treatment room English & French Cuisine V meals Coffee am Tea pm No smoking in restaurant Last d 10pm
ROOMS: s fr £95; d fr £120 **LB**
MEALS: Lunch £9.50-£11.25 Dinner £16.50&alc
CONF: Thtr 500 Class 300 Board 95 Del £120
CARDS:

★★★72% **Beauchief**
161 Abbeydale Rd South S7 2QW (on A621, 3m SW)
☎ 0114 262 0500 FAX 0114 235 0197
COUNTRY CLUB Hotel Group
Popular with both business and leisure guests alike this pleasantly landscaped modern hotel boasts a trout stream running through its grounds. Bedrooms are smart, and the bathrooms have been substantially improved. Public rooms are comfortable and include a choice of bars, including Michel's cellar which serves snacks, and an attractive restaurant. Prompt service is carried out by a friendly team.
41 en suite (bth/shr) No smoking in 21 bedrooms CTV in all

bedrooms STV No dogs (ex guide dogs) Night porter 200P Sauna Solarium Gym Pool table Jacuzzi/spa Wkly live entertainment Xmas English & Continental Cuisine V meals Coffee am Tea pm No smoking area in restaurant Last d 10pm
ROOMS: s £60-£72; d £60-£72 * LB
OFF-PEAK: s £48; d £48
MEALS: Lunch £10.10-£12.10&alc Dinner fr £17.50&alc*
CONF: Thtr 100 Class 50 Board 50 Del from £98
CARDS: 

★★★ 70% *Harley*
334 Glossop Rd S10 2HW (situated west of the city centre on the inner ring road close to its junction with the A57)
☎ 0114 275 2288 FAX 0114 272 2383
RS Sun
Furnished with flair and an individualistic style this red-brick town house style of hotel serves the needs of the business guest with distinction. The public rooms are restricted in their range to a comfortable lounge and an adjoining elegant dining room. Service is simultaneously friendly and professional. The cooking is good and offers freshly cooked modern dishes.
22 en suite (bth/shr) No smoking in 11 bedrooms CTV in all bedrooms STV No dogs (ex guide dogs) Night porter No coaches No children 12yrs English & French Cuisine V meals Coffee am Tea pm Last d 9.45pm
CARDS:

★★★ 69% Charnwood
10 Sharrow Ln S11 8AA (on A621) ☎ 0114 258 9411
FAX 0114 255 5107
Within walking distance of the city, just off London Road, this long established and privately owned hotel offers every comfort for the traveller. There are two styles of dining available in Leo's Brasserie or the more intimate Henfrey's restaurant, where a shorter and more classical menu is provided. Ample comfortable lounges are available, and the bedrooms have been thoughtfully equipped to include trouser presses and mini bars.
22 en suite (bth/shr) (1 fmly) CTV in all bedrooms No dogs (ex guide dogs) Night porter 22P No coaches V meals Coffee am Tea pm
ROOMS: (incl. bkfst) s £75; d £90 * LB
OFF-PEAK: (incl. bkfst) s £45; d £60
CARDS:

★★★ 68% Whitley Hall

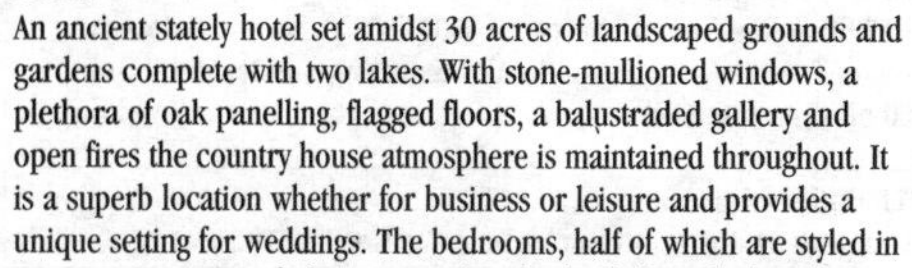

Elliott Ln, Grenoside S30 3NR ☎ 0114 245 4444
FAX 0114 245 5414
RS BH
An ancient stately hotel set amidst 30 acres of landscaped grounds and gardens complete with two lakes. With stone-mullioned windows, a plethora of oak panelling, flagged floors, a balustraded gallery and open fires the country house atmosphere is maintained throughout. It is a superb location whether for business or leisure and provides a unique setting for weddings. The bedrooms, half of which are styled in more contemporary fashion are each individually furnished and decorated.
18 en suite (bth/shr) (1 fmly) CTV in all bedrooms Night porter 100P No coaches Croquet lawn Putting green Wkly live entertainment V meals Coffee am Tea pm No smoking in restaurant Last d 9.15pm
ROOMS: (incl. bkfst) s £62-£78; d £83-£99 LB
OFF-PEAK: (incl. bkfst) s £50-£78; d £60-£99
MEALS: Lunch £13-£15&alc Dinner £19.50-£20.50&alc
CONF: Thtr 70 Class 50 Board 40 Del from £105
CARDS:

★★★ 65% Novotel

50 Arundel Gate S1 2PR (between Registry Office and Crucible/Lyceum Theatres) ☎ 0114 278 1781
FAX 0114 278 7744
A modern, mirrored glass hotel conveniently situated in the heart of Sheffield within walking distance of the shops and many central attractions. Bedrooms are practical, identical in style and most can be converted for family use; some have facilities for disabled guests. Open-plan public areas are spacious and comfortably furnished, and light snacks or meals are available throughout the day; the restaurant is open until midnight The hotel has its own underground car park.
144 en suite (bth/shr) (20 fmly) No smoking in 108 bedrooms CTV in all bedrooms STV Lift Air conditioning 50P Indoor swimming pool (heated) Pool table International Cuisine V meals Coffee am Tea pm Last d mdnt
ROOMS: d £59 * LB
MEALS: Lunch £12 Dinner £15*
CONF: Thtr 200 Class 100 Board 100 Del from £85
CARDS:

★★★ 65% The Regency
High St, Ecclesfield S30 3XB ☎ 0114 246 7703
FAX 0114 240 0081
Closed Xmas & New Year
An imposing stone-built house mansion house in the centre of the village, the restaurant here is popular with locals for its traditional English dishes and grills. A recent extension has created a block of large and thoroughly contempory bedrooms furnished in light oak, with co-ordinated soft furnishings. There are also a large function room and a range of conference rooms.
19 en suite (bth/shr) (1 fmly) CTV in all bedrooms STV No dogs (ex guide dogs) Night porter 80P English & Continental Cuisine V meals Coffee am Tea pm Last d 9.45pm
ROOMS: (incl. bkfst) s fr £59.50; d £71.50-£90 * LB
OFF-PEAK: (incl. bkfst) s fr £39; d £51-£80
MEALS: Lunch £6.50-£10.95&alc Dinner fr £10.95&alc*
CONF: Thtr 200 Class 120 Board 40 Del from £79
CARDS:

★★★ 65% Staindrop Lodge
Ln End, Chapeltown S30 4UH (1m from junct 35 of M1) ☎ 0114 284 6727 FAX 0114 284 6783
Closed 25 & 26 Dec
On the High Green side of Chapeltown a mile from Junction 35 of the M1, Staindrop Lodge is a very well run and kept family-managed hotel. It has a friendly and relaxed atmosphere and has earned a good reputation for the quality of the cooking. Bedrooms are modern and thoughtfully furnished and co-ordinated.
13 en suite (bth/shr) (1 fmly) CTV in all bedrooms No dogs (ex guide dogs) 70P English & French Cuisine V meals Coffee am No smoking in restaurant Last d 9.30pm
ROOMS: (incl. bkfst) s £55-£59; d £69-£75 LB
OFF-PEAK: (incl. bkfst) s £40-£59; d £54-£75
MEALS: Lunch £10.25-£12.25&alc Dinner £17.90-£19.50&alc
CONF: Thtr 90 Class 60 Board 40
CARDS: 

★★★ 65% Swallow
Kenwood Rd S7 1NQ ☎ 0114 258 3811
FAX 0114 250 0138
This former private residence, which has been considerably extended, is peacefully situated in eleven acres of landscaped gardens. It provides varying standards and styles of accommodation, including a number of rooms with balconies overlooking an ornamental lake. Guests can relax in the well equipped leisure club run by very friendly staff, either of the two restaurants or the comfortable, open plan lounge areas, all of which overlook the

contd.

gardens. The hotel has a secure car park and a number of well equipped meeting rooms in the original house.
117 en suite (bth/shr) (33 fmly) No smoking in 8 bedrooms CTV in all bedrooms STV Lift Night porter 200P Indoor swimming pool (heated) Fishing Sauna Solarium Gym Jacuzzi/spa Steam room Xmas English & French Cuisine V meals Coffee am Tea pm No smoking in restaurant Last d 9.45pm
ROOMS: (incl. bkfst) s £95; d £110 * **LB**
OFF-PEAK: (incl. bkfst) s £55; d £80
MEALS: Lunch £13.25&alc Dinner £18&alc*
CONF: Thtr 200 Class 100 Board 60 Del from £85
CARDS:

★★★ 63% **Mosborough Hall**

High St, Mosborough S19 5AE (7m SE on A616)
☎ 0114 248 4353 FAX 0114 247 7042
A historic manor house just four miles from Junction 30 of the M1 surrounded by its own gardens has retained much of its character with some of the original Georgian architecture. Accommodation is very varied ranging from the grand to the cosy, though all are equally well equipped. The house style is informal and the cuisine is both accomplished and ambitious.
23 en suite (bth/shr) (1 fmly) CTV in all bedrooms Night porter 100P Pool table English & French Cuisine V meals Coffee am Tea pm Last d 9.30pm
ROOMS: (incl. bkfst) s £59-£75; d £69-£85 **LB**
OFF-PEAK: (incl. bkfst) s £35-£40; d £62-£70
MEALS: Lunch £9.95-£17.50 High tea £7-£16.95 Dinner £16.95-£21&alc
CONF: Thtr 50 Class 40 Board 40
CARDS:

★★★59% **Rutland**

452 Glossop Rd, Broomhill S10 2PY (on A57, located next to the Royal Hallamshire Hospital)
☎ 0114 266 4411 FAX 0114 267 0348
This business oriented hotel is usefully situated for the city, university and the Royal Hallamshire Hospital. It has evolved from a cluster of period dwellings with more recent conservatory-style additions. The bedrooms are a variety of shapes and sizes - some reasonably spacious, and all furnished in contemporary pastels with light oak fittings.
70 en suite (bth/shr) 17 annexe en suite (bth/shr) (5 fmly) No smoking in 10 bedrooms CTV in all bedrooms Lift Night porter 80P Xmas International Cuisine V meals Coffee am Tea pm No smoking area in restaurant Last d 9.30pm
ROOMS: d £52.50-£57.50 * **LB**
OFF-PEAK: d £35-£39
MEALS: Lunch £8.95-£9.95 Dinner £12.50-£20alc*
CONF: Thtr 100 Class 40 Board 60 Del from £75
CARDS:

★★69% **Andrews Park**
48 Kenwood Rd, Nether Edge S7 1NQ (close to city centre, off the inner ring road) ☎ 0114 2500 111 FAX 0114 2555 423
Situated in a pleasant leafy suburb west of the city this is an immaculately kept small family-operated hotel. All areas have a fresh and inviting appearance, complemented by the hospitality and friendliness provided by the Morris family. Public rooms include a comfortable lounge, and a conservatory-style lounge which can double as a meeting room. The menu is short but offers popular choices and all dishes are freshly cooked.
13 rms (9 bth/shr) (2 fmly) No smoking in 2 bedrooms CTV in all bedrooms Night porter 25P English & French Cuisine V meals Coffee am Tea pm No smoking area in restaurant Last d 10pm
ROOMS: s £35-£45; d £44-£52
OFF-PEAK: s £32; d £40
MEALS: Lunch £9.95-£17.95&alc Dinner £12.95-£18.95&alc
CONF: Thtr 35 Class 25 Board 30 Del from £59
CARDS:

Forte Posthouse Sheffield

Manchester Rd, Broomhill S10 5DX (off A57)
☎ 0114 267 0067 FAX 0114 268 2620
Suitable for both the business and leisure traveller, this bright hotel provides modern accommodation in well equipped bedrooms with en suite bathrooms. For more details about Forte Posthouse hotels, consult the Contents page for the section on Hotel Groups.
135 en suite (bth/shr)
ROOMS: s fr £69; d fr £69 *
CONF: Thtr 300 Class 130 Board 80 Del £99

Travel Inn
Attercliffe Common Rd S9 2LU (from M1 junct34, follow signs to Sheffield city centre. Travel Inn is opposite the Arena) ☎ 0114 242 2802 FAX 0114 242 3703
Purpose-built accommodation, offering spacious, well equipped bedrooms, all with en suite bathrooms. Meals may be taken at the nearby family restaurant. For more information about Travel Inns, consult the Contents page under Hotel Groups.
61 en suite (bth/shr)
ROOMS: d £35.50 *

Travelodge

340 Prince of Wales Rd S2 1FF
☎ 0114 253 0935 FAX 0114 253 0935
This modern building offers accommodation in smart, spacious and well equipped bedrooms, suitable for family use, and all with en suite bathrooms. Meals may be taken at the nearby family restaurant. For information on room rates and to make a booking, call Roomline free of charge on 0800 850950. For more details about Travelodge, consult the Contents page under Hotel Groups.
60 en suite (bth/shr)

⌂ **Cutlers Inn**
George St S1 2PF (city centre adjacent to Crucible Theatre)
☎ 0114 273 9939 FAX 0114 276 8332
Closed 24 Dec-3 Jan
Good-value well equipped accommodation is offered at this modern lodge which stands in the city centre, close to the Crucible and Lyceum theatres. All meals are served in the pleasant franchised Chinese restaurant. At the time of our visit, free parking was available at a nearby car park (check details on booking).
50 en suite (bth/shr) (2 fmly) No smoking in 5 bedrooms CTV in all bedrooms Lift Night porter Chinese Cuisine V meals No smoking in restaurant Last d 10.30pm
ROOMS: s £29.95-£39.95; d £34.95-£44.95
OFF-PEAK: d fr £29.95
MEALS: Lunch £5.95-£10&alc Dinner £5.95-£10&alc*
CARDS:

S

SHEFFORD Bedfordshire Map 04 TL13

★★★60% **Beadlow Manor**
Beadlow SG17 5PH ☎ 01525 860800 FAX 01525 861345
33 en suite (bth/shr) (7 fmly) CTV in all bedrooms Night porter 850P Golf 36 Sauna Solarium Gym Pool table Jacuzzi/spa Italian Cuisine V meals Coffee am Tea pm Last d 9.30pm
ROOMS: (incl. bkfst) s £33-£36; d £49-£55 *
MEALS: Bar Lunch £2.50-£7.50 Dinner £12.50-£17.50*
CONF: Thtr 450 Class 70 Board 70 Del from £84
CARDS:

SHEPPERTON Surrey See LONDON SECTION plan 1 A1

★★★65% ***Shepperton Moat House***
Felix Ln TW17 8NP ☎ 01932 241404
FAX 01932 245231
Closed 27-30 Dec

MOAT HOUSE

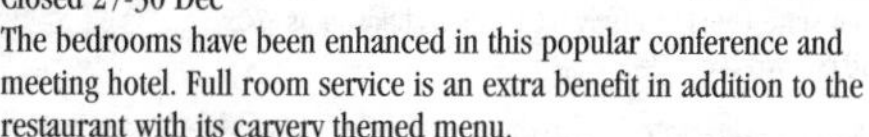

The bedrooms have been enhanced in this popular conference and meeting hotel. Full room service is an extra benefit in addition to the restaurant with its carvery themed menu.
156 en suite (bth/shr) (5 fmly) No smoking in 17 bedrooms CTV in all bedrooms Lift Night porter 225P Snooker Sauna Solarium Gym Putting green English & French Cuisine V meals Coffee am Last d 10pm
CARDS:

SHEPTON MALLET Somerset Map 03 ST64

★★69% **Shrubbery**
Commercial Rd BA4 5BU (turn off A37 at Shepton Mallet onto A371 Wells Rd, hotel 50mtrs past traffic lights in town centre). ☎ 01749 346671 FAX 01749 346581
The Shrubbery Hotel is located in the centre of the town and has the advantage of a good-sized car park. Christopher West returned to the town to manage the hotel recently, following a lifetime in the hospitality industry. Relaxing bedrooms are equipped with remote-control televisions and trouser presses in addition to the usual facilities, while the small restaurant's imaginative set-price menu offers a varied choice of dishes which includes some fish speciality recipes that Mr. West brought back from Spain. Morning coffees and afternoon teas are also available.
8 en suite (bth/shr) (1 fmly) CTV in all bedrooms 20P No coaches Xmas English, Spanish & French Cuisine V meals Coffee am Tea pm No smoking in restaurant Last d 9pm
ROOMS: (incl. bkfst) s £35-£45; d £59.50-£65 **LB**
MEALS: Sunday Lunch £12.95-£14.95 Dinner fr £15.95&alc
CONF: Thtr 100 Class 100 Board 60
CARDS:

★★68% ***Thatched Cottage Inn***
63-67 Charlton Rd BA4 5QF (on A361 Frome road)
☎ 01749 342058 FAX 01749 343265
Situated on the Frome side of the town, this 300-year-old thatched inn retains its original features such as old beams and fireplaces. The first floor bedrooms are spacious, well equipped and have modern bathrooms. In addition to the à la carte menu served in the restaurant, an extensive range of meals is served in the open-plan bar, for those guests looking for informality.
8 en suite (bth/shr) CTV in all bedrooms No dogs (ex guide dogs) Night porter 40P French Cuisine V meals Coffee am Tea pm
CARDS:

SHERBORNE Dorset Map 03 ST61

★★★69% **Eastbury**
Long St DT9 3BY (on A352) ☎ 01935 813131 FAX 01935 817296
This delightful hotel continues to improve under the care of proprietors Tom and Alison Pickford and their young friendly staff. Located in a quiet road in the centre of the town it has its own pretty walled garden. The bedrooms which vary in size, are being steadily upgraded, but all are well equipped. The public rooms include a comfortable lounge and a well stocked bar. The conservatory restaurant offers an interesting menu of carefully prepared local ingredients and benefits from the peace of the garden.
15 en suite (bth/shr) (1 fmly) CTV in all bedrooms STV No dogs (ex guide dogs) 24P No coaches Croquet lawn Xmas English & French Cuisine V meals Coffee am Tea pm Last d 9.30pm
ROOMS: (incl. bkfst) s £45-£55; d £65-£90 **LB**
MEALS: Lunch £10.50-£14.50 Dinner £12-£24.50alc*
CONF: Thtr 60 Class 40 Board 28 Del from £79.50
CARDS:

★★★65% **Antelope**
Greenhill DT9 4EP (just off A30) ☎ 01935 812077
FAX 01935 816473

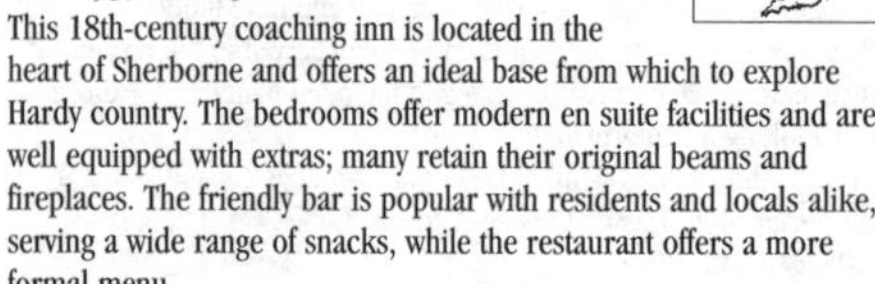

This 18th-century coaching inn is located in the heart of Sherborne and offers an ideal base from which to explore Hardy country. The bedrooms offer modern en suite facilities and are well equipped with extras; many retain their original beams and fireplaces. The friendly bar is popular with residents and locals alike, serving a wide range of snacks, while the restaurant offers a more formal menu.
19 en suite (bth/shr) (1 fmly) No smoking in 1 bedroom CTV in all bedrooms Night porter 22P Xmas English & Continental Cuisine V meals Coffee am Tea pm Last d 9.30pm
ROOMS: (incl. bkfst) s £39.95-£55; d £45-£75 * **LB**
OFF-PEAK: (incl. bkfst) s £35-£49.95; d £40-£65
MEALS: Lunch £5.50-£10&alc Dinner £8-£11&alc
CONF: Thtr 80 Class 60 Board 40
CARDS:

★★★60% **Sherborne**
Horsecastles Ln DT9 6BB (close to A30 on W outskirts of Sherborne) ☎ 01935 813191
FAX 01935 816493

Formerly a Posthouse, this conveniently positioned hotel caters for both business and leisure guests. The bedrooms have been recently refurbished and offer good modern standards of comfort. Staff are very friendly with prompt services carried out by a young, willing team.
59 en suite (bth/shr) (11 fmly) No smoking in 30 bedrooms CTV in all bedrooms Night porter Air conditioning 100P Croquet lawn Putting green Mini driving range Xmas International Cuisine V meals Coffee am Tea pm No smoking in restaurant Last d 10pm
ROOMS: s fr £49.50; d fr £49.50 * **LB**
MEALS: Sunday Lunch £7.50-£9.50 Dinner fr £16.95&alc*
CONF: Thtr 80 Class 30 Board 30 Del from £75
CARDS:

SHERINGHAM Norfolk Map 09 TG14

★★66% **Beaumaris**
South St NR26 8LL ☎ 01263 822370 FAX 01263 821421
Closed 19 Dec-7 Feb
The proprietors and staff offer a warm welcome and personal service at this well established hotel, which sits in a quiet residential road, a short distance from the town centre and seafront. The pleasant public rooms offer a comfortable quiet lounge, a small inviting bar and an adjoining dining room. Bedroom styles and sizes vary: the most recently refurbished bedrooms are particularly cheerful with their co-ordinated bold colour schemes and smart bathrooms; all have a good range of useful facilities.
22 en suite (bth/shr) (5 fmly) CTV in all bedrooms 25P V meals Coffee am Tea pm No smoking in restaurant Last d 8.30pm
ROOMS: (incl. bkfst) s £30-£40; d £60-£80 **LB**
OFF-PEAK: (incl. bkfst) s £25-£35; d £50-£70
MEALS: Sunday Lunch £9.75 Dinner £13.75&alc
CARDS:

★★65% **Southlands**
South St NR26 8LL ☎ 01263 822679 FAX 01263 822679
Closed Oct-Etr
There is a cheerful and friendly environment within this family-run hotel which sits in a residential road a short distance from the town centre. Guests have the use of a spacious comfortable lounge area, a small bar and light dining room, in which a short menu of traditional home cooking is offered. Bedrooms are generally of a reasonable size and traditionally appointed.
16 en suite (bth) (3 fmly) CTV in 18 bedrooms 20P
CARDS:

SHIFNAL Shropshire Map 07 SJ70

★★★★59% **Park House**
Macdonald Hotels
Park St TF11 9BA (leave M54 at junct 4 follow A464 Wolverhampton Rd for approx 2m, under railway bridge and hotel is 100yds on left)
☎ 01952 460128 FAX 01952 461658
Situated in spacious grounds on the A464, as it leaves the town towards Wolverhampton, this hotel's elegant public rooms with chandeliers and high ceilings portray its 17th-Century origins when it was two separate country houses. Now it caters for all contemporary necessities and in addition to spacious and comfortable bedrooms offers a leisure centre and numerous banqueting and conference suites. Modern cooking, provided by Head Chef Timothy Sheery and his team, can be enjoyed in the attractively appointed restaurant which has been given the coveted rosette award.
38 en suite (bth/shr) 16 annexe en suite (bth/shr) (4 fmly) No smoking in 10 bedrooms CTV in all bedrooms STV Lift Night porter 200P Indoor swimming pool (heated) Sauna Solarium Jacuzzi/spa Xmas English & French Cuisine V meals Coffee am Tea pm No smoking in restaurant Last d 9.30pm
ROOMS: s £85; d £103 * **LB**
OFF-PEAK: (incl. bkfst) s fr £50; d fr £80
MEALS: Lunch £11 High tea £9.90&alc Dinner £19.95&alc*
CONF: Thtr 180 Class 100 Board 40 Del from £90
CARDS:

SHIPHAM Somerset Map 03 ST45

★★★69% **Daneswood House**
Cuck Hill BS25 1RD (signposted from A38 Bristol/Bridgwater road)
☎ 01934 843145 & 843945 FAX 01934 843824
RS 24 Dec-6 Jan

Set in well tended gardens with breathtaking views, this Edwardian country house offers a relaxed atmosphere. Owners David and Elise Hodges have made many improvements over the years without obscuring the original features of the building. Individually appointed bedrooms are particularly well equipped for the business traveller, and cottage suites have separate lounges. Chef John Dawson provides a daily-changing fixed-price menu of carefully prepared dishes.
9 en suite (bth/shr) 3 annexe en suite (bth/shr) (3 fmly) CTV in all bedrooms No dogs (ex guide dogs) Night porter 27P No coaches English & Continental Cuisine V meals Coffee am Tea pm No smoking in restaurant Last d 9.30pm
ROOMS: (incl. bkfst) s £59.50-£72.50; d £65-£112.50 * **LB**
MEALS: Lunch £17.95-£22.95 Dinner £17.95-£22.95
CONF: Thtr 40 Board 25 Del from £95
CARDS:

SHIPLEY West Yorkshire Map 07 SE13

★★★70% **Marriott Hollins Hall Hotel**

Marriott HOTELS·RESORTS·SUITES

Hollins Hill, Baildon BD17 7QW (3m N on A6038 Otley road) ☎ 01274 530053 FAX 01274 530187
Situated within its own grounds in an elevated position overlooking Esholt Valley, Hollins Hall is an elegant 19th-century manor house built in the Elizabethan style. Bedrooms are spacious and modern whilst public areas retain a period charm.
59 en suite (bth/shr) (2 fmly) No smoking in 40 bedrooms CTV in all bedrooms STV No dogs (ex guide dogs) Lift Night porter 128P Sauna Solarium English & French Cuisine V meals Coffee am Tea pm No smoking area in restaurant Last d 10pm
ROOMS: (incl. bkfst) s £35-£45; d £70-£90 **LB**
OFF-PEAK: (incl. bkfst) s £29-£39; d £58-£78
MEALS: Lunch £12.95-£16.95 Dinner £14.95-£16.95&alc
CONF: Thtr 200 Class 90 Board 60 Del from £99
CARDS:

SHIPSTON ON STOUR Warwickshire Map 04 SP24

★★63% **The Red Lion**
Main St, Long Compton CV36 5JS (on B3400 between Shipston/Chipping Norton) ☎ 01608 684221
5 en suite (bth/shr) (1 fmly) CTV in all bedrooms 60P Pool table English & French Cuisine V meals Coffee am Last d 9pm
ROOMS: (incl. bkfst) s fr £29.50; d fr £45 * **LB**
MEALS: Lunch £9-£15alc Dinner £9-£20alc
CARDS:

SHIPTON-UNDER-WYCHWOOD Oxfordshire Map 04 SP21

★★63% **Shaven Crown**
OX7 6BA (on A361, halfway between Burford and Chipping Norton opposite village green and church)
☎ 01993 830330 FAX 01993 830330
This charming family-run hotel has an authentic historical atmosphere dating back to the 14th-century: the hotel was formerly a hospice attached to Bruern Abbey. The dramatic reception lounge has an unusual double-collar braced roof and features a collection of period weapons. Bedrooms are sympathetically furnished and all are spacious. There is a cosy bar where meals and real ales are served, or guests can choose to dine in the more formal dining room where the meals are all carefully prepared from fresh ingredients.
9 rms (8 bth/shr) (1 fmly) CTV in all bedrooms No dogs (ex guide dogs) 15P Bowling green Xmas Continental Cuisine V meals Coffee am Tea pm No smoking in restaurant Last d 9.30pm
ROOMS: (incl. bkfst) s £33; d £66-£82 * **LB**
MEALS: Sunday Lunch £11.95-£14.95 Dinner £14.95-£18.50
CARDS:

SHRAWLEY Hereford & Worcester Map 07 SO86

★★★63% **Lenchford**
WR6 6TB (beside B4196, N of its junct with A4133)
☎ 01905 620229 FAX 01905 621125
Closed 25-31 Dec
This much extended late Georgian house occupies a delightful location, alongside the River Severn. The bedrooms vary in size and style, but all have modern equipment and facilities. Bedrooms on ground floor level are available, as is family-bedded accommodation; there are also rooms with balconies overlooking river views, as well as rooms with French windows opening on to the riverside gardens. Public areas include a small à la carte restaurant, a traditionally furnished lounge bar, which has an adjacent area for bar meals, a comfortable lounge and a function room for up to 100 people. There is also an outdoor swimming pool.
16 rms (14 bth 1 shr) (1 fmly) CTV in all bedrooms No dogs 50P Outdoor swimming pool (heated) Fishing Pool table English & French Cuisine V meals Coffee am Last d 9.15pm
ROOMS: (incl. bkfst) s £38.50-£42.50; d £52.50-£55.50 * **LB**
MEALS: Sunday Lunch £10.95-£11.95 Dinner £9.95-£19.95alc*
CONF: Thtr 80 Class 30 Board 30 Del from £70
CARDS:

SHREWSBURY Shropshire Map 07 SJ41
See also Atcham & Nesscliffe

★★★★61% **Albrighton Hall**

Macdonald Hotels

Albrighton SY4 3AG 2.5m N on A528)
☎ 01939 291000 FAX 01939 291123
This historic country house is situated in 14 acres of grounds and gardens including an ornamental lake, just off the A528 on the outskirts of the town. It was built in 1630 and its elegant public rooms with beautiful oak panelling portray the style of the period. Bedrooms in the main house have all been tastefully refurbished and several have four-poster beds. Some of the rooms are in an adjacent house just a few steps away from the main building. There are extensive banqueting and conference facilities and also a modern and very well equipped leisure centre which includes a swimming pool and a squash court.
29 en suite (bth/shr) 10 annexe en suite (bth/shr) (2 fmly) No smoking in 19 bedrooms CTV in all bedrooms STV Night porter 120P Indoor swimming pool (heated) Squash Snooker Sauna

contd.

Solarium Gym Pool table Croquet lawn Jacuzzi/spa Health & leisure club Racquet ball Wkly live entertainment Xmas International Cuisine V meals Coffee am Tea pm No smoking in restaurant Last d 9.45pm
ROOMS: s £59.50-£79; d £79-£95 * **LB**
MEALS: Lunch £9.95-£12.95&alc Dinner fr £21&alc*
CONF: Thtr 300 Class 60 Board 50 Del from £90
CARDS:

★★★ 78% **Albright Hussey**
Ellesmere Rd SY4 3AF (2m N, on A528)
☎ 01939 290571 & 290523 FAX 01939 291143
Owned and enthusiastically run by the Subbiani family since 1967, this immaculately maintained Tudor, timber-framed house offers luxuriously appointed and thoughtfully equipped accommodation, which includes a number of suites and a room with a four-poster bed and whirl-pool bath. At the time of our inspection in early spring more rooms were being added, together with an impressive conference and banqueting facility, lounge and new reception. The innovative skills of head chef Nigel Huxley continue to please and were offered in the form of an extensive carte supplemented by a frequently changing fixed-price menu. A well executed ravioli of seabass served with a light fennel sauce proved a good choice as a first course. A main course of local Ludlow venison, marinated in Beaujolais then pan fried, was beautifully presented and served with an excellent blueberry sauce and accompanied by two pear and cinnamon croquettes. A pudding of whole baked banana served in its skin with a creamy banana mousse and a mint syrup was no less interesting and made a refreshing change.
14 en suite (bth) (4 fmly) No smoking in 3 bedrooms CTV in all bedrooms Night porter 85P Croquet lawn Jacuzzi/spa No children 3yrs Xmas English, French & Italian Cuisine V meals Tea pm No smoking in restaurant Last d 10.15pm
ROOMS: (incl. bkfst) s £55-£90; d £85-£120 * **LB**
MEALS: Lunch £9-£14.50&alc Dinner fr £18.50&alc
CONF: Thtr 250 Class 180 Board 128 Del from £99
CARDS:

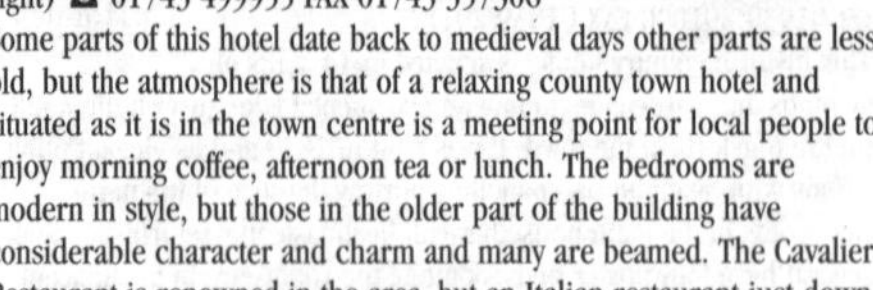

★★★ 68% ***Prince Rupert***
County Hotels
Butcher Row SY1 1UQ (follow signs Railway Station into town centre past St Mary's church and turn right) ☎ 01743 499955 FAX 01743 357306
Some parts of this hotel date back to medieval days other parts are less old, but the atmosphere is that of a relaxing county town hotel and situated as it is in the town centre is a meeting point for local people to enjoy morning coffee, afternoon tea or lunch. The bedrooms are modern in style, but those in the older part of the building have considerable character and charm and many are beamed. The Cavalier Restaurant is renowned in the area, but an Italian restaurant just down the street is also owned by the hotel and is an alternative eating option. Cars can be parked by hotel staff, on request.
65 en suite (bth) (4 fmly) CTV in all bedrooms Lift Night porter 60P Games room English, French & Italian Cuisine V meals Coffee am Tea pm Last d 10.15pm
CARDS:

★★★ 65% **Lord Hill**
Abbey Foregate SY2 6AX (from M54 take A5, at 1st rbt left then right into London Rd. At next rbt (Lord Hill Column) take 3rd exit for hotel on left) ☎ 01743 232601 FAX 01743 369734
Named after the famous memorial column of Lord Hill that stands nearby this is a long-established hotel that has been considerably improved over recent years. Most of the bedrooms are located in a nearby lodge and these provide sound facilities. Extensive function suites are available and there is a choice of restaurants. The Roland restaurant serves more formal meals and the popular Rowlys bar offers less expensive options. These areas together with the foyer lounge area are attractively furnished and decorated.
10 en suite (bth/shr) 24 annexe en suite (bth/shr) CTV in all bedrooms STV Night porter 120P Xmas Continental Cuisine V meals Coffee am Tea pm Last d 10pm
ROOMS: (incl. bkfst) s £49-£52; d £64-£69 * **LB**
OFF-PEAK: (incl. bkfst) s fr £41; d fr £61
MEALS: Lunch fr £11.95&alc Dinner fr £15.95&alc
CONF: Thtr 300 Class 120 Board 150 Del from £65
CARDS:

★★★ 64% **Rowton Castle**
Halfway House SY5 9EP (8m W off A458 Shrewsbury to Welshpool road) ☎ 01743 884044 FAX 01743 884949
This impressive property stands in extensive grounds and formal gardens five miles west of Shrewsbury, set back from the A458 road to Welshpool. Parts of the present building date back to 1696, additions being made during the 19th century. The public areas retain much of their original charm with panelled walls in the restaurant and period-style furnishings. The bedrooms vary in size and style, but all have modern equipment and en suite facilities. Rooms are available for functions, conferences and private dinner parties, and a small shop sells crafts and souvenirs.
19 en suite (bth/shr) (2 fmly) CTV in all bedrooms 100P Croquet lawn Private leisure complex in grounds Xmas English & Continental Cuisine V meals Coffee am Tea pm No smoking in restaurant Last d 9.30pm
ROOMS: (incl. bkfst) s fr £55; d fr £69.50 * **LB**
MEALS: Lunch fr £9.95 Dinner fr £17.50&alc*
CONF: Thtr 150 Class 70 Board 70 Del from £95
CARDS:

See advertisement on opposite page

★★★ 62% **The Lion**
REGAL A Collection of Individual Hotels
Wyle Cop SY1 1UY ☎ 01743 353107
FAX 01743 352744
Charles Dickens and other celebrities have stayed at this 14th-century former coaching inn, which is located in the centre of town, just over the English Bridge. Despite modernisation the hotel retains much of its historic charm and character. Unfortunately some of its elegance has faded, especially in the upstairs corridors, but original beams, ornate carvings, open fires in winter and the impressive Adams-style ballroom help to create a warm and hospitable atmosphere.
59 en suite (bth/shr) (3 fmly) No smoking in 24 bedrooms CTV in all bedrooms Lift Night porter 70P Xmas Traditional Cuisine V meals Coffee am Tea pm No smoking in restaurant Last d 9.30pm
ROOMS: s fr £59; d fr £69 **LB**
OFF-PEAK: s £40-£50; d £50-£59
MEALS: Lunch fr £2.25&alc Dinner £10.95-£21.95alc*
CONF: Thtr 200 Class 80 Board 60 Del from £60
CARDS:

★★ 64% **Abbots Mead**
9 St Julian's Friars SY1 1XL (first left after English Bridge coming into Shrewsbury from S) ☎ 01743 235281 FAX 01743 369133
Tucked away and within easy walking distance of the town centre, this

contd.

is a Grade II listed building. It provides small but pretty bedrooms and these are well equipped with modern amenities. A cosy bar and adjoining foyer lounge area is available for guests and food comes by way of a daily fixed price menu and a larger carte choice. The hotel is run by the friendly Bailey family who, together with local staff, offer a warm welcome to their guests.
14 en suite (shr) CTV in all bedrooms 10P Traditional English and Continental Cuisine V meals Coffee am Tea pm Last d 9pm
ROOMS: (incl. bkfst) s £35.90; d £49.90 * **LB**
OFF-PEAK: (incl. bkfst) s fr £34; d fr £48
MEALS: Dinner £13&alc*
CARDS:

★★64% **Lion & Pheasant**
49-50 Wyle Cop SY1 1XJ (town centre, by English Bridge, 2m from M54 motorway link)
☎ 01743 236288 FAX 01743 244475

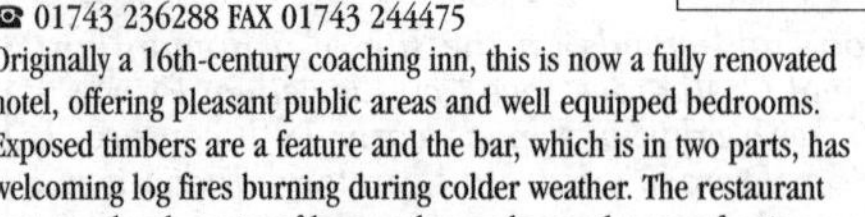

Originally a 16th-century coaching inn, this is now a fully renovated hotel, offering pleasant public areas and well equipped bedrooms. Exposed timbers are a feature and the bar, which is in two parts, has welcoming log fires burning during colder weather. The restaurant captures the character of bygone days and a good range of eating options are available. There are several meeting rooms and an added bonus is the secure car park.
19 rms (17 bth/shr) (1 fmly) CTV in all bedrooms No dogs (ex guide dogs) 20P English & Continental Cuisine V meals Coffee am No smoking in restaurant Last d 9.30pm
ROOMS: (incl. bkfst) s £28.50-£45; d £57-£60 **LB**
MEALS: Lunch fr £8.50 Dinner fr £14&alc*
CONF: Thtr 35 Class 20 Board 20 Del from £65
CARDS:

See advertisement on opposite page

★★64% **Shelton Hall**
Shelton SY3 8BH (2m NW A5) ☎ 01743 343982
FAX 01743 241515
Closed Xmas Day & Boxing Day
The attractive grounds and gardens of this large old house contain examples of rare trees, some of them as much as 300 years old. Friendly owners run the hotel in informal style and offer a range of bedrooms which includes one at ground level as well as family rooms. Public areas are made up of two bars, a pleasant, traditionally furnished restaurant and a function room which can cater for up to 50 delegates. There is ample car parking space.
10 rms (9 bth/shr) (2 fmly) CTV in all bedrooms No dogs 50P No coaches English & Continental Cuisine V meals Coffee am Last d 8.30pm
ROOMS: (incl. bkfst) s £47; d £64 * **LB**
MEALS: Lunch £10.50-£11.50 Dinner £17*
CONF: Thtr 50 Class 24 Board 24 Del from £75
CARDS:

See advertisement on opposite page

Travelodge
Bayston Hill Services SY3 0DA (A5/A49 junct)
☎ 01743 874256 FAX 01743 874256
This modern building offers accommodation in smart, spacious and well equipped bedrooms, suitable for family use, and all with en suite bathrooms. Meals may be taken at the nearby family restaurant. For information on room rates and to make a booking, call Roomline free of charge on 0800 850950. For more details about Travelodge, consult the Contents page under Hotel Groups.
40 en suite (bth/shr)

SIDMOUTH Devon Map 03 SY18

★★★★71% **Victoria**
Esplanade EX10 8RY (on Sidmouth seafront) (Brend)
☎ 01395 512651 FAX 01395 579154
This imposing Victorian building overlooks the sea from an elevated position in its own gardens. Conveniently located within walking distance of the town, it also offers easy access to many areas of interest and beauty on the East Devon coast road. Bedrooms are bright and well furnished, while the lounge area is particularly comfortable. A good selection of dishes makes up the daily-changing menus, and professional service is carried out by a team of friendly, uniformed staff.
61 en suite (bth/shr) (18 fmly) CTV in all bedrooms STV No dogs (ex guide dogs) Lift Night porter 104P No coaches Indoor swimming pool (heated) Outdoor swimming pool (heated) Tennis (hard) Snooker Sauna Solarium Pool table Putting green Jacuzzi/spa Wkly live entertainment ch fac Xmas English & French Cuisine V meals Coffee am Tea pm Last d 9pm
ROOMS: (incl. bkfst) s £62-£94; d £114-£204 * **LB**
OFF-PEAK: (incl. bkfst) s £59-£94; d £108-£204
MEALS: Lunch £11.95-£12.50&alc Dinner £20-£25&alc*
CONF: Thtr 60
CARDS:

See advertisement on opposite page

★★★★70% **Riviera**
The Esplanade EX10 8AY (leave M5 junc 30 & follow A3052)
☎ 01395 515201 FAX 01395 577775
This impeccably maintained Regency property is situated on the seafront overlooking Lyme Bay. The modern bedrooms vary in size but are all tastefully decorated and well equipped; the largest and most comfortable rooms enjoy sea views. Public areas are attractively appointed and facilities include a patio area, a function suite and covered parking.
27 en suite (bth/shr) (6 fmly) CTV in all bedrooms STV Lift Night porter Air conditioning 25P No coaches Wkly live entertainment Xmas English & French Cuisine V meals Coffee am Tea pm Last d 9pm
ROOMS: (incl. bkfst & dinner) s £71-£94; d £126-£172 * **LB**
OFF-PEAK: (incl. bkfst & dinner) s £59-£70; d £104-£126

contd.

MEALS: Lunch £12.50&alc Dinner £22&alc
CONF: Thtr 85 Class 60 Board 30
CARDS:

See advertisement on opposite page

★★★★69% **Belmont**
The Esplanade EX10 8RX (on Sidmouth seafront) (Brend)
☎ 01395 512555 FAX 01395 579101
Built as a private residence in the 18th-century this elegant property retains all the charm of the Georgian period. From its elevated position in several acres of landscaped grounds the Belmont Hotel enjoys glorious views of the sea, the esplanade and the town. There is a choice of comfortable lounges, one no-smoking and one with a bar, and a resident pianist often plays in the stylish restaurant. The bedrooms have been tastefully decorated, furnished with co-ordinating floral fabrics and equipped with modern comforts. A team of friendly staff extend a warm welcome and provide attentive services and extensive leisure facilities are available at the Victoria Hotel a short walk across the garden.
54 en suite (bth/shr) (10 fmly) CTV in all bedrooms STV No dogs (ex guide dogs) Lift Night porter 45P No coaches Putting green Wkly live entertainment ch fac Xmas English & French Cuisine V meals Coffee am Tea pm Last d 9pm
ROOMS: (incl. bkfst) s £54-£96; d £100-£192 * **LB**
MEALS: Lunch £11.50-£12.50&alc Dinner £20-£21.50&alc*
CONF: Thtr 50
CARDS: £

★★★77% **Westcliff**
Manor Rd EX10 8RU ☎ 01395 513252 FAX 01395 578203
Closed Nov-Mar
This delightful family-run hotel, situated in two acres of grounds close to the town centre, enjoys glorious views of the sea and the coastline of East Devon. The elegant lounges are spacious and comfortable, and the cocktail bar has access to a stylish terrace which leads to the outdoor heated pool and croquet lawn in the garden. A choice of dishes is offered from table d'hÙte and a la carte menus, served in the attractive restaurant where staff offer the perfect balance of friendliness and professionalism. Bedrooms provide modern facilities combined with tasteful decor and individual charm; several have balconies and share the wonderful view.
40 en suite (bth/shr) (15 fmly) No smoking in 1 bedroom CTV in all bedrooms STV No dogs Lift 40P No coaches Outdoor swimming pool (heated) Solarium Gym Pool table Croquet lawn Putting green Jacuzzi/spa Mini tennis English & Continental Cuisine V meals Coffee am Tea pm No smoking in restaurant Last d 8.45pm
ROOMS: (incl. bkfst & dinner) s £60.90-£76.65; d £116-£167.90 * **LB**
OFF-PEAK: (incl. bkfst & dinner) s £53.55-£57.75; d £102-£110
MEALS: Sunday Lunch £11 Dinner £19.50&alc
CARDS:

See advertisement on opposite page

★★★66% **Salcombe Hill House**
Beatlands Rd EX10 8JQ ☎ 01395 514697 & 514398
FAX 01395 578310
Closed Nov-Feb
This family run Victorian property is set on the edge of the town in its own grounds, with an outdoor swimming pool and grass tennis court. The public rooms are spacious and comfortably furnished. The bedrooms which are bright and airy and have lovely sea and country views, are being steadily upgraded.
30 en suite (bth/shr) (5 fmly) CTV in all bedrooms Lift Night porter 39P No coaches Outdoor swimming pool (heated) Tennis (grass) Putting green Games room No children 3yrs V meals Coffee am Tea pm Last d 8.30pm
ROOMS: (incl. bkfst) s £43; d £86 *
OFF-PEAK: (incl. bkfst & dinner) s £24; d £48

MEALS: Sunday Lunch £8.50 Dinner £13.75*
CARDS:

★★★65% **Fortfield**
Station Rd EX10 8NU ☎ 01395 512403 FAX 01395 512403
Situated close to the sea this handsome hotel commands impressive sea views. The bedrooms are well sized and are gradually being upgraded. There are extensive public areas including three comfortable lounges and a popular bar. There is a smart indoor swimming pool and sauna; also a table tennis room.
52 en suite (bth/shr) 3 annexe en suite (bth/shr) (7 fmly) CTV in all bedrooms Lift Night porter 60P Indoor swimming pool (heated) Sauna Solarium Health & beauty salon Games room Wkly live entertainment ch fac Xmas V meals Coffee am Tea pm No smoking in restaurant Last d 8.30pm
ROOMS: (incl. cont bkfst) s £31-£36; d £62-£72 * **LB**
OFF-PEAK: (incl. cont bkfst) s £20.50-£25.50; d £41-£51
MEALS: Bar Lunch £7-£8.50 Dinner £16.50*
CONF: Thtr 70 Class 40 Board 20 Del from £40
CARDS: £

★★★57% **Royal Glen**
Glen Rd EX10 8RW ☎ 01395 513221 & 513456 FAX 01395 514922
RS 2-31 Jan
Belonging to the Duke of Kent in the 19th-century, this historic hotel has many royal connections - indeed, the infant Queen Victoria celebrated her first Christmas here. Period furniture abounds in the comfortable bedrooms and cosy lounge. Bedrooms are named after members of the royal family - the most recent bearing the names of the Queen's children. Traditional home-cooked dishes are served, and the hotel also has a heated indoor swimming pool.
33 rms (32 bth/shr) (4 fmly) CTV in all bedrooms 24P No coaches Indoor swimming pool (heated) Xmas English & French Cuisine V meals Coffee am Tea pm No smoking in restaurant Last d 9pm
ROOMS: (incl. bkfst) s £28-£37; d £56-£74 * **LB**
MEALS: Lunch fr £8.50 High tea fr £5.50 Dinner fr £12.50*
CARDS: £

★★❀ 76% **Brownlands**

Sid Rd EX10 9AG (turn off A3052 at Sidford, at Fortescue/Sidford sign, hotel 1m on left)
☎ 01395 513053 FAX 01395 513053
Closed Jan-Feb RS Nov-Dec
Peacefully set in its own beautifully kept grounds on the wooded slopes of Salcombe Hill, this fine Victorian country hotel affords glorious views across the valley to the town and sea front. Brownlands is personally run by the Kendall-Torry Family and their friendly team of staff who provide attentive services. The bedrooms are smartly decorated and well equipped and a choice of comfortable, tastefully furnished lounges includes a cosy bar. Dinner is served in an elegant dining room where the five course set price menu offers imaginative, home cooked dishes. A recent meal started with a light pastry case filled with mushrooms in a cream sauce garnished with asparagus; this was followed by a richly flavoured pea and ham soup, and a tasty liver and bacon casserole served with fresh vegetables was chosen as a main course. Summer pudding was our inspector's choice from the mouthwatering trolley of desserts.
14 en suite (bth/shr) (1 fmly) CTV in all bedrooms 25P No coaches Tennis (hard) Putting green No children 8yrs Xmas International Cuisine V meals Coffee am Tea pm No smoking in restaurant Last d 8pm
ROOMS: (incl. bkfst & dinner) d £101.40-£113.50 * **LB**
OFF-PEAK: (incl. bkfst & dinner) s £53.30-£56.60; d £94.64-£106.60
MEALS: Sunday Lunch £10.75 Dinner £18.95*

See advertisement on opposite page

★★71% **Mount Pleasant**
Salcombe Rd EX10 8JA (turn off A3052 at Sidford x-rds after one & quarter miles turn left into Salcombe Ln, hotel opposite Radway Cinema) ☎ 01395 514694
Closed Dec-Feb
This small private hotel, situated close to the centre of the town and the sea front, offers comfortable accommodation and a relaxed atmosphere in a Georgian building which has been sympathethcially modernised to retain character. The intimate dining room features a short table d'hÙte menu and special requests are catered for. The resident proprietors, the Gleave family, give the Mount Pleasant a friendly, family atmosphere.
16 en suite (bth/shr) (2 fmly) No smoking in 12 bedrooms CTV in all bedrooms 20P No coaches Putting green No children 8yrs Coffee am Last d 7.30pm
ROOMS: (incl. bkfst & dinner) s £37.50-£42; d £75-£84 * **LB**
OFF-PEAK: (incl. bkfst & dinner) s £25-£30; d £50-£60
MEALS: Dinner £12.50-£14*

★★70% **Abbeydale**
Manor Rd EX10 8RP (enter town on A3052 towards seafront, 200 yds before Esplanade turn right into Manor Road)
☎ 01395 512060 FAX 515566
RS 1st wk Aug
A long-established, family-run hotel, the Abbeydale is set in attractive gardens within easy walking distance of the seafront and town centre. Bedrooms are equipped with every modern facility, and there are an attractive lounge and a separate bar-lounge where bar meals are available at lunch time. A short set-price menu is served in the no-smoking dining room.
17 en suite (bth/shr) (2 fmly) CTV in all bedrooms No dogs Lift 24P No coaches No children 4yrs Xmas English & French Cuisine Coffee am Tea pm No smoking in restaurant Last d 8pm
ROOMS: (incl. bkfst) s £25-£40; d £50-£80
MEALS: Lunch £10-£11 Dinner £13-£14

★★70% **Kingswood**
Esplanade EX10 8AX ☎ 01395 516367 FAX 01395 51385
Closed 17 Nov-28 Feb
The Kingswood, which has been owned and run by the Seward family for over forty years, is situated right on the seafront. The attractive Victorian house has been lovingly restored, to retain its charm. The bedrooms all have en suite facilities and pretty décor. There are two comfortable lounges and in the summer guests may enjoy the beautiful flower bedecked patio. The restaurant offers good honest cooking using local ingredients, and the friendly staff ensure that guests are well looked after.
26 rms (25 bth/shr) (7 fmly) CTV in all bedrooms Lift 16P N English & French Cuisine V meals Coffee am Tea pm No smoking in restaurant Last d 7.30pm
ROOMS: (incl. bkfst & dinner) s £30-£36; d £60-£72 * **LB**
OFF-PEAK: (incl. bkfst & dinner) s £25-£29; d £50-£58
MEALS: Bar Lunch £1.95-£4alc Dinner fr £14*
CARDS:

S

★★69% **Devoran**
Esplanade EX10 8AU (turn off B3052 at Bowd Inn follow Sidmouth sign for approx 2m turn left onto sea front, hotel is 50yds along at the centre of Esplanade) ☎ 01395 513151/0800 317171
FAX 01395 579929
Closed mid Nov-mid Mar
This well established family-run hotel, situated on the sea front, forms part of a Victorian terrace which affords fabulous views and easy access to the town centre and gardens. Bedrooms are tastefully decorated and furnished and equipped with modern comforts; many have balconies. Downstairs there is a comfortable lounge, a cosy cocktail bar and an elegant dining room where the menu is based on fresh produce. Alan and Val Clifford have been welcoming guests to the Devoran for 25 years.
23 rms (19 bth/shr) (4 fmly) CTV in all bedrooms Lift 4P Coffee am Tea pm No smoking in restaurant Last d 7.30pm
ROOMS: (incl. bkfst & dinner) s £30.50-£48; d £62-£96 * **LB**
MEALS: Bar Lunch £2.50-£5 High tea fr £4 Dinner £11.75-£14.75*
CARDS:

★★69% **Littlecourt**
Seafield Rd EX10 8HF ☎ 01395 515279
Closed 28 Oct-22 Dec & 29 Dec-29 Apr RS 23-28 Dec
This attractive Regency property is conveniently located for the seafront and town centre. Set in a quiet road in its own pretty gardens, the hotel has an outdoor pool and its own small car park. The bedrooms are bright and comfortable, and most have en suite facilities. There is a spacious lounge overlooking the garden and in the restaurant where traditional home-cooked meals are served, the staff provide friendly relaxed service.
20 rms (19 bth/shr) (3 fmly) No smoking in 7 bedrooms CTV in all bedrooms 17P Outdoor swimming pool (heated) Xmas English & French Cuisine V meals Coffee am Tea pm No smoking in restaurant Last d 8pm
ROOMS: (incl. bkfst & dinner) s £35.50-£48.50; d £71-£97 * **LB**
OFF-PEAK: (incl. bkfst & dinner) s fr £34.70; d fr £69.40
MEALS: Bar Lunch £2.10-£8.50 Dinner £15*
CONF: Thtr 45 Class 22
CARDS:

★★69% **Royal York & Faulkner**
Esplanade EX10 8AZ ☎ 01395 513043
Freephone 0800 220714 FAX 01395 577472
Closed Jan
This fine Regency hotel was the first purpose built hotel in Sidmouth and has been owned by the Hook family for several decades. The family are very much involved in all areas and create a warm friendly atmosphere. The bedrooms, many with sea views, are located on three floors reached by a lift. They are attractively decorated and offer modern en suite facilities. The public areas are spacious and well presented and include smart leisure facilities with a sauna, jacuzzi and fitness area.
68 en suite (bth/shr) (8 fmly) CTV in all bedrooms Lift 7P Snooker Sauna Solarium Gym Jacuzzi/spa Spa pool Indoor short mat bowls Wkly live entertainment Xmas English & French Cuisine V meals Coffee am Tea pm No smoking in restaurant Last d 8.30pm
ROOMS: (incl. bkfst & dinner) s £27.50-£50; d £55-£100 * **LB**
MEALS: Bar Lunch £7.20-£10alc Dinner £13
CARDS:

★★68% **The Salty Monk**
Church St, Sidford EX10 9QP (2m N A3052) ☎ 01395 513174
Centrally situated in the village of Sidford, this small hotel is convenient for Sidmouth and the many areas of great beauty on the east coast of Devon. Bedrooms are warm, comfortable and equipped with hospitality trays. Downstairs, there are a cosy lounge and bar, decorated and furnished in a cottage style in keeping with the building. The restaurant is most attractive and offers a choice of freshly prepared dishes.
8 rms (3 bth 1 shr) No smoking in all bedrooms CTV in all bedrooms 12P No coaches English & French Cuisine V meals Coffee am Tea pm No smoking in restaurant Last d 8.45pm
MEALS: Lunch £5.95-£8.50 Dinner £9.50-£15.95*
CARDS:

★★63% **Sidmount**
Station Rd EX10 8XJ (on B3176, 0.50m from esplanade)
☎ 01395 513432
Closed Nov-Feb
This fine Georgian hotel occupies a superb position overlooking the sea and well tended gardens. The bedrooms are comfortably furnished

and all have modern en suite facilities. The lounge has sea views and the dining room operates a self-service system; the huge dessert table is a speciality.
16 en suite (bth/shr) (1 fmly) No smoking in 14 bedrooms CTV in all bedrooms No dogs 17P No coaches No children 9yrs Coffee am Tea pm No smoking in restaurant Last d 7pm
ROOMS: (incl. bkfst & dinner) s £47; d £82-£86 * **LB**
OFF-PEAK: (incl. bkfst & dinner) s £30-£39; d £56-£66
MEALS: Dinner fr £12

See advertisement on this page

★★56% **Westbourne**
Manor Rd EX10 8RR (200yds from Connaught Gardens)
☎ 01395 513774 FAX 01395 512231
Closed Nov-Feb
This personally managed hotel is located in a quiet residential area of the town, close to the seafront, shops and gardens. Redecoration and improvements have taken place over recent months. In addition to the cosy drawing room, there is a bright sun lounge which overlooks the small, well tended gardens. Home-cooked meals are offered in the dining room from a daily-changing menu. The hotel is popular with older guests, many returning regularly, and staff are friendly and helpful.
12 rms (9 bth/shr) (2 fmly) CTV in all bedrooms 16P No coaches Croquet lawn V meals Coffee am Tea pm No smoking in restaurant Last d 7.30pm
ROOMS: (incl. bkfst) s £22.50-£33; d £45-£66 **LB**
MEALS: Bar Lunch £1.75-£7.50 Dinner £10.50

SILCHESTER Hampshire Map 04 SU66

★★★73% **Romans**
Little London Rd RG7 2PN ☎ 0118 970 0421
FAX 0118 970 0691
Closed 24 Dec-2 Jan
This privately owned Elizabethan house is set in its own grounds in the village of Silchester, between Basingstoke and Reading. The bedrooms, which are being steadily upgraded, are divided between the main house where they are spacious and individually styled, and those in a separate wing, which although attractively decorated are more compact. The public rooms include a comfortable lounge and a pleasant restaurant. Friendly and efficient staff are a strength here.

11 en suite (bth/shr) 14 annexe en suite (bth/shr) (1 fmly) No smoking in 2 bedrooms CTV in all bedrooms STV Night porter 60P No coaches Outdoor swimming pool (heated) V meals Coffee am Last d 9.30pm
ROOMS: (incl. bkfst) s £89; d £99-£135
OFF-PEAK: (incl. bkfst) s £70; d £85-£135
MEALS: Lunch £13.95-£16.95&alc Dinner £13.95-£16.95&alc*
CONF: Thtr 60 Class 15 Board 24 Del £115
CARDS:

SILLOTH Cumbria Map 11 NY15

★★★66% **The Skinburness**
CA5 4QY (2m NE on coast road) ☎ 016973 32332
FAX 016973 32549
A feature of this hotel is its spacious and well equipped bedrooms; several of these have recently been upgraded, arresting a decline that had been noted 12 months ago, and other improvements include the opening of a leisure centre with a pool, gym, sauna, sun beds and sun lounge. There are also a comfortable guests' lounge and a spacious lounge bar where buffet meals have been introduced.
25 en suite (bth/shr) (2 fmly) CTV in all bedrooms 70P Indoor swimming pool (heated) Sauna Solarium Gym Pool table Croquet lawn Jacuzzi/spa Wkly live entertainment ch fac Xmas English & French Cuisine V meals Coffee am Tea pm

ROOMS: (incl. bkfst & dinner) s fr £52.50; d fr £84 * **LB**
OFF-PEAK: (incl. bkfst) s fr £42.50; d fr £62.50
MEALS: Bar Lunch £2.50-£4.95 High tea £2.20-£2.75 Dinner £11.50-£18&alc
CONF: Thtr 120 Class 100 Board 60 Del from £42.50
CARDS:

★★62% **Golf**
Criffel St CA5 4AB (off B5302, in Silloth at t-junction turn left hotel overlooks the corner of the green) ☎ 016973 31438
FAX 016973 32582
Closed 25 Dec
This large family-run hotel lies in the centre of the town and attracts a mixed clientele. Of practical appearance, it offers mainly well proportioned bedrooms, some being furnished in a more modern style than others. There is a cosy and intimate restaurant with a good choice of dishes, or one can dine equally well in the spacious lounge bar.
22 en suite (bth/shr) (4 fmly) CTV in all bedrooms Snooker Pool table English & Continental Cuisine V meals Coffee am Tea pm No smoking area in restaurant Last d 9pm
ROOMS: (incl. bkfst) s £29.50-£44.50; d £44.50-£67 * **LB**
MEALS: Lunch fr £10 Dinner fr £16.50&alc*
CONF: Thtr 100 Class 40 Board 40 Del from £53.50
CARDS:

SIMONSBATH Somerset Map 03 SS73

★★76% **Simonsbath House**

TA24 7SH (situated on the B3223)
☎ 01643 831259 FAX 01643 831557
Closed Dec-Jan
This delightful 17th-century house, the first to be built in the forest of Exmoor, is surrounded by beautiful moorland scenery. Situated in the

contd.

valley of the River Barle which is still home to wild Red Deer, Simonsbath is an ideal position for exploring the wonders of Exmoor either on foot, on horse back or in the car. A relaxing atmosphere pervades throughout the house, which is still essentially a home, with welcoming owners and caring staff. Bedrooms are equipped with modern facilities and thoughtful extras like fresh fruit and bottled water and there is a choice of delightful lounges with original features and log fires on cooler evening. Imaginative dishes, prepared from fresh local ingredients, are served in the hotel's restful dining room whilst the more informal Boevey restaurant in the grounds, is available for lighter meals and snacks.
7 en suite (bth/shr) CTV in all bedrooms No dogs 40P No coaches No children 10yrs No smoking in restaurant Last d 8.30pm
ROOMS: (incl. bkfst) s £54-£64; d £92 **LB**
MEALS: Dinner £21
CARDS:

SITTINGBOURNE See Advertisement on opposite page

SIX MILE BOTTOM Cambridgeshire Map 05 TL55

★★★ 71% **Swynford Paddocks**

CB8 0UE (6m SW of Newmarket, on A1304)
☎ 01638 570234 FAX 01638 570283
Closed 2 days between Xmas & New Year
This elegant country house sits in a pleasant rural setting south-west of Newmarket. Well tended grounds and gardens surround the hotel, which offers a relaxing ambience in comfortable public rooms and attractive bedrooms leading off an impressive balustraded and galleried hall. Some rooms are huge and there are some sumptuous four-poster rooms. Staff provide courteous service and in the restaurant chef Patrick Collins provides an interesting selection of country Irish and French cooking.
15 en suite (bth/shr) CTV in all bedrooms 120P No coaches Tennis (hard) Croquet lawn Putting green Outdoor chess Wkly live entertainment English & Continental Cuisine V meals Coffee am Tea pm No smoking in restaurant Last d 9.30pm
ROOMS: (incl. bkfst) s £80-£105; d £117-£138 * **LB**
MEALS: Lunch fr £17.50&alc Dinner fr £23.95&alc*
CONF: Thtr 30 Board 22 Del from £108
CARDS:

SKEGNESS Lincolnshire Map 09 TF56

★★★ 62% **Crown**
Drummond Rd, Seacroft PE25 3AB (take A52 to town centre, hotel 1m from clock tower) ☎ 01754 610760 FAX 01754 610847
The Crown is quietly located in a pleasant residential area of the town, a stone's throw away from the dunes and sands beyond. It is a friendly hotel with enthusiastic young staff and a public bar with a lively atmosphere.
27 en suite (bth/shr) (7 fmly) STV No dogs (ex guide dogs) Lift Night porter 90P Indoor swimming pool (heated) English & French Cuisine V meals Coffee am Tea pm No smoking area in restaurant
CONF: Thtr 120 Class 130 Board 120
CARDS:

See advertisement on opposite page

★★ 62% ***North Shore***
North Shore Rd PE25 1DN ☎ 01754 763298 FAX 01754 761902
This hotel and golf course is found to the north of the town and stands next to the beach. It caters mainly for the golfing fraternity and also features a golfing shop, whilst the modern bedrooms which vary in size are pleasantly furnished and decorated. The public rooms which are comfortable include a cosy lounge, a pleasant bar and a dining room where a satisfactory choice of dishes is available.
30 en suite (bth/shr) 3 annexe en suite (bth/shr) (4 fmly) CTV in all bedrooms No dogs (ex guide dogs) Night porter 120P Golf 18 Tennis (hard) Snooker Putting green English & Continental Cuisine V meals Coffee am Tea pm Last d 9pm
CARDS:

SKIPTON North Yorkshire Map 07 SD95

★★★ 67% **Randell's**
Keighley Rd, Snaygill BD23 2TA (on A629, 1m from town)
☎ 01756 700100 FAX 01756 700107
(Rosette awarded for dinner only)
This large stone-built hotel is situated just off the by-pass and provides spacious and comfortable accommodation. There are two good lounges and the Waterside Restaurant serves well produced dinners overlooking the Leeds and Liverpool canal. Bedrooms are very well equipped and include trouser presses and satellite television. The hotel offers a well equipped leisure centre which includes a pool and squash courts. There are also extensive conference facilities and children have their own playzone centre.
76 en suite (bth/shr) (10 fmly) No smoking in 14 bedrooms CTV in all bedrooms STV Lift Night porter 200P Indoor swimming pool (heated) Squash Sauna Solarium Gym Pool table Whirlpool spa Steam room ch fac Xmas European Cuisine V meals Coffee am Tea pm No smoking in restaurant Last d 10pm
ROOMS: (incl. bkfst) s £76-£78; d £86-£88 **LB**
OFF-PEAK: (incl. bkfst) s £50-£52; d £65-£67
MEALS: Sunday Lunch £10.95 Dinner £15.95-£16.10&alc
CONF: Thtr 450 Class 180 Board 120 Del from £90
CARDS:

★★ 64% **Herriots**
Broughton Rd BD23 1RT (off A59, opposite station)
☎ 01756 792781 FAX 01756 792781
Formerly the station hotel known as The Midland, this hotel has been extensively refurbished by the resident owner and now provides good all round standards of accommodation. The bedrooms are well equipped and have been prettily decorated whilst the busy bar is traditional in style. A good range of dishes is available either in the bar or the dining room. Service is attentive throughout and solid Yorkshire hospitality is provided. It is only a short walk from the town, and is next to the Leeds Liverpool canal.
13 en suite (bth/shr) (2 fmly) CTV in all bedrooms 25P Bar billiards Wkly live entertainment International Cuisine V meals No smoking area in restaurant Last d 9.30pm
ROOMS: (incl. bkfst) s £45-£55; d £50-£65 * **LB**
MEALS: Bar Lunch £4.50-£12 Dinner £6-£14
CONF: Thtr 35 Class 15 Board 20
CARDS:

Travelodge

Travelodge

Gargrave Rd BD23 1UD (A65/A59 roundabout)
☎ 01756 798091 FAX 01756 798091
This modern building offers accommodation in smart, spacious and well equipped bedrooms, suitable for family use, and all with en suite bathrooms. Meals may be taken at the nearby family restaurant. For information on room rates and to make a booking, call Roomline free of charge on 0800 850950. For more details about Travelodge, consult the Contents page under Hotel Groups.
32 en suite (bth/shr)

SLEAFORD Lincolnshire Map 08 TF04

★★ 70% **Carre Arms**
1 Mareham Ln NG34 7JP (take A153 to Sleaford, hotel on right at level crossing) ☎ 01529 303156 FAX 01529 303139
This comfortable and characterful hotel, which has been totally refurbished in the last few years, is conveniently situated, opposite the station and close to the centre of town. The fresh, spotlessly clean bedrooms, all en suite, are attractively decorated with colourful soft

furnishings and dark pine furniture. A very good range of interesting dishes is available in the Brasserie or the more formal restaurant, and whilst there is no lounge area, there are two comfortable bars and an interesting covered courtyard. The service provided by the young team of staff is cheerful and enthusiastic.
13 en suite (bth/shr) (1 fmly) CTV in all bedrooms No dogs (ex guide dogs) 100P English & Continental Cuisine V meals Coffee am Tea pm
ROOMS: (incl. bkfst) s fr £45; d fr £65 *
MEALS: Lunch fr £9.50
CARDS:

Travelodge

Holdingham NG34 8NP (1m N, at roundabout A17/A15) ☎ 01529 414752 FAX 01529 414752
This modern building offers accommodation in smart, spacious and well equipped bedrooms, suitable for family use, and all with en suite bathrooms. Meals may be taken at the nearby family restaurant. For information on room rates and to make a booking, call Roomline free of charge on 0800 850950. For more details about Travelodge, consult the Contents page under Hotel Groups.
40 en suite (bth/shr)

SLOUGH Berkshire Map 04 SU97
See also Heathrow Airport

★★★★ 67% **Copthorne Slough/Windsor**

MILLENNIUM & COPTHORNE HOTELS

400 Cippenham Ln SL1 2YE (leave M4 junct 6 towards Slough at next rdbt turn left & left again for hotel entrance) ☎ 01753 516222 FAX 01753 516237
Conveniently situated for junction 6 of the M4, this purpose-built modern hotel offers a high standard of accommodation, spacious bedrooms being attractively furnished and thoughtfully equipped.

contd.

Public areas, too, feature a good range of facilities, and there are a smart leisure centre and shop as well as a choice of eating options which includes the informal Verandah. Our one rosette award is for the main restaurant, Reflections, where executive chef Graham Riley offers modern French cuisine in intimate surroundings.
219 en suite (bth/shr) (19 fmly) No smoking in 55 bedrooms CTV in all bedrooms STV No dogs (ex guide dogs) Lift Night porter Air conditioning 320P Indoor swimming pool (heated) Snooker Sauna Solarium Gym Jacuzzi/spa Turkish bath Xmas International Cuisine V meals Coffee am Tea pm No smoking area in restaurant Last d 10pm
ROOMS: s fr £130; d fr £140 * **LB**
OFF-PEAK: s fr £70; d fr £70
MEALS: Lunch £14.50-£18.50 Dinner £18.50&alc*
CONF: Thtr 250 Class 160 Board 18 Del from £155
CARDS:

★★★68% **Heathrow Ambassador**
London Rd, Brands Hill SL3 8QB (approx 0.33m from junc 5 on M4, on right heading towards Colnbrook, behind Texaco garage)
☎ 01753 684001 FAX 01753 685767
Though rather uninspiring from the outside, while stepping over the threshold one is pleasantly surprised to find a smart modern hotel maintained throughout in immaculate condition. Bedrooms are spacious and serve the requirements of business travellers very well. There is a bright and airy restaurant where carvery meals are the main focus, some excellent conference facilities and a smart lobby lounge. Courtesy transport is available to the airport.
112 en suite (bth/shr) (11 fmly) No smoking in 14 bedrooms CTV in all bedrooms STV No dogs (ex guide dogs) Lift 130P Xmas V meals Coffee am Tea pm Last d 10pm
ROOMS: s £79.50-£89.50; d £87.50-£97.50 *
MEALS: Lunch £8.50-£10.50 Dinner £10.75-£14.75&alc*
CONF: Thtr 180 Class 150 Board 80 Del £115
CARDS:

★★★65% **Courtyard by Marriott Slough/ Windsor**

COURTYARD. Marriott

Church St, Chalvey SL1 2NH (from junct 6 of M4 follow A355 to roundabout, turn right hotel approx 50 yds on right) ☎ 01753 551551 FAX 01753 553333
This purpose-built modern hotel is conveniently located for junction 6 of the M4. It has a very good standard of spacious bedrooms which are well equipped and comfortably furnished. Public areas are more restricted but include a pleasant bar and an informal restaurant.
148 en suite (bth/shr) (73 fmly) No smoking in 72 bedrooms CTV in all bedrooms STV No dogs (ex guide dogs) Lift Night porter Air conditioning 162P Gym International Cuisine V meals Coffee am Tea pm Last d 10.30pm
ROOMS: s £77-£85; d £77-£85 * **LB**
OFF-PEAK: s fr £45; d fr £45
MEALS: Lunch £9.75-£14.25&alc Dinner £9.75-£14.25&alc*
CARDS:

★★62% ***King William***

TOBY

399 London Rd, Langley SL3 8PS
☎ 01753 544253 FAX 01753 581054
This old inn offers well equipped bedrooms in a mdern extension. Public areas include a bar and carvery restaurant, which serves traditional food and a selection of grills. Staff are friendly and attentive.
38 en suite (bth/shr) No smoking in 13 bedrooms CTV in all bedrooms No dogs (ex guide dogs) Night porter 100P V meals Coffee am Tea pm Last d 10pm
CARDS:

SOLIHULL West Midlands Map 07 SP17

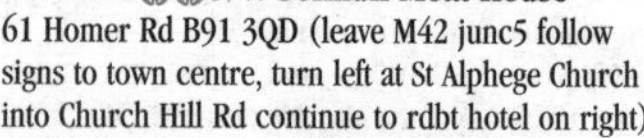

★★★★67% **Solihull Moat House**

MOAT HOUSE

61 Homer Rd B91 3QD (leave M42 junc5 follow signs to town centre, turn left at St Alphege Church into Church Hill Rd continue to rdbt hotel on right)
☎ 0121 623 9988 FAX 0121 711 2696
A large modern hotel is situated in the town centre with landscaped gardens and a spacious car park. Well equipped bedrooms include some executive-style rooms, and decor ranges from English to French and Chinese in inspiration. Pride of place is given to Brookes Restaurant which provides a high standard of British and international cuisine. Head Chef Barrie Corrich's undoubted skills are evident in his ballotine of chicken filled with sweetbreads, and the timbale of oak-smoked salmon stuffed with scrambled egg. Other attractions include an excellent leisure club, aand business and conference facilities. There is also a popular bar, Little J's.
115 en suite (bth/shr) (6 fmly) No smoking in 42 bedrooms CTV in all bedrooms STV Lift Night porter 164P Indoor swimming pool (heated) Sauna Solarium Gym Jacuzzi/spa Beauty salon International Cuisine V meals Coffee am Tea pm No smoking area in restaurant Last d 10pm
ROOMS: s £99-£125; d £99-£135 * **LB**
CONF: Thtr 200 Class 116 Board 102
CARDS:

★★★★62% **Regency**

REGAL A Collection of Individual Hotels

Stratford Rd, Shirley B90 4EB (beside A34, 0.5m from junct 4 of M42) ☎ 0121 745 6119
FAX 0121 733 3801
Continued upgrading and investment at this popular hotel which is very conveniently located for the motor ways, NEC and city centre. Extended over the years it provides a mix of older and more compact newer rooms, all well furnished and equipped. Public areas include a new leisure centre, restaurant and choice of bars in which Morrisey's Irish bar provides a lively and popular alternative.
112 en suite (bth/shr) (10 fmly) No smoking in 17 bedrooms CTV in all bedrooms STV Lift Night porter 275P Indoor swimming pool (heated) Sauna Solarium Gym Jacuzzi/spa Beauty & health salon Wkly live entertainment Xmas International Cuisine V meals Coffee am Tea pm No smoking area in restaurant
ROOMS: s £48-£95; d £63-£105 * **LB**
OFF-PEAK: s £41-£48; d £50-£63

MEALS: Lunch £14.95*
CONF: Thtr 180 Class 80 Board 60 Del from £110
CARDS:

★★★65% **St John's Swallow**
651 Warwick Rd B91 1AT ☎ 0121 711 3000
FAX 0121 705 6629
Much extended since its days as a private residence, this conference and banqueting hotel is conveniently situated for the M42, the NEC and the airport. Bedroom standards vary, the best being the refurbished executive rooms. Public areas are currently rather dated but are scheduled for redevelopment in the near future. There are a smart leisure centre, extensive function facilities and plentiful parking.
177 en suite (bth/shr) (6 fmly) No smoking in 40 bedrooms CTV in all bedrooms STV Lift Night porter 380P Indoor swimming pool (heated) Sauna Solarium Gym Jacuzzi/spa Beauty therapist Wkly live entertainment Xmas English & French Cuisine V meals Coffee am Tea pm No smoking area in restaurant Last d 9.45pm
ROOMS: (incl. bkfst) s £95; d £105 * **LB**
MEALS: Lunch £13.50-£14.50&alc Dinner £19.95*
CONF: Thtr 700 Class 350 Board 60 Del £140
CARDS:

★★56% **Flemings**
141 Warwick Rd, Olton B92 7HW (on A41, near Olton Station)
☎ 0121 706 0371 FAX 0121 706 4494
Closed 24-28 Dec
Situated on the A41 at Olton, this privately owned hotel has been converted from four adjoining houses. It is dated in parts but there are plans to upgrade the hotel soon. Its strength lies in its staff who provide warm and friendly service.
77 en suite (bth/shr) (6 fmly) No smoking in 2 bedrooms CTV in all bedrooms Night porter 80P Snooker International Cuisine V meals Coffee am Tea pm Last d 10pm
ROOMS: (incl. bkfst) s £32-£45; d £43-£56 * **LB**
OFF-PEAK: (incl. bkfst) s £20-£40; d fr £40
MEALS: Lunch fr £6.50&alc High tea fr £5 Dinner fr £8.50*
CONF: Thtr 20 Del from £60
CARDS:

Travel Inn
Stratford Rd, Shirley B90 4EP (on A34)
☎ 0121 744 2942 FAX 0121 733 7075
Purpose-built accommodation, offering spacious, well equipped bedrooms, all with en suite bathrooms. Meals may be taken at the nearby family restaurant. For more information about Travel Inns, consult the Contents page under Hotel Groups.
51 en suite (bth/shr)
ROOMS: d £35.50 *

Travel Inn
Stratford Rd, Hockley Heath B94 6NX
☎ 01564 782144 FAX 01564 783197
Purpose-built accommodation, offering spacious, well equipped bedrooms, all with en suite bathrooms. Meals may be taken at the nearby family restaurant. For more information about Travel Inns, consult the Contents page under Hotel Groups.
40 en suite (bth/shr)
ROOMS: d £35.50 *

SONNING Berkshire Map 04 SU77

★★★ ❀❀ 68% **French Horn**
RG4 6TN (turn left off A4 into Sonning follow road through village over bridge, hotel on right, car park on left) ☎ 01734 692204 FAX 01734 442210
Closed 26-30 Dec

contd.

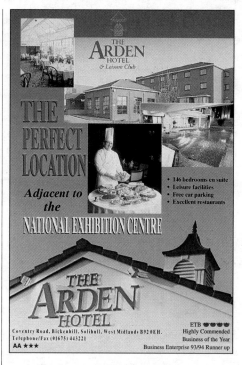

This family-run restaurant with rooms is located in a prime position on the River Thames. The emphasis here is undeniably on the restaurant, where classical French meals are prepared to a high standard and served in traditional fashion. Special mention should be made of the French wine list, which boasts several vintages of first growth clarets. Bedrooms are spacious, some have river views, and there are four large self-contained cottage rooms across the road from the hotel.
12 en suite (bth/shr) 4 annexe en suite (bth/shr) CTV in all bedrooms No dogs (ex guide dogs) 40P No coaches English & French Cuisine V meals Last d 9.30pm
ROOMS: (incl. bkfst) s £90-£120; d £95-£140
MEALS: Lunch £19.50&alc Dinner £30&alc
CONF: Board 20
CARDS: 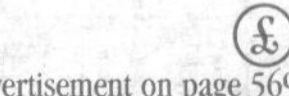

See advertisement on page 569

SOURTON CROSS Devon Map 02 SX59

Travelodge
EX20 4LY (4m W, at junct of A30/A386)
☎ 01837 52124 FAX 01837 52124
This modern building offers accommodation in smart, spacious and well equipped bedrooms, suitable for family use, and all with en suite bathrooms. Meals may be taken at the nearby family restaurant. For information on room rates and to make a booking, call Roomline free of charge on 0800 850950. For more details about Travelodge, consult the Contents page under Hotel Groups.
32 en suite (bth/shr)

SOUTHAMPTON Hampshire Map 04 SU41
See also Shedfield

★★★★★ 70% **De Vere Grand Harbour**

West Quay Rd SO15 1AG (leave M27 junc3 or M3 junc 13 follow Waterfront signs to West Quay Rd)
☎ 01703 633033 FAX 01703 633066
This stunningly modern building stands close to the quayside and benefits from its own large secure car park. The public areas are smart and character has been introduced by the clever use of natural light combined with fresh flower displays, wood panelling and marble. There is an impressive leisure area which includes a good sized pool, a range of conference rooms and a business centre. The hotel has 2 restaurants, Brewsters, which is marketed as the house restaurant, and Allertons, specialising in fish. Bedrooms have been tastefully decorated and furnished, and many have waterfront views and balconies.
172 en suite (bth/shr) No smoking in 139 bedrooms CTV in all bedrooms STV No dogs (ex guide dogs) Lift Night porter 200P Indoor swimming pool (heated) Snooker Sauna Solarium Gym Jacuzzi/spa Steam room Beauty treatments Xmas Continental Cuisine V meals Coffee am Tea pm No smoking area in restaurant Last d 10.30pm
ROOMS: (incl. bkfst) s £115-£125; d £125-£145 **LB**
MEALS: Lunch £12.75-£15.75&alc Dinner £23.50&alc
CONF: Thtr 500 Class 270 Board 48 Del from £140
CARDS:

★★★ 68% **The Woodlands Lodge**
Bartley Rd, Ashurst SO40 7GN ☎ 01703 292257 FAX 01703 293090
This beautifully restored 18th century hunting lodge is set in four acres of attractive gardens and woodland on the edge of the Forest, yet just ten minutes drive from the heart of Southampton and the major roads. The bedrooms are spacious and offer high quality individual decor, all rooms have luxury ensuite facilities with jacuzzi baths. There is a comfortable lounges and the cosy bar opens into the pretty garden. Proprietor Philippa Sherman offers good home-cooked food in the elegant dining room.
16 en suite (bth/shr) (2 fmly) CTV in all bedrooms 40P Jacuzzi/spa Xmas V meals Coffee am Tea pm No smoking in restaurant Last d 8pm
ROOMS: (incl. bkfst) s £69-£89; d £99-£129 * **LB**
MEALS: Bar Lunch fr £2.50 Dinner £19.95&alc*
CONF: Thtr 32 Class 20 Board 32 Del from £99
CARDS:

★★★ 63% **Novotel**

1 West Quay Rd SO15 1RA (turn right onto West Quay Rd at the end of A3024, hotel opposite Dock Gate 10 ☎ 01703 330550 FAX 01703 222158
Spacious, well equipped modern bedrooms are offered at the Novotel, all ideal for families and business guests. Each room has a queen-size double bed and sofa bed plus a good working surface. First, second and fourth floor rooms are now designated no-smoking. Le Grill restaurant is open throughout the day and room service is available between 6am and midnight. Indoor leisure amenities are provided, plus extensive conference and banqueting facilities.
121 en suite (bth/shr) (50 fmly) No smoking in 71 bedrooms CTV in all bedrooms STV Lift Night porter Air conditioning 300P Indoor swimming pool (heated) Sauna Gym International Cuisine V meals Coffee am Tea pm No smoking area in restaurant Last d mdnt
ROOMS: (incl. bkfst) s £59-£65; d £59-£80 * **LB**
MEALS: Lunch £10-£15 Dinner £11-£14&alc*
CARDS:

★★★ 63% **Southampton Park**

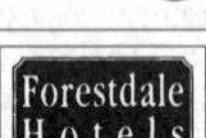

Cumberland Place SO15 2WY (hotel at northern end of the Inner Ring Rd opposite Watts Park & Civic Centre) ☎ 01703 343343 FAX 01703 332538
Closed 25 & 26 Dec nights
Prominently positioned opposite Watts Park in the city centre, this hotel offers a good leisure centre and extensive eating options. Bedrooms standards tend to vary but improvements are planned and all boast a good range of facilities. Parking is found in the multi-storey at the rear of the hotel.
72 en suite (bth/shr) (10 fmly) No smoking in 20 bedrooms CTV in all bedrooms STV Lift Night porter 8P Indoor swimming pool (heated) Sauna Solarium Gym Jacuzzi/spa Massage Jet Steam room English & French Cuisine V meals Coffee am Tea pm Last d 9.45pm
ROOMS: s £57.50-£67.50; d £67.50-£77.50 * **LB**
OFF-PEAK: (incl. bkfst & dinner) s £53.50-£58.50; d £90-£100
MEALS: Bar Lunch fr £1.65 Dinner fr £15.95*
CONF: Thtr 200 Class 60 Board 70 Del from £85
CARDS:

★★★ 61% **County**

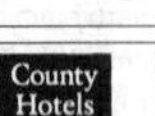
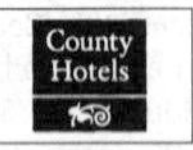

Highfield Ln, Portswood SO17 1AQ (take A335 follow signs for Portswood & univrsity) ☎ 01703 359955 FAX 01703 583910
Set close to the university and within easy reach of the motorway, this hotel attracts conference and business guests during the week. Bedrooms are modern and well furnished, though some are due for redecoration. There is a pub atmosphere in the Cityside Bar, and the restaurant offers a choice of menus in addition to full room service at meal times. Other attractions are plenty of free parking and a mini gym and sauna.
66 en suite (bth/shr) (6 fmly) No smoking in 3 bedrooms CTV in all bedrooms Night porter 100P Sauna Gym Xmas International Cuisine V meals Coffee am Tea pm Last d 10pm
ROOMS: s fr £60; d fr £70 **LB**
OFF-PEAK: s fr £40; d fr £50
MEALS: Lunch £11.45-£15.55&alc Dinner £11.45-£15.55&alc
CARDS: 

S

★★★58% **The Dolphin**

REGAL
A Collection of Individual Hotels

High St SO9 2DS ☎ 01703 339955
FAX 01703 333650
This city centre hotel offers comfortable, character public rooms and a relaxing atmosphere. Bedrooms are well equipped and like the public areas are in the process of gradual upgrading and redecoration. Bar snacks provide an alternative to the restaurant's more formal cuisine. Other facilities include a number of function rooms and a private car park.
73 en suite (bth/shr) (2 fmly) No smoking in 14 bedrooms CTV in all bedrooms Lift Night porter Air conditioning 90P Xmas English & Continental Cuisine V meals Coffee am Tea pm No smoking in restaurant Last d 9.30pm
ROOMS: s fr £55; d fr £65 * **LB**
MEALS: Sunday Lunch fr £9.95 Dinner £15.95&alc*
CONF: Thtr 90 Class 30 Board 45 Del £80
CARDS:

★★67% **Busketts Lawn**
174 Woodlands Rd, Woodlands SO40 7GL (A35 W of city through Ashurst, over railway bridge, sharp right into Woodlands Road)
☎ 01703 292272 & 292077 FAX 01703 292487
This friendly Victorian hotel has been run by the Hayes family for many years and has a loyal following. The bedrooms are comfortable and attractively decorated, with some thoughtful extra touches. The public areas include a cosy guests' lounge, a small bar and a traditional dining room. There is a large function room overlooking the pretty garden: private functions and dinner dances are a speciality here. The swimming pool makes it a popular choice for families.
14 en suite (bth/shr) (3 fmly) CTV in all bedrooms 50P Outdoor swimming pool (heated) Croquet lawn Putting green Football ch fac Xmas English & Continental Cuisine V meals Coffee am Tea pm No smoking in restaurant Last d 8.30pm
ROOMS: (incl. bkfst) s £37.50; d £75 * **LB**
MEALS: Bar Lunch £4.25-£7.50&alc High tea £5.50-£7.50&alc Dinner £16&alc
CONF: Thtr 150 Class 75 Board 40 Del from £75
CARDS:

★★63% **Elizabeth House**
43-44 The Avenue SO17 1XP (on the A33, left hand side travelling towards city centre) ☎ 01703 224327 FAX 01703 224327
This popular city centre hotel is personally run and conveniently located for the airport, docks and Cherbourg ferry. The bedrooms are being steadily upgraded with half of them now very attractively decorated and furnished. There is a cellar bar with a snack menu or guests may dine in the more formal setting of the elegant restaurant.
24 rms (20 bth/shr) CTV in all bedrooms 20P No coaches V meals Coffee am Last d 9pm
ROOMS: (incl. bkfst) s fr £30; d fr £40 * **LB**
MEALS: Lunch fr £10alc Dinner fr £10alc*
CARDS:

★★63% ***Rosida Garden***
25-27 Hill Ln SO15 5AB ☎ 01703 228501 FAX 01703 635501
This popular family-run hotel is ideally located in the city just minutes from the major roads, the docks and ferry ports. The bedrooms all have en suite facilities and are bright and well equipped. There is a smart dining room serving a hearty breakfast and daily changing evening meals. The hotel also has a licensed bar and TV lounge.
27 en suite (bth/shr) (6 fmly) CTV in all bedrooms Night porter 50P Outdoor swimming pool (heated) Coffee am Tea pm
CARDS:

★★61% ***Hotel Ibis***

West Quay Rd, Western Esplanade SO15 1RA
(opposite Central Railway Station) ☎ 01703 634463
FAX 01703 223273

Situated close to the docks and the M27, this modern, budget hotel offers bright, well equipped bedrooms. There are double, twin and interconnecting rooms and recent improvements to the comfort include quilted bedspreads and king size beds. The food and beverage operation is low key with a short choice of hot meals in the evening, an all day snack menu and entirely self-service breakfast buffet.
93 en suite (bth/shr) (8 fmly) No smoking in 27 bedrooms CTV in all bedrooms STV Lift Night porter 280P English & French Cuisine V meals Coffee am Tea pm Last d 10.30pm
CARDS:

★★61% **Star**
26 High St SO14 2NA (enter city from A33 follow signs for city centre at Isle of Wight ferry terminal turn into High St, hotel on right just beyond zebra crossing) ☎ 01703 339939 FAX 01703 335291
Closed 25-26 Dec
This city centre hotel offers a popular public bar serving a range of snacks at lunchtime and in the evening, or for a more formal option there is the restaurant with its carvery lunch and a full carte at night. The bedrooms vary in size and some, which have been recently refurbished are bright and well presented. There are several function rooms including a self contained conference suite.
43 rms (37 bth/shr) No smoking in 7 bedrooms CTV in 45 bedrooms Lift Night porter 30P English & French Cuisine V meals Coffee am Tea pm No smoking area in restaurant Last d 9.30pm
ROOMS: (incl. bkfst) s £42.50-£52.50; d £52.50-£62.50 * **LB**
OFF-PEAK: (incl. bkfst) s £34.50-£52.50; d £44.50-£62.50
MEALS: Lunch £12-£15&alc High tea £3.20-£6alc Dinner £12-£15&alc*
CONF: Thtr 70 Class 25 Board 32
CARDS:

Forte Posthouse Southampton

Herbert Walker Av SO15 0HJ (from M27 follow signs for 'Western Docks 1-10'. Posthouse situated next to Dock Gate 8) ☎ 01703 330777 FAX 01703 332510

Suitable for both the business and leisure traveller, this bright hotel provides modern accommodation in well equipped bedrooms with en suite bathrooms. For more details about Forte Posthouse hotels, consult the Contents page for the section on Hotel Groups.

128 en suite (bth/shr)
ROOMS: s £69; d £69 *
CONF: Thtr 250 Class 80 Board 50 Del £99

Hilton National Southampton

Bracken Place, Chilworth SO16 3RB
☎ 01703 702700 FAX 01703 767233

This is a bright, modern hotel, with an informal restaurant, aimed at both the business and leisure guest. All bedrooms have en suite bathrooms and a range of modern facilities. For more information about Hilton National hotels, consult the Contents page under Hotel Groups.

135 en suite (bth/shr)
ROOMS: s £92-£110; d £92-£110
CONF: Thtr 220 Class 100 Board 40 Del from £95

Travel Inn

Romsey Rd, Nursling SO16 0XJ (off A3057)
☎ 01703 732262 FAX 01703 740947

Purpose-built accommodation, offering spacious, well equipped bedrooms, all with en suite bathrooms. Meals may be taken at the nearby family restaurant. For more information about Travel Inns, consult the Contents page under Hotel Groups.

32 en suite (bth/shr)
ROOMS: d £35.50 *

SOUTH CAVE East Riding of Yorkshire Map 08 SE93

★★65% Fox & Coney Inn

Market Place HU15 2AT (from A63, main Market Weighton to York road, then A1034 into village, close to Midland Bank) ☎ 01430 422275 FAX 01430 421552

An inviting coaching inn standing in the main street and offering a wide range of bar-style meals which are good value for money and are freshly cooked. The newly furnished bedrooms, whilst not large, are all well equipped and pleasantly decorated and furnished. The public areas consist of a large bar and as there is no lounge provided, guests may find comforts rather limited. The staff are friendly and helpful and provide a cheery style of service and there is a car park to the rear of the hotel.

8 en suite (bth/shr) (2 fmly) CTV in all bedrooms STV No dogs (ex guide dogs) 28P No coaches English & French Cuisine V meals Coffee am Tea pm Last d 10pm
ROOMS: s fr £33.50; d fr £42.50 * **LB**
OFF-PEAK: s fr £29.50; d fr £35.50
MEALS: Lunch £5-£10 Dinner £5-£10&alc*
CARDS:

Travelodge

Beacon Service Area HU15 1RZ (A63 eastbound)
☎ 01430 424455 FAX 01430 424455

This modern building offers accommodation in smart, spacious and well equipped bedrooms, suitable for family use, and all with en suite bathrooms. Meals may be taken at the nearby family restaurant. For information on room rates and to make a booking, call Roomline free of charge on 0800 850950. For more details about Travelodge, consult the Contents page under Hotel Groups.

40 en suite (bth/shr)

SOUTHEND-ON-SEA Essex Map 05 TQ88

★★★62% Balmoral

34 Valkyrie Rd, Westcliffe-on-Sea SS0 8BU (off A13)
☎ 01702 342947 FAX 01702 337828

Conveniently situated close to Westcliff Station and a short distance from the town centre and local attractions, the Balmoral was built around the turn of the century and has recently been completely refurbished to a high standard. The bedrooms are well equipped with every amenity and 24-hour room service. Sovereigns Restaurant offers à la carte and fixed-price dining with friendly and conscientious service. There is a small cocktail bar and smart reception sitting area, a furnished patio, and good car parking.

29 en suite (bth/shr) (4 fmly) CTV in all bedrooms STV Night porter 23P No coaches Arrangement with nearby health club ch fac English & French Cuisine V meals Coffee am Tea pm Last d 9.30pm
ROOMS: (incl. bkfst) s £44-£52; d £58-£80 * **LB**
MEALS: Sunday Lunch fr £9.95 Dinner fr £9.95*
CONF: Thtr 16 Board 12
CARDS:

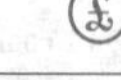

★★★59% Airport

Aviation Way SS2 6UL (turn off A127 at Tesco rdbt follow signs for Aviation Way, turn right at next rdbt straight over rdbt & then left at mini-rdbt, hotel on right) ☎ 01702 279955 FAX 01702 541961

This purpose-built hotel offers motel-style bedrooms which are divided between the main building and several outlying blocks. They are all spacious and equipped with a single and double bed. Public areas are combined into a bar with an informal brasserie with some lounge seating. The night-club opens for three nights a week.

18 en suite (bth/shr) 47 annexe en suite (bth/shr) (65 fmly) No smoking in 13 bedrooms CTV in all bedrooms Night porter 250P Wkly live entertainment Xmas English, French & Italian Cuisine V meals Coffee am Tea pm No smoking in restaurant Last d 10pm
ROOMS: s £60; d £65 * **LB**
OFF-PEAK: (incl. bkfst) s £45; d £55
MEALS: Sunday Lunch fr £10.95 Dinner £12.50-£15.50&alc*
CONF: Thtr 200 Class 120 Board 60 Del £89.50
CARDS:

★★66% Camelia

178 Eastern Esplanade, Thorpe Bay SS1 3AA (from A13 or A127 follow signs to Southend seafront, on seafront turn left, hotel 1m east of the pier) ☎ 01702 587917 FAX 01702 585704

On the seafront at Thorpe Bay, this small hotel provides good modern accommodation of varying sizes. Each bedroom is light and fresh with pastel decor and coordinated soft furnishings; all rooms have modern en suite bathrooms and a full range of thoughtful facilities. The staff provide a friendly informal service within the small bar and spacious air-conditioned restaurant; new this year is a small residents' lounge which has been created adjacent to the restaurant.

16 en suite (bth/shr) (1 fmly) CTV in all bedrooms STV No dogs (ex guide dogs) 100P Wkly live entertainment Xmas English & French Cuisine V meals Last d 10pm
ROOMS: (incl. bkfst) s £42.50-£65; d £55-£80 * **LB**
MEALS: Lunch fr £9.95&alc Dinner fr £12.95&alc
CARDS:

★★64% Schulers Hotel & Restaurant

161 Eastern Esplanade SS1 2YB (from A127 change to A1159 continue to roundabout, turn right into Hamstel Rd and drive straight on into Lifstan Way, at seafront turn right)
☎ 01702 610172 FAX 01702 466835

This small family-run hotel is well known for its large restaurant which dominates the public rooms. It is here that Manfred Schuler presents table d'hÙte and à la carte menus of continental dishes; home-made breads, fish and seafood dishes are strengths of the kitchen. Bedrooms

are bright and modern, affording straightforward levels of comfort.
9 rms (5 bth/shr) (1 fmly) CTV in all bedrooms No dogs (ex guide dogs) 10P No coaches Wkly live entertainment International Cuisine V meals Coffee am Tea pm Last d 10pm
ROOMS: s £24.50-£25.50; d £33.50-£45.50 *
MEALS: Lunch £9.25-£10.50&alc Dinner £9.25-£10.50&alc*
CARDS:

SOUTH MIMMS Hertfordshire Map 04 TL20

Forte Posthouse South Mimms

EN6 3NH (junc 23 on M25 & A1 take services exit off main rdbt then 1st left & follow hotel signs) ☎ 01707 643311 FAX 01707 646728
Suitable for both the business and leisure traveller, this bright hotel provides modern accommodation in well equipped bedrooms with en suite bathrooms. For more details about Forte Posthouse hotels, consult the Contents page for the section on Hotel Groups.
120 en suite (bth/shr)
ROOMS: s £79; d £79 *
CONF: Thtr 170 Class 85 Board 40 Del £109

Travelodge

South Mimms Service Area, Bignells Corner EN6 3QQ (junc 23,M25) ☎ 01707 665440
This modern building offers accommodation in smart, spacious and well equipped bedrooms, suitable for family use, and all with en suite bathrooms. Meals may be taken at the nearby family restaurant. For information on room rates and to make a booking, call Roomline free of charge on 0800 850950. For more details about Travelodge, consult the Contents page under Hotel Groups.
52 en suite (bth/shr)

SOUTH MOLTON Devon Map 03 SS72

RED STAR HOTEL

★★❀❀❀ **Whitechapel Manor**
PRIDE OF BRITAIN MEMBER
EX36 3EG (leave M5 junc27 towards Barnstaple on A361, after 30 minutes turn right at rdbt, after 1m turn right at hotel signpost) ☎ 01769 573377 FAX 01769 573797
A delightful Grade I listed Elizabethan manor house, this hotel is located on the edge of Exmoor. Bedrooms are spacious, stylishly furnished and well equipped, with personal touches such as flowers and quality toiletries. On arrival guests can take tea with home-made cake by the fireside and admire the carved Jacobean fire screen in the Great Hall. The fixed-price menu offers a varied selection of dishes cooked in the modern style. Typical starters might be warm layers of confit of duck leg and crisp potato with shallots, and ravioli of Cornish crab with strips of vegetable and tarragon jus. Main courses may include roast best end of lamb served with an aubergine purée and lamb jus.
10 en suite (bth/shr) (1 fmly) CTV in all bedrooms No dogs (ex guide dogs) 40P No coaches Croquet lawn Xmas English & French Cuisine Coffee am Tea pm No smoking in restaurant Last d 8.45pm
ROOMS: (incl. bkfst) s £70-£85; d £110-£170 * LB
MEALS: Lunch fr £34 High tea fr £10 Dinner fr £34
CONF: Board 24 Del from £129.50
CARDS:

★★❀75% **Marsh Hall Country House**

EX36 3HQ (1.25m N towards North Molton off A361) ☎ 01769 572666 FAX 01769 574230
This delightful small, friendly hotel, personally owned and managed by Tony and Judy Griffiths, stands in beautifully kept grounds not far from the north Devon link road. Dating from the 17th century with a Victorian frontage, Marsh Hall is said to have been built by the local squire for his mistress. Accommodation is furnished in keeping with the style of the house and offers excellent standards of comfort. Public rooms include a peaceful lounge with a supply of reading material and a separate bar lounge. The carefully planned four-course table d'hÙte menu offers a choice of fish, meat and game dishes, and whenever possible, top quality local produce is used. Herbs, vegetables and fruit are home grown, and special diets can be catered for by arrangement.
7 en suite (bth/shr) CTV in all bedrooms No dogs (ex guide dogs) 20P No coaches No children 12yrs Xmas English & Continental Cuisine No smoking in restaurant Last d 8.30pm
ROOMS: (incl. bkfst) s fr £43; d fr £66 * LB
MEALS: Bar Lunch £5-£10 Dinner £18.50*
CARDS:

SOUTH NORMANTON Derbyshire Map 08 SK45

★★★★❀67% **Swallow**

Carter Ln East DE55 2EH (situated on the E side of M1 junct 28 on A38 to Mansfield) ☎ 01773 812000 FAX 01773 580032
A modern hotel conveniently situated just off junction 28 of the M1 motorway. Bedrooms have all up to date facilities and include two rooms designed specially for disabled persons. There are two restaurants, The Pavilion, which has been awarded a rosette for the first time this year and the more informal Lacemaker, which depicts the local lace making industry and is open all day for light meals and afternoon tea. There is a very well equipped conference and banqueting centre and also a Leisure Club, which includes a heated swimming pool. Staff throughout are friendly and helpful and there is a large secure car park.
161 en suite (bth/shr) (6 fmly) No smoking in 100 bedrooms CTV in all bedrooms STV Night porter 200P Indoor swimming pool (heated) Sauna Solarium Gym Jacuzzi/spa Whirlpool Steam room Xmas International Cuisine V meals Coffee am Tea pm No smoking area in restaurant Last d 10.30pm
ROOMS: (incl. bkfst) s £95-£115; d £110-£125 LB
OFF-PEAK: (incl. bkfst) s fr £55; d fr £75
MEALS: Lunch £10.50-£13.50&alc Dinner £15.95-£21&alc*
CONF: Thtr 220 Class 100 Board 60
CARDS:

STOP PRESS! AA Members can book accommodation at many hotels in this guide through the AA Booking Service, usually at attractive discounts. See page 5 for details or telephone 0990 050505

S

SOUTHPORT Merseyside Map 07 SD31
See also Formby

★★★ 68% **Royal Clifton**

Promenade PR8 1RB (hotel on Promenade adjacent to Marine Lake) ☎ 01704 533771
FAX 01704 500657

A long established hotel occupying a prime position on the promenade, the Royal Clifton offers an excellent leisure centre and extensive function and conference facilities. There is a choice of bars, and a comfortable lounge area where a resident pianist recaptures the elegance of an earlier era. Bedrooms are spacious by modern standards and several suites and family rooms are available. All have satellite TV and other contemporary features. Food comes by way of a daily fixed-price menu and a regular carte of popular dishes.

106 en suite (bth/shr) (3 fmly) No smoking in 1 bedroom CTV in all bedrooms STV No dogs (ex guide dogs) Lift Night porter 40P Indoor swimming pool (heated) Sauna Solarium Gym Hair & beauty salon Wkly live entertainment Xmas English Cuisine V meals Coffee am Tea pm No smoking area in restaurant Last d 9.30pm
ROOMS: (incl. bkfst) s fr £67; d fr £85 * **LB**
MEALS: Sunday Lunch £7.50-£12.50 High tea £7.95-£9.95 Dinner £16.50-£17.50&alc*
CONF: Thtr 300 Class 170 Board 60 Del from £79.90
CARDS:

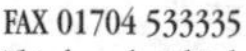

★★★ 67% **Scarisbrick**

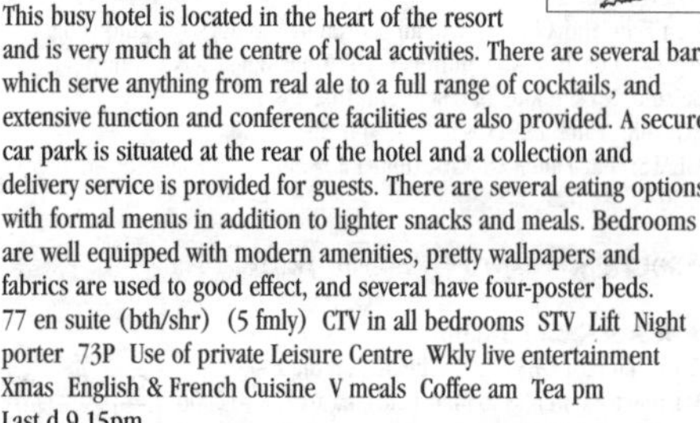

Lord St PR8 1NZ ☎ 01704 543000
FAX 01704 533335

This busy hotel is located in the heart of the resort and is very much at the centre of local activities. There are several bars which serve anything from real ale to a full range of cocktails, and extensive function and conference facilities are also provided. A secure car park is situated at the rear of the hotel and a collection and delivery service is provided for guests. There are several eating options with formal menus in addition to lighter snacks and meals. Bedrooms are well equipped with modern amenities, pretty wallpapers and fabrics are used to good effect, and several have four-poster beds.

77 en suite (bth/shr) (5 fmly) CTV in all bedrooms STV Lift Night porter 73P Use of private Leisure Centre Wkly live entertainment Xmas English & French Cuisine V meals Coffee am Tea pm Last d 9.15pm
ROOMS: (incl. bkfst) s £37-£70; d £44-£120 * **LB**
MEALS: Lunch £8.45-£9.35 High tea fr £4.95 Dinner £12.50-£14.95
CONF: Thtr 200 Class 100 Board 80 Del from £45
CARDS:

★★★ 65% **Stutelea Hotel & Leisure Club**
Alexandra Rd PR9 0NB (off the promenade near town & Hesketh Park) ☎ 01704 544220 FAX 01704 500232

This modern and well appointed hotel is located a short walk from the Marine Lake on the northern side of the town centre. It provides smart bedrooms which include some with four-poster beds and others suitable for families. Several have balconies which overlook the pretty grounds at the rear and some are at ground floor level. As well as a range of comfortable public rooms, residents have use of a fully equipped leisure centre and this also includes a snack bar open all day.

22 en suite (bth/shr) (4 fmly) CTV in all bedrooms STV No dogs (ex guide dogs) Lift Night porter 18P No coaches Indoor swimming pool (heated) Sauna Solarium Gym Pool table Jacuzzi/spa Games room Keep fit classes Steam room Xmas English & French Cuisine V meals Coffee am Tea pm Last d 9pm
ROOMS: (incl. bkfst) s £50; d £75-£80 * **LB**
OFF-PEAK: (incl. bkfst) s £45; d £70-£75
MEALS: Bar Lunch £2-£6 Dinner £12&alc
CONF: Thtr 30 Board 20 Del from £52
CARDS:

★★ 70% **Balmoral Lodge**

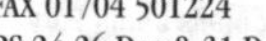

41 Queens Rd PR9 9EX (edge of town on A565 Preston road) ☎ 01704 544298 & 530751
FAX 01704 501224
RS 24-26 Dec & 31 Dec

Situated in a quiet residential area of town, this is a well maintained hotel offering modern accommodation. As well as a cosy bar and open-plan restaurant there is a comfortable lounge for residents. Bedrooms all have en suite bath or shower rooms and one has a four-poster bed for that special occasion. The hotel has its own forecourt car park and a pretty garden.

15 en suite (bth/shr) (1 fmly) CTV in all bedrooms STV No dogs 12P No coaches Sauna English & French Cuisine V meals No smoking in restaurant Last d 8.30pm
ROOMS: (incl. bkfst) s £30-£45; d £55-£60 * **LB**
OFF-PEAK: (incl. bkfst) d £60
MEALS: Dinner £12.95&alc
CARDS:

See advertisement on opposite page

★★ 65% **Bold**
585 Lord St PR9 0BE Near M57 & M58.At the top end of Lord Street near the Casino. ☎ 01704 532578 FAX 01704 532528

This Victorian hotel with its impressive frontage occupies a prime position on the famous Lord Street. The bar with its adjoining bistro is very popular locally and a wide range of snacks and more substantial meals are served throughout the day and evening. Bedrooms all have en suite bath or shower rooms and there are several rooms suitable for families. The hotel has its own night club called Raphael's Bar and there is a rear car park.

23 en suite (bth/shr) (4 fmly) CTV in all bedrooms No dogs (ex guide dogs) Night porter Air conditioning 7P Special rates for local squash club Xmas International Cuisine V meals Coffee am Tea pm Last d 10pm
ROOMS: (incl. bkfst) s £25-£40; d £25-£60 **LB**
OFF-PEAK: (incl. bkfst) s fr £25; d fr £25
MEALS: Lunch £3.95-£4.95&alc Dinner £4.25-£12.95&alc
CONF: Thtr 40 Class 40 Board 11 Del £50
CARDS:

See advertisement on opposite page

★★ 65% **Metropole**
Portland St PR8 1LL (turn left off Lord St after Prince of Wales Hotel & Metropole is directly behind Prince of Wales)
☎ 01704 536836 FAX 01704 549041

Located just off the town's famous Lord Street, this is a family-run hotel with a friendly atmosphere. Bedrooms are bright and modern and public areas include a choice of lounges and a cosy cocktail bar. A good-value daily menu offers a choice of popular meals and there is a full-sized snooker table available for guests.

24 rms (11 bth 10 shr) (3 fmly) CTV in all bedrooms 12P No coaches Snooker Xmas English & French Cuisine V meals Coffee am Last d 8.30pm
ROOMS: (incl. bkfst) s £30-£35; d £50-£60 * **LB**
OFF-PEAK: (incl. bkfst) s fr £25; d fr £40

MEALS: Lunch £5.90-£10.75 Dinner £11-£14.50*
CARDS:

★★63% **Shelbourne**
1 Lord St West PR8 2BH (on A565, Lord St signposted from motorway)
☎ 01704 541252 & 530278 FAX 01704 501293
This is a friendly and family run hotel situated at the west end of Lord Street. Pretty bedrooms are well equipped with modern facilities and one now has been fitted with a four-poster bed, which is proving popular with the many wedding parties using the hotel. Other functions and business meetings are also well catered for. Good-value food is always available and a good lunch time trade has been built up.
20 en suite (bth/shr) (1 fmly) No smoking in 4 bedrooms CTV in all bedrooms 20P V meals Coffee am Tea pm No smoking area in restaurant Last d 9.30pm
ROOMS: (incl. bkfst) s fr £36; d fr £55 * **LB**
MEALS: Lunch £3.95-£5.95 Dinner fr £9.95
CONF: Thtr 150 Class 75 Board 50 Del from £40
CARDS:

★★62% ***Gilton***
7 Leicester St PR9 0ER ☎ 01704 530646 FAX 01704 533791
This small, cosy hotel lies in a quiet residential area of town within easy walking distance of local amenities. Pretty bedrooms are fitted with many extra facilities such as hair-dryers, TVs and clock/radios. The bars and other public rooms are brightly decorated and comfortable. A games room is provided, and weddings and other functions are catered for.
13 en suite (bth/shr) (1 fmly) No smoking in 2 bedrooms CTV in all bedrooms 8P Sauna Jacuzzi/spa Games room V meals Coffee am Tea pm Last d 8.30pm
CARDS:

S

SOUTHSEA See Portsmouth & Southsea

SOUTH SHIELDS Tyne & Wear Map 12 NZ36

★★★61% ***Sea***
Sea Rd NE33 2LD (on A183)
☎ 0191 427 0999 FAX 0191 454 0500
Closed 25-27 Dec
Built as a hotel in the 1930s and now geared to the business market, The Sea sits on the promenade and has fine views over the mouth of the River Tyne. It offers modern bedrooms and a split-level restaurant catering for all tastes.
33 en suite (bth/shr) (2 fmly) CTV in all bedrooms STV Night porter 70P English, French & Italian Cuisine V meals Coffee am Tea pm Last d 9.30pm
CARDS:

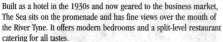

SOUTHWAITE MOTORWAY SERVICE AREA (M6) Cumbria Map 12 NY44

Travelodge
Broadfield Site CA4 0NT (on M6)
☎ Central Res 0800 850950 FAX 01525 878450

This modern building offers accommodation in smart, spacious and well equipped bedrooms, suitable for family use, and all with en suite bathrooms. Meals may be taken at the nearby family restaurant. For information on room rates and to make a booking, call Roomline free of charge on 0800 850950. For more details about Travelodge, consult the Contents page under Hotel Groups.
39 en suite (bth/shr)

SOUTH WALSHAM Norfolk Map 09 TG31

★★★66% **South Walsham Hall**
The Street NR13 6DQ (E of Norwich on B1140 towards Acle)
☎ 01603 270378 & 270591 FAX 01603 270519
South Walsham Hall is located on the fringes of the village, an attractive country house surrounded by expansive lawns, shrubs and trees. Fairhaven Trust Gardens are readily accessible from the hotel grounds, which include leisure facilities under separate management. The small team of staff provide a friendly and enthusiastic service. Accommodation styles and sizes vary, with three grades of bedrooms available, some furnished with period and antique pieces, and the remainder more contemporary in style. The annexe bedrooms were being upgraded on our last visit, examples of the newly refurbished rooms seen were smart with bold colour schemes and comfortable new furnishings.
10 en suite (bth/shr) 6 annexe en suite (bth) (1 fmly) CTV in all bedrooms 25P No coaches Outdoor swimming pool (heated) Tennis (hard) Fishing Xmas English & Continental Cuisine V meals Coffee am Tea pm Last d 9.30pm
ROOMS: (incl. bkfst) s £40-£60; d £70-£90 * LB
CARDS:

SOUTHWELL Nottinghamshire Map 08 SK75

★★★64% **Saracen's Head**
Market Place NG25 0HE (from A1 to Newark take A617 then A612 to centre of town)
☎ 01636 812701 FAX 01636 815408
This half-timbered inn, with rich historical links, is set in the centre of this quiet town. There is a sedate atmosphere in the public areas which include a small bar and a large restaurant. Bedroom styles vary but they are well equipped.
27 en suite (bth/shr) No smoking in 12 bedrooms CTV in all bedrooms Night porter 80P Xmas V meals Coffee am Tea pm No smoking in restaurant Last d 9.30pm
ROOMS: s fr £65; d fr £75 * **LB**
OFF-PEAK: s fr £35; d fr £40
MEALS: Lunch £6.50-£14 Dinner £19.95
CONF: Thtr 120 Class 40 Board 50 Del from £95
CARDS:

SOUTH WITHAM Lincolnshire Map 08 SK91

Travelodge
New Fox NG33 5LN (on A1, northbound)
☎ 01572 767586 FAX 01572 767586
This modern building offers accommodation in smart, spacious and well equipped bedrooms, suitable for family use, and all with en suite bathrooms. Meals may be taken at the nearby family restaurant. For information on room rates and to make a booking, call Roomline free of charge on 0800 850950. For more details about Travelodge, consult the Contents page under Hotel Groups.
32 en suite (bth/shr)

SOUTHWOLD Suffolk Map 05 TM57

★★★69% **Swan**
Market Place IP18 6EG (take A1095 to Southwold, hotel is located in the centre of town, parking is via an archway to the left of the building) ☎ 01502 722186 FAX 01502 724800
RS Xmas-Etr
There is a lovely timeless character to this elegant town hotel. Public areas have open fires in the colder months, and are always cosy and inviting. The restaurant is elegantly decorated, and serves well prepared meals, making the most of fresh local ingredients. Bedrooms are divided between the main house and an annexe with ground floor rooms. Good levels of attentive service add to the charm of this establishment.
27 en suite (bth/shr) 18 annexe en suite (bth/shr) (2 fmly) CTV in all bedrooms Lift Night porter 50P No coaches Croquet lawn Xmas V meals Coffee am Tea pm Last d 9.30pm
ROOMS: (incl. bkfst) s £40-£55; d £84-£149 * **LB**
OFF-PEAK: (incl. bkfst & dinner) s £63-£80; d £100-£130
MEALS: Lunch £12.50-£16.95 High tea £3.50-£4.50 Dinner £19.50-£31.50*
CONF: Thtr 50 Board 12 Del from £110
CARDS:

★★65% **Crown at Southwold**
90 High St IP18 6DP (take A1094 to Southwold to top of High St, hotel on left just before Market Pl) ☎ 01502 722275 FAX 01502 727223
Closed 1st or 2nd wk Jan
The focal point of this small, well maintained hotel remains the nationally recognised restaurant, not least for the quality of its wines and beers. There are two attractively furnished public rooms for business and social functions. Bedrooms are modest but charming, with antique furniture.
12 rms (8 bth 1 shr) (1 fmly) CTV in all bedrooms No dogs (ex guide dogs) 23P No coaches Xmas V meals Coffee am No smoking in restaurant Last d 9.30pm
ROOMS: (incl. cont bkfst) s £41; d £63 *
MEALS: Lunch £12.95-£15.50 Dinner £17.95-£19.95*
CARDS:

SOUTH ZEAL Devon Map 03 SX69

★★65% **Oxenham Arms**
EX20 2JT (just off A30 4m E of Okehampton in centre of village)
☎ 01837 840244 & 840577 FAX 01837 840791
A former monastery, this popular village inn dates back to the 12th century and is full of character, retaining such original features as exposed beams, arched doorways and open fireplaces. The bedrooms

are individually furnished with antiques and good beds, one a four-poster. All have direct-dial telephones, remote control TV and tea trays. The atmosphere is relaxed and informal, and service attentive. The small dining room offers a fixed-price menu.
8 rms (7 bth/shr) CTV in all bedrooms 8P No coaches Xmas International Cuisine V meals Coffee am Tea pm Last d 9pm
ROOMS: (incl. bkfst) s £40-£45; d £50-£60
MEALS: Lunch £9.50-£10.50 High tea £2.50-£3.50alc Dinner £15-£17.50*
CARDS:

SPALDING Lincolnshire Map 08 TF22

★★60% **Cley Hall**
22 High St PE11 1TX (remain on A16 to B1165, take 1st turning on rdbt across mini-rdbt to river turn left) ☎ 01775 725157
FAX 01775 710785
A riverside Georgian house with an adjacent accommodation annexe. Independently owned, the atmosphere is warm and welcoming and the staff are attentive and enthusiastic. In the cellar restaurant, aptly named 'Down Under' the menu ranges from 24oz ribs of beef to green Thai curry and from Mexican-style nachos to fresh grilled Dover sole; the dishes are tasty and enjoyable. The rooms are freshly decorated and the gradual refurbishment programme continues.
4 en suite (bth/shr) 7 annexe en suite (shr) (4 fmly) CTV in all bedrooms 20P ch fac V meals Coffee am Tea pm No smoking area in restaurant Last d 9.30pm
ROOMS: (incl. bkfst) s £30-£48; d £45-£52 * **LB**
OFF-PEAK: (incl. bkfst) s £30; d £45
MEALS: Lunch £10 Dinner £10&alc
CONF: Thtr 40 Class 23 Board 20
CARDS:

STAFFORD Staffordshire Map 07 SJ92

★★★65% **Garth**

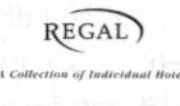

Wolverhampton Rd, Moss Pit ST17 9JR (exit M6 at Junc 13 take A449) ☎ 01785 256124
FAX 01785 255152
RS 25-26 Dec
Conveniently sitated one mile from junction 13 of the M6 on the A449, this much extended hotel offers a good range of conference and banqueting facilities and bedrooms, including family and interconnecting rooms, the oldest of which at the time of our visit were about to be refurbished. The public areas are modern in design and include an attractive restaurant, although guests can choose to eat less formally in the Victorian-style public bar which has access to the gardens.
60 en suite (bth/shr) (4 fmly) No smoking in 28 bedrooms CTV in all bedrooms STV Night porter 175P ch fac Xmas International Cuisine V meals Coffee am Tea pm No smoking area in restaurant Last d 9.45pm
ROOMS: s £59 * **LB**
OFF-PEAK: s £45; d £45
MEALS: Lunch £16-£25alc High tea fr £4 Dinner £16-£25alc*
CONF: Thtr 120 Class 30 Board 48 Del from £70
CARDS:

★★★65% **Tillington Hall**

Eccleshall Rd ST16 1JJ (exit M6 junc 14 take A5013)
☎ 01785 253531 FAX 01785 259223
A converted and extended 19th-century manor house is conveniently situated on the A5013, west of the town centre and close to junction 14 of the M6. Modern bedrooms are split between the original house and an adjoining wing; many have recently been upgraded and the others soon will be. A leisure club includes a swimming pool, a gymnasium and a snooker table. Conference and parking facilities are also available.
90 en suite (bth/shr) (7 fmly) No smoking in 41 bedrooms CTV in all bedrooms STV Lift Night porter 150P Indoor swimming pool (heated) Tennis (hard) Snooker Sauna Solarium Gym Jacuzzi/spa Beauty salon Xmas English, French & German Cuisine V meals Coffee am Tea pm No smoking in restaurant Last d 9.45pm
ROOMS: (incl. bkfst) s £66-£86; d £80-£95 * **LB**
MEALS: Lunch £9&alc Dinner £15.25&alc*
CONF: Thtr 200 Class 80 Board 40 Del from £85
CARDS:

★★62% **Abbey**
65-68 Lichfield Rd ST17 4LW (M6 at Junc 13)
☎ 01785 258531 FAX 01785 246875
Closed 22 Dec-7 Jan
A privately run hotel with a small team of friendly staff, and conveniently situated beside the Lichfield road. The bedrooms vary in size but are all attractively and freshly decorated. A good range of bar snacks are available in the cosy lounge bar and a choice of popular dishes in the restaurant, which guests from the adjoining Windsor Guest House also use.
18 rms (16 bth/shr) (3 fmly) CTV in all bedrooms No dogs (ex guide dogs) 26P No coaches English & French Cuisine V meals Coffee am No smoking in restaurant Last d 8.30pm
ROOMS: (incl. bkfst) s £19-£35; d £40-£50 * **LB**
MEALS: Bar Lunch £3-£6alc Dinner fr £7.50&alc*
CARDS:

★★61% **Vine**
Salter St ST16 2JU (off A34 Queensway ring road)
☎ 01785 244112 FAX 01785 246612
This 17th-century coaching inn with its own small car park stands close to the centre of town. Bedrooms, which are generally spacious and well equipped, include some family rooms. The open-plan ground floor features exposed beams and timbers; there is a lounge area, lounge bar and an attractive restaurant (with a no-smoking area) offering a good range of popular dishes as well as daily specials.
27 en suite (bth/shr) (1 fmly) CTV in all bedrooms No dogs 20P English & French Cuisine V meals Coffee am Tea pm No smoking in restaurant Last d 9pm
ROOMS: (incl. bkfst) s fr £34.50; d fr £40 * **LB**
MEALS: Lunch fr £3.65 Dinner fr £3.65*
CARDS:

STAINES Surrey Map 04 TQ07

★★★66% **The Thames Lodge**

Thames St TW18 4SF (exit M25 at Junc 13)
☎ 01784 464433 FAX 01784 454858
This extended Victorian hotel is situated close to the railway bridge and opposite the local rowing club. It has a riverside setting with its own mooring jetty. There is a broad range of modern bedrooms some of which have river views. There is a popular local pub, the Packhorse, and the more sedate surroundings of the Moorings restaurant.
44 en suite (bth/shr) No smoking in 22 bedrooms CTV in all bedrooms Night porter 60P V meals Coffee am Tea pm No smoking in restaurant
ROOMS: s fr £100; d fr £100 * **LB**
OFF-PEAK: s fr £60; d fr £60
CONF: Thtr 40 Class 30 Board 24 Del from £135
CARDS:

STALHAM Norfolk Map 09 TG32

★★70% **Kingfisher**

High St NR12 9AN (Stalham is by-passed by A149 between Gt Yarmouth & North Walsham, hotel is located just off High St at west end)
☎ 01692 581974 FAX 01692 582544

contd.

S

The Kingfisher hotel sits within the centre of this ancient Broadland market town, just a short walk from Stalham Staithe, where boats may be hired for the day. This small hotel has a friendly and relaxed atmosphere, the hard working resident proprietors ensure that guests receive a warm welcome and helpful service throughout their stay. The bar and restaurant prove to be very popular with locals and visitors, a wide selection of good value fare is available in both areas; bar food is offered from daily blackboard specials, whilst a la carte and daily menus are provided within the restaurant. Bedrooms are well maintained, light and appealing.
17 en suite (bth/shr) (2 fmly) CTV in all bedrooms 40P International Cuisine V meals Coffee am No smoking in restaurant Last d 9pm
ROOMS: (incl. bkfst) s £41-£52; d £50-£69 **LB**
MEALS: Lunch £13.95 Dinner £13.95&alc*
CONF: Thtr 100 Class 40 Board 30 Del from £70
CARDS:

STAMFORD Lincolnshire Map 08 TF00

★★★75% George of Stamford

St Martins PE9 2LB (turn off A1 onto B1081, 1m on left) (Poste)
☎ 01780 55171 FAX 01780 57070
This character coaching inn exudes quality and comfort. The colourful cobbled courtyard is delightful in the summer months, having an almost Mediterranean feel to it as diners eat under the shade of trellises and hanging baskets. The interior is archetypally English country house, though the atmosphere is relaxed and unstuffy. Aesthetically perfect bedrooms are thoughtfully furnished with extras. The wines are superb, both for their quality and range; usefully annoted unrivalled sourcing means that some very fine wines are very affordable and the house wines well above average. Cuisine is very British with some modern influences - a superb full rib of beef cooking under the gueridon had diners drooling. Other dishes include spicy Thai crab cakes and pigeon with lentils and a black pudding polenta, and the dessert selection might offer sherry trifle or Bakewell tart, with some good cheeses as an alternative.
47 en suite (bth/shr) (2 fmly) No smoking in 3 bedrooms CTV in all bedrooms STV Night porter 120P Croquet lawn Xmas English, French & Italian Cuisine V meals Coffee am Tea pm Last d 10.30pm
ROOMS: (incl. bkfst) s £72-£78; d £105-£160 * **LB**
MEALS: Lunch £13.50-£16.50&alc Dinner £19.85-£35alc*
CONF: Thtr 45 Class 25 Board 25 Del from £127
CARDS:

★★★65% Garden House

MINOTEL Great Britain

St Martin's PE9 2LP (take B1081, signposted Stamford. Hotel on left on entering the town)
☎ 01780 63359 FAX 01780 63339
A country house style of hotel within the town retaining a period feel. Improvements have been carefully implemented within the original framework by the resident proprietors Chris and Irene Quinn and these continue gradually. Stone flagged floors lead into an elegant well appointed restaurant and into the garden-style lounge and adjacent comfortable lounge bar. Bedrooms have been updated, relieving their former plainness.
20 en suite (bth/shr) (1 fmly) CTV in all bedrooms 30P Xmas V meals Coffee am Tea pm No smoking area in restaurant Last d 9.30pm
ROOMS: (incl. bkfst) s £45-£65; d £65-£85 * **LB**
MEALS: Lunch fr £14.95 Dinner £15&alc
CONF: Thtr 40 Board 20 Del from £65
CARDS:

★★65% Crown

All Saints Place PE9 2AG (behind the church in the main square)
☎ 01780 63136 FAX 01780 56111
Closed 25 Dec
A friendly and convivial independently-owned 16th century inn tucked away behind the church in the main square. The public rooms, featuring rich wall coverings and fabrics, are warm and inviting and extend to two dining rooms catering for bar meals and more formal restaurant dining. The bedrooms are equally well equipped, spacious and very comfortable.
17 en suite (bth/shr) (2 fmly) CTV in all bedrooms 40P European Cuisine V meals Coffee am Tea pm No smoking area in restaurant Last d 9.30pm
ROOMS: (incl. bkfst) s fr £42; d fr £55 * **LB**
OFF-PEAK: (incl. bkfst) s fr £40; d fr £50
MEALS: Lunch £8-£16.50 Dinner £10.95-£15.95&alc*
CONF: Thtr 50 Class 40 Board 35 Del from £67.50
CARDS:

STANDISH Greater Manchester Map 07 SD51

★★★★67% Kilhey Court

Best Western

Chorley Rd WN1 2XN (on A5106 1.5m N of A49/A5106 junct) ☎ 01257 472100
FAX 01257 422401
A former Victorian mansion now much extended, situated in ten acres of grounds and gardens overlooking Worthington fishing lakes and only a short distance from junction 27 of the M6. Most of the spacious, modern and extremely well appointed bedrooms are situated in a new wing, but a number of luxury suites, which also have spa baths, have been created in the older part of the hotel. The standard of cuisine in The Laureate Restaurant is excellent; in addition to the Laureate with its unique Victorian conservatory there is also a more informal Italian restaurant adjoining the splendid health and leisure club. Staff are professional, friendly and attentive and provide a high standard of service throughout.
61 en suite (bth/shr) (3 fmly) No smoking in 18 bedrooms CTV in all bedrooms STV No dogs (ex guide dogs) Lift Night porter 400P Indoor swimming pool (heated) Golf 18 Fishing Sauna Solarium Gym Jacuzzi/spa V meals Coffee am Tea pm No smoking area in restaurant Last d 10pm
MEALS: Lunch fr £12.95 Dinner fr £22.95*
CONF: Thtr 180 Class 60 Board 60 Del from £125
CARDS:

See advertisement on opposite page

★★★65% Wigan/Standish Moat House

MOAT HOUSE

Almond Brook Rd WN6 0SR (200yds from junct 27 of M6, on A5209) ☎ 01257 499988
FAX 01257 427327
Just a short distance from junction 27 of the M6, this modern hotel is popular with the conference market due to its self contained conference centre and leisure club. Room sizes vary but all are similarly furnished and convenient to use. Almonds restaurant has recently been re-themed and now offers more informal surroundings and menu.
124 en suite (bth/shr) (13 fmly) No smoking in 64 bedrooms CTV in 120 bedrooms Lift Night porter Air conditioning 400P Indoor swimming pool (heated) Sauna Solarium Gym Jacuzzi/spa Xmas

Carvery/Brasserie Cuisine V meals Coffee am Tea pm Last d 10pm
ROOMS: s £35-£70; d £66-£90 **LB**
MEALS: Lunch £5.50-£10&alc Dinner £12.50-£13.50&alc*
CONF: Thtr 170 Class 50 Board 50 Del from £65
CARDS:

STANSTEAD ABBOTS Hertfordshire Map 05 TL31

★★★★63% **Briggens House**
Stanstead Rd SG12 8LD ☎ 01279 829955
FAX 01279 793685

County Hotels

Part of an 80-acre estate, Briggens House dates back to the 17th century and was formerly the home of Lord Aldenham. Conferences are a major part of the operation and there is a good range of meeting rooms; however this does mean there is limited lounge space. The size and style of bedrooms varies: the best are within the original building.

(3 fmly) CTV in 54 bedrooms Lift Night porter 100P Outdoor swimming pool (heated) Golf 9 Fishing Croquet lawn Putting green Wkly live entertainment Xmas International Cuisine V meals Coffee am Tea pm No smoking in restaurant Last d 10pm
ROOMS: s £88; d £99.50 * **LB**
OFF-PEAK: (incl. bkfst) s £47.50; d £95
MEALS: Lunch £16.50&alc Dinner £23.50&alc*
CONF: Thtr 120 Class 50 Board 50 Del £150
CARDS:

STANSTED AIRPORT Essex Map 05 TL52

Hilton National Stansted
Round Coppice Rd CM24 8SE
☎ 01279 680800 FAX 01279 680890

This is a bright, modern hotel, with an informal restaurant, aimed at both the business and leisure guest. All bedrooms have en suite bathrooms and a range of modern facilities. For more information about Hilton National hotels, consult the Contents page under Hotel Groups.
237 en suite (bth/shr)
ROOMS: s £83-£99; d £93-£109 *
CONF: Thtr 300 Class 108 Board 65 Del from £115

Travelodge
Birchanger Green, Old Dunmow Rd
(M11 junct 8) ☎ 01279 656477

Travelodge

This modern building offers accommodation in smart, spacious and well equipped bedrooms, suitable for family use, and all with en suite bathrooms. Meals may be taken at the nearby family restaurant. For information on room rates and to make a booking, call Roomline free of charge on 0800 850950. For more details about Travelodge, consult the Contents page under Hotel Groups.
56 en suite (bth/shr)

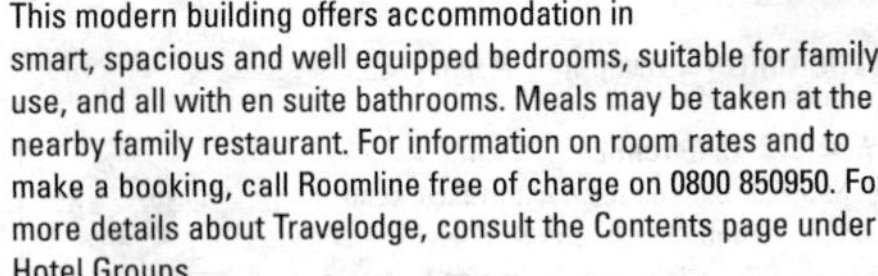

STAVERTON Devon Map 03 SX76

★★ 68% ***Sea Trout Inn***
TQ9 6PA (turn off A38 onto A384 at Buckfastleigh)
☎ 01803 762274 FAX 01803 762506
RS 24-26 Dec
Originally called the Church House Inn, the name of this 15th century building was changed when a previous landlord caught a large sea trout in the nearby river Dart. Nowadays, the fishing theme is evident throughout the inn, whether in the extensive bar areas, the conservatory restaurant or the comfortable cottage style bedrooms. An imaginative range of dishes is offered on the fixed price menu, carte and daily changing blackboard specials. On a recent visit, the wild mushroom soup with sherry was followed by a most enjoyable Oriental duck with black bean sauce.
10 en suite (bth/shr) (1 fmly) CTV in all bedrooms STV 48P No coaches English & French Cuisine V meals Coffee am Last d 9.30pm
CARDS:

STEEPLE ASTON Oxfordshire Map 04 SP42

★★★63% **Hopcrofts Holt**
OX6 3QQ (junct of B4030/A4260) ☎ 01869 340259
FAX 01869 340865
This popular stopover on the main Woodstock to Banbury road is continually improving and with much recent refurbishment to both interior and exterior the hotel is smart and attractive. Bedrooms are generally spacious and well equipped with co-ordinating fabrics used throughout. The staff are professional and extend every courtesy to their guests.
88 en suite (bth/shr) (2 fmly) No smoking in 10 bedrooms CTV in all bedrooms STV Night porter 200P Pool table Xmas English & French Cuisine V meals Coffee am Tea pm Last d 9.45pm
ROOMS: (incl. bkfst) s £69.50; d £85 * **LB**
MEALS: Lunch £7.95-£10.50 Dinner £18-£25*
CONF: Thtr 200 Class 70 Board 50 Del £115
CARDS:

STEVENAGE Hertfordshire Map 04 TL22

★★★68% ***Cromwell***
High St, Old Town SG1 3AZ
☎ 01438 359111 779954 FAX 01438 742169

County Hotels

An enduring appeal and strength of this hotel is the style and the well maintained state of the bedrooms. The public areas preserve a certain dignified country house air about them and there

contd.

are good staffing levels. After a settling-in period, there is hope that the quality of the kitchen's output will improve.
56 en suite (bth/shr) (4 fmly) No smoking in 8 bedrooms CTV in all bedrooms STV Night porter 100P English & French Cuisine V meals Coffee am Tea pm Last d 10pm
CARDS:

★★★63% **Blakemore Thistle**
Blakemore End Rd, Little Wymondley SG4 7JJ
☎ 01438 355821 FAX 01438 742114
(For full entry see Hitchin)

★★★62% **Novotel**
Knebworth Park SG1 2AX (at junct A1/A602)
☎ 01438 742299 FAX 01438 723872

This new red brick building is located in a green belt site yet only seconds off the A1(M). This makes it a popular meeting and conference venue and its informal bar and restaurant are geared around this kind of business. There is an exact and uniform brand standard to all the large bedrooms which now have modem sockets.
100 en suite (bth/shr) (20 fmly) No smoking in 60 bedrooms CTV in all bedrooms STV Lift Night porter 120P Outdoor swimming pool (heated) Pool table Wkly live entertainment International Cuisine V meals Coffee am Tea pm No smoking area in restaurant Last d mdnt
ROOMS: s £59-£62; d £59-£62 *
MEALS: Lunch £14.50&alc Dinner £14.50&alc*
CONF: Thtr 130 Class 80 Board 70 Del from £83
CARDS:

★★★60% ***Hertfordpark***
Danestrete SG1 1EJ (in town centre adjacent to Tesco Superstore) ☎ 01438 779955 FAX 01438 741880

Situated in the heart of the new town, surrounded on all sides by shops, this purpose-built hotel is managing to hold its own. The conference rooms and the restaurant are located on the first floor and the ground floor comprises a coffee lounge area. Bedrooms are well equipped and well laid out but some are awaiting a decorator's touch.
98 en suite (bth/shr) No smoking in 28 bedrooms CTV in all bedrooms Lift Night porter Pool table Wkly live entertainment International Cuisine V meals Coffee am Tea pm Last d 10pm
CARDS:

Forte Posthouse Stevenage
Old London Rd, Broadwater SG2 8DS (off B1970)
☎ 01438 365444 FAX 01438 741308

Suitable for both the business and leisure traveller, this bright hotel provides modern accommodation in well equipped bedrooms with en suite bathrooms. For more details about Forte Posthouse hotels, consult the Contents page for the section on Hotel Groups.
54 en suite (bth/shr)
ROOMS: s £49-£69; d £49-£69 *
CONF: Thtr 60 Class 20 Board 30 Del from £65

Travel Inn
Corey's Mill Ln SG1 4AA (close to A1(M) at intersection of the A602 Hitchin Rd & Corey's Mill Lane) ☎ 01438 351318 FAX 01438 721609

Purpose-built accommodation, offering spacious, well equipped bedrooms, all with en suite bathrooms. Meals may be taken at the nearby family restaurant. For more information about Travel Inns, consult the Contents page under Hotel Groups.
40 en suite (bth/shr)
ROOMS: d £35.50 *

STEYNING West Sussex Map 04 TQ11

★★★70% **The Old Tollgate**
The Street BN44 3WE ☎ 01903 879494
FAX 01903 813399
This popular hotel is situated in the quiet village of Bramber but provides easy access to the coastal towns close by. The restaurant (which offers an impressive visual displayed a al carte buffet) and bar are situated in the original Tollgate Inn building which dates from the early 18th - century with its wood panelling and flagstone floors. bedrooms are especially comfortable well designed and furnished to a high standard with every modern amenity including some with four poster, Jacuzzi and sitting room, family rooms and syndicate rooms. Other facilities include several smart and well equipped adaptable meeting rooms and good facilities for weddings and functions. Service is particularly friendly and helpful.
11 en suite (bth/shr) 20 annexe en suite (bth/shr) (5 fmly) CTV in all bedrooms STV No dogs (ex guide dogs) Lift Night porter 60P No coaches Xmas International Cuisine V meals No smoking area in restaurant Last d 9.30pm
ROOMS: s £58-£78; d £58-£78 * **LB**
MEALS: Lunch £12.45-£14.45 Dinner £17.65
CONF: Thtr 60 Class 32 Board 26 Del from £70.50
CARDS:

STILTON Cambridgeshire Map 04 TL18

★★★67% **Bell Inn**
Great North Rd PE7 3RA ☎ 01733 241066 FAX 01733 245173
Closed 24-25 Dec
A character 16th century Inn sitting in the centre of the village, built around an old courtyard, with good integration of old and new stone buildings. Owners and staff provide a courteous and smiling service within the public areas of the original Inn. The restaurant and village bar are full of character, with exposed beamed ceilings, open log fires and a galleried lounge. Bedrooms are of varying styles, four poster and deluxe rooms supplement standard styles, all rooms are thoughtfully equipped and have modern bathrooms.
19 en suite (bth/shr) (1 fmly) No smoking in 5 bedrooms CTV in all bedrooms STV No dogs (ex guide dogs) Night porter 30P English & French Cuisine V meals Coffee am Tea pm Last d 9.30pm
ROOMS: (incl. bkfst) s £40-£74; d £55-£94 * **LB**
MEALS: Lunch fr £10.95 Dinner fr £16.95&alc*
CONF: Thtr 100 Class 46 Board 46 Del from £75
CARDS:

STOCKBRIDGE Hampshire Map 04 SU33

★★★62% **Grosvenor**
High St SO20 6EU (on the A30 in village centre)
☎ 01264 810606 FAX 01264 810747

Originally a Georgian coaching inn and situated at the heart of this pretty village, the Grosvenor provides a relaxed and informal atmosphere with congenial, character public rooms. There is a traditional bar with log fire, a cosy panelled dining room and choice of bedrooms, either in the main house or a rear extension with smaller, quieter rooms.
25 en suite (bth/shr) No smoking in 3 bedrooms CTV in all bedrooms STV Night porter 60P Snooker Sauna Continental Cuisine V meals Coffee am Tea pm No smoking in restaurant Last d 9.45pm
ROOMS: (incl. bkfst) s £65; d £75-£85 * **LB**
OFF-PEAK: (incl. bkfst & dinner) s £49.50-£60; d £65-£90
MEALS: Lunch £8.95 Dinner £10-£15&alc*
CONF: Thtr 80 Class 20 Board 30 Del £90
CARDS:

STOCKPORT Greater Manchester Map 07 SJ88
See also Manchester Airport

★★★67% **Bramhall Moat House**

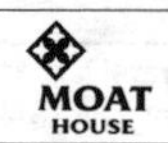

Bramhall Ln South SK7 2EB
☎ 0161 439 8116 & 455 9988 FAX 0161 440 8071
(For full entry see Bramhall)

★★70% **Red Lion Inn**
112 Buxton Rd, High Ln SK6 8ED (beside A6, 1m from Lyme Country Park) ☎ 01663 765227 FAX 01663 762170
This popular inn, where the staff are very friendly and attentive, is conveniently located just a mile from Lyme Hall and sits beside the A6. A very good selection of interesting dishes, including fresh fish, is served in the modern and interestingly decorated brasserie which is open all day. There are no other public areas but the bedrooms, all of which are en suite, are comfortably furnished and thoughtfully equipped.
6 en suite (bth/shr) (1 fmly) CTV in all bedrooms STV No dogs (ex guide dogs) 100P No coaches V meals Coffee am Tea pm Last d 10pm
ROOMS: s £33.50-£46.50; d £44-£58.50 *
OFF-PEAK: s £25.50-£28.50; d £44
MEALS: Lunch fr £8.50&alc Dinner £12-£18alc*
CARDS:

★★67% ***Saxon Holme***
230 Wellington Rd SK4 2QN (N, beside A6) ☎ 0161 432 2335
FAX 0161 431 8076
This long-established privately-owned hotel, situated in a residential area on the A6 north of the town and easily accessible from the M63, offers modern, spacious and well equipped accommodation; the rooms in the new wing offering a higher standard than those in the original house. The restaurant is open from Monday - Thursday inclusive and a full room service menu, offering a good range of light snacks is available at the weekend.
33 en suite (bth/shr) (3 fmly) No smoking in 11 bedrooms CTV in all bedrooms STV Lift Night porter 36P English & French Cuisine V meals Coffee am Tea pm Last d 9pm
CARDS:

★★67% **Wycliffe**
74 Edgeley Rd, Edgeley SK3 9NQ (from M63 junct.11 follow A560 for Stockport, at 1st lights turn right, hotel half a mile on left)
☎ 0161 477 5395 FAX 0161 476 3219
This friendly, family-run and well maintained hotel is quietly situated in a pleasant residential area close to Alexandra Park, just five minutes from junction 11 of the M63. The bedrooms, which vary in size, are modern in style, freshly decorated, well equipped and spotlessly clean. Guests can enjoy a very good range of freshly prepared dishes, which have an Italian theme, in the smart restaurant where service from the staff is prompt and attentive. There is also a comfortable lounge bar and a small sitting room.
20 en suite (bth/shr) CTV in all bedrooms No dogs (ex guide dogs) Night porter 46P No coaches Xmas French & Italian Cuisine V meals Tea pm Last d 9.30pm
ROOMS: (incl. bkfst) s fr £39; d fr £50 *
OFF-PEAK: (incl. bkfst) s fr £32; d fr £40
MEALS: Lunch £7-£11.50&alc Dinner fr £14.50&alc*
CONF: Thtr 20 Class 20 Board 20
CARDS:

★★66% ***Rudyard Toby***
271 Wellington Rd North, Heaton Chapel SK4 5BP
(1.5m N off A6) ☎ 0161 432 2753
FAX 0161 431 0260
This former Victorian gentleman's house situated on the A6 just north of Stockport is convenient for Manchester Airport as well as Manchester city centre. Bedrooms are all very well equipped and have every modern facility suitable for business and leisure users alike. The popular country-style restaurant offers a wide range of dishes, including steaks, chicken and fish, and the menu also has a vegetarian section. The atmosphere is relaxed and informal and the staff are cheerful and friendly.

21 en suite (bth/shr) (2 fmly) No smoking in 10 bedrooms CTV in all bedrooms No dogs Night porter 100P V meals Coffee am Tea pm
CARDS:

Travel Inn

Buxton Rd SK2 6NB (on A6 one and a half miles from town centre) ☎ 0161 480 2968
FAX 0161 477 8320
Purpose-built accommodation, offering spacious, well equipped bedrooms, all with en suite bathrooms. Meals may be taken at the nearby family restaurant. For more information about Travel Inns, consult the Contents page under Hotel Groups.
40 en suite (bth/shr)

Travelodge
Travelodge
London Rd South SK12 4NA (on A523)
☎ 01625 875292 FAX 01625 875292
This modern building offers accommodation in smart, spacious and well equipped bedrooms, suitable for family use, and all with en suite bathrooms. Meals may be taken at the nearby family restaurant. For information on room rates and to make a booking, call Roomline free of charge on 0800 850950. For more details about Travelodge, consult the Contents page under Hotel Groups.
32 en suite (bth/shr)

STOCKTON-ON-TEES Co Durham Map 08 NZ41

★★★★63% **Swallow**

John Walker Square TS18 1AQ ☎ 01642 679721
FAX 01642 601714
Instantly recognisable as the tallest building in Stockton, this modern hotel is conveniently situated right in the centre of town. An on going refurbishment programme to upgrade both the bedrooms and public areas continues. The bedrooms vary in style, but all are spacious and well equipped. The newly refurbished rooms are very smart indeed. The service is friendly and helpful and guests have the choice of eating less formally in the brasserie, as well as the main restaurant.
125 en suite (bth/shr) (12 fmly) No smoking in 65 bedrooms CTV in all bedrooms STV Lift Night porter 400P Indoor swimming pool (heated) Sauna Solarium Gym Jacuzzi/spa Sunbeach tanning area Wkly live entertainment Xmas English & French Cuisine V meals Coffee am Tea pm Last d 10pm
ROOMS: (incl. bkfst) s £88-£105; d £98-£120 * **LB**
OFF-PEAK: (incl. bkfst) d fr £55
MEALS: Lunch £9.50&alc High tea £3-£10alc Dinner £16-£19

contd.

S

CONF: Thtr 300 Class 150 Board 40 Del from £100
CARDS:

★★★ 71% **Parkmore**
636 Yarm Rd, Eaglescliffe TS16 0DH (3m S A19)
☎ 01642 786815 FAX 01642 790485
Standing to the south of Stockton, this extended Victorian house offers every comfort and facility for the commercial traveller and the tourist alike. All the bedrooms are well equipped and have modern fittings whilst the recently refurbished public rooms are most comfortable and inviting. An extensive range of well prepared food is available and there is an Oriental influence with some interesting combinations of flavours being used in the cooking.
55 en suite (bth/shr) (3 fmly) No smoking in 20 bedrooms CTV in all bedrooms STV Night porter 120P Indoor swimming pool (heated) Snooker Sauna Solarium Gym Jacuzzi/spa Beauty salon International Cuisine V meals Coffee am Tea pm No smoking in restaurant Last d 9.30pm
ROOMS: s £56; d £64-£79 * **LB**
OFF-PEAK: s £42-£46; d £53-£58
MEALS: Lunch fr £10.25 Dinner fr £17.25*
CONF: Thtr 140 Class 40 Board 40 Del from £60
CARDS:

★★★ 59% **Billingham Arms**
The Causeway, Billingham TS23 2HD (off A19. Follow signs for Billingham town centre) ☎ 01642 553661 & 360880
FAX 01642 552104
Comfortable, well equipped bedrooms are provided at this busy, town centre hotel. A good range of food is available in two styles of Edwardian restaurants or in the bar, and staff are friendly and helpful.
69 en suite (bth/shr) (6 fmly) No smoking in 4 bedrooms CTV in all bedrooms STV Lift Night porter Air conditioning 152P Solarium Pool table Xmas International Cuisine V meals Coffee am Tea pm Last d 9.45pm
ROOMS: s £21.50-£49; d £43-£64 **LB**
MEALS: Lunch £7-£7.50 Dinner fr £12.95*
CONF: Thtr 300 Class 160 Board 40
CARDS:

See advertisement under BILLINGHAM

★★ 66% **Claireville**
519 Yarm Rd, Eaglescliffe TS16 9BG
☎ 01642 780378 FAX 01642 784109
RS Xmas & New Year
This detached Victorian house stands on the A135 at Eaglescliffe and provides good accommodation for the modern traveller.It is family owned and run and provides friendly service together with a good choice of dishes on the à la carte menu which also includes daily specials. The bedrooms are bright and fresh and have good facilities whilst the public rooms are comfortable and inviting.
18 en suite (bth/shr) (2 fmly) No smoking in 4 bedrooms CTV in all bedrooms STV 30P English & French Cuisine V meals Coffee am Tea pm Last d 8.30pm
ROOMS: (incl. bkfst) s £40-£45; d £50-£58 *
OFF-PEAK: (incl. bkfst) s £33-£40; d £44-£50
MEALS: Lunch fr £9.25 Dinner £12-£19alc
CONF: Thtr 20 Class 20 Board 20 Del from £28
CARDS:

Forte Posthouse Teeside
Low Ln, Stainton Village, Thornaby TS17 9LW (SE on A1044) ☎ 01642 591213 FAX 01642 594989
Suitable for both the business and leisure traveller, this bright hotel provides modern accommodation in well equipped bedrooms with en suite bathrooms. For more details about Forte Posthouse hotels, consult the Contents page for the section on Hotel Groups.
135 en suite (bth/shr)
ROOMS: d £49-£69 *
CONF: Thtr 120 Class 60 Board 70 Del from £65

Travel Inn

Yarm Rd TS18 3RT ☎ 01642 633354
FAX 01642 633339
Purpose-built accommodation, offering spacious, well equipped bedrooms, all with en suite bathrooms. Meals may be taken at the nearby family restaurant. For more information about Travel Inns, consult the Contents page under Hotel Groups.
ROOMS: d £35.50 *

STOKE D'ABERNON Surrey Map 04 TQ15

★★★★ 60% ***Woodlands Park***

Woodlands Ln KT11 3QB (on A245 between Cobham & Leatherhead) ☎ 01372 843933
FAX 01372 842704
Set in ten acres of attractive, well kept lawns and grounds, this 19th-century mansion was built by F C Bryant, of Bryant and May fame, who regularly entertained such celebrities as Lily Langtry and Edward VII, Prince of Wales. The house has been tastefully restored and skilfully extended to provide a range of relaxing bedrooms, all equipped with modern amenities, the best of which have open country views across the M25. There are extensive banqueting and meeting rooms, and the largest can accommodate up to 300 delegates, making this a very popular venue for local wedding receptions. There are two dining options - Langtry's Bar and Brasserie, and the more formal surroundings of the elegant wood-panelled Oak Room.
59 en suite (bth/shr) CTV in all bedrooms STV No dogs (ex guide dogs) Lift Night porter 150P Tennis (hard) Croquet lawn Putting green English & French Cuisine V meals Coffee am Tea pm Last d 9.30pm
CONF: Thtr 250 Class 100 Board 50 Del from £140
CARDS:

STOKE GABRIEL Devon Map 03 SX85

★★★ 71% **Gabriel Court**
TQ9 6SF (off A385) ☎ 01803 782206
FAX 01803 782333
The Beacom family offer warm hospitality at this hotel which dates back, in parts, to 1487 and is set in beautifully kept Elizabethan-style terraced gardens. Bedrooms are individually furnished and decorated, and in the cooler months log fires blaze in the lounges. The dinner menu features mainly traditional British dishes, with fresh vegetables from the hotel garden.
19 en suite (bth/shr) CTV in all bedrooms 20P No coaches Outdoor swimming pool (heated) Tennis (grass) Croquet lawn Xmas English Cuisine Coffee am Tea pm Last d 8.30pm
ROOMS: (incl. bkfst) s £51-£55; d £76 *
MEALS: Sunday Lunch fr £12 Dinner fr £23*
CONF: Board 20
CARDS:

STOKE-ON-TRENT Staffordshire Map 07 SJ84

See also Newcastle-under-Lyme

★★★★ 65% ***Stoke-on-Trent Moat House***

Etruria Hall, Festival Way, Etruria ST1 5BQ (situated on the Festival Park) ☎ 01782 609988
FAX 01782 284500
This large modern hotel was built on the site of the Garden Festival and incorporates Etruria Hall, which was the former home of Josiah Wedgwood. The bedrooms are all very well equipped and include two luxury suites, non smoking bedrooms and rooms for use by disabled

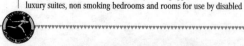

guests. There are excellent facilities for conferences and banquets and there is also a sports and leisure club which includes a heated indoor swimming pool aswell as a gymnasium. A Work Base Business Centre is also available.
143 en suite (bth/shr) (10 fmly) No smoking in 42 bedrooms CTV in all bedrooms STV No dogs (ex guide dogs) Lift Night porter Air conditioning 350P Indoor swimming pool (heated) Snooker Sauna Solarium Gym Leisure club Dance studio ch fac International Cuisine V meals Coffee am Tea pm Last d 10pm
CARDS:

★★★68% **North Stafford**

PRINCIPAL HOTELS

Station Rd, Winton Square ST4 2AE (follow signs for Railway Station) ☎ 01782 744477
FAX 01782 744580

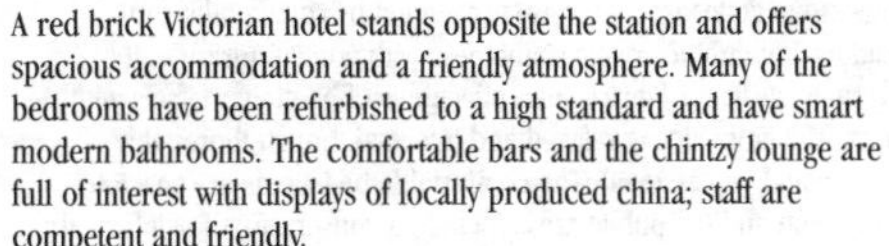

A red brick Victorian hotel stands opposite the station and offers spacious accommodation and a friendly atmosphere. Many of the bedrooms have been refurbished to a high standard and have smart modern bathrooms. The comfortable bars and the chintzy lounge are full of interest with displays of locally produced china; staff are competent and friendly.
69 en suite (bth/shr) (3 fmly) CTV in all bedrooms STV Lift Night porter 120P Wkly live entertainment Xmas English & French Cuisine V meals Coffee am Tea pm No smoking area in restaurant Last d 9.30pm
ROOMS: (incl. bkfst) s fr £72; d fr £92 * **LB**
MEALS: Lunch £5.50-£9.50 Dinner £12.50-£16&alc*
CONF: Thtr 450 Class 100 Board 50 Del from £85
CARDS:

★★★65% ***George***
Swan Square, Burslem ST6 2AE ☎ 01782 577544 FAX 01782 837496
This impressive hotel retains much of the character from when it was built in 1929, including impressively high ceilings and wide corridors. The original bedrooms used to share central bathrooms, but of course are now fully en suite and the rooms themselves, although they vary in size, are attractively decorated and well equipped. There is a handsome lounge on the first floor and a comfortable bar and restaurant. The hotel is ideally situated for visiting the Royal Doulton factory shop which is immediately next door.
30 en suite (bth/shr) (5 fmly) CTV in all bedrooms STV No dogs (ex guide dogs) Lift Night porter 28P Wkly live entertainment English & Continental Cuisine V meals Coffee am Tea pm Last d 9pm
CARDS:

★★★62% **Haydon House**
1-13 Haydon St, Basford ST4 6JD (off A53 near junct with A500)
☎ 01782 711311 FAX 01782 717470
Owned and personally run by the Machin family for the last fifteen years this attractive and comfortable hotel is conveniently situated for the town, surrounding 'Potteries', and the A500. Some of the bedrooms, have recently been redecorated and fitted with new bathrooms and a small number are located in an adjoining annexe; all are comfortable and soundly furnished. The public areas are decorated with a Victorian theme and the Clock restaurant offers a good selection of well produced dishes. The hotel also benefits from a number of meeting rooms and off-street parking.
17 en suite (bth/shr) 14 annexe en suite (bth/shr) (2 fmly) CTV in all bedrooms 52P English & French Cuisine V meals Coffee am Tea pm Last d 10pm
ROOMS: s fr £52.50; d fr £62.50 *
OFF-PEAK: s fr £35; d fr £50
MEALS: Lunch fr £10.50 Dinner fr £14.90&alc*
CONF: Thtr 80 Class 25 Board 30 Del from £70
CARDS:

★★66% ***Trentham Toby***

Longton Rd, Trentham ST4 8BU
☎ 01782 644448 FAX 01782 644936
Closed 24 Dec-1 Jan
Originally a Hunting Lodge and part of the nearby Trentham Estate, this pleasant hotel is conveniently situated three miles from Junction 15 of the M6 and four miles from the centre of Stoke on Trent. The comfortable and very well equipped bedrooms, including family rooms, are accommodated in a purpose-built wing of the hotel. A good range of popular dishes from 'The Toby Grill' menu, including steaks, fish dishes and vegetarian options, can be enjoyed in the spacious restaurant and bar. Bar snacks are served in the attractively decorated and themed public bar and lounge. Two small meeting rooms and ample parking are also available.
30 en suite (bth/shr) (2 fmly) No smoking in 10 bedrooms CTV in all bedrooms STV No dogs (ex guide dogs) Night porter Air conditioning 120P Pool table V meals Coffee am
CARDS:

STONE Staffordshire Map 07 SJ93

★★★70% **Stone House**

Stafford Rd ST15 0BQ (beside A34, 0.5m S of town centre) ☎ 01785 815531 FAX 01785 814764
RS Sat
Conveniently located, this country house has been extended to provide a range of meeting rooms, a health and leisure club and two wings of comfortable, modern bedrooms. Public areas include a lounge, spacious modern restaurant and congenial bar. Prompt services are carried out by a very friendly team.
47 en suite (bth/shr) (1 fmly) No smoking in 30 bedrooms CTV in all bedrooms STV No dogs Lift Night porter 120P Indoor swimming pool (heated) Tennis (hard) Sauna Solarium Gym Putting green Xmas V meals Coffee am Tea pm No smoking in restaurant Last d 9.30pm
ROOMS: s £69; d £69 * **LB**
OFF-PEAK: s £59; d £59
MEALS: Lunch £8-£15 Dinner £12-£20*
CONF: Thtr 190 Class 60 Board 50 Del £99
CARDS:

S

STON EASTON Somerset Map 03 ST65

RED STAR HOTEL

★★★★ **Ston Easton Park**

RELAIS & CHATEAUX. Relais Gourmands

BA3 4DF ☎ 01761 241631
FAX 01761 241377

Set in landscaped gardens and parkland, Ston Easton Park is an impressive stone-built Palladian mansion, containing some of the most exceptional architectural and decorative features to be found in the West of England. Peter and Christine Smedley have restored and refurbished the property recapturing the elegance of the 18th century throughout the spacious public rooms and the individually decorated bedrooms. In the grounds a 17th-century former gardener's cottage provides two luxury suites. Led by Kevin Marchant, a team of professional staff are on hand to provide attentive service. The fixed-price menu of head chef Mark Harrington continues to gain praise, using fresh local produce including vegetables and herbs from the hotel's kitchen gardens. A recent test meal started with a chicken liver parfait, spiked with foie gras and served with Cumberland sauce. This was followed by a roast best end of lamb, topped with a lavender and Meaux mustard crust, the vegetables forming an integral part of the dish. To complete the meal an individual apricot and almond tart served with an Amaretto flavoured crème Anglaise was enjoyed.

18 en suite (bth/shr) 2 annexe en suite (bth/shr) CTV in all bedrooms 52P Tennis (hard) Snooker Croquet lawn Hot air ballooning,Archery,Clay Shooting No children 7yrs Xmas English & French Cuisine V meals Coffee am Tea pm No smoking in restaurant Last d 10pm
ROOMS: s fr £125; d fr £175 **LB**
OFF-PEAK: s fr £125; d fr £175
MEALS: Lunch £26 High tea £5-£15 Dinner £39.50&alc
CONF: Thtr 50 Class 25 Board 26 Del from £120
CARDS:

STONEHOUSE Gloucestershire Map 03 SO80

★★★ 66% **Stonehouse Court**
GL10 3RA (on A419) ☎ 01453 825155 FAX 01453 824611
This hotel is very conveniently located for the M5 and is a popular venue for conferences and weddings, with a superb self-contained function suite which has excellent views over the gardens and pretty canal. The panelled public areas are full of character, and while bedrooms are a little tired a refurbishment programme is planned. The dining room serves appetising tasty food which is prepared with a fair degree of skill and shows a dedicated approach to cooking.
9 en suite (bth/shr) 27 annexe en suite (bth/shr) (1 fmly) No smoking in 4 bedrooms CTV in all bedrooms Night porter 160P Fishing Croquet lawn Bowls Xmas English & French Cuisine V meals Coffee am Tea pm No smoking area in restaurant Last d 9.45pm
ROOMS: (incl. bkfst) s £58-£72; d £85-£110 * **LB**
OFF-PEAK: (incl. bkfst & dinner) d £124-£185
MEALS: Lunch £10.50-£12.50 Dinner fr £19.50*
CONF: Thtr 150 Class 75 Board 50 Del from £110
CARDS:

STONOR Oxfordshire Map 04 SU78

★★★ 77% **Stonor Arms**
RG9 6HE (on B480) ☎ 01491 638345 FAX 01491 638863
This inn-cum-country house lies in the middle of a one street village of picturesque cottages and farms surrounded by rolling hills and meadow. It combines rustic shabbiness with contemporary wall coverings, designer fabrics and collectibles of boating artefacts and prints. The ambience is relaxed and informal though thoroughly attentive and professional. The comfortable bedrooms are spacious and elegant and the public areas include a conservatory for informal dining and a walled garden. The cuisine is good; Cornish scallops were served with a coriander and shallot dressing and followed by tender, pink breast of duck served with a finely judged reduction marred slightly by a pithy lime julienne. A Pithivier of thick chocolate served with a creamy and accurate crème fraiche ice cream was more successful. The wine list is laudable both for the quality of the wines and their vintages. The house selection is probably the best value with an excellent Cosme-Palacio Hermanos white Rioja at around £16.00.
10 en suite (bth/shr) CTV in all bedrooms 27P No coaches Last d 9.30pm
ROOMS: (incl. bkfst) s £85-£95; d fr £95 * **LB**
MEALS: Lunch £20-£27alc Dinner £20-£27alc*
CONF: Thtr 20 Board 12 Del from £130
CARDS:

STOURBRIDGE West Midlands Map 07 SO88

★★ 65% **Talbot**

REGAL A Collection of Individual Hotels

High St DY8 1DW ☎ 01384 394350
FAX 01384 371318
Much of the historical character has been retained at this Tudor and Jacobean coaching inn with its beams and sloping floors. The bedrooms are modernised and attractive, though space is at a premium in some. In addition to the palm-themed restaurant's meals, there is all-day service of bar food and good Italian coffees.
25 en suite (bth/shr) (4 fmly) No smoking in 5 bedrooms CTV in all bedrooms Night porter 25P Pool table International Cuisine V meals Coffee am Tea pm Last d 9.30pm
ROOMS: s fr £45; d fr £55 * **LB**
MEALS: Lunch fr £8.50&alc High tea fr £4.50&alc Dinner fr £16&alc*
CONF: Thtr 130 Class 50 Board 40 Del from £72
CARDS:

STOURPORT-ON-SEVERN Hereford & Worcester Map 07 SO87

★★★ 64% **Stourport Manor**

MENZIES HOTELS

Hartlebury Rd DY13 9LT (E, off B4193)
☎ 01299 289955 FAX 01299 878520
Set back within pretty grounds and gardens yet with good access to major road links, this one-time home of Stanley Baldwin has been extended and developed into a comfortable, modern hotel with extensive conference and function facilities. Well proportioned bedrooms promote good standards of comfort and a range of modern facilities.
68 en suite (bth/shr) (4 fmly) No smoking in 25 bedrooms CTV in all bedrooms No dogs (ex guide dogs) Night porter 200P Outdoor

swimming pool (heated) Golf 8 Tennis (hard) Squash Sauna Gym Pool table Putting green Xmas International Cuisine V meals Coffee am Tea pm No smoking area in restaurant Last d 9.30pm

ROOMS: d fr £59.50 * **LB**
OFF-PEAK: d fr £35
MEALS: Lunch £8.95-£9.95&alc Dinner £12.50-£22.50alc
CONF: Thtr 420 Class 120 Board 80 Del from £85
CARDS:

STOWMARKET Suffolk Map 05 TM05

★★63% **Cedars**

Needham Rd IP14 2AJ (A1308 1m outside Stowmarket on road to Needham Market)
☎ 01449 612668 FAX 01449 674704
Closed 26-30 Dec
A privately-owned commercial hotel based on an old farmhouse still retains some of the original building's character. Bedrooms vary in standard of appointment; some are small and dated but the majority provide comfortable accommodation, furnished to a high standard, and all are well equipped. The bar-type menu served in both the restaurant and bar offers a mixture of fresh and convenience foods. Friendly, helpful staff create an informal atmosphere, and there is ample car parking space.
24 en suite (bth/shr) (2 fmly) CTV in all bedrooms STV 75P English & French Cuisine V meals Coffee am Tea pm Last d 9.45pm
MEALS: Lunch £3-£15alc Dinner £5-£15alc*
CONF: Thtr 180 Class 60 Board 60 Del from £65
CARDS:

Travelodge

IP14 3PY (on A14 westbound) ☎ 01449 615347
FAX 01449 615347
This modern building offers accommodation in smart, spacious and well equipped bedrooms, suitable for family use, and all with en suite bathrooms. Meals may be taken at the nearby family restaurant. For information on room rates and to make a booking, call Roomline free of charge on 0800 850950. For more details about Travelodge, consult the Contents page under Hotel Groups.
40 en suite (bth/shr)

STOW-ON-THE-WOLD Gloucestershire Map 04 SP12

★★★★67% **Wyck Hill House**

Burford Rd GL54 1HY (1.5m SE on A424)
☎ 01451 831936 FAX 01451 832243
Peacefully situated in its own grounds, Wyck Hill was built in the 18th century as a private manor house. Public rooms include the intimate cedar-panelled library, a clubby bar with leather seating and a foyer lounge with a real fire. In the elegant dining room, chef Ian Smith produces dishes such as a sole and stuffed brill terrine, a rabbit and sweetbread boudin ,and a pave of lamb with garlic, thyme and a leek and spinach roulade. Bedrooms are spacious and guests will appreciate the comfortable seating and bathrobes which are provided in every room. However, one of the main strengths of Wyck Hill is the warm welcome created by general manager Peter Robinson and his caring team.
16 en suite (bth/shr) 14 annexe en suite (bth/shr) CTV in all bedrooms Lift Night porter 100P Croquet lawn Archery Clay pigeon shooting British & French Cuisine V meals Coffee am Tea pm No smoking in restaurant Last d 9.30pm
MEALS: Lunch £7.50-£13.95 Dinner £30-£37alc*
CONF: Thtr 50 Class 20 Board 20
CARDS:

★★★74% **Grapevine**
Sheep St GL54 1AU (on A436 towards Chipping Norton. 150 yds on right, facing green)
☎ 01451 830344 FAX 01451 832278
The natural warmth of the welcome and all round hospitality continue to stand out at this extended village centre inn. There are several categories of room varying in size and style of decor. An old grapevine creates the centre piece for the conservatory restaurant where carefully prepared, imaginative meals are served in a professional fashion. A meal might include prawn beignets, noisettes of lamb on a celeriac bed and lemon tart.
13 rms (12 bth/shr) 10 annexe en suite (bth/shr) (2 fmly) CTV in all bedrooms No dogs (ex guide dogs) 23P V meals Coffee am Tea pm No smoking in restaurant Last d 9.30pm
ROOMS: (incl. bkfst) s £60-£100; d £120-£160 **LB**
OFF-PEAK: (incl. bkfst & dinner) s £55-£105; d £110-£170
MEALS: Lunch £9.45-£13.25 High tea £4.35-£5.95 Dinner £19.95-£23.45*
CONF: Thtr 30 Class 18 Board 20 Del from £98
CARDS:

★★★70% **Fosse Manor**

GL54 1JX (1m S on A429, 300yds past junction with A424) ☎ 01451 830354 FAX 01451 832486
Closed 23-28 Dec
This family run hotel, just off the A429 to the south of the town, has a warm friendly atmosphere and this coupled with efficient service makes Fosse Manor an excellent choice. Bedrooms are all individually styled and show a keen eye for detail and colour with bold fabrics and wall coverings being used. The public areas are smart and attractive with a comfortable residents lounge and a cosy bar. For special pampering there is a beauty salon provided and the more active can enjoy a game of outdoor chess. Cuisine is a highlight and the new chef serves some imaginative dishes such as a starter of warm salad of black pudding with crisp bacon, sauté potatoes and poached egg.
16 en suite (bth/shr) 4 annexe en suite (bth) (5 fmly) CTV in all bedrooms 40P Croquet lawn Beautician/Golf practice net ch fac English & Continental Cuisine V meals Coffee am Tea pm Last d 10pm

contd.

ROOMS: (incl. bkfst) s £53-£65; d £80-£150 * **LB**
MEALS: Lunch fr £13.95 Dinner fr £18.95*
CONF: Thtr 40 Class 20 Board 20 Del from £70
CARDS:

★★★67% **The Unicorn**

FORTE Heritage

Sheep St GL54 1HQ (situated at the junct of A429 & A436) ☎ 01451 830257 FAX 01451 831090
A popular hotel dating from the 17th century, with a congenial bar and an attractive restaurant. Bedrooms have benefited from recent refurbishment and offer bright, modern standards of comfort. Friendly service is provided by the manager, Yvonne Dunmur and a small local team. The recruitment of Mark Gilberthorpe to head the kitchen has resulted in enjoyable and imaginative cooking.
20 en suite (bth/shr) No smoking in 11 bedrooms CTV in all bedrooms 45P Xmas V meals Coffee am Tea pm No smoking in restaurant Last d 9.30pm
ROOMS: s fr £75; d fr £95 * **LB**
MEALS: Lunch £11.25-£13.50 Dinner fr £19.95*
CONF: Thtr 25 Class 8 Board 12 Del from £90
CARDS:

★★70% **Stow Lodge**
The Square GL54 1AB (in town centre)
☎ 01451 830485 FAX 8316713
Closed 21 Dec-Jan
A friendly, family-run hotel close to the centre, Stow Lodge offers well maintained accommodation in a variety of styles, in the main building and a converted coach house. The characterful public areas include a lounge with its open fire and a bar with its wooden pew-like seating.
11 en suite (bth/shr) 10 annexe en suite (bth/shr) (32 fmly) No smoking in all bedrooms CTV in all bedrooms No dogs Night porter 30P No coaches No children 5yrs V meals Coffee am No smoking in restaurant Last d 9pm
ROOMS: (incl. bkfst) s £40-£75; d £58-£95 * **LB**
MEALS: Dinner £14.50-£15&alc*
CARDS:

★★66% **Old Farmhouse**
Lower Swell GL54 1LF (1m W on B2052)
☎ 01451 830232 or 0500 657842 (free) FAX 01451 870962
RS 8-23 Jan
In a pretty village just west of Stow, this converted farmhouse is run by the owners. Log fires burn in the bar and the restaurant which serves chef Graham Simmonds' good, hearty food made with local produce. Bedrooms vary in size and there are additional bright and well equipped rooms in a former stable block.
7 rms (4 bth/shr) 7 annexe en suite (bth/shr) (1 fmly) No smoking in 6 bedrooms CTV in all bedrooms 25P Mountain bikes hire/Air pistol range Xmas V meals Coffee am Tea pm No smoking in restaurant Last d 9pm
ROOMS: (incl. bkfst) s £22-£50; d £43-£91 * **LB**
OFF-PEAK: (incl. bkfst) s £18-£45; d £65-£85
MEALS: Lunch £9.99 Dinner £16.50*

CONF: Thtr 30 Board 8 Del from £20
CARDS:

See advertisement on opposite page

★★66% **Old Stocks**
The Square GL54 1AF ☎ 01451 830666 FAX 01451 870014
Closed 18-27 Dec
The sinister past of this pretty Cotswold market town is reflected in the name of this friendly family run hotel. The stocks themselves are still visible outside the hotel on the town square. The hotel is formed from three 16th and 17th-century buildings. The cosy lounge bar and restaurant retain many original features and much of the historical character. Bedrooms are well proportioned and are comfortable with modern facilities.
15 en suite (bth/shr) 3 annexe en suite (bth/shr) (1 fmly) No smoking in 10 bedrooms CTV in all bedrooms 14P ch fac Xmas V meals Coffee am Tea pm No smoking in restaurant Last d 9.30pm
ROOMS: (incl. bkfst) s £40; d £70 * **LB**
MEALS: Sunday Lunch fr £5.95 Dinner £9.50-£15.25*
CONF: Thtr 12
CARDS:

Farmers Lodge
Fosse Way GL54 1JX ☎ 01451 870044 FAX 01451 870539
RS 3rd wk Dec-Jan
Conveniently located between Stow-on-the-Wold and Bourton-on-the-Water, Farmers Lodge is ideally situated for exploring the Cotswolds. Either ground or first floor level bedrooms are available, one room being specifically designed for disabled guests. Breakfast is served in the first floor dining room, while other meals are available in the Farmers Restaurant, a character inn adjoining the lodge, but independently managed.
17 en suite (bth/shr) (4 fmly) No smoking in all bedrooms CTV in all bedrooms STV 60P No coaches English Cuisine V meals Coffee am No smoking area in restaurant Last d 10pm
ROOMS: (incl. cont bkfst) s £39-£43.50; d £39-£48
MEALS: Lunch £14-£25 Dinner £20-£35
CONF: Board 40

STRATFIELD TURGIS Hampshire Map 04 SU65

★★★64% **Wellington Arms**
RG27 0AS ☎ 01256 882214 FAX 01256 882934
Situated at one of the entrances to Stratfield Saye, the ancestral home of the Duke of Wellington, the white Georgian façade of this Grade 11 listed building is a familiar landmark between Basingstoke and Reading on the A33. The bar lounge offers some comfortable seating around a log fire and an extensive selection of bar meals is available. Alternatively there is the option of dining in the restaurant, from both table d'hôte and the à la carte menus. The majority of bedrooms are located in the purpose-built Garden Wing and offer every modern convenience; rooms in the original building are equipped to the same standard though tend to be smaller and can lack certain facilities, but are priced accordingly.
35 en suite (bth/shr) (2 fmly) No smoking in 3 bedrooms CTV in all bedrooms 150P V meals Coffee am Tea pm Last d 9.30pm
ROOMS: (incl. bkfst) s £70-£85; d £80-£95 **LB**
MEALS: Lunch £15.95&alc Dinner £15.95&alc*
CONF: Thtr 100 Class 50 Board 40 Del from £100.95
CARDS:

STRATFORD-UPON-AVON Warwickshire Map 04 SP25

★★★★73% **Billesley Manor**

Billesley, Alcester B49 6NF (off A46 towards Alcester)
☎ 01789 279955 FAX 01789 764145
Lying a short distance away from the bustle of Stratford, in a quiet rural location, this striking Elizabethan manor

house traces its origins to before the Norman conquest. Its many delightful features include a well kept topiary garden and, inside, an abundance of wood panelling and several open log-burning fireplaces. Bedroom styles vary, and some elegantly refurbished rooms enjoy wonderful garden views. The kitchen, under Roger Barstow, goes to great lengths to produce enjoyable dishes.

41 en suite (bth/shr) (6 fmly) No smoking in 5 bedrooms CTV in all bedrooms No dogs Night porter 100P Indoor swimming pool (heated) Tennis (hard) Croquet lawn Putting green Pitch & putt Xmas English & French Cuisine V meals Coffee am Tea pm No smoking in restaurant

ROOMS: s £105; d £155 * **LB**

OFF-PEAK: (incl. bkfst) s £76; d £152

CONF: Thtr 100 Class 60 Board 40 Del £155

CARDS:

See advertisement on this page

★★★★ 72% **Welcombe**
Warwick Rd CV37 0NR (1.5m NE on A439)
☎ 01789 295252 FAX 01789 414666
This Jacobean-style manor house is set in 800 acres of attractively landscaped parkland part of which was once owned by Shakespeare. Bedrooms, all well equipped, are split between the garden wing and the orgiginal house. The sumptuous Caroline has a splendid view of the garden. The public areas are attractive with the wood panelled lounge a special feature. Friendly staff offer traditional standard of service. The dining room offers food prepared with a care for clear flavours, as evidence in an enjoyable starter of roast scallops served with salad leaves and a rocket pesto. A major refurbishment programme should make this hotel one of the finest in the Midlands.
75 en suite (bth/shr) (2 fmly) CTV in all bedrooms STV No dogs (ex guide dogs) Night porter 210P Golf 18 Tennis (hard) Fishing Snooker Putting green Table tennis Wkly live entertainment Xmas V meals Coffee am Tea pm No smoking in restaurant Last d 10pm
ROOMS: (incl. bkfst) s £110; d £150-£500 * **LB**
OFF-PEAK: (incl. bkfst & dinner) s £130; d £195-£225
MEALS: Lunch £19.50-£21.50 High tea £15-£25alc Dinner £32.50&alc
CONF: Thtr 120 Class 55 Board 26 Del from £150
CARDS:

See advertisement on opposite page

★★★★ 69% **The Shakespeare**
FORTE Heritage
Chapel St CV37 6ER (adjoining town hall)
☎ 01789 294771 FAX 01789 415411
Located in the heart of the town, this hotel is a landmark sight with its gabled timber façade. The inside has period character with large, open log-burning fireplaces, creaking stairs and exposed timbers. Bedrooms provide modern and clean comforts. The Garrick restaurant is well run offering dishes that show keen effort and the use of fresh tasting ingredients.
63 en suite (bth/shr) No smoking in 20 bedrooms CTV in all bedrooms Lift Night porter 45P Wkly live entertainment Xmas V meals Coffee am Tea pm No smoking in restaurant Last d 10pm
ROOMS: s £95; d £110-£140 * **LB**
MEALS: Lunch £12.95-£14.95&alc High tea fr £8.95 Dinner £25.95-£40&alc*
CONF: Thtr 120 Class 50 Board 40 Del from £130
CARDS:

★★★★ 66% **Stratford Manor**
Best Western
Warwick Rd CV37 0PY (2.5m on A439)
☎ 01789 731173 FAX 01789 731131
This modern hotel sits in 21 acres of well tended grounds beside the A439, conveniently located for access to junction 15 of the M40. Marston Hotels have implemented considerable changes to services and public areas, so that the hotel now offers courteous professional service and enhanced comfort levels. The bright air-conditioned public areas include a large open-plan lounge bar, a nicely appointed split-level restaurant and an attractive reception lobby. The modern leisure complex offers a good range of amenities and the high-tech gym has recently been extended and upgraded. Conferences are extremely well catered for, the 13 suites and meeting rooms allowing good flexibility.
104 en suite (bth/shr) (8 fmly) No smoking in 52 bedrooms CTV in all bedrooms STV Lift Night porter 220P Indoor swimming pool (heated) Tennis (hard) Sauna Solarium Gym Pool table Jacuzzi/spa Xmas English & Continental Cuisine V meals Coffee am Tea pm No smoking in restaurant Last d 10pm
ROOMS: s £75-£85; d £90-£100 * **LB**
OFF-PEAK: (incl. bkfst & dinner) s £71-£81; d £115-£125
MEALS: Lunch £12.50-£13.50 Dinner £17.50-£19.50&alc
CONF: Thtr 360 Class 200 Board 100 Del from £110
CARDS:

★★★★ 65% **Alveston Manor**
FORTE Heritage
Clopton Bridge CV37 7HP (first roundabout before Clopton Bridge) ☎ 01789 204581
FAX 01789 414095
A striking red brick and wooden front, well tended grounds, and a distinctive giant cedar tree all contribute to the charm of this well established hotel. A rich history surrounds the building and some of the 16th-century decor can be seen in the bar with its panelling. Bedrooms vary in size and character but all provide modern comforts. The menus and wine list add extra interest and the food in the Manor restaurant shows great care and good intentions in producing full flavours. Service is friendly and willing.
106 en suite (bth/shr) No smoking in 30 bedrooms CTV in all bedrooms STV Night porter 200P Xmas V meals Coffee am Tea pm No smoking in restaurant Last d 9.30pm
ROOMS: s £105; d £120-£195 * **LB**
MEALS: Lunch £13.95-£17.95&alc Dinner £25.95-£27.95&alc
CONF: Thtr 140 Class 80 Board 40 Del from £155
CARDS:

★★★★ 64% **Arden Thistle**
THISTLE HOTELS
Waterside CV37 6BA (follow town centre signs turn left into High Street from Bridge Street then 2nd left into Chapel Lane) ☎ 01789 294949
FAX 01789 415874
This popular hotel occupies an enviable position in the heart of Stratford at the water's edge opposite the Royal Shakespeare and Swan theatres. The recently refurbished bedrooms have attractive period-style furniture and guests can choose between a number of types of room. The cooking is bright, well executed and flavoursome, but architectural restraints limit the size of the quiet lounge, the elegant restaurant and terrace, and the cosy theatre bar.
63 en suite (bth/shr) (2 fmly) No smoking in 25 bedrooms CTV in all bedrooms STV No dogs (ex guide dogs) Night porter 70P Xmas English & Continental Cuisine V meals Coffee am Tea pm No smoking in restaurant Last d 10pm
ROOMS: s £78-£85; d £95-£115 * **LB**
MEALS: Lunch £12.50&alc Dinner £24.95&alc*
CONF: Thtr 60 Class 22 Board 30 Del from £100
CARDS:

★★★★ 64% **Stratford Moat House**
MOAT HOUSE
Bridgefoot CV37 6YR (adjoining Stratford Leisure Centre) ☎ 01789 279988 FAX 01789 298589
Popular with both the business guest and overseas groups, this large modern hotel is located right by the River Avon, close to the town centre. It offers spacious bedrooms, a choice of restaurants and bars, an attractive range of shops, a night club and extensive conference/function facilities. Recent upgrading to the exterior and reception lobby has improved the appearance and comfort. Excellent car parking is provided on the premises.
247 en suite (bth/shr) (8 fmly) No smoking in 91 bedrooms CTV in all bedrooms Lift Night porter Air conditioning 350P Indoor

contd.

S

swimming pool (heated) Fishing Snooker Sauna Solarium Gym Pool table Jacuzzi/spa Beautician Hair stylist Video games room ch fac European Cuisine V meals Coffee am Tea pm No smoking area in restaurant Last d 11pm
ROOMS: s £98; d £125 * **LB**
OFF-PEAK: (incl. bkfst) s fr £48; d fr £96
MEALS: Lunch £14.50 High tea £5-£20alc Dinner £14.50&alc*
CONF: Thtr 450 Class 260 Board 100 Del £150
CARDS:

★★★ 77% Salford Hall
WR11 5UT STRATFORD-UPON-AVON
☎ 01386 871300 FAX 01386 871301
(For full entry see Abbot's Salford)

★★★ 68% Grosvenor House
Warwick Rd CV37 6YT (turn off jct 15 on M40 follow Stratford signs to A439 Warwick Rd, hotel is 7m from jct on town centre one way system) ☎ 01789 269213 FAX 01789 266087
Grosvenor House is a friendly hotel which prides itself on the natural charm of its efficient staff. The hotel is located on the main Warwick road a little way from the town centre. Since our last visit a new suite of smart, well appointed rooms has been added, and further upgrading is in progress with the addition of a conservatory. The restaurant has a fascinating trompe l'oeil mural and serves a wide range of popular modern dishes. There are extensive conference and banqueting facilities which are fully equipped for business meetings.
60 en suite (bth/shr) (1 fmly) No smoking in 5 bedrooms CTV in all bedrooms No dogs (ex guide dogs) Night porter 53P Xmas English & Continental Cuisine V meals Coffee am Tea pm No smoking in restaurant Last d 9.30pm
ROOMS: (incl. bkfst) s £72; d £95 **LB**
MEALS: Lunch £10.95&alc Dinner £13.95&alc*
CONF: Thtr 100 Class 50 Board 40 Del £95
CARDS:

See advertisement on page 589

★★★ 63% Charlecote Pheasant Country
CV35 9EW ☎ 01789 470333 FAX 01789 470222
(For full entry see Charlecote)

★★★ 63% The White Swan
Rother St CV37 6NH ☎ 01789 297022
FAX 01789 268773

This character half-timbered building has retained many of its original features and offers cosy, traditionally furnished public areas. Bedrooms come in a variety of shapes and sizes, and all are well equipped with modern facilities. A programme of refurbishment began in 1995.
37 en suite (bth/shr) (3 fmly) No smoking in 12 bedrooms CTV in all bedrooms Night porter 9P Xmas V meals Coffee am Tea pm No smoking in restaurant Last d 9pm
ROOMS: s £50-£75; d £70-£90 * **LB**
OFF-PEAK: s £30-£50; d £40-£70
MEALS: Sunday Lunch £10.95 Dinner £14-£28*
CONF: Thtr 50 Class 25 Board 25 Del from £60
CARDS:

★★★ 60% Falcon
Chapel St CV37 6HA (town centre-opposite Guild Chapel and Nash House)
☎ 01789 279953 FAX 01789 414260

This old town-centre inn offers a choice of bars, a characterful restaurant, and a range of bedrooms. Rooms situated in the new wing have been smartly refurbished; while those in the original part of the buildingare due to be upgraded. A young team of staff offers friendly service.
73 en suite (bth/shr) (13 fmly) No smoking in 27 bedrooms CTV in all bedrooms Lift Night porter 124P Xmas European Cuisine V meals Coffee am Tea pm No smoking area in restaurant Last d 9pm
ROOMS: s £76-£88; d £99-£125 **LB**
OFF-PEAK: s £60-£76; d £85-£99
MEALS: Lunch £9.95-£18.50&alc High tea £6.75-£10.50 Dinner £18.50-£20.50&alc*
CONF: Thtr 200 Class 110 Board 40 Del from £118
CARDS:

★★ 70% Stratford Court
Avenue Rd CV37 6UX ☎ 01789 297799 FAX 01789 262449
Stratford Court is a delightful Edwardian property in a residential suburb of Stratford. The atmosphere is very much one of informal friendliness in charming surroundings. Bedrooms have all been furnished and equipped to a very high standard with the use of some dramatic fabrics and furnishings. Period pieces of furniture live in harmony with modern techniques such as rag rolling. The comfortable lounge and cosy bar are conducive to socialising, and the hands-on approach of the proprietors means guests quickly feel at home. The dinner operation takes a back seat but is a useful standby for guests wishing to eat in rather than explore the town.
13 en suite (bth/shr) (2 fmly) CTV in all bedrooms 20P No coaches No children 14yrs English & French Cuisine V meals Coffee am Tea pm No smoking in restaurant Last d 8.30pm
ROOMS: (incl. bkfst) s £48.50-£55; d £85-£150
MEALS: Dinner fr £17
CARDS:

★★ 70% Stratford House
18 Sheep St CV37 6EF (100yds from the Royal Shakespeare Theatre)
☎ 01789 268288 FAX 01789 295580
RS closed Mon lunch
Personally run by proprietor Sylvia Adcock, this charming small hotel is located in the centre of the old town, just 100 yards from the Royal Shakespeare Theatre. The public areas feature photographs of recent Shakespeare productions, while bedrooms are tastefully furnished and have attractive fabrics. The airy, Shepherd Garden conservatory restaurant is cane-furnished and offers imaginative dishes such as a darne of salmon with lemon butter sauce. A comfortable coffee shop at the front of the hotel is the perfect place to relax and enjoy wonderful home-baking .
11 en suite (bth/shr) (1 fmly) CTV in all bedrooms No dogs (ex guide dogs) Night porter No coaches English & French Cuisine V meals Coffee am Tea pm Last d 9.30pm
ROOMS: (incl. bkfst) s £50-£70; d £82-£88 *
OFF-PEAK: (incl. bkfst) s £50-£65; d £72-£85
MEALS: Bar Lunch £3.50-£5 High tea £3.50-£5 Dinner fr £20alc*
CARDS:

★★ 64% The Coach House Hotel
16-17 Warwick Rd CV37 6YW (in town centre) ☎ 01789 204109 FAX 01789 415916

Well placed within walking distance for the town centre and personally run, this popular hotel, manned by bright and friendly staff, has a thriving cellar restaurant serving a good choice of dishes. Bedrooms are comfortable and well equipped.
10 en suite (bth/shr) 13 annexe rms (10 bth/shr) (3 fmly) No smoking in 5 bedrooms CTV in all bedrooms No dogs (ex guide dogs) 30P Local Leisure centre free to guests English & Italian Cuisine V meals Last d 8.30pm
ROOMS: (incl. bkfst) s £30-£58; d £48-£91 * **LB**
OFF-PEAK: (incl. bkfst) s £28-£58; d £45-£91
MEALS: Sunday Lunch £8.50-£10.50 Dinner £12-£18&alc*
CONF: Thtr 24 Class 24 Board 12 Del from £68
CARDS:

See advertisement on opposite page

Forte Posthouse Stratford upon Avon

FORTE Posthouse

Bridgefoot CV37 7LT (from M40 junct 15,A46 to Stratford,leave at 1st rdbt A439 to town centre,entering town follow one way system left over river bridge hotel by river)
☎ 01789 266761 FAX 01789 414547
Suitable for both the business and leisure traveller, this bright hotel provides modern accommodation in well equipped bedrooms with en suite bathrooms. For more details about Forte Posthouse hotels, consult the Contents page for the section on Hotel Groups.
60 en suite (bth/shr)
ROOMS: s £69-£79; d £69-£79 *
CONF: Thtr 150 Class 100 Del from £105

◯ Quality Stratford Victoria
Arden St CV37 6NX ☎ 01789 271000 FAX 01789 271001
100 en suite (bth/shr) (35 fmly) No smoking in 40 bedrooms CTV in all bedrooms STV Lift Night porter 96P Jacuzzi/spa English & Continental Cuisine V meals Coffee am Tea pm No smoking area in restaurant Last d 10pm
ROOMS: (incl. cont bkfst) s £58.50; d £78.50-£105 * **LB**
MEALS: Lunch £11.50-£15 High tea £3-£10 Dinner £15-£20&alc*
CONF: Thtr 110 Class 66 Board 54 Del from £95
CARDS:

STREATLEY Berkshire Map 04 SU58

★★★★ 66% Swan Diplomat

High St RG8 9HR ☎ 01491 873737
FAX 01491 872554
The beautiful waterside location of the Swan Diplomat makes it a perfect location for a relaxing visit. Bedrooms are spacious and thoughtfully equipped though some are beginning to show signs of age. The attractive restaurant overlooks the Thames and the menu offers a good range of fresh modern dishes. There is a choice of comfortably furnished lounges and seating areas, and in the summer months guests may sit on the terrace. The hotel is well suited to both leisure and business guests with several conference rooms and a modern leisure suite with pool.
46 en suite (bth/shr) No smoking in 2 bedrooms CTV in all bedrooms STV Night porter 135P Sauna Solarium Gym Pool table Croquet lawn Jacuzzi/spa Boat hire Exercise Pool French Cuisine V meals Coffee am Tea pm
CONF: Thtr 80 Class 50 Board 40 Del from £145
CARDS:

See advertisement on page 593

STREET Somerset Map 03 ST43

★★★ 63% Wessex
High St BA16 0EF ☎ 01458 443383 FAX 01458 46589
This purpose built hotel, situated in the centre of the town, with ample parking, is just a short walk from Clarks village. Spacious bedrooms have been equipped with modern facilities, and the public areas include a range of function rooms, a cosy bar, and a comfortable restaurant offering a table d'hôte menu and a choice from the carvery.
50 en suite (bth/shr) (2 fmly) CTV in all bedrooms STV Lift Night porter 90P Xmas V meals Coffee am Tea pm Last d 9pm
ROOMS: (incl. bkfst) s £40-£50; d £50-£60 **LB**
MEALS: Lunch £7.95-£14.50 High tea £3.10 Dinner £14.50
CONF: Thtr 250 Class 150 Board 50 Del from £60
CARDS:

S

STRETTON Rutland Map 08 SK91

★★ 69% **Ram Jam Inn**
Great North Rd LE15 7QX (on northbound carriageway of A1)
☎ 01780 410776 FAX 01780 410361
Closed 25 Dec
One of the most famous landmarks and hostelries along the A1, this inn is easily accessed from either direction of travel. The style is that of a café bar and bistro with rooms. The two distinct influences, continental and English country house, blend well together. Polished pine, terracotta floors and marble tops are interspersed with deep plump sofas, elegant wall coverings and open fires. The atmosphere is relaxed and informal but dedicated to providing good modern English dishes, attentive service and genuine hospitality. The bedrooms meet all the expectations of a higher classification.
7 en suite (bth/shr) (1 fmly) CTV in all bedrooms 64P English & Continental Cuisine V meals Coffee am Tea pm Last d 10pm
ROOMS: s fr £41; d fr £51
OFF-PEAK: (incl. bkfst) s fr £41; d fr £51
MEALS: Dinner £14-£19
CONF: Thtr 60 Class 40 Board 40 Del £72.50
CARDS:

STROUD Gloucestershire Map 03 SO80
See also Amberley

★★★65% **Burleigh Court**
Minchinhampton GL5 2PF (0.75m off A419 E of Stroud)
☎ 01453 883804 FAX 01453 886870
RS Sun
New owners have created a high standard of accommodation at their charming manor house, which is set in landscaped gardens offering wide views of the surrounding vales. Bedrooms are spacious, and several are located in a rear extension close to the outdoor swimming pool. Public areas have a dignified character and there is an inviting atmosphere in the wood-panelled bar.
11 en suite (bth/shr) 6 annexe en suite (bth/shr) (1 fmly) No smoking in 4 bedrooms CTV in all bedrooms STV 41P No coaches Outdoor swimming pool (heated) ch fac English & French Cuisine V meals Coffee am Tea pm No smoking in restaurant Last d 9pm
MEALS: Lunch £14.95-£16.95&alc High tea £6 Dinner £19.95-£21.70&alc*
CONF: Thtr 60 Board 16 Del from £95
CARDS:

★★★62% **The Bear of Rodborough**

Rodborough Common GL5 5DE (1m S on A46, turn left to Rodborough Common) ☎ 01453 878522
FAX 01453 872523
Situated on Rodborough Common, this hotel has the traditional charm and character of an historic inn, retaining many of its original features. The majority of bedrooms have been upgraded and hopefully the remainder, together with the public rooms, will soon benefit from similar good work. A range of meals is available in the bar and the restaurant offers a fixed-price menu.
47 en suite (bth/shr) (1 fmly) No smoking in 15 bedrooms CTV in all bedrooms Night porter 200P Croquet lawn Xmas English & Continental Cuisine V meals Coffee am Tea pm No smoking in restaurant Last d 9.30pm
ROOMS: s £60-£70; d £75-£90 * **LB**
MEALS: Sunday Lunch £12-£18alc Dinner £19.95&alc*
CONF: Thtr 70 Class 25 Board 30 Del from £85
CARDS:

★★65% ***The London Hotel***
30-31 London Rd GL5 2AJ (E, on A419)
☎ 01453 759992 FAX 01453 753363
Catering for a predominantly commercial clientele, this hotel has fresh, well equipped rooms, some of which are compact. Cosy public areas include a small bar and adjacent restaurant where a good range of meals is served. Friendly services are provided by owners Mr and Mrs Portal and their staff.
12 rms (2 bth 6 shr) CTV in all bedrooms No dogs 8P No coaches English & French Cuisine V meals Coffee am Tea pm Last d 9.30pm
CARDS:

★★63% **The Bell**
Wallbridge GL5 3JA (at junct of A419/A46)
☎ 01453 763556 FAX 01453 758611
This well run inn-style hotel offers friendly and informal services supervised by owners Mr and Mrs Williams. Bedrooms are generally spacious and well equipped, and the restaurant serves both bar meals and more formal dinners in the dining room. The bar is popular with both residents and locals alike, with a good range of well kept beers and a convivial atmosphere.
12 rms (10 bth/shr) (1 fmly) CTV in all bedrooms STV 30P Xmas Continental Cuisine V meals Coffee am No smoking in restaurant Last d 9pm
ROOMS: (incl. bkfst) s £28-£50; d £38-£70 **LB**
MEALS: Lunch £9.95-£12.95&alc Dinner £9.95-£12.95&alc*
CONF: Thtr 35 Class 20 Board 16
CARDS:

STUDLAND Dorset Map 04 SZ08

★★ 65% **Manor House**
BH19 3AU ☎ 01929 450288 FAX 01929 450288
Closed 19 Dec-Jan
In a splendid situation overlooking the bay, this friendly family run hotel continues to improve. The bedrooms are modest but well equipped and public areas include a comfortable lounge and a small intimate bar. A varied choice set-price dinner menu, including a selection of fresh local fish and shellfish, is served in the bright conservatory restaurant, and David Rolfe's cooking is uncomplicated but accomplished.
20 en suite (bth/shr) (9 fmly) CTV in all bedrooms 80P Tennis (hard) Croquet lawn No children 5yrs English & French Cuisine V meals Coffee am Tea pm No smoking in restaurant Last d 8.30pm
ROOMS: (incl. bkfst & dinner) d £112-£130 * **LB**
OFF-PEAK: (incl. bkfst & dinner) d £96-£116
MEALS: Sunday Lunch £6.85-£8.35 High tea £4.75 Dinner £18.50*
CONF: Class 25
CARDS:

STURMINSTER NEWTON Dorset Map 03 ST71

★★★ 70% **Plumber Manor**

Hazelbury Bryan Rd DT10 2AF (1.5m SW of Sturminster Newton, off A357 towards Hazelbury Bryan) ☎ 01258 472507 FAX 01258 473370
Closed Feb
This beautiful Jacobean Manor owned by the Prideaux-Brune family is set in its own beautiful grounds, surrounded by farmland. The rooms in the main house are traditionally furnished and retain much of their original character, while the deluxe rooms in the converted barns are more spacious. The hub of the house is the house is the restaurant where Brian Prideaux-Brune has gained a well deserved reputation for his skilfully prepared food; making good use of local ingredients Brian combines traditional favourites with some more imaginative dishes.
6 en suite (bth/shr) 10 annexe en suite (bth/shr) CTV in all bedrooms 30P No coaches Tennis (hard) Croquet lawn English & French Cuisine V meals Last d 9pm
MEALS: Sunday Lunch fr £17.50 Dinner £15-£25
CONF: Thtr 25 Board 12 Del from £100
CARDS:

SUDBURY Derbyshire Map 07 SK13

★★★66% **The Boars Head**

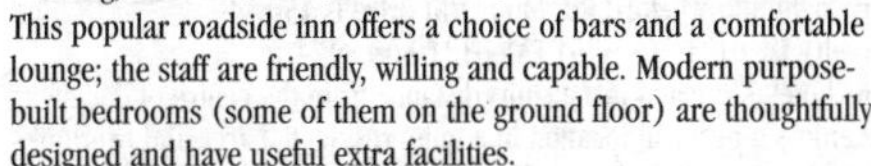

Lichfield Rd DE6 5GX (on A515, close to railway crossing) ☎ 01283 820344 FAX 01283 820075

This popular roadside inn offers a choice of bars and a comfortable lounge; the staff are friendly, willing and capable. Modern purpose-built bedrooms (some of them on the ground floor) are thoughtfully designed and have useful extra facilities.

22 en suite (bth/shr) CTV in all bedrooms STV Night porter 85P Solarium Wkly live entertainment Xmas International Cuisine V meals Coffee am Tea pm Last d 9.30pm

ROOMS: (incl. bkfst) s £35-£57.50; d £45-£69.50 * LB

MEALS: Lunch £11.95&alc Dinner £11.95&alc

CONF: Thtr 35 Class 45 Board 25

CARDS:

See advertisement under BURTON UPON TRENT

SUDBURY Suffolk Map 05 TL84

★★★70% **Mill**

Walnut Tree Ln CO10 6BD ☎ 01787 375544 FAX 01787 373027

This character hotel stands on the banks of the River Stour on the fringe of the town, overlooking open countryside. Smartly maintained public rooms retain much of the character of the building's 300-year history, with open fires, exposed oak beams, and a working mill wheel visible through the glass screens that divide the restaurant and lounge bar areas. Bedroom sizes are quite variable, ranging from the spacious through to the cosy standard rooms. All are attractively furnished and well appointed and most have river or mill pond views.

52 en suite (bth/shr) (2 fmly) CTV in all bedrooms STV Night porter 60P Fishing Xmas English & French Cuisine V meals Coffee am Tea pm No smoking in restaurant Last d 9.30pm

ROOMS: s £50-£60; d £68-£88 LB

MEALS: Lunch £14-£17.50alc Dinner £17.50-£25alc

CONF: Thtr 90 Class 50 Board 40 Del from £70

CARDS:

SUNDERLAND Tyne & Wear Map 12 NZ35

★★★★63% **Swallow**

Queen's Pde, Seaburn SR6 8DB ☎ 0191 529 2041 FAX 0191 529 4227

Situated in an excellent position on the sea front overlooking Whitburn Sands and with its own private car park at the rear, this hotel provides a good standard of accommodation particularly those bedrooms in the original part of the hotel which are spacious and overlook the sea. Some rooms in the newer section are more compact, but modern and tastefully furnished and decorated. The renowned Promenade Restaurant features an unique Victorian "bandstand" and Head Chef Ken Thompson's cooking can be highly recommended. There is also a well equipped Leisure Club which includes a swimming pool and a gymnasium. The smartly dressed staff are helpful and friendly and service is efficient.

65 en suite (bth/shr) (3 fmly) No smoking in 25 bedrooms CTV in all bedrooms STV Lift Night porter 110P Indoor swimming pool (heated) Sauna Solarium Gym Jacuzzi/spa Steam room Wkly live entertainment Xmas English & French Cuisine V meals Coffee am Tea pm Last d 9.45pm

ROOMS: (incl. bkfst) s £80-£130; d £95-£150 * LB

OFF-PEAK: (incl. bkfst) s £48-£70

MEALS: Lunch £10-£13.95&alc Dinner £18.50-£35alc

CONF: Thtr 300 Class 120 Board 90 Del from £115

CARDS:

Travel Inn

Wessington Way, Castletown SR5 3HR (A1231 at junc of A19) ☎ 0191 548 9384 FAX 0191 548 4148

Purpose-built accommodation, offering spacious, well equipped bedrooms, all with en suite bathrooms. Meals may be taken at the nearby family restaurant. For more information about Travel Inns, consult the Contents page under Hotel Groups.

41 en suite (bth/shr)

ROOMS: d £35.50 *

SUTTON Greater London Map 04 TQ26

★★★★63% ***Holiday Inn***

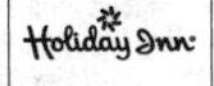

Gibson Rd SM1 2RF (from M25 junct 8 follow A217 then B2230 to hotel entrance) ☎ 0181 770 1311 FAX 0181 770 1539

Located in the centre of town, this busy conference hotel has the added advantage of parking and well maintained leisure facilities with a pool. The top floor offers sweeping views, while another of the four floors is dedicated to executive-style rooms with their own fax machines. Some of the bedrooms are no-smoking and a 24-hour room service is available. An eclectic range of dishes is served in the informal

contd.

atmosphere of Madison's Restaurant, while the Balcony lounge offers alternative menus throughout the day. The smartly presented staff are well meaning and there are flashes of the wonderful hospitality which won the hotel a coveted Courtesy and Care award a few years back.
116 en suite (bth/shr) No smoking in 45 bedrooms CTV in all bedrooms Lift Night porter Air conditioning 120P Indoor swimming pool (heated) Snooker Sauna Solarium Gym Pool table Jacuzzi/spa Steam room Beauty room International Cuisine V meals Coffee am Tea pm Last d 9.30pm
CARDS:

★★60% **Thatched House**
135 Cheam Rd SM1 2BN ☎ 0181 642 3131 FAX 0181 770 0684
Prominently located on the A232 Epsom/Croydon road, this thatched cottage-style hotel is an ideal venue for business and pleasure. It offers a good range of modern bedrooms, cosy public areas, the Devon Dene annexe, meeting and function rooms, and a well maintained rear garden which is often used for wedding receptions. A good choice of dinner dishes including chef's specials and supplementary grills is available Monday to Friday (with limited availability and service by arrangement at weekends). The atmosphere is friendly and relaxed, and conscientious service is well managed by Mr John Jeffs.
27 rms (24 bth/shr) 5 annexe en suite (bth/shr) CTV in all bedrooms 25P No coaches V meals Coffee am Tea pm No smoking area in restaurant Last d 9.15pm
ROOMS: (incl. bkfst) s fr £57.50; d fr £67.50 *
OFF-PEAK: (incl. bkfst) s fr £47.50; d fr £57.50
MEALS: Lunch fr £8.95 Dinner fr £14.50
CONF: Thtr 50 Class 30 Board 26
CARDS:

SUTTON COLDFIELD West Midlands Map 07 SP19

RED STAR HOTEL

★★★★ ⊛⊛⊛ **New Hall**
Walmley Rd B76 8QX (off B4148)
☎ 0121 378 2442 FAX 0121 378 4637

This lovingly preserved hotel, personally run in friendly, attentive style by Caroline and Ian Parkes, is set in 26 acres of sedate gardens. Memorable features include an intact moat, a yew tree walk, an ornamental pool and an archery lawn. Inside there are historic features such as mullioned windows, fine fireplaces and old stained glass. Bedrooms are split between the main building and a cleverly added extension. Public areas are dominated by the restaurant where serious attention is paid to the kitchen's output, which might be described as classically inspired with a light touch and robust flavours. Good examples of the menu style are scallops with polenta and parsley cream, ballotine of rabbit saddle stuffed with a delicate chicken mousse and wrapped in Parma ham, and a confidently flavoured passion fruit soufflé.
62 en suite (bth/shr) CTV in all bedrooms STV No dogs (ex guide dogs) Night porter 70P Golf 9 Fishing Croquet lawn Putting green Golf driving net No children 8yrs Xmas International Cuisine V meals Coffee am Tea pm No smoking in restaurant Last d 10pm
ROOMS: s £100-£135; d £120-£165 * **LB**
OFF-PEAK: s £90-£110; d £114-£154
MEALS: Lunch £16.50-£21.95alc Dinner £27.50-£34.45alc*
CONF: Thtr 50 Class 30 Board 30 Del from £150
CARDS:

★★★69% **Moor Hall**

Moor Hall Dr, Four Oaks B75 6LN (at jct of A38/A453 take A453 towards Sutton Coldfield, at traffic lights turn right into Weeford Rd, Moor Hill drive is 150 yds on left) ☎ 0121 308 3751 FAX 0121 308 8974
This hotel is situated just a short distance from the centre of the city yet enjoys a peaceful location in a quiet residential area and overlooks extensive grounds and the golf course. The executive rooms, in particular, are most spacious and furnished with the comfort of the guest clearly in mind. There is a choice for dining in the evening, with the French restaurant providing an interesting choice from the carte whereas the Country Kitchen offers a more informal atmosphere.
74 en suite (bth/shr) (3 fmly) No smoking in 5 bedrooms CTV in all bedrooms Lift Night porter 164P Indoor swimming pool (heated) Sauna Solarium Gym Jacuzzi/spa Xmas International Cuisine V meals Coffee am Tea pm Last d 10.30pm
ROOMS: (incl. bkfst) s £85-£87; d £98-£100 **LB**
OFF-PEAK: (incl. bkfst) s fr £55; d fr £60
MEALS: Lunch £5.95-£10.95 Dinner £13.50-£21*
CONF: Thtr 320 Class 120 Board 60
CARDS:

★★★65% **Marston Farm**
Bodymoor Heath B76 9JD (take A4091 in direction of Tamworth and turn right for Bodymoor Heath. Turn right after humpback bridge)
☎ 01827 872133 FAX 01827 875043
A well sited hotel both for its proximity to the NEC and its accessibility to the midlands motorway network. Marston Farm has evolved as its name suggests from a vernacular farmhouse extended around a lovely landscaped courtyard. Contemporary furnishings blend well against the remaining rustic architectural features. The style of operation and facilities attract the business guest.
37 en suite (bth/shr) No smoking in 5 bedrooms CTV in all bedrooms STV Night porter 150P Tennis (hard) Fishing Croquet lawn Boules Golf practice net Mountain bikes Xmas English & French Cuisine V meals Coffee am Tea pm No smoking area in restaurant
ROOMS: (incl. bkfst) s £75; d £90 * **LB**
OFF-PEAK: (incl. bkfst) s £37.50; d £75
CONF: Thtr 150 Class 80 Board 50
CARDS:

See advertisement on opposite page

★★★60% **Sutton Court**
60-66 Lichfield Rd B74 2NA (on junct of A5127/A453)
☎ 0121 355 6071 FAX 0121 355 0083
A privately-owned commercial hotel during the week, Sutton Court is a popular marriage and function venue. Rooms are recently redecorated and refurbishment is ongoing. The restaurant, PJ's, has changed and is now a gracious setting for more formal dining.
56 en suite (bth/shr) 8 annexe en suite (bth/shr) (9 fmly) No smoking in 13 bedrooms CTV in all bedrooms STV Night porter 90P Wkly live entertainment Xmas English & French Cuisine V meals

Coffee am Tea pm Last d 9.45pm
ROOMS: s £35-£72; d £39.50-£80 * LB
OFF-PEAK: s £35; d £39.50-£65
MEALS: Lunch £9.50-£16.95&alc Dinner £16.95&alc
CONF: Thtr 90 Class 70 Board 50 Del from £65
CARDS:

★★59% ***The Lady Windsor***
17 Anchorage Rd B74 2PJ ☎ 0121 354 5181 FAX 0121 355 0095
The Lady Windsor is a friendly and welcoming privately owned hotel which has a garden bar and a recently refurbished restaurant. The bedrooms vary but are mostly adequately furnished and maintained and have good facilities.
21 en suite (bth/shr) (2 fmly) CTV in all bedrooms No dogs (ex guide dogs) Night porter 46P No coaches British & Continental Cuisine V meals Coffee am Tea pm Last d 9.30pm
CARDS:

Travelodge
Boldmere Rd B72 5UP (2m S, on B4142)
☎ 0121 355 0017 FAX 0121 355 0017

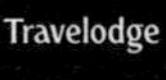

This modern building offers accommodation in smart, spacious and well equipped bedrooms, suitable for family use, and all with en suite bathrooms. Meals may be taken at the nearby family restaurant. For information on room rates and to make a booking, call Roomline free of charge on 0800 850950. For more details about Travelodge, consult the Contents page under Hotel Groups.
32 en suite (bth/shr)

SUTTON IN THE ELMS Leicestershire Map 04 SP59

Mill On The Soar
Coventry Rd LE9 6QD (SE of Leicester, on B4114)
☎ 01455 282419 FAX 01455 285937

The Mill On The Soar is a busy roadside inn which caters especially well for family dining. The accommodation is housed in a separate wing and has the facilities of a higher classification. The public areas centre around the open-plan bar where there is an extensive range of bar meals, informally served. The gardens to the rear lead to a falconry centre, play area, river and small well stocked lake.
20 en suite (bth/shr) (10 fmly) CTV in all bedrooms No dogs (ex guide dogs) 200P Fishing English & French Cuisine V meals Coffee am Tea pm No smoking area in restaurant Last d 10pm
ROOMS: s £28.50-£39.50; d £28.50-£39.50 *
MEALS: Bar Lunch fr £3.50 Dinner fr £4.50
CONF: Thtr 50 Class 20 Board 15
CARDS:

See advertisement on this page

SUTTON ON SEA Lincolnshire Map 09 TF58

★★★ 68% ***Grange & Links***
Sea Ln, Sandilands LN12 2RA (A1111 to Sutton-on-Sea, follow signs to Sandilands) ☎ 01507 441334 FAX 01507 443033
This is a friendly seaside and golfing hotel. There are flexible golfing arrangements and tee off times at the Sandilands Club (a separate bedroom annexe is particularly useful for the latter). The bar is a convivial place to eat or to share experiences of the green. The bedrooms, now completely refurbished, are thoughtfully furnished and modern. Public areas extend to a number of lounges and a cosy restaurant, which offers a good range of generous internationally styled dishes. Sandilands Cod Mornay, pot roasted guinea fowl and Fillet Irlandaise (with Jamesons) feature. Families are made very welcome with acres of lawns and play apparatus in the gardens.
24 en suite (bth/shr) (10 fmly) CTV in all bedrooms STV Night

contd.

porter 60P Golf 18 Tennis (hard) Snooker Croquet lawn Putting green Bowls French Cuisine V meals Coffee am Last d 8.45pm
CARDS:

SUTTON SCOTNEY Hampshire Map 04 SU43

Travelodge (North)

SO21 3JY (on A34 northbound) ☎ 01962 761016
This modern building offers accommodation in smart, spacious and well equipped bedrooms, suitable for family use, and all with en suite bathrooms. Meals may be taken at the nearby family restaurant. For information on room rates and to make a booking, call Roomline free of charge on 0800 850950. For more details about Travelodge, consult the Contents page under Hotel Groups.
31 en suite (bth/shr)

Travelodge (South)

SO21 3JY (on A34 southbound) ☎ 01962 760779
This modern building offers accommodation in smart, spacious and well equipped bedrooms, suitable for family use, and all with en suite bathrooms. Meals may be taken at the nearby family restaurant. For information on room rates and to make a booking, call Roomline free of charge on 0800 850950. For more details about Travelodge, consult the Contents page under Hotel Groups.
40 en suite (bth/shr)

SUTTON UPON DERWENT East Riding of Yorkshire Map 08 SE74

★★64% **Old Rectory**
YO4 5BX v 01904 608548
Closed 2 wks Xmas
This former rectory, owned and run by Mr and Mrs Ward, is in a quiet village location. Its simplicity is valued by many returning guests.
6 rms (5 bth/shr) (2 fmly) CTV in all bedrooms 30P No coaches Coffee am Last d 7.30pm
ROOMS: (incl. bkfst) s £33-£37; d £50-£52 **LB**
MEALS: Dinner £12-£15
CARDS:

SWAFFHAM Norfolk Map 05 TF80

★★★62% **George**

Station Rd PE37 7LJ (turn off A47 signposted Swaffham, hotel opposite the church of St Peter & St Paul) ☎ 01760 721238 FAX 01760 725333
This well established Georgian hotel sits on the corner of the market place, with ample private car parking to the rear. The young staff and enthusiastic proprietors help to make this a friendly establishment. The public rooms offer a pleasant bar where the locals meet, comfortable lounge areas and a formal restaurant, in which daily and à la carte menus are offered. Bar meals are also available. Accommodation styles vary, the more modern bedrooms having fitted dark laminate furniture and cheerful soft furnishings.
27 en suite (bth/shr) (1 fmly) CTV in all bedrooms STV Night porter 100P Xmas English & French Cuisine V meals Coffee am Tea pm No smoking in restaurant Last d 9.30pm
ROOMS: (incl. bkfst) s fr £49; d fr £59 * **LB**
MEALS: Lunch £14.95&alc Dinner £14.95&alc*
CARDS:

SWALLOWFIELD Berkshire Map 04 SU76

★★65% **The New Mill House**
Old Basingstoke Rd RG7 1PY ☎ 0118 9883124 FAX 0118 9885550
Closed 25 Dec-8 Jan RS 10-22 Aug
The Mill House is a comfortable small hotel which is conveniently located close to the M4 between Reading and Basingstoke. A real strength is the warm, friendly family atmosphere which Mr and Mrs Banks the proprietors help create. Bedrooms are spacious and very well equipped with attractive fabrics and some dramatic patchwork bed covers. The restaurant offers a well prepared popular menu and has some pretty views over the attractive garden.
10 en suite (bth/shr) (2 fmly) No smoking in 2 bedrooms CTV in all bedrooms STV 125P Fishing Croquet lawn V meals Coffee am Tea pm No smoking area in restaurant Last d 10.15pm
ROOMS: (incl. bkfst) s £56-£66; d £66-£76 * **LB**
OFF-PEAK: (incl. bkfst) s £40-£50; d £55-£65
MEALS: Sunday Lunch £11.50-£14.50 Dinner £15-£27alc*
CONF: Thtr 90 Class 30 Board 30 Del from £105
CARDS:

SWANAGE Dorset Map 04 SZ07

★★★70% **Purbeck House**
91 High St BH19 2LZ ☎ 01929 422872 FAX 01929 421194
This delightful former convent has been skilfully restored to provide comfortable, well equipped rooms which retain their original character. Public areas have some beautiful features, such as painted ceilings, wood panelling, and fine tiled floors. There is an elegant restaurant and breakfast is served in the conservatory which looks out on the gardens. Staff provide relaxed and friendly service.
18 en suite (bth/shr) (5 fmly) CTV in all bedrooms STV 26P No coaches Croquet lawn Xmas English & French Cuisine V meals Coffee am Tea pm No smoking in restaurant Last d 9pm
ROOMS: (incl. bkfst) s £32.50-£42.50; d £65-£85 **LB**
MEALS: Lunch £9.50-£11.50 Dinner £16.50&alc*
CONF: Thtr 80 Class 60 Del from £55
CARDS:

See advertisement on opposite page

★★★67% **The Pines**
Burlington Rd BH19 1LT (follow A351 to seafront, turn left then take second right and continue to end of road)
☎ 01929 425211 FAX 01929 422075
This popular family-run hotel enjoys a superb location with spectacular views over the sea and Ballard Down. The bedrooms

contd.

continue to improve and have bright attractive co-ordinated décor and modern bathrooms. The public areas are spacious and well maintained with two comfortably furnished lounges. The pretty sea view restaurant offers good value home-cooked food from a daily menu and an additional carte, and the staff offer friendly attentive service.

51 rms (49 bth/shr) (26 fmly) CTV in all bedrooms Lift Night porter 60P No coaches English & Continental Cuisine V meals Coffee am Tea pm No smoking in restaurant

CONF: Thtr 60 Class 60 Board 30

CARDS:

See advertisement on page 597

★★★ 66% **Grand**

Burlington Rd BH19 1LU (on cliff top above town)

☎ 01929 423353 FAX 01929 427068

The Grand enjoys an enviable cliff-top position with spectacular views across Swanage bay, and appeals to both business and pleasure guests. Bedrooms vary in size but are all smartly decorated and many enjoy the glorious views. The public areas are comfortably furnished and well presented with a lounge and conservatory overlooking the well tended gardens. The hotel also has a private beach for guests' use and a well equipped gym and leisure suite. Chef Theresa Reid offers an imaginative daily changing menu in the Renaissance restaurant, where service is carried out by a team of cheerful friendly staff.

30 en suite (bth/shr) (5 fmly) CTV in all bedrooms STV Lift Night porter 15P Indoor swimming pool (heated) Fishing Sauna Solarium Gym Jacuzzi/spa Table tennis Xmas English & French Cuisine V meals Coffee am Tea pm Last d 9.30pm

ROOMS: (incl. bkfst & dinner) s fr £52; d fr £104 * **LB**

OFF-PEAK: (incl. bkfst & dinner) s fr £49.50; d fr £99

MEALS: Sunday Lunch fr £8.95 Dinner fr £15.95*

CARDS:

See advertisement on page 597

SWANWICK See Alfreton

SWAVESEY Cambridgeshire Map 05 TL36

Travelodge

Cambridge Rd CB4 5QR (A604) ☎ 01954 789113

FAX 01954 789113

This modern building offers accommodation in smart, spacious and well equipped bedrooms, suitable for family use, and all with en suite bathrooms. Meals may be taken at the nearby family restaurant. For information on room rates and to make a booking, call Roomline free of charge on 0800 850950. For more details about Travelodge, consult the Contents page under Hotel Groups.

40 en suite (bth/shr)

SWAY Hampshire Map 04 SZ29

★★ 75% **String of Horses**

Mead End Rd SO41 6EH ☎ 01590 682631

FAX 01590 682631

Beautifully situated in four acres of mature grounds adjoining the New Forest this delightful hotel is personally run by Mrs Reardon, who offers a warm welcome. The bedrooms are attractively decorated and offer many thoughtful extras; the bathrooms are particularly impressive: most have extra large round baths and jacuzzis. The public areas are bright and comfortably furnished, enjoying a view across the terrace to the pool and garden. The beamed restaurant offers good freshly prepared meals from a set-price daily menu in addition to a carte.

8 en suite (bth/shr) CTV in all bedrooms No dogs (ex guide dogs) 20P No coaches Outdoor swimming pool (heated) Jacuzzi/spa No children 16yrs Xmas English & French Cuisine V meals Coffee am No smoking in restaurant Last d 8.30pm

ROOMS: (incl. bkfst) s £45-£55; d £70-£100 * **LB**

MEALS: Sunday Lunch fr £12.95 Dinner fr £18.95&alc

CARDS:

★★ 62% **White Rose**

Station Rd O41 6BA (turn off B3055 Brockenhurst/New Milton rd into Sway village centre) ☎ 01590 682754

This popular village centre hotel is family-run and has earned a good local reputation for its wide range of food served in the bar and restaurant. The bedrooms are bright and comfortable; most have en suite facilities. There is an outdoor pool in the peaceful attractive garden.

12 rms (10 bth 1 shr) (2 fmly) CTV in all bedrooms Lift 50P No coaches Outdoor swimming pool Xmas V meals Coffee am Tea pm No smoking in restaurant Last d 9pm

ROOMS: (incl. bkfst) s £39.50-£45; d £59-£70 * **LB**

MEALS: Lunch £5-£10alc Dinner fr £12&alc*

CARDS:

SWINDON Wiltshire Map 04 SU18

★★★★ 72% **De Vere**

Shaw Ridge Leisure Park, Whitehill Way SN5 7DW

☎ 01793 878785 FAX 01793 877822

Situated beside a leisure park on the western edge of the town, the stylish modern hotel offers attractively appointed and comfortable accommodation, popular with the corporate and leisure traveller. Public areas include a marbled lobby, smart lounge and bar and modern leisure facilities. Bedrooms are all to a superior standard with good comfort and level of facilities.

154 en suite (bth/shr) (12 fmly) No smoking in 77 bedrooms CTV in all bedrooms STV Lift Night porter 170P Indoor swimming pool (heated) Snooker Sauna Solarium Gym Jacuzzi/spa Beauty therapist Turkish bath Wkly live entertainment Xmas V meals Coffee am Tea pm No smoking in restaurant Last d 10pm

ROOMS: (incl. bkfst) s £115; d £125 * **LB**

MEALS: Lunch £14.25 Dinner £22&alc*

CONF: Thtr 350 Class 150 Board 80 Del £125

CARDS:

★★★★ 71% **Blunsdon House Hotel & Leisure Club**

Blunsdon SN2 4AD (3m N off A419)

☎ 01793 721701 FAX 01793 721056

This well established family-run hotel, easily accessible from the M4 and the beautiful scenery of the Cotswolds, is set in thirty acres of well tended grounds in the Vale of Cricklade. The emphasis is on personal service, and both the proprietors and staff take pleasure in their guests' comfort. Extensive indoor and outdoor leisure facilities are an added attraction, and the public rooms include three bars and a

choice of eating operations. Carrie's Carverie is ideal for informal dining, whilst The Ridge Restaurant offers more formal surroundings, and an extensive selection of freshly prepared dishes. Bedrooms have been brightly decorated and comfortably furnished.
88 en suite (bth/shr) (10 fmly) No smoking in 44 bedrooms CTV in all bedrooms STV No dogs (ex guide dogs) Lift Night porter 300P Indoor swimming pool (heated) Golf 9 Tennis (hard) Squash Sauna Solarium Gym Pool table Putting green Jacuzzi/spa Skittles Beauty therapy Xmas International Cuisine V meals Coffee am Tea pm Last d 10pm
ROOMS: (incl. bkfst) s £82-£89; d £97-£104 * **LB**
MEALS: Lunch £8.76-£12.75 Dinner £15-£18.50&alc
CONF: Thtr 300 Class 200 Board 40 Del from £97
CARDS:

★★★★65% Swindon Marriott

Pipers Way SN3 1SH (from junct 15 of M4 follow A419, then A4259 to Coate roundabout and B4006 signed 'Old Town') ☎ 01793 512121
FAX 01793 513114
A large and busy hotel, which is ideal for the business and leisure traveller, offering a wide range of services, a choice of eating options and indoor leisure facilities. Bedrooms are comfortable and equipped with modern facilities.
153 en suite (bth/shr) (42 fmly) No smoking in 86 bedrooms CTV in all bedrooms STV Lift Night porter Air conditioning 185P Indoor swimming pool (heated) Tennis (hard) Squash Sauna Solarium Gym Jacuzzi/spa Turkish steam bath & Hair salon English & Continental Cuisine V meals Coffee am Tea pm
CONF: Thtr 250 Class 100 Board 40
CARDS:

★★★❀❀78% The Pear Tree at Purton
Church End SN5 9ED ☎ 01793 772100 FAX 01793 772369
(For full entry see Purton)

★★★70% Stanton House
The Avenue, Stanton Fitzwarren SN6 7SD
☎ 01793 861777 FAX 01793 861857
This extended mansion is situated in its own gardens and grounds in the small, peaceful village of Stanton Fitzwarren, close to Swindon and the M4. The modern public areas include an attractive oak-panelled lounge and an open-plan bar and restaurant. The hotel is operated by a Japanese company, and the Japanese influence is evident both in the menus and service. Business support facilities are available and the friendly team of staff speak both languages. The bedrooms are spacious, equipped with modern facilities and smartly furnished with wood.
86 en suite (bth/shr) No smoking in 3 bedrooms CTV in all bedrooms STV No dogs (ex guide dogs) Lift Night porter 100P No coaches Tennis (hard) Table tennis English & Japanese Cuisine V meals Coffee am
ROOMS: (incl. bkfst) s £65-£90; d £90-£108 * **LB**
OFF-PEAK: (incl. bkfst) s £52-£72; d £60-£72
MEALS: Lunch fr £11*

CONF: Thtr 110 Class 40 Board 40 Del from £110
CARDS:
See advertisement on this page

★★★❀❀68% Chiseldon House
New Rd, Chiseldon SN4 0NE (on B4006)
☎ 01793 741010 FAX 01793 741059
A Grade II listed former manor house, this hotel stands in over three acres of lawned gardens and is convenient for both the M4 and the centre of Swindon. It retains the friendly atmosphere of a home from home, offering accommodation in individually designed bedrooms in light modern styles equipped with both the business and leisure guest in mind. Public areas include an elegant drawing room and various meeting rooms as well as the Orangery Restaurant where chef John Farrow prepares interesting dishes for seasonal menus. A recent inspection meal started with a creamy vegetable soup served with freshly baked bread rolls hot from the oven followed by succulent roast sirloin of beef, the flavour enhanced by a tangy red wine and mustard sauce; the crème brûlée chosen to conclude the meal could only have benefited from a more brittle topping. The pleasant grounds contain a heated outdoor swimming pool and a sun patio.
21 en suite (bth/shr) No smoking in 6 bedrooms CTV in all bedrooms STV Night porter 50P Outdoor swimming pool (heated) Xmas V meals Coffee am Tea pm Last d 9.30pm
ROOMS: (incl. bkfst) s £59.50-£69.50; d £80-£90 **LB**
MEALS: Lunch £12.95-£16.95 Dinner £24.95-£27.50
CONF: Thtr 40 Class 40 Board 20 Del from £101
CARDS:

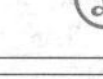

★★★65% Wiltshire

Fleming Way SN1 1TN (opposite police station)
☎ 01793 528282 FAX 01793 541283
RS rest closed Sat lunch

contd.

Conveniently positioned for the town centre this purpose built hotel offers bright, well equipped and furnished bedrooms suitable for both tourists and business guests. There is a choice of bars and the restaurant provides a good choice of dishes. The planned upgrading to the public areas should be completed by the time this Guide goes to press. Staff are well turned out and pleasant, and a good range of room service is provided. Complimentary car parking is available in the adjacent multi-story car park.

93 en suite (bth/shr) No smoking in 26 bedrooms CTV in all bedrooms STV Lift Night porter Xmas English & French Cuisine V meals Coffee am Tea pm No smoking in restaurant Last d 9.45pm
ROOMS: (incl. bkfst) s £75-£85; d £85-£95 * **LB**
OFF-PEAK: (incl. bkfst) s £38-£45; d £76-£90
MEALS: Lunch £9.50-£10.50&alc Dinner £16.50-£17.50&alc*
CONF: Thtr 230 Class 60 Board 60 Del from £100
CARDS:

★★★63% **The Regal**

Oxford Rd, Stratton St Margaret SN3 4TL (3m NE A420) ☎ 01793 831333 FAX 01793 831401
This purpose built hotel is very popular with both the leisure and business guest and is conveniently positioned for both the M4 and the town centre. Bedrooms are well equipped and are in the process of upgrading. The hotel offers a good range of function and meeting rooms.
91 en suite (bth/shr) (13 fmly) No smoking in 50 bedrooms CTV in all bedrooms STV Night porter 150P Pool table Play area Xmas European Cuisine V meals Coffee am Tea pm Last d 10pm
ROOMS: s fr £62; d fr £62 * **LB**
MEALS: Lunch £9.95-£11.95&alc Dinner £11.95-£14.95&alc*
CONF: Thtr 80 Class 40 Board 44 Del £89.50
CARDS:

★★★60% **Goddard Arms**
High St, Old Town SN1 3EG ☎ 01793 692313 FAX 01793 512984
This historic hotel is located in the heart of Old Town, backing onto over fifty acres of natural parkland. Ideally situated for reaching business and nearby tourist centres such as the Cotswolds, Bath and Cheltenham, the hotel is naturally a popular choice. The bedrooms are divided into three wings and are being steadily upgraded. The public areas include a cosy bar with a log fire and selection of real ales, a charming restaurant with food to suit all palates and extensive conference facilities.
18 en suite (bth/shr) 47 annexe en suite (bth/shr) (3 fmly) No smoking in 14 bedrooms CTV in all bedrooms No dogs (ex guide dogs) Night porter 83P English, French & Italian Cuisine V meals Coffee am Tea pm No smoking in restaurant Last d 9.30pm
ROOMS: s £55-£65; d £55-£79 * **LB**
OFF-PEAK: (incl.) s £30-£45; d £60-£79
MEALS: Lunch £11.50-£17.50 Dinner £16-£25&alc
CONF: Thtr 180 Class 100 Board 40 Del from £75
CARDS:

See advertisement on opposite page

★★61% ***Hotel Ibis Swindon***

Delta Business Park, Great Western Way SN5 7XG
(2m from M4 junct 16 & 1m W of town centre)
☎ 01793 514777 FAX 01793 514570
This modern budget hotel is conveniently situated within the Delta Business Park, just 2 miles from the M4. Bedrooms, either twins or doubles, are bright and simple in style though all are en-suite and have satellite TV as an added facility. Open plan public areas include a bar-lounge which is open all day to residents and a dining room serving dinner and a self-service breakfast.
120 en suite (bth/shr) (6 fmly) No smoking in 42 bedrooms CTV in all bedrooms STV Lift Night porter 120P English & Continental Cuisine V meals Coffee am Tea pm Last d 10.30pm
CARDS:

Forte Posthouse Swindon

Marlborough Rd SN3 6AQ (off A4259)
☎ 01793 524601 FAX 01793 512887
Suitable for both the business and leisure traveller, this bright hotel provides modern accommodation in well equipped bedrooms with en suite bathrooms. For more details about Forte Posthouse hotels, consult the Contents page for the section on Hotel Groups.
98 en suite (bth/shr)
ROOMS: s £79; d £79 *
CONF: Thtr 70 Class 30 Board 35 Del from £77

Hilton National

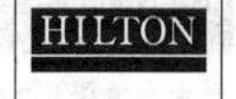

Lydiard Fields, Great Western Way SN5 8UZ (at junct 16 of M4) ☎ 01793 881777 FAX 01793 881881
This is a bright, modern hotel, with an informal restaurant, aimed at both the business and leisure guest. All bedrooms have en suite bathrooms and a range of modern facilities. For more information about Hilton National hotels, consult the Contents page under Hotel Groups.
150 en suite (bth/shr)
ROOMS: s £100-£110; d £110-£120 *
CONF: Thtr 400 Class 136 Board 60 Del from £100

SYMONDS YAT (EAST) Hereford & Worcester Map 03 SO51

★★66% **Saracens Head**
HR9 6JL ☎ 01600 890435
This family-owned and run hostelry stands alongside the River Wye, in the heart of this renowned beauty spot. It provides traditionally furnished but well-equipped accommodation, which includes a family bedded room. The majority of the bedrooms overlook the river. In addition to the cosy residents' lounge, there is a very attractive dining room and a popular bar, which has a lot of character.
9 en suite (bth/shr) TV available No dogs (ex guide dogs) 15P No coaches Fishing Pool table Canoeing Mountain bike hire Wkly live entertainment V meals Coffee am Tea pm Last d 9.30pm
CARDS:

See advertisement on opposite page

★★64% **Royal**
HR9 6JL (off A40 onto B4229, after 0.5m turn right on B4432)
☎ 01600 890238 FAX 01600 890238
Closed 2-16 Jan
This privately-owned and personally-run hotel enjoys a picturesque location, at the foot of a wooded cliff, overlooking the River Wye. It is fronted by pleasant gardens and has ample private parking space. The mainly spacious bedrooms have modern equipment, except for TV, as reception is too poor; the majority of rooms have either river or garden views. Similar views can be enjoyed from the attractively appointed restaurant. Welcoming real fires burn in chilly weather in both the bar and the comfortable lounge. Other facilities include a conference room for up to 35 delegates.

20 en suite (bth/shr) 80P No coaches Fishing Sauna Solarium Abseiling Canoeing Clay pigeon shooting No children 12yrs Xmas British & French Cuisine Coffee am Tea pm Last d 9pm
ROOMS: (incl. bkfst) s £28; d £56-£64 * LB
MEALS: Bar Lunch £5-£12 Dinner fr £17.50&alc
CONF: Thtr 70 Board 30 Del from £70
CARDS:

TALKE Staffordshire Map 07 SJ85

Travelodge

Newcastle Rd ST7 1UP (at junct of A34/A500)
☎ 01782 777148 & 777000 FAX 01782 777148
This modern building offers accommodation in smart, spacious and well equipped bedrooms, suitable for family use, and all with en suite bathrooms. Meals may be taken at the nearby family restaurant. For information on room rates and to make a booking, call Roomline free of charge on 0800 850950. For more details about Travelodge, consult the Contents page under Hotel Groups.
62 en suite (bth/shr)

TALLAND BAY Cornwall & Isles of Scilly Map 02 SX25

★★★ 71% **Talland Bay**
PL13 2JB (signposted from crossroads on A387 Looe/ Polperro road) ☎ 01503 272667 FAX 01503 272940
Closed 2 Jan-10 Feb
This lovely privately-owned old country house is quietly situated in attractive and extensive gardens with panoramic views over Talland Bay. Well co-ordinated bedrooms vary in style, successfully combining traditional comfort with modern facilities, and they are all well equipped; accommodation includes ground-floor rooms as well as some with sea views or four-poster beds. Public areas are made up of two comfortable lounges - one with a log fire and the other for non-smokers - in addition to a cosy bar and an attractive, spacious restaurant offering a choice of menus accompanied by a comprehensive wine list.
16 en suite (bth/shr) 3 annexe en suite (bth) (2 fmly) CTV in all bedrooms 20P No coaches Outdoor swimming pool (heated) Sauna Pool table Croquet lawn Putting green Games room Xmas English & French Cuisine V meals Coffee am Tea pm Last d 9pm
ROOMS: (incl. bkfst & dinner) s £59-£89; d £118-£174 * LB
OFF-PEAK: (incl. bkfst & dinner) s £59-£69; d £118-£138
MEALS: Sunday Lunch £11.50-£17.50 High tea £3-£7.50 Dinner £21-£24.50&alc*
CONF: Thtr 30 Board 30 Del from £70
CARDS:

★★ 67% **Allhays Country House**
PL13 2JB (2.5m from Looe on the A387 towards Polperro until you see Allhays sign follow lane towards sea for 0.75m)
☎ 01503 272434 FAX 01503 272929
Closed 24 Dec-7 Jan
This attractive family home overlooks beautiful Talland Bay from its own well tended gardens on a gently sloping hillside. Some of the bedrooms enjoy fine sea views; all are comfortable and equipped with every modern facility. There is a small dispense bar in the lounge, and a conservatory dining room serves a set meal featuring fresh local fish and home-made puddings.
6 rms (3 bth 1 shr) 1 annexe en suite (bth) (1 fmly) No smoking in 1 bedroom CTV in all bedrooms STV 12P No coaches Croquet lawn Putting green No children 10yrs V meals Coffee am Tea pm No smoking in restaurant Last d 7pm
ROOMS: (incl. bkfst) s £28-£36; d £56-£72 LB
MEALS: Dinner fr £14.50*
CARDS:

T

TAMWORTH Staffordshire Map 07 SK20

★★63% **Globe Inn**
Lower Gungate B79 7AW (follow signs Lower Gungate car park and shops, Hotel is adjacent to car park)
☎ 01827 60455 FAX 01827 63575
This popular inn, recently totally refurbished throughout, offers bright, modern, well equipped bedrooms, all of which have sound en suite facilities. The public areas include a spacious lounge bar, a cosy residents lounge, a meeting room of character and a small dining area where a good range of popular dishes is served. The style of service is informal and none of the usual hotel formalities are enforced. A public car park is available either immediately adjacent to, the hotel.
18 en suite (bth/shr) (2 fmly) No smoking in 2 bedrooms CTV in all bedrooms STV No dogs (ex guide dogs) V meals Coffee am No smoking in restaurant
ROOMS: (incl. bkfst) s £30-£35.25; d £47-£52.25 * **LB**
OFF-PEAK: (incl. bkfst) s £25; d £35
MEALS: Lunch £1.75-£7.95*
CONF: Class 90 Board 90
CARDS:

Travel Inn
Bitterscote, Bonehill Rd B78 3HQ (follow A4091 towards Tamworth) ☎ 01827 54414
FAX 01827 310420
Purpose-built accommodation, offering spacious, well equipped bedrooms, all with en suite bathrooms. Meals may be taken at the nearby family restaurant. For more information about Travel Inns, consult the Contents page under Hotel Groups.
40 en suite (bth/shr)
ROOMS: d £35.50 *

Travelodge

Green Ln, M42 junct 10 B77 5PS (A5/M42 junct 10)
☎ Central Res 0800 850950 FAX 01525 878450
This modern building offers accommodation in smart, spacious and well equipped bedrooms, suitable for family use, and all with en suite bathrooms. Meals may be taken at the nearby family restaurant. For information on room rates and to make a booking, call Roomline free of charge on 0800 850950. For more details about Travelodge, consult the Contents page under Hotel Groups.
63 en suite (bth/shr)

T

TANKERSLEY South Yorkshire Map 08 SK39

★★★68% **Tankersley Manor**
Church Ln S75 3DQ (From M1 junct 36 take A61 Sheffield road. Hotel 0.5 mile on left) ☎ 01226 744700 FAX 01226 745405
Located in a position easily accessible to the M1, this stone-built former farmhouse has been much extended to provide a range of bars and eating areas that have the convivial atmosphere of a country inn, together with a professional and efficient service to guests requiring a more formal style. The bedrooms are furnished in a similar style; modern oak furniture and fittings are brightened by colourful quality soft furnishings and plain decoration. Whilst all the bedrooms are thoughtfully designed the older original rooms have the added character of beams and exposed timbers; another bedroom wing is planned for late 1996.
40 en suite (bth/shr) (1 fmly) No smoking in all bedrooms CTV in all bedrooms STV No dogs (ex guide dogs) Night porter 120P No coaches English & French Cuisine V meals Coffee am Tea pm Last d 9.30pm
ROOMS: (incl. bkfst) s £57.50; d £69.50
OFF-PEAK: (incl. bkfst) s £47.50; d £60
MEALS: Lunch £9.95-£13.50&alc Dinner £16.95-£19.95*
CONF: Thtr 160 Class 80 Board 100 Del from £80
CARDS:

Travel Inn
Maple Rd S74 3DL ☎ 01226 350035
FAX 01226 741524
Purpose-built accommodation, offering spacious, well equipped bedrooms, all with en suite bathrooms. Meals may be taken at the nearby family restaurant. For more information about Travel Inns, consult the Contents page under Hotel Groups.
40 en suite (bth/shr)
ROOMS: d £35.50 *

TAPLOW Buckinghamshire Map 04 SU98

RED STAR HOTEL

★★★★★ 🏵🏵🏵 **Cliveden**
SL6 0JF ☎ 01628 668561 FAX 01628 661837
RELAIS & CHATEAUX. Relais Gourmands
Surrounded by its own 376 acre estate, cared for by the National Trust, Cliveden is a magnificent stately home with a fascinating history, having been owned earlier this century by the Astor family whose influential circle of social and political high-fliers became known as the 'Cliveden Set'. Although it is now one of the world's foremost hotels, it retains the unique atmosphere of a private residence; visitors are referred to as house guests and from the moment of arrival, the welcome suggests that your every need will be anticipated. It is not only for its architecture and gardens that Cliveden is renowned but for its impeccable standards of service. No two bedrooms are the same but all are beautifully decorated in an understated, country-house style to offer the highest levels of comfort. The Great Hall with its fine paintings and Orkney tapestries, leads to a series of day rooms, including the Terrace dining room which overlooks the famous parterre and the French dining room with its splendid gilded panelling. Downstairs, Waldo's is the intimate setting for chef Ron Maxfield's imaginative cuisine which makes unashamed use of the most luxurious of ingredients. There are a number of activities to please those in search of exercise and relaxation, including the secluded outdoor pool, the Pavilion Spa, or maybe a cruise along the Thames in the 'Suzy-Ann' or 'Liddesdale'.
31 en suite (bth/shr) 6 annexe en suite (bth/shr) No smoking in 1 bedroom CTV in all bedrooms Lift Night porter 33P No coaches Indoor swimming pool (heated) Outdoor swimming pool (heated) Tennis (hard) Fishing Squash Riding Snooker Sauna Solarium Gym Jacuzzi/spa Indoor tennis Turkish bath massage Wkly live entertainment ch fac Xmas V meals No smoking in restaurant Last d 9.30pm

ROOMS: s £220; d £398 * **LB**
MEALS: Lunch fr £28 Dinner fr £36
CONF: Thtr 42 Board 28 Del from £245
CARDS:

TARPORLEY Cheshire Map 07 SJ56

★★★ 67% **The Wild Boar**
Whitchurch Rd, Beeston CW6 9NW (2.5m S off A49)
☎ 01829 260309 FAX 01829 261081
This 17th-century black and white half-timbered hotel was once a hunting lodge. It has an elegantly furnished range of bar areas and a smart restaurant. Here Andrew Griffiths offers sound cooking from a daily changing fixed-price menu and an à la carte. Bedrooms are located in a newer building and these are decorated with pretty papers and co-ordinating fabrics. Thoughtful touches include a welcoming glass of sherry, a basket of fresh fruit and a refrigerator complete with a jug of fresh milk. The hotel now holds a licence to perform civil marriages and its function facilities provide an impressive setting for this purpose.
37 en suite (bth/shr) (3 fmly) No smoking in 10 bedrooms CTV in all bedrooms STV Night porter 80P Xmas V meals Coffee am Tea pm Last d 9.30pm
ROOMS: (incl. bkfst) s £50-£70; d £70-£85 **LB**
MEALS: Lunch £14.50&alc Dinner £15.95-£22&alc*
CONF: Thtr 66 Class 33 Board 36 Del £109.50
CARDS: 

★★★ 62% **The Willington Hall**
Willington CW6 0NB (3m NW off unclass road linking A51 & A54)
☎ 01829 752321 FAX 01829 752596
Closed 25 Dec
This privately-owned and personally-run country house, built in 1829, is beautifully situated in extensive parkland close to Chester. It has an informal and relaxed atmosphere created by the owners and their small team of long standing staff. Bedrooms are comfortably furnished with a mixture of antique and modern furniture and many have the feel of a private house. The public areas offer a choice of bars and lounges where real fires burn in winter and in the dining room good, generous home-cooked food is served. Guests can explore the extensive parkland or, if feeling more energetic, enjoy a game of tennis on the hard court.
10 en suite (bth/shr) (1 fmly) CTV in all bedrooms 60P No coaches Tennis (hard) ch fac V meals Last d 9.30pm
ROOMS: s £38-£48; d £68 *
MEALS: Sunday Lunch £15.60-£23.40alc Dinner £15.60-£23.40alc
CONF: Board 16 Del from £94.80
CARDS:

TAUNTON Somerset Map 03 ST22

RED STAR HOTEL

★★★ **Castle**
Castle Green TA1 1NF (from M5 junct 25 follow signs 'Town Centre' then 'Castle & Museum') ☎ 01823 272671
FAX 01823 336066
The mature wisteria-draped façade of this established town centre hotel immediately creates an impression of history and style. There is parking right at the entrance and the Norman Garden is adjacent as is the Castle Museum. Within, there are a range of bedrooms, some recently updated with Laura Ashley fabrics whilst others still await the treatment; the five garden rooms are the most sought after and the stunning penthouse suite offers splendid views. Now in his sixth year, chef Phil Vickery continues to develop his menus, which are imaginative yet simple in their content and provide interesting contrasts in flavours, textures and temperatures with local ingredients being used as much as possible; many firm favourites drawn from his marvellous book collection have to remain on the menus such as old-fashioned style puddings as the baked egg custard tart with nutmeg ice cream and a Rosewater blancmange with pineapple sorbet. The wine list is equally impressive being well chosen and offering informative tasting notes.
36 en suite (bth/shr) CTV in all bedrooms STV Lift Night porter 40P Xmas V meals Coffee am Tea pm No smoking in restaurant Last d 9pm

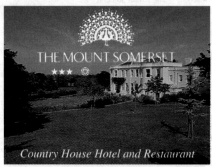

ROOMS: (incl. bkfst) s fr £75; d £115-£185 * **LB**
MEALS: Lunch fr £8.50&alc Dinner £19-£28.50&alc*
CONF: Thtr 100 Class 45 Board 40 Del from £115
CARDS:

T

★★★ 78% **The Mount Somerset Country House**

Henlade TA3 5NB (turn off M5 at junct 25, take A358 towards Chard/Ilminster, at Henlade right into Stoke Rd, left at T junct at end Stoke Rd then right into drive)
☎ 01823 442500 FAX 01823 442900

Set in four acres of landscaped gardens, this gracious Georgian house overlooks the natural beauty of the Quantock and Blackdown Hills, but is only three miles from the centre of Somerset's county town of Taunton, and even closer to junction 25 of the M5. The bedrooms have been sumptuously furnished, in rich colour co-ordinated fabrics and carpeting, and they have all been equipped with every modern comfort. The public areas have similar charm and elegance; they include a choice of lounges with roaring log fires, and the Sedgemoor Suite, ideal for select business meetings and private dining. Attentive service, friendly staff and imaginatively prepared food contributed to the enjoyment of our inspector's stay in this delightful small hotel.

11 en suite (bth/shr) No smoking in 6 bedrooms CTV in all bedrooms STV No dogs Lift Night porter 100P arrangement with health club adjacent Wkly live entertainment Xmas International Cuisine V meals Coffee am Tea pm Last d 10.00pm
ROOMS: (incl. bkfst) s £65-£95; d £80-£160 * **LB**
MEALS: Lunch £15.95-£19.95 High tea £3.50-£10.50 Dinner £22.95-£29.95&alc*
CONF: Thtr 70 Class 30 Board 20 Del from £95
CARDS:

See advertisement on page 603

★★★ 69% **Rumwell Manor**

Rumwell TA4 1EL (leave M5 junct 26 follow signs to Wellington, turn onto A38 to Taunton, hotel is 2.50 miles on right)
☎ 01823 461902 FAX 01823 254861

Situated in well kept gardens and grounds, with distant views of the Blackdown Hills, Rumwell Manor is conveniently positioned for easy access to the centre of Taunton and the M5. Bedrooms vary in size, rooms in the main house having more space and character. In the candlelit restaurant an interesting selection of dishes is offered on the fixed-price and à la carte menus. A cosy bar and adjacent lounge are available for guests.

10 en suite (bth/shr) 10 annexe en suite (bth/shr) (3 fmly) No smoking in 2 bedrooms CTV in all bedrooms 40P No coaches ch fac Xmas English & French Cuisine V meals Coffee am Tea pm No smoking in restaurant Last d 9pm
ROOMS: (incl. bkfst) s £52-£57; d £78-£98 **LB**
MEALS: Lunch £16.50&alc High tea £5 Dinner £16.50&alc
CONF: Thtr 40 Class 24 Board 26 Del from £80
CARDS:

★★ 74% ***Farthings Hotel & Restaurant***

Hatch Beauchamp TA3 6SG (from A358, between Taunton and Ilminster turn into Hatch Beauchamp for hotel in village centre)
☎ 01823 480664 FAX 01823 481118

This charming Georgian hotel, peacefully situated in the country village of Hatch Beauchamp, has a delightful garden and is only a few miles from the centre of the county town of Taunton, the M5 and the A303. Farthings is privately owned and personally managed in a relaxed and friendly fashion. Well equipped bedrooms have been individually decorated and furnished and thoughtful extras have also been added. Public areas include a comfortable lounge and separate bar lounge, and two dining rooms where a varied menu features innovative use of local produce, and the wine list offers an interesting selection.

8 en suite (bth/shr) (1 fmly) CTV in all bedrooms 22P No coaches Croquet lawn ch fac V meals Coffee am Tea pm Last d 9.30pm
CARDS:

★★ 64% **Falcon**

Henlade TA3 5DH (M5 junct 25 1m east of A358 Taunton to Yeovil Road) ☎ 01823 442502 FAX 01823 442670
Closed 25 Dec

Set in well tended gardens, this detached, brick-built Victorian house is just one mile from junction 25 of the M5, alongside the A358. During the week the hotel caters mainly for a business clientele, with leisure guests at the weekend. Bedrooms vary in size and are equipped with the expected facilities. Both fixed-price and à la carte menus are available in the dining room and the adjacent bar provides a popular meeting place.

11 en suite (bth/shr) (2 fmly) No smoking in 3 bedrooms CTV in all bedrooms STV 25P ch fac International Cuisine V meals Coffee am Tea pm No smoking in restaurant Last d 8.30pm
CONF: Thtr 65 Class 40 Board 40
CARDS:

Forte Posthouse Taunton

Deane Gate Av TA1 2UA (adjacent to junct 25 on M5) ☎ 01823 332222 FAX 01823 332266

Suitable for both the business and leisure traveller, this bright hotel provides modern accommodation in well equipped bedrooms with en suite bathrooms. For more details about Forte Posthouse hotels, consult the Contents page for the section on Hotel Groups.

99 en suite (bth/shr)
ROOMS: s fr £79; d fr £79 *
CONF: Thtr 300 Class 110 Board 105 Del £109

Travel Inn

81 Bridgwater Rd TA1 2DU (leave M5 junc 25 towards Taunton then head for Corfe Racecourse)
☎ 01823 321112 FAX 01823 322054

Purpose-built accommodation, offering spacious, well equipped bedrooms, all with en suite bathrooms. Meals may be taken at the nearby family restaurant. For more information about Travel Inns, consult the Contents page under Hotel Groups.

40 en suite (bth/shr)
ROOMS: d £35.50 *

TAUNTON DEANE MOTORWAY SERVICE AREA (M5)

Somerset Map 03 ST12

Roadchef Lodge

Trull TA3 7PF (between junct 25 & 26 of M5)
☎ 01823 332228 FAX 01823 338131

Smart, spacious and well equipped bedrooms, all with en suite bathrooms, are provided by this modern hotel. Meals may be taken at a nearby family restaurant. For more information about RoadChef Lodges, consult the Contents page under Hotel Groups.

39 en suite (bth/shr)
ROOMS: s fr £37.95 *

TAVISTOCK Devon Map 02 SX47

★★★ 62% ***The Bedford***

Plymouth Rd PL19 8BB (situated off the main square in the centre of Tavistock) ☎ 01822 613221
FAX 01822 618034

An impressive castellated stone building, the Bedford is situated near the centre of town and has limited car-parking at the rear. The majority of bedrooms have been upgraded to a good standard with the final stage anticipated in the near future. The corridors are rather drab but work on these is also planned. Character, open plan public rooms are comfortably furnished and a traditional a la carte and set price menus are served in the Woburn Restaurant. Traditional services are carried out by a friendly team.

31 rms (30 bth/shr) (1 fmly) No smoking in 11 bedrooms CTV in all bedrooms 50P V meals Coffee am Tea pm Last d 9pm
CARDS:

★★ 69% **Moorland Hall**
Brentor Rd, Mary Tavy PL19 9PY (4m N, signposted from A386 in Mary Tavy) ☎ 01822 810466
This delightful Victorian country house is set in five acres of gardens and paddocks in a quiet backwater on the edge of Dartmoor. The hotel is run on informal lines by Gillian and Andrew Farr. The main lounge features a roaring fire in chilly weather and is complemented by a well stocked bar. A fixed-price menu based on local produce is offered every evening. Bedrooms, including two ground-floor rooms, are individually decorated and comfortably furnished.
8 en suite (bth/shr) (1 fmly) CTV in all bedrooms 20P No coaches Croquet lawn Bar billiards Xmas English & French Cuisine V meals No smoking in restaurant Last d 8pm
ROOMS: (incl. bkfst) s £40; d £64-£72 *
MEALS: Dinner fr £16.50
CARDS:

TEBAY Cumbria Map 07 NY60

★★★ 65% **Tebay Mountain Lodge**
Orton CA10 3SB (next to Westmorland's Tebay Services on the M6, easily reached from the southbound carriageway using the link road between the two service areas) (Westmorland)
☎ 015396 24351 FAX 015396 24354
Tebay Mountain Lodge is a very welcome addition to this year's guide, offering an idyllic location and superb value for money. Similar to an Alpine lodge in structure, it is accessed from the Westmorland Service area yet is separate from the motorway services. Public areas are simple, though the restaurant is made up of a room decorated with a plethora of original prints and paintings and a conservatory surrounded by grazing meadows. The bedrooms are furnished in a contemporary style and are comfortable, spacious and well equipped. The ambience is friendly and the service accommodating.
30 en suite (bth/shr) (10 fmly) CTV in all bedrooms STV Night porter 32P British & French Cuisine V meals Coffee am Tea pm No smoking in restaurant
ROOMS: s £42; d £45 * LB
MEALS: Dinner £11.25-£25*
CONF: Class 130 Board 300
CARDS:

TEES-SIDE AIRPORT Co Durham Map 08 NZ31

★★★ 64% **St George**
Middleton St George DL2 1RH (turn off A67 by pass directly into Airport grounds) ☎ 01325 332631
FAX 01325 333851
Situated in the airport complex this former war time officers' mess provides recently refurbished, comfortable accommodation with every modern facility, and is very well placed, not only for the airport, but also for major industrial centres nearby. Throughout the hotel there are reminders of its past with paintings, models of war time aircraft and photographs of those who flew them. The restaurant offers French and traditional British cuisine or alternatively meals are also served in the comfortable lounge bar. The staff throughout are courteous and helpful.
59 en suite (bth/shr) (2 fmly) No smoking in 8 bedrooms CTV in all bedrooms Night porter 220P Squash Sauna Solarium Xmas English & French Cuisine V meals Coffee am Last d 9.45pm
ROOMS: (incl. bkfst) s £75; d £85 *
MEALS: Lunch £7.50-£8.95&alc Dinner £16.50&alc*
CONF: Thtr 160 Class 60 Board 50 Del from £80
CARDS:

TEIGNMOUTH Devon Map 03 SX97

★★ 68% **Ness House**
Marine Dr, Shaldon TQ14 0HP (follow signs Shaldon across River Teign) ☎ 01626 873480 FAX 01626 873486
Situated on the outskirts of Shaldon, this elegant Georgian property overlooks the Teign Estuary and the beautiful, unspoilt Devon countryside. The individually furnished and decorated bedrooms are comfortable; luxury bedrooms have a courtesy area with a refrigerator, and most rooms benefit from a balcony with sea views. Guests have the option of either dining by candlelight in the restaurant, or choosing from the extensive range of bar meals which offer good value for money.
7 en suite (bth/shr) 5 annexe en suite (bth/shr) (2 fmly) CTV in all bedrooms STV No dogs (ex guide dogs) 20P No coaches ch fac Xmas English & French Cuisine V meals Coffee am Tea pm No smoking in restaurant Last d 10.15pm
ROOMS: (incl. bkfst) s £39-£60; d £60-£85 * LB
MEALS: Lunch £17.52-£20&alc Dinner £17.50-£20&alc
CARDS:

T

★★65% **Coombe Bank**
Landscore Rd TQ14 9JL (M5 to Exeter follow signs to Torquay, onto B3192 to Teignmouth, turn right into Landscore Road where the Hotel can be found) ☎ 01626 772369
This quietly situated Victorian house is a short walk from the town, harbour and beach. Coombe Bank offers bright comfortable accommodation with private facilities. The public rooms are spacious and well appointed. There is a cosy lounge, and the bar and restaurant on the lower ground floor are attractively decorated. The daily changing menu offers a good range of freshly cooked wholesome meals.
9 en suite (bth/shr) No smoking in all bedrooms CTV in all bedrooms No dogs 9P No coaches Xmas International Cuisine V meals Coffee am Tea pm No smoking in restaurant Last d 9.00pm
ROOMS: (incl. bkfst) s £20-£24; d £40-£48 * **LB**
MEALS: Sunday Lunch £12 Dinner £12
CARDS:

★66% **Glenside**
Ringmoor Rd, Shaldon TQ14 0EP (cross bridge from Teignmouth, turn right and then bear right again signed Ringmore, hotel is on the left) ☎ 01626 872448
Just a stones throw from the southern bank of the Teign Estuary, this cottage-style hotel was built in the 1820s and set in a pretty garden. Keith and Tricia Underwood are friendly hosts, having a relaxed approach to their guests. The majority of bedrooms are en suite, all are well equipped though some of the furnishings are simple. A spacious lounge and cosy bar are available for guests, while in the dining room a limited choice table d'hÙte menu is offered.
9 rms (8 bth/shr) (1 fmly) CTV in all bedrooms 10P No coaches No children 3yrs Xmas
ROOMS: (incl. bkfst) s £19.50-£24.50; d £38-£49 * **LB**

★65% **Belvedere**
Barnpark Rd TQ14 8PJ (near Railway Station) ☎ 01626 774561
Don and Gwen Perkins, who took over the hotel during 1995, endeavour to ensure that guests enjoy a relaxed stay. The bedrooms are well equipped and comfortable, though a programme of upgrading is planned. In the cosy bar, guests partake of a pre-dinner drink, while in the soundly appointed, no smoking dining room, a simple fixed-price menu of home-cooked food is offered. A small range of hot and cold snacks is available in the bar at lunch time; on sunny days these are served on the sun terrace which has fine views over the garden and towards Teignmouth.
13 rms (12 bth/shr) (6 fmly) CTV in all bedrooms No dogs (ex guide dogs) 12P No coaches Xmas V meals No smoking in restaurant Last d 7.30pm
ROOMS: (incl. bkfst) s £20-£23; d £40-£46 * **LB**
MEALS: Bar Lunch £1.30-£4 Dinner £8.50*
CARDS:

TELFORD Shropshire Map 07 SJ60

★★★71% **Madeley Court**

TF7 5DW (M54 juct 4, A4169 Telford, A442 at 2nd rdbt signs for Kidderminster, continue along (ignore sign to Madeley & Kidderminster) 1st left off rdbt) ☎ 01952 680068 FAX 01952 684275
A delightful 16th century manor house sympathetically extended, this hotel is situated beside a lake in the grounds of Madeley Court Mill. The Elizabethan period is reflected in beautifully panelled walls, solid oak spiral staircases and a huge fireplace in the main restaurant. In the older part of the house many of the bedrooms have fine antique furnishings, whilst those in the newer wings have also been comfortably designed and have every modern facility. The great hall is the main restaurant and although executive chef Paul Davis-Clarkson's menus are short they change regularly and the cuisine is of a high standard. For informal meals, the Brasserie in the undercroft caters admirably.
16 en suite (bth/shr) 31 annexe en suite (bth/shr) (1 fmly) No smoking in 2 bedrooms CTV in all bedrooms Night porter 180P Fishing Xmas V meals Coffee am Tea pm No smoking in restaurant Last d 10pm
ROOMS: s £72-£85; d £85-£95 * **LB**
MEALS: Lunch £10-£15 Dinner £10-£15&alc*
CONF: Thtr 200 Class 120 Board 40 Del from £95
CARDS:

★★★69% ***Holiday Inn***
St Quentin Gate TF3 4EH (just off junct 4 of M54) ☎ 01952 292500 FAX 01952 291949
A modern hotel with spacious bedrooms the Holiday Inn is conveniently situated next to the Racquet and Exhibition Centre and Telford Town Park. A feature of the hotel is its Courts Restaurant and Bar, the latter containing many photographs of old tennis scenes, the former well known for its high standard of cuisine, particularly its Japanese cooking. In addition to a good range of Japanese starters and main dishes, there is also Teppan Yaki, where guests can cook their own dishes on hot stones at the table. Instructions are given. British dishes are featured on the main menus which include a Healthy Eating and Vegetarian section. There is also a very good health and leisure club which includes a swimming pool and a fitness room.
100 en suite (bth/shr) No smoking in 35 bedrooms CTV in all bedrooms Lift Night porter 120P Indoor swimming pool (heated) Tennis (hard) Squash Snooker Sauna Solarium Gym Steam room Whirlpool spa English, French & Japanese Cuisine V meals Coffee am Tea pm Last d 10pm
CARDS:

★★★69% ***Telford Moat House***

Forgegate, Telford Centre TF3 4NA (junct 5 M54) ☎ 01952 429988 FAX 01952 292012
Closed 24 Dec-1 Jan (ex Xmas lunch & 31 Dec)
This large modern hotel is situated close to junction 5 of the M54 and provides very good bedroom accommodation and excellent facilities for business meetings, banquets and conferences; there is also a very well equipped leisure centre. A new dining facility has recently been opened: the Casa Med Bar and Brasserie, which provides a wide range of interesting dishes from around the world, not forgetting British favourites such as fish and chips and bread and butter pudding.
147 en suite (bth/shr) (7 fmly) CTV in all bedrooms Lift Night porter 300P Indoor swimming pool (heated) Sauna Solarium Gym Pool table Jacuzzi/spa Childrens play area English & French Cuisine V meals Coffee am
CARDS:

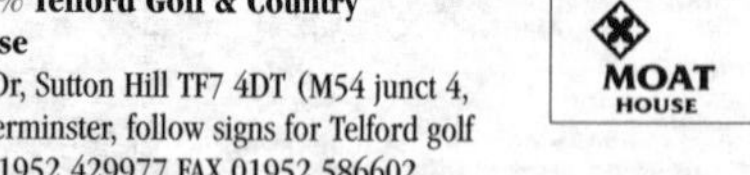

★★★68% **Telford Golf & Country Moat House**
Great Hay Dr, Sutton Hill TF7 4DT (M54 junct 4, A442 - Kiderminster, follow signs for Telford golf club) ☎ 01952 429977 FAX 01952 586602
Situated in a prime position overlooking the Ironbridge Gorge, this hotel and country club offers an excellent range of leisure pursuits with the 18-hole championship course as the main attraction. Many of the bedrooms have now been upgraded and those in the original period house are undergoing a luxurious refurbishment to bring them up to an executive standard. There are numerous eating options including room service, snacks in the coffee lounge, Japanese-style meals in the Kyoto room or traditional menus in the Ironbridge restaurant.
86 en suite (bth/shr) (10 fmly) No smoking in 36 bedrooms CTV in all bedrooms Night porter 200P Indoor swimming pool (heated) Golf 18 Squash Snooker Sauna Solarium Gym Pool table Croquet lawn Putting green Jacuzzi/spa Steam room Masseur Spa pool Beautician Xmas International Cuisine V meals Coffee am Tea pm Last d 10pm

ROOMS: s fr £89; d fr £105 * LB
MEALS: Lunch fr £10.50 High tea fr £2.75 Dinner fr £15.50*
CONF: Thtr 240 Class 140 Board 60 Del from £120
CARDS:

★★★67% **Buckatree Hall**

The Wrekin, Wellington TF6 5AL (exit 7 of M54, turn left and left again for 1m) ☎ 01952 641821
FAX 01952 247540
Privately owned and much extended, this large hotel stands in sizeable wooded grounds with a lake on the slopes of the Wrekin, conveniently close to both the A5 and the M54. Well equipped modern bedrooms include some which are interconnecting and others featuring water beds or balconies; non-smoking rooms can be provided, and an attractive restaurant with picture windows overlooking the grounds also has an area where smoking is prohibited. A pleasant lounge adjoins the lounge bar, extensive function/conference facilities are available, and plans are in hand to create a leisure centre.
64 en suite (bth/shr) (4 fmly) No smoking in 10 bedrooms CTV in all bedrooms STV Lift Night porter 120P Xmas International Cuisine V meals Coffee am Tea pm Last d 9.45pm
ROOMS: (incl. bkfst) s £69-£84.50; d £69-£89.50 * LB
OFF-PEAK: (incl. bkfst & dinner) s £39-£49.50
MEALS: Lunch £9.95&alc Dinner £16.95&alc
CONF: Thtr 166 Class 66 Board 40 Del £89
CARDS:

★★★63% **Valley**

TF8 7DW (M6, M54 junct 6 onto A5223 to Ironbridge) ☎ 01952 432247 FAX 01952 432308
Personally owned and run by the Casson family, this delightfully situated hotel stands in its own grounds and is close to the famous iron bridge. Bedrooms vary in size whilst all are well equipped and pleasingly furnished. A good range of dishes is available in the Chez Maw restaurant and service is very friendly and attentive. The house was once the home of a 19th-century tile manufacture, and much of his work is still in evidence.
35 en suite (bth/shr) CTV in all bedrooms STV No dogs (ex guide dogs) Night porter 100P ch fac International Cuisine V meals Coffee am Tea pm No smoking in restaurant Last d 9.30pm
ROOMS: s £65; d £75 * LB
OFF-PEAK: (incl. bkfst) s £55; d £65
MEALS: Lunch £10.50-£12.50 High tea £2.50-£4.50 Dinner £17.50-£18.50&alc*
CONF: Thtr 250 Class 100 Board 50 Del from £79
CARDS:

★★68% **White House**
Wellington Rd, Muxton TF2 8NG (off A518 Telford-Stafford road)
☎ 01952 604276 & 603603 FAX 01952 670336
This popular commercial hotel has been run by the same family for over thirty years. It is set in pretty lawned gardens with a large car park and provides modern, well equipped bedrooms. A wide range of food is on offer with a good choice of bar meals as well as the more formal carte and fixed price menus. A first floor lounge is available for small meetings.
30 en suite (bth/shr) (3 fmly) CTV in all bedrooms No dogs (ex guide dogs) 100P No coaches Continental Cuisine V meals No smoking area in restaurant Last d 9.30pm
ROOMS: (incl. bkfst) s £50-£55; d £60-£66 LB
OFF-PEAK: (incl. bkfst) s £40; d £50
MEALS: Lunch £8.50-£8.95&alc Dinner fr £12.50&alc
CARDS:

★★63% **Arleston Inn**
The Arleston Ln, Wellington TF1 2LA (from M54 junct 6 take A523 Ironbridge road and right at next roundabout past Lawley School then right into Arleston Lane) ☎ 01952 501881 FAX 01952 506429
This is a small hotel, conveniently located for the M54 and for the industrial and tourist areas of Telford and Ironbridge. It is a split-level building with bedrooms on the upper floor and the bar and restaurant at ground-floor level. The bar has many cosy and intimate areas and a conservatory extension looks out over pretty lawns and gardens. Bedrooms are on the small side but all are attractively decorated and modern facilities are provided.
7 en suite (bth/shr) CTV in all bedrooms No dogs (ex guide dogs) Night porter 40P V meals Last d 9.30pm
MEALS: Lunch £9.15-£16.25alc Dinner £9.15-£16.25alc*
CARDS:

★★63% **Oaks Hotel & Restaurant**
Redhill, St Georges TF2 9NZ (M54 junct 4, A5 Crannock 1.50 miles)
☎ 01952 620126 FAX 01952 620257
This small, family-run hotel has modest and functional bedrooms, and meals are available in the cosy bar or St George's Restaurant. Friendly proprietors play an active role in providing a personal service.
12 en suite (bth/shr) (4 fmly) CTV in all bedrooms No dogs (ex guide dogs) 36P English & French Cuisine V meals Coffee am Last d 9.30pm
ROOMS: (incl. bkfst) s fr £42; d fr £52 * LB
MEALS: Lunch £3.75-£15 Dinner £8-£20*
CONF: Thtr 40 Class 40 Board 25
CARDS:

Travelodge
Travelodge
Whitchurch Dr, Shawbirch TF1 3QA (1m NW, on A5223) ☎ 01952 251244 FAX 01952 251244
This modern building offers accommodation in smart, spacious and well equipped bedrooms, suitable for family use, and all with en suite bathrooms. Meals may be taken at the nearby family restaurant. For information on room rates and to make a booking, call Roomline free of charge on 0800 850950. For more details about Travelodge, consult the Contents page under Hotel Groups.
40 en suite (bth/shr)

TEMPLE SOWERBY Cumbria Map 12 NY62

★★★70% **Temple Sowerby House**
CA10 1RZ (midway between Penrith and Appleby, 7 miles from M6 junct 40) ☎ 017683 61578 FAX 017683 61958
This former Cumbrian farmhouse with Georgian additions is now under the care and direction of Geoffrey and Cecile Temple and is today a very hospitable and civilised small hotel with a relaxed country house atmosphere. Attractive public areas include a choice of comfortable lounges enhanced by real fires, a cosy dispense bar and two elegant candle-lit dining areas featuring honest English fare competently prepared from quality raw ingredients. The variable sized bedrooms, including those in the adjacent Coach House, are quite individual with both traditional and modern furnishings.
8 en suite (bth/shr) 4 annexe en suite (bth/shr) (2 fmly) CTV in all bedrooms 30P No coaches Croquet lawn Badminton Boules Xmas International Cuisine V meals Coffee am Tea pm No smoking in restaurant Last d 9pm
ROOMS: (incl. bkfst) s £55-£60; d £78-£88 * LB
MEALS: Lunch fr £9.95alc Dinner £16-£28alc*
CARDS:

TENBURY WELLS Hereford & Worcester Map 07 SO56

★★65% **Cadmore Lodge**
Berrington Green, St Michaels WR15 8TQ
☎ 01584 810044 FAX 01584 810044
Closed 25 Dec
This small privately owned hotel was built some nine years ago. It

contd.

enjoys a secluded location on a private estate some two and a half miles west of Tenbury Wells, via the A4112. The 70 acres of grounds include a nine-hole golf course, two fishing lakes, a tennis court and a bowling green. The bedrooms, which include family accommodation, are traditionally furnished but have modern equipment and facilities. In addition to the pleasant dining room and lounge bar, the hotel also has a large function room with lake views, which is a popular venue for wedding receptions and conferences.

14 rms (13 bth/shr) (1 fmly) CTV in 9 bedrooms No dogs 60P Indoor swimming pool (heated) Golf 9 Tennis (hard) Fishing Sauna Gym Pool table Jacuzzi/spa Bowling green French Cuisine V meals Coffee am Tea pm Last d 9pm

ROOMS: (incl. bkfst) s £25-£34.50; d £50-£57.50 * **LB**

MEALS: Lunch £10-£11.25&alc High tea £4.25-£10 Dinner £14.50-£20&alc*

CONF: Thtr 100 Class 40 Board 30 Del from £45

CARDS:

See advertisement on opposite page

TETBURY Gloucestershire Map 03 ST89

RED STAR HOTEL

★★★ Calcot Manor

Calcot GL8 8YJ (4m West of Tetbuty W at junc A4135/A46) ☎ 01666 890391 FAX 01666 890394

PRIDE OF BRITAIN MEMBER

This rambling hotel, once part of Kingswood Abbey founded by the Cistercian monks in 1158, is made up of a cluster of imaginatively restored cottages and barns set around a handsome Cotswold farmhouse. Leisure facilities include tennis courts and an outdoor heated swimming pool, and a choice of meeting rooms is available. Bedrooms are attractive and comfortable and range from those in the main house to several situated in the outlying buildings. The public areas retain all the character and charm of the original architecture, with open fireplaces, exposed beams and flagstone floors. The Gumstool, a lively pub/bistro, provides sophisticated pub grub in an informal atmosphere, while the main restaurant offers a certain formality; menus follow the seasons, imaginative dishes are based on local produce, flavours are robust and the wine list is suitably extensive and interesting.

9 en suite (bth/shr) 11 annexe en suite (bth/shr) (4 fmly) CTV in all bedrooms No dogs (ex guide dogs) 82P No coaches Outdoor swimming pool (heated) Croquet lawn Clay pigeon shooting Xmas English & French Cuisine V meals Coffee am Tea pm Last d 9.30pm

ROOMS: (incl. cont bkfst) s £75-£90; d £92-£135 * **LB**

MEALS: Lunch fr £16&alc Dinner fr £22&alc*

CONF: Thtr 60 Class 40 Board 30

CARDS:

RED STAR HOTEL

★★★ Close

8 Long St GL8 8AQ (off B4014 in the centre of Tetbury) ☎ 01666 502272 FAX 01666 504401

THE Virgin HOTEL COLLECTION

In an area that does not lack good hotels, The Close is among the most delightful, steeped in history and with a frontage on the main street of this old Cotswold market town. At the rear is a pretty walled garden and secluded parking, giving direct access to the hotel. Bedrooms, decorated in keeping with the building, are generously furnished with antique pieces, and many retain period features, including original fireplaces. Day rooms include a choice of spacious, comfortable lounges, warmed by open fires in cooler weather, and there are lots of books for guests to browse through. The attractive restaurant overlooks the gardens and offers a good choice of freshly prepared dishes on its menus.

15 en suite (bth/shr) CTV in all bedrooms STV No dogs (ex guide dogs) Night porter 20P No coaches Croquet lawn Xmas V meals Coffee am Tea pm Last d 9.45pm

ROOMS: (incl. bkfst) s £95-£165; d £110-£165 * **LB**

MEALS: Lunch fr £18.50&alc High tea fr £7.90 Dinner fr £25.25&alc*

CONF: Thtr 24 Class 22 Board 20 Del from £140

CARDS:

★★★70% **Priory Inn**

London Rd GL8 8JJ (on A433, Cirencester/Tetbury road 200yds from high st) ☎ 01666 502251 FAX 01666 503534

This stylish hotel brings a touch of Hollywood glitz to the old Cotswold market town of Tetbury. Owners Mr and Mrs O'Toole previously worked in cinema and much of Mr O'Toole's personal memorabilia is displayed in the themed restaurant where you can sit in directors chairs inscribed with the names of tinseltown's brightest stars. The bedrooms are newly refurbished and are stylish with bright fabrics and quality extra touches. The charming residents' lounge has a colonial feel and is well stocked with books and other extra touches.

14 en suite (bth/shr) (1 fmly) No smoking in 3 bedrooms CTV in all bedrooms STV 40P International Cuisine V meals Coffee am Tea pm No smoking area in restaurant Last d 10pm

ROOMS: s £31.50-£34; d £55-£57 * **LB**

MEALS: Lunch fr £6.95 Dinner £9.95&alc*

CONF: Thtr 70 Board 35 Del from £79

CARDS:

★★★65% ***Hare & Hounds***
Westonbirt GL8 8QL (2.5m S on A433)
☎ 01666 880233 FAX 01666 880241
In a convenient location and built of Cotswold stone this family run hotel has comfortable lounges, log fired and congenial bars. Bedrooms are on traditional lines and sizes and styles vary; rooms in the coach house have their own entrances.
22 en suite (bth/shr) 8 annexe en suite (bth/shr) (3 fmly) No smoking in 12 bedrooms CTV in all bedrooms 82P Tennis (hard) Squash Pool table Croquet lawn Table tennis English & French Cuisine V meals Coffee am Tea pm Last d 9pm
CARDS:

★★★65% ***Snooty Fox***
Market Place GL8 8DD (in the centre of the town)
☎ 01666 502436 FAX 01666 503479
This 16th-century coaching inn dominates the pillared Market Place, its façade of mellowed Cotswold stone overlooking the Town Hall. Bedrooms are equipped with every modern facility and many thoughtful extras such as fresh fruit, mineral water and boiled sweets. The bar and coffee lounge are popular with non-residents, but guests can sit quietly in the Drawing Room, and dine in comfort in the elegant oak-panelled restaurant. There is a public car park to the rear of the hotel.
12 en suite (bth/shr) CTV in all bedrooms No dogs (ex guide dogs) V meals Coffee am Tea pm Last d 10pm
CARDS:

★★67% **Hunters Hall Inn**
Kingscote GL8 8XZ (4m W on A4135)
☎ 01453 860393 FAX 01453 860707
This popular 17th-century inn five miles west of Tetbury on the outskirts of the village of Kingscote, features congenial bars with open fires, flagstone floors and beamed ceilings. The bedrooms are housed in an adjacent converted stable block; eight are situated on the ground floor, and two of these are specifically designed to meet the need of disabled guests. An intimate restaurant serves good-value meals which are skilfully created from the freshest of local produce; on a recent visit the fillet of salmon in a blue cheese sauce with asparagus was particularly enjoyable. Service is friendly and efficient.
12 annexe en suite (bth/shr) (1 fmly) CTV in all bedrooms No dogs (ex guide dogs) 120P Xmas V meals Coffee am Tea pm Last d 9.30pm
ROOMS: (incl. bkfst) s £45-£50; d £60-£65 **LB**
MEALS: Bar Lunch £2.50-£9.50alc Dinner £15-£17.50&alc
CONF: Thtr 20 Class 20 Board 30 Del from £65
CARDS:

TEWKESBURY Gloucestershire Map 03 SO83

★★★74% **Puckrup Hall**
Puckrup GL20 6EL (2m N A38) ☎ 01684 296200 FAX 01684 850788
Major changes have taken place to this hotel which proudly boasts of a brand new extension of bedrooms, bars, brasserie, meeting rooms and leisure facilities. These have been added in a sympathetic fashion to the Regency mansion which continues to house the main restaurant. What the original bedrooms might lack in modernity, they make up for by retaining some of the building's Regency character.
84 en suite (bth/shr) (7 fmly) No smoking in 34 bedrooms CTV in all bedrooms STV Lift Night porter 200P No coaches Indoor swimming pool (heated) Golf 18 Fishing Sauna Solarium Gym Croquet lawn Putting green Jacuzzi/spa Beautician Aerobics ch fac Xmas English & French Cuisine V meals Coffee am Tea pm

contd.

ROOMS: s fr £82.50; d £105-£115 * **LB**
CONF: Thtr 250 Class 100 Board 40
CARDS:

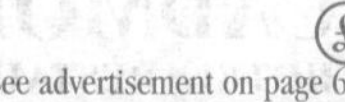

See advertisement on page 609

★★★68% **Tewkesbury Park Hotel**

Lincoln Green Ln GL20 7DN (M5 junct 9 take A438 through Tewkesbury onto A38 passing Abbey on left, Hotel further on right) ☎ 01684 295405
FAX 01684 292386
Enjoying glorious views over the River Severn and the vale of Evesham, Tewkesbury Park was built around an 18th-century mansion. Within the extensive grounds there is an 18-hole golf course and a leisure club, which attract both the corporate and leisure market. Bedrooms are all similarly furnished in a plain style. Smart staff are well meaning and cheerful.
78 annexe en suite (bth/shr) (6 fmly) No smoking in 50 bedrooms CTV in all bedrooms STV Night porter 200P Indoor swimming pool (heated) Golf 18 Tennis (hard) Squash Snooker Sauna Solarium Gym Putting green Jacuzzi/spa Health & beauty salon Xmas French/English Cuisine V meals Coffee am Tea pm No smoking in restaurant Last d 10pm
ROOMS: d fr £79 * **LB**
OFF-PEAK: (incl. bkfst) s fr £79; d fr £79
MEALS: Lunch fr £12.50 Dinner £18*
CONF: Thtr 150 Class 100 Board 50 Del from £118
CARDS:

★★★66% **Bell**

Church St GL20 5SA (on A38 opposite Abbey)
☎ 01684 293293 FAX 01684 295938
RS 28 Dec-4 Jan
A half-timbered former coaching inn situated opposite the Norman Abbey in the town centre, this is said to be one of the oldest buildings of its kind in England. Most of the bedrooms have been refurbished and they are all well equipped. The spacious Priory Restaurant serves a menu with additional dishes at a supplementary charge, and vegetarian dishes are available. A terraced area is popular for bar meals, and, like the restaurant, this is no-smoking. There is a large open fire in the convivial beamed bar.
25 en suite (bth/shr) (1 fmly) No smoking in 6 bedrooms CTV in all bedrooms Night porter 55P Xmas English & French Cuisine V meals Coffee am Tea pm No smoking in restaurant Last d 9.30pm
ROOMS: (incl. bkfst) s £59.50-£65; d £82-£95 * **LB**
MEALS: Lunch £12-£20alc High tea fr £3.50alc Dinner £14.95-£17.95&alc
CONF: Thtr 50 Class 20 Board 25 Del from £85
CARDS:

★★★62% **Royal Hop Pole**

Church St GL20 5RT (M5 junct 9 head for Tewkesbury approx 1.5miles at War Memorial roundabout straight across Hotel is on the right) ☎ 01684 293236
FAX 01684 296680
This historic former coaching inn at the heart of the town dates back to the 14th century - though largely rebuilt in Georgian times - and retains much of its original charm in sloping floors, exposed beams and attractive interior work. Though bedroom renovation is still not completed, all accommodation is equipped with modern facilities, and there are a comfortable traditional lounge, popular bar and cosy restaurant.
24 en suite (bth/shr) 5 annexe en suite (bth/shr) (1 fmly) No smoking in 14 bedrooms CTV in all bedrooms Night porter 30P Xmas V meals Coffee am Tea pm No smoking in restaurant Last d 9.30pm
ROOMS: s £55; d £65 * **LB**
MEALS: Sunday Lunch £8.95-£9.95 Dinner £13.95-£16.95&alc*
CONF: Thtr 25 Board 12 Del from £75
CARDS:

★★67% **Tudor House**

High St GL20 5BH (M5 junct 9 towards Tewkesbury 1.50 miles to the Town Centre, the Hotel can be found in the High Street) ☎ 01684 297755
FAX 01684 290306
Right in the heart of this historic town stands an attractive, cosy, character hotel full of charm. There is an abundance of beams and sloping floors yet rooms offer modern standards of comfort and are equipped with a good range of facilities. For the size of the hotel there is a commendable range of dining options encompassing restaurant, brassiere and bar meals. Friendly service a carried out by an enthusiastic team.
21 en suite (bth/shr) (2 fmly) CTV in all bedrooms 30P English & French Cuisine V meals Coffee am Tea pm Last d 9.30pm
ROOMS: (incl. bkfst) s £35-£50; d £40.50-£65 * **LB**
MEALS: Lunch £7.95-£10.95 Dinner £9.95-£12.95*
CONF: Thtr 12 Class 15 Board 8 Del from £70
CARDS: £

THAME Oxfordshire Map 04 SP70

★★★❀75% **Spread Eagle**
Cornmarket OX9 2BW (town centre on A418 Oxford to Aylesbury Road, exit 6 M40 south exit 8 north) ☎ 01844 213661
FAX 01844 261380
Closed 28-30 Dec
In many ways the Spread Eagle has been a profound influence on hotel keeping as we now know it, and under the Stewardship of the redoutable John Fothergill author of the Innkeepers Diary and father of the "Gentleman Innkeeper" tradition we can draw parallels with many of today's "amateur" hoteliers. The tradition of hospitality from years past is fervently upheld by current proprietors Mr and Mrs Barrington whose benign influence permeates through the hotel and results in a guest focused, friendly yet professional staff. Bedrooms vary in character depending on which part of the much extended property they are in, with the modern wings offering more space but the older areas having more period charm. All rooms are immaculately maintained and have an extensive range of facilities. There are extensive banqueting facilities and the traditional restaurant offers guests choice from a wide selection of menus, including some traditional favourites from Fothergill's day like the incredibly rich Chocolate Mud.
33 en suite (bth/shr) (1 fmly) CTV in all bedrooms No dogs (ex guide dogs) Night porter 80P Xmas English & French Cuisine V meals Coffee am Tea pm Last d 10pm
ROOMS: (incl. cont bkfst) s £82.95-£94.95; d £92.95-£107.95 * **LB**
OFF-PEAK: (incl. cont bkfst) s £69.95-£73.95; d £84.95-£96.95
MEALS: Lunch £18.85-£19.85&alc Dinner £20.75-£21.95&alc*
CONF: Thtr 250 Class 100 Board 50 Del from £105
CARDS:

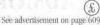

Travelodge
OX9 3XD (A418) ☎ 01844 218740
FAX 01844 218740
This modern building offers accommodation in smart, spacious and well equipped bedrooms, suitable for family use, and all with en suite bathrooms. Meals may be taken at the nearby family restaurant. For information on room rates and to make a booking, call Roomline free of charge on 0800 850950. For more details about Travelodge, consult the Contents page under Hotel Groups.
31 en suite (bth/shr)

THAXTED Essex Map 05 TL63

★★67% **Four Seasons**
Walden Rd CM6 2RE (0.5m N on the B184 at the junction with the B1051 Gt Sampford/Haverhill road)
☎ 01371 830129 FAX 01371 830835
The Four Seasons is a delightful country hotel which sits on the outskirts of the mediaeval town of Thaxted. This attractive building, with lovely plasterwork moulding and weather-boarding, is set in two acres of beautifully kept gardens. Proprietors Mr and Mrs Murfitt maintain high standards of housekeeping and ensure guests receive a courteous personal service at all times. On our last visit, the restaurant and bar were being totally re-styled to give greater flexibility and comfort for guests; in addition there is a quiet residents' lounge available on the first floor.
9 rms (8 bth/shr) No smoking in all bedrooms CTV in all bedrooms No dogs 100P No coaches No children 12yrs No smoking in restaurant
ROOMS: (incl. bkfst) s £45-£50; d £60-£65 * **LB**
MEALS: Lunch £21-£30alc*
CONF: Thtr 70 Class 60 Board 40
CARDS:

THETFORD Norfolk Map 05 TL88
See also Brandon (Suffolk)

★★★59% **The Bell**
King St IP24 2AZ (off A134) ☎ 01842 754455
FAX 01842 755552
Oak beams dating from 1492 are a feature of the hotel's bar and an Elizabethan wall painting is featured in one of the rooms, which also has a four-poster bed and is said to haunted. The majority of bedrooms however are in a newer extension which looks out over the River Ouse. The Bell was once a 15th-century coaching inn on the Cambridge to Norwich run and the older parts of the hotel are reminiscent of this period. The hotel is situated in the centre of the town and overlooks the gilded statue of the 18th century-radical, Thomas Paine, and the parish church.
47 en suite (bth/shr) (1 fmly) No smoking in 20 bedrooms CTV in all bedrooms Night porter 82P Xmas European Cuisine V meals Coffee am Tea pm No smoking in restaurant Last d 9.30pm
ROOMS: s £65-£80; d £75-£90 * **LB**
OFF-PEAK: (incl. bkfst & dinner) d £98-£123
MEALS: Lunch £9.95-£11.95&alc Dinner £16.95-£20.95&alc*
CONF: Thtr 80 Class 45 Board 40 Del from £85
CARDS:

★★69% **Historical Thomas Paine**
White Hart St IP24 1AA (on A1075)
☎ 01842 755631 FAX 01842 766505
This small family owned and managed hotel offers a relaxed and friendly atmosphere, backed up by an efficient informal service. The large bar has recently been refurbished and now offers a lighter and more comfortable environment in which to eat and drink; there is a comprehensive selection of bar meals available. A set priced

contd.

menu is offered in the pleasant small restaurant, and coffee can be taken in comfort in the adjacent lounge. Bedroom styles and sizes vary, each offering a sound level of appointments and comfort.
13 en suite (bth/shr) (1 fmly) CTV in all bedrooms 30P V meals Coffee am Tea pm Last d 9.30pm
ROOMS: (incl. bkfst) s £49-£52; d £59-£62 **LB**
OFF-PEAK: (incl. bkfst) s £38-£45; d £55-£57
MEALS: Lunch £9.50-£17.50 Dinner £17.50-£19.50
CARDS:

THIRSK North Yorkshire Map 08 SE48

★★ 73% **Sheppard's**
Church Farm, Front St, Sowerby YO7 1JF (take A61 Ripon road from Market Sq, at mini roundabout turn left towards Sowerby, hotel on right 0.25m along Sowerby road) ☎ 01845 523655
FAX 01845 524720
Closed 1st wk Jan
This well furnished and very friendly hotel was once a farmhouse and has now been carefully extended to provide comfortable and inviting accommodation; it is found just outside the town in the village of Sowerby. It provides a good range of well produced dishes which are served either in the cosy restaurant or the less formal bistro. Bedrooms are a delight to occupy and have been thoughtfully equipped and very pleasantly furnished. Service is from the Sheppard family who are always on hand to ensure their guests are well cared for.
8 en suite (bth/shr) (1 fmly) No smoking in 2 bedrooms CTV in all bedrooms No dogs 30P No children 10yrs International Cuisine V meals Last d 10pm
ROOMS: (incl. bkfst) s £55-£60; d £70-£80 * **LB**
MEALS: Lunch fr £10.50&alc Dinner £18.80-£26.65alc
CARDS:

★★ 67% **Golden Fleece**

CONSORT HOTELS

42 Market Place YO7 1LL (off A19 at the Thirsk turn off, proceed to the Town Centre, Hotel is situated on the southern edge of Market Place)

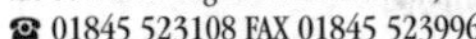

☎ 01845 523108 FAX 01845 523996
Situated in the centre of town, this characterful hotel has been purchased by the Hollins family who have overseen a complete refurbishment. The bedrooms are very well equipped and also include a room with a four-poster bed and all the rooms have been pleasantly decorated. A good range of well prepared food is available and there is a cosy bar as well as a small lounge; meeting rooms are also provided.
18 en suite (bth/shr) (3 fmly) CTV in all bedrooms 50P Xmas English & French Cuisine V meals Coffee am Tea pm Last d 9pm
ROOMS: (incl. bkfst) s fr £55; d £75-£84 * **LB**
MEALS: Lunch £6.50-£15 Dinner fr £16.50&alc*
CONF: Thtr 100 Class 40 Board 40 Del from £58
CARDS:

★★ 62% **Three Tuns Hotel**
Market Place YO7 1LH (A19 A61 8m from A1(17) turn onto A168, onto Town Centre hotel in Market Place)
☎ 01845 523124 FAX 01845 526126
Standing in the corner of the market square and having the benefit of its own car park, this Georgian hotel offers a good standard of both service and accommodation. The bedrooms have been considerably refurbished and there is a wide range of dishes available either in the bar or the spacious rear restaurant.
11 en suite (bth/shr) (3 fmly) CTV in 10 bedrooms 52P Xmas V meals Coffee am Tea pm Last d 9.30pm
ROOMS: (incl. bkfst) s £35-£45; d £55-£60 **LB**
MEALS: Lunch fr £6.95 Dinner fr £10*
CONF: Thtr 50 Board 35
CARDS:

★ 61% **Old Red House**
Station Rd YO7 4LT (1m W) ☎ 01845 524383 FAX 01845 525902
This family-run inn stands next to the railway station and is not far from both the town and the racecourse. It offers adequate accommodation and is good value for money The bedrooms are modern with those in the extension being more spacious than those in the main house. Service is friendly, attentive and polite.
5 en suite (shr) 5 annexe en suite (shr) CTV in all bedrooms 30P Xmas V meals Coffee am Last d 9pm
ROOMS: (incl. bkfst) s fr £19; d fr £32 * **LB**
CARDS:

THORNBURY Gloucestershire Map 03 ST69

RED STAR HOTEL

★★★ **Thornbury Castle**

PRIDE OF BRITAIN MEMBER

BS12 1HH (on A38 travelling N from Bristol take the first turning to Thornbury,at the end of the High St left into Castle St,entrance to Castle on left) ☎ 01454 281182 FAX 01454 416188

Closed 2 days Jan
This beautiful castle was once owned by Henry VIII and its history dates back as far as 1511. Today it is a very comfortable country house hotel, surrounded by its vineyard, gardens and high walls, with distant views over the River Severn into Gloucestershire and Wales. The main apartments have been carefully restored to provide eighteen bedchambers, each individually decorated and equipped with modern creature comforts. The public rooms, with heraldic shields, tapestries, suits of armour and fine antique furniture are similarly impressive and here staff provide attentive services to suit the grandeur of the surroundings.
18 en suite (bth/shr) CTV in all bedrooms No dogs Night porter 40P No coaches Croquet lawn Hot air ballooning Archery No children 12yrs Xmas English & French Cuisine V meals Tea pm No smoking in restaurant
ROOMS: (incl. cont bkfst) s £95; d £110-£220 * **LB**
OFF-PEAK: (incl. cont bkfst) s £75; d £95-£180
CONF: Thtr 36 Class 12 Board 24 Del from £220
CARDS:

See advertisement under BRISTOL

THORNE South Yorkshire Map 08 SE61

★★ 67% **Belmont**
Horsefair Green DN8 5EE (M18 exit 6 A614 signed Thorne Hotel is on the right of the Market place)
☎ 01405 812320 FAX 01405 740508
A popular hotel which is centred around an open-plan bar, reception

and dining area with accommodation above. The bedrooms are purpose built, well equipped and comfortable, furnished with pine and decorated in a cottage style and their bathrooms are modern. Professionally managed, the service is friendly and attentive at all times.

23 en suite (bth/shr) (3 fmly) CTV in all bedrooms Night porter 30P Xmas English & French Cuisine V meals Coffee am Tea pm Last d 10pm

ROOMS: s £48.50-£55; d £63.50-£82.50 * **LB**

MEALS: Lunch £10.95-£12.10&alc Dinner £10.95-£12.10&alc

CONF: Thtr 60 Class 20 Board 25 Del from £69.50

CARDS:

THORNLEY Co Durham Map 08 NZ33

★★63% **Crossways**

Dunelm Rd DH6 3HT (5m SE of Durham City, on A181) ☎ 01429 821248 FAX 01429 820034

Well equipped bedrooms and popular bars are features of this mainly commercial hotel which is situated on the A181, convenient for both the A1 and the A19. A good range of dishes is available in both the attractive split-level restaurant and the bars.

23 en suite (bth/shr) (9 fmly) CTV in all bedrooms STV Night porter 150P Sauna Solarium Xmas English & French Cuisine V meals Coffee am Tea pm Last d 9.45pm

ROOMS: (incl. bkfst) s £39-£55; d £48-£100 * **LB**

MEALS: Lunch £12.50&alc High tea £5.50 Dinner £12.50&alc*

CONF: Thtr 120 Class 80 Board 30 Del from £55

CARDS:

THORNTHWAITE (NEAR KESWICK) Cumbria Map 11 NY22

★★69% **Thwaite Howe**

CA12 5SA (follow signs to Thornthwaite Gallery from A66 approx 3 miles from Keswick) ☎ 017687 78281 FAX 017687 78529

Closed Nov-Feb

Harry and Mary Kay run their traditional country house almost single-handed and their caring approach makes for a relaxed atmosphere. The house is set in two acres of gardens with magnificent views across the valley to the distant fells, which also can be enjoyed from some of the bedrooms. There are a small residents' bar and a comfortable lounge with an open fire in season. Mary serves a good five-course set dinner at 7pm, and Harry has put together an interesting wine list.

8 en suite (bth) No smoking in all bedrooms CTV in all bedrooms 12P No coaches No children 12yrs No smoking in restaurant Last d 7pm

ROOMS: (incl. bkfst & dinner) d £82-£89.50 **LB**

MEALS: Dinner £16.50

CARDS:

See advertisement under KESWICK

★★66% ***Ladstock Country House***

CA12 5RZ ☎ 01768 778210 & 78249

Closed Jan

Set in its own well maintained grounds and enjoying a lovely outlook towards Skiddaw, this fine old oak-panelled house attracts visiting tourists, and is also a popular venue for local conferences and functions. Appealing public areas include an inviting quiet lounge plus a cosy lobby with a welcoming open fire, adjacent to which is the well stocked panelled bar. Bedrooms range from well proportioned front-facing rooms, some of which are appropriately furnished with antiques, to others which are more varied in size, style and quality.

22 rms (11 bth 7 shr) (2 fmly) CTV in all bedrooms No dogs (ex guide dogs) 50P V meals Coffee am Tea pm Last d 8.30pm

CARDS:

THORNTON HOUGH Merseyside Map 07 SJ38

★★★68% **Thornton Hall**

Neston Rd L63 1JF (M53 junct 4 take B5151 Weston onto B5136 to Thornton Hough) ☎ 0151 336 3938 FAX 0151 336 7864

Closed 25-27 Dec & 1 Jan

Set in seven acres of pleasant grounds, this very impressive building was originally built for an 18th-century shipping magnate, and, though the hotel has now been considerably extended, the original hall has preserved its oak panelling and stained glass windows. The restaurant is particularly interesting with its leather and mother-of-pearl ceiling and carved fireplace. Five bedrooms are located in the old part of the house but the majority are housed in modern wings and all are well equipped and comfortable. High quality cooking is provided in the main restaurant and there is also a pub/bistro in the grounds.

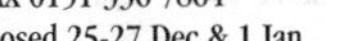

5 en suite (bth/shr) 58 annexe en suite (bth/shr) (4 fmly) CTV in all bedrooms STV Night porter 250P Croquet lawn European Cuisine V meals Coffee am Tea pm Last d 9.30pm

ROOMS: (incl. bkfst) s £70-£75; d £80-£85 **LB**

OFF-PEAK: (incl. bkfst) s £50-£55; d £65-£70

MEALS: Lunch £10&alc Dinner £18.95*

CONF: Thtr 200 Class 80 Board 40 Del £95

CARDS:

THORNTON WATLASS North Yorkshire Map 08 SE28

★67% **Buck Inn**

HG4 4AH (A 684 towards Bedale, B6268 towards Mashan, after 2 miles Thornton Watlass, the Hotel is situated by the Cricket Green) ☎ 01677 422461

Situated overlooking the village green, which completes the English scene with its cricket pitch, this charming inn offers a good all round standard of accommodation. The bedrooms are comfortable whilst the bar is full of character and charm and there is a good range of food available either in the bar or the dining room. Service is friendly and very attentive, and real ale is served in the bar and includes a guest ale.

7 rms (5 bth/shr) (1 fmly) 10P Fishing Pool table Quoits Childrens play area Wkly live entertainment V meals Coffee am Tea pm No smoking in restaurant Last d 9.30pm

ROOMS: (incl. bkfst) s fr £34; d fr £50 * **LB**

MEALS: Lunch fr £10 Dinner fr £12

CARDS:

THORPE (DOVEDALE) Derbyshire Map 07 SK15

★★★66% **Peveril of the Peak**

DE6 2AW ☎ 01335 350333 FAX 01335 350507

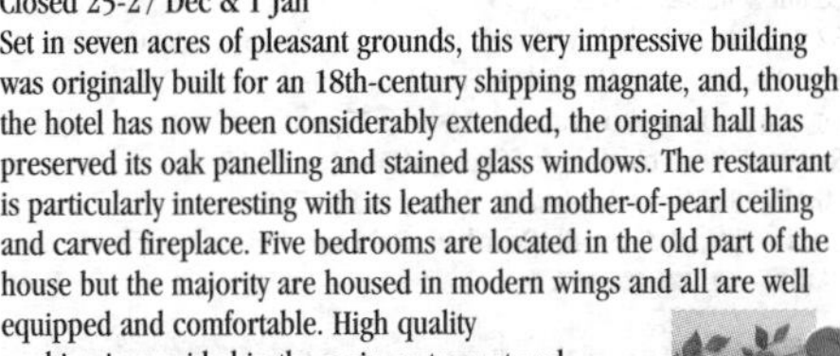

Features of this comfortable hotel, situated amidst some of Derbyshire's finest scenery, are its well appointed bedrooms, comfortable cosy lounges and restaurant which overlooks terraced lawns, rockeries and gardens. Some of the bedrooms are in an extension to the original building, which at one time may have been the local rectory, although it has been a hotel for

contd.

over 100 years and the public areas in particular still maintain Victorian character.
47 en suite (bth/shr) (3 fmly) No smoking in 20 bedrooms CTV in all bedrooms Night porter 60P Tennis (hard) Xmas V meals Coffee am Tea pm Last d 9pm
ROOMS: s £70; d £90 * **LB**
OFF-PEAK: s £70; d £90
MEALS: Lunch £8.50-£15 Dinner £19-£30&alc*
CONF: Thtr 50 Class 30 Board 36 Del from £80
CARDS:

★★★64% **Izaak Walton**
DE6 2AY (1m W on Ilam road) ☎ 01335 350555 FAX 01335 350539
Developed from a rambling 17th-century farmhouse, this hotel is in a delightful position overlooking Dovedale and Thorpe Cloud. Public areas offer a cosy bar and a smart restaurant which has been brightly furnished with bold fabrics. Bedrooms are being upgraded, and the more recently redecorated rooms are very pleasing, with light colour schemes.
32 en suite (bth/shr) (6 fmly) CTV in all bedrooms Night porter 80P Fishing Xmas English & French Cuisine V meals Coffee am Tea pm No smoking in restaurant Last d 9.15pm
ROOMS: (incl. bkfst) s fr £80; d £100-£120 * **LB**
MEALS: Sunday Lunch fr £14 Dinner fr £22.75&alc
CONF: Thtr 50 Class 40 Board 30 Del from £98
CARDS:

THORPE MARKET Norfolk Map 09 TG23

★★68% **Elderton Lodge**
Gunton Park NR11 8TZ ☎ 01263 833547 FAX 01263 834673
Closed 20 Jan-6 Feb
Elderton Lodge, formerly a Shooting Lodge & Dower House to Gunton Hall and favoured retreat of Lillie Langtry, sits in six acres of its own mature grounds adjacent to the thousand acres of Gunton Park, with its herds of roaming deer. A warm welcome and friendly service is assured from the resident proprietors and staff. Public rooms include a small reception foyer, a lounge bar, the Green conservatory and Georgian restaurant, meals are often served in the conservatory in the warmer months; menus offer an interesting selection of carefully cooked and tasty dishes, with game from local estates featuring regularly during the seasons. Bedrooms are individually furnished and decorated, the most recently refurbished rooms are most cheerful with warm rich colour schemes.
8 en suite (bth/shr) (2 fmly) No smoking in 2 bedrooms CTV in all bedrooms 30P No coaches Croquet lawn shooting by arrangement No children 6yrs Xmas French provincial Cuisine V meals Coffee am Tea pm No smoking in restaurant Last d 9pm
ROOMS: (incl. bkfst) s £42-£50; d £64-£70 * **LB**
OFF-PEAK: (incl. bkfst) s £35-£45; d £60-£70
MEALS: Sunday Lunch £5.95-£10.95 Dinner £14.50-£17.50*
CONF: Thtr 30 Class 30 Board 16
CARDS:

THRAPSTON Northamptonshire Map 04 SP97

Travelodge
Thrapston Bypass NN14 4UR (on A14 link road A1/M1) ☎ 01832 735199 FAX 01832 735199

This modern building offers accommodation in smart, spacious and well equipped bedrooms, suitable for family use, and all with en suite bathrooms. Meals may be taken at the nearby family restaurant. For information on room rates and to make a booking, call Roomline free of charge on 0800 850950. For more details about Travelodge, consult the Contents page under Hotel Groups.
40 en suite (bth/shr)

THRUSSINGTON Leicestershire Map 08 SK61

Travelodge
Green Acres Filling Station LE7 8TF (on A46, southbound) ☎ 01664 424525 FAX 01664 424525
Travelodge
This modern building offers accommodation in smart, spacious and well equipped bedrooms, suitable for family use, and all with en suite bathrooms. Meals may be taken at the nearby family restaurant. For information on room rates and to make a booking, call Roomline free of charge on 0800 850950. For more details about Travelodge, consult the Contents page under Hotel Groups.
32 en suite (bth/shr)

THURLESTONE Devon Map 03 SX64

★★★★70% **Thurlestone**
TQ7 3NN (A38 take A384 into Totnes, A381 towards Kingsbridge, onto A379 towards Churchstow, onto B3197 turn into lane signposted to Thurlestone) ☎ 01548 560382 FAX 01548 561069
Set in a superb location overlooking the gardens and the south Devon coast, this long-established hotel, owned by several generations of the Grose family, offers superb leisure facilities among its many attractions. Public rooms are smart and comfortable, and the attitude of the friendly staff is one of the hotel's major strengths. Many of the bedrooms enjoy sea views, while the best 'de luxe' rooms have their own videos and private garaging.The hotel has been awarded a rosette for its food, and the five course dinners offer dishes such as crab with grapefruit, brill with saffron sauce and venison with a port and redcurrant sauce. Afternoon teas in the lounge are a special treat as well.
68 en suite (bth/shr) (16 fmly) CTV in all bedrooms Lift Night porter 119P No coaches Indoor swimming pool (heated) Outdoor swimming pool (heated) Golf 9 Tennis (hard) Squash Snooker Sauna Solarium Gym Croquet lawn Putting green Jacuzzi/spa Games room Badminton ch fac Xmas International Cuisine V meals Coffee am Tea pm No smoking in restaurant Last d 9pm
ROOMS: (incl. bkfst) s £50-£70; d £100-£140 **LB**
OFF-PEAK: (incl. bkfst) s £35-£40; d £70-£80
MEALS: Lunch £12.50-£15alc Dinner £21-£29
CONF: Thtr 140 Class 100 Board 40 Del from £80
CARDS:

★★67% **Heron House**
Thurlestone Sands TQ7 3JY (off A381 3m S of Kingsbridge, turn right signed Hope Cove, continue over x-rds, then fork right 50 yds after Galmpton Village sign) ☎ 01548 561308 & 561600
FAX 01548 560180
With spectacular coast views from its setting between open countryside and a large sandy beach, Heron House has been personally run by the same family for 10 years, and they have created a relaxed and informal atmosphere. A spacious dining room offers a fixed-price menu and a short carte, the lounge/bar has recently been extended and bedrooms are scheduled for refurbishment.

18 en suite (bth/shr) (7 fmly) No smoking in 10 bedrooms CTV in all bedrooms 50P Outdoor swimming pool (heated) Solarium Pool table Golf breaks Xmas V meals Coffee am Tea pm No smoking in restaurant Last d 8.30pm
ROOMS: (incl. bkfst) s £45; d £90-£120 * **LB**
OFF-PEAK: (incl. bkfst) s £30; d £60-£90
MEALS: Lunch £5-£15 Dinner fr £18.50*
CARDS:

See advertisement under SALCOMBE

TICEHURST East Sussex Map 05 TQ63

★★★★67% **Dale Hill Hotel & Golf Club**
TN5 7DQ (situated on B2087 1.25m off A21)
☎ 01580 200112 FAX 01580 201249
This impressive, well designed modern hotel and golf club offers a range of spacious well equipped bedrooms, an open plan ground floor bar and lounge, a separate Spike bar, and a first floor Brasserie and an attractively appointed candlelit restaurant which overlooks the 18th green; the restaurant offers a set priced dinner menu whilst the Brasserie is open all day for light meals and snacks. A good range of leisure facilities are available and two 18 hole golf courses (one of which is under construction and is nearing completion) with resident professional and pro-shop.
26 en suite (bth/shr) (6 fmly) CTV in all bedrooms STV Lift Night porter 220P No coaches Indoor swimming pool (heated) Golf 18 Sauna Solarium Gym Pool table Putting green Xmas V meals Coffee am Tea pm Last d 9.30pm
ROOMS: (incl. bkfst) s £48-£58; d £76-£96 * **LB**
OFF-PEAK: (incl. bkfst) s £43-£48; d £66-£76
MEALS: Lunch fr £9.40 High tea fr £5.25 Dinner £19.95*
CONF: Thtr 44 Class 30 Board 24 Del from £85
CARDS:

TINTAGEL Cornwall & Isles of Scilly Map 02 SX08

★★❀ 72% **Trebrea Lodge**
Trenale PL34 0HR (from A39 take Tintagel sign about 1m before Tintagel turn into Trenale)
☎ 01840 770410 FAX 01840 770092
Closed 5 Jan-10 Feb
This beautifully preserved 18th-century manor house stands in four and a half acres of wooded grounds, commanding superb views across open countryside towards the Atlantic. Tastefully decorated throughout, with antique and period pieces, including a magnificent Jacobean-style bed in one of the en suite bedrooms. Public rooms have a wealth of charm and character, and comprise of two lovely lounges, both with log fires, and also an elegant dining room with oak panelled walls, where a daily-changing set-price menu of honest, unpretentious dishes is served.
6 en suite (bth/shr) 1 annexe en suite (bth/shr) No smoking in all bedrooms CTV in all bedrooms 12P No coaches No children 9yrs English & French Cuisine No smoking in restaurant Last d 6pm
ROOMS: (incl. bkfst) s £52.50-£57.50; d £72-£84 **LB**
MEALS: Dinner £19.50*
CARDS:

See advertisement on this page

★★71% ***The Wootons Country Hotel***
Fore St PL34 0DD ☎ 01840 770170 FAX 01840 770978
This town-centre hotel, close to the sea and surrounded by open country, has been rebuilt and renovated to a high standard. Attractive, comfortable bedrooms with modern facilities have thoughtful extras and the spacious, modern public areas include all-day bars offering a range of dishes and a small restaurant serving evening meals.
11 en suite (bth/shr) CTV in all bedrooms No dogs (ex guide dogs) 35P Snooker Pool table V meals Coffee am Tea pm Last d 9.30pm
CARDS:

★★62% **Bossiney House**
Bossiney PL34 0AX (from A39 take B3263 into Tintagel, then Boscastle road for 0.75m to hotel on left) ☎ 01840 770240 FAX 01840 770501
Closed Nov-Mar
There is a warm and friendly atmosphere at this family-run hotel. Cosy public areas include a TV lounge and a separate lounge/bar. A set-

contd.

price menu with a limited choice is served in the bright dining room and excellent breakfasts are a feature.
17 en suite (bth/shr) 1 annexe en suite (bth) (1 fmly) 30P Indoor swimming pool (heated) Tennis Sauna Solarium Putting green V meals Coffee am Tea pm
ROOMS: (incl. bkfst) s £33-£43; d £56-£76 * **LB**
OFF-PEAK: (incl. bkfst) s £31-£41; d £52-£72
CARDS:

★★55% **Atlantic View**
Treknow PL34 0EJ (B3263 to Tregatta turn left into Treknow, Hotel in situated on road to Trebarwith Strand Beach) ☎ 01840 770221
Closed 23 Dec-2 Jan
Quietly located in a small hamlet, away from the tourist hotspotof Tintagel, this small hotel has sea and rural coastal views. Public rooms include a comfortable lounge, cosy bar, dining room and additional sun lounge. Friendly service is provided by the proprietor and her family.
9 en suite (bth/shr) (2 fmly) CTV in all bedrooms STV 20P No coaches Indoor swimming pool (heated) Solarium Pool table European Cuisine V meals Coffee am Tea pm Last d 9pm
ROOMS: (incl. bkfst) s £19.50-£24; d £39-£48 * **LB**
MEALS: Lunch £2.50-£5.50 Dinner £10-£14
CARDS:

TITCHWELL Norfolk Map 09 TF74

★★72% **Briarfields**
Main St PE31 8BB (A149 coastal road towards Wells-next-sea, Titchwell is the 3rd village & 7m from Hunstanton, hotel is situated on left of main road into village) ☎ 01485 210742 FAX 01485 210933
This friendly small hotel is the result of a careful conversion of a group of traditional Norfolk barns. Guests will find a number of attractive public rooms within the complex, ranging from a small bar with a dining area for bar meals, to a pleasant restaurant serving freshly prepared meals, a cheerful, light breakfast room and a welcoming lounge. Resident owners and their staff provide friendly service in informal style and most of the well proportioned bedrooms are on the ground floor, opening on to a pleasant courtyard.
17 en suite (bth/shr) (2 fmly) No smoking in 15 bedrooms CTV in all bedrooms 30P Snooker Xmas English & French Cuisine V meals Coffee am Tea pm No smoking in restaurant Last d 9.30pm
ROOMS: (incl. bkfst) s £37.50; d £70 * **LB**
MEALS: Lunch £9.95 High tea 85p-£3.50alc Dinner £13.95*
CONF: Board 25
CARDS:

★★❀72% **Titchwell Manor**
PE31 8BB (on A149 between Brancaster and Thorhay on A149 coast road) ☎ 01485 210221 FAX 01485 210104
This delightful family-run hotel is in an unspoilt location looking out towards the sea. Bold colour schemes lend character to the public rooms, and a lighter floral style makes the well equipped bedrooms particularly attractive. Resident owners and their staff provide friendly, cheerful service. The Garden Restaurant makes a delightful setting for interesting menus that include dishes based on local produce, and some unusual soups are a highlight. Good bar meals are also available in more informal surroundings.
11 rms (7 bth/shr) 4 annexe en suite (bth/shr) (2 fmly) CTV in all bedrooms 50P Xmas European Cuisine V meals Coffee am Tea pm Last d 9.30pm
ROOMS: (incl. bkfst) s fr £39; d fr £78 *
OFF-PEAK: (incl. bkfst) s fr £30; d fr £60
MEALS: Lunch £10.95-£20 High tea £5-£15 Dinner £10-£35*
CARDS:

See advertisement on opposite page

TIVERTON Devon Map 03 SS91
See also Burrington

★★★62% **Tiverton**
Blundells Rd EX16 4DB ☎ 01884 256120 FAX 01884 258101
This purpose-built hotel, situated within level walking distance of the town centre and with easy access to the North Devon Link and M5, offers a relaxed atmosphere and spacious accommodation. Bedrooms have been equipped with modern facilities and comfortable sitting areas. The open-plan public rooms include a lounge bar and a restaurant where a wide selection is available from a choice of menus.
75 en suite (bth/shr) (75 fmly) CTV in all bedrooms Night porter 130P Wkly live entertainment ch fac Xmas English, French & Italian Cuisine V meals Coffee am Tea pm No smoking area in restaurant Last d 9.15pm
ROOMS: (incl. bkfst) s £38-£42; d £70-£76 * **LB**
OFF-PEAK: (incl. bkfst) s £38-£42; d £70-£76
MEALS: Lunch £4.80-£12&alc Dinner £6.50-£7.50&alc
CONF: Thtr 250 Class 100 Board 70 Del from £60
CARDS:

★★63% **Hartnoll**
Bolham EX16 7RA (1.5m N on A396)
☎ 01884 252777 FAX 01884 259195
This Georgian country house is situated on the outskirts of Tiverton, and has gardens leading down to the stream. Bedrooms in the main house are well equipped and vary in size whilst those in the cottage across the car park are all on ground level. A conservatory lounge overlooks the gardens, a lounge bar, cosy restaurant and extensive function rooms offer a choice of facilities.
11 en suite (bth/shr) 5 annexe en suite (shr) (2 fmly) CTV in all bedrooms 100P Xmas English & Continental Cuisine V meals Coffee am Tea pm No smoking in restaurant Last d 9pm
ROOMS: (incl. bkfst) s £35-£38; d £50 * **LB**
MEALS: Lunch £12.95-£14.95alc Dinner £12.95-£14.95alc*
CONF: Thtr 150 Class 50 Board 50 Del from £54
CARDS:

See advertisement on opposite page

TODDINGTON MOTORWAY SERVICE AREA (M1)
Bedfordshire Map 04 TL02

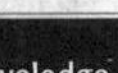

Travelodge
M1 Motorway LU5 6HR (between junct 11 & 12)
☎ Central Res 0800 850950 FAX 01525 878452
This modern building offers accommodation in smart, spacious and well equipped bedrooms, suitable for family use, and all with en suite bathrooms. Meals may be taken at the nearby family restaurant. For information on room rates and to make a booking, call Roomline free of charge on 0800 850950. For more details about Travelodge, consult the Contents page under Hotel Groups.
44 en suite (bth/shr)
ROOMS: s fr £42.95; d fr £42.95 *

TODMORDEN West Yorkshire Map 07 SD92

★★★ 64% **Scaitcliffe Hall**

Burnley Rd OL14 7DQ ☎ 01706 818888 FAX 01706 818825

This 17th-century county house is set in 16 acres of mature woodland, close to the town centre, just off the A646 Burnley Road. It is well furnished and offers well equipped modern bedrooms. A good range of food is available in the converted barn restaurant and service is both warm and friendly. At the time of our visit there were plans to add an extension during the coming winter. The gardens are well cared for and very inviting.

13 en suite (bth/shr) (2 fmly) CTV in all bedrooms STV Night porter 200P Xmas English & Continental Cuisine V meals Coffee am Tea pm Last d 10pm

ROOMS: (incl. bkfst) s £47-£55; d £60-£75 * **LB**

OFF-PEAK: (incl. bkfst) s £35-£42; d £50-£60

MEALS: Lunch £7.45-£8.95 High tea £4.75-£9.75 Dinner fr £16.95

CONF: Thtr 200 Class 100 Del from £79.50

CARDS:

See advertisement on this page

TODWICK South Yorkshire Map 08 SK48

★★★65% ***Red Lion***
Worksop Rd S31 0DJ (on A57) (Whitbread)
☎ 01909 771654 FAX 01909 773704
This former coaching inn retains some of its original character in public rooms which include a choice of bars and a small restaurant, whilst the modern bedrooms are housed in a new and well equipped extension. The hotel is handily located a short distance from junction 31 of the M1. A well established team of staff provides cheerful service.
29 en suite (bth/shr) (1 fmly) No smoking in 9 bedrooms CTV in all bedrooms STV No dogs (ex guide dogs) Night porter 90P English & French Cuisine V meals Coffee am Tea pm Last d 9.45pm
CARDS:

TOLLESHUNT KNIGHTS Essex Map 05 TL91

★★★★71% **Five Lakes Country House, Golf & Country Club**
Colchester Rd CM9 8HX (Kelvedon exit A12 follow signs to Tiptree, over staggered crossroads past Wilkin's Jam Factory,take left fork, approx 2m turn right atT junct) ☎ 01621 868888 FAX 01621 869696
An exceptional range of sporting and leisure amenities are offered at this impressive modern hotel, which stands in 320 acres of panoramic countryside. The well equipped accommodation is luxuriously furnished and includes suites, four-poster rooms and many rooms with marbled bathrooms and separate shower cubicles. Food can be enjoyed throughout the day at Bejerano's Brasserie, while the Camelot Restaurant, offers more formal surroundings. Two 18-hole golf courses are available - the par 71 Links course and the par 72 Lakes Championship course, designed by Neil Coles and used annually by the PGA European Tour. Other facilities include a country club and outstanding conference accommodation.
114 en suite (bth/shr) No smoking in 14 bedrooms CTV in all bedrooms STV Lift Night porter 500P Indoor swimming pool (heated) Golf 18 Tennis (hard) Squash Snooker Sauna Solarium Gym Pool table Putting green Jacuzzi/spa Steam room Health & Beauty Spa Aerobics Xmas English & Continental Cuisine V meals Coffee am Tea pm No smoking area in restaurant Last d 10pm
ROOMS: s fr £85; d fr £115 **LB**
OFF-PEAK: (incl. bkfst) s fr £83.50; d £117-£89
MEALS: Lunch £14.95-£16.50&alc Dinner £16.50-£22.50&alc*
CONF: Thtr 450 Class 180 Board 90 Del from £115
CARDS: Connect

T

TONBRIDGE Kent Map 05 TQ54

★★★58% **The Rose & Crown**
125 High St TN9 1DD ☎ 01732 357966
FAX 01732 357194

REGAL
A Collection of Individual Hotels

This old coaching inn, which sits near the base of the Norman castle, can trace its history back to the 15th century. Bedrooms are divided between a new extension to the rear and the main building. There are signs of wear in places, which are partly offset by the bright floral arrangements. Both the bar - with its cricket memorabilia - and the restaurant are located in the older part of the building.
48 en suite (bth/shr) (3 fmly) No smoking in 20 bedrooms CTV in all bedrooms Night porter 62P Xmas V meals Coffee am Tea pm No smoking in restaurant Last d 9.30pm
ROOMS: s £58.50; d £65 * **LB**
MEALS: Sunday Lunch £3.99-£15&alc Dinner £12.95-£14.95&alc*
CONF: Thtr 100 Class 40 Board 50 Del from £80
CARDS: Connect

Chimneys Motor Inn
Pembury Rd TN11 0NA (S off A21)
☎ 01732 773111 FAX 01732 771534
This new lodge, with a first-floor lounge area, offers a range of smart bedrooms at a very competitive price, the equipment provided including satellite TV. All meals are taken in the adjacent Chimneys Restaurant and bar, which specialises in steaks and grills, though more informal meals can be enjoyed in the bar.
39 en suite (bth/shr) (5 fmly) No smoking in 10 bedrooms CTV in all bedrooms STV No dogs (ex guide dogs) 120P V meals Coffee am Last d 9.45pm
CARDS:

TOPCLIFFE North Yorkshire Map 08 SE47

★★67% **The Angel Inn**
Long St YO7 3RW (turn off the A168 & the Angel Inn is situated in the centre of Topcliffe) ☎ 01845 577237 FAX 01845 578000
This attractive village inn offers a good range of value-for-money dishes from its country-style menu. The pleasant rear garden with its ornamental pool is popular during summer. Bedrooms are well appointed, and a large function room is available. Willing staff provide friendly service.
15 en suite (bth/shr) (1 fmly) CTV in all bedrooms STV No dogs (ex guide dogs) 150P Fishing Pool table English & Continental Cuisine V meals Coffee am Tea pm Last d 9.30pm
ROOMS: (incl. bkfst) s £30-£37.50; d £50-£55 * **LB**
MEALS: Lunch £9.50-£10.95 High tea £6.50&alc Dinner £12.50-£14.95&alc
CONF: Thtr 150 Class 60 Board 50
CARDS: Connect

TORBAY See under Brixham, Paignton & Torquay

TORCROSS Devon Map 03 SX84

★67% **Grey Homes**
TQ7 2TH (take A379 to village square, then take right fork and second turning on left) ☎ 01548 580220
Closed Nov-Mar
Built in the 1920s by the grandfather of the present owner, the hotel is set in six acres of lawns and terraced gardens in an elevated position overlooking this little fishing village. It has a magnificent panoramic view of the whole of Start Bay and Slapton Ley Nature Reserve. Bedrooms all benefit from the view, and are comfortably decorated and furnished. There is a cosy lounge and separate bar, and in the dining room the menu offers a small choice of home-cooked dishes.
7 en suite (bth/shr) (1 fmly) CTV in all bedrooms 15P No coaches Tennis (hard) No children 4yrs English/French Cuisine V meals Coffee am Tea pm No smoking in restaurant Last d 7.30pm
ROOMS: (incl. bkfst) s £30-£32; d £50-£54 * **LB**
MEALS: Dinner £14*
CARDS:

TORMARTON Gloucestershire Map 03 ST77

★★69% **Compass Inn**
GL9 1JB (0.5m from junct 18, M4)
☎ 01454 218242 & 218577 FAX 01454 218741
Closed 24-26 Dec

Best Western

Conveniently positioned just off the M4 this former coaching inn offers a range of facilities to suit the business, conference and leisure guest well. The bars are in the original building while most of the bedrooms are in modern extensions. There are two standards of bedrooms with the executive rooms boasting that little extra in comfort; all are well equipped. The Compass Inn offers a good range of eating options from bar to formal restaurant. Friendly service is carried out by local staff.
28 en suite (bth/shr) (7 fmly) CTV in all bedrooms STV 160P Pool table V meals Coffee am Tea pm Last d 9.30pm
ROOMS: (incl. bkfst) s fr £67.95; d fr £83.95 * **LB**
MEALS: Bar Lunch fr £5 Dinner £15.95-£17.95*
CONF: Thtr 100 Class 30 Board 34 Del from £84.50
CARDS: Connect

TORPOINT Cornwall & Isles of Scilly Map 02 SX45

★★64% **Whitsand Bay Hotel Golf & Country Club**
Portwrinkle PL11 3BU (5m W, off B3247)
☎ 01503 230276 FAX 01503 230329
Standing in six acres of grounds in a secluded fishing hamlet, this unique Tudor-Gothic hotel was rebuilt in 1911. The wood-panelled interior has an interesting architectural style with excellent stained glass windows, and the accommodation has recently been upgraded.
34 rms (32 bth/shr) (10 fmly) CTV in 32 bedrooms 60P Indoor swimming pool (heated) Golf 18 Sauna Solarium Gym Pool table Putting green Beauty salon Steam room Hairdressers ch fac Xmas English & Continental Cuisine V meals Coffee am Tea pm Last d 8.30pm
ROOMS: (incl. bkfst) s £23-£31; d £46-£62 * **LB**
MEALS: Sunday Lunch £7.50 Dinner £15
CONF: Thtr 100 Class 100 Board 40 Del from £40
CARDS:

TORQUAY Devon Map 03 SX96

★★★★★66% **The Imperial**
Park Hill Rd TQ1 1NU ☎ 01803 294301
FAX 01803 298293

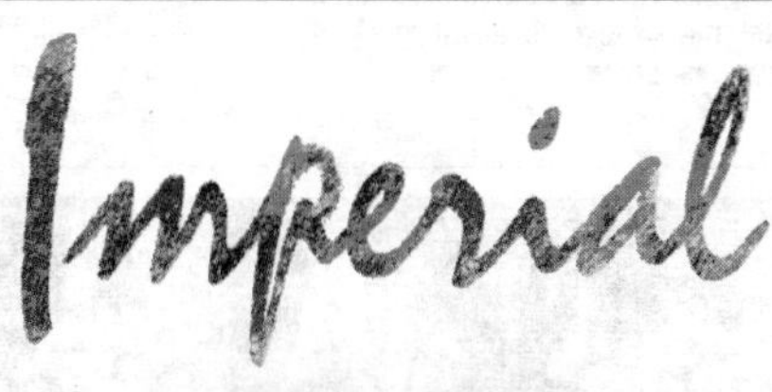

Perched high in an enviable position, the Imperial Hotel boasts commanding views over the bay and coastline beyond. Recently refurbished public rooms have a relaxing ambience and a sense of grandeur befitting its classification. The conservatory Sundeck Restaurant provides an informal brasserie style of dining while the Regatta Restaurant continues on more formal lines with enjoyable cooking. Bedrooms tend to vary in size and some are more opulent than others. However the upgrading programme is ongoing and hopefully those outstanding will receive similar good work in the near future. We await the results of the new management of Frank Tideman who brings with him an established reputation for enthusiasm and dedication.
167 en suite (bth/shr) (7 fmly) No smoking in 67 bedrooms CTV in all bedrooms STV Lift Night porter 180P Indoor swimming pool (heated) Outdoor swimming pool (heated) Tennis (hard) Squash Snooker Sauna Solarium Gym Jacuzzi/spa Health fitness centre Wkly live entertainment English & French Cuisine V meals Coffee am Tea pm Last d 9.30pm
CARDS:

See advertisement on this page

★★★★64% **Palace**
Babbacombe Rd TQ1 3TG ☎ 01803 200200 FAX 01803 299899
An impressive range of leisure facilities - including a health spa, extensive conference facilities and well kept grounds overlooking the park - make The Palace a good choice for both business and pleasure guests. Accommodation has been significantly upgraded, the best rooms having a view of the park or a balcony. Public areas include a choice of lounges, writing rooms, a cocktail bar and a large restaurant

contd.

where traditional cuisine is served. 24-hour room service (including light meals and afternoon tea) is also provided, and general manager Paul Bushby superintends a helpful team of professional staff.
141 en suite (bth/shr) (20 fmly) No smoking in 18 bedrooms CTV in all bedrooms No dogs (ex guide dogs) Lift Night porter 140P Indoor swimming pool (heated) Outdoor swimming pool (heated) Golf 9 Tennis (hard) Squash Snooker Sauna Croquet lawn Putting green Table tennis Wkly live entertainment ch fac Xmas English & French Cuisine V meals Coffee am Tea pm No smoking in restaurant Last d 9.15pm
ROOMS: (incl. bkfst) s £55-£65; d £110-£130 * **LB**
OFF-PEAK: (incl. bkfst & dinner) s £45-£55; d £90-£110
MEALS: Lunch fr £14.50&alc High tea fr £7.50 Dinner fr £21.50&alc*
CONF: Thtr 2000 Class 150 Board 40 Del from £99
CARDS:

See advertisement on opposite page

★★★★62% **Grand**
Sea Front TQ2 6NT (from M5 take A380 to Torquay.At sea front trun 1st right. Hotel on corner,entrance 1st onleft)
☎ 01803 296677 FAX 01803 213462
With fine views over the bay, this Edwardian hotel retains many features of bye-gone times. The greater majority of bedrooms have recently been upgraded, they do however vary in size, from spacious suites to Riviera rooms and rooms that overlook the town. In addition to the smart indoor leisure facilities there is an outdoor pool with patio areas, Bloaters Bar has been upgraded, serving drinks, buffet lunches and afternoon teas; the Gainsborough Restaurant providing the formal dining option. Guests are able to unwind in the Pullman Bar, which has a relaxed, public bar atmosphere.
112 en suite (bth/shr) (30 fmly) No smoking in 30 bedrooms CTV in all bedrooms STV Lift Night porter 35P Indoor swimming pool (heated) Outdoor swimming pool (heated) Tennis (hard) Snooker Sauna Solarium Gym Pool table Jacuzzi/spa Hairdressers Wkly live entertainment ch fac Xmas English & French Cuisine V meals Coffee am Tea pm No smoking in restaurant Last d 9.30pm
ROOMS: (incl. bkfst) s £67-£97.65; d £98-£189 * **LB**
OFF-PEAK: (incl. bkfst) s fr £77; d fr £125
MEALS: Lunch £10.50-£13&alc High tea £6.50-£8.50 Dinner £20.50-£26&alc
CONF: Thtr 350 Class 100 Board 60 Del from £96.50
CARDS:

See advertisement on page 623

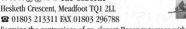

★★★76% **The Osborne**

Hesketh Crescent, Meadfoot TQ1 2LL
☎ 01803 213311 FAX 01803 296788
Forming the centrepiece of an elegant Regency terrace with uninterrupted views over Meadfoot Beach and Torbay, The Osborne has often been described as' Bath by the Sea'. Set in five acres of lovely gardens leading down to the sea, the public areas and some of the bedrooms benefiting from the superb views. Langtry's Restaurant provides the formal eating option; head chef Wayne Maddern continues to produce interesting and imaginative dishes. The Brasserie offers a more relaxed atmosphere and meals and light refreshment throughout the day and evening.
23 en suite (bth/shr) (2 fmly) CTV in all bedrooms STV No dogs (ex guide dogs) Lift Night porter 90P Indoor swimming pool (heated) Outdoor swimming pool (heated) Tennis (hard) Snooker Sauna Solarium Gym Pool table Putting green Plunge pool Wkly live entertainment Xmas International Cuisine V meals Coffee am Tea pm Last d 9.30pm
ROOMS: (incl. bkfst) s £59-£118; d £118-£148 * **LB**
OFF-PEAK: (incl. bkfst) s £41-£82; d £82-£112
MEALS: Bar Lunch fr £7.95alc Dinner fr £16.50&alc*
CONF: Thtr 90 Class 36 Board 42 Del from £78
CARDS:

See advertisement on opposite page

★★★75% **Corbyn Head**
Torquay Rd, Sea Front, Livermead TQ2 6RH
☎ 01803 213611 FAX 01803 296152

CONSORT HOTELS

There are panoramic views across Torbay and the harbour from this hotel. The majority of individually designed bedrooms also benefit from the hotel's seafront position, many rooms having the added bonus of a balcony. Under the direction of the resident proprietors, Julian and Anne Cook and their team of professional staff, guests relax and enjoy the attentive, friendly service. With experience from around the world, chef David Berry has recently taken over in the kitchen, the restaurant gaining a good reputation from both hotel residents and locals alike.
51 en suite (bth/shr) (1 fmly) CTV in all bedrooms No dogs (ex guide dogs) Night porter 50P Outdoor swimming pool (heated) Wkly live entertainment Xmas V meals Coffee am Tea pm No smoking in restaurant Last d 9pm
ROOMS: (incl. bkfst) s £45-£65; d £90-£130 * **LB**
MEALS: Bar Lunch £5-£12 Dinner £21.50-£30
CONF: Thtr 30 Class 20 Board 20
CARDS:

See advertisement on opposite page

★★★72% **Orestone Manor**
Rockhouse Ln, Maidencombe TQ1 4SX (off B3199 coast road, Torquay-Teignmouth) ☎ 01803 328098 FAX 01803 328336
A Georgian lodge, extended in Victorian times, Orestone Manor is situated in a sheltered mature garden with views across Lyme Bay. Bill and Gill Dagworthy took over the hotel during 1995 and are proving to be good hosts. Bedrooms vary in size but all are well equipped and comfortable, and front-facing rooms benefit from delightful views. In the elegantly furnished restaurant two fixed-price menus are offered and guests can 'mix and match' from both. Chef Mike Kukuczka uses much local produce and many innovative ideas for combinating ingredients, which can over complicate the dishes. At times, enthusiastic use of flavourings tends to overpower rather than complement.

contd.

T

18 en suite (bth/shr) (6 fmly) CTV in all bedrooms Night porter 40P No coaches Outdoor swimming pool (heated) Snooker Xmas English & French Cuisine V meals Coffee am Tea pm No smoking in restaurant Last d 8.30pm
ROOMS: (incl. bkfst) s £45-£80; d £73-£120 * **LB**
OFF-PEAK: (incl. bkfst) s £40-£70; d £70-£100
MEALS: Sunday Lunch £8.50-£15.50 Dinner fr £25.50*
CONF: Class 20 Board 16 Del from £90
CARDS:

See advertisement on opposite page

★★★70% **Livermead Cliff**

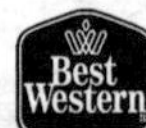

Torbay Rd TQ2 6RQ (on seafront, follow signs 'Livermead, Paignton') ☎ 01803 299666 & 292881 FAX 01803 294496
Situated within walking distance of both the shopping and Riviera centres, this family owned hotel enjoys a superb location; literally on the water's edge. The well equipped bedrooms continue to be upgraded on a rolling basis, with more rooms planned for next winter. The young staff work as a team and have a good rapport with many of the regular hotel guests.
64 en suite (bth/shr) (21 fmly) CTV in all bedrooms Lift Night porter 72P Outdoor swimming pool (heated) Fishing Solarium Sun terrace ch fac Xmas English & Continental Cuisine V meals Coffee am Tea pm Last d 8.30pm
ROOMS: (incl. bkfst) s £34.50-£59; d £67-£114 **LB**
OFF-PEAK: (incl. bkfst) s £33-£57; d £62-£106
MEALS: Lunch £7.95-£8.50&alc High tea fr £7.50&alc Dinner £17.25&alc
CONF: Thtr 100 Class 40 Board 30 Del from £48
CARDS:

★★★68% **Abbey Lawn Hotel**
Scarborough Rd TQ2 5UQ ☎ 01803 299199 FAX 01803 291460
Good standards are achieved at this spacious Georgian hotel, which has been completely refurbished throughout. It is set in a secluded but central location with views overlooking private tennis courts and the bay beyond. Public areas are comfortable, with leather covered furniture, and the conservatory lounge is particularly relaxing. The Leisure Club has an indoor pool and gymnasium, with trained staff in attendance.
56 en suite (bth/shr) No smoking in 2 bedrooms CTV in all bedrooms STV Lift Night porter 50P Indoor swimming pool (heated) Outdoor swimming pool Tennis (hard & grass) Sauna Solarium Gym Pool table Steam room Wkly live entertainment Xmas English & French Cuisine V meals Coffee am Tea pm No smoking in restaurant Last d 8.30pm
ROOMS: (incl. bkfst & dinner) s fr £40; d fr £80 * **LB**
MEALS: Bar Lunch £2.75-£9.50 High tea fr £5.50 Dinner fr £15.25*
CONF: Thtr 120 Class 60 Board 30
CARDS:

See advertisement on page 625

★★★65% **Livermead House**
Torbay Rd TQ2 6QJ (from seafront follow A379 towards Paignton and Livermead) ☎ 01803 294361 FAX 01803 200758
Since it was originally built in 1820, the Livermead House has been extended and extensively modernised. From its seafront location, the hotel has panoramic views over Torbay, from which the lounges and bar benefit. The bedrooms are undergoing a programme of upgrading, using attractively co-ordinated soft furnishings. In the hotel's restaurant, traditional menus with a wide choice of dishes are complemented by a carefully chosen wine list. Over the last few years, the hotel has gained a good reputation locally for functions, even supplying impressive cars for weddings.
66 en suite (bth/shr) (6 fmly) CTV in all bedrooms Lift Night porter 130P Outdoor swimming pool (heated) Squash Snooker Sauna Solarium Gym Wkly live entertainment Xmas English & French Cuisine V meals Coffee am Tea pm No smoking in restaurant Last d 8.30pm
ROOMS: (incl. bkfst & dinner) s fr £62; d fr £124 * **LB**
OFF-PEAK: (incl. bkfst & dinner) s fr £41; d fr £82
MEALS: Lunch £9.75 Dinner £19*
CONF: Thtr 300 Class 150 Board 80 Del from £46
CARDS:

★★★64% ***Belgrave***
Seafront TQ2 5HE ☎ 01803 296666 FAX 01803 211308
This hotel enjoys an enviable location on the seafront, overlooking the bay and Abbey Gardens. Accommodation has recently been refurbished, and the hotel now offers well equipped, spacious bedrooms, the best of them having good sea views or overlooking the swimming pool. Standards of housekeeping are impeccable, and there are both a popular public bar and an open-plan dining room which features live entertainment four nights a week during the season.
68 en suite (bth/shr) (16 fmly) CTV in all bedrooms Lift Night porter 86P No coaches Outdoor swimming pool (heated) Pool table English & French Cuisine V meals Coffee am Tea pm Last d 8.30pm
CARDS:

★★★64% **Toorak**
Chestnut Av TQ2 5JS (opposite Riviera Conference Centre)
☎ 01803 291444 FAX 01803 291666
Guests at the quietly located Toorak share the impressive leisure facilities and entertainment with its adjoining sister hotels. Bedrooms come in two styles, superior and standard, though all are well equipped and modern. In the restaurant a short set-price menu is offered with a few special dishes carrying a supplement, and at lunchtime snacks are served. The hotel is conveniently located for access to the Torquay Riviera Centre.
91 en suite (bth/shr) (29 fmly) CTV in all bedrooms Lift Night porter 90P Indoor swimming pool (heated) Outdoor swimming pool (heated) Tennis (hard) Snooker Sauna Solarium Pool table Croquet lawn Jacuzzi/spa Childrens play area Wkly live entertainment ch fac Xmas English & French Cuisine V meals Coffee am Tea pm No smoking area in restaurant Last d 8.30pm
ROOMS: (incl. bkfst & dinner) s £45-£59; d £90-£118 **LB**
MEALS: Bar Lunch £2.50-£10alc Dinner fr £14*
CONF: Thtr 200 Class 150 Board 80
CARDS:

★★★62% **The Grosvenor**
Belgrave Rd TQ2 5HG (just off sea front)
☎ 01803 294373 FAX 01803 291032
The Grosvenor Hotel, currently undergoing refurbishment by the new management, is situated a short distance from the seafront and is conveniently located for delegates from the Riviera Centre. Bedrooms are mainly spacious and vary in standard. The hotel has conference and function facilities opening onto the gardens, and the Garden Room restaurant is a no-smoking area.
41 en suite (bth/shr) (12 fmly) CTV in all bedrooms STV No dogs (ex guide dogs) Night porter 40P Indoor swimming pool (heated) Outdoor swimming pool (heated) Sauna Solarium Gym Jacuzzi/spa Wkly live entertainment Xmas English & French Cuisine V meals Coffee am Tea pm No smoking in restaurant Last d 8.30pm
ROOMS: (incl. bkfst & dinner) s £39-£60; d £78-£120 * **LB**
OFF-PEAK: (incl. bkfst & dinner) s fr £35; d fr £70
MEALS: Dinner £8.95-£16.95&alc*
CONF: Thtr 275 Class 150 Board 20
CARDS:

★★★61% **Lincombe Hall**
Meadfoot Rd TQ1 2JX ☎ 01803 213361 FAX 01803 211485
Two period houses joined by a covered walkway stand in substantial

contd.

T

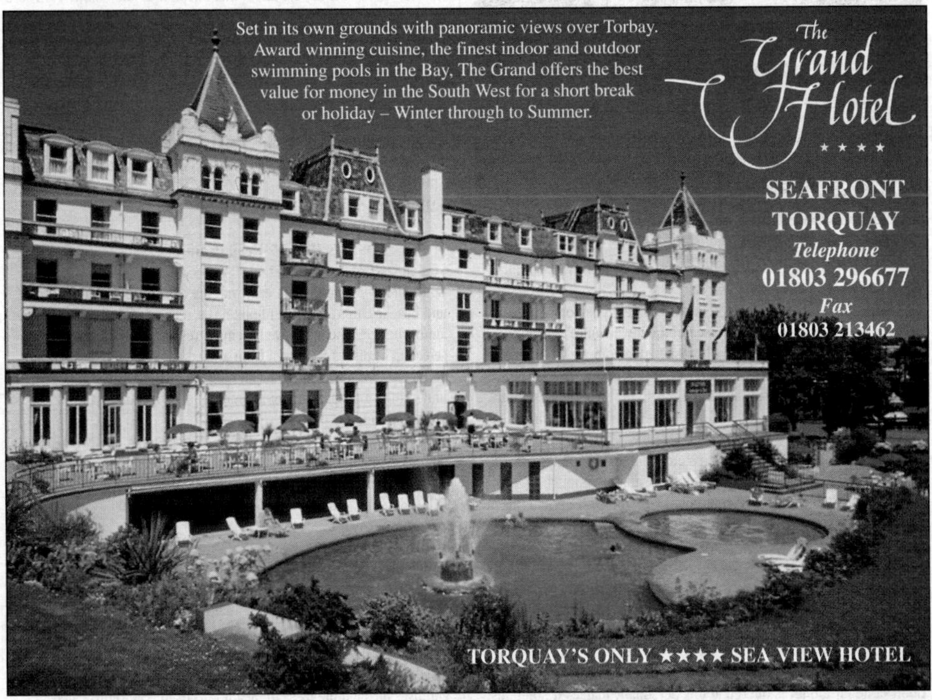

grounds with neat gardens and mature trees. Most of the bedrooms have been recently renovated.
42 en suite (bth/shr) (8 fmly) CTV in all bedrooms Night porter 40P Outdoor swimming pool (heated) Tennis (hard) Sauna Solarium Gym Pool table Putting green Jacuzzi/spa Play area Crazy golf ch fac Xmas V meals Coffee am Tea pm No smoking in restaurant Last d 8.30pm
ROOMS: (incl. bkfst & dinner) s £35-£47.50; d £70-£95 * **LB**
MEALS: Lunch fr £8.95 Dinner fr £12.95*
CONF: Thtr 50 Class 30 Board 20
CARDS:

★★★60% **Kistor**
Belgrave Rd TQ2 5HF (A380 to seafront)
☎ 01803 212632 FAX 01803 293219
Situated in a prime location, the Kistor overlooks the bowling green and is a short walk from the sea front. Now under the new ownership of the Morgan family there is much upgrading in process. The public areas are spacious and comfortable, and there is a swimming pool, sauna and jacuzzi, and also a games room and crazy golf.
56 en suite (bth/shr) (18 fmly) No smoking in 2 bedrooms CTV in all bedrooms STV Lift Night porter 40P Indoor swimming pool (heated) Sauna Gym Pool table Putting green Jacuzzi/spa Games room Table tennis Wkly live entertainment Xmas English & French Cuisine V meals Coffee am Tea pm No smoking area in restaurant Last d 8.30pm
ROOMS: (incl. bkfst) s £33-£43; d £66-£86 * **LB**
OFF-PEAK: (incl. bkfst) s fr £27; d fr £54
MEALS: Lunch £7.50-£8.50 Dinner £7.50-£11&alc*
CONF: Thtr 100 Board 30
CARDS:

★★★56% **Devonshire**
Parkhill Rd TQ1 2DY (from harbour clock tower, turn right up hill)
☎ 01803 291123 FAX 01803 291710
This family-owned hotel is located in a prominent position above the harbour, within easy walking distance of the town centre. Partial renovation has provided some well presented accommodation, and a number of the modern annexe bedrooms are at ground level. Public areas include two lounges, a popular bar and the spacious restaurant where traditional cuisine is served and live entertainment is provided during the season.
59 en suite (bth/shr) 12 annexe en suite (bth/shr) (9 fmly) CTV in all bedrooms Night porter 50P Outdoor swimming pool (heated) Snooker Pool table Wkly live entertainment English & French Cuisine V meals Coffee am Tea pm Last d 8.30pm
CONF: Thtr 20 Class 15 Board 25
CARDS:

See advertisement on opposite page

★★68% ***Coppice***
Babbacombe Rd TQ1 2QJ ☎ 01803 297786 FAX 01803 211085
Closed 16 Dec-3 Mar
Good value for money is offered at this personally managed hotel, just off the Babbacombe Road. Throughout the hotel the staff are friendly and helpful. Public areas are spacious and comfortable,and entertainment is provided on some evenings. The leisure facilities are good and include both indoor and outdoor pools, a mini gym, sauna, solarium and steam room.
40 rms (39 bth/shr) (16 fmly) CTV in all bedrooms Night porter 36P No coaches Indoor swimming pool (heated) Outdoor swimming pool (heated) Sauna Solarium Gym Pool table Putting green Jacuzzi/spa Coffee am Tea pm

★★67% **Albaston House**
27 St Marychurch Rd TQ1 3JF ☎ 01803 296758
Closed Jan
Situated at the top of the town in a residential area, this friendly small hotel is conveniently situated for the shops. The bedrooms vary in size and are attractively decorated; a continuous programme of upgrading is taking place. In addition to the comfortable lounge there is a cosy bar, and a varied set-price menu is offered in the dining room.
13 en suite (bth/shr) (4 fmly) CTV in all bedrooms 12P No coaches English & French Cuisine V meals Coffee am Tea pm Last d 8pm
ROOMS: (incl. bkfst) s fr £35; d fr £66 **LB**
OFF-PEAK: (incl. bkfst) s fr £33; d fr £64
MEALS: Lunch £5-£8 Dinner £10-£12*
CARDS:

★★67% **Ansteys Lea**
Babbacombe Rd, Wellswood TQ1 2QJ (from Torquay harbour take Torwood Street which runs into Babbacombe Road, Hotel is just past St Matthias Church on the left hand side)
☎ 01803 294843 FAX 01803 214333
Closed Jan-Feb RS Dec
There is a friendly atmosphere at this Victorian hotel, which is situated midway between Torquay and Babbacombe just a short walk from Ansteys Cove. Bedrooms are comfortable and well appointed, with modern en suite facilities, direct-dial telephones and colour TV. There is a comfortable lounge/TV room overlooking the garden and a heated outdoor pool surrounded by an attractive terrace. A set dinner menu offers a range of home-cooked dishes and specialises in local fish.
24 en suite (bth/shr) (2 fmly) CTV in all bedrooms No dogs (ex guide dogs) 20P No coaches Outdoor swimming pool (heated) No children 2yrs Xmas English & French Cuisine V meals No smoking in restaurant Last d 7.30pm
ROOMS: (incl. bkfst & dinner) s £23-£31; d £46-£62 * **LB**
MEALS: Dinner £8-£9.95*
CARDS:

★★66% **Oscar's Hotel & Restaurant**
56 Belgrave Rd TQ2 5HY ☎ 01803 293563
Conveniently located within easy walking distance of the town centre and beaches, this family-run hotel has a relaxed and friendly atmosphere. In the attractive basement restaurant, an interesting selection of dishes is offered from a fixed-price menu, the à la carte and daily specials from the blackboard. Bedrooms are currently undergoing a programme of upgrading; all are equipped with modern comforts.
12 rms (9 bth/shr) (2 fmly) CTV in all bedrooms 4P No coaches Xmas International Cuisine V meals No smoking area in restaurant Last d 7.30pm
ROOMS: (incl. bkfst) s £15-£25; d £30-£56 * **LB**
OFF-PEAK: (incl. bkfst) s £15-£18; d £30-£36
MEALS: Dinner £7.50-£8&alc*
CARDS:

★★65% **Hotel Balmoral**
Meadfoot Sea Rd TQ1 2LQ ☎ 01803 293381 & 299224 FAX 01803 299224

Hotel Balmoral is set in a large, peaceful garden with glimpses through the trees to Meadfoot Beach. The refurbished

restaurant and lounge are light and airy, and the bedrooms are in the process of being upgraded. The Heather Bar reflects the Scottish theme, and offers a fine choice of about 60 whiskies.
24 en suite (bth/shr) (7 fmly) CTV in all bedrooms 18P Wkly live entertainment ch fac Xmas English & French Cuisine Coffee am Tea pm No smoking in restaurant Last d 8.30pm
ROOMS: (incl. bkfst & dinner) s £25-£28; d £50-£56 * **LB**
OFF-PEAK: (incl. bkfst & dinner) s £28-£32; d £56-£64
MEALS: Lunch £7.50 Dinner £11.50*
CARDS:

★★65% **Bute Court**
Belgrave Rd TQ2 5HQ ☎ 01803 293771 FAX 01803 213429
This established hotel has been in the Jenkins family since the 1940s and its popularity continues. The bedrooms are neat and well presented and the public rooms are bright and comfortable. The hotel is just a short walk from the seafront and shops.
48 rms (44 bth/shr) (10 fmly) CTV in all bedrooms Lift Night porter 37P Outdoor swimming pool (heated) Snooker Table tennis Darts ch fac Xmas English & Continental Cuisine Coffee am Tea pm Last d 8pm
ROOMS: (incl. bkfst) s £20-£35; d fr £40 * **LB**
MEALS: Dinner £5-£8.50*
CARDS:

★★65% ***Chelston Tower***
Rawlyn Rd TQ2 6PQ ☎ 01803 607351
A fine Victorian house set in two acres of well kept grounds, within walking distance of the town centre and the sea. Linda Wakeman and her family took over the hotel in 1994, and continue to provide a friendly atmosphere. Bedrooms are comfortable,and there are some ground floor and family rooms available. Public areas are spacious and all benefit from fine views over the town.
17 rms (9 bth 4 shr) (8 fmly) 40P Outdoor swimming pool (heated) Snooker Mini golf Games room V meals Coffee am Tea pm Last d 7.30pm
CARDS:

★★65% **Frognel Hall**
Higher Woodfield Rd TQ1 2LD ☎ 01803 298339 FAX 01803 215115
This attractive Victorian Villa is set in its own extensive grounds just a short walk from the seafront in an elevated position. New owners Mr and Mrs Cropper are congenial hosts who enjoy making guests feel at home. Many of the previous staff are still in place ensuring that standards are maintained. The bedrooms are comfortable and public areas are smart and very well presented. Guests have the use of a sauna and solarium and the attractive restaurant serves traditional English food from a table d'hÙte menu.
28 rms (26 bth/shr) (4 fmly) CTV in all bedrooms Lift 25P Sauna Solarium Pool table Croquet lawn Putting green Games room Exercise equipment Wkly live entertainment Xmas English & French Cuisine V meals Coffee am Tea pm No smoking in restaurant Last d 8pm
ROOMS: (incl. bkfst & dinner) s £29-£36 **LB**
OFF-PEAK: (incl. bkfst & dinner) s £22-£27
MEALS: Lunch £6-£10 Dinner fr £11&alc
CONF: Thtr 50 Class 30 Board 15 Del from £30
CARDS:

★★65% **Gresham Court**
Babbacombe Rd TQ1 1HG (0.25m from harbourside)
☎ 01803 293007 & 293658 FAX 01803 215951
Closed mid Dec-late Feb/early Mar
Situated close to the harbour, this long established family-run hotel offers a friendly service. The bedrooms are comfortably furnished and the public areas are modern in decoration. The restaurant offers a choice of menus.

contd.

30 en suite (bth/shr) (6 fmly) CTV in all bedrooms Lift 4P Pool table V meals No smoking in restaurant Last d 8pm
ROOMS: (incl. bkfst & dinner) s £29-£35; d £58-£70 *
MEALS: Bar Lunch £1.50-£3.25 Dinner fr £8.50*
CARDS:

★★65% Red House
Rousdown Rd, Chelston TQ2 6PB
☎ 01803 607811 FAX 01803 200592
A small hotel with bright modern accommodation, the Red House tends to be dominated by its excellent leisure facilities which are used regularly by non-residents. They include a good sized indoor pool, a jacuzzi, table tennis and a mini gym, around which is a coffee bar offering light snacks and refreshments all day. There is also an informal dining room with fixed price menu.
10 en suite (bth/shr) (5 fmly) CTV in all bedrooms 10P No coaches Indoor swimming pool (heated) Outdoor swimming pool (heated) Sauna Solarium Gym Pool table Jacuzzi/spa Games room Xmas English & French Cuisine V meals Coffee am Tea pm No smoking in restaurant Last d 8pm
ROOMS: (incl. bkfst & dinner) s £28-£46; d £56-£72 **LB**
OFF-PEAK: (incl. bkfst & dinner) s £26-£35; d £52-£64
MEALS: Lunch £4.95-£8.45alc High tea £2-£3.95alc Dinner fr £11.95&alc
CONF: Thtr 20 Class 20 Board 16 Del from £45
CARDS:

See advertisement on opposite page

★★65% *Shelley Court*
Croft Rd TQ2 5UD ☎ 01803 295642 FAX 01803 215793
A special feature of this popular hotel is its private path to the seafront, only 250 yards away. Bedrooms have recently been refurbished and are smart, modern and well equipped. Proprietors Jean and Allan May like to offer a complete holiday so provide entertainment most evenings in the season, and a daily-changing menu is presented in the attractive dining room.
27 en suite (bth/shr) (3 fmly) CTV in all bedrooms No dogs 20P Coffee am Last d 7.30pm
CARDS:

★★64% Ellington Court
St Lukes Rd South TQ2 5NZ (from Promenade take Sheddon Hill then take 2nd right) ☎ 01803 294957 FAX 201383
Closed Nov,Jan-Feb
Robbie Marshal and Peter Beardsworth run a very friendly hotel, with a soothing atmosphere. Most of the public rooms have a panoramic view across the bay, which guests can enjoy from the warmth of the double-glazed conservatory with its well stocked bar. Bedrooms vary in size, and some are on the ground floor. The hotel caters for a good range of recreational activities.
14 rms (13 bth/shr) (4 fmly) No smoking in all bedrooms CTV in all bedrooms STV No dogs (ex guide dogs) 10P No coaches Sauna Solarium Gym Pool table Table tennis No children 10yrs Xmas V meals Coffee am Tea pm No smoking in restaurant Last d 7.30pm

ROOMS: (incl. bkfst) s £25-£30; d £50-£60 **LB**
MEALS: Bar Lunch £2.50-£6 Dinner fr £12
CARDS:

★★64% Hotel Sydore
Meadfoot Rd TQ1 2JP ☎ 01803 294758 FAX 01803 294489
Conveniently located midway between the town centre and Meadfoot beach, this Georgian villa is attractively set in two acres of award-winning gardens. Bedrooms are currently being redecorated and refurnished, although they do not have telephones, all rooms have hairdryers and trouser presses. The bar and lounge have individual charm and character, and in the restaurant a well balanced table d'hote menu is available, including a vegetarian choice and featuring traditional British puddings.
11 en suite (bth/shr) (5 fmly) No smoking in all bedrooms CTV in all bedrooms 16P Croquet lawn Bar billiards Xmas V meals Coffee am Tea pm No smoking in restaurant Last d 7.30pm
ROOMS: (incl. bkfst & dinner) s £18.50-£27.50; d £37-£60 * **LB**
OFF-PEAK: (incl. bkfst & dinner) s £16.50-£30; d £50-£45
MEALS: Lunch £8.50 Dinner £8.95*
CARDS:

★★63% Seascape
8-10 Tor Church Rd TQ2 5UT ☎ 01803 292617 FAX 01803 292617
Closed Jan-Feb
A hotel not far from the seafront and near the town centre has now been completely refurbished. Lift access is provided to all floors, the large bar/lounge has a dance floor and there is a separate TV lounge; a dining room overlooking the garden serves fixed-price menus. Most of the bedrooms are of a uniform standard.
62 en suite (bth/shr) (14 fmly) CTV in all bedrooms STV No dogs Lift 27P Sauna Solarium Gym Pool table Table tennis Darts Wkly live entertainment Xmas V meals Tea pm No smoking in restaurant Last d 7.30pm
ROOMS: (incl. bkfst & dinner) s £57-£63; d £54-£58 **LB**
OFF-PEAK: (incl. bkfst & dinner) s £20.50-£25.50; d £38-£52
MEALS: Sunday Lunch £7.50-£9.50 Dinner £7.50-£12.50
CARDS:

★★63% Torcroft
Croft Rd TQ2 5UE ☎ 01803 298292
Colin and Pauline Mayer took over the Torcroft during 1995 and have thoroughly upgraded the hotel in most areas. The family provide a warm and friendly welcome to guests, and in the dining room, a varied choice of dishes is offered and the portions are more than generous. Bedrooms are comfortable and, with the exception of telephones, all facilities are supplied.
15 en suite (bth/shr) (3 fmly) CTV in all bedrooms No dogs 18P No coaches Xmas English & Italian Cuisine V meals No smoking in restaurant Last d 7.30pm
ROOMS: (incl. bkfst) s £20-£24; d £40-£48 **LB**
OFF-PEAK: (incl. bkfst) s £18; d £36
MEALS: Dinner £8-£12
CARDS:

★★62% Sunray
Aveland Rd, Babbacombe TQ1 3PT (opposite Torquay United FC)
☎ 01803 328285 & 966037 FAX 01803 323385
RS Dec-Mar
Established by proprietor Derek Day's father in 1945, this small family-run hotel is in a peaceful residential area close to Cary Parks. Bedrooms are fresh and bright, open-plan public areas have been upgraded in recent years, there is a fully stocked bar and entertainment is provided during the summer.
22 rms (21 bth/shr) (3 fmly) CTV in all bedrooms 16P Xmas English, French & Italian Cuisine V meals Coffee am Last d 8pm
ROOMS: (incl. bkfst & dinner) s £17-£20; d £34-£40 * **LB**
OFF-PEAK: (incl. bkfst & dinner) s £15-£17; d £30-£34

MEALS: Dinner £8.50*
CONF: Class 40 Board 40 Del from £25
CARDS:

★★61% Burlington
462-466 Babbacombe Rd TQ1 1HN (A380 to Torquay, follow signs to seafront, left at harbour, left at clock tower hotel 0.5m on right hand side) ☎ 01803 294374 FAX 01803 200189
A good-value hotel stands about a quarter of a mile from the seafront offering live entertainment most evenings during the season. The dining room serves good, wholesome food. There is also a comfortable bar and a games room.
55 en suite (bth/shr) (7 fmly) CTV in all bedrooms Night porter 20P Indoor swimming pool (heated) Sauna Solarium Pool table Jacuzzi/spa Wkly live entertainment Xmas English, French & Italian Cuisine V meals Coffee am Tea pm No smoking in restaurant
Last d 8pm
ROOMS: (incl. bkfst) s £30-£45; d £50-£80 * **LB**
MEALS: Bar Lunch £1.50-£4 Dinner £8-£14&alc
CARDS:
See advertisement on this page

★★61% *Carlton*
Falkland Rd TQ2 5JJ ☎ 01803 291555 FAX 01803 291666
Situated close to the seafront and the Riviera Leisure Centre, this holiday hotel provides regular entertainment throughout the season, the smart ballroom being a popular venue for dancing. Some of the bedrooms have recently been refurbished and more are due for attention shortly. A short set-price menu is offered in the non-smoking dining room. Guests may use the leisure facilities at the other Torquay Leisure Hotels.
32 rms (31 bth/shr) (15 fmly) CTV in all bedrooms No dogs (ex guide dogs) Lift Night porter 28P Indoor swimming pool (heated) Outdoor swimming pool (heated) Tennis (hard) Snooker Sauna Solarium Gym Childrens playden V meals Coffee am Tea pm
Last d 8pm
CARDS:

★★60% Dunstone Hall
Lower Warberry Rd TQ1 1QS ☎ 01803 293185
Closed Sep-Apr
Facing South, this imposing residence set in an elevated position with glorious views, offers a relaxed atmosphere. Comfortable bedrooms are equipped with modern facilities, and the public areas include a choice of lounges, a conservatory bar and an attractive dining room. An outdoor swimming pool and sun terrace is available in the gardens.
14 rms (13 bth/shr) (3 fmly) CTV in all bedrooms No dogs (ex guide dogs) 18P No coaches Outdoor swimming pool (heated) Pool table V meals Coffee am Tea pm No smoking in restaurant
Last d 7.30pm
ROOMS: (incl. bkfst) s £27-£32.50; d £39-£50 * **LB**
MEALS: Dinner £10.50*
CARDS:

★★60% **Norcliffe**
7 Babbacombe Downs Rd, Babbacombe TQ1 3LF (from M5,take A380, after Sainsburys turn left at traffic lights,across r'about,left next tr.lights into Manor road, from Babbacombe Rdturn left
☎ 01803 328456 FAX 01803 328023
This family-run holiday hotel overlooks the gardens of Babbacombe Downs and has spectacular views of the bay. The dining room, where simple, varied menus are served, has been extended to accommodate extra residents and various functions.
27 en suite (bth/shr) (3 fmly) CTV in all bedrooms Lift 20P Indoor swimming pool (heated) Sauna Xmas V meals Coffee am Tea pm No smoking in restaurant Last d 7.45pm
ROOMS: (incl. bkfst & dinner) s £28.50-£38.50; d £55-£75
OFF-PEAK: (incl. bkfst & dinner) s £25-£35; d £50-£70
MEALS: Bar Lunch £4.50-£10.50 Dinner £8.50-£12.50
CARDS:

★★68% **Roseland**
Warren Rd TQ2 5TT (turn off A379 Torbay Road, up Sheddon Hill and turn left at Warren Road) ☎ 01803 213829 FAX 01803 291266
This former home of Lord Lytton, Viceroy of India, has commanding views over Torbay from its hillside location. Bedrooms vary in size and style but are well equipped, and some have patios with excellent views. A short fixed-price menu is served in the dining room, and there is entertainment in the bar throughout the season. The small leisure complex is made up of a plunge pool, jacuzzi, sauna and solarium.
35 en suite (bth/shr) 1 annexe en suite (shr) (7 fmly) CTV in all bedrooms Lift Night porter Indoor swimming pool (heated) Sauna Solarium Pool table Jacuzzi/spa Games room Wkly live entertainment Xmas V meals Coffee am Tea pm No smoking in restaurant Last d 8pm
ROOMS: (incl. bkfst) s £30-£35; d £50-£60 * **LB**
OFF-PEAK: (incl. bkfst) s £25-£35; d £50-£60
MEALS: Bar Lunch £2-£4 Dinner £5-£14*
CARDS:

★★58% ***Bancourt***
Avenue Rd TQ2 5LG ☎ 01803 295077 FAX 01803 201114
The Proctor and Timms families have recently taken over at the Bancourt, a popular coaching and commercial hotel. Bedrooms are on two floors. The dining room serves a set-price menu at dinner, and there is evening entertainment at times in the ballroom. Guests may relax in the gardens at the rear of the hotel.
40 en suite (bth/shr) (11 fmly) CTV in all bedrooms Night porter 50P Indoor swimming pool (heated) Snooker Games room English, French & Italian Cuisine Coffee am Tea pm Last d 7.30pm
CARDS:

See advertisement on opposite page

★71% **Fairmount House**
Herbert Rd, Chelston TQ2 6RW
☎ 01803 605446 FAX 01803 605446
Closed Nov-Feb
A friendly welcome is assured at this attractive little hotel, which offers

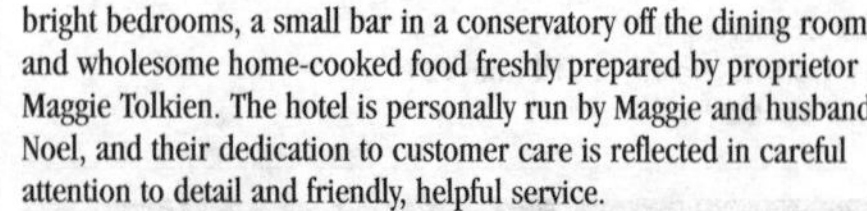

bright bedrooms, a small bar in a conservatory off the dining room, and wholesome home-cooked food freshly prepared by proprietor Maggie Tolkien. The hotel is personally run by Maggie and husband Noel, and their dedication to customer care is reflected in careful attention to detail and friendly, helpful service.
8 en suite (bth/shr) (3 fmly) CTV in all bedrooms 9P English & Continental Cuisine V meals Coffee am No smoking in restaurant Last d 7.30pm
ROOMS: (incl. bkfst) s £23-£30; d £46-£60 * **LB**
MEALS: Sunday Lunch £11.50 Dinner £11.50*
CARDS:

★69% ***Rawlyn House***
Rawlyn Rd, Chelston TQ2 6PL ☎ 01803 605208
Closed Nov-Etr
This Victorian house is located in a quiet area away from the town centre but still within easy reach of the sea front. Bedrooms are bright, airy and well equipped and public areas include a lounge and dining room, with a separate bar displaying a remarkable collection of football pennants. There are also delightful gardens, with a pool, for relaxing in peace.
15 rms (12 bth/shr) 2 annexe en suite (shr) (2 fmly) No smoking in all bedrooms CTV in all bedrooms No dogs 15P No coaches Outdoor swimming pool (heated) Pool table Badminton Table tennis V meals Coffee am Tea pm Last d 7.15pm

★68% **Ashley Rise**
18 Babbacombe Rd, Babbacombe TQ1 3SJ ☎ 01803 327282
Closed Dec-Mar (ex Xmas & New Year)
A popular family-run holiday hotel is located near Babbacombe Downs. Personally run by the proprietors for many years, the hotel has been continually improved, and bedrooms now offer more facilities such as modern en suite shower rooms. Pleasant public areas include a dining room where a small choice of home-cooked dishes are offered from a set-price menu.
25 en suite (bth/shr) (8 fmly) CTV in all bedrooms 14P Solarium Wkly live entertainment Xmas Coffee am No smoking in restaurant Last d 7pm
ROOMS: (incl. bkfst & dinner) s £20-£26; d £40-£52 *
MEALS: Dinner fr £7.50*

★64% **Sunleigh**
Livermead Hill TQ2 6QY (from A380 follow signs to Livermead/sea front,right at sea front proceed along prom,right at Cockington sign,take left hand fork Livermead hill) ☎ 01803 607137
Closed 2 Jan-Mar & Nov-23 Dec
Ray and Carol Smith provide a friendly relaxed environment for their guests at this Victorian property set in its own gardens with views overlooking Torbay. The attractive bar opens into the dining area, where set-price menus are served. A comfortable lounge is also available for guests. The bedrooms are equipped with colour television and beverage-making equipment.
20 en suite (shr) (4 fmly) CTV in all bedrooms 18P Xmas Last d 7pm
ROOMS: (incl. bkfst & dinner) s £25-£35; d £50-£70 **LB**
OFF-PEAK: (incl. bkfst & dinner) s £22-£32; d £44-£54
MEALS: Dinner £9.50*
CARDS:

★63% **Westwood**
111 Abbey Rd TQ2 5NP (near town centre)
☎ 01803 293818 FAX 01803 293818
This friendly, informal hotel is convenient for the town centre and not far from the seafront. Bright bedrooms are and equipped with modern amenities, and there is a first-floor lounge area. Downstairs there is a nicely appointed bar/lounge where entertainment is often provided. Home-cooked dishes are served in the evening in the pretty, no-smoking dining room.
26 en suite (bth/shr) (4 fmly) CTV in all bedrooms No dogs (ex

T

guide dogs) 12P V meals Tea pm No smoking in restaurant Last d 7pm
MEALS: Dinner £7*
CARDS:

★62% **Hotel Fluela**
15-17 Hatfield Rd TQ1 3BW ☎ 01803 297512 FAX 01803 296261
This is a small hotel, located near the town centre and run by the friendly Jarvis family. Bedrooms are very well equipped, several are situated at ground floor level and some are suitable for families. There is a cosy bar for residents, a traditional lounge and a pretty restaurant where good home cooking is served. There is a large car park and guests are assured of excellent value-for-money.
13 en suite (bth/shr) (3 fmly) CTV in all bedrooms No dogs (ex guide dogs) 20P Xmas V meals Coffee am Tea pm No smoking area in restaurant
ROOMS: (incl. bkfst) s £16.50-£20.50; d £33-£41 *
CARDS:

TOTLAND BAY See Wight, Isle of

TOTNES Devon Map 03 SX86
See also Staverton

★★61% **Royal Seven Stars**
The Plains TQ9 5DD (town centre)
☎ 01803 862125 & 863241 FAX 01803 867925
Dating back to 1660, the hotel is centrally situated in the town, at the foot of the main street. Bedrooms are well equipped and currently under a programme of redecoration. In the Brutus Room Restaurant a comprehensive fixed-price menu is offered as well as an extensive range of dishes written on a blackboard; in addition the Carriage Room provides a more informal style of dining throughout the day during the season. A comfortable and quiet lounge is available for guests on the first floor.
18 rms (12 bth/shr) (2 fmly) CTV in all bedrooms 20P Xmas English & Continental Cuisine V meals Coffee am No smoking area in restaurant Last d 9.15pm
ROOMS: (incl. bkfst) s £40-£52; d £54-£60 **LB**
MEALS: Lunch £7.50-£9.50&alc Dinner fr £16.50&alc*
CONF: Thtr 50 Class 20 Board 20
CARDS:

TOWCESTER Northamptonshire Map 04 SP64

★★★64% ***Saracens Head***
219 Watling St NN12 6BX ☎ 01327 350414 FAX 01327 359879
This historic inn is reputed to have inspired Dickens to write the Pickwick Papers. Inside, the building has been attractively and sympathetically upgraded with quality furnishings throughout. Bedrooms are spacious, comfortable and well equipped. Meals can be taken in the pretty restaurant with its feature cartwheels on the ceiling. The food is generally a range of traditional favourites.
21 en suite (bth/shr) (3 fmly) CTV in all bedrooms No dogs (ex guide dogs) 48P International Cuisine V meals Coffee am Tea pm Last d 9.15pm
CARDS:

Travelodge
NN12 6TQ (A43 East Towcester by-pass)
☎ 01327 359105 FAX 01327 359105
This modern building offers accommodation in smart, spacious and well equipped bedrooms, suitable for family use, and all with en suite bathrooms. Meals may be taken at the nearby family restaurant. For information on room rates and to make a booking, call Roomline free of charge on 0800 850950. For more details about Travelodge, consult the Contents page under Hotel Groups.
33 en suite (bth/shr)

TRESCO See Scilly, Isles of

TREYARNON BAY Cornwall & Isles of Scilly Map 02 SW87

★★68% **Waterbeach**
PL28 8JW ☎ 01841 520292 FAX 01841 521102
Closed Nov-Feb
Quietly located three miles from Padstow, with glorious views across rolling hills towards the rugged North Cornish coastline, this friendly hotel remains as popular as ever. It is personally managed by Vicky and Tony Etherington who continue to make improvements year on year. Bedrooms are freshly decorated and public areas are comfortable and well proportioned. Vicky cooks wholesome and generous six-course meals using fresh local produce.
16 rms (7 bth 2 shr) 5 annexe rms (1 bth 3 shr) (6 fmly) CTV in all bedrooms No dogs (ex guide dogs) 20P No coaches Tennis (hard) Putting green ch fac V meals Coffee am Tea pm No smoking in restaurant Last d 8.15pm
ROOMS: (incl. bkfst & dinner) s £33-£41; d £66-£88 *
MEALS: Dinner £12.50*
CARDS:

TRING Hertfordshire Map 04 SP91

★★★★61% ***Pendley Manor***
Cow Ln HP23 5QY ☎ 01442 891891 FAX 01442 890687
An impressive Victorian mansion, Pendley Manor was tastefully extended in 1987 when it became a hotel. The main house retains many features of the era, the galleried staircase being a good example. This leads to the more individually proportioned original bedrooms. New wing rooms are generally quite spacious and all these are similarly well equipped. Guests have the comfort of a spacious drawing room, a small conservatory bar and a restaurant located in the former

contd.

library. Good modern conference rooms with a dedicated business centre are also available.
71 en suite (bth/shr) (4 fmly) CTV in all bedrooms STV Lift Night porter 250P Tennis (hard) Gym Croquet lawn Games room Archery Laser shooting ch fac English & French Cuisine V meals Coffee am Tea pm Last d 9.30pm
CARDS:

★★★64% **Rose & Crown**

High St HP23 5AH (just off the A41 between Aylesbury/Hemel Hempstead, hotel in town centre)
☎ 01442 824071 FAX 01442 890735
This imposing Tudor-style hotel is located in the centre of the town, opposite the church of St Peter and St Paul. The bedrooms vary in size, but most reflect the character of the house which was once owned by Lord Rothschild. Bar meals are served in the refurbished lounge bar, but chef Greig Barnes' imaginative food is best sampled in the smart restaurant.
27 en suite (bth/shr) (2 fmly) No smoking in 5 bedrooms CTV in all bedrooms STV No dogs (ex guide dogs) Night porter 70P Xmas English & Continental Cuisine V meals Coffee am Tea pm No smoking area in restaurant Last d 9.30pm
ROOMS: s £50-£75; d £70-£85 **LB**
MEALS: Lunch £12.95-£14.50 High tea £3.50-£6 Dinner £18.95-£21.95&alc*
CONF: Thtr 80 Class 50 Board 30 Del from £89
CARDS:

Travel Inn

Tring Hill HP23 4LD (on A41 towards Aylesbury)
☎ 01442 824819 FAX 01442 890787
Purpose-built accommodation, offering spacious, well equipped bedrooms, all with en suite bathrooms. Meals may be taken at the nearby family restaurant. For more information about Travel Inns, consult the Contents page under Hotel Groups.
30 en suite (bth/shr)
ROOMS: d £35.50 *

TROUTBECK (NEAR WINDERMERE) Cumbria Map 07 NY40

★★73% **Mortal Man**
LA23 1PL (2.5m N from junct of A591/A592, 1st turning left after Jesus Church) ☎ 015394 33193 FAX 015394 31261
Closed mid Nov-mid Feb
This long established hotel lies in the rural hamlet of Troutbeck in the valley of the same name. It combines the character of a village inn - which indeed it was from the 17th-century - with the charm and relaxation of a country hotel. A cosy lounge adjoins the bar with its beams and open fire, whilst the dining room affords stunning views of the valley. This is also the case with the bedrooms, which are spotlessly clean, nicely furnished and exceptionally well equipped. The emphasis is on enjoyable fresh food and the dessert trolley is worth close scrutiny.
12 en suite (bth/shr) CTV in all bedrooms 20P No coaches No children 5yrs V meals Coffee am Tea pm Last d 8pm
ROOMS: (incl. bkfst & dinner) s £57-£60; d £114-£120 **LB**
OFF-PEAK: (incl. bkfst & dinner) s £50-£52; d £100-£104
MEALS: Sunday Lunch £12.50 Dinner £21

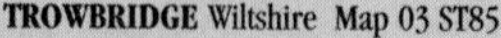

TROWBRIDGE Wiltshire Map 03 ST85

★★66% **Polebarn**
Polebarn Rd BA14 7EW (off A361 in town centre, follow signs 'Police Station') ☎ 01225 777006 FAX 01225 754164
In the heart of Trowbridge, this late Georgian Grade II listed building benefits from its own car park. The bedrooms, though simply decorated, have modern comforts including en suite facilities. There is a cosy bar-lounge and separate restaurant. Herbie and Jill Binder offer a warm welcome and provide friendly service.
12 en suite (bth/shr) (2 fmly) CTV in all bedrooms 12P French Cuisine Last d 8.30pm
ROOMS: (incl. bkfst) s fr £39.50; d fr £50 *
MEALS: Dinner £12.95-£15.45*
CARDS:

★61% **Hilbury Court**
Hilperton Rd BA14 7JW (0.5m from town centre on A361)
☎ 01225 752949 FAX 01225 777990
Hilbury Court is an attractive Georgian property set in beautiful gardens on the outskirts of Trowbridge, within easy reach of many places of interest. Comfortable bedrooms are well equipped, and the spacious public areas are relaxed and informal. A set dinner is served every evening.
14 rms (4 bth 7 shr) (2 fmly) CTV in all bedrooms No dogs (ex guide dogs) 20P No coaches Xmas V meals Coffee am Tea pm No smoking in restaurant Last d 9.30pm
ROOMS: (incl. bkfst) s £45; d £55 *
OFF-PEAK: (incl. bkfst) s £35-£40; d £50-£55
MEALS: Lunch £5.50-£9.50&alc High tea £4.50-£5.80 Dinner £7.90-£9.50&alc
CONF: Thtr 25 Del from £75
CARDS:

TRURO Cornwall & Isles of Scilly Map 02 SW84 During the currency of this guide telephone numbers are due to change.

★★★71% **Alverton Manor**
Tregolls Rd TR1 1XQ (on A390 towards St Austell)
☎ 01872 76633 FAX 01872 222989
This south-facing, impressive sandstone property is quietly located in six acres of terraced gardens and yet within easy walking distance of the city centre. Formerly a convent, over the last few years Alverton Manor has undergone extensive refurbishment. The bedrooms are a particular feature of the hotel, the furnishings being of very good quality and each room having an individual décor. Public areas are stylish and include the library and the former chapel which is now an unusual function room. Both a fixed-price menu and a short carte is available in the candlelit restaurant, with the style of cooking being described as 'Modern British'.
34 en suite (bth/shr) CTV in all bedrooms Lift Night porter 60P Snooker Xmas English & French Cuisine V meals Coffee am Tea pm No smoking in restaurant Last d 9.30pm
ROOMS: (incl. bkfst) s £63-£104; d £99-£130 * **LB**
MEALS: Lunch £9.95-£12.95 Dinner fr £19.50*
CONF: Thtr 370 Class 178 Board 136 Del from £95
CARDS:

See advertisement on opposite page

★★★66% **Brookdale**
Tregolls Rd TR1 1JZ (on main A390)
☎ 01872 73513 & 79305 FAX 01872 72400
Closed Xmas wk
The Brookdale Hotel is an imposing building set in its own gardens with ample car parking space, some of which is covered. The friendly owners and their loyal staff provide professional standards of service. An interesting fixed-price menu is offered in the restaurant, and lighter meals are available either in the bar or guests' rooms. The hotel is within easy walking distance of the city centre.
22 en suite (bth) (1 fmly) CTV in all bedrooms No dogs (ex guide dogs) 60P English, French & Italian Cuisine Last d 8.45pm
ROOMS: (incl. bkfst) s £45-£49; d £60-£65 **LB**
OFF-PEAK: (incl. bkfst) s £35-£40; d £50-£55
MEALS: Dinner £15*
CARDS:

★★★62% **Royal**
Lemon St TR1 2QB ☎ 01872 70345
FAX 01872 42453
Closed 25 & 26 Dec

This hotel is conveniently situated in the city centre and caters well for those travelling on business or on pleasure. Recently refurbished bedrooms are particularly well equipped, with executive rooms including CD players and private fax machines among the amenities provided. Mannings Brasserie is open throughout the day, whether for just coffee, lunch or dinner chosen from the fixed price, carte or daily changing blackboard menu.

37 en suite (bth/shr) (4 fmly) No smoking in 15 bedrooms CTV in all bedrooms STV No dogs (ex guide dogs) Night porter 40P No coaches Snooker Gym English, American & Continental Cuisine V meals Coffee am Tea pm Last d 10pm
ROOMS: (incl. bkfst) s £38-£52; d £55-£69 * **LB**
MEALS: Lunch £3.50-£15 Dinner £14.95&alc*
CONF: Board 12
CARDS:

See advertisement on this page

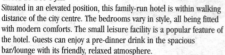

★★60% **Carlton**
Falmouth Rd TR1 2HL ☎ 01872 72450
FAX 01872 223938
Closed 20 Dec-6 Jan
Situated in an elevated position, this family-run hotel is within walking distance of the city centre. The bedrooms vary in style, all being fitted with modern comforts. The small leisure facility is a popular feature of the hotel. Guests can enjoy a pre-dinner drink in the spacious bar/lounge with its friendly, relaxed atmosphere.
31 rms (28 bth/shr) (3 fmly) CTV in all bedrooms 31P Sauna Solarium Gym Jacuzzi/spa V meals No smoking area in restaurant Last d 8pm
ROOMS: (incl. bkfst) s £33.50-£38.50; d £45 **LB**
MEALS: Dinner £8.75&alc
CONF: Thtr 80 Class 40 Board 40
CARDS:
See advertisement on opposite page

★75% **Tregarthen Country Cottage**
Banns Rd TR4 8BW ☎ 01209 890399 FAX 01209 891041
(For full entry see Mount Hawke)

TUNBRIDGE WELLS (ROYAL) Kent Map 05 TQ53

★★★76% **Spa**

Mount Ephraim TN4 8XJ (follow signposts to A264 East Grinstead, hotel is on right hand side)
☎ 01892 520331 FAX 01892 510575
Set in parkland and gardens, this 18th-century country mansion retains much of its original Georgian and Regency character. There is a very good range of bedrooms, the best overlooking the gardens and grounds, and all rooms are equipped to a high modern standard. The wood-panelled public rooms include a comfortable lobby lounge, a well appointed Equestrian bar, and the grand Chandelier Restaurant. Chef Edward Heasman offers a daily fixed-price table d'hÛte menu alongside interesting à la carte alternatives, supported by a good wine list. Service is well managed and attentive; 24-hour room service is also provided.
74 en suite (bth) (10 fmly) No smoking in 13 bedrooms CTV in all bedrooms STV Lift Night porter 120P Indoor swimming pool (heated) Tennis (hard) Sauna Solarium Gym Croquet lawn Putting green Jacuzzi/spa Dance studio Steam room Xmas English & French Cuisine V meals Coffee am Tea pm No smoking area in restaurant Last d 9.30pm
ROOMS: s £69-£75; d £84-£130 * **LB**
MEALS: Lunch fr £3 Dinner fr £19&alc*
CONF: Thtr 340 Class 93 Board 90 Del from £90
CARDS:
See advertisement on opposite page

★★★67% ***Royal Wells Inn***
Mount Ephraim TN4 8BE (on A264)
☎ 01892 511188 FAX 01892 511908
Closed 25-26 Dec
A family-run hotel located high above the town centre, the atmosphere is informal with helpful friendly staff. The accommodation continues to be upgraded, bedrooms are now furnished in modern style, are comfortably appointed and well equipped. The public rooms offer a spacious bar and comfortable lounge. There is a choice of restaurants, the informal brasserie on the ground floor and the more formal conservatory located on the first floor. An interesting menu is offered complemented by a well chosen and reasonably priced wine list; dishes are prepared with sound skills using good quality basic ingredients.
19 en suite (bth/shr) CTV in all bedrooms STV Lift 32P English & French Cuisine V meals Coffee am Last d 10pm
CARDS:

★★69% **Russell**

80 London Rd TN1 1DZ (at junct A26/A264 uphill onto A26, hotel on right) ☎ 01892 544833
FAX 01892 515846
Conveniently close to the town centre, this traditional hotel overlooks the common. Originally three Victorian houses, it has been skilfully converted to provide a range of well proportioned quality furnished bedrooms with modern fittings. Five rooms in a separate building have their own kitchenettes. Public areas are in character with the hotel and include a bar, the attractive Classical Restaurant and full reception facilities. Advertised 24-hour room service is available, along with full lunch provision and attentive service supervised by the resident proprietors.
21 en suite (bth/shr) 5 annexe en suite (bth/shr) (3 fmly) No smoking in 10 bedrooms CTV in all bedrooms STV No dogs (ex guide dogs) Night porter 20P Xmas English & French Cuisine V meals Coffee am Tea pm No smoking in restaurant Last d 9.30pm
ROOMS: (incl. bkfst) s £68; d £82-£99 * **LB**
MEALS: Lunch fr £2.75alc Dinner £10.50-£30alc
CONF: Thtr 40 Class 20 Board 30 Del from £85
CARDS:
See advertisement on opposite page

★★67% ***Swan***
The Pantiles TN2 5TD ☎ 01892 541450 & 527590 FAX 01892 541465
Located in the heart of The Pantiles and dating from the late 1600s, The Swan has been sympathetically restored and upgraded to a high standard by its caring owners David and Noreen Hammond. The atmosphere is friendly and informal and facilities combine to provide a stylish bar-lounge-restaurant, and a public café bar on the lower ground floor leading directly onto The Pantiles. Bedrooms range from luxury suites, two with four-poster beds, to spacious twins and doubles; all have been individually designed and come well equipped with modern facilities.
17 en suite (bth/shr) (1 fmly) CTV in all bedrooms STV No dogs Night porter 18P V meals Coffee am Tea pm Last d 9.30pm
CARDS:

TURNERS HILL West Sussex Map 04 TQ33

RED STAR HOTEL

★★★ **Alexander House**
East St RH10 4QD (on B2110 between Turners Hill and East Grinstead, 6m from junct 10 on M23) ☎ 01342 714914 & 716333 FAX 01342 717328
This splendid country house is set in 135 acres of parkland and attractive well-tended gardens, a perfect venue for afternoon teas in summer. Inside the house the numerous public rooms

T

are attractively decorated and furnished with antique furniture, paintings and beautiful fabrics. In Alexander's restaurant chef Tim Kelsey offers a daily set menu and a seasonally changing carte. A recent meal started with a light sole and lobster terrine served on a bed of pickled samphire with a pimento sauce. Richly flavoured medallions of venison followed, served with leaf spinach and wild mushrooms. A hot Tia Maria soufflé, although rather substantial, was served with a good passion fruit sorbet and fine shortbread biscuits. The bedrooms are all individually decorated and there are six delightful suites, of which two have ornate four-poster beds.

15 en suite (bth/shr) CTV in all bedrooms STV No dogs (ex guide dogs) Lift Night porter 50P No coaches Tennis (hard) Fishing Snooker Solarium Gym Croquet lawn Putting green Clay pigeon shooting Archery Wkly live entertainment No children 7yrs Xmas English & French Cuisine V meals Coffee am Tea pm Last d 9.30pm
ROOMS: (incl. bkfst) s £95; d £125 * **LB**
MEALS: Lunch £18.75&alc Dinner £26&alc*
CONF: Thtr 55 Class 24 Board 24 Del from £150
CARDS:

TURVEY Bedfordshire Map 04 SP95

★★60% ***Laws***
High St MK43 8DB (A428 Bedford-Northampton)
☎ 01234 881213 & 881655 FAX 01234 888864
This attractive stone house in the centre of the village has spacious, comfortable bedrooms in the main building, with more compact rooms in a modern extension; all have modern facilities. The restaurant overlooks the attractive garden and there is a small lounge bar.
23 rms (20 bth/shr) (2 fmly) CTV in 19 bedrooms STV Night porter 35P No coaches Indoor swimming pool (heated) Snooker Sauna Gym Pool table Croquet lawn Jacuzzi/spa Continental Cuisine V meals Coffee am Tea pm Last d 9.30pm
CARDS:

TUTBURY Staffordshire Map 08 SK22

★★★64% **Ye Olde Dog & Partridge**
High St DE13 9LS ☎ 01283 813030 FAX 01283 813178
Closed 25 Dec & 1 Jan
Dating from the 15th century, this High Street hotel is instantly recognisable by its half-timbered black and white frontage. The comfortably furnished public areas, include two bars, a residents lounge and a small function room. The carvery-style restaurant proves popular at both lunchtime and in the evening. The main hotel houses three of the well-appointed bedrooms, the remainder are in a Georgian house immediately opposite reception.

3 en suite (bth/shr) 14 annexe en suite (bth/shr) (1 fmly) No smoking in 3 bedrooms CTV in all bedrooms STV Night porter 150P Wkly live entertainment V meals Coffee am Last d 9.45pm
ROOMS: (incl. bkfst) s £55-£70; d £49.50-£80 * **LB**
MEALS: Lunch £10-£15 Dinner £10-£15*
CONF: Thtr 16 Board 12
CARDS:

See advertisement on opposite page

TWO BRIDGES Devon Map 02 SX67

★★❀74% **Prince Hall**

PL20 6SA (on B3357 1 mile on right from Two Bridges) ☎ 01822 890403 FAX 01822 890676
Closed Jan
Set at the very heart of the Dartmoor National Park, Prince Hall Hotel has some spectacular views. Retaining the atmosphere of a family home, the hotel offers a friendly and relaxed atmosphere. Adam and Carrie Southwell took over the property during 1995, continuing their predecessors' aims. The bedrooms are spacious, well furnished and equipped. Mr Southwell's short table d'h'te menu changes daily, offering a varied choice of dishes based on predominantly local produce. A recent test meal started with a tasty crab thermidor, which was followed by a pan-fried breast of duck served on a bed of sweet and sour red cabbage. Chocolate and brandy marquise came next and the meal was rounded off with a selection of local cheeses. Breakfast was memorable, a selection of starters was offered for guests to help themselves, and the freshly cooked breakfast was served in generous portions. Mrs Southwell leads the small, loyal team of local staff who provide friendly yet efficient service.
8 en suite (bth/shr) (1 fmly) CTV in all bedrooms 13P No coaches Fishing Croquet lawn Xmas English & French Cuisine Coffee am Tea pm No smoking in restaurant Last d 8.30pm
ROOMS: (incl. bkfst & dinner) s £48.50-£50.50; d £56.50-£58.50 * **LB**
MEALS: Dinner £21*
CARDS:

★★❀66% **Two Bridges Hotel**

CONSORT HOTELS

PL20 6SW (junc of B3212 & B3357)
☎ 01822 890581 FAX 01822 890575
As the name implies, this is a rural and attractively located country hotel with a pleasing and friendly atmosphere. Bedrooms tend to vary in size but are individually furnished in keeping with the character of the house. There are two comfortable lounges and a congenial rustic bar which serves locally brewed ales. The pretty restaurant makes a relaxing venue for chefs David Robinson and Danny Kaye to express their enjoyable cooking. Friendly service is carried out by a willing team.
25 en suite (bth/shr) (2 fmly) No smoking in 17 bedrooms CTV in all bedrooms 100P Fishing No children Xmas V meals Coffee am Tea pm No smoking in restaurant Last d 9.30pm
ROOMS: (incl. bkfst) s £38; d £66-£95 **LB**
MEALS: Sunday Lunch £7.50-£12.95 Dinner fr £17.50&alc

CONF: Thtr 150 Class 58 Board 40 Del from £72
CARDS:

TYNEMOUTH Tyne & Wear Map 12 NZ36

★★★62% **Grand**
Grand Pde NE30 4ER ☎ 0191 293 6666 FAX 0191 293 6665
Situated on the seafront, with many of the rooms taking advantage of the view, this family owned hotel has undergone extensive refurbishment over the past couple of years. The bedrooms vary in size but all are attractively decorated and have excellent facilities, the fully tiled bathrooms being a particular feature. The comfortable lounge bar offers a good range of bar meals for residents, while the elegant dining room also enjoys a fine outlook. Conference and banqueting facilities are available.
37 en suite (bth/shr) CTV in all bedrooms No dogs (ex guide dogs) Lift Night porter 19P Xmas European Cuisine V meals Coffee am Tea pm Last d 9.30pm
ROOMS: (incl. bkfst) s £49-£75; d £45-£85 *
OFF-PEAK: (incl. bkfst) s £35-£40; d £45-£75
MEALS: Lunch £4-£7alc Dinner £13.50&alc
CONF: Thtr 120 Class 40 Board 30
CARDS:

See advertisement on this page

★★★61% **Park**
Grand Pde NE30 4JQ (turn off A19 onto A1058 follow signs to Tynemouth at 3rd roundabout follow signs to coast)
☎ 0191 257 1406 FAX 0191 257 1716
RS Xmas & New Year
Built in the 30s and extended in the 60s, this seafront hotel, with its friendly and helpful staff, has been modernised to provide facilities to suit the business traveller. There is a choice of bars and a restaurant with an aquarium of tropical fish and terrapins. Bedrooms come in a variety of styles including some larger ones in a newer wing.
49 rms (43 bth/shr) (4 fmly) CTV in all bedrooms No dogs (ex guide dogs) Night porter 400P Sauna Solarium Gym Pool table Wkly live entertainment English & French Cuisine V meals Coffee am No smoking area in restaurant Last d 9.30pm
ROOMS: (incl. bkfst) s £39.50-£56; d £49.50-£62
OFF-PEAK: (incl. bkfst) s £35-£56; d £45-£56
MEALS: Sunday Lunch £6.50-£12.50 Dinner £13.50-£15.50&alc
CONF: Thtr 500 Class 250 Board 80 Del from £70
CARDS:

Some well known brand-name hotels share a uniform identity and offer the same facilities throughout Britain. The brand standard is accepted by the AA and they therefore have no star rating. See the section on Hotel Groups at the front of the book.

UCKFIELD East Sussex Map 05 TQ42

RED STAR HOTEL

★★★ **Horsted Place Sporting Estate & Hotel**
Little Horsted TN22 5TS (2m S on A26 towards Lewes)
☎ 01825 750581 FAX 01825 750459
Located a short distance off the A26 lies this well maintained example of Gothic revivalist architecture. It sits within its own 1100-acre estate which embraces the East Sussex National Golf Club. The grand design of the house allows for spacious bedrooms, each individually furnished, and looked after with care. In winter, log fires blaze in open hearths in a variety of public rooms which are suitable for private meetings and social gatherings. The kitchen, under the close supervision of chef Alan Garth, eschews flamboyance in favour of exact attention to detail. The style of cooking, rooted in classical training, produces wonderfully tasty food in simple and flawlessly presented guises. An occasional experiment such as a tempura of squid with five spice was sampled at a recent visit; unusually it failed to deliver its promised flavours and could have been less greasy. The rest of the meal comprised was a tender, full tasting, medallion of English venison with glazed apples followed by a perfect strawberry savarin. Afternoon teas can be heartily recommended.
17 en suite (bth/shr) (5 fmly) CTV in all bedrooms STV No dogs (ex guide dogs) Lift 36P Indoor swimming pool (heated) Golf 18 Tennis (hard) Fishing Pool table Croquet lawn Shooting Wkly live entertainment Xmas English & French Cuisine V meals Coffee am Tea pm Last d 9.30pm
ROOMS: s £90-£130; d £90-£130 * **LB**
OFF-PEAK: (incl. bkfst) s £80-£120; d £80-£120
MEALS: Lunch £15.95-£16.95&alc Dinner £28.50&alc
CONF: Thtr 100 Class 50 Board 40
CARDS:

ULLINGSWICK Hereford & Worcester Map 03 SO54

★★ 74% **The Steppes Country House**
HR1 3JG (off A417, 1.5m NW of junct with A465, signposted 'Ullingswick') ☎ 01432 820424 FAX 01432 820042
Closed early Dec-late Jan (ex Xmas & New Year)
Tucked away in this hamlet, Henry and Tricia Howland's 17th-century country house hotel exudes a quaint charm. Painstakingly restored by the owners, it retains many of the original features, with stone floors, beamed ceilings and inglenook fireplaces. Unique country-style bedrooms located in converted barns are set around a courtyard and feature deep armchairs, good quality beds and nice little personal touches, together with a wide range of modern creature comforts. The proprietors are very congenial hosts, Tricia making good use of top quality produce in the tasty, well executed dishes which make up seasonal menus.
6 annexe en suite (bth/shr) No smoking in 4 bedrooms CTV in all bedrooms 8P No coaches No children 12yrs Xmas French Cuisine V meals Coffee am Tea pm No smoking in restaurant Last d 9pm
ROOMS: (incl. bkfst) s £40-£50; d £80-£90 **LB**
MEALS: Bar Lunch £2.95-£7.50 Dinner fr £24&alc
CARDS:

ULLSWATER See Glenridding, Patterdale, Pooley Bridge & Watermillock

UPHOLLAND Lancashire Map 07 SD50

★★★ 68% **Holland Hall**
6 Lafford Ln WN8 0QZ (off A577 on right after Upholland Church) ☎ 01695 624426
FAX 01695 622433
RS 25 Dec
A well positioned hotel with splendid views over the Lancashire countryside. Holland Hall is an extremely good hotel furnished and decorated with richness and character. The lounge in the country house genre, Churchill's in deep reds and greens against oak panelled walls provides a cosy and intimate setting for some fine cuisine. Chef Nigel Smith of "Ready Steady Chef" fame is an accomplished chef producing dishes of interest and quality. The service is friendly and polite. The bar cum pizzeria has a convivial and lively atmosphere and is a fashionable venue and good complementary alternative option for dining. Bedrooms are similarly thoughtfully furnished and well equipped.
28 en suite (bth/shr) 6 annexe en suite (bth/shr) (1 fmly) CTV in all bedrooms No dogs Night porter 200P International Cuisine V meals Coffee am Tea pm Last d 10pm
ROOMS: (incl. bkfst) s £48.50-£56; d £61-£90 * **LB**
MEALS: Lunch fr £10.95 Dinner fr £16.95*
CONF: Thtr 200 Class 140 Board 80 Del from £69
CARDS:

★★★ 65% **Lancashire Manor**
Prescott Rd WN8 9PU (leave M58 at junct 5 follow road round to hotel on one way system)
☎ 01695 720401 FAX 01695 50953
Best Western
A feature of this hotel is the magnificent Great Hall, now used for banquets and weddings, which was built in 1580 and has been sympathetically restored to much of its former splendour. There are also other meeting and function rooms which contain all the latest equipment. Most of the attractively decorated bedrooms are in the newer part of the hotel and include an elegant room with a four-poster bed and also a room with facilities for the disabled. Exposed stone walls in the bar makes it an attractive venue for sampling a wide range of beers, and interesting well cooked dishes are served by friendly staff in Esquires Restaurant.
55 en suite (bth/shr) (2 fmly) No smoking in 9 bedrooms CTV in all bedrooms STV Night porter 200P Putting green English & French Cuisine V meals Coffee am Tea pm No smoking area in restaurant Last d 9.30pm
ROOMS: (incl. bkfst) s £55-£57; d £65-£68 **LB**
OFF-PEAK: (incl. bkfst) s £36; d £52
MEALS: Lunch £6.95-£16.75&alc High tea £3.50-£5.50 Dinner £16.75&alc
CONF: Thtr 180 Class 120 Board 50 Del from £65
CARDS:

UPPER BROUGHTON Nottinghamshire Map 08 SK62

★★ 60% ***Willoughby***
Station Rd LE14 3BH (off A46 at Willoughby/Up Broughton junc)
☎ 01664 823212

A modern red brick building situated beside the A46 offers two distinct styles of bedroom accommodation: rooms in the Lodge wing all have showers, while the standard rooms are generally larger and provided with additional facilities. The public areas are dominated by a spacious, comfortable lounge bar which also has gaming machines and a pool table enjoyed by the predominantly business clientele. The staff are young, efficient and friendly.
75 en suite (bth/shr) No smoking in 4 bedrooms CTV in all bedrooms STV Night porter 300P Riding Games room English & French Cuisine V meals Coffee am Tea pm Last d 9.30pm
CARDS:

UPPER SLAUGHTER Gloucestershire Map 04 SP12

★★★ 79% **Lords of the Manor**

GL54 2JD (2m W of A429) ☎ 01451 820243
FAX 01451 820696
Lords of the Manor is a delightful 17th-century stone-built house set in eight acres of gardens and parkland, including a trout lake. It has benefited from numerous additions over the years, and the latest is a traditional-style courtyard, partly enclosed by new bedrooms with period furniture and thoughtful extras such as sherry, bathrobes, fresh flowers and fruit. Public areas, characterised by antiques, chintz and log fires, include several comfortable lounges and a charming restaurant with an exciting menu. The cooking continues to impress, particularly a fine apple tart with Calvados and sultana ice cream that our inspector still dreams of.
28 en suite (bth/shr) CTV in all bedrooms STV No dogs (ex guide dogs) Night porter 40P Fishing Croquet lawn Xmas V meals Coffee am Tea pm No smoking in restaurant Last d 9.30pm
ROOMS: (incl. bkfst) s £90; d £120-£225 **LB**
MEALS: Lunch £16.95-£22.50&alc Dinner £32.50&alc
CONF: Thtr 30 Class 20 Board 20 Del from £130
CARDS:

UPPINGHAM Leicestershire Map 04 SP89

★★★ 63% **Falcon**
High St East LE15 9PY (off A47) ☎ 01572 823535 FAX 01572 821620
Although it has a rear car park and a secluded garden terrace for the better weather, this 16th century coaching inn fronts the main square of this busy market town. A comfortable bar and lounge occupies the old cobbled yard where coaches and horses once passed and a brasserie serves a wide range of meals and snacks throughout the day and evening. More formal meals are provided in the Garden Terrace Restaurant, and functions and business meetings are well catered for.
25 en suite (bth/shr) (2 fmly) CTV in all bedrooms 28P Xmas English & French Cuisine V meals Coffee am Tea pm No smoking area in restaurant Last d 9.30pm
ROOMS: (incl. bkfst) s £57-£89; d £76-£105 **LB**
OFF-PEAK: (incl. bkfst) s £32-£50; d £68-£89
MEALS: Lunch fr £10.95 High tea fr £4 Dinner fr £16.50*
CONF: Thtr 70 Class 40 Board 30 Del from £95
CARDS:

★★ 71% **Lake Isle**
High St East LE15 9PZ (in the centre of Uppingham via Queen street)
☎ 01572 822951 FAX 01572 822951
Lake Isle began as a restaurant right in the middle of the High Street of this very attractive market town. Under the auspices of the Whitfields - he in the kitchen, she front of house - outbuildings and cottages have been carefully extended into the yards on either side. The total effect is charming: a town house with restaurant which serves fresh, French-influenced cooking on scrubbed pine tables. Tartlets of crab, leg of lamb with a robust minted gravy and a sponge filled lemon tart are typical of the three or five-course set menu. Drinks can be taken around an open log fire, and residents have use of a very comfortable and tastefully furnished first-floor lounge which looks out on to the High Street; bedrooms are varied and fitted with a range of luxuries and facilities that more than meet requirements.
10 en suite (bth/shr) 2 annexe en suite (bth/shr) CTV in all bedrooms 7P No coaches Xmas English & French Cuisine V meals Last d 10pm
ROOMS: (incl. bkfst) s £49-£59; d £69-£79 **LB**
OFF-PEAK: (incl. bkfst) s £43-£55; d £60-£75
MEALS: Lunch £9.50-£13.50 Dinner £21.50-£25.50
CARDS:

★ 68% **Crown**
High St East LE15 9PY (turn off A47 to Corby, turn left at traffic lights and hotel 60 yds on right) ☎ 01572 822302 & 821809
FAX 01572 822942
The Crown is a Grade II listed building, but there is a contemporary feel to the convivial bar and cottage-style restaurant. Although the hotel opens on to the High Street, vehicular access is via North Street East, which runs parallel. The bedrooms are particularly cosy and well stocked.
7 en suite (bth/shr) CTV in all bedrooms 15P No coaches fishing & riding can be arranged V meals Coffee am Tea pm Last d 9.30pm
ROOMS: (incl. bkfst) s £35; d £45 * **LB**
MEALS: Lunch £3-£8alc Dinner £3-£8alc*
CARDS:

UPTON UPON SEVERN Hereford & Worcester Map 03 SO84

★★★ 61% **White Lion**

High St WR8 0HJ ☎ 01684 592551
FAX 01684 592251
Closed 25-26 Dec
Despite its Georgian façade, this town centre inn actually dates back to

contd.

1510 and is the inn depicted in Henry Fielding's novel 'Tom Jones'. Privately owned and personally run by Robert and Bridget Withey, it provides mainly compact accommodation, which includes a bedroom with a four-poster bed. The public areas are not without some character, which is enhanced by oak beams in the restaurant and real fires in the lounge bar. The residents' lounge is also available as a small meeting room.
10 en suite (bth/shr) CTV in all bedrooms 19P English & French Cuisine V meals Coffee am Tea pm Last d 9.15pm
ROOMS: (incl. bkfst) s fr £54.50; d fr £74.50 * **LB**
MEALS: Lunch fr £15.75&alc Dinner fr £15.75&alc*
CONF: Thtr 30 Class 10 Board 20
CARDS:

★★61% **Star**

High St WR8 0HQ (situated close to Juct 1 off M50 on A38 towards Worcester) ☎ 01684 592300 FAX 01684 592929
A converted 17th-century inn standing on the river bank in the centre of the town offers a relaxed, friendly atmosphere. Bedrooms are well equipped but vary in size, and some enjoy fine river views. Downstairs there are an attractive beamed lounge bar and a small wood-panelled country restaurant.
15 en suite (bth/shr) (1 fmly) CTV in all bedrooms STV 10P Xmas European Cuisine V meals Coffee am No smoking in restaurant Last d 9pm
ROOMS: (incl. bkfst) s £45-£50; d £55-£75 * **LB**
OFF-PEAK: (incl. bkfst) s £30-£40; d £40-£60
MEALS: Sunday Lunch £5.95-£11.95alc Dinner £9.95&alc*
CONF: Thtr 60 Class 60 Board 30 Del from £70
CARDS:

UTTOXETER Staffordshire Map 07 SK03

★★64% **Bank House**
Church St ST14 8AG (Church street next to main Paish Church, nearest main road A50 Stoke - Derby) ☎ 01889 566922 FAX 01889 567565
Comfortable, attractively decorated and well equipped accommodation is provided at this tastefully restored hotel, which was the town's first bank. The hotel is situated opposite St Mary's church behind wrought-iron railings and has its own car park accessed from the public pay and display. Guests can choose from a good range of home-cooked bar meals which are served by a friendly and helpful staff, or dine in the well appointed dining room.
14 en suite (bth/shr) (3 fmly) No smoking in 2 bedrooms CTV in all bedrooms 16P ch fac Xmas European Cuisine V meals Coffee am Tea pm No smoking in restaurant Last d 9.30pm
ROOMS: (incl. bkfst) s £49.50-£54.50; d £49.50-£69.50 **LB**
OFF-PEAK: (incl. bkfst) s fr £37.50; d fr £49.50
MEALS: Lunch fr £7.95 Dinner fr £10.95&alc
CONF: Thtr 30 Class 30 Board 35 Del from £78
CARDS:

Travelodge
Ashbourne Rd ST14 5AA (on A50/A5030)
☎ 01889 562043 FAX 01889 562043
This modern building offers accommodation in smart, spacious and well equipped bedrooms, suitable for family use, and all with en suite bathrooms. Meals may be taken at the nearby family restaurant. For information on room rates and to make a booking, call Roomline free of charge on 0800 850950. For more details about Travelodge, consult the Contents page under Hotel Groups.
32 en suite (bth/shr)

UXBRIDGE Greater London Map 04 TQ08

★★★63% **Master Brewer**
Freezeland Way UB10 9NX ☎ 01895 251199 FAX 01895 810330
(For full entry see Hillingdon)

VENTNOR See Wight, Isle of

VERYAN Cornwall & Isles of Scilly Map 02 SW93

★★★★ ❀69% **Nare**
Carne Beach TR2 5PF (from Tregony follow A3078 for approx 1.5m turn left at signpost Veryan, drive straight through village towards sea and hotel) ☎ 01872 501279 FAX 01872 501856
Closed 4 Jan-6 Feb
The Nare Hotel, standing in its own grounds, enjoys fabulous views over the sea. Many of the thoughtfully and tastefully furnished bedrooms have balconies. Fresh flowers and antiques add to the warm and friendly atmosphere and a choice of restaurants offers everything from a light snack to full dinner menus. An indoor swimming pool and extensive leisure facilities and easy access to the beach add up to a super destination for all the family.
36 en suite (bth/shr) (3 fmly) CTV in all bedrooms Lift Night porter 80P No coaches Indoor swimming pool (heated) Outdoor swimming pool (heated) Tennis (hard) Snooker Sauna Solarium Gym Jacuzzi/spa Windsurfing, Health & Beauty Clinic ch fac Xmas English & French Cuisine V meals Coffee am Tea pm Last d 9.30pm
ROOMS: (incl. bkfst) s £50-£115; d £100-£200
MEALS: Lunch £13&alc Dinner £28.50&alc
CARDS:

See advertisement on opposite page

WADEBRIDGE Cornwall & Isles of Scilly Map 02 SW97

★★58% **Molesworth Arms**
Molesworth St PL27 7DP (A30 to Bodmin town centre and follow directions to Wadebridge. Over old bridge turn right and then 1st left) ☎ 01208 812055 FAX 01208 814254
This 16th-century inn still has its original cobbled courtyard and archway entrance. A programme of renovation and improvement has been under way and bedrooms, which retain much of their original character, are now furnished with antiques and have good facilities. The panelled lounge bar provides a wide range of bar meals in a relaxed and informal atmosphere.
16 rms (14 bth/shr) (2 fmly) CTV in all bedrooms STV 16P English Cuisine V meals Coffee am Tea pm Last d 10pm
ROOMS: (incl. bkfst) s £29.50; d £49.50 * **LB**
MEALS: Sunday Lunch £4.25-£7.25alc Dinner £7.50-£10.50alc*
CARDS:

WAKEFIELD West Yorkshire Map 08 SE32

★★★72% **Waterton Park**
Walton Hall, The Balk, Walton WF2 6PW (3m SE off B6378) ☎ 01924 257911 & 249800 FAX 01924 240082
Standing in extensive grounds, surrounded by a moat and with its own large lake, this impressive hotel now boasts a golf course and a well equipped leisure club. The hotel has attractive modern bedrooms and the public rooms include a friendly bar, a cosy lounge and a delightful beamed restaurant. Staff are friendly and provide an attentive style of service. Extensive conference facilities are also available.
30 en suite (bth/shr) 12 annexe en suite (bth/shr) (1 fmly) CTV in all bedrooms STV No dogs Night porter 130P Indoor swimming pool (heated) Golf 18 Fishing Snooker Sauna Solarium Gym Pool table Putting green Jacuzzi/spa Xmas English & French Cuisine V meals Coffee am Tea pm No smoking in restaurant Last d 9.30pm

ROOMS: (incl. bkfst) s £60-£85; d £88-£108 * LB
MEALS: Lunch £11-£11.75 High tea fr £10 Dinner £19-£19.75
CONF: Thtr 120 Class 60 Board 50 Del from £99
CARDS:

★★★71% **St Pierre**

Barnsley Rd, Newmillerdam WF2 6QG (A61 to Newmillerdam, pass dam on left and 500 yds on left hand side) ☎ 01924 255596 FAX 01924 252746
A modern and very well furnished hotel which is found three miles to the south of Wakefield on the A61 Barnsley road. The bedrooms here are quite delightful being very carefully equipped and also offering very good comforts. There is one room suitable for the disabled and one room now has a four-poster bed whilst several are reserved for non-smoking guests. There is a good range of food available in the elegantly furnished and intimate restaurant. Staff are very friendly and helpful.
44 en suite (bth/shr) No smoking in 23 bedrooms CTV in all bedrooms STV Lift Night porter 80P Pool table Xmas English & Continental Cuisine V meals Coffee am Tea pm No smoking area in restaurant Last d 10pm
ROOMS: d £59.50-£82 LB
OFF-PEAK: d £38-£65
MEALS: Lunch £8.95&alc Dinner £13.95-£15.95&alc
CONF: Thtr 130 Class 70 Board 50 Del from £60
CARDS:

★★★68% **Swallow**

Queens St WF1 1JU ☎ 01924 372111 FAX 01924 383648
Situated in the centre of the city, close to the cathedral, this small multi-storey hotel offers a very sound standard of well tended accommodation. Bedrooms are comfortably furnished and equipped with a good range of modern amenities while public areas are largely located on the first floor where there is a pleasant lounge bar and spacious restaurant. Short, frequently changing menus offer an enjoyable and tasty selection of fresh produce which is cooked with care and unexpected flair. Smartly uniformed staff provide friendly and attentive service.
64 en suite (bth/shr) (4 fmly) No smoking in 16 bedrooms CTV in all bedrooms STV Lift Night porter 40P Xmas English & French Cuisine V meals Coffee am Tea pm Last d 9.30pm
ROOMS: (incl. bkfst) s £59.50-£78; d £69.50-£90 * LB
OFF-PEAK: (incl. bkfst) s £39.50-£55; d £49.50-£67
MEALS: Lunch £7.95-£8.95 Dinner £11.50-£15.50*
CONF: Thtr 250 Class 90 Board 40 Del £92
CARDS:

★★★67% **Cedar Court**
Denby Dale Road, Calder Grove WF4 3QZ (adjacent to junct 39 on M1) ☎ 01924 276310 FAX 01924 280221
This large modern hotel is conveniently situated next to junction 39 of the M1 and caters extensively for the commercial and business market. A good range of well produced food is available in the terrace-style restaurant and the service is both warm and friendly.
150 en suite (bth/shr) (11 fmly) No smoking in 59 bedrooms CTV in all bedrooms STV Lift Night porter 350P English & French Cuisine V meals Coffee am Tea pm Last d 10pm
ROOMS: d £80-£90 * LB
OFF-PEAK: d £39.50-£49.50
MEALS: Lunch £9.95-£12.75 Dinner £18.25*
CONF: Thtr 400 Class 200 Del from £75
CARDS:

★★★64% **Stoneleigh**

Doncaster Rd WF1 5HA (1.5m S from Wakefield on A638) ☎ 01924 369461 FAX 01924 201041
Converted from a terraced row of Victorian houses, this very well furnished family owned and run hotel is conveniently situated on the A638 and is within easy reach of the M1, M62 and the A1. The well equipped bedrooms have been attractively decorated whilst the open plan public rooms are inviting and comfortable. A wide range of dishes is offered in the restaurant and good conference and banqueting facilities are also available.
34 rms (32 bth/shr) (3 fmly) CTV in all bedrooms STV No dogs (ex guide dogs) Lift Night porter 80P International Cuisine V meals Coffee am Tea pm Last d 9.30pm
ROOMS: (incl. bkfst) s £43.50-£50; d £53.50-£60 *
OFF-PEAK: (incl. bkfst) s £35.50-£50; d £45.50-£60
MEALS: Lunch £6.95-£9.95&alc Dinner fr £9.50*
CONF: Thtr 200 Class 100 Board 100 Del £70
CARDS:

Campanile

Monckton Rd WF2 7AL (M1, junct 39, 1m towards Wakefield, left onto Monckton Road, hotel on left)
☎ 01924 201054 FAX 01924 201055

contd.

W

The bar and Bistro restaurant provide meals and refreshments. Bedrooms are well equipped and have en suite bathrooms. For more details about Campanile, consult the Contents page under Hotel Groups.
77 annexe en suite (bth/shr)
ROOMS: d £36.50 *
CONF: Thtr 35 Class 16 Board 20 Del £57

Forte Posthouse Wakefield
Queen's Dr, Ossett WF5 9BE (off A638)
☎ 01924 276388 FAX 01924 276437

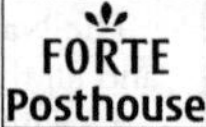

Suitable for both the business and leisure traveller, this bright hotel provides modern accommodation in well equipped bedrooms with en suite bathrooms. For more details about Forte Posthouse hotels, consult the Contents page for the section on Hotel Groups.
99 en suite (bth/shr)
ROOMS: d £69-£79 *
CONF: Thtr 150 Class 100 Board 100 Del from £79

Travel Inn
Holmfield House, Thornes Park, Denby Dale
☎ 01924 367901 FAX 01924 373620

Purpose-built accommodation, offering spacious, well equipped bedrooms, all with en suite bathrooms. Meals may be taken at the nearby family restaurant. For more information about Travel Inns, consult the Contents page under Hotel Groups.
42 en suite (bth/shr)
ROOMS: (incl. bkfst) d £35.50 *

Travelodge
M1 Service Area, West Bretton WF4 4LQ
☎ Central Res 0800 850950
(For full entry see Woolley Edge)

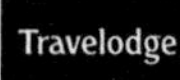

WALLASEY Merseyside Map 07 SJ29

★★71% **Grove House**
Grove Rd L45 3HF ☎ 0151 639 3947 & 0151 630 4558
FAX 0151 639 0028
This immaculately maintained hotel lies in a quiet residential area of the town. It is run by the friendly Burn family who, together with local staff, offer guests a warm welcome. Bedrooms have many extra facilities and, as well as satellite TV, the most recent addition is an iron and ironing board for every room. There are pretty lawns and gardens to the rear which are popular for local weddings and other functions.
14 en suite (bth/shr) (3 fmly) CTV in all bedrooms STV Night porter 28P English & French Cuisine V meals Last d 9.30pm
ROOMS: d £49.50 *
OFF-PEAK: d £45
MEALS: Lunch £10.95&alc Dinner £10.95-£15.95&alc*
CONF: Thtr 60 Class 40 Board 50 Del from £84.40
CARDS:

WALLINGFORD Oxfordshire Map 04 SU68

★★★70% **Springs**
Wallingford Rd, North Stoke OX10 6BE (on the B4009)
☎ 01491 836687 FAX 01491 836877
The Springs Hotel is set in 30 acres of gardens edged by woods in the heart of the Thames Valley. The house dates back to 1874 and offers 30 spacious and well equipped bedrooms, many with balconies. The attractive restaurant enjoys beautiful views over the lake, and the seasonally changing menu presents an interesting range of thoughtfully produced dishes. Public rooms include a lounge with a log fire in the winter months and several private dining rooms. There is also an outdoor pool and tennis court.
30 en suite (bth/shr) CTV in all bedrooms No dogs (ex guide dogs) Night porter 120P Outdoor swimming pool (heated) Tennis (hard) Sauna Croquet lawn Putting green Xmas English & French Cuisine V meals Coffee am Tea pm Last d 9.45pm
ROOMS: s £70-£95; d £95-£125 *
MEALS: Lunch £11.50-£15&alc Dinner £24&alc*
CONF: Thtr 50 Class 16 Board 26 Del from £125
CARDS:

★★★66% **George**
High St OX10 0BS (E side of A329 on N entry to town) ☎ 01491 836665 FAX 01491 825359
It is said that this hotel was opened as the George and Dragon in 1517 and an abundance of beams and uneven floors in the older part of the building gives it considerable character and charm and is reminiscent of its earlier days as a coaching inn. The majority of bedrooms are contained in a newer part of the building and are modern and well equipped, but those in the older part have more individuality. There are a comfortable foyer lounge and two bars as well as the attractively appointed Wealh's Restaurant which offers a good choice of imaginative dishes. Conference and banqueting facilities are available and the hotel has its own car park at the rear.
39 en suite (bth/shr) (1 fmly) No smoking in 9 bedrooms CTV in all bedrooms Night porter 60P English & French Cuisine V meals Coffee am Tea pm Last d 10pm
MEALS: Lunch £5.95-£10.75 Dinner £17.75&alc*
CONF: Thtr 120 Class 60 Board 40 Del from £105
CARDS:

★★★63% **Shillingford Bridge**
Shillingford OX10 8LZ (2m N A329)
☎ 01865 858567 FAX 01865 858636
Situated just outside the village, this popular extended inn boasts a superb riverside location together with its own moorings. The restaurant has benefited from recent refurbishment and makes the most of its setting with large picture windows. Bedrooms are well equipped with the majority upgraded with smart furniture, attractive fabrics and modern bathrooms.
34 en suite (bth/shr) 8 annexe en suite (bth/shr) (6 fmly) No smoking in 5 bedrooms CTV in all bedrooms 100P Outdoor swimming pool (heated) Fishing Squash Wkly live entertainment Xmas International Cuisine V meals Coffee am Tea pm Last d 10pm
ROOMS: (incl. bkfst) s £60-£75; d £85-£95 * **LB**
OFF-PEAK: (incl. bkfst & dinner) s £73.50-£88.50; d £112-£122
MEALS: Lunch £11.95-£16.95 Dinner fr £16.95*
CONF: Thtr 80 Class 36 Board 26 Del from £85
CARDS:

WALSALL West Midlands Map 07 SP09
See also Great Barr

★★★70% **The Fairlawns at Aldridge**
178 Little Aston Rd, Aldridge WS9 0NU (off A452 towards Aldridge at crossroads with A454, Hotel 600 yards on right) ☎ 01922 55122 FAX 01922 743210

RS 24 Dec-3 Jan
Fairlawns is an attractive red-brick building, vastly extended but still retaining the charm and ambience of a small welcoming hotel. John Pette and his loyal team provide an attentive and personal service. The bedrooms are thoughtfully equipped and designed to maximise their comfort. The restaurant continues to offer interesting and competently cooked English dishes and has a fine reputation for its speciality fish dishes; the rhubarb crumble is a must.

35 en suite (bth/shr) (5 fmly) CTV in all bedrooms STV Night porter 80P English & French Cuisine V meals Coffee am Tea pm No smoking area in restaurant Last d 10pm
ROOMS: (incl. bkfst) s £47.50-£79.50; d £87.50-£105 **LB**
OFF-PEAK: (incl. bkfst) s fr £42.50; d £52.50-£59.50
MEALS: Lunch £12.95-£16.95&alc Dinner £22.50-£24.95&alc*
CONF: Thtr 80 Class 40 Board 30 Del from £79.50
CARDS:

★★★66% Boundary
Birmingham Rd WS5 3AB (off M6 at junc 7, A34 to Walsall, Hotel 2 miles on left) ☎ 01922 33555
FAX 01922 612034
FORTE HOTELS
RS 25-30 Dec
Conveniently positioned with good access to the M6 this modern hotel offers a sound standard of accommodation appealing to both the business and family markets. Bedrooms are well equipped, together with a good range of room service, and there is a pleasant restaurant and choice of bars. However its greatest asset are the friendly staff who make staying here enjoyable.
94 en suite (bth/shr) (3 fmly) No smoking in 53 bedrooms CTV in all bedrooms Lift Night porter 250P Tennis (hard) Pool table Wkly live entertainment International Cuisine V meals Coffee am Tea pm Last d 10.30pm
ROOMS: s £59.50; d £59.50 * **LB**
MEALS: Lunch £7.25-£9.50&alc Dinner £14.95&alc*
CONF: Thtr 65 Class 35 Board 30 Del from £59
CARDS:

★★★65% Quality Friendly Hotel
20 Wolverhampton Rd West, Bentley WS2 0BS (junct 10, M6) ☎ 01922 724444 FAX 01922 723148

This modern hotel is conveniently situated just west of junction 10 of the M6 motorway and provides comfortable accommodation in its suites, Premier Plus and standard bedrooms. The suites have small sitting rooms and cooking facilities and are suitable for long stays. Public areas include an open-plan bar, a lounge and restaurant, numerous meeting/function rooms and a modern leisure centre.
155 en suite (bth/shr) (20 fmly) No smoking in 64 bedrooms CTV in all bedrooms STV Night porter 160P Indoor swimming pool (heated) Sauna Gym Jacuzzi/spa Xmas English & Continental Cuisine V meals Coffee am Tea pm No smoking area in restaurant Last d 9.30pm

ROOMS: s £67.50; d £87.50 **LB**
MEALS: Lunch £7.50-£9.95&alc Dinner £13.50&alc
CONF: Thtr 180 Class 80 Board 80 Del from £90
CARDS:

★★★61% Beverley
58 Lichfield Rd WS4 2DJ (1m N on A461)
☎ 01922 614967 & 22999 FAX 01922 724187
This privately owned hotel continues to expand from its origins as a late 19th-century family home. The bedrooms, though well equipped, vary in size and are furnished with traditional dark Stag units. There is a good range of meeting rooms and a bar with a conservatory extension, which now opens onto an attractive patio terrace with pergola. A home-from-home atmosphere is created by the pleasant and welcoming owner and his staff.
30 en suite (bth/shr) (2 fmly) No smoking in 2 bedrooms CTV in all bedrooms No dogs (ex guide dogs) Night porter 68P Sauna Solarium Gym Pool table Croquet lawn Putting green Games room English & French Cuisine V meals Coffee am Tea pm Last d 9.30pm
ROOMS: s £40-£47.50; d £47.50-£55 * **LB**
OFF-PEAK: (incl. bkfst) s £35-£40; d £40-£45
MEALS: Lunch £5-£12.95&alc Dinner fr £14.95&alc*
CONF: Thtr 60 Class 30 Board 30 Del from £65
CARDS:

★★★60% Baron's Court
Walsall Rd, Walsall Wood WS9 9AH (3m NE A461)
☎ 01543 452020 FAX 01543 361276
The Baron's Court Hotel features a strongly themed mock Tudor façade and an interior design of timbers, stone and rough plaster walls. A recent change of management has seen positive moves in services carried out by a friendly team. Bedrooms which are detailed for upgrading are well equipped but tend to vary in size and quality from spacious to more modest rooms.
94 en suite (bth/shr) (2 fmly) No smoking in 19 bedrooms CTV in all bedrooms STV Lift Night porter 200P Indoor swimming pool (heated) Sauna Solarium Gym Pool table Jacuzzi/spa Wkly live entertainment Xmas V meals Coffee am Tea pm No smoking in restaurant Last d 10pm
ROOMS: s £57.50-£78; d £67.50-£88 * **LB**
OFF-PEAK: (incl. bkfst) s £40-£55; d £60-£78
MEALS: Lunch £6-£9.95&alc Dinner £17.95&alc*
CONF: Thtr 200 Class 100 Board 100 Del £88
CARDS:

★★65% Abberley
Bescot Rd WS2 9AD (junct 9 of M6 and A461 towards Walsall, Hotel 200 yards on left) ☎ 01922 27413
FAX 01922 720933

The Abberley, a large period property with gabled ends, offers well designed and soundly maintained bedrooms. There are also a bar-lounge and a more traditional dining room.
28 en suite (bth/shr) (4 fmly) No smoking in 4 bedrooms CTV in all bedrooms STV Night porter 29P Practice golf net Xmas English & French Cuisine V meals Coffee am Tea pm No smoking in restaurant Last d 9pm
ROOMS: (incl. bkfst) s £39.90-£44; d £52.90-£59.90 * **LB**
OFF-PEAK: (incl. bkfst) s £30-£40; d £40-£45
MEALS: Lunch £8.50-£12.50 High tea £4.50-£7.50&alc Dinner £8.50-£10.95&alc
CONF: Thtr 80 Class 60 Board 50 Del from £58
CARDS:

★★60% Bescot
Bescot Rd WS2 9DG (junct 9, M6, off A417)
☎ 01922 22447 FAX 01922 30256
The Bescot, handily placed for quick and easy access to the M6, is a

contd.

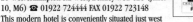

W

privately owned and business oriented hotel. It is well refurbished and the bedrooms, as well as being decorative, have added features.
20 en suite (bth/shr) 13 annexe en suite (bth/shr) (1 fmly) CTV in all bedrooms STV No dogs (ex guide dogs) Night porter 40P International Cuisine V meals Coffee am Tea pm Last d 9.30pm
ROOMS: (incl. bkfst) s fr £39.50; d fr £55 * **LB**
OFF-PEAK: (incl. bkfst) s fr £29.50; d fr £39.50
MEALS: Lunch fr £9.85 Dinner fr £9.85*
CONF: Thtr 80 Class 40 Board 30 Del from £60
CARDS:

WALTERSTONE Hereford & Worcester Map 03 SO32

★★★ 68% **Allt-yr-Ynys Country House Hotel**
HR2 0DU (7m NE of Abergavenny, in Herefordshire, off A465)
☎ 01873 890307 FAX 01873 890539
Queen Elizabeth I is reputed to have once been a guest at this 16th-century house, set in sixteen acres of grounds. The short carte of carefully prepared dishes may feature the likes of crab and prawn salad, roast rack of local lamb on a cake of r^sti potato and warm treacle tart.
4 en suite (bth/shr) 12 annexe en suite (bth/shr) (1 fmly) CTV in all bedrooms 100P Indoor swimming pool (heated) Fishing Sauna Pool table Jacuzzi/spa Clay pigeon range ch fac Xmas English, Welsh, French & Italian Cuisine V meals Coffee am Tea pm No smoking in restaurant Last d 10pm
ROOMS: (incl. bkfst) s £55; d £70 * **LB**
OFF-PEAK: (incl. bkfst & dinner) d £95
MEALS: Lunch £20-£30alc Dinner £20-£30alc*
CONF: Thtr 100 Class 30 Board 40 Del £95
CARDS:

WALTHAM ABBEY Essex Map 05 TL30

★★★★ 65% **Swallow**

Old Shire Ln EN9 3LX (off junct 26 of M25)
☎ 01992 717170 FAX 01992 711841
This modern hotel is conveniently located just off junction 26 of the M25. It is ideal for conferences and meetings but also provides a shuttle bus service to nearby public transport stations for easy access to London. Bedrooms are being refurbished to an attractive and comfortable standard and include modern facilities. Under the conical shapes of the building, there is a focal-point bar, a choice of two restaurants and a large, well frequented leisure centre.
163 en suite (bth/shr) (14 fmly) No smoking in 60 bedrooms CTV in all bedrooms STV Night porter 240P Indoor swimming pool (heated) Sauna Solarium Gym Jacuzzi/spa Steam room Wkly live entertainment Xmas English & Continental Cuisine V meals Coffee am Tea pm No smoking area in restaurant Last d 11pm
ROOMS: (incl. bkfst) s fr £99; d fr £115 * **LB**
OFF-PEAK: (incl. bkfst) s fr £65; d fr £75
MEALS: Lunch £14.50-£16.50&alc High tea £4.50-£4.95 Dinner £18.50-£22.50&alc
CONF: Thtr 250 Class 120 Board 50 Del from £98
CARDS:

WALTON UPON THAMES See Shepperton & Weybridge

WANSFORD Cambridgeshire Map 04 TL09

★★★ 74% **The Haycock Hotel**

PE8 6JA (at junct of A47/A1) ☎ 01780 782223
FAX 01780 783031
This celebrated 17th-century coaching inn is set in delightful grounds beside the River Nene in an unspoilt village of honey stone cottages. A tasteful extension built five years ago offers additional accommodation with an Italian influence, whilst the original bedrooms are traditionally decorated and well appointed. Diners have a choice of eating options, including the popular Orchard Rooms, where light meals are served all day, and the formal dining room which this year has gained rosette recognition for its tasty traditional English dishes cooked in a modern style. The conference suites and dedicated business centre makes this hotel attractive to conference organisers.
51 en suite (bth/shr) (4 fmly) CTV in all bedrooms STV Night porter 300P Fishing Petanque Outdoor chess Xmas V meals Coffee am Tea pm No smoking area in restaurant Last d 9.30pm
ROOMS: (incl. bkfst) s £72.50-£100; d £110-£170 * **LB**
MEALS: Lunch £25-£35alc Dinner £25-£35alc*
CONF: Thtr 250 Class 100 Board 50 Del from £140
CARDS:

WARDLEY Tyne & Wear Map 12 NZ25

Travelodge
Leam Ln, Whitemare Pool NE10 8YB (at junc of A194M/A184) ☎ 0191 438 3333 FAX 0191 438 3333
This modern building offers accommodation in smart, spacious and well equipped bedrooms, suitable for family use, and all with en suite bathrooms. Meals may be taken at the nearby family restaurant. For information on room rates and to make a booking, call Roomline free of charge on 0800 850950. For more details about Travelodge, consult the Contents page under Hotel Groups.
71 en suite (bth/shr)

WARE Hertfordshire Map 05 TL31

★★★★★ 79% **Marriott Hanbury Manor**
SG12 0SD (on A10 12m N of junc 25 of M25)
☎ 01920 487722 FAX 01920 487692
The range of leisure facilities at this impressive Jacobean-style mansion is outstanding. With 200 acres of grounds and gardens, this hotel, the Marriott group's flagship, offers a golf course of growing international reputation, tennis and snooker, together with an excellent health and leisure club with plush swimming pool. Bedrooms come in all sizes, are very comfortably furnished in the country house style, equipped with minibars, and given a personal touch by the provision of fresh flowers and fruit. Smart marbled bathrooms have luxury toiletries and robes. Extensive public areas feature fine wood panelling, crystal chandeliers, antiques, and open fires. There's a shop and a number of options for food and refreshment. The most renowned is the Zodiac Restaurant, where Rory Kennedy continues to maintain high standards of cooking.
69 en suite (bth/shr) 27 annexe en suite (bth/shr) No smoking in 10 bedrooms CTV in all bedrooms STV Lift Night porter 200P Indoor swimming pool (heated) Golf 18 Tennis (hard) Snooker Sauna Solarium Gym Croquet lawn Putting green Jacuzzi/spa Health & beauty treatments Aerobics Xmas English & French Cuisine V meals Coffee am Tea pm No smoking in restaurant Last d 10.30pm
ROOMS: d £168-£232 **LB**
MEALS: Lunch £26.50&alc Dinner £30&alc*

CONF: Thtr 100 Class 54 Board 50
CARDS:

★★★64% ***County***
Baldock St SG12 9DR (on A1170, on left behind fire station) ☎ 01920 465011 FAX 01920 468016
County Hotels
This useful conference hotel is located close to the centre. Bedrooms are colour co-ordinated and have a full range of facilities. There is a bar-lounge and a restaurant with a bright conservatory extension.
50 en suite (bth/shr) (1 fmly) No smoking in 16 bedrooms CTV in all bedrooms Lift Night porter 100P Pool table European Cuisine V meals Coffee am Tea pm Last d 10pm
CARDS:

WAREHAM Dorset Map 03 SY98

RED STAR HOTEL

★★★ ***Priory***
Church Green BH20 4ND ☎ 01929 551666 FAX 01929 554519
This 16th-century priory standing in four acres of beautiful gardens on the banks of the River Frome is steeped in history and has been cleverly converted into a hotel offering luxurious bedrooms, all individually decorated with family antiques. A relaxed atmosphere pervades the public rooms with their log fires and comfortable furnishings, and the friendly staff are attentive. The restaurant is in the vaulted stone cellars and the menu offers enjoyable dishes, for example, delicious chicken liver parfait served with fig chutney and a light sultana brioche, followed by monkfish with a tasty herb crust and a simple provençale-style sauce.
15 en suite (bth/shr) 4 annexe en suite (bth/shr) CTV in all bedrooms No dogs (ex guide dogs) Night porter 25P Fishing Croquet lawn Sailing English & French Cuisine V meals Coffee am Tea pm Last d 10pm
CARDS:

★★★71% **Springfield Country Hotel & Leisure Club**
Grange Rd BH20 5AL (from Wareham take Stoborough road then first right in village to join by-pass. Take first turn immediately on right for hotel) ☎ 01929 552177 FAX 01929 551862
This very smart privately owned hotel is ideally located for the major road routes, yet situated in attractive countryside. The Springfield is a mainly commercial hotel with well equipped comfortable bedrooms and good conference and lounge facilities. The superb modern leisure complex offers a large pool, jacuzzi, training room, games room and snooker room. A new wing of bedrooms was nearing completion at the time of our visit: all will have lovely garden views.
48 en suite (bth/shr) (7 fmly) CTV in all bedrooms STV Lift Night porter 150P No coaches Indoor swimming pool (heated) Outdoor swimming pool (heated) Tennis (hard) Squash Snooker Sauna Solarium Gym Pool table Jacuzzi/spa Steam room Table tennis Beauty treatment English & Continental Cuisine V meals Coffee am Tea pm No smoking in restaurant Last d 9pm
ROOMS: (incl. bkfst & dinner) s £85-£105; d £142-£162 * **LB**
OFF-PEAK: (incl. bkfst) s £66-£86; d £112-£132
MEALS: Lunch £8-£20alc High tea £4-£10alc Dinner £18&alc*
CONF: Thtr 200 Class 50 Board 60 Del from £89.95
CARDS:

★★66% **Kemps Country House**
East Stoke BH20 6AL (mid-way between Wareham/Wool on A352)
☎ 01929 462563 FAX 01929 405287
A warm welcome is guaranteed at this family-run hotel. Bedrooms vary in size, those in the new wing are spacious and modern whilst those in the main house and coach house are more traditional. There are two comfortable lounges, and the restaurant has a conservatory area overlooking the pretty garden. There is a set menu and a carte both offering good range of dishes using locally sourced ingredients, with the emphasis on fresh fish.
5 rms (4 bth/shr) 10 annexe en suite (bth/shr) (4 fmly) CTV in all bedrooms 50P No coaches Xmas English & French Cuisine V meals Coffee am Last d 9.30pm
ROOMS: (incl. bkfst) s £57-£59; d £84-£88 * **LB**
OFF-PEAK: (incl. bkfst) s £50-£52; d £65-£79
CONF: Thtr 50 Class 20 Board 20 Del from £65
CARDS:

★★62% **Worgret Manor**
Worgret Rd BH20 6AB (on A352) ☎ 01929 552957
FAX 01929 554804
This small privately owned hotel is ideally located on the edge of Wareham, with easy access to major routes. The bright, comfortably furnished bedrooms are being steadily upgraded to provide more ensuites. The public areas include a popular bar, a lounge and a restaurant where good home cooked meals are served.
14 rms (1 bth 7 shr) (1 fmly) CTV in all bedrooms Night porter 25P Putting green Free use of local sports centre V meals Coffee am Tea pm No smoking in restaurant Last d 9.30pm
ROOMS: (incl. bkfst) s £40-£50; d £60-£66 * **LB**
MEALS: Lunch £5.50-£16.95&alc Dinner £16.95&alc
CONF: Thtr 90 Del from £95
CARDS:

WARMINSTER Wiltshire Map 03 ST84

★★★★75% **Bishopstrow House**
BA12 9HH (A303, A36, B3414, premises 2m on right)
☎ 01985 212312 FAX 01985 216769
Set in 27 acres of beautiful Wiltshire countryside, this classical creeper-clad Georgian home is filled with fine English antiques, 19th-century oil paintings, log fires and fresh flowers. Bedrooms and suites are equipped with a range of modern facilities, some have whirlpool baths and several are situated around a delightful courtyard. The Mulberry Restaurant and The Wilton Room serve traditional English fare, with an accent on healthy eating, and snacks and afternoon teas are available in an attractive conservatory bar. The Ragdale Spa offers a complete range of health and beauty treatments, and the extensive leisure facilities include indoor and outdoor swimming pools and tennis courts.
30 en suite (bth/shr) (3 fmly) No smoking in 1 bedroom CTV in all bedrooms STV Night porter 60P Indoor swimming pool (heated) Outdoor swimming pool (heated) Tennis (hard) Fishing Sauna Solarium Gym Croquet lawn Clay pigeon shooting Archery Cycling Wkly live entertainment Xmas English & French Cuisine V meals

contd.

W

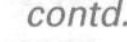

Coffee am Tea pm No smoking in restaurant Last d 9pm
ROOMS: (incl. cont bkfst) s fr £75; d fr £130 * **LB**
OFF-PEAK: (incl. cont bkfst) d fr £100
MEALS: Lunch £12.50-£18 Dinner fr £26.50*
CONF: Thtr 65 Class 32 Board 36 Del from £165
CARDS:

Travelodge
A36 Bath Rd BA12 7RU
☎ Central Res 0800 850950 FAX 01525 878450
This modern building offers accommodation in smart, spacious and well equipped bedrooms, suitable for family use, and all with en suite bathrooms. Meals may be taken at the nearby family restaurant. For information on room rates and to make a booking, call Roomline free of charge on 0800 850950. For more details about Travelodge, consult the Contents page under Hotel Groups.
32 en suite (bth/shr)

WARRINGTON Cheshire Map 07 SJ68

★★★★ 68% **Park Royal International**

Stretton Rd, Stretton WA4 4NS (off M56 junc 10, A49 to Warrington, at traffic lights turn right to Appleton Thorn, hotel 200 yards on right) ☎ 01925 730706 FAX 01925 730740
This large modern hotel is set in rural Cheshire yet only a short distance from the M56 and within easy reach of Manchester International Airport. The bedroom accommodation is very well appointed, all the rooms are spacious, several have their own lounges, and bathroom telephone extensions and fax points are just some of the extra facilities offered. The elegant Harlequin Restaurant provides a high standard of cuisine complemented by an extensive wine list and is well worthy of its rosette award. A feature of the hotel is its extensive conference and banqueting facilities which can accommodate up to 600 delegates.
100 en suite (bth/shr) (6 fmly) CTV in all bedrooms STV Lift Night porter 400P Indoor swimming pool (heated) Squash Sauna Solarium Gym Jacuzzi/spa English & French Cuisine V meals Coffee am Tea pm No smoking area in restaurant Last d 10pm
ROOMS: s fr £91.50; d fr £101.50 * **LB**
MEALS: Lunch £5.95-£14 Dinner £16.45
CONF: Thtr 400 Class 250 Board 90 Del from £80
CARDS:

See advertisement on opposite page

★★★★ 65% **Lord Daresbury**

Chester Rd WA4 4BB ☎ 01925 267331
FAX 01925 265615
(For full entry see Daresbury)

★★★ 66% **Fir Grove**

Knutsford Old Rd WA4 2LD (turn off M6 at junc 20, follow signs for A50, at Warrington stop before the swing bridge over canal, turn right, turn left)
☎ 01925 267471 FAX 01925 601092
A friendly privately-owned hotel conveniently situated for both the M6 and M56 and also the many business organisations in the area. The attractively decorated bedrooms are particularly well designed, and corporate guests in particular will enjoy the congenial atmosphere of the comfortable public areas. There are facilities for conferences and banquets and a small garden in the centre of the hotel is ideal for wedding photographs.
40 en suite (bth/shr) No smoking in 4 bedrooms CTV in all bedrooms STV Night porter 100P Xmas English & French Cuisine V meals Coffee am Tea pm Last d 9.45pm
ROOMS: (incl. bkfst) s fr £59; d fr £70 *
OFF-PEAK: (incl. bkfst) s fr £29; d fr £39
MEALS: Lunch £12.95&alc Dinner £13.95&alc*
CONF: Thtr 200 Class 80 Board 40 Del £75
CARDS:

★★★ 63% **Holiday Inn Garden Court**
Woolston Grange Av, Woolston WA1 4PX (off junct 21 of M6) ☎ 01925 831158 & 838779
FAX 01925 838859
A modern hotel with good bedroom accommodation, but public areas are limited to an informal restaurant and bar, a games room and meeting rooms. Prices however are competitive and there is only one price per room for up to four occupants. There is ample free parking.
98 en suite (bth/shr) (47 fmly) No smoking in 50 bedrooms CTV in all bedrooms STV Lift Night porter 108P Pool table V meals Coffee am Last d 9.45pm
ROOMS: s £66-£69; d £66-£69 * **LB**
OFF-PEAK: (incl. bkfst) s £52-£55; d £52-£55
MEALS: Dinner £12.50-£16&alc*
CONF: Board 14 Del from £85
CARDS:

★★ 70% **Rockfield**
Alexandra Rd, Grappenhall WA4 2EL (turn off M6 at junc 20, A50 to Warrington, at junc of A50/A56 take side road into Victoria Road, Hotel 60 yards on right) ☎ 01925 262898 FAX 01925 263343
This privately owned, personally run hotel is a magnificent Edwardian house set in delightful gardens just off the A50, south of the town centre and near the Manchester Ship Canal swing bridge. Some of the very attractively decorated bedrooms are located in an adjacent, more modern house and all are very comfortably furnished and well equipped. Public areas include a comfortable lounge, a lounge bar and an elegant restaurant offering a wide choice of dishes from carte and fixed-priced menus.
6 en suite (bth/shr) 6 annexe en suite (bth/shr) CTV in all bedrooms STV 25P ch fac Swiss & British Cuisine V meals Coffee am Tea pm No smoking area in restaurant Last d 9pm
MEALS: Lunch £11.50-£12.50 Dinner £14-£15.50&alc
CONF: Thtr 60 Class 40 Board 28
CARDS:

★★ 65% ***Paddington House***
514 Old Manchester Rd WA1 3TZ (junct 21, M6, off A57)
☎ 01925 816767 FAX 01925 816767
Improvements continue to be made at this large hotel, which is conveniently located close to the M6. Many of the bedrooms have been refurbished with attractive colour co-ordinated fabrics. Characterful public areas include an attractive restaurant with exposed Cheshire brick walls, a comfortable conservatory lounge and a spacious lounge bar. There is also a large ballroom, a small meeting room and plenty of parking space.
37 en suite (bth/shr) CTV in all bedrooms Lift Night porter 120P English & French Cuisine V meals Coffee am Last d 9.30pm
CARDS:

★ 68% **Kenilworth**

2 Victoria Rd, Grappenhall WA4 2EN (on A50)
☎ 01925 262323 FAX 01925 268320
Hospitality is a strength of this small privately owned hotel which is situated virtually beside the A50 and conveniently close to the centre of town. The bedrooms, which are already of a very good standard, are constantly being improved; all are en suite and well equipped. Guests have the use of a small comfortable lounge, and a good choice of tasty and carefully prepared home cooked-dishes is available in the small dining room, where the service is very informal, friendly and relaxed.
14 en suite (shr) (2 fmly) CTV in all bedrooms 14P No coaches Cosmopolitan Cuisine V meals Coffee am No smoking in restaurant Last d 8.30pm

ROOMS: (incl. bkfst) s £37-£39; d £47-£49 *
OFF-PEAK: (incl. bkfst) s fr £21; d fr £38
MEALS: Dinner fr £12.50alc*
CONF: Class 20 Board 20 Del from £39.50
CARDS:

Travel Inn
Woburn Rd WA2 8RN (just off junc 9 of M62 towards Warrington) ☎ 01925 414417
FAX 01925 414544

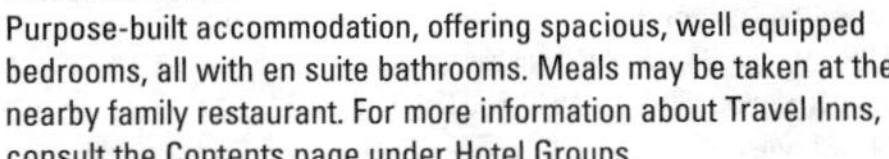

Purpose-built accommodation, offering spacious, well equipped bedrooms, all with en suite bathrooms. Meals may be taken at the nearby family restaurant. For more information about Travel Inns, consult the Contents page under Hotel Groups.
40 en suite (bth/shr)
ROOMS: d £35.50 *

WARWICK Warwickshire Map 04 SP26
See also Barford Honiley and Leamington Spa (Royal)

★★56% **Warwick Arms**
17 High St CV34 4AT (off M40 junc 15, main road into Warwick, premises 100 yards past Lord Leycester Hospital) ☎ 01926 492759
FAX 01926 410587
Set in the heart of this historic city, within easy walking distance of the castle, this hotel is a cherished local landmark offering attractive accommodation and comfortable public rooms.
35 en suite (bth/shr) (4 fmly) CTV in all bedrooms Night porter 21P Xmas English & French Cuisine V meals Coffee am Tea pm Last d 9.30pm
ROOMS: (incl. bkfst) s £49.50; d £59 *
OFF-PEAK: (incl. bkfst) s £30; d £45
MEALS: Lunch fr £8.95alc High tea fr £1.95alc Dinner £5.95-£20alc*
CONF: Thtr 110 Class 50 Board 50 Del from £50
CARDS:

Hilton National Warwick/Stratford
Junction 15 M40, A429, Stratford Rd CV34 6RE (turn off M40 at junc 15, 100 metres from junction on A429 turn into Stratford Road) ☎ 01926 499555
FAX 01926 410020
This is a bright, modern hotel, with an informal restaurant, aimed at both the business and leisure guest. All bedrooms have en suite bathrooms and a range of modern facilities. For more information about Hilton National hotels, consult the Contents page under Hotel Groups.
181 en suite (bth/shr)
ROOMS: s £99-£125; d £99-£125 *
CONF: Thtr 300 Class 100 Board 40 Del from £100

WARWICK MOTORWAY SERVICE AREA Warwickshire
Map 04 SP35

Travelodge
Welcome Break Service Area CV35 0AA (M40 northbound between junct 12 & 13)
☎ 01926 651681
This modern building offers accommodation in smart, spacious and well equipped bedrooms, suitable for family use, and all with en suite bathrooms. Meals may be taken at the nearby family restaurant. For information on room rates and to make a booking, call Roomline free of charge on 0800 850950. For more details about Travelodge, consult the Contents page under Hotel Groups.
56 en suite (bth/shr)

❁ Rosette symbols denote the quality of food in hotel restaurants on a rising scale of 1-5.

Travelodge
Welcome Break Service Area CV35 0AA (M40 southbound between junct 13 & 12)
☎ 01926 651681
This modern building offers accommodation in smart, spacious and well equipped bedrooms, suitable for family use, and all with en suite bathrooms. Meals may be taken at the nearby family restaurant. For information on room rates and to make a booking, call Roomline free of charge on 0800 850950. For more details about Travelodge, consult the Contents page under Hotel Groups.
40 en suite (bth/shr)

WASDALE HEAD Cumbria Map 11 NY10

★★67% **Wasdale Head Inn**
CA20 1EX (turn off the A595 at Gosforth and follow signs to Wasdale Head (approx 9m) the inn is at the head of the valley) ☎ 019467 26229 FAX 019467 26334
Closed mid Nov-27 Dec
This unique hotel is situated at the very end of Wastwater, among some of Cumbria's finest mountain scenery; its comfortable en suite bedrooms and wholesome meals are predictably popular with those walking and climbing in the area. The public rooms are full of character - particularly the residents' bar, with its oak panelling and antique chairs and tables.
9 en suite (bth/shr) (2 fmly) 50P No coaches Pool table V meals Coffee am No smoking in restaurant Last d 9pm
ROOMS: (incl. bkfst) s £29-£34; d £58 *
MEALS: Bar Lunch £2-£6.45alc Dinner £13-£19.50alc*
CARDS:

WASHINGTON Tyne & Wear Map 12 NZ35

★★★67% **Washington Moat House**

Stone Cellar Rd, District 12, High Usworth NE37 1PH (off A1 (M), follow signs for District 12 and Golf Course) ☎ 0191 402 9988 FAX 0191 415 1166

Quietly situated in a residential area and surrounded by its own 18 hole golf course this popular purpose built hotel offers smart, well equipped accommodation. Some suites and family rooms are available. The recently refurbished public areas include an all day coffee shop, restaurant and cocktail bar. The hotel also benefits from a number of well equipped meeting rooms, a business centre and extensive leisure facilities.

105 en suite (bth/shr) (9 fmly) No smoking in 44 bedrooms CTV in all bedrooms Night porter 200P Indoor swimming pool (heated) Golf 18 Squash Sauna Solarium Gym Pool table Putting green Jacuzzi/spa Golf driving range Pitch and putt International Cuisine V meals Coffee am Tea pm No smoking in restaurant Last d 10pm

ROOMS: s fr £75; d fr £90 * **LB**

OFF-PEAK: (incl. bkfst) s fr £45; d fr £60

CONF: Thtr 200 Class 100 Board 80

CARDS:

See advertisement on opposite page

Campanile

Emerson Rd NE37 1LE (turn off A1 at junc 64, A195 to Washington, first left at roundabout into Emerson Road, Hotel 800 yards on left)

☎ 0191 416 5010 FAX 0191 416 5023

The bar and Bistro restaurant provide meals and refreshments. Bedrooms are well equipped and have en suite bathrooms. For more details about Campanile, consult the Contents page under Hotel Groups.

77 annexe en suite (bth/shr)

ROOMS: s fr £36.50; d fr £36.50 *

CONF: Thtr 30 Class 30 Board 25 Del from £57

W

Forte Posthouse Washington

Emerson District 5 NE37 1LB (off A1 (M))

☎ 0191 416 2264 FAX 0191 415 3371

Suitable for both the business and leisure traveller, this bright hotel provides modern accommodation in well equipped bedrooms with en suite bathrooms. For more details about Forte Posthouse hotels, consult the Contents page for the section on Hotel Groups.

138 en suite (bth/shr)

ROOMS: d £49-£69 *

CONF: Thtr 100 Class 40 Board 50 Del from £75

WASHINGTON SERVICE AREA Tyne & Wear Map 12 NZ25

Travelodge

Portobello DH3 2SJ (A1M)

☎ Central Res 0800 850950

This modern building offers accommodation in smart, spacious and well equipped bedrooms, suitable for family use, and all with en suite bathrooms. Meals may be taken at the nearby family restaurant. For information on room rates and to make a booking, call Roomline free of charge on 0800 850950. For more details about Travelodge, consult the Contents page under Hotel Groups.

36 en suite (bth/shr)

WATERGATE BAY Cornwall & Isles of Scilly Map 02 SW86

★★59% **Tregurrian**

TR8 4AB (on B3276, 3m from Newquay)

☎ 01637 860280 FAX 01637 860280

Closed Nov-Feb

Conveniently located for walkers on the coastal path, or families wishing to make use of the famous beach, this personally-run hotel offers value for money accommodation and has well maintained bedrooms. In the dining room, a short fixed-price dinner menu offers straightforward dishes.

27 rms (2 bth 20 shr) (8 fmly) CTV in all bedrooms STV 26P Outdoor swimming pool (heated) Sauna Solarium Pool table Jacuzzi/spa Games room English & Continental Cuisine Coffee am Tea pm Last d 7.30pm

ROOMS: (incl. bkfst) s £17-£29; d £34-£59 * **LB**

MEALS: Dinner fr £8.50

CARDS:

WATERINGBURY Kent Map 05 TQ65

★★★58% **Wateringbury**

Tonbridge Rd ME18 5NS (on the A26 between Maidstone and Tonbridge) ☎ 01622 812632 FAX 01622 812720

This one-time village inn has been extended to include an open plan bar and restaurant area and bedrooms of various styles offering sound standards of comfort.

40 en suite (bth/shr) (1 fmly) No smoking in 17 bedrooms CTV in all bedrooms STV No dogs (ex guide dogs) Night porter 90P Sauna Bar games European Cuisine V meals Coffee am Tea pm Last d 9.45pm

ROOMS: (incl. bkfst) s £59.50-£65; d £71-£80 * **LB**

OFF-PEAK: (incl. bkfst) s £34.50-£40; d £49-£60

MEALS: Lunch £5.75-£20.75alc Dinner £10.50-£20.75alc*

CONF: Thtr 75 Class 40 Board 40 Del from £85

CARDS:

WATERMILLOCK Cumbria Map 12 NY42

RED STAR HOTEL

★★★ **Leeming House**

CA11 0JJ (on A592) ☎ 017684 86622

FAX 017684 86443

This elegant Regency country house is situated on the shores of Ullswater, in 20 acres of landscaped gardens and woodland planted with trees from all parts of the world. The lounges and the graceful, mirrored dining room look out over the terraced lawns towards a magnificent backdrop of Lake District hills. The bedrooms, many with balconies on which breakfast can be taken, have every modern convenience. The hotel is discreetly and effectively managed by Christopher Curry, and all his staff provide the spontaneous warmth of manner for which red star establishments are famous. Dining is also a memorable experience, and Head Chef Adam Marks

produces a daily changing menu which at dinner offers a choice of three, four or five courses.

40 en suite (bth/shr) No smoking in 11 bedrooms CTV in all bedrooms STV Night porter 50P No coaches Fishing Croquet lawn Golf driving net Xmas V meals Coffee am Tea pm No smoking in restaurant Last d 8.45pm
ROOMS: s £95-£125; d £120-£145 * **LB**
OFF-PEAK: s £80-£115; d £110-£135
MEALS: Lunch £17.50&alc High tea £5.25-£9.50alc Dinner £28.50-£35.50*
CONF: Thtr 45 Board 20 Del from £125
CARDS:

★★★ 77% Rampsbeck Country House
CA11 0LP (on A592) ☎ 017684 86442 & 86688
FAX 017684 86688
Closed 3 Jan-early Feb
Rampsbeck country house has much to commend it, not least of which is its wonderful lakeside setting amidst 18 acres of grounds, its warm hospitality and the skilful cooking of chef Andrew McGeorge. There is a series of public rooms including a traditionally styled bar, cosy lounge and the elegant drawing room which is reserved for residents and non-smokers. Bedrooms are all comfortably furnished, most have views and the finest have lovely antique pieces. Dinner is a grand affair with all three menus including a host of extras: delicious canapés, an appetiser, sorbet course and petits fours with coffee. The home-made bread is excellent and pastry is an obvious strength of the brigade. An autumnal meal featured a warm salad of scallops, courgette, water chestnuts, beansprouts and a balsamic dressing - a successful combination of flavours and textures. This was followed by a boned partridge breast, filled with foie gras and wrapped in a delicate flaky pastry, served with a timbale of savoy cabbage filled with a ragout of partridge leg and Cumbrian air dried ham.
20 en suite (bth/shr) No smoking in 2 bedrooms CTV in all bedrooms 30P No coaches Fishing Croquet lawn Xmas English & French Cuisine V meals Coffee am Tea pm No smoking in restaurant Last d 8pm
ROOMS: (incl. bkfst) s £50-£90; d £90-£170 **LB**
OFF-PEAK: (incl. bkfst & dinner) s £65-£116; d £130-£222
MEALS: Lunch £20-£22 Dinner £26-£36*
CONF: Board 20 Del from £85
CARDS:

Remember to return your Prize Draw card for a chance to win a Romantic Weekend for two at a hotel in the Virgin Collection. See inside the front cover for the card and competition details. Remember to fill in your name and full address before posting!

RED STAR HOTEL

★ Old Church
CA11 0JN (5m from junc 40 M6, 2.50m S of Pooley Bridge) ☎ 017684 86204
FAX 017684 86368
Closed Nov-Mar
This fine 18th-century country house sits in its own grounds which lead right down to the shores of Lake Ullswater, giving delightful views of the lake and surrounding fells. Kevin and Maureen Whitemore run their hotel in a friendly and unassuming manner which contributes to the peaceful and relaxing atmosphere. The house is beautifully maintained throughout, with Maureen - a professional interior designer who runs fabric design courses from the hotel - bringing her

contd.

influence to bear on the décor and fabrics. Bedrooms come in three styles, but each room is individual and all excel in comfort, quality and equipment; most face the lake and the superior rooms are delightful. Public areas are well proportioned and very inviting. The lounge has a selection of board games and a host of reading material, whilst one can also relax in the little bar, or in the hall in front of the log fire. Dinner offers a small selection of British dishes perfectly cooked by Kevin Whitemore who's secret is to keep things simple. Breakfasts and the home-baked afternoon teas are equally enjoyable.
10 en suite (bth) CTV in all bedrooms No dogs (ex guide dogs) 30P No coaches Fishing Boat hire Moorings Coffee am No smoking in restaurant Last d 8.30pm
ROOMS: (incl. bkfst) s £59-£99; d £85-£125 * **LB**
MEALS: Dinner £15-£25&alc
CARDS:

WATFORD Hertfordshire Map 04 TQ19

★★★62% **The White House**
Upton Rd WD1 2EL ☎ 01923 237316
FAX 01923 233109
The White House is a well established and privately owned hotel, conveniently situated for access to the underground and railway stations. Public areas have been lifted by the recent redecoration programme and the addition of a smart conservatory restaurant has created a more welcoming environment in which to dine. Bedrooms come in two distinct styles, the modern executive rooms are well appointed, and in comparison, the standard rooms are rather functional. Each room has a range of modern amenities.
60 en suite (bth/shr) 26 annexe en suite (bth/shr) (1 fmly) No smoking in 9 bedrooms CTV in all bedrooms Lift Night porter 40P English & French Cuisine V meals Coffee am Tea pm No smoking in restaurant Last d 9.45pm
ROOMS: (incl. bkfst) s £65-£79; d £79-£99 * **LB**
MEALS: Lunch £9.95-£12.95&alc Dinner £15.35-£17.95&alc*
CONF: Thtr 200 Class 80 Board 50 Del from £70
CARDS:

See advertisement on opposite page

★★★58% **Watford Moat House**

30-40 St Albans Rd WD1 1RN ☎ 01923 429988
FAX 01923 254638
This conference hotel is well placed for the railway station and the town centre. The modern looking bar and restaurant have an informal atmosphere and a style of menu to match. Bedrooms are modern and practically laid out.
90 en suite (bth/shr) (2 fmly) No smoking in 18 bedrooms CTV in all bedrooms No dogs (ex guide dogs) Lift Night porter 116P Xmas V meals Coffee am Tea pm Last d 10pm
ROOMS: (incl. bkfst) s £75-£84.50; d £90-£109 * **LB**
MEALS: Lunch £4.95-£9.95 Dinner fr £14.95*
CONF: Thtr 250 Class 100 Board 80 Del from £109
CARDS:

Hilton National Watford

Elton Way WD2 8HA ☎ 01923 235881
FAX 01923 220836
This is a bright, modern hotel, with an informal restaurant, aimed at both the business and leisure guest. All bedrooms have en suite bathrooms and a range of modern facilities. For more information about Hilton National hotels, consult the Contents page under Hotel Groups.
195 en suite (bth/shr)
ROOMS: s fr £99; d fr £109 *
CONF: Thtr 500 Class 220 Board 50 Del from £140

WEEDON Northamptonshire Map 04 SP65

★★64% **Globe**
High St NN7 4QD (at crossroads of A5/A45)
☎ 01327 340336 FAX 01327 349058
The Globe is a friendly coaching inn which has been owned and managed by the Walton family for many years. Regular guests appreciate the warm and cosy atmosphere and the convenient location, a mere three miles from junction 16 of the M1. Weedon is an antique hunter's delight and the countryside is worth exploring. Bedrooms are bright and attractive and the two bars and restaurant are open all day.
17 en suite (bth/shr) (3 fmly) No smoking in 2 bedrooms CTV in all bedrooms STV 40P Wkly live entertainment International Cuisine V meals Coffee am Tea pm No smoking in restaurant Last d 10pm
ROOMS: (incl. bkfst) s fr £43.50; d fr £52 * **LB**
OFF-PEAK: (incl. bkfst) s fr £29.50; d fr £42.50
MEALS: Lunch £8.95-£17alc Dinner £13.50-£17alc*
CONF: Thtr 35 Board 20 Del from £63
CARDS:

WELLINGBOROUGH Northamptonshire Map 04 SP86

★★★63% **Hind**

Sheep St NN8 1BY (on A509 in town centre)
☎ 01933 222827 FAX 01933 441921
Built as a Jacobean manor house, this town-centre hotel now provides modern comforts. Public areas include meeting rooms and bars which are earmarked for refurbishment by the new owners. Bedrooms are spacious and well designed for both business and leisure users. The car park is reached via a pedestrian walkway.
34 en suite (bth/shr) (2 fmly) No smoking in 5 bedrooms CTV in all bedrooms Night porter 15P Xmas International Cuisine V meals Coffee am Tea pm No smoking in restaurant Last d 9.30pm
ROOMS: d £59.50-£64.50 * **LB**
OFF-PEAK: d £35-£39.50
MEALS: Lunch £8.95-£9.95 Dinner £12.50-£20alc*
CONF: Thtr 130 Class 60 Board 50 Del from £75
CARDS:

W

★★61% **High View**
156 Midland Rd NN8 1NG (turn off A45 onto B573, follow sign post to rail station, at Midland road T junct turn left towards town centre, hotel approx 100yds on left) ☎ 01933 278733 FAX 01933 225948
Closed 25 Dec-1 Jan
This large Victorian house is conveniently located for both the railway station and the town centre. Mr and Mrs Hunter, the resident proprietors, do much to help create the friendly, welcoming atmosphere. Bedrooms are spacious and comfortable, with high standards of housekeeping in evidence. The restaurant operation is rather low-key but provides a useful standby.
14 en suite (bth/shr) (2 fmly) CTV in all bedrooms 9P No children 3yrs V meals No smoking in restaurant Last d 8.30pm
ROOMS: (incl. bkfst) s £36-£46; d £45-£53
OFF-PEAK: (incl. bkfst) s £29-£37; d £39-£44
MEALS: Dinner £4-£15*
CARDS:

★★60% **Columbia**
19-31 Northampton Rd NN8 3HG (access from town centre via Oxford Street) ☎ 01933 229333 FAX 01933 440418
A friendly hotel in the centre of town, the Columbia offers good value accommodation for both business and leisure guests. Bedrooms are due for extensive refurbishment, which will improve the overall quality of the hotel. A conference room is available for both meetings and private dining and the bright restaurant serves an extensive menu of popular items.
29 en suite (bth/shr) (5 fmly) CTV in all bedrooms STV 20P Xmas English, French & Italian Cuisine V meals Coffee am Tea pm No smoking in restaurant Last d 8.45pm
ROOMS: (incl. bkfst) s £49.50; d £65 * **LB**
OFF-PEAK: (incl. bkfst) s £42; d £50
MEALS: Lunch £5.95-£7.95 High tea fr £2.50 Dinner £12-£15.50alc*
CONF: Thtr 30 Class 30 Board 20 Del from £50
CARDS: £

WELLINGTON See Telford

WELLINGTON Somerset Map 03 ST12

★★61% **Beambridge**

Sampford Arundel TA21 0HB (1.5m W on A38)
☎ 01823 672223 FAX 01823 673100
This two-star establishment offers bedrooms which vary in size but are all well decorated and equipped to a standard beyond expectations. A carte is offered in the spacious dining room which features grills and some speciality dishes, while the bar lounge serves a varied choice of bar meals. The large function room is popular locally for weddings and special occasions.
9 en suite (bth/shr) (1 fmly) CTV in all bedrooms No dogs (ex guide dogs) 100P International Cuisine V meals Coffee am No smoking in restaurant Last d 9pm
ROOMS: (incl. bkfst) s £35; d £45 *
MEALS: Lunch £8.85-£15&alc Dinner £8.85-£15&alc*
CONF: Thtr 100 Class 100 Board 50 Del £50
CARDS: £

WELLS Somerset Map 03 ST54

★★★ ❀❀ 70% **One Market Place**
One Market Place BA5 2RW ☎ 01749 672616 FAX 01749 679670
This relaxed and friendly hotel, situated just off the market place and close to the famous cathedral, dates from the 14th century. Bedrooms, all of which have been refurbished to a high standard, are brightly decorated and equipped with modern facilities; many overlook an attractive inner courtyard. The comfortable residents lounge on the first floor, enjoys much of the character of the old building, while the busy bar and restaurant downstairs has a more lively atmosphere. An interesting selection of freshly prepared dishes make up the menu which includes fresh fish, and local game when in season.
24 en suite (bth/shr) CTV in all bedrooms Night porter 30P Squash Xmas English & French Cuisine Coffee am Tea pm No smoking area in restaurant Last d 9.30pm
ROOMS: (incl. bkfst) s £69.50; d £69.50-£79.50 * **LB**
MEALS: Lunch £4.50-£14&alc Dinner £18.50-£20&alc*
CONF: Thtr 150 Class 75 Board 75 Del from £60
CARDS: £

★★★68% **Swan**
Sadler St BA5 2RX (opp cathedral)
☎ 01749 678877 FAX 01749 677647
A long established former coaching inn with what must be the best views of the west front of the cathedral in the city. The individually furnished and decorated bedrooms vary in size and style, the majority of rooms having been re-furbished recently. A third of the rooms have four poster beds, including an unusual single four poster bed. Open fires feature in the panelled public rooms adding to delightful atmosphere. A fixed price menu is served in the dining room, with the added benefit of a roast trolley, rarely seen in smaller hotels today.
38 en suite (bth/shr) (2 fmly) CTV in all bedrooms Night porter 30P Squash Xmas V meals Coffee am Tea pm Last d 9.30pm
ROOMS: (incl. bkfst) s £69.50; d £75-£95 * **LB**
OFF-PEAK: (incl. bkfst) s £60-£67.50; d £75-£87.50
MEALS: Lunch £12.50-£16 Dinner £16.50-£21*
CONF: Thtr 100 Class 30 Board 30 Del from £69.50
CARDS:

W

★★68% **White Hart**

Sadler St BA5 2RR (Sadler St is the start of the one-way system. Hotel opposite the cathedral)
☎ 01749 672056 FAX 01749 672056

This former coaching inn dating from the 15th-century is centrally situated in the small cathedral city. Attractively decorated bedrooms are modern and comfortable, and are located in the main building and adjacent cottages. There are a cosy bar lounge and a spacious, restaurant with an open log fire offering carte, fixed-price and daily menus.

13 en suite (bth/shr) (1 fmly) No smoking in 5 bedrooms CTV in all bedrooms STV 17P Xmas French Cuisine V meals Coffee am Tea pm No smoking area in restaurant Last d 9.30pm
ROOMS: (incl. bkfst) s £45-£50; d £65 **LB**
OFF-PEAK: (incl. bkfst) s £40-£45; d £55-£65
MEALS: Lunch £7.50-£10 Dinner fr £10
CONF: Thtr 60 Class 40 Board 35
CARDS:

★★63% **The Star**

18 High St BA5 2SQ (on A36)
☎ 01749 670500 & 673055 FAX 01749 672654

Right in the heart of the bustling high street, close to the cathedral and market square, this traditional coaching inn offers congenial surroundings full of character and modern comfort. Bedrooms tend to vary in size but have appealing fabrics, mahogany furnishings and modern en suites. The recently refurbished Butchers Restaurant offers a good choice of dishes from daily set and à la carte menus. There is no car park on the premises, but on-street overnight parking and local car parks are close to hand.

12 en suite (bth/shr) (2 fmly) CTV in all bedrooms Xmas V meals Coffee am Tea pm No smoking area in restaurant Last d 9.30pm
ROOMS: (incl. bkfst) s £40-£50; d £55-£65 * **LB**
OFF-PEAK: (incl. bkfst) d £50-£60
MEALS: Lunch £8.95-£12.95&alc Dinner £9.50-£10.50&alc*
CONF: Thtr 130 Class 60 Board 40 Del from £75
CARDS:

★❀67% **Ancient Gate House**

20 Sadler St BA5 2RR (close to the cathedral)
☎ 01749 672029 FAX 01749 670319
Closed 25-26 Dec

Dating from the 14th century, this hotel enjoys an excellent position within he cathedral close. Some rooms have uninterrupted views across the green to the cathedral, particularly impressive at night, when it is floodlit. Two bedrooms are located in the gatehouse itself, which is an ancient monument. The interior is characterised by beams, panelling and steep stone spiral staircases. The Rugatino restaurant on the ground floor provides good home-made value-for-money meals, with a range of traditional Italian dishes.

9 rms (2 bth 5 shr) (1 fmly) CTV in all bedrooms English & Italian Cuisine V meals Coffee am Last d 10pm
ROOMS: (incl. bkfst) s £35-£45; d £55-£65 * **LB**
MEALS: Lunch £5.50-£7.50 Dinner £13.75-£14.50&alc*
CARDS:

WELLS-NEXT-THE-SEA Norfolk Map 09 TF94

★★58% **Crown**

The Buttlands NR23 1EX ☎ 01328 710209
FAX 01328 711432

A part-Tudor inn, peacefully located on the village green which is known locally as the Buttlands, the Crown offers an old-fashioned bar where full meals are served as well as a more formally run restaurant. Bedrooms are modestly furnished and reflect the age and character of the building.

15 rms (5 bth 5 shr) (3 fmly) CTV in all bedrooms 10P No coaches Xmas English & Continental Cuisine V meals Coffee am Tea pm Last d 9.30pm
ROOMS: (incl. bkfst) s £35-£55; d £58-£68 **LB**
MEALS: Lunch £10-£12.50&alc Dinner fr £19.50&alc*
CARDS:

★70% **Scarborough House**

Clubbs Ln NR23 1DP ☎ 01328 710309 & 711661

Both owners work hard to ensure a warm welcome at this hotel, and consistent standards of cooking are maintained in the flint-walled restaurant. Bedrooms in the main building and cottage annexe provide both comfort and local character.

6 en suite (bth/shr) 8 annexe en suite (bth/shr) (1 fmly) CTV in all bedrooms 14P English & French Cuisine V meals No smoking in restaurant Last d 9pm
ROOMS: (incl. bkfst) s £29-£34; d £48-£68 **LB**
MEALS: Dinner £10.95-£13.95
CARDS:

WELWYN Hertfordshire Map 04 TL21

★★★60% **Quality Clock**

Great North Rd AL6 9XA ☎ 01438 716911
FAX 01438 714065

Its convenient location and range of facilities makes this a useful conference venue. The hotel comprises a mixture of architectural styles dominated by a steeple clock. Some of the bedrooms are somewhat dated in style but still provide a range of amenities associated with this type of hotel.

95 en suite (bth/shr) (6 fmly) No smoking in 47 bedrooms CTV in all bedrooms STV Night porter 150P Gym Xmas English & Continental Cuisine V meals Coffee am Tea pm No smoking area in restaurant Last d 9.30pm
ROOMS: s £57.50-£67.50; d £67.50-£77.50 **LB**
MEALS: Lunch £7.50-£9.95&alc Dinner £13.50&alc
CONF: Thtr 250 Class 100 Board 50 Del from £82.50
CARDS:

WELWYN GARDEN CITY Hertfordshire Map 04 TL21

★★★57% **The Homestead Court**

Homestead Ln AL7 4LX (turn off A1000 into Woodhall Lane and left at Pear Tree public house into Cole Green Lane. After 2 mini-roundabouts turn right into Homestead Lane) ☎ 01707 324336 FAX 01707 326447

REGAL
A Collection of Individual Hotels

Staff are cheerful and eager to please at this hotel which is located in the midst of a residential area. Accommodation looks dated but standards of comfort are not compromised. It is advisable to ask for directions when visiting.

58 en suite (bth/shr) No smoking in 25 bedrooms CTV in all bedrooms Lift Night porter 80P Xmas International Cuisine V meals Coffee am Tea pm No smoking area in restaurant Last d 9.45pm
ROOMS: d £70 * **LB**
MEALS: Sunday Lunch £5.95-£14.95&alc Dinner £9.95-£14.95&alc*
CONF: Thtr 80 Class 45 Board 40 Del from £68
CARDS:

W

WEMBLEY Greater London See LONDON SECTION plan 1 C4

Hilton National Wembley

Empire Way HA9 8DS ☎ 0181 902 8839
FAX 0181 900 2201
This is a bright, modern hotel, with an informal restaurant, aimed at both the business and leisure guest. All bedrooms have en suite bathrooms and a range of modern facilities. For more information about Hilton National hotels, consult the Contents page under Hotel Groups.
306 en suite (bth/shr)

WENTBRIDGE (NEAR PONTEFRACT) West Yorkshire Map 08 SE41

★★★68% **Wentbridge House**

WF8 3JJ (off A1) ☎ 01977 620444
FAX 01977 620148
Closed 25 Dec-evening only
Standing in 15 acres of well tended gardens, this delightfully furnished hotel dates back to 1700 and is found conveniently near the A1. There are very well equipped and richly furnished bedrooms whilst the public rooms are attractive and inviting. The Fleur de Lys restaurant is set in two elegant rooms and the cooking of chef Richard Deguil is noteworthy.
16 en suite (bth/shr) 4 annexe en suite (bth/shr) CTV in all bedrooms No dogs (ex guide dogs) 100P No coaches English & French Cuisine V meals Coffee am Last d 9.30pm
ROOMS: (incl. bkfst) s £65-£85; d £75-£95 **LB**
OFF-PEAK: (incl. bkfst) s £48-£58; d £58-£68
MEALS: Lunch fr £14.50&alc Dinner fr £21&alc*
CONF: Thtr 120 Class 60 Board 50 Del from £76.50
CARDS:

WEOBLEY Hereford & Worcester Map 03 SO45

★★🏵🏵74% **Ye Olde Salutation Inn**
Market Pitch HR4 8SJ ☎ 01544 318443 FAX 01544 318216
With a wealth of exposed beams and timbers, log fires and uneven floors, this 15th-century country inn combines period charm with comfortable and modern accommodation. Originally a cider and ale house, the inn has been combined over the years with an adjoining cottage and now offers well equipped bedrooms with en suite bath or shower rooms and such extra facilities as trouser presses and hairdryers. A wide range of good food is available both at the bar and in a restaurant serving imaginative dishes based on fresh local produce; our inspector recently enjoyed the loin of lamb and the bread and butter pudding. Both atmosphere and service are friendly and informal.
4 en suite (bth/shr) No smoking in all bedrooms CTV in all bedrooms STV 14P No coaches Gym No children 14yrs English & French Cuisine V meals Coffee am No smoking in restaurant Last d 9pm
ROOMS: (incl. bkfst) s £36-£40; d £60-£65 *
MEALS: Lunch £9.75&alc Dinner £18.35-£26.05alc*
CARDS:

WEST BAY See Bridport

WEST BEXINGTON Dorset Map 03 SY58

★★🏵67% **Manor**
Beach Rd DT2 9DF ☎ 01308 897616 FAX 01308 897035
This ancient manor house snuggles into the hillside above Chesil Bank, a short stroll from the sea. The attractive bedrooms are all individually furnished and decorated, and have modern en suite facilities. The public areas retain much of their original character, with oak beams and panels, and a popular, stone-lined cellar bar serving a vast bar menu. There are two comfortable lounges overlooking the garden, and the fascinating array of paintings and prints around the house represent proprietor Richard Childs' passion for horse-racing. The restaurant has earned itself a good local reputation and offers an imaginative menu which exploits the abundance of local fish and game. There is a fairly extensive wine list with good European and New World wines and some interesting French country wines.
13 en suite (bth/shr) (1 fmly) CTV in all bedrooms No dogs 28P V meals Coffee am Tea pm Last d 9.30pm
ROOMS: (incl. bkfst) s £47-£51; d £80-£86 **LB**
OFF-PEAK: (incl. bkfst) d £55-£65
MEALS: Lunch £12.50-£14.50alc Dinner £17.95-£20.95alc*
CARDS:

WEST BROMWICH West Midlands Map 07 SP09
See also Great Barr

★★★67% ***Birmingham/West Bromwich Moat House***

Birmingham Rd B70 6RS (off junct 1 of M5)
☎ 0121 609 9988 FAX 0121 525 7403
Well placed for the motorway network, this modern hotel has recently been greatly enhanced by refurbishment of the ground floor and over half of the bedrooms. In addition a small but well equipped gym has been created and a 'Workbase' business centre, both of which will be appreciated by the predominantly business and corporate clientele. The lounge is a popular meeting place and Rafferty's restaurant offers an eclectic menu of sauced dishes, grills and roasts.
171 en suite (bth/shr) (111 fmly) No smoking in 55 bedrooms CTV in all bedrooms Lift Night porter 250P Gym Pool table Games room ch fac English & French Cuisine V meals Coffee am Tea pm Last d 11pm
CARDS:

★★★61% **Great Barr Hotel & Conference Centre**
Pear Tree Dr, Newton Rd B43 6HS BIRMINGHAM
☎ 0121 357 1141 FAX 0121 357 7557
(For full entry see Barr, Great)

WESTBURY Wiltshire Map 03 ST85

★★67% **The Cedar**
Warminster Rd BA13 3PR (on A350, 0.5m from Westbury towards Warminster) ☎ 01373 822753 FAX 01373 858423
Closed 27-29 Dec
This house, converted into a hotel after the last war, was built towards the end of the 18th century. It stands on the edge of Westbury which is close by road to Bath and the many attractions of the county of Wiltshire. Bedrooms have been tastefully decorated, comfortably furnished, and equipped with modern facilities. A range of dishes is offered from various menus in the bar-lounge, and for a more formal occasion there is the Regency Restaurant with its interesting a la carte.
8 en suite (bth/shr) 8 annexe en suite (bth/shr) (4 fmly) CTV in all bedrooms STV 35P No coaches English & Continental Cuisine V meals Coffee am No smoking in restaurant Last d 9pm
ROOMS: (incl. bkfst) s £45-£50; d £55-£65 * **LB**
OFF-PEAK: (incl. bkfst) s £40; d £45-£50
MEALS: Lunch £5.50-£8.50&alc Dinner £12-£17.50alc
CONF: Thtr 40 Class 40 Board 20 Del from £60
CARDS:

WEST CAMEL Somerset Map 03 ST52

★★64% **Walnut Tree**
Fore St BA22 7QW (just off A303 between the Sparkford rdbt and the Yeovilton Air Base) ☎ 01935 851292 FAX 01935 851292
This attractive village inn, situated just off the A303 and close to the
contd.

towns of Yeovil and Wincanton, is the perfect place to break a long journey to Devon and Cornwall. The recently modernised bedrooms have been tastefully decorated and furnished, and well equipped. The restaurant, which is no-smoking, offers many local specialities - Dorset crab, Mendip lamb and Barrow boar marinated in Somerset cider. Traditional beams and exposed walls are features of the bar where a selection of real ales is available.
7 en suite (bth/shr) CTV in all bedrooms No dogs (ex guide dogs) 41P No coaches No children English & French Cuisine V meals Coffee am Last d 9.30pm
ROOMS: (incl. bkfst) s £39.50-£45; d £49.50-£55 *
MEALS: Lunch £2.25-£13.95&alc Dinner £6.95-£13.95&alc*
CARDS:
See advertisement under YEOVIL

WEST CHILTINGTON West Sussex Map 04 TQ01

★★★71% **Roundabout**

Monkmead Ln RH20 2PF (1.75m S via A283)
☎ 01798 813838 FAX 01798 812962

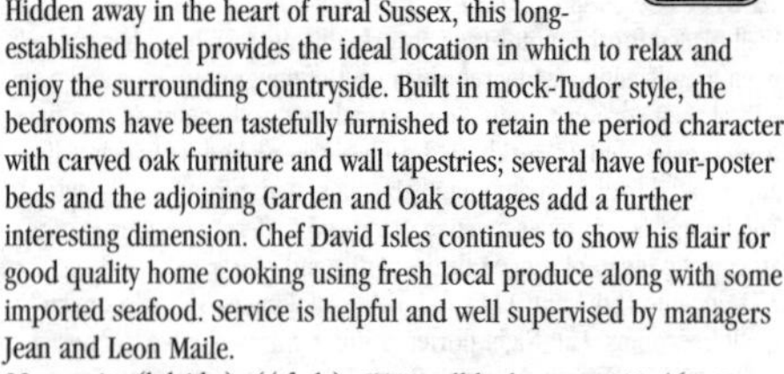

Hidden away in the heart of rural Sussex, this long-established hotel provides the ideal location in which to relax and enjoy the surrounding countryside. Built in mock-Tudor style, the bedrooms have been tastefully furnished to retain the period character with carved oak furniture and wall tapestries; several have four-poster beds and the adjoining Garden and Oak cottages add a further interesting dimension. Chef David Isles continues to show his flair for good quality home cooking using fresh local produce along with some imported seafood. Service is helpful and well supervised by managers Jean and Leon Maile.
23 en suite (bth/shr) (4 fmly) CTV in all bedrooms STV 46P No children 3yrs Xmas English & French Cuisine V meals Coffee am Tea pm Last d 9pm
ROOMS: (incl. bkfst) s £65.95-£68.95; d £89.95-£99.95 * **LB**
MEALS: Lunch £12.70-£15.95&alc Dinner £18.45-£18.95&alc
CONF: Thtr 60 Class 20 Board 26 Del from £81.10
CARDS:
See advertisement on opposite page

WESTCLIFF-ON-SEA See Southend-on-Sea

WEST DRAYTON Hotels are listed under Heathrow Airport

WESTERHAM Kent Map 05 TQ45

★★★68% **Kings Arms**
Market Square TN16 1AN ☎ 01959 562990
FAX 01959 561240
Located in the centre of town, this Georgian hotel has a lot to commend it, not least the quality and standard of food, and the range of well proportioned bedrooms. Other facilities include the Conservatory Restaurant, cocktail bar, downstairs Jail House Bistro and bar and well furnished lounge. The conscientious service and attentive personal supervision of the managers adds a further good dimension. The hotel also benefits from having its own secure car park.
16 en suite (bth/shr) (2 fmly) No smoking in 3 bedrooms CTV in all bedrooms No dogs (ex guide dogs) 70P English & French Cuisine V meals Coffee am Tea pm No smoking area in restaurant Last d 10pm
ROOMS: s £68-£70; d £78-£95 * **LB**
MEALS: Lunch £14.50-£20alc Dinner £18.50-£30alc*
CONF: Thtr 35 Class 14 Board 20 Del from £96
CARDS:

Clacket Lane Lodge
M25 Westbound, Between Junctions 5 + 6
TN16 2ER ☎ 01959 565789 FAX 01959 561311
Smart, spacious and well equipped bedrooms, all with en suite bathrooms, are provided by this modern hotel.

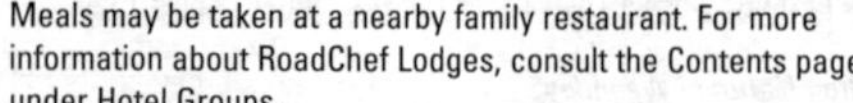

Meals may be taken at a nearby family restaurant. For more information about RoadChef Lodges, consult the Contents page under Hotel Groups.
58 en suite (bth/shr)
ROOMS: d £37.95-£39.95
CONF: Board 30

WESTGATE ON SEA Kent Map 05 TR37

★★60% **Ivyside**
25 Sea Rd CT8 8SB ☎ 01843 831082 FAX 01843 831082
Located facing the sea, this long-established hotel has an extensive range of leisure facilities and accommodation ideally suited for families with children. There are two well furnished bar lounges and a dining room with buffet and a good range of popular menus (including a light refreshment service throughout the day). Bedrooms are modestly furnished but good value, as many special offers and seasonal breaks can be obtained.
75 rms (73 bth/shr) (60 fmly) CTV in all bedrooms STV No dogs Night porter 30P Indoor swimming pool (heated) Outdoor swimming pool (heated) Squash Snooker Sauna Solarium Gym Pool table Jacuzzi/spa Steam room Table tennis ch fac Xmas English & French Cuisine V meals Coffee am Tea pm No smoking in restaurant Last d 8.45pm
ROOMS: (incl. bkfst) s £30-£34; d £50-£58 *
MEALS: Lunch £8.50&alc High tea £2.40-£3.50 Dinner £10&alc*
CONF: Thtr 200 Class 80 Board 80 Del from £46
CARDS:

WESTLETON Suffolk Map 05 TM46

★★73% **The Crown at Westleton**
IP17 3AD ☎ 01728 648777 FAX 01728 648239
This cosy inn at the centre of the village is a popular haunt for locals as well as business and leisure guests. The main, red brick building provides warm hospitality, log fires, and a good choice of eating options. Bedrooms, spread through the main house and three converted outbuildings, vary in size, but all are comfortably furnished and equipped.
10 en suite (bth/shr) 9 annexe en suite (bth/shr) (2 fmly) No smoking in all bedrooms CTV in all bedrooms Night porter 40P Xmas International Cuisine V meals Coffee am No smoking area in restaurant Last d 9.30pm
ROOMS: (incl. bkfst) s £54.50; d £73.50 * **LB**
MEALS: Dinner £17.50-£19.50&alc*
CONF: Thtr 60 Class 40 Board 30 Del £93.95
CARDS:

WEST LULWORTH Dorset Map 03 SY88

★★70% **Shirley**
Main Rd BH20 5RL (on B3070 in centre of village)
☎ 01929 400358 FAX 01929 400358
Closed Dec-Jan
This attractive family-run hotel continues to improve, and has a loyal following. The bedrooms are comfortable and attractively decorated with good modern facilities. The public areas include a smart indoor pool and two lounges. Proprietor Mr Williams offers good home-cooked evening meals in the restaurant where Mrs Williams oversees their team of young friendly staff who provide efficient service in a relaxed atmosphere.
18 en suite (bth/shr) (3 fmly) CTV in all bedrooms 20P No coaches Indoor swimming pool (heated) Jacuzzi/spa Giant chess V meals Coffee am No smoking in restaurant Last d 7.30pm
ROOMS: (incl. bkfst) s £29-£31; d £58-£62 * **LB**
MEALS: Dinner £12-£14&alc*
CARDS:

★★65% **Cromwell House**
Lulworth Cove BH20 5RJ (200 yds beyond end of West Lulworth village, turn left at Lulworth Lodge, Cromwell House 100yds on left)
☎ 01929 400253 & 400332 FAX 01929 400566
Closed 22-28 Dec
Set in an elevated position with spectacular sea and countryside views this family-run hotel continues to improve. The bedrooms are bright and attractive with co-ordinated fabrics and en suite facilities. The traditionally furnished dining room serves good home-cooked meals and is popular for afternoon tea. There is also a comfortable guests' lounge, ideally placed to take advantage of the views.
14 en suite (bth/shr) (2 fmly) CTV in all bedrooms 15P Outdoor swimming pool (heated) V meals Coffee am Tea pm No smoking in restaurant Last d 8.30pm
ROOMS: (incl. bkfst) s £25.50-£36.50; d £51-£61 * **LB**
MEALS: Bar Lunch £1.50-£2.50 High tea £1.50-£3.50 Dinner £7.50-£11&alc
CARDS: 

WESTON-ON-THE-GREEN Oxfordshire Map 04 SP51

★★★ 64% **Weston Manor**
OX6 8QL ☎ 01869 350621 FAX 01869 350901
This imposing Oxfordshire manor house is very popular with the business community and has some impressive conference and banqueting facilities. Bedrooms are split between the main house and a converted coach house and though they vary in size all are particularly well equipped. The public areas are impressive with an imposing foyer lounge and a magnificent vaulted restaurant with minstrels gallery and original panelling.
16 en suite (bth/shr) 20 annexe en suite (bth/shr) (5 fmly) No smoking in 6 bedrooms CTV in all bedrooms No dogs (ex guide dogs) 100P Outdoor swimming pool (heated) Squash Croquet lawn Xmas English & French Cuisine V meals Coffee am Tea pm Last d 9.30pm
ROOMS: (incl. bkfst) s £97.50; d £110 * **LB**
OFF-PEAK: (incl. bkfst) s £85; d £95
MEALS: Lunch fr £17.50 Dinner fr £27.50&alc*
CONF: Thtr 40 Class 20 Board 25 Del from £130
CARDS: 

WESTON-SUPER-MARE Somerset Map 03 ST36

★★★ 68% **Commodore**
Beach Rd, Sand Bay, Kewstoke BS22 9UZ (1.5m NW of town centre)
☎ 01934 415778 FAX 01934 636483
Closed Xmas
This modern hotel, overlooking the sands at Kewstoke, enjoys a relaxed and friendly atmosphere. Bedrooms have been tastefully furnished and well equipped, and some in the main house have sea views. Public areas include a choice of bars and restaurants; snacks, hot specials and a roast are available in the Commodore Lounge and a wider selection of dishes is offered in Alice's Beyond the Pier Restaurant.
12 en suite (bth/shr) 6 annexe en suite (bth/shr) (4 fmly) CTV in all bedrooms No dogs (ex guide dogs) 85P Putting green Adventure play park Wkly live entertainment English & French Cuisine V meals Coffee am Tea pm Last d 9pm
ROOMS: (incl. bkfst) s fr £50; d fr £65 * **LB**
MEALS: Sunday Lunch fr £11.95 Dinner £11.50-£20.15alc*
CONF: Thtr 120 Class 80 Board 72 Del from £65
CARDS: 

★★★61% **The Grand Atlantic**
Beach Rd BS23 1BA ☎ 01934 626543
FAX 01934 415048

A continued major upgrading programme at this

contd.

W

attractive Victorian sea front hotel is all but completed. Most of the refurbished bedrooms now match the public rooms in quality of decor and furnishings. Friendly staff provide traditional services.
76 en suite (bth/shr) (5 fmly) No smoking in 22 bedrooms CTV in all bedrooms Lift Night porter 100P Outdoor swimming pool (heated) Tennis (hard) Xmas English & French Cuisine V meals Coffee am Tea pm No smoking in restaurant Last d 9.30pm
ROOMS: s £50-£55; d £60-£80 * **LB**
MEALS: Sunday Lunch £11.95 Dinner £16.95*
CONF: Thtr 180 Class 80 Board 35 Del from £62.50
CARDS:

★★★59% **Royal Pier**
Birnbeck Rd BS23 2EJ (take A370 and follow seafront 0.5m to Birnbeck Pier) ☎ 01934 626644 FAX 01934 624169
With commanding views over Weston Bay this hotel provides comfortable, traditional public rooms and a choice of bars. Bedrooms tend to vary in size and location and whilst well equipped are in the process of upgrading. Friendly services from local staff.
40 en suite (bth/shr) (4 fmly) No smoking in 2 bedrooms CTV in all bedrooms No dogs (ex guide dogs) Lift Night porter 70P Pool table Xmas European Cuisine V meals Coffee am Tea pm Last d 9.15pm
ROOMS: (incl. bkfst) s £45-£58; d £65-£78 * **LB**
MEALS: Lunch £8.25-£10.95&alc Dinner £14.95&alc*
CONF: Thtr 65 Class 40 Board 30 Del from £65
CARDS:

★★64% **Beachlands**
17 Uphill Rd North BS23 4NG (follow signs for M5/Tauton along seafront for 1m, hotel overlooks golf course)
☎ 01934 621401 FAX 01934 621966
Closed 23 Dec-2 Jan
This small, family-run hotel overlooks the golf course and is situated in a residential area a short stroll from the sea front. The spacious and elegantly decorated public areas include a bar, a choice of lounges and a bright dining room, offering a table d'hÙte menu which changes every day. Bedrooms vary in size but are well equipped for business or leisure use.
17 en suite (bth/shr) (4 fmly) CTV in all bedrooms 21P ch fac English & French Cuisine V meals Coffee am Tea pm No smoking in restaurant Last d 8.30pm
ROOMS: (incl. bkfst) s £32.50-£42.50; d £65 * **LB**
MEALS: Lunch £11.50 High tea £5.50 Dinner £14.75*
CONF: Thtr 80 Class 30 Board 36 Del from £55
CARDS:

★★64% **Rozel**
Madeira Cove BS23 2BU ☎ 01934 415268 FAX 01934 644364
The Rozel Hotel has been in the same family ownership for over 70 years and enjoys an enviable position overlooking the North Shore, with the town centre and all the attractions but a short level walk away. The attractive bar-lounge is tastefully furnished in the style of 'Raffles Hotel' and provides a comfortable place to relax and enjoy the views. Bedrooms have been equipped to meet the needs of both the leisure and business markets. In the restaurant, a short, straightforward menu is available.
46 en suite (bth/shr) (15 fmly) CTV in all bedrooms Lift Night porter 80P Outdoor swimming pool (heated) English & French Cuisine V meals Coffee am Tea pm Last d 8.30pm
CONF: Thtr 160 Class 80 Board 50
CARDS:

Travel Inn

Hutton Moor Rd BS22 8LY ☎ 01934 622625
FAX 01934 627401
Purpose-built accommodation, offering spacious, well equipped bedrooms, all with en suite bathrooms. Meals may be taken at the nearby family restaurant. For more information about Travel Inns, consult the Contents page under Hotel Groups.
40 en suite (bth/shr)
ROOMS: d £35.50 *

WEST RUNTON Norfolk Map 09 TG14

★★71% **Dormy House**
Cromer Rd NR27 9QA (E on A149)
☎ 01263 837537 FAX 01263 837537
Dormy House, on the outskirts of the village, stands on the coast road surrounded by open countryside. This small, family-run hotel offers a friendly and relaxing environment with comfortable public rooms. Diners have a choice of eating venues, with informal meals served in the bar or, alternatively, a wider choice of menus offered within the spacious restaurant. Well equipped, modern bedrooms of generally comfortable proportions are all immaculately maintained and clean; a lift serves most of the accommodation.
16 en suite (bth/shr) (1 fmly) CTV in all bedrooms No dogs Lift 60P No coaches No children 7yrs Xmas English & French Cuisine V meals Coffee am Tea pm No smoking in restaurant Last d 9pm
ROOMS: (incl. bkfst) s £34-£38; d £48-£58 * **LB**
MEALS: Sunday Lunch fr £9.50 Dinner fr £15.50&alc*
CARDS:

WEST THURROCK Essex Map 05 TQ57

Travelodge
RM16 3BG (off A1306 Arterial Rd) ☎ 01708 891111
Central Res 0800 850950 FAX 01525 878450

Travelodge

This modern building offers accommodation in smart, spacious and well equipped bedrooms, suitable for family use, and all with en suite bathrooms. Meals may be taken at the nearby family restaurant. For information on room rates and to make a booking, call Roomline free of charge on 0800 850950. For more details about Travelodge, consult the Contents page under Hotel Groups.
44 en suite (bth/shr)

WESTWARD HO! Devon Map 02 SS42

★★63% **Culloden House**
Fosketh Hill EX39 1JA (on A39 at Bideford, take right turn for Westward Ho!) ☎ 01237 479421
This former Victorian Gentleman's Residence has been converted into a comfortable, small hotel and new owners offer a warm welcome. Bedrooms are clean and modestly furnished, whilst some offer fine views over Bideford Bay and Northam Burrows. The spacious lounge also looks out across the ocean and a freshly prepared dinner is available in the adjacent dining room.
9 rms (2 bth 5 shr) (2 fmly) CTV in all bedrooms 7P No coaches Xmas English & French Cuisine V meals Tea pm No smoking in restaurant Last d 8.30pm
ROOMS: (incl. bkfst) s £25-£33; d £45-£55 * **LB**
OFF-PEAK: (incl. bkfst) s £20-£25; d £40-£50
MEALS: Lunch £7.95-£9.95 Dinner £14.95-£24
CARDS:

WEST WITTON North Yorkshire Map 07 SE08

★★67% **Wensleydale Heifer Inn**

DL8 4LS (A684, at west end of village)
☎ 01969 622322 FAX 01969 624183
Dating in part from the 17th century this famous inn stands in the heart of Wensleydale and retains much of its original charm. The bar and lounge have old beams and open fires and food is provided in the two restaurants, one a bistro and the other a more traditional dining room. Menus are extensive and include daily specials. Bedrooms are

accommodated in the main building as well in a house opposite. Service is friendly and attentive from a smartly turned out staff.

9 en suite (bth/shr) 6 annexe en suite (bth/shr) (1 fmly) CTV in all bedrooms 40P Xmas V meals Coffee am Tea pm Last d 9.30pm
ROOMS: (incl. bkfst) s £49.50-£54; d £64-£85 * LB
MEALS: Sunday Lunch £2.75-£9.50alc High tea £6.50 Dinner £17.50&alc*
CONF: Thtr 20 Class 20 Board 20 Del £75
CARDS:

See advertisement on this page

WETHERBY West Yorkshire Map 08 SE44

★★★ 71% **Wood Hall**
Trip Ln, Linton LS22 4JA (take Harrogate road N from market place and turn left to Linton) ☎ 01937 587271 FAX 01937 584353
RS Sat
Once a boys' school, this magnificent Georgian mansion is set in a lovely location amid open parkland and woods overlooking the River Wharfe. It offers excellent accommodation with generously proportioned, beautifully decorated bedrooms that are well furnished and provide many thoughtful extras. The elegant and ornate reception rooms include a pleasant oak-floored drawing room warmed in winter months by an open log fire, a wood-panelled dining room and a range of private rooms. The food includes some very imaginative oriental-style dishes finding their place amongst more traditional fare.
37 en suite (bth/shr) 6 annexe en suite (bth/shr) CTV in all bedrooms STV Lift Night porter 120P Indoor swimming pool (heated) Fishing Snooker Sauna Solarium Gym Jacuzzi/spa Treatment room for massage and facials Xmas British & French Cuisine V meals Coffee am Tea pm No smoking in restaurant Last d 10pm
ROOMS: (incl. bkfst) s £98-£119; d £109-£130 * LB
MEALS: Lunch £15.95-£28.50 Dinner £28.50
CONF: Thtr 100 Class 60 Board 30 Del £140
CARDS:

WEYBRIDGE Surrey See LONDON SECTION plan 1 A1

★★★★ 71% **Oatlands Park**
146 Oatland Dr KT13 9HB (through Weybridge High Street to top of Monument Hill. Hotel third of a mile on left)
☎ 01932 847242 FAX 01932 842252
Built as a country house in 1974, this impressive and professionally-managed hotel is set in ten acres of well kept grounds overlooking Broadwater Lake. Once inside the glass-covered atrium, the marble-pillared lobby lounge leads into a similarly comfortable and well furnished lounge bar area and the beautifully decorated, well appointed candlelit Broadwater Restaurant. Fully equipped bedrooms include superior, deluxe, and full suites, with several new and very comfortable singles having recently been added. There is a wide range of fully equipped air-conditioned meeting, conference and function rooms, and a fitness centre. Chef John Hayes continues to produce a very enthusiastic style of professional cooking using the best quality

Aberdeen Angus beef, local venison, fresh fish and seafood.
123 en suite (bth/shr) (5 fmly) No smoking in 20 bedrooms CTV in all bedrooms STV Lift Night porter 99P Tennis (hard) Gym Croquet lawn Jogging course Fitness suite Wkly live entertainment International Cuisine V meals Coffee am Tea pm Last d 10pm
ROOMS: (incl. bkfst) s £100-£110; d £130-£145 LB
OFF-PEAK: (incl. bkfst) s £47.50-£85; d £75-£85
CONF: Thtr 300 Class 200 Board 70 Del £145
CARDS:

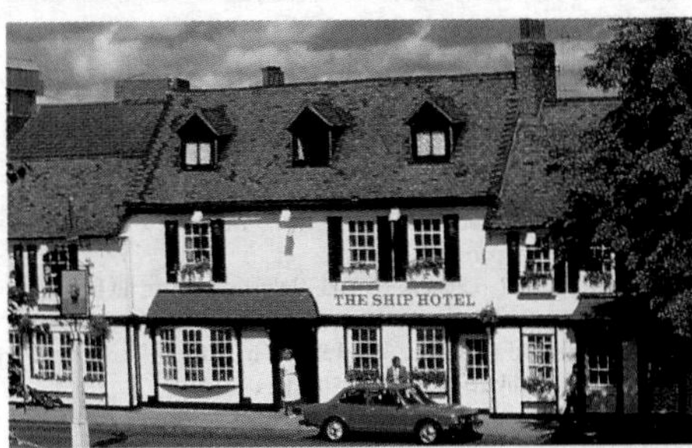

★★★ 71% **Ship Thistle**
Monument Green KT13 8BQ (turn off M25 junc 11, A317, at third roundabout turn left into the High Street, hotel on left) ☎ 01932 848364
FAX 01932 857153
This town centre hotel is sandwiched between a popular bar and L'Escales restaurant, which continues to show keen efforts, now under the new young head chef. One of the most enjoyable features of the hotel is the genuine and caring attitude universally shown by the staff,

contd.

whose behaviour reflects management's positive approach to guest care. Bedrooms are mostly spacious and manage to keep pace with changes to decor and style.
39 en suite (bth/shr) No smoking in 10 bedrooms CTV in all bedrooms STV No dogs (ex guide dogs) Night porter 75P International Cuisine V meals Coffee am Tea pm No smoking in restaurant Last d 9.45pm
ROOMS: s £95-£105; d £105-£115 * **LB**
OFF-PEAK: (incl. bkfst) s fr £43; d £86-£96
MEALS: Lunch £10.75-£13.75 Dinner £17.50&alc*
CONF: Thtr 140 Class 70 Board 60 Del from £137
CARDS:

★★63% ***Kings Manor***
25 Oatlands Rd KT13 9RW ☎ 01932 253277 & 227790 FAX 01932 243910
TOBY
This property has an intimate and well cared for character and it is located in a peaceful residential area. The restaurant, offering the popular range of Toby meals, overlooks a large rear lawn.
19 en suite (bth/shr) (1 fmly) No smoking in 4 bedrooms CTV in all bedrooms No dogs (ex guide dogs) Night porter P V meals Coffee am Last d 9.30pm
CARDS:

WEYMOUTH Dorset Map 03 SY67

★★68% **Bay Lodge**
27 Green Hill DT4 7SW (on A353, 200yds from Lodmoor Country Park) ☎ 01305 782419 FAX 01305 782828
Closed Nov
Located on the edge of town this personally run hotel enjoys spectacular sea views. Barbara and Graham Dubben offer a warm welcome and attentive service. The bedrooms are attractively decorated and well equipped, some with king-size beds and jacuzzi baths. There is a cosy lounge with a log fire; and the restaurant and well stocked bar take advantage of the views. The menu offers a wide range of freshly prepared dishes.
7 en suite (bth/shr) 5 annexe en suite (bth/shr) CTV in all bedrooms 15P Xmas V meals Coffee am Tea pm Last d 5.30pm
ROOMS: (incl. bkfst) s £25-£55; d £48-£66 * **LB**
OFF-PEAK: (incl. bkfst) s £25-£33.50; d £48-£58
MEALS: Sunday Lunch £10 Dinner £8-£14&alc*
CONF: Thtr 25
CARDS:

★★66% **Hotel Rex**
29 The Esplanade DT4 8DN (on seafront opposite Alexandra Gardens) ☎ 01305 760400 FAX 01305 760500
Closed Xmas
This established well managed hotel is in a good central location, close to the ferry and the seafront. The public areas are very smart and attractively decorated in keeping with the Regency period of the building. The bedrooms vary in size but are neat and well equipped; most have sea views. There is a daily-changing and an a la carte menu, both served in the popular Cellar Restaurant. Limited parking at the rear of the hotel must be arranged at the time of booking; there is unrestricted parking at the front of the hotel although this is very busy during the summer.
31 en suite (bth/shr) (5 fmly) CTV in all bedrooms STV Lift Night porter 6P International Cuisine V meals Coffee am Tea pm Last d 10pm
ROOMS: (incl. bkfst) s £42-£52; d £68-£95 **LB**
MEALS: Dinner £10-£12&alc
CONF: Thtr 40 Class 30 Board 25 Del £67
CARDS:

★★65% **Glenburn**
42 Preston Rd DT3 6PZ (3m NE A353) ☎ 01305 832353 0500 543202(FREE) FAX 01305 835610
Closed 25 Dec-1 Jan
Located on the Preston road on the outskirts of the town, the Glenburn is personally run by the Cotton family who create a warm and friendly atmosphere. The bedrooms vary in size but are well maintained and freshly decorated, all have en suite facilities. The smartly furnished restaurant offers an extensive menu, and there is a live band and dancing on some evenings during the winter.
13 en suite (bth/shr) (1 fmly) CTV in all bedrooms No dogs 30P No coaches English & French Cuisine V meals Coffee am Tea pm No smoking in restaurant Last d 8pm
ROOMS: (incl. bkfst) s £30-£35; d £50-£60 * **LB**
CARDS:

★★64% **Crown**
51-52 St Thomas St DT4 8EQ (turn off A35 at Dorchester, take A354 to Weymouth, pass over second bridge, premises on left)
☎ 01305 760800 FAX 01305 760300
Closed 25-26 Dec
Well equipped and comfortable accommodation is offered at this hotel which caters mainly for holidaymakers. There is a choice of restaurants offering a varied menu, and bar snacks are also available. Public areas include a comfortable first-floor lounge. The bedrooms are simply furnished and decorated.
77 en suite (bth/shr) (10 fmly) CTV in all bedrooms STV No dogs (ex guide dogs) Lift Night porter 8P V meals Coffee am No smoking area in restaurant Last d 8pm
ROOMS: (incl. bkfst) s £36-£40; d £56-£60 * **LB**
MEALS: Lunch £5.50-£14alc Dinner £9.50-£12
CONF: Class 140 Board 80
CARDS:

★★62% **Hotel Prince Regent**
The Esplanade DT4 7NR (N end of Weymouth seafront) ☎ 01305 771313 FAX 01305 771313

Closed 23 Dec-2 Jan
This long established seaside hotel has stood on Weymouth promenade since 1855 and is still very much the centre of local activities. Extensive meeting and function facilities are provided and there is a public bar as well as the main hotel bar. Food comes by way of a fixed price menu which is supplemented by a good selection of carte choices. Restaurant manager Victor Caraballo has been at the hotel for nearly 20 years and leads a team of friendly and attentive staff. Bedrooms are functional rather than luxurious but all have en suite facilities and are equipped with modern amenities. Many are suitable for families and several enjoy good sea views. Street parking is available and there is also a small rear car park.
50 en suite (bth/shr) (23 fmly) CTV in all bedrooms STV No dogs Lift Night porter 20P Pool table table tennis English & French Cuisine V meals Coffee am No smoking in restaurant Last d 8.30pm
ROOMS: (incl. bkfst) s £59-£64; d £84-£90 * **LB**
MEALS: Bar Lunch £2.50-£12alc Dinner £11.95-£12.95&alc*

CONF: Thtr 225 Class 1207 Board 70 Del from £60
CARDS:

★★62% **Streamside**

29 Preston Rd DT3 6PX ☎ 01305 833121
FAX 01305 832043
Closed 26-29 Dec
A warm welcome is offered at this family-run hotel on the outskirts of Weymouth. The bedrooms are simply furnished and many of them have en suite facilities. There is a cosy restaurant serving an interesting menu of carefully prepared dishes, and local produce, particularly fish, is used where possible. The spacious function room leading into a pretty garden makes this an ideal venue for weddings.
15 rms (9 bth/shr) (4 fmly) CTV in all bedrooms 20P English & French Cuisine V meals Coffee am Last d 9pm
ROOMS: (incl. bkfst) s £34-£46; d £52-£68 * **LB**
MEALS: Sunday Lunch £5.25-£7.75 Dinner fr £11.75&alc*
CARDS:

★61% **Alexandra**
27/28 The Esplanade DT4 8DN ☎ 01305 785767
Originally two properties, this attractive Georgian building is close to the centre of town on the Esplanade. The hotel offers comfortable public areas including a well stocked bar, traditional lounge and a front-facing dining room where a home-cooked evening meal is served. Most of the bedrooms are bright and attractively furnished.
20 rms (5 bth 9 shr) (4 fmly) CTV in 14 bedrooms 7P V meals Coffee am Tea pm No smoking in restaurant Last d 7pm
CARDS:

WHATTON Nottinghamshire Map 08 SK73

★★64% ***The Haven***
Grantham Rd NG13 9EU (off A52, take turning to Redmile/Belvoir Castle) ☎ 01949 850800 FAX 01949 851454
A much extended smallholding has been converted into a popular roadside inn with a large public bar, budget-priced accommodation and a spacious function room.
33 en suite (bth/shr) (5 fmly) CTV in all bedrooms STV 70P Pool table English, French & Italian Cuisine V meals Coffee am Tea pm Last d 10pm
CARDS:

WHEDDON CROSS Somerset Map 03 SS93

★★ 73% **Raleigh Manor**

TA24 7BB (take A396 N towards Dunster. Turn left 200 yds outside village into private drive)
☎ 01643 841484
Closed mid Nov-mid Mar
The comfortable family home stands in more than an acre of grounds and gardens overlooking Snowdrop Valley. Bedrooms with co-ordinating fabrics and antique furnishings offer comfortable accommodation. There is a choice of lounges with log fires, and interesting home-cooked dishes are featured on the fixed-price menu served in the dining room.
7 en suite (bth/shr) (1 fmly) CTV in all bedrooms 10P No coaches No children 5yrs V meals Coffee am Tea pm No smoking in restaurant Last d 7.30pm
ROOMS: (incl. bkfst & dinner) s £25-£29; d £50-£58 *
MEALS: Dinner £15.50*
CARDS:

STOP PRESS! *AA Members can book accommodation at many hotels in this guide through the AA Booking Service, usually at attractive discounts. See page 5 for details or telephone 0990 050505*

WHICKHAM Tyne & Wear Map 12 NZ26
See also Newcastle upon Tyne

★★★70% **Gibside Arms**
Front St NE16 4JG (turn off A1M towards Whickam on the B6317, B6317 leads onto Whicknam Street, 2m on right)
☎ 0191 488 9292 FAX 0191 488 8000
RS 23-29 Dec
Situated in the old village centre, with fine views over the Tyne Valley, this hotel offers bedrooms which are, for the most part, modern and well appointed (though some in the older part of the building are beginning to look a little dated). Public areas include a number of function/banqueting suites and comfortable smaller lounges as well as the elegant Strathmore Restaurant and spacious Sphinx Bar, both of which look out over the valley.
45 en suite (bth/shr) (2 fmly) CTV in all bedrooms STV Lift Night porter 28P Wkly live entertainment English & French Cuisine V meals Coffee am Tea pm No smoking area in restaurant
ROOMS: s fr £51; d fr £62 * **LB**
OFF-PEAK: (incl. bkfst) s fr £37.50; d fr £45
MEALS: Lunch £8.95&alc Dinner £13.95&alc*
CONF: Thtr 100 Class 50 Board 50 Del from £58.80
CARDS:

WHIMPLE Devon Map 03 SY09

RED STAR HOTEL

★★ **Woodhayes**
EX5 2TD (under 1m from A30, Exeter road)
☎ 01404 822237 FAX 01404 822337
Closed 4 days Xmas
A handsome early-Georgian house, this hotel is set in four acres of gardens and grounds on the edge of the village. Frank and Kathryn Rendle have a natural talent for making guests feel at home, and tea is offered in one of the comfortable lounges while Kathryn explains the dinner menu and enquires as to any dislikes. There are an attractive bar with flagstone floors and antique pine pieces and an elegant dining room where fresh flowers adorn the tables. At a recent inspection meal, the seven-course dinner began with an appetiser of Parma ham and fresh pear, and this was followed by a tasty carrot and orange soup, subtly blended with the added flavour of coriander. Lightly steamed fillet of sea bass was served with dressed salad leaves, and a succulent sirloin of beef was accompanied by a mild grainy mustard sauce, fresh spinach, roast parsnips and creamed potatoes. The dessert selection included date pudding with toffee sauce, crème brûlèe and home-made ice creams, and there is a range of local cheeses to finish. The six

contd.

bedrooms are tastefully furnished and each is equipped with modern comforts and such extras as bottled water and magazines.
6 en suite (bth) CTV in all bedrooms No dogs (ex guide dogs) 12P No coaches Croquet lawn No children 12yrs English & French Cuisine No smoking in restaurant Last d 7.30pm
ROOMS: (incl. bkfst) s fr £85; d fr £130 * LB
MEALS: Lunch £15 Dinner £25*
CARDS:

WHITBY North Yorkshire Map 08 NZ81

★★70% **Saxonville**
Ladysmith Av, (Off Argyle Road) YO21 3HX (A174 on to North Promenade. turn inland at Large building visable on West Cliff into Argyle Road, then first turning on right)
☎ 01947 602631 FAX 01947 820523
Closed mid Oct-Etr
Set in a quiet side road close to the North Promenade, this traditional hotel has now been in the same family ownership for 50 years. It provides modern, well equipped bedrooms, ample comfortable lounges and a very extensive range of well produced dishes served in the inviting restaurant.
24 en suite (bth/shr) (4 fmly) CTV in all bedrooms No dogs (ex guide dogs) 20P V meals Coffee am No smoking in restaurant Last d 8.30pm
ROOMS: (incl. bkfst) s £30-£35; d £60-£70 LB
OFF-PEAK: (incl. bkfst) s fr £27.50; d fr £55
MEALS: Lunch £1.65-£5.50alc Dinner £15.50&alc*
CONF: Thtr 100 Class 64 Board 56 Del from £43.50
CARDS:

See advertisement on opposite page

★★67% **Larpool Hall Country House**

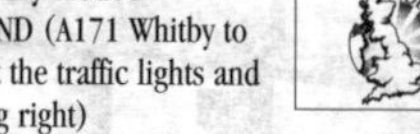

Larpool Dr, Larpool Ln YO22 4ND (A171 Whitby to Scarborough road, turn right at the traffic lights and cross new bridge before turning right)
☎ 01947 602737 FAX 01947 820204
This elegant, stone-built Georgian mansion stands in extensive gardens overlooking the Esk Valley. Public rooms include an attractive restaurant, a comfortable lounge bar, a guests' lounge and a library. Spacious bedrooms, some with antique furniture, all have modern facilities.
20 en suite (bth/shr) (1 fmly) No smoking in 10 bedrooms CTV in all bedrooms No dogs (ex guide dogs) 60P Xmas English & French Cuisine V meals Coffee am Tea pm No smoking in restaurant Last d 9pm
ROOMS: (incl. bkfst) s £39.50-£45; d £70-£110 LB
MEALS: Lunch £9.95-£14.95&alc High tea £5.95-£8.50&alc Dinner £16.95-£19.50&alc*
CONF: Thtr 200 Class 100 Board 70 Del from £69.50
CARDS:

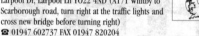

★★67% **White House**
Upgang Lane, West Cliff YO21 3JJ (on A174 beside the golf course)
☎ 01947 600469 FAX 01947 821600
The White House is situated to the north of the town and is only 200 yards from the sea and bordering onto the golf course. It's a friendly hotel offering good all rounds standards of both service and accommodation, whilst an extensive range of food is available and which is served either in the Gallery restaurant or in the cosy bar. There are well equipped bedrooms which now include hairdryers.
12 rms (7 bth 4 shr) (3 fmly) CTV in all bedrooms 50P English & French Cuisine V meals Coffee am Last d 9.30pm
ROOMS: (incl. bkfst) s £26.50-£28.50; d £53-£57 * LB
MEALS: Lunch £8.95 Dinner £11.95*
CARDS:

★★66% **Dunsley Hall**
Dunsley YO21 3TL ☎ 01947 893437 FAX 01947 893505
A gracious turn-of-the-century mansion house set in its own grounds. The new owners Mr & Mrs Ward have already stamped their own refreshingly honest and down to earth approach to hospitality on the hotel, and the welcome is both warm and genuine. The house itself retains its period charm and architectural interest with a wealth of oak panelling and stone mullioned windows. Despite its location, a few miles from the town, the views over the rolling hills and the sea beyond are unrivalled.
17 en suite (bth/shr) (2 fmly) No smoking in 4 bedrooms CTV in all bedrooms 20P Indoor swimming pool (heated) Tennis (hard) Sauna Gym Croquet lawn Putting green Xmas English & French Cuisine V meals Coffee am Tea pm No smoking in restaurant Last d 9.30pm
ROOMS: (incl. bkfst) s £49.95-£59.95; d £79.95-£120 * LB
MEALS: Lunch £2.95-£12.50 Dinner £19.50
CONF: Thtr 60 Class 30 Board 30 Del from £80
CARDS:

See advertisement on opposite page

★★66% **Stakesby Manor**
Manor Close, High Stakesby YO21 1HL (at roundabout junct of A171/B1416 take road for West Cliff. Third turning on right)
☎ 01947 602773 FAX 01947 602140
Closed 25-30 Dec
Standing in its own well tended grounds and about a mile from the sea, this attractive Georgian manor house provides good all round comforts. It is very well furnished throughout and offers well equipped and inviting bedrooms, together with attractive public rooms which include a delightful wood-pannelled dining room. There is a good range of dishes available, either in the bar or dining room, and warm, friendly service is provided by the Hodgson family.
8 en suite (bth/shr) CTV in all bedrooms No dogs (ex guide dogs) 40P No coaches International Cuisine V meals No smoking in restaurant Last d 9.30pm
ROOMS: (incl. bkfst) s fr £44; d £62-£66 LB
MEALS: Lunch £13.50&alc Dinner £13.50&alc
CONF: Thtr 100 Class 46 Board 40
CARDS:

★★62% **Old West Cliff**
42 Crescent Av YO21 3EQ (opposite Whitby Pavilion and Spa, enter Royal Crescent which leads into Crescent Avenue)
☎ 01947 603292 FAX 01947 821716
Closed Nov-Feb
This friendly family-run hotel in a Victorian terrace close to the sea and Crescent Gardens has well equipped bedrooms with modern bathrooms, a comfortable lounge and attractive bar, and a cosy restaurant serving generous meals.
12 en suite (bth/shr) (6 fmly) CTV in all bedrooms No coaches V meals No smoking in restaurant Last d 10pm
ROOMS: (incl. bkfst) s £27; d £44 *
MEALS: Dinner £9.50*
CARDS:

WHITCHURCH Shropshire Map 07 SJ54

★★★59% **Dodington Lodge**
Dodington SY13 1EN (at A41/A49 junct)
☎ 01948 662539 FAX 01948 667992
Dodington Lodge is a family-run hotel with neat modern bedrooms and comfortable public areas. One bedroom has a 4-poster bed and all are equipped with trouser presses. There is a choice of bars and a good range of eating options. The hotel is a popular venue for local functions and meetings, and its car park is secured during the night.
10 en suite (bth/shr) (2 fmly) No smoking in 2 bedrooms CTV in all bedrooms 70P Pool table children's play area pool table V meals

Coffee am Tea pm Last d 9.30pm
ROOMS: (incl. bkfst) s £42.50-£45; d £50-£55 * LB
OFF-PEAK: (incl. bkfst) s fr £35; d fr £42.50
MEALS: Lunch £6.50-£9.50 High tea fr £4.95 Dinner fr £9.95
CONF: Thtr 100 Class 50 Board 40
CARDS:

★★61% **Redbrook Hunting Lodge**
Wrexham Rd SY13 3ET (2.5m W, at A495/A525 junct)
☎ 01948 780204 FAX 01948 780533
Set in several acres of mature grounds, this family run hotel is currently being upgraded under new ownership. Regular carveries supplement a wide range of bar and restaurant meals and these enjoy popular local support. Bedrooms are equipped with modern amenities and facilities are available for weddings and other functions.
13 en suite (bth/shr) (3 fmly) No smoking in 2 bedrooms CTV in all bedrooms 100P Pool table Wkly live entertainment ch fac English & French Cuisine V meals Coffee am Tea pm Last d 10pm
ROOMS: (incl. bkfst) s £39.50-£49.50; d £49.50-£59.50 * LB
MEALS: Lunch £8-£12.75&alc Dinner fr £12.50&alc*
CONF: Thtr 120 Class 40 Board 36 Del from £60
CARDS:

WHITEHAVEN Cumbria Map 11 NX91

★★★63% **Howgate**
Howgate CA28 6PL (on A595 just outside Whitehaven)
☎ 01946 66286 FAX 01946 66286
Friendly staff help to promote a relaxed atmosphere at this hotel which lies on the main road 1.5 miles north of the town. Upgraded and extended, it offers attractively furnished and well proportioned bedrooms as well as a split-level restaurant and two bars.
20 en suite (bth/shr) (1 fmly) No smoking in 8 bedrooms CTV in all bedrooms STV 100P V meals Coffee am Tea pm
ROOMS: (incl. bkfst) s fr £47.50; d fr £63 * LB
OFF-PEAK: (incl. bkfst) s fr £42.50; d fr £53
MEALS: Lunch £8-£14.25*
CARDS:

★★60% **The Chase**
Inkerman Ter CA28 8AA (off A596)
☎ 01946 693656 & 693714 FAX 01946 590807
The Chase is a mainly commercial hotel set in its own grounds just a short distance from the town centre. The bedrooms have good facilities and there is a wide range of food available in either the bar or the restaurant.
11 rms (8 bth/shr) (1 fmly) CTV in all bedrooms 50P English & French Cuisine V meals Last d 9pm
ROOMS: (incl. bkfst) s fr £37; d fr £44
OFF-PEAK: (incl. bkfst) s fr £29; d fr £39
MEALS: Sunday Lunch £5.95 Dinner £6.50-£13.50&alc
CARDS:

WHITLEY BAY Tyne & Wear Map 12 NZ37

★★★64% **Windsor**
South Pde NE26 2RF (A191 into Whitley Bay,at third roundabout take first exit, turn right at lights, turn left at Woolworths, then right)
☎ 0191 251 8888 FAX 0191 297 0272
RS 25 Dec
Modern, well equipped bedrooms of varying sizes, some quite spacious, along with comfortable public areas are features of this business hotel, set between the town centre and the seafront.
63 en suite (bth/shr) (24 fmly) CTV in all bedrooms STV Lift Night porter 32P European Cuisine V meals Coffee am Tea pm
Last d 9.30pm

contd.

ROOMS: (incl. bkfst) s £55-£60; d £60-£65 **LB**
OFF-PEAK: (incl. bkfst) s £40-£55; d £50-£60
MEALS: Bar Lunch £4-£6 Dinner £12.50-£13.50&alc*
CONF: Thtr 100 Class 60 Board 40 Del from £65
CARDS:

See advertisement on opposite page

★★67% **High Point**
The Promenade NE26 2NJ ☎ 0191 251 7782 FAX 0191 251 6318
This modern and stylishly decorated hotel lies on the seafront and provides attractive bedrooms, some of which are very spacious, with comfortable sofas and sea views. There is a small restaurant, but one can also dine in the large split-level bar.
14 en suite (bth/shr) (3 fmly) CTV in all bedrooms STV Night porter 20P Pool table Wkly live entertainment Xmas V meals Coffee am Tea pm Last d 9pm
ROOMS: (incl. bkfst) s £35-£48; d £50-£55 * **LB**
OFF-PEAK: (incl. bkfst) s fr £30; d £45-£50
MEALS: Sunday Lunch fr £7.95 Dinner £10.95-£18*
CARDS:

★★63% ***Park Lodge Hotel***
160-164 Park Av NE26 1AU (on A193, on one-way system after leaving sea front in Whitley Bay) ☎ 0191 253 0288 FAX 0191 297 1006
Closed 24-26 Dec
Liz Carty and her family offer a friendly and relaxing atmosphere at their informally run commercial hotel on the one-way system, close to the seafront. Bedrooms vary in size and standard but are well equipped and attractively decorated. Chef Jason Carty provides skilfully cooked dinners which are an incentive to 'eat in'.
16 rms (12 bth/shr) (1 fmly) CTV in all bedrooms STV No dogs (ex guide dogs) 8P No coaches Solarium Gym Pool table No children European Cuisine Coffee am Tea pm Last d 8.45pm
CARDS:

★★61% **Holmedale**
106 Park Av NE26 1DN (turn off A19 onto A1058, follow signs for A191, when in Whitley Bay follow signs for Tourist info, Hotel on opposite corner) ☎ 0191 251 3903 & 0191 253 1162
FAX 0191 253 0053
Closed evening 24-evening 26 Dec
This family-run hotel has an informal and relaxing atmosphere. Bedrooms come in a variety of sizes but are generally bright and cheery. The attractive dining room has a small lounge bar area adjoining. The dinner menu offers a selection of popular grill dishes supplemented by home-cooked daily specials.
18 en suite (bth/shr) (3 fmly) CTV in all bedrooms 10P Pool table English & Continental Cuisine V meals Last d 8pm
ROOMS: (incl. bkfst) s £25-£35; d £35-£50 * **LB**
OFF-PEAK: (incl. bkfst) s £20-£30; d £30-£50
MEALS: Lunch £4.95-£6.75alc Dinner £8-£15.50alc*
CONF: Thtr 60 Class 50 Board 40 Del from £20
CARDS:

★★61% **Seacrest**
North Pde NE26 1PA ☎ 0191 253 0140 FAX 0191 253 0140
An informal and relaxed atmosphere is a feature of this family-run commercial hotel which lies between the seafront and town centre. Focal-point is the residents lounge bar which has a small games room adjacent. Bedrooms come in two standards, but its worth choosing the larger superior rooms.
24 rms (17 bth/shr) (4 fmly) CTV in all bedrooms Night porter 6P Pool table ch fac Xmas V meals Coffee am Tea pm Last d 8.30pm
ROOMS: (incl. bkfst) s £25-£46; d £40-£55 * **LB**
CONF: Thtr 50 Class 30 Board 30 Del from £39
CARDS:

★60% **Cavendish**
51 Esplanade NE26 2AS (50 yards off Whitley Bay promenade)
☎ 0191 253 3010
This friendly commercial hotel lies close to the seafront and within walking distance of the town centre. It offers unpretentious but reasonably priced accommodation, a small bar and snug, and a cheery restaurant providing a good choice of dishes.
11 rms (5 bth 1 shr) (2 fmly) CTV in all bedrooms STV 12P V meals Last d 9.30pm
ROOMS: (incl. bkfst) s £19.50-£27.50; d £30-£35 * **LB**
MEALS: Lunch £7.50 Dinner fr £4.95*
CARDS:

WHITSTABLE Kent Map 05 TR16

Travelodge
☎ 01227 770254 FAX 01227 770254
Travelodge
This modern building offers accommodation in smart, spacious and well equipped bedrooms, suitable for family use, and all with en suite bathrooms. Meals may be taken at the nearby family restaurant. For information on room rates and to make a booking, call Roomline free of charge on 0800 850950. For more details about Travelodge, consult the Contents page under Hotel Groups.
40 en suite (bth/shr)

WHITTINGTON Shropshire Map 07 SJ33

★61% ***Ye Olde Boot Inn***
SY11 4DG (Frederic Robinson) ☎ 01691 662250
This old coaching inn lies in the village of Whittington, just east of Oswestry picturesquely set opposite the castle and moat. The bars retain much of their original character and are popular locally for their friendly atmosphere and good-value food.
6 en suite (bth/shr) (2 fmly) CTV in all bedrooms 100P V meals Coffee am Tea pm
CARDS:

WICKHAM Hampshire Map 04 SU51

★★74% **Old House**
The Square PO17 5JG (at the junction of the B2177 and the A32)
☎ 01329 833049 FAX 01329 833672
Closed 10 days Xmas, Etr, 2 wks Jul/Aug & BH's RS Mon-Sat
Many original features are retained in this charming Georgian hotel at the centre of the village. Stylishly decorated and comfortable public areas have a warm, friendly atmosphere, while individually decorated bedrooms with modern facilities are furnished with some handsome pieces. The restaurant offers a choice of menus, the enjoyable dishes largely based on fresh produce.
9 en suite (bth/shr) 3 annexe en suite (bth/shr) (1 fmly) CTV in all bedrooms No dogs (ex guide dogs) 12P No coaches French Cuisine V meals Last d 9.30pm

ROOMS: s £65-£75; d £80-£90 * **LB**
MEALS: Lunch £27-£29 Dinner £27-£29*
CARDS:

WIDNES Cheshire Map 07 SJ58

★★★64% ***Hill Crest***

75 Cronton Ln WA8 9AR (on A5080 NW)
☎ 0151 424 1616 FAX 0151 495 1348

This modern hotel is situated north of the town and within easy reach of junction 7 of the M62 motorway. Bedrooms meet modern standards of comfort and those designated as executive rooms are particularly large. A feature of the hotel is its Palms Restaurant, themed as a tropical island, which adjoins the cocktail bar with its baby grand piano. The Nelson Bar has a nautical theme and entertainment is provided at weekends. There are also versatile meeting and conference rooms and good parking facilities.

49 en suite (bth/shr) (1 fmly) No smoking in 3 bedrooms CTV in all bedrooms STV Lift Night porter Air conditioning 150P V meals Coffee am Tea pm Last d 10pm
CARDS:

★★★61% **Everglades Park**

Derby Rd WA8 3UJ ☎ 0151 495 2040 FAX 0151 424 6536

Everglades Park is a modern hotel found on the Warrington road. It provides good sized bedrooms which are adequately furnished and public rooms that are about to be upgraded. Two styles of dining are available and an indoor swimming pool is an added attraction, as are the ample function rooms. A further extension of bedrooms is at present under construction.

67 en suite (bth/shr) (4 fmly) No smoking in 17 bedrooms CTV in all bedrooms Night porter Air conditioning 200P Indoor swimming pool (heated) Pool table Wkly live entertainment ch fac Xmas International Cuisine V meals Coffee am Tea pm Last d 10pm
ROOMS: (incl. bkfst) s £55-£110; d £67-£110 * **LB**
OFF-PEAK: (incl. bkfst) s £31-£70; d £43-£70
MEALS: Lunch £10.50-£12.95&alc Dinner £12.95-£14.95&alc*
CONF: Thtr 200 Class 90 Board 50 Del from £55
CARDS:

See advertisement under LIVERPOOL

WIGAN Greater Manchester Map 07 SD50

★★★★❀❀67% **Kilhey Court**

Chorley Rd WN1 2XN ☎ 01257 472100
FAX 01257 422401
(For full entry see Standish)

★★★65% **Oak**

Riverway WN1 3SS ☎ 01942 826888 FAX 01942 825800

A large, purpose-built hotel opposite Wigan RFC ground, the Oak was opened in 1991 and offers a range of modern bedrooms with a self-service lift operating between all floors. Open-plan public areas include an attractive restaurant, lounge bar and conservatory lounge. A range of function, conference and meeting rooms is also available, most of which open on to a small walled garden and patio area.

88 en suite (bth/shr) (14 fmly) No smoking in 24 bedrooms CTV in all bedrooms STV Lift Night porter 100P Xmas V meals Coffee am Tea pm Last d 9.45pm
ROOMS: s fr £62; d fr £72 * **LB**
OFF-PEAK: s fr £30; d fr £46
MEALS: Lunch £6.95-£8.95&alc Dinner fr £15.95&alc*
CONF: Thtr 170 Class 90 Board 50
CARDS:

★★★65% **Wigan/Standish Moat House**

Almond Brook Rd WN6 0SR ☎ 01257 499988
FAX 01257 427327
(For full entry see Standish)

★★64% **Bel-Air**

236 Wigan Ln WN1 2NU (1m N on A49)
☎ 01942 241410 FAX 01942 243967
Closed 26-30 Dec

This privately owned and personally run hotel offers neat, soundly maintained bedrooms, all with modern furnishings and all but one of them en suite; this room, however, has the use of its own private bathroom. There is a comfortably furnished lounge-bar which at the time of our visit was about to be redecorated. There is also a pleasant restaurant where a good choice of popular dishes is served. The hotel is conveniently located on the A49 to the north of the town centre and within two miles of junction 27 of the M6.

12 en suite (bth/shr) (2 fmly) CTV in all bedrooms 8P English & Continental Cuisine V meals Coffee am Tea pm No smoking in restaurant Last d 8.45pm
ROOMS: (incl. bkfst) s £30-£39.50; d £40-£49.50 *
MEALS: Bar Lunch £2-£4.50 Dinner £6.95-£14.95alc
CONF: Thtr 30 Board 8 Del from £49
CARDS:

Travel Inn

Orrell Rd, Orrell WN5 8HQ ☎ 01942 211516

Purpose-built accommodation, offering spacious, well equipped bedrooms, all with en suite bathrooms. Meals may be taken at the nearby family restaurant. For more information about Travel Inns, consult the Contents page under Hotel Groups.
ROOMS: d £35.50 *

WIGHT, ISLE OF

BONCHURCH See Ventnor

CHALE Map 04 SZ47

★★66% Clarendon Hotel & Wight Mouse Inn
PO38 2HA (on B3099 main coast road)
☎ 01983 730431 FAX 01983 730431
This 17th-century former coaching inn has great charm and a lively atmosphere. Ideally located for visiting Blackgang Chine and local sandy beaches, it is a good choice for families, and children are warmly welcomed and well catered for. The bedrooms are comfortable and attractively decorated, with modern en suite bathrooms and some have beautiful sea views. The cosy dining room offers a wide range of dishes to suit all tastes, and the chef makes good use of local produce. The Wight Mouse pub adjoins the hotel and is popular with locals and visitors alike; there is regular live evening entertainment and food is available throughout the day.
14 rms (4 bth 6 shr) (9 fmly) CTV in all bedrooms 200P Riding Pool table Wkly live entertainment ch fac Xmas International Cuisine V meals Coffee am Tea pm No smoking area in restaurant Last d 10pm
ROOMS: (incl. bkfst) s £25-£35; d £50-£70 * **LB**
OFF-PEAK: (incl. bkfst) s £20-£25; d £40-£50
MEALS: Lunch £8-£12&alc High tea £5-£6&alc Dinner £10-£13.50&alc
CONF: Del from £30
CARDS:

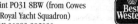

COWES Map 04 SZ49

★★★67% *New Holmwood*

Queens Rd, Egypt Point PO31 8BW (from Cowes Parade turn right by Royal Yacht Squadron)
☎ 01983 292508 FAX 01983 295020
This attractive hotel is situated on the Cowes Esplanade and commands superb views over the Solent. The bedrooms are well equipped and most have now been attractively refurbished with smart new decor. The restaurant takes full advantage of the views with French windows opening onto a terrace. The menu offers a good range of dishes with additional grill, snack and vegetarian menus. There is also a heated outdoor pool with a spa and sun terrace; good conference facilities are available.
25 en suite (bth/shr) CTV in all bedrooms 17P Outdoor swimming pool (heated) French Cuisine V meals Coffee am Tea pm Last d 9.30pm
CARDS:

See advertisement on opposite page

★★61% Fountain
High St PO31 7AN ☎ 01983 292397
FAX 01983 299554
This hotel is conveniently located for the ferry to the mainland. The well maintained bar and informal restaurant have a

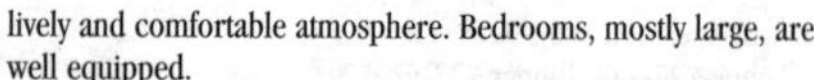

lively and comfortable atmosphere. Bedrooms, mostly large, are well equipped.
20 en suite (bth/shr) (1 fmly) CTV in all bedrooms STV No dogs (ex guide dogs) No coaches European Cuisine V meals Coffee am Tea pm Last d 10pm
ROOMS: (incl. bkfst) s £49.50; d £59.50 * **LB**
OFF-PEAK: (incl. bkfst) s fr £40; d fr £50
MEALS: Sunday Lunch £8.95-£10 Dinner £7.50-£12.50&alc*
CARDS:

FRESHWATER Map 04 SZ38

★★★64% *Albion*
PO40 9RA (off A3055, W of inshore rescue building)
☎ 01983 753631 FAX 01983 755295
Situated right at the water's edge in Freshwater Bay, The Albion enjoys one of the best locations on the island. The public areas are spacious and comfortably furnished, there is a large lounge overlooking the bay, and the bar is very popular with both visitors and locals for its range of snacks. The bedrooms continue to be upgraded, and many of them have balconies.
42 en suite (bth/shr) (28 fmly) CTV in all bedrooms Night porter 75P International Cuisine V meals Coffee am Tea pm Last d 9pm
CARDS:

RYDE Map 04 SZ59

★★★63% Appley Manor
Appley Rd PO33 1PH (on B3330) ☎ 01983 564777
FAX 01983 564704
This Victorian manor has been extensively restored to provide attractive modern accommodation and a popular all-day restaurant. The bedrooms are spacious and well equipped with smart en suite facilities and co-ordinated decor. There is a comfortable residents' lounge and bright breakfast room. The bar and restaurant have already gained a loyal following from locals, businessmen and private parties; the all day menu offers generous portions of traditional and popular dishes.
12 en suite (bth/shr) (2 fmly) No smoking in 3 bedrooms CTV in all bedrooms No dogs (ex guide dogs) Night porter 60P No coaches English, French & Italian Cuisine V meals Coffee am Tea pm No smoking area in restaurant
ROOMS: s fr £25; d fr £35 *
CARDS:

★★65% Biskra House Beach
17 Saint Thomas's St PO33 2DL ☎ 01983 567913 FAX 01983 616976
This relaxing and friendly hotel is personally run by Susan and Guiseppe Cretella, who offer a warm welcome. The Clipper Bar provides a comfortable area in which to take a drink or relax with coffee, and the popular Cellar Restaurant offers good authentic Italian food in the evenings. Lunch is served in the ground floor restaurant overlooking the sea, and light refreshments are also served on the beach terrace. The bedrooms vary in size but most of them have beautiful sea views and balconies; they are all well equipped and have lots of extra home comforts, including mini-bars and bathrobes.
9 rms (8 bth/shr) CTV in all bedrooms STV 12P No coaches English & Italian Cuisine V meals Coffee am Last d 10pm
ROOMS: (incl. bkfst) s £31.50-£35; d £47.50-£57.50 * **LB**
MEALS: Sunday Lunch fr £15.25&alc Dinner fr £15.25&alc
CONF: Board 60 Del from £50
CARDS:

★★61% Yelf's
Union St PO33 2LG ☎ 01983 564062 FAX 01983 563937
This friendly high street hotel is popular with business people, holiday makers and loyal local clientele alike. The public areas are bright and well appointed; the busy bar opens onto a pretty terrace garden and a

comfortable lounge serves snacks and afternoon teas. Bedrooms are spacious and attractively decorated.
21 en suite (bth/shr) (2 fmly) CTV in all bedrooms English Cuisine V meals Coffee am Tea pm No smoking area in restaurant Last d 9pm
ROOMS: (incl. bkfst) s £32.50; d £43.50 *
MEALS: Lunch £9.95-£10.95 Dinner £10.95*
CONF: Thtr 70 Class 10 Board 20 Del from £49.50
CARDS:

ST LAWRENCE Map 04 SZ57

★★66% ***Rocklands***
PO38 1XH ☎ 01983 852964
May-Oct
This handsome property was built in 1842 and stands in its own mature gardens in the village of St Lawrence. Owners Mr and Mrs Exposite offer a warm welcome and create a relaxed and friendly atmosphere. The public areas are peaceful and comfortable, there is a lounge overlooking the garden, a cosy bar and a games room. Michael Exposite prepares generous evening meals using good local fresh produce; the home-made bread and soups are recommended. The bedrooms are attractively decorated and have en suite facilities, there are some ground floor rooms and a chair lift to the first floor.
15 en suite (bth/shr) 4 annexe en suite (bth/shr) (6 fmly) CTV in all bedrooms No dogs (ex guide dogs) 20P Outdoor swimming pool (heated) Snooker Sauna Solarium Gym Croquet lawn Table tennis Games room ch fac English & Continental Cuisine V meals Coffee am Tea pm Last d 8.15pm

SEAVIEW Map 04 SZ69

★★★❀❀77% ***Seaview***
High St PO34 5EX ☎ 01983 612711 FAX 01983 613729
Personally run by Nicholas and Nicola Hayward, manager Mr Leon Gully and their team of friendly staff, Seaview is located close to the sea in the heart of the pretty resort. Three of the individually decorated bedrooms have south-facing balconies and some bathrooms have separate shower cubicles. In addition to the bars and a very elegant first floor drawing room, there is now a choice of eating options with the new Sunshine Room adding to the extent and range of the cuisine. Chef Charles Bartlett and his enthusiastic brigade cook with the freshest top-quality ingredients and, though menus change frequently, such popular dishes as the renowned crab ramekin and fresh lobster retain their place.
16 en suite (bth/shr) (2 fmly) CTV in all bedrooms 12P No coaches English & French Cuisine V meals Coffee am Tea pm Last d 9.30pm
CARDS:

SHANKLIN Map 04 SZ58

★★★64% **Holliers**
5 Church Rd, Old Village PO37 6NU
☎ 01983 862764 FAX 01983 867134
Set amidst thatched cottages in the centre of the Old Town, this 18th-century coaching inn remains popular with both business and leisure guests. The bedrooms are fresh and attractive, and the public areas are spacious and relaxing; they include a smart bar where there is regular live entertainment, and an indoor leisure suite. The first floor lounge offers comfortable tranquillity, and, for a more lively atmosphere, there is the main bar.
30 en suite (bth/shr) (6 fmly) CTV in all bedrooms STV No dogs (ex guide dogs) 50P Indoor swimming pool (heated) Outdoor

contd.

swimming pool (heated) Sauna Solarium Pool table Jacuzzi/spa Xmas European Cuisine V meals Coffee am Tea pm Last d 8.30pm
ROOMS: (incl. bkfst) s £33-£45; d £52-£80
OFF-PEAK: (incl. bkfst) s £33-£40
MEALS: Bar Lunch £2-£15alc Dinner £15.25
CARDS:

★★68% **Keats Green**
3 Queens Rd PO37 6AN (Follow signs Old Village/Ventnor, avoiding town centre, hotel on left past St Saviors church.)
☎ 01983 862742 FAX 01983 868868
Closed Nov-Mar
An attractive property with splendid views out to sea, this hotel continues to flourish under the ownership of Mr and Mrs Bushby, a charming couple who welcome guests warmly. The attractive bedrooms have pretty, coordinated decor, and the public areas are comfortable and stylish, with a relaxed friendly atmosphere. Everyone has a sea-view in the restaurant, where a daily-changing menu is served.
34 rms (33 bth/shr) (3 fmly) CTV in all bedrooms 34P Outdoor swimming pool (heated) V meals Coffee am Last d 8pm
CARDS:

★★66% **Fernbank**
Highfield Rd PO37 6PP ☎ 01983 862790 FAX 01983 864412
Closed Xmas
This friendly hotel, located in a peaceful residential road yet just a few minutes from the Old Village, has beautiful country views. The bedrooms are attractively decorated and include five spacious annexe rooms. There is a bright, pretty restaurant with large bay windows overlooking the garden, as well as a cosy bar. The indoor pool has french-windows opening onto the garden.
19 en suite (bth/shr) 5 annexe en suite (bth/shr) (8 fmly) CTV in all bedrooms 22P No coaches Indoor swimming pool (heated) Sauna Solarium Pool table Jacuzzi/spa Petanque No children 7yrs English, French & Italian Cuisine V meals Coffee am Tea pm Last d 8.30pm
ROOMS: (incl. bkfst & dinner) s £43.50-£48 * **LB**
OFF-PEAK: (incl. bkfst & dinner) s £36.75-£43.50
MEALS: Sunday Lunch £6 Dinner £11*
CARDS:

★★66% **Luccombe Hall**
Luccombe Rd PO37 6RL ☎ 01983 862719 FAX 01983 863082
Closed 2 Jan-6 Feb
Situated in a quiet residential area, Luccombe Hall is set in mature gardens with magnificent views of the sea. The bedrooms vary in size, but are bright and well equipped. The public areas are spacious and relaxing; there is a traditional lounge, an indoor pool, a leisure suite and a squash court. The hotel has a loyal following of regularly returning guests and the family and staff are friendly and helpful.
29 en suite (bth/shr) (14 fmly) CTV in all bedrooms 30P Indoor swimming pool (heated) Outdoor swimming pool (heated) Tennis (grass) Squash Sauna Solarium Gym Pool table Jacuzzi/spa Games room English & Continental Cuisine Coffee am Tea pm Last d 8.30pm
MEALS: Sunday Lunch £6.50-£12 Dinner £16*
CARDS:

★★62% **Melbourne Ardenlea**
Queen's Rd PO37 6AP (turn left at Fiveways Crossroads, off A3055, hotel on right 150yds past the tall spired church) ☎ 01983 862283 FAX 01983 862865
Closed mid Dec-mid Feb RS Nov-mid Dec & mid Feb-Mar
This popular family-run hotel is situated near the old village and the cliffs, making it a favourite with coaching parties. The bedrooms are neat and well presented with modern ensuite facilities. There is a smart indoor pool with a spa bath, and the spacious public areas include a bar and a comfortably furnished lounge with regular live entertainment. There is also a games room for children.

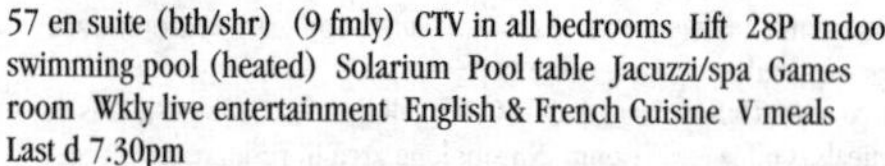

57 en suite (bth/shr) (9 fmly) CTV in all bedrooms Lift 28P Indoor swimming pool (heated) Solarium Pool table Jacuzzi/spa Games room Wkly live entertainment English & French Cuisine V meals Last d 7.30pm
ROOMS: (incl. bkfst & dinner) s £30-£40; d £60-£80 **LB**
OFF-PEAK: (incl. bkfst & dinner) s £25-£30; d £50-£60
MEALS: Lunch fr £10 Dinner £11&alc*
CARDS:

★★61% **Malton House**
8 Park Rd PO37 6AY ☎ 01983 865007
This well presented Victorian villa is conveniently placed for the beach lift and the shops. The bedrooms are neat and brightly decorated, and there is a relaxed and friendly atmosphere in the public areas. A four-course dinner menu is served in the attractive dining room, and there is a well stocked bar.
15 en suite (bth/shr) (3 fmly) CTV in all bedrooms No dogs 12P No coaches Xmas English & Continental Cuisine V meals Last d 8pm
ROOMS: (incl. bkfst) s £20-£24; d £36-£44 *
MEALS: Dinner £9
CARDS:

TOTLAND BAY Map 04 SZ38

★★68% ***Sentry Mead***
Madeira Rd PO39 0BJ ☎ 01983 753212 FAX 01983 753212
Closed 22 Dec-1 Jan
This handsome Victorian property is set in mature grounds in a quiet residential area of West Wight. Proprietors Mike and Julie Hodgson are totally involved in the daily running of the hotel and continue to make improvements. The public areas, which are spacious and comfortable, include a sun lounge overlooking the terrace, a cosy lounge and a smart new bar offering light lunchtime snacks. There is an attractive dining room where Julie provides good quality home-cooked meals. The bedrooms are bright and neatly presented, all have modern en suite facilities.
14 en suite (bth/shr) (4 fmly) CTV in all bedrooms 10P No coaches Putting green European Cuisine Coffee am Tea pm Last d 8pm
CARDS:

VENTNOR Map 04 SZ57

★★★❀68% **The Royal**
Belgrave Rd PO38 1JJ (A3055 main coastal road, into Ventnor follow one way system around Town, after traffic lights turn left into Belgrave road, Hotel is on left) ☎ 01983 852186 FAX 01983 855395
This splendid hotel once favoured by Queen Victoria, is set high above the sea with delightful views over the bay. The public areas are elegant and spacious, and include a sunny conservatory. The bedrooms are being steadily upgraded and the new rooms have bright, co-ordinated decor and quality furnishings. Public rooms include a recently restored bar, serving a range of light dishes throughout the day, and a restaurant with interesting menus and friendly staff. Guests may enjoy the tranquility of the lounge or view the pretty gardens from the sun lounge.
55 en suite (bth/shr) (5 fmly) CTV in all bedrooms Lift Night porter 56P No coaches Outdoor swimming pool (heated) Cocktail Pianist & Harpist Wkly live entertainment ch fac Xmas French Cuisine V meals Coffee am Tea pm Last d 9pm
ROOMS: (incl. bkfst & dinner) s £45-£50; d £110-£120 * **LB**
OFF-PEAK: (incl. bkfst & dinner) s £35-£40; d £90-£100
MEALS: Bar Lunch £3-£14.95alc High tea 75p-£3.50alc Dinner £17.95&alc*
CONF: Thtr 80 Class 80 Board 50 Del from £70
CARDS:

W

★★★65% **Burlington**
Bellevue Rd PO38 1DB ☎ 01983 852113 FAX 01983 852113
Closed Nov-Etr
Situated in a peaceful elevated location, this established family run hotel continues to improve. The bedrooms are comfortable and attractively decorated. The public areas include a cosy lounge overlooking the garden and swimming pool, a smartly furnished bar and a stylish dining room offering good home-cooked meals from a daily changing menu.
23 en suite (bth/shr) (8 fmly) CTV in all bedrooms No dogs 20P No coaches Outdoor swimming pool (heated) Pool table No children 3yrs Coffee am Tea pm No smoking in restaurant Last d 8.30pm
MEALS: Dinner £12.50
CARDS:

★★★ 65% ***Peacock Vane Country House Hotel***
Bonchurch Village Rd, Bonchurch PO38 1RJ ☎ 01983 852019
The history of this unique Victorian country house dates back to 1836, but parts are even earlier and quite historic. The accommodation, whist having been extensively improved and upgraded during the past few years, retains all its original character and charm, furnished with antiques and chandeliers. Bedrooms are individually furnished and decorated and although well equipped TV's are not usually provided. There is a choice of dining options with the Ivory Restaurant and Brasserie, and there is a small cosy bar, but pride of place must go to the exquisitely furnished first floor piano bar and lounge. Service is very friendly and personally supervised by the resident proprietors Larry and Mandy Allen.

★★★63% **Ventnor Towers**
Madeira Rd PO38 1QT (first left after Trinity church, follow road for 0.25m) ☎ 01983 852277
FAX 01983 855536

This family-run hotel enjoys glorious sea views and offers a warm welcome. Locally it is well known for its speciality jazz evenings which take place in the attractive restaurant. The public areas include two lounges, well tended gardens, a swimming pool, tennis court and putting green. The bedrooms which vary in size and style are being continually upgraded, many now having smart new decor.
27 en suite (bth/shr) (4 fmly) CTV in all bedrooms 26P Outdoor swimming pool (heated) Tennis (hard) Croquet lawn Games room Pitch & putt ch fac English & Continental Cuisine V meals Coffee am Tea pm Last d 8.30pm
CONF: Thtr 80 Class 50 Board 35 Del from £65
CARDS:

★★65% **Eversley**
Park Av PO38 1LB (on A3055 west of Ventnor) ☎ 01983 852244
Closed 16 Nov-22 Dec & 28 Dec-15 Feb
This friendly hotel offers bright comfortable accommodation and a cheery atmosphere. The rooms all have modern en suite facilities and are attractively decorated. The lounges are comfortably furnished and the dining room overlooks a pretty garden and the swimming pool.
32 en suite (bth/shr) (8 fmly) CTV in all bedrooms 23P Outdoor swimming pool (heated) Tennis (hard) Pool table ch fac Xmas V meals Coffee am Tea pm Last d 8.30pm
ROOMS: (incl. bkfst) s £24-£28; d £48-£56 **LB**
OFF-PEAK: (incl. bkfst) s fr £20; d fr £40
MEALS: Bar Lunch fr £2.50 Dinner £10-£12
CONF: Class 40 Board 20
CARDS:

★★65% **Highfield**
Leeson Rd, Bonchurch PO38 1PU ☎ 01983 852800 & 854611
Closed 12 Nov-1 Feb
This extended Victorian house stands in an elevated position overlooking the sea and is personally run by Mr and Mrs Flaherty who continue to make improvements. The bedrooms are bright and attractively decorated, all have en suite facilities and most have sea views. There is a comfortable lounge leading to a verandah, and Mrs Flaherty prepares good, home-cooked evening meals.
12 en suite (bth) (1 fmly) CTV in all bedrooms 12P No coaches No children English & French Cuisine V meals Coffee am Tea pm
MEALS: Lunch fr £8.50 Dinner £14.95&alc*
CARDS:

YARMOUTH Map 04 SZ38

★★★❀❀❀79% **George Hotel**
Quay St PO41 0PE (between the castle and the pier)
☎ 01983 760331 FAX 01983 760425

Sitting snugly next to the Tudor castle and within a short stroll of the pier, this historic hotel has been completely transformed by its new owners Jeremy and Amy Willcock, who are committed to making this a very special establishment. The bedrooms are decorated to a very high standard and personalised by the provision of extra touches such as soft fluffy bath robes, top-of-the-range toiletries and even miniature wooden sailing rigs for bath-time entertainment. Foodies will certainly not be disappointed by the kitchen's efforts, driven along by Kevin Mangeolles whose sound technical skills have been refined by some years' experience at a very highly rated Lake District hotel. The food award applies to the restaurant but there is also a very good brasserie.
17 en suite (bth/shr) No smoking in 4 bedrooms CTV in all bedrooms STV 6P No coaches Xmas V meals Coffee am Tea pm Last d 10pm
ROOMS: (incl. bkfst) s £70-£85; d £101.75-£140 *
MEALS: Lunch £22.50&alc Dinner £33.50-£35
CONF: Thtr 40 Class 20 Board 20 Del from £140
CARDS:

WIGTON Cumbria Map 11 NY24

★★59% **Wheyrigg Hall**
Wheyrigg CA7 0DH (4m NW on B5302)
☎ 016973 61242 FAX 016973 61020
Lying on the B5302 Silloth road four miles west of Wigton, this family-run hotel has a friendly and informal atmosphere. Originally a farmhouse which has now been extended, some bedrooms are in an adjoining converted barn and some in a single storey extension which also houses all the public rooms. The bedrooms are all well equipped and include an ideal family suite.
12 en suite (bth/shr) (2 fmly) CTV in 10 bedrooms No dogs (ex guide dogs) 60P Sauna Pool table Wkly live entertainment Xmas English, Italian & French Cuisine V meals Coffee am Tea pm Last d 9pm
ROOMS: (incl. bkfst) s £20-£33; d £35-£48 * **LB**
MEALS: Lunch £7.50-£10 High tea fr £6.50 Dinner fr £15*
CONF: Thtr 100 Board 50
CARDS:

WILLERBY East Riding of Yorkshire Map 08 TA03

★★★70% **Grange Park**
Main St HU10 6EA (turn off roundabout just past Willerby shopping park and turn left at next roundabout (signed Grange Park). Follow road to end) ☎ 01482 656488 FAX 01482 655848

A much extended manor house, this hotel offers a very good range of leisure and conference facilities. Public areas include a choice of bars, an Italian and an English restaurant catering at all times for the formal and the informal. Bedrooms are mainly purpose built and are well equipped.
101 en suite (bth/shr) No smoking in 44 bedrooms CTV in 104

contd.

bedrooms STV Lift Night porter Air conditioning 600P Indoor swimming pool (heated) Gym Hairdressing Beauty clinic ch fac Xmas English & Italian Cuisine V meals Coffee am Tea pm Last d 9pm
ROOMS: s £69-£79; d £79-£89 **LB**
OFF-PEAK: (incl. bkfst & dinner) s £68-£78; d £106-£116
MEALS: Lunch £5.95-£12.95 High tea £4.95-£9.95 Dinner £17.50-£19.50&alc
CONF: Thtr 550 Class 250 Board 80 Del from £85
CARDS:

★★★69% **Willerby Manor**
Well Ln HU10 6ER ☎ 01482 652616 FAX 01482 653901
Very professional and friendly staff ensure that guests have a pleasant stay at this elegant Victorian house standing in well tended gardens and grounds. Set within the village and well signposted, the hotel offers comfortable and spacious accommodation with bedrooms well equipped along modern lines. In the traditional restaurant a good choice of well produced dishes is provided by chef Adam Richardson.
51 en suite (bth/shr) CTV in all bedrooms No dogs (ex guide dogs) Night porter 250P Indoor swimming pool (heated) Sauna Solarium Gym Croquet lawn Jacuzzi/spa Wkly live entertainment V meals Coffee am Tea pm Last d 9.30pm
ROOMS: s £60-£65; d £75-£82 * **LB**
OFF-PEAK: (incl. bkfst) s fr £35; d fr £60
MEALS: Lunch £10.50-£12 Dinner fr £14&alc*
CONF: Thtr 500 Class 200 Board 100 Del from £87
CARDS:

WILLINGTON Co Durham Map 12 NZ13

★★65% **Kensington Hall**
Kensington Ter DL15 0PJ (off A690) ☎ 01388 745071
FAX 01388 745800
This family-owned and run hotel provides modern and well furnished bedrooms together with attractive and comfortable public rooms. It includes two bars and a popular restaurant where a very good range of home-cooked and value-for-money meals is served. Service is friendly and attentive. A function room is attached.
10 en suite (bth/shr) (3 fmly) CTV in all bedrooms No dogs (ex guide dogs) Night porter 40P V meals Coffee am
ROOMS: (incl. bkfst) s £32.50-£35; d £45-£48 * **LB**
MEALS: Lunch £5.45-£6.45&alc Dinner £10.45-£11.45&alc
CONF: Class 80 Board 50 Del from £42.95
CARDS: Connect

WILLITON Somerset Map 03 ST04

★★72% **White House**
Long St TA4 4QW (on A39) ☎ 01984 632306 & 632777
Closed Nov-mid May
This attractive little hotel has been personally run by Dick and Kay Smith for nearly 30 years, in which time they have built up a loyal clientele. The bedrooms vary in size and are attractively furnished. Day rooms include a cosy beamed restaurant and a comfortable bar and lounge. The fixed-price menu changes daily and always includes some tried and tested favourites, a recent inspection meal started with one of these:-a perfectly cooked Gruyère and Parmesan cheese soufflé. A fresh tuna steak was served with a rustic tomato and pepper sauce and fresh seasonal vegetables. The wine list is impressive.
8 rms (5 bth/shr) 4 annexe en suite (bth) (4 fmly) CTV in all bedrooms 12P No coaches English & French Cuisine No smoking in restaurant Last d 8.30pm
ROOMS: (incl. bkfst) s £35-£54; d £62-£92 * **LB**
MEALS: Dinner fr £30

★75% **Curdon Mill**
Vellow TA4 4LS (1m SE off A358)
☎ 01984 656522 FAX 01984 656197
This former water mill is set in attractive, well maintained gardens and is part of a working farm located in the small hamlet of Vellow, off the A358. Richard and Daphne Criddle provide a warm welcome to guests, and accommodation is comfortable and well furnished. The spacious restaurant is located on the first floor and features the original mill workings. The short menu offers a well balanced choice of dishes, using fresh garden and farm produce. Curdon Mill is a popular venue for wedding receptions and small functions.
6 en suite (bth/shr) No smoking in 12 bedrooms CTV in all bedrooms No dogs (ex guide dogs) 100P Outdoor swimming pool (heated) Tennis Fishing Riding Croquet lawn No children 8yrs Xmas V meals Coffee am Tea pm No smoking in restaurant Last d 8.30pm
ROOMS: (incl. bkfst) s fr £35; d £50-£60 *
OFF-PEAK: (incl. bkfst) s fr £30; d £50-£60
MEALS: Sunday Lunch £3.50-£12.50&alc Dinner £19.50-£22.50*
CONF: Thtr 50 Class 50 Board 20 Del from £65
CARDS:

WILMSLOW Cheshire Map 07 SJ88

See also Manchester Airport

★★★★64% **Mottram Hall**
Wilmslow Rd, Prestbury SK10 4QT ☎ 01625 828135
FAX 01625 829284
DE VERE HOTELS
An elegant extended Georgian house stands in 270 acres of parkland and gardens near the pretty Cheshire village of Prestbury, convenient for Manchester Airport and the motorway system. Bedrooms are attractively decorated and well equipped; some rooms are compact, but there are three luxury suites and eight rooms with four-poster beds. Public rooms include the Oak Restaurant, a cocktail bar and extensive function/meeting facilities. There is also a golf course and one of the best leisure complexes in the north of England.
132 en suite (bth/shr) (6 fmly) No smoking in 26 bedrooms CTV in all bedrooms STV Lift Night porter 400P Indoor swimming pool (heated) Golf 18 Tennis (hard) Squash Snooker Sauna Solarium Gym Croquet lawn Putting green Jacuzzi/spa Wkly live entertainment Xmas English & French Cuisine V meals Coffee am Tea pm No smoking area in restaurant Last d 9.45pm
ROOMS: (incl. bkfst) s fr £115; d fr £150 * **LB**
MEALS: Lunch £17-£19 Dinner £24-£30*
CONF: Thtr 275 Class 140 Board 60 Del £150
CARDS:

★★★72% **Stanneylands**
Stanneylands Rd SK9 4EY (leave M56 at junct 5 follow signs to Styal follow B5166 and then B5358, hotel signposted on right hand side)
☎ 01625 525225 FAX 01625 537282
Standing in attractive grounds with fine specimen trees and a small lake, this privately owned hotel offers delightful accommodation. Bedrooms vary in size, but all are attractively decorated with pretty chintz fabrics and thoughtfully equipped with extras such as mineral water and magazines. Cosy public areas feature fine wood panelling and real fires, and during the evening a harpist plays in one of the dining rooms. An interesting range of traditional and modern British dishes is offered from the good value à la carte and daily changing menus. A recent lunch inspection began with a superbly flavoured salmon and mussel sausage served with a small fricassee of sweet leeks. First courses may also include more robust dishes such as an oxtail broth with roast black pudding and flageolet beans. Accurately cooked and deliciously fresh grilled sea bass was a good choice for main course and, to finish, a 'tarte tatin' made with sweet, ripe plums.
32 en suite (bth/shr) CTV in all bedrooms STV No dogs (ex guide dogs) Night porter 80P Wkly live entertainment English &

Continental Cuisine V meals Coffee am Tea pm Last d 10pm
ROOMS: s £45-£85; d £70-£110 **LB**
MEALS: Lunch £11.50-£14.50&alc High tea fr £9.50 Dinner fr £37.50&alc*
CONF: Thtr 100 Class 50 Board 40 Del from £130
CARDS:
See advertisement under MANCHESTER AIRPORT

WIMBORNE MINSTER Dorset Map 04 SZ09

★★★60% **The King's Head**

The Square BH21 1JA (off A31 follow Wimborne town centre signs, car park at rear of hotel on one way system) ☎ 01202 880101 FAX 01202 881667
Located in the square of this attractive county town, the hotel is staffed by a friendly team who contribute to a warm atmosphere. Bedrooms are well equipped and like the public rooms whilst cosy, are now in need of some redecoration. A table d'hÙte and small carte are offered in the formal restaurant, and bar meals are served in the rustic bar.
27 en suite (bth/shr) (1 fmly) No smoking in 8 bedrooms CTV in all bedrooms Lift 25P Xmas V meals Coffee am Tea pm No smoking in restaurant Last d 9pm
ROOMS: s £50-£60; d £60-£80 **LB**
OFF-PEAK: (incl. bkfst) s £35-£60; d £60-£80
MEALS: Sunday Lunch £10.95-£11.95 Dinner £8.95-£13.95&alc
CONF: Thtr 40 Class 30 Board 30 Del from £60
CARDS:

RED STAR HOTEL

★★ **Beechleas**
17 Poole Rd BH21 1QA (on A349) ☎ 01202 841684
FAX 01202 849344
Closed 25 Dec-12 Jan
This handsome Grade II listed Georgian house is situated on the edge of the town and is personally run by Mrs Josephine McQuillan. The bedrooms are all comfortably furnished and individually decorated with attractive co-ordinated fabrics. There is a cosy lounge with a log fire. The conservatory restaurant is a relaxing area in which to enjoy chef Paulina Humphreys' original and carefully prepared dishes. Making full use of local ingredients and herbs from the garden, the meals have a refreshing simplicity. The wine list is carefully chosen and favourably priced with a good choice at each end of the scale, including two wines at specially reduced prices.
5 en suite (bth/shr) 4 annexe en suite (bth/shr) No smoking in all bedrooms CTV in all bedrooms No dogs (ex guide dogs) 9P No coaches Last d 9.30pm
ROOMS: (incl. bkfst) s £60-£80; d £75-£95 * **LB**
CARDS:

★★61% **Coach House Inn**

579 Winborne Rd East, Tricketts Cross BH22 9NW
☎ 01202 861222 FAX 01202 894130
(For full entry see Ferndown)

WINCANTON Somerset Map 03 ST72

★★62% **Holbrook House**
Holbrook BA9 8BS (from A303 at Wincanton, turn left on A371 towards Castle Cary and Shepton Mallet) ☎ 01963 32377
FAX 01963 32681
This charming, if somewhat old-fashioned, country house is set in pretty grounds with mature trees and clipped box hedges. Mrs Taylor provides warm hospitality and is an untiring host. The comfortable lounges have log fires and deep armchairs, while the candlelit dining room offers a short carte of popular dishes.
20 rms (8 bth 8 shr) (2 fmly) CTV in all bedrooms 44P Outdoor swimming pool (heated) Tennis (hard & grass) Squash Croquet lawn Table tennis Xmas European Cuisine V meals Coffee am Last d 9pm
ROOMS: (incl. bkfst) s fr £50; d fr £80 **LB**
MEALS: Lunch £13.50-£14.50&alc Dinner £18-£45alc*
CONF: Thtr 40 Board 20 Del from £70
CARDS:

WINCHESTER Hampshire Map 04 SU42

★★★★78% **Lainston House**
Sparsholt SO21 2LT (3m NW off B3049 towards Stockbridge) ☎ 01962 863588 FAX 01962 776672
Set in 70 acres of beautifully maintained gardens and grounds, this fine William and Mary house retains all its graceful 17th-century style and is now a charming country house hotel. The two dining rooms benefit from a spectacular view and have recently both been upgraded. Chef Friedrich Litty and his team continue to offer interesting dishes from a well balanced carte. Bedrooms vary in size, each individually furnished and decorated to a high standard and well equipped. The public areas reflect the elegance and charm of the period and are tastefully furnished, retaining original features.
38 en suite (bth/shr) (1 fmly) CTV in all bedrooms STV Night porter 150P No coaches Fishing Croquet lawn Putting green Archery Clay pigeon shooting Wkly live entertainment Xmas English & French Cuisine V meals Coffee am Tea pm Last d 10pm
ROOMS: s £105; d £135-£245 * **LB**
MEALS: Lunch fr £19.50 Dinner fr £36&alc*
CONF: Thtr 80 Class 50 Board 40 Del from £170
CARDS:
See advertisement on page 669

★★★★66% **The Wessex**

FORTE Heritage

Paternoster Row SO23 9LQ ☎ 01962 861611
FAX 01962 841503
This large modern hotel offers a wide range of services and amenities, designed with both the leisure and the business traveller in mind. Bedrooms are smart, comfortable and well equipped.
94 en suite (bth/shr) No smoking in 61 bedrooms CTV in all bedrooms STV Lift Night porter 60P Wkly live entertainment Xmas International Cuisine V meals Coffee am Tea pm No smoking area in restaurant Last d 9.30pm
ROOMS: d £79-£89 * **LB**
OFF-PEAK: d fr £59.50
MEALS: Lunch £14.75-£15.50 Dinner £19.95*
CONF: Thtr 100 Class 60 Board 60 Del £120
CARDS:

★★★ 70% ***Royal***
Saint Peter St SO23 8BS ☎ 01962 840840
FAX 01962 841582
This popular city centre hotel is tucked away in a quiet street, and the rooms in the modern wing are spacious and well equipped, overlooking a pretty walled garden. Rooms in the main house vary more in size and have been decorated to retain their original character. An interesting menu of carefully prepared dishes is offered in the air-conditioned conservatory restaurant, and during the summer months there is a daily barbecue lunch in the garden. The lounges are comfortable and elegantly furnished and there is a popular small bar. A new self-contained conference suite is available, with its own parking and several conference rooms.
75 en suite (bth/shr) (1 fmly) No smoking in 6 bedrooms CTV in all bedrooms STV Night porter 59P European Cuisine V meals Coffee am Tea pm Last d 9.30pm
CARDS:

See advertisement on opposite page

★★★64% **Marwell**
Thompson Ln, Colden Common, Marwell SO21 1JY (on B2177 opposite Marwell Zoological Park)
☎ 01962 777681 FAX 01962 777625
RS Sat
This modern hotel is set in the grounds of Marwell Zoological Park. The spacious and well equipped bedrooms are located in three large chalets which are joined to the main building by long glass-sided corridors, and they open out to the woods. Breakfast and dinner are served in La Bambouserie Restaurant which is decorated in colonial style, and a good snack menu is available either in the lounge or bedrooms. The proximity of the zoo is an added interest.
68 en suite (bth/shr) (35 fmly) No smoking in 14 bedrooms CTV in all bedrooms STV No dogs (ex guide dogs) Night porter 85P Indoor swimming pool (heated) Sauna Solarium Gym Pool table Jacuzzi/spa Xmas English & Continental Cuisine V meals Coffee am Tea pm No smoking in restaurant Last d 9.30pm
ROOMS: (incl. bkfst) s fr £80; d fr £90 * **LB**
MEALS: Lunch £10 Dinner fr £15.50*
CONF: Thtr 160 Class 60 Board 60 Del from £85
CARDS:

★★★64% **Winchester Moat House**
Worthy Ln SO23 7AB
☎ 01962 709988 FAX 01962 840862
Situated in a residential area a mile from the city centre, this modern hotel features an attractive tropical atrium housing a health and fitness centre. Bedrooms are a comfortable size and contemporary in style although some are now beginning to show their age. Staff are generally cheerful, friendly and helpful.
72 en suite (bth/shr) (4 fmly) No smoking in 27 bedrooms CTV in all bedrooms Night porter 72P Indoor swimming pool (heated) Sauna Solarium Gym Jacuzzi/spa Steam room Xmas English & French Cuisine V meals Coffee am Tea pm No smoking in restaurant Last d 9.15pm
ROOMS: s £78; d £95 * **LB**
OFF-PEAK: (incl. bkfst) s £38; d £76
MEALS: Lunch £5.95-£13.50&alc Dinner fr £13.50&alc*
CONF: Thtr 200 Class 100 Board 70 Del from £85
CARDS:

★★58% **Harestock Lodge**
Harestock Rd SO22 6NX
☎ 01962 881870 & 880038 FAX 01962 886959
This peaceful Victorian property, already partly restored and upgraded to a good standard, is pleasantly located to the north of the city close to the A34, A303 and M3 road networks. Until the refurbishment is complete, discerning guests should ask for recently upgraded bedrooms. Service is provided by pleasant staff and food is home-cooked and tasty.
18 rms (14 bth/shr) (3 fmly) CTV in all bedrooms 30P Outdoor swimming pool European Cuisine V meals Coffee am Tea pm No smoking area in restaurant Last d 8.45pm
ROOMS: (incl. bkfst) s £35-£45; d £46-£58 **LB**
MEALS: Lunch fr £9.25&alc High tea fr £5 Dinner fr £9.25&alc*
CONF: Thtr 60 Class 30 Board 30 Del from £60
CARDS:

★★54% ***Chantry Mead***
Bereweeke Rd SO22 6AJ ☎ 01962 844166 FAX 01962 852767
Situated just off the Andover road on the northerly city limits. A pleasant looking house, much extended in a quiet leafy area offering some good accommodation in a rather informal atmosphere which suits the commercial worker/traveller.
16 rms (14 bth/shr) (2 fmly) No smoking in 3 bedrooms CTV in all bedrooms STV 20P V meals Coffee am Tea pm Last d 9.30pm
CARDS:

TOWN HOUSE HOTEL

Hotel du Vin & Bistro
14 Southgate St SO23 9EF ☎ 01962 841414 FAX 01962 842458
Robin Hutson's and Gérard Basset's centrally located town house now has a loyal following and offers a relaxed yet lively atmosphere in elegant but informal surroundings. The bedrooms, each sponsored by a different wine house, and so offering considerable originality of style, are very comfortable, with top quality beds and Egyptian linen; all are equipped with mini bar, satellite TV and power shower. The bistro serves imaginative and enjoyable food from a daily changing carte which offers plenty of choice. Gérard Basset's wine list has been selected by a master hand and offers much of interest.
19 en suite (bth/shr) CTV in all bedrooms STV No dogs (ex guide dogs) Night porter 60P No coaches Xmas British & Mediterranean Cuisine V meals Last d 9.30pm
ROOMS: d £75-£99
MEALS: Lunch fr £19.50&alc Dinner £24-£30alc
CONF: Thtr 40 Class 30 Board 25 Del from £129
CARDS:

WINDERMERE Cumbria Map 07 SD49

★★★81% **Gilpin Lodge Country House Hotel & Restaurant**
Crook Rd LA23 3NE
☎ 015394 88818 FAX 015394 88058
Set amid 20 acres of woodlands, moors and delightful country gardens against the backdrop of the lakeland fells Gilpin Lodge exudes quality, comfort and tranquillity. Elegant but cosy this turn of the century house has been tastefully modernised and extended seamlessly and is furnished with a plethora of antiques, flowers, picture lined walls and

W

contd.

real fires on colder days throughout the year. Christine and John Cunliffe are superb hosts both welcoming and friendly in an unpretentious manner but wholly professional. Of the cuisine, the afternoon teas and breakfast are sumptuous for dinner there is plenty of choice both with plainer dishes and those more elaborately sauced. Chef Christopher Davies uses a lot of different and contrasting ingredients which work well together creating some good marriages. A starter of Pigeon, resembling a mini main course, is sliced and served atop a thyme jus with a sausage studded with black pudding and buttery mashed potatoes. A main course of locally and kindly reared calves liver comes with locally cured bacon and onion marmalade. Wines are very good and really varied, sensibly priced with notable choices of wines by the glass and half bottles.

13 en suite (bth/shr) (4 fmly) CTV in all bedrooms No dogs (ex guide dogs) 30P No coaches Croquet lawn Free membership of local Leisure Club No children 7yrs Xmas English & French Cuisine V meals Coffee am Tea pm No smoking in restaurant Last d 8.45pm
ROOMS: (incl. bkfst) s £70-£85; d £90-£140 **LB**
OFF-PEAK: (incl. bkfst) s £65-£70; d £80-£100
MEALS: Lunch £14.50&alc Dinner £27.50
CONF: Thtr 20 Class 16 Board 12 Del from £85
CARDS:

See advertisement on opposite page

★★★ 76% Linthwaite
Crook Rd LA23 3JA ☎ 015394 88600
FAX 015394 88601
(Rosettes awarded for dinner only)
Formerly an Edwardian gentleman's residence, Linthwaite House enjoys a delightful situation, set in fine gardens and grounds high above the lake. Now a small superior hotel, its friendly staff offer service of a high calibre, but the atmosphere is relaxing and unpretentious. Public areas feature two lounges, a conservatory and an attractive restaurant, all of which combine period charm with an old colonial style, and are adorned with lots of memorabilia. Bedrooms are very well equipped and predominantly modern, but with contrasting decor, most opting for a bright uniform style, whilst others are strikingly bold. Food is imaginative and well presented and whilst dinner is the highlight, the interesting lunch menu offering an abundant choice and served in the conservatory, is also well worth considering.
18 en suite (bth/shr) No smoking in 12 bedrooms CTV in all bedrooms STV No dogs (ex guide dogs) 30P No coaches Fishing Croquet lawn Putting green Free use of nearby Leisure Spa Xmas V meals Coffee am Tea pm Last d 8.45pm
ROOMS: (incl. bkfst) s £100-£120; d £120-£200 * **LB**
MEALS: Sunday Lunch fr £13.95 Dinner fr £29.50&alc*
CARDS:

★★★ 71% Wild Boar
Crook LA23 3NF (2.5m S of Windermere on B5284 Crook road) ☎ 015394 45225 FAX 015394 42498
Best Western
Formerly a roadside inn, this long established hotel lies in the peaceful Winster Valley just ten minutes' drive from Windermere. Smart but friendly staff provide attentive service and one can relax by log fires in season. The hotel has been extended over the years and the thoughtfully equipped bedrooms come in a variety of sizes and styles. The dinner menu offers an impressive range of dishes backed by quality British cooking which combines both classical and contemporary styles.
36 en suite (bth/shr) (3 fmly) No smoking in 6 bedrooms CTV in all bedrooms STV 60P Xmas English & French Cuisine V meals Coffee am Tea pm No smoking in restaurant Last d 9.15pm
ROOMS: (incl. bkfst) s £52-£82; d £104-£134 **LB**
MEALS: Lunch £10.45-£12.95&alc Dinner £19.95-£25.50&alc
CONF: Thtr 40 Class 20 Board 26 Del from £65.80
CARDS:

See advertisement on opposite page

★★★ 70% Langdale Chase
LA23 1LW (2m S of Ambleside)
☎ 015394 32201 FAX 015394 32604
This stately late-Victorian country mansion graces and idyllic setting amidst colourful terraced gardens and grounds sweeping down to the shores of Lake Windermere. Delightful views are enjoyed from its public rooms - particular the restaurant - and most of the bedrooms. Inside there are carved fireplaces, oak panelling and a galleried staircase. Upgrading is taking place within the framework of these magnificent features. Many of the bedrooms have been enlarged and there some new ones. Five rooms are still contained in a converted cottage in the grounds, whilst another boasts a unique location, romantically situated over the boathouse on the lake. Cooking is imaginative and service friendly.
32 en suite (bth/shr) (1 fmly) CTV in all bedrooms Night porter 50P No coaches Tennis (grass) Fishing Croquet lawn Putting green Sailing boats Xmas English & French Cuisine V meals Coffee am Tea pm No smoking in restaurant Last d 8.45pm
ROOMS: (incl. bkfst) s £45; d £90-£140 * **LB**
OFF-PEAK: (incl. bkfst) s £40; d £80-£130
MEALS: Lunch £14.50-£15 Dinner £25&alc*
CONF: Thtr 25 Class 16 Board 20 Del from £90
CARDS: 

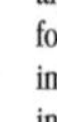

★★★68% **Burn How Garden House Hotel**
Back Belsfield Rd, Bowness LA23 3HH (200mtrs S of Bowness Bay) ☎ 015394 46226 FAX 015394 47000
The hotel lies secluded in beautiful gardens within walking distance of the lakeside and the town's lively shopping areas. Having evolved from 2 private residences, it is unusual in that all the bedrooms are separate to the main reception rooms. Some bedrooms are in the adjacent house and other chalet-style rooms with their own patios or balconies are located in the gardens. All are extremely spacious and furnished with comfort in mind.
The combined lounge and bar opens into the restaurant and has great views.
26 annexe en suite (bth/shr) (10 fmly) CTV in all bedrooms No dogs (ex guide dogs) 30P No coaches Water sports Xmas English & French Cuisine V meals Coffee am No smoking in restaurant Last d 8.30pm
ROOMS: (incl. bkfst) s £38-£65; d £76-£88 * **LB**
OFF-PEAK: (incl. bkfst) s £25-£38; d £50-£70
MEALS: Bar Lunch £2-£7alc Dinner £12.50-£18.50&alc
CARDS:

See advertisement on page 673

★★★68% **Burnside**
Kendal Road, Bowness LA23 3EP ☎ 015394 42211
FAX 015394 43824
A sprawling leisure, self catering and hotel complex set within lovely gardens overlooking the lake. At its heart is a Victorian House vastly extended to include a variety of comfortably furnished lounges, restaurants and some really good modern well equipped bedrooms. The hotel also attracts the larger conference and leisure group bookings.
57 en suite (bth/shr) (15 fmly) No smoking in 18 bedrooms CTV in all bedrooms STV Lift 100P Indoor swimming pool (heated) Squash Snooker Sauna Solarium Gym Jacuzzi/spa Steam room Badminton Beauty salon Wkly live entertainment Xmas V meals Coffee am Tea pm No smoking in restaurant Last d 9.45pm
ROOMS: (incl. bkfst) s fr £66; d £102-£128 * **LB**
OFF-PEAK: (incl. bkfst) s fr £50; d £70-£96
MEALS: Sunday Lunch fr £9.50 High tea fr £6 Dinner fr £18&alc*
CONF: Thtr 100 Class 50 Board 38 Del from £75
CARDS:

★★★67% ***Hillthwaite House***
Thornbarrow Rd LA23 2DF ☎ 015394 43636
FAX 015394 88660
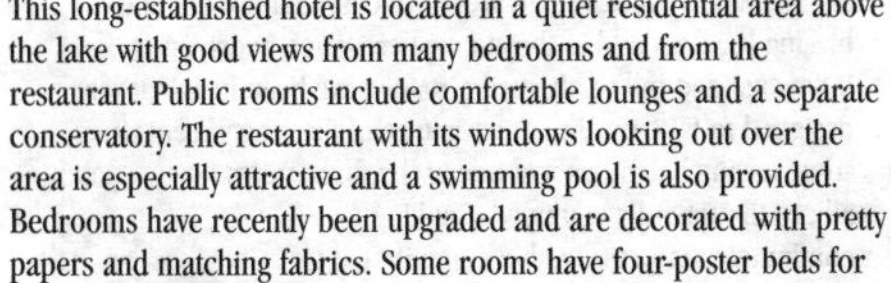
This long-established hotel is located in a quiet residential area above the lake with good views from many bedrooms and from the restaurant. Public rooms include comfortable lounges and a separate conservatory. The restaurant with its windows looking out over the area is especially attractive and a swimming pool is also provided. Bedrooms have recently been upgraded and are decorated with pretty papers and matching fabrics. Some rooms have four-poster beds for

contd.

that special occasion and some are suitable for families. Good kitchen skills are employed and a daily-changing four-course menu is on offer.
30 en suite (bth/shr) (5 fmly) CTV in all bedrooms STV 40P No coaches Indoor swimming pool (heated) Sauna English & French Cuisine V meals Coffee am Tea pm Last d 9.30pm
CARDS:

★★★ 66% **Beech Hill**

CONSORT HOTELS

Newby Bridge Rd, Cartmel Fell LA23 3LR
☎ 015394 42137 FAX 015394 43745
This large hotel stands on the lakeside to the south of Bowness and has a series of terraced extensions leading down to Lake Windermere. There are magnificent views of the lake and distant peaks from the public rooms and also from several bedrooms. Public rooms are very comfortable whilst the bedrooms, which are being continually upgraded, have been well equipped and are generally very spacious. Chef David Swade's dinner is the highlight of any visit to the Beech Hill and offers a daily-changing menu together with the newly added carte.
52 en suite (bth/shr) (3 fmly) CTV in all bedrooms 70P Indoor swimming pool (heated) Fishing Sauna Solarium Wkly live entertainment Xmas English & French Cuisine V meals Coffee am Tea pm No smoking in restaurant Last d 9.30pm
ROOMS: (incl. bkfst) s £49-£54; d £98-£108 * **LB**
MEALS: Lunch £12.95 Dinner £25-£28&alc
CONF: Thtr 120 Class 60 Board 40 Del from £85
CARDS:

★★★ 66% ***Craig Manor***

Lake Rd LA23 3AR ☎ 015394 88877
Built as a gentleman's residence early in the Victorian era, Craig Manor has recently been sympathetically extended and modernised to provide accommodation in well equipped pine-furnished bedrooms, one of which contains a four-poster bed. Rooms at the rear of the hotel - including the spacious restaurant and comfortable lounges - have fine views extending to Lake Windermere and the Langdale Pikes. Ample car parking space is available.
16 en suite (bth/shr)

★★★ 66% **The Old England**

FORTE Heritage

Church St, Bowness LA23 3DF (on A592, behind St Martins church) ☎ 015394 42444
FAX 015394 43432
Situated close to Bowness Pier with gardens running down to the lake and an open air swimming pool on the terrace, this elegant hotel has the atmosphere of a Georgian country house and provides traditional service and comfort in its spacious lounges and public rooms. Bedrooms although modernised have been tastefully furnished and many have fine views over the lake. Some are in a modern wing and are more compact than those situated in the older part of the hotel. The restaurant, in which Head Chef Andrew Hipwell's cooking can be highly recommended is situated at a lower level, but most tables have views over the gardens and lake. The main car park is about 200 yards from the hotel, but valet parking is available on request.
78 en suite (bth/shr) (8 fmly) No smoking in 26 bedrooms CTV in all bedrooms Lift Night porter 82P Outdoor swimming pool (heated) Snooker Golf driving net Xmas V meals Coffee am Tea pm No smoking in restaurant Last d 9.30pm
ROOMS: s £65-£90; d £110-£135 * **LB**
MEALS: Lunch £11.95-£13.95 Dinner £19.95-£21.95&alc*
CONF: Thtr 140 Class 50 Board 42 Del from £110
CARDS:

★★★ 65% **Low Wood**

Best Western

LA23 1LP (3m N A591) ☎ 015394 33338
FAX 015394 34072
An extensive leisure complex which includes a health, beauty and fitness club, and a choice of bars and restaurants, are features of this conference and leisure hotel. With only the main road between it and gardens leading down to the shores of Lake Windermere, it enjoys fine views across the lake to the distant fells.
99 en suite (bth/shr) (10 fmly) No smoking in 9 bedrooms CTV in all bedrooms STV Lift Night porter 200P Indoor swimming pool (heated) Fishing Squash Snooker Sauna Solarium Gym Pool table Croquet lawn Putting green Jacuzzi/spa Water skiing Sub aqua diving Windsurfing Wkly live entertainment Xmas V meals Coffee am Tea pm No smoking in restaurant Last d 9.30pm
ROOMS: (incl. bkfst) s £62-£87; d fr £124 * **LB**
MEALS: Lunch £10-£12.50 High tea £3-£6.50 Dinner £19.50*
CONF: Thtr 340 Class 180 Board 50
CARDS:

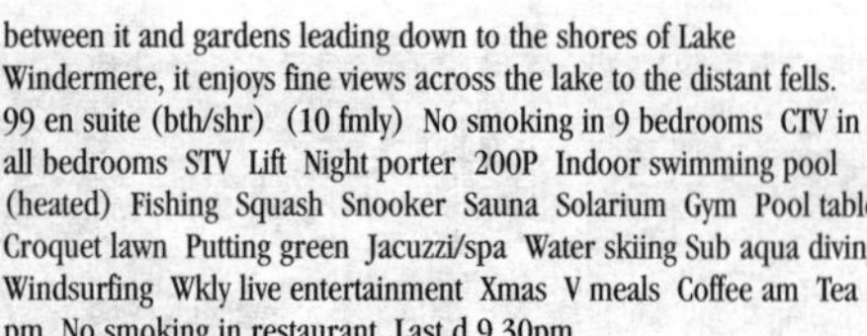

★★★ 63% **The Belsfield**

REGAL
A Collection of Individual Hotels

Kendal Rd, Bowness LA23 3EL
☎ 015394 42448 FAX 015394 46397
In an elevated position overlooking Lake Windermere, this Victorian Hotel has charming and comfortable public areas, however they are beginning to look jaded. Doors from the bar open onto a sunny veranda and there are lovely gardens and an enclosed swimming pool with sliding roof. Bedrooms have recently been upgraded and are now of a sound standard throughout.
64 en suite (bth/shr) (6 fmly) No smoking in 6 bedrooms CTV in all bedrooms Lift Night porter 64P Indoor swimming pool (heated) Snooker Sauna Solarium Putting green Mini golf Wkly live entertainment Xmas V meals Coffee am Tea pm Last d 9.30pm
ROOMS: s £60-£65; d £90-£100 * **LB**
MEALS: Lunch £15-£19 Dinner £15-£19
CONF: Thtr 130 Class 60 Board 50 Del from £75
CARDS:

RED STAR HOTEL

★★ **Holbeck Ghyll Country House**

Holbeck Ln LA23 1LU (3m N off A591)
☎ 015394 32375 FAX 015394 34743
Built as a hunting lodge in the 19th-century, this charming country house lies in gently sloping gardens and grounds offering stunning views of Lake Windermere and the Langdale Fells. David and Patricia Nicholson and their delightful staff have created a first-class hotel where warmth and hospitality are second to none. Public areas are cosy and inviting and blazing log fires add to the atmosphere. Each bedroom is individual and full of character; many have been imaginatively designed to take maximum advantage of the magnificent views, some having balconies and one of the three suites its own patio; all are thoughtfully equipped. Cooking continues to impress, with a commitment to the use of quality ingredients, with even the

W

breads being home-made.
14 en suite (bth/shr) (1 fmly) CTV in all bedrooms STV 22P Tennis (hard) Sauna Gym Croquet lawn Putting green Beautician Steam room Xmas English & French Cuisine V meals Coffee am Tea pm No smoking in restaurant Last d 8.45pm
ROOMS: (incl. bkfst & dinner) s £77.50-£140; d £140-£240 LB
OFF-PEAK: (incl. bkfst & dinner) s £65-£140; d £130-£170
MEALS: Lunch £7.50-£17.50alc Dinner £27.50-£30
CONF: Thtr 45 Class 25 Board 25 Del from £77.50
CARDS:

RED STAR HOTEL

 **Miller Howe**
Rayrigg Rd LA23 1EY (on A592 between Bowness & Windermere) ☎ 015394 42536 FAX 015394 45664
Closed 4 Dec-mid Feb
Miller Howe is perhaps one of the most celebrated Lakeside Country House hotels. Set amidst wooded hillside with gardens and pasture stretching to the water's edge, the views to the fells beyond, from many of the rooms, are stunning. It remains John Tovey's home and is tended with loving care. Whilst the majority of bedrooms are spacious and furnished with an inimitable panache all share similar extra facilities. The set-menu is served at eight pm; it is carefully orchestrated and operates banquet-style with well practised efficiency and just a touch of theatre. The menu itself reads like a journey around England's market gardens and hedgerows; the ingredients are too numerous to mention though diners are reported to enjoy the challenge of identification. Canapés are served, followed by an autumn menu of sausage roll dipped in a rich caramelised onion Madeira jus; fillet of brill; breast of chicken stuffed with stilton and resting on an apple purée gravy; various pungent and tangy vegetables and a choice of puddings.
12 en suite (bth/shr) CTV in all bedrooms 60P No coaches No children 8yrs V meals Coffee am Tea pm No smoking in restaurant Last d 7.30pm
ROOMS: (incl. bkfst & dinner) s £95-£180; d £140-£250 * LB
MEALS: Lunch fr £12.50 Dinner fr £30*
CARDS:

★★ 77% **Lindeth Fell**
Lyth Valley Rd, Bowness LA23 3JP (1m S on A5074)
☎ 015394 43286 & 44287 FAX 015394 47455
Closed mid Nov-mid Mar

Lindeth Fell Hotel is perched high above the town and has superb views over the lake from the front facing reception rooms and bedrooms. It is an Edwardian residence set amidst glorious gardens -a riot of colour in spring and summer, when teas are served on the terrace. Pat and Diana Kennedy and their small staff run the hotel with a keen devotion to the highest standards of courtesy and care. Bedrooms are all most comfortable, furnished with traditional pieces, some gracious, some cosy. The five course dinners offer a straightforward choice of two dishes at each course and exemplify the best of country cooking.
15 en suite (bth/shr) (2 fmly) CTV in all bedrooms No dogs 20P No coaches Tennis (grass) Fishing Croquet lawn Putting green No children 7yrs Coffee am Tea pm No smoking in restaurant Last d 8.30pm
ROOMS: (incl. bkfst & dinner) s £55-£70; d £110-£122 *
MEALS: Sunday Lunch fr £12 Dinner fr £21*
CARDS:

★★ 76% **Fayrer Garden House**
Lyth Valley Rd, Bowness on Windermere LA23 3JP (on A5074) ☎ 015394 88195 FAX 015394 45986
A turn-of-the-century country residence which nestles amongst five acres of beautifully tended gardens high above the lake and away from the hubbub of Bowness. Public areas comprise an elegant panelled hall which leads into a cosy sitting room and a non-smoking drawing room and restaurant, each of which enjoy lake views. The bedrooms are carefully furnished with a mix of the traditional and the contemporary which blend attractively.
The atmosphere is friendly, warm and relaxed and the cuisine is good modern English cooking with its roots in the classical.

contd.

15 en suite (bth/shr) (3 fmly) CTV in all bedrooms 25P No coaches Fishing Free membership of leisure club Xmas V meals Coffee am Tea pm No smoking in restaurant Last d 8.30pm
ROOMS: (incl. bkfst & dinner) s £47.50-£85; d £90-£150 * **LB**
OFF-PEAK: (incl. bkfst & dinner) s £39.50-£75; d £77-£140
MEALS: Bar Lunch fr £3.95alc Dinner £16.95-£19.95&alc
CONF: Thtr 40 Board 30 Del from £75
CARDS:

See advertisement on opposite page

★★ 75% *Quarry Garth Country House Hotel & Restaurant*
Troutbeck Bridge LA23 1LF (on A591)
☎ 015394 88282 FAX 015394 46584
A gracious country house with leaded mullion windows lies secluded in eight acres of beautiful gardens and woodland, its terrace overlooking lawns and a tumbling brook. Combined with this idyllic setting is the friendly and attentive service that helps to create an atmosphere of comfort and relaxation. Bedrooms vary between the spacious master rooms or smaller but appealing cottage-style rooms. There are a delightful lounge with plenty of reading material and two cosy dining rooms where a high standard of cooking is offered. A meal from the carefully chosen four-course dinner menu might start with a terrine of chicken livers studded with apricot and pistachio nuts, served with a port and orange sauce and toasted olive bread. Pan-fried fillet of beef could follow, served on a celeriac rosti with red onion marmalade and a Madeira jus, and desserts include individual apple tart or perhaps chocolate truffle torte.
11 en suite (bth/shr) (2 fmly) CTV in all bedrooms 35P No coaches English & Continental Cuisine V meals Coffee am Tea pm Last d 9pm
CARDS:

★★ 74% Cedar Manor Hotel & Restaurant
Ambleside Rd LA23 1AX (0.25m N on A591 by St Marys Church)
☎ 015394 43192 FAX 015394 45970
This attractive small hotel, built in 1860, sits within its own gardens which are dominated by an Indian Cedar tree, said to be over 200 years old. Inside the house some of the original architectural features have been retained in the public rooms, though bedrooms, some of which are contained in a new wing, or a pretty little cottage to the back, are bright and well equipped. The food created by Lynne Hadley and her team offers a good choice from a table d'hÙte menu, with supplementary dishes being available at a small additional charge. The staff are a real strength and nothing seems to be too much trouble for them.
10 en suite (bth/shr) 2 annexe en suite (bth/shr) (4 fmly) CTV in all bedrooms 15P No coaches Xmas English, French & Italian Cuisine V meals Coffee am Tea pm No smoking in restaurant
ROOMS: (incl. bkfst & dinner) s £29.50-£45; d £59-£70 * **LB**
MEALS: Bar Lunch £3.75-£9.60*
CARDS:

See advertisement on opposite page

★★ 70% Crag Brow Cottage
Helm Rd, Bowness on Windermere LA23 3BU
☎ 015394 44080 FAX 015394 46003
Originally a country residence, Crag Brow lies in its own gardens, shielded from the town by a rocky knoll. Though it is only a stone's throw from the bustling main street, it feels far from the madding crowd. The hotel is attractively furnished throughout and one can relax in either the little bar with its welcoming coal fire in season, or in the lounge. Pride of place, however, must go to the beautiful restaurant with its Italian styling, where three separate dinner menus offer a choice of dishes at different prices. The stylish bedrooms, including a good family room, are not large, but they are extremely well equipped to include clock/radio, hairdryer, trouser press and fruit.
11 en suite (bth/shr) (3 fmly) CTV in all bedrooms STV No dogs (ex guide dogs) 30P Free membership to leisure club Xmas English, French & Italian Cuisine V meals Coffee am Tea pm No smoking in restaurant Last d 8.45pm
ROOMS: (incl. bkfst & dinner) s fr £60; d £100-£110 * **LB**
OFF-PEAK: (incl. bkfst & dinner) s £50; d £80-£100
MEALS: Lunch £7.50-£9.95 Dinner £12.95-£19.95
CARDS:

★★ 70% Glenburn
New Rd LA23 2EE ☎ 015934 42649 FAX 015394 88998
Situated midway between Windermere and Bowness, this family-run hotel offers attractive surroundings. The stylish bedrooms come in a variety of sizes, all being well equipped and including an extensive collection of videos. Public areas are bright and cheery and dinners start conveniently early at 6.30pm.
16 en suite (bth/shr) (4 fmly) CTV in all bedrooms No dogs (ex guide dogs) 17P No coaches No children 5yrs Xmas V meals Coffee am Tea pm Last d 8pm
ROOMS: (incl. bkfst) d £50-£90 * **LB**
MEALS: Dinner £15.50-£16.50alc*
CARDS:

★★ 67% Hideaway
Phoenix Way LA23 1DB ☎ 015394 43070
Closed 3-31 Jan
An attractive Lakeland stone house, the Hideaway Hotel stands in a quiet backwater of Windermere. It is well furnished throughout and offers warm, friendly service.
10 en suite (bth/shr) 5 annexe en suite (bth/shr) (3 fmly) CTV in all bedrooms 16P No coaches Xmas English & Continental Cuisine V meals Coffee am Tea pm No smoking in restaurant Last d 8pm
ROOMS: (incl. bkfst & dinner) s £43-£52; d £76-£108 **LB**
OFF-PEAK: (incl. bkfst & dinner) s £38-£42; d £70-£96
MEALS: Bar Lunch £2-£7 Dinner fr £16.50&alc
CARDS:

See advertisement on opposite page

★★ 67% Lindeth Howe Country House
Longtail Hill, Storrs Park LA23 3JF ☎ 015394 45759
FAX 015394 46368
This fine country house lies secluded in six acres of gardens and its

elevated position gives delightful views of Lake Windermere and distant peaks. Its most famous resident Beatrix Potter lived here for 15 years and the walls are adorned with photographs and other mementoes of her stay. Present owners Clive and Eileen Baxter, supported by their staff, offer a friendly and relaxing atmosphere and the hotel's commitment to home-cooked dishes and fresh ingredients is reflected in the daily changing four course dinner menu. Bedrooms are all different and are being steadily upgraded whilst retaining the charm and character of the house.

14 en suite (bth/shr) (3 fmly) No smoking in 2 bedrooms CTV in all bedrooms STV No dogs 25P No coaches Sauna Solarium Use of adjacent leisure club Xmas V meals Coffee am Tea pm No smoking in restaurant Last d 8.30pm

ROOMS: (incl. bkfst) s fr £48.50; d £64-£104 * **LB**

MEALS: Lunch £8.95-£10.95 High tea £6 Dinner £18*

CARDS:

★★67% Ravensworth

Ambleside Rd LA23 1BA (on A591)

☎ 015394 43747 FAX 015394 43903

This friendly Victorian hotel is conveniently situated on the A591 Ambleside Road not far from the village shops. Guests have use of a cosy lounge and a small bar, and enjoyable evening meals are served in the attractive conservatory restaurant. Bedrooms (including family and four-poster rooms) come in a range of sizes; all are equipped with en suites and other modern facilities and some are situated on the ground floor.

12 en suite (bth/shr) 2 annexe en suite (bth/shr) (1 fmly) CTV in all bedrooms STV 17P No coaches Free membership of local Leisure Club Xmas English & French Cuisine V meals Coffee am No smoking in restaurant Last d 8.15pm

ROOMS: (incl. bkfst) s £27.50-£29.50; d £59-£73 * **LB**

contd.

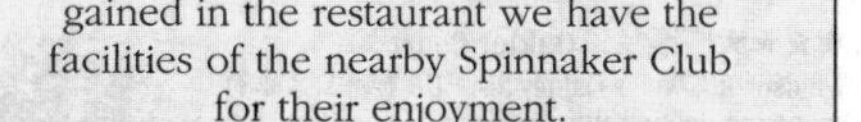

W

OFF-PEAK: (incl. bkfst) s £24.50-£29.50; d £55-£65
MEALS: Dinner £12.95-£15.95
CARDS:

★★64% Applegarth
College Rd LA23 1BU ☎ 015394 43206 FAX 015394 46636
An elegant and individual mansion, built in 1890, is quietly situated within easy reach of all amenities.
16 rms (15 shr) (4 fmly) CTV in all bedrooms 20P No coaches Xmas English & French Cuisine Coffee am Last d 7pm
ROOMS: (incl. bkfst) s £22-£35; d £39-£80 * **LB**
CARDS:

★★63% Cranleigh
Kendal Rd, Bowness on Windermere LA23 3EW (turn left off Lake Road, opposite St Martin's church and continue along Kendal Road for 150mts) ☎ 015394 43293
A relaxing hotel within easy walking distance of town centre. It offers a choice of lounges, an attractive dining room and bedrooms which are split between the main building and a similar one next door. The short dinner menu offers a limited choice, but is modestly priced.
9 en suite (bth/shr) 6 annexe en suite (bth/shr) (3 fmly) CTV in all bedrooms No dogs (ex guide dogs) 17P Free membership of leisure club ch fac V meals Coffee am Tea pm No smoking in restaurant Last d 9pm
ROOMS: (incl. bkfst) s £18-£32; d £36-£64 **LB**
MEALS: Bar Lunch £2-£10 Dinner £9*
CARDS:

★★60% Knoll
Lake Rd, Bowness LA23 2JF (turn off A591 left at Windemere Station) ☎ 01539 443756 FAX 01539 88496
RS Dec-Feb
This late-Victorian house is appealingly old-fashioned and quietly run. It lies just off the main street of Bowness, yet is peacefully secluded in wooded gardens and enjoys fine views of the lake and distant fells.
12 rms (9 bth/shr) (4 fmly) CTV in all bedrooms No dogs 20P Croquet lawn Free membership of local Leisure Club No children 3yrs V meals Coffee am No smoking in restaurant Last d 7.30pm
ROOMS: (incl. bkfst) s £30-£32; d £60-£64 **LB**
MEALS: Dinner £13-£15
CARDS:

★65% Willowsmere
Ambleside Rd LA23 1ES (stay on A591, just past St Marys Church) ☎ 015394 43575 & 44962
RS Dec-Jan
Good all-round standards of comfort are provided at this friendly, family-run hotel. Bedrooms vary in size, but all have their own bathrooms. The lounges are particularly comfortable and guests can enjoy good home cooking in the very attractively decorated dining room.

13 en suite (bth/shr) (7 fmly) CTV in all bedrooms TV in 1 bedroom 20P No coaches English & Austrian Cuisine V meals Coffee am Tea pm No smoking in restaurant Last d 7.30pm
ROOMS: (incl. bkfst) s £25-£27; d £50-£54 * **LB**
OFF-PEAK: (incl. bkfst) s fr £22; d fr £44
MEALS: Bar Lunch £5-£10 Dinner fr £13*
CARDS:

WINDSOR Berkshire Map 04 SU97

★★★★76% Oakley Court
Windsor Rd, Water Oakley SL4 5UR (2m W A308) ☎ 01753 609988 FAX 01628 37011
Oakley Court is a splendid Victorian Gothic mansion situated in extensive grounds which lead down to the Thames where boating can be easily arranged. Only a handful of bedrooms are in the main house, but this should not cause disappointment, as all rooms are spacious, beautifully furnished and most have views of the river. There are two restaurants: the recently re-named Le Boulestin which specialises in modern English and French cuisine with dishes such as a terrine of foie gras and leeks and saltimbocca of red mullet and Boaters Brasserie whith menus that draw inspiration from around the world. Day rooms comprise an elegant drawing room, a clubby bar entertained by a pianist most evenings and a billiards room.
65 en suite (bth/shr) 27 annexe en suite (bth/shr) No smoking in 6 bedrooms CTV in all bedrooms STV No dogs (ex guide dogs) Night porter 120P Golf 9 Fishing Snooker Sauna Solarium Gym Croquet lawn Boating Xmas English & French Cuisine V meals Coffee am Tea pm No smoking area in restaurant Last d 10pm
ROOMS: s £150-£190; d £175-£200 * **LB**
OFF-PEAK: (incl. bkfst) d £120-£180
MEALS: Lunch £22-£23.50 Dinner fr £33*
CONF: Thtr 160 Class 100 Board 48 Del from £205
CARDS:

★★★70% The Castle
High St SL4 1LJ (opposite Guildhall) ☎ 01753 851011 FAX 01753 830244

FORTE Heritage

Situated opposite the Guildhall and in the shadow of Windsor Castle, this popular hotel offers comfortable, well appointed accommodation. Bedrooms vary in size and style from traditional in the original part of the building to modern in a rear extension. Public areas include a choice of eating options, a cocktail bar and small lounge serving afternoon tea.
104 en suite (bth/shr) (40 fmly) No smoking in 32 bedrooms CTV in all bedrooms STV Lift Night porter 156P Xmas English & Continental Cuisine V meals Coffee am Tea pm No smoking in restaurant Last d 10pm
ROOMS: (incl. bkfst) s fr £120; d fr £140 * **LB**
OFF-PEAK: (incl. bkfst) d fr £120
MEALS: Lunch £15.50-£16.50&alc High tea £11.50 Dinner £26.50&alc*
CONF: Thtr 400 Class 250 Board 40 Del from £145
CARDS:

★★72% *Aurora Garden*
14 Bolton Av SL4 3JF ☎ 01753 868686 FAX 01753 831394
This privately run hotel succeeds in creating a naturally friendly setting. It is located in a residential neighbourhood and takes pride in its landscaped water-garden. The restaurant, which overlooks the garden, provides a short choice of interesting and well-prepared dishes. Five new bedrooms have been recently built to a modern and comfortable standard and there are plans to start refurbishing some of the other bedrooms.
15 en suite (bth/shr) (1 fmly) CTV in all bedrooms Night porter 25P English & French Cuisine V meals Coffee am Tea pm Last d 9pm
CARDS:

WINSFORD Somerset Map 03 SS93

★★★72% Royal Oak Inn
Exmoor National Park TA24 7JE (N from Tiverton on A361 for 15m then left to Winsford. First turning left on entering village) ☎ 01643 851455 FAX 01643 851009
Since a disastrous fire in February 1995, the original thatched inn has been totally re-built, sympathetically re-creating its former character. Bedrooms within the inn have been prettily furnished and decorated, using quality soft furnishings. Rooms are also available in a cottage-style court yard. The two bars are each full of character and charm and a new area has been created especially for bar meals. The three comfortable lounges are well furnished and a special feature of the

Royal Oak is the open fires in most of the public rooms. In the restaurant an interesting selection of dishes is offered from a fixed-price menu.

8 en suite (bth/shr) 6 annexe en suite (bth/shr) (1 fmly) CTV in all bedrooms 23P Fishing Hunting Shooting Xmas V meals Coffee am Tea pm Last d 9.30pm
ROOMS: (incl. bkfst & dinner) s £77-£88; d £93.50-£105 **LB**
CARDS:

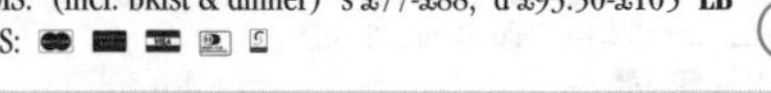

WISBECH Cambridgeshire Map 05 TF40

★★67% **Crown Lodge**

Downham Rd, Outwell PE14 8SE (5m SE, on A1122 close to junct with A1101) ☎ 01945 773391 & 772206 FAX 01945 772668
There is a relaxed and friendly atmosphere at this small, privately run hotel, which continues to offer good value for money. The ground-floor bedrooms are light and inviting, and though they vary in size each is equipped with a range of modern amenities which includes en suite showers or bathrooms. The bistro/bar operation offers a good range of food on bar snack and steak menus supplemented by good-value daily blackboard specials. Guests have the use of a comfortable lounge area and access to a snooker room and squash court. A more recently created function/meeting room is also available.
10 en suite (bth/shr) CTV in all bedrooms 65P Squash Snooker Solarium International Cuisine V meals Coffee am Tea pm No smoking area in restaurant Last d 10pm
ROOMS: (incl. bkfst) s £38.75; d £50 * **LB**
OFF-PEAK: (incl. bkfst) s £35; d £45
MEALS: Lunch £9.45-£17.50&alc Dinner £12.50-£17.50&alc*
CONF: Thtr 70 Class 50 Board 20
CARDS:

★★62% **Rose & Crown Hotel**

Market Place PE13 1DG (in centre of Wisbech, access from A47 & A1101) ☎ 01945 589800 FAX 01945 474610
Spacious public areas have been the first to have benefited from a sympathetic refurbishment programme that will embrace the whole hotel. There is a cosy and popular bar, a coffee shop, a traditional dining room on the first floor overlooking the market square and an attractively laid out ballroom.
20 en suite (bth/shr) (1 fmly) CTV in all bedrooms 17P Pool table International Cuisine V meals Coffee am Tea pm Last d 9.30pm
MEALS: Lunch fr £9.95 Dinner fr £13.50&alc*
CONF: Thtr 120 Class 70 Board 70 Del from £75
CARDS:

WISHAW West Midlands Map 07 SP19

★★★★72% **The Belfry**

B76 9PR (apex of A446 & A4091)
☎ 01675 470301 FAX 01675 470178
Home to the Ryder Cup on three occasions, The Belfry is a haven for golfers and sports enthusiasts, and continues to expand: the latest addition being a dedicated conference centre, new bedrooms and a third golf course. This bustling complex offers a wide variety of bars and restaurants, from the pubby Riley's golf bar to the sophisticated French Restaurant which features both classical dishes and more modern creations. Bedrooms tend to vary in size and style and are housed in various buildings around a central garden with some of the best enjoying views over the golf courses. Conscientious staff are helpful and friendly.
267 en suite (bth/shr) No smoking in 64 bedrooms CTV in all bedrooms STV No dogs (ex guide dogs) Lift Night porter 1500P Indoor swimming pool (heated) Golf 18 Tennis (hard) Squash Snooker Sauna Solarium Gym Pool table Croquet lawn Putting green Jacuzzi/spa Archery Clay pigeon shooting ch fac French Cuisine V meals Coffee am Tea pm Last d 10pm
MEALS: Lunch £16&alc High tea £11.50&alc Dinner £22&alc*
CONF: Thtr 400 Class 220 Board 80 Del from £99
CARDS:

★★★58% ***Moxhull Hall***
Holly Ln B76 9PD (from junc 9 of M42 take A446 N for 2m. Holly Lane signposted on left) ☎ 0121 329 2056 FAX 0121 311 1980
This turn-of-the-century building set among wooded grounds and landscaped gardens retains the style and standards of a bygone era. Bedrooms are housed in either the main building or a converted coach house, the latter tending to be more contemporary in style.
11 en suite (bth/shr) 9 annexe en suite (bth/shr) (3 fmly) CTV in all bedrooms Night porter 60P Croquet lawn English & French Cuisine V meals Coffee am Last d 10pm
CARDS:

Percentage scores give you a comparison of quality within each star rating. See 'How to Use the Guide".

W

WITHERSLACK Cumbria Map 07 SD48

RED STAR HOTEL

★ Old Vicarage Country House
Church Rd LA11 6RS (from A590 take first left in village, signposted to the church and continue for 1m)
☎ 015395 52381 FAX 015395 52373
This former Georgian vicarage lies just outside the village at the end of a long winding lane and is set peacefully amongst the rolling hills. The house retains much of its character in both the suite of lounges and the lovely dining room. The bedrooms in the house are furnished thoughtfully and comfortably with a mix of contemporary cane and antique polished pieces, brought together with good decorative schemes. Rooms in the garden benefit from being purpose-built and are generally very well equipped, with music centres and safes, and are very spacious. Two have their own French windows with a patio area and overlook the woods. The cuisine is good: partner and chef Stanley Reeve concentrates on using quality fresh local produce and preparing relatively straightforward and honest dishes which accentuate these factors. The wine list shows an enthusiasm and devotion to the subject, with most bottles being under £20.00 and well annotated.
9 en suite (bth/shr) 5 annexe en suite (bth/shr) (1 fmly) CTV in all bedrooms 25P No coaches Tennis (hard) Xmas English & Continental Cuisine Coffee am Tea pm No smoking in restaurant Last d 9pm
ROOMS: (incl. bkfst) s £59-£79; d £98-£158 * **LB**
MEALS: Lunch £13.50 Dinner £26.50*
CONF: Thtr 12 Class 12 Board 12 Del from £135
CARDS:

WITHYPOOL Somerset Map 03 SS83

★★72% **Royal Oak Inn**
TA24 7QP (7m N of Dulverton, off B3223)
☎ 01643 831506 & 831236 FAX 01643 831659
Closed 25 & 26 Dec
The Royal Oak combines the character and charm of a typical village inn, with standards which will satisfy the expectations of the discerning guest. There are two bars with inglenook fireplaces, one for residents, the other is very popular with locals, and a good selection of beers and wines is always available. Bedrooms are cosy, well furnished and equipped in a modern style. Good use is made of quality fresh ingredients in the commendable restaurant meals as well as a range of bar food.
8 rms (7 bth) CTV in all bedrooms 20P No coaches Fishing Shooting No children 8yrs V meals Coffee am Last d 9.30pm
ROOMS: (incl. bkfst) s £32-£53; d £64-£76 **LB**
OFF-PEAK: (incl. bkfst) s £28-£32; d £56-£64
MEALS: Sunday Lunch £13.50 Dinner £18-£22&alc
CARDS:

★★71% **Westerclose Country House**
TA24 7QR (signposted in village)
☎ 01643 831302 FAX 01643 831307
Closed 31 Dec-Feb
This family-run hotel, built in the 1920's as a hunting lodge, stands in nine acres of paddocks and gardens above the Barle Valley and the village of Withypool. Bedrooms are individually furnished and decorated, those on the second floor having a cottage atmosphere. Spacious, comfortable public areas include an entrance hall lounge with a wood-burning stove, a cosy sitting room and a plant-filled bar. The Barle Restaurant is well appointed and offers a set menu augmented by a short carte option and a range of vegetarian dishes (the latter by arrangement only).
10 en suite (bth/shr) (1 fmly) CTV in all bedrooms 15P No coaches Fishing Riding Croquet lawn V meals Coffee am Tea pm No smoking in restaurant Last d 9.15pm
ROOMS: (incl. bkfst) s £29-£32.50; d £65-£80 * **LB**
MEALS: Lunch £9-£18alc Dinner £19.75*
CARDS:

WITNEY Oxfordshire Map 04 SP30

★★★66% **Witney Lodge**
Ducklington Ln OX8 7TJ (M40 off junc 9, A34 to A40, exit A415 Witney/Abingdon, Hotel on left) ☎ 01993 779777 FAX 01993 703467
Popular with a business clientele, this modern hotel has well appointed bedrooms with good desks. All rooms are smartly furnished with co-ordinating fabrics and wooden furniture. There is a range of dedicated meeting rooms and the hotel's carvery restaurant offers informal dining. The hotel is within easy reach of the road network.
74 en suite (bth/shr) (10 fmly) No smoking in 16 bedrooms CTV in all bedrooms STV No dogs (ex guide dogs) Night porter Air conditioning 170P Indoor swimming pool (heated) Snooker Sauna Solarium Gym Whirlpool spa Wkly live entertainment Xmas V meals Coffee am Tea pm No smoking area in restaurant Last d 10pm
ROOMS: s £55-£69; d £65-£84 * **LB**
OFF-PEAK: s £49-£69; d £59-£84
MEALS: Lunch £8.95-£15 Dinner fr £11.55*
CONF: Thtr 160 Class 80 Board 46 Del from £105
CARDS:

WIVELISCOMBE Somerset Map 03 ST02

RED STAR HOTEL

★★ **Langley House**
Langley Marsh TA4 2UF (Follow signs to Wivelistone Town Centre, turn right at town centre, Hotel 0.5m on right)
☎ 01984 623318 FAX 01984 624573
Parts of Langley House date back to the 16th century, while later additions add a Georgian elegance. Over the last 10 years Peter and Anne Wilson have lovingly restored and totally refurbished the property, including the four-acre garden. There are deep armchairs in the boldly decorated sitting rooms, and a log fire burns on colder evenings. Bedrooms vary in size; one has a four-poster bed and others have coronet-style drapes. Fresh flowers, books, mineral water and, in winter, hot water bottles are provided. Mr Wilson's set menu continues to please guests. On a recent occasion the meal consisted of a simple starter of a perfectly ripe dessert pear marinated in walnut oil, followed by

a fillet of sea bream topped with Provençal crumbs on a bed of leeks with beurre blanc. The main course was a roasted fillet of Somerset new season lamb, cooked deliciously pink and served with a slightly overpowering pepper-scented coulis. Pierre Wynant's terrine of chocolate completed the meal. The comprehensive wine list features wines from around the world but specialises in the Bordeaux region.

8 en suite (bth/shr) (1 fmly) No smoking in 2 bedrooms CTV in all bedrooms 20P No coaches Croquet lawn ch fac Xmas Coffee am Tea pm No smoking in restaurant Last d 8.30pm
ROOMS: (incl. bkfst) s £68.50-£72.50; d £86-£114 * LB
MEALS: Dinner £25-£29.65*
CONF: Board 20 Del from £118
CARDS:

WOBURN Bedfordshire Map 04 SP93

★★★70% **Bedford Arms**

George St MK17 9PX (off M1 junc 13, left to Woburn, at Woburn left at T-junc, hotel in village)
☎ 01525 290441 FAX 290432

This former inn, situated in the centre of town has recently been completely refurbished and now provides accommodation of the highest standard. The well appointed bedrooms are divided between the original house and a modern extension. A good choice of imaginatively described dishes is available in the restaurant and guests have the choice of enjoying a drink in the cocktail bar, or the beamed Tavistock bar, where lighter meals are also served.

53 en suite (bth/shr) (4 fmly) No smoking in 10 bedrooms CTV in all bedrooms STV No dogs (ex guide dogs) Night porter 80P Wkly live entertainment Xmas International Cuisine V meals Coffee am Tea pm Last d 10.30pm
ROOMS: s £80-£95; d £90-£110 * LB
MEALS: Lunch £13.50-£15.95&alc High tea £5.95 Dinner £18.50&alc*
CONF: Thtr 60 Class 40 Board 40 Del from £90
CARDS:

WOKINGHAM Berkshire Map 04 SU86

★★★★64% ***Reading Moat House***
Mill Ln, Sindlesham RG41 5DF
☎ 01734 499988 FAX 01734 666530

MOAT HOUSE

Standing in its own grounds on the banks of the River Loddon, this modern-style hotel has been sympathetically built around a 19th-century mill which itself now houses the hotel's pub and night club. Other facilities include a Workbase business centre and small but well equipped fitness and bodyclub. Bedrooms reflect the hotel's age but are clean and well maintained. Staff are friendly and willing which helps to maintain a loyal corporate market.

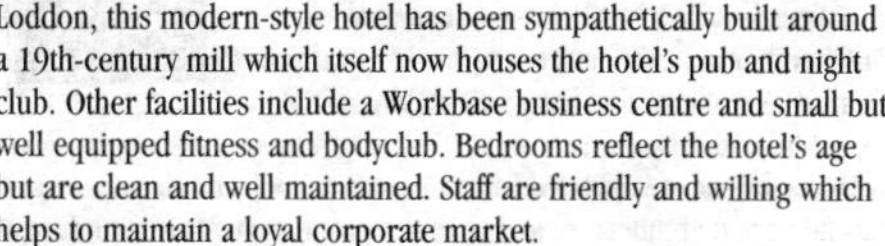

96 en suite (bth/shr) (10 fmly) No smoking in 50 bedrooms CTV in all bedrooms Lift Night porter 350P Fishing Sauna Gym Jacuzzi/spa Steam room Nightclub International Cuisine V meals Coffee am Tea pm Last d 10.30pm
CARDS:

WOLVERHAMPTON West Midlands Map 07 SO99
See also Himley & Worfield

★★★64% **Goldthorn**
Penn Rd WV3 0ER ☎ 01902 29216
FAX 01902 710419

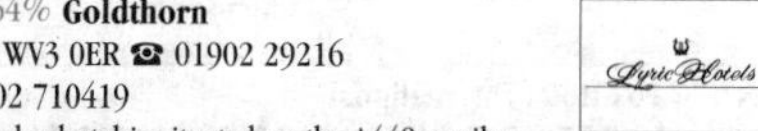

This popular hotel is situated on the A449 a mile south of the town offering comfortable accommodation in well appointed bedrooms. Some rooms are in buildings in the grounds and one can function as a self-contained business centre. Public areas include a panelled lounge bar with an ornate ceiling, the busy Captain's Table bar and an elegant Regency-style restaurant. Meeting/banqueting facilities are available and a new leisure centre is scheduled to open in the summer of 1995.

66 en suite (bth/shr) 27 annexe en suite (bth/shr) (1 fmly) No

contd.

smoking in 39 bedrooms CTV in all bedrooms STV Night porter 120P Indoor swimming pool (heated) Sauna Gym Steam room English & French Cuisine V meals Coffee am Tea pm No smoking in restaurant Last d 9.30pm
MEALS: Lunch £10.45-£11.50&alc Dinner £14.95-£17.50&alc*
CARDS:

★★★64% Novotel
Union St WV1 3JN (junct of town centre and A454)
☎ 01902 871100 FAX 01902 870054

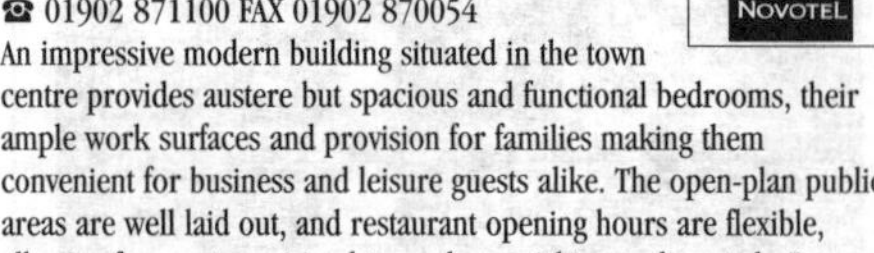

An impressive modern building situated in the town centre provides austere but spacious and functional bedrooms, their ample work surfaces and provision for families making them convenient for business and leisure guests alike. The open-plan public areas are well laid out, and restaurant opening hours are flexible, allowing for guests arriving late or those wishing to dine early. Room service is also available.
132 en suite (bth/shr) (10 fmly) No smoking in 32 bedrooms CTV in all bedrooms STV Lift Night porter 120P Outdoor swimming pool (heated) International Cuisine V meals Coffee am No smoking area in restaurant
ROOMS: s fr £55; d fr £55 * **LB**
CONF: Thtr 200 Class 100 Board 80 Del from £85
CARDS:

★★68% Ely House
53 Tettenhall Rd WV3 9NB (take A41 towards Whitchurch from town centre-ring road. 200yds on left hand side after traffic lights) ☎ 01902 311311
FAX 01902 21098
Ely House has been converted from a private school - it retains its graceful period architecture and spacious proportions. It is a modern and very friendly hotel which has a comfortable lounge in addition to the restaurant and very well equipped bedrooms.
18 en suite (bth/shr) CTV in all bedrooms 20P No coaches No children 7yrs English & Continental Cuisine V meals Coffee am Last d 8.45pm
ROOMS: (incl. bkfst) s £48; d £68 *
OFF-PEAK: (incl. bkfst) s £35; d £48
MEALS: Sunday Lunch £12.50 Dinner £13.50&alc
CARDS:

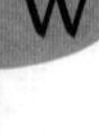

See advertisement on opposite page

★★62% Fox Hotel International
118 School St WV3 0NR ☎ 01902 21680 FAX 01902 711654
Located on the inner ring road this business hotel has been considerably upgraded recently under new ownership. In the well designed bedrooms pretty papers and fabrics are used to good effect. A cosy bar is available where inexpensive meals and snacks are provided and the adjacent restaurant offers more substantial meals. Conference and function rooms are available and staff are friendly and welcoming.
33 en suite (bth/shr) (2 fmly) No smoking in 5 bedrooms CTV in all bedrooms STV No dogs (ex guide dogs) Night porter 20P Xmas International Cuisine V meals Coffee am Tea pm No smoking area in restaurant Last d 10pm
ROOMS: s £22-£27; d £35-£59 * **LB**
MEALS: Lunch £3.95-£5.95alc Dinner £5.65-£14.65&alc
CONF: Thtr 140 Class 100 Board 60 Del from £35
CARDS:

WOOBURN COMMON Buckinghamshire Map 04 SU98

★★66% Chequers Inn
Kiln Ln, Wooburn HP10 0JQ (off M40 junc 2, A40, left to Wooburn Common,Hotel 2.5m on left) ☎ 01628 529575 FAX 01628 850124
This family run country inn with its pretty cottage style bedrooms is popular with locals and also with those exploring the nearby Chilterns. There is a cozy beamed bar which boasts roaring log fires during the winter months, a popular restaurant and facilities for private dining.
17 en suite (bth/shr) CTV in all bedrooms STV No dogs (ex guide dogs) 60P No coaches English & French Cuisine V meals Coffee am Last d 9.30pm
ROOMS: (incl. bkfst) s fr £77.50; d fr £82.50 **LB**
OFF-PEAK: (incl. bkfst) s fr £62.50; d fr £67.50
MEALS: Lunch £17.95&alc Dinner fr £18.95&alc
CONF: Thtr 50 Class 30 Board 20 Del from £70
CARDS:
See advertisement under BEACONSFIELD

WOODBRIDGE Suffolk Map 05 TM24

★★★ 73% Seckford Hall
IP13 6NU (signposted on A12 (Woodbridge bypass). Do not follow signs for town centre)
☎ 01394 385678 FAX 01394 380610
Closed 25 Dec
Seckford Hall is set in peaceful gardens and grounds, an attractive Elizabethan manor house reputed to have been the Court of Queen Elizabeth I. Traditional services are provided in a professional and caring manner by an enthusiastic and friendly team. Diners have the choice of formal dining in the main restaurant or relaxed informal dining in the beamed Courtyard restaurant which serves the smart modern leisure club. Public rooms retain much of their original character, providing guests with quiet comfortable lounge areas, a convivial bar and well appointed restaurant. Bedrooms are well furnished: the spacious Courtyard rooms offer ground floor bedrooms and some smart modern suites.
22 en suite (bth/shr) 10 annexe en suite (bth/shr) (4 fmly) CTV in all bedrooms Night porter 200P Indoor swimming pool (heated) Golf 18 Fishing Solarium Gym Putting green Jacuzzi/spa Xmas International Cuisine V meals Coffee am Tea pm No smoking in restaurant Last d 9.30pm
ROOMS: (incl. bkfst) s £79-£110; d £105-£148 * **LB**
MEALS: Lunch £11.50-£14.95&alc Dinner £23-£35alc*
CONF: Thtr 100 Class 46 Board 40 Del from £110
CARDS:

★★★69% Wood Hall Hotel & Country Club
Shottisham IP12 3EG ☎ 01394 411283 FAX 01394 410007
Woodhall is an elegant Elizabethan Manor House set in ten acres of grounds, which include a walled garden and natural lake. This delightful building has a warm, welcoming atmosphere, the public rooms retaining much of their original character with panelled walls, ornate ceilings and open log fires. The restaurant is effectively a series of three smaller dining rooms, where diners have the choice of an interesting shorter choice daily menu or a more extensive à la carte, which also has vegetarian dishes. Bedrooms come in two styles, the executive rooms are generally spacious and comfortably appointed, and the cottage rooms are of cosier dimensions. All rooms are individually furnished with period-style furniture and co-ordinated soft furnishings. Leisure facilities, a conference and banqueting suite and a night-club are housed in a separate self-contained building.
14 en suite (bth/shr) (1 fmly) CTV in all bedrooms STV 125P Outdoor swimming pool (heated) Tennis (hard) Squash Riding Sauna Solarium Croquet lawn Xmas V meals Coffee am Tea pm No smoking in restaurant Last d 9.30pm
ROOMS: (incl. bkfst & dinner) s £75-£90; d £120-£150 * **LB**
OFF-PEAK: (incl. bkfst & dinner) d £100-£130
MEALS: Lunch £10.95 Dinner £17.50
CONF: Thtr 200 Class 150 Board 70 Del from £86.50
CARDS:

★★★68% Ufford Park Hotel Golf & Leisure

Yarmouth Rd, Ufford IP12 1QW (A12 N to A1152, in Melton turn left at traffic lights, premises 1m on right)
☎ 01394 383555 FAX 01394 383582
This modern hotel complex sits in quiet countryside, within 120 acres of its own mature parkland, on which a challenging 18 hole golf course takes pride of place. The hotel provides light open-plan public areas that include a bar and lounge area, in which an all day menu of snacks and refreshments are served. The restaurant offers value-for-money meals from carvery and à la carte menus. Many of the well appointed bedrooms open onto a terrace with good views of the golf course and countryside. There are plans to extend the public areas and the already good modern leisure complex during 1996/97.
27 rms (25 bth/shr) (2 fmly) No smoking in 4 bedrooms CTV in all bedrooms No dogs (ex guide dogs) Night porter 160P Indoor swimming pool (heated) Golf 18 Sauna Solarium Gym Putting green Jacuzzi/spa Beautician Dance studio Xmas V meals Coffee am Tea pm No smoking in restaurant Last d 9.30pm
ROOMS: (incl. bkfst) s £60-£70; d £70-£90 * **LB**
OFF-PEAK: (incl. bkfst) s fr £55; d fr £65
MEALS: Sunday Lunch £11.50-£14.50 Dinner £15-£17&alc
CONF: Thtr 200 Class 80 Board 80 Del from £84.50
CARDS:

★★63% The Crown
REGAL
A Collection of Individual Hotels
2 Thoro'fare IP12 1AD ☎ 01394 384242
FAX 01394 387192
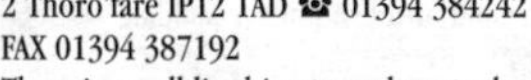
There is a well lived-in atmosphere to the public areas and the bedrooms. More modern and larger bedrooms are housed in a separate building while the main hotel, once a coaching inn, holds the rest. The bar is popular with locals and service is provided in a cheerful manner.
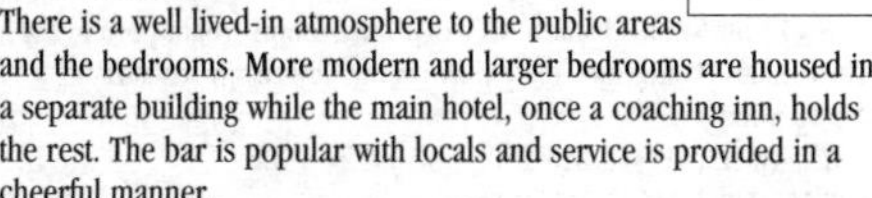
10 en suite (bth/shr) 10 annexe en suite (bth/shr) (2 fmly) No smoking in 6 bedrooms CTV in all bedrooms 35P Xmas International Cuisine V meals Coffee am Tea pm No smoking in restaurant
ROOMS: (incl. bkfst & dinner) s £50-£72; d £70-£114 * **LB**
CONF: Class 35 Board 20 Del from £70
CARDS:

WOODFORD GREEN Greater London
See LONDON SECTION plan 1 G6

★★★65% Epping Forest Moat House
MOAT HOUSE
Oak Hill IG8 9NY ☎ 0181 787 9988
FAX 0181 506 0941
Quietly situated in a residential area on the edge of Epping Forest, this modern hotel is convenient to both the North Circular and M11. Bedrooms have been practically designed with the business person in mind and public areas have recently improved with contemporary styling. The traditional restaurant has been replaced by a more upbeat Brasserie.
99 en suite (bth/shr) No smoking in 30 bedrooms CTV in all bedrooms Lift Night porter 94P Pool table Xmas English & French Cuisine V meals Coffee am Tea pm Last d 10pm
ROOMS: s £75-£85; d £90-£100 * **LB**
OFF-PEAK: s £60-£65; d £65-£70
MEALS: Lunch £12-£16&alc Dinner £12.50-£16.50*
CONF: Thtr 150 Class 60 Board 60 Del from £99
CARDS:

WOODHALL SPA Lincolnshire Map 08 TF16

★★★65% Petwood House
Stixwould Rd LN10 6QF ☎ 01526 352411 FAX 01526 353473
A lovely Edwardian property - its architecture typical of its era - Petwood House has interesting historic connections. The house was built for Lady Weignall on a site chosen by her in the area of her favourite 'pet wood' and was used to visitors from royalty to the 'Dambusters' squadron. It stands in 30 acres filled with mature woodland (at the other side is the town's Kinema), rhododendrons, lawns and gardens. Inside, the hotel furnishings are in character with the original features retained in the elegantly proportioned reception and bedrooms.
46 en suite (bth/shr) No smoking in 6 bedrooms CTV in all bedrooms Lift Night porter 80P Snooker Croquet lawn Putting
contd.

green Complimentary pass to leisure centre Xmas English & French Cuisine V meals Coffee am Tea pm No smoking in restaurant Last d 9pm
ROOMS: (incl. bkfst) s fr £65; d fr £85 * **LB**
MEALS: Sunday Lunch fr £9.50 Dinner fr £16.50&alc
CONF: Thtr 150 Class 60 Board 50 Del from £85
CARDS:

★★★63% **Golf Hotel**
The Broadway LN10 6SG ☎ 01526 353535
FAX 01526 353096
This friendly, traditional hotel stands in seven acres of grounds in the heart of the village, well known for the golf course where Jacklin and Cotton learned their craft. Although public areas retain much of the original character of the house, bedrooms have been modernised to provide a good contemporary standard of accommodation with all the facilities expected of the leisure and business guest. Dinner in the Wentworth restaurant offers fresh local specialities while more informal meals and lunch are served in the Sunningdale Bar.
50 en suite (bth/shr) (4 fmly) CTV in all bedrooms STV Night porter 100P Croquet lawn Xmas V meals Coffee am Tea pm Last d 9.30pm
ROOMS: (incl. bkfst & dinner) s £50-£59; d £60-£79 * **LB**
OFF-PEAK: (incl. bkfst & dinner) s £35-£40; d £50-£60
MEALS: Lunch £8.95 Dinner £14.95&alc*
CONF: Thtr 150 Class 45 Board 50 Del from £75
CARDS:

See advertisement on opposite page

★★63% **Eagle Lodge**
The Broadway LN10 6ST (in the centre of Woodhall Spa)
☎ 01526 353231 FAX 01526 352797
A former nursing home, the bedrooms at this establishment are larger and more comfortably furnished than is usual for this classification. It is set in its own grounds in the centre of the lovely spa resort. The bar is popular for its bar meals, barbecues and jazz nights during the season.
23 en suite (bth/shr) (2 fmly) CTV in all bedrooms STV 70P Wkly live entertainment No children Xmas English & Continental Cuisine V meals Coffee am Tea pm Last d 9.30pm
ROOMS: (incl. bkfst) s fr £39.50; d fr £60 **LB**
MEALS: Lunch £2.95-£7.95&alc Dinner fr £9.95&alc
CONF: Thtr 140 Class 60 Board 24 Del £60
CARDS:
See advertisement on opposite page

WOODSTOCK Oxfordshire Map 04 SP41

★★★❀❀73% **Feathers**
Market St OX20 1SX ☎ 01993 812291 FAX 01993 813158
General manager Tom Lewis and his team clearly enjoy caring for guests. Bedrooms are comfortable and individually decorated, but some of the stairways to them are narrow and steep. Elegant public areas have log fires in winter, and the Whinchat Bar has doors on to the delightful courtyard garden. In the restaurant, head chef David Lewis offers innovative menus in modern British style. A recent test meal included a delicious light smoked haddock soufflé with wild rice and lime, followed by a pot-roasted breast of pheasant with a mellow red wine sauce.
16 en suite (bth/shr) (3 fmly) CTV in all bedrooms STV No coaches Mountain bikes Xmas British with Mediterranean influence Cuisine V meals Coffee am Tea pm No smoking in restaurant
ROOMS: (incl. cont bkfst) s £78-£98; d £99-£150 * **LB**
MEALS: Lunch £16.50-£21&alc Dinner £22.40-£31.40alc*
CONF: Thtr 20 Board 25
CARDS:

★★★❀❀68% **Bear**
Park St OX20 1SZ (opp town hall)
☎ 01993 811511 FAX 01993 813380
Dating from the 13th century this creeper-clad coaching inn retains much of its former character with exposed stone walls, heavily beamed ceilings and a large real fire blazing in the bar. Bedrooms have been tastefully modernised to provide all the expected facilities of both the business and leisure guest but the heart of the hotel is its attractive restaurant where chef Ian Morgan provides diners with an imaginative menu of largely English fare cooked and presented in a modern style. The highlight of a recent meal was crispy duck breast set upon parsnip purée and accompanied by spring greens and a delightful apple cider sauce.
32 en suite (bth/shr) 12 annexe en suite (bth/shr) (2 fmly) No smoking in 15 bedrooms CTV in all bedrooms Night porter 30P Xmas Modern & Traditional English Cuisine V meals Coffee am Tea pm No smoking in restaurant Last d 9.45pm
ROOMS: s £95-£105; d £115-£180 **LB**
MEALS: Lunch £14.95-£18.50&alc Dinner fr £25.95&alc
CONF: Thtr 40 Class 18 Board 26 Del from £120
CARDS:

★★❀62% **Marlborough Arms**
Oxford St OX20 1TS ☎ 01993 811227
This is a really warm and welcoming establishment, its charm and conviviality evocative of the coaching inn era; big open log fires, walls hung with sporting prints, exposed beams and a cobbled courtyard set the scene downstairs. The bedrooms vary in size and are prettily decorated and furnished in Laura Ashley prints. The restaurant is lined with pictures and photographs, many of Winston Churchill who was born just round the corner at the Palace. There are just eight tables, and service is simple but capable. There are both fixed-price and carte menus. One inspection meal started with a very tender carpaccio of beef, served with strips of shaved parmesan and a salad garnish. This was followed by a fresh tasting poached fillet of salmon on a light and creamy dill sauce. There was a good bread and butter pudding to finish.
15 rms (13 bth/shr) (1 fmly) CTV in 12 bedrooms Night porter 20P Xmas V meals Coffee am Tea pm No smoking area in restaurant Last d 10.30pm
ROOMS: (incl. bkfst) s £40-£50; d £50-£75 * **LB**
OFF-PEAK: (incl. bkfst) d £50-£55
MEALS: Lunch £6.95-£12.95&alc High tea £4.95 Dinner £12.95-£15.95&alc
CONF: Class 30 Board 30
CARDS:

WOOKEY HOLE Somerset Map 03 ST54

★★❀ 70% **Glencot House**

Glencot Ln BA5 1BH ☎ 01749 677160
FAX 01749 670210
Tucked away, this late Victorian mansion was built in Jacobean style;

Glencot House overlooks a curve in the river and is set in 18 acres of gardens and grounds which include its own cricket pitch! Over the last eleven years owner Jenny Attia has lovingly restored the property to its former glory, with attractive interior architecture and an extensive range of personal bric-a-brac. Bedrooms are individually furnished and decorated, combining the character of the building with modern comforts. Chef Danny Cannon's fixed price and short carte continue to gain praise, such dishes as a seafood terrine with an avocado sauce or Glencot soup bowl may be offered as a starter, which could be followed by baked fillet of turkey stuffed with apricots and wrapped in smoked bacon.

12 en suite (bth/shr) (2 fmly) No smoking in all bedrooms CTV in all bedrooms 26P Indoor swimming pool (heated) Fishing Snooker Sauna Pool table Table tennis Xmas V meals Tea pm No smoking in restaurant Last d 8.30pm

ROOMS: (incl. bkfst) s fr £55; d £80-£90 * **LB**

MEALS: Bar Lunch £4.50-£9.50alc Dinner fr £22.50alc*

CONF: Thtr 40 Class 22 Board 20 Del from £82.50

CARDS: 

£

WOOLACOMBE Devon Map 02 SS44

★★★ 76% **Watersmeet**

Mortehoe EX34 7EB ☎ 01271 870333 FAX 01271 870890

Closed Dec-mid Feb

This smart, well appointed hotel is set on the water's edge overlooking the bay. Its centrepiece is an attractive restaurant with excellent sea views which serves the unpretentious English cuisine of chef John Physick. The menu is not large but is consistantly improving to offer such meals as the sampled miniature pancakes interleaved with seafood fricassée in a cream and vermouth sauce, followed by marinaded medallions of Exmoor venison on a bed of egg noodles with a red wine and mushroom sauce and, to finish, a Bakewell tart

contd.

and custard. There is a well balanced wine list including a number of good French and New World wines. Young staff provide efficient, attentive and friendly service.

23 en suite (bth/shr) (3 fmly) CTV in all bedrooms No dogs (ex guide dogs) 38P No coaches Outdoor swimming pool (heated) Tennis (grass) Pool table Croquet lawn English & French Cuisine V meals Coffee am Tea pm No smoking in restaurant Last d 8.30pm
ROOMS: (incl. bkfst & dinner) s £65-£90; d £120-£170 * **LB**
MEALS: Sunday Lunch fr £9.50 Dinner £16.50-£25.50*
CONF: Thtr 40 Class 25 Board 25
CARDS:

See advertisement on page 683

★★★67% **Woolacombe Bay**
South St EX34 7BN ☎ 01271 870388 FAX 01271 870613
Closed Jan & 2wks Feb
Situated in six acres of grounds adjacent to Woolacombe beach, this hotel is ideal for families. An extensive range of leisure and sporting facilities is provided, with organised children's activities at certain times of the year. Bedrooms are comfortable and the front-facing rooms have superb sea and coastal views. Public areas are spacious, and in the hotel's restaurant attentive young staff provide friendly service. Bertie's Bar is a popular venue, and Maxwell's Bistro and coffee shop provides an informal eating option. Self-catering apartments are available.
62 en suite (bth/shr) (27 fmly) CTV in all bedrooms STV No dogs Lift Night porter 100P Indoor swimming pool (heated) Outdoor swimming pool (heated) Tennis (hard) Squash Snooker Sauna Solarium Gym Pool table Croquet lawn Jacuzzi/spa Fitness facilities/Table tennis Wkly live entertainment ch fac Xmas English & French Cuisine V meals Coffee am Tea pm Last d 9.30pm
ROOMS: (incl. bkfst & dinner) s £83-£98; d £166-£181 * **LB**
OFF-PEAK: (incl. bkfst & dinner) s £58-£73; d £116-£131
MEALS: Sunday Lunch £8 High tea £7 Dinner £18*
CONF: Thtr 200 Class 150 Board 150
CARDS:

£

See advertisement on opposite page

★★73% **Little Beach**
The Esplanade EX34 7DJ (junct 27 of M5 take A361 through Barnstaple towards Ilfracombe, Woolacombe is signposted at Mullacott Cross roundabout) ☎ 01271 870398
Closed late Oct-early Mar
Stunning views over Morte Bay are a feature of Nola and Brian Wellings' welcoming hotel. The individually decorated bedrooms are pretty and bright, those at the front having balconies. There are cosy public areas and an airy sun room. Brian is an antiques expert and some pieces are offered for sale in the TV lounge. Nola is a keen cook and her five-course dinners are a treat after a day's walking on Exmoor.
10 rms (4 bth 4 shr) No smoking in 8 bedrooms CTV in all bedrooms 8P No coaches No children 6yrs English & Continental Cuisine V meals No smoking in restaurant
ROOMS: (incl. bkfst & dinner) s £35-£39; d £62-£96 **LB**
OFF-PEAK: (incl. bkfst & dinner) d £35-£96
CARDS:

★★60% ***Devon Beach***
The Esplanade EX34 7DJ ☎ 01271 870449 FAX 01271 870506
Closed mid Oct-Etr
The Devon Beach Hotel is right on the seafront with a sun-trap terrace offering fine views over towards Lundy Island. A detailed programme of refurbishment is due to commence during winter 1995/6, with the installation of central heating and a lift. Bedrooms have modern facilities, and some rooms have balconies. Service is friendly and relaxed, provided by a small team of young staff.
33 rms (26 bth) (20 fmly) CTV in all bedrooms 31P Indoor swimming pool (heated) Solarium Pool table ch fac English, French & Italian Cuisine V meals Coffee am Tea pm Last d 8.15pm
CARDS:

★70% **Crossways**
The Esplanade EX34 7DJ (M5 junct 27 then A361 to Barnstaple, follow signs for Ilfracombe and then Woolacombe) ☎ 01271 870395
Closed last Sat in Oct-1st Sat in Mar
This small hotel stands in an elevated position above Combesgate Beach, with direct access to National Trust moorland at the rear. Warm, friendly hospitality comes from the owners Dave and Chris Ellis - and from chirpy zebra finches in the comfortable lounge. The bar has an interesting collection of model cars. The attractive bedrooms are generally of a good size and most have sea views.
9 rms (6 shr) (4 fmly) CTV in all bedrooms 9P No coaches English Cuisine V meals
ROOMS: (incl. bkfst) s £20-£25; d £40-£52 **LB**
OFF-PEAK: (incl. bkfst) s £20-£22; d £40-£44
MEALS: Bar Lunch £1-£3.75alc

WOOLER Northumberland Map 12 NT92

★★62% **Tankerville Arms**
Cottage Rd NE71 6AD (on A697)
☎ 01668 281581 FAX 01668 281387
Closed 22-28 Dec
This long-established hotel and former coaching inn lies on the northern side of the town and offers bedrooms in varying sizes with modern amenities. During the quieter winter months diners can choose from the supper menu which offers a wide range of dishes and is very keenly priced.
16 en suite (bth/shr) (2 fmly) CTV in all bedrooms 100P ch fac V meals Coffee am No smoking in restaurant
ROOMS: (incl. bkfst) s £46.50; d £72 * **LB**
OFF-PEAK: (incl. bkfst) s fr £27; d fr £45
MEALS:*
CONF: Thtr 60 Class 60 Board 30
CARDS:

WOOLLEY EDGE MOTORWAY SERVICE AREA (M1)
West Yorkshire Map 08 SE31

Travelodge
M1 Service Area, West Bretton WF4 4LQ
(between junct 38/39, adj to service area)
☎ Central Res 0800 850950
This modern building offers accommodation in smart, spacious and well equipped bedrooms, suitable for family use, and all with en suite bathrooms. Meals may be taken at the nearby family restaurant. For information on room rates and to make a booking, call Roomline free of charge on 0800 850950. For more details about Travelodge, consult the Contents page under Hotel Groups.
32 en suite (bth/shr)

Travelodge

W

WOOLVERTON Somerset Map 03 ST75

★★68% ***Woolverton House***
BA3 6QS ☎ 01373 830415 FAX 01373 830415
An impressive early 19th-century rectory set in over two acres of gardens and grounds has been converted into a country house hotel offering individually furnished and decorated bedrooms which are all well equipped and complete with minibars. There are an attractive lounge with a conservatory bar overlooking the gardens and an elegant restaurant.
11 en suite (bth/shr) 4 annexe en suite (bth/shr) (1 fmly) No smoking in 4 bedrooms CTV in all bedrooms Night porter 52P No coaches Archery V meals Coffee am Tea pm Last d 9pm
CARDS:

WOOTTON BASSETT Wiltshire Map 04 SU08

★★★69% **Marsh Farm**
Coped Hall SN4 8ER (on B4041, Hook-Purton)
☎ 01793 848044 FAX 01793 851528
Marsh Farm is a personally run hotel in the countryside near Swindon. A modern extension provides well equipped bedrooms while in the original house contains lounges, one with a bar, and an attractive restaurant.
4 en suite (bth/shr) 29 annexe en suite (bth/shr) (1 fmly) CTV in all bedrooms STV No dogs (ex guide dogs) 150P No coaches V meals Coffee am Tea pm No smoking in restaurant Last d 9pm
MEALS: Lunch £10-£13.50&alc Dinner £16.75&alc*
CONF: Thtr 100 Class 50 Board 35 Del £88
CARDS:

WORCESTER Hereford & Worcester Map 03 SO85

★★★68% **Fownes**

City Walls Rd WR1 2AP (beside A38 Inner Ring Road, 100 yds from Cathedral) ☎ 01905 613151
FAX 01905 23742
This former Victorian glove factory has been converted into an interesting modern hotel with nicely furnished and well equipped bedrooms coupled with pleasant public areas. There is a choice of bars, a library and the attractive Kings restaurant. Chef Wayne Meiklejohn produces enjoyable food with bright, honest textures and flavours; good examples from a recent visit included quails' eggs with mushroom purée and fillet of lamb with rabbit mousse.
61 en suite (bth/shr) (4 fmly) CTV in all bedrooms STV Lift 94P Xmas European Cuisine V meals Coffee am Tea pm Last d 9.30pm
ROOMS: s £39-£75; d £85 * **LB**
OFF-PEAK: (incl. bkfst) s £39; d £78
MEALS: Lunch fr £8.95 Dinner fr £15.95&alc*
CONF: Thtr 120 Class 60 Board 50 Del from £105
CARDS:

★★★63% **Star**

Foregate St WR1 1EA (take A44 to city centre, turn right at traffic lights into City Walls Road. Straight ahead at roundabout, turn left at lights then right at lights) ☎ 01905 24308 FAX 01905 23440
A busy city-centre hotel with a pleasing traditional ambience popular with tourists and locals. There are two congenial bars, an all-day coffee shop and a restaurant. Bedrooms vary in size, (some singles being small), but all are attractively furnished and well equipped.
46 en suite (bth/shr) (2 fmly) CTV in all bedrooms Lift Night porter 55P Jacuzzi/spa Xmas International Cuisine V meals Coffee am Tea pm No smoking area in restaurant Last d 9.30pm
ROOMS: s £45-£49; d £52-£55 * **LB**
OFF-PEAK: s £41-£45; d £45-£49
MEALS: Lunch £2.95-£7.95 Dinner £10-£10.50&alc*
CONF: Thtr 150 Class 50 Board 50 Del from £65
CARDS:

★★65% **Loch Ryan Hotel**
119 Sidbury WR5 2DH (on A44 London road)
☎ 01905 351143 FAX 01905 351143
This privately-owned and personally-run hotel is located on the A44 (Evesham Road), close to the city centre and the famous cathedral. It provides soundly maintained, traditionally furnished accommodation, which includes a family-bedded room. The no smoking public areas include a comfortable lounge, a bar and a traditionally furnished dining room.
10 en suite (bth/shr) (1 fmly) CTV in all bedrooms No dogs 10P Coffee am Tea pm No smoking in restaurant Last d 7.30pm
ROOMS: (incl. bkfst) s £38-£45; d £50-£60 * **LB**
OFF-PEAK: (incl. bkfst) s fr £35; d fr £45
MEALS: Lunch £16-£14 High tea fr £2.50 Dinner fr £16
CARDS:

★★64% **Ye Olde Talbot**
Friar St WR1 2NA (in city centre opposite Cathedral)
☎ 01905 23573 FAX 01905 612760
Situated in the city centre close to the cathedral, this former coaching inn offers guests a popular lounge bar, family restaurant and a welcoming and informal atmosphere. Well equipped bedrooms are now scheduled for refurbishment. Limited covered car parking is available to the rear.
29 en suite (bth/shr) (6 fmly) No smoking in 2 bedrooms CTV in all bedrooms STV No dogs (ex guide dogs) Night porter 8P English & Continental Cuisine V meals Coffee am Tea pm No smoking area in restaurant Last d 10pm
ROOMS: (incl. bkfst & dinner) s £49.50; d £59.50 * **LB**
OFF-PEAK: (incl. bkfst) s £35; d £49.50
MEALS: Sunday Lunch £4.95-£7.95 Dinner £8-£12&alc*
CONF: Thtr 15 Class 10 Board 10 Del £78
CARDS:

★63% **Park House**
12 Droitwich Rd WR3 7LJ (on A38) ☎ 01905 21816
This large Victorian house, personally run by owners Sheila and John Smith, and stands on the A38 north of the city centre. Bedrooms, which are well maintained and equipped with modern facilities and furniture, include both a family room and one at ground floor level. There are a pleasant dining room and an inviting lounge.
7 rms (4 shr) (1 fmly) No smoking in all bedrooms CTV in all bedrooms STV 8P No coaches V meals No smoking area in restaurant Last d 6pm
ROOMS: (incl. bkfst) s £25-£30; d £36-£42 **LB**
OFF-PEAK: (incl. bkfst) s £22-£26; d £34-£40
MEALS: Dinner £7.50-£10.50&alc
CARDS:

Forte Posthouse Worcester
High St WR1 2QR (opp Worcester Cathedral)
☎ 01905 726262 FAX 01905 723458
Suitable for both the business and leisure traveller, this bright hotel provides modern accommodation in well equipped bedrooms with en suite bathrooms. For more details about Forte Posthouse hotels, consult the Contents page for the section on Hotel Groups.
95 en suite (bth/shr)
ROOMS: s fr £59; d fr £59 *
CONF: Thtr 130 Class 80 Board 50 Del from £80

WORFIELD Shropshire Map 07 SO79

★★★ ❀❀❀ 76% **Old Vicarage**

WV15 5JZ (off A454 between Bridgnorth & Wolverhampton) ☎ 01746 716497
FAX 01746 716552
Closed 22 Dec-3 Jan

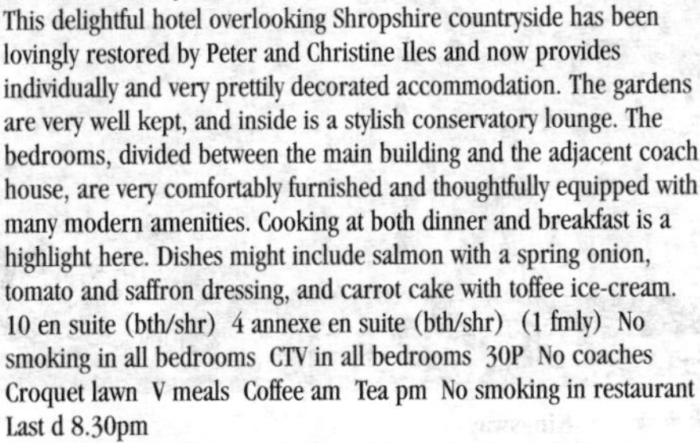

This delightful hotel overlooking Shropshire countryside has been lovingly restored by Peter and Christine Iles and now provides individually and very prettily decorated accommodation. The gardens are very well kept, and inside is a stylish conservatory lounge. The bedrooms, divided between the main building and the adjacent coach house, are very comfortably furnished and thoughtfully equipped with many modern amenities. Cooking at both dinner and breakfast is a highlight here. Dishes might include salmon with a spring onion, tomato and saffron dressing, and carrot cake with toffee ice-cream.
10 en suite (bth/shr) 4 annexe en suite (bth/shr) (1 fmly) No smoking in all bedrooms CTV in all bedrooms 30P No coaches Croquet lawn V meals Coffee am Tea pm No smoking in restaurant Last d 8.30pm
ROOMS: (incl. bkfst) s £68.50-£89.50; d £97-£135 * **LB**
MEALS: Sunday Lunch £15.50 Dinner £25-£30*
CONF: Thtr 30 Class 30 Board 20
CARDS:

WORKINGTON Cumbria Map 11 NY02

★★★ 68% **Washington Central**
Washington St CA14 3AY (off A66) ☎ 01900 65772 FAX 01900 68770
A popular business hotel, this modern brick building is situated in the town centre and provides attractive, well equipped bedrooms. A good range of dinner dishes is served in the Carlton Restaurant, and meals are available throughout the day in the coffee shop.
47 en suite (bth/shr) (4 fmly) CTV in all bedrooms STV No dogs (ex guide dogs) Lift Night porter 60P Indoor swimming pool (heated) Sauna Solarium Gym Jacuzzi/spa English & French Cuisine V meals Coffee am Tea pm No smoking in restaurant Last d 9.30pm
MEALS: Lunch £12.50&alc Dinner £15.75&alc*
CONF: Thtr 300 Class 250 Board 150 Del £65
CARDS:

★★★ 63% **The Hunday Manor**
Hunday CA14 4JF ☎ 01900 61798 FAX 01900 601202
This 18th-century manor house lies in its own grounds amidst farmland two miles south of the town, and enjoys fine panoramic views from its elevated position. A retreat for both business guests and tourists, it is also a popular venue for weddings. Both the bar and foyer lounge have open fires in season, and the restaurant overlooks the gardens.
12 en suite (bth/shr) CTV in all bedrooms STV 40P No coaches Tennis (grass) English & Continental Cuisine V meals Coffee am No smoking area in restaurant Last d 9.30pm
ROOMS: (incl. bkfst) s £50; d £65 * **LB**
OFF-PEAK: (incl. bkfst) s £40; d £50
MEALS: Lunch £7.50-£12.30&alc Dinner £14.50&alc*
CONF: Thtr 30 Class 10 Board 16 Del from £66.45
CARDS:

WORKSOP Nottinghamshire Map 08 SK57

★★★ 70% **Clumber Park**
Clumber Park S80 3PA (on A614, 5m NE) ☎ 01623 835333 FAX 01623 835525

CCH Country Club Hotel Group

In a fine position opposite the National Trust's Clumber Park, this hotel is a popular choice for leisure and business guests. Public rooms are attractively styled and include a conservatory restaurant with an adjoining cocktail bar, and Dukeries Tavern which is conveniently open all day for meals, snacks and drinks. Well

furnished and spacious bedrooms also feature excellent showers.
48 en suite (bth/shr) (6 fmly) No smoking in 18 bedrooms CTV in all bedrooms STV Night porter 200P ch fac Xmas English & Continental Cuisine V meals Coffee am Tea pm No smoking in restaurant Last d 10pm

ROOMS: s £59; d £59 * **LB**
OFF-PEAK: s £45; d £45
MEALS: Lunch £13.95&alc Dinner £15&alc*
CONF: Thtr 270 Class 150 Board 90 Del from £89
CARDS:

★★ 72% **Lion**

112 Bridge St S80 1HT (A57 to town centre, turn at Walkers Garage on right and follow road to Norfolk Arms and turn left) ☎ 01909 477925
FAX 01909 479038
A busy and popular market town inn. With origins firmly in the 16th century the hotel has been vastly, though sympathetically, extended, and offers modern purpose-designed bedrooms and bathrooms. The public

contd.

areas include a good lounge bar and a restaurant. Expected services are supplemented by attentive room service.
32 en suite (bth/shr) (3 fmly) CTV in all bedrooms STV Night porter 50P Sauna Solarium Gym Xmas French Cuisine V meals Coffee am Tea pm Last d 9.30pm
ROOMS: (incl. bkfst) s £47.50-£57.50; d £57.50-£77.50 * **LB**
OFF-PEAK: (incl. bkfst) s fr £35; d fr £45
MEALS: Lunch £3.99-£12.75 High tea fr £4 Dinner £12.75-£16.25*
CONF: Thtr 60 Class 60 Board 60 Del from £70
CARDS:

★★62% **Regancy**
Carlton Rd S80 1PS (adjacent to railway station) ☎ 01909 474108 FAX 01909 479398
A family-owned and much restored former station hotel offers good value for money for well kept accommodation and a convivial atmosphere in the bar and restaurant which also enjoys a good local trade. There is an extra quiet lounge for residents and a substantial range of popular dishes available.
13 rms (7 shr) (1 fmly) CTV in all bedrooms No dogs 30P No coaches V meals Last d 8pm
ROOMS: (incl. bkfst) s £30-£35; d £43-£53 *
MEALS: Lunch £4.50&alc Dinner £8.50-£9.50&alc*
CARDS:

Travelodge

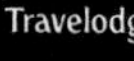

St Anne's Dr, Dukeries Dr S80 3QD (on roundabout junct of A60/A57) ☎ 01909 501528
FAX 01909 501528
This modern building offers accommodation in smart, spacious and well equipped bedrooms, suitable for family use, and all with en suite bathrooms. Meals may be taken at the nearby family restaurant. For information on room rates and to make a booking, call Roomline free of charge on 0800 850950. For more details about Travelodge, consult the Contents page under Hotel Groups.
40 en suite (bth/shr)

WORSLEY Greater Manchester Map 07 SD70

★★★64% **Novotel**

Worsley Brow M28 4YA (adjacent to M62 junc 13)
☎ 0161 799 3535 FAX 0161 703 8207
Regular users of Novotel Hotels will find the art decor style of the public areas at this establishment refreshingly different and those with disabilities will also welcome the lower sections at the reception desk. Bedrooms have also undergone changes, mirrors have been provided for dressing tables together with hairdryers, electrical sockets are better placed and fabrics are much more colourful.
119 en suite (bth/shr) (5 fmly) No smoking in 37 bedrooms CTV in all bedrooms STV Lift 133P Outdoor swimming pool (heated) European Cuisine V meals Coffee am Last d 11.30
MEALS: Bar Lunch £10-£20alc Dinner £13-£16&alc*
CONF: Thtr 220 Class 140 Board 50 Del from £95
CARDS:

WORTHING West Sussex Map 04 TQ10

★★★68% **Beach**
Marine Pde BN11 3QJ ☎ 01903 234001 FAX 01903 234567
The Beach Hotel faces the sea within walking distance of the shops. Extensive traditional services are maintained, and the spacious lounge has made the hotel a popular rendezvous. Most of the good-sized, comfortable bedrooms have sea views and some have balconies. A cocktail bar augments the lounge and large non-smoking restaurant.
80 en suite (bth/shr) (8 fmly) CTV in all bedrooms STV No dogs Lift Night porter 55P Pool table Xmas English & Continental Cuisine V meals Coffee am Tea pm Last d 8.45pm
ROOMS: (incl. bkfst) s £53.25-£62; d £79.50-£89.50 **LB**
OFF-PEAK: (incl. bkfst & dinner) s £45-£55; d £90
MEALS: Lunch fr £13.95&alc Dinner fr £17.50&alc
CONF: Thtr 200 Class 40 Board 12 Del from £55
CARDS:

★★★67% **Kingsway**
Marine Pde BN11 3QQ (A24 to seafront, turn right at pier)
☎ 01903 237542 FAX 01903 204173
This very popular and well managed family-owned hotel continues to improve and upgrade. The atmosphere is friendly and with good team work the staff are conscientious, committed and very willing to please. Bedrooms are well furnished and particularly well equipped with modern facilities, double glazing, and satellite TV. Public rooms comprise a very comfortable double-sided lounge - one side for non smokers -and a bar which offers an extensive range of bar meals. Chef Trevor Lindup offers a choice of menus including carvery and à la carte dishes, with professional standards of cooking. There is also a furnished front terrace for warm sunny days and a lift to all levels.
28 en suite (bth/shr) (2 fmly) CTV in all bedrooms STV Lift Night porter 12P No coaches Xmas English & French Cuisine V meals Coffee am Tea pm No smoking in restaurant Last d 9pm
ROOMS: (incl. bkfst) s £40-£50; d £60-£80 **LB**
MEALS: Sunday Lunch £8.45-£13.95&alc Dinner £15.95&alc
CONF: Thtr 50 Class 20 Board 30 Del from £42
CARDS:

See advertisement on opposite page

★★★66% **Ardington**
Steyne Gardens BN11 3DZ ☎ 01903 230451 FAX 01903 230451
Closed 25 Dec-4 Jan
This family-run hotel has been improved and upgraded over recent years to offer good facilities. All bedrooms are equipped with remote control radio and satellite TV, most have trouser presses and hair dryers, and some are located on the ground floor. Public areas include a spacious and comfortably furnished bar lounge, an attractively appointed restaurant and the Eden and Connaught meeting rooms. Car parking is available.
45 en suite (bth/shr) (4 fmly) No smoking in 10 bedrooms CTV in 47 bedrooms STV Night porter 25P International Cuisine V meals Coffee am Tea pm Last d 8.30pm
ROOMS: (incl. bkfst) s £52-£68; d £72-£88 **LB**
OFF-PEAK: (incl. bkfst) s fr £45; d fr £69
MEALS: Dinner £17&alc
CONF: Thtr 140 Class 60 Board 35 Del from £50
CARDS:

★★★65% **Windsor House**
14/20 Windsor Rd BN11 2LX ☎ 01903 239655 FAX 01903 210763
Closed 24-25 Dec
Located close to the seafront this family-run hotel continues to go from strength to strength with ongoing refurbishment and continued upgrading. There is a good range of bedrooms furnished in the modern style and all equipped to meet the demands of today's discerning traveller. There are a very smart entrance conservatory

reception lobby lounge, an attractive and well appointed restaurant with a weekend carvery option, a comfortable lounge bar, an American pool table and several meeting rooms (the Elizabeth Suite accommodating up to 120 persons). Service is friendly and the atmosphere relaxed and informal, personal supervision being provided by the proprietors Mr and Mrs Armstrong. Room service can also be provided and there is ample forecourt car parking.
30 en suite (bth/shr) (4 fmly) CTV in all bedrooms STV No dogs (ex guide dogs) 18P Pool table English & French Cuisine V meals Coffee am Tea pm No smoking in restaurant
ROOMS: (incl. bkfst) s £49.50-£60; d £65-£95 * **LB**
CONF: Thtr 120 Class 48 Board 40 Del from £82.50
CARDS:

★★★63% **Berkeley**
86-95 Marine Pde BN11 3QD ☎ 01903 820000 FAX 01903 821333
Recently refurbished to a good standard, this popular seafront hotel offers comfortable and well equipped bedrooms with good facilities. All windows are double-glazed and rooms come well equipped with every modern facility to meet the demands of today's discerning traveller. Public rooms comprise a particularly well appointed function room and bar, reception lobby sitting area and separate small lounge, together with a downstairs dining room and bar. There are two lifts, a night porter, 24-hour service of light refreshments and a rear car park.
84 en suite (bth/shr) (2 fmly) CTV in all bedrooms STV Lift Night porter 25P Xmas French & Italian Cuisine V meals Coffee am Tea pm Last d 8.15pm
ROOMS: (incl. cont bkfst) s £49-£53; d £69-£73 * **LB**
OFF-PEAK: (incl. cont bkfst) s fr £39; d fr £39
MEALS: Bar Lunch £1.50-£8.25 Dinner £12.50-£18.50*
CONF: Thtr 120 Class 50 Board 30 Del from £55
CARDS:

★★★59% **Chatsworth**
Steyne BN11 3DU (just beyond the pier) ☎ 01903 236103
FAX 01903 823726
This Georgian-fronted, creeper-clad hotel retaining much of its early 19th-century charm, overlooks Steyne gardens, close to the seafront and town centre. Equally popular for business guests and tourists alike, it offers old-fashioned bedrooms which are well equipped with modern facilities. Refurbished and upgraded public areas comprise the well appointed, attractive Hardwick Restaurant which opens daily for lunch and dinner featuring a fixed-price menu, a combined bar/lounge and a spacious games room with table tennis and two good, full size snooker tables; there is also a function room which can accommodate up to 120 persons. Parking meters and a NCP car park are available.
107 en suite (bth/shr) (5 fmly) CTV in all bedrooms Lift Night porter Snooker Pool table Games room Xmas English & Continental Cuisine V meals Coffee am Tea pm No smoking in restaurant Last d 8.30pm
ROOMS: (incl. bkfst) s £35-£57; d £59-£90 **LB**
MEALS: Lunch fr £11.95 Dinner fr £15.95&alc*
CONF: Thtr 150 Class 60 Board 40 Del from £35
CARDS:

See advertisement on this page

★★62% ***Cavendish***
115/116 Marine Pde BN11 3QG ☎ 01903 236767
FAX 01903 823840

Ideally located facing the sea this very popular hotel is personally run by the Millar family. The atmosphere is relaxed and informal with a friendly cordial traditional bar lounge with TV being regularly used by the locals and featuring real ale and a good range of lunchtime bar food. There is an attractive and well appointed comfortable restaurant which features an a la carte dinner menu and the enthusiastic cooking of Chef Ian Millar. Service is efficient and

contd.

personally supervised by Mr and Mrs Jim Millar who take special care to ensure their guests are made to feel welcome and comfortable.
15 rms (13 bth/shr) (1 fmly) CTV in all bedrooms No dogs (ex guide dogs) Night porter 4P No coaches English & Continental Cuisine V meals Coffee am Last d 9pm
CARDS:

WRIGHTINGTON Lancashire Map 07 SD51

★★★68% **Wrightington Hotel & Restaurant**

Moss Ln WN6 9PB (off junct 27, M6)
☎ 01257 425803 FAX 01257 425830
A modern hotel and leisure club complex close to the M6. The leisure and fitness centre is probably the best, most well equipped and hi tech in the north of England. It comprises; a full size pool, sports injury and rehabilitation clinics, an eighty-eight station gym, hair and beauty treatments with comfortable lounging areas, bar and cafe. The conference facilities are also air conditioned and purpose built. The bedrooms are spacious and comfortable. In the restaurant the cuisine is modern British and is likely in the future to attract a higher award.
47 en suite (bth/shr) (4 fmly) No smoking in 12 bedrooms CTV in all bedrooms STV Night porter 170P Indoor swimming pool (heated) Squash Sauna Solarium Gym Pool table Jacuzzi/spa Fitness Centre, Bar British Cuisine V meals Coffee am Tea pm Last d 9.30pm
ROOMS: (incl. bkfst) s £37-£58; d £47-£72 * **LB**
MEALS: Lunch £8.95 Dinner £16.95*
CONF: Thtr 100 Class 30 Board 30 Del from £75
CARDS:

WROTHAM Kent Map 05 TQ65

Forte Posthouse Maidstone/Sevenoaks

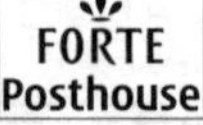

London Rd, Wrotham Heath TN15 7RS ☎ 01732 883311 FAX 01732 885850
Suitable for both the business and leisure traveller, this bright hotel provides modern accommodation in well equipped bedrooms with en suite bathrooms. For more details about Forte Posthouse hotels, consult the Contents page for the section on Hotel Groups.
106 en suite (bth/shr)
ROOMS: s fr £79; d fr £79 *
CONF: Thtr 60 Class 30 Board 30 Del £99

Travel Inn

London Rd, Wrotham Heath TN15 7RX (follow A20 Wrotham & West Malling road) ☎ 01732 884214 FAX 01732 780368
Purpose-built accommodation, offering spacious, well equipped bedrooms, all with en suite bathrooms. Meals may be taken at the nearby family restaurant. For more information about Travel Inns, consult the Contents page under Hotel Groups.
40 en suite (bth/shr)
ROOMS: d £35.50 *

WROXHAM Norfolk Map 09 TG21

★★67% **Broads**
Station Rd NR12 8UR (turn off A1151 onto Station Rd, Hotel 200yds on right) ☎ 01603 782869 & 784157 FAX 01603 784066
A squat, pink-washed, canopied building, taking its name from the adjacent bustling waterways, this hotel is an established favourite for guests touring the countryside by boat, single gauge railway or road. The Bales family are dedicated hosts and the accommodation is modern and well cared for. Entertainment is laid on in the bar-lounge at weekends during the season.
21 en suite (bth/shr) 7 annexe en suite (bth/shr) (1 fmly) CTV in all bedrooms 40P Wkly live entertainment Xmas International Cuisine V meals Coffee am Last d 9.30pm
ROOMS: (incl. bkfst) s £35-£40; d £50-£60 **LB**
MEALS: Lunch £4.75-£10.50 Dinner fr £10.50&alc
CARDS:

WYMONDHAM Norfolk Map 05 TG10

★★70% **Wymondham Consort**

28 Market St NR18 0BB (hotel situated in town centre opposite Barclays Bank) ☎ 01953 606721 FAX 01953 601361
The new proprietors have made considerable improvements to the physical standards and services at this small hotel, formerly known as the Sinclair. Public areas look fresh and inviting following a major redecoration programme, and they include a small no-smoking lounge, a lounge-bar and a pleasant restaurant. A daily fixed-price menu and carte are offered in the restaurant, or lighter snacks can be served in the lounge-bar or to the bedrooms. Accommodation styles and sizes are quite variable, the Heritage bedrooms offering more character with exposed brick work and beams; though thoughtful extras such as fresh fruit and mineral water are provided to all rooms.
20 en suite (bth/shr) (1 fmly) No smoking in 10 bedrooms CTV in all bedrooms 18P Sauna ch fac Home style Cordon Bleu Cuisine V meals Coffee am Tea pm No smoking in restaurant Last d 9pm
ROOMS: (incl. bkfst) s £40-£45; d £55-£65 * **LB**
MEALS: Lunch £10.95 Dinner fr £14.50*
CONF: Thtr 40 Class 30 Board 20 Del from £59
CARDS:
See advertisement on opposite page

★★67% **Abbey**
10 Church St NR18 0PH (take Wymondham sign off A11. Take town centre sign. Hotel opposite Ancient Abbey Church) ☎ 01953 602148 FAX 01953 606247
A charming privately-owned hotel often described as a town house, but in a unique quiet setting opposite the Abbey. Much of its architecture is Victorian, but it also has 16th-century origins and the periods are very much reflected in its character and warmth. The bedrooms vary in both size and shape: some are plainly decorated and others have beams and timber framing, all have modern facilities. There is a comfortable period-style lounge with plenty of reading material and a cosy bar in which pre-dinner drinks can be enjoyed. Mainly British dishes are served in the attractively appointed restaurant.
22 en suite (bth/shr) 1 annexe en suite (bth/shr) (3 fmly) CTV in all bedrooms Lift 4P Xmas English Cuisine V meals Coffee am Tea pm No smoking in restaurant Last d 9.30pm
ROOMS: (incl. bkfst) s £46.50-£55; d £66-£75 **LB**
MEALS: Lunch £4.50-£10 Dinner fr £15
CARDS:
See advertisement under NORWICH

YARCOMBE Devon Map 03 ST20

★★ 74% **The Belfry Country Hotel**

EX14 9BD (on A30) ☎ 01404 861234 & 861588
FAX 01404 861579

Proprietors Jackie and Tony Rees extend a warm welcome to this small hotel where a high standard of accommodation and food is offered in a friendly and relaxing peaceful atmosphere. Tastefully converted from the Victorian village school, original features such as stained glass windows and the brass school bell have been retained. The six bedrooms have been individually furnished and comprehensively equipped, and enjoy views over beautiful Devon countryside. There is a cosy lounge, and the bar forms part of the wood-panelled restaurant. Here, Jackie Rees' home cooking continues to impress. The set and à la carte menus include home-made soups, local meat and game, and delicious puddings with lashings of clotted cream! Yarcombe, once the home of Sir Francis Drake, is ideally placed for exploring Devon, Somerset and Dorset.

6 en suite (bth/shr) (1 fmly) No smoking in all bedrooms CTV in all bedrooms 10P No coaches No children 12yrs Xmas English, French & Italian Cuisine V meals Coffee am Tea pm No smoking in restaurant Last d 8.45pm

ROOMS: (incl. bkfst) s fr £42; d fr £64 * LB
MEALS: Dinner £13.95-£16.95&alc*
CARDS:

YARMOUTH See Wight, Isle of

YATTENDON Berkshire Map 04 SU57

★★ 76% **Royal Oak**

The Square RG18 0UG ☎ 01635 201325
FAX 01635 201926

The Royal Oak, the epitome of an old English country inn with its wisteria-clad walls and attractive garden, has been welcoming guests for 300 years. Bedrooms have been stylishly refurbished to provide delightfully appointed rooms with comfortable beds, rich fabrics and smart modern bathrooms with deep baths and gleaming chrome. Food remains central to the operation and guests can either eat informally in the bar or choose from a full menu in the splendidly decorated restaurant. Chef Robbie Macrae is devises enjoyable dishes based on quality produce. A highlight of a spring meal was some delicious halibut subtly flavoured with lemon grass and thyme and accompanied by a herb sauce and green asparagus spears.

5 en suite (bth/shr) CTV in all bedrooms STV No coaches Croquet lawn Xmas English & French Cuisine V meals Coffee am Tea pm No smoking in restaurant Last d 9.30pm

ROOMS: (incl. bkfst) s £80-£90; d £80-£95 * LB
MEALS: Lunch £18.50-£32alc Dinner £26-£32alc*
CONF: Thtr 30 Class 18 Board 22 Del from £130
CARDS:

YELVERTON Devon Map 02 SX56

★★★ 69% **Moorland Links**

PL20 6DA (on A386) ☎ 01822 852245
FAX 01822 855004

Situated within Dartmoor National Park in 9 acres of mature grounds and gardens this hotel continues to improve. There are 15 stylish executive bedrooms and the existing rooms, whilst less glamorous, are in the process of refurbishment; some have first floor balconies. Breathtaking views can be taken from the majority of bedrooms and restaurant Steve Holmes in the kitchen produces worthy cooking; recent inspection meals have commented favourably on his deliciously light mille fieuille of smoked trout with ginger sauce and confit of duck and pigeon breast topped with cous cous. Scrumptious home made puddings conclude.

45 en suite (bth/shr) (4 fmly) No smoking in 21 bedrooms CTV in all bedrooms Night porter 120P Tennis (hard) Xmas English & French Cuisine V meals Coffee am Tea pm No smoking area in restaurant Last d 9.45pm

ROOMS: (incl. bkfst) s fr £65; d £85-£110 * LB
OFF-PEAK: (incl. bkfst & dinner) s fr £78.50; d £112-£137
MEALS: Lunch £11.45-£14.75 High tea fr £5 Dinner fr £17.25*
CONF: Thtr 120 Class 60 Board 60 Del from £85
CARDS:

See advertisement under PLYMOUTH

YEOVIL Somerset Map 03 ST51
See also Martock & West Camel

★★★ 68% **Yeovil Court**

West Coker Rd BA20 2NE (2.5m W on A30)
☎ 01935 863746 FAX 01935 863990

Situated on the western fringes of the town, this smart modern hotel offers a friendly and relaxed atmosphere. Bedrooms are comfortable and attractively furnished and decorated: four larger rooms offer more

contd.

spacious accommodation and whirlpool baths. It is planned to build a further eight rooms in the courtyard during 1996. The cooking of Howard Mosely continues to please, his à la carte menu offering an interesting selection of dishes, cooked with care and skilfully presented.
15 en suite (bth) 3 annexe en suite (bth) (4 fmly) CTV in all bedrooms 75P Xmas English & French Cuisine V meals Coffee am Tea pm No smoking in restaurant Last d 9.30pm
ROOMS: (incl. bkfst) s fr £59; d fr £69 **LB**
OFF-PEAK: (incl. bkfst) s fr £49; d fr £59
MEALS: Lunch £6.95-£8.95&alc Dinner £14-£25alc*
CONF: Thtr 44 Class 20 Board 28
CARDS:

See advertisement on opposite page

★★★59% **The Manor**

Hendford BA20 1TG ☎ 01935 423116
FAX 01935 706607
This manor house dating from 1735 stands in the centre of Yeovil with its own spacious car park. The well equipped bedrooms are shortly to be upgraded, and the comfortable, traditional public areas include a choice of lounges.
20 en suite (bth/shr) 21 annexe en suite (bth/shr) (2 fmly) No smoking in 12 bedrooms CTV in all bedrooms Night porter 41P Xmas V meals Coffee am Tea pm No smoking in restaurant Last d 9.30pm
ROOMS: s £65-£75; d £75-£90 * **LB**
MEALS: Lunch £10.95&alc High tea fr £6.50 Dinner fr £14.50&alc*
CONF: Thtr 60 Class 35 Board 30 Del from £75
CARDS:

See advertisement on opposite page

RED STAR HOTEL

★ 🏵🏵 **Little Barwick House**

Barwick Village BA22 9TD (turn left off A37, Yeovil/Dorchester road, at first roundabout. Hotel 0.25m on left) ☎ 01935 423902
FAX 01935 420908
Closed Xmas & New Year
This delightful Georgian dower house is set amidst beautiful countryside on the edge of Yeovil. The bedrooms are individually decorated and each have their own character and nice personal touches. Guests enjoy the comfort of a private home with afternoon tea in front of the fire or in the attractive garden. Veronica Colley has prepared an imaginative menu and cooks with care and skill. Homemade ciabatta accompanied a recent starter of lightly sautéed chicken livers on a mixed leaf salad. A confit of duck was combined with sautéed strips of duck breast on a bed of fine noodles with a light oriental sauce flavoured with ginger and spring onion. A rich chocolate pot completed the meal and was rounded off by a full flavoured coffee and petit fours.
6 en suite (bth/shr) CTV in all bedrooms No coaches English & French Cuisine V meals No smoking in restaurant Last d 9pm
ROOMS: (incl. bkfst) s fr £49; d fr £78 * **LB**
MEALS: Dinner £18.90-£25.90*
CARDS:

★63% **Preston**

64 Preston Rd BA20 2DL (from A30 (hospital roundabout) head north on A37 Bristol road for 0.25m. At roundabout take first exit for Preston Road)
☎ 01935 474400 FAX 01935 410142
Peter Goacher and his enthusiastic, friendly staff provide a relaxed and friendly atmosphere at this hotel, conveniently located for the town centre and business areas. Bedrooms are furnished in a mixture of styles and provide excellent facilities for today's travellers. The short fixed-price menu offers a varied choice and good value for money.
5 en suite (bth/shr) 8 annexe en suite (bth/shr) (7 fmly) CTV in all bedrooms 19P English & French Cuisine V meals Coffee am Tea pm No smoking in restaurant Last d 9pm
ROOMS: (incl. bkfst) s £30-£39; d £40-£49 *
CARDS:

YORK North Yorkshire Map 08 SE65

See also Escrick & Pocklington

★★★★65% **Royal York**

Station Rd YO2 2AA (adjacent to railway station)
☎ 01904 653681 FAX 01904 623503
Situated right beside the station this large Victorian hotel, despite recent modernisation, still retains a traditional atmosphere with its lofty public rooms and crystal chandeliers. Contemporary bedrooms are generally spacious - some of the largest being housed in an adjoining garden wing - while others enjoy views of the city walls and Minster. Plentiful and smartly uniformed staff provide friendly and helpful service.
131 en suite (bth/shr) 27 annexe en suite (bth/shr) (4 fmly) CTV in all bedrooms STV Lift Night porter 150P Snooker Sauna Solarium Gym Mini pitch & putt Wkly live entertainment Xmas V meals Coffee am Tea pm No smoking in restaurant Last d 9.45pm
ROOMS: s fr £95; d fr £115 * **LB**
MEALS: Lunch £10.25-£12.50 High tea fr £6 Dinner fr £17.50&alc
CONF: Thtr 280 Class 120 Board 80 Del from £130
CARDS:

See advertisement on opposite page

★★★★64% **Swallow**

Tadcaster Rd YO2 2QQ (W on A1036)
☎ 01904 701000 FAX 01904 702308
Situated outside the city centre in a fine position

contd.

Y

overlooking the racecourse, this modern hotel offers spacious bedrooms, all with useful facilities such as an iron and board and small fridges stocked with complimentary soft drinks. Family rooms are good value and there is a small leisure club. The self-contained management training centre attracts residential and day conferences.
113 en suite (bth/shr) (14 fmly) No smoking in 40 bedrooms CTV in all bedrooms STV Lift Night porter 200P Indoor swimming pool (heated) Sauna Solarium Gym Croquet lawn Putting green Jacuzzi/spa Beauty treatment Xmas English & French Cuisine V meals Coffee am Tea pm No smoking in restaurant Last d 10pm
ROOMS: s fr £96; d fr £125 **LB**
OFF-PEAK: (incl. bkfst & dinner) s fr £70; d fr £140
MEALS: Lunch £10-£15 Dinner fr £18.95*
CONF: Thtr 170 Class 90 Board 40 Del from £95
CARDS:

★★★★58% ***York Viking Moat House***

North St YO1 1JF (between Ouse Bridge and Lendal Bridge) ☎ 01904 459988 FAX 01904 641793
This modern city centre hotel overlooks the River Ouse and as well as the river view York Minster can also be seen from many bedrooms. A busy tourist hotel during the summer months it caters equally well for business clientele throughout the year and has a variety of meeting and function rooms to satisfy most needs. There are two styles of bedroom, those in Garden Court which are compact but functional and have recently been upgraded, and those in the main hotel which are more spacious and feature exceptionally wide windows. Two restaurants provide contrasting eating options including a carvery and there is also a very well equipped gymnasium. Staff are smartly uniformed and service is efficient.
187 en suite (bth/shr) (7 fmly) No smoking in 90 bedrooms CTV in all bedrooms No dogs (ex guide dogs) Lift Night porter 85P Sauna Solarium Gym Jacuzzi/spa Golf driving range International Cuisine V meals Coffee am Tea pm Last d 10pm
CARDS:

RED STAR HOTEL

★★★❀ **The Grange**

Clifton YO3 6AA (on A19)
☎ 01904 644744 FAX 01904 612453
A classical Regency town house which has been carefully restored, the Grange provides an atmosphere of relaxation and warmth and with its open fires and attentive and friendly staff is reminiscent of a country house, yet it is only a short walk from the centre of York. The bedrooms have been individually designed and although they contain every modern facility the furnishings are antique in style and the décor sympathetic with the period. The public rooms are intimate and comfortable and include the one rosette Ivy Restaurant, now incorporating a seafood bar. Downstairs The Brasserie is a popular venue for more informal meals. Christopher Falcus oversees the cooking in the more intimate Ivy Restaurant and his à la carte menu offers a varied choice of both French and traditional British country house dishes including delicious puddings. The wine list contains several fine clarets and also more modest wines including good value house wines and a selection from the New World.
30 en suite (bth/shr) CTV in all bedrooms STV Night porter 26P Xmas English & French Cuisine V meals Coffee am Tea pm Last d 10pm
ROOMS: (incl. bkfst) s £95-£105; d £105-£155 * **LB**
OFF-PEAK: (incl. bkfst & dinner) s £80; d £100
MEALS: Lunch £10-£16&alc High tea £6 Dinner £23&alc
CONF: Thtr 45 Class 20 Board 25 Del £124
CARDS:

RED STAR HOTEL

★★★❀❀❀ **Middlethorpe Hall**

Bishopthorpe Rd YO2 1QB (1.5m SW)
☎ 01904 641241 FAX 01904 620176
RS 25 Dec
On the edge of the racecourse stands this magnificently restored Queen Anne 'Dolls House'. Its square palazzo-like appearance has wings either side and a columned porch to the entrance. The entrance hall leads over a distinctive chequered floor to an intricately carved balustered staircase. The elegant drawing room, converted from the ballroom, is decorated in the country house genre, and the use of pilasters in the dining room probably make it the most ornate in the house. It is here that chef Andrew Wood has built a fine reputation which continues to improve. The menus ring in the seasonal changes - in winter game and wild duck feature prominently. From the gourmet menu a terrine of braised duck legs neatly layered with foie gras and held together by the jelly was complemented by a spiced pear dressing to Puy lentils. Salmis of pheasant comprised the breast lightly pan-fried, the leg braised and topping a delicious purée of Jerusalem artichoke and braised root vegetables. The gravy-like saucing was superb, dark and deep. The soufflé was accomplished, rising temptingly and, on this occasion, filled with a plum purée against a basket of plum sorbet. The service is attentive, professional and discreet at all times. The bedrooms do vary in size though all are furnished with the same degree of thought (and fine antiques). The former stable yard has been rebuilt to provide extra bedrooms.
30 en suite (bth/shr) CTV in all bedrooms No dogs Lift Night porter 70P Croquet lawn No children 8yrs Xmas V meals

Coffee am Tea pm No smoking in restaurant Last d 9.45pm
ROOMS: s £89-£108; d £125-£199 LB
MEALS: Lunch £12.50-£15.50 Dinner fr £25.95&alc*
CONF: Thtr 60 Class 30 Board 25 Del from £125
CARDS:

★★★ 72% **Dean Court**
Duncombe Place YO1 2EF (adjoining York Minster)
☎ 01904 625082 FAX 01904 620305

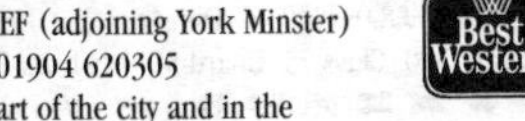

Standing right in the heart of the city and in the shadow of the impressive York Minster, this well furnished hotel has recently been totally refurbished. It provides well equipped and comfortable bedrooms together with several inviting public rooms. Food is highly recommended and is delightfully presented, and there is also a popular tea room. Service and hospitality are both very good and valet car parking is also provided.
41 en suite (bth/shr) (4 fmly) No smoking in 12 bedrooms CTV in all bedrooms No dogs (ex guide dogs) Lift Night porter 25P No

contd.

coaches Xmas English & French Cuisine V meals Coffee am Tea pm Last d 9.30pm
ROOMS: (incl. bkfst) s £75; d £110 * **LB**
MEALS: Lunch £9.75-£13.50 Dinner £16-£23.75*
CONF: Thtr 60 Class 24 Board 32 Del £110.45
CARDS:

See advertisement on page 695

★★★72% **Fairfield Manor Hotel**
Shipton Rd, Skelton YO3 6XW (on A19 Thirsk road 3m from city centre) ☎ 01904 670222
FAX 01904 670311

This large modern hotel stands on the A19 to the north of the city and overlooks pleasant open countryside. Public rooms are spacious and comfortable and a good range of dishes is available in the attractive Kilby's restaurant. Spacious bedrooms are very well equipped and include satellite television. Staff are polite and professional.

90 en suite (bth/shr) (20 fmly) No smoking in 20 bedrooms CTV in all bedrooms STV Lift Night porter Air conditioning 130P Library Xmas French & English Cuisine V meals Coffee am Tea pm No smoking in restaurant Last d 9.30pm
ROOMS: (incl. bkfst) s £79-£89; d £104-£114 **LB**
OFF-PEAK: (incl. bkfst) s £75-£85; d £120-£130
MEALS: Lunch fr £11.95&alc High tea £4.95-£9.95 Dinner £18-£21&alc
CONF: Thtr 250 Class 100 Board 80 Del from £90
CARDS:

★★★72% **Mount Royale**
The Mount YO2 2DA (S on A1036, towards racecourse) ☎ 01904 628856 FAX 01904 611171

Richard and Christine Oxtoby have filled this delightful hotel with paintings, antiques and objets d'art and have created a very special atmosphere. The bedrooms, some of which have separate dressing rooms, are a pleasure to occupy; some overlook the luxurious gardens and yet the house is only a short walk from the city. The food here is not to be missed and is in the very capable hands of Karen Brotherton and her dedicated team. The elegant restaurant offers interesting menus which feature excellent fresh produce. Guests can expect friendly and professional service from a well turned-out team.
23 en suite (bth/shr) (2 fmly) CTV in all bedrooms STV Night porter 18P No coaches Outdoor swimming pool (heated) Snooker Sauna Solarium Gym Beauty treatment centre Wkly live entertainment International Cuisine V meals Coffee am Last d 9.30pm
ROOMS: (incl. bkfst) s £70-£90; d £80-£120 * **LB**
MEALS: Dinner £5.50-£28.50alc*
CONF: Thtr 35 Board 25 Del £120
CARDS:

★★★71% **Parsonage Country House**
Main St YO4 6LE YORK ☎ 01904 728111 FAX 01904 728151
(For full entry see Escrick)

★★★70% **York Pavilion**
45 Main St, Fulford YO1 4PJ (on A19, opposite garage on Fulford Main St) ☎ 01904 622099
FAX 01904 626939

An attractive Georgian house with extensions and standing on the A19 to the south of the city and also enjoying well tended and pleasant gardens. Bedrooms are either in the main house or the converted stables and are all individually designed whilst all have been thoughtfully equipped. Public rooms include a very inviting and comfortable lounge together with an elegant restaurant where modern British cooking is served each evening. The menu changes daily and offers an interesting choice of options. Good conference and banqueting facilities are provided and staff are very friendly and helpful and provide professional service with a smile.

34 en suite (bth/shr) (2 fmly) No smoking in 3 bedrooms CTV in all bedrooms STV No dogs (ex guide dogs) Night porter 72P Xmas V meals Coffee am No smoking in restaurant Last d 9.30pm
ROOMS: (incl. bkfst) s fr £84; d fr £106 **LB**
OFF-PEAK: (incl. bkfst & dinner) d fr £65
MEALS: Lunch £8.95-£10.95 Dinner fr £19.95*
CONF: Thtr 150 Class 75 Board 50 Del from £85
CARDS:

See advertisement on page 695

★★★66% **Ambassador**
125 The Mount YO2 2DA ☎ 01904 641316
FAX 01904 640259

Popular with both tourists and business visitors, this fine Georgian Town House is ideally situated for both the city and the racecourse. Bedrooms are well equipped and generally spacious, with many of them enjoying an outlook over the delightful mature gardens to the rear. The restaurant is most elegant in design, and a peaceful place in which to select from the imaginative menu. Staff are both welcoming and professional, with every attention paid to ensure an enjoyable stay.
24 en suite (bth/shr) (2 fmly) CTV in all bedrooms STV No dogs (ex guide dogs) Lift Air conditioning 35P No coaches Xmas V meals Coffee am Tea pm Last d 9.30pm
ROOMS: (incl. bkfst) s £89-£99; d £105-£115 **LB**
OFF-PEAK: (incl. bkfst & dinner) s £75-£85; d £120-£130
MEALS: Lunch fr £12.95&alc Dinner £19.50-£24.50&alc
CONF: Thtr 50 Class 24 Board 24 Del from £85
CARDS:

★★★64% ***Kexby Bridge***
Hull Rd, Kexby YO4 5LD ☎ 01759 388223 & 388154
FAX 01759 388822
This modern and attractive hotel is found on the A1079 about 5 miles east of York. There are very well furnished bedrooms which are also thoughtfully equipped, whilst the public rooms include a pleasant restaurant with a conservatory and there is a spacious lounge bar. Service is professional and friendly and the hotel is family owned and run.
32 en suite (bth/shr) No smoking in 8 bedrooms CTV in all bedrooms No dogs (ex guide dogs) 60P Fishing English & French Cuisine V meals Coffee am Tea pm
CARDS:

★★★63% ***Monkbar***
Monkbar YO3 7PF (on inner ring road near York Minster) ☎ 01904 638086 FAX 01904 629195

CONSORT HOTELS

This busy hotel stands close to the centre of the city, on the corner of the ring road. Public areas are limited although there is a spacious restaurant, a coffee shop and a pleasant bar. Modern bedrooms are well equipped and service is both friendly and helpful.

contd.

There are plans to add a leisure club in the future as well as further bedrooms.
48 en suite (bth/shr) (3 fmly) CTV in all bedrooms Lift Night porter 50P English & French Cuisine V meals Coffee am Tea pm Last d 10pm
CARDS:

★★★63% *Novotel*

Fishergate YO1 4AD (S off A19)
☎ 01904 611660 FAX 01904 610925
Situated just outside the city walls but within walking distance of the centre of York, this impressive, modern brick building offers spacious and practical accommodation. Good sized bedrooms offer all the usual furnishings and are equipped with a double and single bed, while public areas include the Garden Brasserie which is open for dinner from 5pm to midnight. The hotel also offers a number of meeting rooms and extensive free parking.
124 en suite (bth/shr) (124 fmly) No smoking in 62 bedrooms CTV in all bedrooms STV Lift Night porter 150P Indoor swimming pool (heated) English & French Cuisine V meals Coffee am Tea pm
CARDS:

★★69% **Ashcroft**

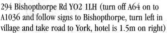

294 Bishopthorpe Rd YO2 1LH (turn off A64 on to A1036 and follow signs to Bishopthorpe, turn left in village and take road to York, hotel is 1.5m on right)
☎ 01904 659286 FAX 01904 640107
Closed 25 & 26 Dec
This Victorian mansion stands on the banks of the River Ouse overlooking the racecourse. Recently fully refurbished, the individually styled bedrooms are really well equipped and mostly spacious. Courtyard rooms are especially popular. The public areas are elegant and stylish and much has been done to restore the house to its former glory.
11 en suite (bth/shr) 4 annexe en suite (bth/shr) (3 fmly) CTV in all bedrooms 40P River moorings Xmas V meals Coffee am Tea pm No smoking in restaurant Last d 8.30pm
ROOMS: (incl. bkfst) s £45-£50; d £75-£80 * **LB**
OFF-PEAK: (incl. bkfst) s £38; d £60-£65
MEALS: Bar Lunch £4-£6 Dinner fr £13.50&alc*
CARDS:

★★69% **Beechwood Close**

19 Shipton Rd, Clifton YO3 6RE
☎ 01904 658378 FAX 01904 647124
Closed 25 Dec
Family owned and run, Beechwood Close is conveniently situated on the A19 about one mile north of the centre of the city. Spacious bedrooms are well equipped and furnished, and the well kept public areas are comfortable. A good selection of wine and food is available in the dining room, with attentive and friendly service. In addition there is generous car parking and a well kept garden to the rear.
14 en suite (bth/shr) (2 fmly) CTV in all bedrooms STV No dogs 36P No coaches V meals Coffee am Tea pm Last d 9pm
ROOMS: (incl. bkfst) s £43.50-£49.50; d £70-£75.50 **LB**
OFF-PEAK: (incl. bkfst) s fr £40; d fr £55
MEALS: Lunch £6.50-£7.25 High tea £6.80-£9.50 Dinner £13.75-£16.75*
CONF: Thtr 60 Class 35 Board 42
CARDS:

★★❀69% **Kilima**

129 Holgate Rd YO2 4DE (on A59, on W outskirts)
☎ 01904 658844 & 625787 FAX 01904 612083
The Kilima was once a Victorian parsonage and is now a well furnished and comfortable hotel which stands in its own grounds. It is within easy walking distance of the city and has the benefit of it own car parking. The well equipped bedrooms are a pleasure to occupy and the inviting public rooms have recently been refurbished. Quality cooking is provided by chef Christopher Betteridge, who offers both fixed price and carte menus with many interesting dishes. The staff are friendly and helpful and provide attentive service.
15 en suite (bth/shr) (1 fmly) CTV in all bedrooms 20P No coaches Xmas English & French Cuisine V meals Coffee am Tea pm No smoking in restaurant Last d 9.30pm
ROOMS: (incl. bkfst) s fr £50; d £79.50-£87.50 * **LB**
MEALS: Lunch £13.95&alc Dinner £17.95&alc
CONF: Thtr 25 Board 14 Del £84.50
CARDS:

★★67% **Heworth Court**

76-78 Heworth Green YO3 7TQ ☎ 01904 425156 FAX 01904 415290
A friendly style of service is provided at this family owned hotel, situated near the eastern walls. Public rooms, styled on Victorian lines, are comfortable and the well furnished bedrooms are equipped with good facilities. Bar meals offer an alternative to the extensive range of food served in the charming restaurant.
15 en suite (bth/shr) 10 annexe en suite (bth/shr) (7 fmly) No smoking in 1 bedroom CTV in all bedrooms No dogs 27P No coaches Xmas English & Continental Cuisine V meals Coffee am Tea pm No smoking in restaurant Last d 9.30pm
ROOMS: (incl. bkfst) s £42-£53; d £44-£76 **LB**
OFF-PEAK: (incl. bkfst) s £33-£43; d £36-£56
MEALS: Lunch £5.95-£16.95&alc High tea £1.10&alc Dinner £9.95-£16.95&alc
CONF: Thtr 50 Class 24 Board 28 Del from £65
CARDS:

See advertisement on page 697

★★67% **Knavesmire Manor**

302 Tadcaster Rd YO2 2HE (follow signs for York (West) A1036)
☎ 01904 702941 FAX 01904 709274
Conveniently located overlooking the racecourse, this ivy-clad Georgian house is furnished with antiques and has other period features around the public rooms. Arnolds Restaurant offers imaginative cooking each evening and the bedrooms are well equipped and pleasantly furnished. The Queen's Suite has a four poster bed and splendid views of the racecourse while some other rooms are found in the modern motel-style garden rooms at the rear. An indoor pool is also provided for guests' use.
12 en suite (bth/shr) 9 annexe en suite (shr) (2 fmly) CTV in all bedrooms STV Lift 27P Indoor swimming pool (heated) Sauna Xmas English & Continental Cuisine V meals Coffee am Tea pm Last d 9pm
ROOMS: (incl. bkfst) s £49-£59; d £69-£79 **LB**
OFF-PEAK: (incl. bkfst) s £39.50-£49; d £49-£59
CONF: Thtr 36 Class 30 Board 28 Del from £59
CARDS:

★★66% **Jacobean Lodge**
Plainville Ln, Wigginton YO3 3RG (between B1363 York/Helmsley and A19 Shipton road) ☎ 01904 762749 FAX 01904 768403
This well furnished and comfortable hotel has been carefully extended from when it was once a farmhouse. It stands in open countryside a short distance from the city and provides modern and well cared for and equipped bedrooms. There is a very good range of home-cooked meals which are served in the bar or the pretty dining room overlooking a pleasant garden and the giant sized chessboard.
8 en suite (bth/shr) 6 annexe en suite (bth/shr) (2 fmly) CTV in all bedrooms 52P Giant chess Childrens play area Wkly live entertainment ch fac English & Continental Cuisine V meals Coffee am Last d 9.30pm
ROOMS: (incl. bkfst) s £34-£36; d £56-£62 * **LB**
OFF-PEAK: (incl. bkfst) d £50-£56
MEALS: Lunch £6.95-£16alc Dinner £10-£25alc
CONF: Thtr 40 Class 30 Board 30 Del from £45
CARDS:

★★65% **Clifton Bridge**
Water End, Clifton YO3 6LL (NW side of city between A19 & A59)
☎ 01904 610510 FAX 01904 640208
Closed 24-25 Dec
This family-owned and run stands close to Clifton Green and the River Ouse and is within walking distance of the city. The house is well furnished and features oak panelled walls in the public rooms whilst the modern bedrooms are well equipped and attractively decorated. Service is both friendly and attentive.
14 en suite (bth/shr) (1 fmly) CTV in all bedrooms 14P English & French Cuisine V meals Coffee am Tea pm No smoking in restaurant Last d 8pm
ROOMS: (incl. bkfst) s £40-£54; d £64 * **LB**
OFF-PEAK: (incl. bkfst) s £35-£40; d £50-£64

contd.

Y

MEALS: Dinner £10&alc
CONF: Thtr 20 Board 16 Del from £50
CARDS:

See advertisement on page 699

★★65% **Hudsons**
60 Bootham YO3 7BZ (situated on the A19 which runs from the north of the city into city centre, just after Bootham Park and before city walls) ☎ 01904 621267 FAX 01904 654719
Standing on the A19 just to the north of the city and within easy walking distance, this family-owned hotel is a pleasing conversion of two Victorian houses and has been carefully extended. Meals are provided either in the bistro or the restaurant and service is friendly and helpful. Bedrooms are modern and well equipped, with some in the main part of the hotel whilst others are in the rear extension.
31 en suite (bth/shr) CTV in all bedrooms STV No dogs (ex guide dogs) Lift 34P Xmas English & French Cuisine V meals Coffee am Last d 9.30pm
ROOMS: (incl. bkfst) s £55-£65; d £80-£90 * **LB**
OFF-PEAK: (incl. bkfst) s £45-£50; d £65-£70
MEALS: Dinner £15-£16&alc*
CONF: Thtr 80 Class 30 Board 25 Del from £81.95
CARDS:

See advertisement on page 699

★★64% **Alhambra Court**
31 St Mary's, Bootham YO3 7DD (off Bootham A19)
☎ 01904 628474 FAX 01904 610690
Closed 24-26 Dec & 1-13 Jan
This attractive Georgian building is set in a quiet side road just a short walk from the city centre. The hotel is family owned and run in a friendly manner, and the pleasant bedrooms are well furnished and equipped. One of the two lounges is reserved for non-smokers, and good home-cooked food is served in the restaurant.
24 en suite (bth/shr) (5 fmly) No smoking in 9 bedrooms CTV in all bedrooms Lift 25P English & French Cuisine No smoking area in restaurant Last d 8.30pm
ROOMS: (incl. bkfst) s £31.50-£39.50; d £45-£62 **LB**
MEALS: Dinner fr £12.50&alc*
CARDS:

See advertisement on page 699

★★64% **Cottage**
3 Clifton Green YO3 6LH ☎ 01904 643711 FAX 01904 611230
Closed 24-26 Dec
This family owned hotel stands overlooking Clifton Green and is only a short walk from the city centre. The bedrooms are bright, fresh and modern and some are found in a rear courtyard. The public rooms, although not over spacious, are well cared for and comfortably furnished. A good range of dishes is available in the cosy dining room and service is friendly and helpful.
16 en suite (bth/shr) 3 annexe en suite (bth/shr) (3 fmly) CTV in all bedrooms STV 10P V meals Coffee am Tea pm Last d 8.30pm
ROOMS: (incl. bkfst) s £30-£45; d £45-£60 * **LB**
MEALS: Dinner £9.50-£11.50&alc*
CARDS:

See advertisement on opposite page

★★64% **Holgate Bridge**
106-108 Holgate Rd YO2 4BB (on A59 Harrogate road close to Holgate Bridge) ☎ 01904 635971 FAX 01904 670049
Closed 24-26 Dec
Convenient for walking to York town centre and situated on the A59, this family owned and run friendly hotel also has the benefit of its own car park to the rear. Bedrooms are bright with good facilities, some overlooking the small well tended garden. Meals are served in the lower ground floor dining room, which has an adjoining bar whilst there is also a cosy lounge opening on to a paved patio.
14 rms (11 bth/shr) (4 fmly) CTV in all bedrooms 14P No coaches V meals No smoking in restaurant Last d 9pm
ROOMS: (incl. bkfst) s £22-£35; d £38-£56 * **LB**
MEALS: Bar Lunch fr £5 Dinner £7.80-£13.85*
CARDS:

See advertisement on opposite page

★★64% **Lady Anne Middletons Hotel**
Skeldergate YO1 1DS (A1036 to W of town, at city wall turn right and first left) ☎ 01904 632257 & 630456 FAX 01904 613043
Closed 24-27 Dec
Located in the heart of the city and having the benefit of its own car park, this collection of historic buildings is now a pleasantly furnished hotel. Adequate lounges are provided and there is also a leisure centre available to guests by prior booking. Bedrooms are either in the main house or in one of the other buildings and they are all well equipped and furnished along modern lines.
40 rms (37 bth/shr) 15 annexe en suite (bth/shr) (3 fmly) No smoking in 15 bedrooms CTV in 52 bedrooms No dogs (ex guide dogs) Night porter 56P Indoor swimming pool (heated) Sauna Solarium Gym No leisure facilities for under 16yrs Xmas V meals Coffee am Tea pm Last d 9pm
ROOMS: (incl. bkfst) s fr £70; d fr £100 * **LB**
OFF-PEAK: (incl. bkfst) s fr £50; d fr £70
MEALS: Lunch £5-£7 Dinner £14.95-£16.95*
CONF: Thtr 50 Class 50 Board 20 Del from £70
CARDS:

★★63% **Elmbank**
The Mount YO2 2DD (on A1036 Tadcaster road following signs for racecourse)
☎ 01904 610653 FAX 01904 627139
CONSORT HOTELS
Celebrating its centenary in 1997, this well furnished hotel is within easy walking distance of the city and is close to the famous racecourse. Bedrooms are well equipped whilst the public rooms include an impressive hall with murals and a magnificent oak staircase. A good range of interesting food is available and the staff are friendly and helpful at all times.
48 rms (46 bth/shr) (5 fmly) CTV in all bedrooms Night porter 20P Sauna Xmas V meals Coffee am Tea pm No smoking area in restaurant Last d 9pm
ROOMS: (incl. bkfst) s £69-£79; d £95-£105 **LB**
OFF-PEAK: (incl. bkfst & dinner) s £74-£84; d £118-£128
MEALS: Sunday Lunch £9.95 High tea £4.95-£9.95 Dinner £16-£18&alc
CONF: Thtr 100 Class 35 Board 40 Del from £70
CARDS:

★★63% **Newington**
147 Mount Vale YO2 2DJ (W on A1036)
☎ 01904 625173 FAX 01904 679937
Standing next to the famous racecourse, this value-for-money hotel provides modern and well equipped bedrooms, some peacefully located in a rear coach house; some of the bedrooms have four-poster beds. The lounges are inviting and a good range of home-cooked food is available in the attractive dining room, whilst service is friendly and attentive. There is also the added attraction of a heated indoor pool.
25 en suite (bth/shr) 15 annexe en suite (bth/shr) (3 fmly) CTV in all bedrooms No dogs Lift 40P Indoor swimming pool (heated) Sauna Xmas V meals Coffee am No smoking in restaurant Last d 9pm
ROOMS: (incl. bkfst) s £40-£42; d £54-£62 **LB**
OFF-PEAK: (incl. bkfst) s £28-£42; d £40-£60
MEALS: Lunch £6.50-£9.50 Dinner £13.95
CARDS:

Y

★★63% **Savages**
St Peters Grove YO3 6AQ (off A19 at Clifton)
☎ 01904 610818 FAX 01904 627729
Closed 25 & 26 Dec
Standing in a quiet side road and within easy walking distance of the city and the Minster, this family-owned and run hotel offers a good all round standard of both accommodation and service. The bedrooms are well equipped and the comfortable lounge is a pleasant room in which to relax both before and after dinner.
20 en suite (bth/shr) (3 fmly) CTV in all bedrooms No dogs (ex guide dogs) 14P V meals Coffee am Tea pm No smoking in restaurant Last d 8.45pm
ROOMS: (incl. bkfst) s £25-£40; d £50-£68 **LB**
OFF-PEAK: (incl. bkfst) s £20-£32; d £40-£60
MEALS: Dinner £11.50-£13
CARDS:

★★62% **Abbots' Mews**
6 Marygate Ln, Bootham YO3 7DE (overlooking Marygate car park)
☎ 01904 634866 FAX 01904 612848
Quietly located within easy walking distance of the city, this Victorian cottage has been carefully converted into a pleasant hotel. Bedrooms are split between the main house and other buildings, but all are well equipped and pleasantly decorated. Public rooms include a cosy bar and a spacious restaurant which overlooks a small floodlit garden and serves a good range of tasty dishes.
12 en suite (shr) 41 annexe en suite (bth/shr) (9 fmly) CTV in 50 bedrooms No dogs (ex guide dogs) 30P Xmas International Cuisine V meals Coffee am Tea pm Last d 9.30pm
ROOMS: (incl. bkfst) s fr £29.50; d fr £49 * **LB**
MEALS: Lunch £7.50-£7.95 Dinner £10&alc*
CONF: Thtr 30 Class 30 Board 20 Del from £68
CARDS:

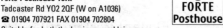

See advertisement on page 701

★★62% ***Elliotts***
Sycamore Place, Bootham YO3 7DW
☎ 01904 623333 FAX 01904 654908
Closed 25 Dec-9 Jan
Elliots Hotel is a handsome Victorian house tucked away from the hustle and bustle yet only a short walk from the centre. It offers good standards of accommodation in a variety of styles and an extensive range of bar and restaurant meals.
18 en suite (bth/shr) (1 fmly) CTV in all bedrooms Night porter 10P V meals Coffee am Tea pm Last d 9.30pm
CARDS:

Forte Posthouse York

Tadcaster Rd YO2 2QF (W on A1036)
☎ 01904 707921 FAX 01904 702804
Suitable for both the business and leisure traveller, this bright hotel provides modern accommodation in well equipped bedrooms with en suite bathrooms. For more details about Forte Posthouse hotels, consult the Contents page for the section on Hotel Groups.
143 en suite (bth/shr)
ROOMS: s fr £69; d £69-£79 *
CONF: Thtr 100 Class 40 Board 40 Del from £65

Travel Inn
Bilborough Top, Colton YO2 3PP (on A64 between Tadcaster & York) ☎ 01937 835067
FAX 01937 835934
Purpose-built accommodation, offering spacious, well equipped bedrooms, all with en suite bathrooms. Meals may be taken at the nearby family restaurant. For more information about Travel Inns, consult the Contents page under Hotel Groups.
60 en suite (bth/shr)
ROOMS: d £35.50 *

YOXFORD Suffolk Map 05 TM36

★★69% **Satis House**
IP17 3EX (set back from A12 midway between Ipswich & Lowerstoft)
☎ 01728 668418 FAX 01728 668640
A 250-year-old listed house features old pieces of furniture and some original Victorian bathrooms adapted for today's guests. Local interest centres on the restaurant, open in the evening and offering a Malaysian-based menu.
8 en suite (bth/shr) CTV in all bedrooms No dogs 30P No coaches Tennis (hard) Sauna Jacuzzi/spa No children 7yrs English, French & Malaysian Cuisine Last d 9.30pm
ROOMS: (incl. bkfst) s £52.50-£55; d £65-£82.50 * **LB**
OFF-PEAK: (incl. bkfst) s £47.50-£52.50; d £60-£75
MEALS: Lunch £10-£12.95 Dinner £15.95-£19.95&alc*
CONF: Thtr 26 Class 20 Board 14 Del from £75
CARDS:  

Y

A

Channel Islands

Directory of establishments in alphabetical order of location.

CHANNEL ISLANDS Map 16

ALDERNEY

★★★63% **Chez André**
Victoria St, St Anne GY9 3TA ☎ 01481 822777 FAX 01481 822962
Closed Nov-Feb
Parts of this family run town centre hotel date back over 200 years. Bedrooms have been individually furnished and equipped with a wide range of modern facilities. Public areas include an attractive and cosy reception lounge and a split-level bar and restaurant serving an extensive selection of fish, meat and vegetarian dishes on fixed-price and carte menus.
11 en suite (bth/shr) (4 fmly) No smoking in 4 bedrooms CTV in all bedrooms No coaches Pool table Wkly live entertainment Xmas English & French Cuisine V meals Coffee am Tea pm No smoking area in restaurant Last d 9pm
ROOMS: (incl. bkfst) s £20-£40; d £40-£80 * **LB**
MEALS: Lunch £7.95-£13.95 Dinner £13.95-£14.95&alc
CARDS:

★★❀❀73% ***Inchalla***
St Anne ☎ 01481 823220 FAX 01481 824045
This delightful modern hotel is located within easy walking distance of the centre of St Anne. Some of the en suite bedrooms enjoy glorious sea views; all are en suite, tastefully appointed and well equipped. An attractive downstairs lounge features cane seating and the personal pieces of the resident proprietor Mrs Valerie Willis. The hotel has relaxing gardens and the island's only jacuzzi, sauna and solarium. Chef Richard Cranfield offers an interesting selection of dishes from a daily changing table d'hÙte and extensive carte menus. At a recent inspection meal, a light and subtly flavoured fish terrine was followed by a tasty cassoulet packed with flageolet beans, bacon, sausage and fresh herbs. Deserts and bread are home-made and a short wine list offers a good choice.
10 en suite (bth/shr) (2 fmly) CTV in all bedrooms STV No dogs 8P No coaches Sauna Solarium Jacuzzi/spa English & French Cuisine V meals Coffee am Tea pm Last d 9pm
CARDS:

GUERNSEY

CATEL (CASTEL)

★★★❀73% **Cobo Bay**
Cobo GY5 7HB (on main coast road)
☎ 01481 57102 FAX 01481 54542
Closed 5 Jan-6 Mar
Overlooking the golden sands at Cobo Bay on the glorious west coast of Guernsey, this family-run hotel provides a range of tastefully decorated and furnished modern bedrooms. The rooms on the front of the building have balconies and enjoy magnificent sea views. Public rooms include the Chesterfield Bar, with its leather sofas and matching easy chairs, the large Cobo suite, available for private functions and the candlelit air-conditioned restaurant. A selection of fish, meat and vegetarian dishes are offered on the menus and the best of fresh local produce is used in the preparation of good food. The resident proprietor extends a personal welcome to guests and along with a friendly team of professionally trained staff carries out attentive services. The hotel benefits from a health suite where facilities include a sauna, Jacuzzi and solarium and also owns the popular Rockmount pub next door.
36 en suite (bth/shr) (1 fmly) CTV in all bedrooms STV No dogs (ex guide dogs) Lift Night porter 60P No coaches Snooker Sauna Solarium Pool table Jacuzzi/spa Wkly live entertainment International Cuisine V meals Last d 9.45pm
ROOMS: (incl. bkfst) s £34-£64; d £68-£88 **LB**
OFF-PEAK: (incl. bkfst) s £29-£39; d £58-£78
CARDS:

★★69% **Hotel Hougue du Pommier**
Hougue Du Pommier Rd GY5 7FQ ☎ 01481 56531 FAX 01481 56260
This former farmhouse dates in part from the 18th-century and much of the original character has been retained in the cosy beamed public areas. Many of the bedrooms have recently been redesigned and completely refurbished to a good standard creating more space and comfort, in line with the de luxe category executive rooms. The good value bar meals are popular, and there is a choice of menus in the oak-panelled bar.Service is friendly and efficient and personally managed by Mr Stephen Bone.
43 en suite (bth/shr) (7 fmly) CTV in all bedrooms STV 87P Outdoor swimming pool (heated) Golf 10 Sauna Solarium Pool table Putting green Games room Table tennis Wkly live entertainment Xmas English & Continental Cuisine V meals Coffee am Tea pm No smoking area in restaurant Last d 9pm
ROOMS: (incl. bkfst) s £27-£41; d £54-£82 **LB**
MEALS: Sunday Lunch fr £8.75 High tea fr £2.75 Dinner fr £14&alc
CARDS:
See advertisement on page 705

FERMAIN BAY

★★★74% **La Favorita**

GY4 6SD ☎ 01481 35666 FAX 01481 35413
Closed 4 Jan-12 Feb
Beautifully located on a hillside overlooking a wooded valley leading down to Fermain Bay, this professionally run hotel has a lot to commend it, not least the range of comfortable bedrooms all furnished and equipped to a modern standard, the best with balcony and sea view. Extensive facilities include La Terrasse Brasserie and Coffee Shop, open throughout the day for all meals and light refreshments, the no-smoking Country House Restaurant and bar-lounge, which features the traditional cooking of chef Kelvin Clark, two elegantly furnished lounges, and good indoor leisure facilities. Service is friendly and particularly well managed by the proprietor Mr Simon Wood.
37 en suite (bth/shr) (6 fmly) No smoking in all bedrooms CTV in all bedrooms No dogs Lift 40P No coaches Indoor swimming pool (heated) Sauna Jacuzzi/spa Xmas English & French Cuisine V meals
contd.

Coffee am Tea pm No smoking in restaurant Last d 9pm
ROOMS: (incl. bkfst) s £49-£65; d £88-£93 **LB**
OFF-PEAK: (incl. bkfst) s £38.50-£45; d £67-£72
MEALS: Sunday Lunch £12 High tea fr £4alc Dinner £14.50-£16.50&alc
CONF: Thtr 70 Class 30 Board 30 Del from £60
CARDS:

★★★67% Le Chalet
GY4 6SD ☎ 01481 35716 FAX 01481 35718
Closed mid Oct-mid Apr

CONSORT HOTELS

Situated in six acres of wooded grounds leading directly down to Fermain Bay, this hotel continues to be a firm favourite with many regular guests. Bedrooms are equipped with modern comforts and the public areas, on two levels and positioned to enjoy the sea views, include a popular bar-lounge, smart restaurant, an attractive residents' lounge and a sun terrace. The more recent addition of a spa bath, sauna, solarium and mini gym is an added attraction.
41 en suite (bth/shr) (5 fmly) CTV in all bedrooms 35P No coaches Indoor swimming pool (heated) Sauna Solarium Jacuzzi/spa English, Austrian & French Cuisine V meals Coffee am Tea pm Last d 9.30pm
ROOMS: (incl. bkfst) s £40-£51.50; d £67-£95 **LB**
OFF-PEAK: (incl. bkfst) s £35-£48; d £55-£70
MEALS: Sunday Lunch fr £9 Dinner fr £13.50&alc
CARDS:

FOREST

★★65% Le Chene
Forest Rd GY8 0AH ☎ 01481 35566 FAX 01481 39456
Closed Nov-25 Apr
Dating from 1842, this former manor house has been skilfully extended to provide a range of well equipped, modern bedrooms. It is attractively set on the side of a hill and the public rooms and some of the bedrooms are located on the lower floor. There is a no-smoking dining room, sun lounge and a beamed cellar bar. Service is particularly friendly, and a cordial atmosphere is generated by the resident proprietors Mr and Mrs Arthur Phillips.
26 en suite (bth/shr) (2 fmly) CTV in all bedrooms No dogs 21P No coaches Outdoor swimming pool No children 12yrs English & Continental Cuisine V meals Coffee am Tea pm No smoking in restaurant Last d 7.30pm
ROOMS: (incl. bkfst) s £31-£41; d £46-£66 *
MEALS: Dinner £12*
CARDS:

PERELLE

★★★❀❀71% L'Atlantique
Perelle Bay GY7 9NA ☎ 01481 64056
FAX 01481 63800
RS Jan & Feb
Located on the west coast road, flanked by sandy beaches, this modern hotel offers accommodation in well equipped mostly non-smoking bedrooms, the best of which have good views over Pirelle Bay. Smart public areas include a very popular and well appointed Victorian-style lounge featuring a wide range of bar meals, while the Green Restaurant and Cocktail Bar - outright winner of the Guernsey Restaurant of the Year Competition for 1994 - offers a more formal and up-market alternative, chef Gary Kindley's imaginative French and modern dishes often making good use of locally caught seafood. A daily-changing fixed-price dinner menu appears alongside the carte, and there is an Epicurean Club menu every third Wednesday and Thursday as well as the serious vegetarian menu which is always available. A meal chosen from the special Competition menu included a well made poached trout and brill sausage (served with a tasty fish stock fumé scented with fennel and Noilly Prat, and accompanied by home-made cumin bread) and a timbale of baked salmon with a sabayon, textured with asparagus points, and scallop sauce; the highlight, however, was the marbled chocolate terrine, flavoured with orange and Tia Maria, and this was followed by freshly brewed coffee and nougat chocolate petit fours. The hotel also features ten self-catering cottages.
23 rms (21 bth/shr) (4 fmly) No smoking in 12 bedrooms CTV in all bedrooms No dogs (ex guide dogs) 80P No coaches Outdoor swimming pool (heated) Tariff prices include car hire International Cuisine V meals Coffee am No smoking area in restaurant Last d 9.30pm
ROOMS: (incl. bkfst) s £39-£47.50; d £68-£85 * **LB**
OFF-PEAK: (incl. bkfst) s £35-£38; d £60-£66
MEALS: Sunday Lunch £9.95 Dinner £14.95&alc*
CARDS:

ST MARTIN

★★★❀70% Hotel Bella Luce
La Fosse GY4 6EB ☎ 01481 38764 FAX 01481 39561
A 12th-century former manor house retains much of its original atmosphere and character. The accommodation has been skilfully extended to create well furnished modern bedrooms, many of which overlook the attractive walled gardens. Public areas include a spacious beamed bar, a traditionally furnished lounge and a double-sided candlelit dining room. Popular bar lunches are served in the garden on sunny days, while the restaurant offers a more formal dinner. The carte and set-price choices feature local produce whenever possible including first class local seafood. Packed luncheons and afternoon teas can also be provided. There are also a laundry room, ample parking space and a swimming pool set in a sun trap in a corner of the grounds.
31 en suite (bth/shr) (9 fmly) CTV in all bedrooms STV Night porter 50P No coaches Outdoor swimming pool (heated) Sauna Solarium ch fac Xmas English & Continental Cuisine V meals Coffee am Tea pm No smoking area in restaurant Last d 9.30pm
ROOMS: (incl. bkfst) s £36-£50; d £70-£95 * **LB**
OFF-PEAK: (incl. bkfst) s £25-£33; d £50-£66
MEALS: Sunday Lunch £9 High tea £2.75 Dinner £15&alc
CARDS:

See advertisement on opposite page

★★★❀69% La Barbarie
Saints Rd, Saints Bay GY4 6ES ☎ 01481 35217 FAX 01481 35208
Dating from the 17th century, this granite-built former priory with modern extensions and an outdoor pool enjoys a peaceful setting with easy access by road to the island's capital St Peter Port. Converted to a hotel in 1950 La Barbarie retains all the character and charm of the original building, now carefully combined with modern facilities and creature comforts. Bedrooms are cottagey in style and tastefully decorated with pretty fabrics and thoughtful touches. The beamed restaurant offers an intimate atmosphere and the cooking skills of Jerry Allen continue to impress. Fresh local fish is a speciality and a wide range of interesting dishes make up the à la carte and fixed-priced menus.
23 en suite (bth/shr) (4 fmly) CTV in all bedrooms No dogs 50P Outdoor swimming pool (heated) Xmas English & French Cuisine V meals Coffee am Tea pm No smoking area in restaurant Last d 9.30pm
ROOMS: (incl. bkfst) s £22-£54.50; d £44-£89 * **LB**
OFF-PEAK: (incl. bkfst) s £18.50-£34.50; d £37-£69
MEALS: Sunday Lunch £9.25 Dinner £13.50-£14.25&alc*
CARDS:

★★★❀68% Idlerocks
Jerbourg Point GY4 6BJ ☎ 01481 37711 FAX 01481 35592
A hospitable family-run hotel, the Idlerocks is set in 5.5 acres of garden and enjoys superb sea views from its cliff-top position.

Extensive upgrading, which is still under way, has provided a range of comfortable no-smoking bedrooms, including some with sea views (a number of which have balconies); standard singles are spacious and there are luxurious mini suites. Guests can dine in either the Admirals Restaurant or the less formal Raffles Lounge and Terrace. Chef Kelvin Clark offers reliable standards of cooking, his set-price and carte menus offering a good range of freshly prepared dishes. Restaurant service is personally supervised by Herbie Witzke, whose attention to detail and customer care is very evident. At the time of our visit there were plans afoot to extend the restaurant and to provide additional and more comfortable lounge facilities.

28 en suite (bth/shr) (4 fmly) No smoking in 11 bedrooms CTV in all bedrooms STV Night porter 100P Outdoor swimming pool (heated) Xmas English & French Cuisine V meals Coffee am Tea pm Last d 9.30pm

ROOMS: (incl. bkfst & dinner) s £46; d £90 * **LB**

OFF-PEAK: (incl. bkfst & dinner) s £30; d £33

MEALS: Sunday Lunch £9.60-£12.50 Dinner £14.50-£18.50&alc*

CONF: Board 30

CARDS:

★★★68% **St Margaret's Lodge**

Forest Rd GY4 6UE (1m W) ☎ 01481 35757 FAX 01481 37594

Conveniently located close to the airport this long established and very popular hotel has a good range of well equipped comfortable bedrooms, some of which overlook the runway along with the swimming pool and gardens, whilst others have a balcony. Chef Kevin Buckley holds out the promise of some good meals to come in the Garden Room Restaurant, and with plans to upgrade and extend the public rooms with a conservatory terrace there will be a lot to commend. Service is professionally managed and personally supervised by the manager Mr Michael Garrett.

47 en suite (bth) (2 fmly) CTV in all bedrooms STV No dogs Lift Night porter 100P Outdoor swimming pool (heated) Sauna Solarium Croquet lawn Putting green Table tennis Xmas English & French Cuisine V meals Coffee am Tea pm No smoking in restaurant Last d 9.30pm

ROOMS: (incl. bkfst) s £28-£42.50; d £56-£112 * **LB**

OFF-PEAK: (incl. bkfst) s £20-£30; d £40-£80

MEALS: Lunch fr £9.95&alc Dinner £15.95&alc

CONF: Thtr 120 Class 80 Board 20 Del from £45

CARDS:  £

See advertisement on page 707

★★★65% **Green Acres**

Les Hubits GY4 6LS (behind parish church, 2m from airport)

☎ 01481 35711 FAX 01481 35978

Peacefully situated in its own grounds overlooking a heated swimming pool and furnished terrace, this well managed hotel in the country parish of St Martins is within walking distance of Fermain Bay and only a mile from the centre of St Peter Port. Comfortable bedrooms are decorated in modern styles and the public areas include a tastefully furnished lounge, a bar lounge and a restaurant. Bar meals are

contd.

popular at lunchtime, and the carte regularly features local seafood.
48 en suite (bth/shr) (3 fmly) CTV in all bedrooms No dogs (ex guide dogs) 75P Outdoor swimming pool (heated) Xmas English & French Cuisine V meals Coffee am Tea pm No smoking in restaurant Last d 8.30pm
ROOMS: (incl. bkfst) s £27.50-£49; d £54-£78 *
MEALS: Sunday Lunch £10 Dinner £14.50&alc*
CONF: Thtr 30 Class 20 Board 20 Del from £45
CARDS:

★★★63% **La Trelade**
Forest Rd GY4 6UB ☎ 01481 35454 FAX 01481 37855
Standing in its own well kept gardens in the country parish of St Martin's, La Trelade is only a stroll away from the rugged cliffs and secluded sandy bays of Guernsey's south coast. Tastefully decorated bedrooms have been equipped with modern comforts and the public areas include a choice of lounges and an attractive bar. Entertainment is provided in the Friday nghtclub, and there is an outdoor heated pool for the more energetic.
45 en suite (bth/shr) (3 fmly) CTV in all bedrooms STV Lift Night porter 120P Outdoor swimming pool (heated) Snooker Pool table Putting green Wkly live entertainment ch fac Xmas English & French Cuisine V meals Coffee am Tea pm No smoking in restaurant Last d 9.30pm
ROOMS: (incl. bkfst) s £20-£39; d £40-£78 * **LB**
MEALS: Lunch £9.25 High tea £3.80-£7.45 Dinner £14&alc*
CONF: Thtr 120 Class 48 Board 40 Del from £58
CARDS:

See advertisement on opposite page

★★72% **Michele**
Les Hubits GY4 6NB ☎ 01481 38065 FAX 01481 39492
Closed Nov-Mar
This modern family run hotel is situated down a quiet lane not far from Fermain Bay in the St Martins district of this picturesque island. Resident proprietors Susie and Roger Edwards have created a delightful small hotel with its own well kept gardens. The atmosphere is relaxed and friendly and Susie and Roger are natural hosts. Bedrooms are brightly decorated with co-ordinating colour schemes, each is en-suite and has been equipped with colour televisions, telephones, tea making facilities and hairdryers. Downstairs is a comfortable bar lounge and a smart No Smoking dining room where a daily four-course dinner is available with a choice of home-cooked dishes.
13 en suite (bth/shr) (3 fmly) CTV in all bedrooms No dogs (ex guide dogs) 13P No coaches Outdoor swimming pool (heated) No children 8yrs V meals No smoking in restaurant
ROOMS: (incl. bkfst & dinner) s £27-£36; d £54-£72 * **LB**
CARDS:

ST PETER PORT

★★★★ 71% **St Pierre Park**
Rohais GY1 1FD ☎ 01481 728282 FAX 01481 712041
Set in 45 acres of mature parkland, complete with lake and nine-hole golf course, this modern, purpose-built hotel has a good range of facilities to offer including a travel agency. All the bedrooms have a balcony or terrace with good views and are comprehensively equipped. Diners can choose between the formal and elegant Victor Hugo restaurant where there is piano entertainment most evenings or the smart but more casual Cafe Renoir. Both have a variety of menus.
135 en suite (bth/shr) (4 fmly) No smoking in 17 bedrooms CTV in all bedrooms STV No dogs (ex guide dogs) Lift Night porter 150P Indoor swimming pool (heated) Golf 9 Tennis (hard) Snooker Sauna Solarium Gym Pool table Croquet lawn Putting green Jacuzzi/spa Trim trail Wkly live entertainment ch fac Xmas V meals Coffee am Tea pm No smoking area in restaurant Last d 10pm
ROOMS: (incl. bkfst) s £115-£125; d £155-£165 * **LB**
MEALS: Lunch £9.95-£11.95&alc High tea fr £4.95 Dinner £18.95&alc*
CONF: Thtr 200 Class 100 Board 30 Del £160
CARDS:

★★★71% **Hotel de Havelet**
Havelet ☎ 01481 722199 FAX 01481 714057
This extended Georgian mansion, set in an elevated position with magnificent views over Castle Cornet, is close to the centre of the town and most of its comfortable bedrooms are set around an inner courtyard balustrade. The indoor swimming pool is an added attraction and the public rooms, situated in the adjoining Coach House, provide a range of eating options. The Wellington Boot restaurant is ideal for more formal dining whilst The Havelet Grill and The Stable Bar offer a more relaxed style. The emphasis is on personal service, and the staff take pleasure in their guests' comfort.
34 en suite (bth/shr) (4 fmly) CTV in all bedrooms STV No dogs 40P No coaches Indoor swimming pool (heated) Sauna Jacuzzi/spa Xmas English, Austrian & French Cuisine V meals Coffee am Tea pm No smoking area in restaurant Last d 9.30pm
ROOMS: (incl. bkfst) s £47.50-£75; d £80-£110 * **LB**
OFF-PEAK: (incl. bkfst) s £42.50-£50; d £68-£78
MEALS: Lunch fr £12alc Dinner fr £14.50&alc
CONF: Thtr 44 Class 24 Board 26 Del from £75
CARDS:

★★★70% ***La Collinette***
St Jacques GY1 1SN ☎ 01481 710331
FAX 01481 713516
Run by the same family for over 36 years, this friendly hotel is quietly situated within walking distance of the town centre. Bedrooms are particularly well furnished and equipped modern standard; most have also been completely upgraded and many overlook the inner swimming pool and attractive garden, with communicating suites being especially suitable for families with young children. Public areas comprise a comfortable reception lounge, a split-level restaurantand the Bear Bar - popular not only for its extensive range of bar meals but because it is the only place on the Island selling Grizzly's real ale - The atmosphere is friendly and welcoming with service provided by cheerful staff and professional management. New self-catering apartments are also available.
27 en suite (bth/shr) CTV in all bedrooms STV No dogs (ex guide dogs) 40P No coaches Outdoor swimming pool (heated) Sauna Gym Jacuzzi/spa ch fac English & Continental Cuisine V meals Coffee am Tea pm Last d 9pm
CARDS:

See advertisement on opposite page

★★★70% **Moore's**
Pollet ☎ 01481 724452 FAX 01481 714037
Moore's Hotel, an elegant blue granite building once the home of the de Saumarez's, one of Guernsey's oldest families, stands on the High Street in the centre of St Peter Port, with parking only five minutes' walk away. Bedrooms, furnished in modern style, fall into three categories, the best having good views and a sunny aspect. For light refreshments and tea during the day there is a patisserie, while for dinner guests can choose between the carvery and the conservatory restaurant; there are also two popular bars. Various ferries depart frequently to France and the other islands from the harbour, which is within strolling distance, and in the summer months courtesy transport is available to and from the other hotels in this well managed group.
46 en suite (bth/shr) 3 annexe en suite (bth/shr) (8 fmly) CTV in all bedrooms STV Lift Night porter No coaches Sauna Solarium Gym Jacuzzi/spa Xmas English & French Cuisine V meals Coffee am Tea pm Last d 9pm
ROOMS: (incl. bkfst) s £42.50-£60; d £75-£140 **LB**

OFF-PEAK: (incl. bkfst) s £35-£40; d £52-£64
MEALS: Lunch fr £9.50&alc High tea fr £5alc Dinner fr £14&alc
CONF: Thtr 40 Class 20 Board 15 Del from £70
CARDS: 

★★★ 68% **La Fregate**
Les Cotils GY1 1UT ☎ 01481 724624 FAX 01481 720443
Overlooking the harbour, this fine hotel enjoys splendid sea views from many of the double-glazed bedrooms. Some rooms have balconies, ideal for al fresco breakfasting. The cooking here is a major attraction, chefs Ossie Steinsdorfer and Gunter Botzenhardt continuing to impress, especially with their sea food specialities. Good use is made of fresh local produce in interesting dishes. There are plans to refurbish the bedrooms, and the lounge, whilst the coctail bar and restaurant combine to form the focal point of the hotel. If it's your first visit it is worth asking directions, as it can be hard to find.
13 en suite (bth/shr) CTV in all bedrooms No dogs 25P No coaches No children 14yrs Continental Cuisine V meals Last d 9.30pm
ROOMS: (incl. bkfst) s £55-£60; d £90-£95 *
OFF-PEAK: (incl. bkfst) d fr £70
MEALS: Lunch fr £12.50&alc Dinner fr £18&alc
CARDS: 

See advertisement on page 709

★★ 68% **Sunnycroft**
5 Constitution Steps GY1 2PN ☎ 01481 723008 FAX 01481 712225
Closed mid Nov-mid Mar
This small personally-managed hotel, situated in an elevated position with glorious views across St Peter Port harbour to the neighbouring islands of Herm, Jethou and Sark, offers comfortable accommodation and a relaxed atmosphere. Access is from an old stepped street and car parking can be arranged nearby. Bedrooms are decorated in modern styles; many have balconies and all are equipped with modern

contd.

facilities. The public rooms include a delightful bar lounge, a cosy sitting room, and an attractive dining room where fresh ingredients are a feature of the daily-changing menus.

12 en suite (bth/shr) CTV in all bedrooms STV No dogs (ex guide dogs) 3P No coaches No children 12yrs International Cuisine V meals Coffee am Tea pm No smoking in restaurant Last d 8pm
ROOMS: (incl. bkfst) s £21.50-£31; d £43-£62
MEALS: Bar Lunch £2.50-£5 Dinner fr £12.50&alc
CARDS:

See advertisement on opposite page

VALE

★★★64% Pembroke Bay
Pembroke Bay GY3 5BY ☎ 01481 47573 FAX 01481 48838
Closed Oct-early Apr
Situated near an excellent bathing beach with its own outdoor heated pool and tennis court, this family-run hotel offers comfortable accommodation with a continental flair. Bedrooms are smart and equipped with modern facilities, and the public areas include a cosy lounge and The Melting Pot Restaurant where interesting dishes are offered; fresh local fish is a speciality.
12 en suite (bth/shr) (2 fmly) No smoking in 6 bedrooms CTV in all bedrooms STV Outdoor swimming pool (heated) Golf 18 Tennis (hard) International Cuisine V meals Coffee am Tea pm Last d 9.30pm
MEALS: Sunday Lunch £7.50-£14.50 Dinner £7.50-£12.50&alc*
CARDS:

★★★60% Peninsula
Les Dicqs ☎ 01481 48400 FAX 01481 48706
The island's newest hotel, built a few years ago, it enjoys a good location in five acres of grounds close to a sandy bay. The spacious accommodation is ideal for families or corporate guests with all rooms furnished in the modern style, with an additional sofa bed and good facilities. The large reception foyer leads into a bar area and the popular restaurant. There are various leisure facilities. There is also good provision for functions and conferences.
99 en suite (bth/shr) (99 fmly) No smoking in 18 bedrooms CTV in all bedrooms STV Lift Night porter 120P Outdoor swimming pool (heated) Putting green Petanque Playground ch fac Xmas English & Continental Cuisine V meals Coffee am Tea pm No smoking area in restaurant Last d 9.30pm
ROOMS: (incl. bkfst) s £35-£53.50; d £56-£97 **LB**
MEALS: Lunch fr £11 Dinner £13.50&alc
CONF: Thtr 250 Class 140 Board 105
CARDS:

VAZON BAY

★★66% *Les Embruns House*
Route de la Margion GY5 7LG ☎ 01481 64834 FAX 01481 66024
This cosy, family-run hotel stands in an acre of gardens with an outdoor swimming pool and sun patio, just minutes from the sands of magnificent Vazon Bay on the west coast of the island. Bedrooms have been equipped with modern comforts and there is a choice of lounges. An extensive choice of dishes is available from various menus with the emphasis on quality ingredients and fresh flavours. At a recent inspection meal, a flavoursome pâté was followed by a succulent breast of chicken served with a creamy asparagus sauce and fresh vegetables. Puddings are home-made and a range of French and New World wines make up the reasonably priced list.
15 en suite (bth/shr) (1 fmly) CTV in all bedrooms 12P Outdoor swimming pool (heated) French Cuisine V meals Coffee am Last d 9pm
CARDS:

See advertisement on page 711

HERM

★★75% White House
GY1 3HR ☎ 01481 722159 FAX 01481 710066
Closed 9 Oct-5 Apr
The White House is the only hotel on this idyllic island, and its resident managers extend every courtesy to guests from the moment that they are met at the jetty. Main house accommodation is augmented by that in two annexes - Foxglove Cottage and Mermaid Cottages, both within walking distance. Bedrooms furnished in modern style (though they have neither telephone nor television) are gradually being upgraded; some of them feature balconies, and most have fine sea views. During the cooler months an open fire burns in the traditional drawing room which extends into the Monk's bar, and another lounge opens onto gardens, terrace and swimming pool. The restaurant specialises in freshly caught seafood (including locally farmed oysters), chef Chris Walder presenting a good-value fixed-price daily menu which vies with the alternative eating options offered by the Sun Inn and seventeenth-century Mermaid Inn. Camping and self-catering accommodation are also available on the island.
16 en suite (bth/shr) 22 annexe en suite (bth/shr) (11 fmly) No dogs No coaches Outdoor swimming pool (heated) Tennis (hard) ch fac English & French Cuisine V meals Coffee am Tea pm No smoking area in restaurant Last d 9pm
ROOMS: (incl. bkfst & dinner) s £48-£63; d £96-£126 *
MEALS: Lunch £9.95-£19.50 Dinner £15.50-£16.50*
CARDS:

JERSEY

ARCHIRONDEL

★★★60% Les Arches
Archirondel Bay JE3 6DR ☎ 01534 853839 FAX 01534 856660
Overlooking the sea and conveniently located on the east coast road this popular, modern and professionally managed hotel has a range of well equipped bedrooms, the best with a balcony and sea view. Public areas comprise an attractive restaurant, spacious lounge, cocktail bar, heated outdoor swimming pool and a night club for sophisticated night owls. The hotel has built up a good reputation for small conferences and seminars, and arrangements for playing golf can readily be obtained from the managing director and proprietor Mr Renzo Martin.
54 en suite (bth/shr) CTV in all bedrooms STV Night porter 120P No coaches Outdoor swimming pool (heated) Tennis (hard) Sauna Gym Pool table Wkly live entertainment ch fac Xmas English & Continental Cuisine V meals Coffee am Last d 8.45pm
ROOMS: (incl. bkfst) s £29-£41; d £58-£82 **LB**
OFF-PEAK: (incl. bkfst) s £27-£38; d £54-£76
MEALS: Lunch £10.50-£18.50 Dinner £14.50-£28
CONF: Thtr 180 Class 120 Board 120 Del from £67
CARDS:

BEAUMONT

★★60% Hotel L'Hermitage
JE3 7BR (on N12) ☎ 01534 33314 & 58272 FAX 01534 21207
Closed Nov-Mar
This sprawling family-run hotel, conveniently situated for the airport, the town of St Helier and the harbour at St Aubin, provides some accommodation in the main house though most of the bedrooms are set around the outdoor pool in the grounds; all the rooms are quite simply furnished, but those with en suite facilities and the ones on higher floors offer views across the bay. Public areas include a modernised bar lounge as well as the spacious dining room where guests choose from a short set-price menu. Separate payment will be requested for drinks and any other additions to the accommodation.
43 en suite (bth/shr) 66 annexe en suite (bth/shr) CTV in all bedrooms No dogs Night porter 100P No coaches Indoor swimming pool (heated) Outdoor swimming pool (heated) Sauna Solarium Jacuzzi/spa Wkly live entertainment No children 14yrs English & French Cuisine Coffee am Tea pm No smoking in restaurant Last d 8pm
ROOMS: (incl. bkfst & dinner) s £25-£37; d £48-£72 *
MEALS: Dinner £8*

GOREY

★★★65% Old Court House
JE3 9FS ☎ 01534 854444 FAX 01534 853587
Closed Nov-Mar
The best bedrooms have balconies which overlook the gardens and heated swimming pool at this well managed and long-established hotel. Spacious public rooms include a comfortable and traditionally-furnished lounge, a large bar and a beamed restaurant. Service is friendly and helpful under the direction of manager Richard Smale, and there are good car parking facilities.
58 en suite (bth/shr) (4 fmly) CTV in all bedrooms STV Lift Night porter 40P Outdoor swimming pool (heated) Sauna Solarium Wkly live entertainment English, French & Italian Cuisine V meals Coffee am Tea pm No smoking area in restaurant
CARDS:

★★70% The Moorings
Gorey Pier JE3 6EN ☎ 01534 853633 FAX 01534 857618
A cosy little hotel beside the harbour, at the foot of Mont Orgueil, enjoys glorious waterfront views from most of its comfortable rooms (some of which have balconies). Attractively decorated and furnished accommodation is equipped with every modern facility, a first-floor TV lounge provides residents with an alternative to the busy bar lounge, and a restaurant popular for its extensive choice of traditional dishes features locally caught fish each day.
16 en suite (bth/shr) CTV in all bedrooms Night porter No coaches Wkly live entertainment Xmas English & Continental Cuisine V meals Coffee am No smoking area in restaurant Last d 10.15pm
ROOMS: (incl. bkfst) s £36-£45; d £72-£90 **LB**
OFF-PEAK: (incl. bkfst) s £32-£38; d £64-£76
MEALS: Lunch £11.50-£26.50&alc Dinner £17.50-£38&alc
CONF: Thtr 20 Class 20 Board 20 Del from £70
CARDS:

GROUVILLE

★★59% Hotel Kalamunda
Gorey Village JE3 9ER ☎ 01534 856656 FAX 01543 856755
This modern hotel stands near the historic village of Gorey, close to the Royal Jersey Golf Club and the town of St Helier. Well equipped en suite bedrooms (some of them on the ground floor) are gradually being upgraded, and there is a small bar lounge as well as the restaurant where a range of menus offers an interesting selection of dishes which always include local fish. A small indoor pool, sauna and solarium are available for guests' use.
29 en suite (bth/shr) (2 fmly) CTV in all bedrooms STV 14P Indoor swimming pool (heated) Sauna Gym Pool table V meals Coffee am Tea pm No smoking in restaurant
CARDS:

L'ETACQ

★★★68% *Lobster Pot Hotel & Restaurant*
JE3 2FB (turn off A12 at St Ouens parish hall onto B64. Hotel signposted at fork junct for B35)
☎ 01534 482888 FAX 01534 481574
Set in a remote position on the coast overlooking St Ouens Bay, this privately-run hotel is, we are informed as we go to press, about to undergo a total refurbishment and is due to close from November 1996 until the early spring of 1997. Exciting plans are afoot, as Kevin-John and Liz Broome, who have been running a highly acclaimed restaurant at St Aubin, Broome's, are joining the Lobster Pot, bringing with them new ideas. Part of the refurbishment concerns the food operation, and in addition to the formal restaurant, there will be a brasserie, installed in the coach house, and opening onto the garden patio. Seafood will continue to feature strongly on all menus.
13 en suite (bth/shr) (1 fmly) CTV in all bedrooms STV No dogs (ex guide dogs) Night porter Air conditioning 56P Wkly live entertainment English, Continental & North American Cuisine V meals Coffee am Tea pm Last d 10pm
CARDS:

ROZEL BAY

RED STAR HOTEL

★★★ Château la Chaire
Rozel Bay JE3 6AJ (from direction of St Helier on B38 turn left in village by the Rozel Bay Inn, hotel 100yds on right) ☎ 01534 863354
FAX 01534 865137
Situated in a wooded valley on the north eastern coast of the island, Chateau La Chaire was built as a gentleman's residence in 1843, with terraced gardens leading down to the picturesque fishing village of Rozel Bay. Many thoughtful extras have been provided in the individually furnished, elegant bedrooms, and there is also a ground-floor suite with direct access on to the terrace. Fresh flowers and a variety of magazines adorn the beautifully decorated drawing room, where guests enjoy an aperitif and canapés before an excellent dinner which is served either in the panelled restaurant or the no-smoking conservatory. Raymond's Bar provides an alternative setting for a relaxing drink.
14 en suite (bth/shr) (1 fmly) CTV in all bedrooms STV No

dogs (ex guide dogs) Night porter 30P No children 7yrs Xmas English & French Cuisine V meals Coffee am Tea pm Last d 10pm
ROOMS: (incl. bkfst) s £59-£111; d £100-£177 * **LB**
MEALS: Lunch £12.95-£15.50 High tea £3.50-£6.95 Dinner fr £21.50*
CARDS:

ST AUBIN

★★★71% **Somerville**
Mont du Boulevard (from village, follow harbour then take Mont du Boulevard and second right hand bend)
☎ 01534 41226 FAX 01534 46621
Closed Nov-mid Apr
Occupying an enviable elevated position overlooking St Aubin's Bay, this handsome and very popular hotel, personally managed by Mr J H Fernandes, offers a good range of bedrooms, the best category being de luxe superior or with a balcony and front-facing open outlook. Service is particularly friendly and cheerful and even more so in the restaurant with Mr George in charge; limited room service can also be obtained up to 11pm. Other facilities include a swimming pool, furnished terraces, split-level bar, small lounge/games room and very good car parking.
59 rms (58 bth/shr) (7 fmly) CTV in all bedrooms STV No dogs Lift Night porter 40P No coaches Outdoor swimming pool (heated) Games room Wkly live entertainment No children 4yrs English & French Cuisine V meals Coffee am Tea pm No smoking area in restaurant Last d 8.30pm
ROOMS: (incl. bkfst) s £30-£50; d £60-£110 *
MEALS: Lunch £6.30-£15 High tea £1.60-£4 Dinner £3-£17alc*
CARDS:

ST BRELADE

★★★★ 75% **The Atlantic**
La Moye JE3 8HE ☎ 01534 44101 FAX 01534 44102
Closed Jan-Feb

Beside La Moye golf course and set in landscaped grounds on a headland overlooking the sea, this modern hotel has undergone radical transformation in recent years. The public areas have been designed in a comfortable Mediterranean style, and there is still a clublike atmosphere in the bar. Most of the bedrooms have balconies and good views, while a few superior rooms on the ground floor are more spacious and have small patios. The cooking of chef Thomas Sleigh offers a variety of dishes on both set-price menu and carte, including traditional, vegetarian and modern innovative ideas. At a recent inspection meal fine fresh scallops came with cured salmon, and pink roasted squab with soft polenta and broad beans.
50 en suite (bth/shr) CTV in all bedrooms STV No dogs (ex guide dogs) Lift Night porter 60P No coaches Indoor swimming pool (heated) Outdoor swimming pool (heated) Tennis (hard) Sauna

contd.

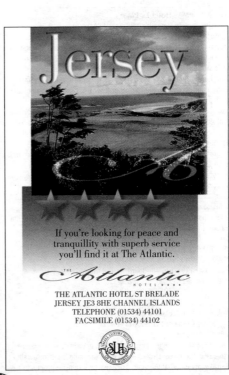

Solarium Gym Jacuzzi/spa Xmas V meals Coffee am Tea pm Last d 9.30pm
ROOMS: (incl. bkfst) s £85-£105; d £110-£200 * LB
MEALS: Lunch fr £15 Dinner fr £22.50&alc*
CONF: Thtr 60 Class 40 Board 20 Del from £135
CARDS:

See advertisement on page 711

★★★★ 74% Hotel L'Horizon
St Brelade's Bay JE3 8EF ☎ 01534 43101
FAX 01534 46269

This pleasant hotel enjoys a near perfect location on the edge of the beach. Under new ownership, the accommodation is undergoing extensive improvements, with most of the bedrooms now complete along with a sumptuous lounge, cocktail bar, reception lobby and the Crystal Restaurant. Phase II is now being planned and will involve major upgrading of the hotel kitchens, leisure centre and the East Wing bedrooms. The Star Grill offers a more formal surrounding to enjoy the skilful cooking of Chef Peter Marek, who continues to produce innovative dishes from interesting à la carte and table d'hôte menus, making use of fresh local produce and seafood. If the Crystal Room Restaurant is open, it provides an alternative dining option along with the new terrace.
107 en suite (bth/shr) (7 fmly) CTV in all bedrooms STV No dogs (ex guide dogs) Lift Night porter 125P No coaches Indoor swimming pool (heated) Sauna Gym Jacuzzi/spa Windsurfing/Water skiing Xmas English, French & Mediterranean Cuisine V meals Coffee am Tea pm No smoking area in restaurant Last d 10pm
ROOMS: (incl. bkfst) s £105-£120; d £155-£180 * LB
OFF-PEAK: (incl. bkfst) s fr £100; d fr £150
MEALS: Lunch fr £12alc High tea £3.75-£6alc Dinner £24&alc
CONF: Thtr 110 Class 58 Board 40 Del from £110
CARDS:

★★★★ 69% Hotel La Place
Route Du Coin, La Haule JE3 8BF ☎ 01534 44261
Converted from an original 17th century farmhouse this charming hotel is quietly located and offers good standards of hospitality and service from a dedicated and conscientious team of well managed professional staff. Under the personal direction of Mr Anthony Gallagher the atmosphere is refined and quietly efficient, and with much of the accommodation set around the inner swimming pool and terrace the rooms have a lot to commend. There is a choice of bedrooms all equipped to a high standard, which range from spacious pool-side to standard bedrooms which are currently being upgraded. Chef Tom Illing offers a fixed-price and a la carte menus and good standards of cooking in Knights Restaurant. There is a very comfortable and elegantly furnished lounge, spacious cocktail bar and, as we go to press, a new all-weather tennis court, conservatory restaurant extension, and a new conference room for up to 60 persons are currently being added.
43 en suite (bth/shr) (1 fmly) No smoking in 25 bedrooms CTV in all bedrooms Night porter 100P Outdoor swimming pool (heated) Tennis (hard) Sauna Croquet lawn ch fac Xmas V meals Coffee am Tea pm No smoking in restaurant Last d 9.30pm
ROOMS: (incl. bkfst) s £85-£105; d £110-£150 * LB
OFF-PEAK: (incl. bkfst) s £70-£85; d £85-£125
MEALS: Lunch £11-£15 Dinner £19&alc
CONF: Thtr 120 Class 40 Board 40 Del from £110
CARDS: £

See advertisement on opposite page

★★★ 75% St Brelade's Bay
JE3 8EF ☎ 01534 46141 FAX 01534 47278
Closed 7 Oct-24 Apr
Now run by Robert Colley, this fine hotel set in eight acres of mature grounds and terraced gardens has been in the same family ownership for five generations. At the time of our visit, an extensive programme of improvements was well under way, beginning with refurbished bedrooms and smart new bathrooms, and the lounge also has been upgraded to a high standard. Other public facilities include a formal restaurant, cocktail bar, heated swimming pool with lunchtime buffet and bar, all-weather tennis courts, a children's play area, games room, teenagers' room, snooker room, sauna, solarium and mini-gym. Children's teas and suppers are provided, special communicating bedrooms are available, and there is a baby listening service. Access to the beach is just across the road.
72 en suite (bth/shr) (50 fmly) CTV in all bedrooms STV No dogs (ex guide dogs) Lift Night porter 60P No coaches Outdoor swimming pool (heated) Tennis (hard & grass) Snooker Sauna Solarium Pool table Croquet lawn Putting green Petanque Mini-gym Wkly live entertainment English & French Cuisine V meals Coffee am No smoking in restaurant Last d 8.45pm
ROOMS: (incl. bkfst) s £52-£90; d £104-£180 *
MEALS: Lunch £12&alc Dinner £18&alc*
CARDS:

★★★ 67% Golden Sands
JE3 8EF ☎ 01534 41241 FAX 01534 499366
Closed Jan-Mar
Located virtually on the beach in the centre of St Brelade's Bay this very friendly and well managed family hotel was completely refurbished and upgraded in 1994, and offers several different styles of bedroom: sea-facing rooms all with a balcony, and spacious other rooms all equipped and furnished to a high standard. There are very good facilities for families with children which include spacious family bedrooms,a professionally supervised playroom and special meal times. Dinner and dance on Saturday night is a feature, and afternoon tea, room service and a night porter are also available, whilst other facilities include a guests' laundry room, courtesy mini bus, and lift to all levels.
62 en suite (bth/shr) (5 fmly) CTV in all bedrooms STV No dogs Lift Night porter Childrens play room Wkly live entertainment ch fac Xmas English & French Cuisine V meals Coffee am Tea pm No smoking in restaurant Last d 9pm
ROOMS: (incl. bkfst) s £23-£43; d £46-£108 *
MEALS: Lunch £8-£11.25 Dinner £10.50*
CARDS: £

★★★ 67% Silver Springs
La Route des Genets JE3 8DB ☎ 01534 46401 FAX 01534 46823
Closed 25 Oct-23 Apr
Modern and purpose-built, this hotel stands in 7 acres of grounds. Bedrooms, several with their own balconies, are all similar in style and furnishings, and there is a choice of comfortable lounges as well as a spacious bar and a restaurant overlooking a private wooded valley. The international staff maintain traditional standards of service and hospitality. Children are both welcomed and properly catered for.
88 en suite (bth/shr) (14 fmly) CTV in all bedrooms STV No dogs Night porter 50P No coaches Outdoor swimming pool (heated) Tennis (hard) Solarium Pool table Croquet lawn Putting green Boules/Children's pool/table tennis No children 9mths ch fac English & French Cuisine V meals No smoking in restaurant Last d 8.45pm
ROOMS: (incl. bkfst & dinner) s £37-£53; d £70-£106 *
MEALS: Dinner fr £13.25*
CARDS: £

See advertisement on opposite page

★★★ 66% *Château Valeuse*
Rue de Valeuse, St Brelade's Bay JE3 8EE
☎ 01534 46281 FAX 01534 47110
Closed Nov-Mar
Once a gentleman's residence, this hotel has been skilfully extended to offer good bedrooms in the main house - some with balcony and sea views - as well as larger rooms in a new wing. Set back from the bay in

contd.

a quiet, elevated position, it has attractive, well-stocked gardens which contain a heated swimming pool and putting green. Public rooms include a comfortable open-plan lounge, a well appointed bar and the Gallery Restaurant. Mary and Tom Jordan are efficient hosts.
34 en suite (bth/shr) (1 fmly) CTV in all bedrooms No dogs Night porter 50P No coaches Outdoor swimming pool (heated) Putting green No children 5yrs English & French Cuisine V meals Coffee am Tea pm Last d 9pm
CARDS:

★★69% **Beau Rivage**
St Brelade's Bay JE3 8EF ☎ 01534 45983 FAX 01534 47127
Closed Nov-late Mar
Occupying a prime seafront location at St Brelade's Bay, this popular holiday hotel has continued to improve in recent years. All the bedrooms have now been refurbished, most of them have excellent sea views and some have balconies. There are two lounges, a sun deck, a public bar with conservatory extension and an attractive dining room; light refreshments are available at all times, and courtesy transport is provided most days.
27 en suite (bth/shr) (9 fmly) CTV in all bedrooms STV No dogs Lift Night porter 14P Sunbathing terrace Video games Wkly live entertainment English, French & Italian Cuisine V meals Coffee am Tea pm No smoking in restaurant Last d 7.45pm
ROOMS: (incl. bkfst & dinner) d £41-£125 * **LB**
MEALS: Bar Lunch £3-£12 Dinner £12.50
CARDS: £

ST HELIER

★★★★❀65% **The Grand**

The Esplanade JE4 8WD ☎ 01534 22301
FAX 01534 37815
This busy hotel overlooks St Aubin's Bay and Elizabeth Castle welcomes both corporate and leisure guests. Bedrooms vary in size, some boasting balconies, while the public areas include two bars a leisure suite and two restaurants. Elaborate French cuisine is served in Victoria's Restaurant, and dishes recently enjoyed here have included calves' liver with sage and onion, and tiger prawns with soy and ginger.
115 en suite (bth/shr) CTV in all bedrooms STV Lift Night porter 27P Indoor swimming pool (heated) Snooker Sauna Solarium Gym Jacuzzi/spa Massage parlour Xmas English, French & Italian Cuisine V meals Coffee am Tea pm No smoking area in restaurant Last d 10pm
ROOMS: (incl. bkfst) s £90-£97.50; d £130-£160 * **LB**
OFF-PEAK: (incl. bkfst) s £75-£80; d £120-£135
MEALS: Lunch £11.50-£16.50&alc Dinner fr £19.50&alc*
CONF: Thtr 180 Class 100 Board 40 Del from £120
CARDS:

★★★❀❀73% **Pomme d'Or**
Liberation Square JE2 3NF (opposite the harbour) ☎ 01534 880110
FAX 01534 37781
Conveniently situated in the centre of the town, this well established hotel with a range of restaurants offers comfortable accommodation and a relaxed atmosphere. Bedrooms have seen the benefit of some refurbishment; all are equipped with modern facilities and the best have sea views and a sunny aspect. For dinner guests can choose between the informal Coffee Shop, the popular Harbour Room Carvery, and for those seeking a more special experience there is La Petite Pomme restaurant where the cooking skills of Steve Le Corre continue to impress. Fresh local ingredients are a feature of the à la carte and monthly-changing table d'hÙte menus, and the wine list is varied and interesting.
147 en suite (bth/shr) (3 fmly) No smoking in 78 bedrooms CTV in all bedrooms STV No dogs (ex guide dogs) Lift Night porter Use of Aquadome at Merton Hotel Xmas International Cuisine V meals Coffee am Tea pm No smoking area in restaurant Last d 10pm
ROOMS: (incl. bkfst) s £70-£72; d £110-£115 **LB**
OFF-PEAK: (incl. bkfst) s £57.50-£60; d £85-£90
MEALS: Lunch £8-£12.50&alc High tea fr £3.50 Dinner £11.50-£15.50&alc
CONF: Thtr 300 Class 120 Board 40 Del from £65
CARDS: £

★★★68% **Beaufort**
Green St JE2 4UH ☎ 01534 32471 FAX 01534 20371
Conveniently situated in the centre of town, this modern hotel has particularly comfortable and well equipped bedrooms, which have been designed to offer every modern amenity. Leisure facilities include an indoor swimming pool and roof terrace, while spacious public areas are made up of the Spanish Suite, Brummels Public Bar and the Rib Room Restaurant where chef Maurice Sones provides professional standards of cooking; 24-hour room service is available.
54 en suite (bth/shr) (4 fmly) CTV in all bedrooms STV No dogs Lift Night porter 60P Indoor swimming pool (heated) Jacuzzi/spa Xmas English & French Cuisine V meals Coffee am Tea pm
ROOMS: (incl. bkfst & dinner) s £52.50-£64.25; d £83-£92.50 * **LB**
MEALS: Sunday Lunch fr £9.75 Dinner fr £11.75*
CONF: Thtr 160 Class 140
CARDS:

See advertisement on page 713

★★★68% **Royal**

CONSORT HOTELS

David Place JE2 4TD ☎ 01534 26521
FAX 01534 24035
This centrally situated hotel has been established for many years and guests return year after year. The bedrooms offer a high degree of comfort and are slowly being upgraded to an even higher standard, while the elegant public areas consist of a very comfortable lounge, a popular bar-cum-lounge, a stylish restaurant and a conservatory breakfast room on the first floor.
86 en suite (bth/shr) (39 fmly) CTV in all bedrooms STV Lift Night porter 28P No coaches Sauna Solarium Jacuzzi/spa Wkly live entertainment Xmas English & French Cuisine V meals Coffee am Tea pm No smoking area in restaurant Last d 9pm
ROOMS: (incl, bkfst) s £49.50-£57.50; d £79-£95 * **LB**
MEALS: Lunch £10.50-£12.50 High tea £3.95-£6.95 Dinner £15*
CONF: Thtr 450 Class 225 Board 30 Del from £70
CARDS: £

See advertisement on opposite page

★★★64% **Rex**
St Saviours Rd JE2 4GJ ☎ 01534 31668 FAX 01534 66922
Closed 16 Oct-13 Apr
Situated within easy, level walking distance of the town centre and the seafront, this popular hotel has been upgraded, providing modern facilities throughout. Public areas include a spacious lounge, well appointed bar and traditionally furnished dining room; there is a lift to all floors. During the season a programme of live entertainment is

S

provided. The management team and staff offer a friendly and helpful standard of service.
53 en suite (bth/shr) (5 fmly) CTV in all bedrooms Lift Night porter 20P No coaches Outdoor swimming pool (heated) Pool table Wkly live entertainment British & Continental Cuisine V meals No smoking in restaurant
CARDS:

★★★64% **Royal Yacht**
The Weighbridge (in town centre, opposite marina and harbour)
☎ 01534 20511 FAX 01534 67729
This long established Victorian town centre hotel features an extensive and very varied range of public rooms which includes several popular bars and a choice of restaurants: the London Grill and the very comfortable and well appointed Victoriana Restaurant. There is also a top floor sun lounge which is ideal for small private meetings, whilst an elegant and very comfortable residents' lounge is on the first floor mezzanine. Room service is available and there is a lift to all levels. Bedrooms are slowly being upgraded and the best rooms are front-facing; all are well equipped and furnished in the modern style.
45 en suite (bth/shr) CTV in all bedrooms STV Lift Night porter Sauna Solarium English, French & Italian Cuisine V meals Coffee am Tea pm Last d 9.30pm
CONF: Thtr 20 Class 20 Board 20
CARDS:

★★★63% **Apollo**
St Saviours Rd JE2 4LA ☎ 01534 25441 FAX 01534 22120
Set in a convenient position in the centre of town, this popular hotel offers comfortable, well equipped bedrooms and a choice of spacious, modern public areas. These include a choice of bars, sitting areas and a quiet lounge as well as a traditional restaurant and pool-side coffee shop. Car parking is available.

contd.

85 en suite (bth/shr) (5 fmly) CTV in all bedrooms STV No dogs (ex guide dogs) Lift Night porter Indoor swimming pool (heated) Sauna Solarium Gym Jacuzzi/spa Xmas English & French Cuisine V meals Coffee am Tea pm Last d 8.45pm
ROOMS: (incl. bkfst) s £37.50-£58.50 * **LB**
MEALS: Sunday Lunch fr £9.50 Dinner fr £11.50*
CONF: Thtr 150 Class 100 Board 80
CARDS:

See advertisement on page 715

★★69% **Berkshire**
25-29 La Motte St JE2 4SZ ☎ 01534 23241 & 23243
FAX 01534 32986
RS 9 Oct-11 May (no half board)
Long established and benefiting from its second generation ownership, this friendly family-run hotel is located in the heart of the business centre of town close to the main shopping precinct. Professionally and personally run by Michael Barnes, the accommodation varies in shape and size with all bedrooms furnished to the same modern standard. Spacious public areas offer a choice of dining options with Lillie Langtry's Bar and Restaurant already establishing itself as one of the capital's top culinary venues, with American chef Stephen Sexton producing imaginative and interesting dishes which reflect his very capable and talented cooking skills. Service is very helpful and attentive and particularly well supervised. Other facilities include a front terrace and an inner courtyard, residents only house bar, and a traditional dining room. Arrival by taxi is recommended.
62 en suite (bth/shr) (6 fmly) CTV in all bedrooms No dogs (ex guide dogs) Night porter Pool table Continental Cuisine V meals Coffee am Tea pm No smoking area in restaurant Last d 9.30pm
ROOMS: (incl. bkfst) s £22-£47.25; d £44-£63 *
MEALS: Lunch £10.50-£13.50 Dinner £17*
CARDS:

★★69% **Sarum Hotel**
19-21 New St John's Rd JE2 3LD ☎ 01534 58163 FAX 01534 31340
Closed 2 Nov-22 Mar
Friendly management in the shape of Barbara and Joseph Arena and their experienced, well-trained staff ensure that this hotel is run to a very high standard at all times. Bright bedrooms are comfortably furnished, and intercom and video channels are provided in all of them. Public rooms which are both smart and inviting include a relaxing small lounge and a well furnished bar. A fixed-price menu is offered in the dining room, and Mr Arena will personally cook an a la carte range of food if given 24 hours notice. Very limited car parking is available behind the hotel.
49 en suite (bth/shr) (9 fmly) CTV in all bedrooms No dogs (ex guide dogs) Lift Night porter 6P Pool table Games room Children's play area Wkly live entertainment ch fac English & Continental Cuisine V meals Coffee am Tea pm No smoking in restaurant Last d 7.45pm
ROOMS: (incl. bkfst & dinner) s £33-£59; d £56-£108 **LB**
MEALS: Bar Lunch £5&alc High tea £3-£5 Dinner £13&alc
CARDS:

★★68% **Graham**
60 Saint Saviours Rd JE2 4LA ☎ 01534 30126 FAX 01534 21246
Closed Nov-late Mar
Located only five minutes' walk from the town centre, this upgraded hotel offers a good standard of accommodation equipped with television and radio intercom. A small, quiet lounge and open-plan bar invite relaxation, while the restaurant is comfortable and smart. Limited 24-hour room service is available, and the bar serves sandwich snacks throughout the day. Live entertainment is provided.
27 en suite (bth/shr) (6 fmly) CTV in all bedrooms No dogs (ex guide dogs) Night porter 11P Outdoor swimming pool Children's play area ch fac English & Continental Cuisine V meals Coffee am Tea pm No smoking in restaurant Last d 7.45pm
ROOMS: (incl. bkfst) d £42-£95 * **LB**
MEALS: Bar Lunch £3-£6 Dinner £12.50
CARDS:

★★65% **Mountview**
New St John's Rd JE2 3LD ☎ 01534 887666 FAX 01534 880746
Closed 18 Oct-6 Apr
This attractive and well managed holiday hotel is located within easy reach of the town centre. Bedrooms are equipped with television, tea trays and a radio-intercom system and there is a lift to most levels. Public rooms include a bar, a non-smoking restaurant and a recently added and wellfurnished lounge. There is some forecourt parking.
35 en suite (bth/shr) (2 fmly) CTV in all bedrooms Lift 16P English & French Cuisine V meals Coffee am Tea pm No smoking in restaurant Last d 7.55pm
ROOMS: (incl. bkfst & dinner) s £37-£48; d £64-£90 **LB**
MEALS: Lunch £8-£13 Dinner £8.50-£14&alc
CARDS:

See advertisement on opposite page

ST LAWRENCE

★★64% **Hotel White Heather**
Rue de Haut, Millbrook JE3 1JQ ☎ 01534 20978 FAX 01534 20968
Closed Nov-Apr
Quietly situated in a fashionable part of town - within walking distance of the seafront and a bus ride from the shopping centre - this friendly hotel offers a range of bedrooms (which are still being improved), many with balconies and sea views. Some are specially suitable for families with children. A comfortable reading room augments a well furnished bar-lounge, and an attractively decorated dining room offers a four course fixed price daily menu. Leisure facilities include an indoor swimming pool and spacious sun terrace. Special inclusive holidays are well worth an enquiry.
33 en suite (bth/shr) (3 fmly) CTV in all bedrooms No dogs 11P Indoor swimming pool (heated) No smoking in restaurant Last d 7.30pm
ROOMS: (incl. bkfst & dinner) s £24.90-£36.60; d £43.80-£67.20 *
MEALS: Dinner £8
CARDS:

ST PETER

★★★67% **Mermaid**
JE3 7BN ☎ 01534 41255 FAX 01534 45826
Situated in 18 acres of gardens and grounds overlooking a small natural lake, the Mermaid Hotel attracts both the business and the leisure traveller. The well equipped bedrooms enjoy tranquil views over the lake, with its own wild life including a pair of swans. In addition to the table d'hÙte menu served in the hotel's dining room, an extensive range of dishes is offered in the renowned Granite Grill room, complemented by a comprehensively stocked wine cellar.
68 en suite (bth/shr) CTV in all bedrooms STV No dogs (ex guide dogs) Night porter 250P Indoor swimming pool (heated) Outdoor swimming pool (heated) Tennis (hard) Sauna Solarium Gym Croquet lawn Putting green Jacuzzi/spa Xmas English & French Cuisine V meals Coffee am Tea pm Last d 9pm
ROOMS: (incl. bkfst) s £36.25-£53.75; d £72.50-£88.50 * **LB**
MEALS: Lunch fr £9.50 Dinner fr £11.50*
CONF: Thtr 100 Class 60 Board 50
CARDS:

See advertisement on this page

ST SAVIOUR

RED STAR HOTEL

★★★★❀❀❀ Longueville Manor

RELAIS & CHATEAUX. Relais Gourmands

JE2 7WF (off St Helier/Grouville Rd A3)
☎ 01534 25501 FAX 01534 31613

With parts dating back to the 13th century, this handsome wisteria-clad manor house stands in 40 acres of well tended gardens and grounds which include a sun terrace, a swimming pool, an ornamental lake with black swans and ducks and a tennis court. Bedrooms are individually furnished with quality, co-ordinating soft furnishings and beautifully decorated. Thoughtful extras such as fresh flowers, magazines, quality toiletries and home-made biscuits are included in all rooms. Larger rooms and suites are available, some with their own balconies or terraces overlooking the gardens. The public areas are elegantly furnished and decorated; in the panelled part of the restaurant there is a no smoking area. Chef Andrew Baird's interesting choice of menus continues to gain praise, the extensive wine list complementing the delicious food.

32 en suite (bth/shr) CTV in all bedrooms STV Lift Night porter 40P No coaches Outdoor swimming pool (heated) Tennis (hard) Xmas English & French Cuisine V meals Coffee am Tea pm No smoking area in restaurant Last d 9.30pm
ROOMS: (incl. bkfst) s £140-£180; d £185-£235 **LB**
OFF-PEAK: (incl. bkfst) s £125-£165; d £155-£215
MEALS: Lunch £18.50 Dinner £31&alc
CONF: Thtr 40 Class 30 Board 30
CARDS:

TRINITY

★★68% **Highfield Country**
Route D'Ebenezer JE3 5DS ☎ 01534 862194 FAX 01534 865342
RS Nov-Mar

The Highfield, quietly set in unspoilt countryside, continues to be improved by proprietors David and Geraldine Lord. Well equipped bedrooms are furnished in modern style, and there is a quiet lounge as well as the bar and conservatory. There is an attractive restaurant, but self-catering apartments are also available, and the well kept gardens and children's play area are added attractions.

38 en suite (bth/shr) (32 fmly) CTV in all bedrooms No dogs Lift 41P No coaches Indoor swimming pool (heated) Outdoor swimming pool Sauna Solarium Gym Pool table ch fac International Cuisine V meals Coffee am Tea pm No smoking in restaurant Last d 8pm
ROOMS: (incl. bkfst & dinner) s £40-£48; d £60-£90 *
MEALS: Dinner £8-£12.50*
CARDS:

£

SARK

★❀ 76% **Stocks Island**

GY9 0SD ☎ 01481 832001 FAX 01481 832130
Closed Oct-Mar

Cars are not allowed on the island of Sark, and travel is either by bicycle, horse and cart, or on foot. Access is by boat from Guernsey or France, and while luggage is taken care of, a short tractor ride up the hill is followed by a 15 minute walk through the meadows to reach Stocks Hotel - the perfect setting in which to forget about all the pressures of 20th-century living. The Armorgie family and their team of staff extend a warm welcome to guests, who are immediately made to feel at home in the surroundings of this elegant stone-built farm house. Bedrooms are traditionally furnished, and some are situated in a Dower house in the garden; since the emphasis is on peace and tranquillity, modern facilities such as televisions, radios, and telephones

17 rms (10 shr) 7 annexe en suite (bth/shr) (4 fmly) No coaches Outdoor swimming pool V meals Coffee am Tea pm No smoking area in restaurant Last d 9pm
ROOMS: (incl. bkfst & dinner) s £40-£55; d £80-£110 * **LB**
MEALS: Lunch £10-£13&alc High tea £4.50-£7.50&alc Dinner £10-£18&alc*
CARDS:

Isle of Man

Directory of establishments in alphabetical order of location.

MAN, ISLE OF Map 06

CASTLETOWN Map 06 SC26

★★★67% Castletown Golf Links
Fort Island IM9 1UA ☎ 01624 822201
FAX 01624 824633

Best Western

A unique setting with sea on three sides and adjoining a Championship Golf Course this hotel has much to offer, not only to those who enjoy golf, but also to those who look for traditional and friendly service in a peaceful and relaxing environment. There are other activities which can be indulged in such as swimming in the indoor heated pool, playing a leisurely game of snooker or walking round the rugged coastline. Bedrooms are modern and well appointed particularly the excellent suites with their own sitting rooms many of which look out over the golf course.
58 en suite (bth/shr) (3 fmly) CTV in all bedrooms STV Night porter 200P Indoor swimming pool (heated) Golf 18 Snooker Sauna Solarium Putting green Xmas European Cuisine V meals Coffee am Tea pm Last d 9pm
ROOMS: (incl. bkfst) s £45-£80; d £70-£110 * **LB**
OFF-PEAK: (incl. bkfst) s £35-£65; d £65-£90
MEALS: Sunday Lunch £15.50-£22.50&alc Dinner £19.50-£25&alc
CONF: Thtr 200 Class 50 Board 20 Del from £85
CARDS:

DOUGLAS Map 06 SC37

★★★★71% Mount Murray Country Club
Santon IM4 2HT (4m SW) ☎ 01624 661111 FAX 01624 611116
A luxury hotel and leisure complex with a sound standard of cooking. In Murray's Restaurant, a seafood terrine would make a good starter, followed by ragout of venison with rösti, navarin of lamb, or darne of salmon from the set-price menu. The 'Menu Gastronimique' offers Dover sole or magret of duck. Charlotte's Bistro is more informal.
90 en suite (bth/shr) (4 fmly) No smoking in 12 bedrooms CTV in all bedrooms No dogs (ex guide dogs) Lift Night porter 400P No coaches Indoor swimming pool (heated) Golf 18 Tennis (hard) Squash Snooker Sauna Solarium Gym Putting green Bowling green Driving range Sports hall ch fac Xmas V meals Coffee am Tea pm No smoking area in restaurant Last d 9.45pm
ROOMS: (incl. bkfst) s £80-£85; d £120-£126 * **LB**
OFF-PEAK: (incl. bkfst) s £60-£65; d £92-£96
MEALS: Lunch £12-£15 High tea fr £5.25 Dinner £12-£15&alc*
CONF: Thtr 300 Class 260 Board 70 Del from £115
CARDS:

★★★72% Empress
Central Promenade IM2 4RA ☎ 01624 661155 FAX 01624 673554
The Empress is an elegant Victorian hotel standing on the promenade and overlooking Douglas Bay. The extensive refurbishment during recent years has provided a well furnished and comfortable hotel. The spacious lounges, with an Art Deco style of decor, have pleasant sea views; the Brasserie restaurant offers a wide choice of dishes which are well prepared. Although some of the bedrooms are not too spacious, they are all very well equipped and pleasantly furnished along modern lines. The staff are friendly, helpful and always willing to be of assistance to guests. A good leisure club is provided and there are also extensive conference facilities.
102 en suite (bth/shr) (20 fmly) CTV in all bedrooms STV No dogs (ex guide dogs) Lift Night porter Indoor swimming pool (heated) Sauna Solarium Gym Jacuzzi/spa Steam room Beautician Wkly live entertainment Xmas International Cuisine V meals Coffee am Tea pm Last d 10.45pm
ROOMS: s £59; d £65 * **LB**
MEALS: Lunch fr £7.50 High tea fr £6.75 Dinner fr £12.50&alc*
CONF: Thtr 200 Class 150 Board 50 Del £95
CARDS:

★★★67% Sefton
Harris Promenade 1MI 2RW ☎ 01624 626011 FAX 01624 676004
This popular Victorian seafront hotel is located next to the Gaiety Theatre, well placed for the town centre. Modern bedrooms have been designed to meet both business and leisure requirements; a number of very well appointed executive rooms have recently been opened, but there is also family accommodation. Public areas provide a wide range of facilities which include a health and leisure club, Harris's Café Bar (in which morning coffee, light lunches, and afternoon teas are served) and The Far Pavilions Restaurant. There is also the Tramshunters Arms, a popular pub renowned for its real ales. A new, fully equipped lecture theatre is also now available, as well as conference and meeting rooms.
79 en suite (bth) (5 fmly) No smoking in 6 bedrooms CTV in all bedrooms STV No dogs (ex guide dogs) Lift Night porter 52P Indoor swimming pool (heated) Sauna Solarium Gym Jacuzzi/spa Steam rooms Beauty therapy service Xmas V meals Coffee am Tea pm No smoking area in restaurant Last d 8pm
ROOMS: (incl. bkfst) s £45-£60; d £60-£79 * **LB**
MEALS: Lunch £7-£14 Dinner £10-£14&alc
CONF: Thtr 90 Class 40 Board 12 Del from £69
CARDS:

★★62% Rutland
Queen's Promenade IM2 4NS ☎ 01624 621218 FAX 01624 611562
Closed Nov-Etr
Rutland is a very friendly family-run hotel under the personal supervision of genial proprietor Ron Wilson. The majority of bedrooms have en suite facilities, and many have fine sea views; all have up-to-date furniture and fittings, and are very well maintained. There is twenty-four-hour room service and also baby listening, if required. Head chef Jim Benson looks after the kitchen, and guests will enjoy dining in a pleasant restaurant overlooking the sea. The residents' lounge bar is known as the Anfield Lounge, and soccer enthusiasts will find much to interest them there, while Champs is one of the Island's most popular night spots for both young and old.
68 en suite (bth/shr) (18 fmly) CTV in all bedrooms No dogs (ex guide dogs) Lift Night porter Pool table Night club Wkly live entertainment V meals Coffee am Tea pm Last d 8pm
ROOMS: (incl. bkfst) s £18.50-£26; d £37-£52 *
MEALS: Bar Lunch £1.30-£3.50 Dinner £7.50-£8.50
CARDS:

PORT ERIN Map 06 SC16

★★★66% Cherry Orchard
Bridson St IM9 6AN (from Seaport/Airport take main road south past Castle Town to Port Erin) ☎ 01624 833811 FAX 01624 833583
This versatile modern hotel is located in the centre of town, close to the bay and the steam railway terminal, and only five miles from the island's airport. It can cater for a wide variety of needs such as families with children, senior citizens, conferences and individual business/leisure travellers will all find it to their liking. The accommodation (which includes family rooms and executive suites) is

contd.

equipped with modern furniture and fittings; and there are also self-catering and long-let apartments. Meeting/banqueting and leisure facilities are available, and the attractive Cherry Tree Grill offers a variety of menus supplemented by substantial meals served in the Morello Bar.

31 en suite (bth/shr) (12 fmly) CTV in all bedrooms STV No dogs (ex guide dogs) Lift Night porter 80P Indoor swimming pool (heated) Sauna Solarium Gym Pool table Jacuzzi/spa Games room ch fac Xmas English & French Cuisine V meals Coffee am Tea pm No smoking area in restaurant Last d 9.45pm

ROOMS: (incl. bkfst) s fr £40; d fr £50 * **LB**

MEALS: Lunch £3-£15alc Dinner £13.75&alc

CONF: Thtr 200 Class 120 Board 70 Del £69

CARDS:

SCOTLAND

Inspectors' Choice Hotel of the Year: Kirroughtree, Newton Stewart

ABERDEEN Aberdeen City Map 15 NJ90
See also Aberdeen Airport & Westhill

★★★★71% **The Marcliffe at Pitfodels**

North Deeside Rd AB1 9YA (turn off A90 onto A93 signposted Braemar. 1m on right after turn off at traffic lights) ☎ 01224 861000 FAX 01224 868860

The charm of this hotel is the fact that the interior belies the young age of the building, with mature grounds helping to create this illusion. Situated off the Deeside road on the western side of the city, it sits well back from the road to offer a quiet oasis of comfort and quality. There is a choice of standard or executive bedrooms, both offering excellent facilities, comfort, and some thoughtful touches. Inviting lounges are complemented by interesting photographs and log fires, while for meals guests can choose between the Conservatory, which is open all day, or the more formal Invery Room. A traditional billiard room is a popular area, while the function suites are extensive and well equipped.

42 en suite (bth/shr) (4 fmly) No smoking in 10 bedrooms CTV in all bedrooms STV No dogs (ex guide dogs) Lift Night porter 160P No coaches Snooker Croquet lawn Putting green Xmas V meals Coffee am Tea pm Last d 10pm
ROOMS: (incl. bkfst) s £115-£155; d £125-£175 * **LB**
OFF-PEAK: (incl. bkfst) s £95-£135; d £105-£155
MEALS: Lunch £20-£35alc Dinner £20-£35alc
CONF: Thtr 500 Class 300 Board 24 Del from £150
CARDS:

See advertisement on opposite page

★★★★ 70% **Ardoe House**

Blairs, South Deeside Rd AB12 5YP (4m W off B9077) ☎ 01224 867355 FAX 01224 861283

Situated just three miles from Aberdeen, this peacefully positioned baronial granite mansion, built in 1878, offers smart, well equipped bedrooms, the majority of the rooms are contained in a sympathetically designed wing. The grand hall and day rooms, such as the cocktail lounge and drawing room feature fine wood panelling, ornate ceilings and some impressive stained glass. In the restaurant a good choice of imaginative dishes, based on seasonal local produce are presented in a modern style. The service is friendly and attentive.

71 en suite (bth/shr) (3 fmly) No smoking in 15 bedrooms CTV in all bedrooms STV Lift Night porter 200P Croquet lawn Putting green Petanque Xmas International Cuisine V meals Coffee am Tea pm No smoking in restaurant Last d 9.45pm
ROOMS: s £79; d £92 * **LB**
OFF-PEAK: s £62.50
MEALS: Lunch £12.50 Dinner £27.50&alc*
CONF: Thtr 200 Class 100 Board 60 Del £135
CARDS:

★★★★63% **The Copthorne Aberdeen**

122 Huntly St AB10 1SU (W of city centre)
☎ 01224 630404 FAX 01224 640573

Peacefully located just off Union Street, close to the shops and within five minutes of the theatre, this well appointed hotel offers spacious well equipped accommodation. Guests have the choice of eating less formally in the comfortable lounge bar, or in the restaurant, where the menus feature a selection of traditional Scottish dishes. The service is friendly and efficient and the hotel is a proud recipient of the 'Investors In People' award.

89 en suite (bth/shr) (15 fmly) No smoking in 14 bedrooms CTV in all bedrooms STV Lift Night porter 20P Wkly live entertainment Xmas Scottish Cuisine V meals Coffee am Tea pm Last d 10pm
ROOMS: s £48-£112; d £72-£122 **LB**
MEALS: Lunch £7.95-£15.95&alc High tea £8-£12alc Dinner fr £15.95&alc
CONF: Thtr 200 Class 100 Board 80 Del from £95
CARDS:

★★★★60% **Holiday Inn Crowne Plaza**

Malcom Rd, Bucksburn AB21 9LN (3m N off A947)
☎ 01224 409988 FAX 01224 714020

This modern, purpose built hotel, which is ideally situated between the city centre and the airport, offers spacious, smartly appointed and well equipped accommodation. The hotel also has a leisure club and impressive conference and banqueting facilities.

144 en suite (bth/shr) (35 fmly) No smoking in 45 bedrooms CTV in all bedrooms STV Lift Night porter 195P Indoor swimming pool (heated) Sauna Solarium Gym Steam room Xmas International Cuisine V meals Coffee am Tea pm No smoking area in restaurant Last d 10pm
ROOMS: s £89-£117; d £99-£117 * **LB**
OFF-PEAK: (incl. bkfst) s £65; d £65
MEALS: Lunch fr £10 Dinner fr £17.50&alc*
CONF: Thtr 500 Class 300 Board 300 Del from £120
CARDS:

★★★★57% **Skean Dhu Altens**

Souter Head Rd, Altens AB12 3LF (3m S off A956, on A90) ☎ 01224 877000 FAX 01224 896964
RS Xmas wk

Situated on the fringe of an industrial estate to the south-east of the city, this 70s purpose-built hotel caters largely for the business guest. Spacious modern public areas include a comfortable bar, a choice of

restaurants, a gift shop and a range of meeting and function rooms. The third floor corridors and bedrooms have recently been refurbished to a particularly smart and attractive standard.
221 en suite (bth/shr) (70 fmly) No smoking in 89 bedrooms CTV in all bedrooms Lift Night porter 300P Outdoor swimming pool (heated) Xmas International Cuisine V meals Coffee am Tea pm No smoking area in restaurant Last d 10.45pm
ROOMS: s £85-£107; d £95-£117 * **LB**
MEALS: Lunch £7.50-£14&alc Dinner fr £16.50&alc*
CONF: Thtr 400 Class 250 Board 100 Del from £67
CARDS:

★★★69% **Caledonian Thistle**

THISTLE HOTELS

10 Union Ter AB10 1WE (follow directions to city centre, Union Terrace is half way along Union St, Aberdeen's main thoroughfare and is opposite Union Terrace Gardens) ☎ 01224 640233 FAX 01224 641627
Situated in the heart of the city, with a car park behind it, this smart hotel offers friendly and quietly attentive service. There are a stylish cocktail lounge, a formal restaurant and a popular continental café/bar where an equally good range of dishes is served in more lively surroundings. Well equipped bedrooms range from spacious suites and executive rooms to smaller standard rooms.
80 en suite (bth/shr) (4 fmly) No smoking in 17 bedrooms CTV in all bedrooms Lift Night porter 25P Xmas International Cuisine V meals Coffee am Tea pm No smoking area in restaurant Last d 10pm
ROOMS: s £108-£168; d £125-£185 **LB**
OFF-PEAK: (incl. bkfst) s £44-£84; d £88-£140
MEALS: Lunch £10.50-£12.75&alc Dinner £21-£26.50&alc*
CONF: Thtr 40 Class 10 Board 20 Del from £110
CARDS:

★★★68% **Atholl**

54 Kings Gate AB15 4YN (in West End 400yds from Anderson Drive, the main ring road) ☎ 01224 323505 FAX 01224 321555
Situated in a west end residential area close to the ring road and not far from the city centre, this privately owned hotel has a relaxed atmosphere which makes it popular with visiting business guests. Bedrooms are situated in either the main house - a splendid turreted building - or in a modern wing, and all are furnished and equipped to a high standard. The bright public areas include a well stocked bar, coffee lounge and tastefully appointed restaurant. A wide range of home cooked dishes is available, with the same imaginative menu offered in both the lounge bar and restaurant.
35 en suite (bth/shr) (1 fmly) No smoking in all bedrooms CTV in all bedrooms STV No dogs (ex guide dogs) Night porter 60P No coaches Scottish Cuisine V meals Coffee am Tea pm Last d 9.30pm
ROOMS: (incl. bkfst) s £70-£76; d £86 **LB**
OFF-PEAK: (incl. bkfst) s £46; d £54
MEALS: Lunch £10-£15 Dinner £10-£15
CONF: Thtr 60 Class 25 Board 25 Del from £112.50
CARDS:

See advertisement on this page

★★★66% **The Craighaar**
Waterton Rd, Bankhead AB21 9HS (NW near the airport off A947)
☎ 01224 712275 FAX 01224 716362
Closed 26Dec & 1-2Jan &
The Craighaar is set in a residential area opposite the bowling green, within a short drive of the airport and the city centre. The well equipped modern bedrooms are attractively decorated and include some unusual gallery suites. Public areas include a conservatory lounge, a lively bar and a choice of restaurants. Friendly staff offer attentive service.
55 en suite (bth/shr) (15 fmly) CTV in all bedrooms STV Night porter 100P Xmas Scottish, French & Italian Cuisine V meals Coffee am Tea pm Last d 9.45pm
ROOMS: (incl. bkfst) s £25-£66.90; d £50-£74.50 **LB**
MEALS: Lunch £9.95-£19.50alc High tea £6.50-£7.50alc Dinner £16.95&alc
CONF: Thtr 90 Class 35 Board 30 Del from £75
CARDS: (£)

★★★ 65% **Maryculter House Hotel** — Macdonald Hotels
AB1 6BB (8 miles along B9077 off the A90 on south side of Aberdeen) ☎ 01224 732124
FAX 01224 733510
Set in five acres of woodland right on the banks of the River Dee, the origins of this hotel go back to the 13th century when the site was a college of the Knights Templar. While much of the hotel is more contemporary, some areas, such as the cocktail bar with its high vaulted ceiling and exposed stone walls, recalls earlier times. The majority of bedrooms are comfortable, furnished with pine and offer extras such as fruit and mineral water. There is a choice of restaurants - the informal Poacher's Bar or the candlelit Priory Room where chef Alfie Murray produces imaginative 4-course dinners featuring seasonal local produce.
24 en suite (bth/shr) (2 fmly) No smoking in 12 bedrooms CTV in all bedrooms STV Night porter 100P Golf 18 Fishing Clay pigeon shooting Wkly live entertainment Xmas European Cuisine V meals Coffee am Tea pm Last d 9.30pm
ROOMS: (incl. bkfst) s £60-£105; d £85-£110 * **LB**
OFF-PEAK: (incl. bkfst) d £75-£95
MEALS: Lunch £4-£15alc Dinner £27.50*
CONF: Thtr 250 Class 120 Board 40 Del £130
CARDS: (£)

★★★62% **Palm Court**
81 Seafield Rd AB15 7YU (take A92 to the Seafield roundabout, drive up Seafield Rd and Hotel is on left hand side)
☎ 01224 310351 FAX 01224 312707
Convenient for both the city centre and ring road, this recently refurbished hotel offers a relaxed, informal atmosphere. The bedrooms are comfortable and well equipped, particularly suited to the business guest, while the attractive decor sets them apart from many commercial hotels. The public areas are limited to the lively bar and adjoining Palm Court restaurant which gives the hotel its name and has an interesting range of African artefacts displayed around its walls and ceiling.
24 en suite (bth/shr) (1 fmly) CTV in all bedrooms STV Night porter 65P International Cuisine V meals Coffee am Tea pm No smoking area in restaurant
ROOMS: (incl. bkfst) s £65-£79.50; d £75-£89.50
OFF-PEAK: (incl. bkfst) s £29.50; d £50
MEALS: Lunch £11.40-£14.65alc Dinner £10.55-£23.45alc
CONF: Thtr 110 Class 80 Board 80 Del £120
CARDS: (£)

★★★61% **Queens**
51-53 Queens Rd AB15 4YP ☎ 01224 209999 FAX 01224 209009
Closed 25-26 Dec & 1-2 Jan
Located on the west side of the city, the hotel has been converted from a large Victorian house and has ample car parking to the front and at the rear. Bedrooms have been furnished to a high standard, with a good range of facilities, particularly for the business traveller. Public areas include a cosy lounge area in the foyer, a large lounge bar and elegant restaurant.
26 en suite (bth/shr) (3 fmly) CTV in all bedrooms STV No dogs Night porter Air conditioning 80P European Cuisine V meals Coffee am Tea pm
ROOMS: (incl. bkfst) s £55-£85; d £65-£95 *
OFF-PEAK: (incl. bkfst) s £35-£65; d £45-£75
CONF: Thtr 600 Class 150 Board 60 Del from £97.50
CARDS: (£)

★★68% ***Waterwheel*** — TOBY
203 North Deeside Rd, Bieldside AB1 9EN
☎ 01224 861659 FAX 01224 861515
Built around one of the last working grain mills in Aberdeen, this Toby Hotel is situated on the Deeside road, about six miles from the city centre. Bedrooms have been refurbished to a high standard and offer excellent facilities for both the tourist and business traveller. Good-value meals are served in either the lounge bar or restaurant, and service throughout the hotel is efficient and friendly
21 en suite (bth/shr) CTV in all bedrooms STV Night porter 95P Wkly live entertainment V meals Coffee am Tea pm Last d 10pm
CARDS:

Travel Inn — travel inn
Murcar, Bridge of Don AB23 8BP (on A92, close to Aberdeen Exhibition Centre) ☎ 01224 821217
FAX 01224 706869
Purpose-built accommodation, offering spacious, well equipped bedrooms, all with en suite bathrooms. Meals may be taken at the nearby family restaurant. For more information about Travel Inns, consult the Contents page under Hotel Groups.
40 en suite (bth/shr)
ROOMS: d £35.50 *

ABERDEEN AIRPORT Aberdeen City Map 15 NJ81
See also Aberdeen

★★★★64% **Aberdeen Marriott**
Overton Circle, Dyce AB21 7AZ (on A947)
☎ 01224 770011 FAX 01224 722347

This modern hotel, which is situated close to the airport and only 15 minutes from the city centre, offers well appointed and equipped accommodation. The smart public areas include an impressive marbled foyer, comfortable lounges and newly refurbished leisure facilities. In the restaurant, guests have the choice of eating from a Brasserie style menu, or from the a la carte which features a good selection of locally supplied fish. A courtesy mini-bus service to and from the airport is available on request. The hotel also has an excellent range of state of the art conference and leisure facilities.
154 en suite (bth/shr) (71 fmly) No smoking in 73 bedrooms CTV in all bedrooms STV Night porter 180P Indoor swimming pool (heated) Sauna Solarium Gym whirlpool ch fac Xmas International, Seafood Cuisine V meals Coffee am Tea pm Last d 10.30pm

contd.

A

ROOMS: s fr £110; d fr £125 * LB
MEALS: Lunch fr £15.95&alc Dinner fr £40&alc*
CONF: Thtr 400 Class 200 Board 30 Del from £56
CARDS:

★★★60% ***Dyce Skean Dhu***
Farburn Ter, Dyce AB21 7DW (off A947)
☎ 01224 723101 FAX 01224 722965

Mount Charlotte Hotels MC

Situated off the A.96, the A.947 and close to the airport, this modern hotel offers motel style accommodation servicing the main Aberdeen offshore industries. Both executive and studio rooms are available and whilst some rooms are rather dated, all are well equipped. A good range of wholesome well prepared dishes are served in the busy restaurant where the service is both friendly and prompt.
220 en suite (bth/shr) No smoking in 14 bedrooms CTV in all bedrooms Night porter 300P Squash Sauna Solarium Gym Pool table International Cuisine V meals Coffee am Tea pm Last d 10pm
CONF: Thtr 400 Board 40 Del from £95
CARDS:

Travel Inn
Burnside Dr, off Riverside Dr, Dyce AB2 0HW
☎ 01224 772787 FAX 01224 772968

Purpose-built accommodation, offering spacious, well equipped bedrooms, all with en suite bathrooms. Meals may be taken at the nearby family restaurant. For more information about Travel Inns, consult the Contents page under Hotel Groups.
40 en suite (bth/shr)
ROOMS: (incl. bkfst) d £35.50 *

ABERDOUR Fife Map 11 NT18

★★66% **Woodside**
High St KY3 0SW (E of Forth Road Bridge, across rbt into town, hotel on left after garage) ☎ 01383 860328 FAX 01383 860920
Situated on the main street, this family-owned hotel dates from 1873, but has undergone considerable refurbishment since a fire in early 1995. There is now a choice between standard and deluxe bedrooms, the latter being larger and better equipped, and all named after Scottish clans. The Clipped Bar was fortunately undamaged, as it has an original stained glass ceiling and wood panelling from the liner Orontes. Both the bar and restaurant menus have a hint of the Orient, as Mrs Austen hails from Singapore.
20 en suite (bth/shr) (1 fmly) CTV in all bedrooms Night porter 30P Xmas Scottish, French & Chinese Cuisine V meals Coffee am Tea pm No smoking area in restaurant Last d 9.30pm
ROOMS: (incl. bkfst) s £47.50-£57.50; d £67.50-£77.50
MEALS: Lunch £5.50-£18&alc Dinner £18&alc
CONF: Thtr 25 Class 40 Board 25 Del £97
CARDS:

See advertisement on opposite page

ABERFELDY Perthshire & Kinross Map 14 NN84

★★63% **"The Weem"**
Weem PH15 2LD (1m NW B846) ☎ 01887 820381
FAX 01887 820187
Situated in the centre of this attractive village, this historic roadside inn has a relaxed, informal atmosphere and offers a good range of bar meals both at lunch and dinner. Bedrooms, including two family suites, provide pleasant, well equipped accommodation, while the public areas include a lounge bar with open plan dining room and a quieter residents' den.
12 en suite (bth/shr) (4 fmly) No smoking in 4 bedrooms CTV in all bedrooms 20P No coaches Shooting Xmas European Cuisine V meals Coffee am Tea pm No smoking in restaurant Last d 8.30pm
ROOMS: (incl. bkfst) s £20-£30; d £40-£60 * LB
OFF-PEAK: (incl. bkfst) s £18-£30; d £30-£50
MEALS: Lunch fr £10alc High tea fr £10alc Dinner fr £13.50alc
CONF: Thtr 60 Class 30 Board 30
CARDS:

See advertisement on opposite page

★❀❀ 74% **Guinach House**
"By The Birks", Urlar Rd PH15 2ET (access off A826 Crieff road) ☎ 01887 820251 FAX 01887 829607
Closed 4 days Xmas
(Rosettes awarded for dinner only)
Lying in secluded gardens on the edge of the town, this small country house hotel is a quiet and informal retreat. Bert and Marian MacKay provide honest and unassuming hospitality which creates a genuine home-from-home atmosphere. The second of Guinach's virtues is its food. Bert - an international master chef - focuses his vast experience on presenting not only the daily-changing dinner menu, but on baking and making jams and preserves, as well as the tasty pre-dinner canapés and after-dinner truffles. The cosy little lounge has lots to read, whilst the attractive dining room boasts some splendid paintings and prints. Bedrooms offer a variety of sizes, some being well proportioned, most furnished in traditional style and all equipped with thoughtful touches.
7 en suite (bth/shr) CTV in all bedrooms 12P No coaches British, French & Italian Cuisine V meals No smoking in restaurant Last d 9.30pm

ROOMS: (incl. bkfst) s £40; d £80 *
MEALS: Dinner £25
CARDS:

ABERFOYLE Stirling Map 11 NN50

★★61% **Altskeith**
Kinlochard FK8 3TL (4m W beside Loch Ard)
☎ 01877 387266 FAX 01877 387223
Enjoying delightful views across Loch Ard, this small family-run hotel is an ideal base from which to explore the Trossachs. The spacious bedrooms have mixed furnishings and there is a small sun lounge exclusively for the use of guests, while the lounge bar is well stocked and a range of bar suppers are also offered there. Free fly fishing on the loch is available to house guests.
6 en suite (bth/shr) (1 fmly) No smoking in all bedrooms CTV in all bedrooms No dogs (ex guide dogs) 20P No coaches Fishing Boats for hire,Shooting Scottish Cuisine V meals Coffee am Last d 8.30pm
ROOMS: (incl. bkfst) s £35-£45; d £66-£70 **LB**
OFF-PEAK: (incl. bkfst) s £33-£39; d £60-£66
MEALS: Lunch £5-£9 Dinner £10.99-£22
CARDS:

ABERLADY East Lothian Map 12 NT47

★★67% **Kilspindie House**
Main St EH32 0RE (on A198 - centre of village on main street)
☎ 01875 870682 FAX 01875 870504
Situated in the centre of an attractive conservation village, this long established family-run hotel is popular with golfers, business guests and tourists alike. Bedrooms are well designed and cheerfully decorated, with a four-poster room available for special occasions. A good range of meals is available either in the lounge bar, dining room or, on warmer evenings, in the enclosed courtyard.
26 en suite (bth/shr) CTV in all bedrooms 30P V meals Coffee am Tea pm No smoking area in restaurant Last high tea 6pm
ROOMS: (incl. bkfst) s £38-£44; d £54-£64 * **LB**
OFF-PEAK: (incl. bkfst) s £38; d £54
MEALS: Sunday Lunch fr £8alc High tea £7-£9.75*
CONF: Thtr 60 Class 40 Board 8 Del from £50
CARDS:

ABERLOUR See Archiestown

ABINGTON South Lanarkshire Map 11 NS92

Travelodge

Welcome Break Service Area ML12 6RE
(off junct 13 of M74) ☎ 01864 502782
This modern building offers accommodation in smart, spacious and well equipped bedrooms, suitable for family use, and all with en suite bathrooms. Meals may be taken at the nearby family restaurant. For information on room rates and to make a booking, call Roomline free of charge on 0800 850950. For more details about Travelodge, consult the Contents page under Hotel Groups.
56 en suite (bth/shr)

ABOYNE Aberdeenshire Map 15 NO59

★★70% ***Birse Lodge***
Charleston Rd AB34 5EL (in centre of Aboyne at western end of village green) ☎ 013398 86253
This long established hotel lies in its own gardens just off the village green and close to the River Dee. It is personally run by owners Trevor and Evelyn O'Halloran who have extended their customer base beyond the fishing and shooting clientele, to appeal to business travellers as

contd.

well. There are inviting lounges, a cosy bar and a traditional dining room adorned with crisp linen and sparkling silver; one can also dine in the popular conservatory. Bedrooms blend traditional furnishings with bold modern décor.
12 en suite (bth/shr) CTV in all bedrooms 30P No coaches Putting green ch fac International Cuisine V meals Coffee am Tea pm Last d 9-9.30pm
CARDS:

ACHNASHEEN Highland Map 14 NH15

★★★ 67% **Ledgowan Lodge**

IV22 2EJ (0.25m on A890 to Kyle of Lochalsh - from Aachnasheen) ☎ 01445 720252 FAX 01445 720240
RS Jan-Feb & Nov-Dec
For over thirty years the Millard family have been welcoming guests to their popular Highland holiday hotel, an ideal base from which one can explore Wester Ross. Relaxing public areas include a choice of comfortable lounges, a coffee shop serving all day meals and snacks, and an attractive dining room with an extensive carte. Bedrooms, solidly traditional, are comfortable and offer all the expected amenities. Staff are friendly and willing to please.
12 en suite (bth/shr) (2 fmly) CTV in all bedrooms STV No dogs 25P International Cuisine V meals Coffee am Tea pm No smoking in restaurant Last d 8.30pm
ROOMS: s £31.50-£45; d £54-£76
OFF-PEAK: s £25-£32; d £50-£70
MEALS: Lunch £15-£25alc Dinner £12.50-£35alc
CARDS:

ALLOA Clackmannanshire Map 11 NS89

★★★ 73% **Gean House**

Gean Park, Tullibody Rd FK10 2HS (W of town centre off B9096) ☎ 01259 219275 FAX 01259 213827
Gean House, built in 1912 as a wedding gift, has been magnificently restored to make an intimate, luxury hotel. The elegant reception rooms have inglenook fireplaces and views over the nearby Ochil Hills, while the dining room has highly polished walnut panels providing a suitable ambience for the imaginative cuisine, which makes good use of local game, fruit and fish. The seven bedrooms are sumptuously furnished, with the three executive rooms being particularly comfortable. Thoughtful touches are evident throughout the hotel, while the well kept gardens help to complete the picture.
7 en suite (bth/shr) CTV in all bedrooms STV No dogs 20P Xmas V meals Coffee am Tea pm No smoking in restaurant Last d 9.30pm
ROOMS: (incl. bkfst) s £80; d £120-£140 *
OFF-PEAK: (incl. bkfst & dinner) s £95; d £150
MEALS: Lunch £15 Dinner £26.50*
CONF: Thtr 50 Class 50 Board 50 Del from £120
CARDS:

ALYTH Perthshire & Kinross Map 15 NO24

★★ 65% **Alyth**
PH11 8AF (turn off A94 for Alyth town centre after 3m hotel on Market Sq) ☎ 01828 632447 FAX 01828 632353
Overlooking the Alyth Burn which flows through the market place, this 18th-century inn now offers modern accommodation in a friendly atmosphere. Bedrooms are bright and practically furnished, while the first floor residents' lounge is a peaceful place to relax. The lively lounge bar has a wide range of malt whiskies, with honest home-cooking being served both there and in the dining room. Golfing packages are a speciality of the hotel and for those wetter days, a full size snooker room is now available.
10 en suite (bth/shr) 3 annexe en suite (shr) (3 fmly) No smoking in 10 bedrooms CTV in all bedrooms STV Snooker Pool table Xmas V meals Coffee am Tea pm No smoking in restaurant Last d 9.30pm
ROOMS: (incl. bkfst) s £35-£40; d £60-£80 **LB**
OFF-PEAK: (incl. bkfst) s £30-£40; d £40-£60
MEALS: Lunch £7.50-£17.50alc High tea £6.25-£12.50alc Dinner £12-£20alc
CARDS:

ANNAN Dumfries & Galloway Map 11 NY16

★★ 66% **Warmanbie Hotel & Restaurant**
DG12 5LL (1.5m E off B722) ☎ 01461 204015 FAX 01461 204015
This elegant Georgian house is set in 45 acres of secluded woodland, close to the River Annan just north of the town. Owned by the Duncan family for more than 40 years, a friendly welcome is assured. Most of the bedrooms have been furnished to retain the character of the house as well as provide excellent modern facilities. Public areas include a small bar, library lounge and fine dining room where a Taste of Scotland can be sampled.
8 en suite (bth/shr) (1 fmly) CTV in all bedrooms 25P Fishing Clay pigeon shooting Xmas V meals Coffee am Tea pm No smoking in restaurant
ROOMS: (incl. bkfst) s £47-£51; d £67-£75.50 * **LB**
OFF-PEAK: (incl. bkfst) s £45-£48; d fr £67.50
MEALS: Lunch £2.50-£8.50*
CONF: Thtr 40 Class 24 Board 20
CARDS:

★★ 61% **Queensberry Arms**

CONSORT HOTELS

DG12 6AD (in town square, 1.5m from A75)
☎ 01461 202024 FAX 01461 205998
This 18th-century coaching inn, with its distinctive black and white facade, is situated in the centre of the town. Public areas are attractive, with a variety of lounges as well as a first floor steakhouse with a nautical theme. Bedrooms vary in size and style.
24 en suite (bth/shr) (3 fmly) CTV in all bedrooms STV Night porter 50P Darts Wkly live entertainment Xmas International Cuisine V meals Coffee am Tea pm No smoking area in restaurant
ROOMS: (incl. bkfst) s fr £45; d fr £55.50 * **LB**
OFF-PEAK: (incl. bkfst) s fr £35; d fr £45
MEALS: Bar Lunch fr £1.20*
CONF: Thtr 70 Class 30 Board 30
CARDS:
See advertisement under GRETNA (WITH GRETNA GREEN)

ANSTRUTHER Fife Map 12 NO50

★★ 60% **Smugglers Inn**
High St KY10 3DQ ☎ 01333 310506 FAX 01333 312706
This historic roadside inn retains much of its original character, particularly in the lounge bar which overlooks Anstruther harbour. There is an attractive restaurant and a first-floor residents' lounge. Bedrooms, some of which also have harbour views, vary in size.
8 en suite (bth/shr) CTV in all bedrooms 12P Scottish, French & Italian Cuisine V meals Coffee am Last d 9pm
ROOMS: (incl. bkfst) s fr £29.50; d fr £59 *

MEALS: Bar Lunch £4.50-£8 Dinner fr £17&alc
CARDS:

ARBROATH Angus Map 12 NO64

★★★69% **Letham Grange**

Colliston DD11 4RL (leave A92 onto A933 to Brechin, Letham Grange signposted at village of Colliston)
☎ 01241 890373 FAX 01241 890414
This splendid listed Victorian mansion is the centrepiece of a golf and sporting complex. Sympathetically restored, the house features magnificent woodwork and fine fireplaces in its elegant public areas, whilst bedrooms retain the character of a country house, an artist having been commissioned to hand-paint many items of furniture. Some rooms are very commodious and all are well equipped. For that unique occasion try the Tower Room set on two levels and with a lounge giving an eagle's eye view of the courses.
19 en suite (bth/shr) 22 annexe en suite (bth/shr) (1 fmly) No smoking in 2 bedrooms CTV in all bedrooms STV Night porter 150P Golf 36 Snooker Croquet lawn Putting green Curling rink Xmas International Cuisine V meals Coffee am Tea pm Last d 10pm
ROOMS: (incl. bkfst) s £65-£85; d £95-£125 **LB**
OFF-PEAK: (incl. bkfst) s fr £49; d fr £80
MEALS: Lunch £7.95-£13.95 High tea fr £5.95 Dinner fr £18.95
CONF: Thtr 700 Class 300 Board 20 Del from £115
CARDS:

See advertisement on this page

★★62% **Hotel Seaforth**
Dundee Rd DD11 1QF (on southern outskirts, on A92)
☎ 01241 872232 FAX 01241 877473
This friendly family-run commercial hotel lies on the southern side of town looking out to sea. Bedrooms come in a variety of styles and sizes, whilst good value meals are offered in both the restaurant and bar, with Arbroath smokies being popular at breakfast.
20 en suite (bth/shr) (2 fmly) CTV in all bedrooms 100P Indoor swimming pool (heated) Snooker Solarium Jacuzzi/spa Xmas Scottish & French Cuisine V meals Coffee am
ROOMS: (incl. bkfst) s £36-£38.50; d £58-£60 * **LB**
CONF: Thtr 120 Class 50 Board 30
CARDS:

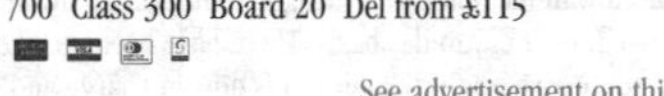

ARCHIESTOWN Moray Map 15 NJ24

★★73% **Archiestown**

AB38 7QX (on B9102, 5m SW of Craigellachie)
☎ 01340 810218 FAX 01340 810239
Closed end Sep - early Feb
Although most of the guests here are fishermen, the relaxed atmosphere would be appreciated by tourists and business guests as well, with the proprietors maintaining a jovial banter with the guests at all times. The public rooms, which include two lounges, are adorned with interesting pictures and other artefacts, while the bistro bar has an array of angling paraphernalia. Bedrooms are very well maintained with attractive floral decor and coordinated soft furnishings. Judith

Bulger keeps the menu here simple, relying on good local produce to create the superb flavours and tastes, and portions are certainly hearty!
8 rms (6 bth) CTV in all bedrooms 20P No coaches International Cuisine V meals Coffee am Tea pm Last d 8.30pm
ROOMS: (incl. bkfst) s £32.50; d £80 *
MEALS: Bar Lunch £2-£20alc Dinner £25&alc
CARDS:

ARDBEG See Bute, Isle of

ARDELVE Highland Map 14 NG82

★★69% **Conchra House**

Sallachy Rd IV40 8DZ ☎ 01599 552233
FAX 01599 555433
Closed 24 Dec-3 Jan
Colin and Mary Deans have lovingly restored this fine Georgian house to create this welcome new addition to the Scottish Country House scene. The house stands in its own grounds under the shadow of Ben Conchra enjoying views over Loch Long, and is a haven of peace with an atmosphere more in keeping with that of a private residence and Colin is a most genial host. There is a lovely sitting room with deep cushioned sofas and a welcoming open fire, and Mary Dean's good home cooking is enjoyable though at peak times it may be necessary to share a table. Bedrooms, though not overly large, are are tastefully decorated and comfortably furnished in pine.
6 rms (3 shr) No smoking in all bedrooms 12P Fishing Pool table Croquet lawn Putting green V meals Coffee am Tea pm No smoking in restaurant Last d 7.30pm
ROOMS: (incl. bkfst) s £30-£40; d £54-£70 *
MEALS: Dinner £14-£19*
CONF: Thtr 45 Class 40 Board 30 Del from £40
CARDS:

★68% **Loch Duich**
IV40 8DY (beside 'Road to the Isles')
☎ 01599 555213 FAX 01599 555214
Closed 4 Jan-1 Mar & 19-28 Dec RS Nov-18 Dec
Improvements have recently taken place at this welcoming family run tourist hotel, a former drovers inn beside the 'Road to the Isles'. Many bedrooms have been refurbished, and more en suite bathrooms added. Relaxing public areas include a choice of lounges, contrasting bars, and an attractive dining room overlooking Eilean Donan Castle.
18 rms (9 shr) (1 fmly) 41P No coaches Fishing,Shooting Wkly live entertainment ch fac Scottish & French Cuisine V meals Coffee am Tea pm No smoking in restaurant Last d 9pm
ROOMS: (incl. bkfst) s £23.50-£28.50; d £25-£28.50 * **LB**
OFF-PEAK: (incl. bkfst) s £20-£25; d £20-£25
MEALS: Bar Lunch £1.75-£10.25alc Dinner £17.50-£18.75*
CONF: Board 40
CARDS:

ARDENTINNY Argyll & Bute Map 10 NS18

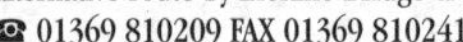

★★67% ***Ardentinny***
PA23 8TR (M8 to Gourock, ferry to Dunoon(every 30mins duration 20mins) 12m N on A880 off A815, alternative route by Erskine Bridge & Loch Lomond)
☎ 01369 810209 FAX 01369 810241
Closed Nov-15 Mar
Relaxed and friendly, this popular tourist hotel (once a coaching inn) has gardens extending down to the picturesque shore of Loch Long. One of its well stocked bars - a firm favourite with visiting yachtsmen - has a nautical theme, the buttery provides a less formal alternative to the spacious traditional dining room, and there is a comfortable lounge. Bedrooms vary in both size and style but all are equipped with the expected amenities; some superior rooms are available.
11 en suite (bth/shr) (1 fmly) CTV in all bedrooms 30P Boating Scottish, French & Italian Cuisine V meals Coffee am Tea pm Last high tea 6.30pm
CARDS:

ARDUAINE Argyll & Bute Map 10 NM71

★★★71% **Loch Melfort**
PA34 4XG (on A816 - midway between Oban and Lochgilphead) ☎ 01852 200233 FAX 01852 200214
Closed 4 Jan-Feb
Under the care and direction of dedicated owners Philip and Rosalind Lewis, this hospitable holiday hotel has an idyllic setting beside the famous Arduaine Gardens with a panoramic outlook over Asknish bay. Most bedrooms are located in the adjoining Cedar wing, accessed by a covered walkway; brightly decorated and with modern furnishings, they enjoy stunning sea views from either a patio or balcony. The main house offers some well proportioned superior rooms. A modern cocktail bar contrasts with the informal atmosphere of the Chart Room bar which is a popular rendezvous for visiting yachtsmen, and an inviting panelled library has well filled book shelves. The attractive restaurant overlooks the bay and offers a daily changing five course fixed price menu supported by a range of seafood specialities and a balanced wine list.

7 en suite (bth/shr) 20 annexe en suite (bth/shr) (2 fmly) CTV in all bedrooms 65P Xmas Scottish & French Cuisine V meals Coffee am Tea pm No smoking in restaurant Last d 9pm
ROOMS: (incl. bkfst) s £62; d £99 **LB**
OFF-PEAK: (incl. bkfst & dinner) s fr £50; d £80-£119
MEALS: Bar Lunch £2.50-£20 Dinner £27.50-£35
CONF: Thtr 30 Board 20
CARDS:
See advertisement under OBAN

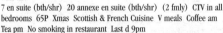

ARDVASAR See Skye, Isle of

ARISAIG Highland Map 13 NM68

RED STAR HOTEL

★★★ **Arisaig House**
Beasdale PH39 4NR (3m E A830)
☎ 01687 450622 FAX 01687 450626
Closed Nov-Mar

This delightful hotel is beautifully situated in woodland, formal gardens and terraces full of rhododendrons, azaleas and roses where guests can wander at leisure. Polished floors, antiques, deep cushioned sofas, real fires and are the hallmarks of the splendid public rooms which enjoy the most wonderful views. Unobtrusive luxury abounds in the indvidually decorated bedrooms in the form of hand-finished sheets, thick bathrobes, fruit bowls and fresh flowers, while old-fashioned courtesies such as evening turndown and service of early morning tea are also provided. Whilst the Smither family are still very much involved with the hotel, their daughter and son in law now manage it on a day to day basis. There have been changes in the kitchen too, where Gary Robinson is now in charge and offers an interesting choice of well executed dishes. A typical dinner may begin with a duck confit served with a warm potato and a small dressed salad, followed by a saddle of hare baked en croute, and finish with a crème brûlée with a tower of spun sugar and good home-made petits fours.
14 en suite (bth) CTV in all bedrooms No dogs (ex guide dogs) 16P No coaches Snooker Croquet lawn No children 10yrs British & French Cuisine V meals Coffee am Tea pm No smoking in restaurant Last d 8.30pm
ROOMS: (incl. bkfst) d £168-£220 * **LB**
MEALS: Lunch £4.25-£25.10alc Dinner fr £33.50*
CARDS:

★★65% **Arisaig**
PH39 4NH (on A830 opposite the harbour - 35 miles west of Fort William) ☎ 01687 450210 FAX 01687 450310
Refurbishment of all the bedrooms is complete at this very comfortable Highland hotel, which occupies an enviable position on the shores of Loch Nan Ceal. The smartly appointed and thoughtfully equipped bedrooms are now all en-suite and some enjoy the most marvellous views across the bay to the isles of Skye, Muck, Rhum and Eigg. The comfortable public areas include a choice of lounges and bars and the atmosphere is very friendly and relaxed.
13 en suite (bth/shr) (2 fmly) CTV in all bedrooms 30P No coaches Pool table ch fac Scottish & French Cuisine V meals Coffee am Tea pm No smoking in restaurant Last d 9pm

ROOMS: (incl. bkfst) s £30-£40; d £60 *
MEALS: Bar Lunch £6.20-£14alc Dinner £17-£22.50*
CARDS:

ARRAN, ISLE OF North Ayrshire Map 10

BRODICK Map 10 NS03

★★★ 76% **Auchrannie Country House**
KA27 8BZ (turn right from Brodick Ferry terminal, through Brodick village, turn second left after Brodick Golf Course clubhouse, 300yds to Hotel)
☎ 01770 302234 FAX 01770 302812
(Rosette awarded for dinner only)
Genuine hospitality together with good food and extensive leisure facilities are all part of the appeal of this renovated and extended Victorian mansion, which stands in 6 acres of wooded and landscaped grounds. Comfortable bedrooms range from 4-poster rooms and suites, to tastefully appointed modern wing rooms. Public areas include a choice of relaxing lounges, a bistro and the more formal Garden Restaurant with its conservatory extension. Here the daily changing fixed-price menu offers the best of Scotland's larder competently prepared by the dedicated kitchen team.
28 en suite (bth/shr) (3 fmly) CTV in all bedrooms STV No dogs (ex guide dogs) Night porter 50P Indoor swimming pool (heated) Snooker Sauna Solarium Gym Hair & beauty salon Aromatherapy Shiatsu Scottish & French Cuisine V meals Coffee am Tea pm Last d 9pm
MEALS: Lunch £9.90-£17.40alc Dinner £22-£23&alc
CONF: Thtr 120 Board 30 Del £75
CARDS:

RED STAR HOTEL

★★ **Kilmichael Country House**
Glen Cloy KA27 8BY ☎ 01770 302219 FAX 01770 302068
Closed Xmas
This attractive house is one of some historical and architectural importance on the island; tucked away in a peaceful glen, it is just a short drive from Brodick and the main ferry terminal. Owners Geoffrey Botterill and Anthony Butterworth, both 'escaped' teachers, have, along with their smiling staff, created a warm and welcoming atmosphere at affordable prices. Accommodation is tastefully appointed with an abundance of flowers, books and interesting knick-knacks. Anthony is responsible for good home cooking and a menu that offers an interesting selection with a French and Italian influence.
6 en suite (bth/shr) No smoking in all bedrooms CTV in all bedrooms 12P No coaches No children 12yrs International Cuisine V meals No smoking in restaurant Last d 8.30pm
ROOMS: (incl. bkfst) s £60; d £76-£106 * **LB**
OFF-PEAK: (incl. bkfst) s £60; d £70-£94
MEALS: Dinner £27.50&alc*
CARDS:

AUCHENCAIRN Dumfries & Galloway Map 11 NX75

★★★ 70% **Balcary Bay**
DG7 1QZ (on coast 2m from village)
☎ 01556 640217 & 640311 FAX 01556 640272
Closed Dec-Feb

This family run country house hotel stands in three acres of its own gardens at the edge of Balcary Bay and offers fine views across the unspoilt Solway coast. The main part of the building dates from 1625, though the accommodation has been sympathetically modernised to ensure that it is comfortable and well equipped. Bedrooms are bright and cheerfully decorated, with those overlooking the bay tending to be more spacious. There is a good choice of public areas including lounges for smokers and non-smokers as well as a pleasant conservatory.
17 en suite (bth/shr) (1 fmly) CTV in all bedrooms 50P No coaches Snooker English & French Cuisine V meals Coffee am Tea pm Last d 8.30pm
ROOMS: (incl. bkfst) s £52-£68; d £94-£106 **LB**
OFF-PEAK: (incl. bkfst & dinner) s £48-£52; d £98-£104
MEALS: Lunch fr £8.95&alc High tea fr £3.95 Dinner fr £21.50&alc
CARDS:

RED STAR HOTEL

★★ *Collin House*
DG7 1QN ☎ 01556 640292
FAX 01556 640276
Closed 4 Jan-1st week Mar

Pam and John Hall are now firmly established at this wonderful little hotel on the Solway coast. Easily spotted from the road because of its pink facade, this Georgian house has been sympathetically extended to offer spacious bedrooms and cosy public areas. Antique furniture is a feature of all the rooms, none of which are fussy but have many attractive touches such as fresh flowers and fluffy towels, while the views are quite spectacular and on a clear day one is able to see the Cumbrian hills. A warming log fire burns in the morning room, and guests are introduced to each other by Pam, who creates an informal and convivial atmosphere. John remains behind the scenes in the kitchen and carefully transforms local produce in to some of the finest dishes in the area; the warm mousse of Arbroath

contd.

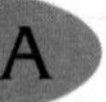

smokie with sauce Vierge was the highlight of a recent meal.
6 en suite (bth/shr) No smoking in 1 bedroom CTV in all bedrooms 15P No coaches
CARDS:

AUCHTERARDER Perthshire & Kinross Map 11 NN91

RED STAR HOTEL

★★★★★ **The Gleneagles Hotel**
PH3 1NF (on A823) (Leading Hotels) ☎ 01764 662231
FAX 01764 662134
Renowned world-wide as a mecca for golfers and as a top class resort destination, Gleneagles commands an imposing position surrounded by its golf courses and extensive policies, in open countryside It offers an outstanding range of sporting activities including an equestrian centre, shooting school, falconry and off-road driving, as well as a country club and health spa to give it all year-round appeal. This grand Edwardian building boasts a fine staircase, wide corridors that stretch forever and a fashionable shopping mall. The drawing room still serves its famous afternoon teas, but it now has a cocktail bar as centre piece. There are lots of dining options, but the elegant Strathearn Restaurant is the place for dinner, with a leaning towards classical dishes such as traditional cock-a-leekie soup, tournedos rossini and crepes suzette cooked at the table. Bedrooms come in a variety of styles and sizes with many enjoying superb views.
234 en suite (bth/shr) No smoking in 60 bedrooms CTV in all bedrooms STV Lift Night porter 200P No coaches Indoor swimming pool (heated) Golf 18 Tennis (hard & grass) Fishing Squash Riding Snooker Sauna Solarium Gym Pool table Croquet lawn Putting green Jacuzzi/spa Bowls Shooting Falconry Esquestrian Wkly live entertainment ch fac Xmas International Cuisine V meals Coffee am Tea pm Last d 10pm
ROOMS: s £130; d £205-£285 * **LB**
MEALS: Lunch £4-£27alc High tea £8-£25alc Dinner £37.50&alc*
CONF: Thtr 360 Class 240 Board 70 Del from £210
CARDS:

★★★ 76% ***Auchterarder House***
PH3 1DZ (NW off B8062) ☎ 01764 663646
FAX 01764 662939
An air of elegance pervades this fine baronial residence which dates from the early 19th-century, and stands in 17 acres of well tended grounds. Bedrooms, named after Scottish clans, are attractively furnished, and have many extra touches such as fresh fruit, sherry and flowers. The impressive public rooms have retained their wood panelling and marble fireplaces, and enjoy superb views over the Perthshire countryside. The cuisine here continues to offer fine Scottish produce cooked with imagination and flair, with the 'Breakfast Salad' the highlight of a recent inspection meal. The wine list is an addictive read, both because of the range of vintages available and the witty quotes which intersperse them. Service is polite with a reserved friendliness.
13 en suite (bth/shr) 2 annexe en suite (bth/shr) CTV in all bedrooms Night porter 40P No coaches Fishing Croquet lawn Putting green No children 11yrs Scottish & French Cuisine V meals Coffee am Tea pm Last d 9.30pm
CARDS:

★★★ 70% **Duchally House**
PH3 1PN (2m SW off A823 Dunfermline road)
☎ 01764 663071 FAX 01764 662464
Some of the bedrooms at this Victorian manor house are large enough to accommodate sofas as well as beds and in the public areas there are traditional open fires. Guests can choose a bistro-style meal, but the main dining room, with its crisp linen and sparkling silver, takes pride of place. A typical three-course meal might start with consommé with Madeira, followed by fillet of beef with mushrooms served on a savoury pancake with mustard sauce, and an unusual iced chocolate and prune terrine with warm chocolate sauce.
13 rms (12 bth/shr) (3 fmly) CTV in all bedrooms 30P Snooker Xmas V meals Coffee am Tea pm Last d 9.30pm
ROOMS: (incl. bkfst) s £60-£70; d £75-£90 * **LB**
OFF-PEAK: (incl. bkfst) s £50-£55; d £65-£70
MEALS: Lunch £12.50-£18.50 Dinner £19.50-£24.50*
CONF: Thtr 50 Class 40 Board 30 Del from £90
CARDS:

★★ 72% **Cairn Lodge**
Orchil Rd PH3 1LX (from the A9 take A824 into Auchterarder then A823 signposted Crieff & Gleneagles in approx 200yds hotel on the Y junct)
☎ 01764 662634 & 662431 FAX 01764 664866
Situated in the heart of Perthshire, just a few minutes from Gleneagles, this elegant, family-run hotel offers high standards of accommodation and cuisine. All the bedrooms have been refurbished to provide both attractive surroundings and many quality touches. There is a popular bar where light meals are served, while fine dining is available in the Capercaillie Restaurant, where guests are recommended to leave room for the deftly prepared desserts. There is also a cosy lounge which overlooks the pretty gardens.
7 en suite (bth/shr) (2 fmly) No smoking in 2 bedrooms CTV in all bedrooms No dogs (ex guide dogs) 40P Putting green Xmas V meals Coffee am No smoking in restaurant Last d 9.30pm
ROOMS: (incl. bkfst) s £45-£75; d £75-£95 *
MEALS: Lunch £11.95-£15.95&alc Dinner £24&alc*
CARDS:

AUCHTERHOUSE Angus Map 11 NO33

★★★ 70% **Old Mansion House**
DD3 0QN (take A923 from Dundee to Muirhead then B954 for 2m hotel is on left) ☎ 01382 320366
FAX 01382 320400
Closed 25 Dec-3 Jan
Nigel and Eve Bell have sympathetically converted this baronial mansion into a tasteful small hotel and restaurant. Now well established, it offers a friendly and relaxing atmosphere. A stone spiral staircase leads from the vaulted entrance to a cosy library bar and the restaurant features a magnificent ornate plaster ceiling and a huge Jacobean fireplace, now a wine store. Dishes blend modern presentation with a more classical style of cooking whilst highlighting Scottish produce. There is also a courtyard bar which offers a more

informal style of catering. The well equipped bedrooms are furnished in the character of a traditional country house.

6 en suite (bth/shr) (2 fmly) CTV in all bedrooms 51P No coaches Outdoor swimming pool (heated) Tennis (grass) Squash Croquet lawn Scottish & French Cuisine V meals Coffee am Tea pm No smoking in restaurant Last d 9.15pm
ROOMS: (incl. bkfst) s £75-£80; d £95-£120 * **LB**
MEALS: Lunch £15.95-£16.95&alc Dinner £25-£30alc
CARDS:

AULTBEA Highland Map 14 NG88

★★69% **Aultbea**
IV22 2HX (turn off A832 at Aultbea signs, hotel will be seen at lochside after 400yds)
☎ 01445 731201 FAX 01445 731214

Many guests return year after year to Peter and Avril Nieto's charming small holiday hotel on the picturesque shore of Loch Ewe. Public areas, where the atmosphere is relaxed, include a comfortable lounge, well stocked bar and the informal Waterside Bistro which offers food and beverages throughout the day. The attractive dining room gives the option of fixed-price and carte menus for dinner. Bedrooms of varying sizes are tastefully decorated and offer traditional comfort and all the usual modern amenities.
8 en suite (bth/shr) 3 annexe en suite (bth/shr) (1 fmly) CTV in all bedrooms 40P No coaches Pool table International Cuisine V meals Coffee am Tea pm Last d 9pm
ROOMS: (incl. bkfst) s £36; d £72-£82 * **LB**
OFF-PEAK: (incl. bkfst) s £32; d £64-£74
MEALS: Bar Lunch £5-£15alc High tea £5-£10alc Dinner £21-£22.50&alc
CARDS:

AVIEMORE Highland Map 14 NH81

★★★66% **Aviemore Highlands**
Aviemore Mountain Resort PH22 1PJ (off A9 signed Aviemore B9152, turn left opposite railway station around Ring road Hotel is 2nd on left)
☎ 01479 810771 FAX 01479 811473

A major transformation is taking place at this popular holiday and conference hotel in the Aviemore Centre. The first phase of improvements involved complete refurbishment of the public areas which now offer tasteful and comfortable modern appointments. At the time of our visit, good progress was being made with upgrading the bedrooms. The completed rooms, with attractive décor and co-ordinated fabrics, are comfortably furnished and offer a wide range of amenities.
102 en suite (bth/shr) (37 fmly) CTV in all bedrooms Lift Night porter 140P Pool table Games room Wkly live entertainment Xmas Scottish, English & French Cuisine V meals Coffee am Tea pm No smoking in restaurant Last d 9pm
ROOMS: s £65-£75; d £75-£85 * **LB**
OFF-PEAK: s £45-£75; d £50-£85
MEALS: Bar Lunch fr £2 Dinner £14.95-£21.50
CONF: Thtr 140 Class 80 Board 60 Del from £65
CARDS:

★★★63% **The Mercury**
Avimore Centre PH22 1PE (from A9 follow directions to Aviemore, hotel is in the Leisure Centre)
☎ 01479 810781 FAX 01479 811167

This popular hotel, conveniently situated in the Aviemore centre, offers comfortable, well appointed accommodation all of which has been refurbished to a high standard. In the bedrooms, good use has been made of bold fabrics and all the rooms have a small kitchenette area. The attractive public areas include a lounge bar with a dance floor where entertainment is regularly provided and a spacious restaurant. The mainly young staff are helpful and friendly.

94 en suite (bth/shr) (85 fmly) No smoking in 6 bedrooms CTV in all bedrooms Lift Night porter 94P Wkly live entertainment ch fac Xmas V meals Coffee am Last d 8.30pm
ROOMS: s £57-£67; d £67-£85 * **LB**
OFF-PEAK: s £37-£57; d £57-£75
MEALS: Lunch £5-£10 Dinner £12-£15*
CONF: Thtr 100 Class 60 Board 50 Del from £70
CARDS:

AYR South Ayrshire Map 10 NS32
See also Maybole

★★★★68% ***Fairfield House***
12 Fairfield Rd KA7 2AR ☎ 01292 267461 FAX 01292 261456
Situated across the park from the seafront and just a short walk from the town centre, this is a fine Victorian mansion that has been restored and extended over recent years. There are superb views over the Firth of Clyde towards the Isle of Arran. Public areas are elegantly furnished and include a modern conservatory brasserie and a fully equipped leisure centre and beauty salon. Most of the bedrooms are in the main hotel and these are spacious and equipped with antique and period furnishings.
24 en suite (bth/shr) 9 annexe en suite (bth/shr) (4 fmly) CTV in all bedrooms STV Night porter 60P Indoor swimming pool (heated) Sauna Solarium Gym Jacuzzi/spa ch fac French Cuisine V meals Coffee am Tea pm Last d 10pm
CARDS:

★★★62% **Savoy Park**
16 Racecourse Rd KA7 2UT
☎ 01292 266112 FAX 01292 611488
This 19th century red sandstone-built hotel has been run by the experienced Henderson family for over 30 years. It stands in its own grounds within walking distance of the town centre and has its own car park. Public rooms feature impressive panelled walls and ornate ceilings and a carte menu supplements the daily fixed-price choice in the restaurant. Bedrooms vary with many rooms spacious

contd.

and furnished in keeping with the character of the building; others are smaller and functionally appointed. The hotel is popular for weddings and other functions and there are facilities for business meetings.
15 en suite (bth/shr) (3 fmly) CTV in all bedrooms Night porter 60P ch fac Xmas Scottish & French Cuisine V meals Coffee am Tea pm No smoking area in restaurant Last d 9pm
ROOMS: (incl. bkfst) s £55-£60; d £70-£90 **LB**
OFF-PEAK: (incl. bkfst) s £50-£55; d £60-£80
MEALS: Lunch £6.50-£20alc High tea £6.95-£8.45alc Dinner £16-£19*
CARDS:

See advertisement on opposite page

★★★59% **Quality Friendly Hotel**

Burns Statue Square KA7 3AT ☎ 01292 263268 FAX 01292 262293
This Victorian railway hotel has been continuously improved in recent years and although some rooms still require upgrading most have now been brought up to a good modern standard. In addition to the elegant cocktail bar and restaurant situated on the first floor, there is also a small leisure club with a jacuzzi bath and gymnasium, and a recently restored conference and banqueting room as well as the popular Piano Bar.
75 en suite (bth/shr) (3 fmly) No smoking in 26 bedrooms CTV in all bedrooms STV Lift Night porter 50P Sauna Solarium Gym Xmas European Cuisine V meals Coffee am Tea pm Last d 9.30pm
ROOMS: s £57.50-£67.50; d £67.50-£77.50 **LB**
MEALS: Lunch £7.95-£9.95&alc Dinner £13.50&alc
CONF: Thtr 180 Class 124 Board 100 Del from £82.50
CARDS:

★★ **Ladyburn**
KA19 7SG ☎ 01655 740585 FAX 01655 740580
(For full entry see Maybole)

★★67% **Elms Court**
Miller Rd KA7 2AX (from A77 onto A719 continue past racecourse,left at traffic lights past railway station turn right & take town centre lane,left at 2nd traffic light) ☎ 01292 264191 & 282332 FAX 01292 610254
This family-run hotel is located within easy walking distance of the shopping centre and the seafront. Public rooms are bright and comfortable and the hotel is very popular locally for its varied choice of menu and specialises in 'Taste of Burns' menus. Bedrooms all have en suite facilities and modern amenities are provided. The hotel has a self-contained function suite and there is an enclosed car park at the rear.
20 en suite (bth/shr) (3 fmly) CTV in all bedrooms Night porter 60P Free entry to local Fitness Centre Xmas Scottish & French Cuisine V meals Coffee am Tea pm No smoking in restaurant Last d 9.30pm
ROOMS: (incl. bkfst) s £35-£50; d £65-£100 **LB**
OFF-PEAK: (incl. bkfst) s £35-£45; d £60-£80
MEALS: Lunch £6.25-£11.50&alc High tea fr £5.95&alc Dinner £13.50-£16&alc*
CONF: Thtr 180 Class 80 Board 60 Del from £55
CARDS:

★★66% **Carrick Lodge**
46 Carrick Rd KA7 2RE (from A77, take A79 until T-junct, then right, hotel on left) ☎ 01292 262846 FAX 01292 611101
This family-run hotel is located in a quiet residential area of the town but not far from the main shopping areas. The bar is divided into two areas and one is impressively wood-panelled. Food options are good, offer value for money, and are popular locally. Bedrooms include several suitable for families and satellite TV is provided. The hotel has its own car park.
8 en suite (bth/shr) (2 fmly) CTV in all bedrooms STV No dogs Night porter 25P V meals Coffee am Tea pm No smoking in restaurant Last d 10pm
ROOMS: (incl. bkfst) s fr £38; d fr £55 * **LB**
MEALS: Lunch £9&alc High tea £6.95 Dinner £12-£16&alc
CONF: Thtr 50 Class 50 Board 50 Del from £50
CARDS:

★63% **Aftongrange**
37 Carrick Rd KA7 2RD (0.5m from rail station & city centre) ☎ 01292 265679
This small hotel is located in a quiet residential part of the town and offers value-for-money accommodation. Bedrooms have all the expected amenities and many have en suite facilities. The bar is popular locally and there is an adjacent games room. Food is wholesome and enjoyable and there is a forecourt car park.
8 rms (1 bth 4 shr) (2 fmly) CTV in all bedrooms 30P Pool table V meals Coffee am Tea pm Last d 8.30pm
ROOMS: (incl. bkfst) s £23-£30; d £40-£50 * **LB**
MEALS: Lunch £5.50-£12.50 High tea £5-£6.25 Dinner £7-£10*

Travel Inn

Kilmarnock Rd, Monkton KA9 2RJ (on A77/A78 roundabout by Prestwick Airport) ☎ 01292 678262 FAX 01292 678248
Purpose-built accommodation, offering spacious, well equipped bedrooms, all with en suite bathrooms. Meals may be taken at the nearby family restaurant. For more information about Travel Inns, consult the Contents page under Hotel Groups.
40 en suite (bth/shr)
ROOMS: d £35.50 *

BALLACHULISH Highland Map 14 NN05
See also North Ballachulish

★★★64% **Ballachulish**
PA39 4JY (on A828, Fort William-Oban road 3m N of Glencoe) ☎ 01855 811606 FAX 01855 821463
Latest improvements at this long established Highland holiday hotel include a smart new bedroom wing where all rooms enjoy glorious views of Loch Linnhe; the creation of an inviting new library lounge to complement the spacious sitting room, and enlargement of the attractive restaurant. There is also a choice of contrasting bars.
54 en suite (bth/shr) (4 fmly) CTV in all bedrooms Night porter 54P Pool table Wkly live entertainment ch fac Xmas International Cuisine V meals Coffee am Tea pm No smoking in restaurant Last d 9.30pm
ROOMS: (incl. bkfst) s £47.50-£54; d £95-£108 * **LB**
OFF-PEAK: (incl. bkfst) s £37.50-£44; d £75-£88
MEALS: Lunch £4.95-£11.95alc High tea £5-£7.50alc Dinner £25&alc
CONF: Thtr 100 Class 50 Board 40 Del from £15.75
CARDS:

See advertisement under FORT WILLIAM

B

The Isles of Glencoe Hotel & Leisure Centre
PA39 4HL (off A82, 1m W of Glencoe)
☎ 01855 811602 FAX 01855 811770
Set on the picturesque shore of Loch Leven, this purpose-built complex, which includes leisure and children's facilities, enjoys spectacular mountain views. The bright airy bedrooms are mostly spacious and offer comfortable modern appointments. Food is available all day in the informal brasserie and 24-hour room service is offered. A visitor centre has been created, and there are plans for future extension.
39 en suite (bth/shr) (6 fmly) CTV in all bedrooms STV Night porter 150P Indoor swimming pool (heated) Fishing Sauna Solarium Gym Jacuzzi/spa Turbo pool Steam room Wkly live entertainment ch fac Xmas International Cuisine V meals Coffee am Tea pm No smoking in restaurant Last d 10pm
ROOMS: (incl. bkfst & dinner) s £53-£66; d £103-£116 * **LB**
OFF-PEAK: (incl. bkfst) s £43-£56; d £86-£112
MEALS: Bar Lunch £3.65-£13.65alc High tea £3.65-£6.30alc Dinner £19.50&alc
CONF: Thtr 150 Class 100 Board 70 Del from £13.50
CARDS:
£
See advertisement under FORT WILLIAM

BALLATER Aberdeenshire Map 15 NO39

★★★ 72% **Darroch Learg**
Braemar Rd AB35 5UX (on A93 at west end of town)
☎ 013397 55443 FAX 013397 55252
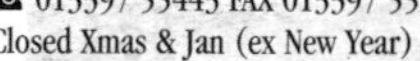
Closed Xmas & Jan (ex New Year)
A delightful country house atmosphere prevails at this charming house which overlooks the golf course and faces towards the River Dee and the mountain of Lochnagar. The public rooms are a pleasure to use and offer peace and tranquillity whilst well tended hillside gardens surround the hotel. Cooking is now in the hands of chef David Mutter who offers two small menus , one changing daily whilst the other changes monthly. Only the best available local produce is used in the cooking and the presentation of the dishes is quite superb. Bedrooms are well equipped and vary in size and shape with some being located in an adjoining mansion. Service is provided by a naturally friendly staff who help to make any stay at Darroch Learg a delightful experience.
13 en suite (bth/shr) 5 annexe en suite (bth/shr) No smoking in 4 bedrooms CTV in all bedrooms 25P No coaches Coffee am Tea pm No smoking in restaurant Last d 9pm
ROOMS: (incl. bkfst) s £40; d £70-£110 **LB**
OFF-PEAK: (incl. bkfst) s £35; d £60-£100
MEALS: Sunday Lunch £3.50-£20.50 Dinner £24.75-£29.75
CONF: Board 25 Del from £69
CARDS:

RED STAR HOTEL

★★ **Balgonie Country House**
Braemar Place AB35 5NQ (turn off A93 (Aberdeen - Perth) on western outskirts of village of Ballater, hotel is sign-posted)
☎ 013397 55482 FAX 013397 55482

Closed 6 Jan-Feb
This award-winning country house hotel lies on the outskirts of the town, in four acres of mature gardens and overlooks Ballater Golf Course and the hills of Glenmuick beyond. Hosts John and Cilla Finnie have built up an enthusiastic following by offering an informal, yet professional level of service, which has guests returning year after year. All the bedrooms are individually decorated to a high standard, and also provide modern amenities. The welcoming public rooms include the cosy bar with a wide range of malt whiskies, the elegant sitting room and the restaurant where David Hindmarsh produces an interesting daily menu, with fresh local produce.

9 en suite (bth/shr) CTV in all bedrooms No dogs (ex guide dogs) 12P No coaches Croquet lawn Xmas French Cuisine V meals Coffee am Tea pm No smoking in restaurant Last d 9pm
ROOMS: (incl. bkfst) s £57.50-£59.50; d £95-£99 **LB**
MEALS: Lunch £16.50-£18.50 Dinner £28.50-£29.50
CARDS:

★★ 64% ***Alexandra***
12 Bridge Square AB35 5QJ ☎ 013397 55376 FAX 013397 55466
Located just off the main A93 on the eastern side of this popular

contd.

Deeside town, the Alexandra offers a warm welcome and good value accommodation. Bedrooms are neat and attractively decorated, with many extra facilities being offered. The buzzing bar attracts both locals and residents', while the restaurant offers home cooked meals at lunch and dinner.
7 en suite (bth/shr) (1 fmly) CTV in all bedrooms 9P Scottish & French Cuisine V meals Coffee am Tea pm Last d 9pm
CARDS:

See advertisement on opposite page

BALLOCH Dumbarton & Clydebank Map 10 NS38

★★★★ 76% **Cameron House Hotel**

G83 8QZ (take A82 to Balloch roundabout and follow signs for Luss. Hotel signposted 1m on right)
☎ 01389 755565 FAX 01389 759522

An exceptionally good range of top quality leisure facilities and outdoor pursuits are available at this superbly positioned hotel on the banks of Loch Lomond. What was originally a private house, has been sympathetically extended and now provides well equipped and smartly appointed accommodation, including a number of magnificent suites. Ornate ceilings, marble fireplaces, deep cushioned sofas and huge arrangements of fresh flowers are the hallmarks of the comfortable public rooms. Jeff Bland's serious cooking can be enjoyed in the Georgian Room, which has views across the loch. He offers an interesting daily changing Market Menu, which is supported by an imaginative carte. A decadently rich parfait of Oban scallops with crispy aubergine and basil served with a gazpacho sauce was one dish typical of his style and enjoyed at a recent dinner inspection. Guests also have the choice of eating less formally in the brasserie.
68 en suite (bth/shr) (9 fmly) No smoking in 18 bedrooms CTV in all bedrooms STV No dogs (ex guide dogs) Lift Night porter 200P Indoor swimming pool (heated) Golf 9 Tennis (hard) Fishing Squash Snooker Sauna Solarium Gym Pool table Croquet lawn Jacuzzi/spa Marina Clay pigeon shooting Beauty salon ch fac Xmas Scottish & French Cuisine V meals Coffee am Tea pm Last d 10pm
ROOMS: (incl. bkfst) s fr £130; d fr £165 * **LB**
MEALS: Lunch £12.50-£22.50 Dinner £16-£40*
CONF: Thtr 300 Class 180 Board 80 Del from £150
CARDS:

See advertisement on opposite page

BALQUHIDDER Stirling Map 11 NN52

★★ 66% **Monachyle Mhor**

FK19 8PQ (11m north of Gallander on A84, turn right at Kingshouse Hotel this road takes you under the A84 towards Balquhidder, the Hotel is 6m on the right) ☎ 01877 384622 FAX 01877 384305

Set amidst 2000 acres of tranquil farmland at the lochhead of a beautiful glen, four miles west of the village, this converted farmhouse provides accommodation with rustic charm and character. Simple cooking brings out natural flavours enhanced by a careful blend of herbs, fruits and vegetables. Our first visit highly praised the choice of dishes available from two set menus, which included roast quail set on red cabbage and garnished with a very tangy apple chutney. The main dish of delicious scallops with spring onions and ginger was set an a bed of squid ink tagliatelli, which all almost melted in the mouth as did the finale of a superb derivation of bread and butter pudding, served as a soufflé. The bedrooms in the main house are pleasantly decorated with good bathrooms whilst those in the adjoining building are more modern. Meals are served in a small extension at the front of the house, which provides lovely views; other public areas include a cosy bar and a separate traditional lounge with the hotel's only TV.
5 en suite (bth/shr) 5 annexe en suite (bth/shr) CTV in 3 bedrooms No dogs (ex guide dogs) Air conditioning 20P No coaches Fishing No children 10yrs Xmas Scottish & French Cuisine V meals Coffee am Tea pm No smoking in restaurant Last d 9pm
ROOMS: (incl. bkfst) d £58-£74
OFF-PEAK: (incl. bkfst) d £58-£74
MEALS: Lunch £10-£17 Dinner £19-£24
CARDS:

See advertisement on opposite page

BANCHORY Aberdeenshire Map 15 NO69

RED STAR HOTEL

★★★ **Banchory Lodge**

AB31 3HS (off A93 13m west of Aberdeen)
☎ 01330 822625 FAX 01330 825019

This impressive Georgian house is reached by a short drive off the main street in the town, and is set in 12 acres of well tended grounds, on the banks of the River Dee. Roaring log fires and an abundance of fresh flowers are features of the two comfortable lounges and other public rooms. The Victorian themed restaurant offers a short table d'hÙte menu in the evenings, on which the local salmon is always available when in season. Bedrooms are individually designed, with swathes of delightful fabrics mixing with some attractive antique furnishings. Hospitality is gracious and attentive, with the front of house staff being particularly impressive.
22 en suite (bth/shr) (11 fmly) CTV in all bedrooms 50P No coaches Fishing Sauna Pool table ch fac English & French Cuisine V meals Coffee am Tea pm Last d 9.30pm
MEALS: Lunch fr £10 High tea fr £8.50 Dinner fr £25.50*
CONF: Class 30 Del from £90
CARDS:

Prices shown in the directory are meant as a guide only and are subject to change without warning. Please check before you book.

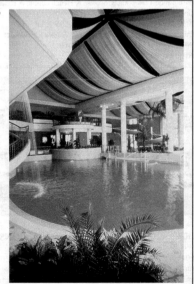

★★★ ♛ 75% **Raemoir House**

Raemoir AB31 4ED (take the A93 to Banchory turn right onto the A980, to Torphins, main drive is 2m ahead at T-junct) ☎ 01330 824884 FAX 01330 822171

This country house hotel has been in the same family for three generations, having been started by the inimitable Kit Sabin, who has been joined in recent years by her daughter and grandchildren. Partly because of this Raemoir has gained a reputation for a special tradition of hospitality. Some of the bedrooms are located in the 'Ha' Hoose which dates from the 16th century, whilst many of the rooms in the main house have pieces of antique furniture, making them individual and memorable. Public areas include the elegant morning room, well stocked bar and sitting room, and the restaurant which offers a range of Scottish fare.

17 en suite (bth/shr) 6 annexe en suite (bth/shr) (1 fmly) CTV in all bedrooms 100P Tennis (hard) Sauna Solarium Gym Croquet lawn Pitch & putt Shooting Stalking ch fac International Cuisine V meals Coffee am Tea pm No smoking in restaurant Last d 9pm

ROOMS: (incl. bkfst) s £52.50-£89; d £85-£145 * **LB**

MEALS: Sunday Lunch £16.50 Dinner £26&alc

CONF: Thtr 40 Class 50 Board 30 Del from £90

CARDS:

★★★ 66% **Tor-na-Coille**

AB31 4AB (on the main A93 Aberdeen/Braemar road, 0.5m west of Banchory town centre, opposite golf course) ☎ 01330 822242 FAX 01330 824012

Closed 25-27 Dec

This handsome ivy-clad Victorian mansion stands in its own wooded grounds set back from the A93. The public rooms are peaceful and comfortable and feature period furniture and have a delightful country house atmosphere. Staff are very friendly and helpful and are always very willing and polite.

24 en suite (bth/shr) (4 fmly) CTV in all bedrooms Lift 130P Squash Croquet lawn Xmas Scottish & French Cuisine V meals Coffee am Tea pm Last d 9.30pm

ROOMS: (incl. bkfst) s £58-£63; d £76-£96 * **LB**

MEALS: Sunday Lunch £11.50-£12.50alc Dinner £22.50&alc*

CONF: Thtr 90 Class 60 Board 30 Del from £79

CARDS:

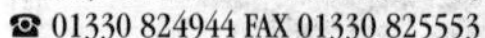

★★ 64% **Burnett Arms**

25 High St AB31 3TD (town centre on north side of A93, 18m from centre of Aberdeen)

☎ 01330 824944 FAX 01330 825553

Centrally located, right on the main street, this former coaching inn is popular with both business guests and tourists. Bedrooms are smartly decorated, though some are larger than others, and all offer good amenities. A wide range of bar meals is available in the lounge bar, while high teas are served in the dining room.

16 en suite (bth/shr) CTV in all bedrooms STV 40P Pool table

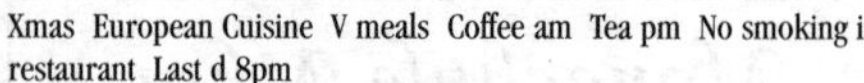

Xmas European Cuisine V meals Coffee am Tea pm No smoking in restaurant Last d 8pm

ROOMS: (incl. bkfst) s £48; d £65 **LB**

MEALS: Lunch £7-£17.50alc High tea £5.80-£11.20alc Dinner £15

CONF: Thtr 100 Class 50 Board 50

CARDS:

See advertisement under ABERDEEN

BANFF Aberdeenshire Map 15 NJ66

★★★ 61% **Banff Springs**

Golden Knowes Rd AB45 2JE (western outskirts of the town of Banff overlooking the beach on the A98 to Inverness road)

☎ 01261 812881 FAX 01261 815546

This purpose built hotel on the western edge of the town is family owned and run, and enjoys spectacular views of Boyndie Bay from many of its rooms and public areas. Bedrooms are well equipped and all have been attractively re-decorated within the last couple of years, to suit the needs of business travellers as well as golfers and tourists.

30 en suite (bth/shr) CTV in all bedrooms STV Night porter 200P Gym Xmas V meals Coffee am Last d 9pm

ROOMS: (incl. bkfst) s £35-£49.50; d £58-£80 **LB**

MEALS: Lunch £4.75-£6&alc Dinner £15.75-£18.95*

CONF: Thtr 400 Class 100 Board 40 Del from £88.50

CARDS:

BARRA, ISLE OF Western Isles

TANGUSDALE Map 13 NF60

★★ 64% **Isle of Barra**

Tangusdale Beach PA80 5XW (turn left after leaving ferry terminal on to the A888, hotel is 2m on the left)

☎ 01871 810383 FAX 01871 810385

Closed 18 Oct-20 Mar

Peacefully situated beside a beautifully sandy bay washed by Atlantic rollers, this modern, family-run hotel is a popular base for visiting tour groups. Public areas boast extensive views and include a choice of contrasting bars, a spacious and comfortable no-smoking lounge and a smart dining room. Bedrooms are of modern design with teak furnishings. Staff are friendly and willing to please.

30 en suite (bth/shr) CTV in all bedrooms 30P Fishing Pool table V meals Coffee am Tea pm No smoking in restaurant Last d 8.30pm

ROOMS: (incl. bkfst) s £38-£46; d £68-£84 **LB**

OFF-PEAK: (incl. bkfst) s £34-£42; d £64-£68

MEALS: Bar Lunch £6.50-£15alc High tea £6.50-£15alc Dinner £14.50-£17.95

CONF: Class 70 Board 60 Del from £52

CARDS:

BARRHEAD East Renfrewshire Map 11 NS45

★★★ 60% **Dalmeny Park Country House**

Lochlibo Rd G78 1LG (on A736 towards Irvine)

☎ 0141 881 9211 FAX 0141 881 9214

This extended 19th-century mansion stands in its own well tended grounds, and as well as appealing to the visiting businessman, it is a popular venue for local functions. Good progress is being made with cosmetic enhancement of bedrooms which range from well proportioned main house rooms to the more compact and functional rooms in the wing. Public areas include a choice of contrasting bars and a spacious restaurant offering both carte and fixed-price menus.

20 en suite (bth/shr) (2 fmly) No smoking in 2 bedrooms CTV in all bedrooms Night porter 150P ch fac Xmas International Cuisine V meals Coffee am Tea pm No smoking area in restaurant Last d 9.30pm

ROOMS: (incl. bkfst) s £55-£61; d £75-£83 *
MEALS: Lunch £10.50&alc High tea £6.25-£9.25
Dinner £14.95-£16.50&alc
CONF: Thtr 200 Class 100 Board 60 Del from £72
CARDS:

See advertisement under GLASGOW

BEATTOCK Dumfries & Galloway Map 11 NT00
See also Moffat

★★★65% **Auchen Castle**

DG10 9SH (1m north of Beattock village access sign posted from A74) ☎ 01683 300407
FAX 01683 300667
Closed 3 wks Christmas-New Year
Conveniently situated just off the A74 north of Moffat, this privately owned and well maintained hotel, which has been in the Beckh family for many years, offers traditional standards of hotel keeping. The main house is Victorian and contains comfortably furnished bedrooms which vary in size, but most benefit from splendid high ceilings and magnificent views. Immediately adjacent to the main building is an annexe where there are ten modern-style bedrooms, with en suite showers, to which a number of improvements are currently being made. The public areas include a very comfortable drawing room, characterful bar and a restaurant which enjoys the most wonderful views and where a choice of good of dishes is available from the daily-changing table d'hÙte menu. The hotel also has a self contained meeting room, well tended gardens and ample car parking.
15 en suite (bth/shr) 10 annexe en suite (shr) (1 fmly) CTV in all bedrooms Night porter 35P Fishing Clay pigeon shooting International Cuisine V meals Coffee am Tea pm Last d 9pm
ROOMS: (incl. bkfst) s £46-£51.50; d £60-£86 **LB**
MEALS: Bar Lunch £1.70-£5.50 Dinner £14.90-£19.50*
CONF: Thtr 40 Board 28
CARDS:

★★59% **Beattock House**
DG10 9QB (off A74) ☎ 01683 300403 FAX 01683 300403
This privately owned and personally-run hotel which has been owned by the Martin family for many years is conveniently situated just off the A74 outside the village. Many of the original features of this Victorian sandstone house have been retained and whilst the bedrooms are rather old-fashioned they are traditionally and comfortably furnished. Some rooms are en suite but others share the most magnificent bathrooms with huge Victorian baths and original fittings. The public areas include an elegant lounge where a fire is lit on cooler evenings, a spacious dining room and small bar.
7 rms (3 shr) (2 fmly) CTV in all bedrooms 30P Fishing V meals Coffee am Tea pm Last d 9pm
ROOMS: (incl. bkfst) s fr £30; d fr £55 * **LB**
OFF-PEAK: (incl. bkfst) s fr £25; d fr £45
MEALS: Lunch fr £8.50 High tea fr £6.50 Dinner fr £14.50
CARDS:

BEAULY Highland Map 14 NH54

★★★68% **Priory**
The Square IV4 7BX (signposted from A832)
☎ 01463 782309 FAX 01463 782531
Occupying a prime position in the village square, this popular business and tourist hotel is easily recognised from the colourful floral baskets and window boxes which adorn the frontage. Attractive public areas include a comfortable foyer lounge and a spacious split-level restaurant offering a range of menus throughout the day. Bedrooms offer every modern comfort together with a wide range of amenities.
22 en suite (bth/shr) (2 fmly) CTV in all bedrooms STV Lift Snooker ch fac Xmas V meals Coffee am Tea pm Last d 9pm
ROOMS: (incl. bkfst) s £35-£44.50; d £62.50-£75 **LB**
OFF-PEAK: (incl. bkfst) s £35; d £55-£62.50
MEALS: Lunch £3.50-£9.50alc High tea £5.95-£11.95alc Dinner £12.50-£17.50&alc*
CONF: Thtr 40 Class 40 Board 30 Del from £59.50
CARDS:

BIGGAR South Lanarkshire Map 11 NT03

★★★70% **Shieldhill**

Quothquan ML12 6NA (turn off A702 onto B7016 Biggar to Carnwath rd in the middle of Biggar, after 2m turn left into Shieldhill rd, Hotel 1.5m on right)
☎ 01899 220035 FAX 01899 221092
Dating from 1199, this impressive mansion house stands in its own grounds amid rolling countryside. At the time of our visit new owners Neil and Joan MacIntosh were still settling in, but it shouldn't take them long to make their mark. The bedrooms - all no-smoking - are very attractive with Laura Ashley decor and antique furnishings, and some have spa baths. Public areas include two elegant lounges, a bar, and a tastefully appointed dining room where a short menu of innovative modern cooking is served.
11 en suite (bth/shr) No smoking in all bedrooms CTV in all bedrooms No dogs (ex guide dogs) 25P No coaches Croquet lawn Cycling No children 11yrs Xmas British & French Cuisine V meals Coffee am Tea pm No smoking in restaurant Last d 9pm
ROOMS: (incl. bkfst) s £68; d £104 * **LB**
OFF-PEAK: (incl. bkfst) s £64; d £94
MEALS: Lunch £2.50-£15 Dinner £27*
CONF: Thtr 25 Class 28 Board 14 Del £115
CARDS:

★★★67% **Tinto**
Symington ML12 6PQ (SW on A72)
☎ 01899 308454 FAX 01899 308520
Situated beside the A72 to the north side of Symington village, this personally run hotel meets the needs of both business people and tourists alike. It is a popular function venue and provides spacious public rooms, including two restaurants where a good range of food is a available. The bedrooms are well equipped and are furnished along modern lines.
29 en suite (bth/shr) (2 fmly) CTV in all bedrooms STV No dogs (ex guide dogs) Night porter 100P Xmas International Cuisine V meals Coffee am Tea pm Last d 9.30pm
ROOMS: (incl. bkfst) s fr £45; d fr £65 * **LB**
MEALS: Lunch £8-£15 High tea £6.95-£13.90 Dinner £13.25-£24.20alc
CONF: Thtr 200 Class 180 Board 30
CARDS:

BIRNAM Perthshire & Kinross Map 11 NO04

★★★64% **Birnam House**
Birnam PH8 0BQ (off A9)
☎ 01350 727462 FAX 01350 728979

CONSORT HOTELS

This imposing baronial style building has a long history as an hotel. Whilst its traditional ambience still prevails, it has been completely refurbished to offer guests a stylish new restaurant and smart well equipped bedrooms.
28 en suite (bth/shr) (6 fmly) CTV in all bedrooms Lift 50P Xmas V meals Coffee am Tea pm No smoking in restaurant Last d 9.30pm
ROOMS: (incl. bkfst) s fr £40; d fr £60 **LB**
MEALS: Bar Lunch £1.50-£11.50alc High tea fr £7.50alc Dinner £12.50-£18.50alc*
CONF: Thtr 150 Class 60 Board 60
CARDS:

BLAIR ATHOLL Perthshire & Kinross Map 14 NN86

★★64% **Atholl Arms**
PH18 5SG (off main A9 to B8079, 1m into Blair Atholl, Hotel is situated at in the village passed the Post Office)
☎ 01796 481205 FAX 01796 481550
Popular with coach parties, holiday-makers and sporting enthusiasts, this long established hotel is close to the gates of Blair Castle at the northern end of the village. There is a magnificent baronial-style dining room with a minstrels' gallery and a small coffee lounge at one side. There is also a cocktail bar, lounge bar and foyer lounge where home baking is served in the afternoons. Bedrooms vary in size and appointment.
30 en suite (bth/shr) (3 fmly) CTV in all bedrooms 103P Fishing Pool table Rough shooting Xmas International Cuisine V meals Coffee am Tea pm No smoking in restaurant Last d 9pm
ROOMS: (incl. bkfst) s £32.50-£39; d £65-£75 * **LB**
OFF-PEAK: (incl. bkfst) s £28.50-£30.50; d £52-£58
MEALS: Lunch £8-£12 Dinner £15.50-£28.50*
CARDS:

See advertisement on opposite page

★★61% **Tilt**
Bridge of Tilt PH18 5SU (1m off main A9 in the village of Blair Atholl, 0.50m from Blair Castle) ☎ 01796 481333 FAX 01796 481335
Closed Jan-Etr
Situated close to the entrance to Blair Castle, this friendly hotel is popular with tourists throughout the summer season. The bar serves a good selection of meals and is divided into smoking and non-smoking sections. Bedrooms in the main house vary in size and appointment, while the seven chalet rooms have recently been refurbished.
28 en suite (bth/shr) (8 fmly) CTV in all bedrooms 40P Fishing Games room Xmas V meals Coffee am Tea pm Last high tea 5.45pm
ROOMS: (incl. bkfst) s fr £28.50; d £57-£75 * **LB**
OFF-PEAK: (incl. bkfst) s fr £26.50; d fr £54
MEALS: High tea fr £7.50*
CARDS:

BLAIRGOWRIE Perthshire & Kinross Map 15 NO14
See also Alyth & Coupar Angus

RED STAR HOTEL

★★★ **Kinloch House**
PH10 6SG (3m W on A923)
☎ 01250 884237 FAX 01250 884333
Closed 20-29 Dec

SMALL LUXURY HOTELS OF THE WORLD

Every guest who comes to this delightful country house is warmly welcomed by David and Sarah Shentall and their friendly staff. The hotel dates from 1840 and stands in 25 acres of parkland grazed by the family's Highland cattle. Thoughtfully appointed and beautifully designed bedrooms are located in both the main house and a newer wing, where the rooms are more spacious and have luxurious bathrooms; four-poster and half-tester beds are also available. The hall and upper gallery have fine oak panelling, while the cocktail bar has a warming log fire on colder days and the conservatory makes a bright alternative. Chef Bill McNicholl continues to produce a range of imaginative and more traditional dishes, all executed with a light, assured touch.

21 en suite (bth/shr) (1 fmly) CTV in all bedrooms 40P No coaches Fishing Croquet lawn ch fac Xmas V meals Coffee am Tea pm No smoking in restaurant Last d 9.15pm
ROOMS: (incl. bkfst & dinner) s fr £83; d fr £176 **LB**
MEALS: Lunch £15.95 Dinner £28.90
CONF: Thtr 12 Class 12 Board 12 Del £98.50
CARDS:

★★65% ***Altamount House***
Coupar Angus Rd PH10 6JN
☎ 01250 873512 & 873814 FAX 01250 876200
Closed 6 Jan-14 Feb

SCOTLAND'S COMMENDED HOTELS

Surrounded by six acres of its own well kept gardens, Altamount House is an elegant Georgian manor which has retained many of its period features including wood panelling and Adam fireplaces in the spacious lounges. The bedrooms vary in size and style, though all are well equipped. There is a good range of menus available, from traditional afternoon teas to four course Taste of Scotland dinners.
7 en suite (bth/shr) (2 fmly) CTV in all bedrooms 43P Coffee am Tea pm Last d 9pm
CARDS:

★★64% **Angus**
46 Wellmeadow PH10 6NQ ☎ 01250 872455 FAX 01250 875615
This well established town centre hotel, popular with tour groups, is centrally located for both the Glenshee ski slopes and other outdoor sporting pursuits. Bedrooms are brightly decorated and have modern appointments together with all the expected amenities. Public areas offer a spacious lounge bar, smart restaurant and leisure facilities; including a swimming pool, solarium and sauna.
86 en suite (bth/shr) (4 fmly) CTV in all bedrooms STV Lift 60P Indoor swimming pool (heated) Squash Sauna Solarium Jacuzzi/spa Wkly live entertainment Xmas British & French Cuisine V meals Coffee am Tea pm No smoking in restaurant Last d 9pm
ROOMS: (incl. bkfst) s £34.50-£45; d fr £69 **LB**
MEALS: Bar Lunch £4.75-£10 Dinner £15-£20*
CONF: Thtr 200 Class 60 Board 40
CARDS:

BOAT OF GARTEN Highland Map 14 NH91

★★★65% **Boat**

PH24 3BH (turn off A9 N of Aviemore onto A95 & follow signposts to Boat of Garten) ☎ 01479 831258 FAX 01479 831414

This long-established family-run Highland golfing and holiday hotel is enjoying more and more success in attracting overseas tour groups. At the time of our visit various improvements were being carried out in both public areas and bedrooms and this, together with the welcoming atmosphere and attentive service, will give the hotel added appeal.

32 en suite (bth/shr) (1 fmly) CTV in all bedrooms 36P Xmas Scottish, English & French Cuisine V meals Coffee am Tea pm No smoking in restaurant Last d 9pm

ROOMS: (incl. bkfst) s £35-£45; d £70-£80 **LB**

OFF-PEAK: (incl. bkfst) s £25-£35; d £50-£60

MEALS: Lunch £10-£20 Dinner £19-£23&alc*

CONF: Thtr 35 Class 20

CARDS:

BOTHWELL South Lanarkshire Map 11 NS75

★★★63% **Bothwell Bridge**

89 Main St G71 8LN ☎ 01698 852246 FAX 01698 854686

Considerably extended, this former mansion house is now a popular business and conference centre and is situated within a mile of the M74 on the edge of Bothwell. The bedrooms are well equipped to meet the needs of today's travellers and there are adequate public rooms, which are in the process of being extended. A very good range of food is available in the pleasant restaurant, with a leaning towards Italian dishes.

90 en suite (bth/shr) (11 fmly) No smoking in 10 bedrooms CTV in all bedrooms STV No dogs (ex guide dogs) Lift Night porter 110P

contd.

Wkly live entertainment Xmas Continental Cuisine V meals Coffee am Tea pm Last d 10.30pm
ROOMS: (incl. bkfst) s fr £58; d fr £68 * **LB**
CONF: Thtr 150 Class 80 Board 350 Del from £85
CARDS:

★★62% **Silvertrees**
Silverwells Crescent G71 8DP (M74 junct 5 follow signs for Hamilton, 1st right at mini roundabout into Silverwells Crescent Hotel is 0.25m on the left) ☎ 01698 852311 FAX 01698 852311 ext200
This personally-owned and run hotel stands in a quiet residential area and is within its own well kept grounds. The bedrooms are located either within the main house or in one of the two annexed houses and are all pleasantly furnished and well equipped. Ornate plaster ceilings feature in the bright and modern public rooms and a good range of dishes is available in the attractive dining room.
7 en suite (bth/shr) 19 annexe en suite (bth/shr) (1 fmly) CTV in all bedrooms STV 100P No coaches ch fac V meals Coffee am Last d 8.45pm
ROOMS: (incl. bkfst) s £55; d £75-£85 *
MEALS: Lunch £11-£11&alc Dinner £16&alc*
CONF: Thtr 200 Class 150 Board 40 Del from £81
CARDS:

BOWMORE See Islay, Isle of

BRAE See Shetland

BRAEMAR Aberdeenshire Map 15 NO19

★★★68% **Invercauld Arms**

AB32 5YR (on the A93 equidistant between Perth and Aberdeen) ☎ 013397 41605 FAX 013397 41428
Set amid spectacular scenery, this traditional Highland hotel offers smart, well appointed accommodation. Whilst the bedrooms vary in size, they are all well equipped and have been very attractively decorated with rich colourful fabrics. The spacious public areas have a very relaxed atmosphere and the service provided by the small team of staff is both attentive and friendly.
The hotel has a small meeting room and 24 room service is also available.
68 en suite (bth/shr) (11 fmly) No smoking in 18 bedrooms CTV in all bedrooms Lift Night porter 80P Wkly live entertainment Xmas International Cuisine V meals Coffee am Tea pm No smoking in restaurant Last d 8.45pm
ROOMS: (incl. bkfst) s fr £70; d fr £95 * **LB**
MEALS: Lunch £11.50&alc High tea £8.50 Dinner £19.50&alc*
CONF: Thtr 60 Class 20 Board 24 Del from £72
CARDS:

★★72% **Braemar Lodge**
Glenshee Rd AB35 5YQ (on the A93 south approach to Braemar) ☎ 013397 41627 FAX 013397 41627
Closed Nov & Dec
Quietly situated in mature gardens just a few minutes' walk from the town centre, this friendly Victorian lodge offers a good standard of accommodation. Bedrooms are comfortable with many nice touches, while the public areas include a wood-panelled bar and a relaxing lounge. The restaurant serves delightful cordon-bleu meals and service is attentive.
7 rms (6 shr) No smoking in all bedrooms CTV in all bedrooms 8P Xmas Scottish & French Cuisine Coffee am No smoking in restaurant Last d 8pm
ROOMS: (incl. bkfst) s £25-£36; d £25-£36 **LB**
MEALS: Dinner £15.50-£19.50
CARDS:

BRECHIN Angus Map 15 NO66

★★58% **Northern**
Clerk St DD9 6AE ☎ 01356 622156 & 625505 FAX 01356 622714
RS 1 & 2 Jan
This family-run hotel is situated in town centre. Many bedrooms have been recently redecorated; the main house rooms are the largest. A café bar is popular with locals, and lunches, high teas and dinners are available in the attractively decorated dining room and adjoining bar.
20 rms (4 bth 12 shr) CTV in 19 bedrooms 20P Pool table Continental Cuisine V meals Coffee am Tea pm
CONF: Thtr 120 Class 80 Board 30
CARDS:

BRIDGEND See Islay, Isle of

BRIDGE OF ALLAN Stirling Map 11 NS79

★★★62% **Royal**
Henderson St FK9 4HG ☎ 01786 832284 FAX 01786 834377
Best Western
Situated on the main street, this popular conference and business hotel is convenient for both the University and the motorway network of Central Scotland. Bedrooms vary in size and are modern in style with good amenities. Henderson's Brasserie is the new restaurant concept which offers excellent value lunches and dinners, while the Kings' bar has a good range of drinks and bar meals.
32 en suite (bth/shr) (2 fmly) CTV in all bedrooms STV Lift Night porter P ch fac V meals Coffee am Tea pm Last d 9.30pm
ROOMS: s £59-£62; d £59-£62 * **LB**
OFF-PEAK: s £42.50-£44.50; d £42.50-£44.50
MEALS: Lunch £8.45-£9.50&alc Dinner £12.45-£13.50&alc*
CONF: Thtr 150 Class 60 Board 50 Del £90
CARDS:
See advertisement under STIRLING

BRIDGE OF CALLY Perthshire & Kinross Map 15 NO15

★63% **Bridge of Cally**
PH10 7JJ (beside bridge over River Ardle (A93))
☎ 01250 886231 FAX 01250 886231
Closed 25-26 Dec
This friendly roadside hotel is located by the bridge, with grounds stretching down to the river. It is especially popular with locals for its bar meals based on fresh Scottish produce, while a more adventurous menu is usually available in the restaurant. Bedrooms are modest in size and comfort, though they are all cosy and warm. The main bar has a roaring log fire throughout the colder months.
9 rms (3 bth 4 shr) CTV in all bedrooms 40P No coaches Fishing V meals Coffee am Tea pm Last d 9.30pm
ROOMS: (incl. bkfst) s £29.50; d £53 *
OFF-PEAK: (incl. bkfst) s £22; d £40
MEALS: Lunch £10-£15alc Dinner £16-£19&alc*
CARDS:

B

BRIDGE OF MARNOCH Aberdeenshire Map 15 NJ55

RED STAR HOTEL

★★ 🏵🏵 **Old Manse of Marnoch**

AB54 5RS (on B9117 less than 1m off A97 route between Huntly and Banff) ☎ 01466 780873 FAX 01466 780873

Closed 2 wks Nov Xmas & New Year

This small luxury hotel has been lovingly created by Patrick and Keren Carter, who are very much involved with ensuring that every guest has a comfortable and relaxing stay. The Old Manse is a Georgian House with an interesting history connected to the local church, which was the foundation for the Free Church of Scotland. The interior has been attractively decorated, and the bedrooms and public areas have many antiques as well as furniture hand crafted by Patrick. Bedrooms are spacious and offer many thoughtful touches, while a middle eastern flavour is found in the lounge. The dining room has a nautical theme and is the setting for Keren's accomplished cooking, which utilises the best local produce, much of it from the hotel's own gardens. The breakfast selection is one of the most extensive and interesting anywhere, and because of this orders are placed the previous evening.

5 en suite (bth/shr) CTV in all bedrooms 10P No coaches No children 12yrs No smoking in restaurant Last d 7.30pm

ROOMS: (incl. bkfst) s £54-£60; d £81-£90 **LB**

MEALS: Dinner £25

CARDS:

BRODICK See Arran, Isle of

BRORA Highland Map 14 NC90

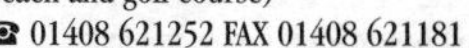

★★★66% **Royal Marine**

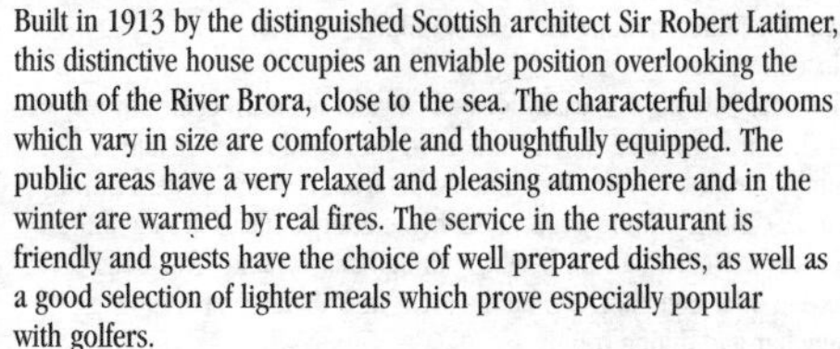

Golf Rd KW9 6QS (turn off A9 in village toward beach and golf course)

☎ 01408 621252 FAX 01408 621181

Built in 1913 by the distinguished Scottish architect Sir Robert Latimer, this distinctive house occupies an enviable position overlooking the mouth of the River Brora, close to the sea. The characterful bedrooms which vary in size are comfortable and thoughtfully equipped. The public areas have a very relaxed and pleasing atmosphere and in the winter are warmed by real fires. The service in the restaurant is friendly and guests have the choice of well prepared dishes, as well as a good selection of lighter meals which prove especially popular with golfers.

11 en suite (bth/shr) (1 fmly) CTV in all bedrooms 40P No coaches Indoor swimming pool (heated) Golf 18 Tennis (hard) Fishing Snooker Sauna Ice curling rink in season Xmas Scottish & French Cuisine V meals Coffee am Tea pm No smoking in restaurant Last d 9pm

ROOMS: (incl. bkfst) s £55-£75; d £90-£120 **LB**

MEALS: Lunch £12.50-£15alc Dinner £15-£25alc

CONF: Thtr 30 Class 20 Board 20 Del from £70

CARDS:

£

★★★64% **The Links**

Best Western

Golf Rd KW9 6QS (turn off A9 in village of Brora towards beach and golf course, hotel overlooks golf course) ☎ 01408 621225 FAX 01408 621383

Closed 31 Oct-Mar

Owned and personally run by The Powell family, this hotel occupies the most enviable position overlooking the golf course and the sea beyond. The spacious bedrooms, where effective decorative use has been made of locally made tweed, include a number of family rooms and suites. Guests can enjoy the marvellous view from the comfortable lounge and restaurant, where a short choice of interesting dishes is available. Nearby Marine Hotel, under the same ownership, has good leisure facilities.

23 en suite (bth/shr) (2 fmly) CTV in all bedrooms 55P Indoor swimming pool (heated) Golf 18 Fishing Snooker Xmas International Cuisine V meals Coffee am Tea pm No smoking in restaurant Last d 9pm

ROOMS: (incl. bkfst) s £48-£65; d £80-£120 **LB**

MEALS: Bar Lunch £5-£15alc Dinner £20-£25&alc

CONF: Thtr 100 Class 40 Board 20 Del from £70

CARDS:

BUCKIE Moray Map 15 NJ46

★★68% **Marine**

Marine Place AB56 1UT ☎ 01542 832249 FAX 01542 834949

Closed 26 Dec, 2 & 3 Jan RS 25 Dec

Situated on the seafront, this friendly hotel has undergone complete refurbishment over the past few years and now offers a good standard of accommodation throughout. Bedrooms are tastefully decorated and well equipped, many having views over the Moray Firth, while a lift provides access for disabled travellers. There is a choice of two bars, the lively Dodger's and the more relaxing Commodore, and for the more energetic there is an exercise room.

12 en suite (bth/shr) (2 fmly) CTV in all bedrooms Lift 30P Snooker Sauna Gym Pool table Jacuzzi/spa petanque Xmas Scottish & French Cuisine V meals Coffee am Tea pm Last d 9pm

ROOMS: (incl. bkfst) s £30-£40; d £50-£60 * **LB**

OFF-PEAK: (incl. bkfst) s £30-£35; d £50-£55

MEALS: Lunch £7.95-£12.15 High tea £6.25-£9.75 Dinner £10.65-£18.35&alc*

CARDS:

★★64% **Mill House**

Tynet AB56 2HJ (on A98 between Buckie and Fochabers)

☎ 01542 850233 FAX 01542 850331

This characterful roadside hotel has been converted from a former meal mill and the original water wheel and machinery, still in working order, is a feature of the entrance hall. A wing of spacious, well equipped bedrooms lies behind the main building, and the conversion has created a popular bar and restaurant, both offering a good range of meals.

15 en suite (bth/shr) (2 fmly) CTV in all bedrooms Night porter 100P Xmas V meals Coffee am Tea pm No smoking in restaurant Last d 8.30pm

ROOMS: (incl. bkfst) s £37; d £57 * **LB**

MEALS: Lunch £4-£7&alc Dinner £9.95-£13.75&alc

CONF: Thtr 100 Class 60 Board 30 Del from £55

CARDS:

B

BUNESSAN See Mull, Isle of

BURNTISLAND Fife Map 11 NT28

★★65% **Inchview Hotel**
69 Kinghorn Rd KY3 9EB (on A921)
☎ 01592 872239 FAX 01592 874866
Forming part of a listed Georgian Terrace, this family-run hotel, enjoys pleasant views over the links and Pettycur Bay. Bedrooms are traditionally furnished, including one with a four-poster bed. The lively lounge bar offers a good range of bar meals and there is an elegant restaurant where flambé dishes are a speciality.
12 en suite (bth/shr) (1 fmly) CTV in all bedrooms 15P Xmas International Cuisine V meals Coffee am Tea pm Last d 9.45pm
ROOMS: (incl. bkfst) s £39.50-£44.50; d £59-£69 * **LB**
MEALS: Lunch £10.50-£12.50&alc Dinner £15.95-£17.95&alc*
CONF: Thtr 80 Class 40 Board 30 Del from £65
CARDS: (£)

BUTE, ISLE OF Argyll & Bute

ARDBEG Map 10 NS18

★★72% **Ardmory House**
Ardmory Rd PA20 0PG (N from Rothesay on A844, 1m turn left up Ardmory Road, Hotel 300mtrs on left)
☎ 01700 502346 FAX 01700 502346
Dedicated owners Donald Cameron and Bill Jeffery are making good progress with refurbishment at this most welcoming of small hotels. Set in its own grounds overlooking the bay, it offers a wonderfully relaxed atmosphere together with outstanding levels of hospitality. Beamed walls and ceilings feature strongly in the public areas which include a cosy bar and an attractive restaurant, where the emphasis is on fresh local ingredients. The no-smoking bedrooms, though not large, are in the process of cosmetic improvement and offer a wide range of amenities as well as thoughtful extras.
5 en suite (bth/shr) No smoking in all bedrooms CTV in all bedrooms 12P V meals Coffee am Tea pm No smoking in restaurant Last d 9pm
ROOMS: (incl. bkfst) s fr £30; d fr £55 *
MEALS: Lunch £5.95-£12.50 High tea fr £5.95 Dinner fr £15.25*
CONF: Thtr 60 Class 30 Board 30
CARDS: (£)

CALLANDER Stirling Map 11 NN60

★★★69% **Roman Camp**
FK17 8BG ☎ 01877 330003 FAX 01877 331533
A tree-lined drive leads from the main road to this 17th-century manor in 20 acres of wooded and lawned grounds beside the River Teith. Efficiently run by the Brown family, the house has a welcoming atmosphere and the charming day rooms are filled with fresh flowers. Bedrooms are very individual and offer thoughtful extras. The candlelit restaurant, with its 16th-century painted ceiling, is the setting for chef Simon Burns' innovative cooking. An inspection meal began with pan-fried salmon set on a pasta biscuit and served with a delicious soy and shallot vinaigrette. Vegetable broth with toasted oatmeal then preceded an accurately roasted best end of lamb with dauphinoise potatoes, timbale of wild mushrooms and a truffle and mint sauce - an interesting blend of natural flavours. Iced praline parfait on a raspberry coulis with fresh strawberries completed a praiseworthy meal.
14 en suite (bth/shr) (3 fmly) CTV in all bedrooms 30P Fishing Xmas Scottish & French Cuisine V meals Coffee am Tea pm No smoking in restaurant Last d 8.30pm
ROOMS: (incl. bkfst) s £89-£129; d £109-£139 **LB**
OFF-PEAK: (incl. bkfst) s £69-£119; d £89-£129
MEALS: Lunch £15-£19 Dinner £34&alc
CONF: Thtr 50 Class 16 Board 20 Del from £105
CARDS:

★★70% **Lubnaig**
Leny Feus FK17 8AS (off A84) ☎ 01877 330376 FAX 01877 330376
Closed Nov-Etr
Set in its own well kept gardens in a quiet residential area, this small hotel is ably run by Crawford and Sue Low, who ensure that guests are made to feel at home. Bedrooms vary in size, but all are attractively decorated and nicely maintained. There are three relaxing lounges, with the kilted Crawford always on hand to provide refreshments. Sue is in charge of the kitchen and produces a short, fixed-price menu which utilises fresh, Scottish ingredients to create tasty, home-cooked dishes.
6 en suite (shr) 4 annexe en suite (shr) CTV in all bedrooms 10P No coaches No children 7yrs International Cuisine No smoking in restaurant Last d 8pm
ROOMS: (incl. bkfst) s £33-£42; d £52-£64 **LB**
OFF-PEAK: (incl. bkfst) s £30-£40; d £46-£54
MEALS: Dinner £11-£18
CARDS: (£)

★★61% **Bridgend House**
Bridgend FK17 8AH (on A81 to Aberfoyle)
☎ 01877 330130 FAX 01877 331512
Situated on the Glasgow road, close to the centre of the town, this informal hotel has an attractive black and white frontage. Bedrooms vary in size, with the age and character of the house being evident with the retention of oak beams and uneven walls. The lounge bar is popular with locals, while the elegant residents' lounge has a warming fire in winter.
6 rms (5 bth/shr) (1 fmly) CTV in all bedrooms STV 30P Xmas V meals Coffee am Tea pm Last d 9pm
ROOMS: (incl. bkfst) s £35; d £51-£59 * **LB**
MEALS: Lunch £3.50-£8.50alc High tea fr £6.25alc Dinner £6-£14alc*
CARDS: (£)

★★61% **Dalgair House**
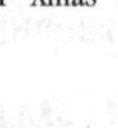
113-115 Main St FK17 8BQ (300 metres beyond access road to golf course on main street)
☎ 01877 330283 FAX 01877 331114
Conveniently situated in the main street, with a car park at the rear, this small family-run hotel is ideally located for exploring the town and local area. Bedrooms, including a large family room, all have bath and shower and are pleasantly decorated. High teas are popular during the summer in the open-plan dining room, which adjoins a small lounge area, and the public bar is situated at the front of the hotel.
8 en suite (bth/shr) (1 fmly) CTV in all bedrooms STV 12P Xmas V meals Coffee am Tea pm Last d 9pm
ROOMS: (incl. bkfst) s £28-£40; d £46-£54 * **LB**
OFF-PEAK: (incl. bkfst) s £28; d £46
MEALS: Lunch £8-£15 High tea £6 Dinner £12&alc*
CARDS: (£)

★66% ***Highland House***
South Church St FK17 8BN (turn off A84 in town centre and follow signs for police station) ☎ 01877 330269
Closed Dec-Feb
This neat little hotel is easily located close to the town centre by way of its attractive frontage which is adorned with window boxes and climbing roses. A warm welcome awaits from resident owners David and Dee Shirley, while good value, home cooked meals are another attraction. Bedrooms are bright, with light fabrics and furnishings belying their compact size. Public areas include a relaxing lounge, snug bar and dining room.
9 rms (7 bth/shr) (1 fmly) No smoking in all bedrooms CTV in all bedrooms No coaches V meals Last d 7.30pm
CARDS:

C

CAMPBELTOWN Argyll & Bute Map 10 NR72

★★65% ***Seafield***
Kilkerran Rd PA28 6JL ☎ 01586 554385 FAX 01586 552741
Enthusiastic owners Alastair and Elizabeth Gilchrist are constantly improving standards at their comfortable small business and tourist hotel, which overlooks the bay. Major alteration and refurbishment has considerably enhanced the public areas which include a new foyer bar-lounge while the attractive restaurant continues to offer an interesting carte with the emphasis on seafood. Bedrooms, both in the main house and garden annexe were scheduled for refurbishment at the time of our visit.
3 en suite (shr) 6 annexe en suite (shr) (1 fmly) CTV in all bedrooms 11P V meals Coffee am Last d 8.30pm
CARDS:

CANNICH Highland Map 14 NH33

★★ 68% **Mullardoch House**
Glen Cannich IV4 7LX (8m W on unclass Glen Cannich road)
☎ 01456 415460 FAX 01456 415460
Peacefully situated at the head of a remote Highland glen amid breathtaking scenery, this former hunting lodge has been converted into a small country house hotel and has been much improved by enthusiastic new owners. Hot drinks and refreshments are served beside a welcoming log fire in a comfortable lounge which shares with the elegant dining room magnificent views across Loch Sealbanach to the Affric Mountains. Bedrooms range from the spacious and tastefully appointed to the smaller and more practical.
6 en suite (bth/shr) (1 fmly) CTV in all bedrooms 12P No coaches Fishing Deer stalking Xmas V meals Coffee am Tea pm Last d 8.30pm
ROOMS: (incl. bkfst) d £72-£86 * **LB**
OFF-PEAK: (incl. bkfst) d £65-£78
MEALS: Bar Lunch fr £3.50alc Dinner fr £21*
CARDS:

CARNOUSTIE Angus Map 12 NO53

★★67% **Carlogie House**
Carlogie Rd DD7 6LD (off A930)
☎ 01241 853185 FAX 01241 856528
Closed 1-3 Jan
This friendly hotel is set in its own grounds on the northern outskirts of the town. There is a spacious lounge bar and conservatory, as well as an attractive dining room. Bedrooms are furnished in a practical manner and are bright, warm and well equipped.
12 en suite (bth/shr) 4 annexe en suite (shr) (2 fmly) CTV in all bedrooms STV No dogs (ex guide dogs) 102P Scottish & French Cuisine V meals Coffee am Tea pm Last d 9pm
ROOMS: (incl. bkfst) s fr £50; d fr £75 * **LB**
MEALS: Lunch fr £19.50&alc High tea fr £7.25&alc Dinner fr £19.50&alc*
CARDS:

★★64% **Glencoe**
Links Pde DD7 7JF (off A92, adjoining Golf Course)
☎ 01241 853273 FAX 01241 853319
New owners have given this elderly hotel a bright, modern image. Guests continue to be drawn predominantly from the golfing fraternity (predictably, since the hotel overlooks the course) and golf is the overriding theme in both bar and dining room. Bedrooms - each of them named after a Scottish championship course - are currently being upgraded.
7 en suite (bth/shr) (4 fmly) CTV in all bedrooms 10P Scottish & French Cuisine V meals Coffee am Tea pm No smoking in restaurant
ROOMS: (incl. bkfst) s fr £39; d fr £60 * **LB**
CARDS:

CARRBRIDGE Highland Map 14 NH92

★★ 71% **Dalrachney Lodge**
PH23 3AT (off A938) ☎ 01479 841252 FAX 01479 841382
The character of this Victorian hunting lodge, set in 14 acres of mature grounds, has been enhanced by the enthusiastic owners Helen and Grant Swanney. Fine pieces of furniture complement the attractive bedrooms, which are spacious and well equipped. Both the restaurant and bar are popular with locals and feature local produce on the menus, while the comfortable lounge is an ideal area to relax. The service is courteous and attentive.
11 en suite (bth/shr) (3 fmly) No smoking in 3 bedrooms CTV in all bedrooms 40P No coaches Fishing Xmas Scottish & French Cuisine V meals Coffee am No smoking in restaurant Last d 9pm
ROOMS: (incl. bkfst) s £30-£45; d £55-£90 **LB**
OFF-PEAK: (incl. bkfst) s £25-£30; d £45-£55
MEALS: Lunch £10-£20&alc Dinner £15-£25&alc
CARDS:

★★66% **Fairwinds**
PH23 3AA ☎ 01479 841240 FAX 01479 841240
Closed 2 Nov-20 Dec
This former Victorian manse has been sympathetically extended and is set back from the road in seven acres of mature gardens. The friendly management couple ensure personal service, and well equipped bedrooms (including one on the ground floor) are individually decorated. The large conservatory serves as a comfortable lounge/dining room, and a wide range of good-value meals is available; the lounge area also has a small honesty bar and a log-burning stove. A selection of self-catering chalets is situated in the hotel grounds, and membership of a local club enables guests to use facilities which include a swimming pool, sauna, steam room, dry ski slope and tennis court for a reasonable fee.
5 en suite (bth/shr) CTV in all bedrooms No dogs (ex guide dogs) 6P No coaches No children 12yrs Regional & Continental Cuisine V meals No smoking in restaurant Last d 8.30pm
ROOMS: (incl. bkfst) s £24-£26; d £45-£54 **LB**
OFF-PEAK: (incl. bkfst) s £23; d £44-£48
MEALS: Dinner £14-£18.50
CARDS:

CARRUTHERSTOWN Dumfries & Galloway Map 11 NY17

★★★69% **Hetland Hall**
DG1 4JX (midway between Annan & Dumfries on A75)
☎ 01387 840201 FAX 01387 840211
This former school is now one of the most well established and popular hotels in the area. An extended Georgian mansion, it is set back from the A75 in 45 acres of parkland which also include a helipad and a putting green. A friendly welcome awaits, with both the proprietors and their staff being attentive and informal in their approach. Bedrooms vary in size and style, depending on whether they are located in the new or old wings, but all are well equipped and attractively decorated. Relaxing lounges with log fires are a feature of

contd.

the public areas, while a chalet to the rear of the hotel houses the leisure centre. A honeymoon suite with a double whirlpool bath and a four-poster bed is available.
27 en suite (bth/shr) (3 fmly) No smoking in 3 bedrooms CTV in all bedrooms STV Night porter 60P Indoor swimming pool (heated) Fishing Snooker Sauna Solarium Gym Putting green Indoor badminton Xmas International Cuisine V meals Coffee am Tea pm No smoking in restaurant Last d 9.30pm
ROOMS: (incl. bkfst) s £65-£78; d £90-£109 * **LB**
OFF-PEAK: (incl. bkfst) s fr £55; d fr £80
MEALS: Lunch £9.50-£16.50&alc Dinner £17.50-£25&alc
CONF: Thtr 200 Class 100 Board 70 Del from £68
CARDS:
See advertisement under DUMFRIES

CASTLE DOUGLAS Dumfries & Galloway Map 11 NX76

★★66% **Douglas Arms**
King St DG7 1DB (by town clock)
☎ 01556 502231 FAX 01556 504000
Dating from 1779, this former coaching inn is situated in the centre of the town, and offers attractive accommodation in a variety of good value standard rooms or more spacious rooms with full en suite facilities. There is a choice of lounges, and also an informal lounge bar combined with a restaurant, which features an interesting painting created by its namesake 'Jessica'.
20 rms (15 bth/shr) (2 fmly) No smoking in 5 bedrooms CTV in all bedrooms STV 14P Pool table Xmas V meals Coffee am Tea pm
ROOMS: (incl. bkfst) s £28-£33; d £52-£62 **LB**
CONF: Thtr 150 Class 30 Board 45
CARDS:

★★66% **Imperial**
King St DG7 1AA (opposite the town library)
☎ 01556 502086 FAX 01556 503009
The black and white façade of this former coaching inn makes it easy to locate at the east end of the main street in this bustling market town. The staff here are cheerful and ensure that guests are made to feel at home. The dining room and spacious residents' lounge are on the first floor, while the cosy lounge bar is the focal point of the hotel. Bedrooms have been enhanced with attractive fabrics.
12 en suite (bth/shr) (1 fmly) No smoking in 6 bedrooms CTV in all bedrooms 29P Pool table Wkly live entertainment V meals Coffee am Tea pm Last d 8.30pm
ROOMS: (incl. bkfst) s £31.50-£33; d £50-£54 * **LB**
MEALS: Lunch £7.50-£9.50&alc High tea £5.95-£6.75 Dinner £12.50-£15&alc*
CONF: Thtr 40 Class 20 Board 20 Del from £50
CARDS:

★★65% ***Urr Valley Country House***
Ernespie Rd DG7 3JG (off A75) ☎ 01556 502188 FAX 01556 504055
Set in 14 acres of mature grounds, this country house-style hotel is on the eastern approach to the town and reached via a long drive. The wood panelled lounge and bar are decorated with memorobilia reflecting the sporting pursuits available locally, whilst roaring log fires create a warming feel in the colder months. Bar meals are popular, whilst the dining room offers great views of the surrounding countryside. Bedrooms are comfortably furnished and have excellent facilities.
16 rms (14 bth/shr) (4 fmly) CTV in all bedrooms 200P Fishing Scottish & French Cuisine V meals Coffee am Tea pm Last d 9pm
CARDS:

★★63% **King's Arms**
St Andrew's St DG7 1EL (through main street, left at town clock, hotel situated on corner site) ☎ 01556 502626 FAX 01556 502097
Closed 25-26 Dec & 1-2 Jan
This former coaching inn dating back 200 years is situated in a quiet road close to the main street. There is a choice of three bars, including a quiet snug, with bar meals available in all. The dining room, which is particularly attractive, features hanging tapestries on the white-painted stone walls and overlooks the courtyard at the centre of the hotel; there is an enclosed car park at the rear.
10 rms (9 bth/shr) (2 fmly) No smoking in 2 bedrooms CTV in all bedrooms 15P Pool table Scottish & French Cuisine V meals Coffee am Tea pm No smoking in restaurant Last d 8.45pm
ROOMS: (incl. bkfst) s £31.50; d £50-£55 * **LB**
OFF-PEAK: (incl. bkfst) s £30-£31.50; d £46-£55
MEALS: Lunch £6-£10.50&alc High tea £6-£8 Dinner £12.50-£15&alc*
CONF: Thtr 35 Class 20 Board 25 Del from £50
CARDS:

CHIRNSIDE Scottish Borders Map 12 NT85

★★68% **Chirnside Hall Country House Hotel**

TD11 3LD (on A6105 Berwick on Tweed/Duns road)
☎ 01890 818219 FAX 01890 818231
Located just outside the village, this friendly country house hotel has a luxurious feel to both the bedrooms and public areas. Deep, comfortable sofas are in plentiful supply in the elegant lounges, while tall backed chairs provide intimacy in the dining room. Bedrooms vary in size, from large 4-poster rooms, to some in the coombs on the second floor. Fresh local produce is treated with honesty, creating tasty dishes with some unusual combinations. The traditional soda bread should not be missed.
10 en suite (bth/shr) (2 fmly) CTV in all bedrooms STV Lift 20P Snooker Putting green Xmas V meals Coffee am Tea pm Last d 8.30pm
ROOMS: (incl. bkfst) s £45-£50; d £80-£90 * **LB**
OFF-PEAK: (incl. bkfst) s £40-£45; d £75-£80
MEALS: Lunch £12.50-£16.75alc Dinner £19.50-£22.50&alc*
CONF: Board 16 Del from £67.50
CARDS:

CLACHAN-SEIL Argyll & Bute Map 10 NM71

★★70% **Willowburn**
PA34 4TJ (0.5m from Atlantic Bridge) ☎ 01852 300276
Closed Nov-Mar
If you are looking for genuine hospitality together with a wonderfully relaxed atmosphere and good food; then a visit to the Todd family's charming small hotel by the shore of Seil Sound is a must. Bedrooms, though not expansive, are cheerfully decorated and comfortably modern in style. There is also a comfortable lounge where guests can unwind. The former cosy bar has been converted into a charming small Bistro offering a reasonably priced list of blackboard specialities. The serious eating is still done in the attractive dining room where Maureen Todd's careful treatment of fresh produce, especially seafood, continues to earn much praise. Her fixed price menu is changed daily and this is supported by a short range of specialities on a supplementary menu.
6 en suite (bth/shr) CTV in all bedrooms 36P No coaches Xmas Scottish & French Cuisine V meals Coffee am Tea pm No smoking in restaurant Last d 8pm
ROOMS: (incl. bkfst & dinner) s £46-£50; d £92-£100 **LB**
MEALS: Bar Lunch £8-£15alc Dinner £19.50&alc*
CARDS:

CLEISH Perthshire & Kinross Map 11 NT09

★★★68% **Nivingston House**

Cleish Hills KY13 7LS (2m W of junct 5 of the M90)
☎ 01577 850216 FAX 01577 850238

Closed 4-20 Jan
Conveniently located for the M90 motorway yet offering the peace and quiet of a rural location, this extended former farmhouse stands in 12 acres of mature grounds. Bedrooms are attractively decorated and offer comfortable accommodation with modern amenities. Public rooms include the relaxing residents' lounge, book-lined library and cosy lounge bar with its well stocked bar. The menu offers some interesting dishes which combine local produce with some more exotic fare, whilst the wine list has a good range of vintages to suit every taste and pocket.
17 en suite (bth/shr) (1 fmly) CTV in all bedrooms 40P No coaches Snooker Croquet lawn Putting green Golf driving range Xmas International Cuisine V meals Coffee am Tea pm Last d 9pm
ROOMS: (incl. bkfst) s £75-£90; d £95-£125 **LB**
MEALS: Lunch £15.50&alc Dinner fr £25&alc
CONF: Thtr 60 Class 40 Board 30 Del from £75
CARDS:

CLYDEBANK Dumbarton & Clydebank Map 11 NS56

★★★★ 69% **Beardmore**
Beardmore St G81 4SA ☎ 0141 951 6000 FAX 0141 951 6018
Initially built to serve the HCI private hospital which it adjoins, this hotel now operates independently. They shares the same elegant entrance and concourse, but otherwise are quite separate. An impressive building, both outside and in, it offers international standards allied to a high level of hospitality. The quality of cooking is also gaining a reputation, with a fine buffet complementing the carte in the evening. The hotel lies on the banks of the River Clyde just off the town centre(follow signs for the hospital).
168 en suite (bth/shr) No smoking in 112 bedrooms CTV in all bedrooms STV Lift Night porter Air conditioning 150P Indoor swimming pool (heated) Sauna Solarium Gym Jacuzzi/spa European Cuisine V meals Coffee am Tea pm Last d 10pm
ROOMS: s fr £110; d fr £110
OFF-PEAK: (incl. bkfst) s £88; d £99
MEALS: Lunch £7.50-£13.50&alc Dinner £7.50-£27.50
CONF: Thtr 170 Class 40 Board 30 Del from £120
CARDS:

★★★ 65% **Patio**
1 South Av, Clydebank Business Park G81 2RW
☎ 0141 951 1133 FAX 0141 952 3713
Situated in the local business park, this modern hotel is ideally located to cater for the business traveller and is also a popular venue for conferences and functions. Contemporary semi open-plan public areas include a bar, restaurant and small lounge. Bedrooms, with lacquered furniture topped with imported Italian marble, are comfortably appointed.
80 en suite (bth/shr) No smoking in 16 bedrooms CTV in all bedrooms Lift Night porter 120P French & Scottish Cuisine V meals Coffee am Tea pm Last d 10pm
ROOMS: s £62; d £72 *
OFF-PEAK: s £45; d £45
MEALS: Lunch fr £12.95&alc Dinner fr £16.50*
CONF: Thtr 150 Class 30 Board 30 Del from £67.50
CARDS:

COLONSAY, ISLE OF Argyll & Bute Map 10

SCALASAIG Map 10 NR39

★ 75% **Colonsay**
PA61 7YP (400mtrs W of Ferry Pier)
☎ 01951 200316 FAX 01951 200353
Closed 6 Nov-27 Dec & 12 Jan-Feb

Colonsay is a remote Hebridean island with a ferry service from the mainland every second day, well worth a visit to sample the genuine hospitality and good food offered by Kevin and Christa Byrne at their refreshingly honest hotel close to the ferry terminal. Relaxing public areas include a choice of lounges and well stocked bars, the latter being a popular rendezvous for islanders and visitors alike. There is also a bookshop and café in an adjoining building. The timber-clad dining room is the setting for Christa's competent cooking; her short table d'hÙte menu is carefully prepared from fresh local ingredients, making dinner one of the highlights. The variable sized bedrooms, some fully timber-clad, offer mixed appointments together with the expected amenities.

10 rms (1 bth 7 shr) 1 annexe en suite (shr) (1 fmly) CTV in all bedrooms 32P No coaches Golf 18 Bicycles Sailing equipment European Cuisine Coffee am Tea pm No smoking in restaurant Last d 8pm
ROOMS: (incl. bkfst & dinner) s £55-£80; d £110-£160 **LB**
MEALS: Dinner £21*
CARDS:

COLVEND Dumfries & Galloway Map 11 NX85

★★ 65% **Clonyard House**
DG5 4QW (through Dalbeattie and turn left onto A710 for aprrox. 4 miles) ☎ 01556 630372 FAX 01556 630422
This family-run hotel is set in seven acres of its own grounds which include a children's play area. It makes a quiet base for exploring the Solway coast. Bedrooms in the main house are particularly spacious and traditional in style, while the ground floor rooms, in the modern wing, have their own patios. The lounge bar and restaurant are enhanced by African artefacts and historic family photographs.
15 en suite (bth/shr) (2 fmly) CTV in all bedrooms 40P No coaches ch fac British & French Cuisine V meals Coffee am Last d 9pm
ROOMS: (incl. bkfst) s £37.50; d £60-£66 * **LB**
OFF-PEAK: (incl. bkfst) s £30; d £55
MEALS: Sunday Lunch £8.50&alc Dinner £12.50&alc*
CARDS:

CONNEL Argyll & Bute Map 10 NM93

★★ 69% **Falls of Lora**
PA37 1PB (off A85, overlooking Loch Etive)
☎ 01631 710483 FAX 01631 710694
Closed 25 Dec & Jan
Situated beside the A85 and overlooking Loch Etive, this welcoming family-run hotel is an ideal base for the touring holidaymaker. Bedrooms, which vary in size and in style, range from spacious luxury rooms to the less expensive standard and compact Cabin rooms. There is a comfortable lounge and a well stocked bar bistro which offers an informal food option to the attractive dining room where local produce, including seafood, features on the carte. Staff are friendly and willing to please.
30 en suite (bth/shr) (4 fmly) CTV in all bedrooms 40P No coaches Scottish & French Cuisine V meals Coffee am Tea pm No smoking area in restaurant Last d 9pm

contd.

ROOMS: (incl. bkfst) s £29.50-£49.50; d £39-£99 * **LB**
MEALS: Bar Lunch £5.75-£12.75alc High tea £6.50-£8alc Dinner £15-£21.50alc*
CONF: Thtr 45 Class 20 Board 15
CARDS:

CONTIN Highland Map 14 NH45

★★★ 73% **Coul House**

IV14 9EY (from South by passing Inverness continue on A9 over Moray Firth bridge, after 5m take 2nd exit at roundabout on to A835 follow to Contin)
☎ 01997 421487 FAX 01997 421945
The genuine warmth of welcome together with good food are all part of the appeal of this lovely Victorian country house which stands in five areas of grounds at the edge of the village. All the expected amenities are provided in the individually decorated bedrooms which offer comfortable modern appointments. The roaring log fire invites relaxation in the pleasant foyer lounge which contrasts with the more refined atmosphere of the charming octagonal drawing room. In the attractive dining room, chef Chris Bentley continues to offer a tempting range of Taste of Scotland specialities, on both the carte and fixed-price menus, which are ably supported by a comprehensive wine list offering some excellent clarets.
20 en suite (bth/shr) (3 fmly) CTV in all bedrooms STV 40P No coaches Pool table Putting green Pitch & putt ch fac Xmas Scottish & International Cuisine V meals Coffee am Tea pm No smoking in restaurant Last d 9pm
ROOMS: (incl. bkfst) s £59.50; d £97-£137 **LB**
OFF-PEAK: (incl. bkfst) s £46-£52; d £70-£122
MEALS: Lunch £19-£30alc Dinner £26.50&alc*
CONF: Thtr 60 Class 40 Board 30 Del from £49.75
CARDS:

★★65% **Achility**
IV14 9EG (on A835,at the northern edge of village)
☎ 01997 421355 FAX 01997 421923
Various improvements are being carried out by enthusiastic owners at this renovated 18th-century former coaching inn just west of the village. Relaxing public areas include a choice of lounges one of which is no-smoking, a well stocked bar with rough-cut stone walls and a beamed ceiling, and an attractive restaurant. Bedrooms, four of which have external access, are brightly decorated and offer comfortable modern furnishings. Staff are friendly and willing to please.
12 en suite (bth/shr) (4 fmly) No smoking in 6 bedrooms CTV in all bedrooms 150P Pool table Xmas Scottish & International Cuisine V meals Coffee am Tea pm No smoking in restaurant Last d 9.30pm
ROOMS: (incl. bkfst) s £35-£40; d £50-£60 **LB**
OFF-PEAK: (incl. bkfst) s £20-£25; d £40-£50
MEALS: Sunday Lunch £8.50&alc High tea £6.95 Dinner £9-£21.45alc
CONF: Class 50 Board 30 Del from £41.50
CARDS:

COUPAR ANGUS Perthshire & Kinross Map 11 NO23

★★★ 71% **Moorfield House**
Myeriggs Rd PH13 9HS ☎ 01828 627303 FAX 01828 627339
Quietly situated midway between Blairgowrie and Coupar Angus, this delightful hotel offers high standards of accommodation and service. Completely refurbished a few years ago, both the bedrooms and public areas exude quality and style. Most of the bedrooms are spacious, with fine views over the countryside, while the public areas include a cosy library, large lounge bar and an elegant restaurant, which is the setting for imaginative and assured cuisine which has earned a two rosette award. The dinner menu might feature a chicken confit with salad leaves and a red wine reduction or a medley of local game with a rich whisky sauce, served on clapshot rösti. There is also a lighter supper menu which is a popular alternative.
12 en suite (bth/shr) No smoking in 4 bedrooms CTV in all bedrooms 100P No coaches French Cuisine Coffee am Tea pm Last d 9.45pm
ROOMS: (incl. bkfst) s £35-£42.50; d £85 **LB**
MEALS: Lunch £11.95 High tea £6.25 Dinner £22.50-£26.50
CONF: Thtr 140 Class 80 Del from £75
CARDS:
See advertisement under BLAIRGOWRIE

CRAIGELLACHIE Moray Map 15 NJ24

★★★ 72% **Craigellachie**

AB38 9SR ☎ 01340 881204 FAX 01340 881253
In the heart of Speyside, this hotel on the edge of the village overlooks the river, and is popular with fishermen as well as business guests and tourists. There is a choice of standard and superior bedrooms, all with attractive fabrics and good facilities. Both the Drawing Room and Library are conducive to relaxation, while for the more active there is a small exercise room, sauna and snooker room. For dining there is a choice of restaurants; the Rib Room which offers a good value carte, and the more formal Ben Aigan restaurant where a set four-course menu changes daily, and tables must be booked 24 hours in advance.
30 en suite (bth/shr) CTV in all bedrooms 50P Fishing Sauna Gym Wkly live entertainment Xmas Scottish & Modern European Cuisine V meals Coffee am Tea pm Last d 9.30pm
ROOMS: (incl. bkfst) s £52-£89; d £104-£131 **LB**
MEALS: Lunch £2.95-£30 High tea fr £2.95 Dinner £30
CONF: Thtr 60 Class 36 Board 24 Del from £120
CARDS:

CRAIL Fife Map 12 NO60

★★63% **Balcomie Links**
Balcomie Rd KY10 3TN (take A917, on approaching Crail follow road for golf course, hotel last large building on left)
☎ 01333 450237 FAX 01333 450540
This friendly family-run hotel is situated close to the golf course on the eastern edge of the village, with the lounge bar and some bedrooms enjoying sea views. The bedrooms vary in size and style, while the attractive bar and restaurant offer pleasant surroundings for the range of good value meals and snacks.
11 en suite (bth/shr) (1 fmly) CTV in all bedrooms 40P Snooker Games room V meals Coffee am Tea pm Last d 8.45pm
MEALS: Lunch £5.95-£12.95 High tea £5.75-£6.75 Dinner £5.95-£12.95alc*
CARDS:

★63% **Croma**
Nethergate KY10 3TU ☎ 01333 450239
Closed Dec-Mar
Situated in a residential area close to the centre of the attractive coastal village, this traditional small hotel offers clean and neat accommodation. Friendly resident proprietors create a comfortable atmosphere.
8 rms (5 bth/shr) (2 fmly) CTV in all bedrooms 6P No coaches V meals Coffee am No smoking in restaurant Last d 9pm
ROOMS: (incl. bkfst) s £20-£25; d £35-£45 * **LB**
OFF-PEAK: (incl. bkfst) d £30-£40
MEALS: Dinner £10

CRIANLARICH Stirling Map 10 NN32

Benmore Lodge

FK20 8QS ☎ 01838 300210
RS Nov-19 Mar

A convenient stop-off point either on the way to the isles or as a base for touring the area, this small lodge offers neat accommodation in timber-built chalets. All of the bedrooms have their own verandah and there are two family rooms with bunk beds. A bar and restaurant are located within the same complex and meals are available all day.
11 annexe en suite (shr) (2 fmly) CTV in all bedrooms 50P Fishing Canoeing Skiing Xmas International Cuisine V meals Coffee am Tea pm Last d 8.45pm
ROOMS: (incl. bkfst) s £36-£38; d £56-£60 * **LB**
OFF-PEAK: (incl. bkfst) s £30-£36; d £50-£56
MEALS: Bar Lunch £8.90-£15 Dinner £15-£16&alc
CARDS:

CRIEFF Perthshire & Kinross Map 11 NN82

★★★70% **Crieff Hydro**
Ferntower Rd PH7 3LQ ☎ 01764 655555
FAX 01764 653087

Situated high above the popular holiday town of Crieff, this multi-faceted hotel has been established for over 125 years, and manages to retain traditional charm, while providing one of the most extensive range of sporting and leisure facilities of any hotel in the country. Friendly, attentive service is also a feature, while a wing of executive bedrooms has recently been added which are particularly suited to the business guest. Families are well catered for with children safely supervised so that adults can also enjoy a break!
198 en suite (bth/shr) 15 annexe en suite (bth/shr) (34 fmly) CTV in all bedrooms No dogs (ex guide dogs) Lift Night porter 205P Indoor swimming pool (heated) Golf 9 Tennis (hard) Fishing Squash Riding Snooker Sauna Solarium Gym Pool table Croquet lawn Putting green Jacuzzi/spa Wkly live entertainment ch fac Xmas International Cuisine V meals Coffee am Tea pm Last d 8.30pm
ROOMS: (incl. bkfst & dinner) s £53.50-£100; d £107-£200 **LB**
OFF-PEAK: (incl. bkfst & dinner) s fr £48.50; d £97-£194
MEALS: Lunch £9 High tea £8.50 Dinner £17
CONF: Thtr 335 Class 125 Board 68 Del £92.50
CARDS:

★★69% **Murraypark**
Connaught Ter PH7 3DJ (off A85 to Perth, near Crieff Golf Club) ☎ 01764 653731 FAX 01764 655311

Set in its own attractive gardens, this popular hotel provides friendly service led by the proprietors, Noel and Ann Scott. Bedrooms vary in size, with the more modern being in the new wing and more traditional style available in the main house. The interesting range of dishes can be taken in either the cosy lounge bar or the dining room which overlooks the garden.
20 en suite (bth/shr) (1 fmly) CTV in all bedrooms 50P Shooting Stalking ch fac Scottish & French Cuisine V meals Coffee am No smoking in restaurant
ROOMS: (incl. bkfst) s £48-£52; d £72-£76 *
MEALS: Bar Lunch £8-£15alc Dinner £19.50-£23&alc*
CONF: Thtr 25 Board 20
CARDS:

★★63% **Crieff**
47-49 East High St PH7 3JA ☎ 01764 652632 & 653854
FAX 01764 655019
Situated on the Perth road close to the town centre, this family-run hotel is popular with business guests, tourists and golfers. A good range of bar meals is offered in the smart lounge bar, while the attractive restaurant has an extensive carte. There is also a panelled public bar.
12 rms (9 bth/shr) (1 fmly) CTV in all bedrooms 9P Sauna Solarium Gym Pool table Hair & beauty salon V meals Coffee am No smoking area in restaurant Last d 9.45pm
ROOMS: (incl. bkfst) s £24-£28; d £49-£54 * **LB**
OFF-PEAK: (incl. bkfst) s £20-£24; d £44-£48
MEALS: Bar Lunch £3-£7alc Dinner £8.95-£12.50alc*
CARDS:

★★60% **The Drummond Arms**
James Square PH7 3HX ☎ 01764 652151 FAX 01764 655222
Situated in the heart of the town, beside the main square, this family-run hotel is popular with tour groups and individual travellers alike. Bedrooms vary in size and style, with practical furnishings and all the expected amenities. Public areas include a choice of bars and dining rooms where reasonably priced home-cooked meals are served.
29 rms (28 bth/shr) 7 annexe en suite (bth/shr) (3 fmly) CTV in all bedrooms Lift 30P Pool table Xmas V meals Coffee am Last d 8.30pm
ROOMS: (incl. bkfst) s £24.50-£26.50; d £49-£51 **LB**
MEALS: Lunch £6-£9 High tea £6.50-£10.75 Dinner £7.50-£13*
CARDS:

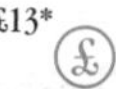

★★59% **Cultoquhey House**
PH7 3NE ☎ 01764 653253 FAX 01764 654535
Closed Feb
Situated in the small village of Gilmerton, just east of Crieff, this country house hotel offers a small piece of Italy in the heart of the Perthshire countryside. The flamboyant owners and their staff provide a relaxed, Mediterranean style service. The bedrooms vary in size and style, with all having smart en-suite facilities. The public areas are grand, with wood panelling and hardwood floors being enhanced with huge oil paintings and stylish fabrics.
20 rms (19 bth/shr) (9 fmly) CTV in all bedrooms STV No dogs 60P Fishing Snooker Shooting Xmas International Cuisine V meals Coffee am Tea pm No smoking in restaurant Last d 10pm
ROOMS: (incl. cont bkfst) s £45-£55; d £60-£80 *
MEALS: Lunch £5&alc High tea £9-£13&alc Dinner £20&alc*
CONF: Del from £65
CARDS:

★68% **Lockes Acre**
7 Comrie Rd PH7 4BP ☎ 01764 652526 FAX 01764 652526
This small Victorian hotel enjoys fine views of the Ochil Hills from its elevated position within attractive wooded gardens on the western side of the town. The welcoming owners, Mr and Mrs Kennedy, are always on hand to advise and assist guests. Bedrooms vary in size, though all are well maintained and housekeeping standards are high. Public areas include a bar, pleasant dining room and relaxing conservatory lounge.
7 rms (4 shr) (1 fmly) CTV in all bedrooms No dogs (ex guide dogs) 35P No coaches International Cuisine V meals Coffee am
MEALS: Lunch £6.55-£12.50alc Dinner £14&alc*
CARDS:

CROCKETFORD Dumfries & Galloway Map 11 NX87

★58% ***Lochview Motel***
Crocketford Rd DG2 8RF ☎ 01556 690281 FAX 01556 690277
Closed 26 Dec & 1 Jan
This good-value motel is an ideal stop-off point on the road to Stranraer. The modest bedrooms are located in a chalet - some having their own veranda. The restaurant overlooks Auchenreoch Loch and offers an all day menu, including specialities for children; home baking and jams are available to take away.
7 en suite (shr) CTV in all bedrooms No dogs 80P Fishing Coffee am Tea pm Last d 8.30pm
CARDS:

For the key to symbols and abbreviations, please see the bookmark inside the back cover

CRUDEN BAY Aberdeenshire Map 15 NK03

★★65% **Red House**
Aulton Rd AB42 7NJ (turn off A952 Aberdeen/Peterhead road at Little Chef onto the A975 towards Cruden Bay, hotel opposite golf course)
☎ 01779 812215 FAX 01779 812320
Popular with golfers, the Red House commands striking views over the links course towards the sea. Completely refurbished, it has smart bedrooms and attractive public areas, which include a comfortable lounge and a restaurant offering a good choice of dishes from both the supper and dinner menus.
6 rms (5 bth/shr) (1 fmly) CTV in all bedrooms STV 40P Pool table V meals Coffee am Tea pm Last d 9pm
ROOMS: (incl. cont bkfst) s £15-£28; d £50-£80 * **LB**
OFF-PEAK: (incl. cont bkfst) s £12-£25; d £40-£60
MEALS: Lunch £7-£11 High tea £4.50-£12 Dinner £14-£25alc*
CARDS:

CULLEN Moray Map 15 NJ56

★★63% **Cullen Bay**
Cullen AB56 4XA (on A98, 0.5m west of Cullen Village)
☎ 01542 840432 FAX 01542 840900
Situated to the west of the town, this family run hotel, as the name suggests, overlooks Cullen Bay. Bedrooms are comfortable and well equipped, some enjoying sea views, while both the lounge bar and restaurant are in a conservatory style with large windows looking out over the bay. Traditional high teas are a popular feature here, with hearty bar meals and dinners also served.
14 en suite (bth/shr) (2 fmly) No smoking in 4 bedrooms CTV in all bedrooms 153P ch fac V meals Coffee am Tea pm No smoking area in restaurant Last d 10pm
ROOMS: (incl. bkfst) s £33-£46; d £55-£61 **LB**
OFF-PEAK: (incl. bkfst) s £33-£35; d £45-£55
MEALS: Lunch £8.95-£9.95&alc High tea £6.50-£15alc Dinner £17.95-£18.95&alc*
CONF: Thtr 100 Class 30 Board 25 Del from £85
CARDS:

See advertisement on opposite page

CUMBERNAULD North Lanarkshire Map 11 NS77

★★★★64% **Westerwood Hotel Golf & Country Club**
1 St Andrews Dr, Westerwood G68 0EW
☎ 01236 457171 FAX 01236 738478
The 18-hole golf course, designed by Seve Ballesteros, together with the range of leisure, conference and function facilities are major attractions at this modern purpose built business hotel. Accommodation ranges from well proportioned suites and executive rooms to the modestly sized standard rooms. All have attractive pastel colour schemes and are smartly furnished, but some may find the shallow baths less than ideal. Increasing demand for a function facility has brought about the demise of the former Old Masters restaurant and the serious eating is now done in the refurbished Tipsy Laird restaurant on the first floor. Here, new chef Anthony Leck's innovative modern style of cooking is producing good results based on sympathetic treatment of the best available fresh raw ingredients.
49 en suite (bth/shr) (20 fmly) No smoking in 4 bedrooms CTV in all bedrooms STV No dogs (ex guide dogs) Lift Night porter Air conditioning 200P Indoor swimming pool (heated) Golf 18 Tennis (hard) Snooker Solarium Gym Pool table Putting green Jacuzzi/spa Steam room Bowling green Driving range Xmas International Cuisine V meals Coffee am Tea pm Last d 10pm
ROOMS: (incl. bkfst) s £82.50-£97.50; d £100-£120 * **LB**
OFF-PEAK: (incl. bkfst) s £30-£60; d £40-£80
MEALS: Lunch £9.50-£9.95&alc Dinner £15&alc*
CONF: Thtr 180 Class 80 Board 40 Del from £99
CARDS:

Travel Inn

4 South Muirhead Rd G67 1AX (from A80 take A8011 following signs to Cumbernauld & then town centre) ☎ 01236 725339 FAX 01236 736380
Purpose-built accommodation, offering spacious, well equipped bedrooms, all with en suite bathrooms. Meals may be taken at the nearby family restaurant. For more information about Travel Inns, consult the Contents page under Hotel Groups.
37 en suite (bth/shr)
ROOMS: d £35.50 *

CUMNOCK East Ayrshire Map 11 NS52

★★57% ***Royal***
1 Glaisnock St KA18 1BP (opposite church in main square)
☎ 01290 420822 FAX 01290 425988
Set in the centre of the town, this mainly commercial hotel offers popular accommodation and value for money prices. Bedrooms are mainly plain and functional whilst the public rooms offer a cosy lounge and an attractive dining room. A good range of food is available, including a high tea menu.
11 rms (6 bth/shr) (1 fmly) CTV in all bedrooms Night porter 10P V meals Coffee am Tea pm Last d 8.45pm
CARDS:

CUPAR Fife Map 11 NO31

★★67% **Eden House**
2 Pitscottie Rd KY15 4HF (overlooking Haigh Park, Cupar on A91, 8 miles west of St.Andrews) ☎ 01334 652510 FAX 01334 652277
Originally built as a home for a Victorian merchant, this friendly family-run hotel on the outskirts of the town has undergone sympathetic refurbishment and extension over the past few years. Bedrooms vary in size, though all have pretty décor and period furnishings. There is a cosy lounge bar, popular with locals, and the conservatory restaurant is the setting for imaginative meals using the best of local produce.
9 en suite (bth/shr) 2 annexe rms (1 bth/shr) (3 fmly) CTV in all bedrooms STV No dogs (ex guide dogs) 18P Wkly live entertainment ch fac V meals Coffee am Tea pm Last d 9.30pm
ROOMS: (incl. bkfst) s £42-£45; d £54-£66 **LB**
MEALS: Lunch fr £18&alc Dinner fr £18&alc*
CONF: Thtr 40 Class 40 Board 40 Del from £55
CARDS:

DALKEITH Midlothian Map 11 NT36

★★62% **Eskbank Motor**
29 Dalhousie Rd EH22 3AT (on B6392)
☎ 0131 663 3234 FAX 0131 660 4347
Set beside the old A7 just south of Eskbank roundabout, this motel operation offers large, well equipped bedrooms contained in a separate annexe. Good value bar-style meals are served in the dining room as well as the bar.
16 en suite (bth/shr) (3 fmly) CTV in all bedrooms STV Night porter 46P Golf parties catered for/Le Boulle rink Wkly live entertainment Xmas International Cuisine V meals Coffee am Tea pm Last d 8.45pm
ROOMS: (incl. bkfst) s £45-£50; d £60-£70 * **LB**
MEALS: Lunch £4.95-£7.50 Dinner £6.50-£15.50*
CONF: Class 20 Board 20
CARDS:

See advertisement under EDINBURGH

DERVAIG See Mull, Isle of

DINGWALL Highland Map 14 NH55

★★ 75% **Kinkell House**
Easter Kinkell, by Conon Bridge IV7 8HY (10m N of Inverness turn off A9 onto B9169 for 1m)
☎ 01349 861270 FAX 01349 865902
Dedicated owners Steve and Marsha Fraser have lovingly restored and sympathetically extended this 19th-century farmhouse to create what is today a most comfortable and appealing small country house hotel. Standing in its own grounds enjoying views over the Cromarty Firth to the Ross-shire hills, the house is located five miles south on the B9169 between the A9 and the A835. Bedrooms in the original house are well proportioned with period furnishings while those in the new extension offer highly polished furnishings on traditional lines. There is a choice of three relaxing and comfortable lounges, the largest of which is a conservatory. Steve Fraser is a genial host while Marsha continues to produce tempting fare from her daily changing fixed price menu featuring the best available local produce, and is served in the elegant dining room.
7 en suite (bth/shr) (1 fmly) No smoking in all bedrooms CTV in all bedrooms 20P No coaches V meals Coffee am Tea pm No smoking in restaurant Last d 9pm
ROOMS: (incl. bkfst) s £38.50-£48.50; d £56-£67 * **LB**
MEALS: Lunch £5-£12.50alc Dinner £10-£20alc*
CARDS:

DIRLETON East Lothian Map 12 NT58

★★★ 64% **The Open Arms**
EH39 5EG ☎ 01620 850241 FAX 850570
Situated in the centre of the attractive East Lothian village, this small hotel offers friendly service and good food. There are two relaxing lounges, with log fires a feature in the winter, and a cosy cocktail bar popular with locals and guests alike. Bedrooms are individually furnished to provide comfortable accommodation. The imaginative dishes served in the restaurant use the best local produce and some old favourites remain on the menu.
10 en suite (bth/shr) CTV in all bedrooms P Xmas V meals Coffee am Tea pm No smoking in restaurant Last d 9.30pm
ROOMS: (incl. bkfst) s fr £74.50; d £119-£149 **LB**
OFF-PEAK: (incl. bkfst) s £40; d £60-£80
MEALS: Lunch fr £16.75&alc High tea £7-£8 Dinner fr £25&alc
CONF: Thtr 100 Class 80 Board 50 Del from £90
CARDS:

DORNIE Highland Map 14 NG82

★★ 64% **Dornie**
Francis St IV40 8DT (follow A87 turn into village of Dornie, hotel on right) ☎ 01599 555205 FAX 01599 555429
RS Jan (ex New Year) & Feb
This well established roadside inn is close to the picturesque Eilean Donan Castle on the shores of Loch Duich. The hotel is run by Ian and Olive Robin who have established themselves at the nearby Robin's Nest restaurant and are building up a good food reputation at the hotel in both the dining room and the bar. Accommodation is bright and mostly en suite with some family units available.
12 rms (1 bth 5 shr) (2 fmly) CTV in all bedrooms 20P No coaches Pool table Wkly live entertainment Xmas Scottish & French Cuisine V meals Coffee am Tea pm Last d 9pm
ROOMS: (incl. bkfst) s £25-£27.50; d £29.50-£35.50 * **LB**
OFF-PEAK: (incl. bkfst) s £25; d £27-£35
MEALS: Lunch £10.95-£24&alc Dinner £18&alc
CARDS:

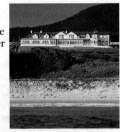

DORNOCH Highland Map 14 NH78

★★ 66% **Dornoch Castle**

Castle St IV25 3SD (2m N, on A949)
☎ 01862 810216 FAX 01862 810981
Closed Nov-Mar
Dominating the main street, this was once the palace of the bishops of Caithness, and parts of the building date from the late 15th century. A comfortable lounge overlooks mature formal gardens, while the wood-panelled, stone-walled bar reflects the building's original character. Bar suppers are available in the Green Room, providing a less formal alternative to restaurant dinner. Bedrooms in the main house are larger than the more modern wing rooms.
4 en suite (bth/shr) 13 annexe en suite (bth/shr) (2 fmly) CTV in all bedrooms Lift 16P No coaches Scottish & Continental Cuisine V meals Coffee am Tea pm No smoking in restaurant
ROOMS: (incl. bkfst) s £39.50; d £70-£83 * **LB**
OFF-PEAK: (incl. bkfst) s £33; d £66-£80
CARDS:

★★ 64% **Burghfield House**
IV25 3HN ☎ 01862 810212 FAX 01862 810404
Closed Nov-Mar (ex Xmas & New Year)
This extended Victorian mansion stands in nearly 6 acres of immaculately kept gardens and has been owned and personally run by the Currie family for 50 years. Bedrooms are located either in the main house or in the Garden Wing annexe, with varying styles of décor and furnishings according to their location. Public areas, including a large lounge, are enhanced with antiques, fresh flowers and real fires, while the bright dining room features a traditional menu with tempting home-made puddings.
14 en suite (bth/shr) 20 annexe rms (16 bth/shr) (8 fmly) CTV in

contd.

all bedrooms Night porter 80P No coaches Sauna Solarium Putting green ch fac Xmas Scottish & French Cuisine Coffee am Tea pm Last d 9.15pm
ROOMS: (incl. bkfst) s £30-£48; d £60-£84 *
MEALS: Bar Lunch £4.50-£10.50 Dinner £14.75-£19.75*
CONF: Thtr 250 Class 170 Board 80
CARDS:

DRUMBEG Highland Map 14 NC13

★★67% Drumbeg
IV27 4NW (on B896) ☎ 01571 833236 FAX 01571 833333
Closed 2 weeks Feb
This small hotel has been extensively modernised by proprietors Jean and John Hay. The location is superb, and surrounded by dramatic countryside this is the ideal base for a walking or fishing holiday. Bedrooms are immaculately maintained and are pretty with floral decor and pine furnishings. Public areas include a comfortable sun lounge, a residents' TV lounge and a busy bar. Dinner is served in the stylish dining room and Jean Hay makes the most of fresh local ingredients.
6 en suite (bth/shr) No smoking in all bedrooms CTV in all bedrooms STV No dogs 30P No coaches Pool table No children Xmas V meals Coffee am Tea pm No smoking in restaurant Last d 9pm
ROOMS: (incl. bkfst) s £38; d £66 *
MEALS: Bar Lunch fr £5 Dinner fr £20&alc
CARDS:

DRUMNADROCHIT Highland Map 14 NH53

★★★69% Polmaily House
IV3 6XT (on A831) ☎ 01456 450343 FAX 01456 450813
Ongoing improvements continue at this relaxed and informal country house hotel which stands in eighteen acres of mixed gardens and woodlands. The emphasis is on the family market and the enthusiastic owners have developed good facilities for children; special children's meals, baby listening and baby sitting facilities are available and there is a choice of outdoor and indoor play areas. Other attractions include an enclosed heated swimming pool and a tennis court. The bar has been repositioned in the new conservatory which is accessed through the comfortable sitting room. There is also a small quiet lounge with well-filled bookshelves and an elegant restaurant. Bedrooms, each with their own colour schemes, are very individual and are comfortably furnished in period style.
10 en suite (bth/shr) (4 fmly) CTV in all bedrooms 20P Indoor swimming pool (heated) Tennis (hard) Croquet lawn Indoor/outdoor childrens play area ch fac Xmas European Cuisine V meals Coffee am Tea pm No smoking in restaurant Last d 9pm
ROOMS: (incl. bkfst) s £44-£62; d £88-£124 * **LB**
OFF-PEAK: (incl. bkfst) s £36-£53; d £72-£106
MEALS: Bar Lunch £5-£10alc Dinner £20&alc
CONF: Thtr 16 Class 8 Board 14
CARDS:

DRYMEN Stirling Map 11 NS48

★★★67% Buchanan Arms
G63 0BQ ☎ 01360 660588 FAX 01360 660943
An extended former coaching inn, situated on the edge of the village, the Buchanan Arms is a popular venue for conferences and weddings. It offers comfortable, well equipped bedrooms furnished in a modern style and public areas which include a beamed bar, the Endrick Lounge and conservatory, and a leisure club.
52 en suite (bth/shr) (3 fmly) No smoking in 6 bedrooms CTV in all bedrooms STV Night porter 100P Indoor swimming pool (heated) Squash Sauna Solarium Gym Jacuzzi/spa Xmas Scottish & French Cuisine V meals Coffee am Tea pm No smoking in restaurant
ROOMS: (incl. bkfst) s £75; d £110 * **LB**
MEALS: Lunch £9.95-£10.50&alc*
CONF: Thtr 150 Class 60 Board 60 Del £99
CARDS:

★★65% Winnock
The Square G63 0BL ☎ 01360 660245 FAX 660267
Surrounding the village green, this 17th-century inn has been extended and modernised to offer accommodation which is comfortable and well equipped. The Highlander Bar is popular with both locals and visitors, with the beer garden providing extra space in the summer. The reception lounge has a warming fire, while the cosy restaurant offers a traditionally Scottish menu. Service is professional and the hotel offers good conference facilities.
49 en suite (bth/shr) (12 fmly) No smoking in 17 bedrooms CTV in all bedrooms No dogs (ex guide dogs) 60P Petanque Wkly live entertainment ch fac Xmas V meals Coffee am Tea pm No smoking in restaurant Last d 9.30pm
ROOMS: (incl. bkfst) s fr £52; d fr £75 * **LB**
OFF-PEAK: (incl. bkfst) s fr £45; d fr £69
MEALS: Lunch £2.75-£9.50&alc High tea fr £6.95 Dinner fr £16.50*
CONF: Thtr 140 Class 60 Board 70 Del from £55
CARDS:

DULNAIN BRIDGE Highland Map 14 NH92

★★★68% *Muckrach Lodge*
PH26 3LY ☎ 01479 851257 FAX 01479 851325
Ongoing improvements have been taking place at this welcoming hotel and the development of a new small conference facility in a separate building should not detract from its country house ambience. New carpeting has enhanced the individually decorated modern bedrooms and personal touches have been reintroduced. Inviting public areas include a spacious and relaxing lounge, a well stocked cocktail bar and an attractive conservatory restaurant which offers the best of Scotland's larder from the carte and daily-changing fixed-price menu.

10 en suite (bth/shr) 4 annexe en suite (bth/shr) (2 fmly) CTV in all bedrooms No dogs (ex guide dogs) 53P No coaches Fishing ch fac British & French Cuisine V meals Coffee am Tea pm Last d 9pm
CARDS:

DUMBARTON Dumbarton & Clydebank Map 10 NS37

★★62% Abbotsford
Stirling Rd G82 2PJ ☎ 01389 733304 FAX 01389 742599
Under the enthusiastic ownership of the McGroarty family, ongoing improvements are taking place at this purpose built business and function hotel, which is conveniently situated beside the A82. Bedrooms, all of which are at ground level, range from upgraded executive rooms with a wide range of amenities, to the somewhat dated standard rooms which are scheduled for refurbishment. Public areas include a popular lounge bar, an attractively refurbished restaurant and a small lounge.
33 en suite (bth/shr) No smoking in 4 bedrooms CTV in all bedrooms STV Night porter 120P European Cuisine V meals Coffee am Tea pm Last d 10pm
ROOMS: (incl. bkfst) s £35-£39.50; d £60-£65 *
OFF-PEAK: (incl. bkfst) s £27.50-£32; d £50-£55
MEALS: Lunch fr £8&alc Dinner fr £13&alc
CONF: Thtr 80 Class 50 Board 30 Del from £60
CARDS:

★★61% ***Dumbuck***
Glasgow Rd G82 1EG ☎ 01389 734336 FAX 01389 734336
Closed 26 Dec & 1-2 Jan
As well as catering for visiting businesspeople, this family-owned hotel is a popular venue for local functions. Bedrooms are modern in style and offer all the expected amenities, though wing rooms are more practical than those in the original house. Public areas include a comfortable foyer lounge, a spacious bar and an attractive restaurant serving a wide range of dishes.
22 en suite (bth/shr) (2 fmly) CTV in all bedrooms STV Night porter 140P Pool table V meals Coffee am Tea pm Last d 9.30pm
CARDS:

Travelodge
Milton G82 2TY (1m E, on A82 westbound)
☎ 01389 765202 FAX 01389 765202
This modern building offers accommodation in smart, spacious and well equipped bedrooms, suitable for family use, and all with en suite bathrooms. Meals may be taken at the nearby family restaurant. For information on room rates and to make a booking, call Roomline free of charge on 0800 850950. For more details about Travelodge, consult the Contents page under Hotel Groups.
32 en suite (bth/shr)

Travelodge

DUMFRIES Dumfries & Galloway Map 11 NX97
See also Carrutherstown

★★★67% **Cairndale Hotel & Leisure Club**
English St DG1 2DF ☎ 01387 254111 FAX 01387 250555
The original sandstone building, close to the high street, has been much extended to provide a wide range of amenities in both the modern bedrooms and the spacious public areas of this hotel. Extensive leisure facilities are available, while a choice of restaurants and a coffee shop offer everything from a quick snack to a formal à la carte meal. The attentive staff ensure efficient service throughout.
76 en suite (bth/shr) (8 fmly) No smoking in 16 bedrooms CTV in all bedrooms STV Lift Night porter 70P Indoor swimming pool (heated) Sauna Solarium Gym Jacuzzi/spa Steam room Toning tables Wkly live entertainment Xmas British, French & Italian Cuisine V meals Coffee am Tea pm No smoking area in restaurant Last d 9.30pm
ROOMS: (incl. bkfst) s £58-£78; d £78-£98 * **LB**
MEALS: Lunch £9.50&alc Dinner £15-£19.50&alc
CONF: Thtr 160 Class 160 Board 40 Del from £55
CARDS:

£

See advertisement on opposite page

★★★63% **Station**
49 Lovers Walk DG1 1LT (opposite the railway station)
☎ 01387 254316 FAX 01387 250388
Opposite the station, this Victorian sandstone hotel is only a short distance from the town centre. Although it retains some of its original character, the bedrooms have been modernised to offer

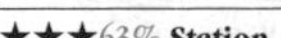

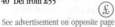

CONSORT HOTELS

contd.

good facilities for both the business traveller and tourist. There is a choice of eating options; the Courtyard Bistro has an informal atmosphere, while the main dining room is more offers a wide ranging menu.

32 en suite (bth/shr) (2 fmly) CTV in all bedrooms STV Lift Night porter 40P ch fac Xmas British, Italian & French Cuisine V meals Coffee am Tea pm No smoking area in restaurant Last d 9.30pm
ROOMS: (incl. bkfst) s £45-£70; d £60-£80 * **LB**
MEALS: Bar Lunch £3.95-£5.50&alc High tea £6-£7.50 Dinner fr £14.50&alc*
CONF: Thtr 60 Class 20 Board 30 Del from £75
CARDS: 

See advertisement on opposite page

Travelodge
Annan Rd, Collin DG1 3SE (on A75)
☎ 01387 750658 FAX 01387 750658

This modern building offers accommodation in smart, spacious and well equipped bedrooms, suitable for family use, and all with en suite bathrooms. Meals may be taken at the nearby family restaurant. For information on room rates and to make a booking, call Roomline free of charge on 0800 850950. For more details about Travelodge, consult the Contents page under Hotel Groups.
40 en suite (bth/shr)

DUNBAR East Lothian Map 12 NT67

★★64% **Redheugh**
Bayswell Park EH42 1AE ☎ 01368 862793
FAX 01368 862793
Closed 25 Dec-2 Jan

The Redheugh Hotel is conveniently situated close to the sea front and the town itself, yet almost hidden away in a quiet residential area. Bedrooms are nicely decorated and furnished, and some of them benefit from sea views. As a small family run hotel, visitors can expect genuine hospitality from the proprietors and can enjoy home cooking, dishes being chosen from a wide selection on the daily changing menu.
10 en suite (bth/shr) (2 fmly) CTV in all bedrooms No coaches No children 8yrs V meals Last d 8.30pm
ROOMS: (incl. bkfst) s £37.50-£39.50; d £57-£61 **LB**
MEALS: Dinner £17.50*
CARDS: 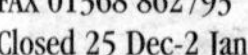

★★61% **Bayswell**
Bayswell Park EH42 1AE ☎ 01368 862225
FAX 01368 862225
A family-run hotel in a quiet area with sea views from its clifftop position. There's a snug bar and a sun lounge where breakfast is served, and a dining room on the first floor next to the residents' lounge. Bedrooms are furnished in different styles.
13 en suite (bth/shr) (4 fmly) CTV in all bedrooms STV 20P Putting green Petanque Wkly live entertainment ch fac Xmas V meals Coffee am Tea pm Last d 9pm
ROOMS: (incl. bkfst) s £39.50-£49.50; d £59-£69 **LB**
MEALS: Bar Lunch fr £9.50 High tea fr £4.95 Dinner fr £12.95
CARDS:

DUNBLANE Stirling Map 11 NN70

RED STAR HOTEL

★★★ **Cromlix House**

Kinbuck FK15 9JT (3 m NE B8033)
☎ 01786 822125 FAX 01786 825450
Closed 2-30 Jan
This delightful country house hotel offers a peaceful haven in the centre of Scotland, and has a welcoming atmosphere which is created by David and Ailsa Assenti and their committed staff. Roaring log fires are a feature of all the public rooms, with the reception hall providing a relaxing area, and the morning room offering large, comfortable sofas. The other day rooms and the dining rooms take advantage of the views over the 3000-acre estate, with a wealth of daffodils in the spring and a blaze of colour in the autumn. Almost half of the bedrooms are suites, though all the rooms are furnished in the style of the house and have every thoughtful extra. The hotel even has its own private chapel, which is popular for weddings. The short dinner carte is well balanced, with local fish and game featuring strongly; tender slices of venison on a redcurrant sauce with a heavenly parsnip purée was the highlight of a recent meal.
14 en suite (bth/shr) CTV in all bedrooms 51P No coaches Tennis (hard) Fishing Croquet lawn Clay pigeon shooting Xmas V meals Coffee am Tea pm No smoking in restaurant Last d 8.30pm
ROOMS: (incl. bkfst) s £95-£150; d £140-£190 * **LB**
OFF-PEAK: (incl. bkfst) s £80-£105; d £135-£165
MEALS: Lunch £18-£26 Dinner £36-£37.50*
CONF: Thtr 40 Class 30 Board 22 Del from £135
CARDS: 

★★64% **Stirling Arms**
Stirling Rd FK15 9EP (on B8033)
☎ 01786 822156 FAX 01786 825300
This 17th-century coaching inn situated beside Allan Water, close to the railway station and within easy reach of the A9, now serves as a friendly family-run business and tourist hotel. Bars are popular with locals, while the attractive panelled Oak Room restaurant offers excellent value in an extensive carte that ranges from light snacks to substantial meals. Bedrooms vary in size but are comfortably modern in style and provide all the expected amenities.
7 rms (1 bth 3 shr) (1 fmly) CTV in all bedrooms STV 9P

International Cuisine V meals Coffee am Last d 9.30pm
ROOMS: (incl. bkfst) s £35-£40; d £48-£60 *
MEALS: Lunch £5.50-£7.95&alc Dinner £16-£20&alc*
CONF: Thtr 30 Class 11 Board 12 Del from £53
CARDS:

DUNDEE Dundee City Map 11 NO43
See also Auchterhouse

★★★★ 62% **Stakis Dundee Earl Grey**
Earl Grey Place DD1 4DE (Stakis)
☎ 01382 229271 FAX 01382 200072
Well equipped accommodation is offered at this purpose built hotel which enjoys an enviable position on the old quayside with views over the Tay estuary to Fife. Over half the bedrooms have been refurbished where effective use has been made of striking fabrics and stylish furnishings. All rooms however are well equipped. Contemporary public areas take advantage of the view, particularly the open-plan bar and restaurant. Dinner menus feature fresh local produce whilst at lunch there is a well displayed carvery buffet. Smartly uniformed staff provide friendly and willing service and the hotel offers good car parking as well as both leisure facilities and a business centre.
104 en suite (bth/shr) (4 fmly) No smoking in 41 bedrooms CTV in all bedrooms STV No dogs (ex guide dogs) Lift Night porter 70P Indoor swimming pool (heated) Sauna Solarium Gym Jacuzzi/spa Exercise equipment Wkly live entertainment Xmas International Cuisine V meals Coffee am Tea pm No smoking area in restaurant Last d 9.30pm
ROOMS: s £88-£103; d £103-£118 * **LB**
MEALS: Lunch £8.60-£11.45 High tea fr £6.95 Dinner £16.50-£18&alc
CONF: Thtr 440 Class 190 Board 130 Del from £65
CARDS:

★★★ 69% **Swallow**

Kingsway West, Invergowrie DD2 5JT (turn off from A90/A929 rdbt following sign for Denhead of Gray, hotel on left) ☎ 01382 641122 FAX 01382 568340
Centred around a magnificent turreted Victorian sandstone house and set in attractive landscaped gardens, this well managed hotel is conveniently situated close to the A90. Whilst some of the bedrooms are compact, all are well equipped and some have been very smartly refurbished; some of the older rooms however are beginning to look a little tired, although plans to refurbish these are well advanced. The good range of public areas include a newly refurbished and very well equipped leisure centre. The smartly uniformed staff are friendly and helpful.
107 en suite (bth/shr) (5 fmly) No smoking in 100 bedrooms CTV in all bedrooms STV Night porter 140P Indoor swimming pool (heated) Sauna Solarium Gym Putting green Jacuzzi/spa Trim trail Mountain bike hire Xmas European Cuisine V meals Coffee am Tea pm No smoking in restaurant Last d 10pm
ROOMS: (incl. bkfst) s fr £88; d fr £115 * **LB**
MEALS: Lunch £5-£12.50&alc Dinner fr £18.50*
CONF: Thtr 80 Class 20 Board 50 Del from £110
CARDS:

★★★ 67% **Invercarse**

371 Perth Rd DD2 1PG (follow signs fo the University) ☎ 01382 669231 FAX 01382 644112
Closed 24-26 Dec & 31 Dec-2 Jan
Set in its own grounds on the east side of the city this fine period house has been tastefully converted and extended to become a smart modern hotel. It offers well equipped bedrooms and public areas which include an attractive cocktail lounge and adjoining two tier lounge bar popular for its range of meals and an alternative eating option to Silks Restaurant.
32 en suite (bth/shr) No smoking in 17 bedrooms CTV in all bedrooms STV Night porter 107P Cosmopolitan Cuisine V meals Coffee am Tea pm Last d 9.30pm
ROOMS: (incl. bkfst) s £63; d £80
OFF-PEAK: (incl. bkfst) s £32; d £64
MEALS: Lunch £10&alc High tea £6.95-£14.25alc Dinner £14.95&alc*
CONF: Thtr 200 Class 100 Board 50 Del from £84
CARDS:

★★★ 63% **Angus Thistle**

101 Marketgait DD1 1QU (500yds from railway station) ☎ 01382 226874 FAX 01382 22564
Forming part of a small shopping centre, this purpose-built city-centre hotel offers a reasonable if somewhat dated standard of accommodation. Bedrooms are comfortably appointed and well equipped, and public areas - most of them on the first floor - include an attractive split-level restaurant and comfortable cocktail bar.
58 en suite (bth/shr) (4 fmly) No smoking in 11 bedrooms CTV in all bedrooms STV Lift Night porter 20P Whirlpool Xmas

contd.

International Cuisine V meals Coffee am Tea pm Last d 9.30pm
ROOMS: s £80-£85; d £95-£105 * **LB**
OFF-PEAK: (incl. bkfst) s fr £37; d fr £74
MEALS: Lunch £5.50-£8.25 Dinner fr £16.50&alc*
CONF: Thtr 500 Class 200 Board 200 Del from £68
CARDS:

★★★62% **Queens**

160 Nethergate DD1 4DU ☎ 01382 322515
FAX 01382 202668
The Queen's is a largely commercial hotel, convenient for the city centre, railway station and university. Bedrooms in a variety of sizes are all well equipped and some offer views of the Tay estuary and bridge. Judges Lounge, on the first floor, looks out over the city and, like the restaurant, features fine ornate ceilings.
47 en suite (bth/shr) (4 fmly) CTV in all bedrooms STV Lift Night porter 80P Wkly live entertainment Continental Cuisine V meals Coffee am Tea pm Last d 9.30pm
ROOMS: (incl. bkfst) s £37-£60; d £50-£80 * **LB**
MEALS: Lunch £8.95&alc High tea £4.50-£11 Dinner £14.95&alc*
CONF: Thtr 160 Del from £65
CARDS:

See advertisement on opposite page

★★68% **The Shaftesbury**

1 Hyndford St DD2 1HQ ☎ 01382 669216
FAX 01382 641598
Formerly the town house of a jute baron who had 17 children, this carefully restored hotel is within walking distance of the university and not far from Ninewells Hospital. Bedrooms have attractive, co-ordinating furniture and fabrics, and the honeymoon suite on the top floor is quite a treat, enjoying fine views across the city and Tay river. There is a cosy lounge and bar, which overlooks the colourful garden, and the elegant restaurant serves a range of Taste of Scotland dishes.
12 en suite (bth/shr) (2 fmly) CTV in all bedrooms 2P No coaches Xmas Scottish & French Cuisine V meals Coffee am No smoking in restaurant Last d 10.45pm
ROOMS: (incl. bkfst) s £39.50-£49.50; d £58-£76 * **LB**
OFF-PEAK: (incl. bkfst) s £38.50-£42; d £54-£58
MEALS: Dinner £15-£18.50&alc
CARDS:

See advertisement on opposite page

Travel Inn

Kingsway West, Invergowrie DD2 5JU (on A972 between Invergowrie & Dundee) ☎ 01382 561115
FAX 01382 568431
Purpose-built accommodation, offering spacious, well equipped bedrooms, all with en suite bathrooms. Meals may be taken at the nearby family restaurant. For more information about Travel Inns, consult the Contents page under Hotel Groups.
40 en suite (bth/shr)
ROOMS: d £35.50 *

Travel Inn
Discovery Quay, Riverside Dr DD1 4XA
☎ 01382 203240 FAX 01382 203237
Purpose-built accommodation, offering spacious, well equipped bedrooms, all with en suite bathrooms. Meals may be taken at the nearby family restaurant. For more information about Travel Inns, consult the Contents page under Hotel Groups.
40 en suite (bth/shr)
ROOMS: d £35.50 *

DUNDONNELL Highland Map 14 NH08

★★★74% **Dundonnell**

IV23 2QS (turn off A835 at Braemore Junction on to A832) ☎ 01854 633204 FAX 01854 633366

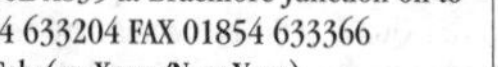

Closed 22 Nov-Feb (ex Xmas/New Year)
Good food together with genuine Highland hospitality ensure that many guests return year after year to Selbie and Flora Florence's comfortable Highland holiday hotel at the head of Little Loch Broom. Bedrooms are nicely presented in the modern style and include a range of Premier and Standard rooms, the former having the best views. The attractive public areas have been transformed following completion of an ambitious refurbishment programme. There is a choice of contrasting bars and comfortable lounges and the upgraded dining room continues to offer a tempting range of Taste of Scotland specialities from the daily changing fixed price menu with seafood featuring strongly.
28 en suite (bth/shr) (2 fmly) CTV in all bedrooms 60P Xmas V meals Coffee am Tea pm No smoking in restaurant Last d 8.30pm
ROOMS: (incl. bkfst) s £44-£50; d £75-£95 * **LB**
OFF-PEAK: (incl. bkfst) s £32.50-£39.50; d £55-£72
MEALS: Bar Lunch £12-£20alc Dinner £23.95-£25*
CARDS:

DUNFERMLINE Fife Map 11 NT08

★★★68% **Keavil House**
Crossford KY12 8QW (2m W A994)
☎ 01383 736258 FAX 01383 621600
Some parts of this extended house are reputed to date from the 16th century, and the hotel enjoys an attractive rural location in a small village just outside Dunfermline. Popular with business guests and family parties, it also provides a pleasant setting for wedding receptions. Some bedrooms in the modern wing have patio doors leading onto the lawns. An interesting choice of dishes is available in the Conservatory restaurant with Chef, Volker Steinemen producing dishes such as courgette and Brie soup, and Tay salmon with a nettle cream sauce. Service throughout is courteous and attentive.
33 en suite (bth/shr) (2 fmly) CTV in all bedrooms STV Night porter 150P Indoor swimming pool (heated) Sauna Solarium Gym Jacuzzi/spa Aerobics studio Steam room ch fac Xmas Scottish & French Cuisine V meals Coffee am No smoking in restaurant Last d 9pm

contd.

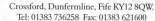

ROOMS: s £62-£79; d £75-£90 **LB**
OFF-PEAK: s £50-£62; d £62-£65
MEALS: Lunch £4.95-£13 Dinner £18.50-£25&alc*
CONF: Thtr 200 Class 60 Board 50 Del from £79.50
CARDS: 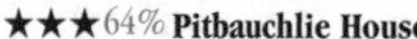

See advertisement on page 757

★★★64% Pitbauchlie House
Aberdour Rd KY11 4PB (1m S of town centre on B916)
☎ 01383 722282 FAX 01383 620738
This family-run hotel, located in a residential area on the south side of the town, has been sympathetically extended to provide modern accommodation in a range of bedroom types. Both the larger executive rooms and the more compact rooms in the main house have been attractively decorated and offer good facilities. Public areas include a choice of bars, a foyer lounge and the restaurant which overlooks the pretty garden. There are also several function and conference rooms.
40 en suite (bth/shr) (2 fmly) CTV in all bedrooms STV Night porter 70P Gym Xmas International Cuisine V meals Coffee am Tea pm No smoking in restaurant Last d 9pm
ROOMS: (incl. bkfst) s £40-£60; d £67-£73 * **LB**
MEALS: Sunday Lunch £8.50-£12.50&alc High tea £7.50 Dinner £12&alc*
CARDS:

★★★62% King Malcolm Thistle
Queensferry Rd, Wester Pitcorthie KY11 5DS (on A823, S of town) ☎ 01383 722611 FAX 01383 730865
THISTLE HOTELS
This modern low rise hotel is situated on the south side of the town besides the A823 and is easily reached from junction 2 of the M90 motorway. Bedrooms, designed for both the business and leisure traveller, are compact and now dated in style, but have every modern facility and for those who may wish to dine in their room a 24 hour menu is provided. Public areas include Richmond's Restaurant and an adjoining cocktail bar and conservatory lounge, Canmore Lodge, which is the hotel's own pub and a comfortably furnished reception foyer. There is also a banqueting suite, a meeting room and ample car parking.
48 en suite (bth/shr) (2 fmly) No smoking in 12 bedrooms CTV in all bedrooms Night porter 60P Wkly live entertainment Xmas Scottish & French Cuisine V meals Coffee am Tea pm Last d 10pm
ROOMS: s £68-£78; d £90-£99 * **LB**
OFF-PEAK: s fr £55; d fr £75
MEALS: Lunch fr £9.95&alc High tea fr £6.50 Dinner fr £15.50&alc*
CONF: Thtr 150 Class 60 Board 50 Del from £85
CARDS:

★★★55% *Pitfirrane Arms*
Main St, Crossford KY12 8NJ ☎ 01383 736132 FAX 01383 621760
The Pitfirrane Arms is located on the main street of this small village on the outskirts of the town. Bedrooms are compact and practical, and the public areas include a choice of bars and a small dining room offering a range of dishes based on world-wide cuisine. The hotel is a popular function venue and attracts mainly business clients.
38 en suite (bth/shr) (1 fmly) CTV in all bedrooms STV No dogs (ex guide dogs) Night porter 72P Sauna Solarium Scottish & French Cuisine V meals Coffee am Tea pm Last d 9.15pm
CARDS:

★★69% Elgin
Charlestown KY11 3EE (3m W of M90, junc 1, on loop road off A985, signposted Limekilns & Charlestown)
☎ 01383 872257 FAX 01383 873044
A friendly family-run hotel with views across the Firth of Forth, the Elgin lies in the village of Charlestown. Bedrooms are bright and attractive, with good facilities for both business travellers and tourists. There is an intimate cocktail bar and restaurant which features a cast of the Elgin marbles above the fireplace. Meals are also served in the large lounge bar.
13 en suite (bth/shr) (3 fmly) CTV in all bedrooms STV No dogs (ex guide dogs) 70P V meals Coffee am Last d 9pm
ROOMS: (incl. bkfst) s £41-£52; d £64-£72 * **LB**
OFF-PEAK: (incl. bkfst) s £35-£41; d £52-£62
MEALS: Bar Lunch £4.50-£12alc High tea £5.50-£7.50alc Dinner £5.50-£15alc*
CARDS:

See advertisement on opposite page

DUNKELD Dundee City Map 11 NO04

RED STAR HOTEL

★★★ Kinnaird
Kinnaird Estate PH8 0LB (4.5m N on B898)
☎ 01796 482440 FAX 01796 482289
RS 6 Jan-16 Mar

This splendid private house is set in its own 9000-acre estate and enjoys spectacular views across the Tay valley. Outdoor sporting activities such as shooting and fishing can be arranged but it is the sumptuous interior that most guests come to appreciate. All of the individually furnished bedrooms have their own gas fire, as well as king-size beds and every possible luxurious touch. Public areas include the Cedar Room, which has deep, comfortable sofas in front of a log fire and there is a billiard room which adjoins it. There is also a quiet study, while the dining room has beautiful hand-painted panels dating from 1860. Chef John Webber has built up a loyal following and some recent dishes sampled included ravioli of rabbit and morels with a white wine and Madeira sauce followed by grilled halibut on a bed of chargrilled Mediterranean vegetables and dribbled with pesto and soy jus. Cakes and pastries are also recommended. The professional service is led by Douglas Jack.
9 en suite (bth/shr) CTV in all bedrooms STV No dogs Lift 22P No coaches Tennis (hard) Fishing Snooker Croquet

lawn Shooting No children 12yrs No smoking in restaurant Last d 9.30pm
ROOMS: (incl. bkfst) s £210-£250; d £220-£260 **LB**
MEALS: Lunch £19.50-£24 Dinner fr £39.50
CONF: Thtr 25 Class 10 Board 15
CARDS:

★★ 64% ***Atholl Arms***
Bridgehead PH8 0AQ ☎ 01350 727219 & 727759 FAX 01350 727219
This former coaching inn, with its distinctive white façade, lies in the centre of the cathedral town, by Dunkeld Bridge overlooking the River Tay. It has been considerable refurbished over the past few years, but retains its traditional appearance and style. The hotel has established a reputation for honest home-cooked meals, which can be enjoyed in either the dining room or the spacious foyer lounge.
16 rms (9 bth/shr) (1 fmly) No smoking in 5 bedrooms CTV in all bedrooms 21P No coaches V meals Coffee am Last d 8.45pm
CARDS:

DUNNET Highland Map 15 ND27

★★60% ***Northern Sands***
KW14 8DX ☎ 01847 85270
Colourful flowering baskets adorn the front of this family run holiday hotel which is situated close to a glorious sandy beach. The well decorated bedrooms are variable in size and offer mixed modern appointments. The comfortable bar is especially popular for it's food operation, an informal alternative to the attractive restaurant where the emphasis is on pasta and grill specialities.
9 en suite (bth/shr) (3 fmly) CTV in all bedrooms No dogs (ex guide dogs) 50P French & Italian Cuisine V meals Coffee am Tea pm Last d 8.30pm
CARDS:

DUNOON Argyll & Bute Map 10 NS17

★★ 76% **Enmore**
Marine Pde, Kirn PA23 8HH (on coastal route between two ferries, 1m N of Dunoon)
☎ 01369 702230 FAX 01369 702148
Closed 2-12 Jan RS Nov-Feb
(Rosette awarded for dinner only)

SCOTLAND'S COMMENDED HOTELS

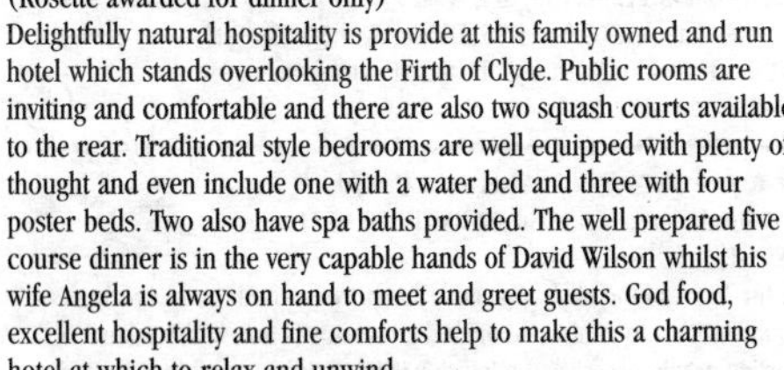
Delightfully natural hospitality is provide at this family owned and run hotel which stands overlooking the Firth of Clyde. Public rooms are inviting and comfortable and there are also two squash courts available to the rear. Traditional style bedrooms are well equipped with plenty of thought and even include one with a water bed and three with four poster beds. Two also have spa baths provided. The well prepared five course dinner is in the very capable hands of David Wilson whilst his wife Angela is always on hand to meet and greet guests. God food, excellent hospitality and fine comforts help to make this a charming hotel at which to relax and unwind.
11 en suite (bth/shr) (2 fmly) CTV in all bedrooms 20P No coaches Squash ch fac Xmas Scottish & French Cuisine V meals Coffee am Tea pm No smoking in restaurant Last d 9.30pm
ROOMS: (incl. bkfst) s £39; d £70-£140 * **LB**
OFF-PEAK: (incl. bkfst & dinner) s £45; d £99
MEALS: Lunch £10-£25 High tea fr £10 Dinner fr £28
CONF: Thtr 14 Class 16 Board 12 Del from £45
CARDS:

★69% **Lyall Cliff**
141 Alexandra Pde, East Bay PA23 8AW (on A815 between Kirn and Dunoon on sea front) ☎ 01369 702041 FAX 01369 702041
Closed 20 Dec-7 Jan RS Nov-Mar
Excellent value for money is offered at this friendly family-run holiday

contd.

hotel on the seafront overlooking the Firth of Clyde. The spotless bedrooms are brightly decorated and furnished in a mixture of modern styles. Following the closure of the small snug bar, drinks are now served on request in the traditional lounge.

10 en suite (shr) (2 fmly) CTV in all bedrooms 12P No coaches No children 3yrs V meals No smoking in restaurant Last d 8pm
ROOMS: (incl. bkfst) s £20-£23; d £34-£40
MEALS: Dinner £9-£12&alc*
CARDS:

DUNVEGAN See Skye, Isle of

DUROR Highland Map 14 NM95

★★ 74% **Stewart**
PA38 4BW (on A828) ☎ 01631 740268
FAX 01631 740328
Closed 16 Oct-Mar
(Rosettes awarded for dinner only)
This friendly, family-run hotel is set in an elevated position in glorious colourful gardens, and offers a good standard of accommodation and service. Bedrooms are contained in a purpose-built extension which is connected internally and are both spacious and well equipped, while the public rooms include a comfortable first-floor lounge, designed to maximise the outstanding loch views, and an elegant restaurant where the seafood is specially recommended.

20 en suite (bth/shr) (2 fmly) CTV in all bedrooms 30P V meals Coffee am Tea pm No smoking in restaurant Last d 9pm
ROOMS: (incl. bkfst) s £43.50; d £87 *
MEALS: Bar Lunch £2.95-£15 Dinner £25
CARDS:

EAST KILBRIDE South Lanarkshire Map 11 NS65

★★★ 63% **Bruce Swallow**
Cornwall St G74 1AF
☎ 013552 29771 FAX 013552 42216
This business hotel forms part of a 1960s shopping centre complex. It offers various styles and grades of rooms, which are reflected in the different tariffs. The best bedrooms are well appointed and equipped. Public areas consist of a comfortable lounge bar and restaurant, and there is a small basement car park. Friendly staff provide an attentive level of service throughout.

78 en suite (bth/shr) No smoking in 23 bedrooms CTV in all bedrooms STV Lift Night porter 35P Xmas Scottish & French Cuisine V meals Coffee am Tea pm No smoking in restaurant Last d 9.45pm
ROOMS: (incl. bkfst) s £55-£75; d £70-£90 * LB
MEALS: Lunch £9.25 Dinner £11.95-£16.95*
CONF: Thtr 200 Class 50 Board 25 Del £85
CARDS:

★★★ 59% **Stuart**
2 Cornwall Way G74 1JR ☎ 013552 21161 FAX 013552 64410
This purpose built business, conference and function hotel is conveniently positioned beside the central shopping area in the centre of town. The spacious lounge bar has recently been upgraded and this is complemented by a split-level cocktail bar which is adjacent to Jellowickis, an informal American themed diner/restaurant offering a varied good value menu. Executive rooms provide the best accommodation standards, the others being somewhat variable in size and functional in style.

39 en suite (bth/shr) (2 fmly) CTV in all bedrooms STV No dogs (ex guide dogs) Lift Night porter Air conditioning Wkly live entertainment European Cuisine V meals Coffee am Tea pm Last d 11pm
ROOMS: (incl. bkfst) s £57-£70; d £80-£100 *
OFF-PEAK: (incl. bkfst) s fr £35; d fr £50
MEALS: Lunch fr £7.95&alc Dinner fr £12.95&alc*
CONF: Thtr 200 Class 80 Board 60
CARDS:

Travel Inn
Brunel Way, The Murray G75 0JY (follow signs for Paisley A726, turn left at Murray roundabout and left into Brunel Way)

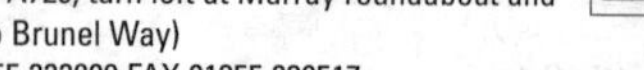

☎ 01355 222809 FAX 01355 230517
Purpose-built accommodation, offering spacious, well equipped bedrooms, all with en suite bathrooms. Meals may be taken at the nearby family restaurant. For more information about Travel Inns, consult the Contents page under Hotel Groups.
40 en suite (bth/shr)
ROOMS: d £35.50 *

EDINBURGH City of Edinburgh Map 11 NT27

★★★★★ 71% **Balmoral**
1 Princes St EH2 2EQ ☎ 0131 556 2414
FAX 0131 557 3747

Restoration of this splendid Edwardian building, with its magnificent clock tower, was completed about 4 years ago and visitors who had known it as The North British Hotel will find much pleasure in its rehabilitation. Traditional afternoon teas and morning coffees are served in the elegant Palm Court lounge, and there are two bars,a cocktail bar with leather seating or alternatively the more lively NB's bar, with live music on some evenings, is an ideal venue for meeting friends or colleagues. The Grill Room restaurant has an excellent reputation for its high standard of cuisine and Stuart Muir, previously of Knockinaam Lodge, is now responsible for the imaginative and creative menus. The Brasserie restaurant provides more informal eating in a bright modern atmosphere. Bedrooms are all comfortably furnished and well equipped and there are excellent suites which have views down Princes Street and towards the Castle.

189 en suite (bth/shr) No smoking in 31 bedrooms CTV in all bedrooms STV No dogs (ex guide dogs) Lift Night porter Air conditioning 50P Indoor swimming pool (heated) Sauna Solarium Gym Beauty salon Steam room Hairdressers Xmas Scottish & French Cuisine V meals Coffee am Tea pm Last d 10.30pm
ROOMS: s £125-£145; d £140-£240 * LB
OFF-PEAK: s £125-£130; d £145-£150
MEALS: Lunch £7.90-£19.95 Dinner £14.50-£29.50*
CONF: Thtr 380 Class 180 Board 30 Del from £105
CARDS:

★★★★★ 70% **Sheraton Grand**
1 Festival Square EH3 9SR ☎ 0131 229 9131
FAX 0131 228 4510
In the heart of the city's west end, this purpose-built hotel overlooks a square with a fountain. Although the exterior is not, at first glance, particularly impressive, the interior is imposing. A marble entrance hall features a grand, central staircase leading to the first floor where there is a lounge and popular cocktail bar and the hotel's two restaurants. The Terrace, which serves brasserie-style cuisine all day, has floodlit views of the Usher Hall and the historic castle beyond. In the Grill Room the cusine is assured and confident, under the supervision of chefs Nicholas Laurent and Philippe Wagenfuhrer, the atmosphere is more sedate, and the decor features the company's own tartan. Modern Scottish dishes are blended with touches of the classical, revealed in dishes such as ravioli of scallops on a bed of rich bisque, and roast pheasant with its juices reduced to a powerful gravy. Desserts are varied - the mille-feuille lightly dusted with chocolate and filled with a sweet chestnut butter cream was ideal.

261 en suite (bth/shr) (23 fmly) No smoking in 67 bedrooms CTV in all bedrooms STV No dogs (ex guide dogs) Lift Night porter Air conditioning 120P Indoor swimming pool (heated) Sauna Solarium

Gym Jacuzzi/spa Wkly live entertainment Xmas Scottish, French & Continental Cuisine V meals Coffee am Tea pm Last d 10.30pm
ROOMS: s £150-£165; d £190-£215 * **LB**
MEALS: Lunch £14-£22.50&alc Dinner £17.50-£28.50&alc*
CONF: Thtr 485 Class 350 Board 120 Del from £171
CARDS:

★★★★★ 66% **Caledonian**

Princes St EH1 2AB (Leading Hotels)
☎ 0131 459 9988 FAX 0131 225 6632
This elegant former railway hotel, affectionately known as "the Caley", is situated at the western end of Princes Street and is a landmark in this part of the city. Many of the comfortable and tastefully furnished and decorated bedrooms have views of the Castle, but others overlook an inner courtyard where the outlook is more restricted. The opulent public rooms include a traditional lounge and a fine staircase which leads to La Pompadour Restaurant, a sumptuous room, presided over with dignity and style by Restaurant Manager Jordi Figuerola and in which fine Scottish dishes, created by head Chef Tony Binks, can be savoured in a relaxed, but luxurious atmosphere. More informal eating can be enjoyed in Carriages Restaurant which occupies an area which was once a railway platform. The hotel now has a gymnasium and there are numerous meeting, conference and banqueting rooms. The staff are all very friendly and helpful combining professionalism with a natural desire to please.
236 en suite (bth/shr) No smoking in 58 bedrooms CTV in all bedrooms STV No dogs (ex guide dogs) Lift Night porter 50P Solarium Gym Wkly live entertainment Xmas Scottish & French Cuisine V meals Coffee am Tea pm No smoking area in restaurant Last d 10pm
ROOMS: s £139-£190; d £209-£299 * **LB**
MEALS: Lunch fr £14.95&alc Dinner £3.50-£16alc*
CONF: Thtr 300 Class 150 Board 60 Del from £150
CARDS:

★★★★ 71% **George Inter-Continental**

INTER·CONTINENTAL HOTELS AND RESORTS

19-21 George St EH2 2PB ☎ 0131 225 1251
FAX 0131 226 5644
Centrally situated behind a classical façade, this long established hotel offers attractive public areas which include a marble floored foyer with fine Corinthian pillars, a popular clubby bar and a choice of eating outlets. The magnificent room which houses Carvers restaurant was built in 1775 and was once an insurance trading hall. However, our award of one rosette is given for the cooking offered in the elegant Chambertin restaurant. Friendly staff offer traditional levels of service which extend to valet parking and evening room servicing. Bedrooms vary in size but are comfortably furnished and continue to be upgraded.
195 en suite (bth/shr) No smoking in 57 bedrooms CTV in all bedrooms STV No dogs (ex guide dogs) Lift Night porter 24P Xmas Scottish, English & French Cuisine V meals Coffee am Tea pm No smoking area in restaurant Last d 10pm
ROOMS: s £135-£160; d £160-£185 * **LB**
OFF-PEAK: (incl. bkfst) s £99-£112; d £120-£140
CONF: Thtr 200 Class 80 Board 80 Del from £99
CARDS:

★★★★ 71% **Marriott Dalmahoy**

Kirknewton EH27 8EB (7m W of Edinburgh on the A71) ☎ 0131 333 1845 FAX 0131 333 1433
Boasting commanding views of the Pentland hills and surrounded by two golf courses, this fine hotel is conveniently positioned for the airport and also has good access to the city. The original Adam house retains much of its original character and the charming bedrooms. The more modern bedroom extensions provide bright, comfortably furnished rooms suitably equipped for both the business and leisure guest. A good range of sporting activities include an attractive leisure club with its own bar and poolside restaurant which is open all day. Our two rosettes award is for the stylish Pentland restaurant where chef Gary Bates offers a more imaginative menu with good use of fresh seasonal produce.

43 en suite (bth/shr) 108 annexe en suite (bth/shr) (3 fmly) No smoking in 57 bedrooms CTV in all bedrooms STV No dogs (ex guide dogs) Lift Night porter 350P Indoor swimming pool (heated) Golf 18 Tennis (hard) Squash Snooker Sauna Solarium Gym Putting green Jacuzzi/spa Health & beauty treatments Steam room Xmas Scottish & French Cuisine V meals Coffee am Tea pm No smoking in restaurant Last d 9.45pm
ROOMS: (incl. bkfst) s £79-£130 * **LB**
MEALS: Lunch fr £14.50 Dinner fr £23.50*
CONF: Thtr 500 Class 150 Board 95 Del £150
CARDS:

★★★★ 68% **Carlton Highland**

SCOTTISH HIGHLAND HOTELS

North Bridge EH1 1SD (on North Bridge which links Princes St to the Royal Mile, opposite 'The Scotsman' offices) ☎ 0131 556 7277 FAX 0131 556 2691
This busy commercial hotel is conveniently located close to the Royal Mile; guests are provided with complimentary overnight permits for a nearby car park. The well equipped bedrooms vary in size but most have recently been upgraded and executive rooms are available for those desiring additional comfort. Public areas include a spacious lounge area, Carlyles (a European style coffee shop), and Quills Restaurant, which serves Scottish and international cuisine in an elegant library setting. A night club, function rooms, shops, food outlets, and an indoor leisure club are also available.
197 en suite (bth/shr) (20 fmly) No smoking in 56 bedrooms CTV in all bedrooms STV Lift Night porter Indoor swimming pool (heated) Squash Snooker Sauna Solarium Gym Pool table Jacuzzi/spa Table tennis Dance studio Creche Wkly live entertainment ch fac Xmas Scottish & French Cuisine V meals Coffee am Tea pm No smoking area in restaurant Last d 10.30pm
ROOMS: (incl. bkfst) s £107-£113; d £166-£176 **LB**
OFF-PEAK: (incl. bkfst) s £58-£76; d £116-£152
MEALS: Lunch fr £9.95&alc High tea fr £8.50 Dinner fr £17&alc
CONF: Thtr 300 Class 120 Board 60 Del from £133
CARDS:

★★★ 64% **Swallow Royal Scot**

111 Glasgow Rd EH12 8NF (on A8 on western outskirts of city) ☎ 0131 334 9191
FAX 0131 316 4507
Conveniently situated for both the airport and city centre, this purpose-built hotel offers well equipped accommodation which is divided between two wings. The rooms are well appointed, although there are a small number in the North wing which are waiting to be refurbished. The public areas include a comfortable Club bar, a restaurant serving carvery and carte meals and a hairdressing salon, all of which lead off the impressive marbled reception foyer. The hotel also has a number

contd.

of very stylish, well equipped meeting rooms. The service provided by the smartly uniformed staff is friendly and helpful.
259 en suite (bth/shr) (17 fmly) No smoking in 102 bedrooms CTV in all bedrooms STV Lift Night porter 300P Indoor swimming pool (heated) Sauna Solarium Gym Jacuzzi/spa Steam room Xmas International Cuisine V meals Coffee am Tea pm Last d 10pm
ROOMS: (incl. bkfst) s £95-£105; d £120-£135 * **LB**
MEALS: Lunch £14-£16 Dinner £21.50*
CONF: Thtr 350 Class 120 Board 45 Del from £120
CARDS:

★★★ 77% **Norton House**
Ingliston EH28 8LX (off A8, 5m W of city centre)
☎ 0131 333 1275 FAX 0131 333 5305
Smart, well equipped accommodation is provided at this much extended Victorian property set in over fifty acres of parkland to the west of the city, close to the airport and the motorway network. The well appointed public areas, which are dressed with fresh flowers and where many of the original features of the house have been retained, include comfortable lounge areas, the Oak bar and the Conservatory restaurant where new head chef Ivor Clark produces a good range of carefully prepared dishes. A recent meal inspection began with a well executed chicken and bacon terrine served with a Kumquat chutney, which was followed by deliciously fresh and accurately cooked fillets of Bream served on a bed of char grilled vegetables. The service in the restaurant is professional and attentive.

47 en suite (bth/shr) (2 fmly) No smoking in 15 bedrooms CTV in all bedrooms STV Night porter 200P Archery Laser clay pigeon shooting ch fac Xmas International Cuisine V meals Coffee am Tea pm Last d 10pm
ROOMS: (incl. bkfst) s £105-£140; d £120-£165 * **LB**
MEALS: Lunch £14.95-£15.50&alc High tea fr £8.50 Dinner fr £22.50&alc*
CONF: Thtr 300 Class 100 Board 60 Del from £135
CARDS:

★★★ 71% **Channings**
South Learmonth Gardens EH4 1EZ
☎ 0131 315 2226 FAX 0131 332 9631
Closed 24-26 Dec
This discreet club-like hotel situated in a quiet cobbled terrace, is made up of five Edwardian townhouses and the character is retained throughout. Welcoming lounges have attractive fireplaces with tiled surrounds and a comfortable, elegant atmosphere. The bedrooms vary in size, with all offering good facilities and additional items to give an individual signature. Downstairs in the smartly decorated brasserie, fresh Scottish produce is served in imaginative and innovative combinations by efficient and friendly staff.
48 rms (47 bth/shr) CTV in all bedrooms STV No dogs Lift Night porter Scottish & French Cuisine V meals Coffee am Tea pm No smoking in restaurant Last d 9.30pm
ROOMS: (incl. bkfst) s £90-£102; d £120-£150 * **LB**
MEALS: Lunch £4-£10 Dinner £18-£22*
CONF: Thtr 35 Board 20
CARDS:

★★★ 70% **King James Thistle**
107 Leith St EH1 3SW ☎ 0131 556 0111
FAX 0131 557 5333

Centrally situated, this modern hotel offers a good standard of accommodation. The executive rooms are particularly smartly appointed: the majority of the other rooms have been refurbished and plans are well advanced for the remainder. Public areas are somewhat restricted, but there is an attractive restaurant with a small adjoining cocktail lounge, and guests have the choice of eating less formally in the St. Jacques Brasserie. A professional standard of service is provided by the friendly and helpful staff. Ask about parking arrangements.

145 en suite (bth/shr) (4 fmly) No smoking in 42 bedrooms CTV in all bedrooms No dogs (ex guide dogs) Lift Night porter 20P Xmas International Cuisine V meals Coffee am Tea pm Last d 10pm
ROOMS: s £70-£110; d £115-£140 * **LB**
OFF-PEAK: (incl. bkfst) s £60-£118; d £118-£140
MEALS: Lunch £12.50-£17.50&alc Dinner £18.50-£19.50&alc*
CONF: Thtr 250 Class 150 Board 40 Del from £110
CARDS:

★★★ 69% **Bruntsfield**
69/74 Bruntsfield Place EH10 4HH (on A702, S of city centre) ☎ 0131 229 1393 FAX 0131 229 5634
This imposing sandstone hotel is sited on the south side of the city opposite Bruntsfield Links, and is convenient for transport in to the city centre. All of the bedrooms have now been refurbished to a high standard and there are plans to add more bedrooms during this year. The Potting Shed restaurant has a friendly atmosphere and offers good value meals, while KB's Bar offers a lively alternative. The staff here are professional and attentive.
50 en suite (bth/shr) (1 fmly) No smoking in 8 bedrooms CTV in all bedrooms STV Lift Night porter 25P Xmas International Cuisine V meals Coffee am Tea pm Last d 9.30pm
ROOMS: s £69-£90; d £79-£130 **LB**
OFF-PEAK: s £50-£65; d £65-£78
MEALS: Lunch £6.50-£12 Dinner £16-£18.50
CONF: Thtr 65 Class 25 Board 20 Del from £80
CARDS:

See advertisement on opposite page

★★★ 69% **Malmaison**
1 Tower Place, Leith EH6 7DB ☎ 0131 555 6868 FAX 0131 555 6999
Converted from the Seaman's Mission building, this stylish hotel offers a French influenced brasserie, where traditional Mediterranean cuisine can be enjoyed until late. A sample meal could include seared plum tomatoes on focaccia toast, coq au vin, and a particularly smooth and creamy crème brûlée to finish.
25 en suite (bth/shr) (6 fmly) CTV in all bedrooms STV Lift Night porter 50P No coaches French & Mediterranean Cuisine V meals Coffee am Last d 10.30pm
ROOMS: d £85 *
MEALS: Lunch £15-£25alc Dinner £15-£25alc

CONF: Thtr 25 Class 10 Board 15
CARDS:

★★★67% ***Braid Hills***
134 Braid Rd, Braid Hills EH10 6JD (2.5m S A702, opposite Braid Burn Park) ☎ 0131 447 8888 FAX 0131 452 8477
Situated in a leafy suburb of Edinburgh with panoramic views over the city, this imposing sandstone hotel was originally built to accommodate golfers visiting the nearby Braid Hills Course. There is a choice of restaurants, the newly refurbished dining room making the most of the view, while the Buckstone Bistro serves lighter meals all day. Bedrooms are well equipped, and there is a choice of lounges where guests can relax. Service is traditional and attentive.
68 en suite (bth/shr) (2 fmly) No smoking in 8 bedrooms CTV in all bedrooms STV Night porter 38P Scottish & French Cuisine V meals Coffee am Tea pm Last d 9.30pm
CARDS:

See advertisement on this page

★★★67% ***Edinburgh Capital Moat House***
187 Clermiston Rd EH12 6UG
☎ 0131 535 9988 FAX 0131 334 9712

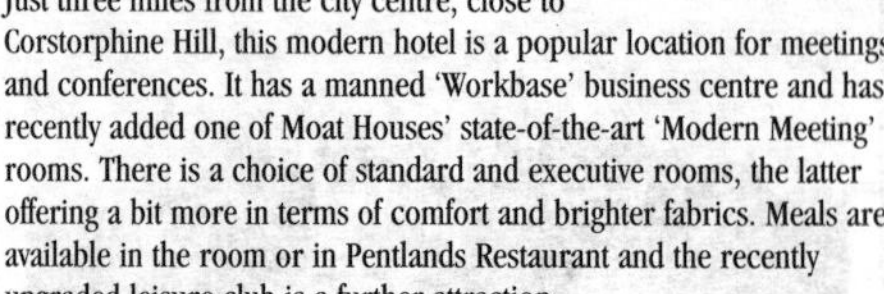

Just three miles from the city centre, close to Corstorphine Hill, this modern hotel is a popular location for meetings and conferences. It has a manned 'Workbase' business centre and has recently added one of Moat Houses' state-of-the-art 'Modern Meeting' rooms. There is a choice of standard and executive rooms, the latter offering a bit more in terms of comfort and brighter fabrics. Meals are available in the room or in Pentlands Restaurant and the recently upgraded leisure club is a further attraction.
111 en suite (bth/shr) (10 fmly) No smoking in 6 bedrooms CTV in all bedrooms Lift Night porter 150P Indoor swimming pool (heated) Sauna Solarium Gym Pool table Jacuzzi/spa Leisure Club steam room Scottish & French Cuisine V meals Coffee am Tea pm Last d 10pm
CARDS:

★★★64% **Barnton Thistle**
Queensferry Rd, Barnton EH4 6AS
☎ 0131 339 1144 FAX 0131 339 5521
This distinctive and well appointed hotel is ideally positioned on the A90, exactly four miles from the city centre, the Forth road bridge and the airport. The comfortable public rooms include a recently refurbished cocktail bar and Crichton's restaurant where guests also have the choice of eating less formally. The bedrooms are well equipped, although some rooms are more compact than others. The hotel also has a well equipped meeting room.
50 en suite (bth/shr) (9 fmly) CTV in all bedrooms STV Lift Night porter 100P Sauna Xmas International Cuisine V meals Coffee am Tea pm Last d 9.45pm
ROOMS: s £85-£95; d £95-£105 * **LB**
MEALS: Lunch £7.50-£12 Dinner £16.95*
CONF: Thtr 150 Class 60 Board 50 Del from £99
CARDS:

★★★63% **Kings Manor**
100 Milton Rd East EH15 2NP
☎ 0131 669 0444 FAX 0131 669 6650
Conveniently situated near to the city bypass, this former laird's house has been sympathetically extended and is now a comfortable, family owned hotel. Public areas include a choice of bars, one a former chapel and full of character. Bedrooms are modern in style and well equipped. A good range of meals is available in the carvery restaurant.
69 en suite (bth/shr) (8 fmly) CTV in all bedrooms STV Lift 100P Scottish & French Cuisine V meals Coffee am Tea pm Last d 9.30pm
ROOMS: (incl. bkfst) s £55-£79; d £74-£110
MEALS: Lunch £6.80-£23.45alc Dinner £9.30-£25.45alc*
CONF: Thtr 140 Class 70 Board 70 Del from £70
CARDS:

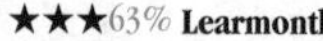

★★★63% **Learmonth**
Learmonth Ter EH4 1PW (just off A90 (Forth Road Bridge road)) ☎ 0131 343 2671 FAX 0131 315 2232
Situated in a Georgian terrace on the northwest fringe of the city centre, this business, conference and tourist hotel has bright, tasteful bedrooms, mostly of a good size. There is a lively brasserie-style bar on the ground floor and a restaurant downstairs. The young staff are obliging and attentive.
62 en suite (bth/shr) (10 fmly) No smoking in 9 bedrooms CTV in all bedrooms Lift Night porter 6P Xmas V meals Coffee am Tea pm Last d 9.30pm
ROOMS: (incl. bkfst) s £80-£85; d £100-£115 **LB**
OFF-PEAK: (incl. bkfst & dinner) s £85-£90; d £128-£145
MEALS: Lunch 95p&alc High tea £5.95-£8.95 Dinner £16.50-£18.50&alc
CONF: Thtr 200 Class 70 Board 80 Del from £70
CARDS:

★★★63% **Roxburghe**
Charlotte Square EH2 4HG
☎ 0131 225 3921 FAX 0131 220 2518
This long established hotel is situated in the oldest part of the New Town at the west end of the city, and is convenient for both city centre shopping and tourist attractions. The style of service is traditional and highly commendable, and the lobby and lounge have a relaxing atmosphere. The elegant Consort Restaurant offers good value meals, particularly for those dining early in the evening, and the cocktail bar is popular with locals as well as guests. Bedrooms vary in size.
75 en suite (bth/shr) CTV in all bedrooms Lift Night porter Xmas Scottish & French Cuisine V meals Coffee am Tea pm No smoking area in restaurant Last d 9.30pm
ROOMS: (incl. bkfst) s £77.50-£99; d £125-£140 * **LB**
OFF-PEAK: (incl. bkfst) s fr £59.50; d fr £75
MEALS: Lunch £8-£12.50 High tea £6-£9.50 Dinner £16.50-£19.50&alc
CONF: Thtr 200 Class 100 Board 60 Del from £70
CARDS:

★★★62% **Holiday Inn Garden Court**
107 Queensferry Rd EH4 3HL (on the A90 approx 1m from city centre)
☎ 0131 332 2442 FAX 0131 332 3408
Popular with tour groups, this bright modern hotel offers competitively priced accommodation in attractive, well equipped bedrooms, many of which enjoy panoramic views of the city. Airy public areas are comfortable if fairly functional and include a fitness room, lounge bar and restaurant which is open for breakfast and dinner.
119 en suite (bth/shr) (53 fmly) No smoking in 59 bedrooms CTV in all bedrooms STV Lift Night porter 80P Gym Xmas International Cuisine V meals Coffee am Tea pm No smoking in restaurant Last d 10pm
ROOMS: s £72.50-£77.50; d £74.50-£84.50 * **LB**
OFF-PEAK: d £69
MEALS: Sunday Lunch £4.95-£14 High tea fr £2alc Dinner £12.95-£15.95&alc*
CONF: Thtr 60 Class 25 Board 30 Del from £72
CARDS:

★★★59% ***Donmaree***
21 Mayfield Gardens EH9 2BX ☎ 0131 667 3641 FAX 0131 667 9130
Located on the south side of the city on the A7, this detached Victorian house offers accommodation in bedrooms of various sizes and styles. There is a comfortable first floor lounge as well as a conservatory at the rear of the hotel, while the restaurant and bar retain an old world elegance.
15 en suite (bth/shr) 2 annexe en suite (bth/shr) No smoking in 2 bedrooms CTV in all bedrooms No dogs (ex guide dogs) Night

porter 6P Scottish & French Cuisine V meals Coffee am Tea pm Last d 10pm
CARDS:

★★★58% **Old Waverley**
43 Princes St EH2 2BY (in the centre of city, opposite the Scott Monument) ☎ 0131 556 4648 FAX 0131 557 6316

Excellently positioned for the station and shopping in Princes Street; this historic building has well equipped bedrooms, varying in size and outlook. The non-smoking restaurant has a choice of carvery or a small a la carte menu and the intimate bar and lounge looks over Princes Street Gardens and the historic Edinburgh skyline.
66 en suite (bth/shr) (6 fmly) No smoking in 8 bedrooms CTV in all bedrooms STV Lift Night porter Xmas International Cuisine V meals Coffee am Tea pm No smoking in restaurant Last d 9.30pm
ROOMS: (incl. bkfst) s £85-£90; d £136-£144 * **LB**
MEALS: Lunch £7 Dinner £16&alc*
CONF: Thtr 50 Class 20 Board 26 Del from £84
CARDS: 

★★★58% **Quality Commodore**
West Marine Dr, Cramond Foreshore EH4 5EP
☎ 0131 336 1700 FAX 0131 336 4934

This much extended hotel where the atmosphere is friendly and relaxed enjoys the most marvellous views over the Firth of Forth. Bedrooms vary in size and style, although all are well equipped. Guests have the use of a small leisure centre and although the public areas are somewhat limited, they are comfortably furnished. Guests can enjoy the view best from the first-floor restaurant.
87 en suite (bth/shr) (6 fmly) No smoking in 30 bedrooms CTV in all bedrooms STV Lift Night porter P Indoor swimming pool (heated) Sauna Solarium Gym Jacuzzi/spa Xmas English & Continental Cuisine V meals Coffee am No smoking area in restaurant Last d 9.30pm
ROOMS: s £67.50; d £87.50 **LB**
MEALS: Lunch £7.95-£9.95&alc Dinner £13.50&alc
CONF: Thtr 200 Class 100 Board 50 Del from £82.50
CARDS: 

★★67% **Allison House**
15/17 Mayfield Gardens EH9 2AX (1m S of city centre on A701)
☎ 0131 667 8049 FAX 0131 667 5001
This family-run hotel has a friendly, informal atmosphere created by the proprietors and their staff, who offer a warm welcome and a high standard of hospitality throughout. The city centre is easily accessible as the hotel is on the main bus routes to Princes Street. Bedrooms are comfortable and well equipped, while the cosy residents' lounge has an honesty bar, and the restaurant provides a good range of home-cooked dishes.
23 rms (21 shr) (5 fmly) CTV in all bedrooms 12P ch fac V meals Coffee am Tea pm Last d 9pm
ROOMS: (incl. bkfst) s £27.50-£42; d £55-£84 **LB**
OFF-PEAK: (incl. bkfst) s £25-£32; d £50-£64

MEALS: Lunch £6.95 Dinner £6.95-£18alc
CONF: Thtr 25 Class 12 Board 16 Del from £50
CARDS:  
See advertisement on this page

★★66% ***Harp Toby***
St John's Rd, Corstorphine EH12 8AX (3.5m W)
☎ 0131 334 4750 FAX 0131 334 6941

TOBY

Modern, well equipped bedrooms are the hallmarks of this friendly hotel which is very conveniently situated beside the A8, between the city centre and the airport. All the rooms are attractively decorated, although some are rather compact. The public areas include a newly refurbished lounge bar and a pleasant restaurant where an extensive range of dishes is available, at both lunch and dinner.
24 en suite (bth/shr) (2 fmly) No smoking in 9 bedrooms CTV in all bedrooms No dogs (ex guide dogs) Night porter 50P V meals Coffee am Tea pm Last d 10pm
CARDS:

★★65% Murrayfield
18 Corstorphine Rd EH12 6HN ☎ 0131 337 1844 FAX 0131 346 8159
Closed 2 days Xmas & 2 days New Year
This friendly business and tourist hotel is situated close to the national rugby stadium and this sporting theme is evident in the newly refurbished bar. The well equipped bedrooms vary in style, from the practical ones in the main house to the smarter style of those in the lodge annexe. The attractive restaurant offers A Taste of Scotland menu and hearty snacks are available all day in the bar and lounge.
23 en suite (bth/shr) 10 annexe en suite (shr) (1 fmly) CTV in all bedrooms Night porter 30P Scottish & European Cuisine Coffee am Last d 9pm
ROOMS: (incl. bkfst) s £52.50-£57.50; d £70-£75 * **LB**
MEALS: Lunch fr £10.50 Dinner fr £14.75alc*
CARDS:

★★64% Rothesay

8 Rothesay Place EH3 7SL (follow M8 into Edinburgh to the Haymarket Station, turn left at traffic lights into Palmerston Place, Rothesay Place is second on right)
☎ 0131 225 4125 FAX 0131 220 4350
This family run hotel is situated in a residential area in the city's West End, a short walk from the centre. In addition to the good value, practical bedrooms in the main hotel, a new wing called the Clan Chieftain's Town House has recently opened, with luxurious accommodation and many modern facilities. There is a cosy bar and comfortable lobby lounge, and the cheerfully decorated restaurant serves a wide selection of home-made Scottish and European cuisine.
46 rms (40 bth/shr) (3 fmly) CTV in all bedrooms Lift Night porter Scottish & French Cuisine V meals Coffee am Tea pm No smoking in restaurant Last d 8.50pm
ROOMS: (incl. bkfst) s £30-£70; d £80-£150
OFF-PEAK: (incl. bkfst) s £30-£65; d £65-£130
MEALS: Dinner £9-£22alc*
CARDS:

★★64% Thrums Private Hotel
14 Minto St EH9 1RQ ☎ 0131 667 5545 & 0131 667 8545
FAX 0131 667 8707
Closed Xmas
Friendly and informal service is provided at this family-run hotel. Licensed to serve drinks to residents and diners only, it has a small bar, but guests will be more comfortable in the lounge. Bedrooms are located in both the hotel and an adjacent house. The former are cheerful and modern while the latter are quite magnificent, being well proportioned and decorated in period style.
6 en suite (bth/shr) 8 annexe rms (7 bth/shr) (5 fmly) CTV in all bedrooms 10P V meals Coffee am Tea pm Last d 8.30pm
ROOMS: (incl. bkfst) s £35-£45; d £60-£70 * **LB**
OFF-PEAK: (incl. bkfst) s £30-£40; d £60-£65
MEALS: Lunch £3-£6&alc High tea £3.50-£4.50&alc Dinner £7-£10&alc
CARDS:

★★63% Iona
Strathearn Place EH9 2AL ☎ 0131 447 6264 & 0131 447 5050
FAX 0131 452 8574
Located in a quiet residential area on the south side of the city, this family-run hotel offers good-value accommodation for both tourists and business travellers. The bedrooms are freshly decorated with bright fabrics, while the popular public bar serves bar meals to supplement the restaurant menus.
17 rms (15 bth/shr) (3 fmly) CTV in all bedrooms 20P No coaches V meals Coffee am Last d 9pm
ROOMS: (incl. bkfst) s £30-£50; d £66-£85 **LB**
OFF-PEAK: (incl. bkfst) s £25-£50; d £56-£85
MEALS: Lunch fr £6.50 Dinner fr £12.95&alc*
CONF: Thtr 40 Board 22 Del from £58
CARDS:

★★59% Orwell Lodge
29 Polwarth Ter EH11 1NH ☎ 0131 229 1044 FAX 0131 228 9492
Closed 25-26 Dec
This Victorian mansion is situated in a quiet residential area in the south west of the city, and convenient for transport in to the city centre. Bedrooms offer good facilities for both the business guest and tourist, while the lounge bar is popular with locals. The smart function room is an attractive setting for weddings and conferences.
10 en suite (bth/shr) No smoking in all bedrooms CTV in all bedrooms No dogs (ex guide dogs) 40P Wkly live entertainment International Cuisine V meals Coffee am Tea pm No smoking in restaurant Last d 8.30pm
ROOMS: (incl. bkfst) s £45-£49; d £70-£80 * **LB**
MEALS: Lunch £12-£15&alc High tea £4-£6alc Dinner £10-£18alc*
CONF: Thtr 250 Class 120 Board 80
CARDS:

TOWN HOUSE HOTEL

The Howard
Great King St EH3 6QH (turn off Princes St into Frederick St for 0.5m and turn right into Great King St. Go past traffic lights, hotel on left)
☎ 0131 557 3500 FAX 0131 557 6515
Quietly situated amongst Edinburgh's elegant Georgian gardens and terraces, this town house hotel offers an ideal city centre location for both the business guest and tourist alike. Bedrooms are sumptuously furnished, with quality touches throughout; bathrooms are equally impressive, many with double sinks and separate shower cubicles. The drawing room offers the opportunity to relax, with deep, plush seats and fresh flowers. The restaurant is situated in the basement and is due to be re-designed, with both new décor and menus proposed. The high standards of cuisine will, of course, remain.
16 en suite (bth/shr) CTV in all bedrooms STV No dogs (ex guide dogs) Lift Night porter Air conditioning 12P No children V meals Coffee am Tea pm No smoking in restaurant Last d 10pm
ROOMS: (incl. bkfst) s £110; d £195 * **LB**
MEALS: Lunch £12-£18alc Dinner £18-£25alc
CONF: Thtr 45 Class 25 Board 25 Del £160
CARDS:

Forte Posthouse Edinburgh
FORTE Posthouse
Corstorphine Rd EH12 6UA (adjacent to Edinburgh Zoo) ☎ 0131 334 0390 FAX 0131 334 9237
Suitable for both the business and leisure traveller, this bright hotel provides modern accommodation in well equipped bedrooms with en suite bathrooms. For more details about Forte Posthouse hotels, consult the Contents page for the section on Hotel Groups.
204 en suite (bth/shr)
CONF: Thtr 120 Class 80 Board 60

Hilton National Edinburgh

69 Belford Rd EH4 3DG ☎ 0131 332 2545
FAX 0131 332 3805
This is a bright, modern hotel, with an informal restaurant, aimed at both the business and leisure guest. All bedrooms have en suite bathrooms and a range of modern facilities. For more information about Hilton National hotels, consult the Contents page under Hotel Groups.
144 en suite (bth/shr)
ROOMS: s fr £97.50; d fr £115.50 *
CONF: Thtr 120 Class 60 Board 45

Travel Inn

288 Willowbrae Rd EH8 7NG (2m from City east)
☎ 0131 661 3396 FAX 0131 652 2789
Purpose-built accommodation, offering spacious, well equipped bedrooms, all with en suite bathrooms. Meals may be taken at the nearby family restaurant. For more information about Travel Inns, consult the Contents page under Hotel Groups.
39 en suite (bth/shr)
ROOMS: d £35.50 *

Travel Inn (City Centre)

1 Morrison St EH3 8DN ☎ 01582 414341
FAX 01582 400024
Purpose-built accommodation, offering spacious, well equipped bedrooms, all with en suite bathrooms. Meals may be taken at the nearby family restaurant. For more information about Travel Inns, consult the Contents page under Hotel Groups.
128 en suite (bth/shr)
ROOMS: (incl. bkfst) d £35.50 *

Travelodge

Dreghorn Link EH13 9QR (6m S, A720 Ring Rd South) ☎ 0131 441 4296 FAX 0131 441 4296
This modern building offers accommodation in smart, spacious and well equipped bedrooms, suitable for family use, and all with en suite bathrooms. Meals may be taken at the nearby family restaurant. For information on room rates and to make a booking, call Roomline free of charge on 0800 850950. For more details about Travelodge, consult the Contents page under Hotel Groups.
40 en suite (bth/shr)

○ **Apex**
31/35 Grassmarket EH1 2HY ☎ 0131 300 3456 FAX 0131 220 5345
99 en suite (bth/shr) No smoking in 78 bedrooms CTV in all bedrooms STV No dogs Lift Night porter 60P V meals Coffee am Tea pm Last d 10pm
ROOMS: d £59.95
MEALS: Lunch £6.95 High tea £6.95 Dinner £11.95
CONF: Thtr 300 Class 150 Board 30 Del from £85
CARDS:

EDZELL Angus Map 15 NO66

★★★62% **Glenesk**
High St DD9 7TF (off A90 just after Brechin Bypass)
☎ 01356 648319 FAX 01356 647333
This family-run hotel beside the golf course is popular not only with golfers, but all types of guests. Public areas include two attractive lounges offering traditional comforts, and bedrooms are comfortable and well equipped.
25 rms (24 bth/shr) (5 fmly) CTV in all bedrooms P No coaches Indoor swimming pool (heated) Golf 18 Snooker Sauna Solarium Gym Pool table Croquet lawn Jacuzzi/spa V meals Coffee am Tea pm
CONF: Board 30
CARDS:

ELGIN Moray Map 15 NJ26

★★★ 73% **Mansion House**

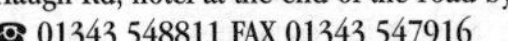

The Haugh IV30 1AW (in Elgin turn off the A96 into Haugh Rd, hotel at the end of the road by the river)
☎ 01343 548811 FAX 01343 547916
Set quietly in gardens by the River Lossie, this turreted, baronial mansion is still within walking distance of the town centre. Facilities include a well equipped leisure centre, a hairdressing and beauty

contd.

salon, a cosy wee bar and an elegant lounge. Meals are available in the restaurant, which offers a contemporary style of cooking from a choice of menus, and in the less formal bistro. Bedrooms come in a variety of styles and sizes, all well equipped and many with four-poster beds.
22 en suite (bth/shr) (3 fmly) CTV in all bedrooms STV No dogs (ex guide dogs) Night porter 150P Indoor swimming pool (heated) Snooker Sauna Solarium Gym Jacuzzi/spa Hairdresser Beauty therapist Steam room Xmas V meals Coffee am Tea pm No smoking in restaurant Last d 9pm
ROOMS: (incl. bkfst) s fr £75; d fr £110 * **LB**
MEALS: Lunch fr £12.95&alc High tea fr £8.50 Dinner fr £23.50&alc*
CONF: Thtr 200 Class 150 Board 50
CARDS:

See advertisement on opposite page

★★★ 70% **Mansefield House**
Mayne Rd IV30 1NY (Entering Elgin on A96 from Inverness side, head for town centre. At roundabout,take a right turn. At mini roundabout we are on the right) ☎ 01343 540883 FAX 01343 552491
Lying in a residential area close to the town centre, this friendly family-run hotel has been sympathetically converted from a Georgian manse. The individually designed bedrooms come in a variety of sizes, all being very well equipped and having smart modern bathrooms. There is a cosy clubby cocktail bar and a stylish restaurant where fresh seafood features prominently on its extensive menu.
20 en suite (bth/shr) (3 fmly) No smoking in 5 bedrooms CTV in all bedrooms STV No dogs (ex guide dogs) Lift 57P No coaches Xmas V meals Coffee am Tea pm No smoking in restaurant
ROOMS: (incl. bkfst) s £60; d £60-£80 *
CARDS:

★★ 67% **Laichmoray**
Station Rd IV30 1QR (opposite the railway station)
☎ 01343 540045 FAX 01343 540055
Situated close to the railway station on the south side of town, this long-established family-run hotel offers well equipped bedrooms in a variety of styles. Service is friendly throughout and a good range of meals is available in both the bar and restaurant.
35 rms (34 bth/shr) (5 fmly) CTV in all bedrooms 60P Pool table Darts Xmas V meals Coffee am Tea pm Last d 9.15pm
ROOMS: (incl. bkfst) s £48; d £72 * **LB**
OFF-PEAK: (incl. bkfst) s £38; d £60
MEALS: Lunch fr £8.95 High tea £8-£12.50 Dinner £11.85-£28.50alc*
CONF: Thtr 200 Class 160 Board 40
CARDS:

ERISKA Argyll & Bute Map 10 NM94

★★★★ 67% ***Isle of Eriska***
PA37 1SD ☎ 01631 720371 FAX 01631 720531
Closed Dec-mid Mar
PRIDE OF BRITAIN MEMBER
Situated in splendid isolation on its own island, this baronial mansion has been run by the Buchanan-Smith family for over 25 years and is now ably managed by Beppo, whose foresight has led to several new developments over the past few years. Guests are free to roam on the island but there is also a leisure centre with a good sized pool and outdoor activities could include golf, tennis or croquet. Bedrooms vary in size, with the largest being on the first floor, though the second floor rooms are cosy and have delightful new bathrooms. Fresh flowers, books, fluffy robes and mini first aid kits are just some of the thoughtful touches. There is a choice of elegant lounges, and in the dining room chef Ewan Clark offers a menu of both traditional and innovative dishes which have earned him the award of two AA rosettes. The highlight of a recent visit had to be watching a pair of badgers feeding on milk and nuts just outside the bar's patio doors, a unique sight!

16 en suite (bth/shr) (1 fmly) CTV in all bedrooms Night porter 36P No coaches Golf 9 Tennis (hard) Riding Croquet lawn Clay pigeon shooting Watersports Last d 9pm
CARDS:

ERSKINE Renfrewshire Map 11 NS47

Forte Posthouse Glasgow/Erskine
North Barr PA8 6AN (off A726) ☎ 0141 812 0123
FAX 0141 812 7642
FORTE Posthouse
Suitable for both the business and leisure traveller, this bright hotel provides modern accommodation in well equipped bedrooms with en suite bathrooms. For more details about Forte Posthouse hotels, consult the Contents page for the section on Hotel Groups.
166 en suite (bth/shr)
ROOMS: d £49-£69 *
CONF: Thtr 600 Class 400 Board 40 Del £99

FALKIRK Falkirk Map 11 NS88

★★ 60% **Comfort Friendly Inn**
Manor St FK1 1NT ☎ 01324 624066
FAX 01324 611785
Situated in the town centre adjoining a shopping mall, this commercial hotel provides functional accommodation, friendly willing service, its own car park and a number of meeting and function rooms. There are good views from the upper floors of the town and the surrounding countryside.
33 en suite (bth/shr) (5 fmly) No smoking in 16 bedrooms CTV in all bedrooms STV Lift Night porter Air conditioning 17P Gym Xmas V meals Coffee am Tea pm No smoking area in restaurant Last d 9.30pm
ROOMS: s £38.50-£49.50; d £38.50-£49.50 **LB**
MEALS: Lunch £7.95-£9.95&alc Dinner £9.75&alc
CONF: Thtr 200 Class 100 Board 87 Del from £65
CARDS:

FORFAR Angus Map 15 NO45

★★★ 64% **Idvies House**
Letham DD8 2QJ (2m outside Letham village, from B9128)
☎ 01307 818787 FAX 01307 818933
Closed 24-30 Dec & 1-2 Jan
A delightful Victorian hotel with an authentic Scottish country house atmosphere. Bedrooms successfully combine period charm with modern equipment, and are mainly spacious and very well furnished. The bar features an impressive range of malt whiskies, and the dinner menu includes A Taste of Scotland dishes.
10 en suite (bth/shr) (1 fmly) CTV in all bedrooms 60P No coaches Squash Snooker Croquet lawn Scottish & French Cuisine V meals Last d 9pm
ROOMS: (incl. bkfst) s fr £50; d fr £68 **LB**
OFF-PEAK: (incl. bkfst) s fr £40; d fr £55

MEALS: Lunch fr £10alc Dinner fr £19.50
CARDS:

FORRES Moray Map 14 NJ05

★★★ 71% **Knockomie**

Grantown Rd IV36 0SG (S on A940 to Grantonn)
☎ 01309 673146 FAX 01309 673290
(Rosettes awarded for dinner only)
This sympathetically extended 19th century Scottish country villa is set in four acres of its own grounds, just south of the town. Most of the bedrooms are furnished with impressive antiques which reflect the period of the house, while some also have four poster or half tester beds. A new bistro bar offers a lighter menu than the short but imaginative dinner table d'hÙte, which uses the best of Moray produce to create some memorable dishes. There are also several private dining rooms available, while the comfortable lounge has a good range of games and the cosy cocktail bar offers a good selection of malts, many from the immediate area.
14 en suite (bth/shr) (1 fmly) No smoking in 3 bedrooms CTV in all bedrooms STV 45P Putting green ch fac Xmas European Cuisine V meals Coffee am Tea pm No smoking in restaurant Last d 9pm
ROOMS: (incl. bkfst) s £71-£104; d £83-£138 **LB**
OFF-PEAK: (incl. bkfst) s fr £45; d fr £60
MEALS: Lunch £15-£20 Dinner £26&alc
CONF: Thtr 40 Class 20 Board 20 Del from £124
CARDS:

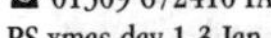

★★ 69% **Ramnee**

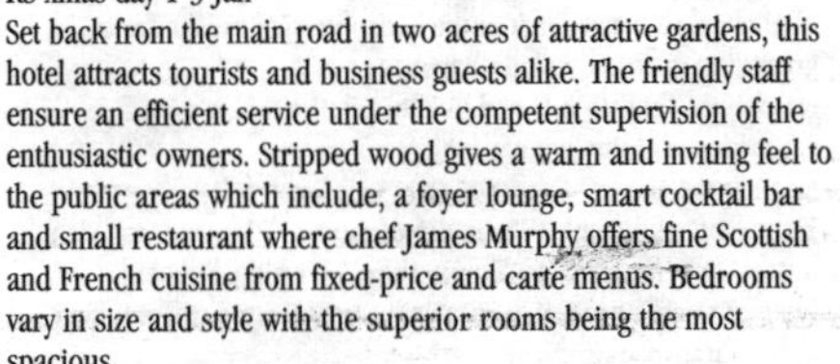

Victoria Rd IV36 0BN (turn off A96 at roundabout on eastern side of Forres, hotel 200yds on right)
☎ 01309 672410 FAX 01309 673392
RS xmas day 1-3 Jan
Set back from the main road in two acres of attractive gardens, this hotel attracts tourists and business guests alike. The friendly staff ensure an efficient service under the competent supervision of the enthusiastic owners. Stripped wood gives a warm and inviting feel to the public areas which include, a foyer lounge, smart cocktail bar and small restaurant where chef James Murphy offers fine Scottish and French cuisine from fixed-price and carte menus. Bedrooms vary in size and style with the superior rooms being the most spacious.
20 en suite (bth/shr) (4 fmly) CTV in all bedrooms STV 50P Scottish & French Cuisine V meals Coffee am Tea pm No smoking in restaurant Last d 9pm
ROOMS: (incl. bkfst) s £52.50-£67.50; d £79-£99 **LB**
OFF-PEAK: (incl. bkfst & dinner) s £55-£75; d £95-£115
MEALS: Lunch £11 High tea £8.25-£19alc Dinner £22&alc
CONF: Thtr 100 Class 30 Board 45 Del £90
CARDS:

See advertisement on this page

FORT AUGUSTUS Highland Map 14 NH30

★★ 69% The Brae
PH32 4DG (Turn left off A82 just before leaving Fort Augustus heading North to Inverness.) ☎ 01320 366289 FAX 01320 366702
Closed Nov-Feb
(Rosette awarded for dinner only)
Many guests return year after year to Andrew and Mari Reive's comfortable small hotel which, from its elevated position off the A82 at the north end of the village, enjoys splendid views of the surrounding hills. Tastefully decorated and comfortably furnished bedrooms, some non smoking, offer the expected amenities apart from telephones. There is a relaxing verandah lounge and a cosy bar, while the attractive dining room is the appropriate setting for Mari's carefully prepared dinners which are based on the best ingredients from Scotland's larder.
7 rms (6 bth/shr) No smoking in 5 bedrooms CTV in all bedrooms 12P No coaches No children 7yrs International Cuisine No smoking in restaurant Last d 8.30pm
ROOMS: (incl. bkfst & dinner) s fr £48; d £96-£106 * **LB**
MEALS: Dinner £22-£25*
CARDS:

★★ 67% Lovat Arms

PH32 4DU (off A82) ☎ 01320 366206 & 366204
FAX 01320 366677
The Lovat Arms enjoys a spectacular location surrounded by Great Glen scenery close to Loch Ness and is an ideal base for exploring the Highlands. It is a friendly family run hotel and offers comfortable bedrooms in a mixture of styles, all well furnished with modern amenities. Public areas include a choice of relaxing lounges, a comfortable bar and a traditional dining room.
21 en suite (bth/shr) (4 fmly) CTV in all bedrooms 60P Pool table Putting green Scottish & French Cuisine V meals Coffee am Last d 8.30pm
ROOMS: (incl. bkfst) s £33.50-£38.50; d £59-£72 **LB**
OFF-PEAK: (incl. bkfst) s £29.50-£33.50
MEALS: Bar Lunch £10-£20alc Dinner £18.50-£21
CARDS:

★★ 64% Inchnacardoch Lodge
Loch Ness PH32 4BL (N of village, off A82) ☎ 01320 366258
Comfortably furnished accommodation is provided at this holiday hotel which enjoys the most wonderful views from its slightly elevated position above Loch Ness. The rooms, including family rooms, are freshly decorated and all are equipped with modern facilities. On cooler days a real fire is lit in the comfortable lounge, which also enjoys the most magnificent views as does the spacious dining room, where a short choice of dishes is available.
12 en suite (bth/shr) (4 fmly) No smoking in all bedrooms CTV in all bedrooms No dogs (ex guide dogs) 40P Fishing No children 10 Xmas International Cuisine V meals Coffee am Tea pm No smoking in restaurant Last d 8.30pm
ROOMS: (incl. bkfst) s £40-£50; d £60-£76 * **LB**
OFF-PEAK: (incl. bkfst) s £30-£45; d £55-£60
MEALS: Lunch fr £7.50 High tea £4.50 Dinner £18
CONF: Class 20 Board 12
CARDS:

FORTINGALL Perthshire & Kinross Map 14 NN74

★★ 59% Fortingall
PH15 2NQ (Take B846 out of Aberfeldy for 6 miles, then turn left (Fortingall) for 3 miles. Hotel is central in village)
☎ 01887 830367 & 830368 FAX 01887 830367
Closed Nov-Feb
This old-fashioned family-run hotel forms the focal point of the attractive conservation village of Fortingall. Bedrooms, though traditional, offer all modern facilities, and a single food menu offers a choice of bar meals and dinner. The hotel is especially popular with tourists and anglers.
9 en suite (bth/shr) (3 fmly) CTV in all bedrooms 20P Fishing Sailing, Pony trekking ch fac V meals Coffee am Tea pm Last d 8.50pm
ROOMS: (incl. bkfst) s £28-£30; d £46-£56 *
MEALS: Lunch £9-£12.50alc Dinner £12.50-£18alc*
CARDS:

FORT WILLIAM Highland Map 14 NN17

RED STAR HOTEL

★★★★ Inverlochy Castle
Torlundy PH33 6SN (3m NE A82)
☎ 01397 702177 FAX 01397 702953
Closed Dec-1 Mar

RELAIS & CHATEAUX. Relais Gourmands

Standing in 500 acres of grounds, in the foothills of Ben Nevis, this fine Victorian building complements its wonderful setting. Public rooms include the Great Hall with its beautiful frescoed ceiling, crystal chandeliers and handsome staircase, an elegant drawing room and two dining rooms. Chef Simon Haigh may be classically trained but this does not prevent him from taking note of modern trends; thus a tomato and filo tart with a salad of cured ham and basil oil sits alongside an accomplished ballotine of foie gras with Madeira jelly. This could be followed by roast duck with lentils and cider fondant potatoes or turbot with roasted Loch Linnhe prawns and a Noilly Prat sauce. Service is suitably polished and welcoming under the direction of Michael Leonard. Each of the bedrooms is furnished with great taste in restful colour schemes and crisp linen, fluffy towels and quality toiletries are evidence of the luxury which features throughout.

17 en suite (bth/shr) CTV in all bedrooms STV No dogs Night porter 18P No coaches Tennis (hard) Fishing Snooker International Cuisine V meals Coffee am Tea pm No smoking in restaurant
ROOMS: (incl. bkfst) s £135-£175; d £240-£280
CARDS:

★★★ 75% Moorings
Banavie PH33 7LY (3m N of Fort William off A830)
☎ 01397 772797 FAX 01397 772441
Closed 22-26 Dec
(Rosettes awarded for dinner only)
This well run hotel stands just north of Fort William in the village of Banavie, alongside 'Neptune's Staircase' (a series of lochs on the

contd.

Caledonian Canal). It has an established reputation for friendly hospitality and the attentive service of the Sinclaire family, but has also become popular for the cuisine of chef Michel Nijsten whose four-course set-price menu offers an imaginative selection of dishes featuring local fish, meat and game together with a good choice of vegetarian fare. The restaurant and an adjacent lounge/function room are both decorated to a Jacobean theme, while the Lower Bar sports an abundance of nautical bric-à-brac. Well equipped bedrooms have modern furnishings and include both a family room and a four-poster.
21 en suite (bth/shr) 3 annexe en suite (shr) (1 fmly) CTV in all bedrooms STV No dogs (ex guide dogs) 60P V meals Coffee am Tea pm No smoking in restaurant Last d 9.30pm
ROOMS: (incl. bkfst) s £44-£75; d £64-£84 **LB**
OFF-PEAK: (incl. bkfst) s £40-£55; d £54-£68
MEALS: Bar Lunch £9-£18.50alc Dinner £23-£27&alc
CARDS:

F

★★★61% **Alexandra**

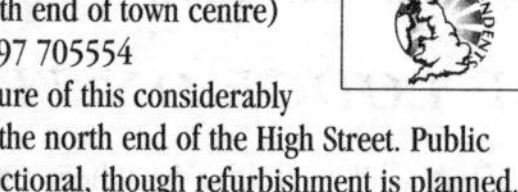

The Parade PH33 6AZ (North end of town centre)
☎ 01397 702241 FAX 01397 705554
Genuine hospitality is a feature of this considerably extended Victorian hotel at the north end of the High Street. Public areas remain somewhat functional, though refurbishment is planned. All day food is available in the coffee shop. Bedrooms range from spacious executive rooms to the more plain and compact standard rooms. Guests are welcome to use the new leisure facilities at the nearby Milton, a sister hotel.
97 en suite (bth/shr) (14 fmly) CTV in all bedrooms Lift Night porter 65P Wkly live entertainment Xmas European Cuisine V meals Coffee am Tea pm No smoking in restaurant
ROOMS: (incl. bkfst) s £59-£69; d £79-£84 * **LB**
OFF-PEAK: (incl. bkfst) s £49-£59; d £69-£79
CONF: Thtr 140 Class 40 Board 26 Del from £49
CARDS:

★★★56% **Mercury**

Achintore Rd PH33 6RW (just south of Fort William centre) ☎ 01397 703117 FAX 01397 700550
Set beside the A82 to the south of town this modern, purpose built hotel enjoys the most marvellous views of Loch Linnhe and the hills beyond. Newly refurbished and smartly appointed bedrooms are available on the ground and first floors, and a programme of refurbishment for the other floors was in hand at the time of our last visit. The open-plan public areas include a lounge bar and carvery restaurant.
86 en suite (bth/shr) (12 fmly) No smoking in 2 bedrooms CTV in all bedrooms Lift Night porter 60P Sauna Pool table Wkly live entertainment Xmas British Cuisine V meals Coffee am Tea pm No smoking in restaurant Last d 9pm
ROOMS: (incl. bkfst) s £39-£70; d £78-£95 * **LB**
OFF-PEAK: (incl. bkfst) s £30-£70; d £60-£95
MEALS: Bar Lunch £3-£9 Dinner £12-£18.50*
CONF: Thtr 60 Class 40 Board 30 Del from £58
CARDS:

★★69% **Nevis Bank**

Belford Rd PH33 6BY (on A82, at junc to Glen Nevis)
☎ 01397 705721 FAX 01397 706275
Situated on the outskirts of the town at the foot of the access road to Ben Nevis, this privately owned hotel offers traditional highland hospitality, with the welcoming staff being both attentive and friendly. Bedrooms are well equipped and many have recently been enhanced with co-ordinating fabrics. There is a choice of two bars and there is also a leisure suite comprising of a gymnasium, sauna and solarium.
31 en suite (bth/shr) 7 annexe en suite (bth/shr) (2 fmly) CTV in all bedrooms 25P Sauna Solarium Gym Pool table Beauty salon Xmas Scottish & French Cuisine V meals Coffee am Tea pm Last d 9pm
ROOMS: (incl. bkfst) s £43-£49; d £58-£70 **LB**
OFF-PEAK: (incl. bkfst) s £41-£43; d £50-£58
MEALS: Bar Lunch £8-£9.20alc Dinner £15.95-£17.45*
CONF: Thtr 40 Class 20 Board 20 Del from £75
CARDS:

See advertisement on opposite page

★★67% **Grand**

Gordon Square PH33 6DX (on A82 at west end of High Street)
☎ 01397 702928 FAX 01397 702928
Closed Jan
Under the direction of Caroline Haines excellent progress is being made in transforming this long-established business and tourist hotel which stands at the south end of the pedestrianised high street. Most bedrooms have been tastefully refurbished to provide comfortable modern standards and the few remaining rooms should be completed for the 1997 season. Public areas include a choice of non-smoking lounges, a well stocked bar and spacious dining room. Staff are friendly and willing to please.
33 en suite (bth/shr) (4 fmly) CTV in all bedrooms STV Night porter 20P Xmas V meals Coffee am Tea pm No smoking in restaurant Last d 8.30pm
ROOMS: (incl. bkfst) s £25-£39.50; d £50-£90 * **LB**
OFF-PEAK: (incl. bkfst) s £25-£35; d £50-£60
MEALS: Bar Lunch £7-£15 High tea £7.50-£11 Dinner £17.50-£25*
CARDS:

★★65% **Imperial**

Fraser's Square PH33 6DW
☎ 01397 702040 & 703921 FAX 01397 706277
A major transformation is taking place at this long established family run hotel in the town centre. When the refurbishment programme is complete, the hotel will be nicely placed to meet the needs of the private sectors of the business and tourist markets. Recent improvements include upgrading of both bars, creation of a new quite first floor lounge together with new conference facilities. Bedrooms are also benefiting from upgrading and smaller rooms are to be enlarged. Staff are friendly and willing to please.
32 en suite (bth/shr) (3 fmly) CTV in all bedrooms 20P Xmas Scottish & French Cuisine Coffee am Tea pm No smoking in restaurant Last d 9.30pm
ROOMS: (incl. bkfst) s fr £46; d fr £76 * **LB**
OFF-PEAK: (incl. bkfst) s fr £35; d fr £56
MEALS: Lunch £3.50-£12.50alc Dinner £12.50-£18.50alc*
CONF: Thtr 60 Class 30 Board 30 Del from £45
CARDS:

See advertisement on opposite page

★★60% **Milton**

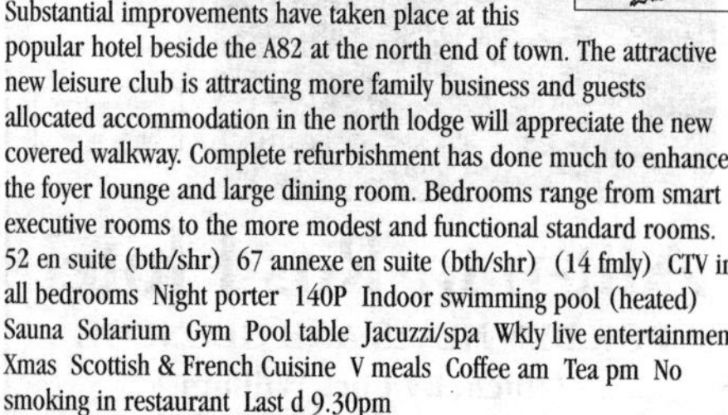

North Rd PH33 6TG (N of town, on A82)
☎ 01397 702331 FAX 01397 703695
Substantial improvements have taken place at this popular hotel beside the A82 at the north end of town. The attractive new leisure club is attracting more family business and guests allocated accommodation in the north lodge will appreciate the new covered walkway. Complete refurbishment has done much to enhance the foyer lounge and large dining room. Bedrooms range from smart executive rooms to the more modest and functional standard rooms.
52 en suite (bth/shr) 67 annexe en suite (bth/shr) (14 fmly) CTV in all bedrooms Night porter 140P Indoor swimming pool (heated) Sauna Solarium Gym Pool table Jacuzzi/spa Wkly live entertainment Xmas Scottish & French Cuisine V meals Coffee am Tea pm No smoking in restaurant Last d 9.30pm
ROOMS: (incl. bkfst) s £59-£69; d £79-£84 * **LB**
OFF-PEAK: (incl. bkfst) s £49-£59; d £69-£79
MEALS: Lunch £7.45-£17alc High tea fr £6.20 Dinner fr £9&alc
CONF: Thtr 220 Class 70 Board 60 Del from £49
CARDS:

FREUCHIE Fife Map 11 NO20

★★65% **Lomond Hills**
Parliament Square KY15 7EY ☎ 01337 857329 & 857498
FAX 01337 858180
A former coaching inn located in the centre of the village, with views of the Lomond Hills, this hotel has been considerably extended whilst retaining some of its original character. There is a choice of lounges as well as a small bar and a panelled restaurant, and though bedrooms vary in size they are well equipped for the business traveller. The indoor leisure centre offers a range of fitness and beauty treatments.
25 en suite (bth/shr) (3 fmly) No smoking in 3 bedrooms CTV in all bedrooms STV 30P Indoor swimming pool (heated) Sauna Solarium Gym Jacuzzi/spa Xmas Scottish & French Cuisine V meals Coffee am Tea pm No smoking area in restaurant Last d 9.15pm
ROOMS: (incl. bkfst) s £48-£50; d £72-£75 * **LB**
OFF-PEAK: (incl. bkfst) s £43.60-£45; d £64.80-£67.50
MEALS: High tea £5.50-£9alc Dinner fr £17.50
CONF: Thtr 200 Class 100 Board 80 Del from £52
CARDS:

GAIRLOCH Highland Map 14 NG87

★★★67% ***Creag Mor***
Charleston IV21 2AH ☎ 01445 712068 FAX 01445 712044
Closed 16 Nov-Feb
Enthusiastic owners Larry and Betty Nieto and their friendly staff extend a warm welcome to all at their comfortable holiday hotel which is situated just south of the village. Bedrooms, though varying in size, are nicely decorated and offer every modern convenience. Relaxing public areas include an inviting split level gallery bar/lounge from which views of the harbour can be enjoyed. Local produce features strongly in the formal dining room and there is also a buttery.
17 en suite (bth/shr) 2 annexe en suite (bth/shr) (1 fmly) CTV in 17 bedrooms Night porter 29P Fishing Pool table French Cuisine V meals Coffee am Tea pm Last d 9.30pm
CARDS:

★★68% **Myrtle Bank**
Low Rd IV21 2BS (off B8012 Melvaig road)
☎ 01445 712004 FAX 01445 712214
Guests are assured of a warm welcome at the MacLean family's comfortable hotel which is situated beside the picturesque shore of Loch Gairloch. The mostly well proportioned bedrooms are comfortably furnished in the modern style and several enjoy views over the loch to the Skye hills beyond. Pleasant public areas include an inviting lounge, well stocked bar and an attractive dining room offering enjoyable Scottish fare which is supported by the ever popular bar food operation.
12 en suite (bth/shr) (3 fmly) CTV in all bedrooms 20P No coaches V meals Coffee am Tea pm No smoking in restaurant Last d 8.30pm
ROOMS: (incl. bkfst) s fr £40; d fr £80 *
OFF-PEAK: (incl. bkfst) s fr £32; d fr £64
MEALS: Bar Lunch £3-£12alc Dinner £22.50*
CARDS:

★★63% **The Old Inn**
Flowerdale IV21 2BD (on A832 - at south end of village near the harbour) ☎ 01445 712006 FAX 01445 712445
A relaxed and informal atmosphere prevails at this former coaching inn which lies south of the village across the road from the old harbour. With a good range of real ales available the two bars are popular and both have recently been refurbished following fire damage. Here you can eat in the informal Bistro or in the main dining room, both offering good food. Good progress is being made with bedroom refurbishment and most are now decorated to a high standard and comfortably furnished.
14 en suite (bth/shr) (4 fmly) CTV in all bedrooms 30P No coaches Xmas Coffee am Tea pm No smoking area in restaurant Last d 9pm
ROOMS: (incl. bkfst) s £27.50-£36.50; d £55-£73 * **LB**
OFF-PEAK: (incl. bkfst) s £27.50-£29.50; d £55-£59
MEALS: Lunch £4.75-£16.75alc High tea £5-£8.50alc Dinner £12.50-£19.50alc
CONF: Class 60 Board 40
CARDS:

GALASHIELS Scottish Borders Map 12 NT43

★★★65% **Woodlands House Hotel & Restaurants**
Windyknowe Rd TD1 1RG ☎ 01896 754722 FAX 01896 754722
This fine Victorian Gothic mansion lies in two acres of grounds in a quiet area above the town. It combines the relaxed atmosphere of a country house with amenities that make it popular with business guests as well as tourists. In addition to the main restaurant which offers a carvery, there is a cosy little steak house, and one can also eat well in the comfortable lounge bar. It's worth asking for one of the lovely large bedrooms.
9 en suite (bth/shr) (3 fmly) CTV in all bedrooms 30P Scottish & French Cuisine V meals Coffee am Last d 9.30pm
ROOMS: (incl. bkfst) s £42; d £68-£74 * **LB**
MEALS: Lunch £7.95 Dinner £18*
CONF: Thtr 40 Class 20 Board 20 Del from £75
CARDS:

★★★64% **Kingsknowes**
Selkirk Rd TD1 3HY (off A7 - at Galashiels/ Selkirk roundabout)
☎ 01896 758375 FAX 01896 750377
A Victorian baronial mansion stands in its own grounds to the south of the town. Family-run, it offers cheerful informal service, with comfortable bedrooms, several being particularly well proportioned. Impressive public rooms feature fine cornices, and include a comfortable lounge, an attractive panelled cocktail bar and the original conservatory, where light lunches are served in summer.
11 rms (10 bth/shr) (3 fmly) CTV in all bedrooms 72P Tennis (hard) English & Continental Cuisine V meals Coffee am Tea pm Last d 9.30pm
ROOMS: (incl. bkfst) s £45-£49; d £70-£74 * **LB**
OFF-PEAK: (incl. bkfst) s fr £40; d fr £56
MEALS: Lunch £7.50-£10.75&alc High tea £6-£7.95&alc Dinner £17.50-£21&alc*
CONF: Thtr 65 Class 45 Board 30 Del from £56.75
CARDS:

★★65% **King's**
56 Market St TD1 3AJ (adjacent to southbound A7 in town centre) ☎ 01896 755497
Closed 1-3 Jan
This friendly family-run hotel lies just off the town centre and provides well equipped modern bedrooms. Good value home-cooked meals are served in the attractive dining room.
7 en suite (bth/shr) (1 fmly) CTV in all bedrooms No dogs (ex guide dogs) Scottish & French Cuisine V meals Coffee am Tea pm Last d 9.30pm
ROOMS: (incl. bkfst) s £39; d £58 * **LB**
OFF-PEAK: (incl. bkfst) s £35; d £50
MEALS: Lunch £8.95&alc High tea £5.95&alc Dinner £15.50&alc
CONF: Thtr 80 Class 30 Board 40 Del from £65
CARDS: 

★★61% **Abbotsford Arms**
63 Stirling St TD1 1BY ☎ 01896 752517 FAX 01896 750744
Closed 24-25 & 31 Dec & 1 Jan
Lying just off the inner ring road and within walking distance of the town centre, this friendly commercial hotel serves food throughout the day, and is popular for its good range of dishes and generous portions, both in the bar and restaurant. .
14 rms (10 bth/shr) (2 fmly) CTV in all bedrooms No dogs (ex guide dogs) Night porter 10P No coaches V meals Coffee am Last d 9pm
ROOMS: (incl. bkfst) s £28-£36; d £44-£55 * **LB**
MEALS: Lunch £7-£15alc High tea £4.95-£6.95alc Dinner £8-£20alc*
CONF: Thtr 150 Class 600 Board 500
CARDS: 

GARVE Highland Map 14 NH36

★★64% **Inchbae Lodge**
Inchbae IV23 2PH (6m W, on A835) ☎ 01997 455269
FAX 01997 455207
Closed 25-29 Dec
Situated some six miles west of the village on the Ullapool road, this relaxing Highland holiday hotel is now under the enthusiastic ownership of Patrick and Judy Price. Bedrooms which have no televisions or telephones to detract from the peace and quiet are well decorated and comfortably furnished in pine, those in the cedar chalet annexe lacking the spaciousness of the main house rooms. There is a choice of comfortable lounges and a well stocked snug bar with beamed ceiling and natural stone walls. Patrick's short fixed price menu featuring the best local produce, is producing some good results.
6 en suite (bth/shr) 6 annexe en suite (shr) (3 fmly) No smoking in all bedrooms 30P No coaches Fishing ch fac Xmas V meals Coffee am Tea pm No smoking in restaurant Last d 8pm
ROOMS: (incl. bkfst) s £32-£37; d £64 * **LB**
MEALS: Bar Lunch £1.85-£10.50alc High tea fr £3.50 Dinner fr £21*
CARDS:

GATEHOUSE OF FLEET Dumfries & Galloway Map 11 NX55

★★★★ 67% **Cally Palace**
DG7 2DL (1m from Gatehouse) ☎ 01557 814341 FAX 01557 814522
Closed 3 Jan-Feb
Set in 500 acres of forest and parkland, this elegant 18th-century country house has widened its appeal with the addition of an 18-hole golf course and well equipped leisure centre. Public rooms have ornate ceilings and marble fireplaces, while the bedrooms are spacious, some with separate sitting areas, and all with thoughtful extra touches like bathrobes and sherry. Service is attentive and friendly and the short dinner menu provides some interesting dishes with a definite Scottish influence.

56 en suite (bth) (7 fmly) CTV in all bedrooms No dogs (ex guide dogs) Lift Night porter 100P No coaches Indoor swimming pool (heated) Golf 18 Tennis (hard) Fishing Sauna Solarium Pool table Croquet lawn Putting green Jacuzzi/spa Table tennis Practice fairway Wkly live entertainment Xmas V meals Coffee am Tea pm No smoking in restaurant Last d 9.30pm
ROOMS: (incl. bkfst & dinner) s £63; d £120-£136 * **LB**
OFF-PEAK: (incl. bkfst & dinner) s £58; d £110-£126
MEALS: Lunch £11&alc Dinner £21.50-£24*
CONF: Thtr 80 Class 40 Board 35 Del £95
CARDS:

★★★64% **Murray Arms**
DG7 2HY (off A75, hotel at edge of town, near clock tower)
☎ 01557 814207 FAX 01557 814370
This traditional inn dates from the 18th-century and offers a relaxed, informal atmosphere to make travellers feel instantly at home. Bedrooms vary in size, though all have been enhanced with attractive fabrics, while the chalet suite offers a comfortable retreat within the hotel gardens. The Lunky Hole dining room is open all day for good value meals, while the cocktail bar and lounges are in several cosy nooks.
12 en suite (bth/shr) 1 annexe en suite (bth/shr) (3 fmly) CTV in all bedrooms Night porter 50P Croquet lawn Xmas V meals Coffee am Tea pm Last d 9.45pm
ROOMS: (incl. bkfst) s £45-£50; d £85-£90 * **LB**
MEALS: Bar Lunch £4-£15alc High tea £5-£10alc Dinner £10-£20alc*
CONF: Thtr 120 Class 50 Board 30 Del from £50
CARDS: 

indicates a Town House Hotel. Please consult the section on AA Star Rating at the front of the book.

GIFFNOCK East Renfrewshire Map 11 NS55

★★★64% **Macdonald Thistle**

Eastwood Toll G46 6RA (On A77 Kilmarnock/Ayr Rd at Eastwood Toll, Giffnock - take first exit onto A726, East Kilbride,then first right to hotel)
☎ 0141 638 2225 FAX 0141 638 6231
A friendly and comfortable, mainly business hotel, the Macdonald is conveniently situated for both the city centre and the airport. The bedrooms are compact but well equipped, although there are four very comfortable suites all with their own sitting rooms. The public rooms include a choice of bars, and French and Scottish cuisine is served in the elegant Oscar's Restaurant. There are also meeting and conference facilities and ample car parking.
56 en suite (bth/shr) (4 fmly) No smoking in 4 bedrooms CTV in all bedrooms STV Night porter 130P Sauna Solarium Pool table Wkly live entertainment Xmas International Cuisine V meals Coffee am Tea pm No smoking area in restaurant Last d 9.45pm
ROOMS: s £79-£92; d £94-£100 * **LB**
OFF-PEAK: s £38-£92; d £73-£100
MEALS: Lunch £13-£14&alc High tea £6-£10 Dinner £17.50-£20.50&alc
CONF: Thtr 160 Class 60 Board 35 Del from £82
CARDS:

GIFFORD East Lothian Map 12 NT56

★★69% **Tweeddale Arms**

EH41 4QU ☎ 01620 810240 FAX 01620 810488
The black and white exterior of this 18th-century country inn beside the village green is enhanced by colourful window boxes and hanging baskets. Modern comforts are effectively combined with old world charm in public areas which include an inviting lounge, an attractive restaurant and a well stocked cocktail bar; bedrooms, though compact, are both comfortable and modern.
16 en suite (bth/shr) (2 fmly) CTV in all bedrooms Xmas V meals Coffee am Tea pm Last d 9pm
ROOMS: (incl. bkfst) s fr £47.50; d fr £65 **LB**
MEALS: Lunch £12.75 High tea £6.50 Dinner £19.50
CARDS:

GLAMIS Angus Map 15 NO34

★★★ 73% ***Castleton House***

DD8 1SJ (Scotland's Heritage) ☎ 01307 840340
FAX 01307 840506
A friendly country house hotel, pleasantly appointed, Castleton House stands in its own grounds just off the A94, about three miles west of Glamis. Bedrooms, which vary in size, have attractive reproduction furniture in elm, colourful soft furnishings and smartly tiled bathrooms. The comfortable lounge is a quiet area, and the bar adjoins the informal conservatory restaurant, which offers an alternative to the elegant dining room. William Little's imaginative cuisine is featured in both.
6 en suite (bth/shr) CTV in all bedrooms No dogs (ex guide dogs) 15P Putting green European Cuisine V meals Coffee am Tea pm Last d 9.30pm
CARDS:

GLASGOW City of Glasgow Map 11 NS56

★★★★★ 64% ***Glasgow Hilton***

1 Williams St G3 8HT ☎ 0141 204 5555
FAX 0141 204 5004
This impressive modern building of polished granite and mirrored glass is situated just off the M8 motorway close to the city centre and has the convenience of its own underground car park although staff will park cars if required. The hotel has been designed to the highest international level, and portrays considerable character in its Raffles Bar which reflects its famous Singapore namesake and in Minsky's New York Deli, based on the original Minsky's which opened in the 1900s. Camerons Restaurant is renowned for its high standard of cuisine, which includes many Scottish delicacies and the Scotch Bar with its fine selection of malts is ideal for drinks before dinner. The bedrooms are spacious and very well equipped, the three top floors of Executive Rooms being of an exceptionally high standard. There is an elegant ballroom and numerous meeting and conference rooms. The Leisure centre includes a swimming pool and a gymnasium.
319 en suite (bth/shr) CTV in all bedrooms STV No dogs (ex guide dogs) Lift Air conditioning 180P No coaches Indoor swimming pool (heated) Sauna Solarium Gym Jacuzzi/spa International Cuisine V meals Coffee am Tea pm Last d 11pm
CARDS:

★★★★ 71% **Glasgow Moat House**

Congress Rd G3 8QT (junct 19 M8, follow signs for SEC (Scottish Exhibition Centre, hotel adjacent to centre) ☎ 0141 306 9988 FAX 0141 221 2022
Smart, very well equipped accommodation, including a number of suites, is available at this impressive hotel which is situated on the banks of the River Clyde. The ultra modern building is one of the tallest in Scotland and is instantly recognisable by its mirrored glass exterior. The comfortable, open-plan public areas, one end of which is decorated with a huge mural depicting much of the city's history, include a choice of restaurants. It is in the smartly appointed Mariner restaurant that head chef Tom Brown produces a range of well prepared and enticing dishes. The hotel also has a range of very well equipped state-of-the-art conference and banqueting facilities.
284 en suite (bth/shr) (45 fmly) No smoking in 120 bedrooms CTV in all bedrooms STV Lift Night porter Air conditioning 300P Indoor swimming pool (heated) Sauna Solarium Gym Wkly live entertainment Xmas International Cuisine V meals Coffee am Tea pm No smoking area in restaurant Last d 10.30pm
ROOMS: s £65-£115; d £85-£125 * **LB**
MEALS: Lunch £14.50-£17.50&alc Dinner £18.95&alc*
CONF: Thtr 800 Class 350 Board 66 Del from £122
CARDS:

See advertisement on opposite page

★★★★66% **Glasgow Marriott**

500 Argyle St, Anderston G3 8RR (off junct 19 of M8)
☎ 0141 226 5577 FAX 0141 221 7676
Smart, well equipped accommodation is provided at this purpose built hotel which is conveniently located just off Junction 19 of the M8. Effective use has been made of colourful fabrics and stylish furnishings in the newly refurbished bedrooms which are equipped to the highest standards. The well appointed public areas include an impressive foyer lounge, which is dressed with fresh flowers as well as extensive leisure facilities, which include squash courts.

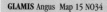

298 en suite (bth/shr) (88 fmly) No smoking in 190 bedrooms CTV in all bedrooms STV Lift Night porter Air conditioning 250P Indoor swimming pool (heated) Squash Sauna Solarium Gym Jacuzzi/spa Heated whirlpool, Hairdresser Xmas European Cuisine V meals Coffee am Tea pm No smoking area in restaurant Last d 10pm
ROOMS: s £79-£104; d £79-£104 * **LB**
OFF-PEAK: s £53-£73; d £53-£73
MEALS: Lunch fr £15 Dinner £14.50-£17.50&alc*
CONF: Thtr 720 Class 450 Board 440 Del from £136
CARDS:

★★★★64% **Glasgow Thistle**

36 Cambridge St G2 3HN (behind Sauchiehall St, opposite back entrance to Marks & Spencer and Boots) ☎ 0141 332 3311 FAX 0141 332 4050

With the major benefit of its own car park, this busy hotel is ideally situated for Sauchiehall Street, the Concert Hall and the Theatre Royal. Refurbishment of the remaining rooms continues, whilst the oldest rooms look very tired indeed; it is hoped that work on these will be finished by late 1996 or early 1997. The newly refurbished rooms however are very attractively decorated, smartly appointed and well equipped. Public areas include a choice of restaurants and bars. There is also a business centre and the hotel has an impressive range of conference and banqueting facilities.

302 en suite (bth/shr) (69 fmly) No smoking in 60 bedrooms CTV in all bedrooms STV Lift Night porter 250P Xmas International Cuisine V meals Coffee am Tea pm Last d 11.30pm
ROOMS: s £90-£130; d £110-£150 * **LB**
OFF-PEAK: s £60-£80; d £70-£95
MEALS: Lunch £13-£18.50&alc High tea £6.50-£9.50 Dinner £18.50-£26.50&alc*
CONF: Thtr 1500 Class 800
CARDS:

★★★★62% **The Copthorne Glasgow**

George Square G2 1DS (take junct 15 from M8 follow signs City Centre/George Sq, travel along Cathedral St past Strathclyde University, turn left into Hanover St)
☎ 0141 332 6711 FAX 0141 332 4264

This imposing Victorian hotel is centrally situated overlooking George Square, close to the Gallery of Modern Art, the Concert Hall and the central business district. Bedrooms vary in size and style, but all are well equipped. Guests have the choice of eating less formally in the smart and very popular café bar or in the restaurant, where the atmosphere is relaxed and a brasserie-style menu is available. One of the most impressive things about the hotel is the friendly and helpful nature of the staff.

141 en suite (bth/shr) (4 fmly) No smoking in 45 bedrooms CTV in all bedrooms STV No dogs (ex guide dogs) Lift Night porter Xmas International Cuisine V meals Coffee am Tea pm No smoking area in restaurant Last d 10pm
ROOMS: s fr £105; d fr £115 **LB**
OFF-PEAK: (incl. bkfst) s fr £45; d fr £65
MEALS: Lunch £12.95-£14.95&alc Dinner fr £16.95&alc*
CONF: Thtr 100 Class 40 Board 40 Del from £130
CARDS:

RED STAR HOTEL

★★★ **One Devonshire Gardens**
1 Devonshire Gardens G12 0UX
☎ 0141 339 2001 FAX 0141 337 1663

This most distinctive hotel, comprising three adjoining (but not interconnecting) town houses, is discreetly situated in a leafy terrace in the city's west side. Get directions if you don't know Glasgow, but expect a great welcome when you arrive. Management and staff are highly attentive without being obtrusive, and nothing appears too much trouble. Bedrooms are bold and striking, with subdued lighting, gentle music, and lavish fruit bowls awaiting each guest; sumptuous fabrics,

contd.

luxurious bathrooms, and exquisite toiletries are further outstanding features. There are two really comfortable, stylish lounges and a restaurant featuring more dramatic decor. Here, chef Andrew Fairlie continues to delight his guests with highly competent cooking. Menus change daily and include a middle course. Highlights of recent meals have included stunning tomato and fennel soup and first-rate beef fillet, perfectly cooked with a red wine sauce.

27 en suite (bth/shr) (3 fmly) CTV in all bedrooms STV Night porter 12P No coaches Scottish & French Cuisine V meals Coffee am Tea pm No smoking in restaurant Last d 10pm
ROOMS: s £135-£145; d £160-£170 *
MEALS: Lunch £25 Dinner £40*
CONF: Thtr 40 Class 20 Board 26
CARDS:

★★★68% **Malmaison**
278 West George St G2 4LL ☎ 0141 221 6400
FAX 0141 221 6411

One of Glasgow's most stylish hotels, the Malmaison successfully combines contemporary bedrooms with a lively brasserie and bar and restricted but friendly service. CD players are a unique feature of all rooms. Menus offer brasserie favourites such as steamed mussels, steak and frîtes and coq au vin and there is a good range of wines, several being available by the glass.

21 en suite (bth/shr) (4 fmly) CTV in all bedrooms STV No dogs (ex guide dogs) Night porter No coaches French & Medditeranean Cuisine V meals Coffee am Last d 10.30pm
ROOMS: (incl. bkfst) s £80-£110; d £80-£110 *
MEALS: Lunch fr £8.50&alc Dinner fr £8.50&alc*
CARDS:

★★★67% **Town House**
54 West George St G2 1NG
☎ 0141 332 3320 FAX 0141 332 9756

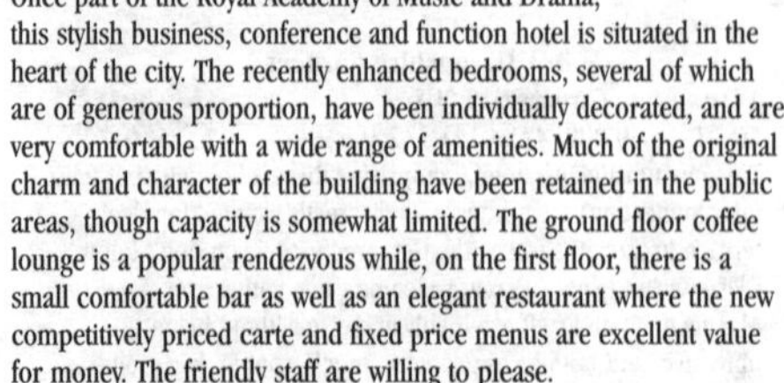

Once part of the Royal Academy of Music and Drama, this stylish business, conference and function hotel is situated in the heart of the city. The recently enhanced bedrooms, several of which are of generous proportion, have been individually decorated, and are very comfortable with a wide range of amenities. Much of the original charm and character of the building have been retained in the public areas, though capacity is somewhat limited. The ground floor coffee lounge is a popular rendezvous while, on the first floor, there is a small comfortable bar as well as an elegant restaurant where the new competitively priced carte and fixed price menus are excellent value for money. The friendly staff are willing to please.
34 en suite (bth/shr) (4 fmly) No smoking in 7 bedrooms CTV in all bedrooms STV No dogs (ex guide dogs) Lift Night porter 5P Xmas V meals Coffee am Tea pm Last d 10pm
ROOMS: s £75-£90; d £85-£115 *

OFF-PEAK: (incl. bkfst) s £65-£80; d £75-£90
MEALS: Lunch £4.50-£9.50&alc Dinner £4.50-£9.51&alc*
CONF: Thtr 180 Class 50 Board 60 Del from £120
CARDS:

★★★66% **Swallow**
517 Paisley Rd West G51 1RW (off junc 23 of M8)
☎ 0141 427 3146 FAX 0141 427 4059

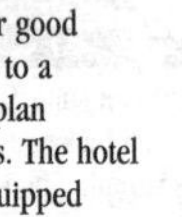

This purpose built hotel is conveniently situated close to Junction 23 of M8 (head towards the city centre) and Bellahouston park, just five minutes from the Burell Collection and ten minutes from the city centre. The bedrooms offer good levels of comfort and the majority have been refurbished to a very high standard indeed. Guests can relax in the open plan public and have use of the usual Swallow leisure facilities. The hotel also has a number of very smartly appointed and well equipped meeting rooms.
117 en suite (bth/shr) (1 fmly) No smoking in 56 bedrooms CTV in all bedrooms STV Lift Night porter 150P Indoor swimming pool (heated) Sauna Solarium Gym Jacuzzi/spa Steam room Xmas Scottish & French Cuisine V meals Coffee am Tea pm Last d 9.45pm
ROOMS: (incl. bkfst) s fr £90; d fr £105 * **LB**
OFF-PEAK: (incl. bkfst) s fr £65; d fr £75
MEALS: Lunch fr £7.95 Dinner fr £16.50*
CONF: Thtr 350 Class 150 Board 30 Del from £100
CARDS:

★★★65% **Ewington**
132 Queens Dr, Queens Park G42 8QW
☎ 0141 423 1152 FAX 0141 422 2030

The welcoming atmosphere together with good food are all part of the appeal of this popular business and tourist hotel on the south side. The comfortable accommodation ranges from well proportioned executive rooms to the variable sized standard rooms. Drinks are dispensed from the trolley in the cocktail lounge and in the attractive restaurant. The short, daily changing fixed-price menu offers uncomplicated and honestly flavoured dishes.
42 en suite (bth/shr) (1 fmly) No smoking in 6 bedrooms CTV in all bedrooms Lift Night porter 8P arrangement with local gym, snooker Xmas International Cuisine V meals Coffee am Tea pm No smoking area in restaurant Last d 9pm
ROOMS: s £75-£85; d £90-£110 **LB**
MEALS: Lunch fr £7.25&alc High tea fr £9alc Dinner £9-£20alc*
CONF: Thtr 70 Class 12 Board 22 Del from £95
CARDS:

★★★64% **Holiday Inn Garden Court**
161 West Nile St G1 2RL (M8 jnct 16, follow signs for Royal Concert Hall, hotel is opposite)
☎ 0141 332 0110 FAX 0141 332 7447

An attractive new hotel situated close to the city centre and providing very good modern accommodation with every facility. A feature is the informal La Bonne Auberge restaurant and bar which is open for breakfast, lunch and dinner and in which a high standard of food and service can be enjoyed. Public areas are limited, but the smartly uniformed staff are friendly and helpful. There is no car park, but a multi story park is almost opposite.
80 en suite (bth/shr) (4 fmly) No smoking in 60 bedrooms CTV in all bedrooms STV No dogs (ex guide dogs) Lift Xmas French Cuisine V meals Coffee am Tea pm No smoking area in restaurant Last d 10.15pm
ROOMS: s £52-£59.90; d £52-£59.90 *
MEALS: Lunch £4-£10alc Dinner £7.95&alc*
CONF: Thtr 80 Class 40 Board 40 Del from £80
CARDS:

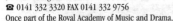

★★★64% **Jurys Glasgow**

Great Western Rd G12 0XP (W of city, off A82)
☎ 0141 334 8161 FAX 0141 334 3846

Situated a short way from the city centre, this modern hotel offers good facilities for both business guests and tourists alike. The bedrooms are well equipped and are in the process of being redecorated and generally upgraded. Public areas include a well equipped leisure centre, a cosy cocktail bar and a spacious split-level restaurant with an extensive range of dishes. The staff provide a warm, friendly and professional style of service.

133 en suite (bth/shr) (15 fmly) No smoking in 55 bedrooms CTV in all bedrooms Lift Night porter 300P Indoor swimming pool (heated) Sauna Solarium Gym Jacuzzi/spa Whirlpool ch fac Xmas Scottish & European Cuisine V meals Coffee am Tea pm No smoking area in restaurant Last d 9.30pm

ROOMS: s fr £85; d fr £85 * **LB**

OFF-PEAK: s fr £60; d fr £60

MEALS: Lunch £5-£10 High tea £2.95-£5.95 Dinner £8-£25&alc

CONF: Thtr 140 Class 80 Board 40 Del from £90

CARDS:

★★★63% **Quality Central**

99 Gordon St G1 3SF (exit 19 of M8, left into Argyle St and left into Hope St) ☎ 0141 221 9680 FAX 0141 226 3948

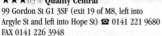

This imposing Victorian hotel, belonging to the golden age of railway transport, is part of Central Station and has direct access to the concourse and also (along one of the platforms) to the multi-storey car park in Oswald Street. Considerable re-furbishment has been carried out recently and both the impressive public rooms and bedrooms now match modern expectations of comfort. There is also a well equipped leisure centre and numerous banqueting and function facilities.

220 en suite (bth/shr) (8 fmly) No smoking in 70 bedrooms CTV in all bedrooms STV Lift Night porter Indoor swimming pool (heated) Sauna Solarium Gym Jacuzzi/spa Hair & beauty salon Steamroom Xmas English & Continental Cuisine V meals Coffee am Tea pm No smoking area in restaurant Last d 9.30pm

ROOMS: s £67.50; d £87.50 **LB**

MEALS: Lunch £7.95-£9.95&alc Dinner £13.50&alc

CONF: Thtr 600 Class 170 Board 40 Del from £95

CARDS:

★★★63% **Tinto Firs Thistle**

470 Kilmarnock Rd G43 2BB (four miles south of Glasgow City Centre on the A77) ☎ 0141 637 2353 FAX 0141 633 1340

This modern hotel is ideally situated in a quiet residential area, just four miles from the city centre and within easy reach of the airport and the noteworthy modern museum which houses the Burrell Collection. The comfortably furnished public areas include a choice of bars, an attractive restaurant and a smartly refurbished boardroom. Whilst the bedrooms are not overly spacious, they are attractively appointed and well equipped.

28 en suite (bth/shr) (4 fmly) No smoking in 4 bedrooms CTV in all bedrooms STV Night porter 46P Xmas International Cuisine V meals Coffee am Tea pm No smoking area in restaurant Last d 10pm

ROOMS: s £78-£85; d £88-£95 **LB**

MEALS: Lunch £9.95-£10.95 High tea fr £6.50 Dinner fr £19.95

CONF: Thtr 200 Class 100 Board 50 Del from £95

CARDS:

★★★62% ***Kelvin Park Lorne***

County Hotels

923 Sauchiehall St G3 7TE
☎ 0141 314 9955 FAX 0141 337 1659

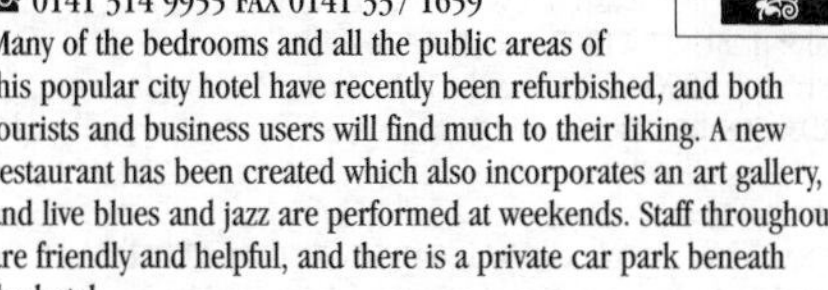

Many of the bedrooms and all the public areas of this popular city hotel have recently been refurbished, and both tourists and business users will find much to their liking. A new restaurant has been created which also incorporates an art gallery, and live blues and jazz are performed at weekends. Staff throughout are friendly and helpful, and there is a private car park beneath the hotel.

98 en suite (bth/shr) (7 fmly) No smoking in 20 bedrooms CTV in all bedrooms No dogs (ex guide dogs) Lift Night porter 40P Wkly

contd.

live entertainment Scottish & French Cuisine V meals Coffee am Tea pm Last d 10.30pm
CARDS:

★★★61% **Carrick**

377 Argyle St G2 8LL (junction 19 M8 bear left onto Argyle St, hotel opposite Cadogan Square)
☎ 0141 248 2355 FAX 0141 221 1014
A modern hotel, centrally situated with compact, but functional and well equipped bedrooms and a popular restaurant on the first floor together with the lounge bar and a number of meeting rooms. Reception is at ground level where there is also some lounge seating and lifts to all floors. Free car parking is available to residents in a car park opposite.
121 en suite (bth/shr) No smoking in 79 bedrooms CTV in all bedrooms No dogs (ex guide dogs) Lift Night porter Xmas Continental Cuisine V meals Coffee am Tea pm
ROOMS: s £55-£65; d £55-£65 * **LB**
OFF-PEAK: s £50-£65; d £50-£65
MEALS: Dinner £12.75-£13.95&alc*
CONF: Thtr 80 Class 40 Board 24 Del from £65
CARDS:

★★★59% **Sherbrooke Castle**
11 Sherbrooke Av, Pollokshields G41 4PG
☎ 0141 427 4227 FAX 0141 427 5685
A turreted building of red sandstone, this impressive hotel stands in a pleasant residential area on the south side of the city and has a thriving conference and function trade. This can, however, put some pressure on the public rooms at times. The bedrooms are well equipped to meet the needs of the modern traveller but do vary in size and shape. Friendly and polite service is provided.
12 en suite (bth/shr) 13 annexe en suite (bth/shr) (2 fmly) No smoking in 4 bedrooms CTV in all bedrooms STV Night porter 50P N Xmas British & French Cuisine V meals Coffee am Tea pm No smoking in restaurant Last d 9.45pm
ROOMS: (incl. bkfst) s £65.50-£99; d £70-£145 **LB**
MEALS: Lunch £5.50-£12.50&alc High tea £6-£10alc Dinner £10.50-£18.50&alc
CONF: Thtr 200 Class 100 Board 50 Del from £60
CARDS:

★★★55% **The Buchanan**

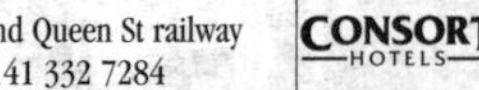

185 Buchanan St G1 2JY (behind Queen St railway station, take second left) ☎ 0141 332 7284
FAX 0141 333 0635
Situated in the heart of the city convenient to central amenities, this long established hotel remains a popular base for visiting tour groups. Public areas are somewhat limited in extent with a minimal lounge seating in the foyer, but there is a choice of bars and a smart restaurant which offers a range of Italian specialities. Many of the various sized bedrooms have benefited from cosmetic enhancement and good progress is being made in upgrading the older bathrooms.
60 en suite (bth/shr) (2 fmly) CTV in all bedrooms No dogs (ex guide dogs) Lift Night porter International Cuisine V meals Coffee am Last d 9pm
ROOMS: (incl. bkfst) s £55-£70; d £70-£90 *
OFF-PEAK: (incl. bkfst) s £50-£60; d £60-£70
MEALS: Lunch £7-£15 Dinner £15-£20&alc*
CONF: Thtr 60 Class 30 Board 25 Del from £70
CARDS:

★★69% **Deauvilles**
62 St Andrews Dr, Pollockshields G41 5EX ☎ 0141 427 1106
Situated in the leafy, up-market suburb of Pollokshields, this elegant Victorian private hotel is very handy for the city either by car or public transport. Marie Campbell has created a fine Dining Club to maximise use of the 3 elegant dining rooms; with breakfast being served in the bright and airy conservatory. Bookings for lunch or dinner is recommended. Most of the bedrooms are comfortable and well furnished.
6 rms CTV in all bedrooms P
ROOMS: (incl. bkfst) s fr £55; d fr £65 *
CARDS:

TOWN HOUSE HOTEL

Devonshire

5 Devonshire Gardens G12 0UX
☎ 0141 339 7878 FAX 0141 339 3980
Standing on the corner of an imposing tree-lined Victorian terrace just yards from its longer established namesake, The Devonshire remains one of the most stylish hotels in the city. Day rooms are limited in extent but the drawing room offers all the charm, elegance and comfort one would expect of such a grand house. Imaginatively prepared Scottish fare is served in the small dining room and there is an extensive 24-hour room service facility available. Bedrooms, many of which are well proportioned, offer designer decor and fabrics to complement the antique pine furnishings. The atmosphere throughout is warmly welcoming and staff unobtrusively attentive.
14 en suite (bth/shr) (3 fmly) CTV in all bedrooms STV Night porter P Xmas Scottish & French Cuisine V meals Coffee am Tea pm Last d 9.45pm
ROOMS: s £95-£125; d £110-£155 **LB**
OFF-PEAK: s £80-£115; d £95-£135
MEALS: Lunch £7.50-£17.50 Dinner £20-£30&alc
CONF: Thtr 50 Class 30 Board 30
CARDS:

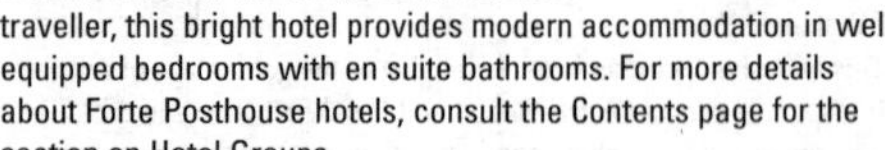

Forte Posthouse Glasgow City

FORTE Posthouse

Bothwell St G2 7EN ☎ 0141 248 2656
FAX 0141 221 8986
Suitable for both the business and leisure traveller, this bright hotel provides modern accommodation in well equipped bedrooms with en suite bathrooms. For more details about Forte Posthouse hotels, consult the Contents page for the section on Hotel Groups.
247 en suite (bth/shr)
ROOMS: s £99; d £99 *
CONF: Thtr 850 Class 450 Board 100 Del £129

Travel Inn

travel inn

Glasgow Zoo, Hamilton Rd G71 7SA
☎ 0141 773 1133 FAX 0141 771 8354
Purpose-built accommodation, offering spacious, well equipped bedrooms, all with en suite bathrooms. Meals may be taken at the nearby family restaurant. For more information about Travel Inns, consult the Contents page under Hotel Groups.
40 en suite (bth/shr)
ROOMS: d £35.50 *

Travelodge

Travelodge

Paisley Rd ☎ 0800 850950 FAX 01384 78578
This modern building offers accommodation in smart, spacious and well equipped bedrooms, suitable for family use, and all with en suite bathrooms. Meals may be taken at the nearby family restaurant. For information on room rates and to make a booking, call Roomline free of charge on 0800 850950. For more details about Travelodge, consult the Contents page under Hotel Groups.
43 en suite (bth/shr)

GLASGOW AIRPORT Renfrewshire Map 11 NS46
See also Howwood

★★★68% ***Glynhill Hotel & Leisure Club***
Paisley Rd PA4 8XB (2m E of A741, off junc 27 of M8)
☎ 0141 886 5555 FAX 0141 885 2838
Conveniently located close to both the motorway and airport, this much extended hotel offers a range of accommodation, as well as extensive leisure and conference facilities. Both the American-style executive bedrooms and the standard rooms offer excellent facilities, and have been enhanced with attractive décor and fabrics. There is a choice of bars and restaurants to suit all tastes and budgets, while the luxurious leisure complex includes a large swimming pool, jacuzzi, saunas and a well equipped gymnasium.
125 en suite (bth/shr) (25 fmly) No smoking in 51 bedrooms CTV in all bedrooms STV Night porter 230P Indoor swimming pool (heated) Snooker Sauna Solarium Gym Jacuzzi/spa Steam room Wkly live entertainment International Cuisine V meals Coffee am Tea pm Last d 10.30pm
CARDS:

★★★64% **Lynnhurst**
Park Rd PA5 8LS ☎ 01505 324331 FAX 01505 324219
Closed 1-3 Jan
Two detached Victorian houses have been linked to create this friendly business hotel on the edge of town, which is also a popular venue for local functions and convenient for holiday-makers using Glasgow Airport. The bright bedrooms are tastefully modern in style and offer a wide range of amenities. Public areas include a spacious bar, conservatory lounge and an attractive panelled dining room with ornate ceiling.
21 en suite (bth/shr) (2 fmly) CTV in all bedrooms STV No dogs (ex guide dogs) 100P Arrangement with local leisure centre European Cuisine V meals Coffee am No smoking area in restaurant Last d 9pm
ROOMS: (incl. bkfst) s £48-£52; d fr £76 **LB**
MEALS: Lunch £7.75-£9&alc High tea £7.75 Dinner £11-£16&alc
CONF: Thtr 160 Class 160 Board 20 Del from £62
CARDS:
£
See advertisement on this page

★★★61% **Dean Park**
91 Glasgow Rd PA4 8YB (3m NE A8 - turn off M8 at junc26 onto A8 for Renfrew, follow road for 200yds, hotel is on the left)
☎ 0141 304 9955 FAX 0141 885 0681
This modern purpose built hotel within easy reach of the airport continues to attract visiting tour groups and is also a popular venue for local conferences and functions. Public areas which are bright and modern, include a comfortable foyer lounge, a well stocked split level bar and attractive restaurant. Bedrooms are not over-large but they are well equipped and a programme of refurbishment is planned.
118 en suite (bth/shr) (6 fmly) No smoking in 6 bedrooms CTV in all bedrooms Night porter 200P Snooker Beautician Xmas French Cuisine V meals Coffee am Tea pm No smoking area in restaurant Last d 9.30pm
ROOMS: s £66; d £86
OFF-PEAK: s £50; d £70
MEALS: Lunch £7.95-£12.95alc Dinner £9.95-£12.95alc
CONF: Thtr 350 Class 150 Board 100 Del £82
CARDS:
£

Forte Posthouse Glasgow Airport
FORTE Posthouse
Abbotsinch PA3 2TR (from E M8 off at junc 28 follow signs for Hotel; from W M8 off at junc 29 follow airport slip road to Hotel)
☎ 0141 887 1212 FAX 0141 887 3738
Suitable for both the business and leisure traveller, this bright hotel provides modern accommodation in well equipped

bedrooms with en suite bathrooms. For more details about Forte Posthouse hotels, consult the Contents page for the section on Hotel Groups.
297 en suite (bth/shr)
ROOMS: d fr £89 *
CONF: Thtr 250 Class 120 Board 20 Del from £75

Forte Posthouse Glasgow/Erskine
FORTE Posthouse
North Barr PA8 6AN
☎ 0141 812 0123 FAX 0141 812 7642
(For full entry see Erskine)

Travel Inn
travel inn
Whitecart Rd PA3 2TH (close to airport terminal follow signs) ☎ 0141 842 1563 FAX 0141 842 1570
Purpose-built accommodation, offering spacious, well equipped bedrooms, all with en suite bathrooms. Meals may be taken at the nearby family restaurant. For more information about Travel Inns, consult the Contents page under Hotel Groups.
81 en suite (bth/shr)
ROOMS: d £35.50 *

GLENCOE Highland Map 14 NN15

★★65% **Glencoe**
PA39 4HW (on A82 in Glencoe village, 15m S of Fort William)
☎ 01855 811245 FAX 01855 811687
This popular and long established family-run hotel is an ideal base from which to explore the Highlands. Situated beside the A82, the atmosphere is relaxed and informal. Some of the bedrooms are quite small, but all have been refurbished and provide bright, modern accommodation. A good range of dishes is available in the restaurant

contd.

which overlooks the Loch, and guests also have use of the foyer lounge and cocktail bar.
15 en suite (bth/shr) (4 fmly) CTV in all bedrooms STV 30P Games room Xmas International Cuisine V meals Coffee am Tea pm No smoking in restaurant Last d 9.30pm
ROOMS: (incl. bkfst) s £34-£46; d £48-£72 **LB**
MEALS: Lunch £7-£12alc Dinner £12.50-£19&alc
CARDS:

GLENEAGLES See Auchterarder

GLENFARG Perthshire & Kinross Map 11 NO11

★★61% **Glenfarg**
Main St PH2 9NU (travelling S on M90, off at junc 9, turn left, Hotel 5m; travelling N on M90, off at junc 8, second left, Hotel 2m)
☎ 01577 830241 FAX 01577 830665
This informal hotel is located in the centre of the village and is popular with golfers using the many local courses. Most of the bedrooms are a good size and have en suite facilities. There is a lively public bar as well as a comfortable lounge area where bar meals are available, while the secluded terrace is pleasant in the summer months.
15 en suite (bth/shr) (3 fmly) CTV in all bedrooms STV 20P Wkly live entertainment Xmas V meals Coffee am Tea pm No smoking in restaurant Last d 9pm
ROOMS: (incl. bkfst) s £25-£32.50; d £40-£59 * **LB**
MEALS: Lunch £7.50-£15 High tea £6.50-£9.50 Dinner fr £14.95*
CONF: Thtr 60
CARDS:

GLENFINNAN Highland Map 14 NM98

★★71% **The Princes House**

Glenfinnan PH37 4LT (15m W of Fort William on A830, 0.5m on right) ☎ 01397 722246
FAX 01397 722307
Closed 4 Jan-Feb & 10-25 Dec RS Mar & Nov
This former coaching inn which has been tastefully modernised is beautifully positioned close the Glenfinnan Monument and the head of Loch Shiel. The Bonnie Prince Charlie theme is discreetly reflected in the relaxing public areas which include a comfortable lounge bar and in Floras Restauarnt, a good choice of dishes, made using the best quality local ingredients, are available. The characterful bedrooms are both generously and thoughtfully equipped. Family owned and personally run, hospitality is an undoubted strength.
8 en suite (bth/shr) (1 fmly) No smoking in all bedrooms CTV in all bedrooms 20P No coaches Fishing Mountain bike hire No children 4yrs Xmas V meals No smoking in restaurant Last d 9pm
ROOMS: (incl. bkfst) s £48-£55; d £76-£90 **LB**
OFF-PEAK: (incl. bkfst) s £40-£45; d £60-£70
MEALS: Lunch fr £8.95 Dinner £15-£28alc
CARDS:

GLENROTHES Fife Map 11 NO20

★★★69% **Balgeddie House**
Balgeddie Way KY6 3ET (from M90 junct 3 take A92. Enter town then over two rbts and 1st left after garage for Cedham Rd. At 2nd rbt into Fortmanthills Rd then 3rd left) ☎ 01592 742511 FAX 01592 621702
This family-run business hotel is well worth seeking out, set in its own, secluded grounds yet surrounded by a modern housing development to the north-west of the town. Spotlessly clean and well maintained, it offers a variety of well equipped bedrooms ranging from spacious first floor rooms to the smaller ones on the top floor, where attractive fabrics have been used to good effect. In addition to the restaurant and cocktail lounge, the Paddock Bar, contained in outside buildings, offers a less formal environment for a meal and a drink.
18 en suite (bth/shr) (3 fmly) CTV in all bedrooms STV No dogs (ex guide dogs) 100P Riding Pool table Croquet lawn Wkly live entertainment Xmas Scottish & French Cuisine V meals Coffee am Tea pm Last d 9.30pm
ROOMS: (incl. bkfst) s £57-£71; d fr £101 * **LB**
OFF-PEAK: (incl. bkfst) s fr £40; d fr £55
MEALS: Lunch £9-£10 High tea £4.95-£7.25 Dinner £16.50*
CONF: Thtr 50 Class 20 Board 25 Del from £65
CARDS:

★★❀71% **Rescobie**
Valley Dr, Leslie KY6 3BQ (at end of village turn W at sharp bend, 50 yards further on turn left)
☎ 01592 742143 FAX 01592 620231
Tucked away in its own grounds, this Edwardian house is conveniently located for both business people and golfing enthusiasts. The owners, Tony and Wendy Hughes-Lewis, provide friendly, attentive service which means that guests return year after year. There is a relaxing lounge, with a log fire in winter and pretty posies of flowers on the mantelpiece. The tiny lounge bar has bright tartan stools, and the restaurant overlooks the garden. Bedrooms vary in size, with those in the main house being the most spacious, though all are well equipped and have smart, fully tiled bathrooms.
10 en suite (bth/shr) (1 fmly) CTV in all bedrooms No dogs (ex guide dogs) 20P No coaches Putting green International Cuisine V meals Coffee am Tea pm Last d 9pm
ROOMS: (incl. bkfst) s £48-£52; d £68-£70 * **LB**
OFF-PEAK: (incl. bkfst) s £35; d £45
MEALS: Lunch £7.50-£11.95alc Dinner £16&alc
CARDS:

Travel Inn
Beaufort Dr, Bankhead Roundabout (from M90 junct3 take A92 to Glenrothes. First rdbt is Bankhead) ☎ 01592 773473 FAX 01592 773453
Purpose-built accommodation, offering spacious, well equipped bedrooms, all with en suite bathrooms. Meals may be taken at the nearby family restaurant. For more information about Travel Inns, consult the Contents page under Hotel Groups.
40 en suite (bth/shr)
ROOMS: (incl. bkfst) d £35.50 *

GLENSHEE (SPITTAL OF) Perthshire & Kinross Map 15 NO16

★★65% **Dalmunzie House**

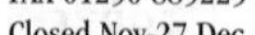

PH10 7QG (turn left off A93 to Spittal of Glenshee, Hotel 400 yards on left) ☎ 01250 885224
FAX 01250 885225
Closed Nov-27 Dec
A striking turreted mansion, set at the end of a long drive in 6,000 acres of its own private glen, boasts a challenging golf course and a fishing river. Very much the home of the delightful owners who, along with their friendly staff, provide an informal and welcoming atmosphere, the hotel is popular with families, golfers, walkers and

field sports enthusiasts. The snug bar and former smoking room have a selection of bar games and a bar billiards table, and there is also a table tennis room and residents' TV lounge; imaginative home-cooked food, based on fresh local ingredients, is served in the dining room. Bedrooms are generally comfortable, although some are plainly furnished, others contain fine period pieces. Ski packages are available for Glenshee, which is only 15 minutes away.
18 rms (16 bth/shr) Lift 32P No coaches Golf 9 Tennis (hard) Fishing Croquet lawn Clay pigeon shooting Deer stalking Xmas V meals Coffee am Tea pm Last d 8.30pm
ROOMS: (incl. bkfst) s £48-£54; d £74-£90 **LB**
OFF-PEAK: (incl. bkfst) s £32-£36; d £50-£64
MEALS: Bar Lunch fr £1.50alc Dinner £17-£20
CONF: Thtr 20 Class 20 Board 20
CARDS:

GLEN SHIEL (SHIEL BRIDGE) Highland Map 14 NG91

★★62% **Kintail Lodge**
IV40 8HL (on A87, at head of Loch Duich)
☎ 01599 511275 FAX 01599 511226
Now owned and personally run by the Fitt family, this former shooting lodge beside the shore of Loch Duich has retained its welcoming atmosphere and continues to appeal to the touring holidaymaker. Public areas include a relaxing sitting room which is comfortably traditional, and there is a choice of contrasting bars as well as an attractive dining room with beamed walls. Bedrooms, many enjoying loch views, are variable in size with mixed appointments.
12 rms (7 bth 3 shr) (2 fmly) CTV in all bedrooms 30P Pool table V meals Coffee am Tea pm No smoking in restaurant
ROOMS: (incl. bkfst & dinner) s fr £39.50; d fr £74.50 * **LB**
OFF-PEAK: (incl. bkfst & dinner) s fr £29.50; d fr £54.50
MEALS: Bar Lunch fr £8.50alc
CARDS:

GOLSPIE Highland Map 14 NH89

★★60% **Golf Links**
KW10 6TT (off A9, Hotel 300 yards along coast road)
☎ 01408 633408
This small family-run hotel is, as its name implies, situated adjacent to the golf course and enjoys fine views over the Dornoch Firth. Bedrooms vary in size and have modest furnishings, though they are all well kept and some have sea views. Public areas include a choice of bars as well as a spacious residents' lounge which retains the stone walls of the original manse which was extended to form the hotel.
9 en suite (bth/shr) (1 fmly) CTV in all bedrooms 20P No coaches Putting green Scottish & French Cuisine V meals Coffee am Tea pm Last d 8.30pm
ROOMS: (incl. bkfst) s £25-£30; d £50 * **LB**
OFF-PEAK: (incl. bkfst) s fr £25; d fr £50
MEALS: Bar Lunch £3.50-£10 Dinner £17.50-£20
CARDS:

GRANGEMOUTH Falkirk Map 11 NS98

★★★63% **Grange Manor**
Glensburgh FK3 8XJ (travelling E; off M9 at junc 6,Hotel 200m on left, travelling W; off M9 at junc 5, A905 for 2 miles) ☎ 01324 474836
FAX 01324 665861
The Wallace family offer a warm welcome to their constantly improving hotel, which is popular with business clientele. Bedrooms vary in size but have been tastefully decorated and provide all the expected facilities. Public areas include an open plan bar/lounge and an attractive restaurant where Craig Davidson offers a short but imaginative range of dishes which are exceptionally good value, particularly at lunchtime. The informal Coach House also provides bar meals and there are good function facilities.

7 en suite (bth/shr) (2 fmly) CTV in all bedrooms No dogs (ex guide dogs) 100P Xmas Scottish & French Cuisine V meals Coffee am Tea pm No smoking area in restaurant Last d 9.30pm
ROOMS: (incl. bkfst) s £64-£69; d £80-£85 * **LB**
MEALS: Lunch £11.25-£11.95 Dinner £18.95&alc
CONF: Thtr 130 Class 63 Board 40 Del from £78
CARDS:

GRANTOWN-ON-SPEY Highland Map 14 NJ02

★★★67% **Garth**

Castle Rd PH26 3HN ☎ 01479 872836 & 872162
FAX 01479 872116
Closed 9-31 Nov
Situated on the main road at the north end of town, this friendly personally run holiday and sporting hotel has a relaxed friendly atmosphere. The brightly decorated bedrooms are comfortable modern in style and offer a wide range of amenities. On the cooler evenings, the two comfortable lounges are warmed by log fires, and the cosy bar is a popular meeting place for diners and residents. Prime Scottish beef, game and seafood feature strongly on the daily changing fixed price menu and the uncomplicated style of cooking allows natural flavours to shine through.
17 en suite (bth/shr) CTV in all bedrooms STV 22P Scottish & French Cuisine V meals Coffee am Tea pm No smoking in restaurant Last d 8.30pm
ROOMS: (incl. bkfst) s £40-£49; d £80-£85 * **LB**
OFF-PEAK: (incl. bkfst) s £30-£40; d £60-£70
MEALS: Sunday Lunch £10-£15 High tea £5-£6 Dinner £15-£24*
CARDS:

★69% **Tyree House**
8 The Square PH26 3HF ☎ 01479 872615
A welcoming atmosphere prevails at this comfortable family run holiday and sporting hotel which stands in the town square. The variable sized bedrooms are decorated to a high standard and are comfortably modern in style. There is no longer a lounge, but the well stocked bar is comfortable and there is an attractive timber clad restaurant. The carte offers a wide range of dishes at competitive prices and is available in both bar and restaurant.
10 en suite (bth/shr) (1 fmly) CTV in all bedrooms 20P No coaches Xmas V meals Coffee am Last d 9pm
ROOMS: (incl. bkfst) s £25-£30; d £44-£50 *
MEALS: Lunch £6-£12 Dinner £10-£15
CARDS:

See advertisement on page 783

G

GRETNA (WITH GRETNA GREEN) Dumfries & Galloway
Map 11 NY36

★★★63% ***Garden House***
Sarkfoot Rd CA6 5EP ☎ 01461 337621 FAX 01461 337692
This modern hotel is just outside the town limits, convenient for the A74 yet only a couple of miles from the famous Blacksmiths' shop. Bedrooms are spacious and ideally equipped for the business traveller, and there is also a honeymoon suite with a four-poster bed and a jacuzzi. The open-plan lounge and dining room are in the large foyer of the hotel, while the indoor leisure centre has a good range of facilities. The Japanese water garden is an attractive area for wedding photographs.
21 en suite (bth/shr) (2 fmly) CTV in all bedrooms STV No dogs (ex guide dogs) 105P Continental Cuisine V meals Coffee am Tea pm
CARDS:

See advertisement on opposite page

★★66% **Solway Lodge**
Annan Rd DG16 5DN ☎ 01461 338266
FAX 01461 337791

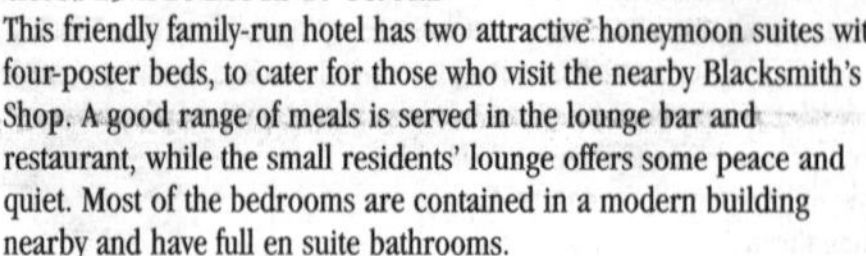

Closed 25 & 26 Dec RS 10 Oct-Mar
This friendly family-run hotel has two attractive honeymoon suites with four-poster beds, to cater for those who visit the nearby Blacksmith's Shop. A good range of meals is served in the lounge bar and restaurant, while the small residents' lounge offers some peace and quiet. Most of the bedrooms are contained in a modern building nearby and have full en suite bathrooms.
3 en suite (bth/shr) 7 annexe en suite (bth/shr) CTV in all bedrooms 25P No coaches V meals Coffee am Tea pm No smoking in restaurant
CARDS:

★★63% **Gretna Chase**
DG16 5JB (off A74 onto B7076, left at top of slip road, Hotel 400 yards on right) ☎ 01461 337517 FAX 01461 337766
This family-run hotel seems to be in no man's land, situated between the signs for Scotland and England, and as such being the first and last hotel in those countries, depending on your direction of travel! Several of the bedrooms have four-poster or half-tester beds and antique furniture. The spacious dining room can accommodate dinner parties and wedding breakfasts, while the cosy lounge bar is popular for meals. In the summer, the hotel's award-winning beer garden comes into its own.
8 rms (3 bth 3 shr) CTV in all bedrooms No dogs (ex guide dogs) 40P English & French Cuisine V meals Coffee am
ROOMS: (incl. bkfst) s £39-£49; d £65-£90 *
MEALS: Lunch £9.50-£20alc*
CONF: Thtr 50 Class 30 Board 20
CARDS:

Travelodge
CA6 5HQ (on A74, northbound) ☎ 01461 337566

Travelodge

This modern building offers accommodation in smart, spacious and well equipped bedrooms, suitable for family use, and all with en suite bathrooms. Meals may be taken at the nearby family restaurant. For information on room rates and to make a booking, call Roomline free of charge on 0800 850950. For more details about Travelodge, consult the Contents page under Hotel Groups.
64 en suite (bth/shr)

GULLANE East Lothian Map 12 NT48

RED STAR HOTEL

★★★ **Greywalls**
Muirfield EH31 2EG (A198, Hotel is signposted at east end of village)
☎ 01620 842144 FAX 01620 842241

Closed Nov-Mar
Immaculate but not intimidating, this fine Luytens house has spectacular views across Muirfield Golf Course as well as its own beautiful gardens designed by Gertrude Jekyll. The array of public areas include a wood-panelled library with an open fire, leather bound books and grand piano, and an adjoining lounge with a fascinating old wooden jigsaw. Bedrooms vary in size, but all are individually styled with attractive furnishings and fabrics, while huge bath sheets, fruit and flowers are just some of the extras to make your stay more enjoyable. A hot water bottle is placed in the bed each evening, and this gives an idea of the kind of attentive and thoughtful service provided at all times. The daily changing dinner menu has a traditional French style though local produce is used much of the time. A light pistachio soufflé was the highlight of a recent meal, which also included loin of lamb with a red wine and tarragon sauce and a vodka and lemon sorbet.

17 en suite (bth/shr) 5 annexe en suite (bth/shr) CTV in all bedrooms STV Night porter 40P No coaches Tennis (hard) Croquet lawn Putting green Coffee am Tea pm No smoking in restaurant Last d 9.15pm
ROOMS: (incl. bkfst) s fr £95; d fr £175 * **LB**
MEALS: Lunch £10-£20&alc Dinner £33*
CONF: Thtr 30 Class 20 Board 20 Del £129.50
CARDS:

HALKIRK Highland Map 15 ND15

★★61% **Ulbster Arms**
Bridge St KW12 6XY (A9 to Latheron from Perth left on to A895)
☎ 01847 831206 & 831641
FAX 01847 831206
Situated beside the River Thurso, this long established Highland hotel has particular appeal for the sporting enthusiast. Public areas, with tartan carpets and timber clad walls are comfortably traditional while bedrooms, most of which are tastefully decorated, offer a mix of modest furnishings the simplest of which are to be found in the annexe rooms.
10 en suite (bth/shr) 16 annexe en suite (bth) CTV in all bedrooms 30P Fishing Pool table V meals Coffee am Tea pm Last d 8.45pm
ROOMS: (incl. bkfst) s £33-£39; d £55-£69 *
OFF-PEAK: (incl. bkfst) s £30-£33
MEALS: Bar Lunch £1.40-£10.95 Dinner £15.50-£19*
CARDS:

HAMILTON South Lanarkshire Map 11 NS75
See also Bothwell

Holiday Inn Express

Strathclyde Country Park ML1 3RB (junct 5 off M74 follow signs for Strathclyde Country park)
☎ 01698 858585
FAX 01698 852375
A new concept in lodges, this attractive building, with Innkeeper's Lodge adjacent, is situated just off junction 5 of the M74 motorway, on the edge of Strathclyde Country Park. Bedrooms include remote control TVs as well as hairdryers and modem points. Rooms for disabled persons and family rooms are available. Continental breakfast is served in a pleasant dining room and there is also vending machines for drinks and snacks. A business centre is also provided.
80 en suite (shr)
ROOMS: (incl. cont bkfst) s fr £45; d fr £45 *
CONF: Thtr 30 Class 10 Board 15

HAMILTON MOTORWAY SERVICE AREA (M74)
South Lanarkshire Map 11 NS75

Roadchef Motorway Lodge
RoadChef Lodge
M74 Northbound ML3 6JW (M74, 1m N of junc 6)
☎ 01698 891904
FAX 01698 891682
Smart, spacious and well equipped bedrooms, all with en suite bathrooms, are provided by this modern hotel. Meals may be taken at a nearby family restaurant. For more information about RoadChef Lodges, consult the Contents page under Hotel Groups.
36 en suite (bth/shr)
ROOMS: d £39.95 *
CONF: Board 20

HARLOSH See Skye, Isle of

HARRIS, ISLE OF Western Isles Map 13

TARBERT Map 13 NB10

★★63% **Harris**
HS3 3DL (on A859) ☎ 01859 502154 FAX 01859 502281
Traditional values of service, hospitality and comfort remain the hallmarks of this welcoming family run holiday hotel which is ideally situated close to the ferry terminal. With friendly and willing local staff, the atmosphere is friendly and appropriately relaxed throughout the public areas which include a snug well stocked bar, choice of lounges with all day snacks available in the sun lounge, and a decidedly traditional dining room which features honest home cooking. The variable sized bedrooms are more mixed in style.
25 rms (12 bth 5 shr) (2 fmly) CTV in 10 bedrooms 30P No coaches Pool table ch fac International Cuisine V meals Coffee am Tea pm No smoking in restaurant
CARDS:

HAWICK Scottish Borders Map 12 NT51

★★71% **Kirklands**
West Stewart Place TD9 8BH (0.5m N from Hawick High Street, 200yds W of A7) ☎ 01450 372263 FAX 01450 370404
Two fine Victorian mansions adjoining this long-established hotel contain several spacious, comfortable bedrooms, while the rest are housed in the main building; all the rooms are equipped to a high standard. Guests can relax in the cosy lounge bar with its display of Toby jugs or in the writing-room/library, and there is also a billiards room. Popular with residents and non-residents alike, this traditional hotel also offers attractive gardens.
5 en suite (bth/shr) 7 annexe en suite (bth/shr) CTV in all bedrooms 20P Snooker Pool table ch fac International Cuisine V meals Coffee am
ROOMS: (incl. bkfst) s £35-£48.50; d £60-£75 * **LB**
OFF-PEAK: (incl. bkfst) d £50-£75
MEALS: Bar Lunch £6-£10alc Dinner £14.50-£16.50&alc
CARDS:

★★61% **Elm House**
17 North Bridge St TD9 9BD (on A7 in centre of Hawick)
☎ 01450 372866 FAX 01450 374715
Situated on the main road through the town, this family-run hotel offers good value accommodation and food. Bedrooms are sensibly furnished and provide all the expected amenities. Inexpensive meals are served either in the lounge bar or restaurant, while the first floor residents' lounge offers a relaxing area. Car parking is available to the rear of the hotel.
7 en suite (bth/shr) 8 annexe en suite (shr) (3 fmly) CTV in all bedrooms 13P European Cuisine V meals Coffee am Tea pm Last d 9.30pm
ROOMS: (incl. bkfst) s fr £30; d fr £42 * **LB**
OFF-PEAK: (incl. bkfst) s fr £28; d fr £38
MEALS: Bar Lunch £3.70-£8 High tea fr £6 Dinner fr £10&alc*
CARDS:

HELENSBURGH Argyll & Bute Map 10 NS28

★★68% **Commodore Toby**

112 West Clyde St G84 8ER (on A814 seafront, 400m W of Pier) ☎ 01436 676924 FAX 01436 676233
RS 27-30 Dec
This attractive hotel with modern bedrooms commands splendid views over the Firth of Clyde from the recently refurbished bars and restaurant and those bedrooms located at the front of the hotel. The popular restaurant has been decorated in three contrasting styles and includes a spacious conservatory eating area. Service throughout is friendly and helpful and the atmosphere is warm and relaxing. All bedrooms are comfortably furnished and have every contemporary facility. Versatile conference and banqueting facilities are available and there is also a large car park at the rear.

45 en suite (bth/shr) (3 fmly) No smoking in 11 bedrooms CTV in all bedrooms STV No dogs (ex guide dogs) Lift Night porter 120P Pool table Xmas V meals Coffee am Tea pm No smoking in restaurant Last d 10pm
ROOMS: (incl. bkfst) s £35-£63; d £65-£78 * **LB**
MEALS: Lunch £7-£15alc High tea £7 Dinner £7-£15alc*
CONF: Thtr 200 Class 100 Board 80 Del from £76.50
CARDS:

HOWWOOD Renfrewshire Map 10 NS36

★★★65% **Bowfield Hotel & Country Club**
Lands of Bowfield PA9 1DB (M8, A737 for 6m, left onto B787, right after 2m, follow road for 1m to Hotel)
☎ 01505 705225 FAX 01505 705230
Set amid open countryside half a mile from the village off the B776, this popular hotel and leisure complex has been created by careful conversion of a former textile mill. Relaxed and informal public areas feature timbered ceilings, brick and white painted stone walls and welcoming open fires. Bedrooms are sensibly located in a quiet wing and offer good modern appointments together with a wide range of amenities.
23 en suite (bth/shr) (3 fmly) CTV in all bedrooms No dogs (ex guide dogs) Night porter 100P Indoor swimming pool (heated) Squash Snooker Sauna Solarium Gym Pool table Jacuzzi/spa Health & beauty treatment rooms Wkly live entertainment International Cuisine V meals Coffee am Tea pm No smoking in restaurant Last d 10pm
ROOMS: (incl. bkfst) s £65; d £90 * **LB**
OFF-PEAK: (incl. bkfst) s fr £55; d fr £76
MEALS: Lunch £6.50-£9.50&alc Dinner £8-£25alc
CONF: Thtr 90 Class 60 Board 20 Del from £92
CARDS:

HUMBIE East Lothian Map 12 NT46

★★★ 62% **Johnstounburn House**
THISTLE HOTELS
EH36 5PL (A68, B6368, 1.5m S of Humbie village is the Hotel) ☎ 01875 833696 FAX 01875 833626
Reached via a long tree-lined drive and surrounded by acres of gardens and the rolling farmland of the Lammermuir hills, this 17th-century country house is a haven of peace and quiet yet it is within easy reach of all that Edinburgh has to offer. Bedrooms are appointed in sympathetic style although they lack several of the modern facilities usually associated with Thistle hotels. The public areas, largely housed on the first floor, offer open fires, fine wood panelling and ornate plasterwork. Service is friendly and relaxed befitting the style of the house.

11 rms (10 bth/shr) 9 annexe en suite (bth/shr) (5 fmly) CTV in all bedrooms STV 100P Fishing Clay pigeon shooting All terrain vehicle Xmas V meals Coffee am Tea pm No smoking in restaurant Last d 9pm
ROOMS: (incl. bkfst) s fr £99; d fr £130 * **LB**
OFF-PEAK: (incl. bkfst) s fr £75; d fr £100
MEALS: Lunch fr £18 Dinner fr £29
CONF: Thtr 50 Class 24 Board 30 Del from £118
CARDS:

HUNTLY Aberdeenshire Map 15 NJ53

★★★ 64% **Castle**
AB54 4SH ☎ 01466 792696 FAX 01466 792641
This impressive 18th century stone building stands behind the ruins of Huntly Castle and is reached by a delightful long drive. The hotel has been pleasantly furnished and provides traditional style bedrooms together with spacious and comfortable public rooms. It is popular with both with the sporting enthusiast and the holiday maker and offers warm and friendly service whilst a good range of food is available either in the bar or attractive restaurant.
20 en suite (bth/shr) (4 fmly) CTV in all bedrooms STV 50P Fishing Croquet lawn Xmas Scottish & French Cuisine V meals Coffee am Tea pm No smoking in restaurant Last d 9pm
ROOMS: (incl. bkfst) s £48; d £68.50 **LB**
MEALS: Bar Lunch £9-£18.25 High tea £7.50-£11.50 Dinner £14.50&alc*
CONF: Thtr 60 Class 40 Board 36 Del £75
CARDS:

INVERARAY Argyll & Bute Map 10 NN00

★64% **Fernpoint**
PA32 8UX (A83 through Inverary, hotel on Pierhead)
☎ 01499 302170 FAX 01499 302366
Closed 5 Jan-5 Feb
A friendly and relaxed style of service is provided at this family-owned and -run hotel which stands on the shores of Loch Fyne. Bedrooms do vary in size but have been tastefully furnished and are well equipped with all the expected amenities. The bar is full of character with open stone walls being a feature a feature of its conversion from a former stable. An extensive range of food is provided and a good selection of malts can be found at the bar.
8 en suite (bth/shr) (3 fmly) CTV in all bedrooms Night porter 15P Affiliated to golf course ch fac European Cuisine V meals Coffee am Tea pm Last d 9pm
ROOMS: (incl. bkfst) s £30-£50; d £50-£70 * **LB**
OFF-PEAK: (incl. bkfst) s £18-£30; d £36-£55
MEALS: Lunch £5-£8 High tea £5.95 Dinner £15.95*
CARDS:

INVERGARRY Highland Map 14 NH30

★★★ 64% **Glengarry Castle**
PH35 4HW ☎ 01809 501254 FAX 01809 501207
Closed 27 Sep-3 Nov
This impressive Victorian baronial mansion is situated in over 50 acres of park and woodland by the shores of Loch Oich, with the ruins of Invergarry Castle within the grounds. Efficiently run by the MacCallum family for nearly 40 years, the hotel has recently undergone tasteful refurbishment, and there is now a choice of smart standard rooms, and more spacious superior rooms, some of which have four-poster or half-tester beds. Public areas include a pine-panelled reception hall, and two lounges which enjoy views of the loch. A traditional-style menu is offered in the restaurant.
26 en suite (bth/shr) (4 fmly) No smoking in 2 bedrooms CTV in all bedrooms 32P No coaches Tennis (hard) Fishing Scottish, English & Continental Cuisine V meals Coffee am Tea pm No smoking in restaurant Last d 8.30pm

contd.

ROOMS: (incl. bkfst) s £47-£57; d £80-£96
OFF-PEAK: (incl. bkfst) s £42-£52; d £70-£86
MEALS: Dinner £21-£23
CARDS:

See advertisement on page 787

INVERMORISTON Highland Map 14 NH41

★★69% **Glenmoriston Arms**
IV3 6YA (at the junct of A82/A877)
☎ 01320 351206 FAX 01320 351308

Enthusiastic new owners Neil and Carol Scott are already beginning to make their mark on this popular and successful former inn which is in an ideal location close to Loch Ness. Bedrooms are traditional in style, but are all comfortably furnished, well equipped and en suite. The characterful public areas include a cosy lounge and a lounge bar where there are 90 single malt whiskies to choose from, including helpful guidance notes! A good standard of food is served in the restaurant and there are also bar meals available for those wishing to eat less formally.
8 en suite (bth/shr) CTV in all bedrooms 28P No coaches Fishing Pool table Stalking Shooting Xmas V meals Coffee am Tea pm No smoking in restaurant Last d 8.30pm
ROOMS: (incl. bkfst) s fr £47.50; d fr £75 * **LB**
OFF-PEAK: (incl. bkfst) s fr £40; d fr £60
MEALS: Bar Lunch £14.80-£16alc Dinner £17.50-£22.50
CARDS:

INVERNESS Highland Map 14 NH64
See also Kirkhill

★★★★67% **Culloden House**
Culloden IV1 2NZ (take A96 from town and turn right for Culloden. After 1m, turn left at White Church after second traffic lights) ☎ 01463 790461
FAX 01463 792181

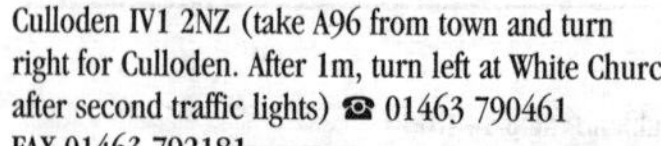

Bonnie Prince Charlie left for the battle of Culloden from this historic house, close to Inverness. The sweeping drive gives a delightful first impression, which is born out by the elegance of the public areas with their fine plasterwork, chandeliers, marble fireplaces and antique furnishings, and the many bedrooms also uphold the character and luxury of the hotel. There is also a separate mansion house, near some interesting tree sculptures, with four sumptuous bedrooms.
20 en suite (bth/shr) 5 annexe en suite (bth/shr) (1 fmly) No smoking in 5 bedrooms CTV in all bedrooms Night porter 30P No coaches Tennis (hard) Snooker Sauna Solarium Croquet lawn No children 10yrs Xmas Scottish & French Cuisine V meals Coffee am Tea pm No smoking in restaurant Last d 9pm
ROOMS: (incl. bkfst) s £125; d £175-£220 * **LB**
OFF-PEAK: (incl. bkfst) s £69-£125; d £99-£175
MEALS: Lunch £12-£25alc Dinner £35*
CONF: Thtr 70 Class 40 Board 30 Del from £110
CARDS:

★★★★67% **Kingsmills**
Culcabock Rd IV2 3LP ☎ 01463 237166
FAX 01463 225208

Set in four acres of colourful and well tended gardens on the southern edge of the town, this well established hotel offers smartly appointed and well equipped accommodation. The impressive public areas, which include a large foyer lounge, cocktail bar and conservatory are decorated with rich fabrics, interesting pictures and prints and large vases of fresh flowers. Guests have the choice of eating less formally in the conservatory or in the restaurant where the service is helpful and friendly. A very well equipped leisure centre is also available.
78 en suite (bth/shr) 6 annexe en suite (bth/shr) (11 fmly) No smoking in 23 bedrooms CTV in all bedrooms STV Lift Night porter 100P Indoor swimming pool (heated) Sauna Solarium Gym Putting green Jacuzzi/spa Hair & beauty salon Steam room Xmas V meals Coffee am Tea pm No smoking in restaurant Last d 9.30pm
ROOMS: (incl. bkfst) s £100-£125; d £135-£160 * **LB**
MEALS: Lunch £9.95-£12 Dinner £21&alc*
CONF: Thtr 80 Class 28 Board 30
CARDS:

★★★74% **Craigmonie**
9 Annfield Rd IV2 3HX (off A9/A96 follow signs Hilton, Culcabock pass golf course second road on right)
☎ 01463 231649 FAX 01463 233720
Many guests return on a regular basis to this most welcoming business and tourist hotel which offers a wide range of leisure facilities. Bedrooms range from the attractive poolside suites with spa bath and balcony, to the variable-sized standard rooms which provide good levels of comfort together with a wide range of amenities. Public areas include a quiet non-smoking lounge and a well stocked and comfortable panelled bar, and guests have the option of dining in Chardonnay which offers a wide range of seafood specialities, or in the informal atmosphere of the Poolside Brasserie.
35 en suite (bth/shr) (3 fmly) No smoking in 10 bedrooms CTV in all bedrooms STV Lift Night porter 60P Indoor swimming pool (heated) Sauna Solarium Gym Jacuzzi/spa Scottish & French Cuisine V meals Coffee am Tea pm No smoking in restaurant Last d 10pm
ROOMS: (incl. bkfst) s £58.50-£63.50; d £78-£97 *
MEALS: Lunch £9.50-£10.50 Dinner £20-£35alc*
CONF: Thtr 150 Class 50 Board 40 Del from £92
CARDS:

★★★72% **Bunchrew House**
Bunchrew IV3 6TA (3m W off A862)
☎ 01463 234917 FAX 01463 710620
This lovely 17th-century mansion is set in 20 acres of wooded grounds right on the shores of the Beauly Firth two miles west of Inverness. Carefully restored, it blends original features such as wood panelling, open fires and large master bedrooms with modern amenities and tasteful décor. Public areas have a relaxing atmosphere, while bedrooms are of a standard to appeal to the international business traveller as well as the tourist. The individually-priced carte offered at dinner places the emphasis on prime Scottish produce, with the quality of its beef and game being of particular merit.
11 en suite (bth/shr) (1 fmly) CTV in all bedrooms STV 40P Fishing Croquet lawn Xmas Scottish & French Cuisine V meals Coffee am Tea pm No smoking in restaurant Last d 9pm
ROOMS: (incl. bkfst) s £55-£78; d £75-£115 **LB**
CONF: Thtr 80 Class 40 Board 30
CARDS:

See advertisement on opposite page

★★★68% **Inverness Thistle**
Millburn Rd IV2 3TR (junc A9/A96)
☎ 01463 239666 FAX 01463 711145
RS 1 Jan

THISTLE HOTELS

This modern hotel, which is ideally situated to allow easy access to both the A9 and A96, offers well equipped accommodation including a number of family rooms and a suite; all but a handful of the rooms have been refurbished. The smartly appointed public areas include an impressive marble foyer and a comfortable and inviting open-plan lounge. A good range of carefully prepared dishes is available in the restaurant which may include dishes such as a timbale of sole mousse wrapped in spinach with an oyster and served with an anchovy butter sauce, or roast leg of Scottish lamb.

118 en suite (bth/shr) (11 fmly) No smoking in 24 bedrooms CTV in all bedrooms STV Lift Night porter 150P Xmas International Cuisine V meals Coffee am Tea pm Last d 9.30pm
ROOMS: s £78-£88; d £100-£115 * **LB**
OFF-PEAK: s fr £55; d fr £70
MEALS: Lunch £5-£12 Dinner fr £16.95&alc
CONF: Thtr 230 Class 72 Board 70 Del from £80
CARDS:

★★★67% **Loch Ness House**
Glenurquhart Rd IV3 6JL (1.5m from town centre, overlooking Tomnahurich Bridge on canal)
☎ 01463 231248 FAX 01463 239327

CONSORT HOTELS

Ongoing improvements continue at this popular business and tourist hotel on the south side of town close to the Caledonian Canal. Welcoming public areas include a comfortable new lounge and a choice of restaurants; one offers Scottish fare and the other specialises in fresh seafood. Bedrooms vary in size with mixed modern appointments.

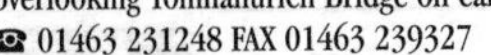

22 en suite (bth/shr) (3 fmly) No smoking in 6 bedrooms CTV in all bedrooms STV 60P No coaches Wkly live entertainment Xmas Scottish & French Cuisine V meals Coffee am Tea pm No smoking area in restaurant Last d 9.30pm
ROOMS: (incl. bkfst) s £52.50-£65; d £95-£120 * **LB**
OFF-PEAK: (incl. bkfst) s £35-£50; d £45-£65
MEALS: Dinner £16.50-£20.50&alc*
CONF: Thtr 150 Class 60 Board 40 Del from £63.50
CARDS:

★★★66% **Lochardil House**
Stratherrick Rd IV2 4LF (follow Island Bank Road for 1m, fork left into Drummond Crescent, into Stratherrick Road,0.5m Hotel on left)
☎ 01463 235995 FAX 01463 713394
A welcoming atmosphere prevails at this castellated Victorian house which has recently been substantially improved to cater for the needs of its predominantly business clientele. Adjacent to the well stocked cocktail bar is the popular conservatory restaurant which offers a wide range of both light and substantial dishes. Bedrooms are comfortably appointed in the modern style.
12 en suite (bth/shr) CTV in all bedrooms STV No dogs (ex guide dogs) 123P No coaches Scottish & French Cuisine V meals Coffee am Tea pm Last d 9pm
ROOMS: (incl. bkfst) s £62.50-£70; d £80-£90 **LB**
OFF-PEAK: (incl. bkfst) s £55-£60; d £70
MEALS: Lunch £6-£15alc Dinner £15-£18.50&alc
CONF: Thtr 120 Class 100 Board 60 Del from £85
CARDS:

★★★61% **Palace**
Ness Walk IV3 5NE (town centre on banks of River Ness) ☎ 01463 223243 FAX 01463 236865
This busy hotel enjoys views of the castle on the other side of the river, and is a popular base for visiting tour groups. Public areas include a spacious lounge, bar and dining room. Some bedrooms have benefited from upgrading, especially those overlooking the river, but others, especially those in the rear annexe, remain compact and somewhat dated in appointment.
42 en suite (bth/shr) 41 annexe en suite (bth/shr) (12 fmly) CTV in all bedrooms Lift Night porter 40P Xmas Scottish & French Cuisine V meals Coffee am Tea pm No smoking in restaurant Last d 9pm
ROOMS: (incl. bkfst) s £59-£69; d £79-£84 * **LB**
OFF-PEAK: (incl. bkfst) s £49-£59; d £69-£79
MEALS: Lunch £7.50-£35 High tea fr £6.20 Dinner fr £9&alc*
CONF: Thtr 100 Class 40 Board 40 Del from £49
CARDS:

RED STAR HOTEL

★★ **Dunain Park**
IV3 6JN (on A82, 1m from Inverness town boundary ☎ 01463 230512
FAX 01463 224532
Closed 10 Jan-20 Feb

SCOTLAND'S COMMENDED HOTELS

Surrounded by greenery on the edge of the capital of the Highlands, Dunain Park is both accessible and restful in its six acres of grounds which incorporate two walled kitchen gardens. A part-Italianate, part-vernacular Georgian villa it is furnished with antiques, modern comforts and plenty of thoughtful extras. The bedrooms are each individually designed with contemporary fabrics complementing the highly polished antique wood furniture; many have small lounges attached and the cottages have open fires. Ann Nicholl's cooking is, as ever, highly regarded with good use made of the region's quality produce.

contd.

Such is the variety of malt whisky on offer that there is a list detailing 200 by year from working distilleries.

14 rms (10 bth/shr) (6 fmly) CTV in all bedrooms 20P No coaches Indoor swimming pool (heated) Sauna Croquet lawn Badminton Xmas Scottish & French Cuisine V meals Coffee am Tea pm No smoking in restaurant Last d 9pm
ROOMS: (incl. bkfst) d £138 **LB**
OFF-PEAK: (incl. bkfst & dinner) d £138
MEALS: Dinner £25-£29.50alc
CARDS:

★★63% **Beaufort**
11 Culduthel Rd IV2 4AG (first left of duel carriage way, past Kingsmills Hotel first right, left at lights onto Southside Road, turn right onto Culdutnel Road) ☎ 01463 222897 FAX 01463 711413
A relaxed, friendly atmosphere prevails at this popular business and tourist hotel situated beyond the castle. Refurbishment is planned for the variable-sized en suite bedrooms which offer all the expected amenities. There is no lounge, but a choice of comfortable lounge bars is available, and in the attractive dining room the new improved carte includes a range of steak and seafood specialities.
36 en suite (shr) (6 fmly) CTV in all bedrooms STV Air conditioning 50P V meals Coffee am Tea pm Last d 9.45pm
ROOMS: (incl. bkfst) s £35-£45; d £50-£65 **LB**
MEALS: Lunch £4.95-£6.50&alc Dinner fr £10&alc*
CARDS:

★★63% **Windsor**
22 Ness Bank IV2 4SF (off B862, hotel below castle on riverside)
☎ 01463 715535 FAX 01463 713262
Closed 23-27 Dec & 30 Dec-4 Jan
Nestling under the castle, this friendly tourist and business hotel has a beautiful location overlooking the River Ness, and yet is only a few minutes' walk from the city centre. All the bedrooms are non-smoking and have been furnished with pine and pretty fabrics; they also provide all the expected amenities. The conservatory dining room offers a short supper menu and a good breakfast buffet, while the cosy lounge is a quiet place to relax.
18 en suite (bth/shr) (5 fmly) No smoking in 16 bedrooms CTV in all bedrooms STV No dogs (ex guide dogs) 14P No coaches V meals No smoking in restaurant Last d 7pm
ROOMS: (incl. bkfst) s £45-£68; d £50-£78 * **LB**
OFF-PEAK: (incl. bkfst) s £45-£65
MEALS: Lunch £12-£28alc Dinner £16-£28&alc
CONF: Class 30
CARDS:

★★60% **Cummings**
Church St IV1 1EN (in town centre, off Union Street onto Church Street) ☎ 01463 232531 FAX 01463 236541
Catering for tour groups and also the visiting businessman, this long-established town centre hotel offers good value for money. The spotless bedrooms are variable in size and offer uniform practical appointments while public areas include a choice of bars, a traditional-style dining room and a popular coffee lounge.
26 rms (23 bth/shr) (3 fmly) CTV in all bedrooms No dogs (ex guide dogs) Lift Night porter 25P Xmas V meals Coffee am Tea pm No smoking in restaurant Last d 8.30pm
ROOMS: (incl. bkfst) s £35-£42; d £60-£70 *
OFF-PEAK: (incl. bkfst) s £30-£35; d £50-£60
MEALS: Lunch £5.30-£6.70 High tea £6.95 Dinner £12-£16
CONF: Thtr 250 Class 90 Board 50 Del from £42
CARDS:

★★59% **Smithton**
Smithton IV1 2NL (A96, 2m turn first right, 2m to Smithton Hotel)
☎ 01463 791999 FAX 01463 794559
This purpose-built hotel lies at the centre of the small village of Smithton, about three miles west of Inverness. Bedrooms are attractively furnished in pine and offer good amenities, while both the lounge and public bars are popular with the locals.
10 en suite (bth/shr) CTV in all bedrooms STV No dogs (ex guide dogs) 60P Pool table Wkly live entertainment Coffee am Tea pm Last d 8pm
ROOMS: (incl. bkfst) s £28.50; d £50-£52 *
CARDS:

Travel Inn

Millburn Rd IV2 3QX ☎ 01463 712010
FAX 01463 717826
Purpose-built accommodation, offering spacious, well equipped bedrooms, all with en suite bathrooms. Meals may be taken at the nearby family restaurant. For more information about Travel Inns, consult the Contents page under Hotel Groups.
40 en suite (bth/shr)
ROOMS: (incl. bkfst) d £35.50 *

INVERURIE Aberdeenshire Map 15 NJ72

★★★★ 70% **Thainstone House Hotel and Country Club**

Macdonald Hotels

AB51 5NT (A96 from Aberdeen, through Kintore, entrance to Hotel at first roundabout)
☎ 01467 621643 FAX 01467 625084
(Rosettes awarded for dinner only)
Set in 40 acres of parkland this elegant 19th century house offers smart, thoughtfully equipped accommodation. Many of the original features of the building have been retained. The impressive public which include a galleried reception hall, cocktail bar a drawing room and other delightful day rooms are enjoyable to use. There is also a very well appointed and equipped leisure centre. Head chef Gordon Dochard makes good use of the finest Scottish ingredients and produces a good choice of carefully prepared dishes such as loin of Scottish lamb, with creamed fennel, grilled kidneys and a port wine sauce.
48 en suite (bth/shr) (3 fmly) CTV in all bedrooms STV No dogs (ex guide dogs) Lift Night porter 100P Indoor swimming pool

(heated) Snooker Gym Jacuzzi/spa Archery Shooting JCB digger driving Xmas V meals Coffee am Tea pm No smoking in restaurant Last d 9.30pm
ROOMS: s fr £94; d fr £110 * **LB**
OFF-PEAK: (incl. bkfst) s fr £59; d fr £78
MEALS: Lunch £12.50-£15.50 Dinner £23.50&alc*
CONF: Thtr 300 Class 100 Board 20 Del from £130
CARDS:

★★★68% **Strathburn**
Burghmuir Dr AB51 4GY (at Blackhall rbt into Blackhall Rd for 100yds then into Burghmuir Drive)
☎ 01467 624422
FAX 01467 625133
This modern hotel is located in a residential area overlooking Strathburn Park. It is popular with business guests who enjoy the relaxed atmosphere, particularly in the refurbished lounge bar and the adjoining restaurant. Bedrooms are attractively decorated, with a soft look to them, and all the expected facilities are provided. There are also some larger executive rooms available.
25 en suite (bth/shr) (1 fmly) No smoking in 12 bedrooms CTV in all bedrooms STV No dogs (ex guide dogs) 40P No coaches V meals Coffee am Tea pm Last d 9.30pm
ROOMS: (incl. bkfst) s £65-£75; d £80-£90 **LB**
OFF-PEAK: (incl. bkfst) s £55-£65; d £65-£75
MEALS: Sunday Lunch £12-£14alc Dinner £18.75&alc
CONF: Thtr 30 Class 24 Board 16 Del from £93.75
CARDS:

IRVINE North Ayrshire Map 10 NS33

★★★★52% **Hospitality Inn**

46 Annick Rd KA11 4LD (access via A71 to Kilmarnock) ☎ 01294 274272
FAX 01294 277287
Standard and executive bedrooms at this large business hotel are roomy, comfortable and fully equipped, while well furnished and spacious public areas include a choice of two restaurants - the more formal Mirage, and the tropical Lagoon with its exotic plants and swimming pool. There is also an open-plan foyer lounge. The hotel attracts a considerable conference trade.
128 en suite (bth/shr) (44 fmly) No smoking in 16 bedrooms CTV in 28 bedrooms STV Night porter Air conditioning 250P Indoor swimming pool (heated) Golf 9 Putting green Jacuzzi/spa Wkly live entertainment Xmas Scottish & French Cuisine V meals Coffee am Tea pm No smoking area in restaurant Last d 10pm
ROOMS: s fr £78; d fr £103 * **LB**
OFF-PEAK: (incl. bkfst) s fr £75; d fr £98
MEALS: Lunch £9.95-£10.95&alc High tea fr £7.95&alc Dinner fr £14.50&alc*
CONF: Thtr 200 Class 120 Board 120 Del from £90
CARDS:

ISLAY, ISLE OF Argyll & Bute Map 10

BOWMORE Map 10 NR35

★★57% ***Lochside***
19 Shore St PA43 7LB (on A846, 100yds from main village square on shore side of road) ☎ 01496 810244 FAX 01496 810390
The unassuming main street frontage belies the lovely outlook over Loch Indaal from the back of this family-run business and tourist hotel. Bedrooms which tend to be compact, are gradually being redecorated. Seafood features strongly in the small dining room and the contrasting bars offer an unrivalled malt whisky selection.
8 en suite (bth/shr) (1 fmly) CTV in all bedrooms Pool table International Cuisine V meals Coffee am Tea pm Last d 9pm
CARDS:

BRIDGEND Map 10 NR36

★★67% ***Bridgend***
PA44 7PQ ☎ 01496 810212 FAX 01496 810673
Ideally situated in the middle of the island, this refurbished Victorian sporting and holiday hotel, with Gaelic-and English-speaking staff, has a wonderfully relaxed and friendly atmosphere. There is a choice of well stocked contrasting bars, a quiet lounge on the first floor, and an attractive dining room offering island produce whenever possible. The variable sized bedrooms offer mixed comfortable appointments along with a wide range of amenities.
10 rms (5 bth 4 shr) (3 fmly) CTV in all bedrooms 30P Fishing Bowls Coffee am Tea pm Last d 8.30pm

PORT ASKAIG Map 10 NR46

★★63% **Port Askaig**
PA46 7RD (at Ferry Terminal) ☎ 01496 840245 FAX 01496 840295
Situated right beside the ferry terminal overlooking the Sound of Islay, this welcoming family-run hotel combines traditional hospitality with modern day amenities. Relaxing public areas include a snug bar, a quiet first-floor lounge and traditional dining room. Bedrooms are variable in size with mixed modern appointments and offer most of the expected amenities.
8 rms (5 bth/shr) (1 fmly) CTV in all bedrooms 21P No coaches No children 5yrs V meals Coffee am Tea pm No smoking in restaurant Last d 9pm
ROOMS: (incl. bkfst) s £35-£39; d £66-£72 **LB**
MEALS: Lunch fr £10alc Dinner £17-£18

ISLE OF
Placenames incorporating the words 'Isle' or 'Isle of' will be found under the actual name, eg Isle of Arran is under Arran, Isle of.

ISLE ORNSAY See Skye, Isle of

JOHN O'GROATS See Halkirk and Lybster

KELSO Scottish Borders Map 12 NT73

★★★ 76% **Sunlaws House Hotel & Golf Course**

PRIDE OF BRITAIN MEMBER

Heiton TD5 8JZ (3m S on A698) ☎ 01573 450331
FAX 01573 450611
Sunlaws House is a fine baronial mansion lying in 200 acres of mature woodland and gardens by the banks of the River Teviot. Owned by the Duke of Roxburgh, it offers a wide range of outdoor sporting activities, including shooting, fishing and falconry, while an 18-hole golf course is in the process of being added. Bedrooms vary in size and are individually furnished with six rooms having been formed out of the original stable block. Public areas are comfortable and relaxing, while fine cuisine continues to be another attraction. Sweet Border lamb with rosemary and tomato jus was the highlight of a recent meal.

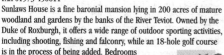

16 en suite (bth/shr) 6 annexe en suite (bth/shr) (2 fmly) CTV in all bedrooms STV Night porter 50P Golf 18 Tennis (hard) Fishing Croquet lawn Shooting Fishing Health & Beauty Saloon Wkly live entertainment Xmas Scottish & French Cuisine V meals Coffee am Tea pm No smoking in restaurant Last d 9.30pm
ROOMS: (incl. bkfst) s £95-£105; d £140-£225 * **LB**
MEALS: Lunch £14-£25 Dinner £27-£40
CONF: Thtr 40 Class 20 Board 20
CARDS:

★★★67% **Ednam House**
Bridge St TD5 7HT ☎ 01573 224168 FAX 01573 226319
Closed 25 Dec-10 Jan
This fine Georgian mansion sits in gardens overlooking the River Tweed, a position which makes it popular with salmon fishers. In the same family ownership since its conversion to a hotel in 1928, it retains an old-fashioned style and traditional values. Bedrooms range from standard to grand, all being well equipped, whilst public areas include three lounges, two bars and a dining room offering honest British cooking.
32 en suite (bth/shr) (2 fmly) CTV in all bedrooms Night porter 102P Croquet lawn V meals Coffee am Tea pm Last d 9pm
ROOMS: (incl. bkfst) s fr £50; d £69-£97 **LB**
MEALS: Sunday Lunch fr £12&alc High tea £7-£11alc Dinner £11-£20*
CONF: Thtr 250 Board 200
CARDS:

★★★61% **Cross Keys**
36-37 The Square TD5 7HL ☎ 01573 223303 FAX 01573 225792
A one-time coaching inn rebuilt in the Georgian era stands overlooking Kelso's fine cobbled square, its window boxes providing a mass of colour in summer. Now a family-run hotel, it has been improved over recent years so that many of the bedrooms offer comfortable modern accommodation; those yet to be upgraded have all the necessary facilities but their style is dated.
24 en suite (bth/shr) (4 fmly) CTV in all bedrooms STV No dogs (ex guide dogs) Lift Night porter Air conditioning Snooker Xmas Scottish & Continental Cuisine V meals Last d 9.15pm
ROOMS: (incl. bkfst) s £41.50-£44.90; d £53-£63 **LB**
OFF-PEAK: (incl. bkfst) s £37.50-£41.50; d £49-£55
MEALS: Lunch £6.90-£9.90 High tea £5.90 Dinner £16.90&alc
CONF: Thtr 280 Class 220 Board 70 Del from £62
CARDS:

KENTALLEN Highland Map 14 NN05

★★ 73% **Ardsheal House**
PA38 4BX (4m S of Ballachulish Bridge on A828 between Glencoe & Appin) ☎ 01631 740227 FAX 01631 740342
A spectacular single track road bordering the shore to Loch Linnhe leads to this fine Scottish mansion, which stands in 900 acres of secluded grounds with views over the loch to the Morvern Hills beyond. This was owner Neil Sutherland's birthplace and, with his managers Michelle and George Kelso, he is intimately involved with the hotel. Bedrooms are very individual in style and offer all modern comforts. Public areas include a choice of three sitting rooms, one with TV, a reception hall with a unique barrel window and an impressive timbered billiard room. The kitchen is George Kelso's domain, and his innovative modern cooking remains a highlight of a visit to Ardsheal; game, prime beef and seafood feature strongly and honest flavours shine through.
13 rms (11 bth/shr) 12P Tennis (hard) Snooker Billards Table ch fac Xmas European Cuisine V meals Coffee am Tea pm No smoking in restaurant Last d 8.30pm

ROOMS: (incl. bkfst & dinner) s fr £85; d £150-£180 * **LB**
OFF-PEAK: (incl. bkfst & dinner) s £55-£65; d £110-£130
MEALS: Lunch £18 High tea £5-£10 Dinner £32.50*
CARDS:

KILCHRENAN Argyll & Bute Map 10 NN02

★★★ 76% **Ardanaiseig**

PA35 1HE (from the A85 take the B845 and follow signs for Kilchrennan turn left into Kilchrenan and follow signs for Ardanaiseig)
☎ 01866 833333 FAX 01866 833222

Peacefully set amid spectacular gardens and breathtaking scenery beside the shore of Loch Awe, Ardanaiseig, built in the Scottish baronial style in 1834, is today a very civilised country house. New owners Mr and Mrs Gray have an antique business in the south and already have introduced many fine pieces of furniture. Charming day rooms include a spacious drawing room, an inviting library bar with an open fire, and an elegant dining room which overlooks the gardens to the loch. Gifted new chef Dale Thornber is producing good results. The short fixed-price menu is supported by a small carte and a carefully chosen and well balanced wine list.

Bedrooms range from well proportioned master bedrooms, which are very individual in style, more modest standard rooms.

14 en suite (bth/shr) No smoking in 2 bedrooms CTV in all bedrooms 22P No coaches Tennis (hard) Fishing Snooker Croquet lawn Putting green Boating Clay pigeon shooting No children 8yrs Xmas V meals Coffee am Tea pm No smoking in restaurant Last d 9pm

ROOMS: (incl. bkfst) s £78-£110; d £96-£160 *
OFF-PEAK: (incl. bkfst) s £72-£102; d £84-£142
MEALS: Lunch £15&alc High tea £2-£6 Dinner £33.50&alc
CONF: Class 30
CARDS:

See advertisement on this page

★★★ 73% **Taychreggan**

PA35 1HQ (west from Glasgow A82 to Crianlarich, west from Cranlarich on A85 to Taynuilt, south for 7m on B845 to Kilchrenan and Taychreggan)
☎ 01866 833211 & 833366 FAX 01866 833244

Standing in a beautifully peaceful location on the shore of Loch Awe, this one-time drovers inn has been skilfully extended and the owner always has improvements in mind. The bedrooms are a delight to occupy; some are very traditional in style, while others have a lighter, more modern feel, and TV and radio do not intrude. In the dining room, chef Neil Melles cooks in the modern style and produces excellent dishes using only the finest and mainly local ingredients. Relaxation is the keynote here and owner Annie Paul and her dedicated staff will ensure that guests want for nothing.

20 en suite (bth/shr) 30P No coaches Fishing Snooker Croquet lawn Boat hire Windsurfing No children 14yrs Xmas International Cuisine V meals Coffee am Tea pm No smoking in restaurant Last d 8.45pm

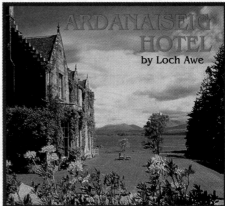

ROOMS: (incl. bkfst & dinner) s £80; d £140-£180 * **LB**
MEALS: Lunch £11-£16 High tea fr £3.50 Dinner fr £28*
CONF: Class 15 Board 20 Del from £100
CARDS:

KILDRUMMY Aberdeenshire Map 15 NJ41

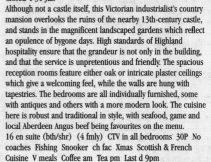

RED STAR HOTEL

★★★ **Kildrummy Castle**

AB33 8RA (off A97, Huntly-Ballater road)
☎ 019755 71288 FAX 019755 71345
Closed 4-31 Jan

Although not a castle itself, this Victorian industrialist's country mansion overlooks the ruins of the nearby 13th-century castle, and stands in the magnificent landscaped gardens which reflect an opulence of bygone days. High standards of Highland hospitality ensure that the grandeur is not only in the building, and that the service is unpretentious and friendly. The spacious reception rooms feature either oak or intricate plaster ceilings which give a welcoming feel, while the walls are hung with tapestries. The bedrooms are all individually furnished, some with antiques and others with a more modern look. The cuisine here is robust and traditional in style, with seafood, game and local Aberdeen Angus beef being favourites on the menu.

16 en suite (bth/shr) (4 fmly) CTV in all bedrooms 30P No coaches Fishing Snooker ch fac Xmas Scottish & French Cuisine V meals Coffee am Tea pm Last d 9pm

contd.

ROOMS: (incl. bkfst) s fr £70; d £115-£145 * **LB**
MEALS: Lunch fr £14.50 Dinner fr £28*
CARDS:

KILFINAN Argyll & Bute Map 10 NR97

★★ 76% **Kilfinan**
PA21 2EP (on B8000 east coast of Loch Fyne, between Otter Ferry and Tignabruaich)
☎ 01700 821201 FAX 01700 821205
Closed Feb

Set amongst thousands of acres of unspoilt west coast countryside on the east shore of Loch Fyne, the Kilfinan Hotel, originally a coaching inn, is a haven for country pursuits and relaxation. Whilst it has retained a certain rustic character it is very comfortable, very hospitable and warm with blazing log fires in the colder months. The cuisine is excellent, with produce supplied on the doorstep, including plentiful game from the adjacent Otter Estate, fresh fish from the loch and local beef. Rolf Mueller accentuates the natural flavours, keeping dishes relatively straightforward.

11 en suite (bth) (1 fmly) CTV in all bedrooms No dogs (ex guide dogs) 40P No coaches Fishing Private beach No children 12yrs Xmas Coffee am Tea pm No smoking in restaurant Last d 8.45pm
ROOMS: (incl. bkfst) s £48-£58; d £72-£92 * **LB**
MEALS: Sunday Lunch £8-£24alc Dinner £26*
CARDS:

See advertisement on opposite page

KILLIECHRONAN See Mull, Isle of

KILLIECRANKIE Perthshire & Kinross Map 14 NN96

★★ 74% **Killiecrankie**
SCOTLAND'S COMMENDED HOTELS
PH16 5LG (turn off A9 at Killiecrankie, hotel is 3m along B8079 on right) ☎ 01796 473220
FAX 01796 472451
Closed 3 Jan-Feb & 2 wk Dec
(Rosettes awarded for dinner only)

This delightful small hotel was formerly a manse, and stands in four acres of well kept gardens and woodland above the River Garry and the historic Pass of Killiecrankie. Resident owners Colin and Carole Anderson and their staff provide friendly, attentive service. The bedrooms are comfortable and attractively furnished in pine and the public areas include a wood-panelled bar and adjoining sun lounge; a quieter residents' lounge is now located on the ground floor. Nicely presented dishes with a predominantly Scottish theme are served in the dining room, while the supper menu is a popular alternative.

10 en suite (bth/shr) (1 fmly) No smoking in 1 bedroom CTV in all bedrooms 30P No coaches Croquet lawn Putting green Xmas V meals Coffee am Tea pm Last d 8.30pm
ROOMS: (incl. bkfst & dinner) s £79; d £158 **LB**
OFF-PEAK: (incl. bkfst & dinner) s £57.50-£70; d £115-£140
MEALS: Bar Lunch £10-£16alc Dinner fr £27*
CARDS:

See advertisement on opposite page

KILLIN Stirling Map 11 NN53

★★★ 60% **Dall Lodge Country House**
Main St FK21 8TN ☎ 01567 820217 FAX 01567 820726

At the north end of the town opposite the River Lochay which flows into Loch Tay is this small well maintained hotel is effectively run by the owners to the required standard. Catering primarily to its residential guests the hotel offers a bright conservatory lounge with a dispense bar and a cosy dining room where carefully prepared and tasty food is provided from a limited choice table d'hÙte menu. There are two ground floor rooms, one of which has been adapted for disabled use, the others being on the 1st floor, several having four poster beds whilst some others are utilitarian by comparison.

10 en suite (bth/shr) (2 fmly) CTV in all bedrooms 20P No coaches Tennis (grass) Scottish, French & Oriental Cuisine V meals Coffee am Tea pm No smoking in restaurant Last d 8.30pm
ROOMS: (incl. bkfst) s £37.50-£39.50; d £59-£71 * **LB**
MEALS: Lunch fr £12.50 Dinner fr £18.50*
CONF: Thtr 20 Class 16 Board 10 Del from £86
CARDS:

See advertisement on opposite page

KILMARNOCK East Ayrshire Map 10 NS43

Travelodge
Kilmarnock By Pass KA1 5LQ (A71)
☎ 01563 573810 FAX 01563 573810
This modern building offers accommodation in smart, spacious and well equipped bedrooms, suitable for family use, and all with en suite bathrooms. Meals may be taken at the nearby family restaurant. For information on room rates and to make a booking, call Roomline free of charge on 0800 850950. For more details about Travelodge, consult the Contents page under Hotel Groups.
40 en suite (bth/shr)

KILWINNING North Ayrshire Map 10 NS34

★★★ 71% ***Montgreenan Mansion House***

Montgreenan Estate KA13 7QZ (4m N of Irvine on A736) ☎ 01294 557733 FAX 01294 850397
This impressive 19th-century mansion set in 50 acres of parkland and wooded grounds has special appeal to the a business clientele who appreciate the peace and tranquillity in contrast to their working lives. The charming public areas retain many of the original features such as ornate ceilings and marble fireplaces and include a splendid drawing room, a welcoming library and a spacious well stocked bar. The elegant restaurant offers a tempting range of seasonal specialities from chef Alan McCall's imaginative daily-changing fixed-price menu which is ably supported by a comprehensive and interesting wine list. Bedrooms range from well furnished standard rooms to spacious and well proportioned superior rooms.
21 en suite (bth/shr) CTV in all bedrooms Lift Night porter 50P No coaches Golf 5 Tennis (hard) Snooker Croquet lawn Clay pigeon shooting Scottish & French Cuisine V meals Coffee am Tea pm Last d 9.30pm
CARDS:

See advertisement on page 795

KINCLAVEN Perthshire & Kinross Map 11 NO13

★★★ 76% **Ballathie House**
PH1 4QN (from A9 2m north of Perth, B9099 through Stanley & signposted or off A93 at Beech Hedge follow signs for Ballathie 2.50m) (Scotland's Heritage) ☎ 01250 883268 FAX 01250 883396
Ballathie House lies beside a river at the end of a long tree-lined avenue; a former mansion, it stands imposingly, its turrets silhouetted against the hills beyond. Inside, its furnishings are of the Scottish country house genre - deep, plump cushioned sofas and armchairs positioned in the various lounges to take advantage of the unrivalled views. The atmosphere is warm and the style informal: the Sportsman's bar is convivial but for most it is a peaceful and tranquil retreat. The cuisine is outstanding. Chef Kevin MacGillivary sources the best local ingredients which he uses with flair and imagination and a good degree of technical know-how.
27 en suite (bth/shr) (2 fmly) CTV in all bedrooms 50P No coaches Tennis (hard) Fishing Croquet lawn Putting green Clay pigeon shooting Xmas V meals Coffee am Tea pm No smoking in restaurant Last d 9pm
ROOMS: (incl. bkfst) s £60-£95; d £155-£180 * **LB**
OFF-PEAK: (incl. bkfst & dinner) s £80-£95; d £138-£180
MEALS: Lunch £11.95-£14.95 Dinner £26-£29*
CONF: Thtr 50 Board 26 Del from £95
CARDS:

***STOP PRESS!** AA Members can book accommodation at many hotels in this guide through the AA Booking Service, usually at attractive discounts. See page 5 for details or telephone 0990 050505*

KINGUSSIE Highland Map 14 NH70

RED STAR HOTEL

★★ **The Cross**
Tweed Mill Brae, Ardbroilach Rd PH21 1TC (from traffic lights in centre of Kingussie, travel uphill along Ardbroilach Rd for 300mtrs, turn left into Tweed Mill Brae) ☎ 01540 661166 FAX 01540 661080
Closed 1-26 Dec & 8 Jan-28 Feb
This cosy and popular hotel was once a tweed mill and retains much of its character. Owners Ruth and Tony Hadley work hard to pamper their guests with excellent service and food. There are nine bedrooms all with their own style, furnished with pine and pretty fabrics and there are many personal touches. The stylish upstairs lounge with its books and smart furnishings is the only area in which smoking is permitted. The restaurant, once a separate establishment in the town's main street, is Ruth Hadley's domain. She is a self-taught cook who understands her ingredients and enhances natural flavours rather than masking them. Tony Hadley is a wine fanatic and his enthusiasm is infectious.
9 en suite (bth/shr) No smoking in all bedrooms TV in all bedrooms No dogs (ex guide dogs) 12P No coaches No children 8yrs Xmas Last d 9pm
ROOMS: (incl. cont bkfst & dinner) s £85-£105; d £170
MEALS: Dinner £35
CARDS:

★★ 75% **The Scot House**

Newtonmore Rd PH21 1HE (from A9 trunk road, take Kingussie exit, Hotel is approx 0.50m at south end of villages main street) ☎ 01540 661351
FAX 01540 661111
Closed 6 Jan-31 Jan
(Rosette awarded for dinner only)
Situated in the centre of the village, this charming small hotel is the creation of the McConnachie and Gilbert families, formerly of the Winking Owl in Aviemore. The combination of quality accommodation together with the genuine warmth of welcome and good food have brought deserved success. The bedrooms have been carefully designed to make best use of available space and are comfortably modern in style. Public areas include a relaxing lounge and a well stocked bar, while the elegant restaurant is an appropriate setting for guests to sample the freshest of local produce which is carefully prepared under the experienced eye of Bill Gilbert.
9 en suite (bth/shr) (2 fmly) CTV in all bedrooms 30P No coaches ch fac V meals Coffee am Tea pm No smoking in restaurant Last d 8.45pm
ROOMS: (incl. bkfst) s £36; d £50-£65 * **LB**
OFF-PEAK: (incl. bkfst) s £30; d £55

MEALS: Bar Lunch £8.50-£15alc Dinner £17&alc*
CARDS:

See advertisement on this page

★★71% **Columba House**

Manse Rd PH21 1JF (at N end of village, off A9)
☎ 01540 661402 FAX 01540 661652
Genuine welcoming hospitality together with honest home cooking and exemplary standards of cleanliness are all part of the appeal of this civilised small holiday hotel; a converted 19th century manse. Bedrooms are comfortably modern in style and offer a wide range of amenities, while public areas include a cosy lounge with dispense bar and an attractive dining room.
7 en suite (bth/shr) (2 fmly) No smoking in 1 bedroom CTV in all bedrooms 12P No coaches Croquet lawn Putting green ch fac V meals Coffee am Tea pm No smoking in restaurant Last d 9.30pm
ROOMS: (incl. bkfst) s £28-£38; d £50-£60 * **LB**
MEALS: Lunch £5-£10alc High tea fr £6alc Dinner fr £17alc
CONF: Class 12 Board 12
CARDS:

See advertisement on this page

★71% **Osprey**
Ruthven Rd PH21 1EN (S end of Kingussie High St)
☎ 01540 661510 FAX 01540 661510
Good food together with genuine welcoming hospitality are all part of the appeal of this charming small family-run hotel on the main street. Bedrooms vary in size and are comfortably furnished in individual traditional styles. There is a choice of inviting lounges where guests can relax before moving to the small intimate restaurant where imaginative Taste of Scotland dishes are competently prepared from quality raw ingredients.
8 en suite (bth/shr) No smoking in 6 bedrooms CTV in all bedrooms No coaches Xmas Coffee am Tea pm No smoking in restaurant Last d 8.30pm
ROOMS: (incl. bkfst & dinner) s £47-£52; d £87-£99 * **LB**
OFF-PEAK: (incl. bkfst & dinner) s £39-£44; d £77-£83
MEALS: Dinner £20.75
CARDS:

KINNESSWOOD Perthshire & Kinross Map 11 NO10

★★66% **Lomond Country Inn**

KY13 7HN (on A911) ☎ 01592 840253
FAX 01592 840693
In the heart of this pretty village close to Loch Leven, this small inn offers a friendly atmosphere and fine views across the loch. Bedrooms are simply furnished and comfortable, with most being in the converted cottages opposite the hotel. Honest cooking is available at good value prices, with fresh local produce being used to create such delights as wild salmon en croute and superb home-made desserts. The cosy bar is popular with locals, and the beer garden is ideal for long summer evenings.

contd.

4 en suite (bth/shr) 7 annexe en suite (bth/shr) (1 fmly) CTV in all bedrooms 50P ch fac Xmas V meals Coffee am Tea pm No smoking in restaurant Last d 9pm
ROOMS: (incl. bkfst) s £40-£45; d £58-£70
CARDS:

KINROSS Perthshire & Kinross Map 11 NO10

★★★71% **Windlestrae Hotel Business & Leisure Centre**
Windlestrae KY13 7AS (leave M90 junc 6 turn E into Kinross, stop at T-junc turn left in approx 350yds Windlestrae on right) ☎ 01577 863217 FAX 01577 864733
This friendly family-run hotel, is secluded in acres of landscaped gardens, just off the main road at the northern end of the town. Public areas are spacious, and include a split-level lounge bar, elegant restaurant and large foyer lounge. The well equipped indoor leisure centre is popular with both locals and guests, while extensive conference facilities include a cinematic theatre. Bedrooms are mostly spacious and offer good facilities.
45 en suite (bth/shr) (10 fmly) No smoking in 8 bedrooms CTV in all bedrooms STV Night porter Air conditioning 80P Indoor swimming pool (heated) Snooker Sauna Solarium Gym Jacuzzi/spa Beautician Steam room Toning tables ch fac Xmas International Cuisine V meals Coffee am Tea pm Last d 9.30pm
ROOMS: (incl. bkfst) s £70-£75; d £105-£112 **LB**
OFF-PEAK: (incl. bkfst) s £65-£70; d £90-£98
MEALS: Lunch £10.50-£17.50&alc Dinner £22.50&alc*
CONF: Thtr 50 Class 60 Board 25 Del from £120
CARDS:

★★★70% **Green**
2 The Muirs KY13 7AS (M90 junct 6 follow signs for Kinross, turn onto A922, the Hotel is situated on this road)
☎ 01577 863467 FAX 01577 863180
Spacious, well equipped bedrooms are an impressive feature of this sympathetically extended hotel, which stands opposite two golf courses, and provides good leisure and conference facilities. Attractive, quality decor has been used throughout the hotel, while the indoor leisure centre includes a good-sized pool as well as a paddling pool for children. A fashionable boutique is also located off the main foyer.
47 en suite (bth/shr) (4 fmly) CTV in all bedrooms STV Night porter 60P Indoor swimming pool (heated) Golf 36 Fishing Squash Sauna Solarium Gym Pool table Croquet lawn Putting green Curling in season ch fac French Cuisine V meals Coffee am Tea pm Last d 9.30pm
ROOMS: (incl. bkfst) s £70-£90; d £110-£125 * **LB**
MEALS: Bar Lunch £8.50-£14alc High tea £8.50-£9.50 Dinner £22.50&alc*
CONF: Thtr 140 Class 100 Board 60
CARDS:

See advertisement on opposite page

★★65% ***Kirklands***
20 High St KY13 7AN ☎ 01577 863313
FAX 01577 863313
Attractive bedrooms are offered at competitive prices at this family-run town centre hotel, where beers and ales are also a speciality. The bedrooms vary in size but all are well equipped and solidly furnished. Extensive public areas include a choice of bars, a coffee lounge and smart restaurant.
9 en suite (bth/shr) CTV in all bedrooms STV No dogs (ex guide dogs) 30P V meals Coffee am Tea pm Last d 9.30pm
CARDS:

MINOTEL Great Britain

Travelodge
Kincardine Rd KY13 7NQ (on A977, off junct 6 of M90) ☎ Central Res 0800 850950
FAX 01577 864108
This modern building offers accommodation in smart, spacious and well equipped bedrooms, suitable for family use, and all with en suite bathrooms. Meals may be taken at the nearby family restaurant. For information on room rates and to make a booking, call Roomline free of charge on 0800 850950. For more details about Travelodge, consult the Contents page under Hotel Groups.
35 en suite (bth/shr)

Travelodge

KINTORE Aberdeenshire Map 15 NJ71

★★60% **Torryburn**
School Rd AB51 0XP (first hotel on the left as you enter Kintore traveling north from Aberdeen on the A96) ☎ 01467 632269
FAX 01467 632271
Closed 1 Jan
The grounds of this popular commercial hotel, situated at the eastern end of the village, contain some adventure equipment for children as well as an outdoor tennis court. Bedrooms are compact but do provide all the necessary facilities. A good range of dishes is offered in both the lounge bar and the more formal Conservatory restaurant.
9 rms (8 shr) (1 fmly) CTV in all bedrooms 30P Tennis (hard) Fishing Snooker Shooting Xmas International Cuisine V meals Coffee am Tea pm Last d 9.15pm
ROOMS: (incl. bkfst) s £37.50; d £52 *
OFF-PEAK: (incl. bkfst) s fr £32.50; d fr £48
MEALS: Lunch £7.10-£9.50 High tea £5.95-£8.95 Dinner £10.95-£15.95*
CONF: Board 50
CARDS:

KIRKCALDY Fife Map 11 NT29

★★★57% **Dean Park**
Chapel Level KY2 6QW (signposted from A92, Kirkcaldy West junc)
☎ 01592 261635 FAX 01592 261371
This extended mansion house is conveniently situated on the edge of the town and is particularly popular for functions and conferences, as it has extensive facilities to provide for these. Bedrooms are modern and functional, some in chalets at the rear of the hotel. Both the bar-lounge and restaurant are bright and offer a range of menus.
20 en suite (bth/shr) 12 annexe en suite (shr) (1 fmly) CTV in all bedrooms STV No dogs (ex guide dogs) Night porter 150P No coaches Scottish, French & Italian Cuisine V meals Coffee am Last d 9.30pm
ROOMS: (incl. bkfst) s fr £55; d fr £75 *
MEALS: Lunch fr £9.75 Dinner fr £15.50*
CONF: Thtr 250 Class 125 Board 54
CARDS:

★★62% **The Belvedere**

Coxstool, West Wemyss KY1 4SL ☎ 01592 654167
FAX 01592 655279
Located in the picturesque village of West Wemyss about four miles from Kirkcaldy, the bedrooms and restaurant at this hotel enjoy superb views across the Firth of Forth. Most of the well equipped bedrooms are contained in a cluster of individual houses, although there are also some in the main house. The bar is small and has a lively atmosphere.
4 en suite (bth/shr) 16 annexe en suite (bth/shr) (2 fmly) CTV in all bedrooms STV 50P Xmas Scottish & Continental Cuisine V meals Coffee am Tea pm Last high tea 6.30pm
ROOMS: (incl. bkfst) s £50; d £70 * **LB**
OFF-PEAK: (incl. bkfst) s fr £40; d fr £50
MEALS: Lunch £12.50-£14.50 High tea fr £4*
CONF: Thtr 18 Class 18 Board 12
CARDS:

KIRKCUDBRIGHT Dumfries & Galloway Map 11 NX65

★★72% **Selkirk Arms**

Old High St DG6 4JG (turn off A75 5m W of Castle Douglas onto A711, 5m to Kircudbright in centre of town) ☎ 01557 330402 FAX 01557 331639
This centrally located 18th-century inn was once visited by Robbie Burns, though it is unlikely that he would recognise the smartly refurbished bedrooms and public areas! Furnished in attractive pine, and with many modern amenities, the bedrooms provide a high standard of accommodation. There is a comfortable bar and adjoining residents' lounge, while the elegant restaurant offers wholesome home cooking. The well presented staff are friendly and cheerful.
15 en suite (bth/shr) 1 annexe en suite (bth/shr) (2 fmly) No smoking in 3 bedrooms CTV in all bedrooms STV 18P Xmas Scottish & Continental Cuisine V meals Coffee am No smoking in restaurant Last d 9.30pm
ROOMS: (incl. bkfst) s £48; d £78 * **LB**
MEALS: Bar Lunch £5-£10alc Dinner £18.50&alc*
CONF: Thtr 70 Class 60 Board 40 Del from £69.50
CARDS:

★★58% **Royal**
St Cuthbert St DG6 4DY (turn off A75 onto A711 hotel is in the centre of Kircudbright, on the corner at crossroads)
☎ 01557 331213 FAX 01557 331513
Located in the centre of the town, this family-run hotel has a striking green façade. Bedrooms provide all the expected amenities. The bar is popular with locals as well as guests, while the Pheasant Grill offers a good selection of steaks with a variety of sauces.
17 en suite (bth/shr) (7 fmly) CTV in all bedrooms Wkly live entertainment V meals Coffee am Tea pm Last d 9pm
ROOMS: (incl. bkfst) s £19-£30; d £38-£50
MEALS: Lunch £5.25-£14.15alc Dinner £6.65-£14.15alc*
CONF: Class 60 Board 60
CARDS:

KIRKHILL Highland Map 14 NH54

★★66% ***Bogroy Inn***
IV5 7PX (at junc A862/B9164) ☎ 01463 831296 FAX 01463 831296
Much improved by its resident owners, the Bogroy Inn is a small country hotel offering an informal, friendly atmosphere which will appeal to both tourists and commercial guests. Compact but comfortable bedrooms are equipped with the expected amenities, and the 'old world' lounge bar provides a popular rendezvous.
6 en suite (bth/shr) (1 fmly) CTV in all bedrooms STV 80P Pool table V meals Coffee am Tea pm Last d 9pm
CARDS:

KIRKWALL See Orkney

KYLE OF LOCHALSH Highland Map 13 NG72

★★★64% **Lochalsh**
Ferry Rd IV40 8AF (turn off A82 onto A87)
☎ 01599 534202 FAX 01599 534881
Enjoying commanding views over the Kyles to Skye from it's position beside the former ferry slip, this friendly hotel is an ideal base for the touring holiday maker. The variably sized modern bedrooms are brightly decorated and have all the expected amenities. Fine views are enjoyed from the public areas, which include an open-plan foyer lounge and cocktail bar as well as an attractive restaurant offering a choice of menus featuring seafood specialities.
38 en suite (bth/shr) (8 fmly) CTV in all bedrooms STV Lift Night porter 20P Scottish & French Cuisine V meals Coffee am Tea pm Last d 9pm
ROOMS: (incl. bkfst) s £60-£80; d £90-£120 * **LB**
MEALS: Lunch £9.50-£12 Dinner £19.50-£30&alc
CONF: Thtr 20 Class 20 Board 20
CARDS:

See advertisement on page 799

★★60% **Kyle**
Main St IV40 8AB (A87 just before new bridge to Skye, turn right into main street) ☎ 01599 534204 FAX 01599 534932
Good progress is being made with bedroom refurbishment at this personally run holiday hotel, which is also a popular base for tour groups. Though compact, the bedrooms are cheerful with enhanced décor, and offer a wide range of amenities. Public areas include an inviting bar with an adjacent small dining area for private use. There is no lounge.
31 en suite (bth/shr) No smoking in 2 bedrooms CTV in all bedrooms STV 80P Xmas Scottish, French & German Cuisine V meals Coffee am Tea pm No smoking in restaurant Last d 9.30pm
ROOMS: (incl. bkfst) s £32-£39; d £60-£72 *
OFF-PEAK: (incl. bkfst) s £30-£32; d £50-£60
MEALS: Bar Lunch £3-£10alc Dinner £6-£15alc
CONF: Class 50
CARDS:

LAIRG Highland Map 14 NC50

★★65% **Overscaig**
Loch Shin IV27 4NY (on A838) ☎ 01549 431203
This welcoming Highland holiday and fishing hotel beside the picturesque shore of Loch Shin, has in recent years been completely refurbished to provide all the expected modern day comforts and amenities. Bedrooms with cheerful decor and comfortable modern furnishings offer all the expected facilities. Public areas include a choice of contrasting bars, a small quiet lounge with lots of books and board games, and a smart dining room overlooking the loch.
9 en suite (bth/shr) (2 fmly) CTV in all bedrooms No dogs (ex guide dogs) 30P No coaches Fishing Xmas Coffee am Tea pm No smoking in restaurant Last d 9pm
ROOMS: (incl. bkfst) s £20-£30; d £40-£60
MEALS: Bar Lunch £3.50-£7 Dinner £3.50-£7&alc

See advertisement on opposite page

LANARK South Lanarkshire Map 11 NS84
See also Biggar

★★★63% ***Cartland Bridge***
Glasgow Rd ML11 9UF
☎ 01555 664426 FAX 01555 663773
Set in 22 acres of grounds, this comfortable hotel which has an informal and relaxed atmosphere offers attractively decorated and well equipped accommodation. Public areas include a conservatory, a choice of bars and a splendid wood-panelled restaurant.
18 en suite (bth/shr) CTV in all bedrooms 200P Last d 9.30pm
CARDS:

LANGBANK Renfrewshire Map 10 NS37

★★★ 72% **Gleddoch House**
PA14 6YE (signposted from B789)
☎ 01475 540711 FAX 01475 540201
Set in extensive grounds high above the River Clyde and with spectacular views across to distant mountains, this fine mansion was originally the home of shipping magnate Sir William Lithgow. Extended and sympathetically converted, it combines the character of a country house with amenities which attract the business and corporate market. Service is smart yet hospitable and its spacious restaurant and clubby cocktail bar with adjoining conservatory provide a tasteful environment. Bedrooms come in a choice of styles, those in the original house retaining much of its character, whist the two wings have a more contemporary touch. The fixed-price and à la carte menus offer a fine selection of dishes.
39 en suite (bth/shr) (4 fmly) No smoking in 6 bedrooms CTV in all bedrooms Night porter 200P Golf 18 Squash Riding Snooker Sauna Clay pigeon shooting Xmas Scottish & French Cuisine V meals Coffee am Tea pm Last d 9pm
ROOMS: (incl. bkfst) s £95; d £140 * **LB**
OFF-PEAK: (incl. bkfst & dinner) s £70; d £70
MEALS: Lunch £15-£18.50&alc High tea £4.50 Dinner £29.50&alc*
CONF: Thtr 100 Class 60 Board 40 Del from £115
CARDS:

LANGHOLM Dumfries & Galloway Map 11 NY38

★★57% **Eskdale**
Market Place DG13 0JH ☎ 013873 80357 & 81178
FAX 013873 80357
This former coaching inn stands in the town's market place, and offers good value, practical accommodation in a friendly atmosphere. The comfortable lounge bar is popular with locals, while the cocktail bar offers an alternative. The dining room has recently been smartly refurbished, as have some of the bedrooms.
15 rms (11 bth/shr) (3 fmly) No smoking in 3 bedrooms CTV in all bedrooms STV 10P Pool table V meals Coffee am Tea pm Last d 8pm
ROOMS: (incl. bkfst) s £26-£34; d £40-£52 *
MEALS: Sunday Lunch £7.95 Dinner £12*
CONF: Thtr 100 Class 30 Board 30 Del from £50
CARDS:

LARGS North Ayrshire Map 10 NS25

★★★66% **Brisbane House**
14 Greenock Rd, Esplanade KA30 8NF (on A78) ☎ 01475 687200
FAX 01475 676295
Situated on the esplanade overlooking the Firth of Clyde, this attractive converted Georgian house makes a comfortable small hotel which is especially popular with the visiting business guest. Apart from the single rooms, which are of limited size, bedrooms are mostly spacious with tasteful modern appointments. The large bar, with its attractive conservatory extension is known for its bar meals, while chef Steve Peddie's competent modern cooking continues to earn praise in the more formal restaurant, from a choice of menus including a carte and speciality seafood menu.
23 en suite (bth/shr) (2 fmly) CTV in all bedrooms No dogs (ex guide dogs) Night porter 60P Jacuzzi/spa International Cuisine V meals Coffee am Tea pm Last d 9pm
MEALS: Lunch £6-£21alc High tea £6.75-£9.75 Dinner £19.75-£28.50&alc*

CONF: Board 50 Del from £80
CARDS:

★★★ 63% *Manor Park*
PA17 5HE (2m N, 200 yds off A78)
☎ 01475 520832 FAX 01475 520832
Standing in 15 acres of well tended grounds and enjoying superb views over the Firth of Clyde, this splendid sandstone house dates back to Victorian times and is well proportioned in all areas. The public rooms include intricate cornices, ornate ceilings and a crackling log fire in the hall on cooler evenings. The bedrooms in the main house are very traditional in style whilst those in the former stable block are more modern and generally less spacious. The hotel provides traditional comforts together with attentive and friendly service.
10 en suite (bth/shr) 13 annexe en suite (bth/shr) CTV in all bedrooms 150P Putting green ch fac British & Continental Cuisine V meals Coffee am Tea pm Last d 9.15pm
CARDS:

★★69% **Elderslie**
John St, Broomfields KA30 8DR ☎ 01475 686460 FAX 01475 689070
A major transformation is taking place at this popular business and tourist hotel, which enjoys views over the Firth of Clyde from its position on the waterfront south of the town centre. Public areas have been tastefully upgraded and offer comfortable modern standards. Bedrooms range from well proportioned superior rooms to the more modest sized standard rooms.
21 rms (10 bth 8 shr) (2 fmly) CTV in all bedrooms Night porter 30P Pool table Jacuzzi/spa Xmas French Cuisine V meals Coffee am No smoking area in restaurant Last d 9pm
ROOMS: (incl. bkfst) s £55; d £75-£100 * **LB**
OFF-PEAK: (incl. bkfst) d £55-£65
MEALS: Bar Lunch £4.70-£9.70alc Dinner £8.35-£20.40alc*
CONF: Thtr 40 Class 20 Board 25 Del from £85
CARDS:

See advertisement on this page

★★67% **Willowbank**
96 Greenock Rd KA30 8PG (on A77)
☎ 01475 672311 FAX 01475 672311
A relaxed friendly atmosphere prevails at this well maintained business and tourist hotel which is also a popular base for visiting tour groups. The well decorated bedrooms tend to be spacious and offer comfortable modern appointments, while public areas include a spacious well stocked bar, a lounge and a dining room.
30 en suite (bth/shr) (4 fmly) CTV in all bedrooms 40P Wkly live entertainment Xmas Scottish, French & Italian Cuisine V meals Coffee am Last d 9pm
ROOMS: (incl. bkfst) s £46-£58; d £72-£96 **LB**
MEALS: Lunch £11.95-£16.95 High tea £5.50-£10.95 Dinner £17-£22.50
CONF: Board 40 Del from £76
CARDS:

★★58% **Springfield**
Greenock Rd KA30 8QL ☎ 01475 673119 & 687475
FAX 01475 673119
Situated on the seafront with views over the Firth of Clyde, this friendly family-run hotel is a popular base for visiting tour groups. Bedrooms are variable in size with mixed modern appointments and offer the expected amenities. The first floor lounge is decidedly traditional in style which contrasts with the more modern appointments of the ground floor public areas.
58 en suite (bth/shr) (4 fmly) CTV in all bedrooms Lift 80P Putting green Wkly live entertainment Xmas Scottish, French & Italian Cuisine V meals Coffee am Tea pm No smoking in restaurant Last d 8.30pm

contd.

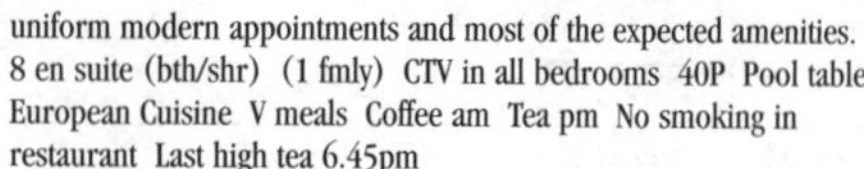

ROOMS: (incl. bkfst) s £48.50; d £67.50 **LB**
MEALS: Lunch £6.50-£10 High tea £5.75-£8 Dinner £10.50-£15.50
CARDS:

LAUDER Scottish Borders Map 12 NT54

★★63% **Lauderdale**

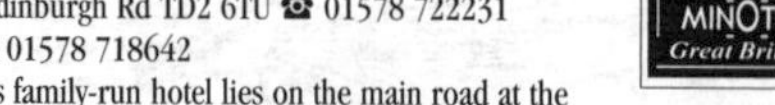

1 Edinburgh Rd TD2 6TU ☎ 01578 722231
FAX 01578 718642
This family-run hotel lies on the main road at the northern end of the town and provides an ideal stop-over for those venturing north and south of the border. In addition to its bright airy bedrooms it has an attractive lounge bar with a range of bar meals to complement its dinner menu. There is also a cosy residents' lounge.
9 en suite (bth/shr) CTV in all bedrooms 50P Scottish & Continental Cuisine V meals Coffee am Tea pm Last d 9pm
ROOMS: (incl. bkfst) s £35; d £52 * **LB**
MEALS: Bar Lunch £5.50-£13.05alc High tea £6.55-£7.55alc Dinner £7.95-£31.50alc*
CARDS:

LERWICK See Shetland

LETHAM Fife Map 11 NO31

★★★61% ***Fernie Castle***

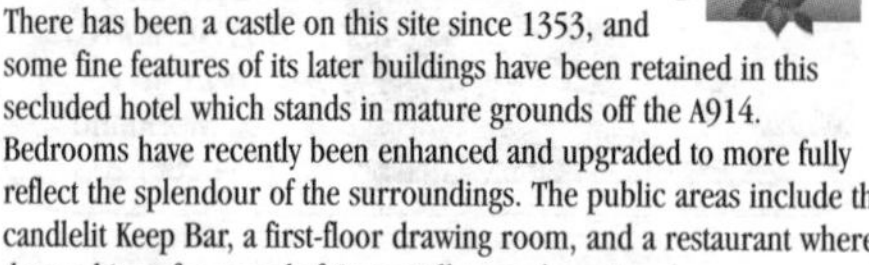

KY7 7RU ☎ 01337 810381 FAX 01337 810422
There has been a castle on this site since 1353, and some fine features of its later buildings have been retained in this secluded hotel which stands in mature grounds off the A914. Bedrooms have recently been enhanced and upgraded to more fully reflect the splendour of the surroundings. The public areas include the candlelit Keep Bar, a first-floor drawing room, and a restaurant where the cooking of young chef Craig Miller can be enjoyed.
15 en suite (bth/shr) (2 fmly) CTV in all bedrooms 80P Scottish & International Cuisine V meals Coffee am Tea pm Last d 9.30pm
CARDS:

LETTERFINLAY Highland Map 14 NN29

★★63% **Letterfinlay Lodge**
PH34 4DZ (7m N of Spean Bridge, on A82) ☎ 01397 712622
Closed Nov-Feb
A welcoming atmosphere prevails at this family run hotel beside the A82 which enjoys a spectacular outlook over Loch Lochy. Relaxing public areas include a choice of lounges, snug bar and an attractive dining room. Bedrooms vary in size and offer both modern and traditional appointments.
13 rms (11 bth/shr) (5 fmly) CTV in all bedrooms 100P No coaches Fishing V meals Coffee am Tea pm No smoking in restaurant Last d 8.30pm
ROOMS: (incl. bkfst) s £25-£40; d £50-£80 * **LB**
MEALS: Sunday Lunch £15.50-£18.50alc Dinner £18.50*
CARDS:

LEUCHARS Fife Map 12 NO42

★★65% **St Michaels Inn**
KY16 0DU (at junction of A919 & A92)
☎ 01334 839220 FAX 01334 838299
A major transformation has taken place at this 200 year old coaching inn which is situated at the junction of the A919 and A92, six miles north of St Andrews. The refurbished public areas have been decorated to a high standard, and include a small tastefully appointed dining room and a comfortable lounge bar with an area set aside for non-smokers. Food is available all day in bar and dining room, and the range of dishes is quite extensive. Bedrooms vary in size but all offer uniform modern appointments and most of the expected amenities.
8 en suite (bth/shr) (1 fmly) CTV in all bedrooms 40P Pool table European Cuisine V meals Coffee am Tea pm No smoking in restaurant Last high tea 6.45pm
ROOMS: (incl. bkfst) s £30-£35; d £50-£58 * **LB**
MEALS: Lunch fr £7.25 High tea £6.25-£9.95*
CONF: Thtr 100 Class 60
CARDS:

See advertisement under ST ANDREWS

LEVEN Fife Map 11 NO30

★★★56% **Caledonian**
81 High St KY8 4NG (follow A912 until Letham Glen rdbt then turn right, 0.5m on turn right into Mitchell St)
☎ 01333 424101 FAX 01333 421241
Purpose-built in the eighties to replace the original hotel, the Caledonian attracts mainly business custom, offering modern but practical accommodation, a spacious lounge bar and small dining room.
24 en suite (bth/shr) (1 fmly) CTV in all bedrooms STV Night porter Wkly live entertainment Xmas Traditional Cuisine V meals Coffee am Tea pm
ROOMS: (incl. bkfst) s £32-£35; d £50-£55 * **LB**
MEALS: Lunch £5.50-£10 High tea £5-£7.50 Dinner £13.50-£18&alc*
CONF: Thtr 140 Class 100 Board 100 Del from £52
CARDS:

LEWIS, ISLE OF Western Isles Map 13

STORNOWAY Map 13 NB43

★★★68% **Cabarfeidh**

PA87 2EU (1m from town centre on main road to Tarbert, turn left at roundabout and take first turn on right) ☎ 01851 702604 FAX 01851 705572
Situated on the edge of town, this welcoming and comfortable modern business and tourist hotel is also a popular venue for local functions and conferences. Warmed by the inviting open fire, the attractive foyer lounge is a comfortable place to relax and there is a choice of contrasting bars as well as a smart split level restaurant which offers a choice of menus. Bedrooms are mostly well proportioned with the standard modern appointments. The local staff are friendly and willing to please.
46 en suite (bth/shr) (36 fmly) CTV in all bedrooms STV Lift Night porter Air conditioning 100P French Cuisine V meals Coffee am Tea pm Last d 9.15pm
ROOMS: (incl. bkfst) s £68-£73; d £90-£95 * **LB**
OFF-PEAK: (incl. bkfst) s £58-£63; d £80-£85
MEALS: Lunch £11.50-£15 Dinner £18.50-£19.50&alc*
CONF: Thtr 350 Class 100 Board 35
CARDS:

LIVINGSTON West Lothian Map 11 NT06

Hilton National Livingston
Almondview EH54 6QB ☎ 01506 431222
FAX 01506 434666
This is a bright, modern hotel, with an informal restaurant, aimed at both the business and leisure guest. All bedrooms have en suite bathrooms and a range of modern facilities. For more information about Hilton National hotels, consult the Contents page under Hotel Groups.
120 en suite (bth/shr)

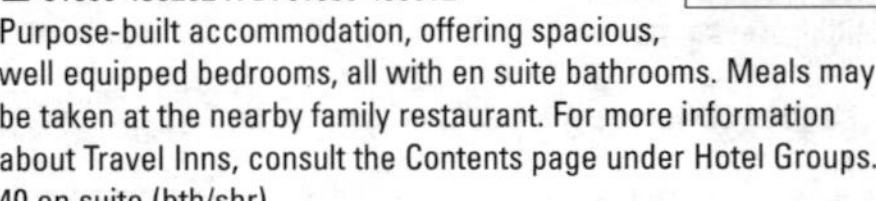

Travel Inn
Deer Park Av, Knightsbridge EH54 8AD
☎ 01506 439202 FAX 01506 438912
Purpose-built accommodation, offering spacious, well equipped bedrooms, all with en suite bathrooms. Meals may be taken at the nearby family restaurant. For more information about Travel Inns, consult the Contents page under Hotel Groups.
40 en suite (bth/shr)
ROOMS: (incl. bkfst) d £35.50 *

LOCHCARRON Highland Map 14 NG83

★★66% Lochcarron
Main St IV54 8YS (E end of village on Lochcarron)
☎ 01520 722226 FAX 01520 722612
New owners, the Graham family have brought a touch of Irish hospitality to this welcoming holiday hotel which overlooks the loch. The tastefully decorated bedrooms, two of which have private sitting rooms, are comfortable with mixed modern appointments and offer all the expected amenities. Meals and light snacks are available throughout the day and these are available in the well stocked bar or alternatively in the dining room where the emphasis is on fresh local seafood.
10 rms (9 bth/shr) (2 fmly) No smoking in 2 bedrooms CTV in all bedrooms 20P No coaches Pool table hunting, shooting & fishing arranged Xmas V meals Coffee am Tea pm No smoking in restaurant
ROOMS: (incl. bkfst) s £30-£39; d £33.50-£39 **LB**
OFF-PEAK: (incl. bkfst) s £25-£30; d £31.50-£39.50
MEALS: Lunch £6-£16.50alc High tea £6-£16.50alc
CARDS:

LOCHEARNHEAD Stirling Map 11 NN52

★65% Lochearnhead
Lochside FK19 8PU ☎ 01567 830229 FAX 01567 830364
Closed mid Nov-end Mar
Opposite the loch side, this friendly family-run hotel has continued to improve over the past couple of years, and now offers bright, well equipped accommodation. An interesting range of dishes, both traditional and innovative, are offered in the attractive restaurant and bar.
12 rms (8 bth/shr) CTV in all bedrooms STV 82P Fishing Squash Water skiing Windsurfing Sailing ch fac Scottish & French Cuisine V meals Coffee am Tea pm Last d 9pm
ROOMS: (incl. bkfst) s £28.25-£36.96; d £45-£57.70 * **LB**
MEALS: Bar Lunch £1-£12.90 High tea £7.50 Dinner £14-£19*
CARDS:

LOCHGILPHEAD Argyll & Bute Map 10 NR88

★★63% The Stag
Argyll St PA31 8NE ☎ 01546 602496 FAX 01546 603549
This long established, family-run commercial and tourist hotel is conveniently situated in the town centre and offers good-value accommodation. Bedrooms have a wide range of amenities though they do tend to be compact. At weekends, live music is a regular feature in the well stocked bar and there is a quiet traditional lounge on the first floor adjacent to the smart dining room.
17 en suite (bth/shr) CTV in all bedrooms STV Pool table Wkly live entertainment V meals Coffee am Tea pm Last d 8.30pm
MEALS: Lunch £5.50-£8.50 Dinner £12-£17&alc*
CARDS:

LOCHINVER Highland Map 14 NC02

★★★77% Inver Lodge

IV27 4LU (A835 to Lochinver continue through village and turn left after village hall, follow private road for 0.50m) ☎ 01571 844496 FAX 01571 844395
Closed 19 Oct-20 Apr
Inver Lodge is a well appointed modern hotel which enjoys superb views from its situation above the village across the river mouth and harbour. Public areas are spacious and comfortable, and good sized bedrooms are smart and well equipped. Fishing is the main attraction of the hotel, and there are useful drying and freezer rooms for successful sportsmen.Both management and staff are most welcoming to their guests and a good range of services is on hand.
20 en suite (bth) CTV in all bedrooms 30P No coaches Fishing Snooker Sauna Solarium Scottish & French Cuisine V meals Coffee am Tea pm No smoking in restaurant Last d 9pm
ROOMS: (incl. bkfst) s £80; d £110-£130 **LB**
OFF-PEAK: (incl. bkfst) d £110
MEALS: Bar Lunch £5-£16alc Dinner £27&alc
CARDS:

See advertisement on this page

LOCHMADDY See North Uist, Isle of

LOCKERBIE Dumfries & Galloway Map 11 NY18

★★★69% Dryfesdale
DG11 2SF (from A74 take 'Lockerbie North' junction)
☎ 01576 202427 FAX 01576 204187
This well maintained hotel, which has recently been bought by the Dunbobbin family, is conveniently situated to the north of the town, just off the A74. The well equipped and attractive bedrooms are divided

contd.

between the main house, which was built as a manse in the 18th-century, and a more recent extension of six spacious ground floor rooms, one specifically designed for wheelchair use. The public areas are spacious and comfortably furnished and in the dining room a good range of interesting, well prepared dishes is available. Lighter meals are served in the bar, where there are also over 100 single malts to choose from.

15 rms (9 bth/shr) (1 fmly) CTV in all bedrooms 50P ch fac Xmas English & French Cuisine V meals Coffee am Tea pm No smoking in restaurant Last d 9pm
ROOMS: (incl. bkfst) s fr £50; d fr £82 * **LB**
OFF-PEAK: (incl. bkfst) s fr £45; d fr £65
MEALS: Lunch fr £11.95 High tea fr £8 Dinner fr £16.95*
CONF: Thtr 80 Board 20 Del from £85
CARDS:

★★69% **Somerton House**
Carlisle Rd DG11 2DR (off A74) ☎ 01576 202583 FAX 01576 204218
This hotel, owned for the last few years by the very hospitable Alex and Jean Arthur, is full of character and retains many of the original Victorian features. It is conveniently situated on the south west side of the town, just three minutes from the A74. An outstanding feature of the bedrooms is their spaciousness and they certainly exceed our requirements as far as comfort and levels of equipment are concerned and one has the most magnificent Victorian bathroom. A very good range of home cooked dishes are available in the small restaurant, opposite which is a comfortably furnished lounge bar where bar snacks are served.

7 en suite (bth/shr) (2 fmly) No smoking in 2 bedrooms CTV in all bedrooms 100P International Cuisine V meals Coffee am Tea pm No smoking in restaurant
CONF: Thtr 25 Class 15 Board 15
CARDS:

★64% **Ravenshill House**
12 Dumfries Rd DG11 2EF (on A709, 400yds from A74 slip road)
☎ 01576 202882 FAX 01576 202882
The atmosphere is welcoming and friendly at this privately owned and personally-run hotel situated in a quiet residential area, in its own gardens, to the west of the town on the Dumfries road, within easy reach from the A74. The public areas include a comfortably furnished lounge bar and a spacious restaurant where a good range of home-cooked dishes is available. The generally spacious and freshly decorated bedrooms include a number of family rooms and all the rooms benefit from having their own en suite facilities. A room is also available for private meetings or functions and there is ample car parking.

7 rms (6 bth/shr) (1 fmly) CTV in all bedrooms 35P Scottish, French, Italian & Indian Cuisine V meals No smoking in restaurant Last d 9.30pm
ROOMS: (incl. bkfst) s £25-£35; d £45-£50 * **LB**
MEALS: Sunday Lunch £10-£13alc Dinner £8.50-£20alc*
CARDS:

LOSSIEMOUTH Moray Map 15 NJ27

★★★62% **Stotfield**
Stotfield Rd IV31 6QS ☎ 01343 812011 FAX 01343 814820
Ongoing improvements are being made at this substantial Victorian hotel, which is located opposite the golf course and enjoys views of the Moray Firth to the hills of Sutherland beyond. Spacious public areas include a comfortable foyer lounge, popular lounge bar and dining room with attractive plaster frieze. An extensive carte is available in the bright sun lounge restaurant, while American-style food is offered in the themed Bourbon Street bar/grill. Bedrooms range from large superior rooms to more modest standard rooms.

45 en suite (bth/shr) No smoking in 10 bedrooms CTV in all bedrooms No dogs 15P Sauna Gym Pool table Xmas European Cuisine V meals Coffee am No smoking in restaurant
ROOMS: (incl. bkfst) s £40; d £61-£76
CONF: Thtr 120 Board 25
CARDS:

LUNDIN LINKS Fife Map 12 NO40

★★★69% **Old Manor**
Leven Rd KY8 6AJ (off A912) ☎ 01333 320368
FAX 01333 320911

CONSORT HOTELS

Located on the outskirts of the village, this converted mansion house is set in its own grounds with impressive views over the Largo Bay and the golf course. Attentive and courteous service is provided throughout the hotel, while the bedrooms offer modern accommodation. Guests have a choice of eating options, with the informal Coachman's Grill and Alehouse offering steaks and seafood, and the fine Aithernie Restaurant providing the setting for chef Alan Brunt's imaginative use of local produce to offer tasty flavour combinations.

25 en suite (bth/shr) (3 fmly) CTV in all bedrooms 80P Golf 18 Scottish & Continental Cuisine V meals Coffee am Tea pm No smoking in restaurant Last d 9.30pm
MEALS: Lunch £11.50-£13&alc High tea £7-£12.50 Dinner £22.50-£27.50&alc
CONF: Thtr 120 Class 60 Board 40 Del from £75
CARDS:

See advertisement on opposite page

LYBSTER Highland Map 15 ND23

★★65% ***Portland Arms***
KW3 6BS ☎ 01593 721208
Enthusiastic owners Gerald and Helen Henderson are making good progress with their improvement programme which has already completely transformed the bar and function room at this popular hotel. The two lounges remain as inviting as ever and enjoyable local fare continues to feature on the varied dinner menu. Bedrooms offer comfort and modern appointments.

19 en suite (bth/shr) (3 fmly) CTV in all bedrooms Night porter 50P Golf 9 Fishing Scottish & French Cuisine V meals Coffee am Tea pm Last d 9.30pm
CARDS:

MACDUFF Aberdeenshire Map 15 NJ76

★★58% **The Highland Haven**
Shore St AB44 1UB ☎ 01261 832408 FAX 01261 833652
Overlooking the harbour, this commercial hotel has a pleasant restaurant and bar on the first floor, which take advantage of the view. Bedrooms are adequately equipped, and a new family suite has been created on the first floor.

24 en suite (bth/shr) (3 fmly) CTV in all bedrooms STV Snooker Sauna Gym Jacuzzi/spa Xmas V meals Coffee am Tea pm Last d 9pm
ROOMS: (incl. bkfst) s £30-£40; d £40-£50 **LB**
OFF-PEAK: (incl. bkfst) d £30-£40
MEALS: Lunch £4.35-£5.65alc High tea £5.35-£14.95alc Dinner fr £16&alc
CONF: Thtr 80 Class 40 Board 30 Del from £55
CARDS:

MALLAIG Highland Map 13 NM69

★★63% **Marine**
PH41 4PY (adjacent to railway terminal first hotel on right off A830)
☎ 01687 462217 FAX 01687 462821
Closed Xmas & New Year RS Nov-Mar
This friendly family-run commercial and tourist hotel is convenient for

the railway station, ferry terminal and harbour. Attractive public areas include a well stocked lounge bar with a small sitting area for residents at one end, and a tastefully appointed restaurant offering a choice of menus, one specialising in fresh local seafood. Bedrooms, some of which have recently been completely refurbished, offer modern standards of comfort.
19 en suite (bth/shr) (2 fmly) CTV in all bedrooms 6P Coffee am Tea pm No smoking in restaurant Last d 9pm
ROOMS: (incl. bkfst) s £30-£35; d £52-£60 * **LB**
OFF-PEAK: (incl. bkfst) s fr £25; d fr £48
MEALS: Bar Lunch fr £9.25alc Dinner fr £14alc*
CARDS:

★★60% **West Highland**
PH41 4QZ ☎ 01687 462210 FAX 01687 462130
Closed 15 Nov-15 Mar RS 15 Mar,1 Nov,15 Nov
From its position on the hill above the town, this family-run hotel enjoys fine views of the Isle of Skye and remains a popular base for visiting tour groups. Bedrooms vary in size and style. A conservatory has recently been completed and plans exist to upgrade the remaining public areas to the same standard as the refurbished dining room.
34 en suite (bth) (6 fmly) CTV in all bedrooms 40P Wkly live entertainment V meals Coffee am Tea pm No smoking in restaurant Last d 9pm
ROOMS: (incl. bkfst) s £30-£32; d £60-£64 * **LB**
OFF-PEAK: (incl. bkfst) s £25; d £50
MEALS: Bar Lunch £2.50-£8alc Dinner £8.50-£17alc
CARDS:

MARKINCH Fife Map 11 NO20

RED STAR HOTEL

★★★★ **Balbirnie House**
Balbirnie Park KY7 6NE (off B9130)
☎ 01592 610066 FAX 01592 610529
This privately owned country house dates from around 1777, and is a fine example of a Georgian Mansion, both inside and out. The 400 acres of parkland that surround it are particularly colourful in the spring, when the vast rhododendron collection is in bloom. Run under the personal supervision of the Russell family, the service is immaculate, with a warmth which makes one feel instantly at ease. Bedrooms are stylishly decorated and furnished with antiques, and many extras such as bathrobes, fruit, flowers and books feature in all of them. The day rooms have original plasterwork and are warmed by log fires and scented by vases of fresh flowers. Chef Robert McPherson uses the best local produce for his imaginative dishes, which include a rabbit

casserole with creamed leeks and a grainy mustard sauce and a mille feuille of meringue filled with chestnut cream.
30 en suite (bth/shr) (9 fmly) CTV in all bedrooms STV Night porter 120P Golf 18 Pool table Croquet lawn Putting green Xmas International Cuisine V meals Coffee am Tea pm No smoking in restaurant Last d 9.15pm
ROOMS: (incl. bkfst & dinner) s £95-£110; d £145-£190 **LB**
OFF-PEAK: (incl. bkfst) d fr £155
MEALS: Lunch £13-£22.50alc Dinner £27.50-£35*
CONF: Thtr 150 Class 70 Board 50 Del from £140
CARDS:

MAYBOLE South Ayrshire Map 10 NS20

RED STAR HOTEL

★★ **Ladyburn**
KA19 7SG ☎ 01655 740585
FAX 01655 740580
RS Nov-Dec 2 weeks, Jan/Mar 4 weeks
(Rosette awarded for dinner only)
Ladyburn lies off the beaten track and enjoys a pastoral landscape a short distance from Turnberry. It is the home of Jane Hepburn and her equally committed and enthusiastic family who appear at the press of a bell. It has the character and ambience of the country house, with fresh flowers and antiques gracing the public rooms and bedrooms and a log fire in the family library. Jane Hepburn's cooking is straightforward

contd.

and very good. The produce is locally bought and flavours are honest and true. Preserves are home-made also. Menus usually include a roast and a soup as regular items.

8 rms (4 bth 3 shr) No smoking in 7 bedrooms CTV in all bedrooms No dogs (ex guide dogs) 12P No coaches Croquet lawn Boules No children 16yrs V meals Last d 8pm
ROOMS: (incl. bkfst) s £70-£90; d £130-£160 * **LB**
MEALS: Lunch £13.50-£16.50 Dinner £27.50-£32.50*
CARDS:

MELROSE Scottish Borders Map 12 NT53

★★★ 65% **Burt's**
The Square TD6 9PN (A6091)
☎ 01896 822285 FAX 01896 822870
Closed 24-26 Dec

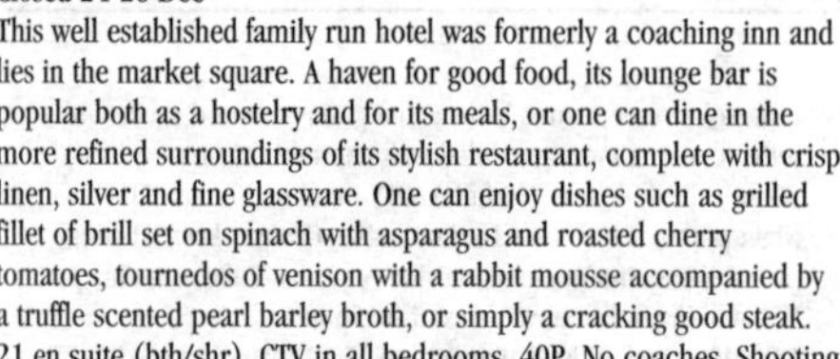

This well established family run hotel was formerly a coaching inn and lies in the market square. A haven for good food, its lounge bar is popular both as a hostelry and for its meals, or one can dine in the more refined surroundings of its stylish restaurant, complete with crisp linen, silver and fine glassware. One can enjoy dishes such as grilled fillet of brill set on spinach with asparagus and roasted cherry tomatoes, tournedos of venison with a rabbit mousse accompanied by a truffle scented pearl barley broth, or simply a cracking good steak.
21 en suite (bth/shr) CTV in all bedrooms 40P No coaches Shooting Salmon Fishing ch fac International Cuisine V meals Coffee am No smoking in restaurant Last d 9pm
ROOMS: (incl. bkfst) s £46-£50; d £78-£82 * **LB**
OFF-PEAK: (incl. bkfst) s £40-£46; d £70-£78
MEALS: Lunch £16.25-£21 Dinner £25-£30&alc*
CONF: Thtr 40 Class 40 Board 26 Del from £80
CARDS:

See advertisement on opposite page

★★ 67% **Bon Accord**
Market Square TD6 9PQ ☎ 01896 822645 FAX 01896 823474
This friendly hotel in the market square offers accommodation in bright, well furnished bedrooms which provide such modern amenities as trouser presses and hair dryers. Though lacking lounge space, it has a choice of bars as well as an attractive dining room.
10 en suite (bth/shr) (1 fmly) CTV in all bedrooms No dogs (ex guide dogs) No children 12yrs Xmas V meals Coffee am Tea pm Last d 8.45pm
ROOMS: (incl. bkfst) s £40; d £68 * **LB**
MEALS: Bar Lunch £10-£20alc Dinner £10-£20alc*
CONF: Thtr 100 Class 60 Board 50 Del from £60
CARDS:

★★ 63% **George & Abbotsford**
High St TD6 9PD ☎ 01896 822308
FAX 01896 822308

This substantial 18th-century former coaching inn stands in the town centre and offers well equipped bedrooms and a lounge bar which complements the restaurant by serving food throughout the day.
30 en suite (bth/shr) (3 fmly) CTV in all bedrooms STV 102P Fishing European Cuisine V meals Coffee am Tea pm Last d 9.30pm
ROOMS: (incl. bkfst) s £30-£49; d £55-£88 * **LB**
OFF-PEAK: (incl. bkfst) s £25-£49; d £50-£88
MEALS: Lunch £7-£16alc Dinner £17.75-£24
CONF: Thtr 180 Class 80 Board 60 Del from £65
CARDS:

MELVICH Highland Map 14 NC86

★★ 61% **Melvich**
KW14 7YJ (on A836, Thurso-Bettyhill)
☎ 01641 531206 FAX 01641 531347
Now owned and personally run by the Martin family, this comfortable Highland hotel, enjoying views over the Halladale Estuary to the Pentland Firth, continues to offer a relaxed welcoming atmosphere. Bedrooms, all located in the wing extension, offer uniform modern appointments together with most of the expected amenities. With its peat fire and fine selection of malts, the informal bar is especially popular and there is a separate comfortable lounge.
14 en suite (shr) CTV in all bedrooms 10P No coaches Fishing Snooker Pool table ch fac Scottish, English, French & Italian Cuisine V meals Coffee am Tea pm Last d 9pm
ROOMS: (incl. bkfst) s £27.50-£32.50; d £50-£60 * **LB**
OFF-PEAK: (incl. bkfst) s £27.50-£30; d £50-£55
MEALS: Bar Lunch £4-£6 High tea £5-£8&alc Dinner £16-£18.50*
CONF: Thtr 60 Board 20
CARDS:

MEY Highland Map 15 ND27

★★ 64% **Castle Arms**
KW14 8XH (on A836) ☎ 01847 851244 FAX 01847 851244
RS Oct-Mar
Genuine hospitality together with personal attention from the resident owner are all part of the appeal of this recently modernised 19th century coaching inn which enjoys uninterrupted views over the Pentland Firth to Orkney. Cosy public areas include a well stocked lounge bar and attractive dining room where seafood specialities are the order of the day. There is also an interesting photographic gallery of the Royal Family. Bedrooms are bright and airy with modern appointments and some are accessed by a covered walkway at the rear of the hotel.
3 en suite (bth/shr) 5 annexe en suite (bth/shr) (1 fmly) CTV in all bedrooms 30P Fishing Pool table ch fac V meals Coffee am Tea pm Last d 9pm
ROOMS: (incl. bkfst) s £33; d £52
OFF-PEAK: (incl. bkfst) s £30; d £47
MEALS: Lunch £6.50 Dinner £15.95&alc*
CARDS:

MILNGAVIE Dumbarton & Clydebank Map 11 NS57

★★★ 65% **Black Bull Thistle**
Main St G62 6BH (leave M8 junc 15 & head north on A879, hotel in Main St) ☎ 0141 956 2291
FAX 0141 956 1896

This one time village inn, which has been extended and modernised in recent years, still retains much of its original character and its well appointed restaurant on the first floor and the adjoining cocktail bar and lounge are warm and enticing areas in which to relax and enjoy the atmosphere of the hotel. There is a public bar downstairs and the hotel has its own tea shop, just down the street. Bedrooms are attractively decorated and have every modern facility and there are also banqueting and meeting facilities.

27 en suite (bth/shr) (2 fmly) No smoking in 8 bedrooms CTV in all bedrooms Night porter 60P International Cuisine V meals Coffee am Tea pm Last d 9.30pm
ROOMS: s £68-£78; d £80-£90 * **LB**
OFF-PEAK: (incl. bkfst) s fr £50; d fr £70
MEALS: Sunday Lunch fr £12.50 Dinner £13.95-£18.25*
CONF: Thtr 30 Class 40 Board 30 Del from £89.25
CARDS:

MOFFAT Dumfries & Galloway Map 11 NT00
See also Beattock

★★★63% **Moffat House**
High St DG10 9HL (at north end of High Street)
☎ 01683 220039 FAX 01683 221288

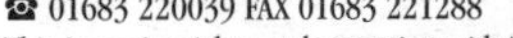

This imposing Adam-style mansion with its large forecourt and extensive gardens at the rear is situated in the centre of the town. The elegant spiral staircase gives an impressive first look at the interior of the hotel, while the public rooms include a number of lounges to suit all moods. Bedrooms, some of which are located in a converted coach house, are attractively decorated and offer modern facilities.

16 en suite (bth/shr) 4 annexe en suite (bth/shr) (2 fmly) CTV in all bedrooms 42P ch fac Scottish & French Cuisine V meals Coffee am Tea pm No smoking in restaurant Last d 8.45pm
ROOMS: (incl. bkfst) s £35-£55; d £65-£84 * **LB**
MEALS: Bar Lunch £3-£15alc Dinner £19.50-£23.50
CONF: Thtr 40 Class 60 Board 40 Del from £65
CARDS:

See advertisement on this page

★★72% **Beechwood Country House**
Harthope Place DG10 9RS (At north end of town)
☎ 01683 220210 FAX 01683 220889
Closed 2 Jan-14 Feb
Once a school for young ladies, this charming Victorian house enjoys an elevated position above the town, giving it an open outlook across the valley. There are two elegant, comfortable lounges, one reserved for non-smokers, which overlook the garden. Bedrooms, all named after local rivers, are tastefully decorated with many nice touches including home-made shortbread and a wide range of toiletries. Carl

contd.

Shaw continues to delight guests with his assured Scottish cuisine served in the candlelit dining room; the five-course dinner is excellent value, but it is advisable to leave room for the large tray of wicked petits fours which accompany the coffee!
7 en suite (bth/shr) (1 fmly) CTV in all bedrooms 15P No coaches Xmas English & French Cuisine V meals Coffee am Tea pm No smoking in restaurant Last d 8.45pm
ROOMS: (incl. bkfst & dinner) s £65; d £108 **LB**
MEALS: Lunch £14 Dinner £22
CARDS:

See advertisement on opposite page

RED STAR HOTEL

★❀❀ **Well View**
Ballplay Rd DG10 9JU (on A708 from Moffat, pass fire station and first left.) ☎ 01683 220184
Closed wk Jan & wk Nov
This delightful Victorian house has a friendly atmosphere, with the Schuckardt family being both welcoming and professional in their approach. The hotel nestles at the foot of hills, but also enjoys an elevated position overlooking this popular Borders town. The bedrooms are comfortably furnished, with one suite on the top floor and a bay-windowed room with a four-poster bed on the first floor. They are furnished in a pleasant style, with attractive quality fabrics and many thoughtful extras. There are two dining rooms and a lounge filled with books, magazines and fresh flowers. Janet Schuckardt is a self-taught chef who has built up a well deserved reputation for her use of local ingredients and imaginative presentation.
6 en suite (bth/shr) No smoking in 4 bedrooms CTV in all bedrooms No dogs (ex guide dogs) 8P No coaches Xmas Scottish & French Cuisine Coffee am Tea pm Last d 8.30pm
ROOMS: (incl. bkfst) s £44; d £72-£78 **LB**
OFF-PEAK: (incl. bkfst) s £38-£40; d £58-£72
MEALS: Lunch £12-£13 Dinner £26-£27.50
CARDS:

MONIAIVE Dumfries & Galloway Map 11 NX79

★★64% **Woodlea**
DG3 4EN (On A702 1.5 miles from Moniaive village)
☎ 01848 200209 FAX 01848 200412
Closed late Oct-Mar
Outdoor and indoor sporting enthusiasts will find plenty to do at this popular hotel, which caters especially for families. The resident owners and their staff can organise sailing, fishing, golf and pony riding, while an indoor pool, games room and tennis courts are all available at the hotel. Dinner orders have to be given earlier in the day, and high teas are arranged for younger children.
12 rms (10 bth) (7 fmly) CTV in all bedrooms STV 20P Indoor swimming pool (heated) Tennis (hard) Sauna Solarium Pool table Croquet lawn Putting green Pony riding Games room Bowls Play area ch fac V meals Coffee am Tea pm Last d 8.30pm
ROOMS: (incl. bkfst) s £24-£39; d £48-£78 * **LB**

MONTROSE Angus Map 15 NO75

★★★63% **Park**

61 John St DD10 8RJ (Off High Street)
☎ 01674 673415 FAX 01674 677091
This family owned and managed hotel is situated close to the town centre, and offers accommodation in both the original building and two extensions. Bedrooms are practically furnished and offer all the expected amenities. There are good conference facilities and the hotel is popular with business guests. At the time of our visit, there were plans to modernise the bar and dining room to create a more informal atmosphere.
59 rms (48 bth 5 shr) (4 fmly) No smoking in 6 bedrooms CTV in all bedrooms Night porter 50P ch fac Xmas Modern International/Scottish & Classical Cuisine V meals Coffee am Tea pm No smoking area in restaurant Last d 9.30pm
ROOMS: (incl. bkfst) s £35-£75; d £55-£90 * **LB**
MEALS: Lunch £4.50-£10 High tea £5.95-£6.50 Dinner £14.50*
CONF: Thtr 150 Class 80 Board 80 Del from £70
CARDS:

MORAR Highland Map 13 NM69

★★63% **Morar**
PH40 4PA (on A830) ☎ 01687 462346 FAX 01687 462130
Closed 22 Oct-Mar
This friendly family-run Highland hotel remains a popular base for visiting tour groups and enjoys superb views over the bay to the islands beyond. The variable sized bedrooms are gradually being enhanced with attractive fabrics, while public areas include an open-plan foyer lounge and small bar. The spacious dining room overlooks the sea and offers satisfying home cooking.
27 en suite (bth) (3 fmly) CTV in all bedrooms 50P Fishing Wkly live entertainment French Cuisine V meals Coffee am Tea pm No smoking in restaurant
ROOMS: (incl. bkfst) s £30-£35; d £60-£70 *
OFF-PEAK: (incl. bkfst) s £25-£30; d £50-£60

MOTHERWELL North Lanarkshire Map 11 NS75

Travel Inn

Glasgow Rd, Newhouse ML1 5SY (leave M74 junc5 onto A725 then follow A8 until M8 roundabout. Turn right onto A73 then first left)
☎ 01698 860277 FAX 01698 861353
Purpose-built accommodation, offering spacious, well equipped bedrooms, all with en suite bathrooms. Meals may be taken at the nearby family restaurant. For more information about Travel Inns, consult the Contents page under Hotel Groups.
40 en suite (bth/shr)
ROOMS: d £35.50 *

MUIR OF ORD Highland Map 14 NH55

★★ 68% **Ord House**
Muir of Ord IV6 7UH (Off A832)
☎ 01463 870492 FAX 01463 870492
May-Oct
Dating back to 1637, this former Laird's house is today a comfortable and relaxing country house hotel which is efficiently run by enthusiastic owners John and Eliza Allen. Set peacefully in 60 acres of lawned and wooded grounds the house offers well proportioned

accommodation in individually designed bedrooms which reflect the original character of the house. Public areas have a comfortable lived in feel and include a choice of inviting lounges with log fires and a small cosy timber clad bar. Upstairs, the L-shaped dining room provides a civilised setting for Eliza's enjoyable country cooking.
11 en suite (bth/shr) 30P No coaches Croquet lawn Putting green Clay pigeon shooting ch fac Scottish & French Cuisine V meals Coffee am Tea pm No smoking area in restaurant Last d 9pm
ROOMS: (incl. bkfst) s £35-£36; d £68-£78 *
MEALS: Bar Lunch £8-£20&alc Dinner £19.50&alc*
CARDS:

★ 77% **Dower House**

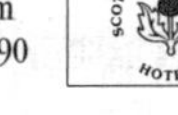

Highfield IV6 7XN (On Dingwall rd A862, 1m from town on left) ☎ 01463 870090 FAX 01463 870090
Closed Xmas day & 1wk Mar
This delightful small hotel lies just a short drive from the village centre. Sheltered in three acres of mature grounds, the house was developed in the cottage orne style around 1800. The cosy lounge has an open fire, books, interesting ornaments and fresh flowers. Robyn Aitchison cooks a set dinner with great skill, and there is an excellent wine list.
5 en suite (bth/shr) 2 annexe en suite (bth) CTV in all bedrooms No dogs 20P Croquet lawn ch fac Xmas No smoking in restaurant Last d 9pm
ROOMS: (incl. bkfst) s £45-£75; d £90-£110 * **LB**
OFF-PEAK: (incl. bkfst) s fr £40; d fr £80
MEALS: Lunch £17.50 Dinner £30*
CARDS:

MULL, ISLE OF Argyll & Bute Map 10

BUNESSAN Map 10 NM32

★ 72% **Assapol House**
PA67 6DW (turn off A849 just after Bunessan School and follow signpost for 1m on minor road)
☎ 01681 700258 FAX 01681 700445
Closed Nov-Mar
(Rosette awarded for dinner only)
Peacefully set by the shore of Loch Assapol, and an ideal base for touring the Ross of Mull, this charming small country house hotel is under the care of Onny Robertson and her son Alex, who have made it a very welcoming and civilised place to stay. Day rooms include a relaxing and recently refurbished drawing room and separate no-smoking sitting room, both comfortably furnished and decorated with many personal ornaments to create a home-like atmosphere. The dining room is quite traditional in style and Onny's uncomplicated and robust home-cooking will satisfy the most hearty of appetites. The menu changes daily and offers choices of starters and puddings, with a set main course. Bedrooms are well equipped and very individual in style.
6 en suite (bth/shr) CTV in all bedrooms No dogs (ex guide dogs) 12P No coaches Fishing No children 10yrs No smoking in restaurant Last d 7.45pm
ROOMS: (incl. bkfst & dinner) s £40-£44; d £86-£104 *
MEALS: Dinner £15
CARDS:

DERVAIG Map 13 NM45

★ 78% **Druimard Country House**
PA75 6QW ☎ 01688 400345 FAX 01688 400345
Closed Nov-Mar
This friendly and small restored Victorian country house within a quiet hamlet on the northwest side of the island is enthusiastically run by Wendy and Haydn Hubbard and their dedicated staff. Wendy's cooking is very much an attraction and in particular pre-theatre dinners are popular as the world's smallest theatre - The Mull Little Theatre is right beside the hotel. The bedrooms offer mixed sizes and are well equipped with pleasant fresh decor;there is a particularly spacious family suite on the top floor. The cosy lounge is available for teas and coffees and the conservatory bar is used for pre-dinner drinks.
6 en suite (bth/shr) (1 fmly) CTV in all bedrooms 20P No coaches Scottish & French Cuisine V meals No smoking in restaurant Last d 8.30pm
ROOMS: (incl. bkfst) s £61.50-£66; d £101-£118 *
MEALS: Dinner fr £17.50*
CARDS:

KILLIECHRONAN Map 10 NM54

★★ 71% **Killiechronan House**
Killiechronan Estate PA72 6JU (leaving ferry turn right to Tobermory A849,in Salen (12m) turn left onto B8035, after 2m turn right to Ulva ferry B8073,Killiechronan House on right)
☎ 01680 300403 FAX 01680 300463
Closed Nov-Mar
Beautifully situated at the head of Loch na Keal in the centre of the Isle of Mull, this recently refurbished house dates from 1840 when it was the lodge house for this vast 6000-acre estate. The comfortable sitting and drawing room offer peaceful relaxation, while the bedrooms have been transformed by the use of high quality fabrics; some have retained their huge original bathrooms. An elegant dining room is the appropriate setting for the good cooking which uses local ingredients, and staff are friendly and courteous at all times. Pony trekking, fishing and shooting can all be arranged through the hotel.
6 en suite (bth) TV available 10P No coaches Fishing Riding No children 12yrs Scottish, French & German Cuisine V meals Coffee am Tea pm No smoking in restaurant Last d 8.30pm
MEALS: Lunch £14.50 Dinner £22.90
CARDS:

PENNYGHAEL Map 10 NM52

★★64% **Pennyghael**
PA70 6HB ☎ 01681 704288
Closed Jan-Mar
A byre has been sympathetically converted and extended to form a charming hotel set on the shore of Loch Scridain on the road to Iona. The lounge and dining room have been reduced in size, and meals are now only served in the evenings by prior arrangement. Two of the bedrooms are on the ground floor and all are comfortable and well equipped.
6 en suite (bth) CTV in all bedrooms 20P No coaches
ROOMS: (incl. bkfst & dinner) s fr £50; d fr £100 *
MEALS: Dinner fr £24.50
CARDS:

TOBERMORY Map 13 NM55

★★★72% **Western Isles**
PA75 6PR ☎ 01688 302012 FAX 01688 302297
Closed 3-22 Jan & 17-28 Dec
Set on a hill with spectacular views over the Bay and Calve Island to the Sound of Mull and the hills beyond, this charming island hotel has been completely transformed by dedicated owners. Recent developments include a new conservatory bar and Spices, a secondary food operation specialising in Eastern cuisine in contrast to the imaginative traditional fare served in the elegant dining room. Bedrooms range from a smart new suite through deluxe and master rooms, to standard rooms; all are decorated to a high standard and feature attractive co-ordinated fabrics and traditional furnishings. Staff are friendly and willing to please.
26 en suite (bth/shr) (2 fmly) CTV in all bedrooms 20P Golf 9 Xmas French Cuisine V meals Coffee am Tea pm No smoking in restaurant Last d 8.30pm
ROOMS: (incl. bkfst) s £37-£44.50; d £83-£98 * **LB**
MEALS: Bar Lunch £4-£10&alc Dinner fr £26*
CONF: Board 30
CARDS: 

See advertisement on opposite page

★68% **Ulva House**
PA75 6PR ☎ 01688 302044
Closed Nov-Feb
Perched on the hilltop overlooking the bay, this charming little hotel offers a friendly welcome and comfortable accommodation. Bedrooms vary in size but are attractively decorated and immaculately maintained. There is a choice of two lounges, one with a bar, and the bright dining room has panoramic views of the area; honest home-cooking is provided at breakfast and dinner. Wildlife tours of the island can be arranged through the owners.
6 rms (1 bth 2 shr) (1 fmly) 8P No coaches ch fac International Cuisine V meals Coffee am No smoking in restaurant Last d 6pm
ROOMS: (incl. bkfst) s £24.95-£42.50; d £49.90-£65 *
MEALS: Lunch £16.50&alc Dinner £16.50&alc

MUSSELBURGH East Lothian Map 11 NT37

Travelodge

Old Craighall EH21 8RE (off A1, 2m from eastern outskirts Edinburgh) ☎ Central Res 0800 850950
FAX 01525 878450
This modern building offers accommodation in smart, spacious and well equipped bedrooms, suitable for family use, and all with en suite bathrooms. Meals may be taken at the nearby family restaurant. For information on room rates and to make a booking, call Roomline free of charge on 0800 850950. For more details about Travelodge, consult the Contents page under Hotel Groups.
45 en suite (bth/shr)

NAIRN Highland Map 14 NH85

★★★★62% **Golf View**
Seabank Rd IV12 4HD (Off A96, next to Nairn Golf Course) ☎ 01667 452301 FAX 01667 455267
With a lovely location overlooking the Moray Firth, this steadily improving hotel is close to both the golf course and the beach. The public areas have undergone a smart refurbishment, whilst the addition of an indoor leisure centre has further enhanced the attractions of the hotel for both business guests and tourists. Bedrooms are also being upgraded to provide a better level of comfort. The staff are friendly and ensure attentive service.
47 en suite (bth/shr) (3 fmly) No smoking in 8 bedrooms CTV in all bedrooms STV Lift Night porter 40P Indoor swimming pool (heated) Tennis (hard) Sauna Solarium Gym Putting green Jacuzzi/spa Xmas Scottish & European Cuisine V meals Coffee am Tea pm No smoking in restaurant Last d 9pm
ROOMS: (incl. bkfst) s £69-£83; d £100-£124 **LB**
OFF-PEAK: (incl. bkfst) s £59-£69; d £70-£100
MEALS: Lunch £9.95-£14&alc Dinner £22.95-£29*
CONF: Thtr 120 Class 40 Board 40 Del from £98
CARDS:

★★★63% **Claymore House**
45 Seabank Rd IV12 4EY (off A96) ☎ 01667 453731 & 453705
FAX 01667 455290
This family-run Victorian hotel is situated in a residential area convenient for the town centre. Improvements have been made to the comfortable bedrooms, which now include one specifically equipped for disabled guests. An attractive conservatory lounge adjoins the well appointed restaurant, and the spacious bar has a lively atmosphere. The hotel is a popular base for both business guests and tourists, and golfing breaks can be arranged.
16 en suite (bth/shr) (2 fmly) No smoking in 4 bedrooms CTV in all bedrooms Night porter 50P Wkly live entertainment ch fac Xmas International Cuisine V meals Coffee am Tea pm No smoking in restaurant Last d 9pm
ROOMS: (incl. bkfst) s £37.50-£45; d £65-£75 **LB**
MEALS: Sunday Lunch £5-£15alc High tea £5.50-£9.50alc Dinner £12-£15&alc
CONF: Class 35 Board 35 Del from £45
CARDS:

★★62% ***Alton Burn***
Alton Burn Rd IV12 5ND ☎ 01667 452051
RS Nov-Mar
This pupose built hotel lies to the west of the town with unrestricted views across the Moray Firth. Bedrooms are practically furnished and enhanced with colourful fabrics, while the family rooms are particularly comfortable. Public areas include a spacious sun lounge and dining room, where a supper menu offers a wide choice of dishes.
19 rms (14 bth 3 shr) 7 annexe en suite (bth/shr) (6 fmly) CTV in all bedrooms 30P Outdoor swimming pool (heated) Tennis (hard) Putting green Games room ch fac International Cuisine V meals

Coffee am Tea pm Last d 9pm
CARDS:

NEWBURGH Aberdeenshire Map 15 NJ92

★★ 68% **Udny Arms**

Main St AB41 0BL (in village centre)
☎ 01358 789444 FAX 01358 789012
This long established hotel stands in the centre of the village, with views over the Ythan estuary. The restaurant is split between a bistro and an elegant Victorian dining room, both with the same menu offering imaginative dishes created with fresh local produce, while the sticky toffee pudding is legendary. There is also a comfortable lounge, characterful bar and an informal café/bar. Bedrooms vary in size, all being attractively decorated and having a good range of amenities for business guests and tourists.
26 en suite (bth/shr) (1 fmly) CTV in all bedrooms 100P Golf 9 Fishing Petanque Scottish & French Cuisine V meals Coffee am Tea pm Last d 9.30pm
ROOMS: s £35-£55; d £70-£90 * **LB**
MEALS: Lunch £15-£40alc Dinner £20-£40alc*
CONF: Thtr 100 Class 30 Board 30 Del £100
CARDS:

See advertisement under ABERDEEN

NEWTON STEWART Dumfries & Galloway Map 10 NX46

HOTEL *of the* YEAR

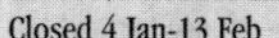
★★★ 76% **Kirroughtree**

Minnigaff DG8 6AN (From A75 take A712, New Galloway rd, for hotel on left)
☎ 01671 402141 FAX 01671 402425
Closed 4 Jan-13 Feb
Standing in an elevated position about a mile outside the town, this impressive 18th-century mansion is surrounded by eight acres of landscaped gardens. The service is impeccable, with the staff being both friendly and attentive whilst retaining a country house approach entirely in keeping with the hotel. All bedrooms have now been upgraded to a high standard, and most are more comfortable and spacious than normally found at this level. The elegant lounge with its reproduction Italian furniture is flanked by two dining rooms where head chef Ian Bennet offers a fine four-course dinner featuring the best of local produce, presented in a delicate and imaginative manner with a good wine list to accompany the meal. Our inspectors have nominated Kirroughtree as AA Hotel of the Year for Scotland for 1996/7.
17 en suite (bth/shr) CTV in all bedrooms 50P Tennis (grass) Croquet lawn Pitch and putt No children 10yrs Xmas Coffee am Tea pm No smoking in restaurant Last d 9pm
ROOMS: (incl. bkfst & dinner) s £66-£76; d £106-£140 * **LB**
OFF-PEAK: (incl. bkfst & dinner) s £59-£70; d £94-£130
MEALS: Sunday Lunch £14-£25alc Dinner £27.50*
CONF: Thtr 30 Class 20 Board 20 Del from £85
CARDS:
See advertisement on page 813

★★★ 59% ***Bruce***
88 Queen St DG8 6JL ☎ 01671 402294 FAX 01671 402294
Located on the main street, this good value hotel takes its name from Robert the Bruce and one of the lounge bars features a spider's web. Some bedrooms have been enhanced with tartan fabrics, though the others remain functional. There are two lounge bars as well as a first floor residents' lounge, while the split-level restaurant can be used for small functions.
contd.

N

20 rms (18 bth/shr) (2 fmly) CTV in 18 bedrooms 20P English & French Cuisine V meals Coffee am
CARDS:

★★67% Creebridge House
DG8 6NP (off A75) ☎ 01671 402121 FAX 01671 403258
RS Nov-Mar
This elegant former shooting lodge has a country house atmosphere, despite being minutes from the town centre. It is surrounded by three acres of woodland and gardens, which the restaurant and comfortable guest lounge overlook. Some of the individually furnished bedrooms also have garden views. There is a large bar/bistro which serves a good range of bar meals, some offering a Taste of Scotland menu, along with the restaurant menus.
20 en suite (bth/shr) (3 fmly) CTV in all bedrooms 50P Fishing Croquet lawn Putting green Xmas Scottish & French Cuisine V meals Coffee am Tea pm Last d 9pm
ROOMS: (incl. bkfst) s £40-£50; d £75-£85 **LB**
MEALS: Sunday Lunch £9.50 Dinner £17.50-£19.50&alc*
CONF: Thtr 70 Class 20 Board 30
CARDS:

NORTH BALLACHULISH Highland Map 14 NN06

★★59% Loch Leven
Onich PH33 6SA (off A82) ☎ 01855 821236
Now a personally run tourist hotel, this 17th-century former coaching inn stands beside the northern shore of Loch Leven close to the Ballachulish bridge. Relaxed public areas include a well stocked bar with a popular menu, a traditional dining room and cosy first-floor lounge. The bedrooms have attractive fabrics and are mostly furnished in pine.
10 en suite (bth/shr) (1 fmly) CTV in all bedrooms 60P Pool table Scottish & Continental Cuisine V meals Coffee am Tea pm No smoking area in restaurant
ROOMS: (incl. bkfst) s £25-£32; d £50-£64 *
OFF-PEAK: (incl. bkfst) s £22-£28; d £44-£56
MEALS: Bar Lunch £3.50-£10alc*
CARDS:

NORTH BERWICK East Lothian Map 12 NT58

★★★63% The Marine

Cromwell Rd EH39 4LZ (from A198 turn into Hamilton Rd at traffic lights then take 2nd right)
☎ 01620 892406 FAX 01620 894480
Well equipped bedrooms of varying size and style are available at this long-established hotel which enjoys the most marvellous views over the golf course and the Firth of Forth beyond. Public areas include a comfortable lounge, a cocktail bar and a number of well appointed meeting rooms. As well as the restaurant, guests have the choice of eating less formally in the bar.
83 en suite (bth/shr) No smoking in 20 bedrooms CTV in all bedrooms Lift Night porter 202P Outdoor swimming pool (heated) Tennis (hard) Squash Snooker Sauna Solarium Putting green Childrens playground ch fac Xmas International Cuisine V meals Coffee am Tea pm No smoking in restaurant Last d 9.30pm
ROOMS: (incl. bkfst) s £55-£75; d £90-£120 * **LB**
OFF-PEAK: (incl. bkfst & dinner) s £45-£79; d £60-£100
MEALS: Lunch £8.95-£12.95 High tea £6.50-£8.50 Dinner £19.95-£25.95
CONF: Thtr 300 Class 150 Board 100 Del from £85
CARDS:

★★64% Point Garry
West Bay Rd EH39 4AW (turn off A198 at North Berwick West Golf Course, onto West Bay Road for 300yds)
☎ 01620 892380 FAX 01620 892848
Closed Nov-Mar
Situated in a quiet residential area on the west side of the town, this Victorian house is popular with golfers, and enjoys fine views over the golf course to the sea. A tranquil atmosphere prevails in the beautifully maintained residents' lounge, while the cocktail bar is an equally welcoming area. Bedrooms vary in size and style.
15 en suite (bth/shr) (7 fmly) CTV in all bedrooms 14P No coaches Snooker International Cuisine V meals Coffee am Tea pm No smoking area in restaurant Last d 9pm
ROOMS: (incl. bkfst) d £50-£90 * **LB**
OFF-PEAK: (incl. bkfst) s £25-£45; d fr £40
MEALS: Lunch £3.50-£14.95 Dinner £14.95-£15.95&alc
CARDS:

★★60% Nether Abbey
20 Dirleton Av EH39 4BQ (On A198)
☎ 01620 892802 FAX 01620 895298
This long established family run hotel is situated on the edge of the town, yet only a short walk from the attractive harbour area. A wide range of speciality ales and a bistro style menu is offered in the Fly Half Bar, a popular place for locals to gather. Bedrooms vary in size and style, most offering comfort and attractive decor.
16 rms (4 bth 6 shr) (5 fmly) CTV in all bedrooms 40P Xmas V meals Coffee am Last d 9.30pm
ROOMS: (incl. bkfst) s £30-£45; d £60-£70 * **LB**
OFF-PEAK: (incl. bkfst) s £25-£30; d £50-£60
MEALS: High tea fr £6.95 Dinner fr £12.50*
CONF: Thtr 80 Class 40 Board 30
CARDS:

NORTH UIST, ISLE OF Western Isles

LOCHMADDY Map 13 NF96

★★65% Lochmaddy
PA82 5AA (100yds from Lochmaddy ferry terminal)
☎ 01876 500331 FAX 01876 500210
CONSORT HOTELS
Conveniently situated beside the ferry terminal, this long established hotel has a welcoming atmosphere and is especially popular with visiting anglers. Other attractions including deerstalking and wildfowling can also be arranged. Public areas include a choice of inviting lounges and contrasting bars while the refurbished dining room offers enjoyable home cooked fare including seafood specialities. Bedrooms provide the expected amenities.
15 en suite (bth/shr) (1 fmly) CTV in all bedrooms 25P No coaches Fishing Pool table Wkly live entertainment V meals Coffee am Tea pm Last d 9pm
ROOMS: (incl. bkfst) s £38.50; d £72
OFF-PEAK: (incl. bkfst) s £30; d £56
MEALS: Bar Lunch £7.50-£12.50alc High tea £7.50-£9.50 Dinner £14.50&alc
CARDS:

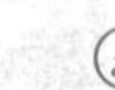

OBAN Argyll & Bute Map 10 NM83

★★★64% *Alexandra*
Corran Esplanade PA34 5AA ☎ 01631 562381 FAX 01631 564497
This privately owned and long established hotel enjoys the most wonderful views of the islands of Kerrera and Mull from its position on the esplanade. Bedrooms are furnished with attractive light wooden furniture and are freshly decorated. Guests have the use of well equipped leisure facilities including a small gym and swimming pool. A good range of popular dishes is available in the attractively decorated restaurant, next door to which is a comfortable lounge bar and a second lounge.
54 en suite (bth/shr) (8 fmly) CTV in all bedrooms Lift Night porter 80P Indoor swimming pool (heated) Snooker Sauna Solarium Gym

Steam room Games room Golf practice nets V meals Coffee am Tea pm Last d 9pm
CARDS:

★★★55% **Caledonian**

Station Square PA34 5RT (Oppoaite Railway station at edge of Oban Bay) ☎ 01631 563133
FAX 01631 562998
The Caledonian is a substantial hotel from the Victorian era and remains a popular base for visiting tour groups. Conveniently situated beside the railway station and ferry terminal, it enjoys a lovely outlook over the bay. As a result of delayed refurbishment, many of the variable-sized bedrooms are functional and show their age. As well as the dining room there is an informal secondary all-day food option. Parking can be difficult.
70 en suite (bth/shr) (10 fmly) CTV in all bedrooms Lift Night porter 6P Xmas Scottish & French Cuisine V meals Coffee am Tea pm No smoking in restaurant Last d 11pm
ROOMS: (incl. bkfst) s £59-£69; d £79-£84 **LB**
OFF-PEAK: (incl. bkfst) s £49-£59; d £69-£79
MEALS: Lunch £7.50-£25 High tea fr £6.20 Dinner fr £9&alc*
CONF: Thtr 120 Class 60 Board 40 Del from £49
CARDS:

★★★53% **Columba**
North Pier PA34 5QD (A82, A85 to Oban town, onto George Street, on approach to mini roundabout turn right, Hotel on left)
☎ 01631 562183 FAX 564683
Situated on the North Pier, this modernised hotel offers very fine views across the bay to the islands of Kerrera and Mull beyond. Bedrooms are well equipped and the public areas can provide food all day, with a reasonably priced menu being available in the attractive restaurant.

contd.

NORTH PIER
OBAN
PA34 5QD
telephone
01631 562183
fax
01631 564683

The newly refurbished 48 bedroomed Columba Hotel situated in the centre of Oban, commands superb views of the Islands. The hotel is ideal from which to explore Argyll and the Islands. Alternatively, enjoy a relaxing meal and a bottle of wine from our extensive wine list in our well appointed restaurant, where our chef prides himself in using carefully selected local produce.

Kirroughtree House ★★★

Newton Stewart, DG8 6AN
Tel: 01671 402141 Fax: 01671 402425

Relax in style at this small and intimate Country House Hotel. Set in eight acres of landscaped gardens, the peace and tranquility of its setting is enhanced by stunning views over Wigtown Bay. All seventeen bedrooms have recently been refurbished to an extremely high standard and many have superb views over the surrounding countryside. Coupled with our outstanding menus and warm welcome this hotel is a must for discerning visitors to the area.

Loch Melfort Hotel ★★★

The finest location on the West Coast of Scotland

Right Beside Arduaine Gardens

The perfect place for a relaxing holiday or short break.
Comfortable accommodation with full ensuite facilities and spectacular views.
Superb cuisine with seafood a speciality.
Non-residents welcome for all meals.

Spring, Autumn and Winter Breaks available together with special Christmas and New Year Holidays.

AA Hotel Inspectors Selected Hotel of the Year Scotland.

Arduaine, by Oban, Argyll PA34 4XG
Tel 01852 200233 Fax 01852 200214

O

There is a public car park on the pier with limited free parking for hotel guests.
48 en suite (bth/shr) (6 fmly) No smoking in 13 bedrooms CTV in all bedrooms Lift Night porter 8P Xmas V meals Coffee am Tea pm No smoking in restaurant Last d 9.30pm
ROOMS: (incl. bkfst) s £49.50-£69.50; d £79-£139 **LB**
MEALS: Lunch £6.50-£11.50 High tea £6.50-£9.50 Dinner £13.95-£16.95&alc
CARDS:

See advertisement on page 813

Courtesy & Care Award

★★❀76% **Manor House**
Gallanach Rd PA34 4LS (Follow signs MacBrayne Ferries and pass ferry entrance for hotel on right) ☎ 01631 562087
FAX 01631 563053
Closed 2-31 Jan
Originally a Georgian dower house and now a comfortable hotel, the Manor House retains much of its original character and charm. It stands close to the town and enjoys superb views over Oban Bay and the nearby islands The staff have been carefully chosen to provide guests with very personal and professional attention and are smartly turned out in tartan. The recently refurbished public rooms are a delight to use and are very comfortable and inviting. The daily changing menu is backed by an extensive carte and cooking is consistent using only the best available produce. Bedrooms have been thoughtfully equipped and are attractively furnished. Owners and staff here have won the AA's Courtesy and Care Award for 1996/7.
11 en suite (bth/shr) CTV in all bedrooms 20P No coaches No children 12yrs Xmas Scottish & French Cuisine V meals Coffee am No smoking in restaurant Last d 9pm
ROOMS: (incl. bkfst & dinner) s £60-£80; d £90-£140 * **LB**
MEALS: Lunch £13.35-£22.90alc Dinner fr £22.90&alc
CARDS:

★★ 67% **Foxholes**
Cologin, Lerags PA34 4SE (3m S, off A816) ☎ 01631 564982
Closed Oct 31 - Apr 1
George and Joan Waugh's charming small country hotel is set amid peaceful countryside in a quiet Glen three miles south of Oban and is an ideal base for the touring holidaymaker. George, a genial host, looks after the front house while Joan provides the tempting fare which is carefully prepared from fresh ingredients. Guests are encouraged to order the main course for the evening meal after breakfast. The non smoking bedrooms are decorated to a high standard and offer comfortable modern furnishings. There is also a wonderfully relaxing lounge with small dispense bar adjacent.
7 en suite (bth/shr) CTV in all bedrooms No dogs 8P No coaches British Cuisine No smoking in restaurant
ROOMS: (incl. bkfst) s fr £35; d fr £50 *

★★65% **Argyll**
Corran Esplanade PA34 5PZ (A85 to town centre, Hotel 500 yards from main rail, taxi and bus terminal) ☎ 01631 562353 FAX 01631 565472

CONSORT HOTELS

A relaxed friendly atmosphere prevails at this family-run hotel which is situated on the seafront beside the North Pier. Ground-floor public areas have recently benefited from refurbishment and the dining room offers an extensive range of dishes from the varied menus. Bedrooms tend to be compact but with modern appointments.
27 en suite (bth/shr) (5 fmly) No smoking in 9 bedrooms CTV in all bedrooms STV Night porter 6P Wkly live entertainment European Cuisine V meals Coffee am Tea pm No smoking in restaurant
CONF: Thtr 600 Class 350 Board 200
CARDS:

See advertisement on opposite page

★★❀64% **Dungallan House**
Gallanach Rd PA34 4PD (at Argyll Square in town centre folow signs for Gallanch, Hotel 0.5m from square) ☎ 01631 563799 FAX 566711
(Rosette awarded for dinner only)
George and Janice Stewart are very caring and friendly hosts at this delightful small hotel which stands in its own well cared for grounds on the edge of town. It enjoys splendid views over the bay and towards the Isle of Mull. The attractive public rooms are comfortable and include a cosy lounge and a spacious bar which features interesting flying boat photographs. The lovely dining room is the perfect setting for Janice's excellent cooking with the menu changing daily. It includes much local produce with an emphasis on fresh fish. The bedrooms were in the midst of being refurbished at the time of our inspection and are mixed in style and type.
13 rms (7 bth 2 shr) CTV in all bedrooms 20P No coaches Xmas V meals Coffee am Tea pm No smoking in restaurant Last d 8.30pm
ROOMS: (incl. bkfst) s £27.50-£40; d £66-£80 * **LB**
MEALS: Lunch £10-£20alc High tea £10-£20alc Dinner £18-£24
CARDS:

See advertisement on opposite page

★★60% **Lancaster**
Corran Esplanade PA34 5AD (on seafront near St Columba's Cathedral) ☎ 01631 562587 FAX 01631 562587
Superb views over the bay to the islands beyond are enjoyed from this friendly tourist hotel, which stands on the waterfront beside the cathedral and is easily recognised by its mock-Tudor exterior. As well as a choice of lounges and bars there is also a range of popular leisure facilities. Bedrooms are neatly furnished to make the best use of space.
27 rms (3 bth 21 shr) (3 fmly) CTV in all bedrooms STV 20P No coaches Indoor swimming pool (heated) Sauna Solarium

contd.

The Lancaster Hotel

OBAN · ARGYLL · PA34 5AD

Tel./Fax 01631 562587

Situated on the sea front within easy walking distance of the town centre. From its public rooms can be seen the magnificent view of Oban Bay with the islands of Kerrera, Lismore and the more distant peaks of Mull in the background. The hotel is readily distinguished by its attractive pseudo-Tudor exterior. The interior is appointed to a high modern standard and can offer guests a wide range of facilities. No coaches.

INDOOR HEATED SWIMMING POOL
SAUNA BATH AND SOLARIUM
FULLY LICENSED · AA ★★

THE FALLS OF LORA HOTEL

AA★★

Oban 5 miles, only 2½-3 hours drive north-west of Glasgow or Edinburgh, overlooking Loch Etive this fine 2-star owner-run Hotel offers a warm welcome, good food, service and comfort. All rooms have central heating, private bathroom, radio, colour television and telephone. From luxury rooms (one with four-poster bed and king size round bath, another with a 7ft round bed and 'Jacuzzi' bathroom en suite) to inexpensive family rooms with bunk beds. FREE accommodation for children sharing parents' room. Relax in super cocktail bar with open log fire, there are over 100 brands of Whisky to tempt you and an extensive Bistro Menu. Fishing, Gliding, Water-sports and Pony Trekking can be arranged. Out of season mini-breaks.

A FINE OWNER-RUN SCOTTISH HOTEL

Connel Ferry, By Oban, Argyll PA37 1PB
Tel: (01631) 710483. Fax: (01631) 710694

Dungallan House Hotel

Gallanach Road, Oban, Argyll PA34 4PD
Telephone: (01631) 563799
Fax: (01631) 566711

George and Janice Stewart look forward to welcoming you to their lovely Victorian Villa set high above Oban. Only half a mile from the town centre with all its facilities yet far enough to be at peace amidst the 5 acres of steep craggy tree-lined cliffs.

The Argyll Hotel

Corran Esplanade · Oban

Telephone: 01631 562353 · Fax: 01631 565472

Situated on the seafront with spectacular views across the sheltered Oban Bay to the magnificent mountains of Mull. The Argyll Hotel is family owned and run priding themselves in doing the utmost to make your stay as comfortable and relaxing as possible. All the bedrooms have been recently refurbished to include en suite facilities. The comfortable restaurant offers a high standard of cuisine using a wide choice of local produce tastefully prepared with a selection of fine wines, malt whiskies and liqueurs to complement your meal. Entertainment can be enjoyed in the lounge bar, provided by local artists. Limited car parking available but there is a large car public car park adjacent to the hotel.

Jacuzzi/spa jacuzzi V meals Coffee am Tea pm Last d 7.45pm
ROOMS: (incl. bkfst) s £25-£30; d £54-£56 *
CARDS:

See advertisement on page 815

OLDMELDRUM Aberdeenshire Map 15 NJ82

★66% Meldrum Arms
The Square AB51 0DS (off the B947, in centre of village)
☎ 01651 872238 FAX 01651 872238
Situated in the centre of the town, this family-run commercial hotel provides good value accommodation and a wide range of meals, including popular high teas. Bedrooms are compact but several have been recently enhanced with bright fabrics and new furnishings. The well stocked lounge bar is also frequented by locals. The local staff create a friendly and welcoming atmosphere.
7 en suite (shr) CTV in all bedrooms No dogs (ex guide dogs) 25P Pool table V meals Coffee am Tea pm
ROOMS: (incl. bkfst) s £35-£37.50; d £45-£50
CONF: Thtr 80 Board 40
CARDS: £

OLD RAYNE Aberdeenshire Map 15 NJ62

★★63% Lodge
AB52 6RY (just off A96) ☎ 01464 851205 FAX 01464 851205
Closed 25-26 Dec & 1 Jan
Good-value accommodation is offered at this friendly family-run hotel. Most bedrooms are in the timber-clad annexe, though there are two rooms in the main house which have recently been refurbished. There is no lounge, but a cosy bar and a small, pretty dining room compensate agreeably.
3 en suite (shr) 4 annexe en suite (bth/shr) (1 fmly) CTV in all bedrooms 20P Coffee am Last high tea 6.30pm
ROOMS: (incl. bkfst) s £40; d £50-£75 * **LB**
MEALS: High tea fr £6.50alc*
CARDS:

ONICH Highland Map 14 NN06

★★★ 69% Allt-Nan-Ros
MINOTEL Great Britain
PH33 6RY (1.5m N of Ballachulish Bridge on A82)
☎ 01855 821210 FAX 01855 821462
Warmly welcoming, the MacLeod family's hotel stands in its own attractive garden and enjoys superb views over Loch Linnhe. The tastefully decorated bedrooms are comfortably furnished in the modern style, and the relaxing public areas include the well stocked bar which leads to the south facing lounge. The recently redecorated T-shaped dining room provides the backdrop for gifted chef Alan Clark's modern style of French cooking which is complemented by the best of Scotland's larder. His imaginative daily fixed-price menu is now supported by a speciality seafood à la carte. The wine list is comprehensive and well chosen.
21 en suite (bth/shr) (2 fmly) CTV in all bedrooms 30P No coaches ch fac Xmas Scottish & French Cuisine V meals Coffee am Tea pm No smoking in restaurant Last d 8.45pm
ROOMS: (incl. bkfst) s £35-£47.50; d £70-£95 **LB**
MEALS: Lunch £7.50-£12.50alc Dinner £22.50&alc
CARDS: £

See advertisement under FORT WILLIAM

★★★67% Onich
CONSORT HOTELS
PH33 6RY (beside A82, 2m N of Ballachulish Bridge)
☎ 01855 821214 FAX 01855 821484
Situated beside the A82 with landscaped gardens sweeping down to the picturesque shore of Loch Linnhe, this friendly family run hotel is an ideal base for the touring holidaymaker. Public areas include a choice of cosy bars and relaxing lounges while the attractive restaurant offers traditional Scottish fare. Bedrooms, many with loch views, offer comfortable modern appointments together with the expected amenities. Staff are especially hospitable and willing to please.
27 en suite (bth/shr) (6 fmly) CTV in all bedrooms STV 50P No coaches Solarium Pool table Jacuzzi/spa Games room Xmas International Cuisine V meals Coffee am Tea pm No smoking in restaurant Last d 9pm
ROOMS: (incl. bkfst) s £43-£47; d £76-£84 **LB**
OFF-PEAK: (incl. bkfst) s £31-£35; d £52-£60
MEALS: Bar Lunch £4.50-£10.75alc Dinner £17.50-£20
CONF: Thtr 30 Del from £65
CARDS: £

See advertisement under FORT WILLIAM

★★★65% Lodge on the Loch

PH33 6RY (beside A82 - 5 miles North of Glencoe and) 10 miles South of Fort William)
☎ 01855 821237 FAX 01855 821238
Closed Nov-Jan (ex Xmas-New Year)
Palm trees grow in the attractive grounds of this comfortableholiday hotel which enjoys a panoramic outlook over Loch Linnhe to the mountains beyond. Public areas have a civilised feel and include an inviting lounge, tastefully appointed restaurant and a snug canopy-draped bar. There is a smart new suite to complement the range of accommodation available.
20 rms (18 bth/shr) (2 fmly) CTV in all bedrooms 25P No coaches Leisure facilities at sister hotel Wkly live entertainment ch fac Xmas International Cuisine V meals Coffee am Tea pm No smoking in restaurant Last d 9.30pm
ROOMS: (incl. bkfst) s £49.50-£56; d £99-£112 * **LB**
OFF-PEAK: (incl. bkfst) s £41-£47.50
MEALS: Sunday Lunch £5.80-£15.50alc High tea £2-£5.50alc Dinner £27.50&alc
CONF: Thtr 50 Class 30 Board 30
CARDS:

See advertisement under FORT WILLIAM

★★63% **Creag Mhor**
PH33 6RY (beside A82) ☎ 01855 821379
RS Late Nov - Jan 17
A relaxed friendly atmosphere prevails at this welcoming family-run holiday hotel which stands in its own well tended grounds beside the A82 overlooking Loch Linnhe. Good progress is being made with cosmetic enhancement of the variable-sized bedrooms many of which enjoy loch views. Public areas include a combined bar/lounge and a spacious traditional dining room offering a tempting range of Scottish fare.
14 rms (9 bth/shr) (3 fmly) CTV in all bedrooms 30P Fishing Xmas V meals Coffee am Tea pm No smoking in restaurant Last d 8.30pm
ROOMS: (incl. bkfst) s £27.50; d £55-£70 * **LB**
OFF-PEAK: (incl. bkfst) s £22.50; d £45-£60
MEALS: Lunch £5.95-£10 Dinner £5.95-£15*
CARDS:
See advertisement under FORT WILLIAM

ORKNEY Map 16

KIRKWALL Map 16 HY41

★★★63% **Ayre**
Ayre Rd KW15 1QX (follow A9 north to Scrabster then P&O car ferry to Stromness, A965 to Kirkwall, Hotel can be found nearby)
☎ 01856 873001 FAX 01856 876289
Completely refurbished in the last few years, this friendly family run hotel beside Kirkwall Bay is an ideal base for the visiting businessman and holidaymaker alike. Bedrooms though variable in size are tastefully decorated and offer comfortable modern furnishings together with the expected amenities. Public areas include a semi open-plan bar/dining room and a small comfortable lounge.
33 en suite (bth/shr) (7 fmly) CTV in all bedrooms STV Night porter 20P No coaches Pool table Wkly live entertainment Scottish & French Cuisine V meals Coffee am Tea pm Last d 9pm
ROOMS: (incl. bkfst) s £54-£74; d £80-£97 *
OFF-PEAK: (incl. bkfst) s £54; d £80-£88
MEALS: Lunch £7.10-£9.75alc Dinner £18.50&alc
CONF: Thtr 150 Class 50 Board 30
CARDS:
See advertisement on this page

★★64% ***Albert***
Mounthoolie Ln KW15 1JZ ☎ 01856 876000 FAX 01856 875397
Close to the harbour and central amenities, this comfortable tourist and commercial hotel stands within the conservation area of old Kirkwall. Public areas include a choice of bars contrasting from the rustic and homely Bothy to the modern style of Matchmakers, while the popular Stables Restaurant with its beamed walls and booth seating, continues offer a range of tempting island produce. Some bedrooms are furnished in pine while others offer solid fitted units.
19 en suite (bth/shr) CTV in 18 bedrooms Last d 9.30pm
CARDS:

PAISLEY Hotels are listed under Glasgow Airport.

PEAT INN Fife Map 12 NO40

RED STAR HOTEL

★★❀❀❀ **Peat Inn**
KY15 5LH (6 miles SW of St Andrews at junct B940/B941) ☎ 01334 840206
FAX 01334 840530
Closed Sun, Mon, Xmas day & New Years day
Situated just six miles from the home of golf, the Peat Inn sits at the crossroads in the centre of the tiny village named after it. The grandly named Residence was added in 1987; eight wonderful suites, each one furnished to the highest standards

contd.

with period French furniture and luxurious marbled bathrooms. Fluffy bathrobes, fresh fruit and a selection of home-made cakes are further treats. However the main point of a visit to the Inn is to sample the refreshing honesty of David Wilson's cuisine. Favourites over the years have been the fish soup, roast salmon with Thai spices, saddle of venison with flageolet beans and red wine sauce, and pigeon with wild mushrooms, brandy and juniper. His other passion is wine, reflected in a wonderful wine list. Continental breakfast served in the room is also memorable with fresh fruit, yoghurt, wonderful pastries and preserves.
8 en suite (bth/shr) CTV in all bedrooms 24P No coaches French Cuisine V meals No smoking in restaurant Last d 9.30pm
ROOMS: (incl. cont bkfst) s £75-£95; d £135 * **LB**
MEALS: Lunch £18.50 Dinner fr £28.50&alc
CARDS:

PEEBLES Scottish Borders Map 11 NT24

★★★ 73% ***Cringletie House***

EH45 8PL (2.5m N on A703) ☎ 01721 730233
FAX 01721 730244
Closed 2 Jan-8 Mar
1996 marked the 25th year at Cringletie for the Maguire family. This imposing turreted baronial mansion is set in 28 acres of gardens and woodland, of which the lovely walled garden is a feature which shouldn't be missed in season. The house is immaculately maintained throughout, with public rooms offering a choice of lounges and a smart conservatory. Unusually the main lounge, with its magnificent ceiling and fireplace, and dining room are on the first floor (there is a lift). All bedrooms enjoy the views. They are attractively decorated and each is individual in size and style, with several boasting fine original fireplaces. The daily-changing dinner menu is short but well structured and offers good honest cooking and accurate flavours.
13 en suite (bth/shr) (2 fmly) CTV in all bedrooms Lift 40P No coaches Tennis (hard) Croquet lawn Putting green International Cuisine V meals Coffee am Tea pm Last d 8.30pm
CARDS:

See advertisement on opposite page

★★★ 71% **Peebles Hydro**
EH45 8LX (On A702, one third mile out of town) ☎ 01721 720602
FAX 01721 722999
This well established family and conference hotel nestles into the hillside on the eastern approach to the town. The welcome is friendly, and the long serving staff are both attentive and caring in their approach. Bedrooms vary in size, though all are well equipped and furnished to a good standard. There is a wide range of leisure activities, both indoors and out, with tennis, pony trekking, dinner dances and swimming all being available. Comfortable public areas overlook the rolling hills.
137 en suite (bth/shr) (25 fmly) CTV in all bedrooms No dogs (ex guide dogs) Lift Night porter 200P Indoor swimming pool (heated) Tennis (hard) Squash Riding Snooker Sauna Solarium Gym Pool table Croquet lawn Putting green Jacuzzi/spa Badminton Beautician Hairdressing Wkly live entertainment ch fac Xmas V meals Coffee am Tea pm Last d 9pm
ROOMS: (incl. bkfst & dinner) s £72.50-£81; d £114.50-£175 **LB**
MEALS: Lunch fr £15 Dinner fr £21
CONF: Thtr 450 Class 200 Board 74 Del from £98
CARDS:

★★★ 67% **Park**
Innerleithen Rd EH45 8BA ☎ 01721 720451 FAX 01721 723510
The Park Hotel is the little sister to the Hydro, with its own individual style, and guests are able to use the extensive leisure facilities nearby. The public areas have been transformed to offer an attractive, tartan-clad bar and a relaxing lounge, while the wood-panelled restaurant enjoys views over the valley. The well equipped bedrooms vary in size, with those in the original house being the most spacious.
24 en suite (bth/shr) CTV in all bedrooms Night porter 50P Putting green Xmas Scottish & French Cuisine V meals Coffee am Tea pm Last d 9pm
ROOMS: (incl. bkfst) s £48.50-£60; d £77-£156 **LB**
OFF-PEAK: (incl. bkfst) s £31-£38; d £62-£80
MEALS: Lunch £8.90-£15 Dinner £18-£18.75
CONF: Thtr 18 Board 10
CARDS:

★★ 67% **Venlaw Castle**
Edinburgh Rd EH45 8QG (off A703) ☎ 01721 720384
Closed Nov-Mar
A fine baronial mansion enjoys a secluded position in wooded grounds high above the town. Some bedrooms are very spacious and the two tower rooms are suitable for families. A comfortable lounge and cosy library bar both have open fires and a wood-floored dining room serves tasty home-cooked dinners. Established family owners provide traditional services.
12 rms (5 bth 5 shr) (4 fmly) CTV in all bedrooms 20P English & French Cuisine V meals Coffee am No smoking in restaurant Last d 8pm
ROOMS: (incl. bkfst) s £36-£38; d £68-£72 **LB**
MEALS: Dinner £11-£16*
CARDS:

See advertisement on opposite page

★★ 64% **Kingsmuir**
Springhill Rd EH45 9EP (Cross Tweed Bridge from High St, then straight ahead up Springhill Rd, hotel is 300 yds on right hand side)
☎ 01721 720151 FAX 01721 721795
This friendly hotel lies in a residential area on the south side of the River Tweed within walking distance of the town centre. Public areas include a choice of lounges and a small bar, whilst bedrooms are thoughtfully equipped.
10 en suite (bth/shr) (2 fmly) No smoking in 5 bedrooms CTV in all bedrooms 35P No coaches V meals Coffee am Tea pm No smoking in restaurant Last d 9.15pm
ROOMS: (incl. bkfst) s fr £43; d fr £74 * **LB**
OFF-PEAK: (incl. bkfst) s fr £36; d fr £64
MEALS: Lunch £10-£15 Dinner £14-£17&alc*
CARDS:

PENNYGHAEL See Mull, Isle of

PERTH Perthshire & Kinross Map 11 NO12

★★★ 74% Murrayshall Country House Hotel & Golf Course
New Scone PH2 7PH ☎ 01738 551171 FAX 01738 552595
Overlooking its own golf course and set in 300 acres of parkland, this magnificent mansion provides excellent facilities for the golfer and business person alike. The public areas are comfortable, with the main house offering a more formal atmosphere than the adjacent clubhouse. The well equipped bedrooms vary from grand rooms in the original house, to less spacious ones in the wing. The Old Masters' Restaurant has delightful decor and views, and offers a good choice of dishes, including several vegetarian options.
19 en suite (bth/shr) (3 fmly) CTV in all bedrooms STV Night porter 50P Golf 18 Tennis (hard) Croquet lawn Putting green Bowling green Driving range V meals Coffee am Tea pm Last d 9.30pm
CARDS:

★★★ 72% **Parklands**

St Leonards Bank PH2 8EB (leave M90 junct 10, after 1 mile turn left at end of park area at traffic lights, hotel on left) ☎ 01738 622451 FAX 01738 622046

(Rosette awarded for lunch only)

This very well furnished hotel is a delightful conversion of two houses and stands in its own well tended gardens. Only a few minutes walk from the city centre, it provides well equipped and mainly spacious bedrooms which have been pleasantly furnished. Dinner is well produced and served in the conservatory restaurant and a good selection of bar meals are now also available. Service is very friendly and attentive whilst the public rooms portray a country house atmosphere and are comfortably furnished.

14 en suite (bth/shr) CTV in all bedrooms STV 40P No coaches International Cuisine V meals Coffee am Tea pm No smoking in restaurant Last d 9pm

ROOMS: (incl. bkfst) s £65-£95; d £75-£125 * **LB**

OFF-PEAK: (incl. bkfst) s £60-£70; d £70-£120

MEALS: Lunch £10.95&alc Dinner £24.95&alc

CONF: Thtr 20 Board 18 Del from £97.50

CARDS:

★★★ 67% **Huntingtower**

Crieff Rd, Almondbank PH1 3JT (3m W off A85)

☎ 01738 583771 FAX 01738 583777

Situated in its own landscaped gardens, just off the Crieff road on the outskirts of the city, this country house style hotel is popular with business people and for weddings. Bedrooms range from spacious masters to more compact standard rooms, and there are several Scandinavian-style chalets in the grounds. There is a choice of eating options, the less formal Conservatory, and the elegant dining room, where a Taste of Scotland is assured, with imaginative dishes being created using the best local produce.

contd.

HUNTINGTOWER
H O T E L
★★★

A magnificent Country House Hotel ~ the finest in PERTH for business or pleasure.

CRIEFF ROAD · PERTH
S C O T L A N D
Tel 01738 · 583771
Fax: 01738 · 583777

ARISTO HOTELS
PERSONALITY HOTELS IN SCOTLAND

PEEBLES · SCOTLAND · EH45 8PL

Set in 28 acres of gardens and woodland – two miles north of Peebles and only 20 miles from Edinburgh.
Magnificent view from all rooms.
Consistently recommended for good food and warm hospitality since 1971 – Good Food Guide 23 years.

One of the most attractive hotels in Scotland

Tel: 01721 730233 Fax: 01721 730 244

Venlaw Castle Hotel ★★

Peebles EH45 8QG
Telephone: 01721 720384

Venlaw Castle Hotel, set in the beautiful Border Hills, with commanding views of the surrounding countryside and the small town of Peebles.
The castle was built in 1782 in the Scottish Baronial Style, on the site of the old Scottish Keep of Smithfield.
This family run hotel, offers all the comforts of the present day, while retaining the atmosphere of gracious living of a bygone age.

15 en suite (bth/shr) 12 annexe en suite (bth/shr) (2 fmly) No smoking in 5 bedrooms CTV in all bedrooms Night porter 100P ch fac Xmas Scottish & Continental Cuisine V meals Coffee am Tea pm Last d 9.30pm
ROOMS: (incl. bkfst) s £71.50; d £90-£95 * **LB**
OFF-PEAK: (incl. bkfst & dinner) s fr £44.50; d fr £89
MEALS: Lunch £9.95-£11.95 Dinner £15.25-£19.75&alc
CONF: Thtr 200 Class 140 Board 30 Del from £56
CARDS:

See advertisement on page 819

★★★61% Lovat

90 Glasgow Rd PH2 0LT (from M90 follow signs for Stirling to rdbt, then turn right into Glasgow Rd, hotel situated 1.50 miles on right) ☎ 01738 636555
FAX 01738 643123
This modern style hotel is very popular for its bar meals and provides recently upgraded bedrooms which are also well equipped. The public rooms include a spacious bar and lounge is found on the first floor whilst the service is friendly and polite from a well turned out staff.
31 en suite (bth/shr) (1 fmly) CTV in all bedrooms STV No dogs (ex guide dogs) Night porter 60P Pool table Xmas V meals Coffee am Tea pm No smoking in restaurant Last d 9.30pm
ROOMS: (incl. bkfst) s £59-£69; d £79-£89 * **LB**
MEALS: Lunch £7.95-£9.95 High tea £6-£8 Dinner £17.95-£19.95&alc*
CONF: Thtr 250 Class 120 Board 70 Del from £72
CARDS:

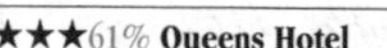

★★★61% Queens Hotel

Leonard St PH2 8HB ☎ 01738 442222
FAX 01738 638496
Located in the heart of the city, close to the railway and bus stations, this large hotel caters for both leisure and business guests, while the function rooms are popular for conferences and dinner dances. Bedrooms vary in size, with a choice of standard or superior, the latter having been more recently refurbished. Public areas include a lounge bar, first floor restaurant and a well equipped leisure centre.
51 en suite (bth/shr) (6 fmly) CTV in all bedrooms STV No dogs (ex guide dogs) Lift Night porter 50P Indoor swimming pool (heated) Sauna Solarium Gym Pool table Jacuzzi/spa Steam room Xmas V meals Coffee am Tea pm No smoking area in restaurant Last d 9.15pm
ROOMS: (incl. bkfst) s £58-£68; d £74-£84 * **LB**
MEALS: Lunch £9.95-£11.95 High tea £6-£8 Dinner £19.95-£21.95&alc*
CONF: Thtr 270 Class 120 Board 70 Del from £82
CARDS:

★★★61% The Royal George

Tay St PH1 5LD ☎ 01738 624455 FAX 01738 630345
What was originally a traditional Scottish coaching inn, this much extended hotel enjoys an enviable position overlooking the River Tay and is fronted by the most magnificent gardens, which each year win the city's garden award. The public areas are both spacious and comfortable, although these areas are beginning to look tired as are a number of bedrooms. This however is more than made up for by the friendly and helpful nature of the largely long standing staff.
42 en suite (bth/shr) No smoking in 14 bedrooms CTV in all bedrooms Night porter 18P Xmas V meals Coffee am Tea pm No smoking in restaurant Last d 9pm
ROOMS: s £60-£67; d £75-£90 * **LB**
MEALS: Sunday Lunch £8.50-£12.50 High tea £5.95-£8.95 Dinner fr £16.95&alc*
CONF: Thtr 120 Class 40 Board 40 Del from £75
CARDS:

★★★60% Quality Station

Leonard St PH2 8HE (from A9 head for city centre and pass Perth Leisure Pool on right. Turn right and head straight for 300yds) ☎ 01738 624141
FAX 01738 639512
This grand Victorian hotel, situated beside the railway stations, offers well appointed accommodation. Whilst the bedrooms very in size and style, the Premier Plus rooms are very spacious and well equipped with trouser presses and mini bars. High ceilings and ornate plasterwork are he hallmarks of the comfortable public areas, which include a cocktail bar with doors which open out on to the garden. The staff are friendly and cheerful.
70 en suite (bth/shr) (4 fmly) No smoking in 25 bedrooms CTV in all bedrooms STV Lift Night porter 70P Gym Mini-gym Xmas English & Continental Cuisine V meals Coffee am Tea pm No smoking area in restaurant Last d 9.30pm
ROOMS: s £57.50-£67.50; d £67.50-£77.50 **LB**
MEALS: Lunch £7.95-£9.95&alc Dinner £13.50&alc
CONF: Thtr 400 Class 150 Board 60 Del from £82.50
CARDS:

★★72% *Newmiln Country Estate*

Guildtown PH2 6AE ☎ 01738 552364
FAX 01738 553505
Situated about four miles north of Perth, this country house hotel is reached through a grand avenue of trees which secludes it from the main road. The elegant public areas are adorned with fresh flowers and feature log fires, with a choice of two lounges available, as well as a spacious dining room. Bedrooms vary in size, some being exceptionally large, and all having antique-style furnishings to give them a luxurious feel. Set 3-course dinners are offered, which allows chef Paul Burns to display his talents of allowing fresh local produce, some of it from the estate itself, to keep its clear flavours, accompanied by delicate sauces or crisp salads. The staff are friendly and attentive.

★★68% Isle of Skye Toby

Queen's Bridge, 18 Dundee Rd PH2 7AB
☎ 01738 624471 FAX 01738 622124
Situated in an elevated position overlooking the city this hotel was originally a 19th century house, but in recent times was

joined to two more houses and is now a comfortable and friendly hotel ideal for touring the area or using as a base for business purposes. The bedrooms are all furnished and decorated to a high standard, two have their own lounges and another has facilities for disabled persons. The Toby Carving Room Restaurant has been attractively designed and incorporates four contrasting styles of décor. Conference and meeting rooms are available and there are adequate parking facilities at the rear.
47 en suite (bth/shr) (37 fmly) No smoking in 19 bedrooms CTV in all bedrooms STV Lift Night porter 70P V meals Coffee am Tea pm No smoking in restaurant Last d 10pm
MEALS: Lunch fr £8.95alc Dinner fr £8.95alc*
CONF: Thtr 130 Class 80 Board 100 Del from £65
CARDS:

★65% **Woodlea**
23 York Place PH2 8EP (take A9 into Perth city centre, hotel is on left next to church & opposite library) ☎ 01738 621744 FAX 01738 621744
Located within easy walking distance of the city, this family owned and run hotel provides modern bedrooms all of which are en suite. A very good range of home cooked food is available with the high tea menu being very popular and good value. There is a small lounge provided for residents.
11 en suite (bth/shr) (1 fmly) CTV in all bedrooms STV No dogs (ex guide dogs) Night porter 4P V meals Tea pm No smoking in restaurant Last d 7.30pm
ROOMS: (incl. bkfst) s £27.50-£35; d £40-£46 **LB**
MEALS: High tea £5.50-£11alc Dinner £12.50-£15

PETERHEAD Aberdeenshire Map 15 NK14

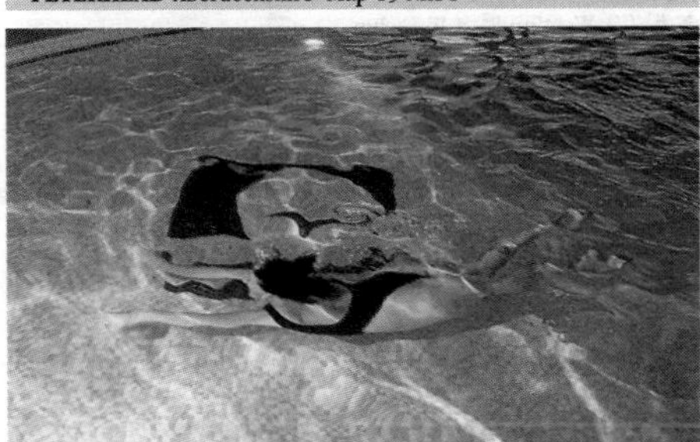

★★★68% **Waterside Inn**
Macdonald Hotels
Fraserburgh Rd AB42 7BN (A952 to roundabout on outskirts of Peterhead and turn left for Fraserburgh - 34 miles North of Aberdeen) ☎ 01779 471121 FAX 01779 470670
This modern hotel is conveniently situated to the north of the town on the Fraserburgh road and offer well equipped accommodation including family rooms and suites. The recently and very smartly refurbished public areas include a cocktail bar and spacious lounge which is warmed by open fires. The restaurant, where a good range of popular dishes are available, enjoys views over the golf course and the river. The service is cheerful and attentive and hotel is family friendly.
69 en suite (bth/shr) 40 annexe en suite (bth/shr) (15 fmly) No smoking in 55 bedrooms CTV in all bedrooms STV Night porter 250P Indoor swimming pool (heated) Snooker Sauna Solarium Gym Jacuzzi/spa Steam room Wkly live entertainment ch fac Xmas Scottish & French Cuisine V meals Coffee am Tea pm Last d 9.45pm
ROOMS: (incl. bkfst) s fr £69.50; d fr £99 * **LB**
MEALS: Lunch £6.50-£13 High tea fr £9 Dinner fr £18.95*
CONF: Thtr 250 Class 100 Board 50
CARDS:

★★★61% **Palace**
Prince St AB42 1PL ☎ 01779 474821 FAX 01779 476119
Situated close to the town centre, this modern commercial hotel has a good range of bars, one of which offers live entertainment on weekend evenings. Bedrooms have recently been refurbished to provide a good standard of accommodation and facilities. Home cooked meals are available in both the restaurant and lounge bar, while home baking can be enjoyed in the coffee shop/diner.
66 en suite (bth/shr) (2 fmly) No smoking in 8 bedrooms CTV in all bedrooms STV Lift Night porter 90P Snooker Pool table Wkly live entertainment Xmas V meals Coffee am Tea pm Last d 9.30pm
ROOMS: (incl. bkfst) s £35-£60; d £49-£70 * **LB**
MEALS: Lunch £10 Dinner £10-£25alc
CARDS:

PITLOCHRY Perthshire & Kinross Map 14 NN95

★★★ 72% **Pine Trees**
Scotland's Commended Hotels
Strathview Ter PH16 5QR ☎ 01796 472121 FAX 01796 472460
Set high above the town in acres of garden and woodland, this magnificent country mansion has many period features; a marble staircase leads up to a drawing room with an ornate plasterwork ceiling and two marble fireplaces. Downstairs there is a cocktail lounge and an elegant dining room where chef Ryan Young has revitalised the cooking. Bedrooms are a blend of the traditional and modern.
20 rms (19 bth/shr) CTV in all bedrooms No dogs (ex guide dogs) 40P No coaches Putting green Xmas Scottish & French Cuisine V meals Coffee am Tea pm Last d 8.30pm
ROOMS: (incl. bkfst) s £48-£53; d £88-£98 * **LB**
MEALS: Lunch fr £12 Dinner fr £25*
CONF: Thtr 20 Board 20
CARDS:

★★★66% **Pitlochry Hydro**

Knockard Rd PH16 5JH (Turn off A9, proceed to town centre. In centre turn right onto A924 Braemar Rd. Hotel is half mile on right) ☎ 01796 472666 FAX 01796 472238
Closed Jan
On the approach to the town, this large resort and conference hotel dominates the skyline of this popular Perthshire town. There is a choice of spacious lounges, while the dining room is traditional in style. Bedrooms are mostly spacious and well equipped; several have views across the Tummel valley. The staff have a professional yet light-hearted approach. There is also a leisure complex with a good-sized swimming pool.
64 en suite (bth/shr) (6 fmly) CTV in all bedrooms STV No dogs (ex guide dogs) Lift Night porter 100P Indoor swimming pool (heated) Snooker Sauna Solarium Gym Croquet lawn Putting green Jacuzzi/spa Xmas Scottish, English & French Cuisine V meals Coffee am Tea pm No smoking in restaurant Last d 8.45pm
ROOMS: (incl. bkfst) s £61-£65; d £110-£116 * **LB**
MEALS: Bar Lunch £5-£10 Dinner fr £15.50&alc
CONF: Thtr 120 Class 40 Board 40 Del from £82
CARDS:

★★★65% **Green Park**
Clunie Bridge Rd PH16 5JY ☎ 01796 473248 FAX 01796 473520
Closed 2 Nov-26 Mar
On the banks of Loch Faskally just on the northern edge of the town, this long-established tourist hotel has a superb setting in award-winning gardens. Bedrooms are comfortable and well maintained, and the lounge gives a panoramic view of the loch and surrounding hills. There is also a bar and traditional-style dining room.

contd.

37 en suite (bth/shr) (10 fmly) CTV in all bedrooms No dogs (ex guide dogs) 50P No coaches Fishing Putting green Table tennis Scottish & French Cuisine V meals Coffee am Tea pm No smoking in restaurant Last d 8.30pm
ROOMS: (incl. bkfst) s £48-£50; d £84-£85 * **LB**
OFF-PEAK: (incl. bkfst) s £38-£40; d £70-£75
MEALS: Bar Lunch fr £6 Dinner fr £19.50&alc*
CARDS:

★★★ 63% Atholl Palace

REGAL A Collection of Individual Hotels

Atholl Rd PH16 5LY ☎ 01796 472400
FAX 01796 473036
The most magnificent views can be enjoyed from this long established hotel set high above the town. The smartly refurbished public areas retain many original features such as high ceilings and ornate plasterwork. These areas, where lounge service is available and guests can also enjoy a lighter meal in the bar, are warmed by log fires in winter. Bedrooms vary in size and style, most enjoying the view. Built in the 'Grand Resort' style, the hotel has a very pleasing and quite unique atmosphere.
76 en suite (bth/shr) (4 fmly) No smoking in 30 bedrooms CTV in all bedrooms Lift Night porter 120P Outdoor swimming pool (heated) Tennis (hard) Snooker Sauna Solarium Pool table Putting green 9 Hole pitch & putt,Games room Xmas British Cuisine V meals Coffee am Tea pm No smoking in restaurant Last d 9pm
ROOMS: (incl. bkfst) s fr £60; d fr £120 * **LB**
OFF-PEAK: (incl. bkfst) s fr £39; d fr £78
MEALS: Bar Lunch £9.95&alc Dinner £17.95&alc*
CONF: Thtr 250 Class 120 Board 60 Del from £75
CARDS:

★★★ 61% *Scotland's*

40 Bonnethill Rd PH16 5BT ☎ 01796 472292 FAX 01796 473284
Close to the town centre, this friendly family-run resort hotel is a popular base for tour groups. Public areas comprise of several traditional lounges and a more modern leisure centre with an adjoining bar lounge, there is also a public bar frequented by the locals. Bedrooms vary in size and style.
60 en suite (bth/shr) (14 fmly) CTV in all bedrooms Lift Night porter 87P Indoor swimming pool (heated) Sauna Solarium Gym Beauty room British & French Cuisine V meals Coffee am Tea pm Last d 8.30pm
CARDS:

★★ ❀ 73% Knockendarroch House

Higher Oakfield PH16 5HT (turn off A9 going N at Pitlochry sign. After railway bridge, take 1st right, then 2nd left) ☎ 01796 473473 FAX 01796 474068
Sitting high above the town, this Victorian mansion enjoys a secluded location with fine views across the town and Tummel Valley. Many guests return year after year, and proprietors John and Mary McMenemie run the hotel in the style of a friendly country house. Bedrooms are spacious and traditionally furnished with individual style. There is a large lounge with comfortable seating and a grand piano; and, as there is no bar, drinks are served in here at any time of day. The short dinner menu offers the best of home cooking which has, again, been awarded our one rosette.
12 en suite (bth/shr) (1 fmly) No smoking in all bedrooms CTV in all bedrooms Night porter 12P No coaches Xmas Scottish & French Cuisine V meals No smoking in restaurant Last d 8pm
ROOMS: (incl. bkfst & dinner) s £46; d £92 **LB**
OFF-PEAK: (incl. bkfst & dinner) s £36; d £72
MEALS: Dinner £14-£18&alc
CARDS:

★★ 70% Acarsaid

8 Atholl Rd PH16 5BX (take main road from A9 Perth to Inverness to Pitlochry, hotel on right hand side as you enter town)
☎ 01796 472389 FAX 473952
Closed 5 Dec-9 Mar

This extended Victorian villa is set back from the main road on the south side of the town. Howard and Mary Williams and their friendly staff ensure that guests are comfortable, providing attractively decorated and thoughtfully arranged bedrooms. There are two lounges, one non-smoking, and a large dining room where healthy eating options feature on the short menu.
18 en suite (bth/shr) (1 fmly) CTV in all bedrooms No dogs 20P No children 10yrs International Cuisine V meals Coffee am Tea pm No smoking in restaurant Last d 8pm
ROOMS: (incl. bkfst) s £25-£35; d £50-£70 **LB**
OFF-PEAK: (incl. bkfst) s £25; d £25-£50
MEALS: Lunch £5-£15alc Dinner £14-£16
CARDS:

See advertisement on opposite page

★★ 70% Westlands of Pitlochry

160 Atholl Rd PH16 5AR (turn off A9 into centre of Pitlochry, hotel situated at north end of town) ☎ 01796 472266 FAX 01796 473994
Fronted by its lawn and garden, this stone-built hotel just north of the town centre creates a pleasing impression. It has an attractive extension with smart bedrooms, a good-sized restaurant and a popular bar which serves light meals.
15 en suite (bth/shr) (2 fmly) CTV in all bedrooms 28P Fishing Xmas International Cuisine V meals Coffee am No smoking in restaurant Last d 9pm
ROOMS: (incl. bkfst) s £36-£41; d £72-£82 * **LB**
OFF-PEAK: (incl. bkfst) s £24.50-£29.50; d £49-£59
MEALS: Bar Lunch £5-£15alc Dinner £17.50
CONF: Thtr 35 Class 24 Board 20 Del from £60
CARDS:

★★ 69% Dundarach

CONSORT HOTELS

Perth Rd PH16 5DJ (S of town centre)
☎ 01796 472862 FAX 01796 473024
Closed Jan RS Dec-early Feb
Popular with tour groups, this fine mansion stands in its own grounds off the main road at the southern end of the town. Lounges are relaxing, bedrooms vary in both size and style and friendly service is provided by the Smail family and their staff.
23 en suite (bth/shr) 3 annexe rms (2 fmly) CTV in all bedrooms 30P Xmas International Cuisine V meals Coffee am Last d 8pm
ROOMS: (incl. bkfst) s fr £52.50; d fr £78 **LB**
MEALS: Lunch fr £12.50 Dinner £14.50-£25alc*
CARDS:

★★ 68% Birchwood

2 East Moulin Rd PH16 5DW (200 m off Atholl Rd on South side of town) ☎ 01796 472477
FAX 01796 473951
Closed Dec-Feb
The enthusiastic proprietors Brian and Ovidia Harmon are closely involved in the day to day running of their hotel, and take the time to

get to know their guests, many of whom return year on year. The hotel lies secluded in its own gardens on the southern side of the town. The wood panelled reception area gives an attractive first impression, and the comfortable lounge has a small dispense bar where drinks are served before dinner. The traditionally furnished bedrooms vary in size, and some are contained in a modern bungalow to the rear of the hotel.
12 en suite (bth/shr) 5 annexe en suite (shr) (4 fmly) CTV in all bedrooms 25P V meals Coffee am Tea pm No smoking in restaurant Last d 8.15pm
ROOMS: (incl. bkfst) s £37.50; d £75 **LB**
OFF-PEAK: (incl. bkfst) s £30; d £60
MEALS: Lunch £5-£10 Dinner £19&alc
CARDS:

★★68% Claymore
162 Atholl Rd PH16 5AR (turn off A9 into Pitlochry, hotel last on right had side after passing through town centre - heading north)
☎ 01796 472888 FAX 01796 474037
Closed 3 Jan-14 Feb
Surrounded by well tended gardens, this family owned and run hotel provides well equipped bedrooms whilst the newly refurbished and extended public rooms include a comfortable lounge and delightful conservatory. A very good range of food is available in either the bar or restaurant and the service is both warm and friendly. The house stands on the main road to the north west of the town.
7 en suite (bth/shr) 4 annexe rms (2 shr) (1 fmly) No smoking in 1 bedroom CTV in all bedrooms 25P No coaches Xmas European Cuisine V meals Coffee am Tea pm No smoking in restaurant Last d 9pm
ROOMS: (incl. bkfst) s £32-£35; d £64-£70 * **LB**
OFF-PEAK: (incl. bkfst) s £27-£29; d £54-£58
MEALS: Bar Lunch £8-£19.10 High tea £5.95-£6.25 Dinner £17.95
CARDS:

★★67% Balrobin
Higher Oakfield PH16 5HT ☎ 01796 472901 FAX 01796 474200
Closed Dec-Feb (ex New Year)
This immaculate hotel with a fine outlook over the surrounding hills offers bedrooms in two modern extensions. The lounge and dining room also have good views and there is a residents' bar.
15 en suite (bth/shr) (2 fmly) CTV in all bedrooms 15P No coaches No children 5yrs Xmas V meals Tea pm No smoking in restaurant Last d 8pm
ROOMS: (incl. bkfst) s £30-£35; d £60-£64 **LB**
OFF-PEAK: (incl. bkfst & dinner) s £33-£36; d £66-£72
MEALS: Dinner £15-£18
CARDS:

★★62% Craigvrack
MINOTEL Great Britain
West Moulin Rd PH16 5EQ (turn off A9 into Pitlochry. Follow sign for Braemar A93, turn right on main street Kirkmichael/Braemar A93 hotel is on the right after 500 mtrs) ☎ 01796 472399 FAX 01796 473990
Located just off the Braemar road, this stone-built house with extensions enjoys an elevated position, giving it panoramic views of the surrounding countryside. Bedrooms vary in size, with most having been recently refurbished to offer modern facilities and attractive décor. There is a small cocktail bar as well as a residents' lounge which adjoins the dining room.
18 rms (16 bth/shr) (2 fmly) CTV in all bedrooms 20P Xmas V meals Coffee am No smoking in restaurant Last d 8.30pm
ROOMS: (incl. bkfst) s £26-£30; d £52-£60 * **LB**
OFF-PEAK: (incl. bkfst) s £21-£25; d £42-£50
MEALS: Bar Lunch £8.60-£16.20 Dinner £16.95-£19.95*
CARDS:

★★60% Craig Urrard
10 Atholl Rd PH16 5BX ☎ 01796 472346
There is an informal atmosphere at this small family-run hotel, which is situated just off the main road on the southern approach to the town. Bedrooms are practically furnished with modern units and neatly kept. Public areas include a small residents' lounge, a cosy bar and a restaurant with sun lounge extension. Bar meals only are served during low season.
10 rms (7 shr) 2 annexe en suite (shr) (2 fmly) CTV in all bedrooms No dogs 12P No coaches
ROOMS: (incl. bkfst) s £23-£27; d £46-£56 *
CARDS:

Highland Gateway Lodge
Perth Rd PH16 5DJ (S of town centre)
☎ 01796 474474 FAX 01796 473024
A lodge standing in the secluded grounds of the Dundarach Hotel but completely separate from it (though guests check in there and can use its facilities) provides accommodation in modern, good-sized bedrooms. Continental breakfast is delivered to rooms or a full breakfast is available in the hotel.
12 en suite (bth) (6 fmly) No smoking in 6 bedrooms CTV in all bedrooms No dogs 12P International Cuisine V meals
ROOMS: s fr £38.95; d fr £38.95
CONF: Thtr 40 Class 24 Board 24 Del from £65
CARDS:

PLOCKTON Highland Map 14 NG83

★★77% Haven

Innes St IV52 8TW (turn off A87 just before Kyle of Loclalsh, after Balmacara there is a signpost to Plockton, hotel on main road just before lochside)

contd.

☎ 01599 544334/544223 FAX 01599 544467
Closed 20 Dec-1 Feb
(Rosette awarded for dinner only)
Regarded by many as one of the best small hotel's on the west coast, this charming village hotel continues to go from strength to strength under the enthusiastic ownership of Annan and Jill Dryburgh. Many of the comfortable and well maintained bedrooms have been cosmetically enhanced while public areas include a choice of comfortable sitting rooms, one for non smokers, and there is also a cosy dispense bar. Dinner in the attractive dining room retains a sense of occasion and Chef Ian James continues to offer carefully prepared dishes from his daily changing fixed price menu. Using only the best available raw ingredients such as game, seafood, prime beef and lamb, dining at the Haven is one of the highlights. Staff are friendly and willing to please.
15 en suite (bth/shr) CTV in all bedrooms 7P No coaches No children 7yrs V meals Coffee am Tea pm No smoking in restaurant
ROOMS: (incl. bkfst) s £53-£55; d fr £110 * **LB**
OFF-PEAK: (incl. bkfst) s fr £50; d fr £100
CARDS:

POLMONT Falkirk Map 11 NS97

★★★69% ***Inchyra Grange***
Grange Rd FK2 0YB (just beyond BP Social Club)
☎ 01324 711911 FAX 01324 716134

Macdonald Hotels

Dating from the 1900's, this former manor house which is ideally situated close to Junction 5 of the M8 and just 20 minutes from both Edinburgh and Glasgow, has been considerably extended to provide spacious, well equipped accommodation. The comfortable public areas include extensive leisure facilities with a second restaurant and plans are well advanced for the addition of a magnificent ballroom which will be completed by the end of 1997. The long established team of staff are friendly and helpful.
43 en suite (bth/shr) (5 fmly) No smoking in 8 bedrooms CTV in all bedrooms Night porter 150P Indoor swimming pool (heated) Snooker Sauna Solarium Gym Jacuzzi/spa Spa bath Steam room Beauty therapy room Scottish & French Cuisine V meals Coffee am Tea pm Last d 9.30pm
CARDS:

PORT APPIN Argyll & Bute Map 14 NM94

RED STAR HOTEL

★★★ ✿✿✿ **Airds**
PA38 4DF ☎ 0163 1730236
FAX 0163 1730535

RELAIS & CHATEAUX. Relais Gourmands

In the heart of R L Stevenson country this former Ferry Inn has been transformed by the Allens into a stylish and peaceful haven of relaxed comfort. Situated amid spectacular scenery with stunning views across Loch Linnhe, scattered with islands, to the Morvern mountains beyond, the simple whitewashed exterior belies the luxury within. Bedrooms may vary in size, but their furnishings are equal in style and quality. The attractive dining room and faces the loch: it is here that Graeme Allen's cooking skills are to be enjoyed. A typical delicious starter was plump juicy scallops lightly toasted and accompanied by a strong, sweet, creamy sauce. Soups are full of body and flavour. The main courses are usually sauced with robust stock reductions accompanying classic dishes such as venison or guinea fowl. There is a good range of desserts and tasty little sweetmeats to follow.

12 en suite (bth/shr) CTV in all bedrooms No dogs (ex guide dogs) 15P No coaches Coffee am Tea pm No smoking in restaurant Last d 8.30pm
ROOMS: (incl. bkfst) s £63; d £160-£180 *
OFF-PEAK: (incl. bkfst) s £50; d £100
MEALS: Dinner £35*
CARDS:

PORT ASKAIG See Islay, Isle of

PORT OF MENTEITH Stirling Map 11 NN50

★★ ✿✿ 75% **Lake**
FK8 3RA (on B8034 to Arnproir)
☎ 01877 385258 FAX 01877 385671

This attractive hotel stands on the shore of Scotland's only lake and is thus unique in both its name and position. The art-deco style is maintained throughout, and the comfortable lounge and conservatory restaurant have stunning views to Inchmahome Priory where Mary, Queen of Scots, took refuge. The bedrooms are furnished and decorated to a high standard, with many extra touches. Chef Stuart Morrison uses fresh ingredients to create mouth-watering dishes: tasty hot canapés were followed by a two-layer chicken and herb terrine on a tomato and mint sauce. A sweet apple sorbet refreshed the palate for a tender fillet of beef with a horseradish sabayon, accompanied by roasted shallots and bacon and a simple selection of fresh vegetables. A light flaky pastry round filled with creamy custard and pieces of plum made an excellent finale, and staff are both friendly and professional.
15 en suite (bth/shr) CTV in all bedrooms 35P No coaches No children 12yrs Xmas Scottish & French Cuisine V meals Coffee am Tea pm No smoking in restaurant Last d 8.30pm
ROOMS: (incl. bkfst & dinner) s £59-£93; d £88-£166 * **LB**
MEALS: Lunch £6-£15.95 Dinner £22.90*
CONF: Thtr 30 Board 20
CARDS:

indicates a Country House Hotel. Please consult the section on AA Star Rating at the front of the book.

PORTPATRICK Dumfries & Galloway Map 10 NX05

★★★66% **Fernhill**

DG9 8TD (turn right off A77 at the War Memorial)
☎ 01776 810220 FAX 01776 810596
Closed Xmas

Set high above the village, this friendly, family-run hotel offers spectacular views of the harbour and across to Ireland. It is conveniently close to Dunskey Golf Course as well as many others in the area, and the garden house, with its four bedrooms, is ideal for parties travelling together. Bedrooms in the main hotel vary in size and furnishings, with the executive rooms offering the most space and comfort. The conservatory restaurant, traditional lounge and smart reception area all overlook the sea.

14 en suite (bth/shr) 6 annexe en suite (bth/shr) (1 fmly) CTV in all bedrooms 50P Xmas Scottish & French Cuisine V meals Coffee am Tea pm Last d 10pm
ROOMS: (incl. bkfst) s £55-£85; d £79-£99 * **LB**
MEALS: Sunday Lunch fr £9.75 Dinner fr £19.50
CONF: Class 30 Board 10 Del from £75
CARDS:

★★★60% **Portpatrick**

DG9 8TQ (A77 Stranraer to Portpatrick. After village sign fork right at war memorial, hotel half a mile on right hand side) ☎ 01776 810333
FAX 01776 810457
Closed mid Nov-early Mar (ex Xmas/New Year)

Popular with golfers and tour groups this large, traditionally managed hotel offers spacious and comfortable accommodation. Perched high on the cliff top overlooking the harbour it enjoys fine panoramic sea views from all of the public rooms. Bedrooms vary in style and have been modernised over the years; some have sea views.

57 en suite (bth/shr) (5 fmly) No smoking in 12 bedrooms CTV in all bedrooms Lift Night porter 60P Outdoor swimming pool (heated) Tennis (grass) Snooker 9 Hole par 3 golf Games room Wkly live entertainment ch fac Xmas English & French Cuisine V meals Coffee am Tea pm Last d 9pm
ROOMS: (incl. bkfst) s £55-£60; d £79-£85 * **LB**
OFF-PEAK: (incl. bkfst) s £45-£50; d £60-£70
MEALS: Bar Lunch £3.50-£7.50 Dinner £16
CONF: Thtr 80 Class 45 Del from £55
CARDS:

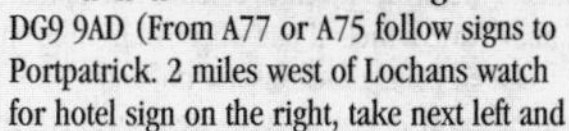

★★❀❀❀ **Knockinaam Lodge**

DG9 9AD (From A77 or A75 follow signs to Portpatrick. 2 miles west of Lochans watch for hotel sign on the right, take next left and follow signs to hotel) ☎ 01776 810471 FAX 01776 810435

This small hotel is building a deserved reputation for both its hospitality, led by Michael Bricker and Pauline Ashworth, and its fine cuisine. The secluded house is beautifully located on the edge of the Irish Sea at the end of a three-mile drive from the main road; it is bordered on three sides by cliffs, while the lawns to the front lead down to the bay. Public areas include a morning room which overlooks the sea, an elegant drawing room and cosy bar, with a wide range of rare malt whiskies. Bedrooms vary in size, but are brightly decorated and have many thoughtful touches. Tony Pierce has taken over as head chef and executes his dishes with a delicate, light touch which has earned him a three rosette award. The chicken and veal sweetbread boudin was the highlight of a recent meal, with a Madeira broth with truffle oil proving an interesting accompaniment. The wine list is very extensive and Michael Bricker is well informed and keen to offer advice.

10 en suite (bth/shr) (6 fmly) CTV in all bedrooms STV 25P No coaches Croquet lawn ch fac Xmas International Cuisine Coffee am Tea pm No smoking in restaurant Last d 9.30pm
ROOMS: (incl. bkfst & dinner) s £90-£115; d £146-£230 * **LB**
OFF-PEAK: (incl. bkfst & dinner) s £65-£75; d £130-£150
MEALS: Lunch £25&alc Dinner £35
CONF: Board 20
CARDS:

PORTREE See Skye, Isle of

PORT WILLIAM Dumfries & Galloway Map 10 NX34

★★★ 65% **Corsemalzie House**

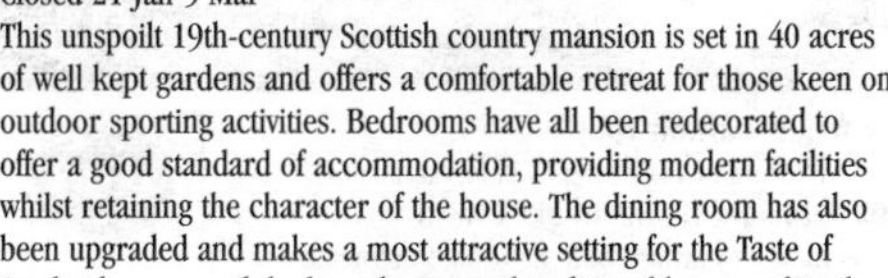

DG8 9RL (on B7005, turn off A714 at Bladnoch)
☎ 01988 860254 FAX 01988 860213
Closed 21 Jan-5 Mar

This unspoilt 19th-century Scottish country mansion is set in 40 acres of well kept gardens and offers a comfortable retreat for those keen on outdoor sporting activities. Bedrooms have all been redecorated to offer a good standard of accommodation, providing modern facilities whilst retaining the character of the house. The dining room has also been upgraded and makes a most attractive setting for the Taste of Scotland menu, and the large lounge and traditional bar complete the public areas.

14 en suite (bth/shr) (1 fmly) CTV in all bedrooms 30P No coaches Fishing Croquet lawn Putting green Game shooting Xmas Scottish & French Cuisine V meals Coffee am Tea pm No smoking in restaurant Last d 8.45pm
ROOMS: (incl. bkfst) s £46-£58; d £92 **LB**
OFF-PEAK: (incl. bkfst) s £35-£48; d £72
MEALS: Lunch £12.75-£14.75 Dinner £19.90-£25.65&alc*
CARDS:

POWFOOT Dumfries & Galloway Map 11 NY16

★★64% **Golf**

Links Av DG12 5PN (turn off A74 at Gretna onto A75 round Annan bypass, hotel sign 2m on turn left follow sign to Powfoot village) ☎ 01461 700254
FAX 01461 700288
This friendly, family-run hotel enjoys views of the Solway Firth, golf course and Cumbrian Mountains from the lounge and some bedrooms. Popular with golfers and business people, it offers a choice of bars, a restaurant, and conference rooms.
19 rms (14 bth/shr) (2 fmly) No smoking in 2 bedrooms CTV in 15 bedrooms No dogs (ex guide dogs) Air conditioning 110P Golf 18 Fishing Pool table Xmas V meals Coffee am Tea pm
ROOMS: (incl. bkfst) s £40-£54; d £60-£74 **LB**
OFF-PEAK: (incl. bkfst) s £35-£50; d £40-£60
CONF: Thtr 150 Class 70 Board 70
CARDS:

POWMILL Perthshire & Kinross Map 11 NT09

★★★ 66% **Whinsmuir Country Inn**
FK14 7NW (on A977) ☎ 01577 840595 FAX 01577 840779
Situated in the small village of Powmill, not far from Dollar, this friendly inn offers good value accommodation and food. Most of the bedrooms are in a new wing, and are spacious and comfortable with good amenities for the business traveller. The bar and restaurant have an informal atmosphere, which aids the digestion of the hearty, and the imaginative cuisine was well worthy of our one rosette award. There is also a quiet lounge and extensive function facilities.
13 en suite (bth/shr) (5 fmly) No smoking in 2 bedrooms CTV in all bedrooms 120P Pool table ch fac Xmas Scottish & European Cuisine V meals Coffee am Tea pm Last d 9.30pm
ROOMS: (incl. bkfst) s £40-£55; d £60-£75 * **LB**
OFF-PEAK: (incl. bkfst) s £35-£45; d £55-£65
MEALS: Lunch £10&alc High tea £7.95 Dinner £12-£24alc
CONF: Thtr 200 Class 200 Board 150 Del from £75
CARDS:

P

PRESTWICK South Ayrshire Map 10 NS32

★★65% **Carlton Toby**

187 Ayr Rd KA9 1TP (on A79 2m from airport)
☎ 01292 476811 FAX 01292 474845
This modern purpose built hotel with colourful gardens, is situated on the A79, one and a half miles from the airport. It offers both well appointed and well equipped accommodation, although plans are well advanced for the refurbishment of the bedroom stock with the work due to commence in the autumn of 1996. The public areas include a lounge bar, a conservatory restaurant with a carvery and a small meeting room.
39 en suite (bth/shr) (2 fmly) No smoking in 9 bedrooms CTV in all bedrooms STV Night porter 100P Wkly live entertainment Xmas European Cuisine V meals Coffee am Tea pm No smoking in restaurant Last d 10pm
ROOMS: (incl. bkfst) s £32-£49.50; d £54-£65 * **LB**
MEALS: Lunch £5-£11.95&alc High tea £5.95-£6.95&alc Dinner £5-£8.95&alc*
CONF: Thtr 30 Class 20 Board 20 Del from £52
CARDS:

★★63% **Parkstone**
Esplanade KA9 1QN ☎ 01292 477286 FAX 01292 477671
Situated on the seafront in a quiet residential area, this is a popular commercial hotel catering for business visitors and, of course, golfers who visit the nearby courses. Bedrooms are all equipped with modern facilities and several are suitable for families. Public areas are smart and cheerful and there is a first-floor ballroom where local functions are held.
15 en suite (bth/shr) (1 fmly) CTV in all bedrooms STV No dogs Night porter 34P V meals Coffee am Last d 8.30pm
ROOMS: (incl. bkfst) s £39.50; d £49.50-£52.50 * **LB**
MEALS: Lunch fr £11.50 High tea fr £7.50 Dinner fr £15.50*
CARDS:

★★61% ***St Nicholas***
41 Ayr Rd KA9 1SY ☎ 01292 479568 FAX 01292 475793
Two adjoining houses have been linked to create this friendly business, tourist and golfing hotel, which stands beside the main road at the south end of town. Bedrooms are variable in size and have a mixture of modern appointments. Recent refurbishment has enhanced the dining room and lounge bar, and further improvements and alterations are planned.
17 rms (12 bth/shr) (2 fmly) No smoking in 5 bedrooms CTV in 13 bedrooms TV in 4 bedrooms No dogs (ex guide dogs) P Pool table Coffee am Tea pm Last high tea 9pm
CARDS:

RENFREW For hotels see Glasgow Airport

RHU Argyll & Bute Map 10 NS28

★★★61% **Rosslea Hall**

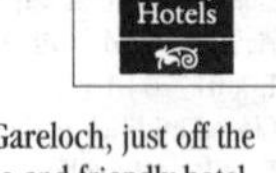

G84 8NF (on A814, past post office)
☎ 01436 439955 FAX 01436 820897
An early Victorian mansion situated in its own attractive grounds and gardens on the shores of Gareloch, just off the A814, 2 miles from Helensburgh, this comfortable and friendly hotel, has recently benefitted from the introduction of The Narrow's Brasserie, instead of a more formal restaurant. This has allowed for a choice of less expensive and lighter meals which are good value and good quality and there is also the option of something more substantial if required.
36 en suite (bth/shr) 9 annexe en suite (bth/shr) (2 fmly) No smoking in 5 bedrooms CTV in all bedrooms STV Night porter Air conditioning 80P Xmas Scottish & French Cuisine V meals Coffee am Tea pm Last high tea 5pm
ROOMS: (incl. bkfst) s fr £70; d fr £82 * **LB**
MEALS: Lunch £15.95&alc High tea £5.85-£9.95*
CONF: Thtr 150 Class 50 Board 30 Del from £100
CARDS:

ROSEBANK South Lanarkshire Map 11 NS84

★★★66% **Popinjay**
Lanark Rd ML8 5QB (on A72 between Hamilton & Lanark) ☎ 01555 860441 FAX 01555 860204
CONSORT HOTELS
This Tudor-style hotel is set in very attractive grounds which extend to the banks of the Clyde. It offers comfortable public areas which include an impressive panelled bar where roaring open fires burn in the colder weather. Local functions are popular, especially weddings, with the gardens providing a lovely backdrop for photographs. Bedrooms are well equipped with modern amenities

which include mini-bars, satellite TV and trouser presses. Private fishing is available and guests have free use of the local golf course.
42 en suite (bth/shr) 5 annexe en suite (bth/shr) (2 fmly) CTV in all bedrooms STV Night porter 300P Fishing ch fac Xmas International Cuisine V meals Coffee am Tea pm Last d 10pm
ROOMS: (incl. bkfst) s £50-£150; d £60-£150 * **LB**
OFF-PEAK: (incl. bkfst) s £25-£150; d £50-£150
MEALS: Lunch £7.95&alc Dinner £14.50&alc*
CONF: Thtr 250 Class 120 Board 60 Del from £75
CARDS:

ROSEHALL Highland Map 14 NC40

★★ 63% ***Achness***
IV27 4BD (just off A837 Bonar Bridge to Lochinver Road)
☎ 01549 441239 FAX 01549 441324
Closed Oct-Feb
Many guests return year after year to this small comfortable Highland fishing hotel which has a relaxed welcoming atmosphere. Built around a rear courtyard, the annexe bedrooms are tastefully decorated and furnished in teak. Main house bedrooms lack en suite facilities and tend to be compact, but they are nicely appointed with pine furnishings. Public areas include a choice of relaxing lounges, one timber-clad, a snug bar and attractive dining room where guests help themselves from the hot buffet table. TV is available on request in bedrooms.
5 rms 7 annexe en suite (bth/shr) TV available 40P No coaches Fishing V meals Coffee am Tea pm Last d 8pm
CARDS:

ROSLIN Midlothian Map 11 NT26

★★ 60% **Roslin Glen**
2 Penicuik Rd EH25 9LH (in the village of Roslin 1ml from the A701 Edinburgh/Peebles Rd. 2mls south of Edin. City bypass)
☎ 0131 440 2029 FAX 0131 440 2229
Set in the heart of the village, this 19th-century hotel is popular with business people and tourists alike. Bedrooms vary in size and have modern furnishings as well as all the expected amenities. The dining room has an inglenook fireplace as a feature, and the extensive menu is served both there and in the lounge bar.
7 en suite (bth/shr) (2 fmly) CTV in all bedrooms STV Night porter 5P No coaches French Cuisine V meals Coffee am Tea pm
ROOMS: (incl. bkfst) s £45-£50; d £55-£65 * **LB**
OFF-PEAK: (incl. bkfst) s fr £42.50; d fr £50
CONF: Thtr 100 Class 50
CARDS:
See advertisement under EDINBURGH

ROSYTH Fife Map 11 NT18

★★ 62% **Gladyer Inn**
Heath Rd, off Ridley Dr KY11 2BT (from junct 1 of M90 travel along Admiralty Road, past roundabout then first road on the left)
☎ 01383 419977 FAX 01383 411728
Located just off the main road, this purpose-built hotel is convenient for the Royal Navy Base. Service is friendly and guests can relax in a comfortable lounge bar and a public bar with entertainment. A small dining room adjoins the function suite, and bedrooms are practical and well equipped.
21 en suite (bth/shr) (3 fmly) CTV in all bedrooms Night porter 81P Pool table Wkly live entertainment Xmas V meals Coffee am Tea pm Last d 9.30pm
ROOMS: (incl. bkfst) s £32-£35; d £50-£55 * **LB**
MEALS: Lunch £5.50-£8.50&alc High tea £5-£6 Dinner £13.50&alc
CONF: Thtr 100 Class 100 Board 80 Del from £50
CARDS:
See advertisement under DUNFERMLINE

ROTHES Moray Map 15 NJ24

★★★ ❀ 71% **Rothes Glen**

AB38 7AQ (3m N, on A941) ☎ 01340 831254
FAX 01340 831566
New owners are making considerable improvements to this impressive Scottish baronial mansion which stands in 10 acres of manicured grounds between Rothes and Elgin. Comfortable public areas retain many of their original late Victorian features, including some fine wood panelling and carved plaster ceilings. A grand piano sits in the lofty foyer and a wide staircase sweeps up to the bedrooms. These vary in size, but most are spacious, with several offering separate sitting rooms and fine views down the attractive Glen of Rothes. One of the most noteworthy rooms is the romantic tower duplex suite. Staff are friendly and the attentive service extends to provision of morning tea and evening room-servicing. The daily changing menu features fresh local produce cooked with care and attention to detail.
16 en suite (bth/shr) (4 fmly) CTV in all bedrooms 40P No coaches Croquet lawn Putting green Xmas V meals Coffee am Tea pm No smoking in restaurant Last d 9pm
ROOMS: (incl. bkfst) s £60-£70; d £90-£100 * **LB**
MEALS: Lunch £10-£16 Dinner £25-£30*
CONF: Thtr 40 Class 20 Board 30 Del from £80
CARDS:

ROY BRIDGE Highland Map 14 NN28

★★ 59% ***Stronlossit***
PH31 4AG ☎ 01397 712253
Closed 10 Nov-10 Dec & Jan
Situated at the east end of the village, this friendly family-run hotel caters for tourists and outdoor enthusiasts. Public areas include a cosy bar, a comfortable lounge and an attractive restaurant, where the carte menu includes a range of grill specialities. Bedrooms vary in size and offer practical modern appointments.
9 en suite (bth/shr) (2 fmly) CTV in all bedrooms 30P V meals Coffee am Tea pm Last d 9.30pm
CARDS:

R

ST ANDREWS Fife Map 12 NO51

★★★★★ 65% **The Old Course Hotel**
KY16 9SP (close to the A91 on the outskirts of the city)
☎ 01334 474371 FAX 01334 477668
Closed 22-28 Dec
Situated on the outskirts of St Andrews - the home of golf - this internationally renowned resort hotel is true to its name, as many of the bedrooms overlook the Old Course itself. The elegant public areas have been extended to offer a choice of lounges, while informal dining is offered in the Conservatory during the summer months. The roof top Road Hole Grill offers spectacular views of the West Sands and the ancient town, while the cuisine is traditional, with some imaginative flair and a choice of menus, including a Gourmet taster menu. Bedrooms, including a range of suites, provide good amenities, and are attractively furnished. There are excellent indoor and outdoor leisure facilities including the hotel's own golf course and a good sized swimming pool. The staff are willing and helpful.
125 en suite (bth/shr) (6 fmly) CTV in all bedrooms STV Lift Night porter 150P Indoor swimming pool (heated) Golf 18 Sauna Solarium Gym Jacuzzi/spa Health spa Steam room Scottish & French Cuisine V meals Coffee am Tea pm No smoking area in restaurant Last d 9.30pm
ROOMS: (incl. bkfst) s £135-£185; d £165-£225 * **LB**
OFF-PEAK: (incl. bkfst & dinner) s £195; d £179
MEALS: Lunch £15-£17.50 High tea £15 Dinner fr £34.50*
CONF: Thtr 300 Class 150 Board 60 Del from £155
CARDS:

★★★★ 64% **Rusacks**
Pilmour Links KY16 9JQ ☎ 01334 474321
FAX 01334 477896

FORTE Heritage

Occupying an enviable position with fine views of the first tee, the 18th green and the sea beyond, this imposing Victorian hotel offers well appointed and equipped accommodation. The friendly staff, led by general manager Ian Fleming, provide an informal but attentive level of service. A lighter lunch menu which features local seafood is served in the Sun Lounge, and in the evening, guests have the option of eating in Champs bistro or the restaurant. For golfers, breakfast is available from 6.00am.
50 en suite (bth/shr) No smoking in 5 bedrooms CTV in all bedrooms STV Lift Night porter 21P Sauna Solarium Xmas V meals Coffee am Tea pm No smoking in restaurant Last d 9.30hrs
ROOMS: (incl. bkfst & dinner) d £65-£90 * **LB**
OFF-PEAK: (incl. bkfst & dinner) d £45-£60
MEALS: Lunch £13.50 Dinner fr £26.50&alc*
CONF: Thtr 150 Class 80 Board 40 Del from £100
CARDS:

Courtesy & Care Award

★★★ 77% **Rufflets Country House**
Strathkinness Low Rd KY16 9TX (1.5m W on B939) ☎ 01334 472594 FAX 01334 478703

SCOTLAND'S COMMENDED HOTELS

This sympathetically extended house stands in 10 acres of award-winning gardens, just over a mile from St Andrews. Proprietor Ann Russell is very much involved with the running of the hotel, and is responsible for some of the bold interior design, which has enhanced both the bedrooms and public areas. There is a choice of standard or superior rooms, the main difference being the views, as all are comfortable and thoughtfully equipped. The Garden Restaurant has an intimate atmosphere, with the Scottish menu including home-grown produce where possible. Owner and staff here have won the AA Courtesy and Care Award for 1996/7.

23 en suite (bth/shr) 3 annexe en suite (bth/shr) (10 fmly) No smoking in 8 bedrooms CTV in all bedrooms No dogs (ex guide dogs) Night porter 52P No coaches Putting green Golf driving net Xmas V meals Coffee am Tea pm No smoking in restaurant Last d 9pm
ROOMS: (incl. bkfst) s £70-£80; d £140-£160 * **LB**
OFF-PEAK: (incl. bkfst) s £50-£55; d £100-£110
MEALS: Lunch fr £15 Dinner fr £27
CONF: Thtr 50 Class 30 Board 25 Del from £109
CARDS:

★★★ 77% **St Andrews Golf**
40 The Scores KY16 9AS (follow signs 'Golf Course' into Golf Place and in 200yds right into The Scores)
☎ 01334 472611 FAX 01334 472188
Overlooking the west sands close to the famous Old Course, this family-run hotel enjoys some wonderful views. The friendly atmosphere and stylish decor make the interior particularly inviting. Bedrooms vary in size, though all are well equipped and have many thoughtful extras. The lobby lounge is a relaxing area, and the 19th hole cocktail bar is well stocked. Meals are served both in the adjoining pub and the elegant dining room, the food in the latter having earned a rosette for its imagination and fine presentation.
23 en suite (bth/shr) (10 fmly) CTV in all bedrooms STV Lift Night porter 6P Scottish & French Cuisine V meals Coffee am Tea pm No smoking in restaurant Last d 9.30pm
MEALS: Lunch fr £15 High tea fr £9.50 Dinner fr £26.50&alc
CONF: Thtr 200 Class 50 Board 30
CARDS:

★★★ 67% ***Scores***
76 The Scores KY16 9BB ☎ 01334 472451
FAX 01334 473947
Closed 21-26 Dec

This friendly hotel, stands close to the first tee of the famous royal and ancient course and is, not surprisingly, a popular choice of golfers from near and far. Bedrooms are furnished in a modern style, with some enjoying spectacular views over the seafront. The all-day coffee shop provides light snacks, while the Scorecards Bar has a display of golf scores which many guests can only dream of. A well constructed menu is offered in Alexander's restaurant.
30 en suite (bth/shr) (1 fmly) CTV in all bedrooms No dogs (ex guide dogs) Lift Night porter 10P No coaches British & French Cuisine V meals Coffee am Tea pm Last d 9.30pm
CARDS:

See advertisement on opposite page

★★67% **Russell Hotel**
26 The Scores KY16 9AS ☎ 01334 473447 FAX 01334 478279
Genuine hospitality is found throughout this family-run hotel, which is situated on the seafront near to both the Old Course and the ruined castle. There is no lounge and the comfortable Victorian bar can get busy. Imaginative meals are served here and in the more intimate supper room. Bedrooms vary in size but are individually decorated and well equipped.
10 en suite (bth/shr) (3 fmly) CTV in all bedrooms STV Night porter No coaches International Cuisine V meals Coffee am No smoking in restaurant Last d 9.30pm
ROOMS: (incl. bkfst) s £35-£60; d £64-£85 * **LB**
OFF-PEAK: (incl. bkfst) d fr £60
MEALS: Bar Lunch £5.20-£9alc Dinner £9.95-£18.50alc
CARDS:

★★61% **Ardgowan**
2 Playfair Ter KY16 9HX ☎ 01334 472970 FAX 01334 478380
Closed 18 Dec-17 Jan RS Nov-17 Dec & 16 Jan-Mar
A family run hotel which stands near the town centre offering well maintained, good value accommodation. Bedrooms, most of which are en suite, are attractively furnished. Popular meals are served in the lounge bar all year round and a restaurant is open during the summer months.
13 rms (11 bth/shr) (2 fmly) CTV in all bedrooms No coaches Scottish & French Cuisine V meals Last d 9.30pm
ROOMS: (incl. bkfst) s £30-£40; d £58-£68 *
OFF-PEAK: (incl. bkfst) s £25-£35; d £48-£58
MEALS: Bar Lunch £5-£10alc Dinner £10-£20alc*
CARDS:

★★ 60% **Parklands Hotel & Restaurant**
Kinburn Castle, Double Dykes Rd KY16 9DS (opposite Kinburn Park and Museum) ☎ 01334 473620 FAX 01334 473620
Closed Xmas/New Year
Located opposite Kinburn Park, this is a popular hotel attracting business visitors and golfers, who play the wealth of local courses. Bedrooms are simply furnished but modern facilities are provided and some are suitable for families. The restaurant serves from a fixed-price menu and this is supplemented with a gourmet choice from Tuesdays to Saturdays. Good kitchen skills are evident and the resulting quality of food has justifiably won our one-rosette award.
15 rms (8 bth 1 shr) (2 fmly) CTV in all bedrooms No dogs (ex guide dogs) 15P International Cuisine Coffee am No smoking in restaurant Last d 8.30pm
ROOMS: (incl. bkfst) s £30-£40; d £50-£70 * **LB**
MEALS: Lunch £10-£15alc Dinner £16.50-£21.50*
CARDS:

ST BOSWELLS Scottish Borders Map 12 NT53

★★★ 76% **Dryburgh Abbey**
TD6 0RQ (off B6356) ☎ 01835 822261
FAX 01835 823945
Best Western
This impressive red sandstone mansion stands in grounds beside the ruins of Dryburgh Abbey, by the banks of the River Tweed. Sympathetically upgraded, it is well maintained and offers inviting public rooms including a choice of lounges, a lounge bar and an attractive first floor restaurant overlooking the river. Bedrooms - each named after a famous fishing fly - are tastefully appointed, thoughtfully equipped and include 2 suites.
25 en suite (bth/shr) 1 annexe en suite (bth/shr) (3 fmly) CTV in 25 bedrooms Lift Night porter 103P Indoor swimming pool (heated) Fishing Putting green Xmas Scottish, English & French Cuisine V meals Coffee am Tea pm No smoking in restaurant Last d 9.15pm

contd.

S

ROOMS: (incl. bkfst) s £62; d £116-£150 **LB**
OFF-PEAK: (incl. bkfst) s £49; d £88-£128
MEALS: Lunch £12.50 Dinner £16-£22.50
CONF: Thtr 200 Class 120 Board 70 Del from £85
CARDS:

★★69% Buccleuch Arms
The Green TD6 0EW (on A68) ☎ 01835 822243 FAX 01835 823965
Formerly a coaching inn dating back to the 16th -century, this roadside hotel stands opposite the village green. Attractively renovated throughout, it offers cosy, well equipped bedrooms, a pleasant lounge with a log fire, a popular wood-panelled lounge bar and a small restaurant, both of which serve a good range of food.
18 rms (17 bth/shr) (1 fmly) CTV in all bedrooms 52P Xmas International Cuisine V meals Coffee am Tea pm No smoking area in restaurant Last d 9.30pm
ROOMS: (incl. bkfst) s £30-£45; d £60-£80 * **LB**
OFF-PEAK: (incl. bkfst) s £25-£45; d £50-£80
MEALS: Lunch £12-£15 High tea fr £6.50 Dinner fr £16.50*
CONF: Thtr 100 Class 40 Board 30 Del from £60
CARDS:

ST FILLANS Perthshire & Kinross Map 11 NN62

★★★67% The Four Seasons Hotel
Loch Earn PH6 2NF (on A85) ☎ 01764 685333 FAX 01764 685333
Closed Jan-Feb RS mid Nov-end Dec
This well established holiday hotel has been run for many years by the Scott family, who maintain a warm and friendly approach to both newcomers and regulars. Some bedrooms enjoy views across Loch Earn, and all are comfortably appointed and traditional in style. There is a choice of lounges including a cosy library. Watching the dusk fall over the gentle waters is only one of the attractions of the dining room, the other being the fine cooking from Andrew Scott, who has a modern, imaginative style of enhancing fine Scottish produce.
12 en suite (bth/shr) (2 fmly) CTV in all bedrooms 25P No coaches Fishing International Cuisine V meals Coffee am Tea pm No smoking in restaurant Last d 9.30pm
ROOMS: (incl. bkfst) s £45-£57.50; d £64-£86 **LB**
OFF-PEAK: (incl. bkfst) s £38.50-£47.50; d £60-£80
MEALS: Lunch fr £14.25 Dinner fr £23.50&alc
CONF: Board 25 Del from £82.50
CARDS:

★★68% Achray House
Loch Earn PH6 2NF (on A85) ☎ 01764 685231 FAX 01764 685320
Closed 4 Jan-1 Feb
Enjoying stunning views of Loch Earn, this friendly hotel is ideally located for exploring Perthshire, with its many activities and attractions. Bedrooms offer a high standard of accommodation, with pretty fabrics and modern pine furnishings. There is a quiet lounge, and the bar is popular both for the selection of whiskies and the wide range of meals. The restaurant offers a good value table d'hÙte menu and more glorious views of the loch.
9 rms (8 bth/shr) (1 fmly) CTV in all bedrooms No dogs (ex guide dogs) 25P No coaches V meals No smoking in restaurant Last d 9.15pm
ROOMS: (incl. bkfst) s fr £44.50; d fr £69 **LB**
OFF-PEAK: (incl. bkfst) s fr £35; d fr £50
MEALS: Sunday Lunch £9-£14alc High tea £9-£14alc Dinner £17.50
CARDS:

SANQUHAR Dumfries & Galloway Map 11 NS70

★★65% Blackaddie House
Blackaddie Rd DG4 6JJ (tune off A76 just N of Sanquhar at Burnside Service Station. Private road to hotel 300m on right) ☎ 01659 50270 FAX 01659 50270
Blackaddie House dates from 1540 and was originally built as a rectory. It is set in its own grounds and is an ideal base for touring the area or indulging in the many local outdoor sporting activities. Personally run by the Cranston family, a pleasant, informal atmosphere prevails. Bedrooms, including some family rooms, are attractively decorated, while the public areas include a spacious lounge, comfortable lounge bar and dining room.
10 en suite (bth/shr) (2 fmly) CTV in all bedrooms No dogs (ex guide dogs) 20P Golf 9 Fishing Riding Game shooting Gold panning Bike hire Xmas Scottish & French Cuisine V meals Coffee am No smoking in restaurant Last d 9pm
ROOMS: (incl. bkfst) s fr £34; d fr £58 **LB**
MEALS: Lunch fr £9.50&alc Dinner £12.50-£30alc*
CONF: Thtr 50 Class 20 Board 20 Del from £48
CARDS:

SCALASAIG See Colonsay, Isle of

SCOURIE Highland Map 14 NC14

★★69% Eddrachilles
Badcall Bay IV27 4TH (2m S on A894)
☎ 01971 502080 FAX 01971 502477
Closed Nov-Feb
Many guests return year after year to the Wood family's delightful holiday hotel which stands peacefully in its own grounds offering spectacular views over the island-studded Badcall Bay. Public areas include a choice of inviting lounges of which the conservatory overlooking the bay is especially popular. There is also a well stocked bar and the dining room, with its natural stone walls and flagstone floor, offers both fixed price and carte menus. The well equipped bedrooms have all been smartly refurnished and upgrade of bathrooms is nearly complete.
11 en suite (bth/shr) (1 fmly) CTV in all bedrooms STV No dogs (ex guide dogs) 25P No coaches Fishing Boats for hire No children 3yrs V meals Coffee am Last d 8pm
ROOMS: (incl. bkfst) s £45.40-£48.50; d £71-£77 * **LB**
OFF-PEAK: (incl. bkfst) s £38.50-£43.50; d £67.30-£71
MEALS: Bar Lunch fr £3.50alc Dinner fr £11.25&alc
CARDS:

★★65% Scourie
IV27 4SX (Hotel situated on A894 in the village of Scourie)
☎ 01971 502396 FAX 01971 502423
Closed mid Oct -end Mar
With extensive fishing rights available on a 25,000 acre estate it is little wonder that the Scourie Hotel is widely regarded as an anglers' paradise. It has a relaxed friendly atmosphere and the touring holidaymaker is also well catered for. Public areas include a choice of inviting lounges, a refurbished bar where many a 'fishy' tale is told, and a smart dining room offering wholesome fare. Bedrooms are smartly decorated and individually furnished, with the usual amenities apart from television.
18 rms (16 bth) 2 annexe en suite (bth) (2 fmly) 30P No coaches Fishing Pool table Coffee am Tea pm Last d 8.30pm
ROOMS: (incl. bkfst) s fr £44; d fr £78
OFF-PEAK: (incl. bkfst) s fr £32; d fr £54
MEALS: Bar Lunch £3.50-£9alc Dinner £15
CARDS:

SELKIRK Scottish Borders Map 12 NT42

★★62% Heatherlie House
Heatherlie Park TD7 5AL (take A707/A708 Peebles road from Walter Scott Monument then 500yds on left)
☎ 01750 21200 FAX 01750 20005
Set in its own gardens off the Peebles road, within walking distance of the town centre, this Victorian mansion is run in the informal style of a

country house. The accommodation is keenly priced and meals are available in both the dining room and bar.
7 rms (6 shr) (2 fmly) CTV in all bedrooms No dogs 12P No coaches European Cuisine V meals No smoking area in restaurant Last d 8.30pm
ROOMS: (incl. bkfst) s £21-£29; d fr £50 * **LB**
MEALS: Bar Lunch £6.30-£10 High tea £6.80-£10 Dinner fr £12&alc*
CARDS:

SHETLAND Map 16

BRAE Map 16 HU36

★★★ 67% **Busta House**
ZE2 9QN (after Brae follow road north, bearing left around Busta Voe, within 1m hotel signposted with Muckle Roe)
☎ 01806 522506 FAX 01806 522588
Closed 23 Dec-2 Jan
A welcoming atmosphere prevails at this charming 16th-century former lairds home which is peacefully set in its own grounds overlooking Busta Voe. Relaxing public areas include a choice of comfortable lounges, a well stocked bar and attractive dining room offering a daily changing five course fixed price menu. Bedrooms, which have been cleverly designed to make best use of available space, are tastefully decorated and offer mixed styles of furnishings.
20 en suite (bth/shr) (2 fmly) CTV in all bedrooms 35P No coaches Sea fishing Water sports International Cuisine V meals Coffee am Tea pm No smoking in restaurant Last d 9pm
ROOMS: (incl. bkfst) s £63; d £86.50 **LB**
MEALS: Sunday Lunch £8.50-£17.20&alc Dinner fr £22.50&alc
CARDS:

LERWICK Map 16 HU44

★★★65% **Lerwick**
15 South Rd ZE1 0RB (signposted from main road)
☎ 01595 692166 FAX 01595 694419
Ongoing improvements are taking place at this popular business and tourist hotel which is situated within a ten minute walk of central amenities and enjoys views over Breiwick Bay to Bressay and Breiwick islands. Refurbishment has transformed the bedrooms, all of which now offer comfortable modern standards, though some are compact. Public areas include a spacious and well stocked bar, attractive restaurant offering varied menus, and an enhanced foyer lounge.
35 en suite (bth/shr) (3 fmly) CTV in all bedrooms STV No dogs (ex guide dogs) Night porter 50P International Cuisine V meals Coffee am Tea pm No smoking area in restaurant Last d 9pm
ROOMS: (incl. bkfst) s fr £68; d fr £85 * **LB**
MEALS: Lunch £12.50 Dinner £19.95
CONF: Thtr 60 Class 40 Board 20
CARDS:

★★★65% **Shetland**
Holmsgarth Rd ZE1 0PW (opposite P&O ferry terminal, on main route north from town centre) ☎ 01595 695515 FAX 01595 695828
Built in 1984 and now under the same ownership as the Lerwick hotel, this modern purpose-built business and tourist hotel is ideally situated at the north end of town directly opposite the main ferry terminal. Public areas are spread over different levels and include an open plan bar/lounge adjacent to reception while on the floor below, you will find the tastefully refurbished Ninian restaurant and Oasis Bistro, the latter offering an informal alternate food option. Bedrooms which are well proportioned include non smoking and ladies rooms, are scheduled for refurbishment by the start of the season.
64 en suite (bth/shr) (4 fmly) No smoking in 14 bedrooms CTV in all bedrooms STV No dogs (ex guide dogs) Lift Night porter 150P French Cuisine V meals Coffee am Tea pm No smoking in restaurant Last d 9.15pm
ROOMS: (incl. bkfst) s fr £73; d fr £85.50 * **LB**
MEALS: Lunch £12.50 Dinner £21.50
CONF: Thtr 320 Class 75 Board 50
CARDS:

UNST Map 16 HP60

★★59% ***The Baltasound***
ZE2 9DS ☎ 01957 711334
This friendly and informal family-run hotel is the most northerly hotel in Britain. Apart from the separate breakfast room, public areas are contained in an open-plan, timber-clad, L-shaped room which includes lounge, bar and dining room. Main house bedrooms are quite practical in style but most accommodation is contained in the log cabins around the grounds and while these are compact, they are comfortable and look more appealing.
10 rms (3 bth/shr) 17 annexe en suite (bth/shr) (17 fmly) CTV in all bedrooms No dogs (ex guide dogs) 20P Fishing Pool table V meals Coffee am Tea pm Last d 8pm

SHIELDAIG Highland Map 14 NG85

★★71% **Tigh an Eilean**
IV54 8XN ☎ 01520 755251 FAX 01520 755321
Closed Nov-Etr
The 'house of the island' is set on the sea-shore amidst whitewashed crofts and fishermen's cottages, sheltered from the elements by pines. The surroundings are rustic, but this belies the contemporary comforts within. Well maintained bedrooms and public areas (which include three comfortable lounges) feature modern furnishings and excellent facilities. A set evening meal offers traditional dishes such as roast rib of beef, chicken supreme and crab dijonaise, all well prepared using fresh local ingredients.
11 en suite (bth/shr) (1 fmly) 15P No coaches Fishing Scottish & French Cuisine Coffee am No smoking in restaurant
ROOMS: (incl. bkfst) s fr £41.50; d fr £91 *
CARDS:

SKEABOST BRIDGE See Skye, Isle of

SKYE, ISLE OF Highland Map 13

ARDVASAR Map 13 NG60

★★71% **Ardvasar**

IV45 8RS ☎ 01471 844223
Closed 24-25 Dec & 1-3 Jan RS Nov-Mar
(Rosette awarded for dinner only)
The genuine warmth of welcome together with good food and a wonderfully relaxed atmosphere continue to entice guests back to Bill and Gretta Fowler's refreshingly honest little hotel situated close to the Armadale ferry terminal. The comfortable bedrooms are mostly furnished in pine and offer all the expected amenities. There is a comfortable and cosy lounge as well as a choice of contrasting bars and in the dining room chef/patron Bill Fowler's competitively priced carte offers a tempting range of Taste of Scotland dishes, prepared from quality island produce.
10 en suite (bth/shr) (3 fmly) CTV in all bedrooms No dogs (ex guide dogs) 30P No coaches Pool table Scottish & French Cuisine V meals Coffee am Tea pm No smoking in restaurant Last d 8.30pm
ROOMS: (incl. bkfst) s £35-£40; d £65-£70 * **LB**
MEALS: Bar Lunch £5-£15 Dinner £12-£25
CARDS:

DUNVEGAN Map 13 NG24

★★65% **Atholl House**
IV55 8WA ☎ 01470 521219 FAX 01470 521481
Closed end Dec-end Feb
Personally run and warmly welcoming, this comfortable village hotel is an ideal base from which to explore the island. Attractive public areas include a choice of comfortable lounges where refreshments are willingly served - there is no bar. The dining room offers carefully prepared and hearty Scottish fare from the carte. Variable sized bedrooms, one with a four-poster, are bright and airy with modern fitted furnishings.
10 rms (7 bth/shr) (1 fmly) CTV in all bedrooms 10P ch fac Xmas V meals Coffee am Tea pm No smoking in restaurant
ROOMS: (incl. bkfst) s £24-£34; d £48-£68 * **LB**
OFF-PEAK: (incl. bkfst) s fr £22; d fr £44
CARDS:

HARLOSH Map 13 NG24

★77% **Harlosh House**
IV55 8ZG (A863 between Roag & Caroy, follow sign for Harlosh)
☎ 01470 521367 FAX 01470 521367
Closed mid Oct-Etr
This extended whitewashed building dates from the late 18th century and has a peaceful location on this small peninsula, with lovely views across to the Cuillin Hills in the south of the island. Peter and Lindsey Elford have built up a regular clientele, many of whom come to enjoy the fine cuisine offered in the cottage-style dining room. Bedrooms are furnished in pine and are simply but tastefully decorated, while an open fire burns in the small lounge. The set menu uses both local ingredients and those from further afield, with the concentration on light, healthy dishes.
6 rms (5 bth/shr) (2 fmly) No smoking in all bedrooms TV available No dogs (ex guide dogs) 10P No coaches International Cuisine Coffee am Tea pm No smoking in restaurant Last d 8.30pm
ROOMS: (incl. bkfst) s £45-£67; d £70-£94
MEALS: Dinner £24.50
CARDS:

ISLE ORNSAY Map 13 NG61

★★73% **Kinloch Lodge**
IV43 8QY (6m S of Broadford on A851, 10m N of Armadale on A851) ☎ 01471 833214/833333
FAX 01471 833277
Closed Dec-14 Mar

SCOTLAND'S COMMENDED HOTELS

At the end of a long bumpy forest track, this former lodge is home to Lord and Lady MacDonald, and guests are made to feel like friends by both the owners and their charming staff. Some rooms have views over Loch Na Dal, and all bedrooms are priced according to their size and location in the building. The two drawing rooms have warm log fires, comfortable settees, and feature family photos throughout. The elegant dining room is the setting for Lady Claire MacDonald's simple but effective cuisine, with fresh produce being enhanced by some superb sauces. The scallop soufflé starter was accompanied by a tart sauce Bercy which cut through the richness of the scallops beautifully, while the lime-flavoured chicken was tender and complemented by a creamy lime and tarragon sauce.

10 rms (8 bth/shr) No smoking in all bedrooms 18P No coaches Fishing Stalking Coffee am Tea pm No smoking in restaurant
ROOMS: (incl. bkfst) s £50-£180; d £100-£180 **LB**
OFF-PEAK: (incl. bkfst) s £50-£100; d £100-£150
MEALS: Dinner £30-£35
CARDS:

★72% **Hotel Eilean Iarmain**
IV43 8QR (A851, A852, right to Isle Ornsay Harbour front) ☎ 01471 833332 FAX 01471 833275
Traditional values of hospitality and comfort have served this 19th-century island inn well over the years and many guests return year after year to enjoy the old world charm and welcoming atmosphere. Bedrooms, including those in the Garden House opposite the main building, are quite individual and appropriately traditional in style. There is a small cosy sitting room and the timber-clad pub often features impromptu ceilidhs, while the attractive candlelit dining room offers innovative Scottish fare which includes local seafood and game, as well as an interesting and well chosen wine list. The Gaelic-speaking staff are naturally friendly and willing to please.
6 en suite (bth/shr) 6 annexe en suite (bth) (2 fmly) No smoking in 6 bedrooms CTV in 3 bedrooms 30P Fishing Shooting Fishing Walking ch fac Xmas V meals Coffee am Tea pm No smoking in restaurant Last d 8.45pm
ROOMS: (incl. bkfst) s £65-£67.50; d £90-£99.50 * **LB**
OFF-PEAK: (incl. bkfst) s fr £58; d fr £84
MEALS: Lunch £16.50 Dinner £28
CONF: Thtr 50 Class 30 Board 25 Del from £94
CARDS:

See advertisement on opposite page

PORTREE Map 13 NG44

★★★69% **Cuillin Hills**
IV51 9LU (Turn right 0.25m North of Portree on A855 and follow signs for hotel) ☎ 01478 612003 FAX 01478 613092
Pleasantly situated just outside the town and enjoying fine views of t he Cuillins, this comfortable hotel stands in its own grounds overlooking the bay. Day rooms include a choice of lounges with comfortable chesterfields, a well stocked bar and an attractive restaurant where chef Jeff Johnson cooks in a modern style, making good use of high quality local ingredients wherever possible. Bedrooms offer all the expected amenities and staff are friendly and willing to please.
16 en suite (bth/shr) 9 annexe en suite (bth/shr) (2 fmly) CTV in all bedrooms 30P No coaches ch fac Xmas Scottish & French Cuisine V meals Coffee am Tea pm No smoking in restaurant Last d 9pm
ROOMS: (incl. bkfst) s £44-£47; d £88-£94 * **LB**
OFF-PEAK: (incl. bkfst) s £34-£37; d £68-£74
MEALS: Sunday Lunch fr £8.95 Dinner £22-£24&alc*
CONF: Thtr 100 Class 60 Board 30 Del from £49
CARDS:

See advertisement on opposite page

★★71% **Rosedale**
IV51 9DB ☎ 01478 613131 FAX 01478 612531
Closed Oct-mid May
The Andrew family are constantly making improvements at their delightful holiday hotel beside the bay, which has been created by the sympathetic conversion of three 19th-century harbour-front buildings. The modern bedrooms vary in size, and all are tastefully decorated and comfortably furnished, as are the lounges and bar. Tony Parkyn has

now taken over the cooking and serves enjoyable three-or five-course meals in the attractive dining room. The fixed-price menu changes daily, and good use is made of high-quality fresh ingredients, featuring much local produce. Staff are hospitable and willing to please.
20 en suite (bth/shr) 3 annexe en suite (bth/shr) (1 fmly) CTV in all bedrooms 10P No coaches No smoking in restaurant Last d 8.30pm
ROOMS: (incl. bkfst) s £35-£40; d £70-£80 **LB**
MEALS: Dinner £20-£25
CARDS:

★★63% **Royal**
IV51 9BU (turn off A850 on to A855, hotel is on corner overlooking the harbour) ☎ 01478 612525 FAX 01478 613198
The new leisure centre is a major attraction at this town centre commercial and tourist hotel which enjoys fine views of the bay from its position above the harbour. Bedrooms are variable in size with somewhat dated appointments, though all the expected amenities are provided. Public areas include a choice of contrasting bars, a comfortable lounge, and Bistro Restaurant. During the high season, live entertainment is provided in the Ceilidh Room.
21 en suite (bth/shr) (5 fmly) No smoking in 4 bedrooms CTV in all bedrooms 14P No coaches Sauna Solarium Gym Pool table Jacuzzi/spa Wkly live entertainment Xmas V meals Coffee am Tea pm No smoking area in restaurant Last d 9.30pm
ROOMS: (incl. bkfst) s £33.50-£42; d £56-£65 **LB**
MEALS: Lunch £7.20-£12.50 Dinner £14.50-£22*
CONF: Thtr 130 Board 16 Del from £55
CARDS:

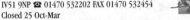

SKEABOST BRIDGE Map 13 NG44

★★★64% ***Skeabost House***
IV51 9NP ☎ 01470 532202 FAX 01470 532454

Closed 25 Oct-Mar
The regular clientele at this family-run hotel consists of fishermen, golfers and those just wanting to get away from it all. Set in superbly kept gardens, the house itself dates from the late 19th century and was the first on the island to be supplied with electricity. It retains a traditional style, with comfortable lounges warmed by log fires and a wood-panelled dining room, while the most modern addition, a large conservatory, offers lighter eating options. Bedrooms vary from the grand master rooms to the more modest second floor rooms, though prices reflect the differences.
21 en suite (bth/shr) 5 annexe en suite (bth/shr) (3 fmly) CTV in all bedrooms Night porter 40P Golf 9 Fishing Snooker Pool table Croquet lawn Putting green Scottish & French Cuisine V meals Coffee am Tea pm Last d 9.30pm
CARDS:

UIG Map 13 NG36

★★67% ***Uig***
IV51 9YE ☎ 01470 542205 FAX 01470 542308

Closed 18 Oct-1 Apr
Enjoying an elevated position on the south side of the village, this family-run country hotel offers fine views across Uig Bay. Bedrooms are available in the main hotel and in a converted steading to the rear, which contains two ground-floor rooms. There is a small residents' lounge and an elegant dining room, while the breathtaking views can be enjoyed from the sun lounge which adjoins the bar. Pony trekking is also available from the hotel.
10 en suite (bth/shr) 7 annexe en suite (bth/shr) (2 fmly) CTV in all bedrooms 20P No coaches Riding V meals Coffee am Tea pm Last d 8.15pm
CARDS:

S

★71% *Ferry Inn*
IV51 9XP (on main road) ☎ 01470 542242
Closed 25 Dec & 1 Jan RS Nov-Etr
Dedicated owner Mrs Campbell demands the highest standards from staff at her welcoming small Highland Inn which is ideally situated close to the Outer Isles ferry terminal. Though compact, the immaculately maintained bedrooms offer sound modern appointments together with a wide range of amenities. There is a relaxing lounge as well as a choice of bars and an attractive dining room offering both gourmet and wholesome fare.
6 en suite (bth/shr) CTV in all bedrooms 12P No coaches V meals Coffee am Last d 8.30pm
CARDS:

SOUTH QUEENSFERRY City of Edinburgh Map 11 NT17

★★★60% **Forth Bridges**

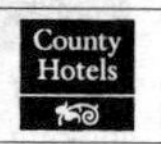

1 Ferrymuir Gate, Forth Bridge EH30 9SF (adjacent to Forth Road Bridge, follow signs - M90 then A8000, hotel on left) ☎ 0131 469 9955 FAX 0131 319 1733
The Firth of Forth with its famous bridges provides a breathtaking backdrop for this modern hotel which is situated only 20 minutes from the centre of Edinburgh. The majority of bedrooms have lovely views and they have recently been upgraded with smart new bathrooms. There is a choice of dining in the informal, themed café bar which overlooks the swimming pool, the more traditional restaurant or room service.
108 en suite (bth/shr) (15 fmly) No smoking in 43 bedrooms CTV in all bedrooms Lift Night porter 200P Indoor swimming pool (heated) Squash Sauna Solarium Gym Jacuzzi/spa Dance studio Xmas Scottish & French Cuisine V meals Coffee am Tea pm No smoking area in restaurant Last d 9.30pm
ROOMS: s £65-£79; d £85-£115 * **LB**
OFF-PEAK: (incl. bkfst) s £41; d £82
MEALS: Lunch £7.50-£12.95 High tea £6.95 Dinner £14-£16.50*
CONF: Thtr 200 Class 90 Board 60 Del from £79
CARDS:

SPEAN BRIDGE Highland Map 14 NN28
See also Letterfinlay and Roy Bridge

S

★★58% *Spean Bridge*
PH34 4ES (beside A82) ☎ 01397 712250 FAX 01397 712001
Closed 24 Dec-2 Jan
A welcoming atmosphere prevails at this long established family run Highland hotel which is a popular base for visiting tour groups. Public areas include a choice of lounges and contrasting bars, and there is also an interesting Commando Exhibition. Bedrooms, including those in the rear annexe, offer mixed practical appointments.
17 en suite (bth/shr) 13 annexe en suite (bth/shr) (3 fmly) CTV in all bedrooms 50P V meals Coffee am Tea pm Last d 9pm
CARDS:

STANLEY Perthshire & Kinross Map 11 NO13

★★65% **The Tayside**
Mill St PH1 4NL (6m N of Perth) ☎ 01738 828249
FAX 01738 827216
(Rosette awarded for dinner only)
Popular with fishermen, this Edwardian hotel is located in the small village of Stanley, not far from Perth. Both the public areas and bedrooms reflect the original character of the building, enhanced by some imaginative interior design. The relaxing bar has a good range of malts, and there is also a quiet lounge. Robust country cooking features in the tartan clad and wood-panelled dining room, with daily specialities supplementing the fixed-price menu.
16 rms (4 bth 10 shr) (2 fmly) CTV in all bedrooms 42P Fishing Pool table Xmas Scottish, English & French Cuisine V meals Coffee am Tea pm Last d 8.30pm
ROOMS: (incl. bkfst) s £42.50-£45; d £65-£70 * **LB**
MEALS: Bar Lunch £3.75-£12.95alc Dinner £16.95-£25&alc
CONF: Thtr 100 Class 75 Board 75
CARDS:

STEWARTON East Ayrshire Map 10 NS44

★★★ 75% **Chapeltoun House**

KA3 3ED (off B796, 2m from SW of town)
☎ 01560 482696 FAX 01560 485100
Located in the peace and tranquillity of 20 acres of mature grounds, this former gentleman's residence is now a fine country house hotel offering comfortable accommodation, good food and warm hospitality. Bedrooms vary in size but all are individually decorated and fitted with period furnishings in keeping with the house's origins. Public rooms are elegant and impressive with a range of sitting rooms; the panelled hall with its open fire is particularly welcoming. The restaurant, which has earned our one-rosette award, attracts a good local following and offers a fixed-price menu of carefully prepared dishes.
8 en suite (bth/shr) CTV in all bedrooms 50P No coaches Fishing No children 12yrs English & French Cuisine V meals Coffee am Tea pm Last d 9.15pm
ROOMS: (incl. bkfst) s £69-£89; d fr £99 * **LB**
OFF-PEAK: (incl. bkfst) d fr £80
MEALS: Lunch fr £15.90 Dinner fr £23.80
CONF: Thtr 60 Class 30 Board 20
CARDS:

STIRLING Stirling Map 11 NS79
See also Bridge of Allan

★★★★69% **Stirling Highland**

Spittal St FK8 1DU (take A84 into Stirling and follow signs to Stirling Castle until you reach the Albert Hall. Turn left and left again, following signs to Castle)
☎ 01786 475444 FAX 01786 462929
(Rosette awarded for dinner only)
On the hill road approaching the castle, this imaginative conversion of the old High School offers spacious modern bedrooms in a purpose built wing that creates the fourth side of the central quadrangle that forms the car park. The original building retains many scholastic features and has incorporated former functions into the names of meeting and public rooms such as the Headmaster's Study for the bar and Latin and History Rooms as private meeting rooms. Scholars Restaurant provides interesting dishes showing flair and imagination whilst Rizzios provides a popular Italian theme. The well equipped leisure complex includes a good sized swimming pool and two squash courts.
76 en suite (bth/shr) (21 fmly) No smoking in 30 bedrooms CTV in all bedrooms STV Lift Night porter 96P Indoor swimming pool (heated) Squash Snooker Sauna Solarium Gym Jacuzzi/spa Steam room Wkly live entertainment Xmas Scottish & Italian Cuisine V meals Coffee am Tea pm No smoking in restaurant Last d 9.30pm
ROOMS: (incl. bkfst) s £88-£91; d £114-£118 * **LB**
OFF-PEAK: (incl. bkfst & dinner) d £138
MEALS: Lunch £5.95-£10.95 Dinner £18.95&alc*
CONF: Thtr 150 Class 80 Board 45 Del from £116
CARDS:

★★64% **Terraces**
CONSORT HOTELS
4 Melville Ter FK8 2ND (off A872) ☎ 01786 472268
FAX 01786 450314
Enjoying an elevated position in a tree-lined terrace, this efficiently run hotel is convenient for the city centre and the Scottish motorway network. The bedrooms vary in size, though all are

well equipped and provide good facilities for the business traveller. Melville's bar and restaurant offer a convivial atmosphere, with the friendly staff ensuring that meal times are a relaxing experience.
18 en suite (bth/shr) (4 fmly) CTV in all bedrooms STV Night porter 25P Wkly live entertainment Xmas International Cuisine V meals Coffee am Last d 9pm
ROOMS: (incl. bkfst) s £59.95-£62.50; d £69.50-£72.50 * **LB**
MEALS: Lunch £5.95-£12.50alc Dinner £5.95-£12.50alc*
CONF: Thtr 130 Class 60 Board 48 Del from £77.50
CARDS:

Travel Inn
Whins of Milton, Glasgow Rd fk7 8ex
☎ 01786 811256

Purpose-built accommodation, offering spacious, well equipped bedrooms, all with en suite bathrooms. Meals may be taken at the nearby family restaurant. For more information about Travel Inns, consult the Contents page under Hotel Groups.
40 en suite (bth/shr)
ROOMS: (incl. bkfst) d £35.50 *

Travelodge
Pirnhall Roundabout, Snabhead FK7 8EU (junct M9/M80) ☎ Central Res 8000 555300
FAX 01525 878450

Travelodge

This modern building offers accommodation in smart, spacious and well equipped bedrooms, suitable for family use, and all with en suite bathrooms. Meals may be taken at the nearby family restaurant. For information on room rates and to make a booking, call Roomline free of charge on 0800 850950. For more details about Travelodge, consult the Contents page under Hotel Groups.
37 en suite (bth/shr)

STONEHAVEN Aberdeenshire Map 15 NO88

★★61% **County**
Arduthie Rd AB39 2EH (off A90, opposite railway station)
☎ 01569 764386 FAX 01569 762214
Located opposite the station on the west side of town, this friendly, family-run hotel offers a range of facilities including two bars and a leisure club, while the function room is popular for weddings and other local functions. Bedrooms vary in size and include a large family room.
14 en suite (bth/shr) (2 fmly) CTV in all bedrooms No dogs (ex guide dogs) 40P Squash Sauna Solarium Gym Pool table Xmas Scottish, English & French Cuisine V meals Coffee am Last d 9pm
ROOMS: (incl. bkfst) s fr £44; d fr £65 * **LB**
OFF-PEAK: (incl. bkfst) s fr £40; d fr £55
MEALS: Bar Lunch £7-£16alc Dinner £10-£22alc
CONF: Thtr 160 Class 100 Board 80
CARDS:

STORNOWAY See Lewis, Isle of

STRACHUR Argyll & Bute Map 10 NN00

★★★61% **Creggans Inn**

PA27 8BX (take A815 to Strachur)
☎ 01369 860279 FAX 01369 860637
A welcoming atmosphere prevails at this long established roadside inn which stands beside the A815 overlooking Loch Fyne. Some of the bedrooms are limited in size but with pretty decor and mixed furnishings they are quite cottagey in style. Public areas include a choice of contrasting bars, two comfortable lounges one of which is upstairs, an attractive split level dining room plus a tea room and gift shop.

contd.

19 en suite (bth/shr) CTV in 9 bedrooms 50P Pool table Xmas V meals Coffee am Tea pm No smoking in restaurant Last d 9pm
ROOMS: (incl. bkfst) s £45-£50; d £80-£90 **LB**
OFF-PEAK: (incl. bkfst) s £40-£45; d £70-£80
MEALS: Sunday Lunch £13.95 High tea £3.50-£8.50 Dinner £23.50&alc
CONF: Thtr 50 Class 50 Board 35 Del from £75
CARDS:

See advertisement on page 835

STRANRAER Dumfries & Galloway Map 10 NX06

★★★★68% **North West Castle**
DG9 8EH (on seafront, close to Stena ferry terminal)
☎ 01776 704413 FAX 01776 702646
Situated on the seafront, close to the ferry terminal, this imposing 19th-century house was built for the Arctic explorer Sir John Ross. It is now owned by the McMillan family, who, together with their long serving staff provide a friendly and professional atmosphere which is hard to beat. Bedrooms are spacious, with a choice of standard or superior rooms, and there are several suites, all of which represent good value, so encouraging guests to return year after year. Public rooms are a mix of traditional and modern, with an elegant Regency dining room and residents' lounge with large leather armchairs, contrasting with the leisure centre, which offers a heated swimming pool and indoor curling rink.
71 en suite (bth/shr) (22 fmly) CTV in all bedrooms No dogs (ex guide dogs) Lift Night porter 100P No coaches Indoor swimming pool (heated) Snooker Sauna Solarium Gym Pool table Jacuzzi/spa Curling (Oct-Apr) Games room ch fac Xmas Scottish & French Cuisine V meals Coffee am Tea pm Last d 9pm
ROOMS: (incl. bkfst) s £50-£67; d £70-£90 * **LB**
MEALS: Lunch £10-£20alc Dinner fr £21&alc*
CONF: Thtr 150 Class 60 Board 40 Del from £70
CARDS:

STRATHAVEN South Lanarkshire Map 11 NS74

★★★66% **Strathaven**
Hamilton Rd ML10 6SZ
☎ 01357 521778 FAX 01357 520789
CONSORT HOTELS
Enthusiastically run by the MacIntyre family, this Robert Adam designed mansion house on the edge of the village has special appeal for the business guest and is a popular venue for local functions. Bedrooms, though variable in size, are comfortable with modern light wood furnishings. Public areas include a spacious lounge and well stocked bar where the bar meals are much in demand. In the more formal restaurant chef Paul Dunn is producing some interesting blends of flavours with his modern style of cooking. Staff are friendly and willing to please.
10 en suite (bth/shr) CTV in all bedrooms STV No dogs (ex guide dogs) Night porter 80P Scottish & French Cuisine V meals Coffee am Tea pm Last d 9.30pm
ROOMS: (incl. bkfst) s £66; d £80 * **LB**
OFF-PEAK: (incl. bkfst) s £30; d £60
MEALS: Lunch fr £10.50&alc Dinner fr £16.95&alc*
CONF: Thtr 180 Class 120 Board 30 Del from £79
CARDS:

STRATHBLANE Stirling Map 11 NS57

★★★64% **Kirkhouse Inn**
G63 9AA ☎ 01360 770621 FAX 01360 770896
Located in the centre of this pretty village below the Campsie Fells, this hotel offers good facilities for both business guests and tourists, being convenient for Glasgow and the Trossachs. Public areas are currently being enhanced and consist of a public bar, lounge bar, foyer lounge and candlelit restaurant. Bedrooms, including one with a four-poster bed, have all the expected amenities.
15 en suite (bth/shr) (2 fmly) CTV in all bedrooms STV Night porter 350P Pool table Beauty therapy room Xmas Scottish & French Cuisine V meals Coffee am Tea pm Last d 9.30pm
ROOMS: (incl. bkfst) s fr £45; d fr £65 * **LB**
OFF-PEAK: (incl. bkfst) s fr £30; d fr £50
MEALS: Lunch fr £12.50 Dinner fr £18.50*
CONF: Thtr 40 Class 20 Board 20
CARDS:

STRATHPEFFER Highland Map 14 NH45

★★70% **Brunstane Lodge**
Golf Rd IV14 9AT ☎ 01997 421261
Closed 1 & 2 Jan
Enjoying an elevated position above this popular spa town, which still retains much of its Victorian architecture, Brunstane Lodge is set in its own immaculately kept landscaped gardens which reflect the high standards offered within the hotel. Enthusiastic owners Alistair and Mary Anne McKay provide a warm welcome for all their guests, and ensure that all the individually decorated bedrooms are well maintained and comfortable. There is a tartan-clad bar which is popular with locals as well as a quieter first-floor residents' lounge and pretty dining room.
7 rms (6 bth/shr) (2 fmly) CTV in all bedrooms No dogs 20P ch fac V meals No smoking in restaurant Last d 8pm
ROOMS: (incl. bkfst) s £25-£28; d £50-£56 * **LB**
MEALS: Bar Lunch £3.50-£5.50 Dinner £15-£17*
CARDS:

STRONTIAN Highland Map 14 NM86

★★76% **Kilcamb Lodge**
PH36 4HY (off A861) ☎ 01967 402257
FAX 01967 402041
Closed Nov-mid Dec & mid Jan-Mar
(Rosettes awarded for dinner only)
Uninterrupted views across Loch Sunart can be enjoyed from this immaculately restored former hunting lodge, where Ann and Peter Blakeway and their small team of staff work tirelessly to ensure guests are well looked after. Crackling fires, deep cushioned sofas, bowls of fresh flowers and plenty of books are the hallmarks of the ground floor rooms. The delightfully furnished bedrooms are not only very comfortable, but thoughtfully equipped with items such as huge fluffy bathrobes. Peter excels in the kitchen where he produces a short choice of well prepared dishes such as roast guinea fowl and a wonderful bread and butter pudding. The staff are very friendly and helpful and the hotel has a very special 'getaway from it all' feel.
11 en suite (bth/shr) (1 fmly) No smoking in all bedrooms CTV in all bedrooms 20P No coaches Mountain bike hire Xmas Scottish & French Cuisine V meals Coffee am Tea pm No smoking in restaurant Last d 7.30pm
ROOMS: (incl. bkfst & dinner) s £62-£75; d £124-£150 * **LB**
MEALS: Bar Lunch £2-£6.50alc Dinner £25*
CONF: Class 30 Board 20
CARDS:

★★62% **Loch Sunart**
PH36 4HZ ☎ 01967 402471
Closed Nov-Mar
The strengths of this family hotel are its splendid Loch side location, the friendly atmosphere and reliable home-cooking. Both the comfortable public areas and the bedrooms are very traditionally furnished and in the absence of telephones and televisions in the rooms, the hotel has a wonderful tranquil feel.
11 rms (10 bth/shr) (1 fmly) 50P No coaches English & French Cuisine V meals Coffee am Tea pm No smoking in restaurant Last d 8.15pm

ROOMS: (incl. bkfst & dinner) s £29; d £58 * **LB**
OFF-PEAK: (incl. bkfst) s £25; d £50
MEALS: Bar Lunch fr £1.65 Dinner £9-£16alc*

★★55% ***Strontian***
PH36 4HZ ☎ 01967 402029 FAX 01967 402314
This old highland inn overlooking Loch Sunart offers cosy, attractively decorated bedrooms furnished with pine. The atmosphere is friendly and informal and guests have the choice of eating in either the bar or restaurant. At the time of our inspection, further improvements were being planned.
7 rms (5 bth/shr) (1 fmly) CTV in all bedrooms 30P No coaches Pool table V meals Coffee am Tea pm Last d 9pm
CARDS:

TAIN Highland Map 14 NH78

★★★68% **Morangie House**
Morangie Rd IV19 1PY (turn right off A9 northwards)
☎ 01862 892281 FAX 01862 892872
Major changes and improvements have taken place at this welcoming family-run business and tourist hotel which enjoys views of the Dornoch Firth from its position at the edge of the village. The attractive new wing bedrooms are comfortably modern, contrasting with the more traditional style of the main house rooms; all are well equipped and include various extras. Remodelled and extended public areas are relaxing and comfortable and an extensive range of dishes is available in both the dining room and smart new Garden Restaurant.
26 en suite (bth/shr) (1 fmly) No smoking in 4 bedrooms CTV in all bedrooms STV Night porter 40P Scottish & Continental Cuisine V meals Coffee am Tea pm Last d 10pm
ROOMS: (incl. bkfst) s £45-£55; d £65-£80 **LB**
MEALS: Lunch £6-£12 High tea £6.50-£8.50 Dinner £17.50&alc*
CONF: Thtr 40 Class 40 Board 24 Del from £75
CARDS:

★★★64% **Mansfield House**

Scotsburn Rd IV19 1PR ☎ 01862 892052
FAX 01862 892260
Standing in its own grounds opposite the Royal Academy this fine mansion house which dates from early this century is now a friendly hotel, ably run by the Lauritson family. There is a choice of standard and de luxe bedrooms, the latter being larger and having antique-style furniture. Public areas feature attractive wood panelling, and guests have a choice of formal or informal dining areas.
8 en suite (bth/shr) 10 annexe en suite (bth/shr) (3 fmly) No smoking in 4 bedrooms CTV in all bedrooms 100P Croquet lawn Xmas International Cuisine V meals Coffee am Tea pm No smoking in restaurant Last d 9pm
ROOMS: (incl. bkfst) s £45-£60; d £70-£90 * **LB**
OFF-PEAK: (incl. bkfst) s £40-£60; d £60-£90
MEALS: Lunch £10-£12alc Dinner £10-£20alc*

CONF: Thtr 40 Class 20 Board 20 Del from £60
CARDS:

See advertisement on this page

★★★58% **Royal**
High St IV19 1AB ☎ 01862 892013 FAX 01862 893450
This friendly Victorian business hotel is located in Tain town centre. There is a smart first floor restaurant and informal dining is available in the basement bistro. Other public areas include a cocktail bar and banqueting facilities on the ground floor. Bedrooms vary in size but are functional and well equipped.
25 en suite (bth/shr) (3 fmly) CTV in all bedrooms Pool table Wkly live entertainment Xmas Scottish & Continental Cuisine V meals Coffee am Tea pm No smoking area in restaurant Last d 9.15pm
ROOMS: (incl. bkfst) s £40; d £60 * **LB**
OFF-PEAK: (incl. bkfst) s £35; d £55
CONF: Thtr 100 Class 20 Board 20 Del from £55
CARDS:

TANGUSDALE See Barra, Isle of

TARBERT See Harris, Isle of

TARBERT LOCH FYNE Argyll & Bute Map 10 NR86

★★★ 64% **Stonefield Castle**
PA29 6YJ (off A83, 2m N) ☎ 01880 820836 FAX 01880 820929
Peacefully set in 60 acres of wooded gardens boasting some fine examples of Himalayan rhododendrons and other exotic shrubs, this sturdy turreted baronial mansion enjoys superb views of Loch Fyne. Ornate plaster ceilings are a feature of the spacious public areas, which include a choice of lounges, a panelled bar and spacious restaurant with a glorious view of the loch. The majority of the

contd.

T

bedrooms are located in the wing extension, they have practical fitted units and are gradually benefiting from cosmetic improvement. Various leisure facilities are available.
33 en suite (bth/shr) (1 fmly) CTV in all bedrooms Lift 50P Outdoor swimming pool (heated) Fishing Snooker Sauna Solarium Xmas European Cuisine V meals Coffee am Tea pm No smoking in restaurant Last d 9pm
ROOMS: (incl. bkfst & dinner) s £51-£69; d £102-£138 * **LB**
OFF-PEAK: (incl. bkfst & dinner) s £40-£55; d £80-£110
MEALS: Lunch fr £9.50&alc Dinner £20.50*
CONF: Thtr 180 Class 100 Board 60 Del from £45
CARDS:

See advertisement on opposite page

TAYNUILT Argyll & Bute Map 10 NN03

★★67% **Brander Lodge**
Bridge of Awe PA35 1HT (2m E of Taynuilt, off A85)
☎ 01866 822243 FAX 01866 822273

CONSORT HOTELS

Brander Lodge is located well back from the A85 two miles east of Taynuilt and is very much a family owned and run hotel. It stands its own grounds close to the River Awe and provides modern and mainly spacious bedrooms which have now had satellite TV added. A comfortable lounge is available whilst the bar and dining room have been pleasantly furnished. Service is friendly and very attentive.
20 en suite (bth/shr) (4 fmly) CTV in all bedrooms STV 60P Pool table Xmas International Cuisine V meals Coffee am Tea pm No smoking in restaurant Last d 9pm
ROOMS: (incl. bkfst) s £30-£38; d £60-£76 * **LB**
OFF-PEAK: (incl. bkfst) s £20-£35; d £40-£70
MEALS: Lunch £1.95-£11.95alc Dinner £16-£18.50*
CARDS:

★★57% ***Polfearn***
PA35 1JQ (turn N off A85, continue 1.5m through village down to Loch Shaw) ☎ 01866 2251
This family owned and run hotel stands one mile north of the village and is close to the shore of Loch Etive. It enjoys delightful all round views and offers friendly and informal service. A good range of food is available either in the bar or the dining room whilst the bedrooms are well equipped.
16 rms (3 bth 11 shr) (2 fmly) CTV in all bedrooms 20P V meals Coffee am Tea pm Last d 9pm
CARDS:

THORNHILL Dumfries & Galloway Map 11 NX89

★★72% **Trigony House**
Closeburn DG3 5EZ (1m S off A76) ☎ 01848 331211
This Edwardian hunting lodge, now an attractive hotel, is set in four acres of mature grounds, just south of Thornhill. Attentive service is provided by the resident owners, Robin and Thelma Pollock. The public areas include a cosy lounge, bar and bright restaurant overlooking the lawn, with fires roaring in all rooms. Bedrooms are immaculately clean, comfortable and well equipped.
8 en suite (bth/shr) CTV in all bedrooms No dogs (ex guide dogs) 30P No coaches No children 8yrs V meals Coffee am No smoking in restaurant Last d 8.45pm
ROOMS: (incl. bkfst) s £36-£40; d £65-£70 * **LB**
MEALS: Bar Lunch £4-£12 Dinner £18.50-£21*
CARDS:

See advertisement on opposite page

THURSO Highland Map 15 ND16

★★63% **Pentland**
Princes St KW14 7AA ☎ 01847 893202 FAX 01847 892761
This long established hotel beside the town square remains a popular venue for local functions. Bedrooms, with all the expected amenities, vary from soundly appointed twin and double rooms to the less impressive utilitarian singles. Ground floor public areas are comfortably modern in style contrasting with the more traditional first-floor lounges.
53 rms (28 bth 11 shr) (4 fmly) CTV in all bedrooms Night porter V meals Coffee am Tea pm Last d 8.30pm
CARDS:

TILLICOULTRY Clackmannanshire Map 11 NS99

★★64% **Harviestoun Country Inn**
Dollar Rd FK13 6PQ ☎ 01259 752522 FAX 01259 752523
Closed 1-2 Jan
This former farmstead and stable block has been sympathetically renovated to create a small hotel full of character. Situated at the east end of the village, the sandstone building surrounds a courtyard on three sides. The lively Brasserie offers both light and substantial dishes, while a good value, no choice menu is offered in the fine dining room on weekend evenings. There is a small well stocked bar and a children's play area in the garden. Bedrooms are neat and cheerful.
10 en suite (bth/shr) (2 fmly) No smoking in all bedrooms CTV in all bedrooms STV 100P Golf 18 Tennis (hard) Fishing Riding Putting green Wkly live entertainment Xmas French Cuisine V meals Coffee am Tea pm No smoking area in restaurant Last d 9.30pm
ROOMS: (incl. bkfst) s £39.95-£49.95; d £49.95-£59.95 * **LB**
OFF-PEAK: (incl. bkfst) s £35.95-£45.95; d £49.95-£55.95
MEALS: Lunch £12-£15&alc High tea £6-£12 Dinner £20-£35alc*
CONF: Thtr 60 Class 30 Board 20 Del from £65
CARDS:

TOBERMORY See Mull, Isle of

TOMINTOUL (NR CARRBRIDGE) Moray Map 15 NJ11

★★★66% **The Gordon Hotel & Cromdales Restaurant**
The Square AB37 9ET ☎ 01807 580206 FAX 01807 580488
The Gordon Hotels stands in the central square of this picturesque Highland village and has been delightfully refurbished over the last couple of years. It provides modern bedrooms, some of which are de luxe whilst other are more standard and all have been pleasantly furnished and equipped. Public rooms offer very comfortable seating in the lounge together with an elegant restaurant where chef Gary Goldie produces his well cooked five course dinners. Service is very friendly and a delightful informal atmosphere prevails throughout the hotel. There is also a 'locals' bar to the rear where the hotels own brewed ales are served
29 en suite (bth/shr) (2 fmly) CTV in all bedrooms STV No dogs (ex guide dogs) Night porter 14P Fishing Xmas French Cuisine V meals Coffee am No smoking in restaurant Last d 9pm
ROOMS: (incl. bkfst) s £27.50-£39; d £55-£73 *
OFF-PEAK: (incl. bkfst) s £27.50-£35; d £55-£65
MEALS: Lunch fr £12.95 High tea fr £5.50 Dinner fr £23.50*
CONF: Thtr 95 Class 50 Board 35 Del from £59.50
CARDS:

TONGUE Highland Map 14 NC55

★★ 69% **Ben Loyal**

IV27 4XE (Tongue lies at the intersection of the A838/A836, hotel is in the centre of village)
☎ 01847 611216 FAX 01847 611212
Closed Nov-Feb RS late Oct-Mar & early Apr

Many guests return time and time again to Mel and Pauline Cook's comfortable holiday and sporting hotel which enjoys a splendid outlook over the Kyle of Tongue and ruins of Varrich Castle. Bedrooms with attractive decor and pretty fabrics are comfortably furnished in pine while public areas include a well stocked bar as well as an inviting and relaxing lounge. Some of the best views are to be had in the attractive dining room which features a short daily changing fixed price menu offering a tempting range of Taste of Scotland specialities.

12 rms (9 bth/shr) CTV in all bedrooms 19P Fishing Pool table Fly fishing tuition V meals Coffee am Tea pm No smoking in restaurant Last d 8.30pm

ROOMS: (incl. bkfst) s £28-£38; d £52-£70 **LB**
OFF-PEAK: (incl. bkfst) s £25-£30; d £50-£60
MEALS: Bar Lunch £7.50-£12alc Dinner £18.50*
CARDS: 

★★58% ***Tongue***

IV27 4XD ☎ 01847 611206 FAX 01847 611345
Closed Oct-Mar

This long established sporting and holiday hotel, a former Victorian hunting lodge, is continuing to be upgraded. Bedrooms, though variable in size, are mostly furnished in period with some fine examples of furniture. Plans are in hand to extend the sun lounge, enhance the traditional dining room, and refurnish the well stocked cocktail bar.

19 rms (16 bth/shr) (2 fmly) No smoking in 10 bedrooms CTV in all bedrooms 30P V meals Coffee am Tea pm Last d 8.15pm
CARDS:

TORRIDON Highland Map 14 NG95

★★★ 75% **Loch Torridon**

IV22 2EY (on A896) ☎ 01445 791242
FAX 01445 791296

This former shooting lodge is set in spectacular romantic scenery overlooking Loch Torridon, with a granite backdrop and Highland cattle grazing nearby. David and Geraldine Gregory are dedicated hosts, always seeking to improve their hotel. The bedrooms vary in size and outlook, and are all smartly decorated; bathrooms are mostly of a generous size. Day rooms include a panelled bar with leather chairs and a fine selection of malt whiskies, an elegant peach and blue lounge and the house's original library. The ceilings have been restored with particular élan. The final touch is the willing service provided by a friendly team of staff.

21 en suite (bth/shr) (4 fmly) No smoking in all bedrooms CTV in all bedrooms STV No dogs (ex guide dogs) Lift 30P No coaches Fishing Pool table Croquet lawn Xmas French Cuisine V meals Coffee am Tea pm No smoking in restaurant Last d 8.30pm

ROOMS: (incl. bkfst) s £75-£150; d £100-£220 * **LB**
OFF-PEAK: (incl. bkfst) s £60-£100; d £80-£180
MEALS: Bar Lunch £9-£12 Dinner £31.50-£36
CARDS:

TROON South Ayrshire Map 10 NS33

★★★★ 65% **Marine Highland**

KA10 6HE (turn off A77 onto B749, hotel on left after 2m past municipal golf course) ☎ 01292 314444
FAX 01292 316922

contd.

What a fine position this hotel has overlooking the 18th fairway of Royal Troon Golf Course. Views from public rooms and from many bedrooms are superb and also extend across the Firth of Clyde to the Isle of Arran beyond. Bedrooms are currently being refurbished and include a range of standard and executive rooms as well as several suites. The superb leisure club has recently been completely upgraded and this has its own bar and snack bar. Further eating options are provided in Fairways restaurant, which has earned our one-rosette award, and in the Crosbie brasserie. Smart public rooms are provided and there are several function suites.

72 en suite (bth/shr) (7 fmly) No smoking in 12 bedrooms CTV in all bedrooms STV Lift Night porter 200P Indoor swimming pool (heated) Tennis (hard) Squash Sauna Solarium Gym Putting green Jacuzzi/spa Aerobics Beautician Steam room Wkly live entertainment Xmas International Cuisine V meals Coffee am Tea pm Last d 10pm

ROOMS: (incl. bkfst & dinner) s £92-£112; d £146-£196 **LB**

OFF-PEAK: (incl. bkfst & dinner) s £55-£69; d £110-£138

MEALS: Lunch £12.50-£14.95 High tea £8.50 Dinner £22-£23.50*

CONF: Thtr 220 Class 120 Del from £100

CARDS:

★★★ 81% Lochgreen House

Monktenhill Rood, Southwood KA10 7EN (off Ayr-Prestwick road)

☎ 01292 313343 FAX 01292 318661

Set in immaculately kept grounds, this splendid mansion enjoys views across the golf links to the sea. Owners Bill and Catherine Costley have expanded the business and doubled the number of bedrooms by converting a stable block in the gardens to the same high standard as in the main house. Bedrooms are very spacious and individually decorated, but the most stunning feature is the luxurious bathrooms, with their highly polished tiles and marble flooring. There are two comfortable lounges, one housing the Lochgreen Malt Whisky collection which should not be missed. There are also several private dining rooms as well as the main, wood panelled restaurant. Bill Costley and his team show imagination and flair in their cooking, with spiced monkfish on noodles with a curry essence being a prime example of how they add an extra dimension to quality ingredients.

7 en suite (bth/shr) 7 annexe en suite (bth/shr) CTV in all bedrooms No dogs Night porter 50P No coaches Tennis (hard) Xmas V meals Coffee am Tea pm No smoking in restaurant Last d 9.30pm

ROOMS: (incl. bkfst) s £95-£110; d £120-£150 *

MEALS: Lunch £16.95-£20 Dinner £28.50

CARDS:

★★★ 74% Highgrove House

Old Loans Rd KA10 7HL ☎ 01292 312511 FAX 01292 318228

Standing on a hillside above the town, this popular business hotel enjoys a spectacular outlook over the Firth of Clyde. Efficient management together with willing staff and a well earned reputation for imaginative cuisine has ensured its continuing success. Bedrooms are attractive and provide all the expected amenities. The elegant split-level restaurant provides a refined setting for chef Jimmy Ellison's innovative modern style of cooking, which features the best of Scotland's larder. Intensely flavoured lobster bisque, pan-fried fillet of salmon with a ginger crust and a tangy lemon butter sauce, and a delicious tiramisu for dessert are typical of his menu. There is also an excellent-value brasserie, and for house guests a fixed-price dinner menu is available on request.

9 en suite (bth/shr) (2 fmly) CTV in all bedrooms No dogs (ex guide dogs) Night porter 50P No coaches French Cuisine V meals Coffee am Last d 9.30pm

CARDS:

★★★ 66% Piersland House

Craigend Rd KA10 6HD ☎ 01292 314747 FAX 01292 315613

Standing in delightful grounds and close to the championship golf course, this fine hotel has been carefully extended over the years and is now a popular venue for both business people and holidaymakers alike. The delightful wood-panelled public rooms offer excellent comforts whilst the well equipped bedrooms are elegantly furnished and are mostly spacious. There are now a few cottage bedrooms to the rear which also include their own lounges. Cooking remains as good as ever and is in the very capable hands of chef John Rae with his style being mainly modern and using only fresh raw ingredients. The staff are very professional and are also friendly and willing.

15 en suite (bth/shr) 11 annexe en suite (bth/shr) (2 fmly) CTV in all bedrooms STV Night porter 150P Croquet lawn Putting green ch fac Xmas British & Continental Cuisine V meals Coffee am Last d 9.30pm

ROOMS: (incl. bkfst) s £79; d £101-£130 * **LB**

OFF-PEAK: (incl. bkfst) d £97.50

MEALS: Lunch £11.50&alc High tea £7.50-£12.50 Dinner £19.95&alc

CONF: Thtr 100 Class 60 Board 30 Del £90

CARDS:

£

See advertisement on opposite page

★★ 62% Craiglea

South Beach KA10 6EG ☎ 01292 311366 FAX 01292 311366

The hallmark of this very traditional-style hotel is the full family involvement combined with plenty of homely comforts. There are ample lounges available and a good range of food is provided either in the bar or the cosy dining room. Although the bedrooms are modestly furnished, they offer comfortable modern appointments. The hotel provides fine sea views to the rear and borders the south links.

20 rms (10 bth/shr) (2 fmly) CTV in all bedrooms 14P V meals Coffee am No smoking in restaurant Last d 8.45pm

CARDS:

TURNBERRY South Ayrshire Map 10 NS20

RED STAR HOTEL

★★★★★ Turnberry Hotel, Golf Courses & Spa

KA26 9LT (off A77) (Leading Hotels)

☎ 01655 331000 FAX 01655 331706

Built at the turn of the century, Turnberry is set in 800 acres of beautiful Ayrshire countryside and offers spectacular views of the Atlantic Ocean. The golf courses have been host to the Open Championship on several occasions and the Ailsa is considered to be one of the best courses in the world. Turnberry, however has other attractions beside golf. The Spa was built in 1991 and as well as a 20 metre pool, there are a number of treatment rooms where guests can be pampered. Apart from the Clubhouse, there are two restaurants; the Bay which specialises in lighter cuisine with a Mediterranean influence, and where diners can eat al fresco on finer days, and the main hotel

restaurant which has a traditional atmosphere, live music nightly and a classical cuisine. Staff are noted for their friendliness, charm and professional service.
132 en suite (bth/shr) CTV in all bedrooms STV Lift Night porter 200P No coaches Indoor swimming pool (heated) Golf 18 Tennis (hard) Squash Riding Snooker Sauna Solarium Gym Putting green Jacuzzi/spa Health spa Wkly live entertainment Xmas Scottish & French Cuisine V meals Coffee am Tea pm Last d 10pm
ROOMS: (incl. bkfst) s £200-£230; d £230-£270 * **LB**
OFF-PEAK: (incl. bkfst) s £150-£175; d £175-£205
MEALS: Lunch fr £21.50&alc Dinner fr £41.50&alc*
CONF: Thtr 160 Class 115 Board 50 Del from £195
CARDS:

★★★ 74% **Malin Court**
KA26 9PB (on A719) ☎ 01655 331457
FAX 01655 331072
RS 25 Dec

Situated near the Firth of Clyde, this very comfortably appointed hotel enjoys lovely views towards the Isle of Arran. Several lounge areas are located throughout the hotel and these take advantage of the views. Standard and executive bedrooms are available: the latter rooms tend to be better equipped and more luxurious but all offer good standards. Business meetings can be catered for and a hairdressing salon is located within the hotel. Food continues to be well cooked and enjoyable and staff go out of their way to look after their guests.
17 en suite (bth/shr) (9 fmly) CTV in all bedrooms STV Lift Night porter 110P V meals Coffee am Tea pm No smoking in restaurant Last d 9pm
ROOMS: (incl. bkfst) s £73-£85; d £105-£130 * **LB**
OFF-PEAK: (incl. bkfst) s £55-£65; d £99-£110
MEALS: Lunch £9.50-£15 High tea £5.95-£7.50 Dinner £19.95-£21.95
CONF: Thtr 120 Class 60 Board 30 Del from £69.50
CARDS:

See advertisement on this page

UDDINGSTON South Lanarkshire Map 11 NS66

★★ 67% **Redstones**
8-10 Glasgow Rd G71 7AS (1m along A721)
☎ 01698 813774 & 814843 FAX 01698 815319
Closed 25 Dec & 1-2 Jan
Created by linking two sandstone Victorian villas, this friendly family-run hotel, within convenient distance of the M74, is especially popular with the business traveller. Tasteful public areas include a well stocked bar, small comfortable lounge and an attractive restaurant offering a wide range of menus. Bedrooms, two of which have four-posters, offer mixed modern appointments together with a good range of amenities.
18 rms (16 bth/shr) CTV in all bedrooms STV No dogs (ex guide dogs) Night porter 33P No coaches Scottish, French & Italian

contd.

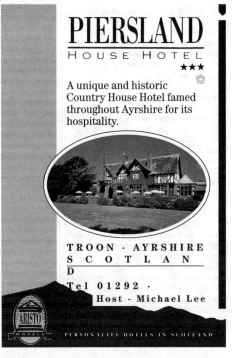

U

Cuisine V meals Coffee am No smoking area in restaurant
Last d 9pm
ROOMS: (incl. bkfst) s £52-£59; d £65-£74.50 *
OFF-PEAK: (incl. bkfst) s £37.50; d £50
MEALS: Lunch £8.50&alc High tea £6.75 Dinner £15.50&alc*
CONF: Thtr 20 Class 16 Board 14
CARDS:

UIG See Skye, Isle of

ULLAPOOL Highland Map 14 NH19

★★69% **Ceilidh Place**
West Argyle St IV26 2TY ☎ 01854 612103 FAX 01854 612886
The Ceilidh Place has for long been regarded by its loyal band of regular followers as being refreshingly different from the normal hotel concept. Here you will find regular and varied live music festivals, drama and exhibitions. Add to this genuine hospitality together with a wonderfully relaxed informal atmosphere, and you begin to understand the appeal. The bookshop has been resited and a new Parlour Bar opened in addition to the original coffee-shop, bar and restaurant, the former serving food all day. Upstairs is the inviting lounge where guests can help themselves from the honesty bar. Bedrooms, with beamed ceilings, are equipped with telephones - CTV is available on request.
13 rms (10 bth) 30P ch fac Xmas International Cuisine V meals Coffee am Tea pm No smoking in restaurant Last d 9.30pm
ROOMS: (incl. bkfst) s £55; d £110 * **LB**
OFF-PEAK: (incl. bkfst) s £35; d £70
MEALS: Bar Lunch £2-£10 Dinner £10-£25*
CONF: Thtr 60 Class 40 Board 24 Del from £20
CARDS:

UNST See Shetland

WALKERBURN Scottish Borders Map 11 NT33

★★★ 61% **Tweed Valley Hotel & Restaurant**
Galashiels Rd EH43 6AA (on A72 overlooking the River Tweed) ☎ 01896 870636 FAX 01896 870639
Closed 25 & 26 Dec
This family-run Edwardian country hotel is set on high ground to the east of the town and enjoys delightful views over the valley of the River Tweed. The house is full of character and oak-panelled public rooms include an attractive restaurant, a cosy diners' bar and a small conservatory. Bedrooms come in a variety of sizes, but it's worth asking about the 4-poster room with its huge antique bath tub. The daily changing dinner menu is augmented by a carte of mainly grills. Look out for dishes featuring fish smoked in the hotel's own smokery - it's delicious.
16 en suite (bth/shr) (2 fmly) CTV in all bedrooms 35P Fishing Sauna Solarium Gym Shooting Stalking Special courses Xmas Scottish, English & French Cuisine V meals Coffee am Tea pm
Last d 9.30pm
ROOMS: (incl. bkfst) s £49-£59; d £78-£98 * **LB**
OFF-PEAK: (incl. bkfst) s £35-£45; d £50-£98
MEALS: Lunch £8.50-£12.50 High tea £5.50-£9.50 Dinner £19-£23&alc*
CARDS:

WESTHILL Aberdeenshire Map 15 NJ80

★★★63% **Westhill**
AB32 6TT (on A944) ☎ 01224 740388
FAX 01224 744354
This purpose-built hotel lies to the west of Aberdeen, and is within a 15 minute drive of the airport and city centre. Popular for conference and business guests, the bedrooms are well equipped, and there is a choice of executive, standard or economy, rooms the latter being in a separate building at the rear of the hotel. There is a choice of bars and a good range of bar suppers prove a popular alternative to the set-price carte offered in the split-level restaurant.
37 en suite (bth/shr) 13 annexe en suite (bth/shr) (2 fmly) No smoking in 8 bedrooms CTV in all bedrooms STV Lift Night porter 350P Wkly live entertainment Xmas International Cuisine V meals Coffee am Tea pm Last d 9.30pm
ROOMS: (incl. bkfst) s £52-£68; d £68-£88 * **LB**
MEALS: Bar Lunch £4.95-£16.50alc High tea £6.25-£7alc Dinner £14.75-£16.25*
CONF: Thtr 300 Class 200 Board 200 Del from £68
CARDS:
See advertisement under ABERDEEN

WHITBURN West Lothian Map 11 NS96

★★★61% **The Hilcroft**
East Main St EH47 0JU (turn off M8 junct 4 follow signs for Whitburn, hotel 0.5m on left from junct)
☎ 01501 740818 FAX 01501 744013
Many improvements have recently been carried out at this purpose built and family run hotel. A popular venue for local functions, it offers a choice of bars - one of them semi open plan with the split level restaurant where both table d'hÙte and à la carte meals are served. The new wing's attractive bedrooms are comfortably furnished in modern style, while those in the main house are more compact and traditional.
31 en suite (bth/shr) (7 fmly) CTV in all bedrooms No dogs (ex guide dogs) Night porter 80P Xmas French & Italian Cuisine V meals Coffee am Tea pm No smoking area in restaurant
Last d 9.30pm
ROOMS: (incl. bkfst) s £40-£52.50; d £45-£65 * **LB**
MEALS: Lunch £8.50-£17.50&alc High tea £5.95-£8.45&alc Dinner £17.50&alc*
CONF: Thtr 200 Class 50 Board 30 Del from £70
CARDS:

WHITEBRIDGE Highland Map 14 NH41

RED STAR HOTEL

★★ **Knockie Lodge**
IV1 2UP (signposted from B862)
☎ 01456 486276 FAX 01456 486389
Closed Oct-Apr
Knockie Lodge is found at the end of the lane which weaves alongside Loch Knockie to the shooting lodge home of the Milward family. Built 200 years ago by the chief of the Clan

Fraser, it remains today a haven of peace and quiet, the atmosphere unsullied by the modern intrusions of television and radio. The warmth of the welcome extended by the truly dedicated owners is natural and evident to all. Its reception rooms, with log fires and a beautiful break fronted antique bookcase, its thoughtfully furnished bedrooms and their views over Loch Nanlann, and the excellent, straightforward but accomplished cuisine, all combine to make for perfect relaxation at a hotel which is very distinctive.
10 en suite (bth/shr) 20P No coaches Fishing Snooker Sailing No children 10yrs No smoking in restaurant Last d 8pm
ROOMS: (incl. bkfst) s £55; d £95-£155
MEALS: Bar Lunch fr £5alc Dinner fr £27.50alc
CARDS:

★★63% ***Whitebridge***
IV1 2UN ☎ 01456 486226 & 486272 FAX 01456 486413
Closed 21 Dec-Feb
This traditional and comfortable family-run hotel is superbly situated close to Loch Ness, half way between Fort Augustus and Inverness. The majority of bedrooms, which vary in size and are all soundly furnished, are en suite. Home-cooked dishes are available in the neatly furnished dining room, and guests also have the use of a cosy lounge with an open fire, and a small public bar.
12 rms (10 bth/shr) (3 fmly) CTV in all bedrooms 32P No coaches Fishing Coffee am Tea pm Last d 8.30pm
CARDS:

WICK Highland Map 15 ND35

★★62% **Mercury**
Riverside KW1 4NL ☎ 01955 603344
FAX 01955 605456
Closed 26 Dec-7 Jan

Mount Charlotte Hotels MCH

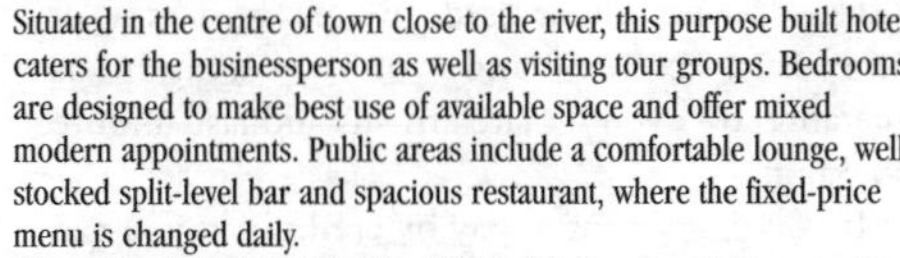

Situated in the centre of town close to the river, this purpose built hotel caters for the businessperson as well as visiting tour groups. Bedrooms are designed to make best use of available space and offer mixed modern appointments. Public areas include a comfortable lounge, well stocked split-level bar and spacious restaurant, where the fixed-price menu is changed daily.
48 en suite (bth/shr) (5 fmly) CTV in all bedrooms Night porter 22P V meals Coffee am Tea pm Last d 8.45pm
ROOMS: (incl. bkfst) s fr £55; d fr £70 * **LB**
MEALS: Lunch £1.50-£10alc Dinner fr £15.50&alc*
CONF: Thtr 180 Class 60 Board 40 Del from £50
CARDS:

★★60% ***Mackay's***
Union St KW1 5ED (opposite Caithness General Hospital)
☎ 01955 602323 FAX 01955 605930
Closed 1-2 Jan
Ongoing improvements are taking place at this long established family run commercial hotel which stands on the south shore of the River Wick. Most public areas, which include a choice of bars and lounges, have benefited from recent upgrade. Bedrooms, with a wide range of amenities, have recently been refurbished.
26 en suite (bth/shr) (4 fmly) CTV in all bedrooms STV Lift Night porter 12P No coaches V meals Coffee am
CARDS:

WALES

Inspectors' Choice Hotel of the Year: Penhelig Arms, Aberdovey

A

ABERCRAF Powys Map 03 SN81

★71% **Maes-Y-Gwernen**

School Rd SA9 1XD ☎ 01639 730218 FAX 01639 730765

Surrounded by pretty gardens and grounds, this gabled house built in 1910 stands in a village in the upper Swansea valley. It offers very comfortable bedrooms, each delightfully decorated in pleasing bold colours and rich soft fabrics. Public areas include a cosy bar, lounge and an attractive conservatory with outside patio.

8 en suite (bth/shr) No smoking in 1 bedroom CTV in all bedrooms 15P No coaches Sauna Solarium Jacuzzi/spa ch fac Xmas European Cuisine V meals Coffee am Tea pm No smoking in restaurant Last d 8.30pm

ROOMS: (incl. bkfst) s £31-£37; d £48-£60

MEALS: Lunch £10.50 High tea £4 Dinner £10.50

CARDS:

ABERDARON Gwynedd Map 06 SH12

★★60% ***Ty Newydd***

LL53 8BE ☎ 01758 760207 FAX 01758 760505

Closed Nov-Feb

This friendly seaside hotel, where the atmosphere is very relaxed, offers simply furnished bedrooms; all the rooms have modern facilities and some enjoy the most marvellous sea views. Guests have direct access from the hotel to the beach, and there is a terrace, with a safe area for children, where snacks, coffee and afternoon tea are available. There is no formal restaurant, but a very good range of bar meals is served in the comfortable lounge bar.

17 rms (8 bth 1 shr) (3 fmly) CTV in 16 bedrooms TV in 1 bedroom No dogs (ex guide dogs) 5P Pool table V meals Coffee am Tea pm Last d 9.30pm

CARDS:

ABERDYFI Gwynedd Map 06 SN69

★★★69% **Trefeddian**

LL35 0SB (0.5m N off A493) ☎ 01654 767213 FAX 01654 767777

Closed 3 Jan-6 Mar

This popular and very well maintained hotel, which has been owned and run personally by the Cave family since 1912, enjoys the most magnificent views over Cardigan Bay from its position 100 feet above sea level. The hotel's many facilities make it attractive to families and there are specific recreation areas for children, for example, after dinner. Bedrooms are freshly decorated, generally spacious and comfortably furnished. A choice of well prepared dishes is available in the restaurant. There are a number of comfortable and smartly decorated lounges.

46 en suite (bth/shr) (7 fmly) CTV in all bedrooms Lift 68P No coaches Indoor swimming pool (heated) Tennis (hard) Snooker Solarium Pool table Putting green Table tennis Play area ch fac Xmas English & French Cuisine V meals Coffee am Tea pm No smoking in restaurant Last d 8.45pm

ROOMS: (incl. bkfst & dinner) s £53-£58; d £106-£116 * **LB**

OFF-PEAK: (incl. bkfst & dinner) s £50-£52; d £100-£104

MEALS: Lunch £8.75-£9.75 Dinner £16.25*

CARDS:

See advertisement on opposite page

★★★ 64% **Plas Penhelig Country House**

LL35 0NA (Welsh Rarebits) ☎ 01654 767676

FAX 01654 767783

Closed Jan & Feb

This characterful country house hotel, set high above the Dovey Estuary, enjoys the most magnificent views. Hospitality is a strength, and the atmosphere is both informal and relaxing; in summer, guests can enjoy a drink on the terrace overlooking the fourteen acres of gardens, or in winter, in front of one of the open fires. Bedrooms are both traditionally and comfortably furnished, as are the public areas which include a wonderful panelled hall, elegant drawing room and the dining room, where a good choice of carefully prepared dishes is available.

11 en suite (bth/shr) CTV in all bedrooms 40P No coaches Croquet lawn Putting green English & French Cuisine V meals Coffee am Tea pm No smoking in restaurant Last d 8.45pm

ROOMS: (incl. bkfst & dinner) s £52.50-£60; d £112-£120 *

MEALS: Lunch fr £13.50 Dinner fr £18.50*

CONF: Thtr 40 Class 20 Board 22

CARDS:

£

See advertisement on opposite page

HOTEL *of the* YEAR

★★ 72% **Penhelig Arms Hotel & Restaurant**

LL35 0LT (take A493 coastal road, hotel faces Penhelig harbour) (Welsh Rarebits)

☎ 01654 767215 FAX 01654 767690

Closed 25 & 26 Dec

Built in the 1700s and originally known as Y Dafarn Fach (The Little Inn), the hotel has kept much of its character. It stands

opposite the old harbour and there are superb views over the Dyfi estuary and mountains beyond from most rooms. Residents and diners have a smaller cocktail bar and there is also a first-floor lounge. Bedrooms are pretty and well equipped and all have excellent armchairs. Robert and Sally Hughes lead a team of friendly staff who offer warm Welsh hospitality. A daily changing fixed-price menu uses local ingredients with fish, lamb and game much in evidence. Not to be missed is the delicious bara brith served with afternoon tea. Our inspectors have nominated Pehelig Arms as AA Hotel of the Year for Wales for 1996/7.

10 en suite (bth/shr) No smoking in all bedrooms CTV in all bedrooms 12P No coaches European Cuisine V meals Coffee am Tea pm No smoking in restaurant Last d 9pm

ROOMS: (incl. bkfst) s £39; d £68 **LB**

MEALS: Lunch fr £12.50 Dinner fr £19.50

CARDS:

★★69% **Harbour**

LL35 0EB (on the A493 coastal road between Dolgellau & Machynlleth) ☎ 01654 767250 FAX 01654 767078

Closed 1-29 Dec

Aberdovey is a pretty seaside village and this family-run hotel looks out over the beach towards the Ynys Las sand dunes. Proprietor Sylvia Graham has considerable interior design talents and this is in evidence throughout the hotel. Bedrooms are exceedingly pretty and rich fabrics and personal touches are used to good effect. Three family suites are available and several rooms have lovely sea views. The lounge bar also looks out over the waterfront and this, like the lounge, is elegantly furnished. Food options are extensive with an all-day family restaurant, the more formal hotel restaurant and a basement wine bar.

9 en suite (bth/shr) (3 fmly) No smoking in 3 bedrooms CTV in all bedrooms International Cuisine V meals Coffee am Tea pm Last d 9pm

ROOMS: (incl. bkfst) s fr £45; d fr £70 *

MEALS: Lunch £3-£15alc High tea £5-£10alc Dinner £10-£15alc*

CONF: Thtr 30 Class 12 Board 12 Del from £70

CARDS:

★69% **Maybank Hotel & Restaurant**

4 Penhelig Rd, Penhelig LL35 0PT ☎ 01654 767500 & 767622

Closed mid Nov-22 Dec & Jan-13 Feb RS 5-15 Nov

Standing in a slightly elevated position, this delightful hotel enjoys superb views over the estuary towards the sand dunes of Ynyslas beyond. In the bedrooms pine furniture and pretty fabrics are used to good effect. There is a cosy bar for pre-dinner drinks and a comfortable first floor lounge is provided which takes advantage of the views. The quality of the food on offer is reflected by our rosette award and local fish catches and meats are always available. Diners choose from a fixed-price menu and extras and specials depend on the market. Sea bass and sewin feature and, of course, Welsh lamb. There is no car park on the premises but the owners have purchased sufficient spaces in the nearby public car park for all their guests.

(1 fmly) No smoking in 6 bedrooms CTV in 6 bedrooms Night porter No coaches ch fac Xmas European Cuisine V meals No smoking in restaurant

ROOMS: (incl. bkfst) s £30.95-£40.95; d £45.90-£57.90 *

OFF-PEAK: (incl. bkfst) d £41.90-£53.90

MEALS: Dinner £19.95-£22.95

CARDS:

Some company-owned hotels have a central reservations telephone number. For the quick-reference list, consult the Contents page.

ABERGAVENNY Monmouthshire Map 03 SO21

See also Walterstone Herefordshire

★★★62% Llansantffraed Court

Llanvihangel Gobion NP7 9BA (on A4598)
☎ 01873 840678 FAX 01873 840674

This impressive country house is set in open countryside, with fine views from most windows. Public rooms are cosily appointed and feature open fires. Bedrooms are fitted with quality furniture and a good range of equipment.

21 en suite (bth/shr) (3 fmly) No smoking in 7 bedrooms CTV in all bedrooms STV Lift Night porter 100P Croquet lawn Xmas International Cuisine V meals Coffee am Tea pm No smoking in restaurant Last d 9.30pm

ROOMS: (incl. bkfst) s £61-£71; d £75-£85 * **LB**

MEALS: Lunch fr £12.95 Dinner £16.25-£18.50*

CONF: Thtr 70 Class 40 Board 40 Del from £80

CARDS:

★★★54% The Angel

Cross St NP7 5EW (on A40 just past Renault garage)
☎ 01873 857121 FAX 01873 858059

The Angel is a 17th-century hostelry with a popular bar and restaurant situated in the centre of the town. Disappointingly, there has been little movement on the upgrading programme since our last visit. Public areas and many bedrooms are now tired and dated.

29 en suite (bth/shr) (2 fmly) No smoking in 6 bedrooms CTV in all bedrooms Night porter 35P Xmas V meals Coffee am Tea pm No smoking in restaurant Last d 9.30pm

ROOMS: s £65; d £75 * **LB**

MEALS: Sunday Lunch fr £10.95 Dinner fr £16.95*

CONF: Thtr 200 Class 60 Board 40 Del from £65

CARDS:

★★70% Llanwenarth Arms

Brecon Rd NP8 1EP (on A40 midway between Abergavenny and Crickhowell beside River Usk) ☎ 01873 810550 FAX 01873 811880

This very pleasant, privately-owned and personally-run hotel dates back to the 16th century, but it has been extensively altered and extended in more recent times. It stands on the A40, on the bank of the River Usk, midway between the towns of Abergavenny and Crickhowell. The traditionally furnished, well equipped bedrooms are located on the ground, lower ground and first floors of a separate, purpose-built building; most of them have views across the river. Public areas include a choice of bars and a bright, traditionally furnished restaurant, which also overlooks the river; there is a pleasant conservatory lounge and an adjacent terrace. Other facilities available to guests include two stretches of salmon and trout fishing. The hotel has a well deserved reputation for its food and a wide range of home-cooked wholesome dishes, prepared from fresh quality produce, is available.

18 en suite (bth/shr) CTV in all bedrooms No dogs 60P No coaches Fishing International Cuisine V meals Coffee am

ROOMS: (incl. bkfst) s £39-£49; d £59 **LB**

MEALS: Lunch £12-£20alc Dinner £12-£20alc

CARDS:

ABERGELE Aberconwy & Colwyn Map 06 SH97

★★★63% Kinmel Manor

St Georges Rd LL22 9AS (at Abergele exit on A55) ☎ 01745 832014 FAX 01745 832014

Parts of this old manor house date back to the early 16th century but it has been considerably extended over the years. It lies in mature grounds and the driveway runs alongside the A55 expressway. Many original features remain, with a beautiful oak fireplace in the hall, and the fireplace in the restaurant depicts the coats of arms of the royal tribes of Wales. Bedrooms have now been equipped with modern fitted furniture and bathrooms have recently been upgraded. Public areas include spacious conference and function facilities as well as a fully equipped leisure centre.

42 en suite (bth/shr) (3 fmly) CTV in all bedrooms STV 120P Indoor swimming pool (heated) Sauna Solarium Gym Jacuzzi/spa Xmas English & French Cuisine V meals Coffee am Tea pm Last d 9.30pm

ROOMS: (incl. bkfst) s £48; d £66 * **LB**

CONF: Thtr 250 Class 100 Board 70 Del £65.50

CARDS: £

ABERPORTH Cardiganshire Map 02 SN25

★★★65% Hotel Penrallt

SA43 2BS ☎ 01239 810227 FAX 01239 811375

Closed 23-31 Dec

This large Edwardian house has many fine original features, including a magnificent stained glass window on the stairway and ornately carved ceiling beams in the oak-panelled restaurant. It occupies an elevated position above the town and commands excellent views of the surrounding area. Leisure facilities located in the extensive grounds and gardens include tennis, pitch and putt and an outdoor swimming pool. Inside, there is a spacious lounge, a choice of bars and a small games room. The well equipped bedrooms include a family bedded room, rooms with balconies, rooms with sea views and three rooms with their own lounges and kitchens, which can also be let as self-catering accommodation.

16 en suite (bth/shr) (2 fmly) CTV in all bedrooms 100P No coaches Outdoor swimming pool (heated) Tennis (hard) Sauna Solarium Gym Putting green ch fac Coffee am Tea pm No smoking in restaurant Last d 9pm

ROOMS: (incl. bkfst) s £50; d £80 * **LB**

MEALS: Sunday Lunch fr £12 High tea fr £6 Dinner fr £16&alc

CONF: Class 60 Board 30

CARDS: £

★★71% Penbontbren Farm

Glynarthen SA44 6PE (3.5m SE off A487) (Welsh Rarebits) ☎ 01239 810248 FAX 01239 811129

Closed 24-28 Dec

This friendly and delightful little hotel is situated on a working farm and has been cleverly developed from former farm buildings. The bedrooms, which include some on ground floor level, are attractively decorated and have modern furnishings, equipment and facilities. A good selection of soundly cooked dishes is available in the very attractive, cottage style restaurant. There is also a bar, a comfortable lounge and a games room. Other facilities include a farm Museum and a nature discovery trail. The hotel is reached from the A487 by following the signs just to the south-west of Sarnau village.

10 annexe en suite (bth/shr) (6 fmly) CTV in all bedrooms 35P No coaches Fishing Farm trail Xmas European Cuisine V meals Coffee am Tea pm Last d 8.15pm

ROOMS: (incl. bkfst) s £38-£43; d £68-£74 **LB**

MEALS: Dinner fr £18alc

CONF: Thtr 35
CARDS:

★★63% **Highcliffe**
SA43 2DA (off B4333) ☎ 01239 810534 FAX 01239 810534
This friendly, privately owned hotel is situated on a hill, a short distance up from the beach. Some of the modern furnished and equipped bedrooms are situated in a separate, purpose built annexe building. Bedrooms with sea views and family bedded rooms are both available. A wide range of dishes is served in the restaurant and there is also an extensive bar meal selection.
9 rms (6 bth 2 shr) 6 annexe en suite (bth) (4 fmly) CTV in all bedrooms 18P Xmas International Cuisine V meals Coffee am Tea pm No smoking in restaurant Last d 8.30pm
ROOMS: (incl. bkfst) s £30.85-£36; d £47-£55 **LB**
OFF-PEAK: (incl. bkfst) s fr £27.50; d fr £44.50
CARDS: £

★73% **Glandwr Manor**
Tresaith SA43 2JH (turn off B4333 towards Tresaith hotel in 1.25m on right) ☎ 01239 810197
Closed Nov-Feb
The Davis family offer warm hospitality at this small hotel set in pleasant grounds at Tresaith. Bedrooms are neat and cosy, and there are several lounges with log fires and an attractive restaurant offering set and à la carte menus.
7 rms (2 bth 3 shr) (2 fmly) No dogs 14P No coaches Coffee am Tea pm No smoking in restaurant Last d 8pm
ROOMS: (incl. bkfst) s fr £28; d fr £56 *
MEALS: Dinner £11-£12&alc*

ABERSOCH Gwynedd Map 06 SH32

★★★69% **Porth Tocyn**
Bwlch Tocyn LL53 7BU (2.5m S follow signs 'Porth Tocyn' and Blue Highway signs marked 'Gwesty/ Hotel') ☎ 01758 713303 FAX 01758 713538
Closed mid Nov-wk before Etr

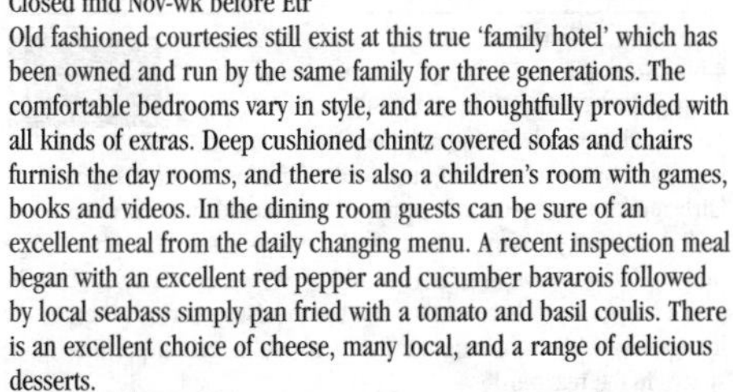

Old fashioned courtesies still exist at this true 'family hotel' which has been owned and run by the same family for three generations. The comfortable bedrooms vary in style, and are thoughtfully provided with all kinds of extras. Deep cushioned chintz covered sofas and chairs furnish the day rooms, and there is also a children's room with games, books and videos. In the dining room guests can be sure of an excellent meal from the daily changing menu. A recent inspection meal began with an excellent red pepper and cucumber bavarois followed by local seabass simply pan fried with a tomato and basil coulis. There is an excellent choice of cheese, many local, and a range of delicious desserts.
17 en suite (bth/shr) (1 fmly) CTV in all bedrooms 50P No coaches Outdoor swimming pool (heated) Tennis (hard) ch fac V meals Coffee am Tea pm Last d 9.30pm
ROOMS: (incl. cont bkfst) s £56.50; d £92-£104 * **LB**
OFF-PEAK: (incl. cont bkfst) s £43.50; d £67-£77.90
MEALS: Sunday Lunch £16 High tea £3-£6 Dinner £20-£26.75*
CARDS:

★★★65% **White House**
LL53 7AG (on A449 from Pwllheli hotel is on the right just before entering Abersoch village) ☎ 01758 713427 FAX 01758 713512
Closed 31 Jan-21 Feb
Located in a slightly elevated position on the approach to the village, there are lovely views over Cardigan Bay and St Tudwals Island from many rooms. These are now all decorated with pretty papers and fabrics and modern facilities are provided. There is a spacious bar and a separate lounge and both are comfortably furnished. A carte and daily menu is on offer, fresh produce is used whenever possible and local fish is always available. The hotel is surrounded by very well maintained lawns and gardens.
11 en suite (bth/shr) (1 fmly) No smoking in 4 bedrooms CTV in all bedrooms 100P Xmas British & Welsh Cuisine V meals Coffee am Last d 9pm
ROOMS: (incl. bkfst) s £31.50-£36.50; d £63-£69 * **LB**
OFF-PEAK: (incl. bkfst) d £55
MEALS: Dinner fr £18.50&alc
CONF: Thtr 100 Class 60 Board 40
CARDS: £

★★★64% ***Abersoch Harbour***
LL53 7HR ☎ 01758 712406
RS Jan & Feb
This holiday hotel is situated in an elevated position overlooking Cardigan Bay with good views of the harbour and Snowdonia. Bedrooms are prettily decorated and include one with a four-poster bed for that special occasion. Some are situated in separate buildings and offer extra privacy. The lounge, which takes advantage of the lovely views, is comfortable and relaxing. There are two bars and, during the season, a bistro provides an alternative place to eat.
9 en suite (bth/shr) 5 annexe en suite (bth/shr) (2 fmly) CTV in all bedrooms No dogs (ex guide dogs) 50P English & French Cuisine V meals Coffee am Tea pm Last d 9.30pm
CARDS:

★★★64% **Riverside**
LL53 7HW ☎ 01758 712419 FAX 01758 712671
Closed Dec-Feb
This popular hotel is full of character and has been owned and enthusiastically run by John and Wendy Bakewell for nearly 30 years. Situated beside the River Soch and overlooking the picturesque harbour, the attractively decorated bedrooms are bright, fresh and well equipped. The spacious and comfortably furnished lounge, which enjoys the most wonderful views, has a spiral staircase leading to the dining room; this has a 'Mediterranean' feel, and a good range of home-cooked dishes is served from the daily-changing fixed-price menu. Guests also have the use of the well tended gardens, the heated indoor swimming pool and even a boat on the river.
12 en suite (bth/shr) (4 fmly) CTV in all bedrooms No dogs (ex guide dogs) 25P No coaches Indoor swimming pool (heated) Sailing Windsurfing ch fac Coffee am Tea pm Last d 8.45pm
ROOMS: (incl. bkfst) s £44-£50; d £64-£84 * **LB**
OFF-PEAK: (incl. bkfst) s £32-£54; d £60-£76
MEALS: Bar Lunch £3-£10&alc High tea £6.50 Dinner £22*
CARDS:

★★76% **Neigwl**
Lon Sarn Bach LL53 7DY (on A499, drive through Abersoch, hotel on the left overlooking the sea) ☎ 01758 712363 FAX 01758 712363
This small, very well maintained hotel has been run by the Heptonstall family for over a decade, and their untiring enthusiasm and dedication ensures that it remains as popular as ever. Bedrooms, whilst not particularly large, are comfortably furnished and attractively decorated; improvements to them are constantly being made. There are a couple of family suites available which are reached externally. The comfortable lounge bar enjoys the most magnificent views, as does the restaurant where the skills of Nigel Higginbottom can be enjoyed. A number of carefully prepared home-cooked dishes are available from the daily changing four-course fixed-price menu where deliciously fresh fish regularly features as well as a chef's dish of the day.
7 rms (1 bth 4 shr) 2 annexe en suite (bth) (2 fmly) CTV in all bedrooms No dogs (ex guide dogs) 30P No coaches ch fac Xmas Coffee am Tea pm Last d 9pm
ROOMS: (incl. bkfst) s fr £42; d fr £70 **LB**
OFF-PEAK: (incl. bkfst) s fr £30; d fr £50
MEALS: Dinner £18-£21
CARDS: 

A

★★ 66% ***Tudor Court***
Lon Sarn Bach LL53 7EB ☎ 01758 713354 FAX 01758 713354
This is a friendly hotel located in the centre of the village. Bedrooms are bright and modern and pretty fabrics are used to good effect. The bar is cosy and welcoming and also features an interesting selection of prints of British war planes, old and new. Local fish catches usually appear on the menu which offers a good range of popular dishes. Special golf packages are on offer and these make use of the many local courses.
8 rms (5 bth 2 shr) (2 fmly) CTV in all bedrooms 14P No coaches European Cuisine V meals Coffee am Tea pm Last d 9.30pm
CARDS:

★★64% **Deucoch**
LL53 7LD (through Abersoch village following signs for Sarn bach. At cross roads in Sarn Bach (approx 1m from village centre) turn right, hotel on top of Hill) ☎ 01758 712680 FAX 01758 712670
This family-owned and -run hotel affords beautiful panoramic views and is located in a quiet position, a little way from the town. It provides modern and comfortable bedrooms whilst a good range of food is provided in the bar or cosy restaurant.
10 rms (3 bth 6 shr) (2 fmly) CTV in all bedrooms STV 30P No coaches Xmas V meals
ROOMS: (incl. bkfst) s £24-£27; d £48-£54 * **LB**
MEALS: Bar Lunch £4-£8 Dinner £13*
CARDS:

ABERYSTWYTH Cardiganshire Map 06 SN58

★★★ 67% **Conrah**
Ffosrhydygaled, Chancery SY23 4DF (on A487, 3.5m S) (Welsh Rarebits) ☎ 01970 617941 FAX 01970 624546
Closed 23-30 Dec
This large country house is set in extensive grounds and gardens, in a rural area some three miles south of Aberystwyth. Privately owned, it provides a high level level of friendly and attentive service. The bedrooms vary in size and style, some being quite spacious, whilst other are compact. Those in the main house are mostly traditional in style and furnishings, whilst the annexe bedrooms are more modern. All the annexe bedrooms are on the ground floor. Public areas have a relaxing atmosphere, with comfortable furnishings. There is an attractive dining room, three lounges, and a small leisure centre with a heated pool and sauna. Fresh local produce is used as much as possible in the kitchens here, and the food is certainly worthy of a mention.
11 en suite (bth/shr) 9 annexe en suite (bth/shr) (1 fmly) CTV in all bedrooms No dogs Lift 60P No coaches Indoor swimming pool (heated) Sauna Croquet lawn Table tennis No children 5yrs International Cuisine V meals Coffee am Tea pm No smoking in restaurant Last d 9pm
ROOMS: (incl. bkfst) s £59-£88; d £88-£110 **LB**
MEALS: Lunch fr £11alc Dinner fr £25.50*
CONF: Thtr 40 Class 20 Board 20 Del from £95.50
CARDS:

See advertisement on opposite page

★★★ 66% ***Belle Vue Royal***
Marine Ter SY23 2BA ☎ 01970 617558 FAX 01970 612190
Closed 24-26 Dec
This family-run hotel stands on the seafront within easy reach of the town centre and other amenities. The individually appointed bedrooms vary in size but all are well equipped and furnished; family rooms, rooms with sea views, non-smoking rooms and a ground-floor room are also available. Public areas have recently been refurbished and include the attractively decorated 'Royals Grill Room', a choice of bars and a residents' lounge. The restaurant is popular with local diners, serving imaginative cuisine from a grill menu and a daily-changing set price carte, both making the most of local fresh produce. One dish recently enjoyed was a shank of Ystwyth lamb infused with rosemary and sweet garlic and served with fried cous cous and a purée of creamed swede and nutmeg.
36 en suite (bth/shr) (7 fmly) No smoking in 8 bedrooms CTV in all bedrooms No dogs (ex guide dogs) Night porter 15P International Cuisine V meals Coffee am Tea pm Last d 9.30pm
CARDS:

★★65% **Four Seasons**
50-54 Portland St SY23 2DX (in town centre, car park entrance in Bath Street) ☎ 01970 612120 FAX 01970 627458
Closed 25-31 Dec
This constantly improving establishment is situated close to the town centre, within easy reach of the seafront. The well equipped bedrooms are tastefully decorated and have co-ordinated soft furnishings and modern furniture; the only room which is not en suite has its own private bathroom. Attractive public areas include a pleasant restaurant, a cosy bar and a room for private meetings. The hotel is popular with commercial visitors but is equally suitable for tourists.
15 rms (14 bth/shr) (1 fmly) CTV in all bedrooms No dogs (ex guide dogs) 10P Welsh, English & Continental Cuisine V meals Coffee am Tea pm No smoking in restaurant Last d 8.30pm
ROOMS: (incl. bkfst) s £45-£50; d £68-£72 **LB**
MEALS: Sunday Lunch £11 Dinner fr £15*
CARDS:

★★ 64% **Groves**
44-46 North Pde SY23 2NF (N on A487, in town centre) ☎ 01970 617623 FAX 01970 627068
MINOTEL Great Britain
This small, privately owned and personally run hotel is situated on the main road, just north of the town centre. It provides fairly modern and quite well equipped accommodation. Facilities include a small pleasant restaurant where a good selection of soundly prepared food, including "Taste of Wales" dishes, is available. There is also a lounge bar, where wholesome bar meals are served. There is a lounge for residents, a room for functions and a few car parking spaces in the rear yard.
9 en suite (bth/shr) No smoking in 1 bedroom CTV in all bedrooms No dogs (ex guide dogs) 8P International Cuisine V meals Coffee am No smoking in restaurant Last d 8.45pm
ROOMS: (incl. bkfst) s fr £45; d fr £55 * **LB**
MEALS: Bar Lunch £1.80-£7.50alc Dinner £15.50-£18*
CONF: Thtr 65 Del from £43.25
CARDS:

★★63% **Richmond**
44-45 Marine Ter SY23 2BX ☎ 01970 612201 FAX 01970 626706
This privately owned hotel has been personally run by the Griffiths family for almost quarter of a century. It is centrally located on the main seafront promenade, and has recently been extensively renovated and refurbished to provide modern accommodation, which includes family rooms and rooms with sea views. The bright and attractive dining room also overlooks the sea, as does the comfortable lounge. Other facilities include a small lounge bar and a self-contained function suite.

15 rms CTV in all bedrooms P
ROOMS: (incl. bkfst) d fr £55 *
CARDS:

AMLWCH See Anglesey, Isle of

AMMANFORD Carmarthenshire Map 03 SN61

★★67% **Mill at Glynhir**
Glyn-Hir, Llandybie SA18 2TE (3m NE off A483) ☎ 01269 850672
Closed Xmas RS 24-30 Dec
This small hotel was once a water-powered flour mill and dates back well over 250 years. It is set in extensive wooded grounds on the side of a valley, and provides individually styled bedrooms, including a suite. All rooms have good modern equipment and en suite facilities. Three bedrooms are located in converted properties adjacent to the main house. There are a cosy dining room and a comfortable lounge, and private fishing is available in the River Loughor, which borders the grounds.
11 en suite (bth/shr) CTV in all bedrooms 20P No coaches Indoor swimming pool (heated) Golf 18 Fishing No children 11yrs Welsh & French Cuisine V meals Coffee am No smoking in restaurant Last d 8.15pm
ROOMS: (incl. bkfst) s £36.50; d £73 * **LB**
MEALS: Dinner £14.50*
CARDS:

ANGLESEY, ISLE OF Anglesey

AMLWCH Map 06 SH49

★★67% **Lastra Farm**
Penrhyd LL68 9TF (after welcome to Amlwch sign turn left across main road, left at T junct on to Rhosgoch road)
☎ 01407 830906 FAX 01407 832522
This modern hotel was originally a 17th-century farm. It lies about half a mile from the town centre and is a popular venue for good-value food. A large conservatory fronted function suite has been built away from the main building and this accommodates local weddings and other events. Bedrooms are pine furnished and pretty papers and fabrics have been used to good effect. Public areas are situated in the old building and these are cosy and comfortable.
6 en suite (bth/shr) (1 fmly) CTV in all bedrooms Night porter 40P Welsh & French Cuisine V meals Coffee am No smoking in restaurant
ROOMS: (incl. bkfst) s fr £26; d fr £46 **LB**
MEALS: Lunch £6.95 Dinner £13.75*
CARDS:

★★60% ***Trecastell***
Bull Bay LL68 9SA (1m N on A5025, adjacent to Golf Club) (Frederic Robinson) ☎ 01407 830651 FAX 01407 832114
Standing in its own grounds with a large car park, this hotel is located near the golf course and enjoys superb views over Bull Bay. There is a modern bar where a good range of meals is served, a separate pool room and a small lounge for residents. Bedrooms are modestly appointed but most have en suite facilities and all have TVs and other modern amenities.
12 rms (8 bth 3 shr) (3 fmly) CTV in 10 bedrooms 60P No coaches Coffee am Last d 8.30pm
CARDS:

BEAUMARIS Map 06 SH67

★★❀❀75% **Ye Olde Bulls Head Inn**
Castle St LL58 8AP (Welsh Rarebits)
☎ 01248 810329 FAX 01248 811294
Closed 25-26 Dec & 1 Jan
This fine old inn is steeped in history with Charles Dickens and Samuel Johnson among its famous past visitors. It was also commandeered by Cromwell's General Mytton as his soldiers laid siege to the nearby castle. Exposed timbers still feature and the bar, with its log fire, has an impressive display of antique weaponry. Modern comforts have been carefully provided and bedrooms now include one with a four-poster bed for that special occasion. With its position on the Menai Straits, fish features prominently on the menus but Welsh lamb, game and other meats are also available. Food is quite rightly taken very seriously and our rosette award is amply justified.
14 en suite (bth/shr) 1 annexe en suite (bth/shr) No smoking in 4 bedrooms CTV in all bedrooms No dogs (ex guide dogs) 8P No coaches V meals Coffee am No smoking in restaurant Last d 9.30pm
ROOMS: (incl. bkfst) s £45-£47; d £75-£77 **LB**
MEALS: Sunday Lunch £14.75-£15.75 Dinner fr £19.95&alc*
CARDS:

★★70% **Bishopsgate House**
54 Castle St LL58 8BB ☎ 01248 810302 FAX 01248 810166
Closed 22 Dec-31 Jan
This is a delightful small hotel, immaculately maintained and offering comfortable modern accommodation. It is located in the centre of the historic town and has quite a history of its own dating back to 1760. The Chinese Chippendale staircase is an impressive feature and the lounge retains its original wall panelling. Bedrooms are pretty and include two with four-poster beds for that special occasion. Others have fine antique beds and all have modern ensuite facilities. The restaurant serves from fixed-price and carte menus and there is a rear car park.
9 en suite (bth/shr) 2 annexe rms No smoking in 2 bedrooms CTV in 9 bedrooms 10P No coaches No children 5yrs English & French Cuisine V meals Coffee am No smoking in restaurant Last d 8.45pm
ROOMS: (incl. bkfst) s £35-£45; d £52-£60 * **LB**
MEALS: Sunday Lunch £7.95-£9.95 Dinner £11.95-£14.95*
CARDS:

★★65% **Bulkeley Arms**

Castle St LL58 8AW ☎ 01248 810415
FAX 01248 810146

Standing on the shores of the Menai Straits, there are superb views from this Grade I listed Georgian building over the Snowdonia mountain range. The hotel offers a choice of bars as well as its own night club facility, and extensive function and meeting rooms are provided. There is a spacious lounge with an adjoining all-day coffee shop and the restaurant serves from a fixed price, regularly changing menu. Many bedrooms are also quite large; these are traditionally furnished and decorated with pretty papers and fabrics and modern amenities are provided. Staff are friendly and attentive and the atmosphere is warm and relaxing.

41 rms (40 bth/shr) (4 fmly) CTV in all bedrooms Lift Night porter 30P Sauna Solarium Gym Jacuzzi/spa Wkly live entertainment Xmas V meals Coffee am Tea pm No smoking in restaurant Last d 9.30pm
ROOMS: (incl. bkfst) s £45-£56; d £70-£95 **LB**
MEALS: Sunday Lunch fr £8.50 Dinner £15.25
CONF: Thtr 200 Class 180 Board 40 Del from £45.50
CARDS:

BENLLECH BAY Map 06 SH58

★★62% **Bay Court**

Beach Rd LL74 8SW (follow the A55 over the Brittania Bridge. Pick up the A5025 signposted Benllech. Turn right at the crossroads towards the beach.) ☎ 01248 852573 FAX 01248 852606

A good range of facilities is offered at this long established hotel, which is situated a short walk from the sandy beach. As well as the bar for residents and diners, there is a public cellar bar popular with locals who come to play darts and pool. Functions and smaller wedding parties are catered for and the bar offers a wide selection of good-value meals. Bedrooms are brightly decorated and include several family suites. Some are located in a nearby building and all are well equipped.

15 rms (2 bth 4 shr) 4 annexe en suite (bth) (5 fmly) CTV in all bedrooms 65P Pool table Xmas English & French Cuisine V meals Coffee am Tea pm No smoking in restaurant Last d 8.30pm
ROOMS: (incl. bkfst) s £18-£23; d £36-£46 **LB**
MEALS: Lunch fr £5.75 Dinner fr £8.50&alc*
CARDS:

HOLYHEAD Map 06 SH28

★★62% **Bull**

London Rd, Valley LL65 3DP (3.50 miles from ferry terminal, on A5 near junct with A5025) ☎ 01407 740351 FAX 01407 742328

This is a busy hotel, located alongside the A5 a few miles east of Holyhead. Bedrooms all have en suite facilities, some are suitable for families and several are situated in nearby buildings. The bars, which are furnished in cottage style, offer a good choice of bar food, and quizzes and other local events are regularly held. There is a large car park.

9 en suite (bth/shr) 5 annexe en suite (bth/shr) (4 fmly) CTV in all bedrooms No dogs (ex guide dogs) 130P International Cuisine V meals Coffee am Tea pm Last d 9.30pm
ROOMS: (incl. bkfst) s £32.75; d £43.75 * **LB**
CARDS:

LLANGEFNI Map 06 SH47

RED STAR HOTEL

★★★ **Tre-Ysgawen Hall**

Capel Coch LL77 7UR (take B5111 from Llangefni for Amlach/Llanerchymedd.Through Rhosmeich,turn right to Capel Coch.Hotel 1 mile on left at end of long drive) ☎ 01248 750750 FAX 01248 750035

Built in 1882, this impressive stone mansion enjoys an enviable position in quiet wooded grounds in the middle of the island. Run very much as a family home, where the style of service is informal, it makes for the perfect 'escape' hotel. Bedrooms are beautifully furnished and good use has been made of pretty fabrics and wallpapers. The fine public rooms all lead in to the magnificent hallway with its impressive oak staircase. The food is very good too. An inspection dinner began with a rich confit of goose breast with an excellent plum compote, accompanied by home-made bread. A highlight of the meal was an intermediate course of deeply flavoured consommé of smoked chicken, garnished with a perfect brunoise of vegetables. Main courses offer interesting combinations such as a cannon of Welsh lamb with a mint mousse set on a tangy Bengal curry sauce with pilau rice. A dish of perfectly cooked Conwy salmon and local monkfish, served with delicious wild mushrooms and laverbread set on a well made white wine butter sauce, confirms that Mark Colley is an able cook who is able to produce imaginative, well timed dishes with some aplomb.

20 en suite (bth/shr) CTV in all bedrooms 100P International Cuisine V meals Coffee am Tea pm Last d 9.30pm
ROOMS: s £71.50-£148; d £93.50-£148 * **LB**
MEALS: Lunch fr £14 Dinner £17.95-£28.35*
CONF: Thtr 120 Board 30
CARDS:

MENAI BRIDGE Map 06 SH57

★★66% **Anglesey Arms**

LL59 5EA (on left after Menai Bridge)
☎ 01248 712305 FAX 01248 712076

Originally a coaching inn but fully modernised over recent years, the hotel lies in pretty gardens, near the famous suspension bridge. Weddings are popular locally and other functions and business meetings are also well catered for. Bedrooms, now completely refurbished, are attractively pine-furnished and modern facilities such as trouser presses and hair dryers are provided. The restaurant, which overlooks the gardens, offers a small fixed-price menu and a wide choice of inexpensive food is served in the lounge bar.

17 rms (10 bth 6 shr) (2 fmly) CTV in 16 bedrooms ch fac Welsh & English Cuisine V meals Coffee am Tea pm

ROOMS: (incl. bkfst) s fr £32.50; d fr £49.50 * **LB**
CONF: Thtr 60 Class 40 Board 40
CARDS:

★★61% ***Gazelle***
Glyn Garth LL59 5PD (2m NE A545) (Frederic Robinson)
☎ 01248 713364 FAX 01248 713167
This cosy little inn is situated on the banks of the Menai Straits with lovely views across to Bangor and Snowdonia beyond. The bar is very popular locally and, as well as a wide range of bar food, the first-floor restaurant offers a further large carte selection; generous portions will satisfy the largest appetites. Bedrooms offer a sound standard of comfort and many have en suite facilities.
9 rms (4 bth 1 shr) CTV in all bedrooms STV No dogs (ex guide dogs) 40P Sailing Sea fishing Watersports Coffee am Tea pm Last d 9pm
CARDS:

TREARDDUR BAY Map 06 SH27

★★★71% **Trearddur Bay**

LL65 2UN (from A5 turn left at lights in Valley towardTrearddur Bay,in Trearddur Bay go to Shell garage on right side,turn left opposite garage,hotel on right) ☎ 01407 860301 FAX 01407 861181
This popular hotel lies next to a lovely beach and provides modern and comfortable accommodation. Bedrooms include several suites, one has a four-poster bed and several are located in a nearby outbuilding. Extensive public rooms include several bars and lounge areas, conference and function facilities, a games room and an indoor swimming pool. The all-day bar serves a good range of inexpensive meals and more formal dining is available in the smart hotel restaurant.
31 en suite (bth/shr) (7 fmly) No smoking in 1 bedroom CTV in all bedrooms STV Night porter 300P Indoor swimming pool (heated) Croquet lawn Children's games room Xmas V meals Coffee am Tea pm No smoking in restaurant Last d 9.30pm
ROOMS: (incl. bkfst) s fr £68; d fr £98 * **LB**
MEALS: Bar Lunch £1.95-£7.95 Dinner £18.50-£22.50&alc*
CONF: Thtr 120 Class 60 Board 40 Del from £85
CARDS:

See advertisement on this page

★★★57% **Beach**
Lon St Ffraid LL65 2YT ☎ 01407 860332 FAX 01407 861140
The Beach is a commercial and leisure hotel located on the approach to the village from the A5 at Valley. The hotel bar is spacious and comfortable and the London Road bar popular with non residents. A simple daily menu is offered in the main restaurant, but a larger range of food is available in the bars or adjoining bistro. Bedrooms are in reasonable condition and improvements are planned over the next couple of years. There is also a leisure club with a snooker hall and squash courts.
27 en suite (bth/shr) (3 fmly) CTV in all bedrooms Night porter 100P Snooker Sauna Gym Pool table Jacuzzi/spa toning tables sun beds Wkly live entertainment ch fac V meals Coffee am Tea pm Last d 9.30pm
ROOMS: (incl. bkfst) s £30-£35; d £60-£65 * **LB**
MEALS: Sunday Lunch £7.50 Dinner £11.50&alc*
CONF: Del from £38
CARDS:

BALA Gwynedd Map 06 SH93

★★★72% **Pale Hall Country House**
Llandderfel LL23 7PS (off the B4401 Corwen/Bala road 4m from Llandrillo)
☎ 01678 530285 FAX 01678 530220
Situated east of the town in the village of Llandderfel, this impressive Victorian mansion is set in several acres of mature parkland. The bedrooms and public areas are elegant and spacious, reflecting the splendour of days gone by. Roaring fires, ornate ceilings and panelled walls feature as well as stained glass windows. Conference facilities are provided and the area is well suited to the outdoor pursuits associated with management training courses. Bedrooms include some with four-

contd.

B

poster and half-tester beds and one room still houses the bath used by Queen Victoria when she once visited the house. Food comes by way of a fixed price menu which is regularly changed. Pigeon, duck and poultry are usually available and the chef's efforts have earned a well deserved one-rosette award.
17 en suite (bth/shr) (2 fmly) No smoking in 5 bedrooms CTV in all bedrooms No dogs 80P Fishing Clay pigeon & Game shooting V meals Coffee am Tea pm No smoking in restaurant Last d 9pm
MEALS: Lunch £14.95 Dinner £23.95*
CONF: Thtr 40 Board 20
CARDS:

★★63% **Plas Coch**
High St LL23 7AB (on A494)
☎ 01678 520309 FAX 01678 521135
Closed 25 Dec
John and Mair Evans offer a genuine Welsh welcome to guests at this 18th-century former coaching inn set in the centre of the lakeside town. Most of the bedrooms have been refurbished in recent years and all modern facilities are provided. There are a comfortable foyer lounge, two bars serving a good range of food and a restaurant where more formal meals are available. It is easy to park on the street outside.
10 en suite (bth/shr) (4 fmly) CTV in all bedrooms No dogs (ex guide dogs) 20P No coaches Windsurfing Canoeing Sailing V meals Coffee am Tea pm No smoking in restaurant Last d 8.30pm
ROOMS: (incl. bkfst) s £39-£51; d £65 **LB**
MEALS: Bar Lunch £7.50-£11.50alc Dinner £14.25-£16.25
CARDS:

BANGOR Gwynedd Map 06 SH57

★★★68% **Menai Court**
Craig y Don Rd LL57 2BG
☎ 01248 354200 FAX 01248 354200
Closed 27 Dec-2 Jan
Elwyn and Judy Hughes of Black and White Minstrel fame extend a warm Welsh welcome to their guests. They are fully involved in all areas and are responsible for the relaxing and friendly atmosphere that prevails. Bedrooms are decorated with pretty papers and fabrics and some have fine views over the Menai Straits. Food is always enjoyable and Judy is responsible for obtaining only the best produce available. Aberdeen Angus, Welsh lamb and local fish are all specialities.
13 en suite (bth/shr) (2 fmly) CTV in all bedrooms STV 22P No coaches British & French Cuisine V meals Coffee am No smoking in restaurant Last d 9.30pm
ROOMS: (incl. bkfst) s £49.50; d £73.50-£80 **LB**
MEALS: Lunch £9.50-£12.95 Dinner £16.95-£18&alc
CONF: Thtr 60 Class 40 Board 30
CARDS:

★★66% **Abbeyfield**
Tal-y-Bont LL57 3UR (turn off A5/A55 at Penrhyn Castle. Hotel 400yds on right) ☎ 01248 352219 & 361299 FAX 01248 362913
Dating back over several centuries, this small and friendly hotel has been a coaching inn and a farmhouse before being converted in 1968. It now provides smart, modern bedrooms, one with a four-poster bed. A good range of bar meals is served as well as a fixed price menu for more formal dining. A comfortable lounge is available together with a bar and pool room. The hotel, previously called Ty Uchaf, is located two miles east of the town in the village of Talybont.
10 en suite (bth/shr) (1 fmly) CTV in all bedrooms No dogs (ex guide dogs) 40P Pool table Wkly live entertainment V meals Coffee am Tea pm Last d 8pm
ROOMS: (incl. bkfst) s £25; d £45 *
MEALS: Bar Lunch £4-£5.20&alc Dinner £11.50&alc*
CARDS:

★★64% **Telford**
Holyhead Rd LL57 2HX (at the foot of Telford suspension bridge, link road A55) ☎ 01248 352543 FAX 01248 352543
This friendly hotel is located alongside the famous suspension bridge of the same name and its gardens reach down to the waterside. Jimmy Bell is the jovial host and, together with his family, offers very flexible services. The hotel is popular with Irish ferry travellers who can book in at any time of the day or night. Bedrooms tend to be compact in size but all are brightly decorated. The cosy bar features a mock-up of the bridge and the adjoining restaurant serves honest cooking in generous portions.
10 rms (4 shr) (2 fmly) No smoking in 2 bedrooms CTV in 9 bedrooms TV in 1 bedroom No dogs (ex guide dogs) Night porter Air conditioning 15P Fishing V meals Coffee am Tea pm Last d 8.30pm
MEALS: Lunch £7-£8.50 High tea fr £3 Dinner £8.50-£12*
CARDS:

Travelodge
Llys-y-Gwynt LL57 4BG (junc A5/A55)
☎ 01248 370345 FAX 01248 370345
Travelodge
This modern building offers accommodation in smart, spacious and well equipped bedrooms, suitable for family use, and all with en suite bathrooms. Meals may be taken at the nearby family restaurant. For information on room rates and to make a booking, call Roomline free of charge on 0800 850950. For more details about Travelodge, consult the Contents page under Hotel Groups.
30 en suite (bth/shr)

BARMOUTH Gwynedd Map 06 SH61

★★68% **Ty'r Graig Castle Hotel**
Llanaber Rd LL42 1YN (1 mile from Barmouth on the Harlech road, seaward side) ☎ 01341 280470
FAX 01341 281260
Closed 27 Dec-31 Jan
Located just north of Barmouth this family-run hotel, built in the Gothic style, was originally the family home of a famous Birmingham gunsmith. Impressive wood panelling and stained glass windows still feature and four of the bedrooms are situated in rounded towers with excellent views over Cardigan Bay. Bedrooms all have modern facilities, one has a four-poster bed, and satellite TV is provided. An elegant lounge is available and the conservatory bar is attractively furnished in cane. Food is well cooked and enjoyable, with a 4-course menu on offer.
12 en suite (bth/shr) No smoking in 1 bedroom CTV in all bedrooms STV 15P No coaches Windsurfing Yachting Sea fishing English & French Cuisine V meals Coffee am Tea pm No smoking in restaurant Last d 8.30pm
ROOMS: (incl. bkfst) s £38; d £59-£71 * **LB**
MEALS: Sunday Lunch £9.95 Dinner £15.50*
CARDS:

★★67% ***Wavecrest***
8 Marine Pde LL42 1NA ☎ 01341 280330
Closed Dec-Etr
Eric and Shelagh Jarman create a very homely atmosphere at this seaside hotel. Most bedrooms enjoy lovely views over Cardigan Bay towards the Cader Idris range of mountains beyond. These are decorated with pretty papers and fabrics and include some suitable for families. The bar and restaurant are in the open-plan mode and there is a quiet seating area on the first-floor landing. Shelagh is an accomplished chef and continues to provide excellent food.
10 rms (3 bth 4 shr) (4 fmly) No smoking in all bedrooms CTV in all bedrooms 2P Last d 7.30pm
CARDS:

B

★★64% **Bryn Melyn**

Panorama Rd LL42 1DQ (off A496)
☎ 01341 280556 FAX 01341 280276
Closed mid Nov-Feb
David and Carol Clay have run this small hotel for over twenty five years and offer warm hospitality to their guests, many of whom return year after year. It lies in an elevated position above the town and there are lovely views over the Mawddach Estuary and Cader Idris. Modern bedrooms are provided and public areas include a lounge and separate conservatory.
9 rms (8 shr) (1 fmly) CTV in all bedrooms 10P No coaches V meals Coffee am No smoking in restaurant Last d 8.30pm
ROOMS: (incl. bkfst) s £31-£37; d £48-£60 **LB**
MEALS: Bar Lunch fr £4.50alc Dinner £14.50-£17alc
CARDS:

BARRY Vale of Glamorgan Map 03 ST16

★★★ 74% **Egerton Grey Country House**
Porthkerry CF62 3BZ (from junct 33 of M4 follow signs for airport and turn left at roundabout for Porthkerry, after 500yds turn left down lane between thatched cottages) (Welsh Rarebits)
☎ 01446 711666 FAX 01446 711690
Conveniently positioned for Cardiff Airport, the hotel is screened from the outside world in seven acres of mature gardens at the head of a steep wooded valley, ending in a golf course and a shingle beach. The house is an elegant former rectory, richly furnished on classical lines, with ornate plasterwork, open fires, paintings, and objets d'art. Bedrooms are mostly well proportioned and individually furnished in period style, some having charming Victorian roll top baths. Craig Brookes heads the kitchens, and his imaginative seasonal menus produce well executed dishes with robust textures and flavours.
10 en suite (bth/shr) (4 fmly) CTV in all bedrooms STV 31P No coaches Tennis (hard) Croquet lawn ch fac Xmas V meals Coffee am Tea pm Last d 9.30pm
ROOMS: (incl. bkfst) s £60-£95; d £95-£120 * **LB**
MEALS: Lunch £18-£25.50 Dinner £18-£25.50
CONF: Thtr 30 Class 30 Board 22 Del from £95
CARDS:
See advertisement under CARDIFF

★★★60% **Mount Sorrel**
Porthkerry Rd CF62 7XY ☎ 01446 740069
FAX 01446 746600

CONSORT HOTELS

This privately owned hotel comprises of two large Victorian houses modernised and extended. It is located close to the town centre. The fairly modern bedrooms fall into two categories, about half being more compact than the others and having more functional furniture. In addition to the cosy, traditionally furnished restaurant and lounge bar, there are function and conference rooms and a leisure centre with a heated swimming pool.
43 en suite (bth/shr) (3 fmly) CTV in all bedrooms Night porter 17P Indoor swimming pool (heated) Sauna Gym Xmas Continental Cuisine V meals Coffee am Tea pm No smoking in restaurant Last d 9pm
ROOMS: (incl. bkfst) s £52-£65; d £60-£75 **LB**
MEALS: Lunch £11.50-£15.50 Dinner £15.50-£19*
CONF: Thtr 150 Class 100 Board 50 Del £85
CARDS:

★★61% **Cwm Ciddy**

Airport Rd CF62 3BA (from junct 33 of M4 follow signs fro airport) ☎ 01446 700075
FAX 01446 700075
RS 24-26 Dec
Conveniently situated for Cardiff Airport, this small hotel offers functional chalet-style accommodation in a very friendly atmosphere. Bedrooms are spacious but simply furnished, while public areas are full of local character with their beamed ceilings and bric-a-brac.
14 en suite (bth) (4 fmly) CTV in all bedrooms STV No dogs (ex guide dogs) 200P No coaches Childrens play area Wkly live entertainment V meals Coffee am No smoking area in restaurant
ROOMS: (incl. bkfst) s fr £49; d fr £59 * **LB**
OFF-PEAK: (incl. bkfst) s fr £37; d fr £55
CARDS:

BEAUMARIS See Anglesey, Isle of

BEDDGELERT Gwynedd Map 06 SH54

★★★68% **Royal Goat**
LL55 4YE (off A498) ☎ 01766 890224 & 890343 FAX 01766 890422
This long established hotel, which is over 200 years old, lies in several acres of mature woodland, with many walks available through the grounds. It provides modern, well equipped bedrooms where pretty wallpapers and floral fabrics are used to good effect. A wide range of bar food is provided for walkers and tourists to the area, and more formal meals are served in the smart restaurant. There is a games room, good conference and function facilities and comfortable bars and lounges. Staff are friendly and many are Welsh speaking.
32 en suite (bth/shr) (3 fmly) No smoking in 10 bedrooms CTV in all bedrooms STV Lift Night porter 100P Fishing Pool table Xmas Welsh & French Cuisine V meals Coffee am Tea pm No smoking in restaurant Last d 10pm
ROOMS: (incl. bkfst) s £42-£48; d £68-£75 * **LB**
MEALS: Lunch £11-£14&alc High tea £5-£9&alc Dinner £14-£17&alc
CONF: Thtr 80 Class 70 Board 70
CARDS:

★★72% ***Tanronnen***
LL55 4YB (Frederic Robinson) ☎ 01766 890258
Set in an area of outstanding beauty, this small hotel offers excellent accommodation with high quality furniture and fittings. Bedrooms are richly furnished and have superb en suite facilities. There are two cosy bars and a warm and relaxing lounge. A coffee lounge serves a good range of bar food and more substantial meals are available in the restaurant. Staff are friendly and attentive.

contd.

7 en suite (bth/shr) (3 fmly) CTV in 8 bedrooms No dogs 15P V meals Coffee am Last d 9pm
CARDS:

★ 67% **Sygun Fawr Country House**

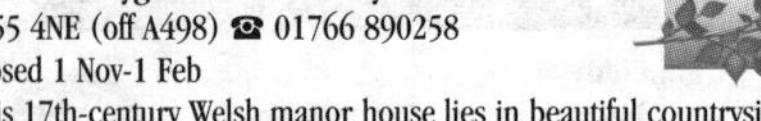

LL55 4NE (off A498) ☎ 01766 890258
Closed 1 Nov-1 Feb
This 17th-century Welsh manor house lies in beautiful countryside within Snowdonia. The surrounding hills are a delight throughout the year but especially impressive during early summer when rhododendron blossoms are to be seen everywhere. Stone walls and exposed timbers abound and a cosy bar is provided in addition to several comfortable sitting rooms. Bedrooms are small but pretty and the views are, of course, superb.
7 en suite (bth/shr) (1 fmly) 20P No coaches Sauna V meals Last d 8pm
ROOMS: (incl. bkfst) d £54 * **LB**
MEALS: Dinner £15-£17&alc*
CARDS:

BENLLECH BAY See Anglesey, Isle of

BERRIEW Powys Map 07 SJ10

★★69% **Lion**
SY21 8PQ (centre of village, next to church) (Welsh Rarebits)
☎ 01686 640452 FAX 01686 640604
This beautifully preserved and impeccably maintained 17th-century inn stands in the village centre, just off the A483, south of Welshpool. It provides well equipped accommodation, which includes a family suite and a room with a four-poster bed. The public areas which are full of character and include a choice of bars and a choice of eating options.
7 en suite (bth/shr) (1 fmly) CTV in all bedrooms No dogs 6P Fishing Welsh & Continental Cuisine V meals Coffee am Last d 9pm
ROOMS: (incl. bkfst) s £50-£59; d £80-£90 * **LB**
MEALS: Sunday Lunch £9-£12 Dinner fr £18&alc*
CARDS:

BETWS-Y-COED Aberconwy & Colwyn Map 06 SH75
See also Llanrwst

★★★69% **Royal Oak**
Holyhead Rd LL24 0AY (on main A5 in centre of town, next to St Mary's church) ☎ 01690 710219 FAX 01690 710603
Formerly a coaching inn on the London to Holyhead road, this is now a fine hotel providing comfortable accommodation. It is located in the centre of the village and overlooks the River Llugwy. Bedrooms include several suitable for families. Various bars are provided and there are no fewer than three eating options. 27 en suite (bth/shr) (5 fmly) No smoking in 1 bedroom CTV in all bedrooms No dogs (ex guide dogs) Night porter 200P Golfing arranged Wkly live entertainment Xmas International Cuisine V meals Coffee am Tea pm No smoking area in restaurant
Last d 8.45pm
ROOMS: (incl. bkfst) s £48-£50; d £76-£80 * **LB**
OFF-PEAK: (incl. bkfst) s £46; d £72
MEALS: Lunch £8.50-£10.50 High tea £5.50-£8.50 Dinner £14.50-£20&alc*
CONF: Board 20
CARDS:

See advertisement on opposite page

★★★68% **Waterloo**
LL24 0AR (close to A5, near Waterloo Bridge)
☎ 01690 710411 FAX 01690 710666
Closed Xmas
This well equipped modern hotel stands alongside the A5, near the famous bridge after which it is named. Extensions made over recent years have increased the number of bedrooms and added a popular leisure centre which includes a coffee shop where light meals are served. Bedrooms have all now been upgraded and several situated in a nearby building have private sitting rooms. There is a large public bar in addition to the cocktail bar and the restaurant.
9 en suite (bth/shr) 30 annexe en suite (bth/shr) (2 fmly) CTV in all bedrooms 200P Indoor swimming pool (heated) Sauna Solarium Gym Pool table Jacuzzi/spa Steam room International Cuisine V meals Coffee am Tea pm Last d 9.30pm
ROOMS: (incl. bkfst) s £46-£51; d £72-£82 **LB**
OFF-PEAK: (incl. bkfst) s £46-£47; d £72-£74
MEALS: Sunday Lunch £8.95-£9.75 Dinner £16.95-£17.50&alc*
CARDS:

See advertisement on opposite page

★★★64% **Craig-y-Dderwen Country House Hotel**
LL24 0AS ☎ 01690 710293 FAX 01690 710292
This Victorian country house hotel is reached by a tree-lined driveway from the end of the famous Waterloo Bridge. Its grounds extend to the River Conwy and famous visitors from the past include Elgar who came for the solitude and relaxation. Bedrooms are comfortable and well decorated and include several with four-poster beds. Bar and lounge areas are smart and cheery and staff are friendly.
17 en suite (bth/shr) (5 fmly) CTV in all bedrooms 50P Jacuzzi/spa Badminton Golf driving range Volleyball ch fac Xmas French Cuisine V meals Coffee am Tea pm No smoking in restaurant
ROOMS: (incl. bkfst) s £55; d £65 * **LB**
MEALS: Lunch £4.50&alc*
CONF: Thtr 50 Del £75
CARDS:

★★★64% **Glan Aber**
Holyhead Rd LL24 0AB ☎ 01690 710325 FAX 01690 710700
Closed 24-26 Dec
Located in the centre of the mountain resort, this is a smart and modern hotel. Bedrooms, which include several suitable for families, are equipped with many extras such as trouser presses and hair

contd.

dryers. The foyer with its open fire also contains a comfortable lounge area and there is a choice of bars and a separate pool room. A recently added facility is a first floor spa complete with jacuzzi and sun beds.
24 en suite (bth/shr) (4 fmly) CTV in all bedrooms STV Lift 21P Fishing Sauna Solarium Pool table Jacuzzi/spa V meals Coffee am Tea pm Last d 8.45pm
ROOMS: (incl. bkfst) s £19-£26; d £38-£52 * **LB**
OFF-PEAK: (incl. bkfst) s £19-£22.50; d £38-£45
MEALS: Lunch £8.25 Dinner £10.50*
CARDS:

See advertisement on page 857

★★★ 62% **Plas Hall**
Pont-y-Pant, Dolwyddelan LL25 0PJ (3m SW A470) ☎ 01690 750206 FAX 01690 750526
Situated in the heart of Snowdonia in an area of outstanding natural beauty, Plas Hall is surrounded by wooded slopes and trout streams. It is popular with tourists, walkers and anglers and is the venue for management training courses in the winter months. Bedrooms, which are pine-furnished, include several with four-poster beds. There is a cosy cocktail bar as well as a games room.
17 en suite (bth/shr) (4 fmly) CTV in all bedrooms STV 36P Fishing Games room Welsh & French Cuisine V meals Coffee am Tea pm No smoking in restaurant Last d 8.30pm
CARDS:

See advertisement on opposite page

RED STAR HOTEL

★★ **Tan-y-Foel Country House**
Capel Garmon LL26 0RE (off A5 at Betws-y-Coed onto A470, travel 2m N sign marked Capel Garmon on right, take this turning towards Capel Garmon for 1.5m hotel sign on left)
☎ 01690 710507 FAX 01690 710681
Set on a hillside with stunning views across the Conwy valley towards the Snowdon range, this immaculately maintained and boldly decorated 16th-century manor house is run by Janet and Peter Pitman and has earned many awards. The two small and cosy lounges have log fires in the winter and are furnished with a host of reading material and objets d'art. The bedrooms, some with four-poster or brass beds, are very comfortable and neatly laid out with many thoughtful extras. The dining room has been extended into a small conservatory area and is a fitting environment to enjoy Janet's fine and artistically presented cooking.
5 en suite (bth/shr) 2 annexe en suite (bth/shr) No smoking in all bedrooms CTV in all bedrooms No dogs (ex guide dogs) 9P No coaches No children 7yrs French Cuisine Coffee am Tea pm No smoking in restaurant Last d 7.30pm
ROOMS: (incl. bkfst) s £53-£76; d £76-£136 * **LB**
MEALS: Dinner £23-£28*
CARDS:

★★ 68% **Park Hill**
Llanrwst Rd LL24 0HD (N on A470)
☎ 01690 710540 FAX 01690 710540
This delightful hotel, situated off the A470 just north of the village, enjoys fine views over the local golf course and Conwy Valley. Accommodation is provided in attractively decorated bedrooms well equipped with modern facilities, public areas include three comfortable lounges as well as a cosy bar, and there is a heated indoor swimming pool. Good home-cooking and ample parking are provided.
11 rms (6 bth 3 shr) (2 fmly) CTV in all bedrooms No dogs (ex guide dogs) 14P No coaches Indoor swimming pool (heated) Sauna Jacuzzi/spa No children 6yrs Xmas Welsh, English & French Cuisine V meals Coffee am Tea pm No smoking in restaurant Last d 7.45pm
ROOMS: (incl. bkfst) s £17.50-£19.50; d £51-£61 * **LB**
MEALS: Dinner £13.50-£14.50*
CARDS:

★★ 67% **Ty Gwyn**
LL24 0SG (at junct of A5/A470, 100yds S of Waterloo Bridge)
☎ 01690 710383 & 710787 FAX 01690 710383
Ty Gwyn is a delightful old coaching inn, situated alongside the A5, near the Waterloo Bridge. Exposed timbers, slab floors, low ceilings and open fires characterise the interior, and both the bedrooms and public rooms are filled with fine period furniture and copper, brass and china pieces. Several rooms have four-poster and half-tester beds, and most have en suite facilities. A wide range of food options is available in the bar and restaurant.
13 rms (2 bth 7 shr) (1 fmly) CTV in 11 bedrooms 16P Xmas English & French Cuisine V meals Coffee am Last d 9pm
ROOMS: (incl. bkfst) s fr £19; d £35-£80 * **LB**
OFF-PEAK: (incl. bkfst) s £19-£40; d £35-£54
MEALS: Lunch fr £11.50 Dinner £14.95-£19.95alc
CARDS:

★ 66% **Fairy Glen**
LL24 0SH (0.5m S of the A5) ☎ 01690 710269 FAX 01690 710269
Closed Dec & Jan
Dating back 300-years, this old coaching inn is located near the famous beauty spot of the same name. The friendly Ball family offer their guests a warm and friendly welcome and the atmosphere is informal and relaxing. Bedrooms come in a range of sizes and all are fitted with televisions and fully-adjustable heating. A comfortable lounge is provided for residents and there is also a cosy bar.
10 rms (5 bth 2 shr) (2 fmly) CTV in all bedrooms Night porter 10P No coaches V meals Coffee am Tea pm No smoking in restaurant Last d 7.30pm
ROOMS: (incl. bkfst) s fr £20; d fr £44 * **LB**
MEALS: Bar Lunch fr £3.50 Dinner fr £11*
CARDS:

BIRCHGROVE Swansea Map 03 SS79

★★ 62% ***Oak Tree Parc***
Birchgrove Rd SA7 9JR (300yds from M4 junc 44)
☎ 01792 817781 FAX 01792 814542
Closed 25-31 Dec
This large detached Victorian house stands in its own extensive gardens, on the B4291, within a few hundred yards of junction 44 of the M4 motorway. Privately owned, it provides well equipped accommodation, which includes family bedded rooms. There is a pleasant restaurant, where a wide range of dishes is available, a small lounge bar and a room for private functions and conferences.

10 en suite (bth/shr) (2 fmly) CTV in all bedrooms Night porter 40P Welsh, English, French & Italian Cuisine V meals Coffee am Tea pm
CARDS:

BLACKWOOD Caerphilly Map 03 ST19

★★★67% ***Maes Manor***
NP2 0AG ☎ 01495 224551 & 220011 FAX 01495 228217
This large former country house was built in 1890. It stands in 9 acres of wooded grounds and pleasant gardens, just north of Blackwood, via the A4048, from which it is signposted. It changed hands in 1995 and the new owner has carried out extensive improvement and renovation work, which has resulted in a dramatic transformation of both the accommodation and the public areas. Just over half the attractively decorated and well equipped, modern bedrooms are located in a converted former coachhouse; several of these are on ground floor level. The attractively appointed public rooms include a choice of bars and a huge, self contained ballroom, which is ideal for large functions or conferences for up to 250 people; another room is available for smaller functions.
8 en suite (bth) 14 annexe en suite (bth) (2 fmly) CTV in all bedrooms Night porter 100P ch fac Welsh, English, French & Italian Cuisine V meals Coffee am Tea pm Last d 9.30pm
CARDS:

BLAENAU FFESTINIOG Gwynedd Map 06 SH74

◯ ***Queens Hotel***
1 High St LL41 3ES ☎ 01766 830055
12 rms

BONTDDU Gwynedd Map 06 SH61

★★★ 72% **Bontddu Hall**
LL40 2SU (on A496) ☎ 01341 430661
FAX 01341 430284
Closed Nov-Etr

Once the country retreat of the Lord Mayor of Birmingham, this fine 19th century house overlooks the Mawddach Estuary and the Cader Idris range of mountains. It lies in 14 acres of mature grounds and the views and location must be one of the loveliest in Wales. The main house features two elegant sitting rooms and the conservatory restaurant has been positioned to enjoy the superb views. Many bedrooms are spacious and appropriately furnished, smaller and more modern rooms are also available and other rooms, which are reached externally, have private balconies. Three suites are available and one of these is fitted with a four-poster bed. Food comes by way of a daily fixed-price menu and fresh and local produce is much in evidence. Didier Bienaime leads the kitchen brigade and his efforts have been rewarded with a second rosette.
15 en suite (bth/shr) 4 annexe en suite (bth/shr) (6 fmly) CTV in all bedrooms 50P No coaches No children 3yrs British & French Cuisine V meals Coffee am Tea pm Last d 9.30pm

ROOMS: (incl. bkfst) s £52.50-£62.50; d £90-£100 * **LB**
MEALS: Lunch fr £12.75 High tea fr £2.50 Dinner fr £23.50&alc*
CARDS:

BRECHFA Carmarthenshire Map 02 SN53

★★ 72% **Ty Mawr Country**
SA32 7RA (off B4310 in centre of village)
☎ 01267 202332 FAX 01267 202437
Closed Xmas week, last week Nov & last two Jan RS Tue
Ty Mawr dates back almost 425 years and has a wealth of character, with exposed stone walls, beams, quarry tiled floors and wood-burning stoves in the dining room, lounge and bar. The house, which stands in an acre of of lovely grounds with the River Marlais flowing through, has been extensively renovated by proprietors Beryl and Dick Tudhope to provide tastefully appointed accomodation. The property includes what was once a small commercial bakery, which is now used for bread-baking lessons. Needless to say, all the bread served here is home-made. The kitchen is Beryl's domain and her set-price menu offers an imaginative choice of seasonal dishes. Dick, an accomplished host, is in charge front of house.
5 rms (4 bth/shr) (1 fmly) No smoking in all bedrooms 45P No coaches International Cuisine V meals Coffee am Tea pm No smoking in restaurant Last d 9.30pm
ROOMS: (incl. bkfst) s £52; d £84 * **LB**
MEALS: Lunch £12.95 Dinner £19-£22
CARDS:

BRECON Powys Map 03 SO02

★★★ 68% **Nant Ddu Lodge**
Cwm Taf CF48 2HY BRECON ☎ 01685 379111 FAX 01685 377088
(For full entry see Nant-Ddu)

See advertisement on page 861

B

★★66% Castle of Brecon
Castle Square LD3 9DB ☎ 01874 624611
FAX 01874 623737
Closed 23-25 Dec

CONSORT HOTELS

This historic former coaching inn dates back to the early 19th century and stands next to the ruined remains of Brecon Castle. As well as being close to the town centre, it overlooks impressive views of the Brecon Beacons National Park and the Usk Valley. Family owned and run, it provides modern equipped accommodation, which includes family bedded rooms, rooms for disabled guests and bedrooms on ground floor level. The latter include several rooms which are located in converted former out-buildings. Public areas include an attractive restaurant with panelled walls and an ornately carved fireplace. There is a choice of two bars, a quiet lounge and a selection of function and conference rooms.

33 en suite (bth/shr) 12 annexe en suite (shr) (4 fmly) CTV in all bedrooms STV 30P V meals Coffee am No smoking in restaurant Last d 8.45pm
ROOMS: (incl. bkfst) s £49; d £70 * **LB**
MEALS: Lunch £8.90-£9.50 Dinner fr £15.90*
CONF: Thtr 170 Class 150 Board 80
CARDS: 

★66% Lansdowne Hotel & Restaurant
39 The Watton LD3 7EG (on A40, close to historic barracks & military museum) ☎ 01874 623321 FAX 01874 624384
A friendly family-run hotel situated just east of the town centre offers good value for money. Most bedrooms have en suite bath or shower rooms, and facilities include TVs and telephones. There are a first-floor residents' lounge, a comfortable bar and a locally popular restaurant which offers a wide range of dishes.
10 rms (3 bth 5 shr) (2 fmly) CTV in all bedrooms No dogs (ex guide dogs) 9P No coaches No children 5yrs English & French Cuisine V meals Coffee am Tea pm No smoking area in restaurant Last d 9.30pm
ROOMS: (incl. bkfst) s £26.50-£27.50; d £45.50-£47.50 * **LB**
OFF-PEAK: (incl. bkfst) s £23.50; d £37.50
MEALS: Lunch £9.75-£10.50&alc Dinner £12.50&alc*
CARDS: 

BRIDGEND Bridgend Map 03 SS97

★★★74% Coed-y-Mwstwr
Coychurch CF35 6AF (leave A473 at Coychurch and turn right at petrol station. Follow signs at top of hill)
☎ 01656 860621 FAX 01656 863122

This lovely Victorian mansion enjoys an enviable, elevated position set back within 17 acres of wooded grounds and overlooking the picturesque Vale of Glamorgan. Many original features of the house have been retained, including an impressive domed ceiling in the oak-panelled restaurant. Bedrooms are spacious, many combining the charm and character of the building with an extensive range of modern facilities. Welcoming log fires blaze in the lounge, and this room adjoins an attractive bar. Friendly staff provide a good level of attentive service and the cooking of Scott Morgan continues to please.
23 en suite (bth/shr) (2 fmly) No smoking in 10 bedrooms CTV in all bedrooms STV Lift Night porter 100P Outdoor swimming pool (heated) Tennis (hard) Snooker Croquet lawn Xmas English & French Cuisine V meals Coffee am Tea pm No smoking area in restaurant Last d 10pm
ROOMS: (incl. bkfst) s fr £85; d fr £125 * **LB**
OFF-PEAK: (incl. bkfst & dinner) d fr £130
MEALS: Lunch £10.95-£12.95&alc High tea fr £5.95 Dinner fr £24&alc*
CONF: Thtr 225 Class 75 Board 60 Del from £100
CARDS: 

★★64% Wyndham
Dunraven Place CF31 1JE ☎ 01656 652080 & 657431
FAX 01656 766438
Extensive renovations have been carried out at this town centre hotel since a change of ownership in September '94. The well equipped bedrooms are modern and brightly decorated and include some family rooms; a comfortable lounge is available for guests and there is a choice of restaurants and bars - one is very popular with locals and provides entertainment at weekends.
24 en suite (bth/shr) (2 fmly) CTV in all bedrooms STV No dogs (ex guide dogs) Night porter 10P Pool table Wkly live entertainment English, French, Italian & Spanish Cuisine V meals Coffee am Tea pm
ROOMS: (incl. bkfst) s fr £30; d fr £45 *
CARDS:

See advertisement on page 861

★★57% *Court Colman*
Pen-y-Fai CF31 4NG ☎ 01656 720212 FAX 01656 724544
This large former country house is set in 6 acres of grounds and is located near Pen-Y-Fai village, north of Bridgend. It provides mainly spacious bedrooms, of varying styles, all of which have a good array of modern equipment. Rooms with four-poster beds and family bedded rooms are both available. Public rooms include a choice of lounges, where welcoming real fires burn during cold weather, a bar, a traditionally furnished restaurant and two large function suites.
32 rms (16 bth 12 shr) (4 fmly) CTV in 34 bedrooms No dogs (ex guide dogs) 80P English & French Cuisine V meals Coffee am Tea pm Last d 9.30pm
CARDS:

Travel Inn
Pantruthyn Farm, Pencoed CF35 5HY (from M4 junct35 take A473 signed Pencoed & Pontyclun. Turn rt at first rdbt - 400yds) ☎ 01656 860133
FAX 01656 864792

Purpose-built accommodation, offering spacious, well equipped bedrooms, all with en suite bathrooms. Meals may be taken at the nearby family restaurant. For more information about Travel Inns, consult the Contents page under Hotel Groups.
40 en suite (bth/shr)
ROOMS: d £35.50 *

Travelodge
Sarn Park Motorway Services CF32 9RW
☎ 01656 659218
(For full entry see Sarn Motorway Service Area)

BUILTH WELLS Powys Map 03 SO05

★★★64% *Caer Beris Manor*
LD2 3NP (SW on A483) ☎ 01982 552601
FAX 01982 552586

This large rambling building retains some of its Elizabethan charm but the main attraction is the location. It is set on a small hill overlooking natural gardens, woods and the River Irfon. The atmosphere is relaxed and the staff are friendly. The accommodation has gradually been improved to modest modern standards.
22 en suite (bth/shr) (1 fmly) CTV in 21 bedrooms STV 32P Fishing Riding Sauna Gym Clay pigeon shooting International Cuisine V meals Coffee am Tea pm Last d 9.30pm
CARDS:

★★62% Pencerrig Country House
LD2 3TF (2m N on A483 towards Llandrindod Wells)
☎ 01982 553226 FAX 01982 552347

CONSORT HOTELS

This comfortable, family-run hotel offers good levels of hospitality and neatly furnished accommodation. Bedrooms, all of which are en suite vary in size and are divided between the original

house and a newer wing. Guests can relax in front of the fire on cooler days, or enjoy a walk in the gardens in the summer, before choosing from the good range of well prepared dishes served in the restaurant. A cosy bar, two well equipped meeting rooms and ample parking are available.

20 en suite (bth/shr) (2 fmly) CTV in all bedrooms 40P Croquet lawn ch fac Xmas Welsh & French Cuisine V meals Coffee am Tea pm No smoking in restaurant Last d 9pm

ROOMS: (incl. bkfst) s £46.75; d £75 * **LB**

OFF-PEAK: (incl. bkfst) s fr £35; d fr £50

MEALS: Lunch £7.95-£9.95&alc Dinner fr £18.50*

CONF: Thtr 75 Class 40 Board 25 Del from £58.25

CARDS:

★★56% **Greyhound Hotel**

3 Garth Rd LD2 3AR (edge of town centre, opposite Police Station)

☎ 01982 553255

The Greyhound lies near the town centre and is used by local groups and diners. Bedrooms are gradually being modernised and further ensuite rooms are planned. Its proximity to several golf courses makes it a popular venue for golf parties and a function room is available for weddings and other events.

11 rms (6 bth/shr) (2 fmly) CTV in all bedrooms 25P Pool table Xmas V meals Coffee am Tea pm No smoking in restaurant Last d 9.30pm

ROOMS: (incl. bkfst) s £16.50-£22.50; d £33-£45 * **LB**

MEALS: Lunch £5-£9.50 Dinner £4.95-£9.95*

CONF: Thtr 100 Class 75 Board 50 Del from £43

CARDS:

C

CAERNARFON Gwynedd Map 06 SH46

★★★ 79% **Seiont Manor**
Llanrug LL55 2AQ (E on A4086) ☎ 01286 673366
FAX 01286 672840
Set in tranquil Welsh countryside, Seiont Manor has been developed with great skill, using local materials and converting original barns. The buildings overlook an attractive courtyard, a formal herb garden and the surrounding fields. Bedrooms are a fine size, decorated with taste and an extensive range of amenities includes video, safes, bidets and minibars. The public rooms are comfortable and elegant with interesting ornaments and an abundance of fresh flowers. In the kitchen, Richard Treble is well established, and his honest, capable cooking features local produce.
A high level of service is provided by a friendly and professional team. Further improvements are planned.
28 en suite (bth/shr) (7 fmly) No smoking in 4 bedrooms CTV in all bedrooms STV Night porter 150P Indoor swimming pool (heated) Fishing Sauna Solarium Gym Jacuzzi/spa Xmas French Cuisine V meals Coffee am Tea pm Last d 10pm
ROOMS: (incl. bkfst) s £79-£95; d £125-£140 * **LB**
MEALS: Lunch £10-£14&alc High tea £3.50-£5.95alc Dinner £22.95&alc*
CONF: Thtr 100 Class 40 Board 40 Del from £1100
CARDS:

★★ 73% **Ty'n Rhos Country House & Restaurant**
Llanddeiniolen LL55 3AE (situated in the hamlet of Seion between B4366 and B4547) ☎ 01248 670489 FAX 01248 670079
Closed 24-28 Dec
Lynda and Nigel Kettle extend a warm welcome to visitors to their converted farmhouse, which is set in the lovely countryside between Snowdon and the Menai Straits. The lounge, with its slate inglenook fireplace, is elegantly furnished and there is a small bar for pre-dinner drinks. Food is fresh and local whenever possible and a set daily menu is augmented by a large à la carte. Bedrooms are pine-furnished and comfortably furnished and 3 new bedrooms have recently been completed in nearby buildings. Small meetings can also be catered for.
11 en suite (bth/shr) 3 annexe en suite (bth/shr) No smoking in 3 bedrooms CTV in all bedrooms No dogs (ex guide dogs) 14P No coaches Croquet lawn No children 6yrs V meals No smoking in restaurant Last d 8.30pm
ROOMS: (incl. bkfst) s £40-£45; d £60-£80 * **LB**
MEALS: Dinner £21-£24.50alc*
CARDS:

★★ 65% **Menai Bank**
North Rd LL55 1BD (on A487 towards Bangor)
☎ 01286 673297 FAX 01286 673297
Closed Xmas
Located at the entrance to the town centre from the Bangor direction, this hotel was built as a private residence at the turn of the century. Many original features remain with stained glass windows, slate fireplaces and ornate cornices much in evidence. Bedrooms are modern and well equipped and there is a spacious and very comfortable lounge which, like many bedrooms, looks out over the Menai Straits.
15 rms (5 bth 6 shr) (3 fmly) No smoking in 5 bedrooms CTV in all bedrooms 10P Pool table Coffee am No smoking in restaurant Last d 7.30pm
ROOMS: (incl. bkfst) s £20-£38; d £32-£53 * **LB**
MEALS: Dinner £15
CARDS:

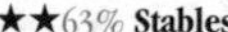

★★ 63% **Stables**
LL54 5SD ☎ 01286 830711 & 830935 FAX 01286 830413
(For full entry see Llanwnda)

CAPEL CURIG Aberconwy & Colwyn Map 06 SH75

★★ 64% **Cobdens**
LL24 0EE (on A5, 4m N of Betws-y-Coed)
☎ 01690 720243 FAX 01690 720354
For over 200 years this hotel has been a centre for the outdoor pursuits found in the area. It is situated at the foot of Moel Siabod and lies in the heart of Snowdonia with the River Llugwy running alongside. Many bedrooms take advantage of the lovely views and these are modern and well equipped. Two have adjoining rooms which are suitable for families. There are two bars and one of these has an impressive, exposed rock face. The hotel is run by an enthusiastic team and offers a full range of good-value meals.
17 rms (16 bth/shr) (2 fmly) CTV in all bedrooms 60P No coaches Outdoor swimming pool Fishing Xmas V meals Coffee am Tea pm No smoking in restaurant Last d 9.30pm
ROOMS: (incl. bkfst) s £27-£30; d £54-£60 *
MEALS: Lunch £6-£10alc Dinner £10-£17alc
CONF: Thtr 40 Class 30 Board 25 Del from £55
CARDS:

CARDIFF Cardiff Map 03 ST17
See also Barry

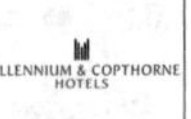

★★★★ 68% **The Copthorne Cardiff-Caerdydd**
Copthorne Way, Culverhouse Cross CF5 6XJ (exit at junct 33 of M4 and take A4232 for 2.5m in direction of Cardiff West and then A48) ☎ 01222 599100 FAX 01222 599080
The Copthorne is a comfortable and popular modern hotel with bright open-plan public areas. The comprehensively equipped bedrooms are nicely presented with bold colours and fabrics and deep armchairs. Connoisseur rooms provide extra luxury and the use of their own club lounge. A leisure complex, business centre and conference facilities are available. Guests can dine in Raglans Restaurant, overlooking the lake in the grounds, or less formally in Beauchamps Brasserie.
135 en suite (bth/shr) (10 fmly) No smoking in 50 bedrooms CTV in all bedrooms STV Lift Night porter 225P Indoor swimming pool (heated) Snooker Sauna Solarium Gym Jacuzzi/spa Steam room Wkly live entertainment International Cuisine V meals Coffee am Tea pm Last d 10pm
ROOMS: s £60-£99; d £70-£109 **LB**
MEALS: Lunch £13.95-£17 Dinner fr £17*
CONF: Thtr 300 Class 140 Board 80
CARDS:

★★★★ 64% **Jurys Cardiff**
Mary Ann St CF1 2EQ (next to ice rink, opposite Cardiff International Arena) (Jurys) ☎ 01222 341441 FAX 01222 223742
Formerly the Cardiff International Hotel, this large, modern, purpose-built establishment has recently changed ownership and has been renamed Jurys Cardiff Hotel. It is conveniently located in the city centre and stands opposite the Cardiff International Arena. The well equipped accommodation includes executive bedrooms, full suites, rooms designed for the convenience of disabled guests and no-smoking rooms. The attractive public areas are located around the unusual central foyer, which has been designed to resemble a small town square, complete with a clock tower. In addition to the busy bar and attractively appointed restaurant, there is also a spacious and comfortable lounge. Facilities include rooms for small conferences and other functions.
143 en suite (bth/shr) No smoking in 12 bedrooms CTV in all bedrooms STV No dogs (ex guide dogs) Lift Night porter 55P Wkly live entertainment Xmas International Cuisine V meals Coffee am

Tea pm No smoking area in restaurant Last d 10pm
ROOMS: d £99-£109 * **LB**
MEALS: Lunch £12.95 Dinner fr £14.95&alc*
CONF: Thtr 44 Class 20 Board 12
CARDS:

★★★★63% **Park Thistle**
Park Place CF1 3UD ☎ 01222 383471
FAX 01222 399309

THISTLE HOTELS

This Victorian hotel in the heart of the city has just benefited from a major face-lift to its public rooms. It now boasts a grand lobby, stylish brasserie restaurant and congenial sports bars as recent additions. Bedrooms tend to vary in size and spaciousness but are comfortable and attractively furnished; the new rooms offer that little extra in space. Formally dressed staff offer attentive service.
136 en suite (bth/shr) (7 fmly) No smoking in 30 bedrooms CTV in all bedrooms STV No dogs (ex guide dogs) Lift Night porter 70P Xmas English & French Cuisine V meals Coffee am Tea pm Last d 9.45pm
ROOMS: s £95; d £105-£210 * **LB**

OFF-PEAK: (incl. bkfst) s £62; d £84
MEALS: Lunch £7.95-£12.25&alc High tea £11.75 Dinner £8.95-£16.25&alc*
CONF: Thtr 300 Class 170 Board 100 Del from £115
CARDS:

★★★★62% **Cardiff Marriott**
Mill Ln CF1 1EZ (from M4 junct 29 follow signs into City Centre. Turn left into High Street opposite Cardiff Castle, then second left) ☎ 01222 399944
FAX 01222 395578

Centrally positioned, this large, busy hotel is ideal for the business and leisure traveller. A wide range of services is offered, together with a choice of eating options and indoor leisure facilities. Bedrooms are comfortable and well equipped and at the time of our last visit were programmed for upgrading.
182 en suite (bth/shr) (78 fmly) No smoking in 91 bedrooms CTV in all bedrooms STV Lift Night porter Air conditioning 100P Indoor swimming pool (heated) Squash Sauna Solarium Gym Jacuzzi/spa

contd.

Turkish bath Beauty Therapist Wkly live entertainment Welsh, English & French Cuisine V meals Coffee am Tea pm No smoking area in restaurant Last d 10pm
ROOMS: (incl. bkfst) s £86-£96; d £96-£106 **LB**
OFF-PEAK: (incl. bkfst) s £58-£78; d £68-£84
MEALS: Lunch £9.95-£15.50 High tea fr £6 Dinner £13.95-£16.95*
CONF: Thtr 300 Class 200 Board 100 Del from £110
CARDS:

★★★ 73% **Manor Parc Country Hotel & Restaurant**
Thornhill Rd, Thornhill CF4 5UA (on A469)
☎ 01222 693723 FAX 01222 614624
Closed 24-26 Dec
A popular business hotel conveniently positioned in rural surroundings just ten minutes' drive from the city centre offers immaculate, comfortable bedrooms, most of which have stylish Italian furnishings and accessories. A recently constructed conservatory restaurant features interesting Italian cuisine based on quality fresh ingredients - in particular, fish - and serves exquisite coffee. Service is of a high standard throughout the hotel.
12 en suite (bth/shr) (2 fmly) CTV in all bedrooms No dogs (ex guide dogs) Night porter 70P No coaches Tennis (hard) International Cuisine V meals Coffee am Tea pm Last d 10pm
ROOMS: (incl. bkfst) s £57.50; d £85 * **LB**
CONF: Thtr 120 Class 80 Board 50
CARDS:

★★★ 72% **Quality Friendly**

Merthyr Rd, Tongwynlais CF4 7LD (junct 32/M4, take exit for Tongwynlais off large roundabout)
☎ 01222 529988 FAX 01222 529977
This new hotel and leisure complex in a very convenient motor way location, with good car parking and access to the city and major link roads, offers bright, open-plan public areas and comfortable quality bedrooms, including a range of mini-suites. Friendly, smartly dressed staff offer a wide range of services.
95 en suite (bth/shr) (6 fmly) No smoking in 47 bedrooms CTV in all bedrooms STV Lift Night porter Air conditioning 100P Indoor swimming pool (heated) Sauna Gym Xmas English & Continental Cuisine V meals Coffee am Tea pm No smoking area in restaurant
ROOMS: s £67.50; d £87.50 **LB**
MEALS: Lunch £7.50-£9.95&alc Dinner £13.50&alc
CONF: Thtr 180 Class 80 Board 40 Del from £90
CARDS:

★★★ 71% **New House Country**
Thornhill CF4 5UA (on A469)
☎ 01222 520280 FAX 01222 520324
This impressive Georgian mansion is set in extensive grounds and enjoys panoramic views across Cardiff. It is situated to the north of the city, via the A469 and the entrance is on the left, a short distance from where the road crosses the M4. Most of the spacious and comfortable bedrooms are located in a purpose-built separate building, and suites and rooms with four-poster beds are both available. The attractively appointed public rooms include a choice of lounges, one of which contains a bar and has a welcoming open fire, while the other can also be hired as a private dining room.
5 en suite (bth/shr) 28 annexe en suite (bth/shr) (3 fmly) No smoking in 3 bedrooms CTV in all bedrooms No dogs (ex guide dogs) Night porter P Xmas English & French Cuisine V meals Coffee am Tea pm No smoking area in restaurant Last d 9.30pm
ROOMS: (incl. bkfst) s fr £65; d fr £80 * **LB**
MEALS: Lunch fr £12.95&alc Dinner fr £17&alc*
CONF: Thtr 200 Class 150 Board 200 Del from £90
CARDS:

★★★ 68% **Cardiff Moat House**

Circle Way East, Llanederyn CF3 7XF (off A48)
☎ 01222 589988 FAX 01222 549092
Situated on the outskirts of the city but with good access to the M4 and city centre, this modern hotel offers spacious, attractively furnished bedrooms and bright open-plan public areas. Facilities include a carvery restaurant, a lounge bar, leisure club and congenial basement sports bar. The hotel is especially popular with conference and corporate guests.
132 en suite (bth/shr) (4 fmly) No smoking in 40 bedrooms CTV in all bedrooms STV Lift Night porter 300P Indoor swimming pool (heated) Sauna Solarium Gym Jacuzzi/spa Baby pool Xmas Welsh & Continental Cuisine V meals Coffee am Tea pm Last d 10pm
ROOMS: s fr £75; d fr £90 * **LB**
OFF-PEAK: (incl. bkfst) s fr £45; d fr £50
MEALS: Lunch £11.50 Dinner £11.95-£16.95&alc
CONF: Thtr 290 Class 130 Board 65 Del from £99
CARDS:

★★★ 68% **Cardiff Bay**
Schooner Way, Atlantic Wharf CF1 5RT
☎ 01222 465888 FAX 01222 481491
This mid-Victorian warehouse has been cleverly converted into a good modern hotel. It is located in the heart of Cardiff's waterside development area, and provides attractively appointed, well equipped accommodation. Public areas include a choice of comfortable lounges and bars. The hotel has extensive conference and function facilities and is a popular venue for wedding receptions. There is also a leisure club. At the time of our last inspection, plans were in hand to expand the hotel substantially.
65 en suite (bth/shr) (6 fmly) No smoking in 50 bedrooms CTV in all bedrooms STV Lift Night porter 150P Sauna Solarium Gym Pool table Jacuzzi/spa Wkly live entertainment Xmas Continental Cuisine V meals Coffee am Tea pm Last d 10pm
ROOMS: s £78; d £90 * **LB**
OFF-PEAK: (incl. bkfst) s £44.95; d £59.90
MEALS: Lunch £9-£11&alc High tea £2.75-£6.55 Dinner £14&alc*
CONF: Thtr 400 Class 200 Board 60
CARDS:

See advertisement on opposite page

★★ 70% **Masons Arms**

Tyn-y-Parc Rd, Whitchurch CF4 6BG (on the A470, 3m from city centre) ☎ 01222 692554
FAX 01222 693724
Situated three miles from the centre of the city beside the A470, convenient for junction 32 of the M4, this well managed hotel offers a good standard of accommodation. Bedrooms are attractively appointed, comfortably furnished and equipped with all modern amenities. Public areas include a choice of bars and a popular restaurant which includes a good-value carvery. Smartly dressed staff are efficient and friendly.
30 en suite (bth/shr) (4 fmly) No smoking in 14 bedrooms CTV in all bedrooms STV No dogs (ex guide dogs) Night porter 150P Pool table V meals Coffee am Tea pm

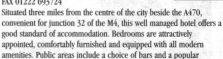

ROOMS: (incl. bkfst) s fr £60; d fr £69 * **LB**
OFF-PEAK: (incl. bkfst) s fr £31; d fr £52
CONF: Thtr 120 Class 80 Board 60 Del from £80
CARDS:

★★65% Sandringham
21 St Mary St CF1 2PL (access via junct 29 on M4, follow 'City Centre' signs) ☎ 01222 232161 FAX 01222 383998
This city centre hotel is conveniently close to the main shopping areas, the railway and bus stations, the castle and the National Rugby Stadium. It provides modern furnished and equipped bedrooms and offers a choice of bars and eating options, one of which is the venue for live jazz entertainment, five nights a week.
28 en suite (bth/shr) (1 fmly) CTV in all bedrooms No dogs (ex guide dogs) Night porter Wkly live entertainment V meals Coffee am Tea pm No smoking area in restaurant
ROOMS: (incl. bkfst) s £52; d £57 * **LB**
OFF-PEAK: (incl. bkfst) s £39; d £44
CONF: Thtr 100 Class 700 Board 60 Del from £55
CARDS:

See advertisement on this page

C

★★59% ***Lincoln***
118 Cathedral Rd CF1 9LQ ☎ 01222 395558 FAX 01222 230537
Two Victorian houses have been converted into a small, informally run hotel, well positioned near Sophia Gardens and the National Sports Stadium. Bedrooms are bright, modern and well equipped, the lounge is cosy and meals are taken in a charming dining room.
17 en suite (bth/shr) (1 fmly) CTV in all bedrooms 18P English & French Cuisine V meals Coffee am Tea pm Last d 8.30pm
CARDS:

See advertisement on opposite page

★★58% **The Phoenix**
199-201 Fidlas Rd, Llanishen CF4 5NA
☎ 01222 764615 & 764619 FAX 01222 747812
Closed 24-25 Dec
This popular hotel in the northern suburbs of the city provides well equipped, compact bedrooms. There are good facilities, and the public areas are well maintained and comfortable.
21 en suite (bth/shr) (1 fmly) CTV in all bedrooms Night porter 25P Snooker V meals Coffee am Tea pm Last d 10pm
ROOMS: (incl. bkfst) s £30-£37; d £41.85-£51.85. *
MEALS: Lunch £5.95-£8.50&alc Dinner fr £5.95&alc*
CONF: Thtr 120 Class 70 Board 30
CARDS:

Campanile
Caxton Place, Pentwyn CF2 7HA (take Pentwyn exit from A48 and follow signs for Pentwyn Industrial Estate)
☎ 01222 549044 FAX 01222 549900

The bar and Bistro restaurant provide meals and refreshments. Bedrooms are well equipped and have en suite bathrooms. For more details about Campanile, consult the Contents page under Hotel Groups.
50 annexe en suite (bth/shr)
ROOMS: d £36.50 *
CONF: Thtr 30 Class 16 Board 16 Del from £49

Forte Posthouse Cardiff City
Castle St CF1 2XB ☎ 01222 388681
FAX 01222 371495
Suitable for both the business and leisure traveller, this bright hotel provides modern accommodation in well equipped bedrooms with en suite bathrooms. For more details about Forte Posthouse hotels, consult the Contents page for the section on Hotel Groups.
155 en suite (bth/shr)
ROOMS: d £79 *
CONF: Thtr 170 Class 65 Board 50 Del from £85

Forte Posthouse Pentwyn
Pentwyn Rd, Pentwyn CF2 7XA (off A48(M))
☎ 01222 731212 FAX 01222 549147
Suitable for both the business and leisure traveller, this bright hotel provides modern accommodation in well equipped bedrooms with en suite bathrooms. For more details about Forte Posthouse hotels, consult the Contents page for the section on Hotel Groups.
142 en suite (bth/shr)
ROOMS: d £69-£79 *
CONF: Thtr 140 Class 70 Board 40 Del from £69

Travel Inn
Newport Rd CF3 8UQ (on the old A48)
☎ 01633 680070 FAX 01633 681143
Purpose-built accommodation, offering spacious, well equipped bedrooms, all with en suite bathrooms. Meals may be taken at the nearby family restaurant. For more information about Travel Inns, consult the Contents page under Hotel Groups.
47 en suite (bth/shr)
ROOMS: d £35.50 *

Travelodge
Cardiff West CF72 8SA (M4, junct 33/A4232)
☎ 01222 891141 FAX 01222 892497
This modern building offers accommodation in smart, spacious and well equipped bedrooms, suitable for family use, and all with en suite bathrooms. Meals may be taken at the nearby family restaurant. For information on room rates and to make a booking, call Roomline free of charge on 0800 850950. For more details about Travelodge, consult the Contents page under Hotel Groups.
50 en suite (bth/shr)

Travelodge
Circle Way East, Llanederyn CF3 7ND (4m NE of city centre, off A48(M))
☎ 01222 549564 FAX 01222 549564
This modern building offers accommodation in smart, spacious and well equipped bedrooms, suitable for family use, and all with en suite bathrooms. Meals may be taken at the nearby family restaurant. For information on room rates and to make a booking, call Roomline free of charge on 0800 850950. For more details about Travelodge, consult the Contents page under Hotel Groups.
32 en suite (bth/shr)

CARDIGAN See Gwbert-on-Sea

CARMARTHEN Carmarthenshire Map 02 SN42

★★★60% **The Ivy Bush Royal**
Spilman St SA31 1LG ☎ 01267 235111
FAX 01267 234914
This character property offers congenial public rooms. The bedrooms tend to vary in size and comfort and although they are well equipped they do show signs of age. A programme of upgrading is, however, detailed. Service in the bar and restaurant is prompt and professional.
73 en suite (bth/shr) (4 fmly) No smoking in 21 bedrooms CTV in all bedrooms Lift Night porter 78P Xmas V meals Coffee am Tea pm No smoking in restaurant Last d 9.30pm
ROOMS: (incl. bkfst) s fr £60; d fr £75 * **LB**
MEALS: Sunday Lunch fr £9.50 Dinner fr £14.75*
CONF: Thtr 250 Class 50 Board 40 Del from £75
CARDS:

★★65% **Falcon**
Lammas St SA31 3AP ☎ 01267 234959 & 237152 FAX 01267 221277
Closed 25-26 Dec RS Sun
This small, pleasant, privately owned hotel is conveniently situated in the town centre. It provides modern furnished and equipped accommodation, which is equally suitable for both business people

and tourists. The public areas comprise of a pleasant lounge, a small bar and an attractive restaurant where a good choice of both popular favourites and more adventurous dishes is available. Young Head Chef William Noblett is becoming quite well known throughout Wales for both his skills and his keenness to promote traditional Welsh dishes. He uses only the best available fresh produce and goes to great lengths to obtain as much of it as possible locally.
14 en suite (bth/shr) (1 fmly) CTV in all bedrooms 30P V meals Coffee am Tea pm No smoking area in restaurant
ROOMS: (incl. bkfst) s £42.50-£47.50; d £52.50-£57.50 *
CONF: Thtr 100 Class 50 Board 40 Del from £69.95
CARDS:

★★ 64% **Cothi Bridge**
Pontargothi, Nantearedig SA32 7NG (due E from Carmarthen towards Llandeilo hotel on A40 6m from Carmarthen, after stone bridge on right hand side) ☎ 01267 290251 FAX 01267 290156
Located east of the town in the village of the same name, this hotel has been completely upgraded over recent years. Bedrooms are decorated with pretty wallpapers and modern facilities are provided. The bar is popular with both locals and tourists for its wide range of food, and more substantial meals are provided in the restaurant which runs alongside the River Cothi. Staff are friendly and helpful and the atmosphere is relaxing.
13 rms (3 bth 8 shr) (1 fmly) No smoking in 2 bedrooms CTV in all bedrooms 50P Fishing V meals Coffee am Tea pm Last d 9.30pm
ROOMS: (incl. bkfst) s £33; d £48 * **LB**
MEALS: Lunch £15&alc Dinner £15&alc*
CONF: Thtr 50 Class 30 Board 25 Del from £55
CARDS:

CHEPSTOW Monmouthshire Map 03 ST59

★★★★ 72% **Marriott St Pierre**
St Pierre Park NP6 6YA (2.5m W off A48)
☎ 01291 625261 FAX 01291 629975
A popular golf and leisure hotel, St Pierre is ideally placed close to the M4 and Severn Bridge and only two hours from London and Birmingham. The £3 million investment here has resulted in elegant public rooms combined with well equipped and inviting bedrooms either in the main house or the suites in the adjacent cottage complex. The combination of modern creature comforts and the character of the old building, which is surrounded by its own championship golf course, makes a stunning complex. Rene Brunet manages with dedication and this enthusiasm is reflected in the genuine hospitality and willingness of the staff.
Executive chef Mark Lindsey continues to please with enjoyable cooking that make the best use of quality ingredients.

143 en suite (bth/shr) (4 fmly) No smoking in 73 bedrooms CTV in all bedrooms STV No dogs (ex guide dogs) Night porter 420P Indoor swimming pool (heated) Golf 18 Tennis (hard) Squash Snooker Sauna Solarium Gym Croquet lawn Putting green

contd.

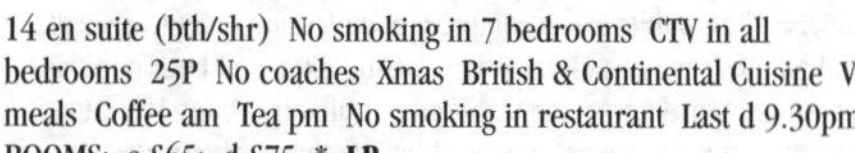

C

Jacuzzi/spa Health spa Xmas V meals Coffee am Tea pm No smoking in restaurant Last d 9.45pm
ROOMS: d £115-£165 * **LB**
MEALS: Lunch £5-£15 Dinner £18-£25*
CONF: Thtr 220 Class 160 Board 90 Del from £115
CARDS:

★★★62% **The Old Course**
Newport Rd NP6 5PR (leave M48 junct 22, then A466 and A48 into town for hotel on left) ☎ 01291 626261 FAX 01291 626263
This hotel with its own large car park stands beside the A48 just south of the town centre and within easy reach of junction 22 of the M4. Modern bedrooms are well equipped, while public areas include a comfortable foyer lounge, an attractively furnished restaurant and a spacious lounge bar. There are also a spacious ballroom and other function/conference rooms. A lift serves all floors.
31 en suite (bth/shr) (1 fmly) CTV in all bedrooms Lift Night porter 180P Xmas Welsh & French Cuisine V meals Coffee am Tea pm No smoking in restaurant Last d 9.30pm
ROOMS: d £42.50 **LB**
OFF-PEAK: d £39.50
MEALS: Lunch £9.50-£14.50&alc Dinner £18.50&alc
CONF: Thtr 240 Class 70 Board 70 Del from £77.50
CARDS:

★★❀66% **Beaufort**
Beaufort Square NP6 5EP ☎ 01291 622497 FAX 01291 627389
This town centre former coaching inn dates back to the 16th century. Privately owned and personally run, it has been considerably improved in recent times. The bedrooms have modern furnishings and equipment; family-bedded rooms and rooms on the ground floor of a rear annexe building, are available. Public areas include a popular bar and pleasant restaurant, which thanks to the skills of head chef Justin Sterry has a well deserved reputation for its food. Other facilities include a small conference room.
18 en suite (bth/shr) (2 fmly) CTV in all bedrooms STV 14P English & French Cuisine V meals Coffee am Tea pm No smoking area in restaurant Last d 9.30pm
ROOMS: s £36-£38; d £47-£49 * **LB**
OFF-PEAK: s £32-£42
MEALS: Lunch £9.90-£9.95 Dinner £12.95-£18.50
CONF: Thtr 40 Class 25 Board 20 Del from £60
CARDS:

★★66% **The George**
Moor St NP6 5DB (M48, jct 2,follow signs for town centre adjacent to 16th century town gate)
☎ 01291 625363 FAX 01291 627418

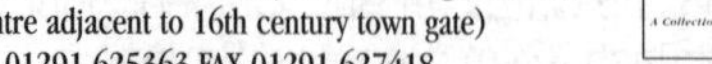

REGAL
A Collection of Individual Hotels

Situated next to the 16th-century town gate, the George retains much of the character of a traditional posting house. However it has moved with the times and the restaurant now sports a more informal bistro menu and bedrooms have been attractively styled with contemporary fabrics.

14 en suite (bth/shr) No smoking in 7 bedrooms CTV in all bedrooms 25P No coaches Xmas British & Continental Cuisine V meals Coffee am Tea pm No smoking in restaurant Last d 9.30pm
ROOMS: s £65; d £75 * **LB**
OFF-PEAK: (incl. bkfst) s £51; d £82
MEALS: Sunday Lunch £10.95 Dinner £12.20-£22.50alc*
CONF: Thtr 50 Class 20 Board 30 Del from £80
CARDS:

★★65% **Castle View**
16 Bridge St NP6 5EZ (opposite the castle)
☎ 01291 620349 FAX 01291 627397
Closed 1-19 Jan
Parts of this interesting property date back some 300 years, and as the name would suggest, it overlooks Chepstow castle. Now a privately owned hotel, it provides bedrooms with modern equipment and furniture, some located in separate buildings, and these include two on the ground floor of a house which stands at the bottom of the pleasant garden; family-bedded rooms are available. Public areas include a lounge bar and a pleasant traditionally furnished dining room. Although the hotel does not have its own car park, there is a public one immediately opposite.
9 en suite (bth/shr) 4 annexe en suite (bth) (7 fmly) CTV in all bedrooms STV No coaches V meals Coffee am Last d 9pm
ROOMS: s £37.50-£39.95; d £49.50-£57.95 * **LB**
OFF-PEAK: d £49.50
MEALS: Lunch £9.95 Dinner £13.95-£17.85*
CARDS:

CHIRK Wrexham Map 07 SJ23

★★★67% **Hand**
Church St LL14 5EY (in the centre of Chirk on the B5070)
☎ 01691 772479 FAX 01691 773472
This recently refurbished Grade II listed building, a stopping place for mail coaches during James I's reign, is conveniently situated in the centre of town just off the A5. Comfortable bedrooms are attractively decorated and well equipped, including one with a four poster bed. Guests have use of the public bar and pleasant gardens, as well as a choice of two restaurants - the Regency provides a more formal eating option while the Castle Room serves a range of lighter meals and bar snacks.
16 en suite (bth/shr) (1 fmly) CTV in all bedrooms STV 50P Sauna Solarium Gym Pool table ch fac Xmas English Cuisine V meals Coffee am Tea pm Last d 9.30pm
ROOMS: (incl. bkfst) s £37.50-£39.50; d £66-£86 * **LB**
MEALS: Lunch £5.95-£9.95&alc Dinner £14.50&alc*
CONF: Thtr 250 Class 225 Board 200 Del from £84.75
CARDS:

COLWYN BAY Aberconwy & Colwyn Map 06 SH87

★★★67% **Norfolk House**
Princes Dr LL29 8PF ☎ 01492 531757 FAX 01492 533781
This long established hotel is located within easy walking distance of the seafront and town centre. It lies in its own grounds and staff and proprietors are friendly and welcoming. Several comfortable lounges are provided and there is a cosy bar and several meeting rooms. Bedrooms include several suitable for families and all are decorated with pretty papers and fabrics.
23 en suite (bth/shr) (3 fmly) CTV in all bedrooms Lift Night porter 30P English & French Cuisine V meals Coffee am Tea pm Last d 9pm
ROOMS: (incl. bkfst) s £41-£43; d £50-£65 * **LB**
OFF-PEAK: (incl. bkfst) s £35; d £50-£56
MEALS: Dinner fr £16*

CONF: Thtr 35 Class 15 Board 20
CARDS:

See advertisement on this page

★★★64% **Hopeside**
Princes Dr, West End LL29 8PW (turn off A55 at Rhos-on-Sea exit, turn left at lights, hotel 50 yds on right)
☎ 01492 533244 FAX 01492 532850
Situated in a quiet area of the town, the main shopping centres and the seafront are both within easy walking distance of the Hopeside Hotel. The pretty bedrooms are mostly pine furnished and all are equipped with trouser presses and extra personal touches like fresh fruit and bottled water. Business meetings and local functions are well catered for and the hotel is now licensed to perform marriage ceremonies. Extensive food options are available and staff and management are friendly and enthusiastic.
19 rms (11 bth 5 shr) No smoking in 4 bedrooms CTV in all bedrooms STV Night porter 25P Solarium Xmas English & French Cuisine V meals Coffee am Tea pm Last d 9pm
ROOMS: (incl. bkfst) s £39-£55; d £56-£65 * **LB**
MEALS: Lunch £5-£15&alc Dinner £10-£16&alc*
CONF: Thtr 50 Class 35 Board 26 Del from £60
CARDS:

See advertisement on this page

★★★60% **Colwyn Bay**
Penmaenhead LL29 9LD (2m E A547, follow signs 'Old Colwyn')
☎ 01492 516555 FAX 01492 515565
This long established hotel occupies a unique position on the cliffs above the resort and bay. There are lovely views from the bedrooms but those from the restaurant are particularly impressive. Public areas include a comfortable foyer lounge, and extensive facilities are

contd.

Penmaenhead
Old Colwyn
Colwyn Bay
Clwyd LL29 9LD
Tel: 01492 516555
Fax: 01492 515565
Previously called Hotel 70°

Occupying an enviable position commanding panoramic views of the Irish Sea, Colwyn Bay and the dramatic mountains of Snowdonia.
This splendid modern Hotel offers a very high standard of comfort, service and luxury throughout. All bedrooms en suite with full facilities and sea views.
Elegant restaurant serving excellent cuisine in superb surroundings.
Ideally located for touring Snowdonia National Park and Conwy. Numerous golf courses nearby for the discerning golf enthusiast.
Excellent conference and banqueting facilities available for up to 200 persons.

Norfolk House Hotel

★★★

PRINCES DRIVE, COLWYN BAY
NORTH WALES LL29 8PF
Telephone (01492) 531757
Fax (01492) 533781

Discover old-fashioned courtesy, cordial hospitality and comfort in this family-owned hotel, with a relaxed and welcoming atmosphere. Excellent food and service. Pretty bedrooms, all en-suite, comfortable lounges and charming restaurant and bar. Situated close to beach, town and railway station. Pleasant gardens. Large Car Park. Ideal centre for touring North Wales. Short breaks a speciality.

Hopeside Hotel

AA ★★★ **WALES TOURIST BOARD**

A quality hotel that is aimed towards the business and leisure traveller alike

★ All rooms en-suite (some executive)
★ All rooms colour television/radio
★ All rooms international direct dial telephone
★ Two conference rooms/two syndicate rooms
★ Award winning restaurant
★ Solarium
★ Week/weekend breaks (two family rooms)
★ Some non-smoking bedrooms

WEST END, COLWYN BAY
CLWYD LL29 8PW
Tel: 01492 533244 Fax: 01492 532850

available for functions and business meetings. Bedrooms, although well equipped, are now in need of modernisation.

43 en suite (bth/shr) (1 fmly) CTV in all bedrooms 100P Xmas English & French Cuisine V meals Coffee am Tea pm
ROOMS: s £32.95-£33.95; d £39.95-£41.95 * **LB**
OFF-PEAK: s £30.95
CONF: Thtr 200 Class 140 Board 40 Del from £59
CARDS:

See advertisement on page 869

★★66% **Ashmount**

College Av, Rhos-on-Sea LL28 4NT (A55, take turning for Rhos-on-Sea.Turn left on promenade,pass harbour on right then take fourth turning left into College Ave,hotel 100yds on left)
☎ 01492 544582 FAX 01492 545479
Run by Gill and Les Stott for many years, this long-established hotel is located near the promenade at Rhos-on-Sea. Bedrooms are attractively decorated and all are equipped with modern facilities; many are located at ground-floor level and these are suitable for less mobile guests. A cosy bar is provided and there is a small sun lounge which is furnished with comfortable cane seating. The restaurant also has an adjacent sitting area. Food comes by way of a fixed-price menu offering a good range of popular dishes.
17 en suite (bth/shr) (4 fmly) No smoking in 4 bedrooms CTV in all bedrooms Night porter 10P Xmas English & French Cuisine V meals Coffee am Tea pm No smoking in restaurant Last d 8.30pm
ROOMS: (incl. bkfst) s £34; d £51.50-£64 **LB**
OFF-PEAK: (incl. bkfst) s £34; d £49-£61
MEALS: Lunch fr £7.50 Dinner £13.50&alc
CONF: Board 25 Del from £50
CARDS:

See advertisement on opposite page

★★64% ***Whitehall***
Cayley Promenade, Rhos on Sea LL28 4EP ☎ 01492 547296
Closed Nov-Etr
This family-run holiday hotel is located opposite the seafront at Rhos-on-Sea and has lovely views from the lounge and from many bedrooms. These are well maintained and decorated with pretty papers and fabrics. Family rooms are provided and most have en suite facilities. There is a comfortable lounge for residents and a cosy bar for pre-dinner drinks. Good home cooking is served and there is a rear car park.
13 rms (1 bth 6 shr) (2 fmly) CTV in all bedrooms 5P No coaches V meals Coffee am
CARDS:

★★61% **Edelweiss**
Lawson Rd LL29 8HD (coming from east take B5104 turn left at lights and round a right hand bend, turn left at give way on main road then 4th left into Lawson Rd) ☎ 01492 532314 FAX 01492 534707
This traditional holiday hotel is situated in its own grounds in a quiet area of the resort. Beaches and the town centre are within easy walking distance and ample car parking is provided. Pretty bedrooms include several multi-purpose units which can be converted into family rooms or private lounge areas. All have modern facilities and en suite bath or shower rooms. Public areas are comfortably furnished and a games room is provided.
26 en suite (bth/shr) (6 fmly) No smoking in 5 bedrooms CTV in all bedrooms STV Air conditioning 26P Solarium Children's play area Games room ch fac Xmas Welsh, English, French & Italian Cuisine V meals Coffee am Tea pm No smoking in restaurant Last d 7.30pm
ROOMS: (incl. bkfst) s £28-£35; d £46-£60 * **LB**
MEALS: Bar Lunch £1.25-£9.25alc Dinner £12.50-£18.45&alc*
CONF: Thtr 70 Class 50 Board 30 Del from £35
CARDS:

★★61% **Fairways**
12 Ellesmere Rd LL29 8RP ☎ 01492 530528 FAX 01492 534558
Located just a short walk from the town centre and promenade, this cosy hotel offers comfortable accommodation in bedrooms which, though compact, have en suite facilities and bright decor; some of them are suitable for family use. Residents also have the use of a small bar, a welcoming lounge and good parking facilities.
9 en suite (bth/shr) (4 fmly) No smoking in 1 bedroom CTV in all bedrooms 4P No coaches Xmas V meals Coffee am Tea pm
ROOMS: (incl. bkfst) s £18-£20; d £36-£40 * **LB**
CARDS:

★★61% **Lyndale**
410 Abergele Rd, Old Colwyn LL29 9AB (Exit A55 Old Conwyn, turn left. At roundabout through village 1 mile. On A547)
☎ 01492 515429 FAX 01492 518805
This family-run hotel is located at the eastern side of the resort, alongside the A547 at Old Colwyn. Bedrooms have modern facilities, including en suite bath or shower rooms, and one has a four-poster bed for that special occasion. Weddings and other functions can be catered for as well as business meetings, and public rooms are comfortable and cosy. The hotel has its own forecourt car park.
14 en suite (bth/shr) (3 fmly) CTV in all bedrooms 20P Xmas European Cuisine V meals Coffee am Tea pm
ROOMS: (incl. bkfst) s £25-£28; d £44-£48 * **LB**
OFF-PEAK: (incl. bkfst) s £20-£28; d £35-£48
MEALS: Lunch £5.50-£8.50 Dinner £9.50-£11&alc*
CARDS:

★★59% ***Rhos Abbey***
111 Rhos Promenade, Rhos on Sea LL28 4NG (directly opposite the harbour) ☎ 01492 546601 FAX 01492 543056
Improvements are slowly being made to the bedrooms of this popular seafront hotel; some rooms have been re-carpeted and some redecorated, but many still remain quite dated. The pleasant public areas, however, are spacious and retain many of the building's original features, such as the stained-glass windows and the ornate ceiling in the lounge bar. Regular entertainment is provided, and a short range of popular dishes is available in the restaurant.
32 en suite (bth/shr) (7 fmly) CTV in all bedrooms Lift 100P Wkly live entertainment V meals Coffee am Tea pm Last d 7.30pm
CARDS:

★65% **Marine**
West Promenade LL28 4BP (Turn off A55 at Old Colwyn to seafront. Turnleft, slow down after pier. Turn left just before traffic lights, car park on corner) ☎ 01492 530295
Closed Oct-Mar
Brian and Sue Owen offer warm hospitality to their guests, and many of them return year after year as a result. The hotel is well maintained and provides modern and well equipped bedrooms. Guests have use of a cosy bar and a spacious and comfortable lounge. There is a forecourt car park and the hotel is located on the promenade with superb sea views from many rooms.

14 rms (11 shr) (4 fmly) CTV in all bedrooms 11P No coaches English Cuisine V meals Coffee am Tea pm No smoking in restaurant Last d 7pm
ROOMS: (incl. bkfst) s £16.75-£23; d £31.50-£40 * **LB**
MEALS: Bar Lunch £3-£6 Dinner £8*
CARDS:

CONWY Aberconwy & Colwyn Map 06 SH77
See also Rowen

★★★62% **The Castle**
High St LL32 8DB ☎ 01492 592324
FAX 01492 583351

A historic former coaching inn situated in the town centre with the convenience of its own car parks, opposite and at the rear. Fine original oil paintings by a local artist are features of the public rooms and are particularly impressive in the attractively appointed restaurant. Bedrooms, furnished in modern style, provide good facilities and one room has a beautifully carved four-poster bed which was made in 1570.
29 en suite (bth/shr) (1 fmly) No smoking in 10 bedrooms CTV in all bedrooms Night porter 30P Xmas V meals Coffee am Tea pm No smoking in restaurant Last d 9pm
ROOMS: s £60; d £70 * **LB**
MEALS: Sunday Lunch £10.95 Dinner £15.95&alc*
CONF: Thtr 35 Class 20 Board 20 Del from £65
CARDS:

RED STAR HOTEL

★★✿✿✿ **The Old Rectory Country House**
Llanrwst Rd, Llansanffraid Glan Conwy LL28 5LF (0.5m south from A470/A55 junct)
(Welsh Rarebits) ☎ 01492 580611 FAX 01492 584555
Closed 14 Dec-Jan
Michael and Wendy Vaughan have created a haven of peace and tranquillity in this superb, small hotel which was the home of the local rectors for many centuries. It is set in terraced gardens which overlook Conwy Estuary and the famous castle and there are lovely views towards the hills of Snowdonia beyond. Bedrooms are tastefully furnished in tune with the building and many thoughtful extra comforts are provided. Two bedrooms are located in converted buildings in the grounds and these can be used as a family suite if required. The sitting room and restaurant are elegantly appointed and the crowning glory is the superb quality of Wendy's cooking. The daily menu offers a choice only for the sweet course but any likes and dislikes are taken care of. Dishes are not only appealing to the eye, their flavours are honest and Wendy Vaughan has a flair for interesting combinations of ingredients.
4 en suite (bth/shr) 2 annexe en suite (bth/shr) No smoking in 4 bedrooms CTV in all bedrooms 10P No coaches No children 5yrs British & French Cuisine Tea pm No smoking in restaurant Last d 7.30pm
ROOMS: (incl. bkfst) s £79-£89; d £99-£129 * **LB**
MEALS: Dinner £29.50
CARDS:

★★✿71% **Castle Bank**
Mount Pleasant LL32 8NY (follow one way system through town to Bangor Archway and turn left into Mount Pleasant) ☎ 01492 593888
Closed Jan RS mid Dec & early-mid Feb
This is a peaceful and relaxing hotel which is located near the old town walls. Sean and Marilyn Gilligan are the very friendly owners and they offer warm hospitality to their guests. Marilyn is an accomplished cook and provides good reliable meals from a fixed-price menu that changes daily and uses fresh produce where possible. Sean looks after the bar and other front-of-house duties. Bedrooms and public areas are comfortably furnished and well maintained.
9 rms (8 shr) (3 fmly) No smoking in all bedrooms CTV in all bedrooms No dogs 12P No coaches International Cuisine V meals No smoking in restaurant Last d 8pm
ROOMS: (incl. bkfst) s fr £25; d fr £53 * **LB**
MEALS: Sunday Lunch fr £9 Dinner fr £13*
CARDS:

★★65% **Sychnant Pass**
Sychnant Pass Rd LL32 8BJ (turn off A55 for Conwy, follow one way traffic, through arch and turn left on Mount Pleasant St, turn right onto Sychnant Pass, hotel 1.5m on right)
☎ 01492 596868 FAX 01492 596868

contd.

Closed 23 Dec-31 Jan
Located at the entrance to the pass of the same name this hotel appeals to a wide range of visitors to the area. It looks out over the mountains nearby and there is a peaceful and relaxing atmosphere throughout. Bedrooms include some suitable for families and several are located at ground-floor level. Public areas are in the open-plan style with an attractive restaurant and foyer sitting area. A small bar is also provided and a spacious lounge is available for residents. Owners and staff are friendly and attentive and enjoyable food is provided.
10 en suite (bth/shr) (2 fmly) CTV in all bedrooms No dogs (ex guide dogs) 20P No coaches British & Welsh Cuisine V meals Coffee am Tea pm No smoking in restaurant Last d 9pm
ROOMS: (incl. bkfst) s £30; d £60 * **LB**
OFF-PEAK: (incl. bkfst) s £25; d £50
MEALS: Bar Lunch fr £3.50 Dinner £17*
CARDS:

○ **Groes Inn**
Tyn-y-Groes LL39 8TN ☎ 01492 650545
14 en suite (bth/shr)

CRICCIETH Gwynedd Map 06 SH43

★★★ 70% **Bron Eifion Country House**
LL52 0SA (1m W on A497 - outside village of Criccieth going west on A497 towards Pwllheli 0.25m on right hand side) ☎ 01766 522385
FAX 01766 522003
This impressive country house hotel lies to the west of the resort in several acres of mature grounds and well maintained gardens. The central hall is most impressive with its Oregon pine panelling and minstrel's gallery. There is a separate lounge for residents and the restaurant with its picture windows looks out on to the gardens. Bedrooms are mostly spacious and several have four-poster beds for those special occasions. Functions and business conferences are catered for and smart staff are attentive and friendly.

19 en suite (bth/shr) (2 fmly) CTV in all bedrooms STV 80P Croquet lawn Putting green Clock golf Xmas International Cuisine V meals Coffee am Tea pm No smoking in restaurant Last d 8.30pm
ROOMS: (incl. bkfst) s £55-£65; d £82-£105 * **LB**
OFF-PEAK: (incl. bkfst) s £50-£55
MEALS: Lunch £11.95-£12.50 Dinner £19.50-£30&alc
CONF: Thtr 30 Class 25 Board 25 Del from £65
CARDS:

See advertisement on opposite page

★★ 69% **Parciau Mawr**
High St LL52 0RP ☎ 01766 522368
Closed Nov-Mar
The original part of this delightful hotel dates back over 300 years and lies in attractive grounds on the northern edge of the town. The same friendly family have been in charge for many years and such is the warmth of their hospitality that most of their visitors are returning after previous stays. Bedrooms are fresh and brightly decorated, several are suitable for families and 6 are located in converted outbuildings. There is a choice of comfortable lounges, a neat bar and a very impressive restaurant, created from an old barn.
6 en suite (bth/shr) 6 annexe en suite (shr) (1 fmly) CTV in all bedrooms 30P No coaches No children 5yrs English & French Cuisine Coffee am Tea pm
ROOMS: (incl. bkfst) s £29.50; d £48-£53 * **LB**
CARDS:

★★ 68% **Caerwylan**
LL52 0HW ☎ 01766 522547
Closed Nov-Etr
This traditional holiday hotel has been run by the caring Davies family for over 30 years. It is perched above the seafront and there are lovely views from many rooms of the famous castle and of Cardigan Bay. Bedrooms are well decorated and equipped with modern amenities, all have en suite bath or shower rooms and several have private sitting areas. Lounge areas are comfortably furnished and a five-course table d'hÙte menu is served for residents. Staff and owners are friendly and attentive to their guests and a warm and relaxing atmosphere prevails.
25 en suite (bth/shr) CTV in all bedrooms Lift 16P Coffee am Tea pm No smoking in restaurant Last d 7.30pm
ROOMS: (incl. bkfst) s fr £18; d fr £36 * **LB**
MEALS: Sunday Lunch fr £7.70 Dinner fr £9.50*
CARDS:

★★ 67% **Gwyndy**
Llanystumdwy LL52 0SP (turn off A497 into village of Llanystumdwy follow road for 0.25m, hotel is next to church) ☎ 01766 522720
Closed Nov-Mar
This friendly hotel has been run by the same family for over 35 years. During this time the original 17th-century cottage has been converted to provide comfortable lounges and other public areas with exposed timbers and inglenook fireplaces in abundance. The ten modern bedrooms are situated in a nearby building and these are spacious and have en suite facilities.
10 annexe en suite (bth/shr) (5 fmly) CTV in all bedrooms 20P No coaches Fishing British & French Cuisine Coffee am Tea pm Last d 8.30pm
ROOMS: (incl. bkfst) s £29; d fr £48
MEALS: Sunday Lunch £6-£12 Dinner £11.95-£14.95*

★★ 62% **Lion**
Y Maes LL52 0AA (turn off A497 in the centre of Criccieth on to village green north, hotel located on green)
☎ 01766 522460 FAX 01766 523075
RS Nov-Mar
This family-run hotel is located in the centre of the resort. It stands in pretty gardens and continues to be improved. Twelve additional bedrooms have recently been created in the grounds and these have fine views of the castle and over Cardigan Bay. Extensive function facilities are available and these are put to good use locally. Regular live entertainment is provided during the season.
33 en suite (bth/shr) 12 annexe en suite (bth/shr) (6 fmly) CTV in all bedrooms Lift 30P Pool table Wkly live entertainment ch fac Xmas Welsh & French Cuisine V meals Coffee am Tea pm No smoking in restaurant Last d 8.30pm
ROOMS: (incl. bkfst) s £28.50; d £55 * **LB**
OFF-PEAK: (incl. bkfst) s £24.50; d £47
MEALS: Lunch £4.95-£9.45 Dinner £15-£18*
CARDS:

★★ 62% ***Plas Isa***
Porthmadog Rd LL52 0HP (E on A497)
☎ 01766 522443 FAX 01766 523423
Closed 24-28 Dec
This busy hotel is located at the eastern side of the town and many public rooms and bedrooms enjoy lovely views of the castle and of

Cardigan Bay. Bedrooms all have modern facilities and there is one family suite available. There is a cosy bar, a comfortable conservatory lounge, and food comes by way of a fixed-price and additional carte menu. The hotel has its own car park.
14 en suite (bth/shr) (3 fmly) CTV in all bedrooms STV 14P Chinese, French, Indian & Italian Cuisine V meals Coffee am Last d 8.45pm
CARDS:

CRICKHOWELL Powys Map 03 SO21

Courtesy & Care Award

★★★ 68% **Bear**
NP8 1BW (on A40) ☎ 01873 810408 FAX 01873 811696
A delightful, personally run hotel, based on a former coaching inn dating from the 15th century, the Bear is owned by Mrs Hindmarsh and her son, who ensure that guests are welcomed with true hospitality. Public areas are full of charm and character and bedrooms, most of which are in a separate building overlooking the rear courtyard, are furnished to a high standard and in keeping with the style of the hotel. Family and four-poster rooms are available. Executive chef Graham Mahlia is producing good results in the kitchens. The hotel has lovely gardens. Owners and staff have won the AA Courtesy and Care Award for 1996/7.

contd.

C

13 en suite (bth/shr) 13 annexe en suite (bth) (6 fmly) CTV in all bedrooms 38P English & French Cuisine V meals Coffee am No smoking area in restaurant Last d 9.30pm
ROOMS: (incl. bkfst) s £42-£70; d £56-£90 *
MEALS: Lunch £15-£25&alc Dinner £18-£27alc
CONF: Thtr 60 Class 30 Board 20 Del from £99
CARDS:

See advertisement on page 873

★★★60% ***Manor***
Brecon Rd NP8 1SE (on A40) ☎ 01873 810212 FAX 01873 811938
In an elevated position above the town, this completely modernised hotel was the birthplace of Sir George Everest, in whose honour the mountain was named.
17 en suite (bth/shr) (1 fmly) CTV in all bedrooms No dogs (ex guide dogs) Night porter 200P Indoor swimming pool (heated) Sauna Solarium Gym Jacuzzi/spa Beauty salon Steam room V meals Coffee am Tea pm
CARDS:

★★71% **Gliffaes Country House**
NP8 1RH (W, 1m from A40 - 2m west of Crickhowell)
☎ 01874 730371 FAX 01874 730463
This impressive, Italianate country house dates back to the 18th century and is quietly located some three miles west of Crickhowell, signposted from the A40. It is set in extensive grounds and magnificent gardens with many rare species of trees. A picturesque section of the River Usk flows through the grounds and provides good trout and salmon fishing for the guests. The hotel is privately owned and run by the Brabner family, who have been here almost half a century. The accommodation, which includes three rooms in a lodge some quarter of a mile from the main house, are well proportioned and comfortable. All have period-style furnishings, including antique pieces, but modern equipment. The public rooms have a wealth of charm-welcoming log fires burn in the main lounge and there is also a conservatory lounge which overlooks the terrace. Mark Coulton has recently been promoted to head chef and we are confident that he will soon be earning a high reputation for his talents.
19 en suite (bth/shr) 3 annexe en suite (bth/shr) (3 fmly) CTV in all bedrooms 34P Tennis (hard) Fishing Snooker Croquet lawn Putting green Painting ch fac European Cuisine V meals Coffee am Tea pm No smoking in restaurant Last d 9.15pm
ROOMS: (incl. bkfst) s £36-£69; d £72-£108 * **LB**
MEALS: Sunday Lunch £19.50 Dinner £21
CONF: Board 16
CARDS:

★★68% **Ty Croeso**
The Dardy, Llangattock NP8 1PU (at the Action Garage on A40 take opposite road and go down the hill over the river bridge. Turn right and after 0.5m turn left and hotel signposted)
☎ 01873 810573 FAX 01873 810573
Closed 2 Jan for 3 weeks
This stone built property dates back to 1822, when it was built as the infirmary for the local workhouse. Now a privately owned and personally run, friendly little hotel, it provides soundly maintained modern bedrooms and attractive, traditionally furnished public areas. These include a cosy bar and a very pleasant lounge, where welcoming real fires burn during cold weather. A good choice of dishes are served in the attractive restaurant, including a "Taste of Wales" selection. From its elevated position above the Brecon and Monmouth canal the hotel commands good views over Crickhowell to the hills beyond.
8 en suite (bth/shr) (1 fmly) CTV in all bedrooms 20P No coaches Xmas International Cuisine V meals Coffee am Tea pm Last d 9pm
ROOMS: (incl. bkfst) s £30; d £55-£65 * **LB**
MEALS: Sunday Lunch £8.95 Dinner £14.95&alc*
CARDS:

★★66% **Dragon**
High St NP8 1BE (off A40 in town centre)
☎ 01873 810362 FAX 01873 811868
This 18th-century hostelry has been owned and personally run by Christine and Alan Thomas since 1978, since when they have consistently improved the accommodation whilst preserving the building's character. Bedrooms range in style from modern to period, but all are similarly well equipped, including family rooms and two in a cottage behind the hotel. The cottage style bar and restaurant both have low, beamed ceilings and the bar has a cheery open fire. In the kitchens, chef Shaun Ellis has earned a well deserved reputation for good food. Meals from his set-price menu can be chosen as either two or three courses and there are also daily specials.
12 en suite (bth/shr) 2 annexe en suite (bth/shr) (2 fmly) No smoking in 5 bedrooms CTV in all bedrooms No dogs 14P No coaches Xmas British Cuisine V meals Coffee am Tea pm No smoking in restaurant
ROOMS: (incl. bkfst) s £35-£45; d £50-£56 * **LB**
CARDS:

CROSS HANDS Carmarthenshire Map 02 SN51

Travelodge
SA14 6NW (on A48, westbound)
☎ 01269 845700 FAX 01269 845700

Travelodge

This modern building offers accommodation in smart, spacious and well equipped bedrooms, suitable for family use, and all with en suite bathrooms. Meals may be taken at the nearby family restaurant. For information on room rates and to make a booking, call Roomline free of charge on 0800 850950. For more details about Travelodge, consult the Contents page under Hotel Groups.
32 en suite (bth/shr)

CRUGYBAR Carmarthenshire Map 03 SN63

★★72% **Glanrannell Park**
SA19 8SA (from A40 take A482 to Lameter after 5.5m follow signs to hotel. From Llandeilo take B4302 for 10.5m , hotel is signposted) (Welsh Rarebits) ☎ 01558 685230 FAX 01558 685784
Closed Nov-Mar
David and Bronwen Davies have welcomed guests to Glanrannell Park for over 20 years. The hotel is fronted by a lake, where guests are invited to feed the Chinese carp after dinner, and is set in 23 acres of mature grounds. There are two very comfortable lounges, and the fixed-price menu offers good honest cooking based on local produce.
8 en suite (bth) (2 fmly) CTV in all bedrooms 33P No coaches Fishing International Cuisine Coffee am Tea pm No smoking in restaurant Last d 8pm
ROOMS: (incl. bkfst) s £33-£37; d £56-£64 **LB**

MEALS: Bar Lunch £2.50-£10 High tea £3.50-£6 Dinner £16-£17&alc
CARDS:

See advertisement on this page

CWMBRAN Torfaen Map 03 ST29

★★★★63% **Parkway**

Cwmbran Dr NP44 3UW (Leave M4 junc.26 onto A4042. First exit at roundabout onto A4051 Cumbrian Drive.3rd exit at 2nd roundabout and 1st turning right) ☎ 01633 871199 FAX 01633 869160
Closed 24-31 Dec

This large, privately owned, purpose built hotel complex is situated between Cwmbran and junction 26 of the M4 motorway. It provides well equipped, modern accommodation, which includes a full suite, bedrooms on ground floor level, interconnecting rooms, rooms for disabled guests and no smoking rooms. The public areas include a spacious lounge which also doubles as a coffee shop during the day, a lounge bar and a compact restaurant, where guests can choose from either the a la carte selection of popular dishes, or the carvery buffet. Other facilities include conference suites and a well equipped leisure club

70 en suite (bth/shr) (4 fmly) No smoking in 24 bedrooms CTV in all bedrooms STV Night porter 300P Indoor swimming pool (heated) Sauna Solarium Gym Jacuzzi/spa Steam room Wkly live entertainment V meals Coffee am Tea pm Last d 10pm
ROOMS: s £59.50-£73; d £69.50-£82.50 * **LB**
MEALS: Lunch fr £12.95 Dinner fr £12.95&alc*
CONF: Thtr 550 Class 280 Board 144 Del from £57.25
CARDS:

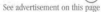

See advertisement on this page

D

DEGANWY Aberconwy & Colwyn Map 06 SH77

★★65% ***Bryn Cregin***
Ty Mawr Rd LL31 9UR ☎ 01492 585266 FAX 01492 596203
Once the private home of a retired ship's captain, this friendly hotel looks out over the Conwy Estuary. The restaurant, which enjoys fine views, is in two parts and doubles as a venue for local weddings and other functions. Bedrooms are decorated with pretty papers and fabrics and some are quite spacious.
17 en suite (bth/shr) CTV in all bedrooms 30P International Cuisine V meals Coffee am Tea pm Last d 9pm
CARDS:

DEVIL'S BRIDGE Cardiganshire Map 06 SN77

★★66% ***Hafod Arms***
SY23 3JL ☎ 01970 890232
Closed 2-31 Jan
The hotel was built as a hunting lodge in 1787 and was once part of a vast estate. It stands at the head of the famous Mynach Falls, overlooking a spectacular wooded gorge, next to the legendary Devils Bridge. The well maintained accommodation includes a large room with a four-poster bed and a family suite. Public areas include a choice of bars and lounges, and there is also a Victorian style tea room, which is open to the public. Wholesome dinners are served in the traditionally furnished restaurant.
15 rms (11 bth/shr) (1 fmly) CTV in all bedrooms 60P No children 12yrs International Cuisine V meals Coffee am Tea pm Last d 9pm
CARDS:

DINAS MAWDDWY Gwynedd Map 06 SH81

★★63% ***Buckley Pines***
SY20 9LP ☎ 01650 531261
This peaceful, rural hotel is situated in a lovely area of Wales and enjoys fine views over the adjacent river, meadowland and wooded slopes. Bedrooms are modern and well decorated, cheerful log fires burn in both the bar and the comfortable lounge, and the restaurant offers a carte of enjoyable dishes.
10 rms (3 bth 2 shr) (1 fmly) CTV in all bedrooms 40P Fishing Pool table V meals Coffee am Tea pm Last d 8.30pm
CARDS:

DOLGELLAU Gwynedd Map 06 SH71

★★★ 74% **Penmaenuchaf Hall**
Penmaenpool LL40 1YB (on A493 towards Tywyn) (Welsh Rarebits)
☎ 01341 422129 FAX 01341 422129
Built as a summer and sporting residence in 1860 by a cotton magnate, this fine country house stands in 21 acres of magnificent woodland and terraced gardens off the A493 Tywyn road at the foot of the Cader Idris mountain range and above the Mawddach Estuary. Bedrooms vary in size but all are comfortable, well equipped and individually decorated to a high standard. Log fires burn in the various elegant sitting rooms, and there are separate panelled meeting rooms. Leisure facilities include a snooker room and several miles of fishing on the rivers Mwddach and Wnion. Local fresh produce and herbs from the hotel's own garden are used to produce menus that have won deserved appreciation.
14 en suite (bth/shr) (3 fmly) No smoking in 1 bedroom CTV in all bedrooms No dogs (ex guide dogs) 40P Fishing Snooker Croquet lawn No children 8yrs ch fac Xmas V meals Coffee am Tea pm No smoking in restaurant Last d 9.30pm
ROOMS: (incl. bkfst) s £50-£95; d £95-£150 **LB**
MEALS: Lunch £12.95-£14.95&alc High tea £7-£15alc Dinner fr £23&alc*
CONF: Thtr 50 Class 30 Board 25 Del from £95
CARDS:

★★★ 70% **Dolmelynllyn Hall**
Ganllwyd LL40 2HP (5m N of Dolgellau on A470)
☎ 01341 440273 FAX 01341 440273
Closed Dec-Feb
Situated off the A470 in the village of Ganllwyd, which is about five miles north of Dolgellau, this fine house dates in part back to the 16th century. It is surrounded by beautiful wooded slopes and the drive is lined with beech trees. There are superb views from many bedrooms over the area and the conservatory bar looks out over the attractive gardens. Bedrooms are spacious and comfortable, one has a four-poster bed and many have settees and armchairs. As well as the cane-furnished bar there is an elegant lounge and many original stained glass windows still survive.
10 en suite (bth/shr) No smoking in all bedrooms CTV in all bedrooms STV 20P No coaches Fishing No children 10yrs V meals Coffee am Tea pm No smoking in restaurant
ROOMS: (incl. bkfst) s £47.50-£55; d £80-£95 **LB**
OFF-PEAK: (incl. bkfst) s £42.50-£50; d £75-£85
MEALS: Bar Lunch £5-£10.50alc High tea £5-£8.50alc
CONF: Thtr 20 Class 20 Board 20
CARDS:

Courtesy & Care Award

★★ 73% **Dolserau Hall**
LL40 2AG (1.5m outside town between A494 to Bala and A470 to Dinas Mawddwy) ☎ 01341 422522 FAX 01341 422400
Closed mid Nov-early Feb (ex Xmas & New Year)
This Victorian country house lies in several acres of pleasant grounds that extend to the River Wnion. Bedrooms and the Winter Garden Restaurant look out over fields of grazing sheep and a more peaceful location would be difficult to find. Bedrooms have all been upgraded over recent years and most have comfortable armchairs and settees. Reception for

terrestrial TV services tends to be patchy so full satellite coverage is provided instead. Several elegant sitting rooms are available with log fires. Chef Huw Roberts offers a fixed-price daily-changing menu comprising four courses and his cooking continues to be consistently enjoyable. Owners and staff here have won the AA Courtesy and Care Award for 1996/7.
15 en suite (bth/shr) (3 fmly) CTV in all bedrooms STV Lift 70P No coaches No children 6yrs Xmas V meals No smoking in restaurant Last d 8.30pm
ROOMS: (incl. bkfst & dinner) s £51-£59; d £96-£112 **LB**
OFF-PEAK: (incl. bkfst & dinner) s £44-£50; d £80-£100
MEALS: Dinner £20
CARDS:

★★69% **George III**
Penmaenpool LL40 1YD (2m W on A493)
☎ 01341 422525 FAX 01341 423565
This delightful hotel is situated near the toll bridge which spans the Mawddach Estuary at Penmaenpool. Built in 1650 as a ships' chandler and a pub, a wealth of exposed timbers and inglenook fireplaces remain in the main building. Nearby, in what was Victorian railway station buildings until the Beeching cuts of the sixties, several bedrooms have been created and these are every bit as comfortable as those in the main building. Most bedrooms have beautiful views over the estuary. Twelve miles of river and lake fishing are available for residents, and mountain bikes can be hired for exploring the surrounding countryside. The hotel has been owned for the last few years by the Cartwright family and they, together with local staff offer a warm welcome and a relaxing atmosphere.
6 en suite (bth/shr) 6 annexe en suite (bth/shr) CTV in all bedrooms 60P Fishing Free fishing permits Mountain bike hire Welsh, English & French Cuisine V meals Coffee am Tea pm No smoking in restaurant Last d 9.30pm
ROOMS: (incl. bkfst) s £50; d £70-£88 **LB**
MEALS: Sunday Lunch £11.95 Dinner £15-£20alc*
CARDS:

★★66% ***Fronoleu Farm***
Tabor LL40 2PS ☎ 01341 422361 & 422197
This 400-year-old stone-built farmhouse lies in a remote setting about a mile east of Dolgellau, in the shadow of Cader Idris and enjoying superb views of the Mawddach Estuary. It has recently been extended to provide a wing of six good quality modern bedrooms, including some with four-poster beds and others suitable for family use; a large self-contained function suite has also been created. Other facilities include a cosy bar and a comfortable lounge where welcoming fires burn in cold weather. A very pleasant cottage-style restaurant - popular with locals - serves generous portions of grill-type dishes.
10 rms (6 bth/shr) (3 fmly) CTV in all bedrooms 40P ch fac Welsh, French & Italian Cuisine V meals Coffee am Tea pm Last d 10pm

★★64% ***Royal Ship***
Queens Square LL40 1AR (Frederic Robinson) ☎ 01341 422209
Standing in the heart of this country market town, the Royal Ship dates from 1813 when it was a coaching inn. There are three bars and several lounges, all most comfortably furnished and appointed. It is very much the centre of local activities and a wide range of food is always available. Bedrooms are well fitted out, all with modern amenities.
24 rms (18 bth/shr) (4 fmly) CTV in all bedrooms No dogs (ex guide dogs) Lift 8P V meals Coffee am Tea pm Last d 9.30pm
CARDS:

See advertisement on this page

★69% **Clifton House**
Smithfield Square LL40 1ES (off A470) ☎ 01341 422554
Closed Nov-Mar
For many years the Meirionnydd County Gaol, this building dates back to the 18th century. It is located in the centre of the market town and now provides modern accommodation. Many old features have been retained, however, with exposed timbers, uneven floors and low ceilings much in evidence. Most bedrooms have en suite bath or shower rooms and one is situated at ground floor level. All have such amenities as TVs and hairdryers. Chef proprietor Pauline Dix serves from a carte menu with blackboard specials of fresh fish catches. Food is carefully cooked and worthy of our one-rosette award. Not to be missed, if available, is the rich bread pudding.
6 rms (4 bth/shr) CTV in all bedrooms No dogs (ex guide dogs) 2P No coaches V meals No smoking in restaurant Last d 9pm
ROOMS: (incl. bkfst) s £27.50-£35; d £39-£52
OFF-PEAK: (incl. bkfst) s £22.50-£30; d £32-£49
MEALS: Dinner £14-£22alc*
CARDS:

DOLWYDDELAN Aberconwy & Colwyn Map 06 SH75

★★63% **Elen's Castle**
LL25 0EJ (on A470, 5m S of Betws-y-Coed)
☎ 01690 750207 FAX 01690 750207
This small hotel is situated in a beautiful village in the heart of Snowdonia. It was a beer house in the 18th century and the original bar, with its slab floor, remains an impressive feature. The lounge is in two sections and, as well as restaurant dinners, there is a good range of popular bar meals. Bedrooms are modestly appointed but a start has been made to improve these through the introduction of pretty fabrics. Two rooms have four-poster beds and a family suite of two rooms is available. The hotel has its own car park.

contd.

8 rms (7 bth/shr) (2 fmly) CTV in 9 bedrooms STV 40P Fishing Sauna Xmas Welsh & Continental Cuisine V meals Coffee am Tea pm No smoking in restaurant Last d 9pm
ROOMS: (incl. bkfst) s fr £15; d £30-£56 **LB**
OFF-PEAK: (incl. bkfst) s fr £14; d £28-£56
MEALS: Lunch £1.95-£8.95 High tea fr £3.25 Dinner £13.95
CARDS:

D

EGLWYSFACH Cardiganshire Map 06 SN69

RED STAR HOTEL

★★ **Ynyshir Hall**
SY20 8TA (off A487, 5.5m S of Machynlleth, signposted from the main road)
☎ 01654 781209 FAX 01654 781366

Ynyshir Hall was once the shooting lodge of a large estate owned by Queen Victoria. Most of the estate is now an RSPB reserve. The lodge, together with 12 acres of mature attractive grounds, is now owned by Bob and Joan Reen, who have turned it into a delightful hotel, which is a haven of relaxing tranquillity, warm hospitality and fine food. The tastefully appointed bedrooms are all individual in style and are furnished with fine antique and period pieces. All are similarly well equipped and have good quality en-suite facilities. The many thoughtful extra welcoming touches include good toiletries, and mineral water. Some rooms have their own separate lounges and in the case of one ground floor room, this takes the form of a conservatory. No smoking bedrooms are available. Bob Reen is a talented artist and many fine examples of his work are displayed in the attractive public rooms. These comprise of an elegant dining room, a comfortable drawing room and a cosy bar. Chefs Ian White and Chris Dawson produce a short, daily set price menu, which takes account of freshly available produce, much of it local. Welsh Black Beef, Welsh Lamb, free range ducks, shellfish and venison are all represented.
8 en suite (bth/shr) No smoking in 4 bedrooms CTV in all bedrooms 20P No coaches Croquet lawn No children 9yrs Xmas Welsh, English & French Cuisine V meals Coffee am Tea pm No smoking in restaurant Last d 8.30pm
ROOMS: (incl. bkfst) s £85-£105; d £110-£160 * **LB**
OFF-PEAK: (incl. bkfst) s £75-£95; d £100-£150
MEALS: Lunch fr £19alc Dinner fr £29alc
CONF: Thtr 25 Class 20 Board 18 Del from £129.50
CARDS:

Percentage scores give you a comparison of quality within each star rating. See 'How to Use the Guide".

EWLOE Flintshire Map 07 SJ36

★★★★ 69% **St David's Park**
St Davids Park CH5 3YB (take A494 Queensferry to Mold for 4m,then take left slip road B5127 towards Buckley) ☎ 01244 520800 FAX 01244 520930

Best Western

This modern hotel provides excellent conference and function facilities in addition to a fully equipped leisure club. Spacious public areas are attractively decorated and comfortably furnished. Bedrooms include several with four-poster beds, and many specially designed for disabled guests; there are also family rooms and private suites. The Fountains restaurant serves from a daily fixed price-menu, a large carte and a further 'Gourmet' selection. Staff are friendly and attentive. Reduced green fees are offered on the nearby Northop Country Park championship golf course.
145 en suite (bth/shr) (26 fmly) No smoking in 54 bedrooms CTV in all bedrooms STV Lift Night porter 240P Indoor swimming pool (heated) Golf 18 Tennis (hard) Snooker Sauna Solarium Gym Pool table Jacuzzi/spa Steam bath Beauty therapist Wkly live entertainment Xmas V meals Coffee am Tea pm No smoking in restaurant Last d 10pm
ROOMS: s £89-£139; d £99-£139 * **LB**
OFF-PEAK: s £63-£139; d £83-£139
MEALS: Lunch £11.95-£17.50&alc Dinner £17.50&alc
CONF: Thtr 270 Class 150 Board 40 Del from £105
CARDS:
See advertisement under CHESTER

FISHGUARD Pembrokeshire Map 02 SM93

★★ 72% **Tregynon Country Farmhouse Hotel**
Gwaun Valley SA65 9TU (at cross roads of B4313/B4329 take B4313 towards Fishguard, then first right and first right again proceed for 1.5m hotel drive on left)
☎ 01239 820531 FAX 01239 820808
Closed 2wks in winter
Located in the beautiful Gwaun Valley, this 16th-century farmhouse has been sympathetically converted by Peter and Jane Heard into a comfortable hotel. An impressive stone inglenook fireplace dominates the sitting room, so large that guests may sit within it. There is a cosy bar adjacent, and and the restaurant offers a daily changing menu of organic produce. The hotel has its own traditional smoke house for gammon and bacon, and also offers an interesting choice of home-made icecreams. Bedrooms are comfortably furnished and several are located in nicely converted outbuildings.
3 en suite (shr) 5 annexe en suite (bth/shr) (2 fmly) No smoking in all bedrooms CTV in all bedrooms No dogs P No coaches Xmas V meals Coffee am Tea pm No smoking in restaurant Last d 7.30pm
ROOMS: (incl. bkfst) d £46-£67 * **LB**
MEALS: Dinner £15.95&alc*
CARDS:

★★64% **Cartref**
15-19 High St SA65 9AW ☎ 01348 872430 FAX 01348 872430
A warm welcome is assured at this very friendly small hotel in the town centre. Bedrooms are well equipped and modern, there is a comfortable lounge, a pleasant bar and an attractive restaurant. The hotel's own car park is small, but there is a public one close by.
12 rms (6 bth/shr) (2 fmly) CTV in 7 bedrooms Night porter 4P No coaches Welsh & Continental Cuisine V meals Coffee am Tea pm No smoking in restaurant Last d 9pm
ROOMS: (incl. bkfst) s £15-£27; d £36-£45 * **LB**
MEALS: Lunch £6.75&alc Dinner fr £7.50&alc*
CARDS: 

See advertisement on this page

★★63% **Abergwaun**
The Market Square SA65 9HA (on A40)
☎ 01348 872077 FAX 01348 875412
This privately owned and personally run hotel dates back some 200 years and was once a coaching inn. It is conveniently situated in the town centre and although it does not have a car park, free public facilities are situated nearby. The bedrooms, which include a family room and a room with a four-poster bed, are bright and attractively decorated and have modern furnishings and equipment. Bar meals are served in the spacious lounge bar, or alternatively, guests can eat in Bumbles bistro next door.
11 rms (7 bth/shr) (1 fmly) CTV in all bedrooms 2P Pool table English, French & Italian Cuisine V meals Coffee am Tea pm Last d 9pm
ROOMS: (incl. bkfst) s £22.50; d £48 *
MEALS: Lunch £2.25-£15alc Dinner £1.65-£15alc*
CONF: Thtr 50 Class 20 Board 24 Del from £32.50
CARDS: 

GLYN CEIRIOG Wrexham Map 07 SJ23

★★★61% **Golden Pheasant**
LL20 7BB (take B4500 at Chirk, continue along this road for 5m, follow hotel signs) ☎ 01691 718281 FAX 01691 718479
This creeper clad country hotel dates back over 200 years and lies in the beautiful Ceiriog Valley which is a popular venue for outdoor sports and other activities. Comfortable public rooms are provided and the Pheasant bar with its flag floors and log fire is a striking feature. Modern facilities are provided in bedrooms and a programme of upgrading was under way at the time of our last visit.
19 en suite (bth/shr) (5 fmly) CTV in all bedrooms 45P Pool table Xmas English & French Cuisine V meals Coffee am Tea pm No smoking area in restaurant Last d 8.30pm
ROOMS: (incl. bkfst) s £30-£40; d £55-£75 * **LB**
MEALS: Lunch £11.95 High tea £3.50-£5 Dinner £14.95-£17.95
CONF: Thtr 60 Board 10 Del from £61.45
CARDS:

GWBERT-ON-SEA Cardiganshire Map 02 SN15

★★★65% **Cliff**
SA43 1PP ☎ 01239 613241 FAX 01239 615391
Set in 30 acres of land, this large hotel enjoys a quite spectacular location on a headland overlooking Cardigan Bay and the Teifi estuary. An extensive programme of renovation and improvement work has recently been completed and the standard of the accommodation has been considerably upgraded. The en suite bedrooms are categorised into four types, depending upon their size and location. All are soundly decorated, have good modern furniture and are well equipped; some ground floor rooms are available. The spacious public areas include a choice of bars and lounges, a games room, a souvenir shop and a large function room. The 18-hole Cardigan Golf Course adjoins the hotel grounds.
70 en suite (bth/shr) (4 fmly) No smoking in 10 bedrooms CTV in all bedrooms Lift Night porter 100P Outdoor swimming pool (heated) Golf 9 Squash Snooker Sauna Solarium Gym Pool table Putting green Sea fishing Xmas Welsh, English & French Cuisine V meals Coffee am Tea pm Last d 8.45pm
ROOMS: (incl. bkfst) s £37.50-£63; d £75-£116 * **LB**
OFF-PEAK: (incl. bkfst) s £32-£56; d £64-£102
MEALS: Sunday Lunch fr £8.95 Dinner £13.95&alc*
CONF: Thtr 200 Class 100 Board 64 Del from £57.50
CARDS:

See advertisement under CARDIGAN

HALKYN Flintshire Map 07 SJ27

Travelodge

CH8 8RF (on A55, westbound)
☎ 01352 780952 FAX 01352 780952
This modern building offers accommodation in smart, spacious and well equipped bedrooms, suitable for family use, and all with en suite bathrooms. Meals may be taken at the nearby family restaurant. For information on room rates and to make a booking, call Roomline free of charge on 0800 850950. For more details about Travelodge, consult the Contents page under Hotel Groups.
31 en suite (bth/shr)

HARLECH Gwynedd Map 06 SH53
See also Talsarnau

★64% **Noddfa**
Lower Rd LL46 2UB (on A496, hotel opposite Royal St David's Golf Club) ☎ 01766 780043 FAX 01766 781105
RS Nov-Mar
From its elevated position this cosy hotel with fine views of the Lleyn *contd.*

Peninsula also overlooks the local championship golf course and the sea. Bedrooms are well decorated and several have en suite bathrooms. Eric Davies is an expert on medieval weaponry and many examples are on display. He gives archery lessons in the grounds as well as organising tours of the castle. His wife Gillian provides honest and enjoyable cooking.
6 rms (4 bth/shr) (1 fmly) CTV in all bedrooms No dogs (ex guide dogs) 15P No coaches Archery No children 3yrs Xmas International Cuisine No smoking in restaurant Last d 8pm
ROOMS: (incl. bkfst) d £45 * **LB**
MEALS: Dinner £7-£16alc*
CARDS:

HAVERFORDWEST Pembrokeshire Map 02 SM91

★★65% Hotel Mariners

MINOTEL Great Britain

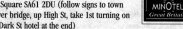

Mariners Square SA61 2DU (follow signs to town centre, over bridge, up High St, take 1st turning on the right Dark St hotel at the end)
☎ 01437 763353 FAX 01437 764258
Closed 26-27 Dec & 1 Jan

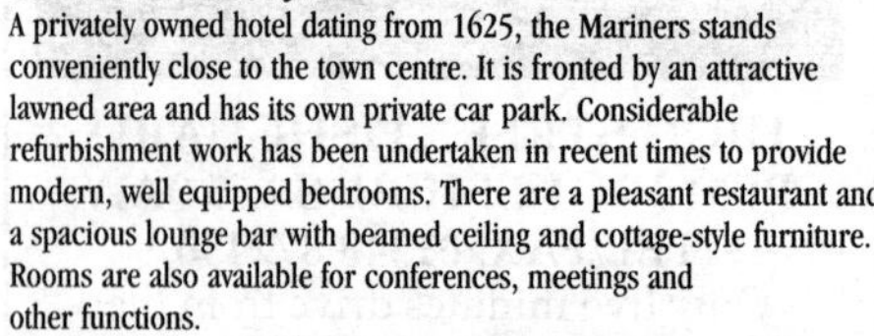

A privately owned hotel dating from 1625, the Mariners stands conveniently close to the town centre. It is fronted by an attractive lawned area and has its own private car park. Considerable refurbishment work has been undertaken in recent times to provide modern, well equipped bedrooms. There are a pleasant restaurant and a spacious lounge bar with beamed ceiling and cottage-style furniture. Rooms are also available for conferences, meetings and other functions.
29 en suite (bth/shr) (5 fmly) No smoking in 3 bedrooms CTV in all bedrooms Night porter 50P Short mat bowls English & French Cuisine V meals Coffee am Tea pm Last d 9.15pm
ROOMS: (incl. bkfst) s £47.50-£54.75; d £67.50-£73 **LB**
MEALS: Dinner £13.50-£14.50
CONF: Thtr 50 Class 28 Board 28
CARDS:

★★65% Wilton House
6 Quay St SA61 1BG ☎ 01437 760033 FAX 01437 760297
Situated close to the river in the town centre, this personally run hotel offers traditionally furnished accomodation with modern facilities. Family bedded rooms and a room at ground floor level are both available. Public areas include a couple of shops and a bar/bistro which serves a good range of value-for-money dishes. The outdoor heated swimming pool is a recent addition.
9 en suite (bth/shr) (3 fmly) CTV in all bedrooms No dogs (ex guide dogs) Night porter 6P No coaches Outdoor swimming pool (heated) V meals Coffee am Tea pm Last d 8.30pm
ROOMS: (incl. bkfst) s fr £35; d fr £52.50 *
MEALS: Lunch £2.05-£4.95alc Dinner £5.75-£9.95alc*
CARDS:

★★62% Castle
Castle Square SA61 2AA (from the main roundabout into Haverfordwest take the town centre turn off, follow the road for approx 200yds, hotel on right hand side)
☎ 01437 769322 FAX 01437 769493
This early 19th-century inn, which stands in the town centre, was extensively renovated by the present owners in 1990. It provides attractively decorated, modern and well equipped bedrooms, which are suitable for both business people or tourists. A good choice of popular dishes, including grills, is served in the restaurant. Other facilities include a lively bar.
9 en suite (bth/shr) (1 fmly) CTV in all bedrooms No dogs (ex guide dogs) Night porter No coaches V meals Coffee am No smoking area in restaurant Last d 9.30pm
ROOMS: (incl. bkfst) s £37.50; d £50 *
MEALS: Sunday Lunch £4.95-£7.75 Dinner £4.95-£11.95&alc*
CARDS:

★★60% Pembroke House
Spring Gardens SA61 2EJ ☎ 01437 763652
Part of an attractive Georgian terraced property, this privately owned hotel with its own rear car park is situated close to the town centre. Accommodation, which includes family rooms, is modestly furnished but well equipped. There are a pleasant lounge with a small bar and a smaller lounge which contains a pool table. A wide range of popular dishes is served in the split-level restaurant.
21 rms (13 bth 6 shr) (4 fmly) CTV in all bedrooms STV 18P V meals Coffee am Tea pm Last d 9.30pm
ROOMS: (incl. bkfst) s £38; d £55 * **LB**
MEALS: Dinner £10.50-£20alc*
CARDS:

HAY-ON-WYE Powys Map 03 SO24

★★★67% The Swan-at-Hay
Church St HR3 5DQ ☎ 01497 821188 FAX 01497 821424
This former coaching inn was built in 1821 and stands on the road to Brecon, just south of the town centre. In more recent times it has been extensively renovated by the present owners, Rosemary and Colin Vaughan, to provide well equipped accommodation, which includes a variety of bedroom styles and sizes. Public areas comprise an attractive, traditionally furnished restaurant overlooking the lovely garden, a comfortable lounge and a choice of bars. There is also a large function room and a smaller room for meetings or private dinner parties.

15 en suite (bth/shr) 3 annexe en suite (bth/shr) (1 fmly) CTV in all bedrooms 18P Fishing Xmas V meals Coffee am Tea pm Last d 9.30pm
ROOMS: (incl. bkfst) s £40-£50; d £60-£80 **LB**
MEALS: Lunch £8.95-£18.50 Dinner £15-£18.50&alc*
CONF: Thtr 140 Class 60 Board 50 Del from £65
CARDS:

★★68% Old Black Lion
26 Lion St HR3 5AD ☎ 01497 820841
Parts of this 17th-century coaching inn are reputed to date back to the 13th-century. Oliver Cromwell stayed here whilst his army besieged Hay Castle. The quaint bar and restaurant, with their low beamed ceilings, still retain much of the original character. The bedrooms, some of which are located in a separate annexe, have modern equipment and facilities. The culinary skills of Head Chef John Morgan have earned the inn a reputation for its good food and both the restaurant and bar meal operation are extremely popular.
6 rms (5 shr) 4 annexe en suite (bth/shr) (2 fmly) CTV in all bedrooms 20P No coaches Fishing No children 5yrs Xmas International Cuisine V meals Coffee am Tea pm No smoking in restaurant Last d 9.30pm
ROOMS: (incl. bkfst) s £20.95; d £45.90-£49.90 **LB**
OFF-PEAK: (incl. bkfst) d £42.90-£45.90
MEALS: Sunday Lunch £9.75-£10.95&alc Dinner £14-£20alc
CARDS:

★★65% Kilverts
The Bull Ring HR3 5AG (in centre of town, close to Butter Market)
☎ 01497 821042 & 820564 FAX 01497 821580
This Victorian property has a wealth of charm and character and is located close to the town centre. Well equipped bedrooms are provided, and there is a pleasant bistro style restaurant where an interesting selection of imaginative dishes are served. There is musical entertainment every Thursday night in the cosy bar, and also a comfortably furnished quiet lounge.
11 en suite (bth/shr) (1 fmly) CTV in all bedrooms 15P No coaches Croquet lawn European Cuisine V meals Coffee am Last d 10pm

ROOMS: (incl. bkfst) s £24-£27; d £48-£60 * **LB**
MEALS: Bar Lunch £2.50-£10.50alc Dinner fr £15&alc
CARDS:

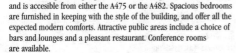

HOLYHEAD See Anglesey, Isle of

HOLYWELL Flintshire Map 07 SJ17
See also Nannerch

★★67% **Stamford Gate**
Halkyn Rd CH8 7SJ (take Holywell turn off A55 on to A5026, hotel 1m on right) ☎ 01352 712942 FAX 01352 713309
This popular commercial hotel is located north of the town on the approach from the A55 expressway. Bedrooms are well equipped with modern amenities and satellite TV has recently been fitted. The bars and marine-themed restaurant have built up a fine local reputation and good facilities are provided for weddings and other functions. Guests have the option of taking breakfast in their bedrooms or in an attractive conservatory.
12 en suite (bth/shr) CTV in all bedrooms STV No dogs 100P Wkly live entertainment English & Italian Cuisine V meals Coffee am Last d 10pm
ROOMS: (incl. bkfst) s £33.50-£38; d £36-£45 *
MEALS: Lunch £7.75-£8.50&alc Dinner fr £13.50&alc
CONF: Thtr 60 Class 30 Board 30
CARDS:

ISLE OF Placenames incorporating the words 'Isle' or 'Isle of' will be found under the actual name, eg Isle of Anglesey is under Anglesey, Isle of.

KNIGHTON Powys Map 07 SO27

★★72% **Milebrook House**
Milebrook LD7 1LT (2m E, off A4113)
☎ 01547 528632 FAX 01547 520509
RS Mon

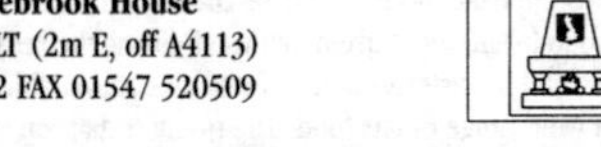

This small hotel stands one-and-a-half miles east of town in three acres of grounds which include a wild flower paddock with an abundance of wildlife; there is also a vegetable and herb garden where much of the produce used in the kitchen is grown. Beryl Marsden offers two fixed-price menus of two or three courses which have established an enviable local reputation. Public areas include a residents' sitting room and a cane-furnished bar, while six bedrooms furnished in pine all have en suite bath and shower rooms. Guests may fish in the River Teme.
10 en suite (bth/shr) (2 fmly) No smoking in 4 bedrooms CTV in all bedrooms No dogs 20P Fishing Croquet lawn Badminton Xmas English & French Cuisine V meals Coffee am Last d 9pm
ROOMS: (incl. bkfst) s £46; d £68-£72 **LB**
OFF-PEAK: (incl. bkfst) s £42; d £63-£67
MEALS: Lunch £10.75 Dinner £17.45-£20.45&alc
CARDS:

LAMPETER Cardiganshire Map 02 SN54
See also Crugybar

★★★70% **Falcondale Mansion**
SA48 7RX ☎ 01570 422910 FAX 01570 423559
This large Italianate mansion enjoys an idyllic setting in 14 acres of picturesque grounds outside Lampeter, and is accesible from either the A475 or the A482. Spacious bedrooms are furnished in keeping with the style of the building, and offer all the expected modern comforts. Attractive public areas include a choice of bars and lounges and a pleasant restaurant. Conference rooms are available.

19 en suite (bth/shr) (8 fmly) CTV in all bedrooms STV No dogs Lift 80P Tennis (hard) Fishing 18 Hole putting green Xmas English & French Cuisine V meals Coffee am Last d 9.30pm
ROOMS: (incl. bkfst) s £49.50; d £70-£80 * **LB**
MEALS: Dinner £17.95&alc
CONF: Thtr 60 Class 15 Board 30
CARDS:
See advertisement on this page

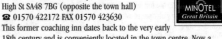

★★66% **Black Lion Royal Hotel**
High St SA48 7BG (opposite the town hall)
☎ 01570 422172 FAX 01570 423630
MINOTEL Great Britain
This former coaching inn dates back to the very early 18th century and is conveniently located in the town centre. Now a small, privately owned and personally run hotel, it provides friendly hospitality and well equipped bedrooms; family-bedded rooms are available. At the time of our last inspection, extensive improvements were being made in all the public areas, which include two bars, one of which is combined with an informal-style restaurant; there is also
contd.

L

another more formal eating option. Other facilities include a function room for up to 140 people.
15 en suite (bth/shr) (4 fmly) CTV in all bedrooms STV 30P Pool table British Cuisine V meals Coffee am Tea pm Last d 8.45pm
ROOMS: (incl. bkfst) s fr £35; d fr £55 * **LB**
MEALS: Lunch £6.50-£10.50 Dinner £11.50-£18.50alc*
CARDS:

LAMPHEY See Pembroke

LANGLAND BAY Swansea Map 02 SS68
See also Mumbles and Swansea

★★ 70% **Langland Court**
Langland Court Rd SA3 4TD (take B4593 towards Langland and turn left at St Peter's church)
☎ 01792 361545 FAX 01792 362302

This large Victorian house retains many of its original features, including the impressive stairway. Set in extensive gardens, it is situated in a quiet residential area, close to Langland Bay. Privately owned and personally run, in a friendly manner, it provides well equipped accommodation, which includes family rooms and bedrooms on the ground floor of a converted former coach house. The traditionally furnished public areas include a lounge bar and the "Oak Room" restaurant. The popular "Polly's" wine bar provides a second and less formal eating option. Other facilities include a large self contained function suite.

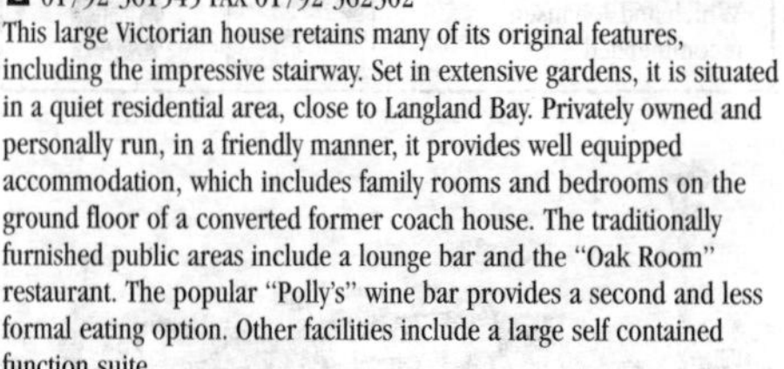

16 en suite (bth/shr) 5 annexe en suite (bth/shr) (5 fmly) No smoking in 2 bedrooms CTV in all bedrooms No dogs (ex guide dogs) 49P ch fac Welsh, English & Continental Cuisine V meals Coffee am No smoking in restaurant Last d 9.30pm
ROOMS: (incl. bkfst) s £50-£65; d £70-£82 * **LB**
MEALS: Lunch £9.95-£14.25&alc Dinner £18.95-£20.25&alc*
CONF: Thtr 150 Class 60 Board 40 Del from £77
CARDS:
See advertisement under SWANSEA

★ 66% **Wittemberg**
Rotherslade Rd SA3 4QN ☎ 01792 369696 FAX 01792 366995
Closed Jan
This small private hotel is located a very short walk from the sandy beaches of Langland Bay. Mumbles is just one mile away, with the city of Swansea and the Gower also within easy reach. Bedrooms are neat and comfortably furnished; all are equipped with TVs and hair dryers and some are suitable for families. Andrew and June Thomas are the owners and their welcome is naturally warm and friendly. June provides wholesome meals using only fresh produce whilst Andrew waits on guests and looks after the bar.
12 rms (10 shr) (2 fmly) CTV in all bedrooms 12P No coaches Jacuzzi/spa Xmas V meals No smoking in restaurant Last d 8.30pm
ROOMS: (incl. bkfst) s £28-£38; d £42-£55 * **LB**
MEALS: Dinner £15&alc*
CARDS:

LLANBEDR Gwynedd Map 06 SH52

★★ 66% ***Cae Nest Hall***
LL45 2NL ☎ 01341 241349
This is a quiet and relaxing country house hotel set in pleasant lawns and gardens and dating back to the 15th century. Bedrooms and ensuite facilities have been refurbished over recent years and pretty papers and fabrics are much in evidence. Family rooms are provided, one has a four poster bed and most of the others have attractively canopied beds. Log fires feature throughout the public rooms which include a flag-floored bar and a comfortable sitting room.
9 en suite (bth/shr) (2 fmly) CTV in all bedrooms 8P No coaches V meals

★★ 64% **Ty Mawr**
LL45 2NH (travelling from Harlech turn left just before bridge, hotel opposite war memorial) ☎ 01341 241440
Closed 24-26 Dec
This is a popular holiday hotel, family-run and situated in pleasant grounds opposite the River Artro. The slab-floored bar opens out onto the grounds and these are much used during the season by holiday-makers and tourists. A choice of real ales is available here together with a wide range of bar food. The pretty restaurant serves more substantial meals and there is a cosy lounge for residents. Bedrooms are modern and brightly decorated and the owners and local staff are friendly and helpful.
10 en suite (bth/shr) (2 fmly) CTV in all bedrooms STV 30P No coaches ch fac Welsh English French & Indian Cuisine V meals Coffee am Tea pm No smoking in restaurant
ROOMS: (incl. bkfst) s £20-£30; d £40-£60 **LB**
MEALS: Lunch fr £6.50&alc Dinner fr £10&alc*
CONF: Class 25
See advertisement on opposite page

LLANBERIS Gwynedd Map 06 SH56

★★★ 65% **Royal Victoria**
LL55 4TY ☎ 01286 870253 FAX 01286 870149
This early Victorian property is situated between the lakes of Peris and Padarn, at the foot of the Llanberis Pass, just to the west of Snowdon. It is set in 30 acres of grounds and gardens. All areas of the hotel have benefited from recent refurbishment work and it provides sound, modern furnished and equipped accommodation, which is equally suitable for both tourists and business people, including delegates using the extensive conference facilities. Public areas include a choice of traditionally furnished bars, a spacious restaurant, which has a conservatory extension, and ample lounge space. It is a popular venue for coach party holidays.
114 en suite (bth/shr) (1 fmly) CTV in all bedrooms STV Lift Night porter 60P Pool table V meals Coffee am Tea pm No smoking in restaurant Last d 8.30pm

ROOMS: (incl. bkfst) s £43; d £86 * **LB**
OFF-PEAK: (incl. bkfst) s £41.50; d £83
MEALS: Lunch £7-£10.50alc High tea £4.50-£7alc Dinner £9.95-£14.95*
CONF: Thtr 130 Class 50 Board 40 Del from £55
CARDS:

★★65% **Padarn Lake**
High St LL55 4SU (opposite the church)
☎ 01286 870260 FAX 01286 870007
Run by the same friendly family for nearly 20 years, this fully modernised hotel lies in the centre of the mountain resort. There is a choice of bars and several lounge areas are also provided. Bedrooms have pretty papers, en suite facilities and modern fitted furniture. There are also several inter-connecting rooms which are suitable for families. Local weddings and other functions are well catered for and a wide choice of food is available. The hotel has its own car park.
18 en suite (bth/shr) (4 fmly) CTV in all bedrooms 15P Xmas V meals Coffee am Last d 9pm
ROOMS: (incl. bkfst) s fr £31; d fr £52 * **LB**
MEALS: Sunday Lunch fr £5.95 Dinner fr £11.95&alc*
CARDS:

★62% ***Gallt-y-Glyn***
Caernarfon Rd LL55 4EL (W on A4086) ☎ 01286 870370
Closed 25 Dec
This small, friendly hotel is situated on the approach to the village from Caernarfon. Helen and Peter Rayment offer a warm welcome to their guests and the atmosphere is relaxed. Bedrooms are modestly furnished and equipped but provide value for money accommodation for visiting tourists and climbers. There is a comfortable TV lounge, a bar and sun terrace looking out over the nearby mountains, and a large car park.
9 rms (5 shr) (1 fmly) No smoking in 1 bedroom CTV in 2 bedrooms No dogs (ex guide dogs) 12P No coaches V meals Last d 7.30pm
CARDS:

LLANDEGLA Denbighshire Map 07 SJ25

★★★ 69% **Bod Idris Hall**

LL11 3AL (Welsh Rarebits) ☎ 01978 790434
FAX 01978 790335
Closed Jan
A beautifully preserved manor house, steeped in history and legend stands in 11 acres of ornamental gardens inclding a lake and swans. Guests cannot fail to be influenced by these magical surroundings. The interior of the hotel preserves magnificent stonework, fine oak panelling, inglenook fireplaces and an original duelling staircase. Bedrooms are furnished with fine period pieces and there are many four-poster beds. Modern comforts, however, are not lacking. Chef Phillip Weale prepares enjoyable and daily-changing menus, using Welsh produce wherever possible. The hotel organises tours of the grounds and gardens, which usually culminates in a delicious cream tea.
9 en suite (bth/shr) 2 annexe en suite (bth/shr) (2 fmly) No smoking in 4 bedrooms CTV in all bedrooms 80P Fishing Clay pigeon & Driven shooting Falconry Xmas V meals Coffee am Tea pm No smoking in restaurant Last d 9.30pm
ROOMS: (incl. bkfst) s fr £80; d £105-£125 **LB**
OFF-PEAK: (incl. bkfst) s fr £55; d £70-£90
MEALS: Sunday Lunch £15-£20 Dinner £26.50-£30&alc
CONF: Thtr 50 Class 25 Board 20 Del from £65
CARDS:

LLANDEILO Carmarthenshire Map 03 SN62

★★★68% **The Plough Inn**
Rhosmaen SA19 6NP (1m N, on A40)
☎ 01558 823431 FAX 01558 823969
Closed 25 Dec RS Sun
This popular, well run hotel, close to the A40 on the east side of the town, overlooks the lovely Towy valley. Bedrooms are well furnished and most are spacious enough to accommodate king-size beds and settees, so standards of comfort are high. There are two bars which attract a flourishing local clientele and serve a wide range of food. There is also a restaurant with its own cocktail bar offering an extensive menu, and the first-floor Penlan Lounge serves delicious afternoon teas.
12 en suite (bth/shr) CTV in all bedrooms STV No dogs 70P Sauna Gym Italian & Continental Cuisine V meals Coffee am Tea pm Last d 9.30pm
ROOMS: (incl. cont bkfst) s fr £45; d £60-£65
MEALS: Lunch £8.50-£27 Dinner £13.50-£27
CONF: Thtr 45 Class 24 Board 24
CARDS:

See advertisement on page 883

★★★64% ***Cawdor Arms***
Rhosmaen St SA19 6EN ☎ 01558 823500 FAX 01558 822399
This Georgian property is situated in the town centre. The public areas have been completely refurbished to a good standard, using period-style furnishings to complement the age and character of the building. There is a large restaurant, which can be partitioned to accommodate private parties. Work was about to begin on an upgrade as we went to press.
12 en suite (bth/shr) (1 fmly) No smoking in 2 bedrooms CTV in all bedrooms Night porter 13P International Cuisine V meals Coffee am Tea pm Last d 10pm
CARDS:

LLANDRILLO Denbighshire Map 06 SJ03

RED STAR HOTEL

★★ **Tyddyn Llan Country House Hotel & Restaurant**
LL21 0ST (on B4401, Corwen-Bala road)
☎ 01490 440264 FAX 01490 440414
A sympathetically restored and extended Georgian property, this hotel with beautiful gardens stands west of the village, surrounded by lovely countryside. Peter and Bridget Kindred, who have created this comfortable environment, lavish care and attention on their guests. An inventive four-course fixed-price dinner menu of competently prepared dishes uses local produce - including herbs from the garden - whenever possible, while attractively decorated bedrooms are well furnished with a mixture of period and locally crafted furniture; they contain no television sets, however, which is possibly why guests mix so well in the relaxing lounges.
10 en suite (bth/shr) (2 fmly) CTV in all bedrooms 30P No coaches Fishing Croquet lawn Xmas V meals Coffee am Tea pm No smoking in restaurant Last d 9pm
ROOMS: (incl. bkfst) s £60-£65; d £92-£102 * **LB**
MEALS: Lunch £11-£15 Dinner £23-£25*
CONF: Thtr 50 Class 30 Board 20 Del from £98
CARDS:

LLANDRINDOD WELLS Powys Map 03 SO06
See also Penybont

★★★66% **Hotel Metropole**
Temple St LDI 5DY (on A483 in centre of town)
☎ 01597 823700 FAX 01597 824828
Best Western
A large Victorian hotel situated in the town centre with an ample car park at the rear. The elegant public rooms are reminiscent of the period, but recent refurbishment of the main lounge has created a comfortable and relaxing area with more modern furnishings. Other facilities include a swimming pool beneath a Victorian style conservatory, Spencers Bar and Pantry in which afternoon tea is served and numerous banqueting and conference suites. Bedrooms are traditional in style and have every modern facility. Most of the staff have worked at the hotel for many years and are friendly and helpful.
121 en suite (bth/shr) (2 fmly) No smoking in 10 bedrooms CTV in all bedrooms Lift Night porter 150P Indoor swimming pool (heated) Sauna Solarium Jacuzzi/spa Beauty salon Rowing & Cycling machines Xmas English & Continental Cuisine V meals Coffee am Tea pm Last d 9pm
ROOMS: (incl. bkfst) s £63-£83; d £83-£103 * **LB**
MEALS: Lunch £8.15-£9.75 Dinner £17.95
CONF: Thtr 300 Class 200 Board 80 Del £90
CARDS:

★★65% **The Bell Country Inn**
Llanyre LD1 6DY (1.5m NW on Rhayader Road) ☎ 01597 823959 FAX 01597 825899
This old former drovers inn has been much extended and modernised in recent times. It is situated in the village of Llanyre, which is one and a half miles north-west of Llandrindod Wells, via the A4081. Privately owned and personally run, it provides well equipped modern accommodation, which includes a bedroom on ground floor level which has been specially designed for disabled guests. Public areas include a spacious lounge bar, an attractively appointed dining room and a separate breakfast room, which is also available for private functions. An à la carte menu, plus a selection of bar meals, gives a wide choice of dishes.
9 en suite (bth/shr) (2 fmly) No smoking in 2 bedrooms CTV in all bedrooms STV 20P Fishing Pool table ch fac Xmas English & French Cuisine V meals Coffee am Tea pm No smoking area in restaurant Last d 9.30pm
ROOMS: (incl. bkfst) s fr £35; d fr £60 * **LB**
MEALS: Bar Lunch £5-£6 High tea fr £7.50 Dinner fr £15*
CONF: Thtr 40 Class 20 Board 20 Del from £60
CARDS:

★★60% ***Hotel Commodore***
Spa Rd LD1 5ER (in centre of town off A483 to left if travelling from south, right if travelling from north)
☎ 01597 822288 FAX 01597 824828
This Victorian hotel stands in the centre of the spa resort. Facilities have been improved over recent years and all rooms now have en suite

bathrooms. Many family rooms are also available, one with a private lounge. Extensive public rooms regularly host live entertainment and the old public bar has been converted to an all-day American restaurant. Meeting rooms are available for conferences and functions, there is a hotel car park and guests have use of the modern leisure complex in a nearby sister hotel.
28 en suite (bth/shr) 22 annexe en suite (bth) (4 fmly) CTV in all bedrooms Lift Night porter 100P Indoor swimming pool (heated) Squash English & Continental Cuisine V meals Coffee am Tea pm Last d 10pm
CARDS:

LLANDUDNO Aberconwy & Colwyn Map 06 SH78

RED STAR HOTEL

★★★ **Bodysgallen Hall**
LL30 1RS (on A470 Llandudno link road)
☎ 01492 584466 FAX 01492 582519
This impressive country house hotel remains one of the finest of its type in the principality. Dating from the 17th century, it is set in 200 acres of attractive gardens and parkland and there are superb views towards Conwy Castle and Snowdonia. Public rooms include a large entrance hall and first floor drawing room. Both are oak-panelled and there are stone mullioned windows and splendid fireplaces. Bedrooms are mostly spacious and all are fitted with fine antique pieces. Those in buildings in the grounds have private sitting rooms. Food is always an enjoyable experience here, and the braised turbot chosen by our inspector at a recent vist was accurately cooked to preserve its superb flavour and texture. A fully equipped business centre is provided in the grounds and a new leisure centre has recently been completed.

19 en suite (bth/shr) 16 annexe en suite (bth/shr) (3 fmly) CTV in all bedrooms Night porter 70P No coaches Indoor swimming pool (heated) Tennis (hard) Sauna Solarium Gym Croquet lawn Jacuzzi/spa Sports & Beauty facility Wkly live entertainment No children 8yrs Xmas V meals Coffee am Tea pm Last d 9.30pm
ROOMS: s £79-£85; d £115-£135 * **LB**
MEALS: Lunch £11.50-£16 Dinner £27.50-£36*
CONF: Thtr 50 Class 30 Board 26 Del from £98
CARDS:

★★★75% **Empire**
Church Walks LL30 2HE ☎ 01492 860555 FAX 01492 860791
Closed 20-30 Dec
(Rosette awarded for dinner only)
This established hotel has been in the same family for more than fifty

years and benefits from the dedicated service of long serving staff. The luxurious bedrooms have cast iron beds, fine French linen and beautiful paintings together with thoughtful modern facilities such as videos, safes and fridges. Watkins & Co restaurant offers an interesting daily changing dinner menu; alternatively, lighter meals are served in the Coffee shop overlooking the indoor pool.
50 en suite (bth/shr) 8 annexe en suite (bth/shr) (4 fmly) CTV in all bedrooms STV No dogs (ex guide dogs) Lift Night porter 40P No coaches Indoor swimming pool (heated) Outdoor swimming pool (heated) Sauna Jacuzzi/spa Wkly live entertainment Xmas French Cuisine V meals Coffee am Tea pm No smoking area in restaurant Last d 9.30pm
ROOMS: (incl. bkfst) s £50-£60; d £70-£90 **LB**
MEALS: Sunday Lunch £10.50-£12.50 Dinner £17.50-£22.50
CONF: Thtr 36 Class 20 Board 20 Del from £60
CARDS:

See advertisement on thise page

★★★67% **Imperial**
The Promenade LL30 1AP
☎ 01492 877466 FAX 01492 878043
The Imperial is a long established hotel, fully modernised over recent years and now offering a full range of leisure and business facilities. It is part of the resort's imposing Victorian seafront and there are good views from many bedrooms. These are decorated with pretty papers and fabrics and include several spacious suites. Lounge areas are comfortable and spacious and, as well as several function suites, there is a fully equipped leisure club. Food continues to be carefully cooked and enjoyable with a well chosen monthly menu as well as daily specials.
100 en suite (bth/shr) (10 fmly) CTV in all bedrooms STV Lift Night porter 40P Indoor swimming pool (heated) Snooker Sauna

contd.

Solarium Gym Beauty therapist Hairdressing Xmas V meals Coffee am Tea pm No smoking in restaurant Last d 9.30pm
ROOMS: (incl. bkfst) s £65-£85; d £95-£175 * **LB**
MEALS: Lunch £12 Dinner £20-£25*
CONF: Thtr 150 Class 800 Board 50 Del from £95
CARDS:

See advertisement on opposite page

★★★63% Gogarth Abbey
West Shore LL30 2QY ☎ 01492 876211 FAX 01492 875805
Standing on the West Shore, this long-established hotel has lovely views over the Conwy Estuary and Snowdonia. The public rooms are quite delightful and comfortably inviting. It was here that Lewis Carroll created Alice in Wonderland. Bedrooms do vary in both quality and size.
40 en suite (bth/shr) (4 fmly) CTV in all bedrooms STV Night porter 40P Indoor swimming pool (heated) Sauna Solarium Pool table Croquet lawn Putting green Table tennis Boules Wkly live entertainment Xmas English & French Cuisine V meals Coffee am Tea pm No smoking in restaurant Last d 9pm
ROOMS: (incl. bkfst) s £40; d £80 **LB**
OFF-PEAK: (incl. bkfst) s £35; d £70
MEALS: Lunch £4.95-£8.95 Dinner fr £17.50
CONF: Thtr 50 Class 40 Board 40 Del from £60
CARDS:

L

★★★62% St George's
Lyric Hotels
The Promenade LL30 2LG
☎ 01492 877544 FAX 01492 877788
One of the first major hotels to be built in the town, its public rooms and facade still portray many Victorian features and the classical nineteenth century painted ceiling in the Wedgewood Room, is particularly noteworthy. Bedrooms vary in position, shape and size, some are compact, some less well decorated than others, but all are equipped with every modern convenience and those at the front have splendid views over the sea. A programme of upgrading is continuous and much is being done to considerably improve all aspects of the hotel. The staff are friendly and helpful and both lounge and room service exceed expectations.
87 en suite (bth/shr) (4 fmly) No smoking in 8 bedrooms CTV in all bedrooms STV Lift Night porter 36P Sauna Solarium Gym Jacuzzi/spa Hairdressing Health & beauty salon English French & Welsh Cuisine V meals Coffee am Tea pm No smoking in restaurant Last d 9.15pm
MEALS: Sunday Lunch fr £7.95 High tea fr £3.95 Dinner fr £15.50*
CARDS:

★★★61% Chatsworth House
Central Promenade LL30 2XS ☎ 01492 860788 FAX 01492 871417
Standing in a central position on the Promenade, this Victorian hotel enjoys superb views over the bay and caters well for families. It offers a wide range of entertainment and has the benefit of an indoor pool, a sauna and a children's paddling pool. Bedrooms are modern and well equipped and the spacious public rooms are comfortably furnished; service is friendly and attentive.
72 en suite (bth/shr) (19 fmly) CTV in all bedrooms Lift Night porter 9P Indoor swimming pool (heated) Sauna Jacuzzi/spa D British Cuisine V meals Coffee am Tea pm No smoking area in restaurant Last d 8.30pm
MEALS: Lunch £6-£7.50 Dinner £11*
CARDS:

★★★59% Risboro
Clement Av LL30 2ED ☎ 01492 876343 FAX 01492 879881
This popular family hotel, situated close to the base of The Great Orme, is the sister hotel to The Gogarth Abbey and has been owned by the Irving family for many years. Bedrooms, some of which have been refurbished, vary in size, but are soundly furnished and quite well equipped. Guests have the use of a good size indoor swimming pool, solarium, sauna and gym. Amongst the quite extensive public areas are a comfortable lounge with a small terrace and a large restaurant overlooking the pool where a range of popular dishes is served.
65 en suite (bth/shr) (7 fmly) CTV in all bedrooms STV Lift Night porter 40P Indoor swimming pool (heated) Squash Riding Sauna Solarium Gym Jacuzzi/spa Table tennis Wkly live entertainment Xmas English & French Cuisine V meals Coffee am Tea pm
ROOMS: (incl. bkfst) s fr £40; d fr £80 * **LB**
CONF: Thtr 150 Class 100 Board 80 Del from £60
CARDS:

RED STAR HOTEL

★★ ❀❀❀ *St Tudno*
Promenade LL30 2LP (on reaching Promenade drive towards the pier, hotel is opposite pier entrance & gardens)
(Welsh Rarebits) ☎ 01492 874411 FAX 01492 860407
This is a delightful seaside hotel offering warm hospitality and comfortable accommodation. It lies on the promenade near the Great Orme and all the resort's amenities are within walking distance. Bedrooms are individually decorated with pretty wallpapers and rich fabrics and several have views over the bay. Public rooms are comfortable and there is an indoor swimming pool and a small car park. The 'Garden Room' restaurant provides superb food as our three-rosette award indicates. A five-course menu is on offer and local lamb and fish are usually available. Starters can include fish cakes served with laver bread or a hot pot of Conwy mussels, and at a recent inspection, the main course was a delicious collop of monkfish baked to perfection. Hospitality here is warm and genuine and guests are really made to feel special.
21 en suite (bth/shr) (4 fmly) CTV in all bedrooms STV Lift 9P No coaches Indoor swimming pool (heated) Wkly live entertainment V meals Coffee am Tea pm Last d 9.30pm
CARDS:

★★73% Dunoon
Gloddaeth St LL30 2DW ☎ 01492 860787
FAX 01492 860031
Closed mid Nov-mid Mar
This soundly furnished and very comfortable hotel has been run by the experienced Chadderton family for nearly half a century. Traditional services are provided and staff are very friendly and attentive. Panelled public areas are impressive and the bar features an antique cooking range that has been handed down through the generations. Bedrooms are smart and modern, some are suitable for families and satellite television is provided.
56 en suite (bth/shr) 14 annexe en suite (bth) (22 fmly) CTV in all

bedrooms STV Lift 24P Solarium Pool table Jacuzzi/spa English & French Cuisine V meals Coffee am Tea pm Last d 8pm
ROOMS: (incl. bkfst) s £35-£39; d £50-£78
MEALS: Lunch £8-£9.50 Dinner £12-£15.50
CARDS:

★★70% Belle Vue
26 North Pde LL30 2LP (follow the promenade towards the pier, as the road bends the Belle Vue Hotel is on the left)
☎ 01492 879547 FAX 01492 870001
Closed Dec-Feb RS Nov & Mar
Located under the Great Orme with shops and other amenities within easy walking distance, this hotel is very well maintained and offers modern accommodation. A lift serves the bedrooms, each of which has its own video player for which a large library of films is available. A comfortable lounge and separate bar is provided and the restaurant serves enjoyable food.
15 en suite (bth/shr) (3 fmly) CTV in all bedrooms Lift 14P No coaches No children 3yrs International Cuisine V meals Coffee am Last d 8pm
ROOMS: (incl. bkfst) s £22.50-£26.50; d £45-£57 * **LB**
MEALS: Dinner £10&alc*
CARDS:

★★69% Epperstone
15 Abbey Rd LL30 2EE ☎ 01492 878746 FAX 01492 871223
Closed possibly January
This charming small holiday hotel stands in its own award-winning garden in a residential area within easy reach of the shops and seafront. Many original features have been retained, and there is a choice of lounges (including a Victorian conservatory) as well as a small, intimate dining room where good-value five-course dinners are served. Attractively decorated bedrooms have comfortable appointments and a wide range of facilities.
8 en suite (bth/shr) (5 fmly) No smoking in 1 bedroom CTV in all bedrooms STV 8P No coaches Xmas Home cooking Cuisine Coffee am Tea pm No smoking in restaurant Last d 7.30pm
ROOMS: (incl. bkfst) s £25-£27; d £50-£54 * **LB**
OFF-PEAK: (incl. bkfst) s £22-£25; d £44-£50
MEALS: High tea £5-£8 Dinner £12.50-£13.50
CARDS:

★★69% Sandringham
West Pde LL30 2BD (Enter Llandudno on A470 follow signs for West Shore, hotel is located in centre of West Shore Promenade)
☎ 01492 876513 & 876447 FAX 01492 872753
RS 25 & 26 Dec
This family-run holiday hotel is situated on the pretty West Shore and enjoys superb views over the Conwy Estuary to Snowdonia beyond. Public rooms are spacious and comfortable and, as well as the main restaurant which serves a daily changing fixed price menu, there is a further buttery where a large carte selection is available. Bedrooms are freshly decorated and well equipped with modern amenities and David and Yvonne Kavanagh, together with local staff, offer a warm welcome to their guests.
18 en suite (bth/shr) (3 fmly) CTV in all bedrooms STV No dogs 6P Xmas English & Continental Cuisine V meals Coffee am Last d 8.30pm
ROOMS: (incl. bkfst) s £24-£28; d £48-£52 **LB**
MEALS: Lunch £9.50 Dinner £12.95-£13.95
CARDS:

★★69% Tan-Lan
Great Orme's Rd, West Shore LL30 2AR
☎ 01492 860221 FAX 01492 860221
Closed 26 Oct-21 Mar
This very well maintained hotel, where the hospitality displayed by its owners Jennifer and Tony Fossi is a real strength, is ideally situated in a quiet street just off the seafront, under the Great Orme. Bedrooms, including a number of family rooms and a ground-floor suite are all en suite, freshly decorated and quite well equipped. There is a comfortably furnished lounge in addition to a lounge bar, and in the restaurant a good, five-course dinner is served. The hotel also benefits from its own car park.
17 en suite (bth/shr) (3 fmly) CTV in all bedrooms 15P No coaches English,French,Italian & Vegetarian Cuisine V meals Coffee am Tea pm No smoking in restaurant Last d 7.45pm
ROOMS: (incl. bkfst) s £26.50-£28; d £49-£50 **LB**
OFF-PEAK: (incl. bkfst) s fr £23; d £45-£50
MEALS: Lunch £7.95-£8.50 Dinner £13*
CARDS:

★★68% Sunnymede
West Pde LL30 2BD ☎ 01492 877130
Closed mid Nov-Feb
Guests have been returning year after year to this family-run hotel which is located on the resort's West Shore. Many bedrooms face the seafront and have lovely views over the Conwy Estuary to Snowdonia beyond. Bedrooms are attractively decorated and one has a four-poster bed for that special occasion. Excellent lounge facilities are provided and the experienced Seddon family extend a warm welcome to their guests.
18 rms (14 bth 3 shr) (3 fmly) CTV in all bedrooms STV 18P Xmas V meals Coffee am Tea pm Last d 7.30pm
ROOMS: (incl. bkfst & dinner) s £31-£38; d £62-£76 * **LB**
OFF-PEAK: (incl. bkfst) s £29-£32; d £58-£64
MEALS: Bar Lunch £2.50-£10 Dinner £12.50&alc*
CARDS:

For the key to symbols and abbreviations, please see the bookmark inside the back cover

★★68% **White Court**
2 North Pde LL30 2LP (enter Llandudno on A470,travel down Promenade with sea on right,turn left at Cenotaph, hotel is on right)
☎ 01492 876719 FAX 01492 871583
Closed Nov-12 Feb
This immaculately maintained small hotel is situated almost on the seafront and close to the main shopping centre. Many bedrooms have sea views and are quite spacious. Two have four-poster beds and all have modern en suite facilities. There is a comfortably furnished lounge and separate bar, and the pretty restaurant serves enjoyable food.
13 en suite (bth/shr) (3 fmly) No smoking in all bedrooms CTV in all bedrooms No dogs (ex guide dogs) No coaches A completely non-smoking hotel English & French Cuisine V meals No smoking in restaurant Last d 7.30pm
ROOMS: (incl. bkfst) s £30-£50; d £40-£70 **LB**
MEALS: Dinner £12-£16*
CARDS:

★★67% **Banham House**
2 St Davids Rd LL30 2UL (from Llandudno Station turn left, at traffic lights turn left into Trinity Avenue, take 3rd exit on right opposite school) ☎ 01492 875680 FAX 01492 875680
Closed 31 Dec-2 Jan
This small hotel is located in a quiet part of the resort but is within easy walking distance of the shops and seafront. Patricia and Tony Sharp are the welcoming owners and nothing is too much trouble for them. Bedrooms are freshly decorated and many extra facilities are provided. There is a comfortable lounge for residents, a small bar and a choice from fixed price or carte menus. The hotel has its own forecourt car park and only non-smokers are accommodated.
6 en suite (bth/shr) No smoking in all bedrooms CTV in all bedrooms No dogs 5P No coaches A non-smoking hotel No children 12yrs Xmas V meals Coffee am No smoking in restaurant Last d 9.30pm
ROOMS: (incl. bkfst) s £30; d £46 *
MEALS: Lunch £9 Dinner £9&alc

★★67% **Bromwell Court**
Promenade LL30 1BG ☎ 01492 878416 FAX 01492 874142
Closed Nov-Mar
This is a friendly holiday hotel situated on the Craig-y-Don promenade. Bedrooms are smart, modern and well decorated, and hair dryers and trouser presses are provided in each. Many bedrooms face the sea and these have good views over the bay towards the Great and Little Ormes. A comfortable lounge is available for residents and there is also a cosy bar. The hotel is run by the friendly Ireland family who offer a genuinely warm welcome to their guests.
11 en suite (bth/shr) (2 fmly) CTV in all bedrooms No coaches V meals No smoking in restaurant Last d 7.30pm
ROOMS: (incl. bkfst) s £19-£23; d £37-£42 * **LB**
OFF-PEAK: (incl. bkfst) s £17.50-£19; d £35-£40
MEALS: Bar Lunch £2.50-£5.50alc Dinner fr £10.50

★★67% **Bryn-y-Bia Lodge**
Craigside LL30 3AS (take Promenade towards Little Orme, hotel on right at the Little Orme)

☎ 01492 549644 & 540459
Closed 23-31 Dec
Set in its own walled grounds with attractive gardens and ample parking, this family-run hotel lies on the eastern side of the Promenade, near the Little Orme. Views from many rooms sweep over the bay towards the Great Orme and an atmosphere of tranquillity prevails. The restaurant's fixed-price four-course menu offers a range of freshly prepared dishes, and prettily decorated bedrooms include one with a four-poster bed.
13 en suite (bth/shr) (2 fmly) CTV in all bedrooms 20P No coaches ch fac English & Continental Cuisine V meals Coffee am No smoking in restaurant Last d 8pm
ROOMS: (incl. bkfst) s £29-£38; d £60-£68 **LB**
OFF-PEAK: (incl. bkfst) s £27-£29; d £52-£58
MEALS: Dinner fr £18&alc*
CARDS:

★★67% **Merrion**
Promenade, South Pde LL30 2LN
☎ 01492 860022 FAX 01492 860378
Closed 1-28 Feb
This very popular hotel has been run by the same caring family for three generations. It is situated in a prime position on the promenade with the Great Orme and main shopping centre nearby. Many bedrooms overlook the sea front and several of these have private balconies. The pretty restaurant offers a fixed-price menu with several choices and a good range of comfortable lounges is provided including an entertainment section and a function suite. The hotel also offers speciality breaks throughout the year. Staff are smartly turned out and friendly and many guests visit the hotel regularly.
65 en suite (bth/shr) (6 fmly) CTV in all bedrooms Lift Night porter 30P Wkly live entertainment Xmas British Cuisine Coffee am Last d 8.30pm
ROOMS: (incl. bkfst & dinner) s £38-£49.50; d £76-£99 * **LB**
MEALS: Lunch £8-£10 Dinner £15-£19
CONF: Thtr 100 Class 100 Board 100 Del from £40
CARDS:

★★67% **Stratford**
8 Craig-y-Don Pde, Promenade LL30 1BG (from A55 take A470 to Llandudno at 3rd roundabout take Craig-y-don sign to Promenade)
☎ 01492 877962 FAX 01492 877962
Closed Dec-Feb
Located on the Craig-y-Don promenade, there are superb views from many rooms over the bay towards Great Orme. Bedrooms are decorated with pretty papers and fabrics and include several with canopied beds. A ground floor room is also available for less-mobile guests. A comfortable lounge is provided and good home-cooking is the order of the day.
9 en suite (bth/shr) (4 fmly) CTV in 10 bedrooms STV No coaches V meals
ROOMS: (incl. bkfst) s £22; d £38-£48 * **LB**
CARDS:

★★67% **Tynedale**
Central Promenade LL30 2XS (on promenade opposite bandstand)
☎ 01492 877426 FAX 01492 871213
This holiday hotel is situated opposite the bandstand in the centre of the promenade. Many bedrooms look out over the bay and there are fine views of the Great Orme. Public areas include several comfortable lounges and live entertainment is regularly provided in the brightly decorated bar. Bedrooms are bright and modern and several are situated at ground floor level. A modern lift serves all floors, and the hotel has its own rear car park.
56 en suite (bth/shr) (4 fmly) CTV in all bedrooms No dogs (ex guide dogs) Lift Night porter 30P Wkly live entertainment Xmas English & French Cuisine V meals Coffee am Tea pm No smoking in restaurant Last d 8.30pm
ROOMS: (incl. bkfst) s £21-£25; d £42-£64 * **LB**
OFF-PEAK: (incl. bkfst) s £19-£25; d £38-£60
MEALS: Lunch £6.50-£8.95 High tea £2.95-£3.95 Dinner £9.50-£11.50*
CARDS:

★★67% **Wilton**
South Pde LL30 2LN ☎ 01492 876086 & 878343 FAX 01492 876086
Closed 28 Nov-6 Feb
This small hotel is maintained in excellent condition and provides

good quality, modern facilities. It lies just off the promenade and is near the main shopping area. Bedrooms are colourful and brightly decorated with rich fabrics and wallpapers. Four-poster beds are available and some rooms are suitable for families. There is a comfortable lounge bar for residents and, as well as unrestricted street parking, there is a small rear car park.
14 en suite (bth/shr) (7 fmly) CTV in all bedrooms STV 3P No coaches V meals No smoking in restaurant
ROOMS: (incl. bkfst) s £24-£44; d £48 * **LB**
OFF-PEAK: (incl. bkfst) s £22; d £44

See advertisement on this page

★★66% **Rose Tor**
124 Mostyn St LL30 2SW ☎ 01492 870433 FAX 01492 871545
Closed 23-29 Dec
Conveniently located for the main shopping area and the promenade, this friendly hotel offers modern accommodation. Ground floor areas have been completely altered during 1995. A popular carvery serves two restaurants and the bar and lounge areas are bright and spacious. Bedrooms are decorated with pretty papers and fabrics, two now have four-poster beds and several family rooms are available. Live entertainment is provided during the season.
24 en suite (bth/shr) (3 fmly) CTV in all bedrooms V meals Coffee am Tea pm Last d 9pm
ROOMS: (incl. bkfst) s £24-£45; d £42-£90 * **LB**
MEALS: Lunch fr £7.50 Dinner fr £9.95&alc*
CARDS:

★★66% ***Waverley***
North Pde LL30 2LP ☎ 01492 876933 FAX 01492 876933
Closed 1 Nov-31 Mar
This friendly family-run hotel occupies an elevated position under the Great Orme with superb views over the bay from the lounge and dining room and from many bedrooms. Some rooms have pretty four-poster beds for that special occasion and two rooms are located at ground-floor level. All are well equipped with modern facilities. A sauna, sunbed and small gymnasium are also available for guests.
10 en suite (bth/shr) (4 fmly) CTV in all bedrooms STV No coaches Sauna Solarium Gym V meals Coffee am Tea pm Last d 7pm

★★65% **Bedford**
Promenade LL30 1BN ☎ 01492 876647 FAX 01492 860185
Located on the promenade at the eastern side of the resort this is a friendly and relaxing hotel. Bedrooms are attractively fitted with good quality Italian furniture and many are suitable for families. Several have fine views over the bay towards the Great Orme and one of these has a four-poster bed for that special occasion. Comfortable lounges are provided and a special bonus is an Italian restaurant and pizzeria which supplements the hotel dining room.
27 en suite (bth/shr) (2 fmly) No smoking in 3 bedrooms CTV in all bedrooms STV Lift Night porter 21P Xmas British, French & Italian Cuisine V meals Coffee am Tea pm Last d 10.15pm
ROOMS: (incl. bkfst) s £25-£28; d £46-£56 * **LB**
OFF-PEAK: (incl. bkfst) s £23-£26; d £40-£50
MEALS: Lunch £11-£14&alc Dinner £11-£14&alc*
CONF: Thtr 30 Class 20 Board 20 Del from £50
CARDS:

★★65% **Fairhaven Christian Hotel**
3 Craig-y-Don Pde, Promenade LL30 1BG (on the Promenade,300 yards west of the North Wales Theatre)
☎ 01492 878447 FAX 01492 870185
RS Nov-Jan
Owned by John and Kathleen Hammond and run with enthusiasm and commitment, this neatly maintained hotel on the promenade at the quiet end of the town offers informal Christian fellowship. The

contd.

comfortable bedrooms are very well equipped and some enjoy the most beautiful sea views. There is a cosy lounge and in the dining room a short menu of home-cooked dishes is on offer.
11 en suite (bth/shr) (2 fmly) No smoking in all bedrooms CTV in all bedrooms No dogs (ex guide dogs) No coaches Non-smoking hotel Xmas V meals No smoking in restaurant
ROOMS: (incl. bkfst) s £18.50-£21.90; d £37-£43.80 * **LB**

See advertisement on page 889

★★65% **White Lodge**
9 Neville Crescent, Central Promenade LL30 1AT ☎ 01492 877713
Closed Nov-Mar
Right in the centre of the promenade, this small hotel is run by the friendly and welcoming Rigby family. Bedrooms are neat and well decorated with clever use made of pretty fabrics and canopied beds. All have en-suite bathrooms and many have lovely views over the bay to the two Ormes. There is a comfortable lounge, in addition to the pleasant dining room and cosy bar.
12 en suite (bth/shr) (4 fmly) CTV in all bedrooms STV 12P No coaches No children 5yrs British Cuisine Coffee am Tea pm
ROOMS: (incl. bkfst) s £29-£32; d fr £48 * **LB**
CARDS:

★★64% **Bryn-y-Mor**
North Pde LL30 2LP ☎ 01492 876790
Closed Dec-Feb
This family-run hotel is located near the pier and there are magnificent views over the bay from many bedrooms and from the lounge and bar. The restaurant is located at a lower level and opens out on to a sun terrace. Bedrooms are equipped with modern facilities, with several suitable for families. Fay and Brian Sherlock are the very friendly owners, with Fay responsible for honest home cooking which includes a good choice for vegetarians.
11 en suite (bth/shr) (2 fmly) No smoking in 4 bedrooms CTV in all bedrooms No dogs 1P International Cuisine V meals Last d 7pm
ROOMS: (incl. bkfst) s £20-£22; d £40-£44 * **LB**
MEALS: Dinner £10-£12
CARDS:

★★64% **Castle**
Vaughan St LL30 1AG (From A55 take A470, the hotel is 1st on left when entering Llandudno, by Asda)
☎ 01492 877694 & 876868 FAX 01492 872974
Closed Jan
This busy holiday hotel with its rear car park is centrally located with the shops and promenade nearby. Several bars are provided and live entertainment is held regularly. Lounges are spacious and comfortable and one is reserved for non-smokers. Two lifts serve all floors and bedrooms are brightly decorated and equipped with modern facilities.
55 en suite (bth/shr) (19 fmly) CTV in all bedrooms Lift Night porter 30P Pool table Wkly live entertainment Xmas V meals Coffee am Tea pm No smoking in restaurant Last d 7.30pm
ROOMS: (incl. bkfst) s £20-£30; d £40-£60 * **LB**
MEALS: Bar Lunch fr £1.50 Dinner £7.50-£8.50
CONF: Thtr 80 Class 60 Board 30 Del £35
CARDS:

★★64% **Headlands**
Hill Ter LL30 2LS ☎ 01492 877485
Closed Jan-Feb
This family run hotel occupies a superb position under the Great Orme. There are excellent views over the seafront and Snowdonia from most bedrooms and all public areas. Bedrooms, most of which have en suite bath or shower rooms, include several with canopied or four poster beds and some situated at ground floor level. Comfortably furnished public areas include a good range of sitting rooms, a small bar and a first floor bay with Victorian stained-glass windows.
17 rms (15 bth/shr) (4 fmly) CTV in all bedrooms 7P No coaches No children 5yrs Xmas Coffee am Last d 8.30pm
ROOMS: (incl. bkfst) s £28; d £56 * **LB**
MEALS: Bar Lunch £1.50-£3alc Dinner fr £16.50*
CARDS:

★★64% **Kensington**
Central Promenade LL30 1AT (Situated on the promenade, 500 yards from The North Wales Theatre & Conference Centre)
☎ 01492 876784 FAX 01492 874184
Closed 24 Dec-30 Jan RS 2 Jan-14 Jan
This privately owned holiday hotel is located on the central promenade. There are superb views from many rooms over the seafront and of both the Great and Little Orme. Bedrooms are modern and freshly decorated and all have en suite bath or shower rooms. A lift serves all floors and there is a rear car park. There are two lounges for residents and live entertainment is provided in the bar. The Beardmore family and their staff are friendly and welcoming.
36 en suite (bth/shr) 12 annexe en suite (bth) (18 fmly) CTV in all bedrooms No dogs (ex guide dogs) Lift 39P Wkly live entertainment Xmas V meals Coffee am Tea pm No smoking in restaurant
ROOMS: (incl. bkfst & dinner) s £34-£42; d £52-£76 * **LB**
OFF-PEAK: (incl. bkfst & dinner) d £52-£70
CONF: Thtr 120 Class 100 Board 50 Del from £48
CARDS:

See advertisement on opposite page

★★63% **Ormescliffe**
East Pde LL30 1BE ☎ 01492 877191 FAX 01492 860311
Closed 2 Jan-2 Feb
This is a long established holiday hotel, with a friendly atmosphere, located on the eastern end of the promenade and convenient for the theatre and conference centre. Many of the well equipped bedrooms afford sweeping views across the bay, there is a ballroom and live entertainment takes place regularly.
62 en suite (bth/shr) (7 fmly) CTV in all bedrooms Lift Night porter 15P Snooker Pool table Table tennis Xmas Coffee am Tea pm Last d 7.45pm
ROOMS: (incl. bkfst & dinner) s £41.50; d £83 * **LB**
OFF-PEAK: (incl. bkfst & dinner) s £38.50; d £77
MEALS: Bar Lunch £1-£3.50 Dinner £9.50-£10.50*
CONF: Thtr 120 Class 120 Board 80
CARDS:

★★63% **Royal**
Church Walks LL30 2HW (Opposite Great Orme Tram Station)
☎ 01492 876476 FAX 01492 870210
This family-run hotel is located in the shelter of the Great Orme and has pretty lawns and gardens. There are fine views over the town and seafront from many rooms and the main shopping centre is nearby. Modern facilities are provided in bedrooms and some of these are situated on the ground floor. There are spacious public areas and regular live entertainment is provided for the many tour groups that are catered for. It is also a popular venue for golf parties and other groups.
38 rms (36 bth/shr) (7 fmly) CTV in all bedrooms No dogs (ex guide dogs) Lift Night porter 20P Pool table Putting green ch fac Xmas V meals Coffee am No smoking in restaurant Last d 8pm
ROOMS: (incl. bkfst) s £20-£30; d £40-£70 **LB**
MEALS: Lunch fr £3.25 Dinner fr £14.50*
CARDS:

★★63% **Sherwood**
Promenade LL30 1BG ☎ 01492 875313 FAX 01492 875313
Closed Xmas & New Year RS Nov-Feb
This family-run hotel is situated on the promenade at Craig-y-Don and there are superb views of the bay and of both the Ormes from many bedrooms. These are modern and brightly decorated as are the public rooms. Linda and Michael Bentley are the friendly owners and a warm

welcome is extended to their guests, many of whom return year after year. The hotel has a large rear car park.
15 en suite (bth/shr) (5 fmly) CTV in all bedrooms STV 15P Pool table Games room Indoor golf V meals Coffee am Tea pm No smoking in restaurant Last d 8pm
ROOMS: (incl. bkfst) s £22-£24; d £42-£46 * **LB**
OFF-PEAK: (incl. bkfst) s £21-£23; d £40-£44
MEALS: Dinner £9-£10
CARDS:

★★62% ***Branksome***
Lloyd St LL30 2YP ☎ 01492 875989 & 878808 FAX 01492 875989
Closed Jan-Feb
This well maintained holiday hotel is situated midway between the town's two shores and within easy walking distance of the main shopping areas. It offers brightly decorated and modern bedrooms and public areas include a games room and a popular bar. Live entertainment is provided and there is a small car park.
49 rms (44 bth/shr) (8 fmly) CTV in all bedrooms Night porter 16P V meals Coffee am Tea pm Last d 7pm

★★62% **Evans**
Charlton St LL30 1RU ☎ 01492 860784 FAX 01492 860784
Closed 14-22 Dec & 27-29 Dec
This friendly, privately owned and personally run hotel which provides comfortable, well appointed bedrooms, including family rooms, is ideally positioned for the station, shops and Promenade. The spacious, attractively decorated public areas include a well equipped games room and a comfortable lounge bar, where regular evening entertainment is held. Dinner is served until 7.00 pm, although a cold supper will very willingly be provided for later arrivals.
50 rms CTV in all bedrooms P
ROOMS: (incl. bkfst) d £49 *

★★61% **Somerset**
St Georges Crescent, Promenade LL30 2LF
☎ 01492 876540 FAX 01492 876540
Closed Nov-Feb
This popular resort hotel is located in the centre of the promenade and near the main shopping centre. Many bedrooms overlook the sea front and all have ensuite bath or shower rooms. Public areas are quite extensive with guests also having use of an adjoining sister hotel. Regular entertainment is held and there is a rear car park.
37 en suite (bth/shr) (4 fmly) CTV in all bedrooms Lift Night porter 20P Pool table Games room Xmas British Cuisine V meals Coffee am No smoking in restaurant Last d 7.30pm
ROOMS: (incl. bkfst & dinner) s £30-£32; d £38-£39.50 * **LB**
MEALS: Lunch £6.75 Dinner £12-£13.50*
CARDS:

★★61% **Wavecrest**
St Georges Crescent, Central Promenade LL30 2LF (on promenade behind Marks & Spencer) ☎ 01492 860615 FAX 01492 876540
Closed Nov-Mar
This popular holiday hotel occupies a prime sea front position and is yet just a few yards from the main shopping centre of the resort. Bedrooms are all equipped with ensuite bath or shower rooms and many have glorious views over the bay. Several lounges are available and guests also have use of the public rooms of the adjoining, sister hotels. Regular entertainment is held and there is a rear car park.
41 en suite (bth/shr) (7 fmly) CTV in all bedrooms Lift Night porter 12P Xmas British Cuisine V meals Coffee am No smoking in restaurant Last d 7.30pm
ROOMS: (incl. bkfst & dinner) s £30-£32; d £38-£39 **LB**
MEALS: Lunch £6.75 Dinner £12.50-£13.50*
CARDS:

★★60% **Esplanade**
Glan-y-Mor Pde, Promenade LL30 2LL (turn off A55 at Llandudno junct & proceed on A470) ☎ 01492 860300 FAX 01492 860418
Located in the centre of the promenade, this long-established hotel is also conveniently sited for the main shopping area and other amenities. A programme of bedroom refurbishment is ongoing and bathrooms are also being modernised. Many rooms have excellent sea views. Regular live entertainment is held and there is a buttery where snacks and teas are served all day.
59 en suite (bth/shr) (15 fmly) CTV in all bedrooms Lift Night porter 30P Pool table Table tennis Wkly live entertainment Xmas Traditional British Cuisine V meals Coffee am Tea pm Last d 8.30pm
ROOMS: (incl. bkfst) s £21-£47.50; d £42-£80 * **LB**
OFF-PEAK: (incl. bkfst) s £21-£29; d £42-£58
MEALS: Sunday Lunch £8.50 Dinner £12.50-£16.50*
CONF: Thtr 120 Class 60 Board 50 Del from £33
CARDS: £

★★60% **Southcliffe**
Hill Ter LL30 2LS ☎ 01492 876277
Closed Nov-15 Dec & 5 Jan-Mar
This holiday hotel, which stands under the Great Orme and high above the promenade, affords superb views over the bay. Public rooms are comfortably furnished and include a bar and sun terrace. There is one four-poster bed for that special occasion and several rooms enjoy the views. Regular live entertainment is held during the season and Ann Goldsmith and her team are friendly and welcoming.
30 rms (19 bth/shr) (7 fmly) No smoking in all bedrooms CTV in all bedrooms 3P Wkly live entertainment No children 7yrs Xmas V meals Coffee am Tea pm No smoking in restaurant Last d 8.30pm
ROOMS: (incl. bkfst) s fr £26; d fr £52 * **LB**
MEALS: Lunch £5-£7 Dinner £7-£10*
CONF: Thtr 60 Class 40 Board 40 Del from £30 £

★67% **Concord**
35 Abbey Rd LL30 2EH ☎ 01492 875504
Closed mid Oct-mid Mar
Located between the resort's two shores this is a very friendly and relaxing family-run hotel. Hospitality is warm and welcoming with the experienced Price family always on hand. Bedrooms are bright and cosy and pretty papers and fabrics are used to good effect. Several rooms are suitable for families and one is located at ground floor level. A comfortable lounge is provided for residents and good home cooking is the order of the day.
11 en suite (bth/shr) (7 fmly) No dogs (ex guide dogs) 11P No coaches No children 5yrs Coffee am No smoking in restaurant
ROOMS: (incl. bkfst) s £20; d £40
OFF-PEAK: (incl. bkfst) s £19; d £38

★67% **Gwesty Leamore**
40 Lloyd St LL30 2YG ☎ 01492 875552
Closed Dec
This very Welsh hotel has been run for many years by Fred and Beryl Owen. It lies in a quiet part of the resort but is a short walk from the promenade and shopping centre. Bedrooms are bright and cheerful and modern facilities are provided. There is a small foyer bar for residents and a comfortable sitting room. Beryl provides good home cooking, Welsh wines are available, and guests dine to a background of Welsh choral music.
12 rms (1 bth 6 shr) (4 fmly) CTV in all bedrooms STV No dogs (ex guide dogs) 4P No coaches V meals Last d 7pm
ROOMS: (incl. bkfst) s £22-£25; d £36-£38 * **LB**
MEALS: Bar Lunch £3-£6 Dinner £8-£10*
£

★67% **Oak Alyn**
Deganwy Av LL30 2YB (Situated in the cen..e of Llandudno, 200 yards from the Town Hall, opposite the Catholic Church) ☎ 01492 860320
Closed Nov-Feb RS Mar
This very well maintained holiday hotel has been run by the same caring and friendly family for many years. It lies a short distance from the sea front and the main shopping centre is nearby. Bedrooms are fresh and bright, all have ensuite bath or shower rooms and televisions are provided. There is a comfortable lounge for residents as well as a small bar and a large forecourt car park. Food is freshly cooked and enjoyable.
12 en suite (bth/shr) CTV in all bedrooms 14P No children 12yrs British & Continental Cuisine V meals Coffee am No smoking area in restaurant Last d 7.30pm
ROOMS: (incl. bkfst) s £17.25-£19.25; d £34.50-£38.50 * **LB**
MEALS: Bar Lunch £2.50 Dinner £8.50
CARDS:

★67% **Tan-y-Marian**
87 Abbey Rd, West Shore LL30 2AS ☎ 01492 877727
Closed Oct-Mar
This small and friendly hotel is located adjacent to the West Shore and beneath the Great Orme. Pretty bedrooms are provided and these, like the rest of the hotel, are freshly decorated and very well maintained. There is a comfortable television lounge for residents, a cosy foyer bar and good home cooking is the order of the day. Car parking is provided and the welcoming Owen family extend a warm welcome to their guests.
7 rms (1 bth 4 shr) (1 fmly) No dogs 5P No coaches
ROOMS: (incl. bkfst) s £19-£24; d £34-£40 *

★66% ***Brigstock***
1 St David's Place LL30 2UG ☎ 01492 876416
Closed Dec-Jan
Situated in a quiet residential area of the town and within easy walking distance of the shopping centre and sea front, this hotel is bright and sparkling throughout. Bedrooms are equipped with modern facilities and pretty fabrics and wallpapers are used to good effect. Pauline and Ray Southon extend a warm welcome to their guests and only non-smokers are accommodated.
10 rms (3 bth 3 shr) (2 fmly) No smoking in all bedrooms CTV in all bedrooms No dogs 5P No coaches No children 3yrs V meals Last d 4.30pm

★66% **Ravenhurst**
West Pde LL30 2BB (on West Shore, opposite boating pool)
☎ 01492 875525
Closed Dec-Feb
This long-established family-run hotel is situated on the pretty West Shore. Many bedrooms face the Conwy Estuary and there are good views towards the hills of Snowdonia. Bedrooms are well decorated and include several family suites of adjoining rooms. A choice of sitting rooms is provided.
25 en suite (bth/shr) (3 fmly) CTV in all bedrooms 15P V meals Coffee am Tea pm Last d 6pm
ROOMS: (incl. bkfst & dinner) s £24-£27; d £48-£54 * **LB**
OFF-PEAK: (incl. bkfst & dinner) s £22-£25
MEALS: Lunch fr £5 Dinner fr £10*
CARDS:

★65% ***Clontarf***
1 Great Ormes Rd, West Shore LL30 2AR ☎ 01492 877621
Mar-Oct
A stone's throw away from the West Shore, in a residential area at the foot of the Great Orme, this solid detached period house offers a warm welcome. Bedrooms vary in size, and it is worth asking for one of the larger. In the comfortable lounge guests can enjoy a drink from the dispense bar as they watch TV, and the attractive dining room serves honest home-cooked meals. Expect to be asked for your dinner choice at breakfast or on arrival.
9 rms (5 bth/shr) (2 fmly) No dogs 9P No coaches No children 8yrs Last d 6pm

★65% **Warwick**
56 Church Walks LL30 2HL ☎ 01492 876823
This large house dates back to the 1880's and has been in the present owner's family for nearly 60 years. It stands beneath the Great Orme and from its elevated position, it commands views across the town to the hills beyond. It is within a few minutes walk of the shops and other amenities. Personally run in an informal and friendly manner, it provides modern equipped accommodation, which includes family bedded rooms. In addition to the pleasant dining room, there is a comfortable lounge and a lounge bar. The house is fronted by an attractive terraced garden, part of which has been converted into a small car park.
15 rms CTV in all bedrooms P
ROOMS: (incl. bkfst) s fr £24; d fr £48 *
CARDS:

★61% **Min-y-Don**
North Pde LL30 2LP ☎ 01492 876511 FAX 01492 878169
Closed Dec-Jan
This relaxing holiday hotel is situated on the pier end of the promenade and is within easy walking distance of the main shopping centre. It is run by the friendly Verma family and offers pretty bedrooms, many of which have good sea views. Most have ensuite facilities and such amenities as televisions and radios are provided. Public rooms are modern and smart and regular live entertainment is held. There is a small car park.
28 rms (2 bth 17 shr) (12 fmly) CTV in all bedrooms No dogs Air conditioning 7P Xmas V meals Coffee am Tea pm Last d 7.30pm
ROOMS: (incl. bkfst) s £20-£22; d £38-£42 * **LB**
MEALS: Lunch £5.95-£6.95 Dinner £6.95-£7.95*
CARDS:

★59% **Quinton**
36 Church Walks LL30 2HN (150yds from St George's church) ☎ 01492 876879 & 875086 FAX 01492 876879
Situated in a quiet side road and only a short walk from the town, this personally-owned and -run hotel offers good value for money. The well equipped bedrooms are gradually being improved, whilst a cosy lounge is provided for guests, together with a basement bar with a pool table.
15 rms (4 bth 5 shr) (7 fmly) CTV in all bedrooms STV 10P Pool table ch fac Xmas Coffee am Tea pm No smoking in restaurant
ROOMS: (incl. bkfst) s £15-£19; d £30-£38 * **LB**
MEALS: Lunch £3.50-£7*

LLANELLI Carmarthenshire Map 02 SN50

★★★63% **Diplomat**
Felinfoel SA15 3PJ
☎ 01554 756156 FAX 01554 751649
This large Victorian house, now a privately owned hotel, has been much extended in recent times. It is located at Felinfoel, on the A476 road to Llandeillo. It provides modern furnished and equipped accommodation. Some of the bedrooms are on the ground and first floor of a separate house in the grounds. In addition to the lounge bar and restaurant, facilities include a large function room, a conference room and a well equipped leisure club.
23 en suite (bth/shr) 8 annexe en suite (bth/shr) (2 fmly) CTV in all bedrooms Lift 300P Indoor swimming pool (heated) Sauna Solarium Gym Turkish bath Wkly live entertainment English,French & Welsh Cuisine V meals Coffee am Tea pm Last d 10.45pm
MEALS: Lunch £6.95-£12.95&alc Dinner £15.95&alc*
CONF: Thtr 300 Class 100 Del from £75
CARDS:

★★65% **Ashburnham**
Ashburnham Rd, Pembrey SA16 0TH (take A484 for Pembrey, look out for hotel sign on entering village)
☎ 01554 834343 & 834455 FAX 01554 834483
RS 25 Dec
This privately owned hotel is located at Pembrey, to the west of Llanelli, via the A484 road to Carmarthen. Amelia Earhart stayed here, in 1928, after landing her seaplane at nearby Burry Port, at the end of her historic Atlantic crossing from Canada. The hotel was built in the early part of the last century, but has been considerably upgraded in more recent times. The attractively appointed restaurant and lounge bar are both contained in conservatory extensions. The well equipped bedrooms have modern furnishings and include family bedded rooms. Other facilities include a meeting room and a large, self contained function suite.
12 en suite (bth/shr) (2 fmly) CTV in all bedrooms STV Night porter 100P No coaches Pool table ch fac V meals Coffee am Tea pm No smoking in restaurant Last d 9.30pm
ROOMS: (incl. bkfst) s fr £40; d fr £52 *
MEALS: Lunch fr £7.95 High tea fr £4.50 Dinner fr £8.95*
CONF: Thtr 150 Class 150 Board 80 Del from £55
CARDS:

★★63% **Miramar**
158 Station Rd SA15 1YU (opposite railway station) ☎ 01554 754726 & 773607 FAX 01554 772454
This pleasant, small, privately owned and personally run hotel stands opposite the railway station. It provides modern furnished, well equipped accommodation. Facilities include a choice of restaurants, which provide a wide range of dishes, including several Portuguese. One of the restaurants is available as a function room. The hotel also has a pleasant lounge bar.
10 rms (1 bth 7 shr) CTV in all bedrooms STV No dogs (ex guide dogs) 10P International Cuisine V meals
ROOMS: (incl. bkfst) s £16-£20; d £30-£36

MEALS: Lunch £5.25-£8.75*
CARDS:

LLANFYLLIN Powys Map 06 SJ11

★★ 74% **Bodfach Hall**
SY22 5HS (0.5m W at the end of the A490, on the B4393)
☎ 01691 648272 FAX 01691 648272
Closed 3 Nov-1 Mar
Ian Gray and his family have been welcoming guests to their delightful home for more than 20 years. The well maintained, 17th century country house is surrounded by farmland, parkland and extensive gardens and is situated just north of the town. It provides well equipped accommodation, which includes family bedded rooms. The public rooms have a wealth of charm, which is enhanced by original features such as the oak panelling in the dining room. Other facilities include a comfortable lounge, a bar, a conservatory lounge and a room for private meetings and other functions.
9 en suite (bth/shr) (2 fmly) CTV in all bedrooms STV 20P No coaches Fishing Putting green V meals Coffee am Last d 8.45pm
ROOMS: (incl. bkfst) s £34.50; d £69-£72 * **LB**
MEALS: Sunday Lunch £7.50-£9.50 Dinner fr £13.50
CARDS:

LLANGAMMARCH WELLS Powys Map 03 SN94

RED STAR HOTEL

★★★ **Lake Country House**
LD4 4BS (from Builth Wells head W on A483 to Garth (6m approx) turn left for Llangammarch Wells follow signs for hotel)

☎ 01591 620202 & 620474 FAX 01591 620457
An exceptional hotel in exceptional surroundings, the Lake embodies many of the traditions of hotel keeping with its exemplary hospitality and service, and also provides the wealth of facilities associated with modern establishments. Owners Mr and Mrs Mifsud exert a benign influence, with the result that staff are totally guest-focused and nothing seems too much trouble. The house itself is Victorian in origin and is surrounded by landscaped gardens which feature some lovely walks. The bedrooms are carefully styled with comfort the priority and regular guests quickly choose favourites. Chef Richard Arnold is an assured master of his craft, cooking with a great respect for his ingredients; his afternoon teas are a real Edwardian treat. Mr Mifsud is a great wine enthusiast.
19 en suite (bth/shr) (1 fmly) No smoking in 6 bedrooms CTV in all bedrooms Night porter 72P No coaches Golf 6

contd.

Tennis (hard) Fishing Snooker Pool table Croquet lawn Putting green Clay pigeon shooting Xmas English & French Cuisine Coffee am Tea pm No smoking in restaurant Last d 9pm
ROOMS: (incl. bkfst) s £78; d £120-£162 * **LB**
MEALS: Lunch £16.50 Dinner £28.50
CONF: Thtr 80 Class 30 Board 25 Del from £72
CARDS:

LLANGEFNI See Anglesey, Isle of

LLANGOLLEN Denbighshire Map 07 SJ24
See also Glyn Ceiriog

★★★ 69% ***Bryn Howel***
LL20 7UW (2m E on A539) ☎ 01978 860331
FAX 01978 860119
Closed 24-26 Dec

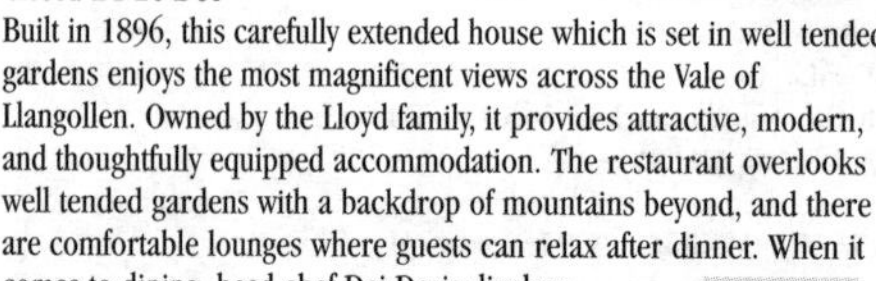

Built in 1896, this carefully extended house which is set in well tended gardens enjoys the most magnificent views across the Vale of Llangollen. Owned by the Lloyd family, it provides attractive, modern, and thoughtfully equipped accommodation. The restaurant overlooks well tended gardens with a backdrop of mountains beyond, and there are comfortable lounges where guests can relax after dinner. When it comes to dining, head chef Dai Davis displays well accomplished cooking skills in his Welsh-influenced cuisine, and produces excellent, imaginative menus.

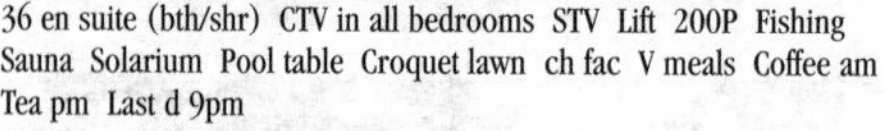

36 en suite (bth/shr) CTV in all bedrooms STV Lift 200P Fishing Sauna Solarium Pool table Croquet lawn ch fac V meals Coffee am Tea pm Last d 9pm
CARDS:

★★★67% **The Wild Pheasant Hotel & Restaurant**
Berwyn Rd LL20 8AD ☎ 01978 860629
FAX 01978 861837
Located in 17 acres of mature grounds, this 19th-century house has been carefully extended over recent years. It now provides modern, well equipped bedrooms and, to meet the demands of the many wedding parties 2 of the rooms have been fitted with 4-poster beds. The large foyer lounge area takes the form of a village square, complete with several mock shop fronts to add authenticity. Bar food is popular and a more formal menu is available in the attractive restaurant.
34 en suite (bth/shr) (2 fmly) CTV in all bedrooms No dogs (ex guide dogs) 250P Xmas Welsh & Continental Cuisine V meals Coffee am Tea pm No smoking in restaurant Last d 10pm
ROOMS: (incl. bkfst) s £48-£50; d £78 * **LB**
OFF-PEAK: (incl. bkfst) s £40-£48; d £55-£78
MEALS: Sunday Lunch £8.95-£9.50 High tea £6.25-£6.75 Dinner £15.50-£18.95&alc*
CONF: Thtr 200 Class 120 Board 50 Del from £45
CARDS:

★★★62% **The Royal**
Bridge St LL20 8PG ☎ 01978 860202
FAX 01978 861824
Queen Victoria once stayed at this hotel, which changed its name from The Kings Head in her honour, at the time it was also active with the passing trade of coaches carrying the Irish mail. It stands in the centre of the town, overlooking the River Dee, and several of its comfortable and recently modernised bedrooms have views over the river as does the Berwyn Restaurant which has also recently been refurbished.
33 en suite (bth/shr) (3 fmly) No smoking in 8 bedrooms CTV in all bedrooms 20P Fishing Pool table Xmas International & British Cuisine V meals Coffee am Tea pm No smoking in restaurant Last d 9pm
ROOMS: (incl. bkfst) s £35-£41; d £70-£82 * **LB**
OFF-PEAK: (incl. bkfst & dinner) s fr £26; d fr £52
MEALS: Sunday Lunch £10.95 High tea £5-£7.50 Dinner £13.95*
CONF: Thtr 70 Class 30 Board 20 Del from £70
CARDS:

★★★60% **Hand**
Bridge St LL20 8PL ☎ 01978 860303
FAX 01978 861277

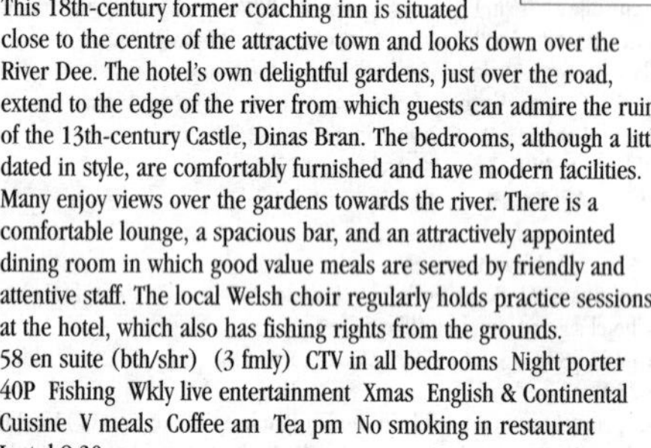

This 18th-century former coaching inn is situated close to the centre of the attractive town and looks down over the River Dee. The hotel's own delightful gardens, just over the road, extend to the edge of the river from which guests can admire the ruins of the 13th-century Castle, Dinas Bran. The bedrooms, although a little dated in style, are comfortably furnished and have modern facilities. Many enjoy views over the gardens towards the river. There is a comfortable lounge, a spacious bar, and an attractively appointed dining room in which good value meals are served by friendly and attentive staff. The local Welsh choir regularly holds practice sessions at the hotel, which also has fishing rights from the grounds.
58 en suite (bth/shr) (3 fmly) CTV in all bedrooms Night porter 40P Fishing Wkly live entertainment Xmas English & Continental Cuisine V meals Coffee am Tea pm No smoking in restaurant Last d 8.30pm
ROOMS: (incl. bkfst) s £55; d £70 * **LB**
OFF-PEAK: (incl. bkfst) s £40; d £60
MEALS: Sunday Lunch fr £8 High tea fr £4.75 Dinner fr £13.95*
CARDS:

LLANGURIG Powys Map 06 SN98

★★67% ***Glansevern Arms***
Pant Mawr SY18 6SY (4m W on A44) ☎ 0686 440240
This pleasant hotel has been personally run by the same owner for over 30 years. Surrounded by impressive mountain scenery, it stands on the A44 some 5 miles west of Llangurig. The traditionally furnished bedrooms are soundly maintained and all have modern equipment and en suite facilities. Thoughtful touches include electric blankets. Public areas offer an attractive dining room with traditional furniture and some fine antique pieces. In cold weather, welcoming log fires burn in both bars and in the spacious lounge.
7 en suite (bth/shr) CTV in all bedrooms 40P No coaches Coffee am Last d 8pm

LLANGYBI Monmouthshire Map 03 ST39

★★★★ 60% **Cwrt Bleddyn Hotel & Country Club**
NP5 1PG (From A449 take A472 through Usk. Turn left after river bridge. Hotel is 4 miles on right)
☎ 01633 450521 FAX 01633 450220

Located in extensive parkland, this hotel dates in part from the 14th

century, and offers a variety of accommodation to suit all tastes. Bedrooms, some in buildings in the grounds, tend to vary in style and include a number of high quality suites. A talented kitchen team produces worthy cooking standards with imaginative dishes making good use of quality produce and fresh ingredients. A recent test meal began with a tasty seafood bisque, followed by breast of pigeon served with a red wine and shallot glaze. Saucing is excellent. A prune and almond tart, and light bread and butter pudding with apricot sauce and vanilla crème anglaise scored equally well.
29 en suite (bth/shr) 7 annexe en suite (bth/shr) (5 fmly) CTV in all bedrooms Night porter 100P Indoor swimming pool (heated) Tennis (hard) Squash Snooker Sauna Solarium Gym Croquet lawn Boules Clay pigeon shooting ch fac Xmas Welsh & Modern European Cuisine V meals Coffee am Tea pm No smoking in restaurant Last d 10pm
ROOMS: (incl. bkfst) s £85; d £105 * **LB**
MEALS: Lunch fr £14.50&alc Dinner fr £24.50&alc*
CARDS:

LLANRWST Aberconwy & Colwyn Map 06 SH76
See also Betws-y-Coed

★★★ 65% ***Plas Maenan Country House***
Conway Valley LL26 0YR (3m N) ☎ 01492 660232
FAX 01492 660551
This long established hotel looks out over the lovely Conwy valley from an elevated position. It stands in some 12 acres of mature grounds and is very popular for local weddings. In addition, it is now licensed to conduct civil marriages. The hall and staircase are impressively panelled and there are several function rooms where business meetings can be held. A wide range of bar food is on offer and the conservatory restaurant serves a good choice of more formal meals. Bedrooms include one full suite as well as several family rooms. Friendly staff offer a warm welcome and ensure a relaxing atmosphere.
15 en suite (bth/shr) (2 fmly) CTV in all bedrooms 100P Welsh, English & French Cuisine V meals Coffee am Tea pm Last d 8.45pm
CARDS:

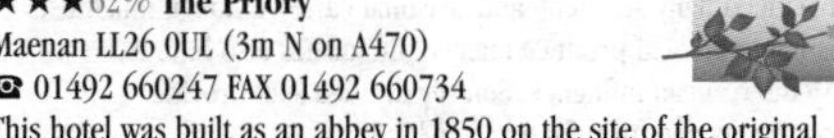

★★★62% **The Priory**
Maenan LL26 0UL (3m N on A470)
☎ 01492 660247 FAX 01492 660734
This hotel was built as an abbey in 1850 on the site of the original 13th-century Cistercian monastery. It lies in several acres of mature grounds alongside the A470, and an impressive feature is the galleried Victorian staircase seen on entering the hall. There are just 12 bedrooms, all well equipped with modern facilities and two with four-poster beds. Two bars are provided and there is a large car park.
12 en suite (bth/shr) (2 fmly) CTV in all bedrooms 60P Fishing Clay pigeon shooting Wkly live entertainment Xmas Welsh, English & French Cuisine V meals Coffee am Tea pm Last d 8.45pm
ROOMS: (incl. bkfst) s £39; d £49 * **LB**
OFF-PEAK: (incl. bkfst) s £45; d £69-£74
MEALS: Lunch £6.95-£15 Dinner £12.50-£17.50*
CONF: Class 50 Board 50 Del from £60
CARDS:

See advertisement on this page

★★62% **Eagles**
Ancaster Sq LL26 0LG ☎ 01492 640454 FAX 01492 640454
Set in the beautiful Conwy valley this family run hotel is very much the centre for local activities. Popular bars serve from an extensive range of menus and the pretty restaurant offers a more formal daily fixed-price choice. There is a large ballroom which is the venue for many local functions and there are ample facilities for business and other meetings. Bedrooms are generally spacious and modern facilities are provided.
12 en suite (bth/shr) (5 fmly) CTV in all bedrooms 60P Fishing Sauna Solarium Pool table Welsh, English & French Cuisine V meals Coffee am Tea pm No smoking in restaurant Last d 8.30pm
ROOMS: (incl. bkfst) s £25-£28; d £35-£40 * **LB**
MEALS: Lunch £6.50-£7.50 Dinner £11.50-£12.50&alc*
CONF: Class 30 Board 20 Del from £30
CARDS:

LLANTWIT MAJOR Vale of Glamorgan Map 03 SS96

★★67% **West House Country Hotel & Restaurant**
West St CF61 1SP (Welsh Rarebits)
☎ 01446 792406 & 793726 FAX 01446 796147
Tucked away in the heart of the village, yet convenient for the M4 and Cardiff Airport, this friendly hotel has a relaxed, welcoming atmosphere. The original 18th century farmhouse has been sympathetically converted, bedrooms are bright and well equipped, and there is a congenial bar and an intimate restaurant. There is also a comfortable conservatory lounge overlooking the small surrounding garden.
21 en suite (bth/shr) CTV in all bedrooms STV Night porter 60P ch fac English & French Cuisine V meals Coffee am Tea pm No smoking in restaurant Last d 9.45pm
ROOMS: (incl. bkfst) s £48-£58; d £65-£72.50 * **LB**
MEALS: Lunch £5.50-£10.95 Dinner £14.95&alc
CONF: Class 70 Del from £60
CARDS:

LLANWDDYN Powys Map 06 SJ01

★★★ 72% **Lake Vyrnwy**
Lake Vyrnwy SY10 0LY (on A4393,200yds past dam)
☎ 01691 870692 FAX 01691 870259
Overlooking a lake and surrounded by woodland, this long-established hotel has been greatly improved. It has elegant sitting rooms and a

contd.

restaurant with a conservatory, and there is also a separate village pub. Bedrooms are furnished with fine antiques and many have views over the lake and the Berwyn mountains. Chef Andrew Wood, as well as using produce from the garden, makes his own bread. Delicious canapés are served before the four-course, fixed-price menu which is changed daily. Many recreational pursuits are available.
35 en suite (bth/shr) (4 fmly) CTV in all bedrooms 70P Tennis (hard) Fishing Riding Game shooting Sailing Cycling Archery Xmas V meals Coffee am Tea pm No smoking in restaurant Last d 9.15pm
ROOMS: (incl. bkfst & dinner) s £63.80-£102; d £81.80-£132.80 * LB
MEALS: Lunch £13.75-£14.75 Dinner fr £22.50
CONF: Thtr 120 Class 60 Board 40 Del £110
CARDS: 

LLANWNDA Gwynedd Map 06 SH45

★★63% **Stables**
LL54 5SD (3m S of Caernarfon, on A499)
☎ 01286 830711 & 830935 FAX 01286 830413
This hotel comes in two parts with the restaurant and bar situated in a converted stable. Bedrooms are in a comparatively modern block set slightly away from the main house, are brightly decorated and include one with a four-poster bed. This building also contains a breakfast room and reception area. All rooms open out onto pleasant lawns where a swimming pool is available during the summer months. Weddings and other functions can be arranged and the popular restaurant specialises in charcoal grills.
14 annexe en suite (bth/shr) (2 fmly) CTV in all bedrooms 40P Outdoor swimming pool Riding Guests may bring own horse to stables ch fac Xmas International Cuisine V meals No smoking area in restaurant Last d 9.30pm
ROOMS: s £35-£45; d £50-£60 * LB
MEALS: Sunday Lunch £9.95&alc Dinner £14&alc
CONF: Thtr 50 Class 30 Board 30 Del from £45
CARDS: 

LLANWRTYD WELLS Powys Map 03 SN84

★ 70% **Carlton House**
Dolycoed Rd LD5 4RA (centre of town)
☎ 01591 610248 FAX 01591 610242
(Rosettes awarded for dinner only)
This late Edwardian house has a wealth of charm, which is enhanced by period furnishings and an abundance of bric-a-brac in the public areas. Personally run in an informal and very hospitable manner by proprietors Alan and Mary Ann Gilchrist, it is a haven of relaxation, with a well deserved reputation for its food. During a recent inspection, dishes enjoyed included beautifully fresh king scallops, perfectly seared and served in a subtly flavoured Thai fish consommé. This was followed by new season Welsh lamb of the highest quality supplied by the local butcher. The meal was rounded off by a quite delicious sticky toffee pudding.
6 rms (4 bth/shr) (2 fmly) CTV in all bedrooms No coaches Pony trekking Mountain biking V meals No smoking in restaurant Last d 8.30pm
ROOMS: (incl. bkfst) s £37.50; d £55-£64 LB
MEALS: Dinner £19.50&alc
CARDS: 

Some well known brand-name hotels share a uniform identity and offer the same facilities throughout Britain. The brand standard is accepted by the AA and they therefore have no star rating. See the section on Hotel Groups at the front of the book.

LLYSWEN Powys Map 03 SO13

RED STAR HOTEL

★★★★ **Llangoed Hall** 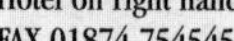

LD3 0YP (follow A470 through village for 2m. Hotel on right hand side) ☎ 01874 754525
FAX 01874 754545
Surrounded by formal gardens and parkland deep in the valley of the Wye and enjoying views of the Black Mountains, Sir Bernard Ashley's splendid largely Edwardian home continues to impress. Inviting day rooms with deep-cushioned sofas, interesting memorabilia and large wood-burning open fires include a small library complete with billiard table and a morning room with a grand piano. Not unsurprisingly, much is made of Laura Ashley furnishings and fabrics which blend well with the antiques that adorn both the public areas and bedrooms; the latter are equally comfortable with several having their own seating areas. The elegant dining room with its yellow picture-lined walls and cornflower blue chairs is a handsome setting for chef Ben Davies' enticing menus which feature a well balanced daily set menu and seasonal carte. Although much use is made of local produce many of the dishes also have a Mediterranean influence. Smartly dressed staff provide courteous and unstuffy service which extends to early morning tea and thorough evening room servicing.
23 en suite (bth) (5 fmly) CTV in all bedrooms STV No dogs (ex guide dogs) Night porter 85P No coaches Tennis (hard) Fishing Croquet lawn Maze No children 8yrs Xmas V meals Coffee am Tea pm No smoking in restaurant Last d 9.30pm
ROOMS: (incl. bkfst) s fr £95; d fr £155 * LB
MEALS: Lunch £13-£16.75&alc Dinner £29.50&alc*
CONF: Thtr 55 Class 30 Board 28 Del from £145
CARDS:

★★ 66% **Griffin Inn**
LD3 0UR (on A470) ☎ 01874 754241 FAX 01874 754592
This long established country inn has justifiably gained a wide international reputation, offering a convivial atmosphere in two bars which bustle with visitors and locals alike. It is popular with shooting parties and fishermen, and suitable venues for both sports can, on request, be arranged by the hotel. Huge log fires burn in a restaurant which has now deservedly gained a rosette award for its very enjoyable dishes, created with flair and imagination. Much of the food used in the kitchen is locally caught, with Wye salmon, trout, hare and venison usually available. Bedrooms are plainly appointed, with few modern frills, but decor and maintenance standards are high. Two comfortable lounges are provided on the first floor.

8 rms (7 bth/shr) 14P No coaches Fishing V meals Coffee am No smoking in restaurant Last d 9pm
ROOMS: (incl. bkfst) s £34.50-£37.50; d £45-£60 * **LB**
MEALS: Lunch £10-£15 Dinner £15-£17.50&alc*
CARDS:

MACHYNLLETH Powys Map 06 SH70
See also Eglwysfach

★★65% **Wynnstay Arms**

Maengwyn St SY20 8AE (at junct of A487/A489)
☎ 01654 702941 FAX 01654 703884
This privately-owned hotel is conveniently situated in the town centre. It provides well equipped comfortable accommodation which, at the time of our last visit, was about to be refurbished. Public areas include a choice of comfortable lounges, a lounge bar and a traditionally furnished restaurant. Other facilities include a room for private meetings.
20 en suite (bth/shr) (3 fmly) No smoking in 7 bedrooms CTV in all bedrooms 30P Xmas International Cuisine V meals Coffee am Tea pm No smoking area in restaurant Last d 9pm
ROOMS: (incl. bkfst) s fr £37.50; d £55-£65 **LB**
OFF-PEAK: (incl. bkfst) s fr £32.50; d £45-£55
MEALS: Lunch £5.95-£8.95 Dinner £14.95&alc*
CONF: Thtr 40 Class 20 Board 24 Del from £65
CARDS:  

MAGOR MOTORWAY SERVICE AREA Monmouthshire
Map 03 ST48

⇧ **First Motorway Lodge**
Magor Service Area NP6 3YL (junct 23 M4)
☎ 01633 881887 FAX 01633 881896
This modern building provides smart, spacious and well equipped bedrooms, all with en suite bathrooms. Meals may be taken at a nearby family restaurant.
43 en suite (bth/shr) No smoking in 23 bedrooms CTV in all bedrooms STV No dogs (ex guide dogs) 180P V meals Coffee am Tea pm No smoking area in restaurant
ROOMS: s £39.95; d £39.95
CARDS:

MALLWYD Gwynedd Map 06 SH81

★61% **Brigand's Inn**
SY20 9HJ ☎ 01650 531208 FAX 01650 531460
This old coaching inn which dates back to the 15th century is located at the junction of the A470 and the A458. It lies in the heart of Wales and offers a wide range of country pursuits including private fishing, organised shooting parties and country walks. There is a cosy bar and a residents' lounge which features a blazing fire when needed. Beams and exposed timbers abound as well as uneven floors. Bedrooms are neat and well maintained and several have en suite bath or shower rooms.
12 rms (4 bth 1 shr) (2 fmly) 50P Fishing Shooting Xmas V meals Coffee am Tea pm No smoking area in restaurant Last d 9.15pm
ROOMS: (incl. bkfst) s £23-£26; d £40-£46 * **LB**
OFF-PEAK: (incl. bkfst) s £20-£23
MEALS: Lunch £7.95-£15.50 Dinner £14.50-£15.50*
CARDS:

MANORBIER Pembrokeshire Map 02 SS09

★★63% **Castle Mead**
SA70 7TA (A4139 towards Pembroke from Tenby,turn onto B4585 into village and follow signs to beachand castle. Hotel on left above beach)
☎ 01834 871358 FAX 871358
Closed Nov-Feb RS B & B only
This historic hotel occupies a delightful position at the head of a picturesque valley leading to a beach, and for neighbours it has, on the one side a Norman church, on the other a Norman castle. Lorna and Geoff Greasley run their hotel in an informal and friendly style and go to great lengths to make their guests feel welcome. All the bedrooms provide good modern standards of comfort, and three are housed on the ground floor of a nicely converted former coach-house. Rooms catering for families are also available. Day rooms include two comfortable lounges, a small bar and a dining room looking out down the valley. In summer, weather permitting, afternoon teas are served on the lawn.
5 en suite (bth) 3 annexe en suite (bth/shr) (2 fmly) No smoking in 2 bedrooms CTV in all bedrooms 20P No coaches V meals Coffee am Tea pm Last d 8.30pm
ROOMS: (incl. bkfst) s £29.50-£31.50; d £59-£60 * **LB**
OFF-PEAK: (incl. bkfst) s £27.50-£29.50; d £55-£59
MEALS: Sunday Lunch £8.50 Dinner £11.50*
CARDS: 

MENAI BRIDGE See Anglesey, Isle of

MERTHYR TYDFIL Merthry Tydfil Map 03 SO00
See also Nant-Ddu

★★★59% ***Baverstock***
The Heads Of Valley Rd CF44 0LX (approx 3m from Merthyr Tydfil on the A465 westbound) ☎ 01685 386221 FAX 01685 723670
Bright open-plan public rooms and extensive function and meeting rooms are available at this busy commercial hotel on the Heads of the Valley road. Bedrooms are small but well equipped.
53 en suite (bth/shr) (3 fmly) CTV in all bedrooms STV Night porter 300P Pool table Snooker table European Cuisine V meals Coffee am Tea pm Last d 9.45pm
CARDS:

★★68% **Tregenna**
Park Ter CF47 8RF ☎ 01685 723627 & 382055 FAX 01685 721951
Tregenna is a deservedly popular, family-run hotel, a short walk from the town centre. Bedrooms around the car park are large, and though some in the main house are compact, all have excellent facilities. There is a modern bar where bar meals are served. The main restaurant offers a lengthy carte with additional specials.
24 en suite (bth/shr) (9 fmly) CTV in all bedrooms STV Night porter 60P Xmas English, Indian, Italian & Philippino Cuisine V meals Coffee am Tea pm No smoking area in restaurant Last d 10pm
ROOMS: (incl. bkfst) s £40-£45; d £53-£57 * **LB**
MEALS: Lunch fr £9.95 Dinner fr £9.95
CONF: Thtr 70 Class 70 Board 30
CARDS: 

⇧ **Little Diner/Drive Inn**
Dowlais Top CF48 2YE (NE of town, directly at junct of A470/A465)
☎ 01685 723362 FAX 01685 376540
Closed Dec24-25
This small American-style diner is situated on the A465, near its junction with the A470, at Dowlais Top, to the north of Merthyr Tydfil. It provides well equipped modern accommodation, equally suitable for both tourists and travelling business people.
6 en suite (bth/shr) (1 fmly) CTV in all bedrooms Air conditioning 32P No coaches Coffee am Tea pm No smoking area in restaurant
ROOMS: (incl. bkfst) s fr £29; d fr £32.31 *
CARDS:

MILFORD HAVEN Pembrokeshire Map 02 SM90

★★ 63% **Lord Nelson**
Hamilton Ter SA73 3AW (follow signs for railway station and docks)
☎ 01646 695341 FAX 01646 694026
An old stone-built inn overlooking the harbour first opened in 1795 and was renamed after a visit from Nelson. Bedrooms vary in size. A four-poster, family rooms, interconnecting rooms and no-smoking rooms are all available. The attractive restaurant serves generous meals - mainly grills - and there is a lounge bar, popular with the locals.
32 en suite (bth/shr) (1 fmly) No smoking in 2 bedrooms CTV in all bedrooms No dogs (ex guide dogs) Night porter 26P English, French & Italian Cuisine V meals Coffee am Last d 9.30pm
ROOMS: (incl. bkfst) s £30-£42; d £50-£65 * **LB**
OFF-PEAK: (incl. bkfst) s £25-£36; d £40-£55
MEALS: Bar Lunch £6-£10.40 Dinner £10.95&alc*
CONF: Class 40
CARDS:

MISKIN Rhondda Cynon Taff Map 03 ST08

★★★★ 65% **Miskin Manor**
CF72 8ND (leave M4 at junct 34 & follow hotel signs)
☎ 01443 224204 FAX 01443 237606
Closed 25-26Dec. 1Jan
This large stone built manor house is set in 20 acres of wooded grounds and gardens on the banks of the River Ely, yet is convenient for junction 34 of the M4. The public areas are full of charm and character, with ornate ceilings and original wood panelling. The recently refurbished bedrooms have period style furniture and are both spacious and comfortable. They include a suite, rooms with four-poster beds, and rooms on ground floor level. Facilities include extensive function and conference suites and a well equipped health and leisure centre.
32 en suite (bth/shr) No smoking in 12 bedrooms CTV in all bedrooms STV No dogs (ex guide dogs) Night porter 150P No coaches Indoor swimming pool (heated) Squash Snooker Sauna Solarium Gym Croquet lawn Jacuzzi/spa Steam room Badminton Clay pigeon shoot Xmas V meals Coffee am Tea pm Last d 9.45pm
ROOMS: (incl. bkfst) s £80-£85; d £100-£175 * **LB**
MEALS: High tea £6.50-£9.50 Dinner £19.95&alc*
CONF: Thtr 200 Class 60 Board 65 Del £95
CARDS:

MOLD Flintshire Map 07 SJ26
See also Nannerch & Northop Hall

★★★ 65% **Beaufort Palace**
Alltami Rd, New Brighton CH7 6RQ (A55 - take Mold slip road, A494.Through Alltami traffic lights. Over mini r'about by petrol station towards Mold,A5119. Hotel 100yds on right)
☎ 01352 758646 FAX 01352 757132
The Beaufort Park is a well maintained modern hotel conveniently situated a short distance from the North Wales Expressway. Spacious lounge areas are provided with comfortable cane seating, and the coffee lounge has an attractive balcony setting. Squash courts and a games room are avialable for guests to use. Bedrooms include several semi-suites, others suitable for families and many for non-smokers.
106 en suite (bth/shr) (4 fmly) No smoking in 10 bedrooms CTV in all bedrooms Night porter 200P Squash Pool table Darts Wkly live entertainment Xmas International Cuisine V meals Coffee am Tea pm No smoking area in restaurant Last d 9.30pm
ROOMS: (incl. bkfst) s fr £70; d fr £85 * **LB**
MEALS: Lunch £8.95-£12.50 Dinner fr £19.50*
CONF: Thtr 250 Class 120 Board 50 Del from £80
CARDS:

★★ 65% **Bryn Awel**
Denbigh Rd CH7 1BL (NW edge of town, on A541)
☎ 01352 758622 FAX 01352 758625
Public areas and bedrooms at this family run hotel are attractively decorated with pretty papers and rich fabrics. Many bedrooms are located in a nearby building and facilities provided include satellite television. The bar offers a large selection of inexpensive meals whilst the restaurant serves from a carte choice of popular dishes. Staff and owners Terry and Heather Lally are friendly and welcoming.
7 en suite (bth/shr) 10 annexe en suite (bth/shr) No smoking in 5 bedrooms CTV in all bedrooms 44P English & Continental Cuisine V meals Coffee am Tea pm Last d 9.30pm
ROOMS: (incl. bkfst) s £38-£40; d £48-£55 * **LB**
MEALS: Lunch £7.50-£12.50&alc Dinner fr £12&alc
CONF: Thtr 35 Class 20 Board 20 Del from £50
CARDS:

MONMOUTH Monmouthshire Map 03 SO51

★★ 68% **Riverside**

Cinderhill St NP5 3EY (leave A40 signposted Rockfield & Monmouth hotel on left beyond garage & before roundabout) ☎ 01600 715577 & 713236
This privately-owned hotel is situated close to the famous 13th-century Monnow Bridge, with its fortified gatehouse, over the River Monmouth. It provides modern furnished and equipped accommodation, which includes two ground floor rooms, each with an entrance from the car park. Facilities include an attractive restaurant, a pleasant bar, a comfortable conservatory lounge and a function room for up to 120 people.
17 en suite (bth/shr) (2 fmly) No smoking in 2 bedrooms CTV in all bedrooms STV 30P Pool table Xmas European Cuisine V meals Coffee am Tea pm No smoking in restaurant Last d 9.30pm
ROOMS: (incl. bkfst) s £35-£49; d £50-£69 * **LB**
MEALS: Bar Lunch £3.95-£10.95alc Dinner £3.95-£19.95alc
CONF: Thtr 200 Class 100 Board 80 Del from £39.95
CARDS:

MONTGOMERY Powys Map 07 SO29

★★ 67% **Dragon**

SY15 6PA (behind the Town Hall) ☎ 01686 668359
FAX 01686 668359
Originally a coaching inn dating back to the middle of the 17th century, The Dragon is today a modern hotel within a historic building. Many of the original features remain, the old courtyard now being enclosed to provide a seating area. The bar and lounge contain timbers and masonry reputed to have come from the nearby castle after it was destroyed by Cromwell. Quaint, cosy bedrooms include one in the form of a semi-suite. The bar areas are comfortable, and an extensive choice of food is available.
15 en suite (bth/shr) (5 fmly) No smoking in 2 bedrooms CTV in all bedrooms 21P Indoor swimming pool (heated) Xmas Welsh & French Cuisine V meals Coffee am Tea pm No smoking area in restaurant Last d 9pm
ROOMS: (incl. bkfst) s £42-£49.50; d fr £69 * **LB**
MEALS: Lunch fr £16.50&alc Dinner fr £16.50&alc*
CARDS:

MUMBLES (NEAR SWANSEA) Swansea Map 02 SS68
See also Langland Bay and Swansea

★★ 72% ***Hillcrest House***
1 Higher Ln SA3 4NS ☎ 01792 363700
Quietly located in a residential area, Hillcrest House is a modern property with interesting decor. Each bedroom is individually themed with adventurous touches spanning three continents. 'Botswana' has a four-poster bed and safari pictures, for example, while 'Scotland' has

touches of the Highlands. In the restaurant chef/proprietor Yvonne Scott changes the short carte on a regular basis. Using fresh local produce, dishes are created with imagination and attention to detail.
7 rms

★63% **St Anne's**
Western Ln SA3 4EY ☎ 01792 369147 FAX 01792 360537
Offering fine views across Swansea Bay, this popular holiday hotel offers mainly spacious, modern bedrooms, and a comfortable open-plan lounge. Service is informal and friendly and the hotel has the bonus of its own car park.
23 rms (22 bth/shr) 4 annexe rms (2 shr) (1 fmly) CTV in all bedrooms STV 50P Snooker Gym International Cuisine V meals Coffee am Tea pm No smoking area in restaurant Last d 8.30pm
ROOMS: (incl. bkfst) s £30-£33; d £47-£54.50 * **LB**
OFF-PEAK: (incl. bkfst) s £20-£33; d £40-£54.50
MEALS: Lunch £8.75-£10.75 Dinner £10.75&alc
CARDS:

NANNERCH Flintshire Map 07 SJ16

★★70% **The Old Mill Private Hotel**

Melin-y-Wern, Denbigh Rd CH7 5RH (on A541 seven miles west of Mold,in hamlet of Melin-y-Wern - do not turn off A541 into Nannerch) ☎ 01352 741542
FAX 01352 740254
Closed 24-31 Dec
This delightful small hotel is set in pretty landscaped gardens with the River Wheeler running alongside. Originally the stable block of the nearby Wern Mill, it now provides six pine-furnished bedrooms, three of which are reached externally. Trouser presses and hair dryers are included in the many extras provided. There is a cosy cane-furnished lounge for residents and an adjoining room contains information on the touring spots of North Wales. A fixed-price menu offers good wholesome food and the very friendly owners are Neil and Susan Evans. Please note that only non-smokers are accommodated.
6 en suite (bth/shr) (2 fmly) No smoking in all bedrooms CTV in all bedrooms 12P No coaches British Cuisine V meals Coffee am No smoking in restaurant Last d 7pm
ROOMS: (incl. bkfst) s £36-£39.75; d £54-£58.50 **LB**
MEALS: Dinner £13.25-£20.50
CARDS:

NANT-DDU (NEAR MERTHYR TYDFIL) Powys Map 03 SO01

★★★68% **Nant Ddu Lodge**
Cwm Taf CF48 2HY (6 miles north of Merthyr Tydfil)
☎ 01685 379111 FAX 01685 377088
RS 24-30 Dec
This Georgian hotel is set in the impressive scenery of the Brecon Beacons National Park in its own extensive grounds. The present owners, the Ronson family, have tastefully extended and extensively upgraded the accommodation and public areas. The attractively decorated, well equipped bedrooms include family bedded rooms and four bedrooms on the ground floor of a separate building. Facilities include a bright and attractive bistro style restaurant, a traditionally furnished bar a comfortable quiet lounge and a room for private meetings and dinner parties. The hotel has a well deserved reputation for its food.
12 en suite (bth/shr) 4 annexe en suite (bth/shr) (1 fmly) CTV in all bedrooms STV 80P No coaches International Cuisine V meals Coffee am No smoking area in restaurant Last d 9.30pm
ROOMS: (incl. bkfst) s £45; d £50-£59.50 * **LB**
MEALS: Lunch £12-£20alc Dinner £12-£20alc
CONF: Thtr 30 Class 15 Board 20 Del from £50
CARDS:
See advertisement under BRECON

NEATH Neath Port Talbot Map 03 SS79

★★65% **Castle Hotel**

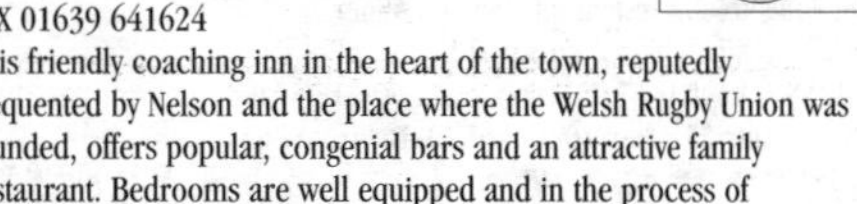

The Parade SA11 1RB (in town centre near railway station) ☎ 01639 641119 & 643581
FAX 01639 641624
This friendly coaching inn in the heart of the town, reputedly frequented by Nelson and the place where the Welsh Rugby Union was founded, offers popular, congenial bars and an attractive family restaurant. Bedrooms are well equipped and in the process of redecoration.
28 en suite (bth/shr) (3 fmly) No smoking in 4 bedrooms CTV in all bedrooms STV No dogs (ex guide dogs) Night porter 26P Xmas English & Continental Cuisine V meals Coffee am Tea pm No smoking area in restaurant Last d 10pm
ROOMS: s £49.50; d £59.50 * **LB**
OFF-PEAK: (incl. bkfst) s £40; d £50
MEALS: Lunch £4.95-£7.25 Dinner £8.50-£13.50&alc*
CONF: Thtr 160 Class 75 Board 50 Del from £65
CARDS:

NEVERN Pembrokeshire Map 02 SN03

★★65% **Trewern Arms**
SA42 0NB (off A487 coast road - midway between Cardigan and Fishguard) ☎ 01239 820395 FAX 01834 811 679
This charming extended 18th-century inn is set in a secluded valley. Bedrooms are spacious and modern and there are quite extensive comfortable public rooms.
9 en suite (bth/shr) (3 fmly) CTV in all bedrooms No dogs 100P Fishing Riding Solarium Gym Pool table Xmas V meals Coffee am
ROOMS: (incl. bkfst) s fr £30; d fr £45 *
MEALS: Sunday Lunch fr £8.50*
CARDS:

NEWPORT Newport Map 03 ST38

★★★★65% **Celtic Manor Hotel, Golf & Country Club**
Coldra Woods NP6 2YA (leave M4 at junction 24, take A48 towards Newport town centre. Celtic Manor is 1st right turn past Newbridge Networks) ☎ 01633 413000 FAX 01633 412910
Perched high above the M4, this classical manor house with modern facilities was due to have a new championship golf course open by mid 1995. Comfortable bedrooms have quality furnishings and there are two restaurants - Hedleys best displays the talents of Trefor Jones; our inspector enjoyed rabbit terrine, scallops with chanterelles and a trio of fillets of beef, lamb and veal with pasta.
72 en suite (bth/shr) (1 fmly) No smoking in 10 bedrooms CTV in all bedrooms STV No dogs Lift Night porter Air conditioning 150P Indoor swimming pool (heated) Golf 36 Sauna Solarium Gym Putting green Jacuzzi/spa Golf Academy Wkly live entertainment ch fac Xmas English & French Cuisine V meals Coffee am Tea pm No smoking area in restaurant Last d 10pm
ROOMS: s fr £89; d fr £99 * **LB**

contd.

N

MEALS: Lunch £6.95-£15.95&alc Dinner fr £19.50&alc*
CONF: Thtr 320 Class 80 Board 60 Del from £119
CARDS:

See advertisement on opposite page

★★★65% **Newport Lodge**
Bryn Bevan, Brynglas Rd NP9 5QN
☎ 01633 821818 FAX 01633 856360
This privately owned, personally run, purpose built, modern hotel is situated on Bryn Bevan hill, above the tunnel through which the M4 motorway runs. It is reached from junction 26 of the M4 by following the road towards Newport and then taking the second left turn. From its elevated position, the hotel commands views of the motorway and the surrounding countryside. It provides well equipped accommodation, a pleasant bistro restaurant and a Victorian style bar. A second bar is also available for private meetings.
27 en suite (bth/shr) (7 fmly) CTV in all bedrooms Night porter 63P Xmas British & French Cuisine V meals Coffee am Tea pm No smoking area in restaurant Last d 9.45pm
ROOMS: (incl. bkfst) s £52; d £72 * **LB**
MEALS: Lunch fr £7.95 Dinner £12.50-£17.50alc*
CONF: Thtr 25 Class 20 Board 20 Del from £64
CARDS:

★★★62% **Kings**

High St NP9 1QU (from town centre, take left hand road (not flyover) right hand lane to next roundabout, 3rd exit off across front of hotel then left for carpark)
☎ 01633 842020 FAX 01633 244667
Closed 26Dec- 1Jan
This privately owned hotel is located in the town centre and the car park has to be accessed by driving through a pedestrianised area. It provides soundly maintained, well equipped, modern furnished accommodation, which includes family bedded rooms. Public areas offer a choice of bars and three eating options, one of which is a Chinese restaurant. Other facilities include no less than three function rooms.
47 en suite (bth/shr) (15 fmly) CTV in all bedrooms STV No dogs (ex guide dogs) Lift Night porter 50P Pool table Wkly live entertainment Xmas V meals Coffee am Tea pm Last d 9pm
ROOMS: s £45-£52; d £57-£65 *
MEALS: Bar Lunch £3-£10 Dinner £8-£20*
CONF: Thtr 150 Class 700 Board 50 Del from £75
CARDS:

See advertisement on opposite page

Hilton National Newport
HILTON
The Coldra NP6 2YG (close to junc24 M4)
☎ 01633 412777 FAX 01633 413087
This is a bright, modern hotel, with an informal restaurant, aimed at both the business and leisure guest. All bedrooms have en suite bathrooms and a range of modern facilities. For more information about Hilton National hotels, consult the Contents page under Hotel Groups.
119 en suite (bth/shr)
ROOMS: s £90-£105; d £180-£210 *
CONF: Thtr 500 Class 250 Board 100 Del from £90

NEW QUAY Cardiganshire Map 02 SN35

★★62% ***Black Lion***
SA45 9PT ☎ 01545 560209 FAX 01545 560585
This privately owned hotel, which dates back to the 18th century, is situated on the road which leads to the harbour and beach. From the rear, it commands views of the bay and surrounding coast line. The accommodation includes family bedded rooms. There is a quaint bar and a pleasant restaurant, which has an abundance of Dylan Thomas memorabilia. Other facilities include a beer garden and childrens play area.
8 rms (6 bth/shr) (3 fmly) CTV in all bedrooms Air conditioning 20P No coaches boules pitch Wkly live entertainment British & Continental Cuisine V meals Coffee am Last d 9.30pm
CARDS:

See advertisement on opposite page

NEWTOWN Powys Map 06 SO19

★★64% **Elephant & Castle**
Broad St SY16 2BQ ☎ 01686 626271 FAX 01686 622123
RS 24-26 Dec
A much extended old hostelry, the Elephant & Castle is situated in the town centre alongside the River Severn. Bedrooms come in a variety of sizes and styles, and some are on the ground and first floors of a separate 16th-century timber-framed building which was originally a bothy. All have modern equipment and en suite facilities. The recently refurbished lounge bar looks very attractive and there is also a pleasant restaurant. Extensive banqueting and conference facilities are available.
24 en suite (bth/shr) 11 annexe en suite (bth/shr) (1 fmly) CTV in all bedrooms STV No dogs (ex guide dogs) Night porter 15P Solarium Gym V meals Coffee am Tea pm No smoking in restaurant
ROOMS: (incl. bkfst) s £36-£45; d £52-£65 *
MEALS: Lunch fr £9
CARDS:

NORTHOP Flintshire Map 07 SJ26

★★★ 75% ***Soughton Hall***
CH7 6AB ☎ 01352 840811 FAX 01352 840382
Closed 1st 2 wks Jan
Built as a Bishop's Palace in 1714 this is a truly elegant and unique country house. It has been lovingly restored by John and Rosemary Rodenhurst and its previous splendour is evident throughout. Bedrooms are individually decorated and each is furnished with fine antiques and rich fabrics. Day rooms, as you would expect, are extensive and the house is surrounded by beautiful lawns and gardens. Michael Carney looks after the kitchens and offers an imaginative carte supplemented by market-available fish dishes.
12 en suite (bth/shr) CTV in all bedrooms No dogs Night porter 40P Tennis (hard) croquet No children 12yrs V meals Coffee am Tea pm Last d 9.30pm
CARDS:

NORTHOP HALL Flintshire Map 07 SJ26

★★★64% **All Seasons Lodge**
Gateway Services, Westbound A55 CH5 6HB (follow M56,M53,M55 signposted for Conway North Wales,hotel located on A55 on the westbound route)
☎ 01244 550011 FAX 01244 550763
Closed 25-27 December
This modern commercial hotel offers good-value accommodation

which is well equipped and well maintained. Bedrooms all have bed settees which can be used for families and satellite TV is provided. The conservatory restaurant offers a wide choice of food and there is an adjacent bar for residents. Several conference suites are provided and up to 200 guests can be accommodated for weddings and other functions. The hotel is conveniently located alongside the A55 some ten minutes' drive from Chester.

55 en suite (bth/shr) (38 fmly) No smoking in 18 bedrooms CTV in all bedrooms STV No dogs (ex guide dogs) Night porter Air conditioning 185P French Cuisine V meals Coffee am No smoking area in restaurant Last d 10pm
ROOMS: s £36.50; d £39.50 *
MEALS: Dinner fr £12.50&alc*
CONF: Thtr 300 Class 140 Board 90 Del from £72
CARDS: 

Travelodge

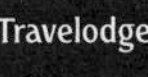

CH7 6HB (on A55, eastbound) ☎ 01244 816473
FAX 01244 816473
This modern building offers accommodation in smart, spacious and well equipped bedrooms, suitable for family use, and all with en suite bathrooms. Meals may be taken at the nearby family restaurant. For information on room rates and to make a booking, call Roomline free of charge on 0800 850950. For more details about Travelodge, consult the Contents page under Hotel Groups.
40 en suite (bth/shr)

OXWICH Swansea Map 02 SS48

★★65% **Oxwich Bay**
Oxwich Bay SA3 1LS (turn left at x-rds in Oxwich village hotel at end of road) ☎ 01792 390329 FAX 01792 391254
Closed 24-25 Dec

contd.

This family-run hotel is superbly located fronting Oxwich Bay, one of the beauty spots of the Gower Peninsula. Guest rooms are modern with attractive coordinating decor and soft furnishings. The hotel's lounge bar, which can get very busy in summer, serves popular bar snacks, and table d'hÙte and à la carte menus are available in the restaurant.
13 en suite (bth/shr) (4 fmly) CTV in all bedrooms STV 250P V meals Coffee am Tea pm No smoking area in restaurant Last d 10pm
ROOMS: (incl. bkfst) s £35-£53; d £59-£79 **LB**
OFF-PEAK: (incl. bkfst) s £30-£48; d £42-£68
MEALS: Lunch £9.95&alc High tea £2.50-£3.95&alc Dinner £14&alc*
CONF: Thtr 75 Class 40 Board 40 Del from £65.95
CARDS:

PEMBROKE Pembrokeshire Map 02 SM90

★★★ 74% **Court**
Lamphey SA71 5NT (from Carmarthen,end M4,take A477 to Pembroke.Just before Pembroke turn left at Village Milton. In Lamphey village our drive is on right - clear) ☎ 01646 672273 FAX 01646 672480
This impressive Georgian mansion was built in 1823. Set in extensive landscaped grounds and gardens, it is located close to the village of Lamphey, to the east of Pembroke. Now a privately owned hotel, it provides well equipped, good quality accommodation, which includes bedrooms on the ground floor of a converted coach house. The tastefully appointed, comfortable public areas include a conservatory, which is used as an informal eating option to the elegant Georgian restaurant. Facilities here include a conference suite with syndicate rooms, a very well equipped leisure centre and two all weather tennis courts.

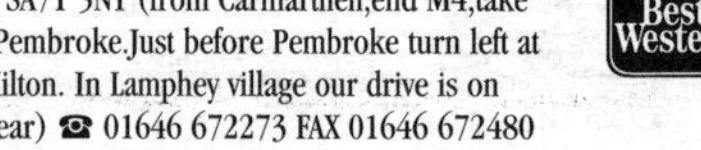

26 en suite (bth/shr) 11 annexe en suite (bth/shr) (15 fmly) CTV in all bedrooms STV 50P Indoor swimming pool (heated) Tennis (hard) Sauna Solarium Gym Jacuzzi/spa Yacht charter Xmas English & French Cuisine V meals Coffee am Tea pm No smoking in restaurant Last d 9.30pm
ROOMS: (incl. bkfst) s £65-£75; d £75-£125 **LB**
OFF-PEAK: (incl. bkfst & dinner) s £39.50-£81; d £79-£127
MEALS: Sunday Lunch £9.95-£17.95&alc High tea fr £2.95 Dinner fr £17.95&alc
CONF: Thtr 80 Class 60 Board 40 Del from £95
CARDS:

See advertisement on opposite page

★★70% **Bethwaite's Lamphey Hall**
Lamphey SA71 5NR (on A4139 Pembroke/Tenby Road in centre of village, opposite parish church) ☎ 01646 672394 FAX 01646 672369
A small village hotel with well kept gardens, Lamphey Hall is back under the careful ownership of the Bethwaite family who, along with a team of willing staff, afford a warm welcome and assure guests of attentive services. The hotel has a range of well equipped bedrooms, a relaxing lounge and a cosy bar. Dinner can be taken in the informal bistro or in the smart surroundings of the a la carte restaurant.
10 en suite (bth/shr) (2 fmly) CTV in all bedrooms 32P No coaches Xmas English & French Cuisine V meals Coffee am
ROOMS: (incl. bkfst) s fr £35; d fr £50 * **LB**
CARDS:

★★60% **Holyland Tavern & Hotel**
Holyland Rd SA71 4PP ☎ 01646 681444 FAX 01646 621544
This large country house, which dates back some 300 years, is set in four and a half acres of grounds and gardens, on the A4075, just to the north-east of Pembroke. It changed hands in 1995 and the new owners have carried out many improvements. Bedrooms all have modern equipment and facilities. Family rooms are available, as is a bridal suite with a four-poster bed. In addition to the lounge bar and attractive restaurant, there is also a function room for up to 160 people.
12 en suite (bth/shr) (2 fmly) CTV in all bedrooms STV Night porter 30P Wkly live entertainment Xmas English & French Cuisine V meals Coffee am Tea pm Last d 9pm
ROOMS: (incl. bkfst) s £25-£30; d £50-£70 * **LB**
OFF-PEAK: (incl. bkfst) s £17.50-£25; d £35-£50
MEALS: Lunch £5-£12&alc Dinner £10-£14.50*
CONF: Del from £45
CARDS:

★★60% **Old Kings Arms**
Main St SA71 4JS (situated in Main Street Pembroke. Approach from Carmarthen,Tenby or Pembroke Dock)
☎ 01646 683611 FAX 01646 682335
Closed 25-26 Dec & 1 Jan
This former coaching inn in the town centre has been in the same private ownership for more than 30 years. The public areas, which include two bars and a quaint cottage-style restaurant, have a lot of charm and character, enhanced by exposed stone walls, stone-flagged floors, beams, an inglenook fireplace and an abundance of bric-a-brac. The bedrooms, although well equipped, are rather functional and do not have a great deal of quality.
21 en suite (bth/shr) CTV in all bedrooms 21P V meals Coffee am Last d 10pm
ROOMS: (incl. bkfst) s £32.50-£37; d fr £37 *
MEALS: Lunch £7.95-£18alc Dinner £13.95-£18alc
CARDS:

PEMBROKE DOCK Pembrokeshire Map 02 SM90

★★★64% **Cleddau Bridge**
Essex Rd SA72 6UT ☎ 01646 685961 FAX 01646 685746
This modern, purpose-built hotel is situated at the end of the Cleddau Bridge, about half a mile from the town centre, from where it overlooks impressive views of both the bridge and the River Cleddau. The modern furnished and equipped bedrooms, which include two suites, are all situated on ground floor level. In addition to the à la carte and set-price menus in the attractive restaurant, there is also a bistro-style food operation in the lounge bar. Other facilities include an outdoor heated swimming pool and two function and conference suites.
24 en suite (bth/shr) (2 fmly) CTV in all bedrooms STV Night porter 120P Outdoor swimming pool Xmas V meals Coffee am Tea pm No smoking area in restaurant
ROOMS: (incl. bkfst) s fr £55; d fr £59.50 * **LB**
MEALS: Lunch £7.50-£12.95&alc*
CARDS:

PENARTH Vale of Glamorgan Map 03 ST17

★66% **Walton House**
37 Victoria Rd CF64 3HY (from M4 junction 33 into Penarth)
☎ 01222 707782 FAX 01222 711012
RS Sun
A well-established, family-run hotel set back in pretty gardens, this sympathetically restored Victorian house provides comfortable public rooms and a welcoming atmosphere. Bedrooms vary in size, some being quite compact, but all are well equipped.
13 rms (11 bth/shr) CTV in all bedrooms No dogs (ex guide dogs) 16P No coaches English, French, Italian & Spanish Cuisine V meals Last d 9pm
ROOMS: (incl. bkfst) s £20-£35; d £47 *
MEALS: Dinner fr £13.50&alc*
CARDS:

★ Hotels with a Red Star Award offer outstanding quality of accommodation and service within their classification. There is a full list at the front of the book.

PENCOED Bridgend Map 03 SS98

★★★72% *St Mary's Hotel & Country Club*

St Marys Golf Club CF35 5EA (just off junct 35 of M4)
☎ 01656 861100 FAX 01656 863400

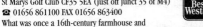

What was once a 16th-century farmhouse and buildings together with the surrounding land, has been developed into a modern hotel and golfing complex, with two golf courses close to junction 35 of the M4 motorway, on the outskirts of Pencoed. The good quality accommodation is spacious, comfortable and well equipped, and there are bedrooms on ground-floor level, one of which has been adapted for guests with disabilities. Public areas include a choice of bars, and "Rafters" restaurant, with its rustic charm enhanced by exposed rafters and stone walls. The pleasant conservatory adjacent to the bar is available for private functions and is a a popular venue for weddings. Other facilities include a conference room in the oldest part of the original house which still has the original inglenook fireplace.

24 en suite (bth/shr) (18 fmly) CTV in all bedrooms STV No dogs (ex guide dogs) Night porter 140P Golf 27 Tennis (hard) Fishing Riding Floodlit driving range ch fac International Cuisine V meals Coffee am Tea pm Last d 10pm

CARDS:

See advertisement under BRIDGEND

Travelodge

Old Mill, Felindre Rd CF3 5HU (on A473)
☎ 01656 864404 FAX 01656 864404

This modern building offers accommodation in smart, spacious and well equipped bedrooms, suitable for family use, and all with en suite bathrooms. Meals may be taken at the nearby family restaurant. For information on room rates and to make a booking, call Roomline free of charge on 0800 850950. For more details about Travelodge, consult the Contents page under Hotel Groups.

40 en suite (bth/shr)

PENMAEN Swansea Map 02 SS58

★★61% *Nicholaston House*

Nicholaston SA3 2HL ☎ 01792 371317

This 19th-century hotel commands a superb position looking out over Oxwich Bay. Accommodation, with sea or country views, has modern furnishings. The restaurant, bar and small lounge overlook the bay and there is a separate breakfast room.

13 en suite (bth/shr) (4 fmly) No smoking in 1 bedroom CTV in all bedrooms 40P No coaches Snooker Welsh & French Cuisine V meals Coffee am Tea pm Last d 9pm

CARDS:

PENRHYNDEUDRAETH Gwynedd Map 06 SH63

★★★ 78% The Hotel Portmeirion

Portmeirion LL48 6ET (2m W, Portmeirion village is S off A487) (Welsh Rarebits)
☎ 01766 770228 FAX 01766 771331

Closed 10 Jan-4 Feb

The location of this high quality hotel, with the sandy estuary at the front and wooded slopes to the rear, must be one of the finest in Wales. It is also part of the famous Italianate village and many of the bedrooms are located here, with most having commanding views. All are individually furnished and decorated, rich fabrics and colours abound and there are many fine antiques; several rooms also have private sitting rooms and balconies. Public rooms are elegant and spacious and these, like the restaurant, look out over the sea towards Snowdonia. Colin Pritchard now leads the kitchen team and produces attractive and enjoyable dishes from a daily-changing menu that uses fresh local produce. Most of the staff are Welsh-speaking and hospitality is warm and friendly.

14 en suite (bth/shr) 23 annexe en suite (bth/shr) (4 fmly) CTV in all bedrooms STV No dogs Night porter 40P No coaches Outdoor swimming pool (heated) Tennis (hard) Xmas V meals Last d 9.30pm

ROOMS: s £65; d £110 * **LB**
OFF-PEAK: s £55; d £90
MEALS: Lunch £13.50-£16 Dinner £25
CONF: Thtr 100 Del from £125
CARDS:

PENYBONT Powys Map 03 SO16

★★64% Severn Arms

LD1 5UA (hotel is situated 5 miles from LLandrindod Wells on the A44 at the junction with the A488) ☎ 01597 851224 & 851344
FAX 01597 851693

Closed xmas

This former coaching inn dates back to the early 19th century, when it was apparently relocated from the other side of the river; it stands on the A44 in the village centre. The traditionally furnished bedrooms are well equipped and family-bedded rooms are available. In addition to the traditionally furnished dining room there are two bars, both with character, and a comfortable lounge for resident guests. Outside is a pleasant lawned garden and patio area.

10 en suite (bth/shr) (6 fmly) CTV in all bedrooms 62P Fishing Pool table ch fac V meals Coffee am No smoking area in restaurant Last d 8.45pm

ROOMS: (incl. bkfst) s £28; d £50 * **LB**
MEALS: Sunday Lunch £6.70 Dinner fr £12
CARDS:

P

PONTERWYD Cardiganshire Map 06 SN78

★★60% ***Dyffryn Castell***
SY23 3LB (beside A44, 2m E) ☎ 01970 890237
Dating back some 400 years, this former coaching inn stands amidst the magnificent scenery of the Plynlimon Mountains, alongside the A44, some 13 miles east of Aberystwyth. The majority of bedrooms have en suite facilities and several are equipped for family occupancy. Guests have a choice of eating in the bright dining room or in the lounge bar. Other facilities include a games room with pool tables and darts, and a lounge for residents.
9 rms (3 bth 3 shr) (6 fmly) No smoking in 2 bedrooms CTV in 6 bedrooms 75P Games room V meals Coffee am Last d 6pm
CARDS:

PONTYPRIDD Rhondda Cynon Taff Map 03 ST08

★★★66% **Heritage Park**
Coed Cae Rd, Trehafod CF37 2NP (off A4058, next to the Rhondda Heritage Park) ☎ 01443 687057 FAX 01443 687060
This is a modern red brick building with bright, comfortable bedrooms, richly styled with bold fabrics, quality furnishings and deep tub chairs. There is a welcoming open plan bar leading to the loft restaurant - a galleried bistro with highly polished floors and pine furniture. A variety of value-for-money dishes is offered from the daily blackboard as well as the carte, and service is friendly.
50 en suite (bth/shr) (4 fmly) No smoking in 20 bedrooms CTV in all bedrooms STV Night porter 146P Indoor swimming pool (heated) Sauna Solarium Gym Jacuzzi/spa Xmas English & French Cuisine V meals Coffee am Tea pm Last d 10pm
ROOMS: s fr £42.95; d fr £47.95 * **LB**
MEALS: Lunch £7.95-£13&alc Dinner £10-£17&alc*
CONF: Thtr 200 Class 160 Board 80 Del from £57.50
CARDS:

★★★63% **Llechwen Hall**
Llanfabon CF37 4HP (1m off A470) ☎ 01443 742050 & 740305 FAX 01443 742189
This one-time farmhouse and Victorian gentleman's residence stands in six acres of grounds overlooking four surrounding valleys. It has been transformed into a small quality hotel of character, run on formal lines with prompt services provided by well turned out staff. Bedrooms are tastefully decorated with bold fabrics and have Victorian-style bathrooms. There is a choice of two restaurants, one with a carte for more intimate and formal dining.
12 en suite (bth/shr) (1 fmly) CTV in all bedrooms STV 100P ch fac Xmas French Cuisine V meals Coffee am Tea pm Last d 9.45pm
ROOMS: (incl. bkfst) s £38.50-£48.50; d £48.50-£68.50 * **LB**
MEALS: Lunch £8.95-£10.95&alc Dinner £10.95-£15&alc
CONF: Thtr 80 Class 30 Board 40 Del from £65
CARDS:

PORT EINON Swansea Map 02 SS48

★68% **Culver House**
SA3 1NN (in village continue past church turn right at post office, 50 yards on turn left, hotel a further 100yds on left) ☎ 01792 390755
This privately-owned and personally-run small hotel is quietly situated, close to the beach. Most of the modern furnished and equipped bedrooms have sea views; family-bedded rooms are available. Only two rooms lack an en suite shower and wc, and each of these has a private bathroom nearby. There is a comfortable lounge containing a bar, and a bright pleasant restaurant.
10 rms (8 shr) (3 fmly) No smoking in all bedrooms CTV in all bedrooms 8P No coaches Xmas V meals Coffee am Tea pm No smoking in restaurant Last d 8.30pm
ROOMS: (incl. bkfst) s £19-£28; d £38-£56 **LB**
MEALS: Lunch £9.95&alc Dinner £11&alc
CARDS:

PORTHCAWL Bridgend Map 03 SS87

★★★61% **Atlantic**
West Dr CF36 3LT ☎ 01656 785011 FAX 01656 771877
This is a busy seafront hotel situated within easy walking distance of the town centre. Its bar is popular for coffees and teas and a wide range of bar food is also available. More formal meals are served in the hotel's restaurant with a daily fixed-price menu as well as an extensive carte choice provided. Bedrooms are fresh and well decorated and many have good sea views that extend towards North Devon and Somerset; some are suitable for families and one has a four-poster bed for that special occasion.
18 en suite (bth/shr) (2 fmly) CTV in all bedrooms STV Lift 20P Xmas V meals Coffee am Tea pm Last d 9.45pm
ROOMS: (incl. bkfst) s £49.50; d £65 * **LB**
OFF-PEAK: (incl. bkfst) s £30; d £50
MEALS: Lunch £13.60-£26.20alc Dinner £12.50&alc*
CARDS:

★★★61% **Seabank**
The Promenade CF36 3LU
☎ 01656 782261 FAX 01656 785363

In a prominent seafront position, this established hotel offers commanding views and bright, comfortable public areas. Since our last visit a number of bedrooms have benefited from quality upgrading, and similar good work is planned for the remainder. Popular for conferences, it provides good access to the M4 and is also a convenient base from which to tour the peninsula.
61 en suite (bth/shr) (1 fmly) No smoking in 6 bedrooms CTV in all bedrooms STV Lift Night porter 150P Sauna Solarium Gym Pool table Xmas English & French Cuisine V meals Coffee am Tea pm No smoking area in restaurant Last d 10pm
ROOMS: (incl. bkfst) s £54.50; d £69.50-£95 * **LB**
OFF-PEAK: (incl. bkfst) s £27.50-£54.50; d £40-£69.50
MEALS: Lunch £4.95-£7.95 Dinner £7.50-£14.50&alc*
CONF: Thtr 350 Class 130 Board 70 Del from £70
CARDS:

★★61% ***Glenaub***
50 Mary St CF36 3YA ☎ 01656 788242
A cosy family-run hotel a short walk from the sea front, the Glenaub is popular with both business guests and tourists. Bedrooms are functional and well equipped, and the restaurant offers long hours of service.
18 en suite (bth) CTV in all bedrooms No dogs 12P No coaches International Cuisine V meals Coffee am Tea pm Last d 10pm
CARDS:

PORT TALBOT Neath Port Talbot Map 03 SS79

★★★64% **Aberavon Beach**
SA12 6QP (M4 junction 41 (A48) and follow signs for Aberavon and Aberavon beach)
☎ 01639 884949 FAX 01639 897885

This privately owned hotel stands on the sea front overlooking Swansea Bay. It was purpose built some 25 years ago and provides fairly modern accommodation which was being refurbished at the time of our last inspection. Family rooms, including a pair of interconnecting rooms, are available, and there are also two executive rooms. In addition to the bright open-plan public areas and restaurant there are good leisure facilities and two self-contained function suites.
52 en suite (bth) (6 fmly) CTV in all bedrooms Lift Night porter 150P Indoor swimming pool (heated) Sauna Jacuzzi/spa All weather leisure centre Wkly live entertainment Xmas Welsh, English & French Cuisine V meals Coffee am Tea pm No smoking area in restaurant

Last d 10.15pm
ROOMS: (incl. bkfst) s fr £55; d fr £60 * **LB**
OFF-PEAK: (incl. bkfst) s fr £46; d fr £50
MEALS: Lunch fr £9 Dinner fr £14.50*
CONF: Thtr 300 Class 200 Board 50 Del from £55
CARDS:

Travel Inn

Baglan Rd SA12 8ES (on roundabout junc 42 M4)
☎ 01639 813017 FAX 01639 823096
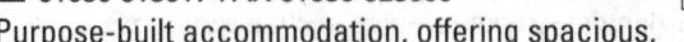
Purpose-built accommodation, offering spacious, well equipped bedrooms, all with en suite bathrooms. Meals may be taken at the nearby family restaurant. For more information about Travel Inns, consult the Contents page under Hotel Groups.
40 en suite (bth/shr)
ROOMS: d £35.50 *

PRESTEIGNE Powys Map 03 SO36

★★70% **Radnorshire Arms**
High St LD8 2BE ☎ 01544 267406
FAX 01544 260418
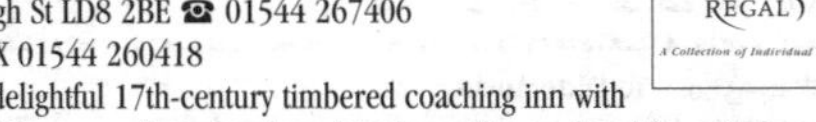
A delightful 17th-century timbered coaching inn with public rooms featuring the original panelling and real fires. Bedrooms are split between the main building and a new one across the pretty garden; the majority are spacious with good seating and a full range of facilities. A welcoming atmosphere is created by management couple Aidan and Denise Treacey who run the property as their own.
8 en suite (bth/shr) 8 annexe en suite (bth/shr) (10 fmly) No smoking in 8 bedrooms CTV in all bedrooms 55P ch fac Xmas British Cuisine V meals Coffee am Tea pm No smoking in restaurant Last d 9.00pm
ROOMS: (incl. bkfst & dinner) s £57-£64.50; d £94-£109 * **LB**
OFF-PEAK: (incl. bkfst & dinner) s £39-£46.50; d £58-£73
MEALS: Lunch £9.95-£11.95 Dinner £15.95&alc*
CONF: Thtr 30 Class 15 Board 18 Del from £75
CARDS:

PWLLHELI Gwynedd Map 06 SH33

★65% **The Seahaven**
West End Pde LL53 5PN (take road to Promenade, hotel on sea front adjacent to golf course & leisure complex)
☎ 01758 612572 FAX 01758 612572
Colin and Diane Theakston, owners of this small hotel, make every effort to ensure their guests are comfortable and well looked after. Bedrooms, half of which are en suite, are bright, freshly decorated and well equipped; some enjoy the most superb views across Cardigan Bay. There is a comfortably furnished lounge, next door to which is a bar and a spacious dining room where a small choice of good, home-cooked dishes is available. The hotel is on the seafront, conveniently situated for the nearby golf course, with the new marina also within very easy reach.
10 rms (5 shr) (3 fmly) CTV in all bedrooms No coaches No children 3yrs Coffee am Tea pm No smoking in restaurant Last d 7.15pm
ROOMS: (incl. bkfst) s £23; d £33-£38 * **LB**
OFF-PEAK: (incl. bkfst) s £20; d £30-£35
MEALS: Dinner £8.50
CARDS:

REDBROOK Wrexham Map 07 SJ54

★★61% **Redbrook Hunting Lodge**
Wrexham Rd SY13 3ET ☎ 01948 780204 FAX 01948 780533
(For full entry see Whitchurch (Shropshire))

REYNOLDSTON Swansea Map 02 SS48

★★ 77% **Fairyhill**
SA3 1BS (just outside Reynoldston off the A4118 from Swansea in the middle of the Gower Peninsula)
(Welsh Rarebits) ☎ 01792 390139
FAX 01792 391358
This 18th-century mansion is delightfully set in 24 acres of wooded grounds in the heart of the Gower. Owning partners, Jane and Peter Camm, Jane's brother Andrew Hetherington and Paul Davies have made many improvements to the accommodation and continue to do so. They are all actively involved in the day-to-day running, ensuring that their guests get the warmest hospitality and the best of care. Chef Paul Davies has a well deserved reputation for the quality of his imaginative cuisine. At a test meal, seared scallops with black fettucini on a creamy saffron sauce was followed by prime fillet of Welsh beef topped with sun-dried tomato butter served on rösti potato. The meal was rounded off by a delicious creamed rice with griddled pineapple and toasted coconut.
8 en suite (bth/shr) CTV in all bedrooms 50P No coaches Croquet lawn No children 8yrs V meals Coffee am Last d 9.15pm
ROOMS: (incl. bkfst) s £75-£140; d £85-£150 **LB**
MEALS: Lunch £7.50-£17.50 Dinner £22-£27
CARDS:

RHOSSILI Swansea Map 02 SS48

★★63% ***Worms Head***
SA3 1PP ☎ 01792 390512 FAX 01792 391115
This privately-owned hotel occupies a superb cliff-top location, from where it commands panoramic sea and coastal views. It provides modern furnished and equipped accommodation, which includes both no smoking bedrooms and family rooms. Public areas include a choice of bars and a bright restaurant.
18 rms (4 bth 8 shr) No smoking in 5 bedrooms CTV in all bedrooms 10P Last d 9pm
CARDS:

RHYL Denbighshire Map 06 SJ08

★★61% **Marina**
Marine Dr LL18 3AU ☎ 01745 342371 FAX 01745 342371
A seafront hotel which is located near the Sun Centre and just a short walk from the resort's shopping areas. Bedrooms, which have modern facilities, include several suitable for families and many have fine sea views. There is a choice of bars, a games room and several function suites are available.
29 en suite (bth/shr) (6 fmly) CTV in all bedrooms No dogs (ex guide dogs) Lift Night porter 75P Pool table Wkly live entertainment Xmas V meals Coffee am Tea pm
ROOMS: (incl. bkfst) s £27.50; d £55 * **LB**
OFF-PEAK: (incl. bkfst) s £22.50
CARDS:

ROSSETT Wrexham Map 07 SJ35

★★★ 73% **Llyndir Hall**
LL12 0AY (5m S of Chester follow signs for Pulford on B5445 on entering Rossett hotel is set back off road)
☎ 01244 571648 FAX 01244 571258
Located on the English/Welsh border, this comfortable, modern hotel is easily reached off the A483 between Wrexham and Chester. It lies in several acres of mature grounds and contains extensive function and conference facilities as well as a fully equipped leisure centre. Bedrooms are spacious and trouser presses are provided in addition to standard facilities. The lounge is elegantly furnished and, as well as the hotel bar, the leisure centre has an extra facility where snacks and

contd.

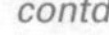

light meals are provided. Jeremy Stone leads the kitchen team in the main restaurant and food continues to be enjoyable, worthy of our one-rosette award.

38 en suite (bth/shr) No smoking in 12 bedrooms CTV in all bedrooms STV No dogs (ex guide dogs) Night porter 80P Indoor swimming pool (heated) Solarium Gym Croquet lawn Jacuzzi/spa Steam room Xmas English & French Cuisine V meals Coffee am Tea pm No smoking in restaurant Last d 9.30pm
ROOMS: (incl. bkfst) s £70-£77; d £100-£115 * **LB**
OFF-PEAK: (incl. bkfst) s £60-£65; d £90-£100
MEALS: Lunch £12.50-£14.50&alc High tea £3.50-£10 Dinner £18.95-£20.95&alc
CONF: Thtr 140 Class 60 Board 40 Del from £100
CARDS:
See advertisement under CHESTER

★★★ 71% **Rossett Hall**

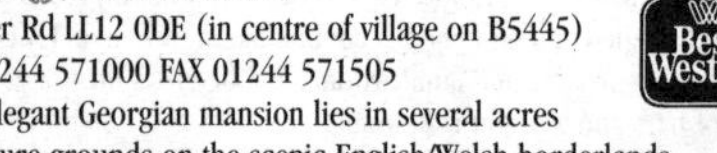

Chester Rd LL12 0DE (in centre of village on B5445)
☎ 01244 571000 FAX 01244 571505
This elegant Georgian mansion lies in several acres of mature grounds on the scenic English/Welsh borderlands. Bedrooms are spacious and comfortably furnished, several have attractive canopied beds and some are suitable for disabled visitors. The restaurant offers a choice of two fixed price menus and food is carefully cooked and enjoyable. Public areas include good function and conference facilities as well as relaxing lounge areas.
30 en suite (bth/shr) (2 fmly) No smoking in 5 bedrooms CTV in all bedrooms STV No dogs (ex guide dogs) Night porter 90P Xmas International Cuisine V meals Coffee am Tea pm Last d 10pm
ROOMS: s £65-£70; d £80-£85 * **LB**
MEALS: Lunch £11.50&alc Dinner £18.50&alc*
CONF: Thtr 200 Class 100 Board 100
CARDS:

R

ROWEN Aberconwy & Colwyn Map 06 SH77

★★ 64% **Tir-y-Coed Country House**
LL32 8TP (turn off B5106 into unclassified road signposted Rowen, hotel is on fringe of village) ☎ 01492 650219
Closed Xmas & New Year RS Nov-Feb
A very pleasant country house hotel set in mature grounds, situated a few minutes from the village, in the picturesque Conwy Valley. Bedrooms are brightly decorated and include some suitable for families. The choice of food is not extensive, but it is enjoyable and cooked with care. There is a small bar and a very comfortable residents' lounge.
7 en suite (bth/shr) 1 annexe en suite (shr) (1 fmly) CTV in all bedrooms 8P No coaches ch fac British Cuisine Coffee am Tea pm No smoking in restaurant Last d 7.30pm
ROOMS: (incl. bkfst) s fr £28; d fr £52 **LB**
OFF-PEAK: (incl. bkfst) s fr £25; d fr £45
MEALS: Bar Lunch £3-£8alc Dinner £11.75
CARDS:

RUTHIN Denbighshire Map 06 SJ15

★★★ 64% **Ruthin Castle**

LL15 2NU ☎ 01824 702664 FAX 01824 705978
Ruthin Castle is situated in 30 acres of splendid gardens and parkland and although the main part was not built until the early 19th century there are many ruins in the grounds from much earlier days and remains of the steep walls overlooking the moat are still very much in evidence. Inside the hotel the public rooms are particularly elegant and include the fine, wood panelled, Library Bar, the sumptuous salon and the very comfortable Cornwallis lounge. There is also a mediaeval banqueting hall, which was one of the first of its kind in Britain, a tea room and a billiards room. Bedrooms are not quite as elegant as the public areas, but have every modern facility and are gradually being refurbished.
58 en suite (bth/shr) (6 fmly) CTV in all bedrooms No dogs (ex guide dogs) Lift Night porter 200P Fishing Snooker International Cuisine V meals Coffee am Tea pm
CONF: Thtr 150 Class 100 Board 30
CARDS:

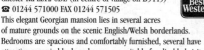

★★ 66% **Ye Olde Anchor Inn**
Rhos St LL15 1DX (on the junction of the A494 and A575)
☎ 01824 702813 FAX 01824 703050
Once an 18th-century drovers inn, this is now a fully modernised market town inn offering friendly hospitality and good food in abundance. Low ceilings and exposed timbers remain and warm fires burn during colder weather. Bedrooms are neat and pretty and satellite TV is provided. Some inter connecting rooms are available and these prove popular with families. The restaurant has built up a sound local reputation. Fresh fish is usually available - look out for blackboard specials, and desserts are all home-made. The bar and restaurant revolve around the enthusiastic and very friendly owners, Rod and Jean England who are fully committed to the well-being of their guests.
14 en suite (bth/shr) (1 fmly) CTV in all bedrooms STV 20P Xmas English & French Cuisine V meals Coffee am Tea pm No smoking in restaurant Last d 9.30pm
ROOMS: (incl. bkfst) s £27.50; d £44 * **LB**
MEALS: Lunch fr £8.45&alc High tea £5-£6.50 Dinner fr £19alc
CONF: Del £35
CARDS:

Clwyd Gate Inn & Motel
Mold Rd (A494), Llanbedr LL15 1YF (A494 Mold-Ruthin road approx 1m from Ruthin) ☎ 01824 704444 & 702667 FAX 01824 703513
This very modern complex is located above the A494 between Mold and Ruthin at Llanbedr. Bed and breakfast accommodation is provided and other meals are available at the nearby inn. One bedroom is situated in the main building and this is spacious and has its own lounge area; the other rooms are reached externally. There are two family units and a further seven double or twin bedded rooms as well as two self-catering cottages. Facilities provided include satellite TV and there is a swimming pool, sauna and jacuzzi. All bedrooms have patio areas and enjoy lovely views over the area.
10 en suite (bth/shr) (2 fmly) CTV in all bedrooms STV 30P Indoor swimming pool (heated) Sauna Jacuzzi/spa
ROOMS: (incl. cont bkfst) s £35.25; d £49.50 *
OFF-PEAK: (incl. cont bkfst) s £35.25; d £49.50

ST ASAPH Denbighshire Map 06 SJ07

★★★ 65% ***Talardy Park***
The Roe LL17 0HY (at A525's junct with A55 coastal expressway)
☎ 01745 584957 FAX 01745 584385
Smart modern bedrooms are offered at this popular commercial hotel. One has a four-poster bed and is ideal for weddings and other special occasions. There are a comfortable residents' lounge, a well equipped

bar and a wide range of food options. The restaurant has a popular carvery, supplementing its carte choice, and the coffee shop serves bar food from a blackboard menu. There is a large car park and, also in the grounds, a night club where regular entertainment is held.
18 en suite (bth/shr) (1 fmly) CTV in all bedrooms STV Night porter 100P ch fac European Cuisine V meals Coffee am Tea pm Last d 9.30pm
CARDS:

★★★64% **Oriel House**
Upper Denbigh Rd LL17 0LW (turn off A55 on to A525, left at cathedral 1 mile along A525 on right hand side)
☎ 01745 582716 FAX 01745 585208
Closed 26 Dec
Situated in several acres of mature grounds, Oriel House lies alongside the A525, on the Denbigh road, in the lovely Vale of Clwyd. Except for two small singles, bedrooms are quite spacious. One has a four-poster bed and all are well decorated. Function facilities are good with business meetings well catered for and the hotel is also very much in demand for local weddings. Public bars and lounges are comfortable and two full-sized snooker tables are available. Food options are extensive with a large carte menu in addition to the fixed-price and bar meal selection.
19 en suite (bth/shr) (1 fmly) CTV in all bedrooms STV 200P Fishing Snooker English & French Cuisine V meals Coffee am Tea pm Last d 9.30pm
ROOMS: (incl. bkfst) s £40-£47; d £66 * **LB**
MEALS: Lunch £10 Dinner £15.95&alc*
CONF: Thtr 250 Class 150 Board 50 Del from £70
CARDS:

★★68% **Plas Elwy Hotel & Restaurant**
The Roe LL17 0LT (close to A55 at junct with A525)
☎ 01745 582263 & 582089 FAX 01745 583864
Closed 26-31 Dec
This very friendly small hotel run by Caroline and Phillip Woolley dates in part from 1850 and has a modern extension housing spacious bedrooms and a small lounge. Rooms in the main building are rather smaller but these, like the others, are well equipped with modern facilities. The restaurant specialises in steaks but other dishes are also available. There is a cosy bar for residents.
7 en suite (bth/shr) 6 annexe en suite (bth/shr) (2 fmly) CTV in all bedrooms No dogs (ex guide dogs) 28P No coaches British Cuisine V meals Coffee am No smoking in restaurant Last d 10pm
ROOMS: (incl. bkfst) s £38.50-£44; d £55-£65 * **LB**
MEALS: Sunday Lunch £4-£9 Dinner fr £3.50&alc*
CARDS:

ST CLEARS Carmarthenshire Map 02 SN21

★★66% **Forge Restaurant & Motel**
SA33 4NA (1m E, beside A40) ☎ 01994 230300 FAX 01994 231577
Closed 25 & 26 Dec
This friendly motel-style operation offers well equipped rooms in annexes set well back from the road. A busy restaurant/diner provides meals all day and evening.
18 annexe en suite (bth/shr) (8 fmly) CTV in all bedrooms 80P No coaches Indoor swimming pool (heated) Sauna Gym British Cuisine V meals Coffee am Tea pm Last d 9.30pm
ROOMS: (incl. bkfst) s fr £37.50; d fr £55 *
OFF-PEAK: (incl. bkfst) s fr £33.75; d fr £49.50
MEALS: Lunch £6.50-£15 High tea £6.50-£15 Dinner £6.50-£15*
CARDS:

ST DAVID'S Pembrokeshire Map 02 SM72

★★★ 68% **Warpool Court**
SA62 6BN (from Cross Square bear left beside Cartref Restaurant down Goat Street. Pass Farmers Arms on right, follow road to left and signposted at fork) ☎ 01437 720300 FAX 01437 720676
Closed Jan
This large and impressive stone-built Victorian property was originally erected as the cathedral choir school. Set in lovely gardens, it occupies a superb coastal position on the outskirts of the city, from where it overlooks St Brides Bay and the islands. There are various kinds of bedrooms, including family rooms and those with sea views. In addition to the spacious restaurant and lounge bar, there are two comfortable lounges, one of which has a log fire in cold weather. New chef John Daniels produces a seasonally changing, imaginative menu, making good use of available fresh produce.
25 en suite (bth/shr) (4 fmly) CTV in all bedrooms 100P Indoor swimming pool (heated) Tennis (hard) Sauna Gym Pool table Croquet lawn Childrens play area ch fac Xmas English & French

contd.

Cuisine V meals Coffee am Tea pm No smoking in restaurant Last d 9.15pm
ROOMS: (incl. bkfst) s £64-£80; d £98-£118 * LB
MEALS: Lunch £16.95 High tea £4.50-£7.50 Dinner £28
CONF: Thtr 40 Class 25 Board 25
CARDS:

See advertisement on page 907

★★67% Old Cross
Cross Square SA62 6SP (right in centre of St Davids facing Cross Square) ☎ 01437 720387 FAX 01437 720394
Closed Xmas-1 Mar
The original parts of this attractive property date back to the 18th century. Fronted by its own pleasant garden, it stands in the centre of St Davids, opposite the old market square. Privately owned and personally run in a very friendly manner, it provides soundly maintained, well equipped, modern accommodation, which includes family rooms and bedrooms for non-smokers. In addition to the lounge bar and the pleasant dining room, the public areas include a choice of lounges, one of which is for non-smokers.
16 en suite (bth/shr) (1 fmly) No smoking in 5 bedrooms CTV in all bedrooms No dogs (ex guide dogs) 18P No coaches ch fac European & Oriental Cuisine V meals Coffee am No smoking in restaurant Last d 8.30pm
ROOMS: (incl. bkfst) s £33-£42; d £62-£72 LB
MEALS: Bar Lunch £7.50-£12alc Dinner £16&alc
CARDS:

★★67% St Non's Hotel
Catherine St SA62 6RJ (from Cross Square in St Davids bear left between Midland bank and Restaurant,follow road for 700yds, hotel on the left) (Welsh Rarebits) ☎ 01437 720239 FAX 01437 721839
Closed Dec
St Non's Hotel takes its name from the mother of St David, the Patron Saint of Wales. It is situated close to both the famous cathedral and 14th century Bishops Palace. New owners in January 1996 have made a great many improvements, providing well-equipped modern accommodation, which includes family bedded rooms and bedrooms on ground floor level. The pleasant and attractively appointed public areas include a bright restaurant, a lounge bar and a choice of lounges, including one for non-smokers, which is spacious and comfortably furnished.
21 en suite (bth/shr) (4 fmly) CTV in all bedrooms 40P English Cuisine V meals Coffee am Tea pm No smoking in restaurant Last d 9pm
ROOMS: (incl. bkfst) s £52; d £80 LB
OFF-PEAK: (incl. bkfst) s £47; d £70
MEALS: Bar Lunch £2.50-£18.50 High tea fr £4.25 Dinner £18.50
CONF: Thtr 32 Class 32 Board 32
CARDS:

SARN PARK MOTORWAY SERVICE AREA (M4) Bridgend Map 03 SS98

Travelodge
Travelodge
Sarn Park Motorway Services CF32 9RW (junction 36, M4) ☎ 01656 659218
This modern building offers accommodation in smart, spacious and well equipped bedrooms, suitable for family use, and all with en suite bathrooms. Meals may be taken at the nearby family restaurant. For information on room rates and to make a booking, call Roomline free of charge on 0800 850950. For more details about Travelodge, consult the Contents page under Hotel Groups.
40 en suite (bth/shr)

SAUNDERSFOOT Pembrokeshire Map 02 SN10

★★★67% St Brides

St Brides Hill SA69 9NH (on Tenby road, overlooking the harbour) ☎ 01834 812304 FAX 01834 813303
Closed 1-10 Jan
St Brides is in a prominent position with excellent views of the harbour from many of the bedrooms. The hotel has been professionally run by the same family for 25 years, and offers spacious public rooms and a range of well equipped bedrooms, some with their own lounges.
43 en suite (bth/shr) (2 fmly) No smoking in 6 bedrooms CTV in all bedrooms STV Night porter 70P Outdoor swimming pool (heated) Wkly live entertainment Xmas English & French Cuisine V meals Coffee am Tea pm Last d 9.15pm
ROOMS: (incl. bkfst) s £58-£80; d £94-£135 * LB
MEALS: Sunday Lunch £11-£14&alc Dinner £18.50-£21&alc
CONF: Thtr 150 Class 80 Board 60 Del from £60
CARDS:

See advertisement on opposite page

★★65% Jalna
Stammers Rd SA69 9HH ☎ 018341 812282 FAX 01834 812282
This privately owned and personally run, friendly hotel is situated just 200 yards from the sea front and harbour. It provides very soundly maintained accommodation, which includes bedrooms on ground floor level and family bedded rooms. The only room without an en-suite facility has its own private bathroom immediately opposite. Facilities include a lounge bar, a bright and attractively decorated dining room, a small no smoking lounge and a solarium.
13 en suite (bth/shr) (7 fmly) No smoking in 6 bedrooms CTV in all bedrooms 14P Solarium V meals Coffee am No smoking in restaurant Last d 5.30pm
ROOMS: (incl. bkfst) s £20-£30; d £40-£50 * LB
MEALS: Dinner £7.50-£9.50*
CARDS:

★★64% *Merlewood*
St Brides Hill SA69 9NP ☎ 01834 812421 & 813295
Closed Nov-Etr
This well-maintained modern hotel is situated off St Brides Hill, a few minutes' walk from the village centre and the beach. Bedrooms have modern furnishings, equipment and facilities and there are both family and ground floor rooms. There are lovely views and spacious grounds in which to relax.
34 rms (17 bth 13 shr) (8 fmly) CTV in all bedrooms No dogs (ex guide dogs) 34P Outdoor swimming pool (heated) Wkly live entertainment V meals Tea pm Last d 8pm
CARDS:

★★64% Rhodewood House
St Brides Hill SA69 9NU (M4, take A48 to Carmarthen then A40 to St Clears,then A477 to Kilgetty,then A478 to Tenby,turn left onto B4316 signposted Saundersfoot) ☎ 01834 812200 FAX 01834 811863
Set in gardens containing a children's play area, this privately owned and personally run hotel is situated a few hundred yards uphill from

the sea front and harbour. It provides well equipped accommodation which includes no smoking bedrooms and family bedded rooms. Public areas include a lounge bar, a snooker room and a large dining room, where entertainment is provided.
44 en suite (bth/shr) (6 fmly) No smoking in 6 bedrooms CTV in all bedrooms STV 70P Snooker Wkly live entertainment ch fac Xmas V meals Coffee am No smoking area in restaurant Last d 9.30pm
ROOMS: (incl. bkfst) s £24-£33; d £38-£56 * **LB**
OFF-PEAK: (incl. bkfst) s fr £23; d fr £36
MEALS: Sunday Lunch £5.50 Dinner £9.50*
CONF: Thtr 100 Board 100
CARDS:

★★59% **Cwmwennol Country House**
Swallow Tree Woods SA69 9DE ☎ 01834 813430 FAX 01834 813430
This privately owned and personally run hotel stands amidst three acres of woodland, south of the town centre, a short walk from a sandy beach. It provides well equipped accommodation, which includes family bedded rooms. Public areas include a pleasant restaurant, a function room and a cosy bar, where welcoming real fires burn during cold weather.
13 en suite (bth/shr) (3 fmly) CTV in all bedrooms 35P Solarium Xmas English & French Cuisine V meals
ROOMS: (incl. bkfst) s £25; d £40 **LB**
CARDS:

SWANSEA Swansea Map 03 SS69
See also Langland Bay, Mumbles, Oxwich & Port Talbot

★★★★61% **Swansea Marriott**

The Maritime Quarter SA1 3SS (M4 junction 42,take A483 to the City Centre past Leisure Centre, follow signs to Maritime Quarter) ☎ 01792 642020
FAX 01792 650345
Attractively positioned on the marina with commanding views over the bay this large and busy hotel is ideal for the business and leisure guest. It offers a choice of eating options and indoor leisure facilities. Bedrooms are comfortable and equipped with modern facilities.
117 en suite (bth/shr) (51 fmly) No smoking in 50 bedrooms CTV in all bedrooms STV No dogs (ex guide dogs) Lift Night porter Air conditioning 122P Indoor swimming pool (heated) Sauna Gym Jacuzzi/spa Xmas European Cuisine V meals Coffee am Tea pm Last d 10.30pm
ROOMS: s £76-£84; d £76-£94 * **LB**
OFF-PEAK: (incl. bkfst) s £58-£78; d £78-£98
MEALS: Lunch £9-£14 Dinner £16&alc*
CONF: Thtr 250 Class 90 Board 22 Del from £89
CARDS:

★★★61% **Fforest**

Pontardulais Rd, Fforestfach SA5 4BA (on A483 1.5m S of M4 junc 47) ☎ 01792 588711
FAX 01792 586219
Conveniently positioned with good access to the town and major link

contd.

roads, this popular commercial hotel offers well equipped bedrooms and informal, open-plan public rooms and a family restaurant. An upgrading programme is planned for the bars.
34 en suite (bth/shr) No smoking in 4 bedrooms CTV in all bedrooms No dogs (ex guide dogs) Night porter 150P Sauna Solarium Xmas V meals Coffee am Tea pm No smoking area in restaurant Last d 10.30pm
ROOMS: (incl. bkfst) s £59.50; d £65 * **LB**
OFF-PEAK: (incl. bkfst) s £40; d £45
MEALS: Lunch £6-£7.30 Dinner £10-£14.50&alc*
CONF: Thtr 250 Class 80 Board 40 Del from £70
CARDS:

★★ 77% **Fairyhill**
SA3 1BS (Welsh Rarebits) ☎ 01792 390139 FAX 01792 391358
(For full entry see Reynoldston)

★★ 72% **Beaumont**
72 Walter Rd SA1 4QA (on A4118)
☎ 01792 643956 FAX 01792 643044
A little gem of hospitality, comfort and good food, the Beaumont is still being improved by owners Wynne Jones and John Colenso. The bedrooms have quality furnishings and modern facilities. Crisp linen and quality appointments in the conservatory restaurant mark the beginning of chef Brian Evans' domain. Imaginative use of fresh ingredients reflects his international experience, demonstrated by a rich mushroom soufflé and a bold ragout of beef bourguignonne.
17 en suite (bth/shr) No smoking in 1 bedroom CTV in all bedrooms 10P No coaches Welsh, French & Italian Cuisine V meals Coffee am Tea pm
ROOMS: (incl. bkfst) s fr £52.25; d fr £65 * **LB**
CARDS:
See advertisement on page 909

★★ 72% **Windsor Lodge**
Mount Pleasant SA1 6EG (M4 exit 42 onto A483,turn right at lights past Sainsburys,turn left at station,turn rightimmediately after 2nd set of lights)
☎ 01792 642158 & 652744 FAX 01792 648996
Closed 25-26 Dec

Still continuing to generate praise Ron and Pam Rumble's delightful Georgian house promotes charm and character nicely tempered with a high standard of modern comfort. Established here for some considerable time the house is personally run with good back-up from a keen local team of staff who create a welcoming atmosphere. All bedrooms are well equipped and since our last visit are significantly upgraded, all with en-suite and many enlarged. The hotel offers a range of services, including room service, normally associated with higher classification hotels. One of the main strengths of the hotel is the cooking from Ron which has depth and makes good use of quality products with honest textures and flavours.
18 en suite (bth/shr) (2 fmly) CTV in all bedrooms 26P No coaches Sauna English, French & Welsh Cuisine V meals Coffee am No smoking in restaurant Last d 9.30pm
ROOMS: (incl. bkfst) s £40-£50; d £50-£60 * **LB**
MEALS: Lunch £10-£25 High tea £5-£10 Dinner £15-£28
CARDS:
See advertisement on opposite page

★★ 62% ***Oak Tree Parc***
Birchgrove Rd SA7 9JR ☎ 01792 817781 FAX 01792 814542
(For full entry see Birchgrove)

★★ 61% ***Nicholaston House***
Nicholaston SA3 2HL ☎ 01792 371317
(For full entry see Penmaen)

★ 65% **Parkway**
253 Gower Rd, Sketty SA2 9JL (A4118 situated between Sketty and Killoy) ☎ 01792 201632 FAX 01792 201839
Closed 25 Dec-5 Jan
This friendly and popular hotel, personally owned and run by Mr and Mrs Wearing, is an extended house, recently upgraded, with modern, well equipped bedrooms and comfortable open-plan public rooms. The hotel is set back in its own small garden.
13 en suite (shr) CTV in all bedrooms 16P No coaches Outdoor swimming pool British Cuisine V meals Last d 8pm
ROOMS: (incl. bkfst) s £35; d £49 * **LB**
MEALS: Dinner £9.50&alc
CARDS:
See advertisement on opposite page

Forte Posthouse Swansea
The Kingsway Circle SA1 5LS ☎ 01792 651074
FAX 01792 456044
FORTE Posthouse
Suitable for both the business and leisure traveller, this bright hotel provides modern accommodation in well equipped bedrooms with en suite bathrooms. For more details about Forte Posthouse hotels, consult the Contents page for the section on Hotel Groups.
99 en suite (bth/shr)
ROOMS: s £79-£89; d £79-£89 *
CONF: Thtr 230 Class 80 Board 30 Del from £109

Hilton National Swansea
Phoenix Way, Swansea Enterprise Park SA7 9EG (1m S M4,jct 44 & 45, SW of Llansamlet)
☎ 01792 310330 FAX 01792 797535
HILTON
This is a bright, modern hotel, with an informal restaurant, aimed at both the business and leisure guest. All bedrooms have en suite bathrooms and a range of modern facilities. For more information about Hilton National hotels, consult the Contents page under Hotel Groups.
120 en suite (bth/shr)
ROOMS: s £65-£89; d £65-£89 *
CONF: Thtr 170 Class 80 Board 40 Del from £65

Travelodge

Travelodge

Junction 47 M4 Motorway, Penllergaer SA4 1GT (M4 junct 47) ☎ 01792 896222 FAX 01792 898806

This modern building offers accommodation in smart, spacious and well equipped bedrooms, suitable for family use, and all with en suite bathrooms. Meals may be taken at the nearby family restaurant. For information on room rates and to make a booking, call Roomline free of charge on 0800 850950. For more details about Travelodge, consult the Contents page under Hotel Groups.

50 en suite (bth/shr)

ROOMS: s fr £39.95; d fr £39.95 *

CONF: Thtr 25 Class 32 Board 20

TALSARNAU Gwynedd Map 06 SH63

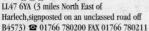

RED STAR HOTEL

★★ **Maes y Neuadd**

LL47 6YA (3 miles North East of Harlech,signposted on an unclassed road off B4573) ☎ 01766 780200 FAX 01766 780211

Dating back to the 14th century this former manor house has been transformed by the Slatter and Horsfall families into a fine hotel. It lies in its own peaceful and beautiful grounds in the heart of the Snowdonia National Park with views of Snowdon and the Estuary. Bedrooms are furnished with fine antique and period pieces and many have been comfortably and attractively

contd.

T

redecorated. Four rooms are in a converted coach house close to the front door. Welcoming log fires burn throughout the public areas in the colder months and, in the better weather, afternoon teas are served on the patio. Chef Peter Jackson leads the kitchen team and provides a daily-changing innovative five-course menu.

12 en suite (bth/shr) 4 annexe en suite (bth/shr) CTV in all bedrooms 50P No coaches Croquet lawn Xmas British Cuisine V meals Coffee am Tea pm No smoking in restaurant Last d 9pm
ROOMS: (incl. bkfst & dinner) s £76-£169; d £152-£209 * LB
OFF-PEAK: (incl. bkfst & dinner) s £72-£159; d £136-£188
MEALS: Lunch £8-£14.95 Dinner £23-£29*
CONF: Thtr 20 Class 20 Board 16
CARDS:

★★66% **Tregwylan**
LL47 6YG (0.5m N, on A496) ☎ 01766 770424 FAX 01766 771317
Closed Jan-mid Feb
The views from this cosy hotel over Cardigan Bay are really superb. It is set in mature grounds in a slightly elevated position and looks out over the estuary towards Portmeirion. Pretty bedrooms are provided, several have attractive canopied beds and facilities include trouser presses and hairdryers. Warm hospitality is a prominent feature here and the Edwards family, who have been welcoming their guests for over 20 years, are genuinely friendly and caring.
10 en suite (bth/shr) (3 fmly) CTV in all bedrooms No dogs (ex guide dogs) 20P No coaches V meals Coffee am Tea pm No smoking in restaurant
ROOMS: (incl. bkfst) s £26-£32; d £52-£56 * **LB**
MEALS: Dinner fr £14.50
CARDS:

★★63% **Estuary Motel**
LL47 6TA (4m N of Harlech, on the A496) ☎ 01766 771155
This family run hotel was built in the early 'seventies' in the form of a motel. It has been refurbished over recent years and now offers sound modern accommodation. The bedrooms, which are reached externally, are all at ground-floor level and most have comfortable cane seating. Public areas are in the open-plan mode and include a small lounge and foyer area and a cosy bar.
10 en suite (bth/shr) (2 fmly) CTV in all bedrooms Night porter 30P No coaches Xmas British Cuisine V meals Coffee am Tea pm Last d 8.45pm
ROOMS: (incl. bkfst) s £25; d £40-£46 **LB**
MEALS: Dinner £8-£16alc*
CARDS:

For the key to symbols and abbreviations, please see the bookmark inside the back cover

TAL-Y-BONT (NEAR CONWY) Gwynedd Map 06 SH76

★★67% **Lodge**
LL32 8YX (on B5106, hotel on right hand side of the road when entering village) ☎ 01492 660766 FAX 01492 660534
RS Nov
A small friendly hotel, the Lodge is situated alongside the B5106 in the heart of the lovely Conwy valley. Bedrooms, in a separate building near the main hotel, all have en suite bathrooms and good quality modern furnishings. The comfortable lounge and bar has a cheerful open fire in the colder months and the attractive restaurant serves a large choice of dishes from fixed-price and à la carte menus. The hotel has its own kitchen garden, producing soft fruit, vegetables and herbs, and honest cooking served in enormous portions has earned the restaurant a large local following.
10 annexe en suite (bth) CTV in all bedrooms 50P British & French Cuisine V meals Coffee am Tea pm No smoking in restaurant Last d 8.30pm
ROOMS: (incl. bkfst) s £25-£35; d £50-£70 * **LB**
MEALS: Lunch fr £5.95&alc Dinner fr £14.95&alc*
CARDS:

TAL-Y-LLYN Gwynedd Map 06 SH70

★★71% **Minffordd**

LL36 9AJ (at junct of A487/B4405)
☎ 01654 761665 FAX 01654 761517
Closed Jan-Feb RS Nov-Dec
Originally a 17th-century drovers' inn, this hotel enjoys a spectacular location at the foot of Cader Idris. Bedrooms are well equipped, and the cottage atmosphere is enhanced by low beams, exposed stone, slate, and log fires in winter. The welcoming public areas include a pleasant bar, parlour and sun room, with the heart of the hotel firmly in the dining room. A short menu is available offering the best local produce, carefully prepared.
6 en suite (bth/shr) No smoking in all bedrooms No dogs (ex guide dogs) 12P No coaches No children 3yrs British Cuisine Coffee am Tea pm No smoking in restaurant Last d 8pm
ROOMS: (incl. bkfst & dinner) s £62-£65; d £92-£110 **LB**
MEALS: Dinner £18.50
CARDS:

★★69% **Tyn-y-Cornel**
LL36 9AJ (1.5m from junct B4405/A487, on shore of lake) ☎ 01654 782282 FAX 01654 782679
This delightful hotel is located on the banks of Tal-y-Llyn and under the shadow of Cader Idris. Visitors have use of the hotel's superb fishing, with brown trout, sea trout and salmon. Brightly decorated bedrooms are modern and well furnished, all have en suite facilities and several are housed in adjacent buildings. The spacious lounge features a welcoming log fire when needed and the pretty restaurant offers a fixed-price menu. There are attractive grounds with ample car parking, and the team of friendly staff is enthusiastic and caring.
8 rms (6 bth/shr) 9 annexe en suite (bth/shr) (2 fmly) CTV in all bedrooms 61P No coaches Fishing Sauna Solarium Croquet lawn Xmas Welsh & Continental Cuisine V meals Coffee am Tea pm No smoking in restaurant Last d 9pm
ROOMS: (incl. bkfst & dinner) s fr £62.50; d fr £125 *
OFF-PEAK: (incl. bkfst & dinner) s fr £50; d fr £100
MEALS: Lunch £11.25 Dinner £18
CARDS:

TENBY Pembrokeshire Map 02 SN10

★★★70% **Atlantic**
Esplanade SA70 7DU ☎ 01834 842881 & 844176
FAX 01834 842881 ex 256
Closed 21 Dec-15 Jan

T

Occupying a prime position above the South Beach, and enjoying views of the sea and Caldey Island, this popular hotel has private access to the beach. The tastefully decorated and furnished bedrooms vary in size, some being very spacious. Some have sea views, and there are ground floor and family rooms available. All have good modern equipment and en-suite facilities. The elegant public rooms have period furnishings, and include a comfortable lounge and a spacious restaurant, which offers a good choice of dishes. The hotel has its own leisure centre, with pool, spa bath, solarium and steam room.
42 en suite (bth/shr) (11 fmly) No smoking in 2 bedrooms CTV in all bedrooms STV Lift Night porter 30P Indoor swimming pool (heated) Solarium Jacuzzi/spa Steam room Welsh & French Cuisine V meals Coffee am Tea pm Last d 8.30pm
ROOMS: (incl. bkfst) s £46; d £70-£100 * **LB**
MEALS: Bar Lunch fr £2.25alc High tea £3.99-£7.50 Dinner £12-£16.50
CONF: Thtr 40 Class 30 Board 20 Del from £57
CARDS:

★★★64% **Fourcroft**
North Beach SA70 8AP ☎ 01834 842886 FAX 01834 842888
Once a row of Georgian houses, this friendly hotel stands on the cliffs above the harbour and north beach. Bedrooms have modern furnishings and family rooms are available. The restaurant is bright and attractive, and public areas also include a bar and a choice of lounges.
46 en suite (bth/shr) (9 fmly) CTV in all bedrooms Lift Night porter 6P Outdoor swimming pool (heated) Sauna Pool table Jacuzzi/spa Table tennis Indoor bowls Snooker ch fac Xmas International Cuisine V meals Coffee am Tea pm No smoking in restaurant Last d 8.30pm
ROOMS: (incl. bkfst) s £31-£46; d £54-£84 * **LB**
MEALS: Lunch £4.50-£15 High tea £4-£8 Dinner £15-£16&alc
CONF: Thtr 80 Class 50 Board 40 Del from £60
CARDS:

★★68% **Heywood Mount**
Heywood Ln SA70 8DA ☎ 01834 842087 FAX 01834 842087
This 18th-century house stands in extensive gardens within easy reach of both the town centre and the beach. The well equipped bedrooms are attractively decorated with modern furnishings and include ground floor rooms, non-smoking rooms and a two-bedroom family suite. Other accommodation comprises a comfortable lounge, a spacious dining room and an adjoining lounge bar. Ample car parking is available.
21 en suite (bth/shr) (4 fmly) No smoking in 4 bedrooms CTV in all bedrooms No dogs (ex guide dogs) 25P ch fac Xmas British and Continental Cuisine V meals Tea pm No smoking in restaurant Last d 9pm
ROOMS: (incl. bkfst & dinner) s £35-£45; d £70-£90 * **LB**
OFF-PEAK: (incl. bkfst & dinner) s £30-£40; d £60-£80
MEALS: Lunch £8-£12.50&alc Dinner fr £12.50&alc
CONF: Class 50 Board 30 Del from £60
CARDS:

★★64% ***Bellini's***
The Esplanade SA70 7DU ☎ 01834 843333
RS Nov-May
This privately owned and personally run hotel is situated just outside the town walls, at the end of The Esplanade, from where it commands views across South Beach to Caldey Island. Bedroom sizes vary from spacious to compact, but all are well equipped. Rooms with a sea view are available. Bellini's bar/restaurant provides a good choice of Italian dishes in the evening, and it is also open throughout the day for coffee and bar snacks.
15 en suite (bth/shr) 3 annexe en suite (bth/shr) (5 fmly) CTV in all bedrooms STV No dogs No coaches Italian Cuisine Coffee am Tea pm
CARDS:

★★59% **Albany**
The Norton SA70 8AB (follow signs for North Beach - hotel is almost opposite Tourist Info Office) ☎ 01834 842698
This privately owned hotel is conveniently located for access to the North Beach and is within easy reach of the town centre. It provides fairly modern accommodation which includes family bedded rooms. There is a choice of bars and lounges and a pleasant garden with a patio. The hotel is popular with coach parties.
24 en suite (bth/shr) (2 fmly) CTV in all bedrooms Wkly live entertainment Xmas French Cuisine V meals Coffee am Tea pm Last d 8pm
ROOMS: (incl. bkfst) s £24-£29; d £48-£54 * **LB**
OFF-PEAK: (incl. bkfst) s £19-£23; d £38-£46
MEALS: Lunch £9.50 Dinner £12.95-£16.95&alc
CARDS:

★★55% **Royal Lion**
High St SA70 7EX ☎ 01834 842127 FAX 01834 842441
Closed mid Oct-May
This privately owned hotel occupies a prime position overlooking both the harbour and beach. Bedrooms with sea views are available; at the time of our last inspection, plans were in hand to extensively refurbish the bedrooms. Leisure facilities are available and these are situated at the sister hotel, the Royal Gate, which is next door. A private car park for hotel guests is also available and situated a couple of minutes' walk away.
21 en suite (bth/shr) (8 fmly) CTV in all bedrooms Lift Night porter 30P Leisure Complex available next door Welsh & English Cuisine No smoking in restaurant Last d 8.30pm
ROOMS: (incl. bkfst) s fr £35; d fr £65 **LB**
MEALS: Dinner fr £14
CONF: Thtr 70 Board 30 Del from £65
CARDS:

★67% **Hammonds Park**
Narberth Rd SA70 8HT ☎ 01834 842696 FAX 01834 844295
This small, friendly hotel in attractive gardens is very hospitably run by Shirley and Bryn Draper - she hailing from New Zealand and he very much a native Welshman. Well equipped modern bedrooms include some on the ground floor. A conservatory serves as a restaurant and lounge, the separate TV lounge includes an exercise area, and a dark room is available for film developing.
10 en suite (bth/shr) (5 fmly) No smoking in all bedrooms CTV in all bedrooms 11P Gym Jacuzzi/spa Dark room ch fac Welsh & New Zealand Cuisine V meals Coffee am Tea pm No smoking in restaurant Last d 7.30pm
ROOMS: (incl. bkfst) d £38-£44 * **LB**
OFF-PEAK: (incl. bkfst) s £17-£36; d £32-£38
MEALS: Dinner £9&alc
CONF: Class 10
CARDS:

THREE COCKS Powys Map 03 SO13

★★❀❀73% **Three Cocks**
LD3 0SL (on A438, between Brecon & Hereford, next to BP petrol station) ☎ 01497 847215
FAX 01497 847215
Closed Dec & Jan RS Sun lunch & Tue
This delightful 15th-century inn is situated in fantastic Welsh countryside with the Brecon Beacons as a backdrop. The inn retains many original features such as the cobbled courtyard and exposed oak beams, but modern creature comforts are not forgotten, with a relaxing, comfortably furnished lounge. Bedrooms offer sound standards of comfort, with some excellent period pieces of furniture. The dining room forms a showcase for the talents of owner Michael Winstone, a Belgian national who derives inspiration from his

contd.

homeland. Only the finest ingredients are used, with Welsh lamb and Cornish seafood frequently featuring on the interesting menu. Be sure to sample some of the excellent selection of Belgian beers.
7 rms (5 bth 1 shr) (2 fmly) No dogs (ex guide dogs) 40P No coaches Continental Cuisine V meals Coffee am
ROOMS: (incl. bkfst) d £62 **LB**
CARDS:

TINTERN Monmouthshire Map 03 SO50

★★ 68% ***Royal George***

NP6 6SF (on A466) ☎ 01291 689205
FAX 01291 689448
This privately-owned and personally-run hotel has a well deserved reputation for friendly hospitality and good food. Parts of the property date back to 1598, when it was an Iron Master's cottage; it became a coaching inn in the 17th century. Set in lovely gardens with a stream running through, it is situated close to the famous abbey. Most of the modern equipped bedrooms are located in purpose-built separate buildings, overlooking the garden. Ground-floor bedrooms, family-bedded rooms and rooms with balconies are all available. The public rooms are not without character and include a choice of bars. Other facilities include a function room for up to 160 people.
5 rms (2 bth/shr) 14 annexe en suite (bth/shr) (13 fmly) No smoking in 7 bedrooms CTV in all bedrooms 50P English & French Cuisine V meals Coffee am Tea pm Last d 9.30pm
CARDS:

★★ 67% **Parva Farmhouse Hotel & Restaurant**

NP6 6SQ (N of village, on A466 - junction 22 of M4)
☎ 01291 689411 & 689511 FAX 01291 689557
(Rosette awarded for dinner only)
This sympathetically converted 17th-century Wye farmhouse is conveniently located next to the river. Comfortable, recently upgraded bedrooms combine modern conveniences with charm and character, and a relaxed atmosphere makes the hotel popular with both business and leisure users. The food is excellent, fresh local produce being used to create well presented dishes with honest flavours and textures.
9 en suite (bth/shr) (3 fmly) CTV in all bedrooms STV 10P Cycle hire European Cuisine V meals Last d 8.30pm
ROOMS: (incl. bkfst) s £42-£44; d £60-£64 **LB**
CONF: Thtr 16 Class 12 Board 12 Del from £60
CARDS:

T

TREARDDUR BAY See Anglesey, Isle of

TREFRIW Aberconwy & Colwyn Map 06 SH76

★★ 74% **Hafod House**

LL27 0RQ (on B5106 - between A5 at Betws-y-Coed and A55 at Conwy) ☎ 01492 640029
FAX 01492 641351
Closed 1Dec-31Jan Exc.Xmas/NY
Norman and Val Barker have built up this former farmhouse into a fine modern hotel. It is located in the picturesque Conwy Valley and many of the pine-furnished bedrooms have private balconies that take advantage of the views. Bedrooms are provided with many thoughtful extras with baskets of fresh fruit and even Welsh joke books to while away the time. A comfortable sitting room is provided and there is a cosy bar for residents. A fixed-price menu of enjoyable, attractively presented food changes daily and diners can opt for as many courses as they wish.
7 en suite (bth/shr) CTV in all bedrooms No dogs (ex guide dogs) 20P No children 11yrs Xmas English & French Cuisine V meals Coffee am Tea pm No smoking in restaurant Last d 9.30pm
ROOMS: (incl. bkfst) s £34.50; d £69 * **LB**
OFF-PEAK: (incl. bkfst) s £24.50; d £49
MEALS: Lunch £10.95 Dinner £14.95-£19.95alc*
CARDS:

TYWYN Gwynedd Map 06 SH50

★★ 58% **Corbett Arms**
Corbett Square LL36 9DG (near cinema)
☎ 01654 710264 FAX 01654 710359
An improvement programme was well underway at this long established hotel at the time of our visit in the spring. All the bedrooms have been refurbished and now provide bright and well equipped accommodation which varies in size. The hotel has two bars and a short choice of simply prepared dishes is offered in the restaurant, where the service is very informal and relaxed.
40 en suite (bth/shr) (2 fmly) No smoking in 2 bedrooms CTV in all bedrooms Lift 60P Pool table Wkly live entertainment Xmas English Cuisine V meals Coffee am Tea pm No smoking in restaurant Last d 9.30pm
ROOMS: (incl. bkfst) s £26-£32; d £44-£54 * **LB**
OFF-PEAK: (incl. bkfst) s £22; d £39
MEALS: Lunch £6.95-£9&alc Dinner £7.95-£11.95&alc
CONF: Thtr 80 Class 35 Board 35 Del from £60
CARDS:

★ 62% **Greenfield**
High St LL36 9AD (on A493, opposite leisure centre - short distance from railway station) ☎ 01654 710354 FAX 01654 710354
Closed Dec RS Nov-Mar
This small family-run hotel is situated in the centre of the town opposite the leisure centre and enjoys views over the Cader Idris mountains. Bedrooms (some of them suitable for families) are modestly furnished but equipped with modern amenities. The residents' dining room offers a fixed-price menu, and, in season, there is a separate restaurant open to the public where a good range of light meals is offered alongside the more formal carte. There are a cosy bar and a small lounge on the second floor. The hotel does not have a car park, but street parking is available.
8 rms (5 bth/shr) (2 fmly) CTV in all bedrooms No dogs (ex guide dogs) No coaches V meals Coffee am Last d 8.30pm
ROOMS: (incl. bkfst) s £17-£20.50; d £32-£37
MEALS: Lunch £4.25-£7.25 Dinner £7.25&alc

USK Monmouthshire Map 03 SO30

★★★ 73% **Glen-yr-Afon House**
Pontypool Rd NP5 1SY (just outside town, on Pontypool rd - A472)
☎ 01291 672302 & 673202 FAX 01291 672597
This elegant gabled Victorian house with modern extensions is situated in well kept gardens and grounds, five minutes' walk from the centre of Usk. The beautiful scenery of the Wye Valley, the Brecon Beacons and the Black Mountains is all within easy reach, making Glen-Yr-Afon and ideal base for touring. The bedrooms have recently been upgraded - all are tastefully decorated and furnished and equipped with modern comforts. A choice of comfortable lounges is available and the library is popular for special functions. Fresh produce is used in the

production of the dishes offered from a choice of interesting menus, and under the personal supervision of the resident proprietors, a team of willing staff carry out attentive services.
27 en suite (bth/shr) (2 fmly) No smoking in 14 bedrooms CTV in all bedrooms STV Lift Night porter 101P Croquet lawn Xmas V meals Coffee am Tea pm Last d 8.45pm
ROOMS: (incl. bkfst) s £54.05-£58.75; d £65.80-£70.50 * **LB**
MEALS: Lunch fr £13.50&alc High tea fr £5.50 Dinner fr £18&alc
CONF: Thtr 200 Class 100 Board 20
CARDS:

See advertisement on this page

★★★ 69% **Three Salmons**
Bridge St NP5 1BQ (on A472 - junction 24 M4 to A449,first exit - Usk)
☎ 01291 672133 FAX 01291 673979
Set in the town centre, this former coaching inn has been extensively renovated, resulting in a vast improvement in the standard of accommodation. The spacious en suite bedrooms are all attractively furnished and well equipped. Family, four poster and ground floor rooms are all available and most bedrooms are located in a separate building across the road which has been converted from a former coach house and shop. Public areas include a tastefully appointed restaurant, a pleasant lounge bar and various function rooms, one with a magnificent Victorian lantern ceiling. A pleasant garden and an ample car park are both found to the rear of the hotel.
10 en suite (bth/shr) 14 annexe en suite (bth/shr) CTV in all bedrooms No dogs Night porter 45P International Cuisine V meals Coffee am No smoking area in restaurant Last d 9pm
ROOMS: (incl. bkfst) s £46-£49.50; d £70-£84 * **LB**
OFF-PEAK: (incl. bkfst) s £43-£46; d £65-£78
MEALS: Lunch fr £17.95&alc Dinner fr £17.95&alc*
CONF: Thtr 80 Class 15 Board 32 Del from £76
CARDS:

WELSHPOOL Powys Map 07 SJ20

★★ 72% **Golfa Hall**
Llanfair Rd SY21 9AF (1.5 mile west of Welshpool on the A458 to Dolgellau) ☎ 01938 553399 FAX 01938 554777
A delightful small hotel, situated in well maintained mature grounds off the A458 Dolgellau road, overlooking the hills surrounding Powys castle. Four of the bedrooms are located in an adjoining building, and all are modern and well equipped. There is a choice of cosy lounges. The restaurant offers a choice of menus. Private functions and business meetings can be catered for.
10 en suite (bth/shr) 4 annexe en suite (bth/shr) (3 fmly) CTV in all bedrooms 100P Xmas British Cuisine V meals Coffee am Tea pm No smoking in restaurant Last d 9pm
ROOMS: (incl. bkfst) s £45-£55; d £65-£79 * **LB**
MEALS: Lunch £9.95-£14.95&alc Dinner £14.95&alc*
CONF: Thtr 85 Class 50 Board 36 Del £70
CARDS:

★★ 67% **Royal Oak**
SY21 7DG (by traffic lights at A483/A458 intersection)
☎ 01938 552217 FAX 01938 552217
Dating back over 350 years, this traditional hotel stands in the centre of this old market town. It has been modernised over recent years and now provides well equipped bedrooms, all of which are en-suite. There is an attractive restaurant featuring exposed beams, and a choice of bars as well as a comfortable lounge. There are also extensive meeting and function rooms.
24 en suite (bth/shr) (2 fmly) CTV in all bedrooms 60P Xmas Welsh, English, French & Italian Cuisine V meals Coffee am Tea pm No smoking area in restaurant Last d 9.30pm
ROOMS: (incl. bkfst) s fr £45; d £70-£80 * **LB**
OFF-PEAK: (incl. bkfst & dinner) s fr £45; d £160-£180

MEALS: Lunch £9.50-£12.75 High tea fr £7.50 Dinner £13.50-£17alc
CONF: Thtr 120 Class 120 Board 120 Del from £70
CARDS:

WHITEBROOK Monmouthshire Map 03 SO50

★★ 73% **Crown at Whitebrook**
NP5 4TX (turn W off A466, 50yds S of Bigsweir Bridge)
☎ 01600 860254 FAX 01600 860607
Closed 2 wks Jan & 2 wks Aug
The delightful countryside of the Wye Valley is just one of the attractions of the Crown at Whitebrook. Roger and Sandra Bates' fine restaurant with rooms offers some of the most exciting cookery in Wales with careful use of quality ingredients a keynote. Roger coordinates the front of house with skill and aplomb, and his small team of staff are friendly and attentive. The kitchen is the domain of award-winning chef Sandra who chooses her ingredients with care and uses restraint and attention in their combination. At a recent meal a starter of local black pudding served with caramelised apples, smoked bacon and a Calvados cream sauce was an excellent example of a classic combination. Welsh lamb is used to good effect in dishes such as roast loin of lamb with a herb crust, roast shallots and a rosemary jus. Bedrooms are pretty and well appointed, and the comfortable lounge is an ideal venue to peruse Roger's excellent wine list.
12 en suite (bth/shr) CTV in all bedrooms 40P No coaches French Cuisine V meals Last d 9pm
ROOMS: (incl. bkfst) s fr £43; d fr £33 * **LB**
OFF-PEAK: (incl. bkfst) s fr £33; d £33-£40
MEALS: Lunch £15.95-£16.95 Dinner £26.95-£27.95*
CONF: Thtr 18 Class 18 Board 18 Del from £95
CARDS:

W

WREXHAM Wrexham Map 07 SJ34

★★★66% **Cross Lanes Hotel & Restaurant**
Cross Lanes, Bangor Rd, Marchwiel LL13 0TF
(3m SE of Wrexham, on A525) ☎ 01978 780555
FAX 01978 780568

CONSORT HOTELS

Closed 25 Dec (night) & 26 Dec
Built as a private house in 1890, this delightful hotel, standing in over 6 acres of beautiful grounds three miles from Wrexham, retains much of its original charm and has wonderful oak panelling in the hall dating from 1620 and rescued from a grand old house - Emral Hall at Worthenbury. Accommodation meets the needs of today's traveller and offers a fine selection of well produced food. Bedrooms are well equipped and the hotel caters for conferences, weddings and functions. Staff are very attentive.
16 en suite (bth/shr) (1 fmly) CTV in all bedrooms 80P Indoor swimming pool (heated) Sauna Croquet lawn Putting green Fishing rights International Cuisine V meals Coffee am Tea pm No smoking area in restaurant Last d 9.15pm
ROOMS: (incl. cont bkfst) s £58-£68; d fr £84 **LB**
OFF-PEAK: (incl. cont bkfst) s fr £49; d fr £68
MEALS: Lunch £11.50-£12.50&alc Dinner £18.50-£19.75&alc*
CONF: Thtr 100 Class 60 Board 40 Del from £76
CARDS:

★★★ 65% ***Llwyn Onn Hall***
Cefn Rd LL13 0NY ☎ 01978 261225
FAX 01978 363233

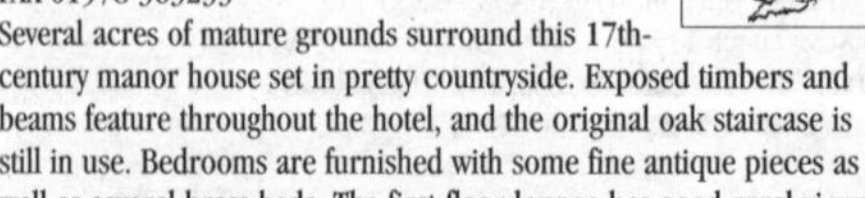

Several acres of mature grounds surround this 17th-century manor house set in pretty countryside. Exposed timbers and beams feature throughout the hotel, and the original oak staircase is still in use. Bedrooms are furnished with some fine antique pieces as well as several brass beds. The first-floor lounge has good rural views, and a blackboard menu is offered in the bar, which has a log fire; restaurant meals are also available.
13 en suite (bth/shr) (1 fmly) No smoking in 4 bedrooms CTV in all bedrooms No dogs (ex guide dogs) 40P V meals Coffee am Tea pm Last d 10pm
CARDS:

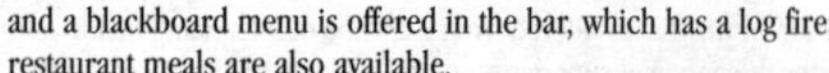

See advertisement on this page

★★★60% **Wynnstay Arms**
Yorke St LL13 8LP ☎ 01978 291010 FAX 01978 362138
This large commercial hotel has a Georgian frontage and lies in the town centre just off the pedestrian precincts. Extensive function and conference facilities are provided and there is a choice of bars. Bedrooms are rather functional by modern standards but all are equipped with trouser presses and other modern amenities.
76 en suite (bth/shr) (16 fmly) No smoking in 4 bedrooms CTV in all bedrooms No dogs (ex guide dogs) Lift Night porter 70P V meals Coffee am Tea pm No smoking area in restaurant Last d 9.45pm
ROOMS: s £35-£39.95; d £52.50 *
OFF-PEAK: s £27.95-£35; d £34.50-£52.50
MEALS: Lunch £7.95-£8.50 Dinner fr £9.95&alc*
CONF: Thtr 50 Class 10 Board 20 Del from £57.95
CARDS:

Travel Inn
Chester Rd, Gresford LL12 8PW ☎ 01978 853214
FAX 01978 856838

Purpose-built accommodation, offering spacious, well equipped bedrooms, all with en suite bathrooms. Meals may be taken at the nearby family restaurant. For more information about Travel Inns, consult the Contents page under Hotel Groups.
38 en suite (bth/shr)
ROOMS: d £35.50 *

Travelodge
Wrexham By Pass, Rhostyllen LL14 4EJ (2m S, A483/A5152 roundabout) ☎ 01978 365705
FAX 01978 365705

This modern building offers accommodation in smart, spacious and well equipped bedrooms, suitable for family use, and all with en suite bathrooms. Meals may be taken at the nearby family restaurant. For information on room rates and to make a booking, call Roomline free of charge on 0800 850950. For more details about Travelodge, consult the Contents page under Hotel Groups.
32 en suite (bth/shr)

IRELAND

Inspectors' Choice Hotel of the Year: Park Hotel, Kenmare

A

ADARE Co Lmerick Map 01 B3

RED STAR HOTEL

★★★★❀ **Adare Manor**

(situated on the N21 from Shannon to Killarney in Adare village) ☎ 061 396566 FAX 061 396124

This magnificent gothic mansion, once the home of the Earls of Dunraven, is situated in 840 acres of woodland and formal gardens beside the River Maigue. Public areas are opulent yet comfortable, especially the Long Gallery, a majestic banqueting room. There is a Cocktail bar and the less formal Tack room, and a wide variety of bedrooms include thirteen staterooms, all with views of the gardens. An 18-hole championship golf course designed by Robert Trent Jones Senior was opened in 1995 and many other leisure and conference facilities are available.

64 en suite (bth/shr) CTV in all bedrooms STV No dogs (ex guide dogs) Lift Night porter 150P Indoor swimming pool (heated) Golf 18 Fishing Riding Snooker Sauna Gym Putting green Clay pigeon shooting.archery Wkly live entertainment Xmas Irish & French Cuisine V meals Coffee am Tea pm No smoking area in restaurant Last d 9.30pm

ROOMS: s IR£112-IR£315; d IR£112-IR£315 **LB**

OFF-PEAK: s IR£112-IR£168; d IR£112-IR£168

MEALS: Lunch IR£14.95-IR£22 Dinner IR£32.50&alc*

CONF: Thtr 300 Class 150 Board 50 Del from IR£118

CARDS:

★★★❀❀❀76% **Dunraven Arms**

(South West Ireland.14 miles from Limerick City. The N20 changing onto the N21. The first building as you enter the village of Adare) ☎ 061 396633 FAX 061 396541

This lovely old-style country inn dates from 1792, and is situated in the midst of thatched cottages in one of Ireland's prettiest villages. Although additions and major refurbishment have taken place, the style and charm of Dunraven have been carefully preserved. The comfortable bedrooms are equipped with all modern facilities, many with their own dressing rooms. The pleasant restaurant is professionally run with tempting dishes and has won a number of awards. Other nearby attractions include hunting, fishing and golf, and the hotel has its own leisure centre.

66 en suite (bth/shr) (1 fmly) CTV in all bedrooms STV Night porter 90P Indoor swimming pool (heated) Golf 18 Sauna Jacuzzi/spa Fully equipped gym & studio Wkly live entertainment Xmas Irish & French Cuisine V meals Coffee am Tea pm Last d 9.30pm

ROOMS: s fr IR£80; d fr IR£110 * **LB**

OFF-PEAK: s fr IR£65; d fr IR£88

MEALS: Lunch IR£12.95 Dinner IR£22.95

CONF: Thtr 300 Class 200 Board 50

CARDS:

AGHADOWEY Co Londonderry Map 01 C6

★★68% **Brown Trout Golf & Country Inn**

209 Agivey Rd BT51 4AD (on A54, 7miles north of Kilrea on the right) ☎ 01265 868209 FAX 01265 868878

Located south of Coleraine on the A54 by the banks of the Agivey River is this well established family run Inn which makes a very special effort to cater for golfers using their own attractive 9 hole course. Attentive and friendly service is provided by Bill O'Hara and his pleasant staff. Spacious bedrooms are within a self contained courtyard area, all rooms are freshly decorated and very well maintained and have a useful range of facilities. The character restaurant, which is located on the first floor overlooking the 9th green, serves hearty home cooked food and offers a reasonably priced wine list; all day service of food is available in the spacious bar lounge.

17 en suite (bth/shr) (11 fmly) CTV in all bedrooms 80P No coaches Golf 9 Fishing Gym Putting green Wkly live entertainment ch fac Xmas Traditional Cuisine V meals Coffee am Tea pm No smoking in restaurant Last d 9.30pm

ROOMS: (incl. bkfst) s £40-£60; d £60-£80 **LB**

MEALS: Bar Lunch £2.75-£9.95alc High tea £6.25-£9.95alc Dinner £7.50-£11.50alc

CONF: Thtr 40 Class 24 Board 28 Del from £45

CARDS:

AHERLOW Co Tipperary Map 01 B3

★★★65% ***Aherlow House***

☎ 062 56147 FAX 062 56212

Near Bansha on the N24.Located in coniferous forest with superb views of the Galtee Mountains, this Tudor-style house offers comfortable public rooms, including a relaxing drawing room, a spacious lounge bar, and restaurant, all of which have views of the forest. Accommodation is well equipped, and a new wing has recently been added. The attentive staff create a warm and friendly atmosphere, and golf, fishing, riding and climbing can be arranged.

30 en suite (bth/shr) (5 fmly) CTV in all bedrooms STV No dogs (ex guide dogs) Lift Night porter 203P English & French Cuisine V meals Coffee am Tea pm Last d 9.30pm

CARDS:

ANNALONG Co Down Map 01 D5

RED STAR HOTEL

★★❀❀ **Glassdrumman Lodge**

85 Mill Rd BT34 4RH ☎ 013967 68451 FAX 013967 67041

This tremendous little hotel has been developed over the years from the original farm to a coffee shop, then restaurant, and eventually a fully fledged hotel. The philosophy of warm hospitality and simple excellence has remained, though, and despite thoughts of even more bedrooms in the next year or so, there is no doubt that such virtues will remain intact. The attractive accommodation includes two sumptuous suites accessed from the courtyard, and all rooms are supplied with fresh flowers, iced water, and fruit as well as offering stunning views of either the coast or the Mourne mountains. The lounges, restaurant, and dining room, with its boardroom-sized pine table, are all nicely appointed and feature cosy open fires. Stephen Webb, self-taught chef, continues to cook consistently

well. His generous 6-course dinners feature local prawns and salmon, together with home-reared pork and chicken. Leave room for good home baking and a hearty Ulster breakfast.

8 en suite (bth/shr) 2 annexe en suite (bth/shr) CTV in all bedrooms STV 10P No coaches Tennis (hard) Xmas English & French Cuisine V meals
ROOMS: (incl. bkfst) s £75-£85; d £100-£125 * **LB**
CONF: Board 20 Del from £95
CARDS:

ATHLONE Co Westmeath Map 01 C4

★★★ 69% **Hodson Bay**
Hodson Bay, Kiltoom (from N6 take N61 to Roscommon. Take right turn - hotel situated 1/2 mile on Lough Ree)
☎ 0902 92444 FAX 0902 92688
On the Co Roscommon side of the River Shannon and right on the shore of Lough Ree, this historic hotel has recently been reconstructed and extended to provide comfortable accommodation. With a golf course to the rear and a marina to the front, most of the rooms have excellent views.
97 en suite (bth/shr) (23 fmly) CTV in all bedrooms STV No dogs (ex guide dogs) Lift Night porter 300P Indoor swimming pool (heated) Golf 18 Tennis (hard) Fishing Sauna Solarium Gym Steam room Wkly live entertainment Xmas Irish & French Cuisine V meals Coffee am Tea pm No smoking area in restaurant Last d 9.30pm
ROOMS: (incl. bkfst) s fr IR£83; d fr IR£105 * **LB**
OFF-PEAK: (incl. bkfst) s fr IR£66; d fr IR£88
MEALS: Lunch IR£9.50-IR£12.50 Dinner IR£18.50-IR£20.50&alc
CONF: Thtr 1000 Class 300 Board 300 Del from IR£88
CARDS:

See advertisement on this page

★★★ 64% **Prince of Wales**
(in centre of town, opposite Bank of Ireland)
☎ 0902 72626 FAX 0902 75658
This modern town centre hotel has a large comfortable restaurant and pleasant, friendly staff.

73 en suite (bth/shr) (15 fmly) No smoking in 4 bedrooms CTV in all bedrooms STV No dogs (ex guide dogs) Night porter 35P Wkly live entertainment Xmas French Cuisine V meals Coffee am Tea pm Last d 9.30pm
ROOMS: (incl. bkfst) s IR£35-IR£45; d IR£33-IR£42.50 * **LB**
OFF-PEAK: (incl. bkfst) s IR£35-IR£40; d IR£33-IR£35
MEALS: Lunch IR£7-IR£10.50 High tea IR£6-IR£12 Dinner IR£17.95&alc*
CONF: Thtr 270 Class 140 Board 50 Del from IR£70
CARDS:

★★ 66% **Royal Hoey**
Mardyke St ☎ 0902 72924 & 75395 FAX 0902 75194
Closed Xmas
Upholding a tradition of warm hospitality is the priority at this family-run hotel in the centre of town. Bedrooms are well appointed, and snacks are available all day in the coffee shop.
38 en suite (bth/shr) (8 fmly) No smoking in 10 bedrooms CTV in all bedrooms STV No dogs (ex guide dogs) Lift Night porter Air conditioning 50P Wkly live entertainment ch fac Irish, English & Italian Cuisine V meals Coffee am Tea pm Last d 8pm
ROOMS: (incl. bkfst) s IR£30-IR£40; d IR£55-IR£70 * **LB**
MEALS: Lunch IR£9.50-IR£12 High tea IR£4-IR£10 Dinner IR£16-IR£18&alc*
CONF: Thtr 250 Class 130 Board 40
CARDS:

BALLINA Co ayo Map 01 B4

★★★ 57% **Downhill**
☎ 096 21033 FAX 096 21338
Closed 23-25 Dec
This family owned and managed hotel is set in beautiful grounds; the

contd.

atmosphere is peaceful and facilities include a health and leisure centre, with salmon fishing and golf available nearby. Variety is the keynote in the restaurant where good value, well prepared dishes are served, and entertainment is provided in 'Frogs' piano bar.
50 en suite (bth/shr) (13 fmly) CTV in all bedrooms STV No dogs (ex guide dogs) Night porter 300P Indoor swimming pool (heated) Tennis (hard) Squash Snooker Sauna Solarium Gym Pool table Jacuzzi/spa Sunbed,step aerobics,steam room Irish & French Cuisine V meals Coffee am Tea pm No smoking in restaurant Last d 9.15pm
ROOMS: (incl. bkfst) s IR£53-IR£60; d IR£82-IR£97.50 * **LB**
MEALS: Lunch IR£10-IR£12 High tea IR£5-IR£12alc Dinner IR£15-IR£22*
CONF: Thtr 500 Class 250 Board 150
CARDS:

BALLINASLOE Co Galway Map 01 B4

★★★67% **Hayden's**
(located on the main Dublin/Galway road N6)
☎ 0905 42347 FAX 0905 42895
Closed 24-26 Dec
This hotel has been family owned and managed for four generations. It is renowned for hospitality and good food, either in the coffee shop, serving tasty home-made snacks throughout the day, or the Garbally Restaurant with its extensive à la carte menu - both overlooking a garden.
48 en suite (bth/shr) (7 fmly) CTV in all bedrooms STV No dogs Lift Night porter 100P Wkly live entertainment International Cuisine V meals Coffee am Tea pm Last d 9.15pm
ROOMS: s IR£30-IR£35; d IR£50-IR£60 **LB**
MEALS: Lunch IR£10-IR£11.50 High tea IR£10-IR£17alc Dinner IR£17.95-IR£19
CONF: Thtr 300 Class 160 Board 50 Del from IR£55
CARDS:

BALLYBOFEY Co Donegal Map 01 C5

★★★62% **Kee's**
Stranolar (1m NE on N15) ☎ 074 31018 FAX 074 31917
This delightful hotel, once a coaching inn, stands on the main street with a large car park to the rear. Recent refurbishment has improved many areas including the pleasant leisure centre. Meals are carefully prepared from fresh produce and the atmosphere is friendly.
36 en suite (bth/shr) (5 fmly) CTV in all bedrooms STV Night porter 90P Indoor swimming pool (heated) Sauna Solarium Gym Mountain bikes for hire Wkly live entertainment Xmas V meals Coffee am Tea pm No smoking area in restaurant Last d 9.30pm
ROOMS: (incl. bkfst) s IR£36-IR£42; d IR£60-IR£72 **LB**
MEALS: Sunday Lunch IR£10 Dinner IR£18&alc*
CONF: Thtr 250 Class 100 Board 30
CARDS:

BALLYCONNELL Co Cavan Map 01 C4

★★★★66% **Slieve Russell Hotel & Country Club**
☎ 049 26444 FAX 049 26474
An imposing building stands in extensive gardens amidst 300 acres of lake and woodland. Attractive public areas include a welcoming foyer lounge, the Fountain Room, bars and two restaurants. Bedrooms are tastefully appointed and comprehensively equipped, and while those in the newer wings are more spacious, all are comfortable and well maintained. Excellent leisure facilities are available at the Country Club, and there is also fishing.
151 en suite (bth/shr) (74 fmly) CTV in all bedrooms STV No dogs (ex guide dogs) Lift Night porter 600P Indoor swimming pool (heated) Golf 18 Tennis (hard) Squash Snooker Sauna Solarium Gym Pool table Jacuzzi/spa Wkly live entertainment ch fac Xmas Irish & French Cuisine V meals Coffee am Tea pm No smoking area in restaurant Last d 9.45pm
ROOMS: (incl. bkfst) s IR£65-IR£85; d IR£120-IR£155 * **LB**
OFF-PEAK: (incl. bkfst) s IR£65-IR£70; d IR£120-IR£130
MEALS: Lunch IR£12-IR£15 Dinner IR£15-IR£25&alc*
CONF: Thtr 800 Class 450 Board 40 Del from IR£103
CARDS:

BALLYCOTTON Co Cork Map 01 C2

★★★65% **Bay View**
(turn off N25 at Castlemartyr and follow signs to Ballycotton)
☎ 021 646746 FAX 021 646075
Closed Nov-Apr
This hotel has been rebuilt to very high standards, reflecting the owner's wish to retain the character of the original building while providing modern comforts and facilities. It has an attractive gabled exterior and inside the public areas are spacious. Bedrooms are comfortable, some with superb views over Ballycotton Bay. Staff are friendly and efficient.
35 en suite (bth/shr) CTV in all bedrooms STV No dogs (ex guide dogs) Lift Night porter Air conditioning 40P Cruiser for hire Wkly live entertainment V meals Coffee am Tea pm No smoking area in restaurant Last d 9pm
ROOMS: (incl. bkfst) s IR£67; d IR£110 * **LB**
OFF-PEAK: (incl. bkfst) s IR£56; d IR£88
MEALS: Sunday Lunch IR£13.50 Dinner IR£25*
CONF: Thtr 60 Class 30 Board 24 Del from IR£90
CARDS:

See advertisement on opposite page

BALLYGALLY Co Antrim Map 01 D5

★★★60% ***Ballygally Castle***
274 Coast Rd BT40 2QR (Hastings)
☎ 01574 583212 FAX 01574 583681
Closed 24 & 25 Dec
This hotel stands on the A2 coast road, from where it enjoys good sea views, it also has attractive gardens which are a feature of the hotel; they have a trout stream running through the grounds. The original castle was built by the Shaw family in 1625, this building contains the olde worlde Dungeon bar, a conference room for up to 50 delegates, and four of the bedrooms. A wing added in more recent times contains the remaining bedrooms, the self-contained function suite, the lounge, and the split level restaurant, which overlooks the walled garden. Bedrooms vary in size and styles, some furnishings are now quite modest, yet all have a good array of modern equipment, including satellite TV, trouser press, and hairdryer.
30 en suite (bth/shr) (1 fmly) CTV in all bedrooms STV No dogs (ex guide dogs) Night porter 100P Tennis (hard) Fishing Putting green Wkly live entertainment French Cuisine V meals Coffee am Tea pm Last d 9.30pm
CARDS:

BALLYHEIGE Co Kerry Map 01 A2

★★★58% **The White Sands**
☎ 066 33102 FAX 066 33357
Closed Nov-Feb
This seaside hotel, in a village near Tralee, has warm attractive colour schemes, a good restaurant, two cosy bars and a pleasant staff. There is a car park to the rear with a sandy beach and a championship golf course nearby.
75 en suite (bth/shr) CTV in all bedrooms STV Night porter Air conditioning P Golf 9 ch fac V meals Coffee am Tea pm
ROOMS: (incl. bkfst) s IR£39; d IR£70 * **LB**
OFF-PEAK: (incl. bkfst) s IR£32; d IR£58
CARDS:

BALLYLICKEY Co Cork Map 01 B2

★★★ 73% **Sea View**
(3 miles from Bantry on the Glengarriff side of N71)
☎ 027 50073 & 50462 FAX 027 51555
Closed mid Nov - mid Mar
Irish hospitality is legendary, and there is nowhere better to sample it than at this delightful country house overlooking Bantry Bay. Set in well tended gardens back from the main Bantry/Cork road, it has cosy lounges with turf fires and comfortable, pleasantly redecorated bedrooms. The hotel caters for the fishing and golfing enthusiast and is also a good touring base for West Cork and Kerry.
17 en suite (bth/shr) (3 fmly) CTV in all bedrooms STV 32P V meals Coffee am Tea pm Last d 8.45pm
ROOMS: (incl. bkfst) s IR£40-IR£65; d IR£60-IR£110 * **LB**
OFF-PEAK: (incl. bkfst) s IR£40-IR£55; d IR£60-IR£90
MEALS: Lunch fr IR£12.50 Dinner fr IR£23.50*
CARDS: 

BALLYMENA Co Antrim Map 01 D5

★★★★ 71% **Galgorm Manor**

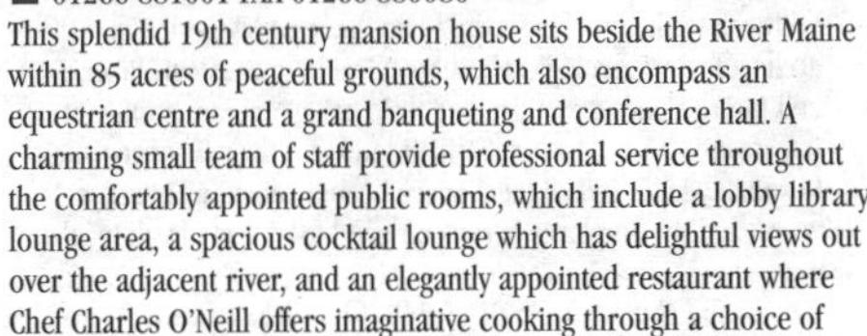

BT42 1EA (1m outside Ballymena on A42, between Galgorm & Cullybackey)
☎ 01266 881001 FAX 01266 880080
This splendid 19th century mansion house sits beside the River Maine within 85 acres of peaceful grounds, which also encompass an equestrian centre and a grand banqueting and conference hall. A charming small team of staff provide professional service throughout the comfortably appointed public rooms, which include a lobby library lounge area, a spacious cocktail lounge which has delightful views out over the adjacent river, and an elegantly appointed restaurant where Chef Charles O'Neill offers imaginative cooking through a choice of

contd.

daily and a la carte menus. Locals and guests find the character of 'Ghillies' bar a relaxing and informal environment in which to take a drink or light meal. The majority of bedrooms are of good proportions and all are well equipped; there are three bedrooms furnished with antique and period furnishings which are more appealing to leisure guests.
23 en suite (bth/shr) (6 fmly) CTV in all bedrooms STV No dogs (ex guide dogs) Night porter 170P No coaches Fishing Riding Clay pigeon shooting Archery Wkly live entertainment Xmas Irish & French Cuisine V meals Coffee am Tea pm Last d 9.30pm
ROOMS: (incl. bkfst) s fr £99; d fr £120 * **LB**
OFF-PEAK: (incl. bkfst) s fr £80; d fr £100
MEALS: Lunch £12-£19 Dinner £19-£21&alc
CONF: Thtr 500 Class 200 Board 12 Del from £99
CARDS:

See advertisement on page 921

★★★68% **Country House Hotel**

CONSORT HOTELS

20 Doagh Rd BT42 3LZ (from Belfast exit off M2 at junct 5, proceedalong A57 to Larne, turn left for Doagh and take B59 to Ballymena the hotel is 6m on the right hand side) ☎ 01266 891663 FAX 01266 891477
Closed 25 & 26 Dec
The Country House is located in quiet countryside a few miles from the outskirts of Ballymena; take the Larne road, turn right on B59 and the hotel is 2 miles on the left. This modern hotel provides a restaurant, bar and spacious foyer lounge areas, the most comfortable conservatory is occasionally used for small meetings. Bedroom styles and sizes vary, but each room is equally well equipped and has modern en-suite facilities. A leisure club is available to all residents, this includes a good multi-gym, cardio-vascular suite and a beauty salon. The modern dedicated conference centre is both extensive and well equipped, recognised as one of the top meeting venues in Northern Ireland, and the banqueting facilities are also worthy of note.
38 en suite (bth/shr) CTV in all bedrooms Night porter 250P Sauna Solarium Gym Jacuzzi/spa French Cuisine V meals Coffee am Tea pm Last d 9.15pm
ROOMS: (incl. bkfst) s £70; d £80 * **LB**
MEALS: Lunch fr £10.95 Dinner £16.95&alc*
CONF: Thtr 150 Class 80 Board 50 Del £110
CARDS:

BALLYNAHINCH Co Galway Map 01 A4

★★★★73% **Ballynahinch Castle**
(take Roundstone turn off from N59, 3m after Recess)
☎ 095 31006 & 31086 FAX 095 31085
Closed Feb & 20-26 Dec
Situated at the foot of Ben Lettery, the hotel stands on the banks of the famous salmon river, the Ballnahinch, in 350 acres of grounds with woodlands and scenic walks. Bedrooms are spacious, individually designed and comfortably equipped, and there is a timeless quality about this historic house where antique furnishings harmonise with modern facilities and staff offer a warm welcome. In the popular Castle Bar, ghillie meets fishing enthusiast, and a marvellous atmosphere builds up. During the season there is often a fine salmon to display and game and fresh local produce inspire the menus offered in the charming restaurant. Understated elegance and informality are the keynotes here.
28 en suite (bth/shr) CTV in all bedrooms STV No dogs (ex guide dogs) Night porter 45P No coaches Tennis (hard) Fishing Wkly live entertainment Xmas Irish & French Cuisine V meals Coffee am Tea pm Last d 8.30pm
ROOMS: (incl. bkfst) s IR£84.70-IR£95.70; d IR£132-IR£154 * **LB**
OFF-PEAK: (incl. bkfst) s IR£66-IR£73.70; d IR£99-IR£114.40
MEALS: Bar Lunch IR£4.50-IR£20alc Dinner IR£25.30-IR£35*
CARDS:

BALLYVAUGHAN Co Clare Map 01 B3

RED STAR HOTEL

★★★ **Gregans Castle**
(3.5m S on N67) ☎ 065 77005 FAX 065 77111
Closed late Oct-27Mar
Standing at the foot of Corkscrew Hill with dramatic views over Galway Bay, the hotel is situated in an area which is rich in archaeological, geological and botanical interest. Hosts Peter and Moira Haden are warm and welcoming, and are a mine of information about the area. A high level of personal service and hospitality have earned them special commendations in recent years, and the emphasis here is on good food using fresh local produce.
22 en suite (bth/shr) No dogs 25P No coaches Croquet lawn Irish & French Cuisine V meals Coffee am Tea pm Last d 8.30pm
ROOMS: (incl. bkfst) s fr IR£90; d fr IR£120 **LB**
OFF-PEAK: (incl. bkfst) s fr IR£78; d fr IR£96
MEALS: Bar Lunch IR£10.50-IR£36alc Dinner IR£28&alc*
CARDS:

BALTIMORE Co Cork Map 01 B1

★★★65% **Baltimore Harbour**
(S from Cork city N71 to Skibbereen, continue on R595 8m to Baltimore) ☎ 028 20361 FAX 028 20466
Closed Dec-Mar ex Xmas
Famous as a sailing base, Baltimore has much to offer visitors, and this smart new hotel adds to its attractions. Set in a delightful position overlooking the harbour, with spacious, interconnecting public areas. The restful lounge has deep sofas and a turf fire, and the bar and garden room open on to the patio and gardens. The staff are young, friendly, and enthusiastic, and fresh local ingredients are served in the dining room. Bedrooms are well appointed and all have sea views.
30 en suite (bth/shr) (20 fmly) No smoking in 3 bedrooms CTV in all bedrooms No dogs (ex guide dogs) Night porter 50P Xmas Irish & International Cuisine V meals Coffee am Tea pm Last d 9.15pm
ROOMS: (incl. bkfst) s fr IR£55; d fr IR£74 **LB**
OFF-PEAK: (incl. bkfst) s fr IR£47; d fr IR£64
MEALS: Sunday Lunch IR£11.50 Dinner IR£15.50-IR£18.50*
CONF: Thtr 120 Class 100 Board 30 Del from IR£75
CARDS:

BANGOR Co Down Map 01 D5

★★★74% **Clandeboye Lodge**

10 Estate Rd, Clandeboye BT19 1UR (from Belfast on A2 take Ballysallagh road.500 yards turn left and take

Crawfordsburn road.Hotel is on left.) ☎ 01247 852500
FAX 01247 852772
Closed 24-26 Dec
(Rosettes awarded for dinner only)
Clandeboye Lodge sits within several acres of wooded and landscaped grounds adjacent to the Blackwood Golf Course, approximately three miles from Bangor. It consists of two separate buildings, one housing function rooms and a country-style pub,serving bar meals and snacks at lunch and dinner, the other is the main hotel building, with a foyer bar and lounge, and a smart restaurant offering an interesting choice of menus. Bedrooms are attractive, comfortable and very well equipped; thoughtful extras such as mineral water, fresh fruit and bathrobes are standard.
43 en suite (bth/shr) (2 fmly) No smoking in 13 bedrooms CTV in all bedrooms STV Lift Night porter 250P Petanque court European Cuisine V meals Coffee am Tea pm No smoking area in restaurant Last d 9.45pm
ROOMS: s £87-£92; d £100-£105 * **LB**
OFF-PEAK: (incl. bkfst) s £55-£60; d £75-£80
MEALS: Bar Lunch £3.50-£7 Dinner £18-£19&alc
CARDS:

★★★70% **Marine Court**
18-20 Quay St BT20 5ED ☎ 01247 451100 FAX 01247 451200
This newly created hotel is situated overlooking the marina on Bangor's seafront, offering modern accommodation and a smart range of public rooms. Visitors have a selection of dining options, with all day service of snacks available in the coffee shop (soon to be converted to the piano bar), bar meals in the lively environment of Calico Jack's nautical themed bar, and formal dining in the Stevedore Restaurant. There is a good range of conference and function rooms, a modern high-tech gym and an 18 metre-swimming pool, sauna and spa. Accommodation is light and inviting, with cheerful fabrics and modern ash furniture. The rooms are well equipped and have generous writing surfaces and modern bathrooms with power showers.
51 en suite (bth/shr) (11 fmly) No smoking in 16 bedrooms CTV in all bedrooms STV No dogs (ex guide dogs) Lift Night porter 30P Indoor swimming pool (heated) Solarium Gym Jacuzzi/spa Wkly live entertainment Xmas French Cuisine V meals Coffee am Tea pm No smoking area in restaurant Last d 9pm
ROOMS: (incl. bkfst) s fr £80; d fr £90 * **LB**
OFF-PEAK: (incl. bkfst) s fr £65; d fr £75
MEALS: Lunch £5-£12&alc High tea £5-£10 Dinner £12-£15&alc
CONF: Thtr 350 Class 100 Board 20 Del from £19
CARDS:

★★★63% **Royal**
Seafront BT20 5ED (take A2 from Belfast. Proceed through Bangor town centre to seafront.Turn right-Hotel 300 yards overlooking Marina) ☎ 01247 271866 FAX 01247 467810
Closed 25 Dec
This well established hotel overlooks the new harbour and marina of this revitalised east coast resort. The new owners are currently in the process of major refurbishment of the public areas, creating a more welcoming and comfortable environment. Bedrooms are also scheduled for new soft furnishings in the early part of 1996, creating a more decorative and cheerful feel to presently rather plain, yet pleasant rooms; the front rooms have fine views out over the harbour.
34 en suite (bth/shr) CTV in all bedrooms STV No dogs (ex guide dogs) Lift Night porter Wkly live entertainment French Cuisine V meals Coffee am Last d 9.15pm
ROOMS: (incl. bkfst) s £54.50-£65; d £70-£85 **LB**
OFF-PEAK: (incl. bkfst) s £40-£50; d £50-£60
MEALS: Lunch £8-£11 High tea £9-£12 Dinner £16-£20&alc
CONF: Thtr 80 Class 60 Board 40 Del from £90
CARDS:

BANTRY Co Cork Map 01 B2

★★★58% ***Westlodge***
☎ 027 50360 FAX 027 50438
Closed 23-27 Dec
This modern, busy hotel is set in its own grounds on the outskirts of the town and overlooking the bay. A new leisure centre opened in 1995.
90 en suite (bth/shr) (20 fmly) CTV in all bedrooms No dogs (ex guide dogs) Night porter Air conditioning 400P Indoor swimming pool (heated) Tennis (hard) Squash Snooker Sauna Solarium Gym Pool table Putting green Jacuzzi/spa Pitch & Putt Wkly live entertainment ch fac V meals Coffee am Tea pm Last d 9pm
CONF: Thtr 400 Class 200 Board 24
CARDS:

BELFAST Map 01 D5

Courtesy & Care Award

★★★★71% **Culloden**
Bangor Rd, Holywood BT18 0EX (on A2) (Hastings)
☎ 01232 425223 FAX 01232 426777
Closed 24 & 25 Dec
Time never stands still at this, one of Northern Ireland's foremost hotels, and improvements are continually being made in many areas. Sitting in 12 acres of landscaped grounds, this skilfully extended baronial mansion enjoys fabulous views over Belfast Lough. There are many fine original features to admire in the day rooms, which have been much enhanced by recent refurbishment. Bedrooms provide ample space and modern comforts and friendly staff offer a wide range of services. Guests can choose between two restaurants and there is also an attractively designed leisure club. Management and staff here have won the AA Courtesy and Care Award for 1996/7.
87 en suite (bth/shr) No smoking in 9 bedrooms CTV in all bedrooms STV No dogs (ex guide dogs) Lift Night porter 500P Indoor swimming pool (heated) Tennis (hard) Squash Snooker Sauna Solarium Gym Croquet lawn Putting green Jacuzzi/spa Hair & Beauty Salon Aromatherapist Xmas Irish & Continental Cuisine V meals Coffee am Tea pm Last d 9.45pm
ROOMS: s fr £120; d fr £150 * **LB**
OFF-PEAK: (incl. bkfst & dinner) s £64-£74; d £98-£118
MEALS: Lunch £21.50&alc Dinner £21.50&alc*
CONF: Thtr 500 Class 250 Board 70 Del from £75
CARDS:

B

★★★★68% Europa
Great Victoria St BT2 7AP (Leave Westlink at Grosvenor Rd R'about, turn left into Grosvenor Rd.At traffic lights turn rht,then 1st left into Glengall St) (Hastings) ☎ 01232 327000 FAX 01232 327800
Closed 24-25 Dec
Peaceful times in Belfast have been celebrated with the new-look Europa finally playing it's part as a truly International hotel. Major refurbishment has seen the provision of outstanding business and conference facilities and stunning public rooms. A plethora of eating options are on offer, from Irish Stew in the Lobby bar and snacks in the Brasserie to the more elaborate cuisine of the Gallery restaurant - all served by willing staff. Bedrooms remain less impressive, but are nevertheless perfectly serviceable and well equipped for the modern business person.
184 en suite (bth/shr) No smoking in 57 bedrooms CTV in all bedrooms STV Lift Night porter Hairdressing & Beauty salon Wkly live entertainment International & French Cuisine V meals Coffee am Tea pm No smoking area in restaurant Last d 10pm
MEALS: Lunch fr £13.50&alc Dinner fr £23.50*
CONF: Thtr 800 Class 400 Board 50 Del from £71.50
CARDS:

★★★★63% Stormont
587 Upper Newtonards Rd BT4 3LP (4m E, off the A20) (Hastings)
☎ 01232 658621 FAX 01232 480240
Closed 25 Dec
Situated beside the A20 on the outskirts of the city, this busy purpose-built hotel stands overlooking the grounds of Stormont Castle. Accommodation has been completely refurbished to offer light modern appointments - the few remaining older bathrooms are scheduled to be refurbished in '95/'96 - and 24-hour room service is provided. Public areas include a small cocktail bar, open-plan lounge areas and a choice of food outlets; the split-level brasserie is open all day for light meals and refreshments while the McMasters restaurant offers interesting cuisine in a more formal environment. Extensive conference and banqueting facilities, including the modern, well equipped Confex centre, are also available.
109 en suite (bth/shr) (10 fmly) No smoking in 23 bedrooms CTV in all bedrooms STV No dogs (ex guide dogs) Lift Night porter 600P Wkly live entertainment Xmas French Cuisine V meals Coffee am Tea pm Last d 9.45pm
ROOMS: s £95; d £125 * **LB**
MEALS: Lunch £6-£18 Dinner £23.95&alc
CONF: Thtr 400 Class 120 Board 80 Del from £100
CARDS:

★★★66% Lansdowne Court
657 Antrim Rd BT15 4EF ☎ 01232 773317 FAX 01232 370125
Closed 25 & 26 Dec
Conveniently situated on the A6, just north of the city centre, close to the zoo and castle and not far from the International airport, this hotel is in good condition following a refurbishment in the past few years. There's secure car parking and accommodation is bright and well equipped. The extensive bar and informal Palm Court restaurant are both popular, and there's live entertainment most evenings. For businesses, the wide range of banqueting and meeting rooms include some air conditioned facilities. Staff are willing and cheerful.
25 en suite (bth/shr) (3 fmly) CTV in all bedrooms STV No dogs (ex guide dogs) Night porter 50P Wkly live entertainment traditional Cuisine V meals Coffee am Tea pm Last d 9.30pm
ROOMS: (incl. bkfst) s £75; d £95
OFF-PEAK: (incl. bkfst) s fr £38; d fr £55
MEALS: Sunday Lunch £9.95 Dinner £15*
CONF: Thtr 250 Class 60 Board 40
CARDS:

★★★65% *Malone Lodge*
60 Eglantine Av BT9 6DY
☎ 01232 382409 FAX 01232 382706
CONSORT HOTELS
Located in a tree lined street close to both the university and west end of the city, this hotel offers bright modern accommodation, a comfortable and popular lounge, in addition to a pleasant bar. The attractively decorated split level dining room offers good value table d'hote lunches and a la carte dinners and a range of bar meals are also available

★★★62% Dukes
65 University St BT7 1HL . ☎ 01232 236666 FAX 01232 237177
Converted from a Victorian terraced house in the south side, close to the university, this modern hotel is especially popular with business guests. Bedrooms are generally spacious, with pastel colour schemes and light wood contract furnishings. Public areas include a choice of bars, a small restaurant and a multi-gym, and a smartly turned out staff provides attentive service.
21 en suite (bth/shr) (2 fmly) No smoking in 11 bedrooms CTV in all bedrooms STV No dogs (ex guide dogs) Lift Night porter No coaches Sauna Gym Xmas European Cuisine V meals Coffee am Tea pm Last d 10pm
ROOMS: (incl. bkfst) s fr £87.50; d fr £105 * **LB**
OFF-PEAK: (incl. bkfst) s fr £55; d fr £62
MEALS: Lunch £9.50-£9.95&alc High tea £4.50-£6.95 Dinner £15-£20&alc*
CONF: Thtr 110 Class 50 Board 30 Del from £110
CARDS:

★★★61% *Aldergrove Airport Hotel*
Belfast International Airport BT29 4AB
☎ 01849 422033 FAX 01849 423500
A strikingly modern hotel which sits just yards from the main airport terminal building. The accommodation provides quite well proportioned bedrooms that are practical but rather functional in appointment, all with en suite bathrooms and double glazed windows. Visitors have the option of informal dining within the bar and foyer lounge area from an all-day menu of light meals and refreshments, or alternatively more formal meals within the restaurant. Residents have the use of a small leisure area which includes a sauna and fitness room.
108 en suite (bth/shr) (31 fmly) No smoking in 36 bedrooms CTV in all bedrooms No dogs (ex guide dogs) Lift Night porter Air conditioning 100P Sauna Gym International Cuisine V meals Coffee am Tea pm Last d 10pm
CARDS:

★★★59% Plaza
15 Brunswick St BT2 7GE ☎ 01232 333555 FAX 01232 330070
A popular hotel with the business community for its very central location in the heart of the city, close to City Hall. Accommodation sizes do vary, most rooms tending to be more compact in nature, but all with a good range of facilities and en suite bathrooms. Public areas include a small foyer lounge, and a semi open-plan bar and conservatory restaurant, while new this year is Spinners public bar which is themed around Irish Linen. Although there is no car park at the hotel there are preferential arrangements with a local multi-storey car park for guests cars, approximately a 5 minute walk from the hotel.
76 en suite (bth/shr) No smoking in 22 bedrooms CTV in all bedrooms STV No dogs (ex guide dogs) Lift Night porter Beauty salon Wkly live entertainment Xmas European Cuisine V meals Coffee am Tea pm No smoking area in restaurant Last d 10pm
ROOMS: s £60-£75; d £70-£85 **LB**
MEALS: Lunch £6.95-£13.95 High tea £6.95-£9.95 Dinner £9.95-£14.95
CONF: Thtr 65 Class 50 Board 34 Del from £102
CARDS:

★★🏵🏵74% **Rayanne Country House & Restaurant**
60 Desmesne Rd BT18 9EX ☎ 01232 425859 FAX 01232 425859
Rayanne is a small country house which sits close to the Holywood Golf Course, approximately 6 miles East of Belfast. You are assured of a warm welcome from the enthusiastic and friendly proprietors, Anne and Raymond McClelland, who work extremely hard to ensure that each guest receives a caring and attentive service throughout their stay. The public rooms are cosy and very well appointed, these include two small comfortable lounges and an elegantly appointed dining room, where Raymond presents a carte of interesting and varied dishes; please note that on Sunday and Monday evenings there is a restricted meal service. Bedrooms are individually furnished, most with period furnishings and cheerful colour schemes, each has a range of thoughtful extras, such as home-made cookies, fruit and mineral water.
6 en suite (bth/shr) (1 fmly) No smoking in all bedrooms CTV in all bedrooms No dogs (ex guide dogs) 15P No coaches International Cuisine V meals Coffee am Tea pm
ROOMS: (incl. bkfst) s £39-£57; d £55-£75 * **LB**
CARDS:

★★64% **Balmoral**
Blacks Rd, Dunmurry BT10 0ND (take M1,3 miles exit at Suffolk slip road, turn right and hotel is approx 300 yards)
☎ 01232 301234 FAX 01232 601455
Closed 25 Dec
This recently refurbished hotel in Dunmurry village can be reached either by leaving the M1 motorway (southbound) at the Dunmurry junction or by turning west from the main Belfast to Lisburn road at Black's Road. Smart, spacious public rooms offer guests and the local community a choice of bars and eating options, while bedrooms at present vary in both size and style - the older wing bedrooms being due for refurbishment late in '95. There is a good range of large function suites, and secure car parking is provided.
44 en suite (bth/shr) CTV in all bedrooms STV Night porter Air conditioning 300P Xmas V meals Coffee am Tea pm No smoking area in restaurant Last d 9.30pm
ROOMS: (incl. bkfst) s £45; d £65 * **LB**
MEALS: Lunch £10-£13&alc Dinner £12.50-£14&alc
CONF: Thtr 150 Class 100 Board 80 Del £65
CARDS:

★★59% ***Renshaws***
75 University St BT7 1HL ☎ 01232 333366 FAX 01232 333399
Renshaws is a commercial hotel situated near the university, and the bar is a popular rendezvous for students. Bedrooms have recently been refurbished, and public areas include a split-level bistro/bar, which is due to be extended, and a restaurant where Indian cuisine is the speciality. A range of European dishes is also available.
20 en suite (bth/shr) (2 fmly) No smoking in 6 bedrooms CTV in all bedrooms STV No dogs Lift Night porter European & Indian Cuisine V meals Coffee am Tea pm
CARDS:

Forte Posthouse Belfast

FORTE Posthouse

Kingsway, Dunmurry BT17 9ES (6 miles SW of Belfast City Centre on A1)
☎ 01232 612101 FAX 01232 626546
Suitable for both the business and leisure traveller, this bright hotel provides modern accommodation in well equipped bedrooms with en suite bathrooms. For more details about Forte Posthouse hotels, consult the Contents page for the section on Hotel Groups.
82 en suite (bth/shr)
ROOMS: s fr £79; d fr £79 *
CONF: Thtr 450 Class 230 Board 80 Del from £65

BIRR Co Offaly Map 01 C3

★★66% ***County Arms***
(on N52) ☎ 0509 20791 & 20193 FAX 0509 21234
This fine Georgian house, built in 1810, has outstanding and well preserved interior features. The hotel offers a warm, cosy atmosphere and its garden and glasshouses provide fresh produce for the restaurant.
18 en suite (bth/shr) (4 fmly) CTV in all bedrooms STV No dogs (ex guide dogs) Night porter 150P Squash Irish & French Cuisine V meals Coffee am Tea pm Last d 9.30pm
CARDS:

BLARNEY Co Cork Map 01 B2

★★★68% **Blarney Park**
(Off village green) ☎ 021 385281 FAX 021 381506
The hotel stands within 10 acres of gardens beneath the woods of Blarney Castle grounds. Staff are friendly and accommodation is comfortable. Tea and coffee are served in the fine residents' lounge where guests can relax on sofas in front of a welcoming fire.The hotel also has a smart bar with a convivial atmosphere - 'Paddy Coles' For the more energetic, there is also an excellent leisure centre featuring a pool with a 40-metre water slide and there are good facilities for children, with plenty of play space in the grounds.
76 en suite (bth/shr) (20 fmly) No smoking in 2 bedrooms CTV in all bedrooms STV No dogs (ex guide dogs) Night porter 100P Indoor swimming pool (heated) Tennis (hard) Sauna Gym Steam room Childrens pool & playroom Wkly live entertainment ch fac Xmas V meals Coffee am Tea pm No smoking area in restaurant Last d 9.30pm
ROOMS: s IR£49-IR£65; d IR£78-IR£104 * **LB**
MEALS: Lunch IR£12 High tea IR£7.50 Dinner IR£18.50&alc*
CONF: Thtr 300 Class 130 Board 80 Del IR£63
CARDS:

★★★68% ***Christy's***
☎ 021 385011 FAX 021 38350
Closed 24-31 Dec RS Good Friday
This hotel is part of the famous Blarney Woollen Mills complex and stands within sight of the historic castle. All the rebuilding and refurbishment carried out to transform this former mill building into a modern, comfortable hotel lies hidden behind the original 150-year-old façade. Staff are pleasantly attentive and the Restaurant and Library have a relaxing atmosphere. Adjacent to the hotel is an interesting shopping complex which includes Christy's Pub and self-service restaurant.
49 en suite (bth/shr) (2 fmly) No smoking in 10 bedrooms CTV in all bedrooms No dogs (ex guide dogs) Night porter 200P Squash Sauna Solarium Gym Badminton courts Fitness classes V meals Coffee am Tea pm Last d 9.30pm
CARDS:

BLESSINGTON Co Wicklow Map 01 D3

★★★56% **Downshire House**
(on N81) ☎ 045 865199 FAX 045 865335
Closed 22 Dec-6 Jan
This welcoming, small Georgian hotel is gradually being sensitively restored and extended. Bedrooms are comfortable, and a programme of redecoration is planned. The food here is good, and our inspector particularly praised his traditional roast pork, which was followed by a light-as-air Bakewell tart. The hotel has lovely gardens.
14 en suite (bth/shr) 11 annexe en suite (bth/shr) CTV in all bedrooms No dogs (ex guide dogs) Night porter 30P Tennis (hard) Croquet lawn Table tennis V meals Coffee am Tea pm No smoking area in restaurant Last d 9.30pm

contd.

ROOMS: (incl. bkfst) s IR£45; d IR£75 *
MEALS: Lunch IR£9.50-IR£12 High tea IR£7-IR£20alc Dinner IR£15-IR£20alc*
CONF: Thtr 40 Class 20 Board 20
CARDS:

BOYLE Co Roscommon Map 01 B4

★★64% **Royal**
(in town centre) ☎ 079 62016 FAX 079 62016
Closed Xmas
Recent refurbishment to public areas has taken place at this family-run town-centre hotel. The lounge is a comfortable and well furnished lounge and a new bar and coffee shop provides good food service throughout the day in addition to the restaurant. Good car parking is provided.
16 en suite (bth/shr) (5 fmly) CTV in all bedrooms STV Night porter 120P Golf 9 Irish, French & Italian Cuisine V meals Coffee am Tea pm No smoking area in restaurant Last d 9pm
ROOMS: (incl. bkfst) s IR£32.50-IR£37.50; d IR£57.50-IR£75 * **LB**
MEALS: Lunch IR£9.95-IR£13.50 Dinner IR£15.50-IR£19.50*
CARDS:

BRAY Co Wicklow Map 01 D4

★★★58% **Royal**
Main St (going south on N11.First exit for Bray,2nd exit from roundabout,through 2 sets traffic across bridge,main street,hotel on the left side) ☎ 01 2862935 FAX 01 2867373 / 2761387
The Royal Hotel is situated on the main street near the seafront, just seven miles from the Dun Laoghaire ferryport. Recent refurbishment has improved overall standards and added a new well equipped leisure centre. Free car parking is available.
91 en suite (bth/shr) (3 fmly) CTV in all bedrooms No dogs (ex guide dogs) Lift Night porter 100P Indoor swimming pool (heated) Sauna Solarium Gym Jacuzzi/spa Children's pool Whirlpool spa creche Wkly live entertainment ch fac Xmas European Cuisine V meals Coffee am Tea pm No smoking area in restaurant Last d 10.30pm
ROOMS: (incl. bkfst) s IR£60-IR£110; d IR£90-IR£150 * **LB**
MEALS: Lunch fr IR£11.25 Dinner fr IR£15
CONF: Thtr 450 Class 300 Board 100 Del from IR£65
CARDS:

BUNRATTY Co Clare Map 01 B3

★★★63% **Fitzpatrick Bunratty Shamrock**
(take Bunratty by-pass, exit off Limerick/Shannon dual carriageway) ☎ 061 361177 FAX 061 471252
RS 24-25 Dec
Situated in the picturesque village of Bunratty, famous for its medieval castle, this modern ranch-style building is surrounded by lawns and flower beds. Bedrooms and public rooms are timbered, and there is a helipad in the grounds.
115 en suite (bth/shr) (6 fmly) No smoking in 2 bedrooms CTV in all bedrooms STV No dogs (ex guide dogs) Night porter 150P Indoor swimming pool (heated) Sauna Gym Jacuzzi/spa Steam room Wkly live entertainment ch fac Xmas European Cuisine V meals Coffee am Tea pm Last d 9.45pm
ROOMS: s fr IR£83; d fr IR£90 * **LB**
MEALS: Lunch IR£11.50 High tea fr IR£2.50 Dinner fr IR£20.50
CONF: Thtr 1100 Class 900 Board 12 Del from IR£90
CARDS:

CAHERDANIEL Co Kerry Map 01 A2

★★★57% ***Derrynane***
☎ 066 75136 FAX 066 75160
Closed Oct-Apr
This company-owned hotel on the Ring of Kerry caters mainly for holidaymakers and some coach parties. Accommodation offers all the expected modern standards of comfort.
75 en suite (bth) (30 fmly) CTV in all bedrooms STV Night porter 60P Outdoor swimming pool Tennis (hard) Fishing Snooker International Cuisine V meals Coffee am Tea pm Last d 9pm
CARDS:

CARNLOUGH Co Antrim Map 01 D6

★★69% **Londonderry Arms**
20 Harbour Rd BT44 0EU (14m N from Larne on the coast road)
☎ 01574 885255 FAX 01574 885263
The Londonderry Arms sits in the heart of this small fishing village, a striking Georgian coaching inn with ivy clad exterior, which was formerly owned by Sir Winston Churchill. At the time of our last inspection the hotel was in the midst of a major refurbishment, which had upgraded most of the accommodation, shortly to be followed by alterations to the public rooms which should further enhance the comfort levels to guests. New bedrooms are cheerfully furnished and decorated, and the modern bathrooms looked particularly smart. The hotel is known for its friendly relaxed atmosphere and good levels of traditional services.
35 en suite (bth/shr) (5 fmly) CTV in all bedrooms No dogs Lift Night porter 50P Fishing Cycles available Wkly live entertainment Xmas V meals Coffee am Tea pm
ROOMS: (incl. bkfst) s fr £45; d fr £70 * **LB**
CARDS:

CARRICKFERGUS Co Antrim Map 01 D5

★59% **Dobbins Inn**
6-8 High St BT38 7AP ☎ 01960 351905 FAX 01960 351905
Closed 25 & 26 Dec RS Good Friday
Dating from the 16th century, this friendly, family-run hotel in the town centre has good-value accommodation. Bedrooms are modest, while public areas keep much of the original character with beamed restaurant and nautical themes in the bar. In addition, it has a popular coffee shop.
13 en suite (bth/shr) (2 fmly) CTV in all bedrooms Night porter Wkly live entertainment English & French Cuisine V meals Coffee am Tea pm Last d 9.15pm
ROOMS: (incl. bkfst) s fr £42; d fr £62 * **LB**
MEALS: Sunday Lunch £8 High tea £5-£9alc Dinner £10-£15alc
CARDS:

CARRICKMACROSS Co Monaghan Map 01 C4

★★★★❀❀71% **Nuremore**
(1.5m N of Carrickmacross, on main Dublin/Derry road) ☎ 042 61438 FAX 042 61853
Nuremore describes itself as a business hotel but has been developed to meet the needs of a wide range of guests. The emphasis is on comfort, quality service and good food together with a wide range of leisure facilities. All its rooms have a superb outlook over the fine golf course and gardens.
69 rms CTV in all bedrooms STV No dogs (ex guide dogs) Lift Air conditioning 200P No coaches Indoor swimming pool (heated) Golf 18 Tennis (grass) Fishing Squash Snooker Sauna Solarium Gym Putting green Jacuzzi/spa Xmas European Cuisine V meals Coffee am Tea pm Last d 9.30pm

ROOMS: (incl. bkfst) s IR£75-IR£85; d IR£120-IR£130 * **LB**
MEALS: Lunch IR£13.50 Dinner IR£23.50*
CONF: Thtr 250 Class 55 Board 30 Del IR£110
CARDS:

CASHEL Co Galway Map 01 A4

RED STAR HOTEL

★★★ **Cashel House**

(turn S off N59, hotel 1m W of Recess)
☎ 095 31001 FAX 095 31077
Closed 10 Jan-10 Feb
Award winning gardens are the setting for this gracious country house hotel, which overlooks Cashel Bay. Rich fabrics and antique furnishings contribute to the atmosphere of luxury and peaceful elegance created by the McEvilly family. The comfortable lounges have turf fires and antique furnishings, and the restaurant offers local produce such as Connemara lamb, skilfully prepared. Bedrooms are appealing, and luxury suites are available.
32 en suite (bth/shr) (4 fmly) CTV in all bedrooms STV 40P No coaches Outdoor swimming pool Tennis (hard) Fishing Riding No children 5yrs Xmas Irish & French Cuisine V meals Coffee am Tea pm Last d 9pm
ROOMS: (incl. bkfst) s IR£55.13-IR£78.75; d IR£110.26-IR£157.50 * **LB**
MEALS: Bar Lunch IR£9-IR£25alc Dinner IR£29-IR£34&alc
CARDS:

★★★ 76% **Zetland House**
(take N59 from Galway direction Clifden,afterrecess turn left direction Carna,take first right,Zetland House is on right)
☎ 095 31111 FAX 095 31117
Closed Nov- Apr
Set in very attractive gardens featuring an unusual mix of rock formation, flowers, shrubs and woodland, this peaceful and comfortable country house overlooking Cashel Bay is enhanced by attractive furnishings and decor. Public areas include a fine lounge and reading room as well as a smart cocktail bar; many of the bedrooms have sea or garden views - and the dining room has both. Warm hospitality is matched by good food and service, and leisure facilities include private fishing, shooting parties (snipe and woodcock) and tennis. Riding is available close by.
19 en suite (bth/shr) (10 fmly) CTV in all bedrooms STV 32P Tennis (hard) Fishing Snooker Croquet lawn V meals Coffee am Tea pm No smoking in restaurant Last d 8.45pm
ROOMS: (incl. bkfst) s IR£76.75-IR£141.26; d IR£110-IR£181.50 **LB**
OFF-PEAK: (incl. bkfst) s IR£63-IR£116; d IR£87-IR£155
MEALS: Lunch IR£10-IR£30alc Dinner IR£29&alc
CARDS:

CASHEL Co Tipperary Map 01 C3

★★★★ 63% **Cashel Palace Hotel**
(in centre of town) ☎ 062 62707 FAX 062 61521
Originally built as a Bishop's palace in the 18th century, this fascinating hotel has been carefully modernised to retain its historic character and atmosphere, with furnishings and decor reflecting the period. It stands in mature gardens, set against the backdrop of the Rock of Cashel where the ancient kings of Ireland held court, and a private path leads up to the Rock. Two restaurants and a pub give a good choice of eating styles, and the Vincent O'Brien library, warmed by a traditional peat fire, houses a well-stocked cocktail bar.
13 en suite (bth/shr) No smoking in 6 bedrooms CTV in all bedrooms STV No dogs (ex guide dogs) Lift Night porter 50P No coaches Fishing Xmas V meals Coffee am Tea pm No smoking area in restaurant
ROOMS: (incl. bkfst) s IR£195-IR£225; d IR£195-IR£225 *
OFF-PEAK: (incl. bkfst) s IR£150-IR£195; d IR£150-IR£195
MEALS: Lunch IR£3.50-IR£20alc Dinner IR£16-IR£35alc*
CONF: Thtr 100 Class 50 Board 50
CARDS:

CASTLEBAR Co Mayo Map 01 B4

★★★ 62% **Breaffy House**

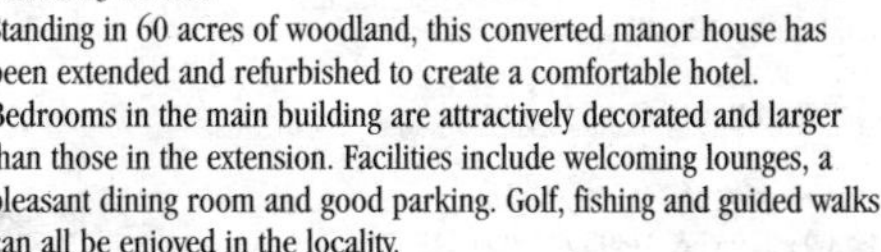

(on N60 in direction of Tuam and Galway)
☎ 094 22033 FAX 094 22276
Closed 23-26 Dec
Standing in 60 acres of woodland, this converted manor house has been extended and refurbished to create a comfortable hotel. Bedrooms in the main building are attractively decorated and larger than those in the extension. Facilities include welcoming lounges, a pleasant dining room and good parking. Golf, fishing and guided walks can all be enjoyed in the locality.
62 en suite (bth/shr) (3 fmly) CTV in all bedrooms STV No dogs (ex guide dogs) Lift Night porter 300P Gym Croquet lawn Crazy golf Irish & French Cuisine V meals Coffee am Tea pm Last d 8.45pm
ROOMS: (incl. bkfst) s IR£50-IR£53; d IR£80-IR£88 **LB**
MEALS: Lunch IR£9.50 Dinner IR£18*
CONF: Thtr 250
CARDS:

★★ 65% ***Welcome Inn***
☎ 094 22288 & 22054 FAX 094 21766
Closed 23-25 Dec
This town-centre hotel offer a range of modern facilities behind its Tudor frontage, including a new banqueting/conference centre. Bedrooms are well equipped and there is a night club with disco on some evenings as well as traditional music nights in the summer.
43 en suite (bth/shr) (5 fmly) CTV in all bedrooms No dogs (ex guide dogs) Night porter 100P Irish & French Cuisine V meals Coffee am Tea pm Last d 9.15pm
CARDS:

CASTLECONNELL Co Limerick Map 01 B3

★★★ 65% **Castle Oaks House**

☎ 061 377666 FAX 061 377717
Closed 25 Dec
This Georgian mansion is set next to the River Shannon in 25 acres of mature grounds with pretty gardens and country walks. An excellent leisure centre has recently been added and golf, angling, pony treking and water sports are available locally. As

contd.

with many houses of this era bedroom sizes vary. Good parking facilities are provided.
20 en suite (bth/shr) (9 fmly) CTV in all bedrooms STV No dogs (ex guide dogs) Night porter 400P Indoor swimming pool (heated) Tennis (hard) Fishing Sauna Gym Jacuzzi/spa Angling centre Wkly live entertainment French Cuisine V meals Coffee am Tea pm Last d 9.45pm
ROOMS: (incl. bkfst) s IR£46-IR£54; d IR£60-IR£75 * **LB**
MEALS: Lunch IR£9.75-IR£12 High tea fr IR£9 Dinner IR£9.01-IR£19.95
CONF: Thtr 350 Class 95 Board 40 Del from IR£65
CARDS:

CAVAN Co Cavan Map 01 C4

★★★64% **Kilmore**
Dublin Rd (approx 2 miles from Cavan on N3)
☎ 049 32288 FAX 049 32458
Set on a hillside on the outskirts of Cavan, easily visible from the main N3 route, this completely refurbished, very comfortable hotel features spacious public areas. The good food served in the well appointed Annalee Restaurant is particularly appreciated by guests returning from a day's fishing, golf, windsurfing or boating - all these activities being available nearby. On-site car parking is available.
39 en suite (bth/shr) (17 fmly) CTV in all bedrooms STV No dogs (ex guide dogs) Night porter Air conditioning 450P Wkly live entertainment Xmas European Cuisine V meals Coffee am Tea pm No smoking area in restaurant Last d 9.15pm
ROOMS: (incl. bkfst) s IR£42-IR£47; d IR£74-IR£78 * **LB**
MEALS: Lunch IR£9.95-IR£10.95 Dinner IR£18.50-IR£20.50*
CONF: Thtr 300 Class 200 Board 60
CARDS:

CLIFDEN Co Galway Map 01 A4

★★★ 73% **Rock Glen**
☎ 095 21035 & 21393 FAX 095 21737
Closed 29 Oct-14 Mar
John and Evangeline Roche run this converted 18th-century shooting lodge set in its own grounds. The emphasis is on traditional hospitality, with award-winning cuisine under John's personal supervision. There are comfortable lounges with turf fires, and a cosy convivial cocktail bar. A leisurely feeling of well-being pervades the hotel.
29 en suite (bth/shr) (3 fmly) CTV in all bedrooms STV No dogs (ex guide dogs) 50P Tennis (hard) Snooker Croquet lawn Putting green Wkly live entertainment Irish & French Cuisine V meals Coffee am Tea pm
CARDS:

★★★69% **Abbeyglen Castle**
Sky Rd (take N59 from Galway to Clifden. Hotel is 1/2 mile from Clifden on the Sky Road) ☎ 095 21201 FAX 095 21797
Closed 11 Jan-1 Feb
Set in its own grounds with panoramic views over Clifden Bay, this friendly family-run hotel gives high priority to hospitality and good food. Musical evenings are a regular occurrence, creating a good atmosphere in the cosy bar with its turf fires. Extensive grounds include a helipad.
34 en suite (bth/shr) No smoking in 10 bedrooms CTV in all bedrooms STV 40P No coaches Outdoor swimming pool (heated) Tennis (hard) Snooker Sauna Putting green Wkly live entertainment Xmas International Cuisine V meals Coffee am Tea pm Last d 10pm
ROOMS: (incl. bkfst) s IR£52.50-IR£75; d IR£67.50-IR£99 * **LB**
MEALS: Sunday Lunch IR£5-IR£11alc Dinner IR£16.50-IR£24&alc
CONF: Thtr 100 Class 50 Board 40 Del from IR£72.50
CARDS:

★★★67% **Ardagh**
Ballyconneely Rd (N59 Galway to Clifden, signposted for Ballyconneely) ☎ 095 21384 FAX 095 21314
Closed Nov-Mar
A family-run hotel enjoys in a quiet location, just over a mile from Clifden. The restaurant overlooks the bay and serves award-winning food with good attention to detail, and fine lounges take full advantage of the views of Ardbear Bay.
21 en suite (bth/shr) (2 fmly) CTV in all bedrooms No dogs 35P No coaches Coffee am Tea pm Last d 9.30pm
ROOMS: (incl. bkfst) s IR£57.50-IR£65; d IR£78-IR£95 * **LB**
MEALS: Dinner IR£23.50*
CARDS:

CLONMEL Co Tipperary Map 01 C2

★★★72% **Minella**
☎ 052 22388 FAX 052 24381
Closed 25 Dec
This mansion stands in nine acres of grounds on the banks of the River Suir. The public rooms are in the main building, while the east wing extension houses comfortable, well equipped bedrooms, some with jacuzzis. All rooms have good views. The hotel is owned and managed by the Nallen family.
70 en suite (bth/shr) (8 fmly) No smoking in 8 bedrooms CTV in all bedrooms STV No dogs Night porter 100P Fishing V meals Coffee am Tea pm No smoking area in restaurant Last d 9.30pm
ROOMS: (incl. bkfst) s IR£45-IR£70; d IR£70-IR£110 * **LB**
MEALS: Lunch IR£12-IR£15 Dinner IR£22-IR£25*
CONF: Thtr 500 Class 300 Board 20 Del from IR£85
CARDS:

★★★63% ***Clonmel Arms***
Sarsfield Rd ☎ 052 21233 FAX 052 21526
In the town centre, backing onto the River Suir, this friendly hotel is owner managed. Refurbishment of the bedrooms is now under way and a number have been completed, combining richly coloured fabrics with cherry wood furniture. The popular buttery serves food all day, while the restaurant offers more formal dining.
31 en suite (bth/shr) (4 fmly) CTV in all bedrooms STV Lift Night porter Wkly live entertainment ch fac Irish & European Cuisine V meals Coffee am Tea pm Last d 10.30pm
CARDS:

COLLOONEY Co Sligo Map 01 B5

★★★62% **Markree Castle**
(turn off N4 at Collooney Crossroads just north of junct with N17, 7m S of Sligo, hotel gates on right hand side after 0.5 m)
☎ 071 67800 FAX 071 67840
This magnificent castle dates back to 1640 and is the ancestral home of Charles Cooper, the present owner, whose family tree is depicted in the stained glass window over the staircase. Considerable restoration work has taken place to transform this historic building into an hotel, and the imposing Knockmuldowney Restaurant gives a taste of the style, though service is informal.
30 en suite (bth/shr) (2 fmly) CTV in all bedrooms Lift 60P Riding Croquet lawn Coffee am Tea pm No smoking in restaurant Last d 9.30
ROOMS: (incl. bkfst) s IR£63-IR£74; d IR£96-IR£106 **LB**
MEALS: Sunday Lunch IR£12.50 Dinner IR£19.50-IR£24.90*
CONF: Thtr 50 Class 30 Board 20
CARDS:

All AA-classified hotels now have an entry on the AA Internet site, address: http://www.theaa.co.uk/hotels The information is also available through CompuServe.

CORK Co Cork Map 01 B2

★★★★ 70% Jurys
Western Rd (close to city centre, on main Killarney road as you exit Cork) (Jurys) ☎ 021 276622 FAX 021 274477
Closed 25-27 Dec
Jurys enjoys a riverside setting near the University and within walking distance of the city centre. Public areas include the Pavilion cocktail bar and lounge, two restaurants, 'Cork's' pub, indoor and outdoor heated pools and conference/banqueting facilities. Bedrooms are well equipped, staff are courteous and car parking is provided.
185 en suite (bth/shr) (23 fmly) CTV in all bedrooms STV No dogs (ex guide dogs) Lift Night porter 350P Indoor swimming pool (heated) Outdoor swimming pool (heated) Squash Sauna Gym Jacuzzi/spa Wkly live entertainment ch fac International Cuisine V meals Coffee am Tea pm No smoking area in restaurant Last d 10.45pm
ROOMS: s fr IR£115.88; d fr IR£135.88 * **LB**
MEALS: Lunch fr IR£14.50 Dinner IR£18-IR£26*
CONF: Thtr 600 Class 400 Board 60
CARDS:

★★★★ 66% Fitzpatrick Silver Springs
Tivoli (from N8 south-bound take Silver Springs exit. Turn right across overpass - hotel is on right) ☎ 021 507533 FAX 021 507641
Closed 24-25 Dec
A charming hotel enjoys an elevated setting overlooking the River Lee on the outskirts of the city. Guests have a choice of Executive or Standard rooms and there are spacious lounges and two restaurants. Good leisure facilities and parking are an added attraction.
109 en suite (bth/shr) (50 fmly) No smoking in 4 bedrooms CTV in all bedrooms STV Lift Night porter 450P Indoor swimming pool (heated) Golf 9 Tennis (hard) Squash Snooker Sauna Gym Pool table Jacuzzi/spa aerobics classes Wkly live entertainment Xmas V meals Coffee am Tea pm No smoking area in restaurant Last d 10pm
ROOMS: s IR£83-IR£90; d IR£96-IR£121 **LB**
MEALS: Lunch IR£13.50 Dinner IR£18.75&alc*
CONF: Thtr 800 Class 500 Board 50 Del IR£98
CARDS:

★★★ 69% Arbutus Lodge
Middle Glanmire Rd, Montenotte ☎ 021 501237 FAX 021 502893
Closed 24-28 Dec RS Sun
A period town house stands in a residential suburb above attractive terraced gardens overlooking the city. An intimate and friendly atmosphere is created by the owners who offer good service and hospitality. A variety of well equipped bedrooms are available, many with period furnishings; the elegant dining room has a good reputation for food and wine - the selection of the wine list being a particular passion of owner Declan Ryan. Four suites of rooms with kitchens are housed in an elegant nearby building and are ideal for guests who want privacy allied to the convenience of having the full hotel services only a minute's stroll away.
16 en suite (bth/shr) 4 annexe en suite (bth/shr) CTV in all bedrooms STV No dogs (ex guide dogs) Night porter 35P No coaches Tennis (hard) Irish & French Cuisine Coffee am Last d 9.30pm
ROOMS: (incl. bkfst) s fr IR£50; d fr IR£85 *
MEALS: Lunch IR£15.25&alc Dinner IR£25&alc*
CONF: Thtr 100 Class 60 Board 30 Del from IR£85
CARDS:

★★★ 64% *Metropole*
MacCurtain St ☎ 021 508122 FAX 021 506450
This city-centre hotel features secure free car parking in the rear garage. The Metropole has undergone major changes recently, with a new leisure centre which includes supervised crîche. The Waterside café overlooks the swimming pool and has been well designed with good use of natural light. Refurbishment of the bedrooms was completed in spring 1996. Conference rooms, a bar and a choice of restaurants are also available.
108 en suite (bth/shr) (3 fmly) No smoking in 6 bedrooms CTV in all bedrooms STV No dogs (ex guide dogs) Lift Night porter 50P Indoor swimming pool (heated) Snooker Sauna Solarium Gym Jacuzzi/spa Wkly live entertainment ch fac V meals Coffee am Tea pm Last d 8.45pm
CARDS:

★★★ 58% Jurys Inn
Anderson's Quay (on E side of city, on the river Lee)
☎ 021 276444 FAX 021 276144
Closed 24-26 Dec
133 en suite (bth/shr) CTV in all bedrooms STV No dogs (ex guide dogs) Lift 22P International Cuisine V meals Coffee am No smoking area in restaurant Last d 9.30pm
ROOMS: s IR£42-IR£53; d IR£42-IR£53
MEALS: Dinner fr IR£14*
CARDS:

★★ 57% Vienna Woods
Glanmire (off R639) ☎ 021 821146 FAX 021 821120
This 18th-century house is situated in 20 acres of garden and woodlands overlooking Cork Harbour.
20 en suite (bth/shr) (2 fmly) CTV in all bedrooms STV 150P English & French Cuisine V meals Coffee am Tea pm
ROOMS: (incl. bkfst) s IR£28-IR£35; d IR£50-IR£70 *
OFF-PEAK: (incl. bkfst) s IR£25-IR£28; d IR£44-IR£50
CONF: Thtr 250 Class 150 Board 15
CARDS:

Travelodge
Travelodge
Blackash ☎ 01 21310722 FAX 01 21310707
This modern building offers accommodation in smart, spacious and well equipped bedrooms, suitable for family use, and all with en suite bathrooms. Meals may be taken at the nearby family restaurant. For information on room rates and to make a booking, call Roomline free of charge on 0800 850950. For more details about Travelodge, consult the Contents page under Hotel Groups.
40 en suite (bth/shr)

COURTMACSHERRY Co Cork Map 01 B2

★★ 64% Courtmacsherry
☎ 023 46198 FAX 023 46137
Closed Oct-Mar
This Georgian house is set in attractive grounds near the beach in an area well known for its bird life. The hotel is family-run, Terry Adams supervising a kitchen which produces good quality cooking and Carole running a riding school that offers instruction for all ages. Fishing and tennis are also available.
13 rms (9 bth 1 shr) (1 fmly) CTV in all bedrooms STV 60P Tennis (hard & grass) Riding International Cuisine V meals Coffee am Tea pm Last d 9pm
ROOMS: (incl. bkfst) s IR£46-IR£52.50; d IR£78 **LB**
OFF-PEAK: (incl. bkfst) s IR£40-IR£45; d IR£64
MEALS: Sunday Lunch IR£12-IR£14 Dinner IR£16-IR£18.50&alc*
CARDS:

COURTOWN HARBOUR Co Wexford Map 01 D3

★★ 68% Courtown
(5m off N11) ☎ 055 25210 & 25108 FAX 055 25304
Closed Nov-16 Mar
Situated in a picturesque seaside resort, this long-estabished family-
contd.

C

run hotel is noted for good food and the friendly atmosphere of its lounge bars. Summer entertainment takes the form of dinner theatre shows.
21 en suite (bth/shr) (4 fmly) CTV in all bedrooms No dogs (ex guide dogs) Night porter 10P Indoor swimming pool (heated) Golf 18 Tennis (hard & grass) Fishing Squash Riding Sauna Solarium Gym Jacuzzi/spa Steam room Massage Crazy golf Wkly live entertainment ch fac Irish, English & French Cuisine V meals Coffee am Tea pm Last d 9.30pm
ROOMS: (incl. bkfst) s IR£33-IR£38; d IR£60-IR£70 * **LB**
MEALS: Lunch IR£10-IR£10.50 High tea IR£10-IR£10.50 Dinner IR£19.50-IR£20
CARDS:

★★63% **Bay View**
☎ 055 25307 FAX 055 25576
Closed Nov-14 Mar
Overlooking the beach and harbour, this family-run hotel complex offers a range of leisure facilities. Many of the bedrooms have sea views.
17 en suite (bth/shr) (12 fmly) CTV in all bedrooms No dogs (ex guide dogs) 30P Tennis (hard) Squash Coffee am Tea pm
CARDS:

CRAWFORDSBURN Co Down Map 01 D5

★★★66% ***Old Inn***
15 Main St BT19 1JH (turn off A2 at junction for Crawfordsburn on B20 1m on left from junction) ☎ 01247 853255 FAX 01247 852775
The Old Inn, reputed to be one of Ireland's oldest hostelries, retains great character throughout its public rooms, which include cosy bars and charming restaurants; the bistro offers an informal alternative to the busy main restaurant. Accommodation sizes and styles differ: the newly refurbished rooms look smart and inviting, with good use of bold cheerful colour schemes through the décor and quality soft furnishings.
33 en suite (bth/shr) CTV in all bedrooms STV No dogs Night porter 65P V meals Coffee am Tea pm Last d 9.30pm
CARDS:

CUSHENDALL Co Antrim Map 01 D6

★★63% **Thornlea**
6 Coast Rd BT44 0RU (centre of village)
☎ 012667 71223 FAX 012667 71362
Thornlea sits in the centre of the village, a friendly family-run hotel which offers good value practical holiday accommodation. Public areas consist of a lounge bar that looks out over the adjoining golf course and a restaurant which offers high tea and daily menus; the public rooms have recently been redecorated in lighter more appealing colour schemes. Bedroom sizes are quite variable and they tend to be furnished in functional style; however they are all well maintained and carefully cleaned.
13 en suite (bth/shr) (3 fmly) CTV in all bedrooms No dogs (ex guide dogs) 20P Xmas V meals Coffee am Tea pm Last d 9.15pm
ROOMS: (incl. bkfst) s £35; d £55 * **LB**
MEALS: Lunch fr £8.70 High tea fr £7.20 Dinner fr £9.25*
CONF: Thtr 80 Class 20 Board 20
CARDS:

DALKEY Co Dublin Map 01 D4

★★❀❀61% **Dalkey Island**
Coliemore Harbour (2 miles from Dun Laoghaire and Ferry Port on the coast road) ☎ 01 2850377 FAX 01 2850141
This recently refurbished Georgian-style building enjoys a spectacular setting near Dalkey village in south County Dublin, just a short distance from the Old Coliemore Harbour. There are spectacular sea views from most rooms and from the excellent Lighthouse Restaurant.
20 en suite (bth/shr) (2 fmly) CTV in all bedrooms STV No dogs (ex guide dogs) Night porter 100P No coaches Xmas V meals Coffee am Tea pm No smoking area in restaurant Last d 10.30pm
ROOMS: (incl. bkfst) s IR£38-IR£50; d IR£70-IR£100 *
MEALS: Lunch fr IR£13.50 Dinner fr IR£15.50*
CARDS:

DINGLE Co Kerry Map 01 A2

★★★❀❀71% **Skellig**
☎ 066 51144 FAX 066 51501
Closed mid Nov-mid Mar
Best Western
On the outskirts of town overlooking the bay, this modern hotel has bright airy bedrooms and pleasant public areas, making it an excellent base for holidaymakers.
115 en suite (bth/shr) TV available STV No dogs (ex guide dogs) Night porter Indoor swimming pool (heated) Tennis (hard) Snooker Sauna Solarium Wkly live entertainment French Cuisine V meals Coffee am Tea pm Last d 9.15pm
ROOMS: (incl. bkfst) s IR£55-IR£70; d IR£90-IR£120
MEALS: Lunch IR£10.50 Dinner IR£21.50&alc
CARDS:

DONEGAL Co Donegal Map 01 B5

★★★❀❀❀71% **Harvey's Point Country**
Lough Eske (From Donegal, take N56.Take 1st right signposted Loch Eske/Harvey's Point. Hotel is approx 10 mins drive)
☎ 073 22208 FAX 073 22352
Closed weekdays Nov-Mar
This modern hotel is in a superb lakeside location on Lough Eske, and was built with guests' peace and comfort in mind. There are spacious public rooms, excellent cuisine and a wide range of facilities.
20 en suite (bth/shr) 12 annexe en suite (shr) CTV in all bedrooms STV Night porter 200P Tennis (hard) Fishing Wkly live entertainment No children 10yrs Xmas Irish, French & Swiss Cuisine V meals Coffee am Tea pm Last d 9.30pm
ROOMS: (incl. bkfst) s IR£55-IR£60.50; d IR£88-IR£99 **LB**
MEALS: Lunch IR£9.50-IR£12.50 Dinner IR£22.50-IR£25
CONF: Thtr 400 Class 400 Board 50 Del from IR£90
CARDS:
See advertisement on opposite page

★★★63% **Abbey**
The Diamond (located in centre of Donegal Down - N15 fromSligo)
☎ 073 21014 FAX 073 21014
Closed 25-27 Dec
Mainly commercial but with some tourist trade in season, this owner-managed hotel is situated in the centre of town.
49 en suite (bth/shr) (5 fmly) CTV in all bedrooms STV Lift Night porter Air conditioning 40P International Cuisine V meals Coffee am Tea pm No smoking area in restaurant Last d 9.30pm
ROOMS: (incl. bkfst) s IR£30-IR£35; d IR£60-IR£70 * **LB**
OFF-PEAK: (incl. bkfst) s IR£28-IR£35; d IR£55-IR£65
MEALS: Lunch fr IR£10&alc High tea IR£6-IR£15 Dinner IR£15*
CONF: Del from IR£38
CARDS:

DOOLIN Co Clare Map 01 B3

★★★58% **Aran View House**
Coast Rd (approx 100 yards from the church on the top of hill on coast road) ☎ 065 74061 74420 FAX 065 74540
Closed 1 Nov-1 Apr
Situated in 100 acres of rolling farmland and commanding panoramic views of the Aran Islands, this hotel offers attractive and comfortably furnished accommodation. Owned and managed by John and Teresa

Linnane, the atmosphere is convivial and there is traditional music and song in the bar three times a week.
13 en suite (bth/shr) 6 annexe en suite (bth/shr) (1 fmly) CTV in all bedrooms P Pool table V meals Coffee am Tea pm Last d 9pm
ROOMS: (incl. bkfst) s IR£40-IR£45; d IR£60-IR£80 * **LB**
OFF-PEAK: (incl. bkfst) s IR£35-IR£40; d IR£55-IR£60
MEALS: Dinner IR£18&alc*
CARDS:

See advertisement on this page

DROGHEDA Co Louth Map 01 D4

★★★68% ***Boyne Valley Hotel & Country Club***
☎ 041 37737 FAX 041 39188
This historic mansion stands in 16 acres of gardens and woodlands on the outskirts of Drogheda. The last phase of a major refurbishhment has now been completed and adds an extensive leisure/fitness centre with a 20-metre pool to the amenities. Much emphasis is placed here on good food and attentive service and all the accommodation is well furnished and provides high standards of comfort.
35 en suite (bth/shr) (4 fmly) CTV in all bedrooms Night porter 200P Indoor swimming pool (heated) Golf Putting green Jacuzzi/spa Pitch & putt Wkly live entertainment Irish & French Cuisine V meals Coffee am Tea pm Last d 10pm
CARDS:

★★★58% **The Westcourt**
West St (located on Main St, 'West St' approx 200yds from St Peters Church) ☎ 041 30965 FAX 041 30970
Closed 25 Dec
The Westcourt is a long established hotel, recently rebuilt to a high standard and linked to a shared indoor car park, which is free to guests. Although the absence of a lift is a disadvantage, the three floors of bedrooms are modern, comfortable and well equipped. The all-day food service is also popular.
27 en suite (bth/shr) (9 fmly) No smoking in 6 bedrooms CTV in all bedrooms STV No dogs (ex guide dogs) Night porter 150P nightclub Wkly live entertainment Xmas French, Italian & Spanish Cuisine V meals Coffee am Tea pm Last d 10pm
ROOMS: (incl. bkfst) s fr IR£37.50; d IR£75-IR£100 * **LB**
MEALS: Lunch IR£8.95-IR£9.95 Dinner IR£11.95&alc*
CONF: Thtr 350 Class 200
CARDS:

DUBLIN Co Dublin Map 01 D4

★★★★★ 62% **Berkeley Court**
Lansdowne Rd (Leading Hotels) ☎ 01 6601711 FAX 01 6602365
This fine flagship hotel of the Doyle Group, on Dublin's famous Lansdowne Road, is the embodiment of elegance, warmth and comfort. Dine in the Berkely Room Restaurant or the less formal Conservatory Restaurant, or just relax over a drinkin the richly wood panelled Roayl Court Bar. Excellent conference and banqueting suites.
188 en suite (bth/shr) (10 fmly) No smoking in 15 bedrooms CTV in all bedrooms STV No dogs (ex guide dogs) Lift Night porter 156P Gym Xmas Irish & French Cuisine V meals Coffee am Tea pm No smoking area in restaurant Last d 10.30pm
ROOMS: s IR£165; d IR£185 * **LB**
MEALS: Lunch IR£15.75 Dinner IR£25.50*
CONF: Thtr 450 Class 250
CARDS:

★★★★ 72% **Conrad International**
Earlsfort Ter ☎ 01 6765555 FAX 01 6765424
Very centrally located, just off St Stephens Green, this hotel stands opposite the National Concert Hall and a short distance from shops and places of interest. Facilities include two restaurants - the award-

contd.

winning Alexandra and a more informal brasserie which offers good-value menus in cheerful surroundings - as well as Alfie Byrnes Dublin Pub and a popular lobby lounge where full floor service is available. Spacious, well appointed bedrooms include some suites, and good facilites are provided for corporate guests. There is an underground car park (with valet service available).
191 en suite (bth/shr) No smoking in 60 bedrooms CTV in all bedrooms STV No dogs (ex guide dogs) Lift Night porter Air conditioning 80P Wkly live entertainment Xmas Irish & Continental Cuisine V meals Coffee am Tea pm Last d 11pm
ROOMS: s fr IR£175; d fr IR£200 * **LB**
MEALS: Lunch fr IR£16&alc High tea fr IR£5 Dinner fr IR£30&alc*
CONF: Thtr 370 Class 150
CARDS:

★★★★ 70% **Jurys**
Pembroke Rd, Ballsbridge (Jurys) ☎ 01 6605000 FAX 01 6605540
Both business guests and holidaymakers will find something that appeals in this conveniently located hotel to the south of the city centre. All bedrooms have been recently refurbished, and a wide range of accommodation is available, including the luxurious rooms and suites in the Towers wing. The two restaurants include the Embassy Room, which overlooks the pool.
292 en suite (bth/shr) No smoking in 80 bedrooms CTV in all bedrooms No dogs (ex guide dogs) Lift Night porter 280P Indoor swimming pool (heated) Outdoor swimming pool (heated) Whirlpool Masseuse Xmas International Cuisine V meals Coffee am Tea pm Last d 10.15pm
ROOMS: s fr IR£145.12; d fr IR£167.63 **LB**
MEALS: Lunch fr IR£13 Dinner fr IR£27*
CONF: Thtr 850 Class 450 Board 100 Del from IR£113
CARDS:

★★★★ 68% ***Burlington***
Upper Leeson St ☎ 01 6605222 FAX 01 6603172
Extensive refurbishment continues to enhance this comfortable hotel which enjoys a south central location a few minutes from the city. Recent additions include the smart Diplomat restaurant and residents' bar to complement the popular Buck Mulligans Dublin pub. The bedrooms are well appointed and the executive rooms have comfortable upholstered furniture, fax points and voice mail; suites and non-smoking room are also available.
450 en suite (bth/shr) CTV in all bedrooms No dogs Lift Night porter 400P Use of facilities at fitness club Irish & French Cuisine V meals Coffee am Tea pm Last d 10pm
CARDS:

★★★★ 67% **Shelbourne**
St Stephen's Green (in city centre)
☎ 01 6766471 FAX 01 6616006
This Georgian hotel overlooking St Stephen's Green at the heart of the city is famous for the drafting of the Irish constitution in 1922. Its public areas are a popular meeting place, and there are two busy bars as well as the Lord Mayor's Lounge where afternoon tea is served. Bedrooms vary in size and outlook, and many have now been smartly refurbished.
164 en suite (bth/shr) (3 fmly) No smoking in 9 bedrooms CTV in all bedrooms Lift Night porter Beauty Salon Xmas Irish Classical Cuisine V meals Coffee am Tea pm No smoking area in restaurant Last d 10.30pm
ROOMS: s IR£174.50-IR£206; d IR£206-IR£235 * **LB**
OFF-PEAK: s IR£156.40-IR£206; d IR£180-IR£235
MEALS: Lunch IR£15.50&alc Dinner fr IR£23&alc*
CONF: Thtr 400 Class 180 Board 60 Del from IR£160
CARDS:

See advertisement on opposite page

★★★★ 66% **Gresham**
O'Connel St ☎ 01 8746881 FAX 01 8787175
The Gresham stands on Dublin's main thoroughfare near the financial centre, shops and cultural attractions of the city. A commitment to traditional standards of hotel keeping are evident; a concierge parks the car in the secure car park and then helpful hall porters take over. Bedrooms (including penthouse suites) are well equipped, thoughtfully providing newspapers and magazines, and there is a foyer lounge serving snacks and afternoon tea; a popular spot in which to relax. Other facilities include a gym, a business centre and conference/board rooms. There is also the Aberdeen restaurant and 24-hour room service.
200 en suite (bth/shr) (4 fmly) No smoking in 6 bedrooms CTV in all bedrooms STV No dogs (ex guide dogs) Lift Night porter 74P Irish & International Cuisine V meals Coffee am Tea pm Last d 10pm
ROOMS: s IR£130-IR£190; d IR£150-IR£190 * **LB**
MEALS: Lunch fr IR£12&alc Dinner fr IR£19&alc*
CONF: Thtr 300 Class 200 Board 100
CARDS:

See advertisement on opposite page

★★★ 75% **Hibernian**
Eastmoreland Place, Ballsbridge
☎ 01 6687666 FAX 01 6602655
RS 24-29 Dec

This fine Victorian building, very close to the south city centre off Baggot Street, has recently been refurbished as a town centre hotel. The rich, luxurious decor features well upholstered furniture and dramatic colour schemes, and there is access by lift to the individually decorated bedrooms. Manager David Butt and his professional staff create a friendly atmosphere, and the food has won praise from our inspector, with dishes such as a feuilleté of asparagus with poached quail's eggs and a tarragon hollandaise, followed by medallions of veal with a risotto of apple and vegetables and a calvados sauce. The coffee and kahlua mousse served with a confit of kumquats rounded off the meal to perfection and testified to the expertise of a confident, innovative chef.
41 en suite (bth/shr) CTV in all bedrooms STV No dogs Lift Night porter 25P Irish & French Cuisine V meals Coffee am Tea pm No smoking area in restaurant
ROOMS: (incl. bkfst) s IR£110; d IR£150-IR£180 * **LB**

MEALS: Lunch IR£13.95*
CONF: Board 18
CARDS:

★★★68% ***Doyle Montrose***
Stillorgan Rd ☎ 01 2693311 FAX 01 2691164
Smartly decorated, attractive, comfortable bedrooms have resulted from the refurbishment of this hotel which overlooks the campus of University College. The public areas include good lounge space, a carvery bar and a more formal restaurant. The hotel is in a quiet suburb a short distance from the city.
179 en suite (bth/shr) (6 fmly) No smoking in 12 bedrooms CTV in all bedrooms STV No dogs (ex guide dogs) Lift Night porter 150P Wkly live entertainment V meals Coffee am Tea pm Last d 10.30pm
CARDS:

★★★❀❀68% **Marine**
Sutton Cross (from City centre follow signs to Hawth)
☎ 01 8390000 FAX 01 8390442
Closed 25-27 Dec
On the north shore of Dublin Bay with attractive gardens and seashore walks, the hotel has undergone extensive refurbishments. Bedrooms are attractively decorated and well equipped, and public rooms are spacious. It is close to the Howth rapid railway into the city centre, and the famous Portmarnock Golf Course.
26 en suite (bth/shr) CTV in all bedrooms STV No dogs (ex guide dogs) Night porter 150P No coaches Indoor swimming pool (heated) Sauna International Cuisine V meals Coffee am Tea pm No smoking area in restaurant Last d 10.30pm
ROOMS: (incl. bkfst) s IR£60-IR£80; d IR£45-IR£60 **LB**
MEALS: Lunch IR£11.50-IR£13.50 Dinner IR£19.95-IR£22&alc
CONF: Thtr 220 Class 140 Board 40 Del from IR£74
CARDS:

★★★67% ***Doyle Skylon***
Drumcondra Rd ☎ 01 8379121 FAX 01 8372778
In a convenient location on the main airport road, with easy access to the city centre. Extensive refurbishment has resulted in very well appointed bedrooms, with facilities including dual voltage plugs and fax lines. There is a spacious lobby lounge and comfortable air conditioned bar, and a restaurant where good value food is served. There is private car parking.
92 en suite (bth/shr) (10 fmly) CTV in all bedrooms No dogs Lift Night porter P European Cuisine V meals Coffee am Tea pm
CARDS:

★★★66% **Temple Bar**
Fleet St, Temple Bar ☎ 01 6773333 FAX 01 6773088
Closed 24-29 Dec
This stylish new hotel lies in the heart of old Dublin and is ideally situated for sampling the cultural life of the city. Comfortable, well equipped bedrooms are moderately priced, and food is served throughout the day. The hotel is suitable for the disabled and offers facilities for small to medium conferences.
108 en suite (bth/shr) (24 fmly) No smoking in 10 bedrooms CTV in all bedrooms STV No dogs (ex guide dogs) Lift Night porter European Cuisine V meals Coffee am Tea pm Last d 10.30pm
ROOMS: (incl. cont bkfst) s IR£80-IR£95; d IR£95-IR£120 **LB**
MEALS: Lunch IR£8.75-IR£9.25&alc Dinner IR£15-IR£17&alc*
CONF: Thtr 35 Class 20 Board 20
CARDS:

★★★65% **Adams Trinity**
28 Dame Ln (in city centre, from O'Connell St go over O'Connell Bridge, take right pass Trinity College on to Dame St, hotel on the left)
☎ 01 6707100 FAX 01 6707101
Closed 24-26 Dec

contd.

28 en suite (bth/shr) (4 fmly) CTV in all bedrooms STV No dogs (ex guide dogs) Lift Night porter V meals Coffee am No smoking area in restaurant Last d 9pm
ROOMS: (incl. bkfst) s fr IR£75; d fr IR£120 *
MEALS: Lunch IR£10-IR£15&alc Dinner IR£12-IR£18&alc*
CARDS:

See advertisement on opposite page

★★★ 65% **Longfield's**
Fitzwilliam St ☎ 01 6761367 FAX 01 6761542
RS 23 Dec-27 Jan
This intimate town house hotel is situated close to the city centre. Particular emphasis is placed on personalised service, good food and a relaxed atmosphere.
26 en suite (bth/shr) CTV in all bedrooms STV No dogs (ex guide dogs) Lift Night porter No coaches French Cuisine V meals Coffee am Tea pm No smoking area in restaurant
CARDS:

★★★ 65% **Stephen's Hall**
The Earlsfort Centre, Lower Leeson St (from N11 into Dublin hotel is on left after Hatch St junction) ☎ 01 6610585 FAX 01 6610606
RS 24 Dec-4 Jan
A famous landmark in central Dublin, located by St Stephens Green, this hotel offers a wide range of all suite accommodation which makes it ideal for both corporate and leisure guests. The choice includes penthouses, townhouses, double and single suites and four studios; every room has a well equipped kitchen with microwave. Bar space is limited to a counter in the attractive bistro restaurant where a range of good food is served. Underground car parking is available - ask at reception for directions.
37 en suite (bth/shr) (9 fmly) CTV in all bedrooms STV No dogs (ex guide dogs) Lift Night porter 40P European & Modern Irish Cuisine V meals Coffee am No smoking area in restaurant
Last d 10pm
ROOMS: s IR£100; d IR£140 * **LB**
MEALS: Lunch IR£9.50-IR£15 Dinner IR£10-IR£20alc
CONF: Thtr 30 Board 20
CARDS:

★★★ 64% **Abberley Court**
Belgrad Rd, Tallaght ☎ 01 4596000 FAX 01 4621000
Closed 25 Dec
Conveniently placed beside a spacious complex of shops, cinema and restaurants, this hotel is very smartly furnished and public areas include a spacious lounge bar serving food all day long, and the first-floor Court Restaurant. There is security surveillance of the car park and nearby are a leisure and fitness centre, bowling and golf.
40 en suite (bth/shr) (38 fmly) CTV in all bedrooms No dogs (ex guide dogs) Lift Night porter 500P Irish & Continental Cuisine V meals Coffee am Tea pm No smoking area in restaurant
Last d 9.30pm
ROOMS: (incl. bkfst) s IR£79-IR£95; d IR£98-IR£125 **LB**
OFF-PEAK: (incl. bkfst) s IR£71.50-IR£79; d IR£98
MEALS: Lunch IR£12.95-IR£14.95 Dinner IR£15.50-IR£22.95
CONF: Thtr 200 Class 70 Board 70 Del from IR£105
CARDS:

★★★ 64% **Doyle Tara Tower**
Merrion Rd ☎ 01 2694666 FAX 01 2691027
Situated on the coast road south of Ballsbridge, this modern hotel has recently been refurbished and one of the striking new features is a most comfortable lounge adjacent to the lobby and adjoining the bar. Sofas and armchairs invite relaxation and soft furnishings are in jewel-toned colours. Bedrooms are well equipped with all the expected modern facilities.
113 en suite (bth/shr) (2 fmly) CTV in all bedrooms STV No dogs (ex guide dogs) Lift Night porter 140P European Cuisine V meals Coffee am Tea pm
ROOMS: (incl. bkfst) s IR£78-IR£102; d IR£107-IR£131.50 *
CONF: Thtr 300 Class 100 Board 40
CARDS:

★★★ 61% **Doyle Green Isle**
Naas Rd (on N7,6 miles SW of the city centre)
☎ 01 4593406 FAX 01 4592178
This hotel has been subject to a major reconstruction programme, undertaken to provide up-to-date accommodation and facilities in line with those found in others of the group.
90 en suite (bth/shr) CTV in all bedrooms No dogs (ex guide dogs) Lift Night porter 250P Irish French & Italian Cuisine Coffee am Tea pm Last d 10pm
MEALS: Lunch IR£12-IR£15&alc Dinner IR£17-IR£19&alc
CONF: Thtr 300 Class 100 Board 100 Del from IR£106
CARDS:

★★★ 60% **Bewley's**
Newlands Cross, Naas Rd (from M50 take N7 Naas road, hotel is short distance from junc of N7 with Belgard Rd at Newlands Cross)
☎ 01 464 0140 FAX 01 464 0900
Closed 24-26 Dec
This brand new hotel on the outskirts of Dublin West has a bright, airy atmosphere, with a spacious lobby and residents' lounge and a restaurant with self-service breakfast and snacks available all day, plus a separate section with waitress service for more formal evening meals. Bedrooms are very good value, as all are equipped for family use and are also furnished to a high standard.
126 en suite (bth/shr) (126 fmly) No smoking in 63 bedrooms CTV in all bedrooms STV No dogs (ex guide dogs) Lift Night porter 200P V meals Coffee am Tea pm No smoking area in restaurant Last d 10pm
ROOMS: s IR£49-IR£59; d IR£49-IR£59 *
MEALS: Lunch IR£6-IR£12alc Dinner IR£15-IR£20alc*
CARDS:

★★★ 57% **Jurys Christchurch Inn**
Christchurch Place (Jurys) ☎ 01 4540000 FAX 01 4540012
Closed 24-26 Dec
This bustling, budget, 'one-price' hotel is only a few minutes' walk from the city centre, opposite the 12th-century Christ Church Cathedral. Less emphasis on traditional room service and porterage takes nothing from its popularity.
182 en suite (bth/shr) No smoking in 37 bedrooms CTV in all bedrooms No dogs (ex guide dogs) Lift Night porter International Cuisine V meals Coffee am No smoking area in restaurant
Last d 9.30pm
ROOMS: s fr IR£55; d fr IR£55 *
MEALS: Dinner IR£14*
CARDS:

★★ 64% **Harding**
Copper Alley, Fishamble St, Christchurch (located at the top of Dame st beside Christchurch cathedral, on the edge of Dublin's Temple Bar area) ☎ 01 6796500 FAX 01 679 6504
Situated at the heart of the fascinating Temple Bar area of the city opposite the 12th-century Christchurch Cathedral, this purpose-built hotel run by cheerful young staff has a friendly atmosphere and offers good-value accomodation. Its Peruvian-style bar and Fitzers Restaurant are popular meeting places, while in the vicinity are plenty of lively bars, restaurants and good shops.
53 en suite (shr) (14 fmly) CTV in all bedrooms No dogs (ex guide dogs) Lift European Cuisine V meals Coffee am Tea pm No smoking area in restaurant
ROOMS: s IR£45; d IR£55-IR£60
MEALS: Dinner IR£7-IR£15&alc*
CARDS:

Forte Posthouse Dublin
Cloghran (located on Dublin Airport complex)
☎ 01 8444211 FAX 01 8446002
Suitable for both the business and leisure traveller, this bright hotel provides modern accommodation in well equipped bedrooms with en suite bathrooms. For more details about Forte Posthouse hotels, consult the Contents page for the section on Hotel Groups.
188 en suite (bth/shr)
ROOMS: s IR£89.50-IR£112; d IR£89.50-IR£112 *
CONF: Thtr 150 Class 70 Board 40 Del from IR£119

Travelodge
Swords By Pass ☎ 01 8409233 FAX 01 8409257
This modern building offers accommodation in smart, spacious and well equipped bedrooms, suitable for family use, and all with en suite bathrooms. Meals may be taken at the nearby family restaurant. For information on room rates and to make a booking, call Roomline free of charge on 0800 850950. For more details about Travelodge, consult the Contents page under Hotel Groups.
40 en suite (bth/shr)

◯ ***The Herbert Park Hotel***
Ballsbridge ☎ 01 6672200
Due to open 1 July 1996

DUNDALK Co Louth Map 01 D4

★★★65% **Ballymascanlon House**
(north of Dundalk take T62 to Carlingford. Hotel is approx 3/4 mile) ☎ 042 71124 FAX 042 71598
Ballymascanlon House is a warm and comfortable hotel with its own extensive grounds including an 18-hole golf course. Most rooms have excellent views, and there is plenty of car parking. A major construction programme is due to have been completed in October 1996, includding the provision of a range of superior bedrooms and a new leisure centre.
55 en suite (bth) (11 fmly) CTV in all bedrooms STV Lift Night porter 250P Indoor swimming pool (heated) Golf 18 Tennis (hard) Sauna Gym Jacuzzi/spa Wkly live entertainment Irish & French Cuisine V meals Coffee am Tea pm Last d 9.30pm
ROOMS: (incl. bkfst) s IR£55-IR£65; d IR£80-IR£95 **LB**
MEALS: Lunch IR£12-IR£13 High tea IR£20.50-IR£23&alc Dinner IR£24-IR£26&alc
CONF: Thtr 300 Class 160 Del from IR£93
CARDS:

★★★60% **Fairways Hotel & Leisure Centre**
Dublin Rd (On N1 2 miles south of Dundalk)
☎ 042 21500 FAX 042 21511
Closed 25 Dec
48 en suite (bth/shr) (2 fmly) CTV in all bedrooms STV Night porter 300P Indoor swimming pool (heated) Tennis (hard) Squash Snooker Sauna Solarium Gym Jacuzzi/spa Badminton court Wkly live entertainment European Cuisine V meals Coffee am Tea pm No smoking area in restaurant Last d 10pm
ROOMS: (incl. bkfst) s IR£50-IR£55; d IR£75-IR£85 * **LB**
MEALS: Lunch IR£10.30-IR£11.30 Dinner IR£15-IR£16*
CONF: Thtr 350 Class 250
CARDS:

★★60% ***Imperial***

Park St ☎ 042 32241 FAX 042 37909
Closed 25 Dec
This busy town-centre hotel is on the main Dublin to Belfast road and offers well equipped bedrooms, and a comfortable

contd.

bar where guests can order bar food all day. There is also a restaurant and coffee shop. The hotel caters for trade shows and meetings and has good parking facilities.
47 en suite (bth) (47 fmly) CTV in all bedrooms Lift Night porter 25P V meals Coffee am Tea pm Last d 9.30pm
CARDS:

DUNFANAGHY Co Donegal Map 01 C6

★★70% Arnold's
(on N56 from Letterkenny hotel is on right on entering the village)
☎ 074 36208 & 36142 FAX 074 36352
Closed Nov-mid Mar
This family owned and managed hotel has been going for three generations. It offers good food and friendly, efficient service. The hotel has well cultivated mature gardens and splendid views over Sheephaven Bay and Horn Head.
32 en suite (bth/shr) (10 fmly) CTV in all bedrooms STV No dogs (ex guide dogs) Night porter 60P Tennis (hard) Fishing Riding Croquet lawn Putting green 9 Hole pitch `n' putt Wkly live entertainment V meals Coffee am Tea pm
ROOMS: (incl. bkfst) s IR£40-IR£60; d IR£80 * **LB**
OFF-PEAK: (incl. bkfst) s IR£52; d IR£60
MEALS: Bar Lunch fr IR£4.50alc*
CARDS:

★★65% Carrig Rua
(on N56) ☎ 074 36133 FAX 074 36277
Closed Nov-17 Mar RS 17 Mar-Etr
This old former coaching inn, now a modern family-run hotel, offers a high standard of comfort and personal attention. Most of the bedrooms have views of the sea and Horn Head, and the hotel is situated near a safe sandy beach.
22 en suite (bth/shr) (10 fmly) CTV in all bedrooms 14P Wkly live entertainment French Cuisine V meals Coffee am Tea pm No smoking area in restaurant Last d 9pm
ROOMS: (incl. bkfst) s IR£30-IR£37; d IR£60-IR£74 * **LB**
MEALS: Lunch IR£8.50-IR£10.50 High tea IR£7.50-IR£18alc Dinner IR£18-IR£22&alc
CARDS:

DUNGANNON Co Tyrone Map 01 C5

⇧ Cohannon Inn
212 Ballynakilly Rd BT71 6HJ (400 yards from junction 14 on M1)
☎ 01868 724488 FAX 01868 724488
This Auto Lodge is located just off junction 14 of the M1 (follow the 'services' signs). The modern building offers sound accommodation suitable for overnight stops, each of the light, spacious bedrooms having a modern en suite bath or shower room as well as colour TV, radio alarm and tea-making facilities. An executive bedroom and one designed for disabled guests are also available. The adjacent Cohannon Inn serves food and drink from 7.30am until 9.30pm.
50 en suite (bth/shr) (20 fmly) No smoking in 15 bedrooms CTV in all bedrooms No dogs (ex guide dogs) Night porter 100P Wkly live entertainment V meals Coffee am Tea pm No smoking area in restaurant Last d 10pm
ROOMS: s fr £31.95; d fr £63.90 *
MEALS: Lunch £2.95-£7.99 High tea £3.95 Dinner £3.95-£9.95
CONF: Thtr 150 Class 150 Board 100 Del from £24
CARDS:

DUNGARVAN Co Waterford Map 01 C2

★★★59% *Lawlors*
☎ 058 41122 & 41056 FAX 058 41000
An ideal touring centre, this family-run, streetside hotel caters for both leisure and business guests.
89 en suite (bth/shr) (8 fmly) CTV in all bedrooms Lift Night porter P V meals Coffee am Tea pm Last d 10pm
CARDS:

DUN LAOGHAIRE Co Dublin Map 01 D4

★★★61% Royal Marine
Marine Rd (follow signs for 'Car Ferry')
☎ 01 2801911 FAX 01 2801089
Superbly set in four acres overlooking Dun Laoghaire harbour, the Victorian Royal Marine has long been a local landmark with an imposing façade. Ongoing refurbishment has provided the hotel with a range of contemporary facilities including a restaurant, bars, conference and meeting rooms, the popular Bay Lounge, and attractive gardens. Car parking facilities are good, the seaport and railway are close by, and there is easy access to the city centre
104 en suite (bth/shr) CTV in all bedrooms STV No dogs (ex guide dogs) Lift Night porter 450P Wkly live entertainment Xmas Irish & French Cuisine V meals Coffee am Tea pm
ROOMS: s IR£100-IR£170; d IR£120-IR£170 * **LB**
CONF: Thtr 700 Class 300
CARDS:
See advertisement under DUBLIN

★★70% Pierre
Victoria Ter, Seafront ☎ 01 2800291 FAX 01 2843332
Closed 24-27 Dec
Friendliness is the keynote at this prominent seaside hotel overlooking the car ferry. Bedrooms, which are steadily being improved, are well equipped and comfortable.
32 rms (30 bth/shr) (5 fmly) No smoking in 4 bedrooms CTV in all bedrooms No dogs (ex guide dogs) Night porter 20P No coaches Wkly live entertainment V meals Coffee am Tea pm Last d 10pm
MEALS: High tea IR£8-IR£10 Dinner IR£15-IR£20&alc*
CONF: Thtr 100 Class 40 Board 30
CARDS:

EMO Co Laois Map 01 C3

★★60% *Hotel Montague*
Portlaoise ☎ 0502 26154 FAX 0502 26229

This modern roadside establishment, recently remodelled and extended, caters for holiday and commercial trade.
75 en suite (bth/shr) (2 fmly) CTV in all bedrooms Night porter P European Cuisine V meals Coffee am Tea pm Last d 9.30pm
CARDS:

ENNIS Co Clare Map 01 B3

★★★68% Auburn Lodge
Galway Rd (Galway Rd on the outskirts of Ennis N18)
☎ 065 21247 FAX 065 21202
This smart modern hotel has recently benefitted from extensive refurbishment to the public areas. These include a fine new reception

foyer and lounge, and a traditional style pub with carvery. There are two restaurants, and the en suite bedrooms are of a good size, featuring colour TV, telephones, hair dryers and tea trays. The hotel also offers a tennis court and car park.
100 en suite (bth/shr) (70 fmly) No smoking in 15 bedrooms CTV in all bedrooms STV No dogs (ex guide dogs) Night porter 200P Tennis (hard) Xmas European Cuisine V meals Coffee am Tea pm No smoking area in restaurant Last d 9.30pm
ROOMS: (incl. bkfst) s IR£30-IR£50; d IR£50-IR£80 * **LB**
OFF-PEAK: (incl. bkfst) s IR£25-IR£40; d fr IR£40
MEALS: Lunch IR£8-IR£10 Dinner IR£18.95-IR£20&alc*
CONF: Thtr 600 Class 200 Board 150 Del from IR£60
CARDS:

★★★ 65% **Temple Gate**
The Square (fronm Ennis follow signs for Temple Gate)
☎ 065 23300 23322 FAX 065 23322
This smart new hotel in the centre of Ennis is painted in a soft yellow shade, making it easy to identify, and it incorporates a 19th-century gothic building which adds interest to the architecture and decor. Oak furniture and relaxing colour schemes feature in the comfortable bedrooms, while public areas include the Bistro, Macauleys Pub and a good foyer lounge.
34 en suite (bth/shr) (6 fmly) No smoking in 10 bedrooms CTV in all bedrooms STV No dogs (ex guide dogs) Lift Night porter 52P Wkly live entertainment Irish & French Cuisine V meals Coffee am Tea pm
ROOMS: s IR£42.50-IR£45; d IR£65-IR£80 **LB**
OFF-PEAK: s IR£35-IR£42.50; d IR£60-IR£70
MEALS: Lunch IR£9.75-IR£12 Dinner IR£13.50-IR£24&alc
CONF: Board 35 Del from IR£50
CARDS:

★★★65% **West County Conference & Leisure Hotel**
Best Western
Clare Rd (10mins walk from Ennis Town, next to St Flannans College) ☎ 065 28421 FAX 065 28801
Extensive refurbishments have taken place here, and are continuing with the opening of the new Leisure Centre in summer 1996. The comfortable new lounge is an ideal spot in which to relax, and is in addition to the spacious foyer lounge. Many of the bedrooms have been upgraded, and refurbishment of the rest is continuing. All have telephones, TV and hair dryers. The new conference centre has all the latest equipment including international video conference facilities. There is a good car park.
110 en suite (bth/shr) (8 fmly) No smoking in 4 bedrooms CTV in all bedrooms STV No dogs (ex guide dogs) Lift Night porter 300P Indoor swimming pool (heated) Snooker Sauna Solarium Gym Pool table Jacuzzi/spa Aerobics classes Massage Wkly live entertainment Xmas Irish & French Cuisine V meals Coffee am Tea pm No smoking area in restaurant Last d 10.15pm
ROOMS: s IR£30-IR£49; d IR£60-IR£80 * **LB**
MEALS: Lunch fr IR£9.35&alc High tea IR£8-IR£9.50 Dinner IR£12.50-IR£19.50&alc*
CONF: Thtr 1000 Class 800 Board 50
CARDS:

★★66% **Queen's**
Abbey St (in the centre of town adjacent to ruins of Franciscan Friary)
☎ 065 28963 FAX 065 28628
Closed 25 Dec
Recently modernised, this family-run, town-centre hotel is convenient for Shannon Airport and Bunratty Castle.
52 en suite (bth/shr) (20 fmly) No smoking in 5 bedrooms CTV in all bedrooms STV No dogs (ex guide dogs) Lift Night porter Wkly live entertainment Xmas Irish & Continental Cuisine V meals Coffee am Tea pm
ROOMS: (incl. bkfst) s IR£30-IR£45; d IR£40-IR£90 * **LB**
OFF-PEAK: (incl. bkfst) s IR£25-IR£30; d IR£36-IR£60
MEALS: Lunch IR£9-IR£19*
CARDS:

★★62% **Magowna House**
Inch, Kilmaley (turn off N18 in Ennis onto R474 via Ennis Golf Club, hotel off road on right 4m from Ennis) ☎ 065 39009 FAX 065 39258
Closed 24-26 Dec
A small family-run hotel with good standards of comfort and enjoyable meals stands in 14 acres of grounds just off the R474 road to Ennis Golf Club and Kilmaley at Inch. Good local fishing, boats for hire, and a golf practice area are among the amenities in the neighbourhood.
10 en suite (bth/shr) (3 fmly) No smoking in 4 bedrooms CTV in 5 bedrooms 25P 3 hole pitch & putt Boat for hire V meals Coffee am Tea pm No smoking area in restaurant Last d 9.30pm
ROOMS: (incl. bkfst) s IR£30-IR£33; d IR£46-IR£52 **LB**
OFF-PEAK: (incl. bkfst) s IR£30; d IR£46
MEALS: Lunch IR£9.95 High tea IR£6.50-IR£10.50 Dinner IR£16.50
CONF: Class 50 Board 20 Del from IR£45
CARDS:

ENNISCORTHY Co Wexford Map 01 D3

★56% ***Murphy-Flood's***
Market Square ☎ 054 33413 FAX 054 33413
Closed 25 Dec
A family-run hotel in the centre of a lively market town, Murphy-Flood's has a comfortable bar where carvery lunches, grills and snacks are served throughout the day. The hotel is currently undergoing refurbishment.
21 rms (5 bth 13 shr) (2 fmly) No smoking in 2 bedrooms CTV in all bedrooms No dogs (ex guide dogs) Night porter Wkly live entertainment V meals Coffee am Tea pm Last d 9.30pm
CARDS:

ENNISKERRY Co Wicklow Map 01 D3

★★ 65% **Enniscree Lodge Hotel & Restaurant**
Glencree Valley (off N11) ☎ 01 2863542 FAX 01 2866037
Enniscree is a comfortable lodge in a panoramic location overlooking the forests and parkland of the Glencree Valley. There are two lounges and a bar with a blazing log fire. The bedrooms vary in size, have standard modern facilities, and most have forest views. The adjoining restaurant enjoys a well deserved reputation for good food. Our inspector enjoyed sautéed wild mushrooms enhanced by a delicately flavoured orange cream sauce that displayed a light, sure touch which was apparent in all the following courses. The dessert-tasting plate deserves a special mention - a selection of tiny delicious temptations which included a vacherin with rich chocolate pastry cream, lemon chiffon crîpe and passion fruit ice cream.
10 en suite (bth/shr) (1 fmly) CTV in all bedrooms No dogs (ex guide dogs) 20P No coaches Xmas Irish & French Cuisine V meals Coffee am Tea pm No smoking area in restaurant Last d 9.15pm
ROOMS: (incl. bkfst) s IR£45-IR£50; d IR£75-IR£80 *
MEALS: Lunch IR£14.50 Dinner IR£21-IR£26*
CONF: Board 14

ENNISKILLEN Co Fermanagh Map 01 C5

★★★54% **Killyhevlin**
BT74 4AU (2m S, off A4) ☎ 01365 323481 FAX 01365 324726
In a fine situation overlooking Lough Erne, this family-owned hotel is popular for weddings and functions, for which it has extensive modern facilities. Bedrooms range from the spacious, with balconies and lough views, to some rather smaller rooms. The public areas have all been refurbished.

contd.

E

44 en suite (bth/shr) 26 annexe rms (34 fmly) CTV in 44 bedrooms No dogs (ex guide dogs) Night porter 500P Fishing International Cuisine V meals Coffee am Tea pm Last d 9.15pm
CARDS:

★65% **Railway**
BT74 6AJ ☎ 01365 322084 FAX 327480
Closed 25 Dec
The Byrne family have been welcoming guests to their small comfortable hotel on the edge of the town centre since 1855. A railway theme is strongly maintained throughout the public areas, and it is popular with local people who enjoy the extensive range of food which is available throughout the day. Bedrooms are tastefully decorated and offer modern appointments together with a wide range of amenities, although some are rather compact. The local staff are very friendly and attentive.
19 en suite (bth/shr) (4 fmly) CTV in all bedrooms STV Night porter Golf Wkly live entertainment ch fac V meals Coffee am Tea pm No smoking area in restaurant
ROOMS: (incl. bkfst) s £27.50-£32.50; d £55-£65 *
CONF: Board 100
CARDS:

G

GALWAY Co Galway Map 01 B4

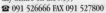

RED STAR HOTEL

★★★★ **Glenlo Abbey**
p.o.Box 86 Bushypark (2.5 miles from Galway City Centre on the N59)
☎ 091 526666 FAX 091 527800
This restored 18th-century abbey stands on a landscaped 134-acre estate overlooking the beautiful loch. The handsome original building now houses a board room and other conference and banqueting facilities, including a business centre. The bedrooms, and all that appeals to the guest in search of a relaxing holiday are in a well designed modern wing, with restaurants, cocktail and cellar bars and a library. Leisure facilities are also available in the grounds.
45 en suite (bth/shr) No smoking in 10 bedrooms CTV in all bedrooms STV No dogs (ex guide dogs) Lift Night porter 150P Golf 18 Fishing Putting green Boating Clay pigeon shooting Wkly live entertainment Xmas Irish & Continental Cuisine V meals Coffee am Tea pm No smoking area in restaurant Last d 10pm
ROOMS: s IR£110-IR£135; d IR£135-IR£150 * **LB**
MEALS: Lunch IR£14-IR£16 Dinner IR£19-IR£30alc*
CONF: Thtr 80 Class 60 Board 40 Del from IR£145
CARDS:

★★★★64% **Ardilaun House**
Taylor's Hill (take 4th left after 4th roundabout leading from main Dublin road) ☎ 091 521433 FAX 091 521546
Closed 22-28 Dec
The comfortable public rooms at this hotel include large lounges, and the bedrooms are also spacious and well furnished. Warmly inviting, the hotel successfully marries traditional standards of service with tasteful furnishings and modern facilities.
90 en suite (bth/shr) (19 fmly) No smoking in 6 bedrooms CTV in all bedrooms STV Lift Night porter 200P Snooker Sauna Gym Wkly live entertainment Xmas V meals Coffee am Tea pm Last d 9pm
ROOMS: (incl. bkfst) s IR£60-IR£65; d IR£100-IR£115 * **LB**
OFF-PEAK: (incl. bkfst) s IR£45-IR£48; d IR£70-IR£75
MEALS: Lunch fr IR£10.75 Dinner fr IR£17.75*
CONF: Thtr 450 Class 200 Board 60
CARDS:
See advertisement on opposite page

★★★67% **Galway Ryan**
Dublin Rd (1m from city centre, on main Dublin/Galway Road N6)
☎ 091 753181 FAX 091 753187
Closed 25Dec
This modern hotel has undergone major recent refurbishment to all public areas, which now include a spacious, well decorated lounge and a new leisure club.
96 en suite (bth/shr) (96 fmly) No smoking in 6 bedrooms CTV in all bedrooms STV No dogs Lift Night porter 100P Indoor swimming pool (heated) Sauna Gym Jacuzzi/spa Sports hall,steam rooms Wkly live entertainment ch fac French Cuisine V meals Coffee am Tea pm Last d 9.30pm
ROOMS: s IR£50-IR£85; d IR£90-IR£120 * **LB**
MEALS: Bar Lunch IR£5-IR£10 Dinner fr IR£15&alc
CONF: Thtr 80 Class 110 Board 30
CARDS:
See advertisement under DUBLIN

★★★60% **Victoria**
Victoria Place, Eyre Square ☎ 091 567433 FAX 091 565880
This new city-centre hotel is conveniently located off Eyre Square, a few minutes' walk from a public car park. Bedrooms are well

equipped, while other facilities include 24-hour room service, a good bar and a pleasant restaurant. The atmosphere is relaxing and staff are friendly and attentive.
57 en suite (bth/shr) (20 fmly) No smoking in 1 bedroom CTV in all bedrooms STV No dogs (ex guide dogs) Lift Night porter Xmas V meals Coffee am Tea pm Last d 10pm
ROOMS: (incl. bkfst) s fr IR£60; d IR£75-IR£85 *
OFF-PEAK: (incl. bkfst) s fr IR£45; d IR£55-IR£65
MEALS: Bar Lunch IR£1.95-IR£5.95&alc Dinner IR£15.50-IR£17.50&alc*
CONF: Thtr 50 Class 30 Board 25
CARDS:

★★★59% **Jurys Galway Inn**
Quay St (Jurys) ☎ 091 566444 FAX 091 568415
Closed 23-27 Dec
This modern budget hotel stands at the heart of the city opposite the famous Spanish Arch. To the rear of the hotel are an attractive patio and a garden bounded by the river. The 'one price' room rate and comfortable bedrooms ensure its popularity and this is an ideal base from which to tour the area.
128 en suite (bth/shr) CTV in all bedrooms No dogs (ex guide dogs) Lift Wkly live entertainment International Cuisine V meals Coffee am No smoking area in restaurant Last d 9.30pm
ROOMS: s IR£42-IR£48; d IR£60
MEALS: Lunch fr IR£5.50 Dinner fr IR£14.50
CONF: Thtr 40 Class 40 Board 40
CARDS:

★★58% **Lochlurgain**
22 Monksfield, Upper Salthill (hotel is off main Salthill road (R336) 200m the Galway side of Salthill r'about,behind Bank of Ireland and beside RC church) ☎ 091 529595 FAX 091 22399
Closed 2 Nov-13 Mar
This family-run hotel is situated close to the promenade and beach.
13 en suite (bth/shr) (3 fmly) CTV in all bedrooms STV No dogs (ex guide dogs) 8P No coaches English & French Cuisine Coffee am Tea pm No smoking in restaurant Last d 8pm
ROOMS: (incl. bkfst) s IR£25-IR£49.50; d IR£45-IR£95 * **LB**
MEALS: Lunch IR£9.50-IR£11.50 Dinner IR£9.50-IR£17.50
CARDS:

GARRYVOE Co Cork Map 01 C2

★★67% **Garryvoe**
(turn off N25 onto L72 at Castlemartyr between Midelton and Youghal. Drive straight on for four miles) ☎ 021 021 646718 FAX 021 646824
Closed 25 Dec
A comfortable, family-run hotel with caring staff, the Garryvoe has recently been refurbished. It is in a delightful position facing a sandy beach, and the first floor residents' lounge overlooks the sea. There are a hotel bar, and a public bar where locals meet and chat.
19 en suite (bth/shr) (2 fmly) CTV in all bedrooms No dogs (ex guide dogs) P Tennis (hard) Putting green ch fac Swiss Cuisine V meals Coffee am Tea pm No smoking area in restaurant
Last d 8.45pm
ROOMS: (incl. bkfst) s fr IR£35; d fr IR£60 * **LB**
OFF-PEAK: (incl. bkfst) s fr IR£30; d fr IR£50
MEALS: Lunch IR£9-IR£11 High tea IR£1.45-IR£4.20 Dinner IR£19
CONF: Thtr 400 Class 250 Del from IR£35
CARDS:

GLENDALOUGH Co Wicklow Map 01 D3

★★★64% **The Glendalough**
☎ 0404 45135 FAX 0404 45142
Closed 1 Dec-Jan
Forest and mountains provide the setting for this long-established hotel run by the Casey family and situated beside the famous monastic site. The hotel has been refurbished, and additional new bedrooms, many with lovely views, are now available. The charming restaurant overlooks river and forest, and bar food is also served. The whole area is ideal for hill walking, golf and trout fishing.
44 en suite (bth/shr) (3 fmly) CTV in all bedrooms STV No dogs (ex guide dogs) Lift 100P Fishing Pool table Wkly live entertainment European Cuisine V meals Coffee am Tea pm
Last d 9pm
ROOMS: (incl. bkfst) s IR£50-IR£55; d IR£60-IR£80 * **LB**
MEALS: Lunch IR£8.50-IR£10.50 High tea fr IR£4 Dinner fr IR£17
CONF: Thtr 200 Class 150 Board 50
CARDS:

GOREY Co Wexford Map 01 D3

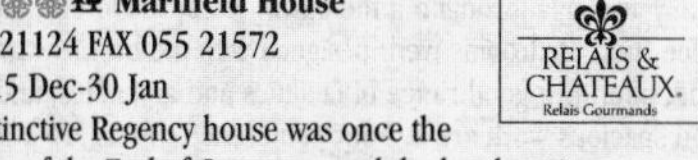

★★★ **Marlfield House**
☎ 055 21124 FAX 055 21572
Closed 15 Dec-30 Jan

RELAIS & CHATEAUX.
Relais Gourmands

This distinctive Regency house was once the residence of the Earl of Courtown, and the hotel retains an atmosphere of elegance and luxury throughout its well proportioned day rooms, which include an entrance foyer, library, drawing room and dining room leading into a fine conservatory which looks out over the grounds and a wild-life preserve. Bedrooms are in keeping with the style of the downstairs rooms and there are some superb suites. Druids

contd.

Glen and several other golf courses are within easy reach of Marlfield House.

19 en suite (bth/shr) (3 fmly) CTV in all bedrooms STV 50P No coaches Tennis (hard) Sauna Croquet lawn Jacuzzi/spa Irish & French Cuisine V meals Coffee am Tea pm Last d 9pm
ROOMS: (incl. bkfst) s IR£80-IR£93.50; d IR£143-IR£161 * **LB**
OFF-PEAK: (incl. bkfst) s fr IR£83
MEALS: Lunch fr IR£18 Dinner fr IR£32
CONF: Thtr 60 Class 40 Board 24
CARDS:

GOUGANE BARRA Co Cork Map 01 B2

★★62% ***Gougane Barra***
(off N22) ☎ 026 47069 FAX 026 47226
Closed 7 Oct-14 Apr
Right on the lake shore, this hotel has been in the Lucey family for generations. Recent refurbishments have improved the restaurant, bedrooms and bathrooms, all of which have lovely views. Guests can be met from their train, boat or plane by prior arrangement.
28 en suite (bth/shr) CTV in all bedrooms STV No dogs (ex guide dogs) P No coaches Fishing No children 6yrs Irish & French Cuisine V meals Coffee am Tea pm Last d 8.30pm
CARDS:

HILLSBOROUGH Co Down Map 01 D5

★★★69% **White Gables**

14 Dromore Rd BT26 6HS (join M2 (Belfast) then M1 west,join A1 atjunc. 7 to Dublin. Take Hillsborough turn, go through village, hotel is on right hand side)
☎ 01846 682755 FAX 01846 689532
Closed 24-25 Dec
A personal and friendly service is one of the strengths at this modern hotel which sits on the outskirts of Hillsborough, conveniently located for access to junction 7 of the M1 and the A1. Public areas include a smart reception lobby with comfortable sofas, a light modern restaurant, lounge bar and a small coffee shop; refreshments are readily available throughout the day in either the lounge bar or the coffee shop. Bedrooms were designed with the business traveller in mind, offering a good range of facilities and amenities, and generally good spacious work areas. Four conference rooms are available for small and large functions.
31 en suite (bth/shr) (2 fmly) CTV in all bedrooms STV No dogs (ex guide dogs) Night porter Xmas French Cuisine V meals Coffee am Tea pm No smoking area in restaurant Last d 9.15pm
ROOMS: s £65-£95; d £85-£105 *
OFF-PEAK: s £40-£50; d £50-£60
MEALS: Lunch £15-£16.50&alc Dinner fr £19.50&alc*
CONF: Thtr 120 Class 40 Board 25 Del from £76.35
CARDS:

HOWTH Co Dublin Map 01 D4

★★★66% ***Howth Lodge***
☎ 01 8321010 FAX 01 8322268
Closed 22-27 Dec
Overlooking Dublin Bay, Howth Lodge has fine sea views and has access to sandy beaches. Conveniently situated 25 minutes from Dublin Airport, Howth is a quaint fishing village, and fresh fish features daily on the restaurant and the bistro menus. The bistro is a new addition to the hotel and opens for lunch and in the evening. The bar has a smart new pub theme decor, which has worked very successfully and opens out on to a beer garden in the summer. Bedrooms vary in size; most are in the new wing extension and are spacious with all modern facilities. There is also a secure car park.
46 en suite (bth/shr) (5 fmly) CTV in all bedrooms STV No dogs (ex guide dogs) Lift Night porter 200P Indoor swimming pool (heated) Sauna Solarium Gym Jacuzzi/spa Leisure Club beauty salon Wkly live entertainment Irish & French Cuisine V meals Coffee am Tea pm Last d 9.30pm
CARDS:

INISHANNON Co Cork Map 01 B2

★★70% ***Inishannon House***
(off N71 at eastern end of village) ☎ 021 775121 FAX 021 775609
Closed 15 Jan-15 Mar
Conal and Vera O'Sullivan took over this charming country house in 1989 and have been restoring it since then. The River Bandon flows by the house, and there are attractive walks and gardens. Good food is prepared from the freshest ingredients, with seafood a speciality.
13 en suite (bth/shr) 1 annexe en suite (bth/shr) (4 fmly) CTV in all bedrooms STV 100P Fishing Wkly live entertainment Irish & French Cuisine V meals Coffee am Tea pm Last d 9.30pm
CARDS:

IRVINESTOWN Co Fermanagh Map 01 C5

★★66% **Mahons**
BT74 1GS (on A32 midway between Enniskillen and Omagh - beside town clock in centre of Irvinestown)
☎ 013656 21656 FAX 013656 28344
Closed 25 Dec
The Mahon family have been welcoming guests to this well run business and tourist hotel for over 100 years. Continuing improvements successfully combine the character of the property with modern day comforts, and the hotel offers very well maintained accommodation. Public areas are full of character, decorated with objets d'art and bric-à-brac; they include a pleasant bar, a choice of lounges and an attractive restaurant.
18 en suite (bth/shr) (4 fmly) CTV in all bedrooms STV 40P Tennis (hard) Riding Solarium Pool table Wkly live entertainment V meals Coffee am Tea pm Last d 9.30pm
ROOMS: (incl. bkfst) s fr £35; d fr £60 * **LB**
OFF-PEAK: (incl. bkfst) s fr £30; d fr £55
MEALS: Lunch fr £9.50 High tea fr £12.50 Dinner fr £14.50
CONF: Thtr 450 Class 200 Del £40
CARDS:

KELLS Co Meath Map 01 C4

★★62% ***Headfort Arms***
Ceanannus ☎ 046 40063 & 40121 FAX 046 40587
Closed Good Fri & 25 Dec
18 en suite (bth/shr) (4 fmly) CTV in all bedrooms STV Night porter 6P Irish & Continental Cuisine V meals Coffee am Tea pm
CARDS:

KENMARE Co Kerry Map 01 B2

HOTEL *of the* YEAR

★★★★ **Park**

(on R569) ☎ 064 41200 FAX 064 41402
Closed 2 Jan-5 Apr & 5 Nov-23 Dec
The Park is synonymous with all the expectations of a luxurious country house hotel. On the famous Ring of Kerry, it stands above terraced gardens which overlook the estuary of the Kenmare River, with a glorious backdrop of mountains. Splendid antique furnishings, warm hospitality and sheer professionalism combine to draw guests back here time after time, and the restaurant offers very good food and fine wines. Our inspectors have nominated Park Hotel as AA Hotel of the Year for Ireland for 1996/7.
49 en suite (bth/shr) (2 fmly) CTV in all bedrooms STV No dogs (ex guide dogs) Lift Night porter 60P Tennis (hard) Snooker Gym Croquet lawn Putting green Wkly live entertainment Xmas V meals Coffee am Tea pm Last d 8.45pm
ROOMS: (incl. bkfst) s IR£118-IR£142; d IR£210-IR£302 **LB**
MEALS: Bar Lunch IR£6-IR£18 Dinner IR£29-IR£39&alc
CONF: Thtr 60 Class 40 Board 28
CARDS:

RED STAR HOTEL

★★★★ **Sheen Falls Lodge**

(from Kenmare take N71 to Glengarriff over the suspension bridge, take the first turn left)
☎ 064 41600 FAX 064 41386
Closed 30 Nov-21 Dec & 2 Jan-6 Feb
This beautifully appointed hotel is situated beside the cascading Sheen Falls in 300 acres of glorious coutryside. The falls are floodlit at night, creating a magical atmosphere which can be enjoyed from the public rooms, not least the restaurant where head chef Fergus Moore and his brigade produce food to match the dramatic views. A luxurious lounge, well stocked library, billiards room and cocktail bar are conducive to relaxation and bedrooms, in three grades, are all comfortable and well equipped. The grounds are magnificent, and all manner of outdoor sports and pursuits are readily available.
40 en suite (bth/shr) (14 fmly) CTV in all bedrooms STV No dogs (ex guide dogs) Lift Night porter 75P Tennis (hard) Fishing Riding Snooker Sauna Solarium Gym Croquet lawn Jacuzzi/spa Table tennis Steamroom Shooting (clay) Wkly live entertainment Xmas V meals Coffee am Tea pm No smoking area in restaurant Last d 9.30pm
ROOMS: s IR£135-IR£185; d IR£160-IR£240 **LB**
MEALS: Sunday Lunch IR£17.50 Dinner IR£29.80-IR£37.50
CONF: Thtr 150 Class 65 Board 50 Del from IR£175
CARDS:

★★★60% ***Dromquinna Manor***
Blackwater Bridge ☎ 064 41657 FAX 064 41791
Situated in the scenic Ring of Kerry in a beautiful setting with 42 acres of woodland and rolling lawns sweeping down to the banks of the Kenmare River, this lovely hotel is continually being improved by dedicated owners Mr and Mrs Robertson. The heart of the hotel is the panelled Great Hall, with its traditional open fireplace, and there are other pleasant sitting rooms, as well as the Dragon Bar. Bedrooms vary in size, the largest being at the front, and do ask about the much sought-after treehouse suite, perched 15ft above ground on the base of a huge tree. On the riverside are the informal Boathouse bistro, a marina providing every facility for sailing, fishing and watersports, with a shallow pool, playground and small beach for children. Six golf courses and riding stables nearby add to the attractions of the natural countryside.
30 en suite (bth/shr) (3 fmly) CTV in all bedrooms No dogs (ex guide dogs) Night porter 80P Outdoor swimming pool Tennis (hard) Fishing Riding Pool table Croquet lawn International Cuisine V meals Coffee am Tea pm Last d 9.30pm
CARDS:

See advertisement on page 943

KILKEE Co Clare Map 01 B3

★★60% ***Halpin's***
Erin St ☎ 065 56032 FAX 065 56317
Closed 3 Jan-15 Mar
The finest tradition of personal service is offered at this family-run hotel which has a commanding view over the old Victorian town. The attractive bedrooms have recently been refurbished.
12 en suite (bth/shr) (6 fmly) No smoking in 4 bedrooms CTV in all bedrooms STV No dogs Night porter Air conditioning Golf 18 Tennis (hard) V meals Coffee am Tea pm Last d 9pm
CARDS:

KILKENNY Co Kilkenny Map 01 C3

★★★68% **Hotel Kilkenny**
College Rd (follow ring road to Callan/Clonmel rdbt hotel located 150yds off last exit) ☎ 056 62000 FAX 056 65984
Set in five acres of wooded grounds on the outskirts of Kilkenny, this hotel has facilities for both holidaymakers and business guests. There has recently been an extensive refurbishment, with new bedrooms and

contd.

an attractive new restaurant which enjoys views of landscaped gardens. There is also a comfortable bar and a conservatory lounge.
80 en suite (bth/shr) (20 fmly) CTV in all bedrooms STV No dogs (ex guide dogs) Night porter 250P Indoor swimming pool (heated) Tennis (hard) Sauna Solarium Gym Jacuzzi/spa Wkly live entertainment Xmas French Cuisine V meals Coffee am Tea pm No smoking area in restaurant Last d 10pm
ROOMS: (incl. bkfst) s IR£45-IR£60; d IR£95-IR£120 * **LB**
OFF-PEAK: (incl. bkfst) s IR£40-IR£55; d IR£85-IR£100
MEALS: Lunch IR£8.50-IR£11 High tea IR£6.50-IR£8.50 Dinner IR£16-IR£18
CONF: Thtr 500 Class 250 Del from IR£57.50
CARDS:

★★★68% **Newpark**
☎ 056 22122 FAX 056 61111
Situated in parkland on the outskirts of Kilkenny, this friendly hotel features a well equipped leisure centre, conference/banqueting facilities, a pleasant restaurant and good car parking. Recent refurbishments include a light-filled extension to the attractive dining room, and the new residents' lounge is comfortable and well decorated.
84 en suite (bth/shr) (42 fmly) No smoking in 8 bedrooms CTV in all bedrooms STV No dogs (ex guide dogs) Night porter 350P Indoor swimming pool (heated) Tennis (hard) Sauna Solarium Gym Jacuzzi/spa Plunge pool Wkly live entertainment ch fac Xmas International Cuisine V meals Coffee am Tea pm No smoking area in restaurant Last d 9.30pm
ROOMS: s IR£39-IR£50; d IR£63-IR£77 **LB**
MEALS: Lunch IR£8.50-IR£11.95 High tea fr IR£10 Dinner fr IR£18.95*
CONF: Thtr 600 Class 300 Board 50
CARDS:

★★57% **Club House**
Patrick St (city centre) ☎ 056 21994 FAX 056 21994
This 200 year old hotel is located in the city centre and has its own car park to the rear of the building. The en suite bedrooms have all been refurbished, and ten more have recently been added. There is a lounge bar with an open fire, a Georgian dining room, and a function suite. Personally supervised by the owner, this is a comfortable and friendly hotel.
32 en suite (bth/shr) CTV in all bedrooms STV Night porter 80P Squash Sauna Solarium Gym Irish & French Cuisine V meals Coffee am Tea pm No smoking area in restaurant
ROOMS: (incl. bkfst) s IR£38-IR£49.50; d IR£65-IR£88 * **LB**
OFF-PEAK: (incl. bkfst) s IR£33-IR£44; d IR£55-IR£77
CONF: Thtr 100 Class 75 Board 35
CARDS:

KILL Co Kildare Map 01 D4

★★★62% **Ambassador**
(20/25 mins from Dublin centre on the N7 fromDublin to the South and South West) ☎ 045 877064 FAX 045 877515
Set beside the N7 - an easy turn off the motorway near Goffs Bloodstock Sales Complex, 16 miles from Dublin - this recently refurbished hotel offers comfortable, well appointed accommodation. The Ambassador Lounge carvery (open until 10pm) provides an alternative to the more formal Diplomat Restaurant's menus, and public areas also include a bar and conference/banqueting facilities. Parking facilities are good, and equestrian centres, fishing, golf, Curragh Race Course and Mondello racing circuit are all easily accessible.
36 en suite (bth/shr) (36 fmly) CTV in all bedrooms STV No dogs (ex guide dogs) Night porter 150P Wkly live entertainment Xmas European Cuisine V meals Coffee am Tea pm Last d 10pm
ROOMS: (incl. bkfst) s IR£44-IR£57; d IR£75-IR£95 * **LB**
MEALS: Lunch IR£11.50 High tea IR£3.50-IR£6.50 Dinner IR£18.50*
CONF: Thtr 300 Class 140 Board 60 Del from IR£72
CARDS:

KILLARNEY Co Kerry Map 01 B2

★★★★❀❀❀78% **Aghadoe Heights**
(hotel is 10 miles south of Kerry Airport and3 miles north of Killarney. It is signposted off the N22 Tralee road) ☎ 064 31766 FAX 064 31345
In a superb setting, high up overlooking the Killarney Lakes, this hotel has a rather solemn exterior which gives no hint of the luxury and hospitality to be found within. The award-winning restaurant continues to receive well deserved recognition and standards of service have also brought accolades, including our own Courtesy and Care Award.
60 en suite (bth/shr) (5 fmly) CTV in all bedrooms STV No dogs Night porter 120P Indoor swimming pool (heated) Golf 18 Tennis (hard) Fishing Sauna Solarium Gym Jacuzzi/spa Steamroom Plunge pool Wkly live entertainment Xmas French Cuisine V meals Coffee am Tea pm Last d 9.30pm
ROOMS: (incl. bkfst) s IR£85-IR£125; d IR£120-IR£175 **LB**
MEALS: Lunch IR£19.50&alc Dinner IR£31.50&alc*
CONF: Thtr 100 Class 70 Board 40 Del from IR£125
CARDS:

★★★★❀70% **Muckross**
Muckross Village (from Killarney take road to Kenmare, hotel 2.5miles on left)
☎ 064 31938 FAX 064 31965
Closed Dec-Feb
Set in the heart of the Killarney National Park, this 18th-century hotel has been luxuriously refurbished to a high standard. Relaxing lounge areas feature comfortable furniture, warm colour schemes and chandeliers. Bedrooms are attractively decorated and well equipped. The adjacent thatched pub, Molly Darcys, offers an alternative to the formal Bluepool restaurant and has live entertainment.
27 en suite (bth/shr) (2 fmly) No smoking in 2 bedrooms CTV in all bedrooms STV No dogs (ex guide dogs) Night porter 250P European Cuisine V meals Coffee am Tea pm No smoking in restaurant
ROOMS: (incl. bkfst) s IR£60-IR£80; d IR£90-IR£120 * **LB**
OFF-PEAK: (incl. bkfst) s IR£45-IR£60; d IR£70-IR£80
MEALS: Dinner IR£16.95-IR£20.95&alc*
CONF: Thtr 200 Class 80 Board 40
CARDS:
See advertisement on opposite page

★★★★❀❀69% **Killarney Park**
Kenmare Place ☎ 064 35555 FAX 064 35266
Located on the edge of town, this charming purpose-built hotel combines elegance with comfort. The entrance lobby with blazing fire gives the first hint of the warmth of atmosphere created by both the innovative decor, rich in colours and fabrics and the friendly efficient staff. Public rooms and bedrooms are very comfortable.
44 en suite (bth/shr) (4 fmly) No smoking in 10 bedrooms CTV in all bedrooms STV No dogs (ex guide dogs) Lift Night porter Air conditioning 70P Indoor swimming pool (heated) Gym Steam room Wkly live entertainment Xmas V meals Coffee am Tea pm Last d 9.30pm
ROOMS: (incl. bkfst) s IR£70-IR£100; d IR£110-IR£150 **LB**
MEALS: Lunch IR£13.50-IR£15alc Dinner IR£20-IR£25alc
CONF: Thtr 150 Class 100 Board 40
CARDS:

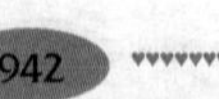

Courtesy & Care Award

★★★ 75% **Cahernane**
Muckross Rd ☎ 064 31895 FAX 064 34340
Closed 2 Nov-Mar
This fine old country mansion with a magnificent mountain backdrop enjoys panoramic views from a setting in its own grounds beside the lake shore. One's immediate impression is of comfort and warmth, blazing fires, wood floors, elegant period furnishings, flowers and the glow of silver - all combining to make guests feel very welcome. A pleasant, smartly uniformed staff provides unobtrusively good service, and skilfully prepared award-winning food displays innovative touches. Facilities include comfortable lounges, bar, shop,

contd.

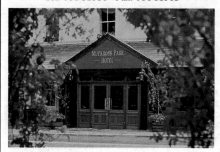

tennis and easy car parking. Owners and staff here have won the AA Courtesy and Care Award for 1996/7.
14 en suite (bth/shr) 33 annexe en suite (bth/shr) No dogs (ex guide dogs) Night porter 50P Tennis (hard) Fishing Croquet lawn Wkly live entertainment Xmas Irish, French, German & Italian Cuisine V meals Coffee am Tea pm No smoking in restaurant Last d 9.30pm
ROOMS: (incl. bkfst) s IR£80-IR£85; d IR£102.50-IR£130 **LB**
MEALS: Bar Lunch IR£3-IR£5 Dinner IR£20-IR£27.50&alc
CARDS:

★★★64% ***Castlerosse***
☎ 064 31144 FAX 064 31031
Closed Dec-Feb
Set in 6,000 acres of lakeland overlooking Lough Leane, this beautifully situated hotel offers warm hospitality and good food as well as special facilities on the adjoining championship golf courses. Boating and fishing trips are available on the nearby lakes.
110 en suite (bth/shr) (27 fmly) No smoking in 4 bedrooms CTV in all bedrooms Lift Night porter 100P Indoor swimming pool (heated) Snooker Sauna Gym Jacuzzi/spa Golfing & riding arranged Wkly live entertainment International Cuisine V meals Tea pm Last d 9.30pm
CARDS:

★★★64% ***Gleneagle***
☎ 064 31870 FAX 064 32646
Set in 25 acres of parkland, this hotel has fine leisure facilities, including a swimming pool, gym, tennis and creche. Hospitality is a priority with the O'Donoghue family, who create a good atmosphere. There are spacious lounges, two bars, coffee shop and a restaurant which offers a range of interesting dishes. Menus demonstrate good cooking skills and imaginative presentation. The bedrooms vary, those in the new wing are very comfortable, whilst those in the original section of the building are more compact. Conference and banqueting facilities are available, and there is entertainment during the summer months.
200 en suite (bth/shr) (17 fmly) CTV in all bedrooms STV Lift Night porter 500P Indoor swimming pool (heated) Golf 36 Tennis (hard) Fishing Squash Snooker Sauna Solarium Gym Pool table Jacuzzi/spa Table tennis Steam room Beauty therapist V meals Coffee am Tea pm
CARDS:

See advertisement on opposite page

★★★63% **Killarney Ryan**
Cork Rd (on N22 route) ☎ 064 31555 FAX 064 32438
Closed Dec & Jan
This hotel is conveniently located on the outskirts of Killarney. Excellent leisure facilities have recently been added, and a crèche is provided in summer with 'Friendly Fellows' to supervise. Guests will also enjoy the hotel grounds.
168 en suite (bth/shr) (168 fmly) No smoking in 20 bedrooms CTV in all bedrooms STV No dogs (ex guide dogs) Lift Night porter 150P Indoor swimming pool (heated) Tennis (hard) Sauna Jacuzzi/spa Steamroom/Crazy Golf Wkly live entertainment ch fac French Cuisine V meals Coffee am Tea pm Last d 10pm
MEALS: Dinner fr IR£16.50*
CONF: Thtr 50 Class 25 Board 20
CARDS:
See advertisement under DUBLIN

★★★63% **Royal**
College St (across the street from bus/train station)
☎ 064 31853 & 31854 FAX 064 34001
An intimate family-run hotel very conveniently situated in the centre of town, offering personal, friendly service in comfortable surroundings. The bedrooms are well appointed, all have en suite facilities, and there is a lift to all floors.
49 en suite (bth/shr) (12 fmly) No smoking in 6 bedrooms CTV in all bedrooms STV Lift Night porter Air conditioning Wkly live entertainment V meals Coffee am Tea pm No smoking area in restaurant Last d 9pm
ROOMS: (incl. bkfst) s IR£45-IR£85; d IR£80-IR£120 **LB**
OFF-PEAK: (incl. bkfst) s IR£35-IR£50; d IR£60-IR£80
MEALS: Lunch IR£10.50-IR£13 Dinner IR£18.50-IR£21
CONF: Thtr 60 Class 40 Board 30
CARDS:

★★★62% **Lake**
Muckross Rd (Kenmare road out of Killarney)
☎ 064 31035 FAX 064 31902
Closed Dec-Feb
This former mansion is superbly located in lovely countryside with lake and mountain views and woodland walks. A programme of refurbishment of bedrooms is well advanced. Public rooms are spacious and a good standard of hospitality and service is provided by the owners.
72 rms (65 bth/shr) (10 fmly) CTV in all bedrooms STV No dogs (ex guide dogs) Night porter Air conditioning 122P Tennis (hard) Fishing Pool table Putting green Wkly live entertainment Irish, French & Italian Cuisine V meals Coffee am Tea pm No smoking area in restaurant Last d 9pm
ROOMS: (incl. bkfst) s IR£48-IR£57; d IR£66-IR£84 **LB**
MEALS: Lunch IR£8-IR£11 Dinner IR£19-IR£20
CONF: Thtr 80 Class 60 Board 60 Del from IR£40
CARDS:

★★★61% **White Gates**
Muckross Rd ☎ 064 31164 FAX 064 34850
Distinctive blue and ochre paintwork draws the eye to this newly opened hotel on the Kenmare road. The same flair for colour combinations is evident throughout the interior, and bedrooms are particularly attractive. The natural harmony of wood and stone is a feature of the well designed lounge bar and the restaurant, with its conservatory front, is filled with light. There is also a very comfortable lounge.
27 en suite (bth/shr) CTV in all bedrooms STV No dogs (ex guide dogs) Night porter 50P Wkly live entertainment V meals Coffee am Tea pm
ROOMS: (incl. bkfst) s IR£49; d IR£70 *
OFF-PEAK: (incl. bkfst) s IR£44; d IR£64
MEALS: Bar Lunch IR£4.95-IR£8.50*
CARDS:

★★★59% **International**
Kenmare Pl (town centre)
☎ 064 31816 FAX 064 31837
Closed 23-27 Dec

This is a golfer's paradise, with two championship courses almost on

the doorstep and several others within easy driving distance of this recently refurbished hotel. Family-owned, it is also conveniently situated for shops and all the town-centre facilities. Staff are friendly and obliging, bedrooms have co-ordinated decor and high quality furnishings and public rooms are spacious and comfortable.
75 en suite (bth/shr) (6 fmly) CTV in all bedrooms STV Lift Night porter V meals Coffee am No smoking area in restaurant Last d 9pm
ROOMS: (incl. bkfst) s IR£35-IR£52; d IR£50-IR£80 **LB**
MEALS: Lunch fr IR£8&alc High tea fr IR£5&alc Dinner fr IR£12.50&alc
CONF: Thtr 100 Class 50 Board 25
CARDS:

★★63% ***Arbutus***
College St ☎ 064 31037 FAX 064 34033
Closed 19-30 Dec
33 en suite (bth/shr) (4 fmly) CTV in all bedrooms STV No dogs (ex guide dogs) Night porter V meals Coffee am Last d 9pm
CARDS:

See advertisement on this page

★★62% ***Scotts***
College St ☎ 064 31060 FAX 064 31582
Coffee am Tea pm Last d 9pm
CARDS:

KILLINEY Co Dublin Map 01 D4

★★★66% ***Fitzpatrick Castle***
☎ 01 2840700 FAX 01 2850207
This converted castle with modern extensions is set in its own attractive gardens and grounds with views over Dublin Bay. There is a helipad, and a courtesy coach is available for transfers to and from the airport.
90 en suite (bth/shr) (6 fmly) No smoking in 6 bedrooms CTV in all bedrooms No dogs (ex guide dogs) Lift Night porter 300P Indoor swimming pool (heated) Tennis (hard) Squash Sauna Solarium Gym Beauty salon Hairdressing salon Wkly live entertainment International Cuisine V meals Coffee am Tea pm Last d 10.30pm
CARDS:

★★★63% **Court**
(head towards Killiney Bay seafront & hotel)
☎ 01 2851622 FAX 01 2852085
In its own grounds overlooking Killiney Bay, this attractive converted Victorian mansion is in a convenient location, only 12 miles from Dublin and close to the fast commuter train service. Conference facilities include six-booth simultaneous translating equipment.
86 en suite (bth/shr) (29 fmly) No smoking in 8 bedrooms CTV in all bedrooms No dogs (ex guide dogs) Lift Night porter 200P Xmas International Cuisine V meals Coffee am Tea pm Last d 10pm
ROOMS: s IR£78.75-IR£90; d IR£95.62-IR£106.87 * **LB**
OFF-PEAK: (incl. bkfst) s IR£61.31; d IR£88.87
MEALS: Lunch IR£12.50 High tea IR£10 Dinner IR£22.50*
CONF: Thtr 300 Class 180 Board 60 Del IR£101.25
CARDS:

KINSALE Co Cork Map 01 B2

★★★68% **Trident**
Worlds End ☎ 021 772301 FAX 021 774173
Closed 25-26 Dec
Located at the harbour's edge, the Trident Hotel has its own marina with boats for hire. Many of the bedrooms have superb views and two have balconies. The restaurant and lounge both overlook the harbour and pleasant staff provide hospitable service.
58 en suite (bth/shr) (2 fmly) CTV in all bedrooms STV No dogs

contd.

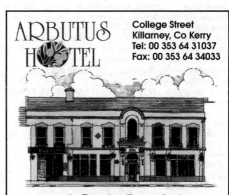

(ex guide dogs) Lift Night porter 60P Sauna Gym Pool table Jacuzzi/spa Steam room Games room Xmas Irish & European Cuisine V meals Coffee am Tea pm No smoking area in restaurant Last d 9.45pm
ROOMS: (incl. bkfst) s IR£54-IR£74; d IR£78-IR£118 * **LB**
MEALS: Sunday Lunch IR£9.50-IR£12 Dinner IR£18-IR£20&alc*
CONF: Thtr 250 Class 170 Board 60 Del from IR£90
CARDS:

LAHINCH Co Clare Map 01 B3

★★★59% Aberdeen Arms

LAHINCH ☎ 065 81100 FAX 065 81228
A popular and recently modernised hotel offering well equipped bedrooms and very comfortable day rooms where guests can expect to mingle with the golfing fraternity playing the famous Lahinch Links Course.
55 en suite (bth/shr) CTV in all bedrooms STV No dogs (ex guide dogs) Night porter 85P Snooker Sauna Pool table Jacuzzi/spa Xmas European Cuisine V meals Coffee am Tea pm No smoking area in restaurant Last d 9pm
ROOMS: (incl. bkfst) s IR£57; d IR£90 * **LB**
OFF-PEAK: (incl. bkfst) s fr IR£45; d fr IR£70
MEALS: Sunday Lunch IR£9.50-IR£14.50 Dinner IR£17-IR£23&alc*
CONF: Thtr 200 Class 100 Board 50 Del from IR£64.50
CARDS:

L

LIMAVADY Co Londonderry Map 01 C6

★★★★71% Radisson Roe Park Hotel & Golf Resort

BT49 9LB (on the A2 Londonderry/Limavady road, 16m from Londonderry, 1m from Limavady) ☎ 015047 22222 FAX 01547 22313
Radisson Roe Park is a newly-built hotel and conference complex that sits amongst its own well established parkland golf course on the outskirts of Limavady. The accommodation is quite spacious, cheerfully furnished and well appointed, and the public areas include a choice of bars and dining options; dinner in the Courtyard restaurant offers a good standard of cuisine from daily and à la carte menus. The Fairways leisure club offers a full range of modern amenities and beauty services: the swimming pool and state-of-the-art fitness suite are particularly popular. The impressive conference and banqueting facilities are extensive, flexible and hi-tech, equally suitable for both large and small functions.
64 en suite (bth/shr) (15 fmly) CTV in all bedrooms STV No dogs (ex guide dogs) Lift Night porter Air conditioning 300P Indoor swimming pool (heated) Golf 18 Fishing Riding Sauna Solarium Gym Pool table Putting green Jacuzzi/spa Floodlit driving range Practice area Wkly live entertainment Xmas French Cuisine V meals Coffee am Tea pm No smoking area in restaurant Last d 10pm
ROOMS: (incl. bkfst) s £70-£85; d £90-£110 * **LB**
MEALS: Lunch £12.50 Dinner £23.50&alc*
CONF: Thtr 500 Class 300 Board 100 Del from £115
CARDS:

LIMERICK Co Limerick Map 01 B3

★★★★68% *Castletroy Park*

Dublin Rd (off N7) ☎ 061 335566 FAX 061 331117
Encircled by gardens, this creatively designed hotel seems filled with light and combines modern comforts with attractive decor. Business guests will welcome the fax and computer points in the bedrooms. McLaughlin's Restaurant serves good food and is a popular meeting place. The hotel caters excellently for both business and leisure, and is near the University of Limerick, off the N7.
107 en suite (bth/shr) No smoking in 41 bedrooms CTV in all bedrooms STV No dogs (ex guide dogs) Lift Night porter 160P Indoor swimming pool (heated) Sauna Gym Jacuzzi/spa Running track Steam room International Cuisine V meals Coffee am Tea pm Last d 9.30pm
CARDS:

★★★69% Jurys

Ennis Rd (Jurys) ☎ 061 327777 FAX 061 326400
Closed 24 & 25 Dec
Professional standards of service are the norm at this comfortable hotel, in four acres of grounds and landscaped gardens beside the River Shannon, yet just a short stroll from the city centre. The award-winning Copper Room restaurant is a favourite with our inspectors; it offers a wide range of food, including vegetarian, and speciality flambé dishes. There are excellent leisure facilities.
95 en suite (bth/shr) No smoking in 8 bedrooms CTV in all bedrooms STV No dogs (ex guide dogs) Night porter 180P Indoor swimming pool (heated) Tennis (hard) Sauna Gym Jacuzzi/spa Steam room Wkly live entertainment Xmas International Cuisine V meals Coffee am Tea pm Last d 10pm
ROOMS: s IR£94.60; d IR£116.60 * **LB**
MEALS: Sunday Lunch IR£11-IR£30&alc Dinner IR£15&alc*
CONF: Thtr 200 Class 100 Board 45
CARDS:

★★★69% Limerick Ryan

Ennis Rd (on N22, Ennis road) ☎ 061 453922 FAX 061 326333
Conveniently situated close to the city, in its own grounds, the Limerick Ryan has smart public areas located in the original part of this refurbished period house. Spacious lounges and restaurants, and a cocktail bar with a fire, sofas and a pianist, are warm and relaxing. The well equipped bedrooms are located in the modern extension, and 24-hour room service is available. Other facilities include conference suites, a business centre, patio gardens and a large car park.
181 en suite (bth/shr) (181 fmly) No smoking in 19 bedrooms CTV in all bedrooms STV Lift Night porter 180P gym nearby available free to guests Wkly live entertainment Xmas French Cuisine V meals Coffee am Tea pm
ROOMS: s IR£55-IR£90; d IR£70-IR£100 * **LB**
MEALS: Lunch IR£10.50-IR£18.50 Dinner IR£18-IR£22&alc*
CONF: Thtr 130 Class 60 Board 40
CARDS:
See advertisement under DUBLIN

★★★62% *Two Mile Inn*

Best Western

Ennis Rd (on N22, near Bunratty Castle & airport)
☎ 061 326255 FAX 061 453783
Situated on the outskirts of Limerick city near Bunratty Castle and Shannon Airport, the Two Mile Inn has new and comfortable bedrooms built to a very high standard with attractive furnishings. The restaurant is very good value.
123 en suite (bth/shr) (30 fmly) CTV in all bedrooms STV No dogs

(ex guide dogs) Night porter 300P Irish & Continental Cuisine V meals Coffee am Tea pm Last d 10pm
CARDS:

See advertisement on this page

★★★57% **Green Hills**
Caherdavin ☎ 061 453033 FAX 061 453307
Set in 3.5 acres of lovely landscaped gardens, this hotel has recently been refurbished and extended, adding some large, comfortable and well appointed bedrooms. It has superb conference and leisure facilities.
59 en suite (bth/shr) (3 fmly) CTV in all bedrooms STV No dogs Night porter 150P Indoor swimming pool (heated) Tennis (hard) Sauna Solarium Gym Jacuzzi/spa Beauty parlour Massage Xmas International Cuisine V meals Coffee am Tea pm Last d 9.30pm
ROOMS: (incl. bkfst) s IR£55-IR£70; d IR£80-IR£110 * **LB**
OFF-PEAK: (incl. bkfst) s IR£50; d IR£75
MEALS: Lunch IR£9.50-IR£11.50 Dinner IR£19.50-IR£22*
CONF: Thtr 400 Class 250 Board 50
CARDS:

See advertisement on this page

★★63% **Woodfield House**
Ennis Rd (on outskirts of city on main Shannon road)
☎ 061 453022 FAX 061 326755
Closed 25 Dec
This intimate little hotel stands on the N18 a short distance from the city centre. It offers well equipped en suite bedrooms, a restaurant, a lounge bar and good car parking.
21 en suite (bth/shr) (3 fmly) CTV in all bedrooms STV No dogs (ex guide dogs) Night porter Air conditioning 80P ch fac V meals Coffee am Tea pm Last d 9.30pm
ROOMS: (incl. bkfst) s IR£40-IR£45; d IR£69-IR£75 * **LB**
MEALS: Lunch IR£10.95-IR£13.95&alc High tea IR£9-IR£13 Dinner IR£16.95-IR£19.50&alc*
CONF: Thtr 150 Class 80 Board 80
CARDS:

★★59% **Royal George**
O'Connell St ☎ 061 414566 FAX 061 317171
Closed 25 Dec RS 24 Dec
The Royal George is a city centre hotel with car parking to the rear. Many of the bedrooms have been refurbished and are equipped with satellite TV, telephones, hairdryers and hospitality trays. A new addition, a traditional Irish bar, An Sìbìn, is proving popular, and has live music five nights a week. Other facilities include a lounge bar, self-service bistro grill, and a restaurant.
54 en suite (bth/shr) (6 fmly) CTV in all bedrooms STV Lift Night porter 30P Free access to fitness club Wkly live entertainment European Cuisine V meals Coffee am Tea pm Last d 9.45pm
ROOMS: (incl. bkfst) s IR£35-IR£39; d IR£55-IR£65 *
OFF-PEAK: (incl. bkfst) s IR£29.50-IR£35; d IR£50-IR£55
MEALS: Lunch fr IR£8.95 High tea IR£8.95 Dinner IR£14.50*
CONF: Thtr 70 Class 35 Board 30
CARDS:

L

LISDOONVARNA Co Clare Map 01 B3

★★❀❀70% **Sheedy's Spa View Hotel & Orchid Restaurant**
☎ 065 74026 FAX 065 74555
Closed Oct-14 Mar
This well run family hotel provides warm hospitality, comfort, and good food from its award-winning restaurant. It is situated beside the spa complex in well tended gardens in an area which abounds in interest.
11 en suite (bth/shr) No dogs 42P No coaches Tennis (hard) Irish, English & French Cuisine V meals Coffee am Tea pm No smoking in restaurant
ROOMS: (incl. bkfst) s IR£35-IR£40; d IR£50-IR£63.50 *
CARDS:

LONDONDERRY Co Londonderry Map 01 C5

★★★65% ***Everglades***
Prehen Rd BT47 2PA (1m from city centre) (Hastings)
☎ 01504 46722 FAX 01504 49200
Closed 25 Dec
Everglades is a modern purpose built hotel that sits beside the A5 and the River Foyle to the south of the city centre. Accommodation and public rooms are of a comfortably modern style, offering guests a good range of amenities and services, which include a choice of lounge areas, a well stocked bar and a restaurant providing set-priced and carte menus. A major refurbishment is planned during 1996 to further upgrade the quality of the hotel, and this should make the hotel even more appealing to both the business and tourist markets.
52 en suite (bth/shr) (1 fmly) CTV in all bedrooms STV No dogs (ex guide dogs) Lift Night porter Air conditioning 250P International Cuisine V meals Coffee am Tea pm Last d 9.30pm
CARDS:

LUCAN Co Dublin Map 01 D4

★★★66% **Finnstown Country House Hotel & Golf Course**
Newcastle Rd (on B200) ☎ 01 6280644 FAX 01 6281088
An impressive range of leisure facilities is offered at this 18th-century house set in 22 acres of woodland.
25 en suite (bth/shr) 20 annexe en suite (bth/shr) No smoking in 27 bedrooms CTV in all bedrooms STV Night porter 90P Indoor swimming pool (heated) Golf 9 Tennis (hard) Sauna Solarium Gym Pool table Croquet lawn Turkish bath Table tennis Massage Wkly live entertainment ch fac Xmas International Cuisine V meals Coffee am Tea pm Last d 9.30pm
ROOMS: (incl. bkfst) s IR£75-IR£85; d IR£110-IR£130 * **LB**
MEALS: Lunch IR£14.95 Dinner IR£20.50-IR£24&alc*
CONF: Thtr 60 Class 45 Board 32 Del from IR£110
CARDS:
See advertisement under DUBLIN

★★★55% **Lucan Spa**
(just off N4, 7 miles from Dublin centre)
☎ 01 6280494 FAX 01 6280841
Closed 25 Dec
This long established, modernised hotel is equipped for business conferences and meetings.
59 en suite (bth/shr) (15 fmly) CTV in all bedrooms STV No dogs (ex guide dogs) Night porter Air conditioning 90P Wkly live entertainment European Cuisine V meals Coffee am Tea pm No smoking area in restaurant Last d 9.45pm
ROOMS: (incl. bkfst) s IR£42.50; d IR£70 * **LB**
OFF-PEAK: (incl. bkfst) s IR£37.50; d IR£65
MEALS: Lunch IR£8.50-IR£12 High tea IR£11-IR£12 Dinner IR£16.50-IR£17.50
CONF: Thtr 600 Class 250 Board 80
CARDS:
See advertisement on opposite page

MACROOM Co Cork Map 01 B2

★★❀70% **Castle**
Main St (on N22) ☎ 026 41074 FAX 026 41505
Closed 25-27 Dec
Refurbishment has added to the attraction of this smart stone-built hotel. Accommodation is comfortable with well appointed en suite bedrooms. The restaurant offers good food and a range of bar meals is also available. There are a relaxing lounge, a private dining/meeting room and a gym, steam room and rackets court. Golf can be played nearby.
26 en suite (bth/shr) (5 fmly) CTV in all bedrooms STV No dogs Night porter Air conditioning 6P Squash Sauna Gym Sunbed & Steamroom Wkly live entertainment V meals Coffee am Tea pm No smoking area in restaurant Last d 9pm
ROOMS: (incl. bkfst) s IR£46.75; d IR£63.50 * **LB**
OFF-PEAK: (incl. bkfst) s IR£40.50; d IR£51
MEALS: Lunch IR£9.50-IR£12&alc High tea IR£8.50-IR£12.50&alc Dinner IR£15-IR£18.50&alc*
CONF: Board 20
CARDS:

★★61% **Victoria**
(in the centre of Macroom opposite the Town Hall, on the N22) ☎ 026 41082 & 42143 FAX 026 42148
Closed 25-28 Dec
Set in a good touring location, this town-centre hotel has recently been undergoing refurbishment. The cosy lounge bar has been redesigned and is now very smart with vibrant fabrics, comfortable seating and a large stone fireplace. Bar food is available and further upgrading is planned.
16 en suite (bth/shr) (10 fmly) CTV in all bedrooms STV Night porter 4P Wkly live entertainment Irish, French, Italian & American Cuisine V meals Coffee am Tea pm Last d 9pm
ROOMS: (incl. bkfst) s IR£34-IR£38; d IR£48-IR£50 * **LB**
OFF-PEAK: (incl. bkfst) s IR£23; d IR£44
MEALS: Lunch fr IR£10 High tea fr IR£10 Dinner fr IR£15
CARDS:

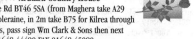

MAGHERA Co Londonderry Map 01 C5

★★❀❀80% **Ardtara Country House**
8 Gorteade Rd BT46 5SA (from Maghera take A29 towards Coleraine, in 2m take B75 for Kilrea through Upperlands, pass sign Wm Clark & Sons then next left) ☎ 01648 44490 FAX 01648 45080
Ardtara is a charming 19th-century house, set in its own grounds on the outskirts of the village of Upperlands in South Londonderry. Marie Boyle and her small team of staff create a friendly and relaxed atmosphere, and service is both attentive and caring. The stylish public rooms include a drawing room, smaller lounge with board games and TV, and a pretty conservatory. Freshly prepared Irish country house cooking is served in the wood-panelled dining room, which is notable for its equine frieze and large skylight. The individually styled bedrooms are furnished with antique and period pieces, and the bathrooms, each with a powerful shower and generous bath, are elegantly appointed.
8 en suite (bth/shr) CTV in all bedrooms No dogs (ex guide dogs) Night porter 100P Tennis (hard) practice tee No children 12yrs Xmas V meals Coffee am Tea pm No smoking in restaurant Last d 9pm
ROOMS: (incl. bkfst) s £80; d £95 * **LB**
OFF-PEAK: (incl. bkfst) s £60; d £80
MEALS: Lunch £12.50-£15 Dinner fr £22&alc*

CONF: Board 20
CARDS:

MALLOW Co Cork Map 01 B2

RED STAR HOTEL

★★★ **Longueville House**

(3m W, on N72) ☎ 022 47156 & 47306
FAX 022 47459
Closed 22 Dec-1 Mar
This 18th-century Georgian mansion, set in a wooded estate, boasts many fine features; your comfortable bedroom might overlook the river valley or a courtyard maze, the two elegant sitting rooms have fine examples of Italian plasterwork. An Adams mantlepiece graces the Presidents Restaurant where chef William O'Callaghan shows flair, courage and sureness of touch in the preparation of an exciting range of dishes based on excellent fresh produce.
20 en suite (bth/shr) (4 fmly) No smoking in 5 bedrooms CTV in all bedrooms STV No dogs 53P No coaches Fishing Snooker Croquet lawn Billiards Table tennis Irish & French Cuisine V meals Coffee am Tea pm No smoking in restaurant Last d 9pm
ROOMS: (incl. bkfst) s IR£55-IR£58; d IR£134-IR£144 * **LB**
OFF-PEAK: (incl. bkfst) s IR£55-IR£58; d IR£106-IR£116
MEALS: Sunday Lunch IR£18-IR£25 Dinner IR£29-IR£40
CONF: Thtr 25 Class 12 Board 14 Del from IR£110
CARDS:

MIDLETON Co Cork Map 01 C2

★★★ 66% ***Midleton Park***
☎ 021 631767 FAX 021 631605
This purpose-built hotel - situated in an area with much to recommend it, just off the N25 Cork/Rosslare route ten miles from Cork - features fine, spacious and well appointed en suite bedrooms; a comfortable restaurant offers good food and attentive service. Both conference/banqueting facilities and on-site parking are available.
40 en suite (bth/shr) (10 fmly) CTV in all bedrooms No dogs (ex guide dogs) Night porter 300P Irish & French Cuisine V meals Coffee am Tea pm Last d 9.30pm
CARDS:

MONAGHAN Co Monaghan Map 01 C5

★★★★ 56% ***Hillgrove***
Old Armagh Rd (turn off N2 at Cathedral, continue for a quarter of a mile, on left just beyond Cathedral) ☎ 047 81288 FAX 047 84951
44 en suite (bth/shr) (2 fmly) CTV in all bedrooms STV No dogs

(ex guide dogs) Lift Night porter Air conditioning 430P Wkly live entertainment European Cuisine V meals Coffee am Tea pm Last d 10pm
CARDS:

★★★ 64% **Four Seasons Hotel & Leisure Club**
Coolshannagh (on N2, 0.5m from town centre)
☎ 047 81888 FAX 047 83131
Closed 24-26 Dec
This modern single storey hotel is set back from the road in its own grounds and car park. A good choice of food is served at the bar, carvery and the restaurant. The hotel is suitable for disabled guests. It also has a fitness centre.
44 en suite (bth/shr) (6 fmly) CTV in all bedrooms STV No dogs (ex guide dogs) Night porter 200P Indoor swimming pool (heated) Fishing Riding Sauna Solarium Gym Jacuzzi/spa steam room Wkly live entertainment European Cuisine V meals Coffee am Tea pm No smoking area in restaurant Last d 9.30pm
ROOMS: (incl. bkfst) s IR£36-IR£50; d IR£68-IR£150 * **LB**
MEALS: Lunch IR£9-IR£12.50 High tea IR£7.50-IR£15 Dinner IR£20-IR£25
CONF: Thtr 450 Class 250 Board 35
CARDS:

NEWBRIDGE Co Kildare Map 01 C3

★★★ 68% **Keadeen**
☎ 045 431666 FAX 045 434402
37 en suite (bth/shr) CTV in all bedrooms STV No dogs (ex guide dogs) Night porter Air conditioning 200P Indoor swimming pool (heated) Sauna Solarium Gym Jacuzzi/spa Xmas French Cuisine V meals Coffee am Tea pm Last d 9.45pm
ROOMS: (incl. bkfst) s IR£60-IR£150; d IR£90-IR£200 * **LB**

contd.

MEALS: Lunch IR£11-IR£38 Dinner IR£22-IR£38*
CARDS:

NEWCASTLE Co Down Map 01 D5

★★★65% **Slieve Donard**
Downs Rd BT33 0AH (follow the A2 from Belfast into Newcastle.Asyou enter the town centre bear left onto Downs Road) (Hastings)
☎ 013967 23681 FAX 013967 24830
Nestling at the foot of the beautiful Mourne Mountains, in six acres of grounds that extend to the shoreline, this impressive red brick Victorian hotel has a wide range of leisure, function and conference facilities. Public rooms include lounge areas, a panelled restaurant and a choice of bars, the public bar being separately located in the entrance to the grounds. Currently, the hotel is under going a major refurbishment to two floors of the accommodation, which will bring a consistently high standard to all the bedrooms; recent examples are tastefully refurbished and offer a very good range of amenities.
134 en suite (bth/shr) No smoking in 12 bedrooms CTV in all bedrooms STV No dogs (ex guide dogs) Lift Night porter 500P Indoor swimming pool (heated) Tennis (hard) Sauna Solarium Gym Putting green Jacuzzi/spa Xmas European Cuisine V meals Coffee am Tea pm Last d 9pm
ROOMS: (incl. bkfst) s fr £75; d fr £110 **LB**
MEALS: Lunch £14.50-£18 Dinner £18&alc*
CONF: Thtr 800 Class 120 Board 70 Del £90
CARDS:

★★64% **Enniskeen House**
98 Bryansford Rd BT33 0LF (from Newcastle town centre follow signs for Tollymore Forest Park, hotel 1 mile on left)
☎ 013967 22392 FAX 013967 24084
Closed 12 Nov-14 Mar
Set in its own grounds in a quiet residential area north of the town centre, this friendly family-run hotel offers unpretentious, traditional accommodation, many rooms enjoying fine mountain and sea views.
12 en suite (bth/shr) (1 fmly) No smoking in 3 bedrooms CTV in all bedrooms No dogs Lift 45P V meals Coffee am Tea pm No smoking in restaurant Last d 8.30pm
ROOMS: (incl. bkfst) s £40-£47; d £65-£78 * **LB**
MEALS: Lunch £8.50-£11.50 High tea £6.25-£10.75 Dinner fr £14.50*
CARDS:

NEWMARKET-ON-FERGUS Co Clare Map 01 B3

★★★64% **Clare Inn**
(on N18, 9 miles from Shannon International Airport)
☎ 061 368161 FAX 061 368622
The Clare Inn is set in open countryside in the centre of an 18-hole golf course just 10 minutes from Shannon Airport. It is a comfortable hotel with excellent leisure facilities and friendly staff to ensure an enjoyable stay.
121 en suite (bth/shr) (20 fmly) No smoking in 4 bedrooms CTV in all bedrooms STV No dogs (ex guide dogs) Night porter 150P Indoor swimming pool (heated) Golf 18 Tennis (hard) Fishing Sauna Solarium Gym Pool table Jacuzzi/spa Bowls Cruiser for hire Wkly live entertainment Xmas Irish & Continental Cuisine V meals Coffee am Tea pm No smoking area in restaurant Last d 10pm
ROOMS: s IR£35-IR£55; d IR£60-IR£85 * **LB**
OFF-PEAK: s IR£25-IR£55; d IR£35-IR£85
MEALS: Sunday Lunch IR£10.50 Dinner IR£20*
CONF: Thtr 400 Class 300 Board 70 Del from IR£57
CARDS:

indicates a Town House Hotel. Please consult the section on AA Star Rating at the front of the book.

NEW ROSS Co Wexford Map 01 C3

★★59% **The Old Rectory**
Rosbercon (when you are in New Ross cross the bridge, turn off to the right and follow road for 200 yds up hill, hotel is on the right)
☎ 051 421719 FAX 051 422974
Closed Jan
12 en suite (bth/shr) CTV in all bedrooms STV No dogs (ex guide dogs) 37P V meals Coffee am No smoking area in restaurant Last d 9.30pm
ROOMS: (incl. bkfst) s IR£35-IR£45; d IR£50-IR£70 **LB**
MEALS: Lunch IR£8.50-IR£11.50 Dinner IR£15.95-IR£17.95&alc
CONF: Thtr 80 Class 48 Board 20 Del from IR£58
CARDS:

NEWTOWNABBEY Co Antrim Map 01 D5

★★★60% **Chimney Corner**
630 Antrim Rd BT36 8RH (off M2 at Sandyknowes onto A6, hotel 1m on left) ☎ 01232 844925 & 844851 FAX 01232 844352
Closed 24-26 Dec
This busy commercial hotel, which is built around a 19th century inn, is handy for Belfast and the International airport; stands beside the A6 Belfast Antrim road with convenient access to the M2 motorway. The well equipped bedrooms have recently been refurbished, the new co-ordinated colour schemes give the rooms an added lift. There have been improvements in the public areas too, the restaurant has been moved into the original Inn, and has been refurbished in a sympathetic style, enhancing the character of the room with cheerful soft furnishings.
63 en suite (bth/shr) CTV in all bedrooms STV No dogs (ex guide dogs) Night porter 306P Tennis (hard) Sauna Gym Pool table Bicycles Wkly live entertainment British & French Cuisine V meals Coffee am Tea pm Last d 9.45pm
ROOMS: (incl. bkfst) s £75; d £95
OFF-PEAK: (incl. bkfst) s £38; d £55
MEALS: Lunch £9.95 Dinner £15.95
CONF: Thtr 220 Class 100 Board 60
CARDS:

OMAGH Co Tyrone Map 01 C5

★★63% ***Royal Arms***
51 High St BT78 1BA ☎ 01662 243262 FAX 01662 245011
Closed 25 Dec
Dating back to 1787, this long-established family-run commercial hotel is situated in the centre of town. Bedrooms vary in size but are modern in style and offer practical modern appointments. The bar/lounge is a popular local rendezvous, and an attractive restaurant with a heavily beamed ceiling offers a good choice of dishes on its fixed-price menu and carte. Less formal meals are available in the bar/bistro, and staff are friendly and willing to please. Function rooms include a theatre.
19 en suite (bth/shr) (1 fmly) CTV in all bedrooms Night porter 250P Snooker Golf & Fishing can be arranged V meals Coffee am Tea pm Last d 9.30pm
CARDS:

OUGHTERARD Co Galway Map 01 B4

★★★63% **Ross Lake House**
Rosscahill (on N59, Galway - Clifden road) ☎ 091 550109 & 550154 FAX 091 550184
Closed Nov-mid Mar
This modern Georgian-style house is situated at the end of a winding country road in a panoramic garden setting. It is family run and offers well furnished accommodation and a comfortable, relaxed atmosphere.

13 en suite (bth/shr) 150P Tennis (hard) V meals Coffee am Tea pm Last d 9pm
ROOMS: (incl. bkfst) s IR£48.50-IR£54; d IR£77-IR£88 **LB**
MEALS: Dinner IR£19*
CARDS:

PARKNASILLA Co Kerry Map 01 A2

★★★★ 79% **Great Southern**
(on Kenmare road 2m from village) ☎ 064 45122 FAX 064 45323
Closed 5 Jan-14 Feb
The Great Southern is superbly located on Kenmare Bay with fine sea views from many of its bedrooms. There are spacious, comfortable lounges, the excellent Pygmalion Retaurant and an impressive range of leisure facilities. Above all, it is the warmth of the welcome from the friendly and attentive staff that distinguishes this hotel.
26 en suite (bth/shr) 59 annexe en suite (bth/shr) (6 fmly) CTV in all bedrooms STV No dogs (ex guide dogs) Lift Night porter 60P Indoor swimming pool (heated) Golf 9 Tennis (hard) Fishing Riding Snooker Sauna Pool table Croquet lawn Jacuzzi/spa Bike hire Windsurfing Clay pigeon Wkly live entertainment International Cuisine V meals Coffee am Tea pm No smoking area in restaurant Last d 8.45pm
MEALS: Bar Lunch IR£7&alc Dinner IR£25*
CONF: Thtr 100 Class 80 Board 20
CARDS:

PORTAFERRY Co Down Map 01 D5

★★★ 66% **Portaferry**
10 The Strand BT22 1PE (situated on Lough Shore opposite ferry terminal) ☎ 012477 28231 FAX 012477 28999
Closed 24-25 Dec
(Rosette awarded for dinner only)
Originally a terrace of 18th-century dwellings, this is now a charming waterside inn, which offers tastefully furnished public rooms and well appointed accommodation. John and Marie Herlihy are enthusiastic hosts, and they and their staff work hard to provide professional service and a relaxing atmosphere. Interesting dishes are served from both set-price and carte menus. The quiet first-floor drawing room enjoys delightful views over the lough, which are shared by a good number of the light and airy en suite bedrooms.
14 en suite (bth/shr) CTV in all bedrooms No dogs (ex guide dogs) 6P Irish & Continental Cuisine V meals Coffee am Tea pm Last d 9pm
ROOMS: (incl. bkfst) s £55; d £90 * **LB**
MEALS: Lunch £13.50-£17.50 Dinner £19.50-£22.50&alc*
CARDS:

PORTBALLINTRAE Co Antrim Map 01 C6

★★ 60% **Beach House**

The Sea Front BT57 8RT (on the sea front) ☎ 012657 31214 FAX 012657 31664
Efficiently run by the third generation of the Maclean family, this resort hotel enjoys sea views from the Donegal coast to the Giant's Causeway. Bedrooms are mostly well proportioned. There are a large dining room, a bar made to resemble a 1920s cruise liner and a comfortable lounge.
32 en suite (bth/shr) (17 fmly) CTV in all bedrooms STV No dogs (ex guide dogs) Night porter 40P Pool table Table tennis Xmas European Cuisine V meals Coffee am Tea pm No smoking area in restaurant Last d 9pm
ROOMS: (incl. bkfst) s £45-£48; d £70-£76 **LB**
OFF-PEAK: (incl. bkfst) s £35-£40; d £54-£60
MEALS: Lunch £8-£9 High tea £7-£12alc Dinner £13-£16
CONF: Class 150 Board 35
CARDS:

PORTLAOISE Co Laois Map 01 C3

★★★ 62% ***Killeshin***
Dublin Rd (on N7) ☎ 0502 21663 FAX 0502 21976
Major refurbishment has taken place throughout the hotel, most notably in the public areas. A smart new entrance and foyer lounge have comfortable sofas and a relaxing atmosphere, and the most recent addition is a conference suite. There is also a lounge bar, a restaurant, and private banqueting facilities are available. The recently refurbished bedrooms are well equipped with modern facilities.
44 en suite (bth/shr) (8 fmly) No smoking in 11 bedrooms CTV in all bedrooms STV Night porter 400P Wkly live entertainment V meals Coffee am Tea pm Last d 9.30pm
CARDS:

PORTRUSH Co Antrim Map 01 C6

★★★ 61% **Causeway Coast**
36 Ballyreagh Rd BT56 8LR (on A2 between Portrush & Portstewart, opposite Ballyreagh Golf Course)
Best Western
☎ 01265 822435 FAX 01265 824495
This modern hotel sits facing the Atlantic sea, on the A2 coast road between Portrush and Portstewart, opposite the Ballyreagh Golf Club. The accommodation is modern, practical and well equipped; 10 of the bedrooms are of a condominium style with small fitted kitchen units. Public areas offer a choice of eating outlets, with informal dining in the lively wine bar or alternatively formal menus are available in the small dining room; service tends to be rather informal. A good modern conference centre is available, separate self-contained facilities which offer flexible combinations for large and small meetings.
21 en suite (bth/shr) (2 fmly) CTV in all bedrooms STV No dogs (ex guide dogs) Night porter 180P Snooker ch fac Xmas British & French Cuisine V meals Coffee am Tea pm Last d 9pm
ROOMS: (incl. bkfst) s £46-£53; d £75 * **LB**
OFF-PEAK: (incl. bkfst) d £65-£75
MEALS: Sunday Lunch £8.95-£9.95 Dinner £14-£16.50*
CONF: Thtr 500 Class 170 Board 108
CARDS:

PROSPEROUS Co Kildare Map 01 C4

★★ 59% ***Curryhills House***
(5m from N7 and N4) ☎ 045 868150 FAX 045 868805
Closed 23-30 Dec
This 19th-century house with a modern bedroom extension stands in 100 acres of gardens and parklands.
10 en suite (bth/shr) (10 fmly) CTV in all bedrooms STV No dogs (ex guide dogs) Air conditioning 50P No coaches Coffee am
CARDS:

RATHMULLAN Co Donegal Map 01 C6

★★★ 69% **Fort Royal**
Fort Royal (take L77 from Letterkenny, through Rathmullen village, hotel is signposted) ☎ 074 58100 FAX 074 58103
Closed Nov-Etr
Period house in a lovely location on the shores of Lough Swilly, with private access to a secluded sandy beach. The hotel has been refurbished to a high standard, and the decor throughout is delightful. Comfortable public rooms include a charming dining room, and an attractive restaurant, serving freshly prepared cuisine,both of which benefit from views of the grounds and lake shore. The individually styled bedrooms are well equipped, and the atmosphere is very pleasant, from the moment guests are welcomed with afternoon tea in a cosy room with a blazing log fire.
11 en suite (bth/shr) 4 annexe en suite (bth) (3 fmly) CTV in all

contd.

R

bedrooms 40P No coaches Golf 9 Tennis (hard) Squash Irish & French Cuisine V meals Coffee am Last d 9pm
ROOMS: (incl. bkfst) s IR£63-IR£76.75; d IR£87-IR£110 **LB**
MEALS: Sunday Lunch IR£14.50 Dinner IR£19.50-IR£23*
CARDS:

★61% **Pier**
(on sea front, near harbour) ☎ 074 58178 & 58115 FAX 074 58115
Closed Nov-May RS Apr-May & Oct
Standing directly opposite a safe sandy beach on the western shores of Lough Swilly, this pleasant hotel has been refurbished by its friendly owners. There are a comfortable lounge and dining room, a cosy bar, and en suite bedrooms. A good angling centre and golf course are available nearby.
10 en suite (bth/shr) (2 fmly) No dogs (ex guide dogs) Wkly live entertainment Coffee am Tea pm No smoking area in restaurant Last d 9.30pm
ROOMS: (incl. bkfst) s fr IR£23; d fr IR£46 *
OFF-PEAK: (incl. bkfst) s fr IR£20; d fr IR£40
MEALS: Sunday Lunch IR£8 Dinner IR£14*
CARDS:

RATHNEW Co Wicklow Map 01 D3

RED STAR HOTEL

★★★ **Tinakilly Country House & Restaurant**
(500 metres from town on R750 Wicklow rd)
☎ 0404 69274 FAX 0404 67806
We are pleased to welcome Tinakilly Country House to the ranks of our Red Star award winners. Built in 1870, it is an elegant house is set in seven acres of 19th-century gardens with breathtaking views of the sea. It offers the highest standards of accommodation and hospitality, its bedrooms tastefully decorated with period furnishings and some four-poster beds. Country house cuisine is served, including fresh fish, game and home-grown vegetables.
29 en suite (bth/shr) CTV in all bedrooms No dogs (ex guide dogs) 60P Tennis (hard) Croquet lawn Putting green Mapped garden walks Jogging route Wkly live entertainment Xmas Coffee am Tea pm Last d 9pm
ROOMS: (incl. bkfst) s IR£96-IR£118; d IR£132-IR£160 * **LB**
OFF-PEAK: (incl. bkfst) s IR£96-IR£108; d IR£116-IR£140
MEALS: Lunch IR£18.50 Dinner IR£32*
CONF: Thtr 80 Class 60 Board 40 Del from IR£150
CARDS:

★★★59% ***Hunter's***
(1m from village off N11) ☎ 0404 40106 FAX 0404 40338
Closed 24-26 Dec
The hospitable Gelletlie family forms the fifth generation of Hunters who have been hosts at this delightful hotel which is one of Ireland's oldest coaching inns. Over the years they have made many improvements to introduce modern facilities, but none of this has detracted from the character of the original building. It is also noted for its prize-winning gardens bordering the River Vartry, where afternoon tea in summer is a special treat. The restaurant has a good reputation for carefully prepared dishes which make the best use of high quality local produce. An ideal centre for touring or for golf, Hunters caters equally well for the business traveller.
16 en suite (bth/shr) (2 fmly) CTV in all bedrooms No dogs (ex guide dogs) 50P No coaches Irish, English & French Cuisine Coffee am Tea pm Last d 9pm
CARDS:

RECESS Co Galway Map 01 A4

★★★74% **Lough Inagh Lodge**

Inagh Valley (off N59) ☎ 095 34706 & 34694
FAX 095 34708
Closed 28 Oct - 27 Mar
This 19th-century shooting lodge has been skilfully restored and upgraded into a luxurious hotel. It is in a superb location, fronted by a good fishing lake and with lovely mountain views. Large lounges with blazing fires and a cosy oak-lined bar offer great warmth and comfort. The spacious, high-ceilinged bedrooms are beautifully furnished. Food and presentation are excellent, and overall a friendly informal atmosphere prevails.
12 en suite (bth/shr) CTV in all bedrooms Air conditioning 16P No coaches Fishing Fishing arranged Irish & French Cuisine V meals Coffee am Tea pm No smoking area in restaurant
ROOMS: (incl. bkfst) s fr IR£69; d fr IR£102 * **LB**
OFF-PEAK: (incl. bkfst) s fr IR£40; d fr IR£80
MEALS: Bar Lunch IR£2.50-IR£12.50
CONF: Thtr 20 Class 20 Board 20 Del IR£85
CARDS:

RENVYLE Co Galway Map 01 A4

★★★68% **Renvyle House**
(signposted fron turn off for Recess)
☎ 095 43511 FAX 095 43515
Closed 7 Jan-3 Mar
Once the home of Oliver St John Gogarty, this historic country house is set on the shore of the Atlantic ocean, in the wild splendour of Connemara. The hotel is warmly inviting with log fires and comfortable public rooms. Good leisure facilities include hard tennis courts, snooker room, outdoor pool, and a 9-hole golf course.
65 en suite (bth/shr) CTV in all bedrooms STV No dogs (ex guide dogs) Night porter 100P Outdoor swimming pool (heated) Golf 9 Tennis (hard) Fishing Riding Snooker Croquet lawn Boating Lawn bowls Bicycle hire Wkly live entertainment ch fac Xmas International Cuisine V meals Coffee am Tea pm
ROOMS: (incl. bkfst) s IR£40-IR£100; d IR£80-IR£160 * **LB**
CONF: Thtr 120 Class 70 Board 20
CARDS:

ROSCOMMON Co Roscommon Map 01 B4

★★★60% **Abbey**

Galway Rd (on N63 opposite railway station)
☎ 0903 26240 & 26505 FAX 0903 26021
Closed 25-26 Dec
This family-run hotel is a converted 19th-century manor house, centrally located in attractive grounds with its own car park. It caters

for tourist and commercial trade, offering a good standard of public rooms. Bedroom refurbishment has left many rooms comfortable and up-to-date.
25 en suite (bth/shr) (2 fmly) No smoking in 2 bedrooms CTV in all bedrooms STV No dogs Night porter 45P No coaches Irish & French Cuisine V meals Coffee am Tea pm No smoking area in restaurant Last d 9.30pm
ROOMS: (incl. bkfst) s IR£45-IR£55; d IR£70-IR£80 *
OFF-PEAK: (incl. bkfst) s IR£35-IR£40; d IR£60-IR£70
MEALS: Lunch IR£9.75-IR£14.95 High tea IR£7.50 Dinner IR£17.50-IR£22.50*
CONF: Thtr 300 Class 200 Board 25 Del from IR£65
CARDS:

ROSCREA Co Tipperary Map 01 C3

★★★63% Grant's
Castle St ☎ 0505 23300 FAX 0505 23209
This attractive hotel stands opposite the 13th-century castle and Heritage Centre and is as inviting inside as out. Bedrooms are pleasantly furnished in warm-toned colours and there is an excellent, oak-panelled foyer lounge with deep leather armchairs and sofas. There is a choice of two restaurants, the Lemon Tree and the Bistro, as well as an informal pub with a cafe-bar area, Kitty's Tavern.
25 en suite (bth/shr) (3 fmly) CTV in all bedrooms No dogs (ex guide dogs) Night porter 30P Wkly live entertainment Irish & French Cuisine V meals Coffee am Tea pm Last d 9.30pm
ROOMS: (incl. bkfst) s IR£35; d IR£65 *
MEALS: Lunch IR£8.96 Dinner IR£18.50&alc*
CONF: Thtr 300 Class 150 Board 30 Del from IR£57
CARDS:

ROSSLARE Co Wexford Map 01 D2

★★★★76% Kelly's Resort
☎ 053 32114 FAX 053 32222
Closed mid Dec-late Feb
Comfort, a friendly atmosphere, attractive decor, professional service and award-winning food all combine to make this a very special place to stay, as the many regularly returning guests will agree. Since 1895 successive generations of the Kelly family have extended and improved the original building to create this truly fine hotel, with an emphasis on all-year-round family holidays. There is plenty to do, or guests can relax in one of the many comfortable lounges, and entertainment is provided nightly in the hotel's own ballroom. A lasting impression of a stay at the hotel is the effort made by the Kellys to cater in every possible way for their guests. Menus are varied and generous, reflecting careful preparation, and fresh local fish and shellfish are very popular.
99 annexe en suite (bth/shr) (15 fmly) CTV in all bedrooms STV No dogs Lift Night porter 99P No coaches Indoor swimming pool (heated) Tennis (hard) Squash Snooker Sauna Solarium Gym Pool table Croquet lawn Jacuzzi/spa Bowls Plunge pool Badminton Crazy golf Wkly live entertainment ch fac English & French Cuisine Coffee am Tea pm Last d 9pm
MEALS: Lunch IR£14-IR£15 Dinner IR£23*
CONF: Thtr 30 Class 30 Board 20
CARDS:

★★★58% Cedars
(off N25) ☎ 053 32124 FAX 053 32243
Closed Jan-14 Apr
Situated five minutes' drive from Rosslare ferryport and close to the 'blue flag' beach, this hotel has pleasant public areas and spacious bedrooms. It has recently undergone extensive refurbishment, and there are pleasant public areas and spacious family bedrooms. There are two restaurants and two bars, the Casket Lounge and the Casablanca, with nightly entertainment during the summer.
34 en suite (bth/shr) (34 fmly) CTV in all bedrooms No dogs (ex guide dogs) Night porter Air conditioning 150P ch fac Xmas French Cuisine V meals Coffee am Tea pm No smoking area in restaurant Last d 9.30pm
ROOMS: (incl. bkfst) s IR£42-IR£55; d IR£64-IR£80 * LB
MEALS: Lunch IR£9.95-IR£10.95 Dinner IR£15.95&alc*
CONF: Thtr 350 Class 250 Board 40
CARDS:

See advertisement on this page

ROSSLARE HARBOUR Co Wexford Map 01 D2

★★★56% Hotel Rosslare
☎ 053 33110 FAX 053 33386
Ideally situated for the car ferryport, this hotel overlooks the harbour and is a short distance from sandy 'blue flag' beaches. A friendly atmosphere and good food are the priorities, and there is an interesting old bar full of seafaring lore and local history, with a pleasant beer garden outside.
25 rms (22 bth/shr) (6 fmly) CTV in all bedrooms Night porter P Fishing Snooker Sauna Wkly live entertainment International Cuisine V meals Coffee am Tea pm Last d 9pm
ROOMS: (incl. bkfst) s IR£39-IR£49; d IR£58-IR£78 * LB
OFF-PEAK: (incl. bkfst) s IR£29-IR£35; d IR£50-IR£58
MEALS: Lunch fr IR£9.50 Dinner fr IR£18*
CONF: Thtr 120 Class 80 Board 50
CARDS:

ROSSNOWLAGH Co Donegal Map 01 B5

★★★ 73% ***Sand House***
☎ 072 51777 FAX 072 52100
Closed mid Oct-Etr
Set in a crescent of golden sands five miles north of Ballyshannon, this owner-managed hotel is well known for its hospitality, good cuisine and personal service. Many rooms have sea views, and a conservatory lounge overlooking Donegal Bay provides a relaxing retreat. The beach at Rossnowlagh is ideal for safe bathing and surfing.
46 en suite (bth/shr) (6 fmly) Night porter 42P Tennis (hard) Croquet lawn Putting green Miniature golf Surfing Wkly live entertainment Irish & French Cuisine V meals Coffee am Tea pm Last d 9pm
CARDS:

ROUNDSTONE Co Galway Map 01 A4

★★ 69% **Eldons**
(off N59 through Toombedla then lt to village)
☎ 095 35933 & 35942 FAX 095 35871
Closed 6 Nov-14 Mar
This distinctive blue and yellow painted building is situated on the main street of this picturesque fishing village. From Galway take the N59 to Clifden, near Recess turn left to Cashel and follow the coastline. The Conneely family are welcoming hosts and they maintain high standards throughout their hotel. Noleen runs Bedla, the popular seafood restaurant, where fresh lobster, crab and prawns are served.
13 en suite (bth/shr) CTV in all bedrooms No dogs Lift Wkly live entertainment V meals Coffee am Tea pm No smoking area in restaurant Last d 9.30pm
ROOMS: (incl. bkfst) s IR£30-IR£40; d IR£40-IR£60 **LB**
OFF-PEAK: (incl. bkfst) s fr IR£25; d fr IR£40
MEALS: Lunch IR£10.50 Dinner IR£12.50-IR£20*
CARDS:

SALTHILL See Galway

SHANNON Co Clare Map 01 B3

★★★ 67% **Oak Wood Arms**
(1m from Shannon Airport on main Airport road)
☎ 061 361500 FAX 061 361414
Closed 24-25 Dec
75 en suite (bth/shr) (2 fmly) No smoking in 16 bedrooms CTV in all bedrooms STV No dogs (ex guide dogs) Night porter Air conditioning 200P Sauna Solarium Gym French Cuisine V meals Coffee am Tea pm Last d 9.45pm
ROOMS: (incl. bkfst) s IR£58-IR£70; d IR£80-IR£120
OFF-PEAK: (incl. bkfst) s IR£46-IR£58; d IR£72-IR£80
MEALS: Lunch IR£12-IR£15 Dinner IR£19.75-IR£25&alc*
CONF: Thtr 200 Class 160 Board 20
CARDS:

SLANE Co Meath Map 01 D4

★★ 60% **Conyngham Arms**
(from N2 turn onto N51, hotel is 25 yards on the left)
☎ 041 24155 FAX 041 24205
Closed Good Fri & Xmas
Situated in the picturesque village near the famous prehistoric tombs of New Grange, the hotel has very comfortable public rooms including the unique Estate Agent's Restaurant. Five new bedrooms have recently been added and are equipped with excellent bathrooms. There are attractive gardens to the rear, and this is an ideal location from which to explore the historic area which includes Tara and the Boyne Valley. Fishing, horse riding and tennis are available locally.
16 rms (15 bth/shr) (4 fmly) CTV in all bedrooms STV No dogs (ex guide dogs) 12P Irish & French Cuisine V meals Coffee am Tea pm Last d 9.45pm
ROOMS: (incl. bkfst) s IR£35-IR£41.25; d IR£57.50-IR£65.75 **LB**
MEALS: Sunday Lunch IR£10.50-IR£11.50 High tea IR£8.90-IR£10alc Dinner IR£15-IR£17.95alc
CONF: Thtr 150 Class 120
CARDS:

SLIGO Co Sligo Map 01 B5

★★★ 70% **Sligo Park**
Pearse Rd (on N4) ☎ 071 60291 FAX 071 69556
RS 24-26 Dec
Set in seven acres of parkland on the southern edge of Sligo, this recently refurbished hotel is an ideal touring centre for the many attractions of Yeats country and is also near Rosses Point Golf Club. Most of the bedrooms have recently been upgraded and offer all modern facilities, in particular the excellent 'executive' rooms. The restaurant is particularly attractive and inviting. A comprehensive leisure centre is an added attraction, and there are good beaches not far away.
89 en suite (bth/shr) No smoking in 4 bedrooms CTV in all bedrooms No dogs (ex guide dogs) Night porter 200P Indoor swimming pool (heated) Tennis (hard) Snooker Sauna Solarium Gym Jacuzzi/spa Steam room Plunge pool Wkly live entertainment Xmas Irish & French Cuisine V meals Coffee am Tea pm No smoking area in restaurant Last d 9.15pm
ROOMS: (incl. bkfst) s IR£57-IR£62; d IR£90-IR£99 **LB**
OFF-PEAK: (incl. bkfst) s IR£52-IR£57; d IR£80-IR£85
MEALS: Lunch IR£6.95-IR£10 Dinner IR£15.50-IR£18.95*
CARDS:

★★★ 65% **Tower**
Quay St (in the centre of Sligo) ☎ 071 44000 FAX 46888
58 en suite (bth/shr) No smoking in 12 bedrooms CTV in all bedrooms No dogs (ex guide dogs) Lift Night porter Air conditioning 20P V meals Coffee am No smoking in restaurant Last d 9.30pm
ROOMS: (incl. bkfst) s IR£51-IR£58; d IR£86 * **LB**
OFF-PEAK: (incl. bkfst) s IR£54; d IR£78
MEALS: Lunch IR£9.50-IR£12 Dinner IR£16.95-IR£18*
CARDS:

★★ 60% **Ballincar House**
Rosses Point Rd, Ballincar ☎ 071 45361 FAX 071 44198
A friendly, relaxed atmosphere is one of the characteristics of this converted country house, set in six acres of mature gardens midway between Sligo and Rosses Point. The attractively redecorated restaurant overlooks gardens where good food in comfortable surroundings makes dining an enjoyable experience. Parking is provided and the hotel is suitable for both tourists and business guests.
25 en suite (bth/shr) (11 fmly) No smoking in 6 bedrooms CTV in all bedrooms STV No dogs (ex guide dogs) Night porter 100P Tennis (hard) Snooker Sauna Xmas French & International Cuisine V meals Coffee am Tea pm No smoking area in restaurant Last d 9pm
ROOMS: (incl. bkfst) s IR£45-IR£60; d IR£86-IR£104 * **LB**
OFF-PEAK: (incl. bkfst) s IR£35-IR£49; d IR£70-IR£82
MEALS: Lunch IR£11-IR£15 Dinner IR£15-IR£20&alc
CONF: Thtr 90 Class 50 Board 50 Del from IR£59
CARDS:

★★ 60% **Silver Swan**
(situated in the town centre) ☎ 071 43231 FAX 071 42232
Closed 25 & 26 Dec
Family owned, this hotel is situated on the banks of the Garavogue River in the heart of Sligo and attracts both business guests and tourists. Recently redecorated bedrooms are well furnished and

comfortable with good bathrooms, some with aero-spa baths. The Horseshoe Bar is a popular spot for snacks and drinks and there is a car park to the rear.
29 en suite (bth/shr) CTV in all bedrooms No dogs (ex guide dogs) Night porter 40P Wkly live entertainment French Cuisine V meals Coffee am Tea pm No smoking in restaurant Last d 10pm
ROOMS: (incl. bkfst) s IR£35-IR£49; d IR£60-IR£85 *
OFF-PEAK: (incl. bkfst) s IR£32-IR£42; d IR£55-IR£65
MEALS: Lunch IR£9.95-IR£13 Dinner IR£18.75-IR£21*
CONF: Thtr 100 Class 60 Board 30 Del from IR£65
CARDS:

STRAFFAN Co Kildare Map 01 D4

RED STAR HOTEL

★★★★★ ❀❀❀ **The Kildare Hotel & Country Club**

RELAIS & CHATEAUX. Relais Gourmands

(from Dublin take N4,take exit for R406 hotelentrance is on right in Straffan)
☎ 01 6273333 FAX 01 6273312
In the heart of horse-breeding territory, in 330 acres of parkland beside the River Liffey, this very grand and luxurious hotel is known not only for its Arnold Palmer designed golf course, and private fishing, but also for its country elegance and the quality of its decor and furnishings. Paintings, antiques and rugs enhance the atmosphere, and bedrooms are well furnished and comfortable. The new Arnold Palmer Conference/Banqueting room and new Clubhouse Restaurant for members provide fine facilities overlooking the course. Chef Michel Flamme produces a choice of menus, featuring dishes cooked in French or speciality Irish style. Ray Carroll has brought together a team whose professionalism and charm combine to make a stay here a real pleasure.
36 en suite (bth/shr) 7 annexe en suite (bth/shr) (10 fmly) CTV in all bedrooms STV No dogs Lift Night porter 205P Indoor swimming pool (heated) Golf 18 Tennis (hard) Fishing Squash Snooker Sauna Solarium Gym Pool table Croquet lawn Putting green Jacuzzi/spa Beauty salon Driving range Wkly live entertainment Irish, French & Italian Cuisine V meals Coffee am Tea pm Last d 9.45pm
MEALS: Lunch fr IR£25 Dinner fr IR£39*
CONF: Thtr 160 Class 80 Board 100
CARDS:

★★★ ❀❀ 76% **Barberstown Castle**
☎ 01 6288157 & 6288206 FAX 01 6277027
Closed 24-26 Dec
Embracing a heritage that dates from the 13th century, the castle has been elegantly refurbished and decorarted in glowing colours to provide the highest standards of comfort. Inviting public rooms range from the original castle keep, now housing one of the two restaurants, to the soft warmth of the drawing room and cocktail bar. A new wing of high quality bedrooms has recently been added.
22 en suite (bth/shr) 4 annexe en suite (bth/shr) CTV in all bedrooms STV No dogs Night porter 200P No children 12yrs V meals Coffee am Tea pm Last d 9.30pm
ROOMS: (incl. bkfst) s IR£71.50; d IR£121 *
MEALS: Lunch IR£15.50&alc Dinner IR£25&alc*
CONF: Thtr 50 Class 40 Board 30
CARDS:

THOMASTOWN Co Kilkenny Map 01 C3

RED STAR HOTEL

★★★★ ❀ **Mount Juliet**
☎ 056 24455 FAX 056 24522
Closed 1st 2wks Jan
Set in 1500 acres of parkland, including a Jack Nicklaus designed golf course where the Irish Opens were played in 1993 and 1994, this beautiful Palladian mansion is now a very special hotel. The elegant and spacious public rooms retain much of the original architectural features, including ornate plasterwork and fine Adam fireplaces in the cocktail bar, restaurant and drawing room. Many sporting and leisure activities are catered for and in Hunters Yard there is moderately priced accommodation for parties.
32 en suite (bth/shr) 21 annexe en suite (bth/shr) CTV in all bedrooms STV No dogs (ex guide dogs) Night porter 200P Indoor swimming pool (heated) Golf 18 Tennis (hard) Fishing Riding Snooker Sauna Gym Croquet lawn Putting green Beauty salon Archery Shooting Cycling Xmas International Cuisine V meals Coffee am Tea pm Last d 9.30pm
ROOMS: s IR£125-IR£155; d IR£125-IR£270 **LB**
OFF-PEAK: s IR£115-IR£125; d IR£115-IR£200
MEALS: Bar Lunch IR£13.50-IR£16.50alc Dinner IR£19.50-IR£33*
CONF: Thtr 50 Class 36 Board 20
CARDS:

TIPPERARY Co Tipperary Map 01 C3

★57% **Royal**
Bridge St ☎ 062 33244 FAX 062 33596
16 en suite (bth/shr) (3 fmly) CTV in all bedrooms No dogs 200P Wkly live entertainment V meals Coffee am Tea pm No smoking area

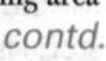

contd.

T

in restaurant Last d 9pm
ROOMS: (incl. bkfst) s IR£30; d IR£60 * **LB**
OFF-PEAK: (incl. bkfst) s IR£25; d IR£50
MEALS: Lunch IR£8-IR£10 Dinner IR£12-IR£14
CONF: Class 80
CARDS:

TRALEE Co Kerry Map 01 A2

★★★64% **Abbey Gate**
Maine St (in town centre) ☎ 066 29888 FAX 29821
Closed 25 Dec
The Abbey Gate is a smartly appointed new hotel, conveniently situated in the town centre with parking in front. The well equipped bedrooms have modern facilities, and there are five suitable for those with mobility problems. Public areas include a spacious foyer and lounge area with attractive decor, a traditional pub, 'The Old Market Place' where carvery lunches are served, a cocktail bar, the Vineyard Restaurant, and banqueting and conference suites.
100 en suite (bth/shr) (4 fmly) CTV in all bedrooms No dogs (ex guide dogs) Lift Night porter 20P Wkly live entertainment Xmas International Cuisine V meals Coffee am Tea pm No smoking area in restaurant Last d 9.30pm
ROOMS: (incl. bkfst) s IR£45-IR£95; d IR£70-IR£98 * **LB**
OFF-PEAK: (incl. bkfst) s IR£38-IR£45; d IR£50-IR£70
MEALS: Lunch IR£10-IR£10.50 Dinner IR£18.50&alc
CONF: Thtr 350 Class 250 Board 25 Del from IR£50
CARDS:

★★★64% ***The Brandon***
☎ 066 23333 FAX 066 25019
This modern hotel, completely refurbished, is situated in the town centre. It has excellent leisure facilities and is a golfer's paradise, within 30 minutes' of six superb courses.
160 en suite (bth/shr) (2 fmly) CTV in all bedrooms STV No dogs (ex guide dogs) Lift Night porter 200P Indoor swimming pool (heated) Sauna Solarium Gym Concessionary Green fees Coffee am Tea pm Last d 9.15pm
CARDS:

WATERFORD Co Waterford Map 01 C2

★★★★❀❀75% **Waterford Castle**
The Island (from N25 take R684 in direction of Dunmore East for approx 2m and then signposted turn to the left for ferry) ☎ 051 878203 FAX 051 879316
This distinctive hotel, formerly a castle, as its name suggests, stands on an island reached by a chain-link ferry off the main Waterford-Dunmore road (route 683). Inside the ivy-clad walls the entrance lobby features 16th-century oak panelling, Portland stone and graceful arches; beyond reception are comfortable lounges and a dining room serving enjoyable meals.
19 en suite (bth/shr) CTV in all bedrooms STV No dogs (ex guide dogs) Lift Night porter 40P Indoor swimming pool (heated) Golf 18 Tennis (hard) Croquet lawn Putting green Clay pigeon shooting Wkly live entertainment ch fac Xmas Irish & French Cuisine V meals Coffee am Tea pm Last d 9.30pm
ROOMS: s IR£150; d IR£220 * **LB**
OFF-PEAK: s IR£100-IR£120; d IR£110-IR£150
MEALS: Lunch IR£16 Dinner IR£33*
CONF: Thtr 35 Class 18 Board 20 Del from IR£120
CARDS:

★★★66% ***Jurys***
Ferrybank (on N25 half a mile from city centre) (Jurys)
☎ 051 832111 FAX 051 832863
Situated in parkland overlooking the city, this large modern hotel has spacious public rooms and caters for tourists and the commercial trade.
98 en suite (bth/shr) (20 fmly) No smoking in 4 bedrooms CTV in all bedrooms No dogs (ex guide dogs) Lift Night porter 300P Indoor swimming pool (heated) Tennis (hard) Sauna Solarium Gym Jacuzzi/spa steam room plunge pool jacuzzi International Cuisine V meals Coffee am Tea pm
CONF: Thtr 700 Class 400 Board 100
CARDS:

★★★64% **Granville**
The Quay ☎ 051 855111 FAX 051 870307
Closed 25-26 Dec
This longstanding quayside hotel has been much modernised and offers bright, airy bedrooms and spacious public rooms.
74 en suite (bth/shr) (35 fmly) No smoking in 11 bedrooms CTV in all bedrooms No dogs (ex guide dogs) Lift Night porter 300P Wkly live entertainment International Cuisine V meals Coffee am Tea pm Last d 10.20pm
ROOMS: (incl. bkfst) s IR£52.50-IR£57.50; d IR£80-IR£90 * **LB**
MEALS: Lunch IR£7.50-IR£11 High tea IR£6.30-IR£7.50 Dinner IR£14-IR£17*
CONF: Thtr 200 Class 150 Board 30 Del from IR£55
CARDS:

★★★62% **Tower**
The Mall (opposite Reginald's Tower in the centre of town)
☎ 051 875801 FAX 051 870129
Closed 25-28 Dec
Now completely upgraded, the hotel offers a full range of banqueting, conference and leisure facilities - the latter including a new swimming pool with air conditioned fitness centre - as well as an attractive restaurant and a pleasant bar overlooking the river. Helpful, friendly staff provide good service throughout.
141 en suite (bth/shr) (10 fmly) CTV in all bedrooms No dogs (ex guide dogs) Lift Night porter 60P Indoor swimming pool (heated) Sauna Solarium Gym Jacuzzi/spa Wkly live entertainment European Cuisine V meals Coffee am Tea pm No smoking area in restaurant Last d 9.30pm
ROOMS: (incl. bkfst) s fr IR£75; d fr IR£120 **LB**
MEALS: Lunch IR£12-IR£16 Dinner IR£15-IR£17&alc*
CONF: Thtr 650 Class 300 Board 100 Del from IR£75
CARDS:

★★★59% **Bridge**
The Quay ☎ 051 77222 FAX 051 77229
This busy hotel stands near the City Bridge, convenient for the shops and all local amenities. Extensive refurbishment has created really comfortable bedrooms and public areas include a country-style bistro, a restaurant, a traditional Irish pub and a relaxing lounge bar.
96 en suite (bth/shr) CTV in all bedrooms STV No dogs Lift Night porter Air conditioning Wkly live entertainment V meals Coffee am Tea pm
ROOMS: (incl. bkfst) s IR£36-IR£45; d IR£65-IR£80 * **LB**
OFF-PEAK: (incl. bkfst) s fr IR£35
CONF: Thtr 400 Class 300
CARDS:

★★66% **Dooley's**
30 The Quay (on N25) ☎ 051 73531 FAX 051 70262
Closed 25-27 Dec
This hotel overlooks Quayside and is easily accessible, with a car park opposite. It is a friendly hotel that has comfortable bedrooms and is popular with local diners. The seafood menu, in addition to the à la carte, provides fresh fish caught daily.
35 rms (34 bth/shr) No smoking in 3 bedrooms CTV in all bedrooms STV No dogs (ex guide dogs) Night porter International Cuisine V meals Coffee am Tea pm Last d 9.30pm
ROOMS: (incl. bkfst) s IR£38.50-IR£41.80; d IR£77 * **LB**

OFF-PEAK: (incl. bkfst) s fr IR£38.50; d IR£55-IR£57
MEALS: Lunch IR£8.60-IR£9.95 High tea IR£5-IR£10alc Dinner IR£13-IR£15&alc*
CONF: Thtr 60 Class 40 Board 30
CARDS:

WATERVILLE Co Kerry Map 01 A2

★★★ 70% **Butler Arms**
(centre of Watreville village on seafront. N70 Ring of Kerry)
☎ 066 74144 FAX 066 74520
Closed Jan-Apr & Oct-Dec
Situated on the Ring of Kerry overlooking the ocean, the Butlers Arms has been owned by the same family for over three generations and offers high traditional standards of service. Most of the bedrooms have marble bathrooms and enjoy sea views, whilst public areas include spacious lounges and a billiards room. An 18-hole championship golf course is opposite.
30 en suite (bth/shr) (1 fmly) CTV in all bedrooms STV No dogs (ex guide dogs) Night porter 30P Tennis (hard) Fishing Snooker Irish/French Cuisine V meals Coffee am Tea pm No smoking area in restaurant Last d 9.15pm
ROOMS: (incl. bkfst) s IR£65-IR£90; d IR£90-IR£110 **LB**
MEALS: Bar Lunch IR£3-IR£20alc Dinner IR£24.50&alc
CARDS:

WESTPORT Co Mayo Map 01 B4

★★★65% ***Hotel Westport***
The Demesne, Newport Rd ☎ 098 25122 FAX 098 26739
Closed 24 & 25 Dec
Situated on its own land adjacent to the grounds of Westport House, this hotel has a bedroom block with modern amenities and caters for leisure and commercial guests.
49 en suite (bth/shr) (5 fmly) CTV in all bedrooms No dogs (ex guide dogs) Night porter 100P V meals Coffee am Tea pm Last d 9pm
CARDS:

★★ 71% **The Olde Railway**
The Mall (overlooking the Carrowbeg River in the town centre)
☎ 098 25166 & 25605 FAX 098 25090
Set on a tree-lined mall overlooking the river, this extensively refurbished old coaching inn offers a welcoming atmosphere with blazing turf fires. The en suite bedrooms vary in size; some are very spacious, and all come equipped with TVs. Communal areas include an attractively furnished bar, a comfortable lounge and a new Conservatory Restaurant with access to the patio and barbecue area. Car parking is available at the rear.
24 en suite (bth/shr) (2 fmly) CTV in all bedrooms STV No dogs (ex guide dogs) Night porter 34P Fishing & Shooting arranged Wkly live entertainment V meals Coffee am Tea pm No smoking area in restaurant Last d 9.30pm
ROOMS: (incl. bkfst) s IR£45-IR£65; d IR£65-IR£90 * **LB**
OFF-PEAK: (incl. bkfst) s IR£35-IR£45; d IR£50-IR£75
MEALS: Bar Lunch IR£3.95-IR£8.95 Dinner IR£17.50-IR£19.50
CONF: Thtr 140 Class 100 Board 100 Del from IR£55
CARDS:

WEXFORD Co Wexford Map 01 D3

★★★72% ***Talbot***
Trinity St (on waterfront on Rosslare side of town)
☎ 053 22566 FAX 053 23377
Centrally situated on the quayside, this hotel has been extensively refurbished, giving all the bedrooms custom-made oak furniture, attractive decor and new bathrooms. Day rooms include a spacious foyer, comfortable lounge, and a bar with an open fireplace. Cuisine is informal, in the country-kitchen style. There are good leisure facilities and an adjoining car park.
100 en suite (bth/shr) (12 fmly) No smoking in 10 bedrooms CTV in all bedrooms STV Lift Night porter 60P Indoor swimming pool (heated) Squash Snooker Sauna Solarium Gym Games room Beauty salon International Cuisine V meals Coffee am Tea pm Last d 8.45pm
CARDS:

★★★ 67% **Ferrycarrig**
Ferrycarrig (on N11 by Slaney Estuary,beside Ferrycraig Castle)
☎ 053 20999 FAX 053 20982
The Ferrycarrig Hotel is a modern four-storey hotel in a lovely location on a sea inlet on the edge of Wexford and beside the National Heritage Park. In addition to the lovely views, smart new public rooms, refurbished bedrooms and excellent food and service ensure an enjoyable stay here.
39 en suite (bth/shr) (2 fmly) CTV in all bedrooms STV No dogs (ex guide dogs) Lift Night porter 235P Sauna Solarium Gym Wkly live entertainment Xmas Irish & French Cuisine V meals Coffee am Tea pm Last d 9.15pm
ROOMS: (incl. bkfst) s IR£35.50-IR£45; d IR£71-IR£90 * **LB**
OFF-PEAK: (incl. bkfst) s IR£35-IR£40
MEALS: Lunch IR£11&alc Dinner IR£25&alc*
CONF: Thtr 400 Class 250 Board 60
CARDS:

★★★ 66% **Whitford House**
New Line Rd ☎ 053 43444 & 43845 FAX 053 46399
RS 24 Dec-31 Jan
A smart modern hotel in a rural setting on the edge of Wexford offering large, comfortable bedrooms with luxury en suite bathrooms, charming lounges and a popular restaurant. The proprietor Mrs Kay Whitty continually improves the facilities and levels of comfort available to her guests, many of whom return again and again. Both an indoor swimming pool and hard tennis court are provided, and there is good car parking.
23 en suite (bth/shr) (10 fmly) CTV in all bedrooms No dogs Night porter 140P Indoor swimming pool (heated) Tennis (hard) Childrens playground Wkly live entertainment French Cuisine Coffee am Tea pm Last d 8.45pm
ROOMS: (incl. bkfst) s IR£26.50-IR£29.50; d IR£49-IR£55 * **LB**
MEALS: Sunday Lunch IR£11.50 Dinner IR£13.95-IR£19.50*
CARDS:

★★★64% **White's**
George St ☎ 053 22311 FAX 053 45000
Best Western
Closed 24 Dec-26 Dec
This historic former coaching inn has recently been refurbished, but retains much of its charm. The entrance is through a modern extension, and entertainment is provided in the converted saddlery and forge.
76 en suite (bth/shr) 6 annexe en suite (bth/shr) (1 fmly) CTV in all bedrooms STV No dogs (ex guide dogs) Lift Night porter 100P Sauna Solarium Gym Jacuzzi/spa Nightclub Wkly live entertainment Xmas International Cuisine V meals Coffee am Tea pm Last d 9pm
ROOMS: (incl. bkfst) s IR£47.50-IR£60; d IR£69-IR£90 **LB**
OFF-PEAK: (incl. bkfst) s IR£42.50-IR£48; d IR£59-IR£66
MEALS: Lunch IR£9.95-IR£11 Dinner IR£18-IR£22*
CONF: Thtr 400 Class 300 Board 30
CARDS:

★★ 70% ***Wexford Lodge***
(beside Wexford Bridge on R741) ☎ 053 23611 FAX 053 23342
Closed 1-15 Nov & 24-29 Dec
This family-run hotel is situated adjacent to the town bridge overlooking the River Slaney and the harbour. Public rooms are good

contd.

W

and all the bedrooms are of an excellent standard.
19 en suite (bth/shr) (5 fmly) CTV in all bedrooms No dogs (ex guide dogs) 30P French Cuisine V meals Coffee am Tea pm
CARDS:

WICKLOW See Rathnew

WOODENBRIDGE Co Wicklow Map 01 D3

★★64% **Woodenbridge**
(between Avoca & Arklow) ☎ 0402 35146 FAX 0402 35573
This comfortable hotel in the Vale of Avoca, about an hour's drive from the ferry ports of Dun Laoghaire and Rosslaire, and not far from the N11 Dublin to Wexford road, has been given a new lease of life by its new owners the O'Brien family who have recently extended it by creating 12 new bedrooms and a conference/banqueting suite. Hospitality and good food are the focus of their concerns. Golf and fishing are on the doorstep.
23 en suite (bth/shr) (13 fmly) CTV in all bedrooms STV No dogs Lift Night porter 100P Snooker Pool table Wkly live entertainment ch fac V meals Coffee am Tea pm No smoking area in restaurant Last d 9.30pm
ROOMS: (incl. bkfst) d IR£30-IR£33 * **LB**
OFF-PEAK: (incl. bkfst) s IR£30-IR£33; d IR£30
MEALS: Lunch fr IR£10.95 Dinner IR£15.95-IR£18.95&alc*
CONF: Thtr 200 Class 200 Board 200
CARDS:

YOUGHAL Co Cork Map 01 C2

★★❀❀64% **Devonshire Arms**
Pearse Square ☎ 024 92827 & 92018 FAX 024 92900
Closed Xmas
Stephen and Helen O'Sullivan have been restoring this 19th-century hotel with much care and attention to detail. It offers good food in both the restaurant and the bar.
10 en suite (bth/shr) (3 fmly) CTV in all bedrooms No dogs (ex guide dogs) 20P Irish & French Cuisine V meals Coffee am Tea pm
ROOMS: (incl. bkfst) s IR£40; d IR£60-IR£66
OFF-PEAK: (incl. bkfst) s IR£35; d IR£55-IR£60
CONF: Class 150
CARDS:

Premier Selected Guest Houses, Farmhouses and Inns

Premier Selected guest houses, farmhouses and inns hold 5 Qs - the AA's highest rating for the Bed & Breakfast listing scheme. They are equivalent to small hotels, though they may not offer the full range of conventional services or meals that is traditionally available in hotels. They have no entries in the Hotel Guide directory but telephone numbers have been included so that intending guests can inquire direct about details of the accommodation.

ENGLAND

BERKSHIRE

MAIDENHEAD:
Beehive Manor Tel: 01628 20980
NEWBURY:
Rookwood Farmhouse Tel: 01488 608676

BUCKINGHAMSHIRE

BEACONSFIELD:
George Hotel Tel: 01494 673086

CHESHIRE

CHESTER:
Redland Private Hotel Tel: 01244 671024
KNUTSFORD:
Laburnum Cottage Tel: 01565 872464
MALPAS:
Laurel Farm Tel: 01948 860291
Tilston Lodge Tel: 01829 250223
NANTWICH:
Oakland House Tel: 01270 67134

CORNWALL

CRACKINGTON HAVEN:
Manor Farm Tel: 1840 230304
Trevigue Farm Tel: 01840 230418
Treworgie Barton Tel: 01840 230233
FALMOUTH:
Prospect House Tel: 01326 373198
HAYLE:
Treglisson Tel: 01736 753141
LIZARD:
Landewednack House Tel: 01326 290909
LOOE:
Coombe Farm Tel: 01503 240223
PADSTOW:
St Petroc's House Tel: 01841 532700

POLPERRO:
Trenderway Farm Tel: 01503 72214
ST BLAZEY:
Nanscawan House Tel: 01726 814488
ST HILARY:
Ennys Farm Tel: 01736 740262

CUMBRIA

AMBLESIDE:
Grey Friar Lodge
Country House Tel: 01539 433158
Rowanfield Tel: 01539 433686
BOLTONGATE:
Old Rectory Tel: 016973 71647
Hazel Bank Tel: 01768 777248
CARLISLE:
Number Thirty-One Tel: 01228 597080
COCKERMOUTH:
Low Hall Tel: 01900 826654
CONISTON:
Coniston Lodge Tel: 01539 441201
Wheelgate Tel: 01539 441418
GRANGE-OVER-SANDS:
Greenacres Tel: 01539 534578
KENDAL:
Lane Head Country
House Tel: 01539 731283
Low Jock Scar Tel: 01539 823259

KESWICK:
Derwent Cottage Tel:01768 774838
KIRKBY LONSDALE:
Cobwebs Tel: 015242 72141
Hipping Hall Tel: 015242 71187
LONGTOWN:
Bessiestown Farm Tel: 01228 577219
LORTON:
New House Farm Tel: 01900 85404
NEAR SAWREY:
Ees Wyke Tel: 015394 36393
ROSLEY:
Causa Grange Tel: 016973 45358

DERBYSHIRE

ASHBOURNE:
Biggin Mill House Tel: 01335 370414
DOVERIDGE:
Beeches Farmhouse Tel: 01889 590288
HOPE:
Underleigh House Tel: 01433 621372
SHOTTLE:
Dannah Farm Country Guest House Tel: 01773 550273
WESTON UNDERWOOD:
Park View Farm Tel: 01335 360352

DEVON

AXMINSTER:
Millbrook Farmhouse Tel: 01297 35351
BOVEY TRACEY:
Front House Lodge Tel: 01626 832202
CHUMLEIGH:
Old Bakehouse Tel: 01769 580074
CROYDE:
Whiteleaf at Croyde Tel: 01271 890266
DARTMOUTH:
Boringdon House Tel: 01803 832235
Broome Court Tel: 01803 834275
Ford House Tel: 01803 834047
Hedley House Tel: 01803 835849
HORN'S CROSS:
Lower Waytown Tel: 01237 451787
LYDFORD:
Moor View House Tel: 01822 820220
LYNMOUTH:
Bonnicott House Tel: 01598 753346
LYNTON:
Victoria Lodge Tel: 01598 753203
MORCHARD BISHOP:
Wigham Tel: 01363 877350
MORETONHAMPSTEAD:
Blackaller Hotel Tel: 01647 440322
Gate House Tel: 01647 440479
PARKHAM:
Old Rectory Tel: 01237 451443
POUNDSGATE:
Leusdon Lodge Tel: 01364 631304
SIDMOUTH:
Broad Oak Tel: 01395 513713
SOUTH MOLTON:
Kerscott Farm Tel: 01769 550262
TEIGNMOUTH:
Thomas Luny House Tel: 01626 772976
TIVERTON:
Hornhill Farm Tel: 01884 253352
TOTNES:
Waterman's Arms Tel: 01803 732214
TORQUAY:
Mulberry House Tel: 01803 213639
WEST DOWN:
Long House Tel: 01271 863242

DORSET

DORCHESTER:
Yalbury Cottage Tel: 01305 262382
HORTON:
Northill House Tel: 01258 840407

CO DURHAM

FIR TREE:
Greenhead Tel: 01388 763143

ESSEX

COLCHESTER:
Hockley Place Tel: 01206 251703

GLOUCESTERSHIRE

CHELTENHAM:
Cleeve Hill Tel: 01242 672052
Lypiatt House Tel: 01242 224994
CHIPPING CAMPDEN:
Malt House Tel: 01386 840295
CLEARWELL:
Tudor Farmhouse Tel: 01594 833046
FRAMPTON ON SEVERN:
Old School House Tel: 01452 740457
GUITING POWER:
Guiting Guest House Tel: 01451 850470

LECHLADE:
Cottage-by-the-Church Tel: 01367 860613
MORETON-IN-MARSH:
College House Tel: 01451 832351

RENDCOMB:
Shawswell Tel: 01285 831779
TETBURY:
Tavern House Tel: 01666 880444

GREATER MANCHESTER

ALTRINCHAM:
Ash Farm Tel: 0161 929 9290

HAMPSHIRE

BROCKENHURST:
Thatched Cottage Tel: 01590 23090
HAYLING ISLAND:
Cockle Warren Tel: 01705 464961
ODIHAM:
Poland Mill Tel: 01256 702251
RINGWOOD:
Little Forest Lodge Tel: 01425 478848
ROMSEY:
Highfield House Tel: 01794 340727
SWAY:
Nurse's Cottage, The Tel: 01590 683402
WINCHESTER:
Wykeham Arms Tel: 01962 853834
WOODFALLS:
Woodfalls Inn Tel: 01725 513222

HEREFORD & WORCESTER

BROADWAY:
Old Rectory Tel: 01386 853729
WHITNEY-ON-WYE:
Rhydspence Inn Tel: 01497 831262

KENT

BENENDEN:
Crit Hall Tel: 01580 240609
CANTERBURY:
Magnolia House Tel: 01227 765121
Old Rectory Tel: 01227 730075
Thanington Hotel Tel: 01227 453227
Thruxted Oast Tel: 01227 730080
CRANBROOK:
Hancocks Farmhouse Tel: 01580 714645
HAWKHURST:
Conghurst Farm Tel: 01580 753331

PENSHURST:
Swale Cottage Tel: 01892 870738
SITTINGBOURNE:
Hempstead House Tel: 01795 428020
TONBRIDGE:
Goldhill Mill Tel: 01732 851626
TUNBRIDGE WELLS, ROYAL
(see also Frant, Sussex East):
Danehurst House Tel: 01892 527739

LANCASHIRE

CARNFORTH:
New Capernwray Farm Tel: 01524 734284
SLAIDBURN:
Parrock Head Farm House Hotel Tel: 01200 446614
THORNTON:
Victorian House Tel: 01253 860619
YEALAND CONYERS:
Bower, The Tel: 01524 734585

LONDON:

E11: **Lakeside** Tel: 0181 9896100
NW3: **Sandringham** Tel: 0171435 1569
W7: **Wellmeadow Lodge** Tel: 0181 567 7294

NORTHUMBERLAND

CORBRIDGE:
Courtyard, The Tel: 01434 606850

NOTTINGHAMSHIRE

NORTH WHEATLEY:
Old Plough Tel: 01427 880916

OXFORDSHIRE

BURFORD:
Andrews Hotel Tel: 01993 823151
Elm House Tel: 01993 823611
OXFORD:
Cotswold House Tel: 01865 310558
Fallowfields Tel: 01865 820416
THAME:
Upper Green Farm Tel: 01844 212496

SHROPSHIRE

CHURCH STRETTON:
Rectory Farm Tel: 01694 751306
LUDLOW:
Line Farm Tel: 01568 780400
MARKET DRAYTON:
Stoke Manor Tel: 01630 685222

SOMERSET

BATH:
Apsley House Hotel Tel: 01225336966
Dorian House Tel: 01225 426336
Gaites House Tel: 0117 932 9800
Haydon House Tel: 01225 444919
Holly Lodge Tel: 01225 424042
Leighton House Tel: 01225 314769
Lodge Hotel Tel: 01225 858467
Meadowland Tel: 01225 311079
Monkshill Tel: 01225 833028
Newbridge House Tel: 01225 446676
Old School House Tel: 01225 859593

BEERCROCOMBE:
Frog Street Farm Tel: 01823 480430
Whittles Farm Tel: 01823 480301

BRIDGWATER:
Woodlands Tel: 01278 423442

BUCKLAND ST MARY:
Keymer Cottage Tel: 01460 234460

CASTLE CARY:
George Hotel Tel: 01963 350761

CREWKERNE:
Broadview Tel: 01460 73424

DUNSTER:
Dollons House Tel: 01643 821880

KILVE:
Hood Arms Tel: 01278 741210

LANGPORT:
Hillards Farm Tel: 01458 251737

NORTON ST PHILIP:
Monmouth Lodge Tel: 01373 834367

RODE:
Irondale Tel 01373 830730

SOMERTON:
Lydford House Tel: 01963 240217
Lynch Country House Tel: 01458 272316

WATCHET:
Chidgley Hill Farm Tel: 01984 640403

WEST BAGBOROUGH
Bashfords Farmhouse Tel: 01823 432015
Tilbury Farm Tel: 01823 432391

WELLS:
Beaconsfield Farm Tel: 01749 870308
Infield House Tel: 01749 670989
Littlewell Farm Tel: 01749 677914

YEOVIL:
Holywell House Tel: 01935 862612

STAFFORDSHIRE

AUDLEY:
Domvilles Farm Tel: 01782 720378

OAKAMOOR:
Bank House Tel: 01538 702810

STOKE-ON-TRENT:
Hanchurch Manor Tel: 01782 643030

SUFFOLK

BURY ST EDMUNDS:
Twelve Angel Hill Tel: 01284 704088

FRESSINGFIELD:
Chippenhall Hall Tel: 01379 586733

SUSSEX (EAST)

ARLINGTON:
Bates Green Tel: 01323 482039

BATTLE:
Brakes Coppice Farm Tel: 01424 830347

FRANT:
Old Parsonage Tel: 01892 750773

HARTFIELD:
Bolebrook Watermill Tel: 01892 770425

HASTINGS:
Bryn-y-Mor Tel: 01424 722744
Parkside House Tel: 01424 433096

LEWES:
Fairseat House Tel: 01825 722263

RUSHLAKE GREEN:
Great Crouch's Tel: 01435 830145

RYE:
Green Hedges Tel: 01797 222185:
Jeakes House Tel: 01797 222828
Old Vicarage Hotel Tel: 01797 225131
Old Vicarage Guest House
Tel: 01797 222119
Playden Cottage Tel: 01797 2322234

UCKFIELD:
Hooke Hall Tel: 01825 761578

WINCHELSEA:
Country House at Winchelsea
Tel: 01797 226669

SUSSEX (WEST)

BEPTON:
Park House Tel: 01730 812880

BILLINGSHURST;
Old Wharf Tel: 01403 784096

BOSHAM:
Kenwood Tel: 01243 572727

ROGATE:
Mizzards Farm Tel: 01730 821656

SUTTON:
White Horse Tel: 01798 869221

TYNE & WEAR

TYNEMOUTH:

Hope House Tel: 0191 257 1989

WARWICKSHIRE

WARWICK:

Shrewley House Tel: 01926 842549

WILTSHIRE

ALDERTON:

Manor Farm Tel: 01666 840271

BRADFORD ON AVON:

Bradford Old Windmill Tel: 01225 866842
Burghope Manor Tel: 01225 723557
Fern Cottage Tel: 01225 859412
Widbrook Grange Tel: 01225 863173

CALNE:

Chilvester Hill House Tel: 01249 813981

LACOCK:

At the Sign of the Angel Tel: 01249 730230

LITTLE CHEVERELL:

Little Cheverell House Tel: 01380 813322

MARLBOROUGH:

Laurel Cottage Tel: 01672 841288

MIDDLE WINTERSLOW:

Beadles, The Tel: 01980 862922

TROWBRIDGE:

Old Manor Tel: 01225 777393

WEST GRAFTON:

Mayfield Tel: 01672 810339

YORKSHIRE (NORTH)

HARROGATE:

Ruskin Hotel Tel: 01423 502045

REETH:

Arkleside Hotel Tel: 01748 884200

RICHMOND:

Whashton Springs Farm Tel: 01748 822884

STARBOTTON:

Hilltop Tel: 01756 760321

YORK: **Arndale Hotel** Tel: 01904 702424

CHANNEL ISLANDS

GUERNSEY, ST PETER PORT:

Midhurst House Tel: 01481 724391

SCOTLAND

ABERDEEN CITY

ABERDEEN:

Ewood House Tel: 01224 648408

ABERDEENSHIRE

ABOYNE:

Arbor Lodge Tel: 01339 886951

ANGUS

ARBROATH:

Farmhouse Kitchen Tel: 01241 860202

FORFAR:

Finavon Farmhouse Tel: 01307 850269

ARGYLL & BUTE

CONNEL:

Ards House Tel: 01631 710255

TOBERMORY:

Strongarbh House Tel: 01688 2328

CITY OF EDINBURGH

EDINBURGH:

Drummond House Tel: 0131 557 9189
Elmview Tel: 0131 2281973

FIFE

ABERDOUR:

Hawkcraig House Tel: 01383 860335

ANSTRUTHER:

Hermitage Guest House Tel: 01333 310909

AUCHTERMUCHTY:

Ardchoille Tel: 01337 828414

CUPAR:

Todhall House Tel: 01334 656344

HIGHLAND

BOAT OF GARTEN:

Heathbank Tel: 01479 831234

CONON BRIDGE:

Kinkell House Tel: 01349 861270

DORNOCH:

Highfield Tel: 01862 810909

FORT WILLIAM:

The Grange Tel: 01397 705516
Ashburn House Tel: 01397 706000
Torbeag House Tel: 01397 772412

GRANTOWN-ON-SPEY;

Ardconnel Tel: 01479 872104
Culdearn House Tel: 01479 872106

INVERNESS:
Ballifeary Tel: 01463 235572
Culduthel Hotel Tel: 01463 240089
Moyness House Tel: 01463 233836

MORAY

ELGIN:
Croft, The Tel: 01343 546004
Pines, The Tel: 01343 542766

PERTH & KINROSS

ABERFELDY:
Fernbank House Tel: 01887 820345
ALYTH:
Drumnacree House Tel: 01828 632194

RENFREWSHIRE

PAISLEY:
Myfarrclan Tel: 0141 884 8285

SCOTTISH BORDERS

COLDINGHAM:
Dunlaverock House Tel: 01890 771450
GALASHIELS:
Maplehurst Tel: 01896 754700
JEDBURGH:
The Spinney Tel: 01835 863525

SOUTH AYRSHIRE

BALLANTRAE:
Cosses Country House Tel: 01465 831363

SOUTH LANARKSHIRE

ABINGTON:
Glentewing Farm Tel: 01864 504221

STIRLING

BRIG O' TURK:
Dundarroch Tel: 01877 376200
CALLANDER:
Arran Lodge Tel: 01877 330976

WALES

ABERCONWY & COLWYN

LLANDUDNO:
Bryn Derwyn Tel: 01492 876804

DENBIGHSHIRE

RUTHIN:
Eyarth Station Tel: 01824 703643

GWYNEDD

BARMOUTH:
Plas Bach Tel: 01341 281234
BONTDDU:
Borthwnog Hall Tel: 01341 430271
LLANFACHRETH:
Ty Isaf Farmhouse Tel: 01341 423261
LLANWNDA:
Pengwern Farm Tel: 01286 830717

POWYS

NEWTOWN:
Dyffryn Farmhouse Tel: 01686 688817
PENYBONT:
Ffaldau Country House Tel: 01597 851421

NEATH/PORT TALBOT

NEATH:
Green Lanterns Tel: 01639 631884

IRELAND

CO. TYRONE

DUNGANNON:
Grange Lodge Tel: 01868 784212

CO. CORK

FERMOY:
Ballyvolane House Tel: 025 36349
KANTURK:
Assolas Country House Tel: 029 50015

CO. DUBLIN

DUBLIN:
Aberdeen Lodge Tel: 01 283 8155
Ariel House Tel: 01 668 5512
Cedar Lodge Tel: 01 668 4410
Grey Door Tel: 01 676 3286
DUN LAOGHAIRE:
Chestnut Lodge Tel: 01 2807860

CO. GALWAY

GALWAY:
Killeen House Tel: 091 24179

CO. KERRY

KILLARNEY:
Earls Court Tel: 064 34009
Kathleen'sCountry House Tel: 064 32810

CO. LONDONDERRY

COLERAINE:

Greenhill House Tel:01 265 868241

CO. TIPPERARY

NENAGH:

St Davids Country House Tel: 067 24145

CO. WESTMEATH

MULLINGAR:

Crookedwood House Tel: 044 72165

CO. WEXFORD

ROSSLARE HARBOUR:

Churchtown House Tel: 053 32555

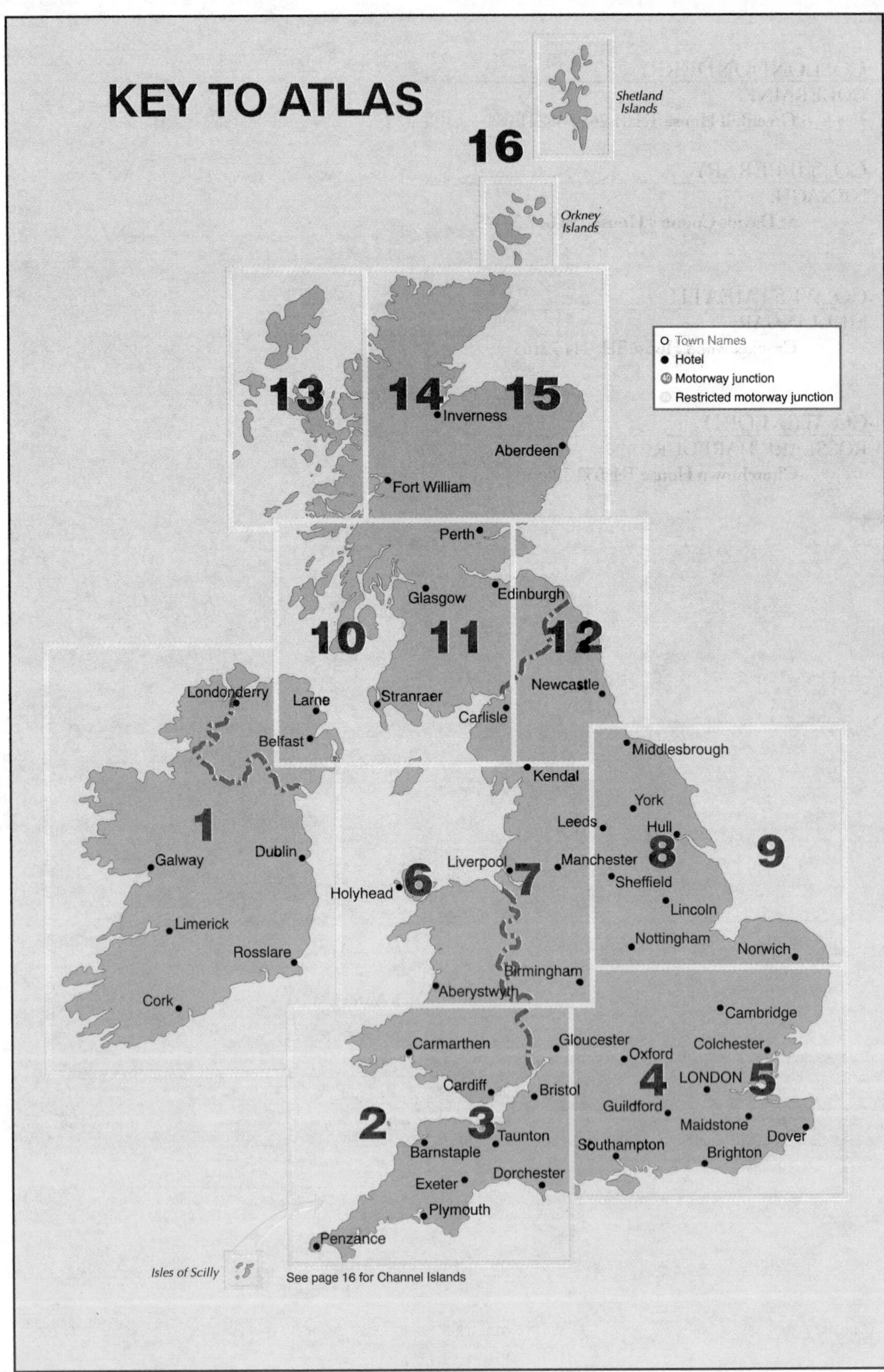
KEY TO ATLAS
Shetland Islands
16
Orkney Islands
Town Names
Hotel
Motorway junction
Restricted motorway junction
13
14
15
Inverness
Aberdeen
Fort William
Perth
Glasgow
Edinburgh
10
11
12
Londonderry
Larne
Stranraer
Newcastle
Carlisle
Belfast
Middlesbrough
Kendal
York
Leeds
Hull
1
Galway
Dublin
Liverpool
Manchester
8
9
Holyhead
6
7
Sheffield
Lincoln
Limerick
Nottingham
Rosslare
Norwich
Birmingham
Cork
Aberystwyth
Cambridge
Carmarthen
Gloucester
Colchester
Oxford
4
LONDON
5
Cardiff
Bristol
Guildford
2
3
Maidstone
Taunton
Dover
Barnstaple
Southampton
Brighton
Exeter
Dorchester
Plymouth
Penzance
Isles of Scilly
See page 16 for Channel Islands

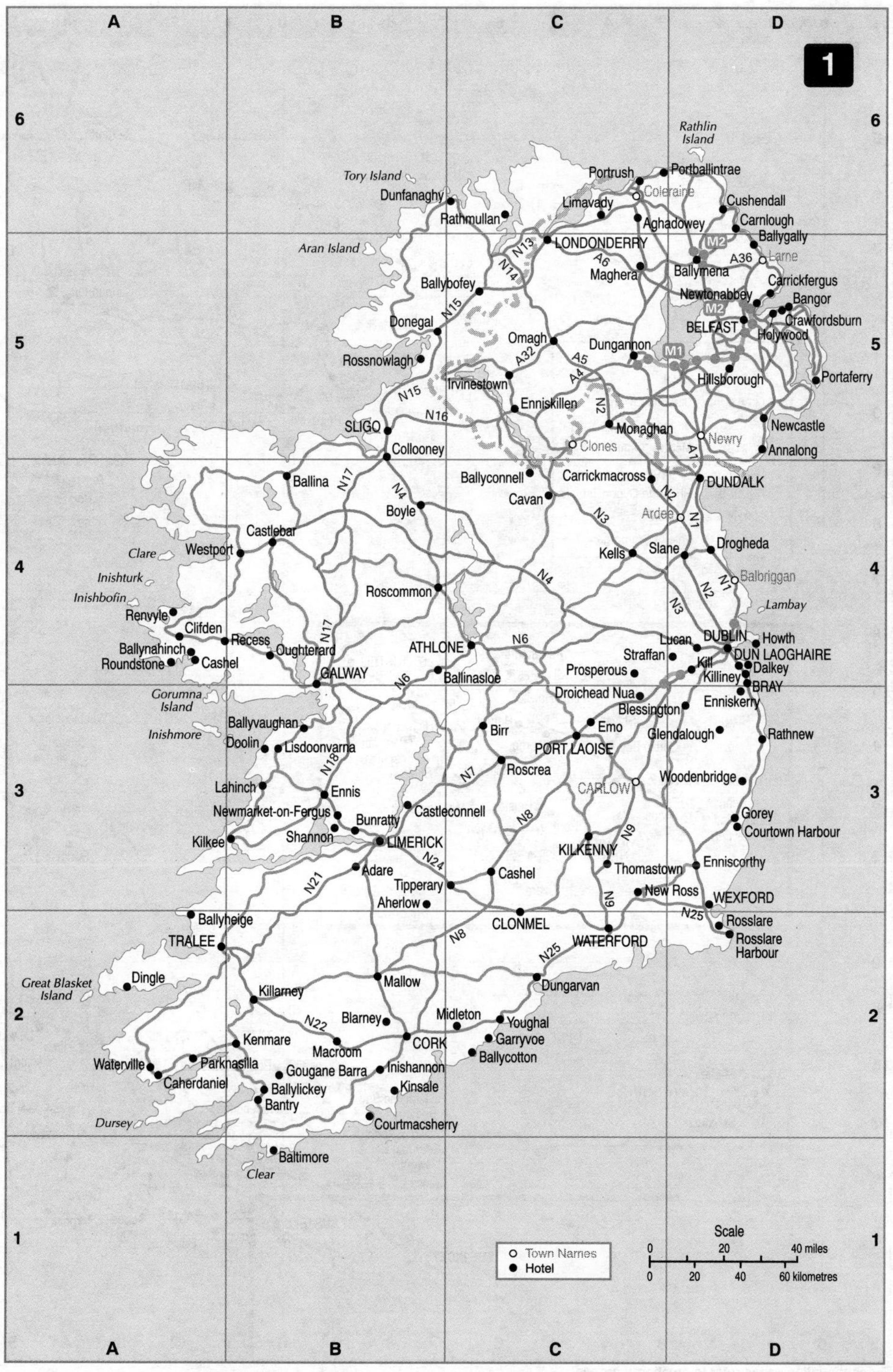

A
B
C
D
1
6
5
4
3
2
1
Rathlin Island
Tory Island
Aran Island
Portrush
Portballintrae
Coleraine
Dunfanaghy
Limavady
Cushendall
Rathmullan
Aghadowey
Carnlough
LONDONDERRY
Ballygally
M2
A36
Larne
N13
A6
N14
Maghera
Ballymena
Ballybofey
Carrickfergus
Newtonabbey
Bangor
M2
N15
BELFAST
Crawfordsburn
Donegal
Omagh
Holywood
Dungannon
M1
A32
A5
Rossnowlagh
Portaferry
A4
Hillsborough
Irvinestown
N15
N2
Enniskillen
N16
Newcastle
SLIGO
Monaghan
Newry
Clones
A1
Annalong
Collooney
Ballyconnell
Carrickmacross
DUNDALK
N17
Ballina
N4
N2
Cavan
Boyle
N3
Ardee
N1
Castlebar
Drogheda
Kells
Slane
Clare
Westport
Inishturk
N4
N1
Balbriggan
Inishbofin
Roscommon
N2
N3
Lambay
Renvyle
Clifden
N17
N6
Lucan
DUBLIN
Howth
Recess
ATHLONE
Straffan
DUN LAOGHAIRE
Ballynahinch
Oughterard
Kill
Roundstone
Cashel
Prosperous
Dalkey
Killiney
GALWAY
N6
Ballinasloe
BRAY
Gorumna Island
Droichead Nua
Enniskerry
Blessington
Ballyvaughan
Emo
Inishmore
Birr
Glendalough
Rathnew
Doolin
Lisdoonvarna
PORT LAOISE
N18
Roscrea
N7
Woodenbridge
Lahinch
CARLOW
Ennis
Castleconnell
Gorey
Newmarket-on-Fergus
N8
Bunratty
N9
Courtown Harbour
Kilkee
Shannon
LIMERICK
KILKENNY
N24
Enniscorthy
Adare
Cashel
Thomastown
N21
Tipperary
New Ross
WEXFORD
Aherlow
N9
N25
Ballyheige
CLONMEL
Rosslare
TRALEE
N8
WATERFORD
Rosslare Harbour
N25
Great Blasket Island
Dingle
Mallow
Dungarvan
Killarney
N22
Blarney
Midleton
Youghal
Kenmare
CORK
Garryvoe
Macroom
Ballycotton
Waterville
Parknasilla
Gougane Barra
Inishannon
Caherdaniel
Ballylickey
Kinsale
Bantry
Dursey
Courtmacsherry
Baltimore
Clear
Town Names
Hotel
Scale
0
20
40 miles
0
20
40
60 kilometres

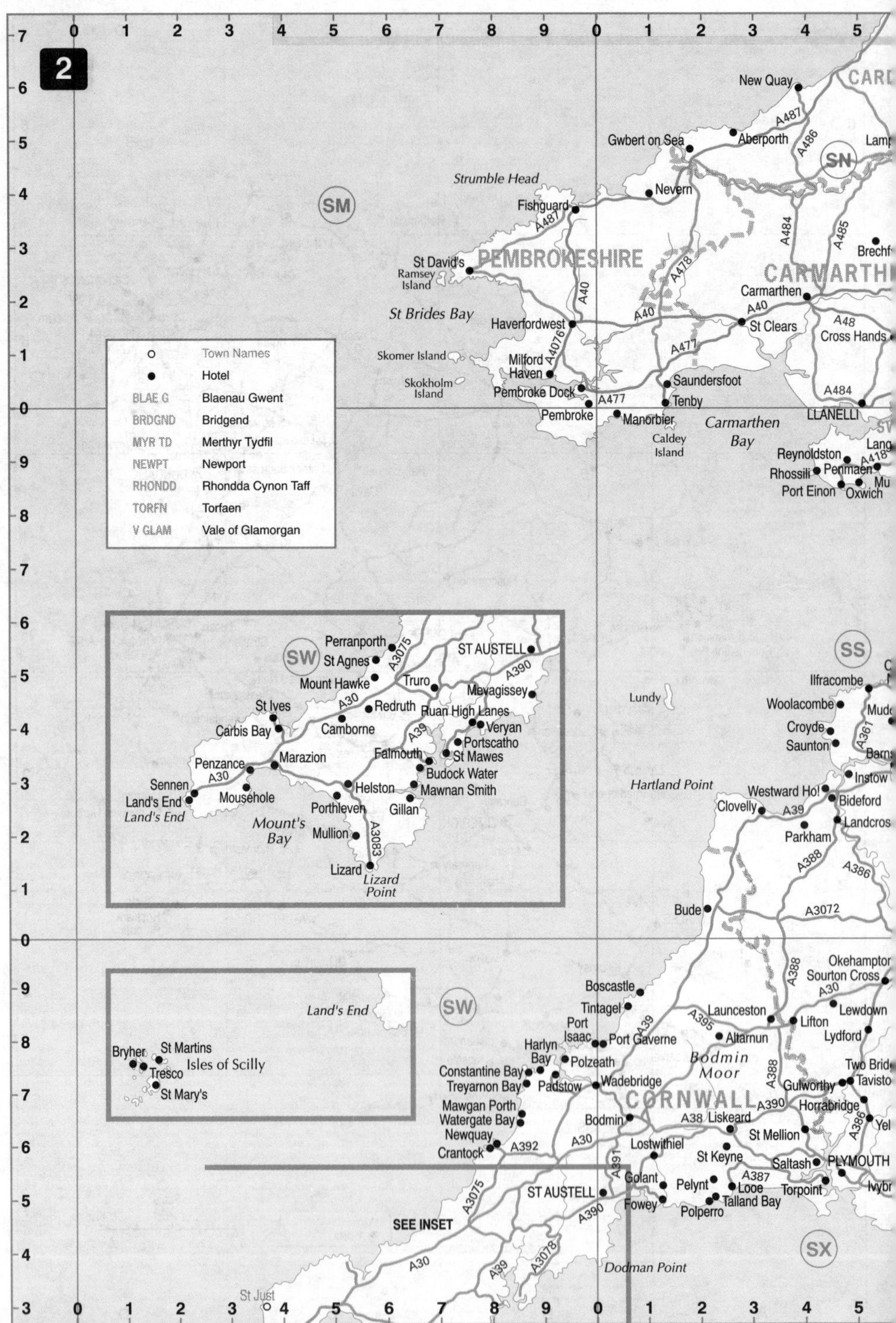

For continuation pages refer to numbered arrows

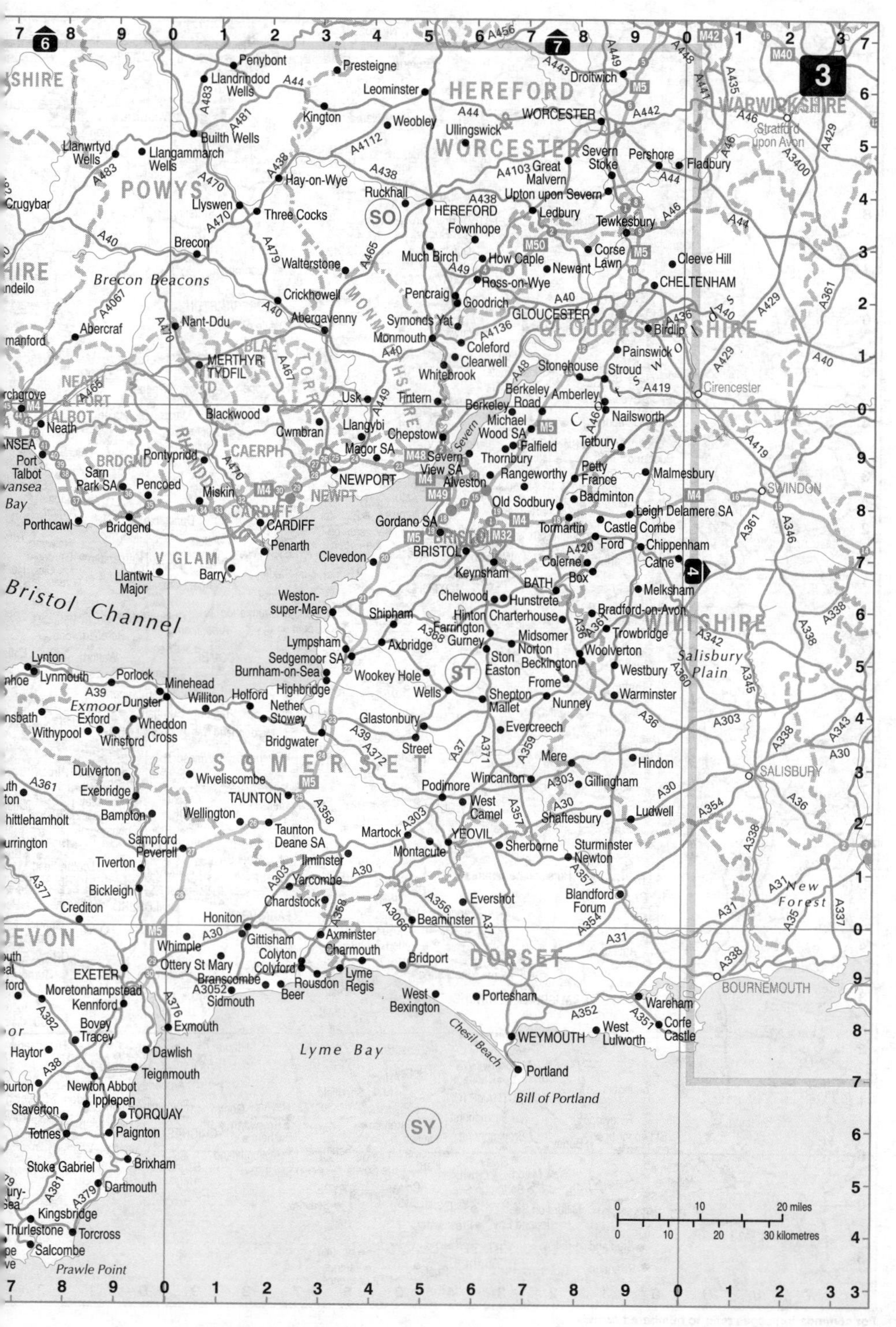

3
HEREFORD & WORCESTER
WARWICKSHIRE
POWYS
GLOUCESTERSHIRE
WILTSHIRE
SOMERSET
DEVON
DORSET
MONMOUTHSHIRE
CAERPHILLY
CARDIFF
NEWPORT
V GLAM
NEATH PORT TALBOT
BRIDGEND
RHONDDA
MERTHYR TYDFIL
Cotswolds
Brecon Beacons
Exmoor
Salisbury Plain
New Forest
Bristol Channel
Lyme Bay
Chesil Beach
Bill of Portland
Prawle Point
SO
ST
SY
Penybont
Presteigne
Llandrindod Wells
Leominster
Kington
Weobley
Builth Wells
Llanwrtyd Wells
Llangammarch Wells
Hay-on-Wye
Llyswen
Three Cocks
Brecon
Walterstone
Crickhowell
Abergavenny
Nant-Ddu
Abercraf
Crugybar
Ruckhall
HEREFORD
Ullingswick
WORCESTER
Droitwich
Stratford upon Avon
Pershore
Fladbury
Severn Stoke
Great Malvern
Upton upon Severn
Ledbury
Tewkesbury
Fownhope
Much Birch
How Caple
Ross-on-Wye
Newent
Corse Lawn
Cleeve Hill
CHELTENHAM
Pencraig
Goodrich
Symonds Yat
Monmouth
Coleford
Clearwell
Whitebrook
GLOUCESTER
Birdlip
Painswick
Stonehouse
Stroud
Amberley
Nailsworth
Cirencester
Tintern
Usk
Llangybi
Chepstow
Berkeley Road
Michael Wood SA
Falfield
Thornbury
Tetbury
Malmesbury
Magor SA
Severn View SA
Alveston
Rangeworthy
Petty France
Badminton
Old Sodbury
Tormarton
Leigh Delamere SA
Castle Combe
SWINDON
Blackwood
Cwmbran
Pontypridd
NEWPORT
Miskin
CARDIFF
Penarth
Barry
Llantwit Major
Porthcawl
Bridgend
Pencoed
Sarn Park SA
Port Talbot
Neath
Swansea Bay
Gordano SA
BRISTOL
Clevedon
Keynsham
Ford
Chippenham
Colerne
Box
Calne
BATH
Melksham
Chelwood
Hunstrete
Bradford-on-Avon
Weston-super-Mare
Shipham
Hinton Charterhouse
Farrington Gurney
Midsomer Norton
Trowbridge
Lympsham
Axbridge
Sedgemoor SA
Ston Easton
Woolverton
Beckington
Westbury
Burnham-on-Sea
Highbridge
Wookey Hole
Wells
Frome
Shepton Mallet
Nunney
Warminster
Lynton
Lynmouth
Porlock
Minehead
Dunster
Williton
Holford
Nether Stowey
Exford
Wheddon Cross
Withypool
Winsford
Bridgwater
Glastonbury
Street
Evercreech
Mere
Hindon
SALISBURY
Dulverton
Exebridge
Bampton
Wiveliscombe
TAUNTON
Wellington
Taunton Deane SA
Podimore
Wincanton
Gillingham
West Camel
Shaftesbury
Ludwell
Sampford Peverell
Tiverton
Bickleigh
Crediton
Martock
Montacute
YEOVIL
Sherborne
Sturminster Newton
Ilminster
Yarcombe
Chardstock
Evershot
Blandford Forum
Beaminster
Honiton
Axminster
Charmouth
Gittisham
Colyton
Colyford
Whimple
Ottery St Mary
Branscombe
Rousdon
Beer
Lyme Regis
Bridport
EXETER
Moretonhampstead
Kennford
Sidmouth
West Bexington
Portesham
Wareham
BOURNEMOUTH
Corfe Castle
West Lulworth
WEYMOUTH
Portland
Exmouth
Bovey Tracey
Haytor
Dawlish
Teignmouth
Newton Abbot
Ipplepen
TORQUAY
Staverton
Totnes
Paignton
Brixham
Stoke Gabriel
Dartmouth
Kingsbridge
Thurlestone
Torcross
Salcombe
M4
M5
M32
M48
M49
M50
M40
M42
A44
A49
A40
A438
A470
A465
A4103
A46
A429
A419
A420
A361
A303
A30
A36
A37
A39
A338
A350
A354
A357
A358
A31
A35
A352
A351
A376
A380
A381
A379
A382
A38
A3052
20 miles
0
10
20
30 kilometres

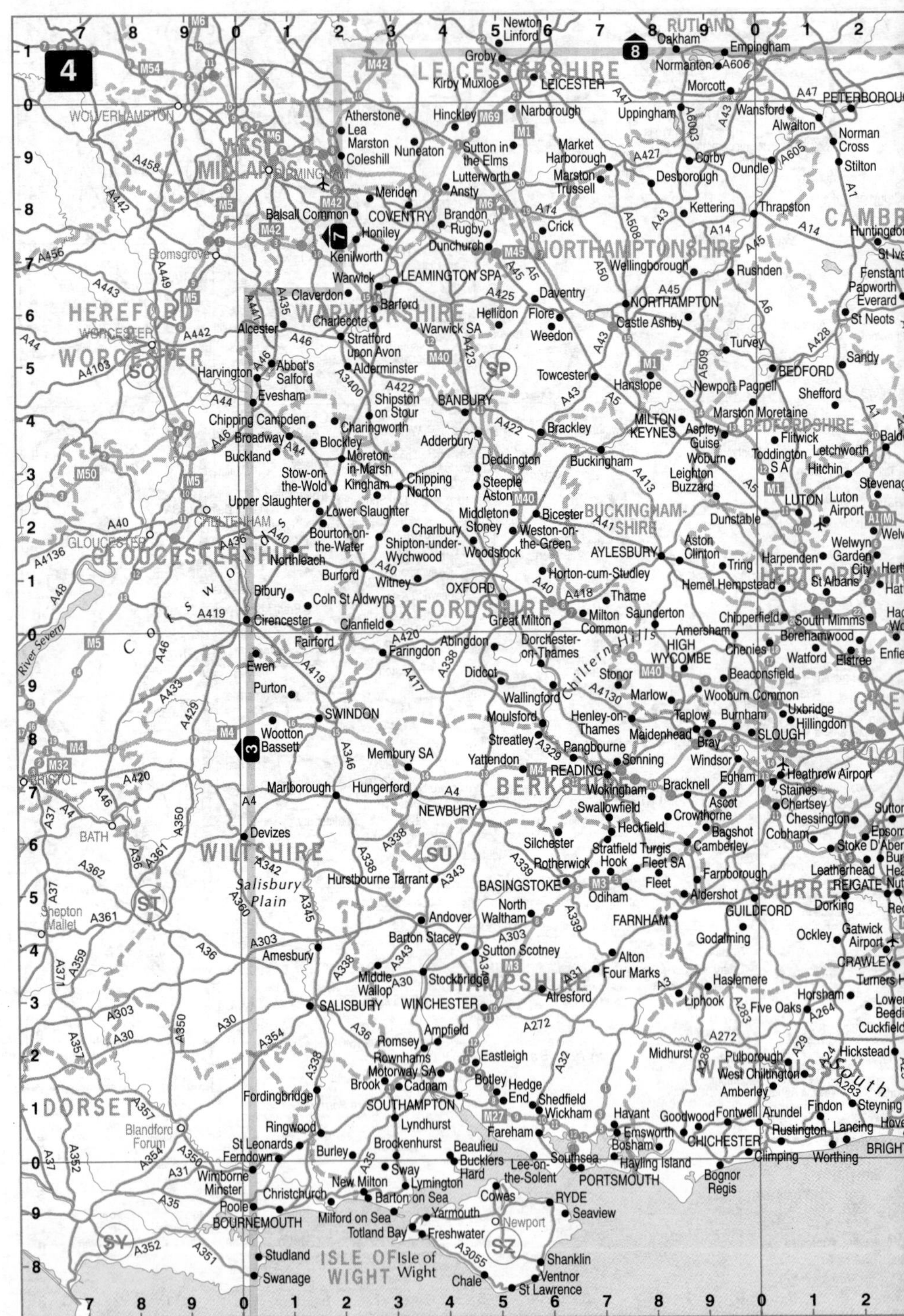

For continuation pages refer to numbered arrows

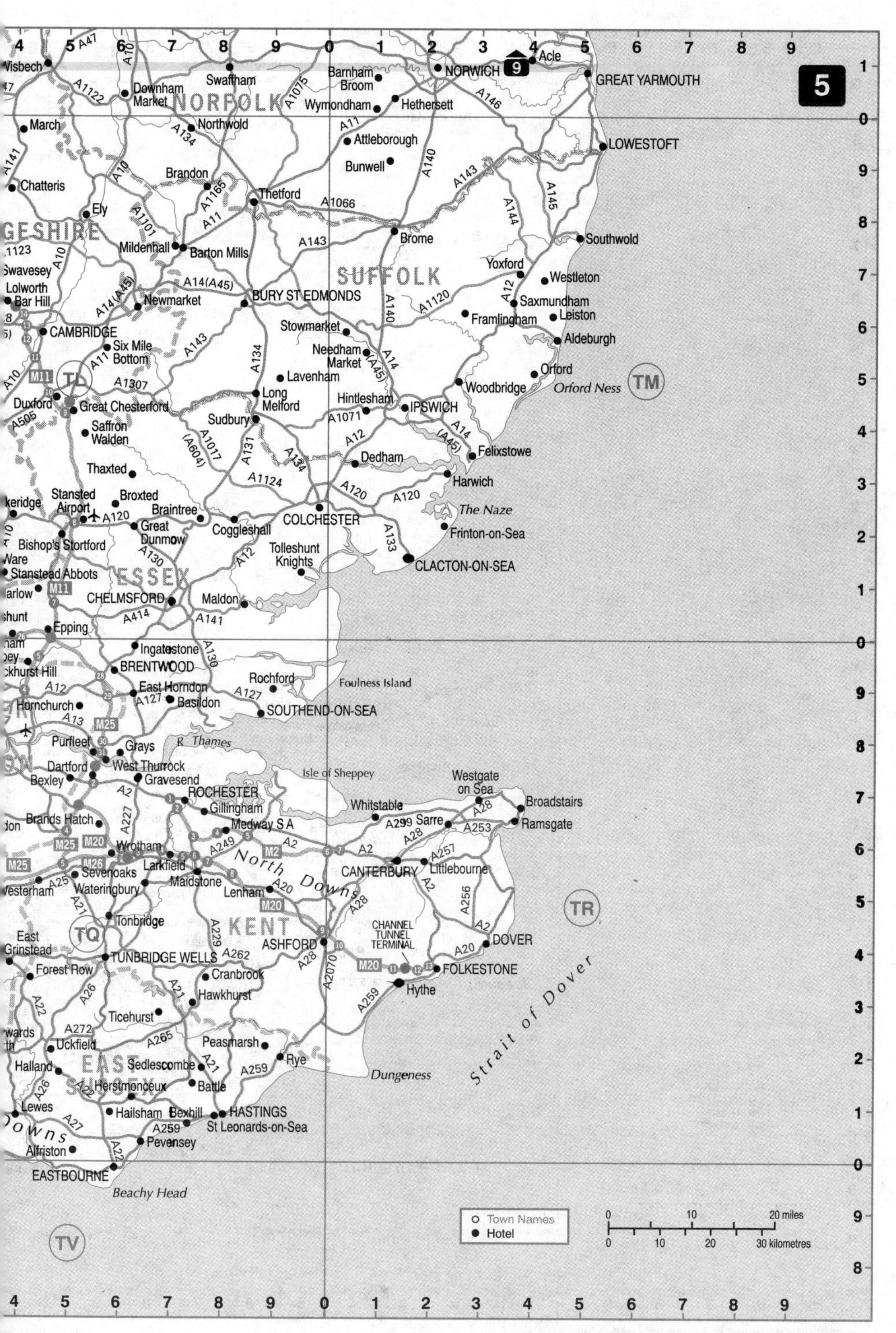
5
NORFOLK
SUFFOLK
ESSEX
KENT
EAST SUSSEX
Wisbech
Swaffham
Downham Market
Barnham Broom
Wymondham
Hethersett
NORWICH
Acle
GREAT YARMOUTH
March
Northwold
Attleborough
Bunwell
LOWESTOFT
Chatteris
Brandon
Thetford
Ely
Brome
Southwold
Mildenhall
Barton Mills
Yoxford
Westleton
Swavesey
Lolworth
Bar Hill
Newmarket
BURY ST EDMONDS
Saxmundham
Framlingham
Leiston
CAMBRIDGE
Stowmarket
Aldeburgh
Six Mile Bottom
Needham Market
Lavenham
Orford
Orford Ness
Woodbridge
Duxford
Great Chesterford
Long Melford
Hintlesham
IPSWICH
Saffron Walden
Sudbury
Felixstowe
Dedham
Thaxted
Harwich
Stansted Airport
Broxted
Braintree
The Naze
Great Dunmow
Coggleshall
COLCHESTER
Frinton-on-Sea
Bishop's Stortford
Tolleshunt Knights
CLACTON-ON-SEA
Stanstead Abbots
CHELMSFORD
Maldon
Epping
Ingatestone
BRENTWOOD
Rochford
Foulness Island
East Horndon
Basildon
Hornchurch
SOUTHEND-ON-SEA
Purfleet
Grays
R Thames
Dartford
West Thurrock
Bexley
Gravesend
Isle of Sheppey
Westgate on Sea
Broadstairs
ROCHESTER
Gillingham
Whitstable
Sarre
Ramsgate
Brands Hatch
Medway S A
Wrotham
Larkfield
North Downs
CANTERBURY
Littlebourne
Sevenoaks
Maidstone
Lenham
Westerham
Wateringbury
Tonbridge
CHANNEL TUNNEL TERMINAL
DOVER
East Grinstead
ASHFORD
TUNBRIDGE WELLS
FOLKESTONE
Forest Row
Cranbrook
Hythe
Hawkhurst
Strait of Dover
Ticehurst
Uckfield
Peasmarsh
Rye
Halland
Sedlescombe
Dungeness
Herstmonceux
Battle
Lewes
Hailsham
Bexhill
HASTINGS
St Leonards-on-Sea
Pevensey
Alfriston
EASTBOURNE
Beachy Head
TL
TM
TQ
TR
TV
Town Names
Hotel
0 10 20 miles
0 10 20 30 kilometres

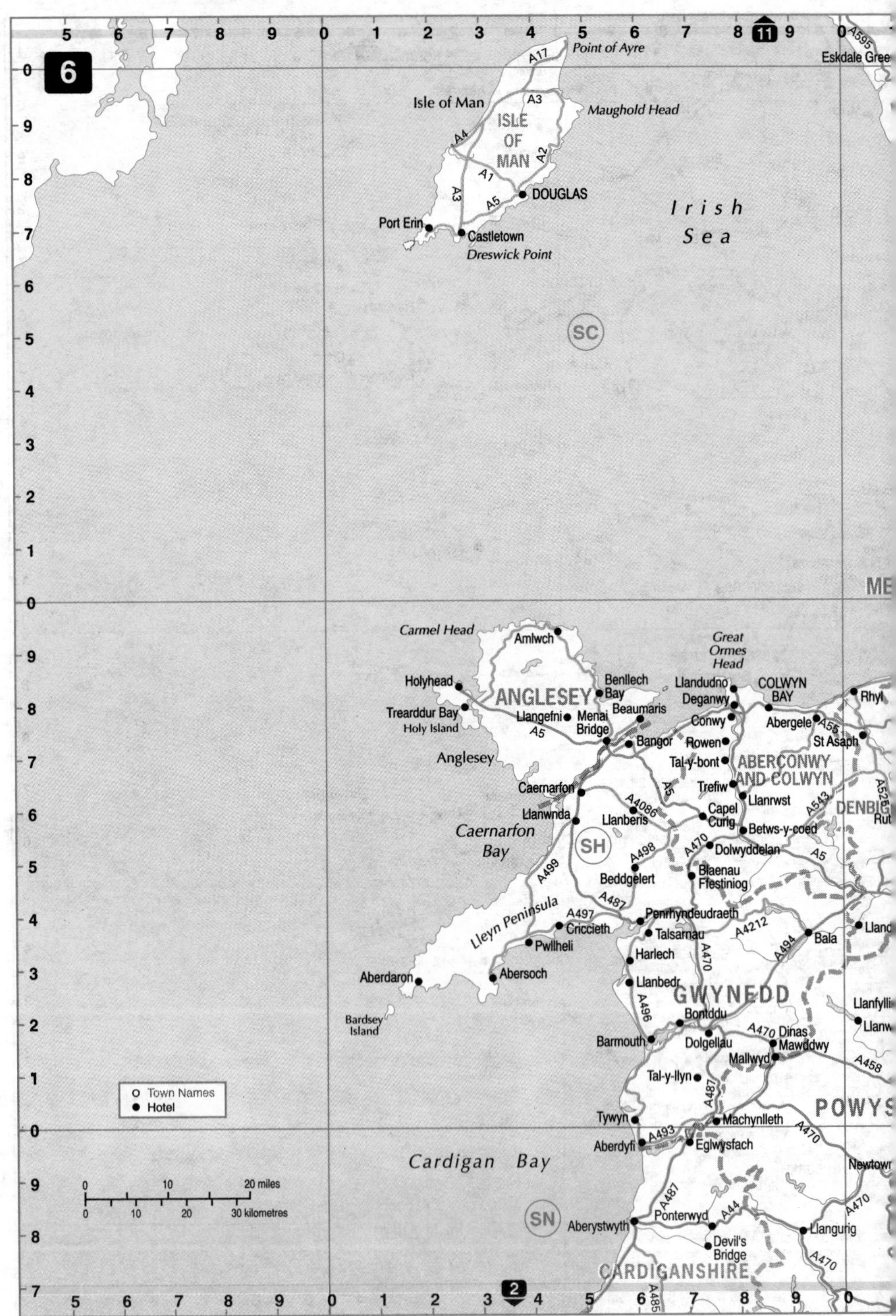
6
Point of Ayre
Isle of Man
ISLE OF MAN
Maughold Head
DOUGLAS
Port Erin
Castletown
Dreswick Point
Irish Sea
Eskdale Green
SC
Carmel Head
Amlwch
Great Ormes Head
Holyhead
ANGLESEY
Benllech Bay
Llandudno
Deganwy
COLWYN BAY
Rhyl
Treardur Bay
Holy Island
Llangefni
Menai Bridge
Beaumaris
Conwy
Abergele
St Asaph
Bangor
Rowen
Anglesey
Tal-y-bont
ABERCONWY AND COLWYN
Caernarfon
Trefiw
Llanrwst
DENBIG
Llanwnda
Llanberis
Capel Curig
Betws-y-coed
Caernarfon Bay
SH
Dolwyddelan
Blaenau Ffestiniog
Beddgelert
Lleyn Peninsula
Penrhyndeudraeth
Criccieth
Talsarnau
Bala
Pwllheli
Harlech
Aberdaron
Abersoch
Llanbedr
GWYNEDD
Llanfyllin
Bardsey Island
Bontddu
Dinas Mawddwy
Barmouth
Dolgellau
Mallwyd
Tal-y-llyn
Town Names
Hotel
POWYS
Tywyn
Machynlleth
Aberdyfi
Eglwysfach
Cardigan Bay
Newtown
0 10 20 miles
0 10 20 30 kilometres
SN
Aberystwyth
Ponterwyd
Llangurig
Devil's Bridge
CARDIGANSHIRE
11
2
For continuation pages refer to numbered arrows

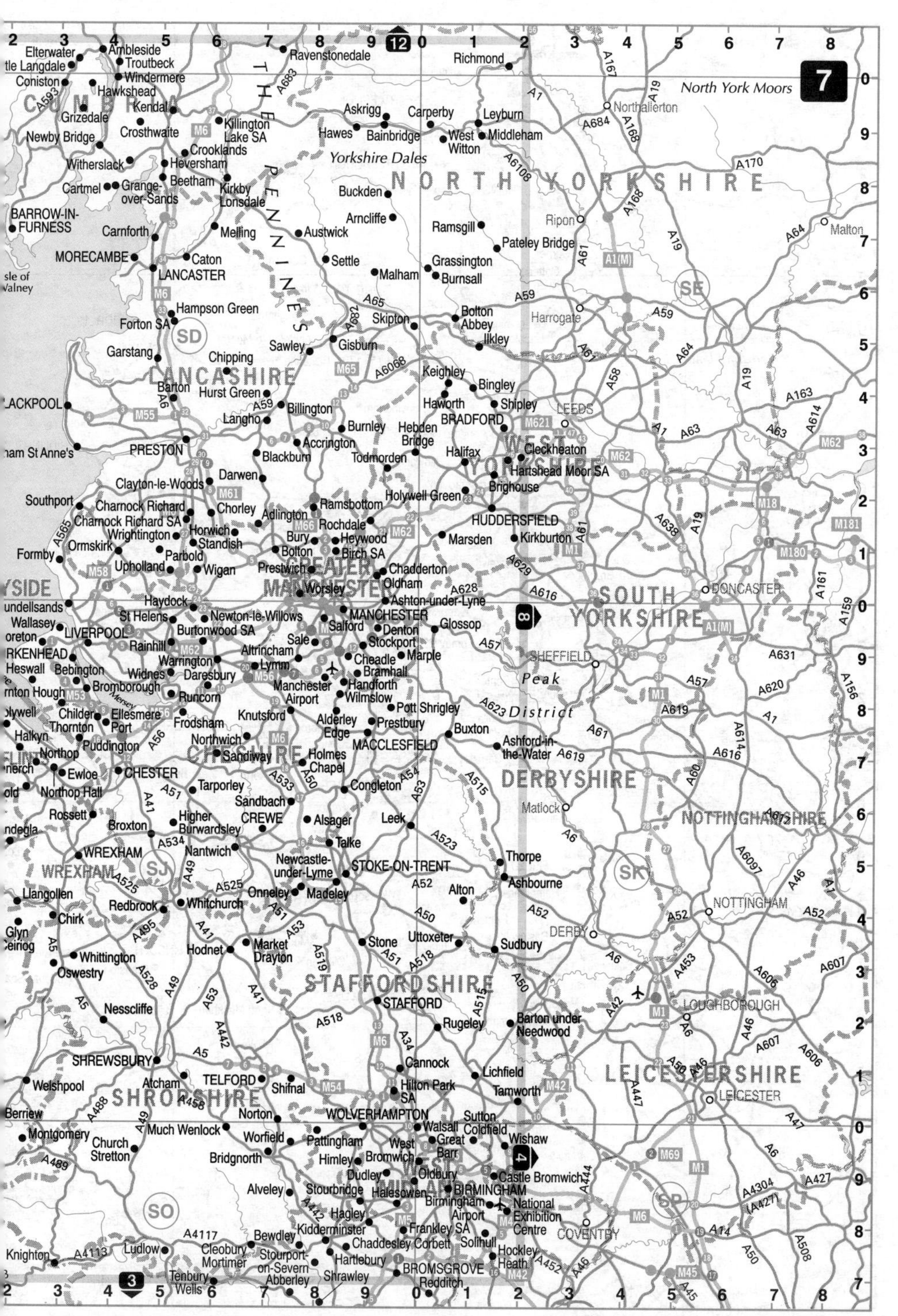
7
North York Moors
12
8
4
3
NORTH YORKSHIRE
Yorkshire Dales
THE PENNINES
LANCASHIRE
WEST YORKSHIRE
SOUTH YORKSHIRE
GREATER MANCHESTER
CHESHIRE
DERBYSHIRE
NOTTINGHAMSHIRE
STAFFORDSHIRE
SHROPSHIRE
LEICESTERSHIRE
WEST MIDLANDS
WREXHAM
CUMBRIA
Peak District
Elterwater
Little Langdale
Ambleside
Troutbeck
Coniston
Windermere
Hawkshead
Grizedale
Kendal
Crosthwaite
Newby Bridge
Witherslack
Cartmel
Grange-over-Sands
Heversham
Beetham
Crooklands
Killington Lake SA
Kirkby Lonsdale
BARROW-IN-FURNESS
Carnforth
Melling
MORECAMBE
Caton
LANCASTER
Isle of Walney
Hampson Green
Forton SA
Garstang
Chipping
Barton
Hurst Green
BLACKPOOL
Langho
Billington
PRESTON
Lytham St Anne's
Blackburn
Accrington
Burnley
Clayton-le-Woods
Darwen
Southport
Charnock Richard
Charnock Richard SA
Chorley
Adlington
Horwich
Wrightington
Ormskirk
Standish
Parbold
Formby
Upholland
Wigan
Bolton
Bury
Heywood
Birch SA
Rochdale
Ramsbottom
Prestwich
Chadderton
Oldham
Worsley
Ashton-under-Lyne
Crosby
Blundellsands
Haydock
St Helens
Newton-le-Willows
MANCHESTER
Salford
Denton
Wallasey
Moreton
LIVERPOOL
Burtonwood SA
Rainhill
BIRKENHEAD
Heswall
Bebington
Widnes
Warrington
Altrincham
Sale
Stockport
Lymm
Cheadle
Bramhall
Daresbury
Manchester Airport
Handforth
Wilmslow
Bromborough
Runcorn
Thornton Hough
Holywell
Childer Thornton
Ellesmere Port
Frodsham
Knutsford
Alderley Edge
Prestbury
Pott Shrigley
Halkyn
Northop
Puddington
Northwich
Sandiway
MACCLESFIELD
Holmes Chapel
Ewloe
Northop Hall
CHESTER
Tarporley
Sandbach
Congleton
Rossett
Higher Burwardsley
CREWE
Alsager
Broxton
Llandegla
Talke
Leek
WREXHAM
Nantwich
Newcastle-under-Lyme
STOKE-ON-TRENT
Llangollen
Onneley
Madeley
Redbrook
Whitchurch
Chirk
Glyn Ceiriog
Hodnet
Market Drayton
Whittington
Oswestry
Stone
Uttoxeter
Sudbury
Nesscliffe
STAFFORD
Rugeley
Barton under Needwood
SHREWSBURY
Welshpool
Atcham
TELFORD
Shifnal
Cannock
Hilton Park SA
Lichfield
Tamworth
Berriew
Norton
WOLVERHAMPTON
Walsall
Sutton Coldfield
Montgomery
Much Wenlock
Church Stretton
Worfield
Pattingham
West Bromwich
Great Barr
Wishaw
Bridgnorth
Himley
Dudley
Oldbury
Castle Bromwich
Alveley
Stourbridge
Halesowen
BIRMINGHAM
Birmingham Airport
National Exhibition Centre
Hagley
Kidderminster
Frankley SA
Solihull
Bewdley
Chaddesley Corbett
Cleobury Mortimer
Stourport-on-Severn
Hartlebury
Hockley Heath
Knighton
Ludlow
Tenbury Wells
Abberley
Shrawley
BROMSGROVE
Redditch
COVENTRY
Ravenstonedale
Richmond
Northallerton
Askrigg
Carperby
Leyburn
Hawes
Bainbridge
West Witton
Middleham
Buckden
Arncliffe
Ramsgill
Ripon
Malton
Austwick
Pateley Bridge
Settle
Grassington
Malham
Burnsall
Harrogate
Skipton
Bolton Abbey
Ilkley
Gisburn
Sawley
Keighley
Bingley
Haworth
Shipley
LEEDS
BRADFORD
Hebden Bridge
Todmorden
Halifax
Cleckheaton
Hartshead Moor SA
Brighouse
Holywell Green
HUDDERSFIELD
Marsden
Kirkburton
DONCASTER
Glossop
Marple
SHEFFIELD
Buxton
Ashford-in-the-Water
Matlock
Thorpe
Ashbourne
Alton
NOTTINGHAM
DERBY
LOUGHBOROUGH
LEICESTER
SE
SD
SJ
SK
SO
SP

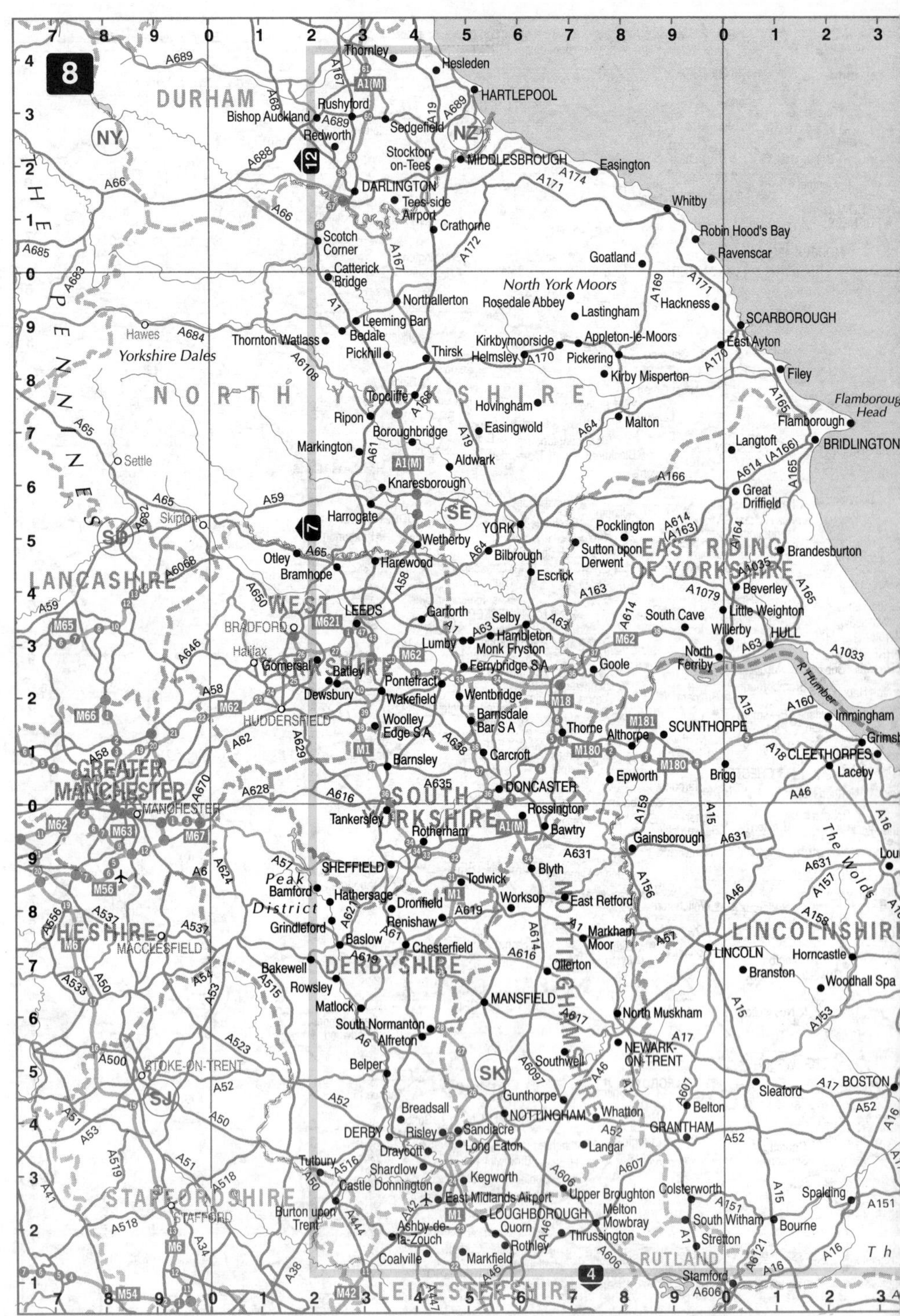

For continuation pages refer to numbered arrows

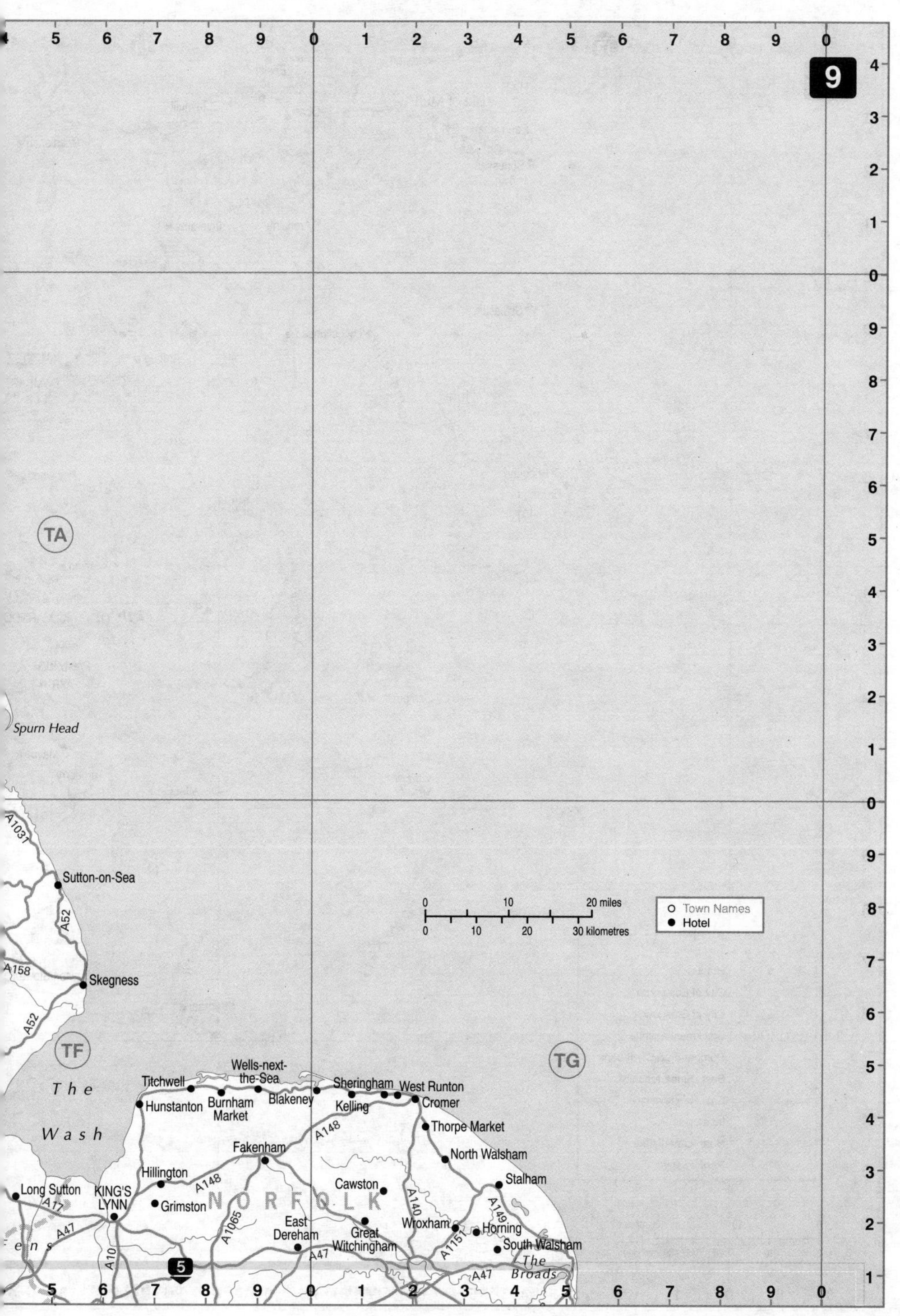
9
TA
Spurn Head
Sutton-on-Sea
Skegness
TF
The Wash
Titchwell
Hunstanton
Burnham Market
Wells-next-the-Sea
Blakeney
Sheringham
West Runton
Kelling
Cromer
Thorpe Market
North Walsham
Stalham
Fakenham
Hillington
Grimston
Long Sutton
KING'S LYNN
NORFOLK
Cawston
East Dereham
Great Witchingham
Wroxham
Horning
South Walsham
The Broads
Fens
TG
5
0 10 20 miles
0 10 20 30 kilometres
Town Names
Hotel
A1031
A52
A158
A148
A17
A47
A10
A1065
A140
A1151
A149

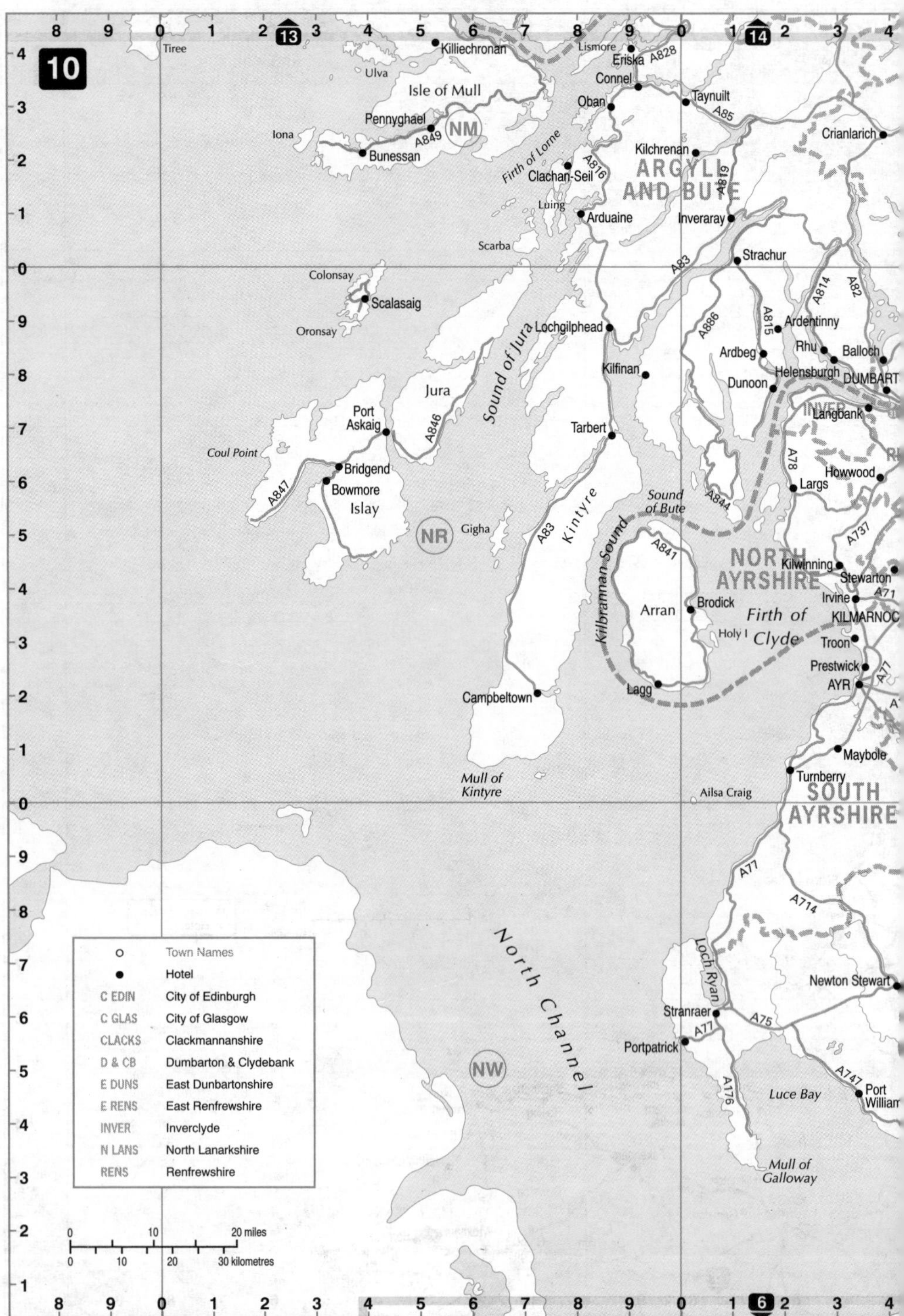

For continuation pages refer to numbered arrows

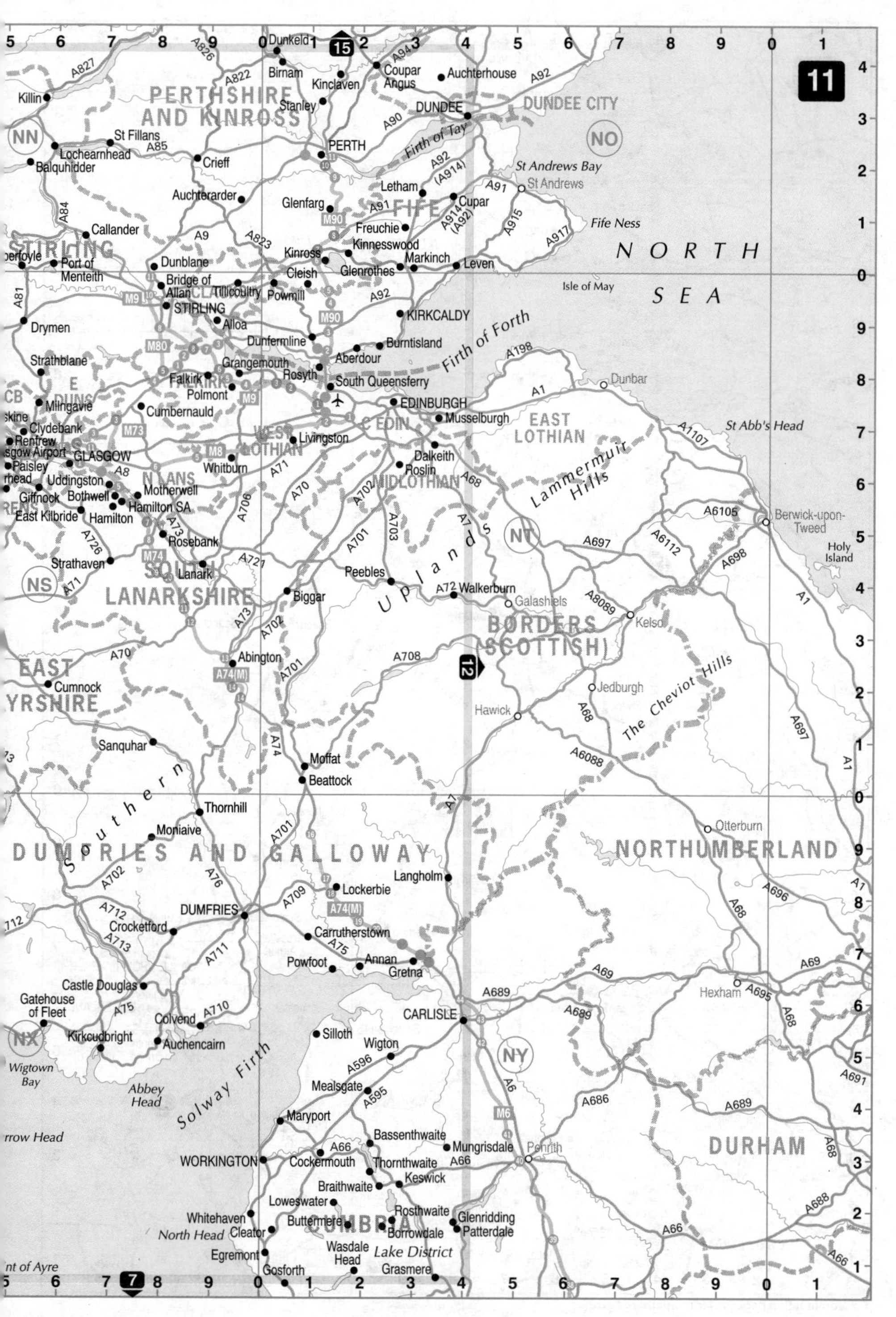

For continuation pages refer to numbered arrows

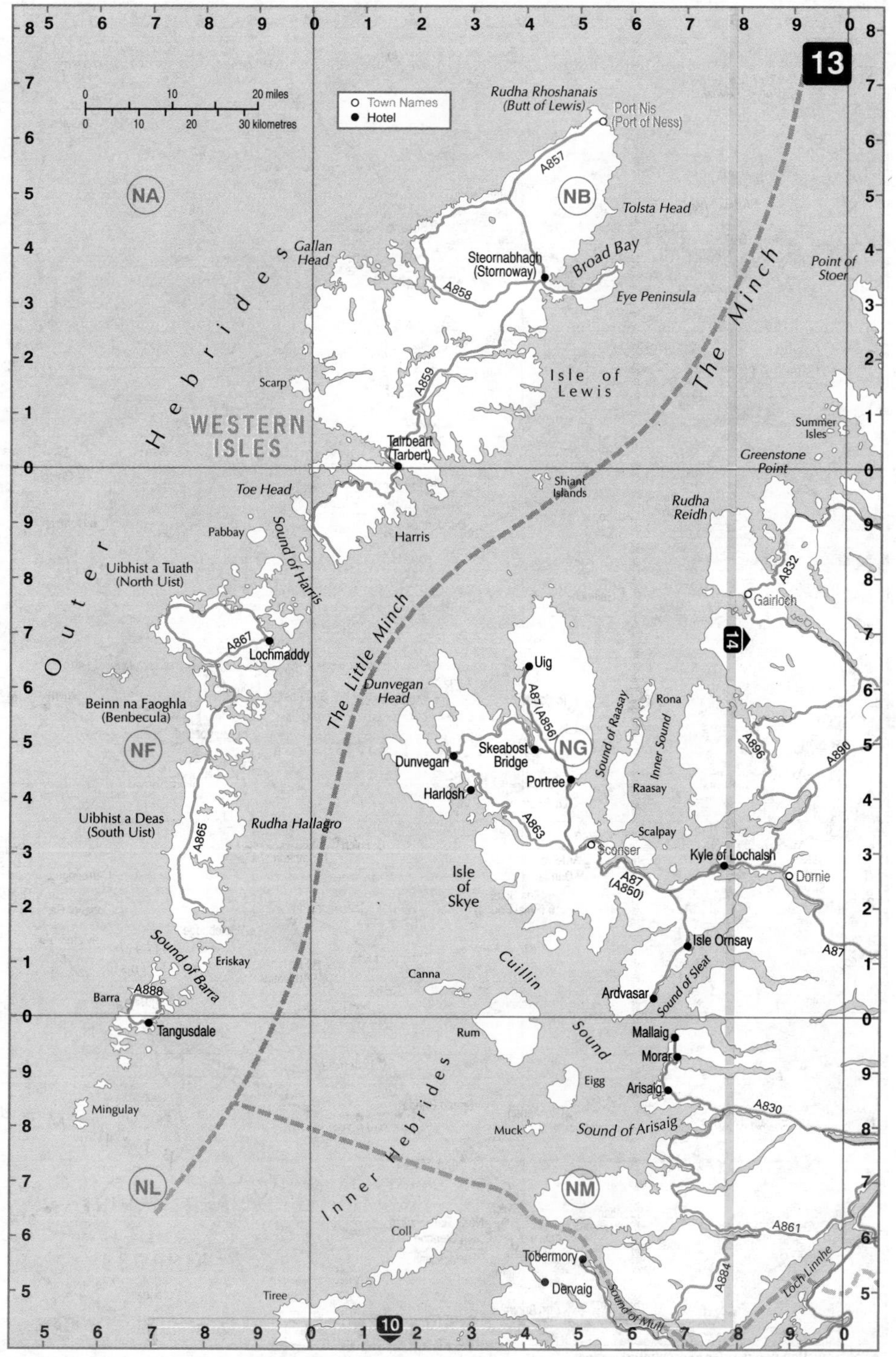
13
Town Names
Hotel
0 10 20 miles
0 10 20 30 kilometres
NA
NB
NF
NG
NL
NM
Rudha Rhoshanais
(Butt of Lewis)
Port Nis
(Port of Ness)
A857
Tolsta Head
Gallan Head
Steornabhagh
(Stornoway)
Broad Bay
A858
Eye Peninsula
Point of Stoer
The Minch
Outer Hebrides
Isle of Lewis
Scarp
A859
WESTERN ISLES
Tairbeart
(Tarbert)
Summer Isles
Greenstone Point
Toe Head
Shiant Islands
Rudha Reidh
Pabbay
Sound of Harris
Harris
Uibhist a Tuath
(North Uist)
A832
Gairloch
A867
Lochmaddy
The Little Minch
14
Uig
Dunvegan Head
A87 (A856)
Sound of Raasay
Rona
Beinn na Faoghla
(Benbecula)
Inner Sound
Skeabost Bridge
Dunvegan
Portree
A896
A890
Harlosh
Raasay
Uibhist a Deas
(South Uist)
A865
Rudha Hallagro
A863
Scalpay
Sconser
Kyle of Lochalsh
Dornie
Isle of Skye
A87
(A850)
Sound of Barra
Isle Ornsay
Eriskay
Cuillin Sound
A87
Canna
Barra
A888
Ardvasar
Sound of Sleat
Tangusdale
Rum
Mallaig
Morar
Arisaig
Eigg
Mingulay
A830
Muck
Sound of Arisaig
Inner Hebrides
A861
Coll
Tobermory
Dervaig
A884
Loch Linnhe
Tiree
Sound of Mull
10

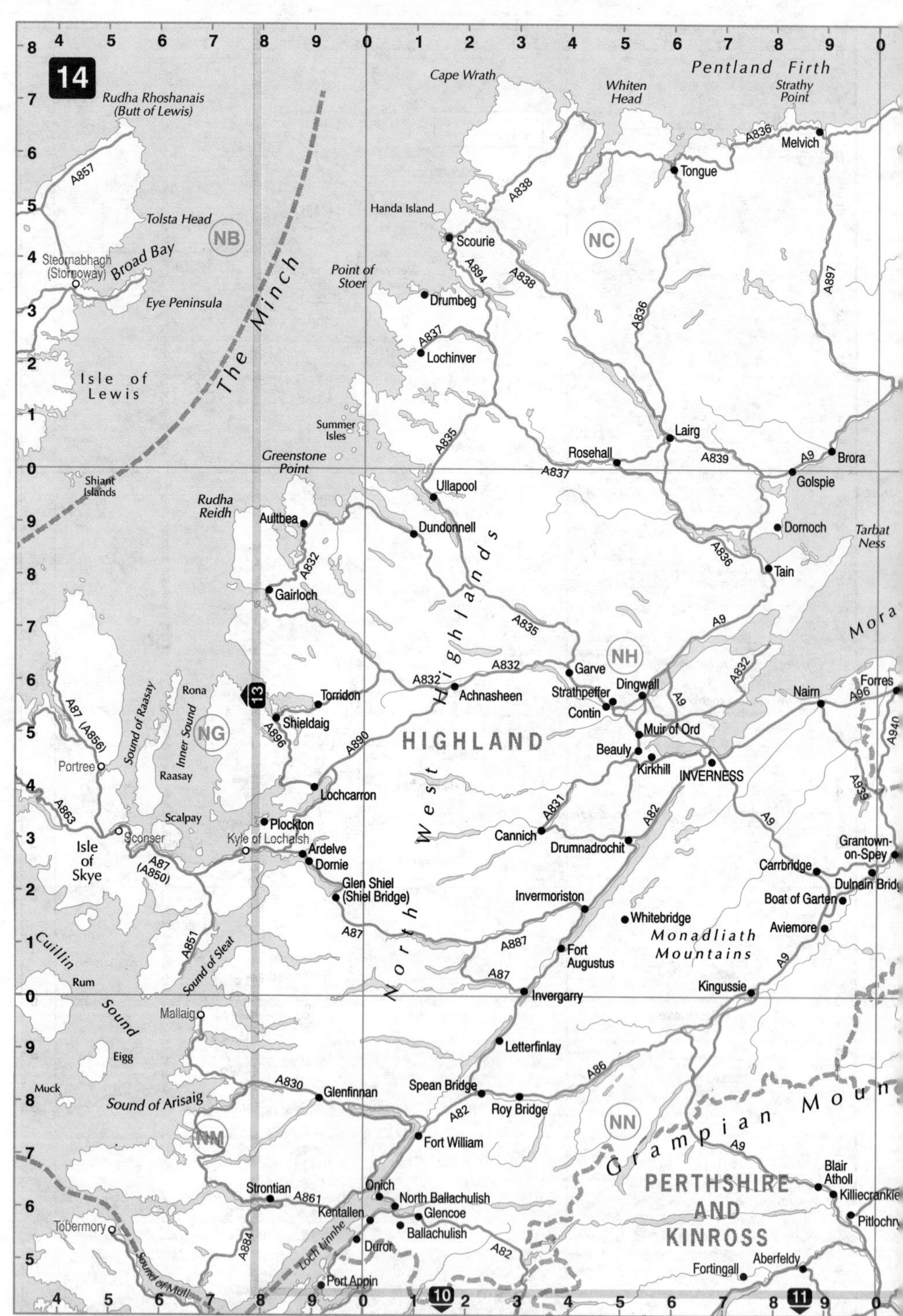

For continuation pages refer to numbered arrows

15
Dunnet Head
Island of Stroma
Duncansby Head
Mey
Dunnet
A836
John O'Groats
Thurso
A9
Halkirk
Noss Head
Wick
ND
A9
(A895)
A99
(A9)
Lybster
Firth
Lossiemouth
Buckie
Cullen
Banff
Macduff
Fraserburgh
Elgin
(A92)
A90
A98
A95
A941
Bridge of Marnoch
A950
Rothes
NJ
NK
Peterhead
Archiestown
Craigellachie
A97
A947
A952
(A92)
MORAY
A920
Huntly
A90
(A952)
Cruden Bay
A95
A941
A96
A920
A97
Old Rayne
Oldmeldrum
ABERDEENSHIRE
Newburgh
Inverurie
Tomintoul
Kildrummy
Kintore
Aberdeen Airport
A939
A944
A944
ABERDEEN CITY
Westhill
ABERDEEN
A939
A97
A980
A93
A93
Aboyne
Braemar
Ballater
Banchory
A90
A957
Stonehaven
Town Names
Hotel
A92
Glenshee (Spittal of)
NO
Edzell
A93
A90
ANGUS
Brechin
0
10
20 miles
Montrose
A935
0
10
20
30 kilometres
Bridge of Cally
A932
Lunan Bay
Alyth
Forfar
Blairgowrie
A933
Glamis
12

16

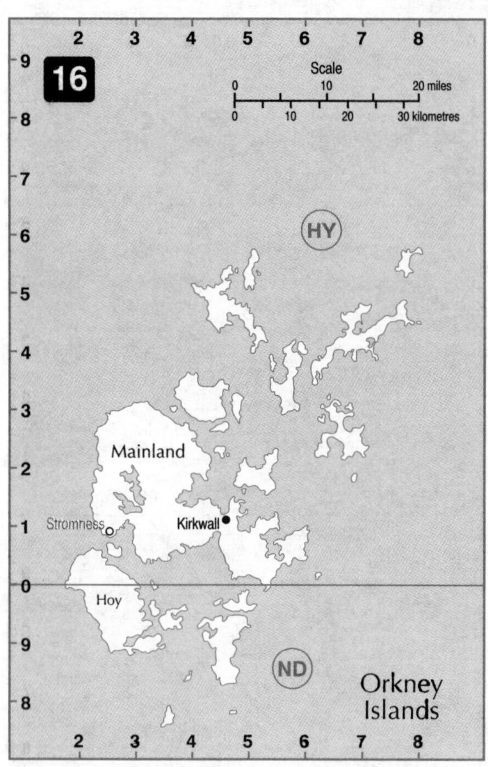

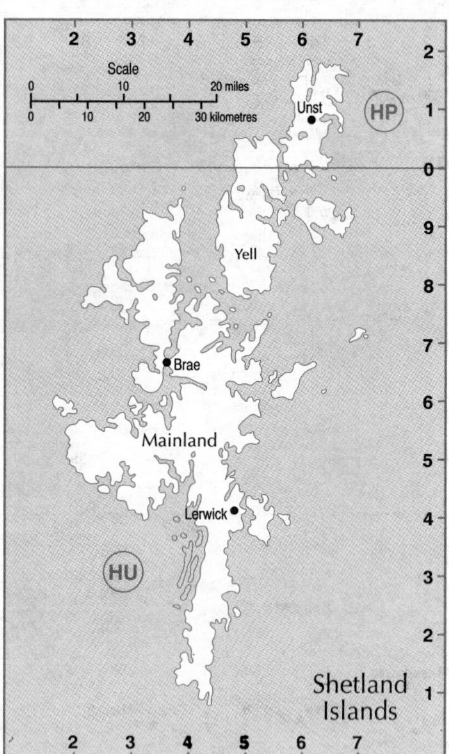

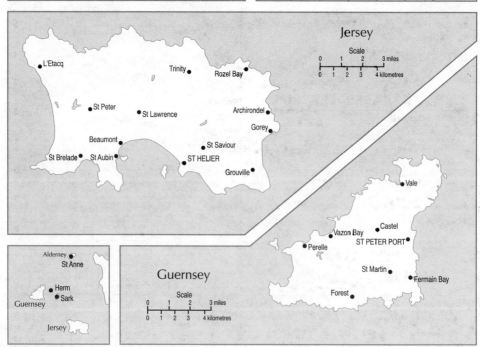

Jersey

Scale
0 1 2 3 miles
0 1 2 3 4 kilometres

L'Etacq
Trinity
Rozel Bay
St Peter
St Lawrence
Archirondel
Gorey
Beaumont
St Saviour
St Brelade
St Aubin
ST HELIER
Grouville

Alderney
St Anne
Herm
Sark
Guernsey
Jersey

Guernsey

Scale
0 1 2 3 miles
0 1 2 3 4 kilometres

Vale
Castel
Vazon Bay
ST PETER PORT
Perelle
St Martin
Fermain Bay
Forest

Please write to: Editor, AA Hotel Guide, Publishing Division, The Automobile Association, Fanum House, Basingstoke RG21 4EA

Please use this form to recommend any hotel where you have stayed which is not already in our guide.

If you have any comments about your stay at a hotel listed in the guide, we shall be grateful if you will let us know, as feedback from readers helps us to keep our guide accurate and up to date. Please note, however, that if you have a complaint to make during a stay, we do recommend that you discuss the matter with the hotel management there and then so that they have a chance to put things right before your stay is spoilt.

Please note that the AA does not undertake to arbitrate between you and the hotel management, or to obtain compensation or engage in protracted correspondence.

Readers' Report form

Your name (block capitals) ....

....

....

Your address (block capitals) ....

....

....

....

....

....

Comments ....

....

....

....

....

....

HOTEL GUIDE 1997

Readers' Report form

HOTEL GUIDE 1997

Please post to: The Editor, AA Hotel Guide, Editorial Department, The Automobile Association, Fanum House, Basingstoke, Hampshire RG21 2EA

Please write to: Editor, AA Hotel Guide, Publishing Division,
The Automobile Association, Fanum House,
Basingstoke RG21 4EA

Please use this form to recommend any hotel where you have stayed which is not already in our guide.

If you have any comments about your stay at a hotel listed in the guide, we shall be grateful if you will let us know, as feedback from readers helps us to keep our guide accurate and up to date. Please note, however, that if you have a complaint to make during a stay, we do recommend that you discuss the matter with the hotel management there and then so that they have a chance to put things right before your stay is spoilt.

Please note that the AA does not undertake to arbitrate between you and the hotel management, or to obtain compensation or engage in protracted correspondence.

Readers' Report form

Your name (block capitals) ....

....

....

Your address (block capitals) ....

....

....

....

....

....

Comments ....

....

....

....

....

....

HOTEL GUIDE 1997

Readers' Report form

HOTEL GUIDE 1997

Please post to: The Editor, AA Hotel Guide, Editorial Department, The Automobile Association, Fanum House, Basingstoke, Hampshire RG21 2EA

Please write to: Editor, AA Hotel Guide, Publishing Division,
The Automobile Association, Fanum House,
Basingstoke RG21 4EA

Please use this form to recommend any hotel where you have stayed which is not already in our guide.

If you have any comments about your stay at a hotel listed in the guide, we shall be grateful if you will let us know, as feedback from readers helps us to keep our guide accurate and up to date. Please note, however, that if you have a complaint to make during a stay, we do recommend that you discuss the matter with the hotel management there and then so that they have a chance to put things right before your stay is spoilt.

Please note that the AA does not undertake to arbitrate between you and the hotel management, or to obtain compensation or engage in protracted correspondence.

Readers' Report form

Your name (block capitals) ....

....

....

Your address (block capitals) ....

....

....

....

....

....

Comments ....

....

....

....

....

....

HOTEL GUIDE 1997

Readers' Report form

HOTEL GUIDE 1997

Please post to: The Editor, AA Hotel Guide, Editorial Department,
The Automobile Association, Fanum House, Basingstoke,
Hampshire RG21 2EA

Please write to: Editor, AA Hotel Guide, Publishing Division,
The Automobile Association, Fanum House,
Basingstoke RG21 4EA

Please use this form to recommend any hotel where you have stayed which is not already in our guide.

If you have any comments about your stay at a hotel listed in the guide, we shall be grateful if you will let us know, as feedback from readers helps us to keep our guide accurate and up to date. Please note, however, that if you have a complaint to make during a stay, we do recommend that you discuss the matter with the hotel management there and then so that they have a chance to put things right before your stay is spoilt.

Please note that the AA does not undertake to arbitrate between you and the hotel management, or to obtain compensation or engage in protracted correspondence.

Readers' Report form

Your name (block capitals) ....

....

....

Your address (block capitals) ....

....

....

....

....

....

Comments ....

....

....

....

....

....

HOTEL GUIDE 1997

Readers' Report form

HOTEL GUIDE 1997

Please post to: The Editor, AA Hotel Guide, Editorial Department, The Automobile Association, Fanum House, Basingstoke, Hampshire RG21 2EA

Special AA Membership Offer

Join today and you gain all the benefits of membership of the AA - the 4th Emergency Service - as well as being able to use your AA Hotel Guide Discount Card.

You're the Member, Not the Car

AA membership is personal - that means whatever car you are in, even if you are travelling simply as a passenger, you can use your AA cover to get you out of trouble.

Priority for Motorists at Risk

The AA has the world's largest patrol force and helps someone out of trouble every 7 seconds. Over 80 per cent of breakdowns are fixed at the roadside, and priority is given to lone women and members in vulnerable situations.

Option 100 - Roadside Assistance
Option 200 - Roadside Assistance and Relay
Option 300 - Roadside Assistance, Relay and Home Start
Option 400 - Roadside Assistance, Relay, Relay Plus and Home Start

The affordable options are designed to make membership easy. Available as Single, Joint or Family membership, you simply select the level of cover that's right for you.

The photograph on this and the following pages is the Lythe Hill Hotel at Haslemere, Surrey.

AA Membership Benefits

extend beyond motoring emergencies and include:

- AA Handbook
- AA Magazine
- AA Member Benefits booklet
- Route planning services
- Legal and technical information services

To join or for further details, call today free on 0800 919 595, quoting ref HGPC

When you join* you will receive a free copy of the AA's celebrated BEST RESTAURANTS guide

- **Over 1700 British restaurants with AA Rosette Awards for culinary excellence**
- **More than 900 colour photographs of restaurants**
- **Up-to-date details and maps**
- **Lively, readable descriptions**
- **Published October 1996**
- **Price £13.99**

*This offer is not available in conjunction with any other promotional offer and is only available for new members joining by bank direct debit or credit card continuous authority. Offer closes 31st December 1997.

The AA Hotel Guide Discount Card

The AA Hotel Guide Discount Card (see opposite) entitles AA members to Discounts off certain Hotel Accommodation and Special Deals with Europcar Interrent on Car Hire (see below for details).

To join the AA and gain all the benefits of AA membership as well as the benefits of the discount card, see the Special Membership Offer on the previous page. Apply to join today!

Terms of the Discount Scheme

AA members may use the AA Discount Card to claim a minimum 10 per cent discount off their room bill at more than 1800 hotels listed in the directory.

Hotels which have agreed to participate in the scheme in 1997 display a £ symbol by their directory entry.

The discount applies to the full-tariff room rate only and may not be claimed for restaurant or bar bills.

Cardholders must show a valid AA membership card with this discount card at reception when they check in to the hotel so that their bill can be made out correctly at the end of their stay.

This is very important because so many hotel accounts are computerised and it may cause difficulty if an account has to be adjusted at check-out stage. The hotel will be within its rights to refuse to allow a discount if a customer has not confirmed their entitlement to discount on checking in.

In the case of a joint booking for a group of individuals, the discount applies to the accommodation of the cardholder only. However, if the cardholder has booked a double, family room or suite, the discount will apply to the full-tariff rate for that accommodation.

Please note that the discount may only be claimed from participating hotels which display the £ symbol alongside their entry in the directory, and that the bill must be settled before you leave the hotel.

The discount does not apply:

- to company accounts
- to agency bookings
- to rooms booked at bargain rates
- in conjunction with any other offers

EUROPCAR INTERRENT

EXCLUSIVE TO AA MEMBERS - EUROPCAR'S LOWEST PRICE GUARANTEE

IF YOU CAN FIND CAR RENTAL FOR LESS, EUROPCAR WILL NOT ONLY MATCH IT -WE'LL BETTER IT BY £5.00.

We're so confident that we offer AA Members the best value car and van rental there is that, if you can find a lower rental rate locally in the UK, for the same vehicle group over the same time period - from Avis, Hertz, Budget, Alamo or Eurodollar - we'll match it and take another £5.00 off your bill.

To book, and for details of your nearest Europcar Intererent rental station, just call 0345 626640 and quote the unique AA contract ID number 84074202. Please present your AA Hotel Guide discount card or AA Membership Card when you collect the car.

Conditions:

1. Local area definition - with a 5-mile radius of the Europcar rental station from which you have arranged to collect the car.
2. Price comparisons can only be made with other international car rental companies - Avis, Hertz, Budget, Alamo, Eurodollar.
3. All rentals are subject to Europcar's standard terms and conditions of rental.
4. Applies to UK rentals only, subject to availability.
5. Valid until 31 December 1997.